FOURTH CANADIAN EDITION

# EXPLORING THE DIVERSITY OF LIFE
# BIOLOGY

Peter J. Russell

Paul E. Hertz

Beverly McMillan

M. Brock Fenton
*Western University*

Denis Maxwell
*Western University*

Tom Haffie
*Western University*

Bill Milsom
*University of British Columbia*

Todd Nickle
*Mount Royal University*

Shona Ellis
*University of British Columbia*

With contributions by Ivona Mladenovic, Simon Fraser University

**NELSON**

# NELSON

**Biology, Fourth Canadian Edition**

by Peter J. Russell, Paul E. Hertz, Beverly McMillan, M. Brock Fenton, Denis Maxwell, Tom Haffie, Bill Milsom, Todd Nickle, Shona Ellis

**VP, Product Solutions, K–20:**
Claudine O'Donnell

**Senior Publisher, Digital and Print Content:**
Paul Fam

**Marketing Manager:**
Tia Nguyen

**Content Manager:**
Toni Chahley

**Photo and Permissions Researcher:**
Kristiina Paul

**Senior Production Project Manager:**
Imoinda Romain

**Production Service:**
MPS Limited

**Copy Editor:**
Frances Robinson

**Proofreader:**
MPS Limited

**Indexer:**
MPS Limited

**Design Director:**
Ken Phipps

**Higher Education Design Project Manager:**
Pamela Johnston

**Interior Design Modifications:**
Ken Cadinouche

**Cover Design:**
Courtney Hellam

**Cover Image:**
© Seth Casteel

**Art Coordinator:**
Suzanne Peden

**Managing Designer:**
Courtney Hellam

**Illustrator(s):**
Articulate Graphics, Steve Corrigan, Crowle Art Group, Patrick Gnan, Dave McKay, MPS Limited, Allan Moon, Ann Sanderson, Ralph Voltz

**Compositor:**
MPS Limited

**Library and Archives Canada Cataloguing in Publication**

Russell, Peter J., author
Biology : exploring the diversity of life / Peter J. Russell, Paul E. Hertz, Beverly McMillan, M. Brock Fenton, University of Western Ontario, Denis Maxwell, University of Western Ontario, Tom Haffie, University of Western Ontario, Bill Milsom, University of British Columbia, Todd Nickle, Mount Royal University, Shona Ellis, University of British Columbia ; with contributions by Ivona Mladenovic, Simon Fraser University. — Fourth Canadian edition.

Includes index.
Issued also in 3 volumes.
Issued in print and electronic formats.
ISBN 978-0-17-671888-6 (hardcover).—
ISBN 978-0-17-682709-0 (PDF)

1. Biology—Textbooks.
2. Textbooks. I. Title.

QH308.2.R88 2018  570  C2017-904622-5
                          C2017-904623-3

ISBN-13: 978-0-17-671888-6
ISBN-10: 0-17-671888-5

For, and because of,
our generations of students.

# About the Canadian Authors

M. B. Fenton

**M. B. (Brock) Fenton** received his Ph.D. from the University of Toronto in 1969. Since then, he has been a faculty member in biology at Carleton University, then at York University, and then at Western University. In addition to teaching parts of first-year biology, he has also taught vertebrate biology, animal biology, and conservation biology, as well as field courses in the biology and behaviour of bats. He has received awards for his teaching (Carleton University Faculty of Science Teaching Award; Ontario Confederation of University Faculty Associations Teaching Award; and a 3M Teaching Fellowship, Society for Teaching and Learning in Higher Education) in addition to recognition of his work on public awareness of science (Gordin Kaplan Award from the Canadian Federation of Biological Societies; Honorary Life Membership, Science North, Sudbury, Ontario; Canadian Council of University Biology Chairs Distinguished Canadian Biologist Award; The McNeil Medal for the Public Awareness of Science of the Royal Society of Canada; and the Sir Sandford Fleming Medal for public awareness of Science, the Royal Canadian Institute). He also received the C. Hart Merriam Award from the American Society of Mammalogists for excellence in scientific research. Bats and their biology, behaviour, evolution, and echolocation are the topics of his research, which has been funded by the Natural Sciences and Engineering Research Council of Canada (NSERC). In November 2014, Brock was inducted as a Fellow of the Royal Society of Canada.

Alan Noon

**Denis Maxwell** received his Ph.D. from the University of Western Ontario in 1995. His thesis, under the supervision of Norm Hüner, focused on photosynthetic acclimation in green algae. Following his doctorate, he undertook postdoctoral training at the Department of Energy Plant Research Laboratory at Michigan State University, where he studied the function of the mitochondrial alternative oxidase. After taking up a faculty position at the University of New Brunswick in 2000, he moved in 2003 to the Department of Biology at Western University. Denis served as Associate Chair for Undergraduate Education for the Department of Biology from 2009 to 2016. Currently, he is Assistant Dean for the Faculty of Science, with a portfolio that includes Recruitment and First-Year Studies and outreach. He has taught first-year Biology to over 15 000 students, most of the time with Tom Haffie.

Tom Haffie

**Tom Haffie** is a graduate of the University of Guelph and the University of Saskatchewan in the area of microbial genetics. Tom has devoted his 33-year career at Western University to teaching large biology classes in lecture, laboratory, and tutorial settings. He led the development of the innovative core laboratory course in the Biology program; he was an early adopter of computer animation in lectures; and, most recently, has overseen a deep blended redesign of introductory biology informed by a students-as-partners approach to development. He is the founding coordinator of the biennial Western Conference on Science Education. He holds a University Students' Council Award for Excellence in Teaching, a UWO Edward G. Pleva Award for Excellence in Teaching, a UWO Fellowship in Teaching Innovation, a Province of Ontario Award for Leadership in Faculty Teaching (LIFT), and a Canadian 3M National Teaching Fellowship for excellence in teaching. Tom is currently a Teaching Fellow for Science at Western University.

**Bill Milsom** (Ph.D., University of British Columbia) is a professor in the Department of Zoology at the University of British Columbia, where he has taught a variety of courses, including first-year biology, for almost 40 years. His research interests include the evolutionary origins of respiratory processes and the adaptive changes in these processes that allow animals to exploit diverse environments. He examines respiratory and cardiovascular adaptations in vertebrate animals in rest, sleep, exercise, altitude, dormancy, hibernation, diving, and so on. This research contributes to our understanding of the mechanistic basis of biodiversity and the physiological costs of habitat selection. His research has been funded by NSERC, and he has received several academic awards and distinctions, including the Fry Medal of the Canadian Society of Zoologists, the August Krogh Distinguished Lectorship Award of the American Physiological Society, the Bidder Lecture of the Society for Experimental Biology, and the Izaak Walton Killam Award for Excellence in Mentoring. He has served as the President of the Canadian Society of Zoologists and as President of the International Congress of Comparative Physiology and Biochemistry.

**Todd Nickle** received his Ph.D. from Oklahoma State University in 1998, and has been teaching biology at Mount Royal University ever since. He advocates Active Learning: students come to class prepared to *work* with material rather than just hear about it. Student preparation involves reading the text and applying the concepts to online exercises, the results of which inform what the next lecture will be about. Class time focusses on exploring connections between concepts and ideas in biology and how they relate to other disciplines, which inspired him to coauthor a handbook for first-year science students (*Science*³). His interest in promoting best teaching practices among educators had him confirm the Alberta Introductory Biology Association as an official Society of Alberta; Todd is currently President. His work put him in the first cohort of Full Professors at Mount Royal University in 2012, garnered the 2015 ACIFA Innovation in Teaching Award, and the Distinguished Faculty Award from MRU in 2016.

**Shona Ellis** (M.Sc., University of British Columbia) is a professor of teaching in the Botany Department and Associate Head of Biology at the University of British Columbia. She developed a keen interest in forests and the ocean growing up on the central coast of British Columbia. As an undergraduate, Professor Ellis pursued her interests in botany and entomology. Her M.Sc. research incorporated tissue culture, phytochemistry, and plant anatomy. As a teaching assistant, she realized a passion for teaching and joined the teaching faculty at the University of British Columbia in 1998. She teaches botany courses that have included nonvascular and vascular plants, economic botany, bryology, and plant systematics, as well as introductory biology. Professor Ellis has taught in a number of settings: large and small lectures, laboratories, and fieldtrips. While she feels the best classroom is outdoors, she integrates online technologies into all her courses; she is an early adopter of online teaching and learning resources. Professor Ellis has received two Killam Teaching Awards and the Charles Edwin Bessey Teaching Award from the Botanical Society of America.

# About the U.S. Authors

**Peter J. Russell** received a B.Sc. in Biology from the University of Sussex, England in 1968 and a Ph.D. in Genetics from Cornell University in 1972. He has been a member of the Biology Faculty of Reed College since 1972, and is currently a Professor of Biology, Emeritus. Peter taught a section of the introductory biology course, a genetics course, and a research literature course on molecular virology. In 1987 he received the Burlington Northern Faculty Achievement Award from Reed College in recognition of his excellence in teaching. Since 1986, he has been the author of a successful genetics textbook: current editions are *iGenetics: A Molecular Approach, iGenetics: A Mendelian Approach,* and *Essential iGenetics.* Peter's research was in the area of molecular genetics, with a specific interest in characterizing the role of host genes in the replication of the RNA genome of a pathogenic plant virus, and the expression of the genes of the virus; yeast was used as the model host. His research has been funded by agencies including the National Institutes of Health, the National Science Foundation, the American Cancer Society, the Department of Defense, the Medical Research Foundation of Oregon, and the Murdoch Foundation. He has published his research results in a variety of journals, including *Genetics, Journal of Bacteriology, Molecular and General Genetics, Nucleic Acids Research, Plasmid,* and *Molecular and Cellular Biology.* Peter has a long history of encouraging faculty research involving undergraduates, including cofounding the biology division of the Council on Undergraduate Research, in Washington, D.C. in 1985. He was Principal Investigator/Program Director of a National Science Foundation Award for the Integration of Research and Education (NSF-AIRE) to Reed College, 1998–2002.

Aaron Kinard

**Paul E. Hertz** was born and raised in New York City. He received a B.S. in Biology from Stanford University in 1972, an A.M. in Biology from Harvard University in 1973, and a Ph.D. in Biology from Harvard University in 1977. While completing field research for the doctorate, he served on the Biology Faculty of the University of Puerto Rico at Rio Piedras. After spending two years as an Isaac Walton Killam Postdoctoral Fellow at Dalhousie University, Paul accepted a teaching position at Barnard College, where he has taught since 1979. He was named Ann Whitney Olin Professor of Biology in 2000, and he received the Barnard Award for Teaching Excellence in 2007. In addition to serving on numerous college committees, Paul chaired Barnard's Biology Department for eight years and served as Acting Provost and Dean of the Faculty from 2011 to 2012. He is the founding Program Director of the Hughes Science Pipeline Project at Barnard, an undergraduate curriculum and research program that has been funded continuously by the Howard Hughes Medical Institute since 1992. The Pipeline Project includes the Intercollegiate Partnership, a program for local community college students that facilitates their transfer to four-year colleges and universities. He teaches one semester of the introductory sequence for Biology majors and pre-professional students, lecture and laboratory courses in vertebrate zoology and ecology, and a year-long seminar that introduces first-year students to scientific research. Paul is an animal physiological ecologist with a specific research interest in the thermal biology of lizards. He has conducted fieldwork in the West Indies since the mid-1970s, most recently focusing on the lizards of Cuba. His work has been funded by the NSF, and he has published his research in *The American Naturalist, Ecology, Nature, Oecologia,* and *Proceedings of the Royal Society.* In 2010, he and his colleagues at three other universities received funding from NSF for a project designed to detect the effects of global climate warming on the biology of *Anolis* lizards in Puerto Rico.

Courtesy of Beverly McMillan

**Beverly McMillan** has been a science writer for more than 25 years. She holds undergraduate and graduate degrees from the University of California, Berkeley, and is coauthor of a college text in human biology, now in its 11th edition. She has also written or coauthored numerous trade books on scientific subjects and has worked extensively in educational and commercial publishing, including eight years in editorial management positions in the college divisions of Random House and McGraw-Hill.

# Brief Contents

# Contents

# Preface

Welcome to an exploration of the diversity of life. The main goal of this textbook is to guide you on a journey of discovery about life's diversity across levels ranging from molecules to genes, cells to organs, and species to ecosystems. Along the way, we will explore many questions about the mechanisms underlying diversity as well as the consequences of diversity, for our own species and for others.

## An emphasis on the diversity of life …

At first glance, the riot of life that animates the biosphere overwhelms our minds. One way to begin to make sense of this diversity is to divide it into manageable sections on the basis of differences. We also consider features found in all life forms to stress similarities as well as differences. We examine how different organisms solve the common problems of finding nutrients, energy, and mates on the third rock from our Sun. What basic evolutionary principles inform the relationships among life forms regardless of their different body plans, habitats, or life histories? Unlike many other first-year biology texts, this book has chapters integrating basic concepts such as the effects of genetic recombination, light, and domestication across the breadth of life from microbes to mistletoe to moose. As you read this book, you will be referred frequently to other chapters for linked information that expands the ideas further.

Evolution provides a powerful conceptual lens for viewing and understanding the roots and history of the diversity of living things. We will demonstrate how knowledge of evolution helps us appreciate the changes we observe in organisms. Whether the focus is the conversion of free-living prokaryotic organisms into mitochondria and chloroplasts or the steps involved in the domestication of rice, selection for particular traits over time can explain the current condition.

Examining how biological systems work is another theme pervading this text and underlying the idea of diversity. We have intentionally tried to include examples that will tax your imagination, from sea slugs that steal chloroplasts for use as solar panels, to the molecular basis of high altitude adaptations in deer mice, to adaptive radiation of viruses. In each situation, we examine how biologists have explored and assessed the inner workings of organisms, from gene regulation to the challenges of digesting cellulose.

Solving problems is another theme that runs throughout the book. Whether the topic is gene therapy to treat a disease in people, increasing crop production, or reducing the incidence of human obesity, both the problem and the solution lie in biology. We will explore large problems facing planet Earth and the social implications that arise from them.

## Emphasizing the big picture …

Many biology textbooks use the first few chapters to review fundamentals of chemistry and biochemistry as well as information on the scientific method. Instead of focusing on this background information, we have used the first chapter, in particular, to immediately engage students by conveying the excitement that is modern biology. We have put important background information in the centre of the book as a distinct reference section entitled *The Chemical and Physical Foundations of Biology*. With their purple borders, these pages are distinct and easy to find, and have become affectionately known as *The Purple Pages*. These pages enable information to be readily identifiable and accessible to students as they move through the textbook rather than being tied to a particular chapter. In this edition, the concepts of atoms, molecules, and macromolecules are connected through the theme of "emergent properties." By considering how the "stuff of life" interrelates as a function of increasing complexity rather than just memorizing the attributes of individual items, students can better grasp *why* biology works the way it does, rather than be awed by how much information we know about it.

We hope that Canadian students will find the subject of biology as it is presented here accessible and engaging because it is presented in familiar contexts. We have highlighted the work of Canadian scientists, used examples of Canadian species, and referred to Canadian regulations and institutions.

## Focusing on research to help students engage the living world as scientists …

A primary goal of this book is to evoke and sustain students' curiosity about biology, rather than dulling it with a mountain of disconnected facts. We can help students develop the mental habits of scientists and a fascination with the living world by conveying our passion for biological research. We want to excite students not only with *what biologists know* about the living world but also with *how they know it* and *what they still need to learn*. In doing so, we can encourage some students to accept the challenge and become biologists themselves, posing and answering important new questions through their own innovative research. For students who pursue other careers, we hope that they will leave their introductory—and perhaps only—biology course armed with intellectual skills that will enable them to evaluate future knowledge with a critical eye.

In this book, we introduce students to a biologist's "ways of learning." Research biologists constantly integrate new observations, hypotheses, questions, experiments, and insights with existing knowledge and ideas. To help students engage the world as biologists do, we must not simply introduce them to the current state of knowledge, we must also foster an appreciation of the historical context within which those ideas developed, and identify the future directions that biological research is likely to take.

Because advances in science occur against a background of research, we also give students a feeling for how biologists of the past formulated basic knowledge in the field. By fostering an appreciation of such discoveries, given the information and theories available to scientists in their own time, we can help students understand the successes and limitations of what we consider cutting edge today. This historical perspective also encourages students to view biology as a dynamic intellectual enterprise, not just a collection of facts and generalities to be memorized.

We have endeavoured to make the science of biology come alive by describing how biologists formulate hypotheses and evaluate them using hard-won data; how data sometimes tell only part of a story; and how the results of studies often end up posing more questions than they answer. Our exploration of the Tully Monster in Chapter 27 is a case in point. Since its fossil discovery and description, this mainly soft-bodied animal has been tentatively classified with species in five different groups of animals. Through this example, and throughout Chapter 27, we explore the current recognition that the historical and traditional grouping of animals into protostomes and deuterostomes is more artificial than real.

Although students might prefer simply to learn the "right" answer to a question, they must be encouraged to embrace "the unknown," those gaps in knowledge that create opportunities for further research. An appreciation of what biologists do *not* yet know will draw more students into the field. And by defining *why* scientists do not understand interesting phenomena, we encourage students to think critically about possible solutions and to follow paths dictated by their own curiosity. We hope that this approach will encourage students to make biology a part of their daily lives by having informal discussions and debates about new scientific discoveries.

## Presenting the story line of the research process ...

Science is by its nature a progressive enterprise in which answers to questions open new questions for consideration. In preparing this book, we developed several special features to help students broaden their understanding of the material presented and of the research process itself:

- The chapter openers, titled **Why It Matters,** are engaging, short vignettes designed to capture students' imaginations and whet their appetites for the topic that the chapter addresses. In many cases, this feature uses current Canadian examples and tells the story of how a researcher or researchers arrived at a key insight, or how biological research solved a major societal problem, explained a fundamental process, or elucidated a phenomenon. The Why It Matters feature links the insight from the vignette to the contents of the chapter to spark student interest in the topic at hand.

- Three types of specially designed *research figures* provide more detailed information about how biologists formulate specific hypotheses and test them by gathering and interpreting data. **Experimental Research** figures describe specific studies in which researchers used both experimental and control treatments, either in the laboratory or in the field, to test hypotheses or answer research questions by manipulating the system they studied. **Observational Research** figures describe specific studies in which biologists have tested hypotheses by comparing systems under varying natural circumstances. **Research Method** figures provide examples of important techniques, such as light and electron microscopy, the polymerase chain reaction, making a knockout mouse, DNA microarray analysis, plant cell culture, producing monoclonal antibodies, radiometric dating, and cladistic analysis. Each *Research Method* figure leads a student through the purpose of the technique and protocol, and describes how scientists interpret the data it generates.

## Integrating effective, high-quality visuals into the narrative ...

Today's students are accustomed to receiving ideas and information visually, making the illustrations and photographs in a textbook and the fully integrated online resources critically important. From the first Canadian edition, our illustration program has provided an exceptionally clear supplement to the narrative in a style that is consistent throughout the book. Graphs and anatomical drawings are annotated with interpretive explanations that lead students, step by step, through the major points they convey.

Over subsequent editions, we have continued to enhance the illustration program, focusing on features that reviewers and users of the book identified as the most useful pedagogical tools. In revising the text, we reevaluated each illustration and photograph, and made appropriate changes to improve their utility as teaching tools.

For this most recent edition, we have made some exciting new additions to our illustration program through the creation of **Chapter Roadmaps** and **Summary Illustrations** for every chapter the book. Chapter Roadmaps appear at the beginning of each chapter and provide a visual overview of the chapter contents. Connections between topics across chapters are emphasized to give students a sense of how the content of each chapter fits within the larger context of the book, and biology as a whole. At the end of each chapter, we have created vivid and engaging

Summary Illustrations that depict the core concepts—and teaching heart—of the chapter. These illustrations provide students with a visual overview of the connections between key concepts, and provide a unique touchstone to review and gauge understanding of the chapter contents.

## Organizing chapters around important concepts …

As authors and university teachers, we understand how easily students can get lost within a chapter. When students request advice about how to read a chapter and learn the material in it, we usually suggest that, after reading each section, they pause and quiz themselves on the material they have just encountered. After completing all the sections in a chapter, they should quiz themselves again, even more rigorously, on the individual sections and, most important, on how the concepts that were developed in the different sections fit together. Accordingly, we have adopted a structure for each chapter to help students review concepts as they learn them.

- The organization within chapters presents material in digestible sections, building on students' knowledge and understanding as they acquire it. Each major section covers one broad topic.
- **Study Break** questions follow every major section. These reading comprehension questions encourage students to pause at the end of a section and review what they have learned before going on to the next topic within the chapter. If a student isn't able to answer a study break question, they can immediately revisit the previous section to solidify their understanding. We feel that this is a better learning tool than directly providing the answers to these questions. If the answer does not come easily, then rereading the material associated with the answer is as important as seeing the answer itself.
- **Self-Test Questions** are found at the end of each chapter. These chapter review questions are organized according to Bloom's taxonomy into three sections: Recall/Understand, Apply/Analyze, and Create/Evaluate. This structure allows students to review the material in a sequence that moves from the basic knowledge of factual material, to more challenging and sophisticated applications of that knowledge, to novel situations. Answers to the Self-Test Questions are found in an appendix at the back of the book.
- *The Chemical and Physical Foundations of Biology,* also known as **The Purple Pages,** keep background information out of the main text, allowing students to focus on the bigger picture.
- *Unit 5: The Diversity of Life,* also known as **The Green Pages,** contains readily identifiable chapters that introduce the tremendous variability among living organisms.

## Effectively introducing digital solutions into your classroom—online or in class—is now easier than ever …

The fourth Canadian edition of *Biology: Exploring the Diversity of Life* represents a fully integrated package of print and media, providing comprehensive learning tools and flexible delivery options. In preparing this edition, we conducted extensive research to determine how instructors prefer to present online learning opportunities. The result of this research is a new MindTap course organized around the instructors' preferred workflow. Instructors can now select just the content they want to assign, chosen from a comprehensive set of learning materials provided with the course for each chapter. Many types of learning activities are assignable and offer students immediate feedback and automated instructor assessment.

Research also indicates that online content is most effective when it enhances conceptual understanding through the use of relevant applications. In this edition, we have developed new assessable online learning activities that provide students the opportunity to explore and practice biology the way scientists practice biology:

- *Interpret the Data* exercises have been enhanced by an additional online exercise to further develop student quantitative analysis and mathematical reasoning skills.
- The *Design an Experiment* feature is delivered online as a guided learning activity that takes the student through the process of designing an experiment.
- *Conceptual Learning Activities* are repeatable in alternate versions to help students learn the material.

The *Instructor Resource Center* provides everything you need for your course in one place. This collection of lecture and class tools is available online for instructors only via **www .nelson.com/instructor.** There you can access and download PowerPoint presentations, images, the Instructor's Manual, the Test Bank, videos, animations, and more.

To maximize the chances of producing a useful text that draws in students (and instructors), we sought the advice of colleagues who teach biology (members of the MindTap Advisory Board). We also asked students (members of the Student Advisory Boards) for their advice and comments. These groups evaluated the effectiveness of important visuals in the textbook, evaluated draft chapters, and provided valuable feedback on the MindTap, but any mistakes are ours.

In summary, we have applied our collective experience as teachers, researchers, and writers to create a readable and understandable foundation for students who may choose to enrol in more advanced biology courses in the future. Where appropriate, we provide straightforward explanations of fundamental concepts from the evolutionary perspective that binds together all the biological sciences. Recognizing that students in an introductory biology course face a potentially daunting quantity of ideas and information, we strive to provide an appropriate balance between factual and conceptual material, taking great care to provide clear explanations of how scientists draw conclusions from empirical data. Our approach helps students understand how we achieved our present knowledge. Clarity of presentation, thoughtful organization, a logical and seamless flow of topics within chapters, and carefully designed illustrations are key to our approach.

We hope that you are as captivated by the biological world as we are, and are drawn from one chapter to another. But don't stop there; use the digital and other resources to broaden your search for understanding, and, most important, observe and enjoy the diversity of life around you.

M. Brock Fenton
Denis Maxwell
Tom Haffie
Bill Milsom
Todd Nickle
Shona Ellis
London, Calgary, and Vancouver
January 2018

# New to This Edition

The enhancements we have made in the fourth Canadian edition of *Biology: Exploring the Diversity of Life* reflect our commitment to providing a textbook that introduces students to new developments in biology while fostering active learning and critical thinking.

Our revisions to the new edition were guided by five important principles:

- Reduce the size of the book
- Ensure content is relevant and engaging for students and instructors
- Emphasize connections
- Support concepts with visuals wherever possible
- Extensively revise and rewrite Unit Four: Evolution and Classification

## A streamlined textbook …

In response to feedback from students and instructors across the country, we have made some important changes that have resulted in a briefer edition.

### Organizational Changes

By combining and reorganizing information, we have reduced the number of chapters in the book from 52 to 46. The material on protostomes and deuterostomes has been combined into a single super chapter on animals. Using the latest research as our guide, Chapter 27: Animals captures the excitement of how new developments in molecular phylogenetic techniques have resulted in many taxonomic reclassifications as well as changes to phylogenies. This chapter features a unique research box on the Tully Monster as a case in point.

We have also streamlined our coverage of systems and processes in animals by combining reproduction and development to create Chapter 44: Animal Reproduction. The chapters on neural control and neural integration have been combined to create Chapter 45: Control of Animal Processes: Neural Control.

We have also rewritten former Chapter 33: Putting Selection to Work and Chapter 52: Conservation and Evolutionary Physiology into a collection of case studies and placed them on the MindTap for the book.

### Streamlined Pedagogy and Prose

Our revisions to the fourth Canadian edition were also informed by a desire to reduce redundancy across the book, including only essential, testable information. As a result, students and instructors will find an efficient use of prose across the new edition, as well as extensive use of cross-references to other chapters, where necessary. The feature boxes "Molecule behind Biology," "People behind Biology," and "Life on the Edge" have also been moved from the book to the Instructor's Manual, allowing instructors to continue to draw upon these engaging stories and vignettes, without increasing the length of the textbook.

## Engaging and relevant content …

From personal genome reports to cues to recognizing human female ovulation, the new edition is full of engaging examples that reflect everyday biology and its impact on society. In addition to references to Canadian research and researchers throughout the book, our MindTap features profiles of 13 former biology students, and what they have done with their biology degrees in "Where Are They Now?"

## Emphasizing connections …

We recognize that part of the challenge of an introduction to biology course lays in covering a large breadth of knowledge while making meaningful connections across topics, concepts, and the discipline as a whole. In *Biology: Exploring the Diversity of Life*, every chapter begins with a **Chapter Roadmap** that provides students with a visual overview of the chapter contents, while making connections between parts of the chapter and other chapters in the book. Within chapters, students will find cross-references and connections to other chapters where a concept is explored further or from a different perspective. Furthermore, every chapter concludes with a **Summary Illustration,** a two-page spread that synthesizes, integrates, and illustrates connections between important concepts covered in the chapter.

## Clear and thoughtful visuals …

Each of the figures in the new edition delivers a clear and thoughtful message that is tied directly to the discussion it accompanies. The new edition contains over 200 new and 55 revised figures. We have further enhanced this connection through the refinement and integration of research figures. **Experimental Research, Observational Research,** and **Research Methods** are further highlighted in a vivid new design, drawing attention to how biologists formulate and test specific hypotheses by gathering and interpreting data.

## Extensively Revised Unit Four: Evolution and Classification

The fundamental concepts of evolution are essential for students to grasp as they explain the diversity of living organisms as well as the commonalities that organisms possess. That said, many first-year students come to university with a poor understanding of evolutionary principles; whether it's the importance of chance mutation as a driver of evolutionary change or that evolution can occur in the absence of natural selection.

With this in mind, we have extensively revised this unit to focus more clearly on conveying the fundamental concepts of evolution, to provide greater clarity on the processes that cause evolutionary change, as well as to make critical connections between evolution and genetics. Chapter 16: Evolution by Natural Selection now includes a section and Research Figure focused on experimental evolution in *E. coli,* as well as a concluding figure that explains the major misconceptions students have concerning evolution and natural selection. Chapter 17: Microevolution: Changes Within Populations has been rewritten to make stronger connections to genetics, which are often not made in the context of evolution, by fully explaining terms such as *allele, gene, gene pool,* and *locus.* This chapter also emphasizes the role of random mutation in evolution and its importance in introducing genetic novelty. Chapter 18: Speciation and Macroevolution has improved flow and clarity, including simpler and more informative figures. Chapter 19: Systematics and Phylogenetics: Revealing the Tree of Life is now its own dedicated chapter. This allows for more clear discussion of the tools and approaches used today to infer evolutionary histories. Great care has been taken to clearly define and present concepts of homology and convergent evolution.

## Major revisions to selected chapters are listed below:

### Chapter 1: Light and Life

- Streamlined to be more concise

### Chapter 2: The Cell: An Overview

- NEW Research Figure about cell fractionalization

### Chapter 3: Energy and Enzymes

- More precise description of fundamentals of thermodynamics
- Improved and clarified figures related to exergonic and endergonic reactions

### Chapter 4: Cell Membranes and Signalling

- NEW Research Figure: Frye–Edidin Experiment Demonstrating that the Phospholipid Bilayer Is Fluid
- NEW Research Figure: Freeze Fracture

### Chapter 5: Cellular Respiration

- Clarified section on chemical basis of cellular respiration to include stronger connections with Chapter 3

### Chapter 6: Photosynthesis

- Clarified and improved selected figures

### Chapter 7: Cell Cycles

- NEW Why It Matters about algal blooms in Lake Erie
- NEW material on DNA packaging
- NEW figure clarifying replicated versus unreplicated chromosomes

### Chapter 8: Genetic Recombination

- Added explicit reference to cytokinesis
- Specified creation of haploid cells

### Chapter 9: The Chromosomal Basis of Mendelian Inheritance

- NEW Canadian Why It Matters about the spirit bears of British Columbia
- Enhanced discussion connecting genes/alleles to proteins and protein products, and to the expression of alleles in the phenotype as dominant/recessive

### Chapter 10: Genetic Linkage, Sex Linkage, and Other Non-Mendelian Inheritance Mechanisms

- NEW Canadian Why It Matters about disease incidence in Quebec
- NEW figures and examples dealing with translocations, imprinting, and pedigree analysis

### Chapter 11: DNA Structure, Replication, and Repair

- NEW Canadian Why It Matters about woolly mammoths in Canada
- Highlighted mechanisms of repair of DNA damage

### Chapter 12: Gene Structure, Expression, and Mutation

- NEW Canadian Why It Matters about poisonous mushrooms in British Columbia
- Expanded material on mutations and how they can affect protein function
- NEW discussion about ENCODE versus the junk DNA debate
- Expanded and clarified discussion of mutagenesis

### Chapter 13: Regulation of Gene Expression

- NEW Why It Matters featuring epigenetic regulation of honeybee castes

- Updated material on lncRNA
- Updated material on cancer genetics

## Chapter 14: DNA Technologies

- NEW section on CRISPR and qPCR
- Clarified and expanded Health Canada position on genetically modified foods
- Added material on knockout mouse protocol

## Chapter 15: Genomics

- Fully updated
- NEW section on comparative genomics
- Linked advances in sequencing technologies from Sanger to early next-gen methods to DNA replication outlined in Chapter 11
- Enhanced explanation of principles behind BLAST

## Chapter 16: Evolution: The Development of the Theory

- Completely rewritten with a greater focus on fundamental concepts of evolution and less emphasis on historical development
- NEW Why It Matters about antibiotic resistance
- Section and Experimental Research Figure focused on experimental evolution in *E. coli*
- Concluding figure explains the major misconceptions students have with evolution and natural selection

## Chapter 17: Microevolution: Changes within Populations

- Completely rewritten with greater clarity on the processes that cause evolutionary change
- Stronger connections with genetics by fully explaining terms such as allele, gene, gene pool, locus
- Emphasis on the role of random mutation, the different types and when they occur, that may drive the introduction of genetic novelty

## Chapter 18: Speciation and Macroevolution

- Improved flow and clarity of the writing
- Simpler and more informative figures

## Chapter 19: Systematics and Phylogenetics: Revealing the Tree of Life

- In the previous edition, systematics and phylogenetics were grouped with the history of life (geological record) as a single chapter. This made it somewhat disjointed. In this edition, systematics and phylogenetics is its own dedicated chapter. This allows for clearer discussion of the tools and approaches used today to infer evolutionary histories.

- The concepts of homology and convergent evolution are more clearly presented.

## Chapter 20: Humans and Evolution

- Unchanged from previous edition

## Chapter 21: Defining Life and Its Origins

- In this edition, this chapter includes a section on the fossil record.
- Expanded section discussing possible energy sources for early life
- More in-depth discussion on LUCA

## Chapter 22: Viruses, Viroids, and Prions: Infectious Biological Particles

- NEW Canadian example about tracking viral disease
- NEW Research Figure: A New Discovery for Hepatitis C Therapy

## Chapter 23: Bacteria and Archaea

- Phylogenetic tree updated to reflect latest research
- NEW Research Figure: Genetic Recombination in Bacteria
- NEW discussion of a recent finding of a group within Archaea (Lokiarchaeota) that has a number of genes in common with eukaryotes

## Chapter 24: Protists

- Phylogenetic tree updated to reflect latest research
- Incorporated recent research on Diplonemids that had been previously known from only a single environmental gene from marine planktonic samples
- NEW Research Figure: Isolation and Identification of Marine Diplonemids

## Chapter 25: Fungi

- Incorporated information on a recent discovery in lichens related to the third symbiont, a basidiomycete yeast that is part of the symbiosis that influences the morphology of lichen
- Added material on the *Puccinia*–grain interaction
- NEW Research Figure: Hidden Third Partner in Lichen Symbiosis

## Chapter 26: Plants

- NEW Research Figure: Exploring a Possible Early Angiosperm Adaptation for Efficient Photosynthesis in Dim Environments
- Extensive revision of key figures for clarity

## Chapter 27: Animals

- NEW chapter that combines both protostomes and deuterostomes
- Includes latest research on phylogenetic tree
- NEW Research in Biology box on the Tully Monster

## Chapter 28: Conservation of Biodiversity

- NEW Why It Matters featuring the extinction of passenger pigeons
- NEW section on the Anthropocene
- Enhanced discussion of human impact on landscapes
- NEW material on ecosystem services
- NEW discussion of the impact of wolf predation on populations of caribou

## Chapter 29: Population Ecology

- NEW Why It Matters about the other malaria
- NEW Research Figure: Evaluating Density-Dependent Interactions between Species
- NEW section on Human Administered Population Control

## Chapter 30: Species Interactions and Community Ecology

- NEW Why It Matters about oxpeckers and their hosts
- NEW coverage of blood feeders
- NEW material on venoms, how animals use them and how they work

## Chapter 31: Ecosystems

- NEW Why It Matters about cave ecosystems
- Updated discussion of mass mortality
- Enhanced discussion of urban ecosystems

## Chapter 32: Animal Behaviour

- NEW Why It Matters about bird migration
- NEW discussion about changing behaviour, featuring moose, salt, and cars
- NEW coverage of echolocation
- NEW material on the evolution of human language

## Chapter 33: Organization of the Plant Body

- Incorporation of current research that demonstrates, with the discovery of new transcription factors, that there is an unexpectedly complex regulatory network governing secondary wall development
- NEW Research Figure: Networking the Secondary Cell Wall

## Chapter 34: Transport in Plants

- NEW Research Figure: Translocation Pressure

## Chapter 35: Reproduction and Development in Flowering Plants

- NEW section explaining the genetics behind the ABC model of floral development
- NEW section showing how plant tissue culture can generate virus-free plants from infected donors

## Chapter 36: Plant Nutrition

- Assimilation of nutrients connected with material in *The Purple Pages*

## Chapter 37: Plant Signals and Responses to the Environment

- Updated section on Darwin's experiments using light and oat coleoptiles

## Chapter 38: Introduction to Animal Organization and Physiology

- NEW Research Figure: Demonstration of the Use of the Bill for Thermoregulation in Birds

## Chapter 39: Animal Nutrition

- NEW Research Figure: Association of Bacterial Populations in the Gut Microbiome with Obesity in Humans
- NEW definition of essential nutrients, malnutrition, and undernutrition
- NEW figure illustrating intracellular digestion

## Chapter 40: Gas Exchange: The Respiratory System

- NEW Why It Matters, featuring a discussion of adaptations that allow animals to live in oxygen-limited environments (burrows, during diving, at altitude)
- NEW Research Figure: Demonstration of a Molecular Basis for High-Altitude Adaptation in Deer Mice

## Chapter 41: Internal Transport: The Circulatory System

- NEW Why It Matters, featuring the effects of animal body size on resting heart rate (but not longevity)
- NEW Research Figure: Demonstration of a Vasodilatory Signalling Molecule

## Chapter 42: Regulation of the Internal Environment: Water, Solutes, and Temperature

- NEW Research Figure: ADH-Stimulated Water Reabsorption in the Kidney Collecting Duct

- Added new section on the regulation of mammalian kidney function
- Refined discussion to clarify the difference between osmolality and osmolarity

## Chapter 43: Control of Animal Processes: Endocrine Control

- NEW Why It Matters, featuring endocrine control of mating behaviour in elk
- NEW Research Figure: Demonstration That Epinephrine Acts by Binding to a Plasma Membrane Receptor

## Chapter 44: Animal Reproduction

- NEW chapter created by combining reproduction and development
- Added sexual reproduction as a route for infection
- Clarified discussion of where organelles were in the sperm
- NEW Research Figure: Vocal Cues of Ovulation in Human Females

## Chapter 45: Control of Animal Processes: Neural Control

- NEW chapter created by combining neural control and integration
- Clarified the difference between the spike initiation zone and the axon hillock
- Clarified resting and membrane potential
- NEW Concept Fix addressing passive versus gated channels
- Enhanced discussion of the refractory period and why it is important for nerve conduction
- NEW Research Figure: Demonstration of Chemical Transmission of Nerve Impulses at Synapses

## Chapter 46: Muscles, Skeletons, and Body Movements

- NEW Concept Fix addressing the misconceptions about muscles getting smaller as they contract
- More human examples integrated throughout
- NEW Research Figure: The Sliding Filament Model of Muscle Contraction

# Welcome to *Biology: Exploring the Diversity of Life,* 4Ce

*Biology: Exploring the Diversity of Life* and MindTap engage students so they learn not only WHAT scientists know, but HOW they know it and what they still need to learn.

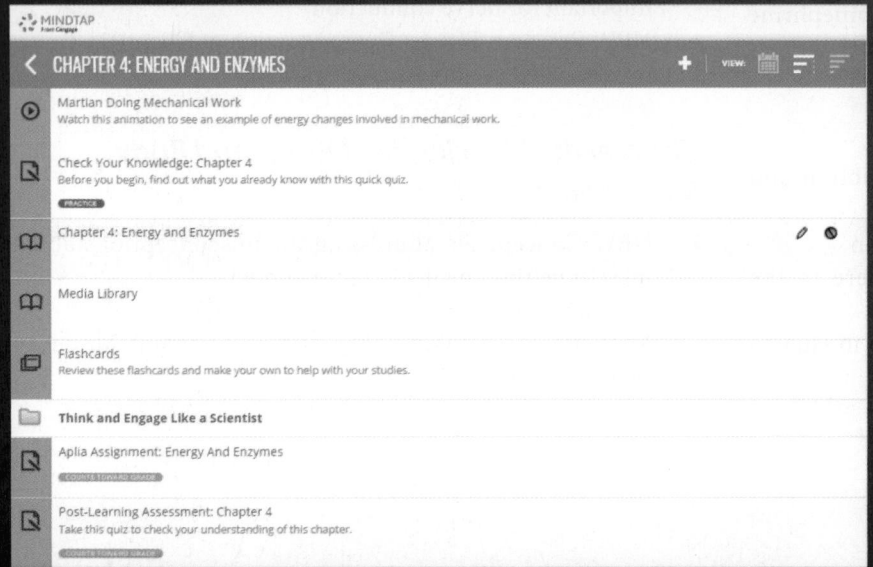

◀ **Engage, Adapt, and Master!** Stay organized and efficient with **MindTap**—a single destination with all the course material and study aids you need to succeed. Built-in apps leverage social media and the latest learning technology to help you succeed. Our customized learning path is designed to help you engage with biological concepts, identify gaps in your knowledge, and master the material!

▼ **Adapt!** Reinforce your knowledge of concepts by working through our Biology MindTap Study Guide, which includes

- animations and videos
- topic maps, learning outcomes, and study strategies
- multimodal quiz questions with instant feedback
- vocabulary flashcards
- chapter summaries

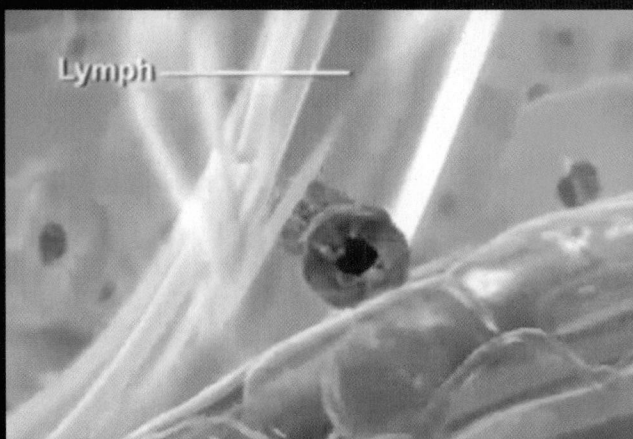

▲ **Engage!** The learning path for each chapter begins with an engaging video designed to pique your interest in the chapter contents. Take the tutorial quiz to assess gaps in your knowledge, and strengthen your knowledge of concepts by reviewing the ebook.

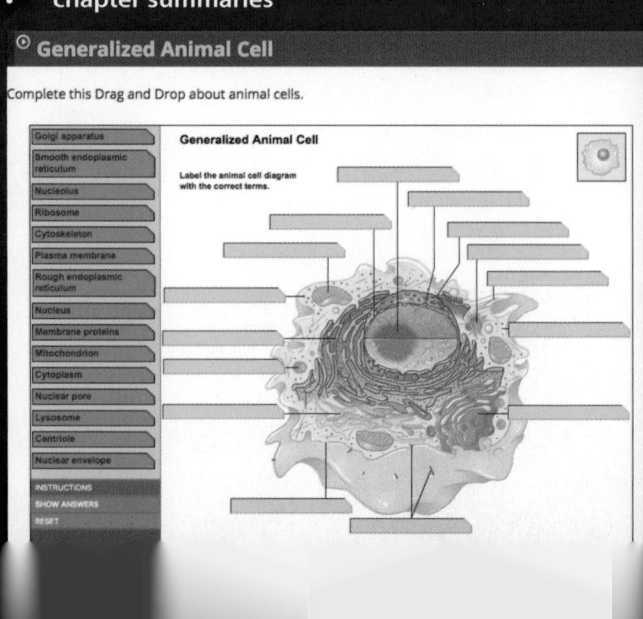

## Interpret the Data

Investigators studying protein changes during aging examined enzyme activity in cells extracted from the nematode worm *Caenorhabditis elegans*. The cell extracts were treated to conserve enzyme activity, although the investigators noted that some proteins were broken down by the extraction procedure. The extracts were centrifuged, and seven fractions were collected in sequence to isolate the location of activity by protease enzymes called cathepsins. Examine the activity profiles in the Figure. In which fraction and, hence, in which eukaryotic cellular structure are these enzymes most active?

**Figure    Distribution of Enzyme Activity in Fractions from Centrifugation of an Organelle Pellet.**

The fractions are numbered 1 to 7 from the top to the bottom of the centrifuge tube. Fraction 1 contains cytosolic contents and is the supernatant, and fraction 7 contains cellular debris and membrane fragments.

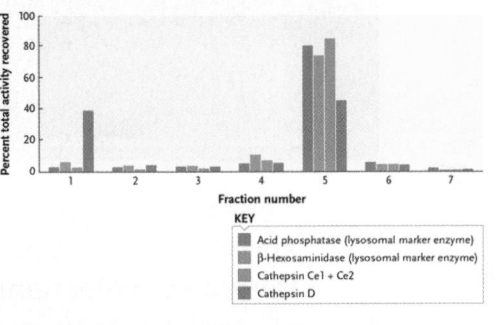

**KEY**
- Acid phosphatase (lysosomal marker enzyme)
- β-Hexosaminidase (lysosomal marker enzyme)
- Cathepsin Ce1 + Ce2
- Cathepsin D

---

Determine which strand is which, and complete the blanks to identify them.

The following strand presents the sequence of the _____.

5'– G* – GCCACC **AUG**GGACCC........ [ nontemplate DNA / template DNA / mature mRNA ] ........CCA**UAG**

The following strand presents the sequence of the _____.

5' ...TATAAAA... GCCACC **ATG**GGACCC................................CCA**TAG**

The following strand presents the sequence of the encoded polypeptide.

N terminus — **Met** AA₂ AA₃ ................................ AA_n

The following strand presents the sequence of the _____.

3' ...ATATTTT... CGGTGG **TAC**CCTGGG................................GGT**ATC**

The blue-colored region is the _____.

---

◀ **Master!** Think and engage like a scientist by taking gradable short-answer quizzes:

- **Apply Evolutionary Thinking** questions ask you to interpret a relevant topic in relation to the principles of evolutionary biology.
- **Design an Experiment** challenges your understanding of the chapter and helps you deepen your understanding of the scientific method as you consider how to develop and test hypotheses about a situation that relates to a main chapter topic.
- **Interpret the Data** questions help you develop analytical and quantitative skills by asking you to interpret graphical or tabular results of experimental or observational research experiments for which the hypotheses and methods of analysis are presented.

Test your mastery of concepts with **Aplia for Biology,** a series of **Conceptual Problem Sets** that complement the text and help you learn and understand key concepts through focused assignments, an engaging variety of problem types, exceptional text/art integration, and immediate feedback.

Assess your knowledge of chapter concepts by taking the **Post-Learning Assessment,** a set of higher-level quiz questions designed to test the depth of your understanding.

# Active Learning

Visually stunning features that engage your students in the process of learning because an engaged student is a successful student.

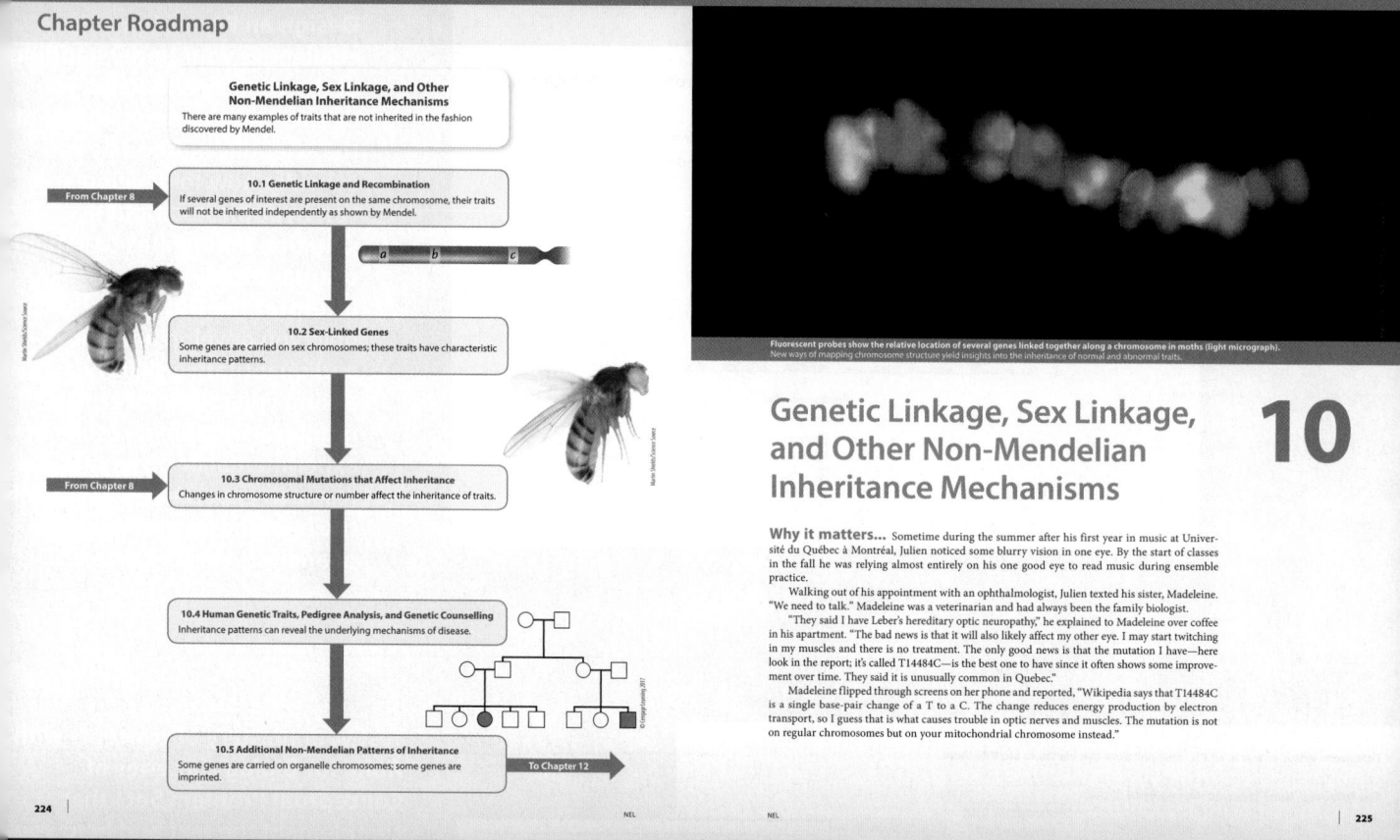

## Chapter Roadmap

**Genetic Linkage, Sex Linkage, and Other Non-Mendelian Inheritance Mechanisms**
There are many examples of traits that are not inherited in the fashion discovered by Mendel.

From Chapter 8

**10.1 Genetic Linkage and Recombination**
If several genes of interest are present on the same chromosome, their traits will not be inherited independently as shown by Mendel.

**10.2 Sex-Linked Genes**
Some genes are carried on sex chromosomes; these traits have characteristic inheritance patterns.

From Chapter 8

**10.3 Chromosomal Mutations that Affect Inheritance**
Changes in chromosome structure or number affect the inheritance of traits.

**10.4 Human Genetic Traits, Pedigree Analysis, and Genetic Counselling**
Inheritance patterns can reveal the underlying mechanisms of disease.

**10.5 Additional Non-Mendelian Patterns of Inheritance**
Some genes are carried on organelle chromosomes; some genes are imprinted.

To Chapter 12

Fluorescent probes show the relative location of several genes linked together along a chromosome in moths (light micrograph). New ways of mapping chromosome structure yield insights into the inheritance of normal and abnormal traits.

## Genetic Linkage, Sex Linkage, and Other Non-Mendelian Inheritance Mechanisms — 10

**Why it matters...** Sometime during the summer after his first year in music at Université du Québec à Montréal, Julien noticed some blurry vision in one eye. By the start of classes in the fall he was relying almost entirely on his one good eye to read music during ensemble practice.

Walking out of his appointment with an ophthalmologist, Julien texted his sister, Madeleine. "We need to talk." Madeleine was a veterinarian and had always been the family biologist.

"They said I have Leber's hereditary optic neuropathy," he explained to Madeleine over coffee in his apartment. "The bad news is that it will also likely affect my other eye. I may start twitching in my muscles and there is no treatment. The only good news is that the mutation I have—here look in the report; it's called T14484C—is the best one to have since it often shows some improvement over time. They said it is unusually common in Quebec."

Madeleine flipped through screens on her phone and reported, "Wikipedia says that T14484C is a single base-pair change of a T to a C. The change reduces energy production by electron transport, so I guess that is what causes trouble in optic nerves and muscles. The mutation is not on regular chromosomes but on your mitochondrial chromosome instead."

224 — NEL — NEL — 225

▲ **Chapter Roadmaps** The Chapter Roadmaps provide a visual overview of the major sections in the chapter and show the connections between the topics in the chapter and other chapters in the book.

**Why It Matters ...** Why It Matters draws students in with an engaging vignette that is linked to the concepts discussed in the chapter.

**Concept Fix Icons** Concept Fixes draw on the extensive research literature dealing with misconceptions commonly held by biology students. Strategically placed throughout the text, these short segments help students identify—and correct—a wide range of misunderstandings. ▼

## STUDY BREAK QUESTIONS

1. What are the three interrelated systems that contribute to the eukaryotic cell cycle?
2. What is a chromosome composed of?
3. When is a chromosome composed of two chromatids?

▲ **Study Breaks** The Study Breaks fall at the end of each major section and encourage students to pause and review what they have learned before going on to the next topic within the chapter.

**CONCEPT FIX** Coming out of high school, many students think that ATP is a product of the respiratory ETC. This is a misconception that we need to fix. The generation of ATP by the ATP synthase complex is linked, or coupled, to electron transport by the proton gradient established across the inner mitochondrial membrane. But electron transport and the chemiosmotic generation of ATP are separate and distinct processes and are not always completely coupled (**Figure 5.17**). For example, it is possible to have high rates of electron transport (and thus high rates of oxygen consumption) and yet no ATP generated by chemiosmosis. This uncoupling of the two processes occurs when mechanisms prevent the formation of a proton-motive force. ◖

## FIGURE 10.2 Experimental Research

### Evidence for Gene Linkage

**Question:** Do the purple-eye and vestigial-wing genes of *Drosophila* assort independently?

**Experiment:** Morgan crossed true-breeding, wild-type flies having red eyes and normal wings with purple-eyed, vestigial-winged flies. The F1 dihybrids were all wild type in phenotype. Next he crossed the F1 dihybrid flies with purple-eyed, vestigial-winged flies (this is a testcross) and analyzed the phenotypes of the progeny.

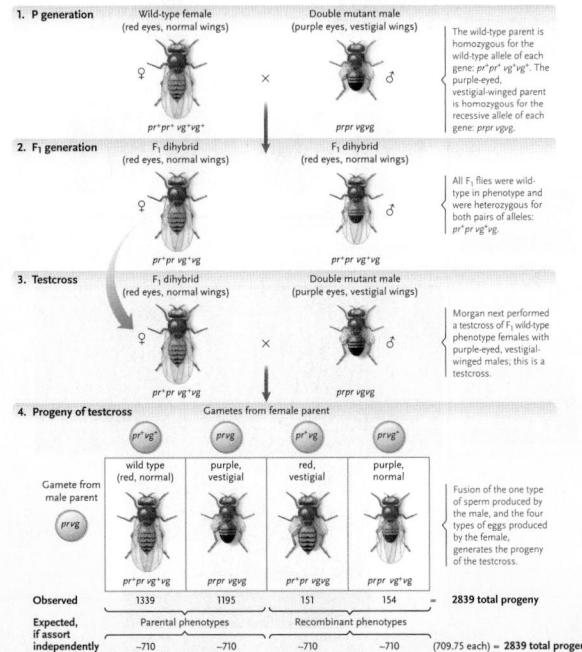

**Results:** 2534 of the testcross progeny flies were parental—wild-type or purple, vestigial—while 305 of the progeny were recombinant—red, vestigial or purple, normal. If the genes assorted independently, the expectation is for a 1:1:1:1 ratio for testcross progeny: approximately 1420 of both parental and recombinant progeny.

**Conclusion:** The purple-eye and vestigial-wing genes do not assort independently. The simplest alternative is that the two genes are linked on the same chromosome. The small number of flies with recombinant phenotypes is explained by crossing-over.

◀ **Experimental Research Figures** Experimental Research figures describe specific studies in which research used both experimental and control treatments—either in the laboratory or in the field—to test hypotheses or answer research questions by manipulating the system they studied.

**Research Method Figures** Research Method Figures provide examples of important techniques, lead students through the purpose of the technique and protocol, and describe how scientists interpret the data generated. ▼

## FIGURE 14.3 Research Method

### Identifying a Recombinant Plasmid Containing a Gene of Interest

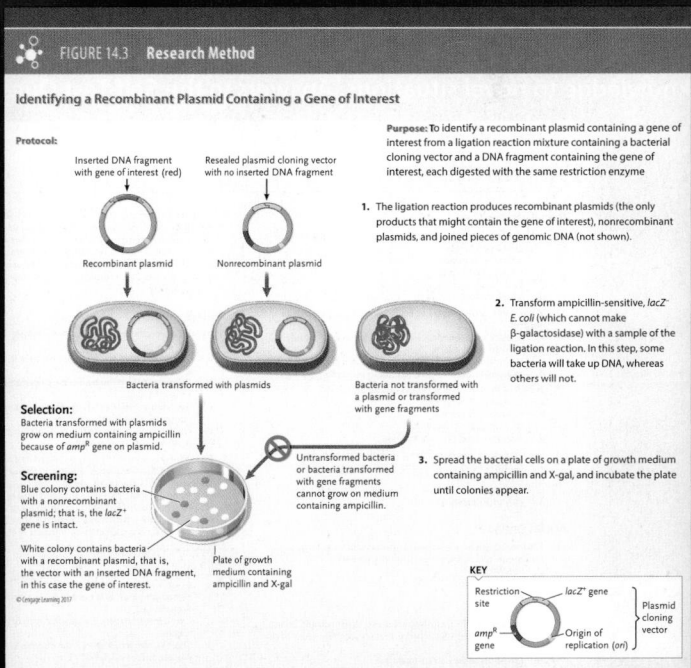

**Interpreting the Results:** All the colonies on the plate contain plasmids because the bacteria that form the colonies are resistant to the ampicillin present in the growth medium. Blue–white screening distinguishes bacterial colonies with nonrecombinant plasmids from those with recombinant plasmids. Bacteria making up blue colonies contain nonrecombinant plasmids. These plasmids have intact *lacZ+* genes and produce β-galactosidase, which changes X-gal to a blue product. Bacteria that form the white colonies contain recombinant plasmids. Each recombinant plasmid has a DNA fragment (in this example, the gene of interest) inserted into the *lacZ* gene, so β-galactosidase cannot be produced. As a result, bacteria with recombinant plasmids cannot convert X-gal to the blue product and the colonies are white. Culturing a white colony produces large quantities of the recombinant plasmid that can be isolated and purified for analysis and/or manipulation of the gene = "gene of interest".

## FIGURE 18.16 Observational Research

### Chromosomal Similarities and Differences among Humans and the Great Apes

**Question:** Does chromosome structure differ between humans and their closest relatives among the apes?

**Hypothesis:** Large-scale chromosome rearrangements contributed to the development of reproductive isolation between species within the evolutionary lineage that includes humans and apes.

**Prediction:** Chromosome structure differs markedly between humans and their close relatives among the great apes: chimpanzees, gorillas, and orangutans.

**Method:** Jorge J. Yunis and Om Prakash, of the University of Minnesota Medical School, used Giemsa stain to visualize the banding patterns on metaphase chromosome preparations from humans, chimpanzees, gorillas, and orangutans. They identified about 1000 bands that are present in humans and in the three ape species. By matching the banding patterns on the chromosomes, the researchers verified that they were comparing the same segments of the genomes in the four species. They then searched for similarities and differences in the structure of the chromosomes.

**Results:** Analysis of human chromosome 2 reveals that it was produced by the fusion of two smaller chromosomes that are still present in the other three species. Although the position of the centromere in human chromosome 2 matches that of the centromere in one of the chimpanzee chromosomes, in gorillas and orangutans it falls within an inverted segment of the chromosome.

**Conclusion:** Differences in chromosome structure between humans and both gorillas and orangutans are more pronounced than they are between humans and chimpanzees. Structural differences in the chromosomes of these four species may contribute to their reproductive isolation.

Source: © Cengage Learning 2017. Based on J. J. Yunis and O. Prakash. 1982. The origin of man: A chromosomal pictorial legacy. *Science* 215:1525–1530.

▲ **Observational Research Figures** Observational Research Figures describe specific studies in which biologists have tested hypotheses by comparing systems under varying natural circumstances.

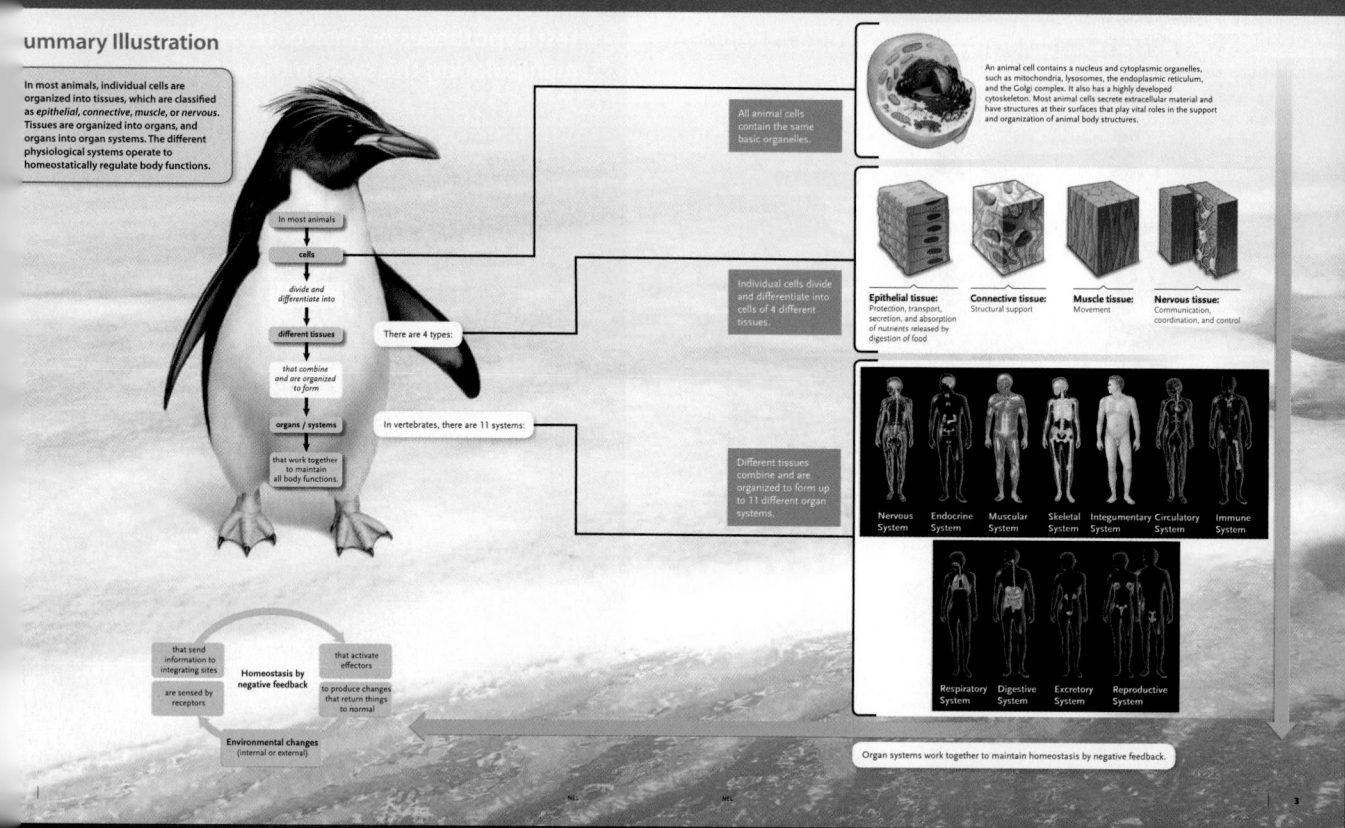

## SELF-TEST QUESTIONS

### Recall/Understand

1. Which of these factors is found in organic molecules that are considered good fuels?
   a. many C—H bonds
   b. many C=C double bonds
   c. an abundance of oxygen
   d. a high molecular weight

2. What is one of the places in a cell where cellular respiration occurs?
   a. in plant mitochondria, but not in animal mitochondria
   b. in plant chloroplasts
   c. in the mitochondria of both animals and plants
   d. in animal mitochondria, but not in plant mitochondria

3. Which of these processes occurs during glycolysis?
   a. oxidation of pyruvate
   b. reduction of glucose
   c. oxidative phosphorylation
   d. substrate-level phosphorylation

4. Which of these processes links glycolysis and the citric acid cycle?
   a. chemiosmosis
   b. formation of G3P
   c. reduction of NAD$^+$
   d. pyruvate oxidation

### Apply/Analyze

5. The breakdown of fats releases fatty acids. In what form do the carbon molecules enter the respiratory pathway?
   a. as NADH
   b. as acetyl-CoA
   c. a glucose
   d. as pyruvate

6. You are reading this text while breathing in oxygen and breathing out carbon dioxide. Which two processes are the sources of the carbon dioxide?
   a. glycolysis and pyruvate oxidation
   b. glycolysis and oxidative phosphorylation
   c. pyruvate oxidation and the citric acid cycle
   d. the citric acid cycle and oxidative phosphorylation

7. Under conditions of low oxygen, what key role is played by fermentation in overall metabolism?
   a. It regenerates the NAD$^+$ required for glycolysis.
   b. It synthesizes additional NADH for the citric acid cycle.
   c. It allows for pyruvate to be oxidized in mitochondria.
   d. By activating oxidative phosphorylation, it allows for the synthesis of ATP.

8. Suppose you are a doctor and your patient complains of feeling hot all the time, even on the coldest winter days. The young man perspires constantly and his skin is always flushed. He also eats a lot but is rather thin. You perform some laboratory tests, and find that the patient consumes lots of oxygen in his metabolic pathways. What would you suspect this patient suffers from and why?

### Create/Evaluate

9. In cellular respiration, which of the following does the term uncoupled refer to specifically?
   a. The two parts of glycolysis are running independently of each other.
   b. Respiratory electron transport is operating, but chemiosmosis is inhibited.
   c. Respiratory electron transport is operating, but proton pumping is inhibited.
   d. Oxidative phosphorylation is occurring, but the proton-motive force remains high.

10. Phosphofructokinase (PFK) is regulated by a number of metabolites. In addition to those mentioned in the text, which one of the following would also make sense?
   a. Pyruvate could function as an activator of PFK.
   b. Glucose could function as an inhibitor of PFK.
   c. ADP could function as an activator of PFK.
   d. Acetyl-CoA could act as an activator of PFK.

11. Which of these statements best describes the "paradox of aerobic life"?
   a. Humans are completely protected from the toxic effects of oxygen.
   b. Hydrogen peroxide is formed when a single electron is donated to O$_2$.
   c. Cytochrome oxidase is a major source of reactive oxygen species.
   d. Strict anaerobes often lack the enzyme(s) superoxide dismutase and/or catalase.

12. Compare direct burning of glucose and cellular respiration with reference to their progression.

13. Distinguish between reduction and oxidation during redox reactions.

14. Explain what happens with hydrogen and its bonding electrons during cellular respiration.

15. Cyanide is a strong toxin that reacts with the final protein in the electron transport chain (ETC). Explain why it can kill a human within a few minutes.

# Appendix A: Answers to Self-Test Questions

### Chapter 1
1. a  2. a  3. d  4. a  5. c  6. d  7. c  8. a  9. b  10. a  11. c  12. b  13. d

14. Eyes are usually not exposed to full sunlight for a very long period of time, such as the photosynthetic apparatus is. Damage due to exposure of photosystems can be repaired by removing damaged proteins and replacing them with newly synthesized ones, which is not possible in a damaged eye.

15. Melanin protects skin cells because it absorbs ultraviolet light, and it is increasingly synthesized upon exposure to the Sun, which results in the darker shade of her skin.

### Chapter 2
1. d  2. c  3. c  4. a  5. a  6. b  7. b  8. a  9. d  10. a  11. d  12. d  13. c

14. ribosomes, rough ER, transport vesicle, Golgi complex, secretory vesicle, plasma membrane

15. Anchoring junctions function to reinforce cell-to-cell connections made by adhesion molecules. Tight junctions seal the spaces between cells. Gap junctions create direct channels for communicating between adjacent cells.

### Chapter 3
1. c  2. d  3. b  4. a  5. b  6. c  7. c  8. d  9. c  10. d

11. As they dissolve, the sugar molecules raise their entropy. However, the crystals re-form because the water decreases in its order, changing from compact liquid to disordered vapour.

12. Any substance in ordered state (minimum entropy) will contain molecules with maximum free energy. On the contrary, any substance in disordered state (maximum entropy) will contain molecules with minimum free energy. The relationship is reversed.

13. In an exergonic reaction, reactants contain more free energy than the products; energy is released and the reaction is spontaneous. In an endergonic reaction, reactants contain less free energy than the products; energy is required and the reaction is not spontaneous.

14. At any time in a cell, there must be exergonic reactions happening to provide enough energy for endergonic reactions. In addition, the energy released by exergonic reactions must be higher than the energy needed for endergonic reactions because some energy is always transferred to heat (second law of thermodynamics).

### Chapter 4
1. a  2. c  3. b  4. c

5. Some proteins perform transport; others have enzymatic activities; some are a part of signal transduction process; and others are involved in attachment and/or recognition.
6. b  7. c  8. b  9. c  10. c  11. b  12. a  13. d

14. Passive transport occurs down the concentration gradient of the solute, and active transport occurs against the gradient of the transported solute. Active transport therefore requires a protein and energy to perform.

15. They are both a form of passive transport, but facilitated diffusion utilizes proteins to speed up the transport of solute across the membrane.

### Chapter 5
1. a  2. c  3. d  4. d  5. b  6. c  7. a

8. This patient might have defective mitochondria in his cells. This condition is common in a number of diseases. The reason why it was suspected is that, based on his symptoms, probably little ATP is synthesized, in spite of high oxygen consumption, since

his cells dissipated a lot of heat (the patient was hot all the time).
9. b  10. c  11. d

12. Direct burning of glucose is an uncontrolled process; cellular respiration occurs in a series of steps and is therefore a form of controlled combustion.

13. Reduction is the acceptance of electrons during a redox reaction. Oxidation is the loss of electrons during a redox reaction.

14. Hydrogen and its electrons move from sugar to oxygen, forming water.

15. The process of oxidative phosphorylation produces the large number of ATP molecules needed for the endergonic reactions in the cell that we are so dependent on. One of the major sequences of proteins embedded in the mitochondrial membrane—called the electron transport chain—can accept electrons rich in energy. As the energized electrons fall from protein to protein in the ETC, they deposit energy that they carry. At the end of the ETC, there must be oxygen ions present to accept these energetically depleted electrons. If these energy-depleted electrons are not carried away by the oxygen ions, ATP production would stop. Cyanide exerts its deadly effects by reacting with the final protein in ETC, blocking oxygen from accepting electrons from this protein.

### Chapter 6
1. d  2. c  3. c  4. a  5. c

6. A group of pigment proteins form an antenna complex that surrounds a reaction centre. Light energy absorbed anywhere in the antenna complex is transferred to a special chlorophyll molecule in the reaction centre. The absorbed light is converted to chemical energy when an excited electron from the chlorophyll a is transferred to a primary

## Secondary Structure

The amino acid chain of a protein, rather than being stretched out in linear form, is folded into arrangements that form the protein's secondary structure. Secondary structure is based on hydrogen bonds between atoms of the backbone. More precisely, the hydrogen bonds form between the hydrogen atom attached to the nitrogen of the backbone and the oxygen attached to one of the carbon atoms of the backbone. Two highly regular secondary structures are the alpha helix and the beta sheet. In the alpha helix, side chains project outward, supporting the tertiary level of structure. Beta sheets have the side chains sticking out from the plane of the sheet alternating to either side, again supporting the overall structure. A third, less regular arrangement, the coil or loop, imparts flexibility to certain regions of the protein. Most proteins have segments of all three arrangements.

## The α-Helix

A model of the α-helix (below, left), a coil shape formed when hydrogen bonds form between every N—H group of the backbone and the C=O group of the amino acid four residues earlier. In protein diagrams (below, right), the α-helix is depicted as a cylinder or barrel.

## The β-Sheet

A β-sheet is formed by side-by-side alignment of β-strands (picture below shows two strands). The sheet is formed by hydrogen bonds between atoms of each strand. In protein diagrams, the β-strands are depicted as ribbons with arrowheads pointing toward the C-terminal.

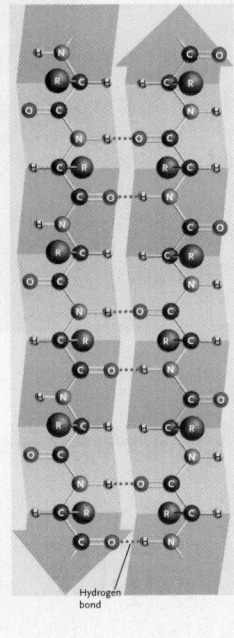

Ball-and-stick model of α helix

Cylinder representation of α helix

Amino acid side group

Hydrogen bond

Hydrogen bond

Peptide bond

Hydrogen bond

◄ *The Purple Pages:* **The Chemical and Physical Foundations of Biology** While many textbooks use the first few chapters to introduce and/or review, we believe that the first chapters should convey the excitement and interest of biology itself. We therefore placed important background information about biology and chemistry in the reference section entitled *The Chemical and Physical Foundations of Biology,* in the centre of the book. With their purple borders, these pages are distinct and easy to find and have become affectionately known as *The Purple Pages.* References to material covered in *The Purple Pages* are set in purple throughout the text.

**The Green Pages: Unit 5: The Diversity of Life** We emphasize the richness and tremendous variability among living organisms in *The Green Pages.* With their green borders, these pages identify chapters that introduce and explore the tree of life. ▼

---

FIGURE 25.1 **Example of a wood decay fungus: sulfur shelf fungus (*Polyporus*)**

essential components in all ecosystems and Earth's premier decomposers **(Figure 25.1)**.

Despite their profound impact on ecosystems and other life forms, most of us have only a passing acquaintance with fungi, perhaps limited to the mushrooms on our pizza or the invisible but annoying types that cause skin infections, such as athlete's foot. This chapter provides you with an overview of fungal biology. We begin with the features that set fungi apart from all other organisms, and discuss the diversity of fungi existing today before revisiting associations between fungi and other organisms.

### 25.1 General Characteristics of Fungi

We begin our survey of fungi by examining the features that distinguish fungi from other forms of life, how fungi obtain nutrients, and adaptations for reproduction and growth that enable fungi to spread far and wide through the environment.

Fungi are heterotrophic eukaryotes that obtain carbon by breaking down organic molecules synthesized by other organisms. Although all fungi are heterotrophs, fungi can be divided into two broad groups based on how they obtain carbon. If a fungus obtains carbon from non-living material, it is a **saprotroph**. Fungi that decompose dead plant and animal tissues, for example, are saprotrophs. If a fungus obtains carbon from living organisms, it is a **symbiont**. Symbiosis is the living together of two (or sometimes more) organisms for extended periods; symbiotic relationships range along a continuum from **parasitism**, in which one organism benefits at the expense of the other, to **mutualism**, in which both organisms benefit. Although we often think of fungi as decomposers, fully half of all identified fungi live as symbionts with another organism.

a. Multicellular fungus

Fruiting Body

Honey mushroom (*Armillaria ostoyae*)

Fungal hyphae

Mycelium

b. Rhizomorphs

FIGURE 25.2 **Fungal structure: mycelia, hyphae. (a)** Illustration of the mycelium of a mushroom-forming fungus, which consists of branching septate hyphae. Inset: Micrograph of fungal hyphae **(b)** Rhizomorph – a cordlike aggregation of hyphae formed by some basidiomycete fungi.

Regardless of their nutrient source, fungi feed by **absorptive nutrition**: they secrete enzymes into their environment, breaking down large molecules into smaller soluble molecules that can then be absorbed into their cells. This mode of nutrition means that fungi cannot be stationary, as they would then deplete all the food in their immediate environment. Instead, fungi have evolved the ability to proliferate quickly through their environment, digesting nutrients as they grow. How can fungi proliferate so quickly? Although some fungi grow as unicellular yeasts, which reproduce asexually by **budding** or binary fission (see Figure 25.13), most are composed of **hyphae** ("web"; singular, *hypha*; **Figure 25.2**), fine filaments that spread through whatever substrate the fungus is growing in—soil, decomposing wood, your skin—forming a network, or **mycelium** (Figure 25.2). Hyphae are essentially tubes of cytoplasm surrounded by cell walls made of chitin, a polysaccharide also found in the exoskeletons of insects and other arthropods.

Hyphae grow only at their tips, but because a single mycelium contains many, many tips, the entire mycelium

grows outward very quickly. Together, this **apical growth** and absorptive nutrition account for much of the success of fungi. As the hyphal tips extend, they exert a mechanical force, allowing them to push through the substrate, releasing enzymes and absorbing nutrients as they go. Fungal species differ in the particular digestive enzymes they synthesize, so a substrate that is a suitable food source for one species may be unavailable to another. Although there are exceptions, fungi typically thrive only in moist environments, where they can directly absorb water, dissolved ions, simple sugars, amino acids, and other small molecules. When some of a mycelium's hyphal filaments contact a source of food, growth is channelled in the direction of the food source.

Nutrients are absorbed at the porous tips of hyphae; small atoms and molecules pass readily through these tips, and then transport mechanisms move them through the underlying plasma membrane. Some hyphae have regular cross-walls, or **septa** ("fences" or "walls"; singular, *septum*), that separate a hypha into compartments **(Figure 25.3)**, whereas others lack septa and are effectively one large cell. But even septate hyphae should be thought of as interconnected compartments rather than separate cells, as all septa have pores that allow cytoplasm and, in some fungi, even nuclei and other large organelles to flow through the mycelium. By a mechanism called **cytoplasmic streaming** (flow of cytoplasm and organelles around a cell or, in this case, a mycelium), nutrients obtained by one part of a mycelium can be translocated to other non-absorptive regions, such as reproductive structures.

When a fungus releases enzymes into its substrate, it faces competition from bacteria and other organisms for the nutrients that are now available. How can a fungus prevent these competitors from stealing the nutrients that it has just expended energy and resources to obtain? Many fungi produce antibacterial compounds and toxins that inhibit the growth of competing organisms. Many of these compounds are **secondary metabolites**, which are not required for day-to-day survival but are beneficial to the fungus. As we will see, many of these compounds not only are important in the life of a fungus but also benefit organisms associated with the fungus. Many are also of commercial or medical importance to humans; for example, the antibiotic penicillin is a secondary metabolite produced by a species of *Penicillium*.

Fungi reproduce by spores, and this spore production can be amazingly prolific, with some species of fungi producing billions of spores per day **(Figure 25.4)**. These spores are microscopic, featherlight, and able to survive in the environment for extended periods after they are released. Reproducing via such spores allows fungi to be opportunists, germinating only when favourable conditions exist and quickly exploiting food sources that occur unpredictably in the environment. Releasing vast numbers of spores, as some fungi do, improves the odds that the spores will germinate and produce a new individual.

Spores can be produced asexually or sexually; some fungi produce both asexual and sexual spores at different stages of their lives. Sexual reproduction in fungi is complex. In all organisms, sexual reproduction involves three stages: the fusion of two haploid cells (**plasmogamy**), bringing together their two nuclei in one common cytoplasm. Cytoplasmic fusion in most organisms is quickly followed by nuclear fusion (**karyogamy**), but in fungi the cells can remain bi-nucleate as the organism grows. Nuclear fusion is often followed by meiosis to produce genetically distinct haploid spores. As we will see, fungi are unique in that plasmogamy and karyogamy can be separated in time for durations ranging from seconds to many years.

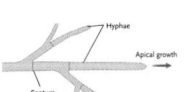

Hyphae

Apical growth

Septum

FIGURE 25.3 **Septa.** In some fungi, septa divide each hypha into separate compartments.

FIGURE 25.4 **Spore production by fungal fruiting bodies.** Some fruiting bodies can release billions of spores per day.

# Student and Instructor Resources

Succeed in the course with these dynamic resources!

## MindTap

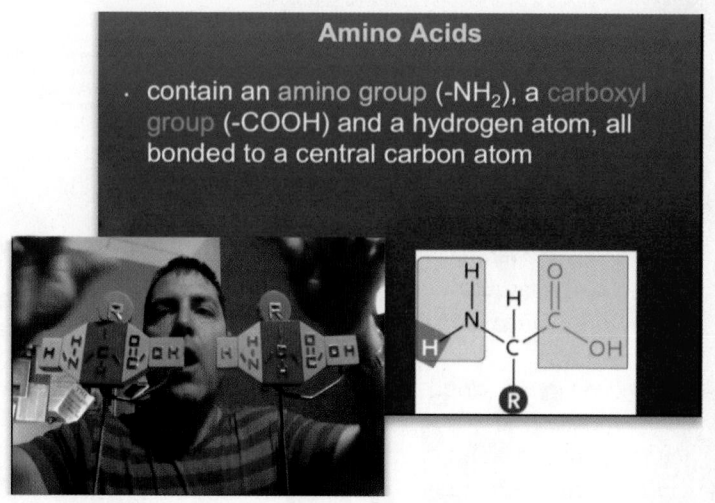

With relevant assignments that guide students to analyze, apply, and elevate thinking, **MindTap** allows instructors to measure skills and promote better outcomes with ease. Including interactive quizzing, this online tutorial and diagnostic tool identifies each student's unique needs with a pre-test. The learning path then helps students focus on concepts they're having the most difficulty mastering. It refers to the accompanying MindTap Reader eBook and provides a variety of learning activities designed to appeal to diverse ways of learning. After completing the study plan, students take Aplia problem sets and then take a post-test to measure their understanding of the material. Instructors have the ability to customize the learning path, add their own content, and track and monitor student progress by using the instructor Gradebook and Progress app.

Students stay organized and efficient with MindTap, a single destination with all the course material and study aids students need to succeed. Built-in apps leverage social media and the latest learning technology. For example,

- ReadSpeaker will read the text to you.
- Flashcards are prepopulated to provide you with a jump start for review, or you can create your own.
- You can highlight text and make notes in your MindTap Reader. Your notes will flow into Evernote, the electronic notebook app that you can access anywhere when it's time to study for the exam.
- Self-quizzing allows you to assess your understanding.

The **MindTap** resources were developed by Dora Cavallo-Medved of the University of Windsor, Reehan Mirza of Nipissing University, Roy Rea of the University of Northern British Columbia, and Miranda Meents.

Also available in MindTap for Biology are engaging and informative videos that accompany *The Purple Pages*. From matter to polypeptides, author Todd Nickle, of Mount Royal University (pictured), will walk you through these foundational concepts, strengthening your understanding and helping you build a strong base of knowledge and understanding for biology.

Visit www.nelson.com/student to start using MindTap. Enter the Online Access Code from the card included with your textbook. If a code card is *not* provided, you can purchase instant access at NELSONbrain.com.

## Aplia for Biology

Strengthen your understanding of biology with Aplia™!

Aplia's focused assignments and active learning opportunities help students learn key concepts by randomized, automatically graded questions, exceptional text/art integration, and immediate feedback. Aplia has a full course management system that can be used independently or in conjunction with other course management systems such as Blackboard and WebCT.

This innovative, easy-to-use, interactive technology gives students more practice, with detailed feedback to help students learn with every question!

Aplia's focused assignments and active learning opportunities (including randomized questions, exceptional text/art integration, and immediate feedback) get students involved with biology and help them think like scientists.

Interactive problems and figures help students visualize dynamic biological processes and integrate concepts, art, media, and homework practice.

For more information, visit **www.aplia.com/biology.**

The Aplia course for *Biology: Exploring the Diversity of Life,* Fourth Canadian Edition, was prepared by Anna Rissanen of Memorial University and Todd Nickle of Mount Royal University.

**The Nelson Education Teaching Advantage (NETA)** program delivers research-based instructor resources that promote student engagement and higher-order thinking to enable the success of Canadian students and educators. To ensure the high quality of these materials, all Nelson ancillaries have been professionally copy-edited.

Be sure to visit Nelson Education's **Inspired Instruction** website at **www.nelson.com/inspired/** to find out more about NETA. Don't miss the testimonials of instructors who have used NETA supplements and have seen student engagement increase!

**NETA Test Bank:** This resource was written by Ivona Mladenovic of Simon Fraser University. It includes over 2500 multiple-choice questions written according to NETA guidelines for effective construction and development of higher-order questions. The Test Bank was copy-edited by a NETA-trained editor for adherence to NETA best practices. Also included are true/false, essay, short-answer, matching, and completion questions. Test Bank files are available in Microsoft Word format from your Nelson publishing representative.

The **NETA Test Bank** is available in a new, cloud-based platform. **Nelson Testing Powered by Cognero®** is a secure online testing system that allows you to author, edit, and manage test bank content from any place you have Internet access. No special installations or downloads are needed, and the desktop-inspired interface, with its drop-down menus and familiar, intuitive tools, allows you to create and manage tests with ease. You can create multiple test versions in an instant and import or export content into other systems. Tests can be delivered from your learning management system, your classroom, or wherever you want. Nelson Testing Powered by Cognero can be accessed through www.nelson.com/instructor.

**NETA PowerPoint:** Microsoft PowerPoint® lecture slides for every chapter were created by Jane Young of the University of Northern British Columbia. There is an average of 80 slides per chapter, many featuring key figures, tables, and photographs from *Biology: Exploring the Diversity of Life,* Fourth Canadian Edition. The PowerPoint slides also feature "build slides"—selected illustrations with labels from the book that have been reworked to allow optimal display in PowerPoint. NETA prin-

ciples of clear design and engaging content have been incorporated throughout, making it simple for instructors to customize the deck for their courses.

**Image Library:** This resource consists of digital copies of figures, short tables, and photographs used in the book. Instructors may use these jpegs to customize the NETA PowerPoint slides or create their own PowerPoint presentations.

**NETA Instructor's Manual:** This resource was written by Tamara Kelly of York University and Tanya Noel of the University of Windsor. It is organized according to the textbook chapters and addresses key educational concerns, such as typical stumbling blocks students face and how to address them. Other features include tips on teaching using cases as well as suggestions on how to present material and use technology and other resources effectively, integrating the other supplements available to both students and instructors. This manual doesn't simply reinvent what's currently in the text, it helps the instructor make the material relevant and engaging to students.

**TurningPoint®:** Another valuable resource for instructors is **TurningPoint® classroom response software** customized for *Biology: Exploring the Diversity of Life,* Four Canadian Edition, by Jane Young at the University of Northern British Columbia. Now you can author, deliver, show, access, and grade, all in PowerPoint, with no toggling back and forth between screens! JoinIn on TurningPoint is the only classroom response software tool that gives you true PowerPoint integration. With JoinIn, you are no longer tied to your computer. You can walk about your classroom as you lecture, showing slides and collecting and displaying responses with ease. There is simply no easier or more effective way to turn your lecture hall into a personal, fully interactive experience for your students. If you can use PowerPoint, you can use JoinIn on TurningPoint! (Contact your Nelson publishing representative for details.) These contain poll slides and pre- and post-test slides for each chapter in the text.

# Acknowledgements

We thank the many people who have worked with us on the production of this text, particularly Paul Fam, Senior Publisher, whose foresight brought the idea to us and whose persistence saw the project through.

We are also grateful to the members of the MindTap Advisory Board and the Student Advisory Boards for the fourth Canadian edition, who provided us with valuable feedback and alternative perspectives (special acknowledgments to these individuals are listed below).

We also thank Richard Walker at the University of Calgary and Ken Davey at York University, who began this journey with us but were unable to continue. We are very grateful to Heather Addy of the University of Calgary for her significant contributions to the first three editions.

We are especially grateful to Toni Chahley, Content Manager, who kept us moving through the chapters at an efficient pace, along with Charu Verma, Project Manager, and Imoinda Romain, Senior Production Project Manager. A very special thanks to Kathy Hamilton, for her guidance and helpful suggestions with the summary illustrations, and we are very grateful to Roy Rea of the University of Northern British Columbia for his critical read of Chapter 27, and his significant contribution to the summary illustrations for Chapters 27–32. We thank Kristiina Paul, our photo researcher, for her hard work with the numerous photos in the book, and Frances Robinson for her careful and thoughtful copy-editing. Finally, we thank Kim Carruthers, Marketing Manager, for making us look good.

Brock Fenton thanks Allan Noon for offering advice about taking pictures; Laura Barclay, Jeremy McNeil, Tony Percival-Smith, C. S. (Rufus) Churcher, and David and Meg Cumming for the use of their images; Karen Campbell for providing a critical read of Putting Selection to Work; and Michael Owen for his outstanding contribution to Chapter 27: Animals.

Tom Haffie would like to acknowledge the cheerful and insightful editorial work of Jennifer Waugh on Chapter 16 and the conscientious research assistance of Dr. Aniruddho Chokroborty-Hoque.

Denis Maxwell would like to thank David Brock for helping fine-tune the coverage of thermodynamics in Chapter 3.

Todd Nickle thanks his family, students, and colleagues for humouring his mad exploits and for their understanding when he doesn't make things easy on himself—or others—as he explores insane and sometimes creative ways to repurpose old ways of doing things.

The authors are all indebted to Ivona Mladenovic of Simon Fraser University for her excellent work on the Self-Test Questions, and Johnston Miller, whose extensive background research anchored our Concept Fixes in the education literature.

It is never easy to be in the family of an academic scientist. We are especially grateful to our families for their sustained support over the course of our careers, particularly during those times when our attentions were fully captivated by bacteria, algae, fungi, parasites, snakes, geese, or bats. Saying "yes" to a textbook project means saying "no" to a variety of other pursuits. We appreciate the patience and understanding of those closest to us that enabled the temporary reallocation of considerable time from other endeavours and relationships.

Many of our colleagues have contributed to our development as teachers and scholars by acting as mentors, collaborators, and, on occasion, "worthy opponents." Like all teachers, we owe particular gratitude to our students. They have gathered with us around the discipline of biology, sharing their potent blend of enthusiasm and curiosity, and leaving us energized and optimistic for the future.

## Editorial and Student Advisory Boards

We were very fortunate to have the assistance of some extraordinary students and instructors of biology across Canada who provided us with feedback that helped shape this textbook into what you see before you. As such, we would like to say a very special thank you to the following people:

### MindTap Advisory Board

Brett Couch, University of British Columbia
Stewart Daly, Marianopolis College
Jon Houseman, University of Ottawa
William Huddleston, University of Calgary
Ivona Mladenovic, Simon Fraser University
Ken Otter, University of Northern British Columbia
Lisa Prichard, MacEwan University
Roy Rea, University of Northern British Columbia
Frieder Schoeck, McGill University
Marina Silva-Opps, University of Prince Edward Island
Matt Smith, Wilfrid Laurier University
Chris Todd, University of Saskatchewan
Paula Wilson, York University
Ken Wilson, University of Saskatchewan

(Top) Ivona Mladenovic, Ken Wilson, Jon Houseman, Stewart Daly, Frieder Schoeck; (bottom) William Huddleston, Chris Todd, Lisa Prichard

Paula Wilson, York University

Ken Otter, University of Northern British Columbia

Roy Rea, University of Northern British Columbia

Matt Smith, Wilfrid Laurier University

## University of British Columbia

Shown above are members of the University of British Columbia Student Advisory Board. From left to right: Kristina Balce, Amy Dhillon, Humaam Hamado, Ebi Oliya, Laura Fash, Sina Soleimani, Adam Book, Ashley Pinter, Garrett Huwyler, Quinn Stewart, Gavindeep Shinger. Not pictured: Kendrix Kek, Hassan Ali

## University of Calgary

Shown above are members of the University of Calgary Student Advisory Board. From left to right: Gina Mannella, Jesse Provick, Amanda Bennett, Leesa Le, Vivian Nguyen

## Mount Royal University

Depicted above are members of the Student Advisory Board at Mount Royal University. From left to right, back row: Evan Olar, Moroni Lopez, Taelor Evans, Todd Nickle, Jonathan Roveredo, Darlene Skagen, Andrew Roberts, Surafel Girma, Danielle Schmidt, Laura Villarraga Ulloa. Front row: Kyle Poffenroth, Heaven Berhe Sium, Aderinsoye Ademoye, Ravneet Gill, Meena Kanthimathinathan, Alexandra Presbitero, Anastasia Socolnicova. Not pictured: Ashley Chicote, Cassidy Fleming

Nelson would like to thank some of the current student users of *Biology: Exploring the Diversity of Life,* in particular the students at Western University's Biology 1001A course who shared their feedback via their participation in a student focus group early in the development process.

# BIOLOGY OF THE CELL

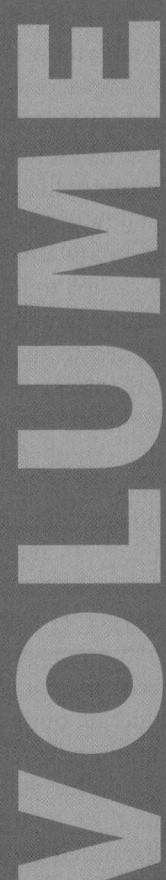

VOLUME 1

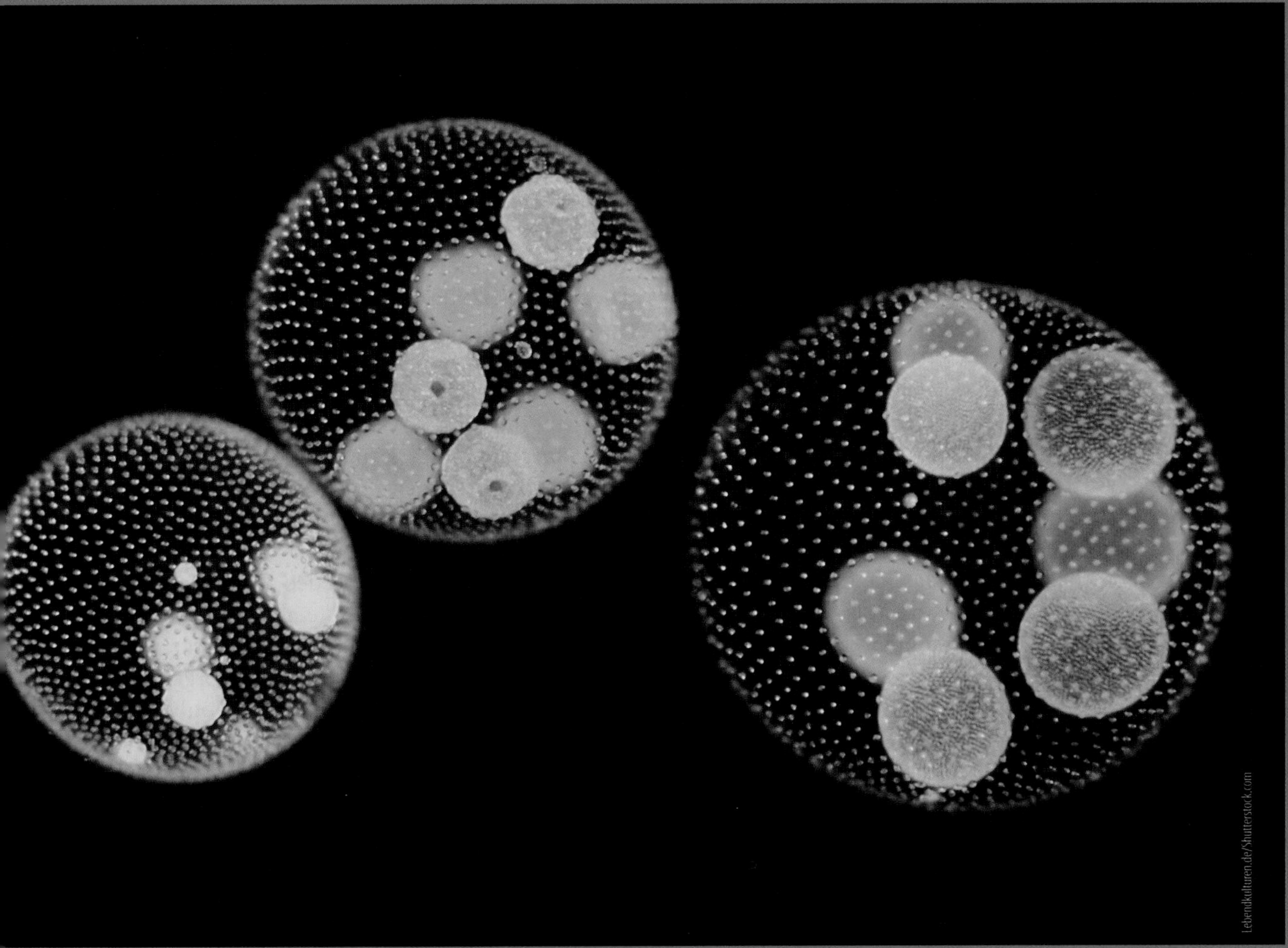

Lebendkulturen.de/Shutterstock.com

***Volvox* is a genus of green algae.** As photosynthetic eukaryotes, *Volvox* cells exist in colonies of thousands of cells. Some of the cells are vegetative (non-reproductive); a smaller number of much larger reproductive cells are found in the interior of the colony.

There is a huge diversity of life on Earth; some estimates peg the total number of species at over 1 billion (with most yet to be described!). Yet, what this opening volume of the textbook should covey to you is that underlying that diversity is a remarkable level of similarity. From monkeys to mycoplasma to monocots, everything that is alive on Earth employs a variation on that remarkable innovation: the cell. No matter if that cell is communicating with other cells in the brain of a fruit fly, or capturing sunlight in a spruce needle, or driving the muscles of a sprinting cheetah, or thriving in the mineral-rich water of deep-sea vents, no matter what their role or activity, all cells share a remarkably long list of common features. Volume 1 explores these common features in detail.

The invention of the microscope allowed scientists to finally understand how living organisms were built from cells, which to early scientists were astonishingly small. Further work clearly delineated two major divisions in cell types: those without a nucleus (prokaryotic) and those with a nucleus (eukaryotic). And within both these groups there are clear subdivisions: for example, plants, fungi, and animal cells, in eukaryotes.

The chapters of Unit 1 talk a lot about energy because without it living cells would die. Like the non-living world, all forms of life abide by the foundational laws of thermodynamics and need to bring in energy and matter from the environment to maintain their highly ordered state. In part, energy is required to build complex things (e.g., proteins) out of simpler things (amino acids). In addition to energy, the evolution of life is tied to the development of a remarkable group of proteins called *enzymes*, which when they get tied to a biochemical reaction can increase its rate by $10^{10}$ times!

Another remarkable feature of cells that we dedicate a chapter to in Unit 1 is membranes. These self-forming lipid bilayers act as the gatekeepers of the cell: they allow certain things in but keep other things out. How they do this is by acting in concert with membrane-specific proteins that shuttle molecules from one side to another. Membrane proteins also play a remarkable role in transducing signals from outside the cells and compartments to the inside. As we will see, the transduction of signals associated with hormones, for example, can profoundly affect cell function.

What you may not realize is that virtually all the energy used by living systems comes ultimately from sunlight being harvested and converted into a useable chemical form through photosynthesis. This process evolved perhaps as early as 3.5 billion years ago and used photons of light energy to extract electrons from water, releasing oxygen as a by-product. The rise in oxygen in an atmosphere that previously had none led to an explosion of life as the mechanism of cellular respiration evolved that could use that oxygen, and enabled cells to produce huge amounts of energy.

The chapters of Units 2 and 3 are dedicated to molecular biology and genetics, the central player being the gene. All cells possess genes that are coded by the molecule DNA that, through the process of transcription, get copied into RNA. All cells contain ribosomes where some kinds of RNAs get translated into **proteins**, the fundamental structural, functional, and regulatory molecule of the cell.

Genes are stretches of DNA sequence in an organism that collectively comprise a kind of library of information about how a cell functions. Recent advances in technology have made it relatively easy to determine the entire DNA sequence of an organism, including individual humans. As a result, modern biology is awash in the As, Ts, Gs, and Cs of DNA sequence revealed by thousands of sequencing projects. New insights into evolutionary history as well as gene structure and function are arising from bioinformatic analysis of such extensive data sets.

The elegant double-strandedness of DNA, whereby two long strands of nucleotides are held together by hydrogen bonds formed between complementary base pairs, affords a straightforward mechanism for replication that was recognized early on by Watson and Crick. Although conceptually simple, the mechanism for unwinding the DNA **double helix** and polymerizing new complementary bases is rather complicated and managed by a suite of interacting enzymes. Again, we see that all DNA on the planet is replicated using variations on one underlying strategy.

DNA genes provide the cell with needed RNA by transcription. One remarkable feature of all protein-coding genes is that, with minor exceptions, the information they carry is specified by a universal code. That is, a gene from one organism can be "understood" by any other organism, even if only distantly related: a gene from a spider can be expressed by a goat; a gene from a jellyfish can be expressed in a flower. The field of genetic engineering is devoted to developing the tools and applications of this technology for moving genes from one organism to another.

In a story that is about to come full circle, synthetic biologists have extensively customized naturally occurring cells and have made important advances toward their ultimate goal of creating novel life forms artificially in the lab. As students of biology in the early twenty-first century, you can well expect to witness a momentous event in Earth's history, the creation of one life form by another.

# Chapter Roadmap

## Light and Life

Light serves two important functions for life on Earth: First, it is the ultimate source of energy for almost all organisms. Second, light provides many organisms with information about the physical world that surrounds them.

### 1.1 The Physical Nature of Light

To be used as a source of energy or information, photons of light must be absorbed by a molecule.

**To Purple Pages →**

### 1.2 Light as a Source of Energy

The energy of light can be used in photosynthesis to convert carbon dioxide into carbohydrates.

**To Chapter 6 →**

### 1.3 Light as a Source of Information

The photoreceptor, a pigment molecule bound to a protein, is the common molecule used in sensing light in the environment.

**To Chapter 37 →**

**To Chapter 45 →**

### 1.4 The Uniqueness of Light

Light possesses an ideal amount of energy: enough energy to excite electrons, but not enough to directly destroy biological molecules.

### 1.5 Light Can Damage Biological Molecules

Organisms possess mechanisms to both protect themselves from the damaging effects of light and repair the inevitable damage that light causes.

### 1.6 Using Light to Tell Time

Organisms have evolved circadian clocks, which allow them to keep track of time on a daily and seasonal scale.

Anita Patterson Peppers / Shutterstock.com

### 1.7 The Role of Light in Behaviour and Ecology

The light environment of a particular habitat plays a central role in adaptation. It leads to unique colouration that may serve to attract a mate or hide from predators.

**To Chapter 30 →**

**To Chapter 32 →**

### 1.8 Organisms Making Their Own Light

Some organisms generate their own light to attract a mate or prey, or for communication.

**Paintings by Claude Monet (1840–1926).** Compared to his early works, including *The Water Lily Pond* **(a)**, his later paintings, including *The Japanese Footbridge* **(b)**, bordered on the abstract, with almost complete loss of light blue. Monet suffered from cataracts, a degenerative vision disease, diagnosed in 1912.

# Light and Life

1

**Why it matters . . .** Claude Monet (1840–1926), a French painter, is considered by many to be the master of the impressionist form that rose to prominence in the late nineteenth century. Impressionism as an art movement was characterized by the use of small visible brush strokes that emphasized light and colour, rather than lines, to define an object. The artists used pure, unmixed colour, not smoothly blended, as was the custom at the time. For example, instead of physically mixing yellow and blue paint, they placed unmixed yellow paint on the canvas next to unmixed blue paint so that the colours would mingle in the eye of the viewer to create the impression of green. The impressionists found that they could capture the momentary and transient effects of sunlight and the changing colour of a scene by painting *en plein air* (in the open air), outside the studio, where they could more accurately paint the reflected light of an immediate scene.

Interestingly, compared with his early works, which included *The Water Lily Pond* (1899), Monet's later paintings verge on the abstract, with colours bleeding into each other and with a lack of rational shape and perspective. For example, *The Japanese Footbridge* is an explosion of orange, yellow, and red hues, with heavy, broad brush strokes, leaving the viewer barely able to discern the vague shape of the arched bridge. In many of Monet's later works, the colours in his paintings became more muted, far less vibrant and bright, with a pronounced colour shift from blue–green to red–yellow and an almost total absence of light blues. The sense of atmosphere and light that he was famous for in his earlier works disappeared.

Although the change in Monet's paintings could easily be explained by an intentional change in style or perhaps an age-related change in manual dexterity, Monet himself realized that it was not his style or dexterity that had changed but, rather, his ability to see. Monet suffered from cataracts, a vision-deteriorating disease diagnosed in both eyes when he was 72. A cataract is a change in the lens of the eye, making it more opaque, which changes the ability to see different colours of light.

In this chapter, the first of the 46 of this textbook, we introduce you to the science of biology by using light as a central connecting theme. Light is arguably the most fundamental of natural phenomena, and foundational experiments into the nature of light were a key part of the scientific revolution that took place in the sixteenth and seventeenth centuries. Beyond formally defining light and discussing its properties, in this chapter we explore the huge diversity of areas of biology that light influences, from the molecular to the ecological. This introductory tour is not intended to be complete or exhaustive but to simply set the stage for the topics that come in subsequent chapters.

## 1.1 The Physical Nature of Light

Light serves two important functions for life on Earth: First, it is the ultimate source of energy that sustains virtually all organisms. Second, light provides many organisms with information about the physical environment in which they live. These two roles for light are nicely illustrated by the green alga *Chlamydomonas* **(Figure 1.1)**. *Chlamydomonas* is a single-celled, photosynthetic eukaryote that is commonly found in ponds and lakes. *Chlamydomonas* contains a single large chloroplast that harvests light energy and uses it to make energy-rich molecules through the process of photosynthesis. In addition, each cell contains a light sensor called an *eyespot* that allows *Chlamydomonas* to gather information about the direction and intensity of the light in its environment. With this information, cells can move toward or away from the light source using a pair of flagella. Regardless of whether the light is used as a source of energy or as a source of information about the environment, both rely on the same fundamental properties of light.

### 1.1a What Is Light?

Through the process of nuclear fusion, the Sun transforms a staggering $3.4 \times 10^{38}$ hydrogen nuclei into helium each second **(Figure 1.2)**. In the process, about 4 million tonnes of matter are converted into energy. This energy is given off by the Sun as *electromagnetic radiation*, which travels in the form of a wave at a speed of $1.1 \times 10^9$ km/h (the speed of light) and reaches Earth in just over 8 minutes. Electromagnetic radiation is generated at a range of wavelengths **(Figure 1.3)**: cosmic rays have a wavelength of less than one picometre ($10^{-12}$ m); radio waves have a wavelength longer than one kilometre ($10^6$ m). The complete range of wavelengths of electromagnetic radiation is referred to as the **electromagnetic spectrum**.

So what is light? **Light** is most commonly defined as the portion of the electromagnetic spectrum that we can detect with our eyes. As shown in Figure 1.3, this is a very narrow portion of the total electromagnetic spectrum, spanning only the wavelengths from about 400 to 700 nm.

The physical nature of light has been the focus of scientific inquiry for hundreds of years, and in many ways it remains a mystery. Unlike the atoms that make up matter, light has no mass. And although the results of some experiments suggest

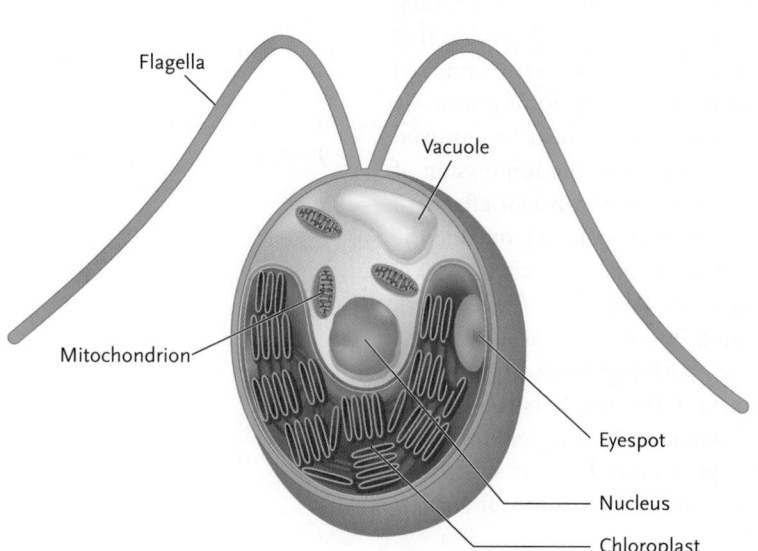

**FIGURE 1.1** *Chlamydomonas.* Each cell contains a single chloroplast used for photosynthesis, as well as an eyespot for sensing light in the environment.

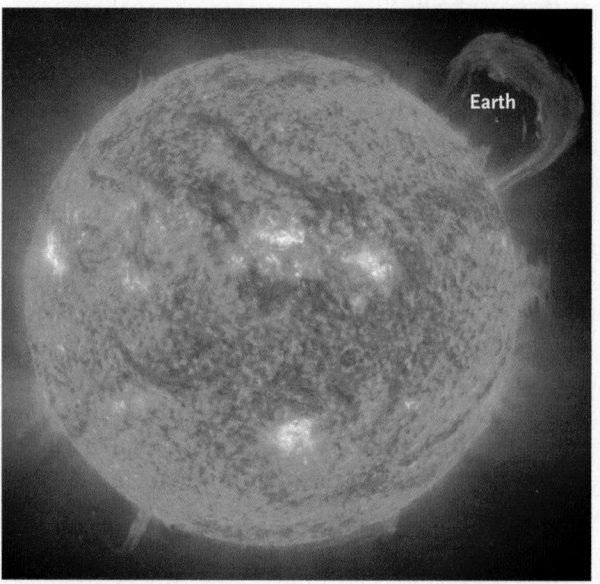

**FIGURE 1.2** **The Sun.** Like most stars, the Sun generates electromagnetic radiation as a result of the nuclear fusion of hydrogen nuclei into helium. Note the superimposed image of Earth used to illustrate the relative sizes.

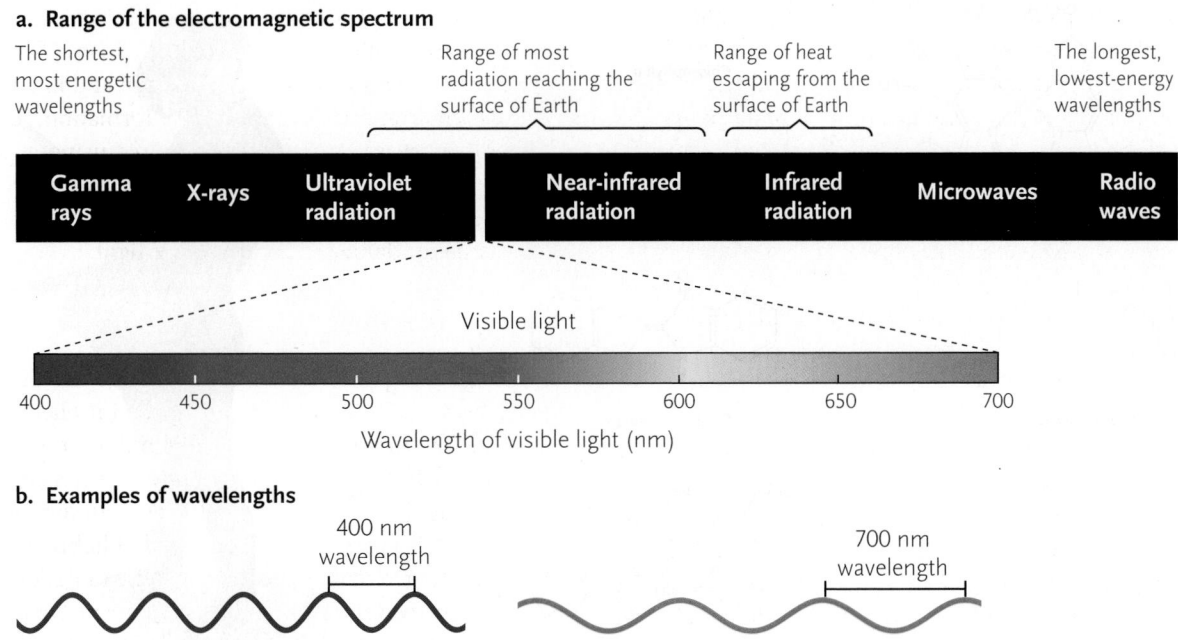

**a. Range of the electromagnetic spectrum**

The shortest, most energetic wavelengths

Range of most radiation reaching the surface of Earth

Range of heat escaping from the surface of Earth

The longest, lowest-energy wavelengths

| Gamma rays | X-rays | Ultraviolet radiation | Near-infrared radiation | Infrared radiation | Microwaves | Radio waves |

Visible light

400    450    500    550    600    650    700

Wavelength of visible light (nm)

**b. Examples of wavelengths**

400 nm wavelength

700 nm wavelength

**FIGURE 1.3 The electromagnetic spectrum. (a)** The electromagnetic spectrum ranges from gamma rays to radio waves; visible light and the wavelengths used for photosynthesis occupy only a narrow band of the spectrum. **(b)** Examples of wavelengths show the difference between the longest and shortest wavelengths of visible light.

that light behaves as a wave as it travels through space, other experiments indicate that light behaves more like discrete particles of energy called **photons**. In the end, we are left with a compromise description: light is best understood as a wave of photons. An important aspect of light to remember is that there is an inverse relationship between the energy of a photon and the wavelength of light. Looking at Figure 1.3, this means that shorter-wavelength blue light consists of photons of higher energy than red light, which has a longer wavelength and thus photons of lower energy.

## 1.1b Light Interacts with Matter

Although light has no mass, it is still able to interact with matter and cause change. This change is what allows the energy of light to be used by living things. When a photon of light hits an object, the photon has three possible fates: it can be reflected off the object, transmitted through the object, or absorbed by the object. To be used as a source of energy or information by an organism, the light must be absorbed. Light is absorbed when the energy of the photon is transferred to an **electron** within a molecule. This transfer of energy excites the electron, moving it from its ground state to a higher energy level that is referred to as an *excited state* **(Figure 1.4)**.

Molecules differ considerably in their ability to absorb photons of light. There is a major class of molecules that is very efficient at absorbing photons of specific wavelengths; those molecules are called **pigments (Figure 1.5)**. As you would expect, there is a huge diversity of pigments, including chlorophyll *a*, which is involved in photosynthesis; retinal, which is involved

in vision; and indigo, which is used to dye jeans their distinctive blue colour.

An important question we can ask is: What is it about pigments that enable them to capture light? At first glance, the molecules shown in Figure 1.5 seem to be very different from each other structurally. However, they all have a common feature critical to light absorption: a region where carbon atoms are covalently bonded to each other with alternating single and double bonds. This bonding arrangement is called a *conjugated system,* and it results in the delocalization of electrons. These electrons are not closely associated with a particular atom or involved in bonding to another atom, and instead are available to absorb the energy of a photon of light.

While the presence of a conjugated system is common to all pigments, differences in the arrangement of the conjugated

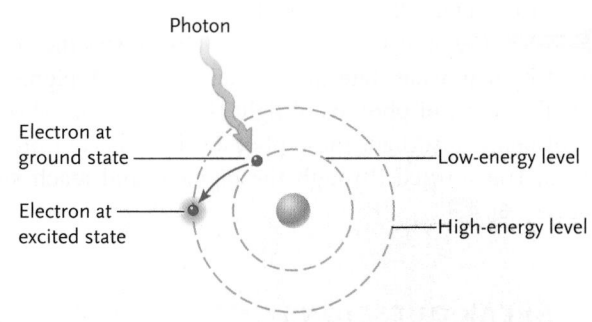

Photon

Electron at ground state — Low-energy level

Electron at excited state — High-energy level

**FIGURE 1.4 The absorption of a photon by a molecule results in the energy being transferred to an electron.** This causes the energy to move to a higher-energy, excited state.

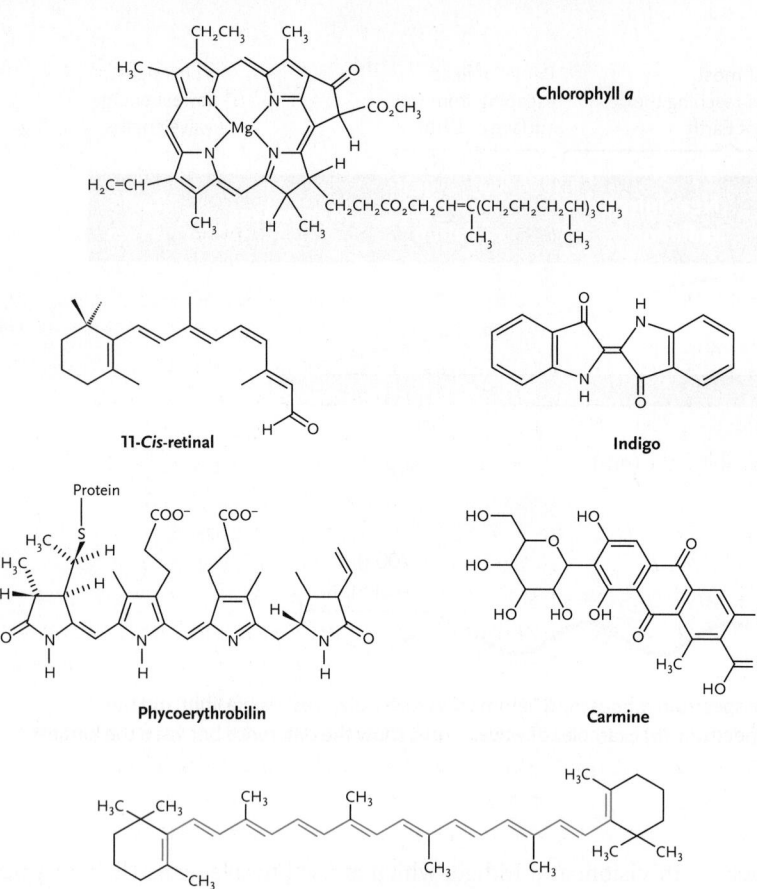

FIGURE 1.5 **Structure of some common pigments.** Chlorophyll *a*, photosynthesis; 11-*cis*-retinal, vision; indigo, dye; phycoerythrobilin, red photosynthetic pigment found in red algae; carmine, scale pigment found in some insects; beta-carotene, an orange accessory photosynthetic pigment. A common feature of all these pigments that is critical for light absorption is the presence of a conjugated system of double/single carbon bonds (shown in red for beta-carotene).

system as well as differences in the overall chemical structure explain why each type of pigment absorbs light of only certain wavelengths. This is because, for a photon to be absorbed, the energy of the photon must match the amount of energy needed to move a delocalized electron from its ground state to a specific excited state. If the energies don't match, then the photon of light is not absorbed and instead is transmitted through the molecule or reflected off the molecule.

**CONCEPT FIX** The ability of pigments to absorb specific wavelengths of light is what determines their colour. A pigment's colour is the result of photons of light that it *does not* absorb. Instead of being absorbed, these photons are reflected off the pigment or transmitted through the pigment and reach your eyes **(Figure 1.6)**.

## STUDY BREAK QUESTIONS

1. What has to occur for a photon to be absorbed?
2. What structural feature is common to all pigments?

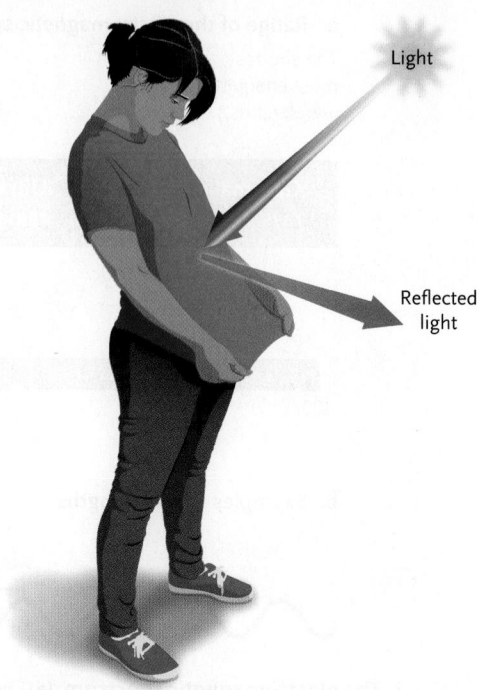

FIGURE 1.6 **Why the T-shirt is red.** Pigment molecules bound to the fabric of the shirt absorb blue, green, and yellow photons of light. Red photons are not absorbed and are instead transmitted through the shirt or are reflected.

## 1.2 Light as a Source of Energy

The ultimate source of the energy used by almost all organisms that make up the biosphere is light from the Sun. The energy of electromagnetic radiation is made accessible through the ability of plants and related organisms to convert the energy of photons into chemical energy. Through photosynthesis, plants absorb photons of light and use that energy to convert carbon dioxide and water into sugars and other molecules.

Following light absorption by the pigment chlorophyll, the high potential energy of excited-state electrons is used in photosynthetic electron transport to synthesize the energy-rich compounds NADPH (nicotinamide adenine dinucleotide phosphate) and ATP (adenosine triphosphate). These molecules are in turn consumed in the biochemical reactions of the Calvin cycle of photosynthesis to convert carbon dioxide into carbohydrates **(Figure 1.7)**. Although the energy of one photon is very small, the photosynthetic apparatus within the chloroplast of a single plant leaf absorbs millions of photons each second. And a single cell within a typical plant leaf contains hundreds of chloroplasts!

While photosynthesis converts carbon dioxide into carbohydrates, it is the process of cellular respiration, which is found in all organisms, that breaks down carbohydrates and other energy-rich molecules, trapping the released energy as ATP (Figure 1.7). The value of ATP is that it is the universal energy

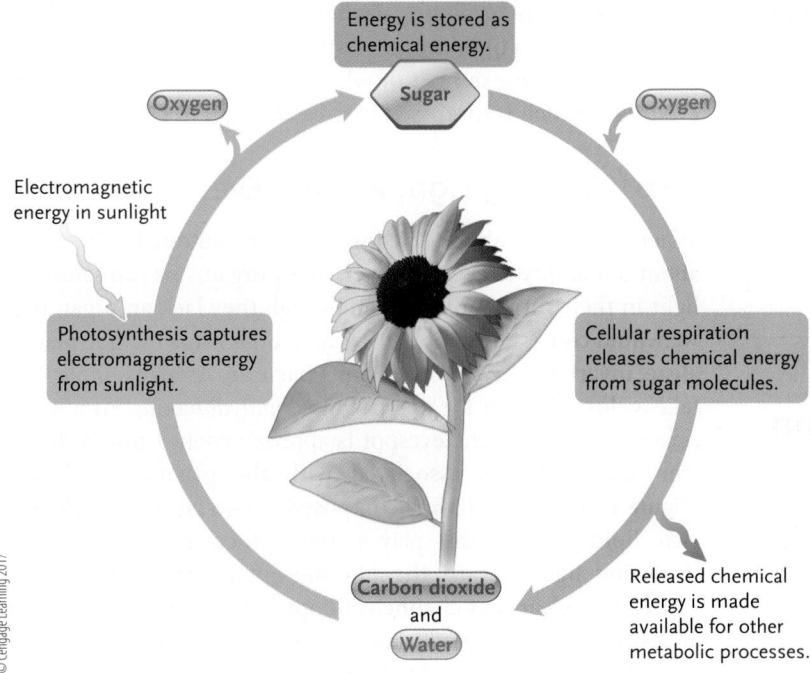

© Cengage Learning 2017

**FIGURE 1.7 Photosynthesis converts light energy into chemical energy.**
Photosynthesis uses the energy in sunlight to build sugar molecules from carbon dioxide and water, releasing oxygen as a by-product. The process of cellular respiration breaks down the products of photosynthesis and releases usable energy.

currency, and can be readily used for the energy-requiring metabolic and biosynthetic processes that are required to maintain all life.

Photosynthesis is the dominant process of the biosphere that directly uses the light of the Sun as a source of energy, but you may be surprised to know that it isn't the only one. Another light-driven process used to acquire energy is found in a group of microbes called *Halobacterium*. These organisms are not eukaryotes or even bacteria, but rather they belong to the third domain of life, the Archaea. We will introduce you to the three domains of life in Chapter 21, and will discuss the Archaea in greater detail in Chapter 22. Most often found in extreme habitats, *Halobacterium* contains a pigment–protein complex called *bacteriorhodopsin*, which is found on the plasma membrane and functions as a light-driven proton pump. When the pigment component of bacteriorhodopsin captures a photon of light, it triggers changes in the protein component, resulting in the specific transport of protons out of the cell. The resulting difference in $H^+$ concentration across the plasma membrane represents a source of energy that is used by the enzyme ATP synthase to generate ATP from ADP and inorganic phosphate (Pi) **(Figure 1.8)**. Like all organisms, the

**a. *Halobacterium salinarum***

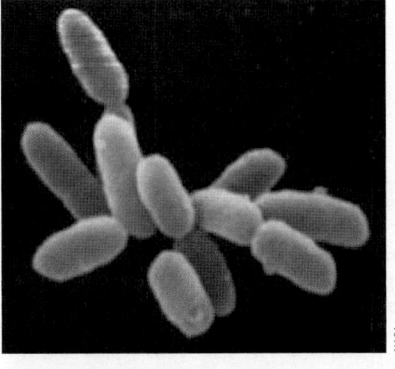

NASA

**b. Hutt Lagoon, Western Australia**

J Marshall – Tribaleye Images / Alamy Stock Photo

**FIGURE 1.8 *Halobacterium* is a genus of Archaea that have a light-driven proton pump.**
**(a)** Electron micrograph of a colony of *Halobacterium salinarum*. **(b)** Species of *Halobacterium* thrive in high-salt environments, such as Hutt Lagoon in Australia. The pink colour of the water is due to the presence of bacteriorhodopsin within individual cells. **(c)** A model of bacteriorhodopsin shows the pigment retinal bound to a protein. **(d)** Bacteriorhodopsin functions as a light-driven proton pump, the proton gradient being used to synthesize ATP.

**c. A model of bacteriorhodopsin**

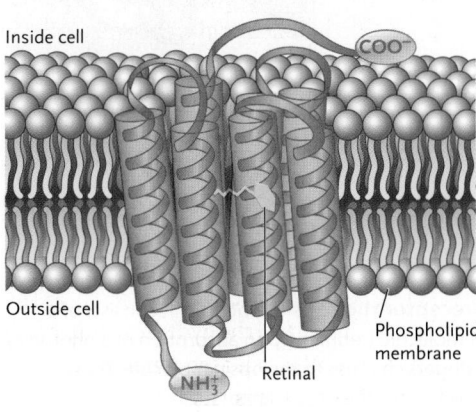

**d. Bacteriorhodopsin-driven ATP formation**

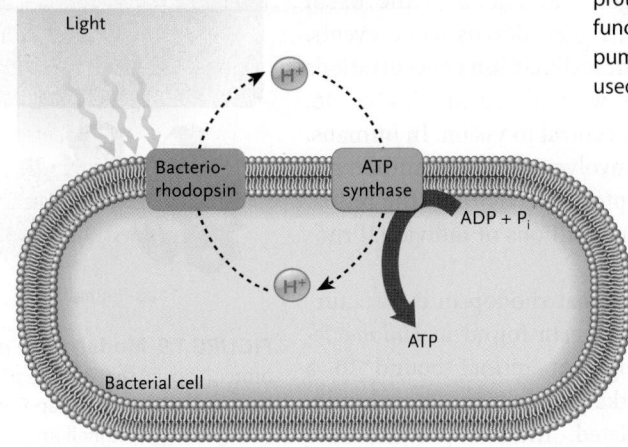

CHAPTER 1 LIGHT AND LIFE

ATP generated by *Halobacterium* is used for a range of energy-requiring reactions necessary for life.

**STUDY BREAK QUESTIONS**
1. What is the definition of photosynthesis?
2. How is light absorption linked to ATP synthesis in *Halobacterium*?
3. *Halobacterium* uses light energy but is not considered to be photosynthetic. Why not?

# 1.3 Light as a Source of Information

As mentioned in *Why It Matters*, the deterioration of Monet's eyesight changed the way he saw the world, thus changing the way he painted. This reminds us that many organisms use light to sense their environment—to provide them with crucial information about what is around them. The experience of trying to perform even the simplest of tasks in a dark room makes you quickly realize how important the ability to sense light has become. The change in Monet's eyesight during his later life also suggests that not every person, and certainly not every species, sees the world in the same way.

## 1.3a Rhodopsin, the Universal Photoreceptor

Almost all organisms that sense light for information do so using a fundamental light-sensing system called a *photoreceptor*. By far, the most common kind of photoreceptor in nature is rhodopsin **(Figure 1.9)**, which is a key component of the eye in all animals and insects. Each rhodopsin molecule consists of a protein (opsin) that binds a single pigment molecule (retinal). Opsins are membrane proteins that span a membrane multiple times and form a complex, with the retinal molecule at the centre (Figure 1.9). We will talk much more about membrane proteins in Chapter 4.

As shown in Figure 1.9, absorption of a photon of light causes the retinal pigment molecule to change shape. This change triggers alterations to the opsin protein, which in turn trigger downstream events, including alterations in intracellular **ion** concentrations and electrical signals. As we will see in Chapter 46, these electrical signals are central to vision. In humans, light captured by the eye involves about 125 million rod and cone cells (photoreceptor *cells*) that line the retina. Each of these cells contains millions of individual rhodopsin molecules.

You may have noticed that rhodopsin is structurally similar to bacteriorhodopsin found in *Halobacterium*: both have the pigment retinal bound to a membrane protein. Remarkably, however, the molecules are not evolutionarily related. The two proteins have entirely different evolutionary histories but, over time, have evolved to have a high degree of structural and functional similarity. This is an example of what is referred to as *convergent evolution*, which is discussed in greater detail in Chapter 16.

## 1.3b Sensing Light without Eyes

When we think about sensing light, we automatically think about our ability to see. However, many organisms can sense the light in their surroundings even though they lack an organ that we would consider to be an eye. These organisms include plants, algae, invertebrates, and even some bacteria. As an example, let's take a closer look at the eyespot of *Chlamydomonas*. As a light-sensitive structure, the eyespot is approximately 1 μm in diameter and is closely associated with the plasma membrane **(Figure 1.10)** of the cell. It is composed of two layers of pigment-rich, lipid globules that play a role in focusing and directing incoming light toward the photoreceptor channelrhodopsin. Evidence is clear that channelrhodopsin and bacteriorhodopsin are evolutionarily related, sharing a common ancestor. The eyespot allows the cell to sense light direction and intensity. Using a pair of flagella, *Chlamydomonas* can respond to light by swimming toward or away from the light source in a process called *phototaxis*. This allows the cell to stay in the optimum light environment to maximize light capture for photosynthesis. Although evolutionarily related to bacteriorhodopsin, channelrhodopsin

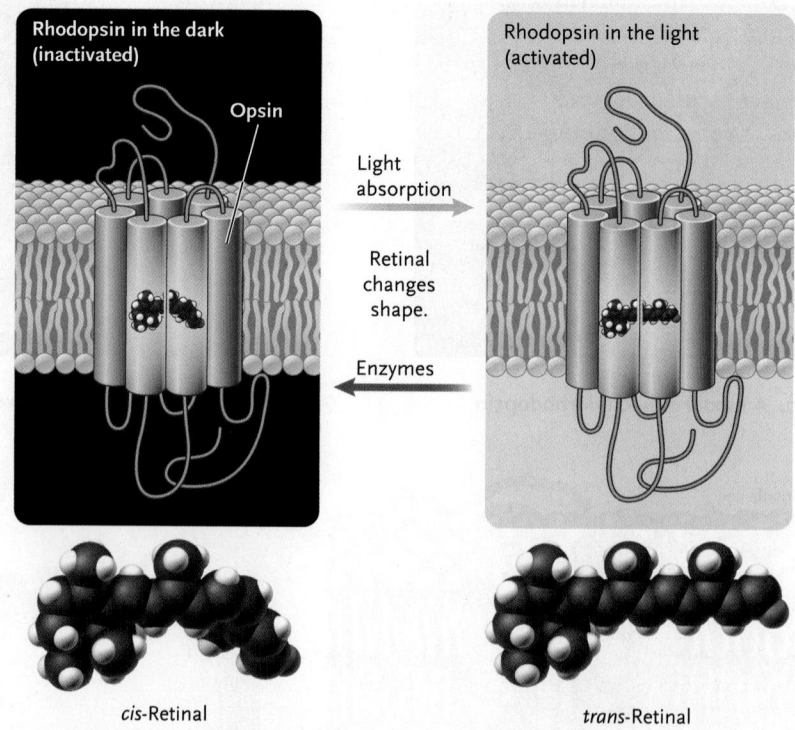

**FIGURE 1.9 Model of the photoreceptor rhodopsin.** Rhodopsin consists of a protein (opsin) that binds a pigment molecule (retinal). Upon absorption of a photon of light, retinal changes shape, which triggers changes to the opsin molecule. These changes trigger signalling events, which allow the organism to "see."

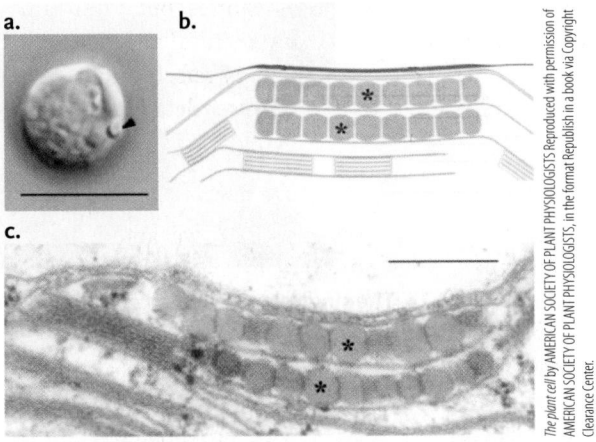

FIGURE 1.10 **The eyespot of *Chlamydomonas*. (a)** Light microscope image of one *Chlamydomonas* cell. Arrowhead points to the eyespot. Bar = 10 μm. **(b)** Drawing of the eyespot apparatus with the asterisks indicating the orange pigment-rich, globule layers that are found inside the chloroplast outer membrane. **(c)** Transmission electron micrograph of the same area. The eyespot contains the photoreceptor molecule channelrhodopsin (not shown). Bar = 300 nm.

is not linked to ATP formation. Instead, it is part of a **signal transduction** pathway: light absorption by channelrhodopsin triggers rapid changes in the concentrations of ions, including potassium and calcium, which generate a cascade of electrical events. These, in turn, change the beating pattern of the flagella used for locomotion. Signal transduction is introduced in Chapter 4 and touched on in a number of other chapters.

In plants, a photoreceptor called *phytochrome* senses the light environment and is critical for *photomorphogenesis,* the normal developmental process activated when seedlings are exposed to light **(Figure 1.11)**. Phytochrome is present in the cytosol of all plant cells, and when a seedling is exposed to wavelengths of red light, phytochrome becomes active and initiates a signal transduction pathway that reaches the nucleus. In the nucleus, these signals activate hundreds of genes, many of which code for proteins involved in photosynthesis and leaf development. DNA, genes, and gene expression are topics that are discussed in the chapters of Unit 3; plant development is the focus of Chapter 36.

## 1.3c The Eye

The **eye** is the organ animals use to sense light. What distinguishes the eye from the eyespot of *Chlamydomonas* is vision. The process of vision requires not only an eye to focus and absorb incoming light but also a brain, or at least a simple nervous system, that interprets the electrical signals sent from the eye. The eye and brain are thought to have co-evolved over time because detailed visual processing occurs in the brain rather than in the eye. So improved vision required not only the eye to develop greater sophistication but the brain as well. Essentially, we see not with our eyes but with our brain. We discus both the eye and the brain in much greater detail in Chapter 46.

The simplest eye is the *ocellus* (plural: *ocelli*), which consists of a cup or pit lined with up to 100 photoreceptor cells. A common group of organisms that possesses ocelli are flatworms of the genus *Planaria* **(Figure 1.12)**. Information sent to the cerebral ganglion from individual eyes enables the worms to orient themselves so that the amount of light falling on the two ocelli remains equal and diminishes as they swim. This

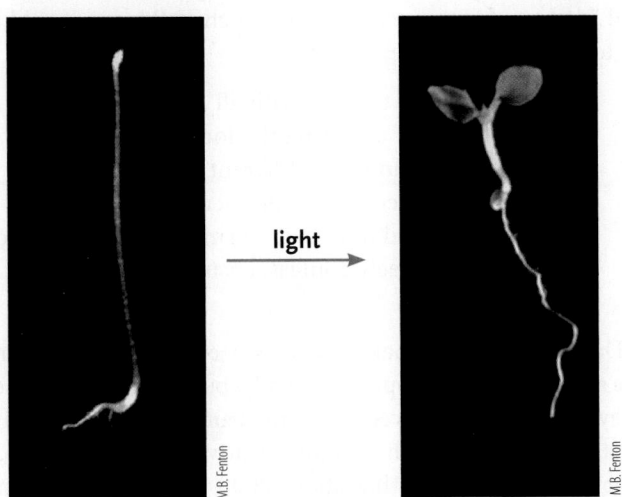

FIGURE 1.11 **Photomorphogenesis.** Shifting a seedling from darkness to light triggers a developmental program within the plant called *photomorphogenesis.* Light sensed by the photoreceptor phytochrome initiates the program that involves the activation of hundreds of genes.

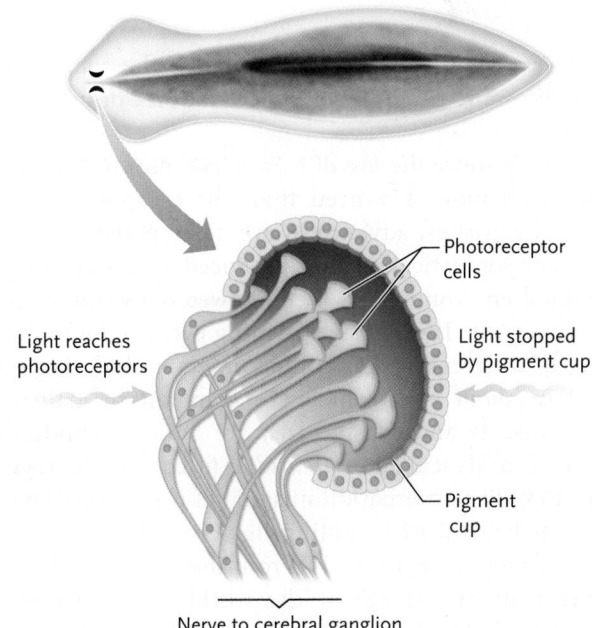

FIGURE 1.12 **The ocellus of Planaria, a flatworm, and the arrangement of photoreceptor cells that allows worms to orient themselves in response to light**

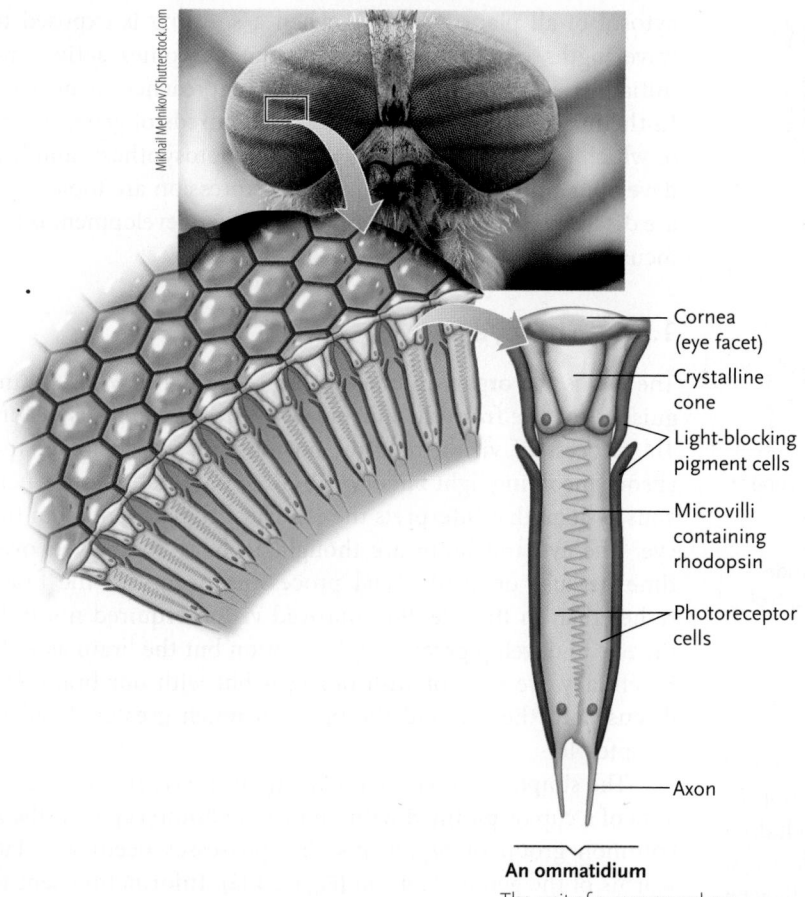

FIGURE 1.13 **The compound eye of a deer fly.** Each ommatidium has a cornea that directs light into the crystalline cone; in turn, the cone focuses light on the photoreceptor cells. A light-blocking pigment layer at the sides of the ommatidium prevents light from scattering laterally in the compound eye.

Cornea (eye facet)

Crystalline cone

Light-blocking pigment cells

Microvilli containing rhodopsin

Photoreceptor cells

Axon

**An ommatidium**
The unit of a compound eye

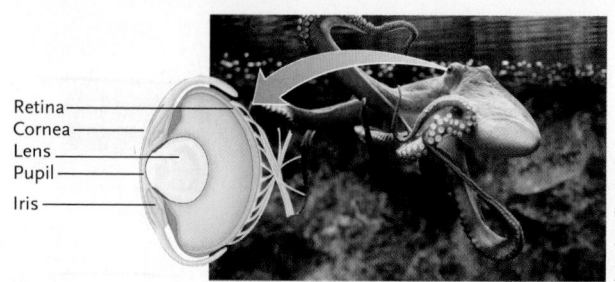

FIGURE 1.14 **The single-lens eye of a cephalopod mollusc (an octopus)**

Retina
Cornea
Lens
Pupil
Iris

reaction carries them directly away from the source of the light and toward darker areas, where the risk of predation is smaller.

In many ways, the eye of a *Planaria* (plural: *Planarians*) is not much more advanced than the eyespot of *C. reinhardtii*. The greatest advance in eye development came with the greater sophistication that produced an actual image of the lighted environment, which allowed objects and shapes to be discerned. These image-forming eyes are found in two distinctly different types: compound eyes and single-lens eyes. *Compound eyes,* which are common in arthropods such as insects and crustaceans, are built of hundreds of individual units called *ommatidia* fitted closely together **(Figure 1.13)**. Each ommatidium samples only a small part of the visual field, with incoming light being focused onto a bundle of photoreceptor cells. From these signals, the brain receives a mosaic image of the world. Because even the slightest motion is detected simultaneously by many ommatidia, organisms with compound eyes are extraordinarily good at detecting movement, a lesson soon learned by fly-swatting humans.

The other major type of eye is called the *single-lens eye* **(Figure 1.14)**, or camera-like eye, and is found in some invertebrates and most vertebrates, including humans. Unlike compound eyes, in a single-lens eye, as light enters through the transparent cornea, a lens concentrates the light and focuses it onto a layer of photoreceptor cells at the back of the eye, the retina. The photoreceptor cells of the retina send information to the brain through the optic nerve.

## 1.3d Darwin and the Evolution of the Eye

Stop for a second and think about how remarkable eyes and the brain are, and how complex the act of seeing is. Because of the inherent complexity of the organs involved, many people have a hard time thinking that these are products of evolution. Well, when Charles Darwin presented his theory of evolution by natural selection in *On the Origin of Species by Means of Natural Selection* (1859), he also recognized that what he called "organs of extreme perfection," such as the eye, would be hard to explain. He wrote:

> To suppose that the eye, with all its inimitable contrivances for adjusting the focus to different distances, for admitting different amounts of light, and for the correction of spherical and chromatic aberration, could have been formed by natural selection, seems, I freely confess, absurd in the highest possible degree.

Darwin proposed that the eye as it exists in humans and other animals did not appear suddenly, but correctly surmised that eyes must have evolved over time from a simple, primitive eye. Starting with a patch of light-sensitive cells on the skin, a recent study concluded that about 2000 small improvements over time would gradually yield a single-lens eye in less than 500 000 years **(Figure 1.15)**. Considering that animals with primitive eyes appeared in the **fossil** record about 500 million years ago, the single-lens eye found in humans could have evolved

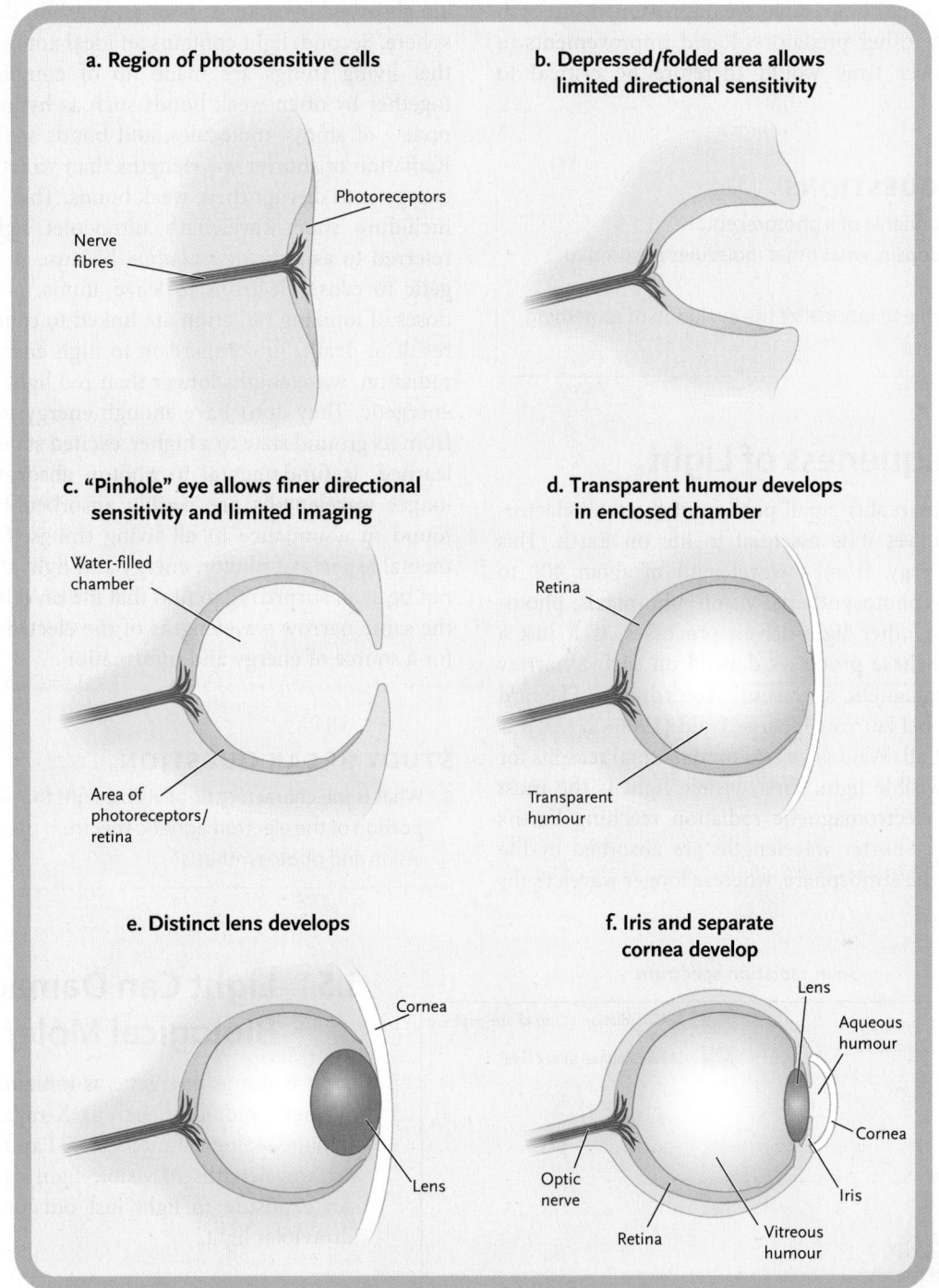

**FIGURE 1.15 The evolution of the eye.** Starting with a layer of light-sensitive cells, research suggests that a camera-like eye could evolve in less than 500 thousand years. The evolution of a more sophisticated eye can be explained by the huge advantage that improved eyesight would give an organism.

more than 1000 times. This kind of timing supports fossil evidence that indicates that the eye evolved independently at least 40 times in different animal lineages before converging into a handful of fundamental designs found today.

It is somewhat surprising that something so complex as the eye could evolve 40 or more different times. However, recently it has been shown that most eyes have fundamental similarities in their underlying developmental program. For example, a diversity of organisms have recruited a similar set of highly conserved genes to orchestrate eye development. This includes a gene called *Pax6* that has been identified as a master control gene that is almost universally employed for eye formation in animals. And let's not forget that what drove eye evolution in many different animal phyla is the huge advantage that eyesight, and then improved eyesight, would have to an animal. The development of heightened visual ability in a predator, as an example, would force comparable eye improvements in both prey and potentially other predators. Rapid improvements in eye development over time would therefore be critical to survival.

**STUDY BREAK QUESTIONS**

1. What are the components of a photoreceptor?
2. In addition to rhodopsin, what other molecules are used to sense light?
3. How was Darwin able to rationalize the evolution of something so complex as the eye?

## 1.4 The Uniqueness of Light

Visible light is a remarkably small portion of the total electromagnetic spectrum, yet it is essential to life on Earth. This narrow band of energy, from a wavelength of about 400 to 700 nm, is used for photosynthesis, vision, phototaxis, photomorphogenesis, and other light-driven processes. Is it just a coincidence that all these processes depend on such a narrow band of the electromagnetic spectrum? According to Harvard physiologist and Nobel laureate George Wald (1906–1997), it is not a coincidence at all. Wald gave two fundamental reasons for the dominance of visible light. First, visible light is the most dominant form of electromagnetic radiation reaching Earth's surface **(Figure 1.16)**. Shorter wavelengths are absorbed by the ozone layer high in the atmosphere, whereas longer wavelengths are absorbed by water vapour and carbon dioxide in the atmosphere. Second, light contains an ideal amount of energy. Recall that living things are made up of complex molecules held together by often weak bonds such as hydrogen bonds. (For a review of atoms, molecules, and bonds see *The Purple Pages*.) Radiation of shorter wavelengths than violet light is sufficiently energetic to disrupt these weak bonds. This higher energy light, including short-wavelength ultraviolet light and X-rays, is referred to as *ionizing radiation* because it is sufficiently energetic to cause electrons to leave atoms, producing ions. Low doses of ionizing radiation are linked to cancer, and high doses result in death. In comparison to high energy electromagnetic radiation, wavelengths longer than red light are not sufficiently energetic. They don't have enough energy to move an electron from its ground state to a higher, excited state, which, as we have learned, is fundamental to photon absorption. Furthermore, longer wavelengths are readily absorbed by water, which is found in abundance in all living things. Given these fundamental aspects of photon energy and light absorption, it would not be at all surprising to find that life on other planets relies on the same narrow wavelengths of the electromagnetic spectrum for a source of energy and information.

**STUDY BREAK QUESTION**

1. What is the characteristic of visible light that makes it the portion of the electromagnetic spectrum that is used for both vision and photosynthesis?

## 1.5 Light Can Damage Biological Molecules

Light is not as energetic as ionizing forms of electromagnetic radiation such as X-rays, but light can still damage biological molecules. Exposure to high-intensity wavelengths of visible light can be damaging, as can exposure to light just outside the visible range, ultraviolet light.

### 1.5a Damage Is an Unavoidable Consequence of Light Absorption

The photoreceptor cells that line the human retina can be damaged by exposure to bright light. The high-energy environment associated with pigment molecules and excited electrons can result in what is referred to as *photo-oxidative damage*. The absorption of excess light energy can result in excited electrons being donated to $O_2$, producing what are called *reactive oxygen species*. These forms of oxygen, which include the molecule hydrogen peroxide, can

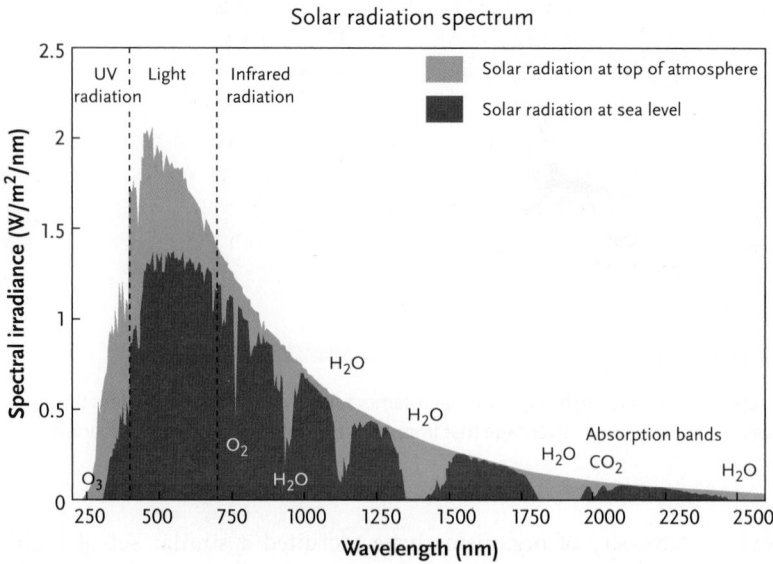

Solar radiation spectrum

**FIGURE 1.16 Electromagnetic radiation reaching the top of Earth's atmosphere (orange) and at sea level (red).** As the energy passes through the atmosphere, short-wavelength radiation (250–300 nm) gets absorbed by ozone ($O_3$). Other wavelengths get partially absorbed by other gases, including $O_2$, $H_2O$, and $CO_2$. Compared to the electromagnetic radiation that reaches the outer atmosphere, the radiation reaching Earth's surface is reduced in both short wavelengths and long wavelengths, with visible wavelengths the most dominant.

damage proteins and other molecules, often resulting in a loss of function. Damaged rhodopsin molecules are unable to be repaired and excessive damaged can result in cell death of rod and cone cells.

Unlike eyes, the photosynthetic apparatus of plants and algae is often exposed to full sunlight for hours, and thus is particularly susceptible to photo-oxidative damage. A typical chloroplast contains hundreds of photosystems, each one trapping the energy of thousands of photons each second. However, unlike the photoreceptor molecules of the retina, damaged photosystems can be repaired by a very efficient mechanism that involves removing damaged proteins and replacing them with newly synthesized copies. In fact, under normal light conditions, a single photosystem II **(Figure 1.17)** complex needs to be repaired about every 20 minutes. Because damage to the photosynthetic apparatus is unavoidable, a mechanism of efficient repair must have developed early during the evolution of life so that photosynthesis could be maintained even under high light conditions. This mechanism involves high rates of protein synthesis, a process that is discussed in Chapter 12.

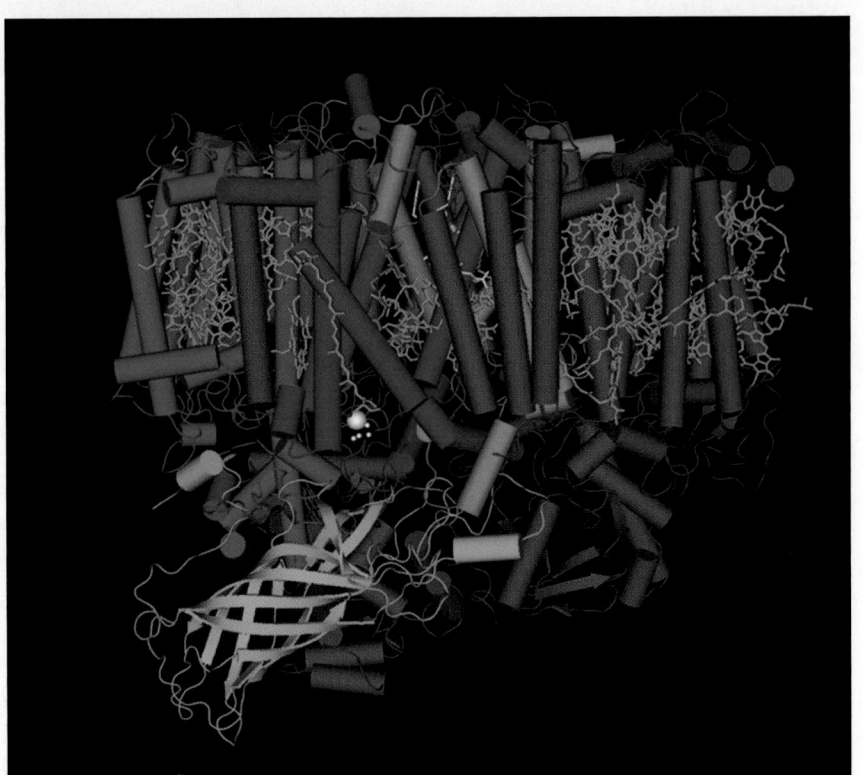

Courtesy of Curtis Neveu

**FIGURE 1.17 Molecular model of the structure of photosystem II.** The coloured ribbons and rods represent proteins to which pigments and other cofactors are precisely bound. Light absorption results in unavoidable damage to proteins. An efficient repair system maintains photosystem function even under high light conditions.

## 1.5b Ultraviolet Light Is Particularly Harmful

Ultraviolet light is electromagnetic radiation that has a wavelength between blue light (400 nm) and X-rays (200 nm). Because it consists of wavelengths that are shorter than visible light, the energy of the photons of ultraviolet light is greater and more damaging to biological molecules. Life on Earth is protected from the shortest-wavelength and most-damaging form of ultraviolet light by the atmosphere's ozone layer. While short wavelengths of ultraviolet light are absorbed by ozone, longer wavelengths of ultraviolet light reach Earth's surface within visible light.

Ultraviolet light can be destructive to a range of biological molecules; however, it is the structure of DNA that is particularly susceptible to damage **(Figure 1.18)**. The interaction of ultraviolet light with nucleotide bases that make up DNA can result in the formation of a dimer—two neighbouring bases become linked together covalently. Dimers change the shape of the double-helix structure of DNA and prevent its replication, as well as hinder gene transcription. These processes are discussed in detail in Chapter 12. Although there is an elaborate process by which nucleotide dimers are detected and repaired,

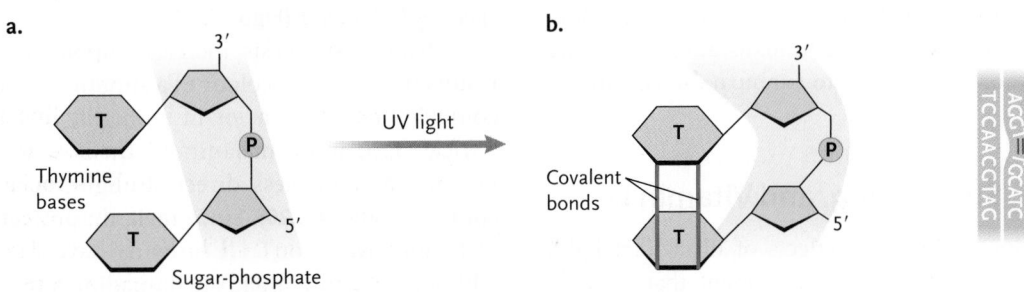

**FIGURE 1.18 Ultraviolet light can damage DNA.** Ultraviolet light absorbed by DNA can cause the formation of thymine dimers. Although cells have an efficient mechanism to repair damage to DNA, the formation of dimers can lead to mutation.

FIGURE 1.19    **Research Method**

## Using Spectrophotometry to Determine an Absorption Spectrum

Spectrophotometry measures the capacity of pigment molecules to absorb light of specific wavelengths. White light from a bulb is separated into its different wavelengths by a prism. Using a movable slit, light of only a specific wavelength is passed through the sample. Usually, the sample is pigment molecules dissolved in a suitable solvent. Positioned after the sample chamber is a detector, which measures the amount of light that passed through the sample. By comparing the amount of light that passed through the sample with the amount that entered the sample, the amount of light that is absorbed is calculated and presented on a digital display. In the example shown, the larger the number the more light at that wavelength was absorbed (and the less light was transmitted through the sample).

To produce an absorption spectrum, you would do this experiment at a range of wavelengths from 400 nm (blue) to 700 nm (red).

**Experiment:** β-carotene is the most abundant pigment found in carrots. We can isolate β-carotene by grinding carrot tissue in the presence of a solvent. Because β-carotene is non-polar, it is extracted using a non-polar solvent such as hexane or acetone. After filtering the extracts to remove debris, you can use the technique of spectrophotometry to determine at which wavelengths β-carotene absorbs.

**Results:** By determining the absorbance of a pigment extract from carrots at a range of wavelengths from 400 to 700 nm, you can produce an absorption spectrum for that pigment. As shown below, the pigment isolated from carrots absorbs strongly in the blue region of the spectrum. It does not absorb any light of longer wavelengths (green through red).

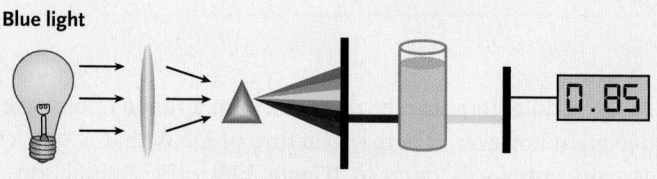

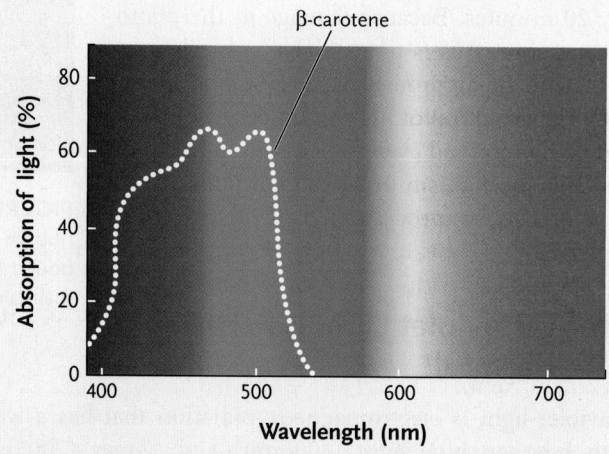

**Absorption spectrum for β-carotene**

---

their formation can give rise to mutations and they have been linked to skin cancer.

For most organisms, exposure to ultraviolet light is unavoidable. Because of this, organisms use a range of behavioural, structural, and biochemical mechanisms to protect themselves from its damaging effects. For example, many animals are protected by fur or feathers covering their skin. Organisms with naked skin, such as humans and whales, are less protected and more susceptible to sunburn due to ultraviolet light exposure.

## 1.5c    Melanin, Suntanning, and Vitamin D

To protect cells from the harmful effects of ultraviolet light, many organisms synthesize melanin, a pigment that strongly absorbs ultraviolet light. Melanin is a remarkable pigment found in all branches of the tree of life. Along with playing a key role in ultraviolet light protection in organisms as diverse as microbes

and humans, it is also the major component of the ink released by cephalopods such as squid.

Melanin is very efficient at absorbing ultraviolet light, and yet it dissipates over 99% of this energy harmlessly as heat. The specific wavelength of radiation that a pigment such as melanin can absorb can be determined using an instrument called a *spectrophotometer* **(Figure 1.19)**.

Melanin synthesis increases upon Sun exposure, which results in the brown colour of a suntan. In general, people from countries receiving a lot of sunlight, including countries of Africa, have more melanin in their skin than people from regions receiving less direct sunlight, such as Scandinavian countries **(Figure 1.20)**. Since melanin protects us from ultraviolet light, why don't all humans have high melanin levels? Although melanin filters out damaging ultraviolet wavelengths, humans require some ultraviolet radiation to synthesize vitamin D, which is critical for normal bone development. People with high melanin levels who live in regions that do not

**FIGURE 1.20 People differ in the amount of melanin in their skin cells.**

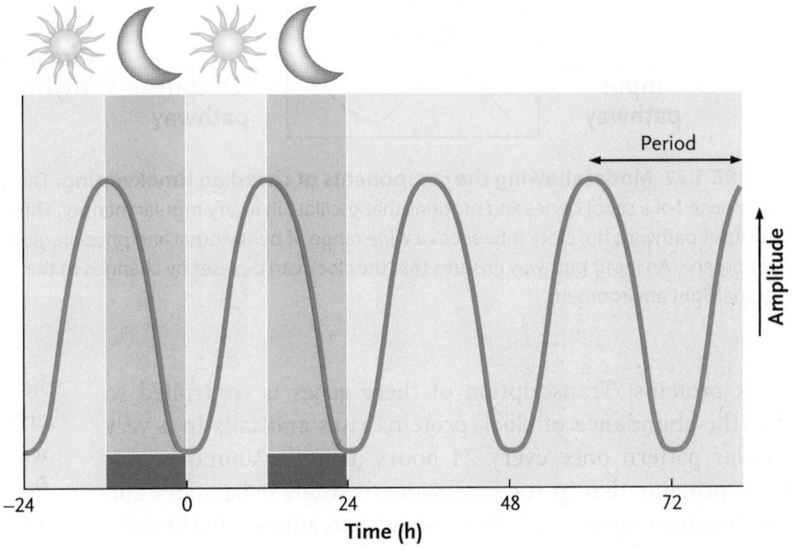

**FIGURE 1.21 Circadian rhythms are oscillations in behaviour and physiology that have a period of approximately 24 hours.** These rhythms are set by the external light environment but can run for some time (free-running) even in the absence of environmental light oscillations.

receive abundant sunlight are susceptible to vitamin D deficiency. This could occur, for example, for someone of African descent living in Winnipeg. However, in much of the developed world, vitamin D deficiency is rare because many foods, such as milk, yogurt, and grain products, are fortified with this essential nutrient.

**STUDY BREAK QUESTIONS**

1. What biological molecules are particularly susceptible to damage by ultraviolet radiation?
2. What role does vitamin D serve in protecting humans from ultraviolet light?

## 1.6 Using Light to Tell Time

As it revolves around the Sun once a year, Earth rotates on its axis once every 24 hours. These two motions result in very predictable changes to the light and temperature at Earth's surface, giving rise to the seasons and day/night respectively. The rhythmic and predictable nature of light and darkness during the 24-hour day has led to the evolution of many physiological and behavioural phenomena that display diurnal (*daily*) and seasonal rhythmicity.

### 1.6a Circadian Rhythms Are Controlled by a Biological Clock

The daily cycling of some biological phenomena is due simply to an organism responding to changes in sunlight. For example, photosynthesis and vision occur during the day and not in darkness because they require photons of light. However, the diurnal cycling of other phenomena called **circadian** (*circa* = "around"; *diem* = "day") **rhythms** is quite different **(Figure 1.21)**. Circadian rhythms are not driven by an organism constantly detecting changes in daylight, but rather are governed by an internal *biological clock* (also known as the *circadian clock*). Phenomena that are classified as circadian rhythms and thus are controlled by a biological clock include sleep–wake cycles, body temperature, metabolic processes, cell division, and the behaviours associated with foraging for food and **mating**.

A key attribute of all biological clocks is that, while they are set by the external light environment, they can run for a long time independent of external conditions—a phenomenon called *free-running*. This is analogous to winding an old-fashioned wrist watch. Once it is wound it can function for a long time without being rewound. The free-running nature of circadian rhythms was first described in 1729 by the French astronomer Jean-Jacques d'Ortous de Mairan. He found that the daily rhythmic movements of certain plant leaves continued when he placed the plants in complete darkness. In humans, the free-running nature of circadian rhythms is shown by the fact that daily fluctuations in body temperature and hormone levels, for example, will occur even if an individual is subjected to conditions of constant light or darkness.

A key question we can ask at this stage is, What is the physical basis of a biological clock? A requirement of anything that keeps time is the presence of something that oscillates. In the case of a traditional clock or watch, it's often a crystal or a pendulum (tick, tock, tick, tock…). By comparison, a biological clock is built around a small set of so-called *clock genes* and

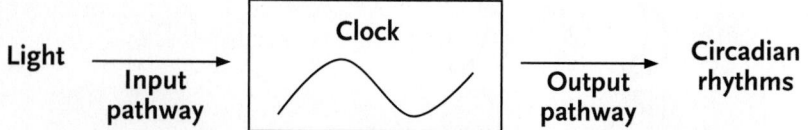

FIGURE 1.22 **Model showing the components of circadian timekeeping.** The clock is composed of a set of genes and proteins that oscillate in a very regular manner. Through an output pathway, the clock influences a wide range of behavioural and physiological phenomena. An input pathway ensures that the clock can be reset by changes to the external light environment.

clock proteins. Transcription of these genes is controlled so that the abundance of clock proteins rises and falls in a very regular pattern once every 24 hours. It is the abundance of these proteins that in turn influences various behaviours and physiological processes that show circadian rhythmicity **(Figure 1.22)**.

Circadian rhythms have been found in all organisms in which they have been searched, including species from a diverse array of phyla such as bacteria, fungi, animals, and plants. The widespread occurrence of circadian rhythms suggests that there is a selective advantage to being able to tell time. So why are circadian rhythms and the use of an underlying biological clock advantageous? The presence of biological clocks enhances an organism's ability to survive under ever-changing environments by giving them the ability to anticipate or predict when a change will occur, instead of just responding after a change has occurred. This ability to predict change is seen as advantageous and increases survivability because it enables organisms to restrict their activities to specific, most beneficial times of the day. Such activities include foraging for food, finding a mate, and avoiding predators, just to name a few. Let's work through some specific examples. In insects, emergence of adults from the pupal case is under circadian control and occurs close to dawn. This is the time of the day when the humidity in the air is highest, which is thought to prevent desiccation (drying out) of the insects, which in turn enhances their survival. In many organisms, proteins required for DNA replication are controlled by a biological clock and are synthesized at dusk.

This allows for DNA replication to occur at night, which protects replicating DNA from damaging ultraviolet radiation during the day.

## 1.6b Biological Clocks Track the Changing Seasons

Not only are biological clocks central to diurnal behaviour and physiology, but they also have been shown to be critical to an organism's ability to keep track of the time of year. Organisms keep track of the changing seasons in part by being able to measure day length, or *photoperiod*. Changes in day length and thus seasons occur because Earth is tilted on its axis as it orbits the Sun (see *The Purple Pages*). In the Northern Hemisphere, the longest and shortest days of the year are June 21 and December 21 respectively.

Being able to determine the time of year assures that, for both plants and animals, certain phenomena occur under the most appropriate environmental conditions. This means that the onset of flowering occurs in the spring or summer for most angiosperm plant species, and that leaf drop followed by entrance into dormancy occurs in the autumn for deciduous trees in temperate climates. In animals, a huge range of phenomena are linked to being able to sense the time of year. Changes in photoperiod have been shown to provoke changes in colour of fur and feathers, and trigger migration, entry into hibernation, and changes in sexual behaviour **(Figure 1.23)**.

## 1.6c Jet Lag and the Need to Reset Biological Clocks

In humans, the central biological clock is found in a very small part of the brain, the suprachiasmatic nucleus (SCN; **Figure 1.24**). This central clock can receive direct light inputs through the optic nerve of the eye so that it can be reset periodically. The SCN regulates the timing events in peripheral tissues, in part, through the release during the night of the hormone melatonin from the pineal gland.

FIGURE 1.23 **Changes in photoperiod trigger behavioural and developmental changes.** Biological clocks keep track of day length, which is critical for organisms to ensure that specific events occur only at certain times of the year. Examples of photoperiod-dependent phenomena are leaf-drop in trees and colour change in the coat of the Arctic fox (*Vulpes lagopus*).

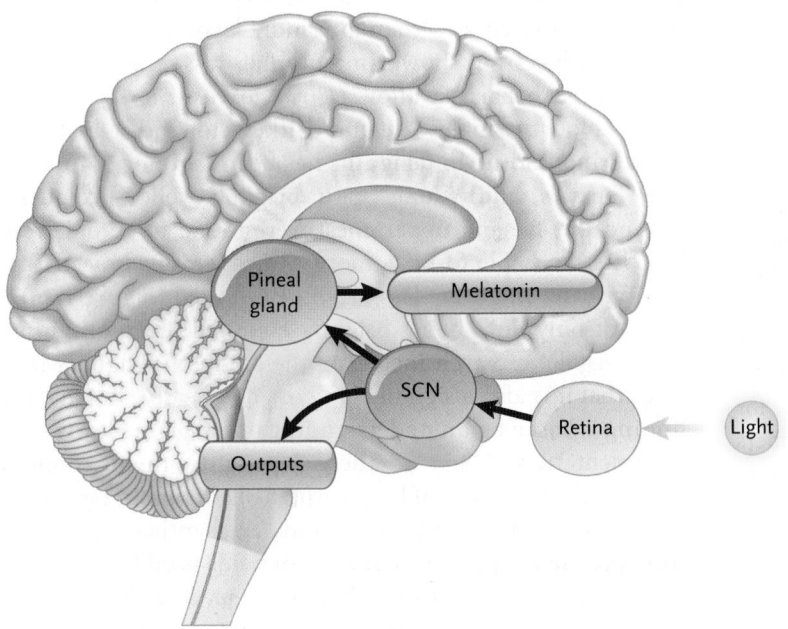

**FIGURE 1.24 In humans, central timekeeping is found in the brain.** The suprachiasmatic nucleus (SCN) within the brain is the central biological clock in humans. It is set by direct light input from the eye. It controls circadian rhythms directly through an output pathway or through the synthesis of the hormone melatonin by the pineal gland.

an eight-hour flight from Paris to Toronto starting at 2 p.m. **(Figure 1.25).** When you arrive in Toronto, your body feels like it is 10 p.m. and expects it to be dark. But because of the six-hour time zone change, when you step off the plane in Toronto it is only 4 p.m. and still daylight. The external light environment is out of synchronization with your internal biological clock. It is this confusion that results in the symptoms of jet lag, which can include lack of appetite, fatigue, insomnia, and mild depression. The clearly defined health effects of jet lag indicate that a range of behavioural and physiological processes are intimately linked to circadian timekeeping. They also show that biological clocks cannot be automatically reset to new light conditions, but instead they often take a few days to adjust. Poor synchronization between circadian clocks and the external light environment is a particular problem for shift workers (e.g., nurses, police officers, fire fighters), who usually alternate working a few weeks during the day followed by shifts at night. While there is growing evidence that this lack of synchronization is unhealthy, low-dosage melatonin given when these shift workers want to sleep seems to help.

Several conditions can interfere with normal circadian cycling. Probably the best example is jet lag, which occurs when you travel rapidly east or west across many time zones, putting your circadian cycling out of synchronization with the external light environment. As an example, let's say you take

**STUDY BREAK QUESTIONS**

1. Why isn't photosynthesis considered to have a circadian rhythm?
2. What is the advantage to having a biological (circadian) clock?
3. What is the biological explanation for jet lag?

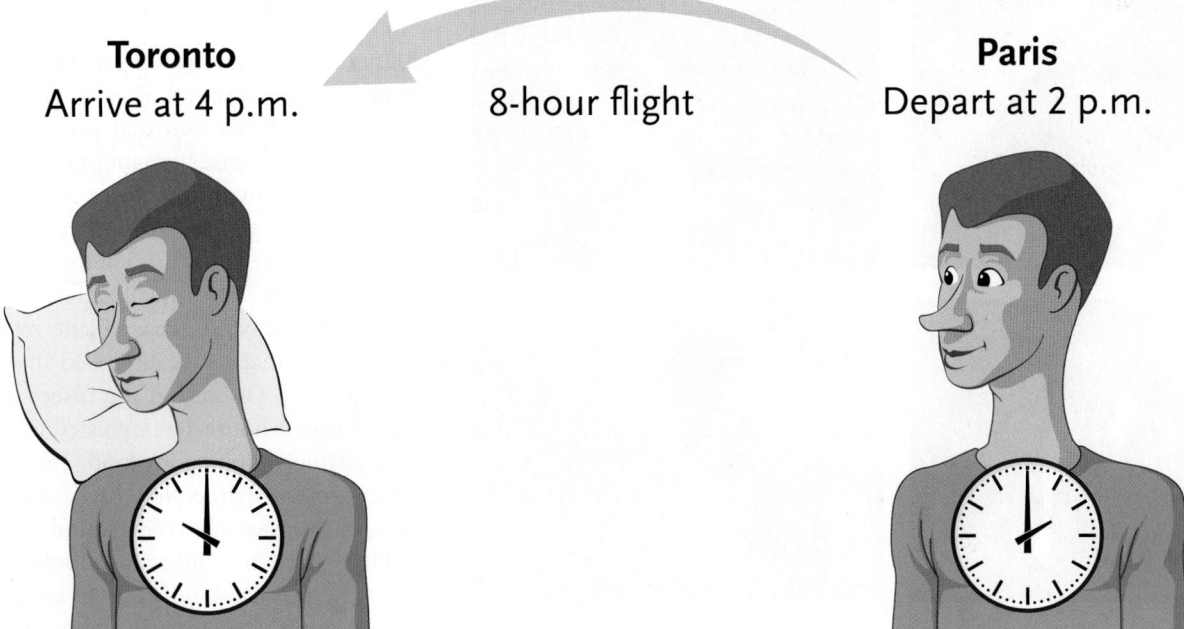

## Toronto
### Arrive at 4 p.m.

**8-hour flight**

## Paris
### Depart at 2 p.m.

**FIGURE 1.25 Jet lag.** Flights over many time zones result in your biological clock becoming out of synchronization with the external light environment. This results in a number of unpleasant responses that are collectively referred to as *jet lag*. The effects subside as the clock within the suprachiasmatic nucleus is reset to the new light environment.

## 1.7 The Role of Light in Behaviour and Ecology

Nature provides a great range of light environments, ranging from the total darkness of caves and the deep ocean to the stark brightness of deserts and polar regions. Differences in the intensity and spectral composition of the light environment influence how a population may adapt to a specific habitat and, in so doing, contribute to the huge diversity of organisms we find on Earth. We will discuss species diversity in the eight chapters that make up Unit 6, and gain an appreciation for how organisms interact with each other and the environment (ecology) in the chapters of Unit 7. As we will see in the next few sections, for many animals, unique colorations may serve to attract members of the same species, while in plants they often serve to attract animal pollinators.

### 1.7a Using Colour as a Signal: Animals

In animals, bright coloration is thought to serve a valuable role in communication. Research suggests that what is most often communicated by their colouring is an individual's worth as a rival or a mate. A range of particularly colourful fish and bird species have become model systems used by ecologists investigating the role of colour in communication; biochemists are interested in the actual pigments that account for the colour and how they are made.

In the Eclectus parrot (*Eclectus roratus*), the female is more brightly coloured (in terms of standing out from its surroundings) than the male **(Figure 1.26)**. This is an exception to the general rule that the male of a species is usually more brightly coloured and therefore more conspicuous than the female. It has been shown in a number of species, including the European barn swallow (*Hirundo rustica rustica*), that more colourful males are more likely to find a mate. An interesting finding in penguins has been that, for both males and females, individuals with brighter yellow colouring around the eye and upper chest were found to be older and healthier and able to raise more chicks in a given year than mating pairs that were less brightly coloured (Figure 1.26).

Not only does being brightly coloured make an animal more visible, research including the study of penguins indicates that it is also a sign of being in good health. In part, this finding is based on an understanding of the pigments used for ornamentation. Many of these belong to the **carotenoid** family—the structure of beta-carotene is shown in Figure 1.5. Unlike in plants, where carotenoids are synthesized in cells from precursor molecules, the carotenoids used for colouring in birds are obtained from what birds eat, and they circulate in the bloodstream before being deposited in feathers. Biochemical studies have shown that carotenoids play an important role in breaking down potentially harmful reactive oxygen species. Thus, a more brightly coloured individual suggests a good diet rich in molecules that maintain good health. In addition to carotenoids, different types of melanin-based pigments are also found in darker and brown colorations in birds. Finally, the biochemistry of some pigments is particularly interesting; for example, the dominant psittacofulvins pigments of parrots are found nowhere else in nature.

### 1.7b Using Colour as a Signal: Plants

Although humans marvel at the diversity of colours and patterns in flowers, botanists correctly concluded centuries ago that such displays were not designed to please humans but rather to attract pollinators. Pollination involves the movement of pollen from the anthers (male parts) of one flower to the stigmas (female parts) of the same flower or other flowers to effect fertilization and the production of fruit and seeds. Plant reproduction, including pollination, is discussed in more detail in Chapter 35. Of course, the insect or bird visiting a flower is not really interested in pollination, they are simply looking for food. This reward may be the protein-rich pollen itself, the sugar-rich nectar, or the waxes or resins found in the flower.

Plants that use animals as pollinators must attract the correct candidates to ensure efficient pollination, in part because the excess pollen or nectar can be energetically costly for the plant to produce. The dependence of a specific plant species on certain animals to act as pollinators, and

**FIGURE 1.26 Coloured plumage of four avian species often used in studies of the role of colour in behaviour.** Clockwise from top left: Eclectus parrot (*Eclectus roratus*) showing a green male and red female, European barn swallow (*Hirundo rustica rustica*), red-winged blackbird (*Agelaius phoeniceus*), and King penguin (*Aptenodytes patagonicus*)

FIGURE 1.27 **Flowering plants and their animal pollinators**

the reliance of certain animals on particular flowers as a food source, has led to the co-evolution of flower–pollinator associations. Mentioned in the 1877 publication *Fertilisation of Orchids*, by Charles Darwin, co-evolution refers to the fact that, over evolutionary time, a change in one species triggers changes in the other. The result is that specifics of flower shape, colour, and smell make them more attractive to specific groups of potential pollinators **(Figure 1.27)**. For example, the food reward of the flower has become an important part of the pollinator's diet, and the colour and shape of the flower coincide with the

visual preferences and shape, respectively, of the animal pollinator.

The visual systems of pollinators differ considerably among broad groupings such as bees, bats, and birds. Through co-evolution, these differences have led to flower colour being a key factor that attracts specific groups of pollinators. For example, whereas hummingbirds can perceive colour across a broad range of wavelengths, bees are unable to see red. This explains why hummingbirds dominate the pollination of red-coloured flowers, and bees are attracted primarily to blue and yellow flowers. In addition, bees and some other insects can also see in the ultraviolet region of the electromagnetic spectrum, and are particularly attracted to flowers that strongly reflect ultraviolet radiation. The role of ultraviolet light in flower–pollinator interactions is widely studied, and these studies have been aided by the development of photographic approaches that readily capture the ultraviolet radiation reflected off flowers. It is striking how different flowers look that were photographed using this technique compared to flowers photographed using visible wavelengths. The organization of distinct ultraviolet-reflecting pigments reveals patterning that is undetectable to humans. In general, it is shown that the region around the anthers and stigma is darker, and thus more easily detected by the pollinating insects **(Figure 1.28)**.

## STUDY BREAK QUESTIONS

1. What is a potential advantage for a parrot in being brightly coloured?
2. Why is it important for flowering plants to be able to attract specific species of animals?

FIGURE 1.28 **Two species of flowering plants (angiosperms) that are pollinated by bees: *Oenothera biennis* (top) and *Ranunculus ficaria* (bottom).** Photographs capturing visible light are shown on the left; photographs capturing only ultraviolet light are shown on the right.

## 1.8 Organisms Making Their Own Light: Bioluminescence

Many organisms, including certain bacteria, algae, fungi, insects, squid, and fish, are able to make their own light, a process called *bioluminescence* **(Figure 1.29)**. Recall from Section 1.1 that, in the process of light absorption by a pigment, the energy of a photon is transferred to an electron, raising it from the ground state to an excited state. Bioluminescence is essentially the same process in reverse (Figure 1.29). Chemical energy in the form of ATP is used to excite an electron in a **substrate** molecule from the ground state to a higher excited state, and when the electron returns to the ground state, the energy is released as a photon of light. The conversion of the

CHAPTER 1 LIGHT AND LIFE

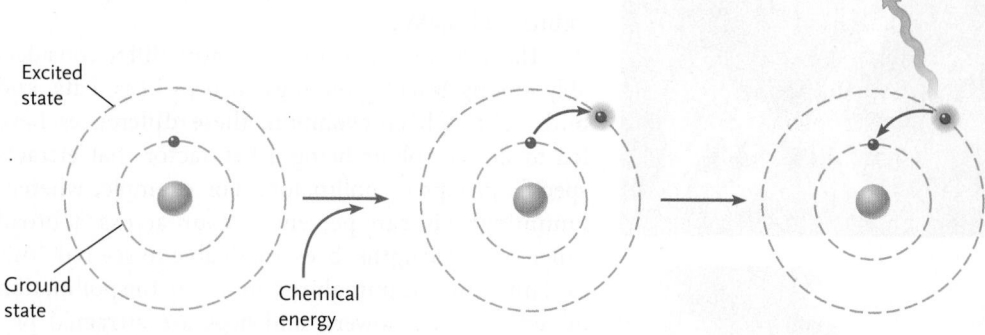

**FIGURE 1.29 Bioluminescence.** Chemical energy is used to excite an electron in a molecule. A photon of light is released when the electron decays back down to the ground state.

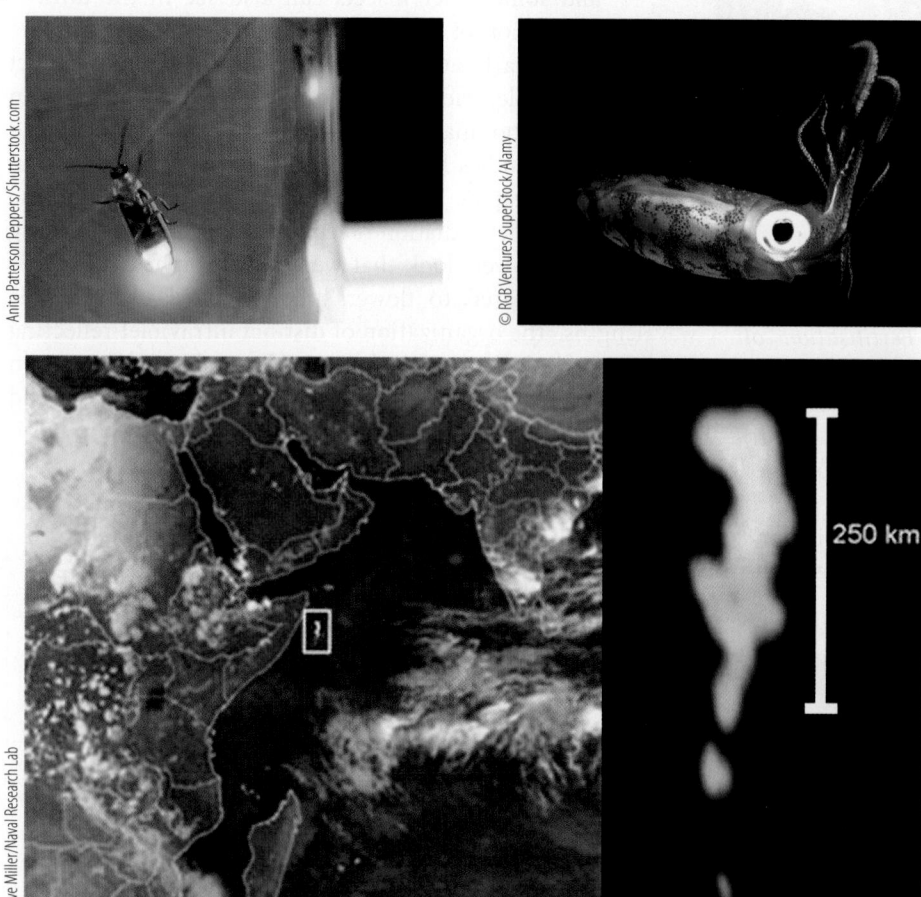

**FIGURE 1.30 Examples of bioluminescence. (a)** Bioluminescent insect. **(b)** Bioluminescent squid. **(c)** Satellite image of a "milky sea," a bloom of bioluminescent bacteria off the east coast of Africa

scare off potential predators. In these tiny organisms, bioluminescence is triggered simply by a disturbance of the water surrounding them. When a predator such as a small fish swims close to a dinoflagellate at night, the resulting burst of light produced by all the dinoflagellates in the vicinity lights up the water around the fish. This defensive behaviour makes the fish clearly visible to its own predators.

Some marine bacteria use bioluminescence in a type of communication called *quorum sensing.* Individual bacteria often release compounds into their environment at concentrations too low to elicit a response from their neighbours. However, as a bacterial population grows, its size reaches a threshold, a quorum, whereby the concentration of compounds is high enough to elicit a physiological response in all members of the population. The response results in the activation of certain genes, including those that encode for proteins required for bioluminescence. Quorum sensing is now believed to be the basis for what are termed "milky seas" **(Figure 1.30).** This strange phenomenon of light on the surface of the ocean has been reported many times over the past several hundred years by sailors, and is mentioned in Jules Verne's classic book *Twenty Thousand Leagues Under the Sea.*

chemical energy in ATP into light is very efficient. Considering that up to 95% of the energy of an incandescent light bulb is lost as heat, it is remarkable that less than 5% of the energy in ATP is lost as heat during the process of bioluminescent light production. This extraordinary efficiency is essential because high heat production would be incompatible with life.

Bioluminescent organisms generate light for a range of uses. These include attracting a mate or prey, camouflage, and communication. For example, dinoflagellates, which are unicellular algae, use bioluminescence as an alarm mechanism to

Many bioluminescent organisms are marine and are most abundant below 800 m, a depth to which sunlight does not penetrate. Bioluminescence has not been reported in land plants or higher vertebrates. Why is bioluminescence absent in these organisms? We do not yet have the answers to this or other questions about bioluminescence, reminding us how much there is still to discover about life on Earth.

In closing, this introductory chapter discussed one phenomenon, light, and how it affects the biology of Earth. From absorption of a single photon by a pigment molecule in a single cell to affecting the composition of entire ecosystems, the influence of light spans all levels of biological organization. This chapter touched on many topics, including physics and chemistry, photosynthesis, genes and proteins, evolution and natural selection, and ecology and behaviour. As you work through the remaining chapters of this textbook, you will learn much more about these topics.

**STUDY BREAK QUESTIONS**

1. Compare and contrast the process of bioluminescence with light absorption.
2. Given that bioluminescence takes energy on the part of the organism, what are some roles that it may serve?

## SELF-TEST QUESTIONS

### Recall/Understand

1. Which of the following are the components of a photoreceptor?
   a. a pigment molecule bound to a protein
   b. two complementary proteins that are involved in photosynthesis
   c. a group of many pigment molecules
   d. two molecules of chlorophyll

2. Which of these statements is a characteristic of the eyespot of *Chlamydomonas reinhardtii*?
   a. It is unable to generate an image.
   b. It is not composed of photoreceptors.
   c. It is unable to detect changes in light intensity.
   d. It is unable to activate a signal transduction pathway when it absorbs light.

3. Which of these statements is an example of jet lag?
   a. a condition experienced when someone travels slowly over many time zones with lots of stops
   b. a condition that occurs even when the external environment and the events in the suprachiasmatic nucleus are synchronized
   c. a condition resulting from taking melatonin pills
   d. a condition experienced when someone travels continuously over many time zones with no stops

4. Which of these statements is a characteristic of bioluminescence?
   a. It requires ATP.
   b. It cannot occur in complete darkness.
   c. It is found only in Bacteria and Archaea.
   d. Like vision, it requires the absorption of a photon of light.

5. Which of these statements characterizes rhodopsin?
   a. It is found only in plants.
   b. It is found only in animals.
   c. It is the most common photoreceptor.
   d. It is the only receptor found in animals.

6. Which of the following is illustrated by the peppered moth?
   a. light pollution
   b. circadian rhythm
   c. light sensitivity
   d. camouflage

### Apply/Analyze

7. Which of these statements *best* describes light?
   a. Like sound, light is a form of electromagnetic radiation.
   b. Light of a longer wavelength contains more energy than light of a shorter wavelength.
   c. Visible light is more energetic than radio waves.
   d. A photon of red light contains more energy than a photon of blue light.

8. Suppose that you have found an organism with compound eyes. Which of these organisms is it most likely to be?
   a. an insect
   b. a vertebrate

   c. a *Planaria*
   d. *C. reinhardtii*

9. Suppose that you are diving in an ocean and a squid sprays you with its ink. You collect a sample of its ink for further testing in the lab. Which of these components would you most likely find as the major one in this ink?
   a. melatonin
   b. melanin
   c. melanoma
   d. melanocyte

### Create/Evaluate

10. For a photon of light to be used by an organism, which of these actions must occur?
    a. The photon must be absorbed.
    b. The photon must be reflected off a substance.
    c. The photon must interact with a protein in the plasma membrane.
    d. The photon must oxidize a molecule.

11. Which of these light forms is the major source of harmful effects for human skin?
    a. light that is emitted from fluorescent bulbs
    b. light that is emitted from halogen bulbs
    c. light that has shorter wavelength and higher frequency than visible light
    d. light that has longer wavelength and shorter frequency than visible light

12. Light represents only a very narrow region of the electromagnetic spectrum; however, it is the dominant form of electromagnetic radiation used in biology. Which of these statements is the reason why?
    a. Light contains the most energy per photon.
    b. Light can excite electrons within molecules without destroying them.
    c. Light is the only form of electromagnetic radiation to reach Earth's surface.
    d. All other wavelengths of electromagnetic radiation are too destructive to biological molecules.

13. Which of these statements is the *best* example of the free-running nature of circadian rhythms?
    a. speech patterns in humans
    b. reproduction patterns in humans
    c. absence of hormonal level fluctuations in people subjected to constant light
    d. daily fluctuations in body temperature in people subjected to constant darkness

14. How do eyes and the photosynthetic apparatus compare regarding damage caused by light?

15. Suppose a friend asked you to explain to her why her skin gets a darker shade after suntanning. What would you tell her?

# Chapter Roadmap

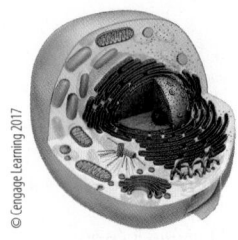

## The Cell: An Overview
The cell is the basic structural and functional unit of all living organisms.

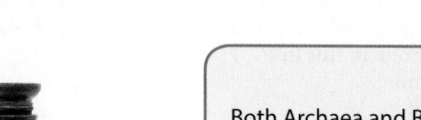

### 2.1 Basic Features of Cell Structure and Function
The diversity of life on Earth hides the fact that all life is built on cells that share a long list of similar structures and functions.

**To Purple Pages**

### 2.2 Prokaryotic Cells
Both Archaea and Bacteria are characterized by cells that lack internal, membrane-bound organelles.

**To Chapter 22**

### 3.3 Eukaryotic Cells
Eukaryotic cells have a complex cell architecture that includes a nucleus and cytoplasmic organelles.

**To Chapters 24–27**

### 2.4 Specialized Structures of Plant Cells
Chloroplasts, large and highly specialized vacuoles, and cell walls give plant cells their distinctive characteristics.

**To Chapter 6**

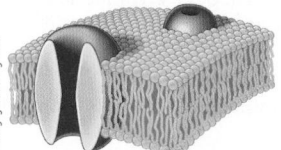

### 2.5 The Animal Cell Surface
Animal cells have specialized structures that help hold cells together, produce avenues of communication between cells, and organize body structures.

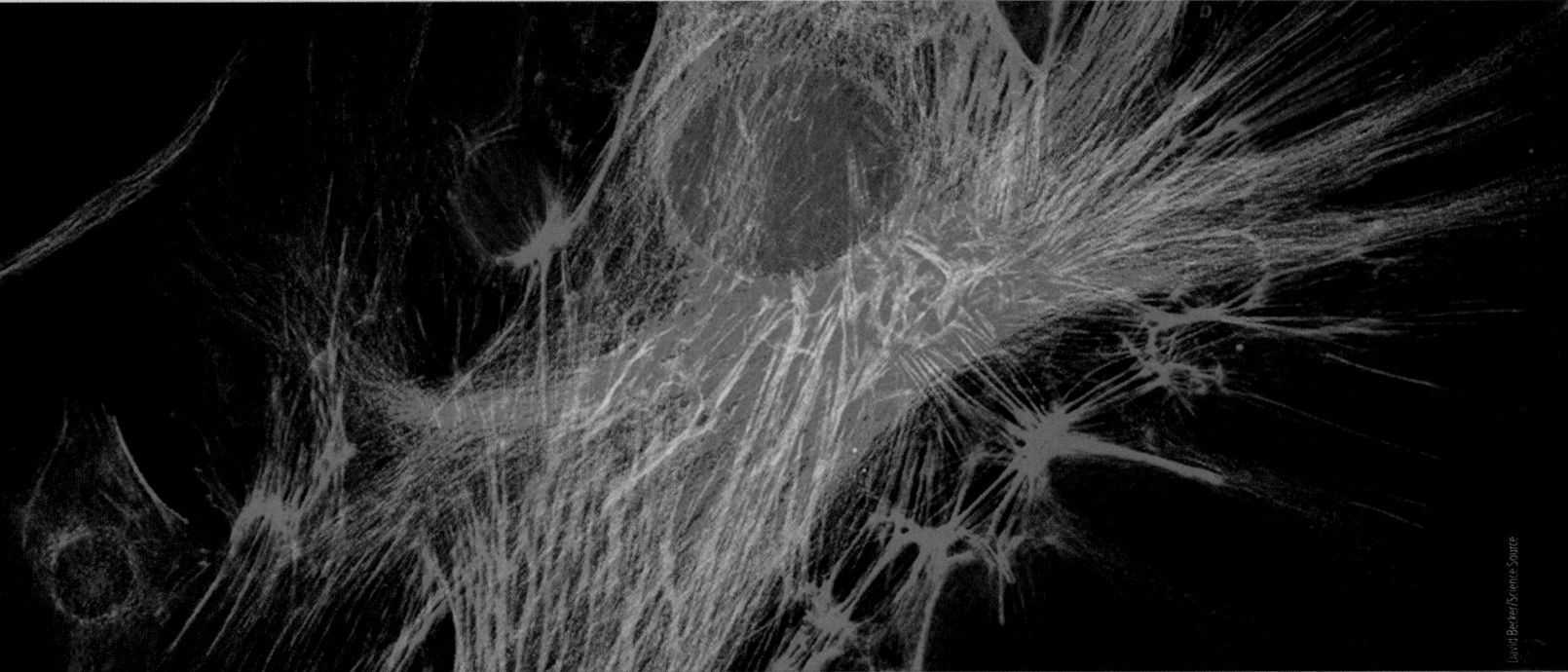

**Cells fluorescently labelled to visualize their internal structure (confocal light micrograph).** Cell nuclei are shown in blue, and parts of the cytoskeleton in red and green.

# The Cell: An Overview

# 2

**Why it matters . . .** In the mid-1600s, Robert Hooke, Curator of Instruments for the Royal Society of England, was at the forefront of studies applying the newly invented light microscopes to biological materials. When Hooke looked at thinly sliced cork from a mature tree through a microscope, he observed tiny compartments **(Figure 2.1a)**. He gave them the Latin name *cellulae*, meaning "small rooms"—giving us the biological term *cell*. Hooke was actually looking at the walls of dead cells, which is what cork consists of.

Reports of cells also came from other sources. By the late 1600s, Anton van Leeuwenhoek (Figure 2.1b), a Dutch shopkeeper, observed "many very little animalcules, very prettily a-moving" using a single-lens microscope of his own construction. Leeuwenhoek discovered and described diverse protists, sperm cells, and even bacteria, organisms so small that they would not be seen by others for another two centuries.

In the 1820s, improvements in microscopes brought cells into sharper focus. Robert Brown, an English botanist, noticed a discrete, spherical body inside some cells; he called it a *nucleus*. In 1838, German botanist Matthias Schleiden speculated that the nucleus had something to do with the development of a cell. The following year, the zoologist Theodor Schwann of Germany expanded Schleiden's idea to propose that all animals and plants consist of cells that contain a nucleus. He also proposed that even when a cell forms part of a larger organism, it has an individual life of its own. However, an important question remained: Where do cells come from? A decade later, the German physiologist Rudolf Virchow answered this question: From his studies of cell growth and reproduction, Virchow proposed that cells arise only from preexisting cells by a process of division.

**FIGURE 2.1 Investigations leading to the first descriptions of cells. (a)** The cork cells drawn by Robert Hooke and the compound microscope he used to examine them. **(b)** Anton van Leeuwenhoek holding his microscope, which consisted of a single, small sphere of glass fixed in a holder. He viewed objects by holding them close to one side of the glass sphere and looking at them through the other side.

Thus, by the middle of the nineteenth century, microscopic observations had yielded three profound generalizations, which together constitute what is now known as the **cell theory**:

1. All organisms are composed of one or more cells.
2. The cell is the basic structural and functional unit of all living organisms.
3. Cells arise only from the division of preexisting cells.

These tenets were fundamental to the development of biological science.

This chapter provides an overview of our current understanding of the structure and functions of cells, emphasizing both the similarities among all cells and some of the most basic differences among cells of various organisms. The variations in cells that help make particular groups of organisms distinctive are discussed in later chapters. This chapter also introduces some of the modern microscopes that enable us to learn more about cell structure.

# 2.1 Basic Features of Cell Structure and Function

As the basic structural and functional units of all living organisms, cells carry out the essential processes of life. They contain highly organized systems of molecules, including the nucleic acids DNA and RNA, which carry hereditary information and direct the manufacture of cellular molecules. Cells use chemical molecules or light as energy sources for their activities. Cells also respond to changes in their external environment by altering their internal reactions. Further, cells duplicate and pass on their hereditary information as part of cellular reproduction. All these activities occur in cells that, in most cases, are invisible to the naked eye.

As we will discuss in detail in Chapter 21, all forms of life can be divided into one of three domains: Bacteria, Archaea, and Eukarya. Some organisms in each domain are unicellular. This includes almost all bacteria and archaeans; some eukaryotes, including protists, such as the green alga *Chlamydomonas*; and some fungi, such as yeast. Each of these cells is a functionally independent organism capable of carrying out all activities necessary for living. In more complex multicellular organisms, including plants and animals, the activities of life are divided among varying numbers of specialized cells. However, individual cells of multicellular organisms are potentially capable of surviving by themselves if placed in a chemical medium that can sustain them.

If cells are broken open, the property of life is lost: they are unable to grow, reproduce, or respond to outside stimuli in a coordinated, potentially independent fashion. This fact confirms the second tenet of the cell theory: Life as we know it does not exist in units more simple than individual cells. *Viruses*, which consist only of a nucleic acid molecule surrounded by a protein coat, cannot carry out most activities of life. Their only capacity is to infect living cells and direct them to make more virus particles of the same kind. (Viruses are discussed in Chapter 22.)

## 2.1a Cells Are Visualized Using a Microscope

As shown in **Figure 2.2**, cells representing all three domains of life assume a wide variety of forms. Individual cells range in size from tiny bacteria to an egg yolk, a single cell that can be several centimetres in diameter. Yet, all cells are organized according to the same basic plan, and all have structures that perform similar activities.

Most cells are too small to be seen by the unaided eye: humans cannot see objects smaller than about 0.1 mm in diameter. The smallest bacteria have diameters of about 0.5 μm (a micrometre is one thousandth of a millimetre). The cells of multicellular animals range from about 5 to 30 μm in diameter. Your red blood cells are 7–8 μm across—a string of 2500 of these cells is needed to span the width of your thumbnail. Plant cells range from about 10 μm to a few hundred micrometres in diameter. (**Figure 2.3** explains the units of measurement used in biology to study molecules and cells.)

To see cells and the structures within them we use **microscopy**, a technique for producing visible images of objects, biological or otherwise, that are too small to be seen by the human

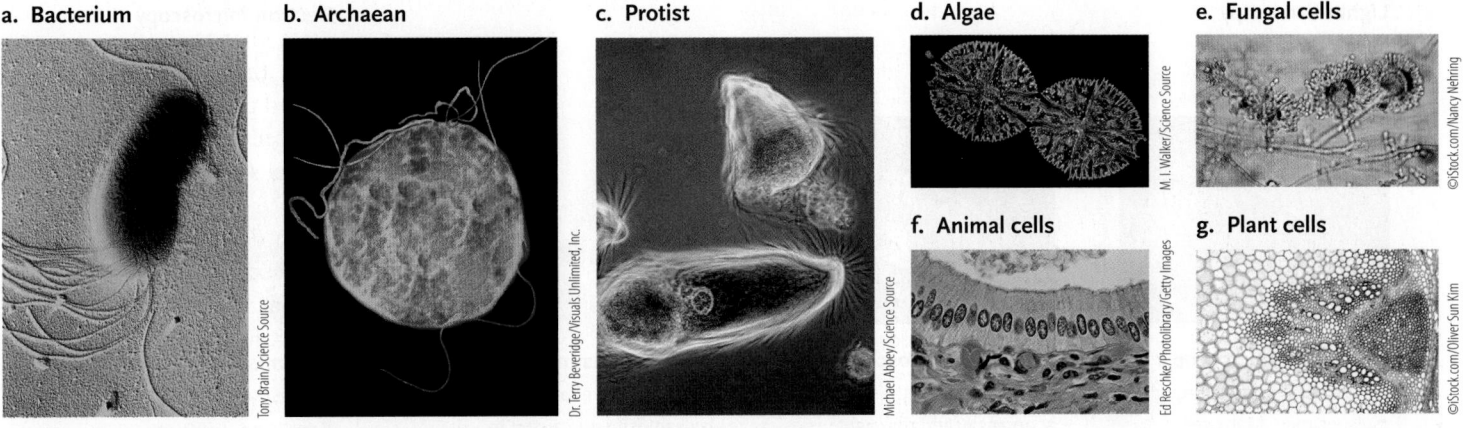

**FIGURE 2.2 Examples of the various kinds of cells: (a)** a bacterial cell with flagella, *Pseudomonas fluorescens*; **(b)** an archaean, the extremophile *Sulfolobus acidocaldarius*; **(c)** *Trichonympha*, a protist that lives in a termite's gut; **(d)** two cells of *Micrasterias*, an algal protist; **(e)** fungal cells of the bread mould *Aspergillus*; **(f)** cells of a surface layer in the human kidney; **(g)** cells in the stem of a sunflower, *Helianthus annuus*

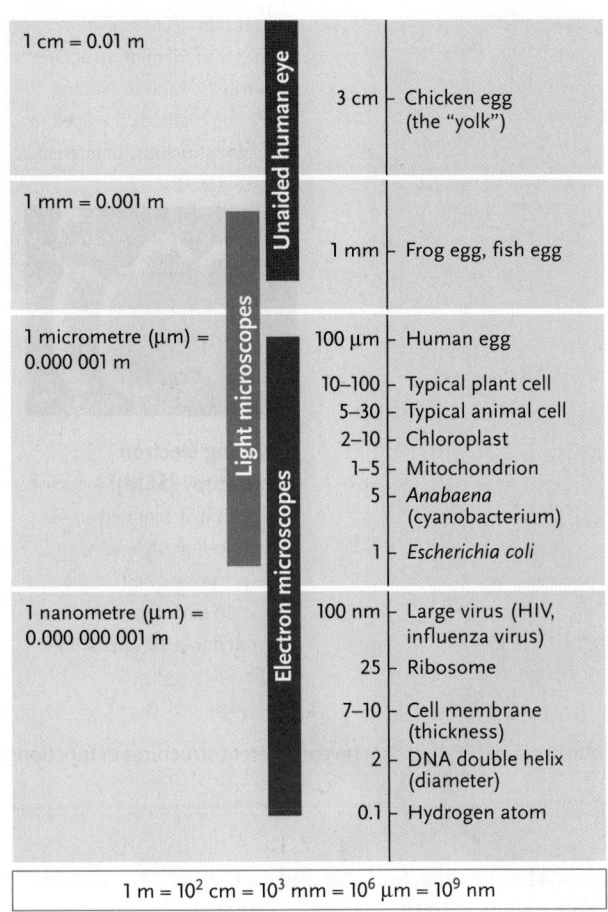

**FIGURE 2.3 Units of measure and the ranges in which they are used in the study of molecules and cells.** The vertical scale in each box is logarithmic.

eye (**Figure 2.4**). The instrument of microscopy is the **microscope**. The two common types of microscopes are **light microscopes**, which use light to illuminate the specimen (the object being viewed), and **electron microscopes**, which use electrons to illuminate the specimen. Different types of microscopes give different magnifications and resolutions of the specimen. Just as

for a camera or a pair of binoculars, **magnification** is the ratio of the object as viewed to its real size, usually given as something like 400:1. **Resolution** is the minimum distance by which two points in the specimen can be separated and still be seen as two points. Resolution depends primarily on the wavelength of light or electrons used to illuminate the specimen: the shorter the wavelength, the better the resolution. Hence, electron microscopes have higher resolution than light microscopes. Biologists choose the type of microscopy technique based on what they need to see in the specimen; selected examples are shown in Figure 2.4.

Why are most cells so small? The reason can be explained by how the surface area-to- volume ratio of a cell changes as it gets bigger (**Figure 2.5**). For example, doubling the diameter of a cell increases its volume by eight times but increases its surface area by only four times. The significance of this relationship is that the volume of a cell determines the amount of chemical activity that can take place within it, whereas the surface area determines the amount of substances that can be exchanged between the inside of the cell and the outside environment. Nutrients must enter cells constantly, and wastes must leave constantly. However, past a certain point, increasing the diameter of a cell gives a surface area that is insufficient to maintain an adequate nutrient–waste exchange for its entire volume. At that point, cell growth must stop or the cell must divide into two separate smaller cells that could grow larger.

## 2.1b Cells Have a DNA-Containing Central Region That Is Surrounded by Cytoplasm

All cells are bounded by the **plasma membrane**, a bilayer made of lipids with embedded protein molecules (**Figure 2.6**). The lipid bilayer is a hydrophobic barrier to the passage of water-soluble substances, but selected water-soluble substances can penetrate cell membranes through **transport protein** channels. The selective movement of ions and water-soluble molecules

## Light microscopy

Micrographs are of the protist *Paramecium*.

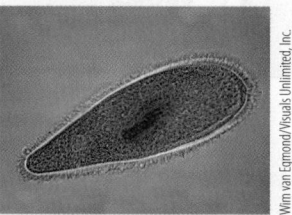 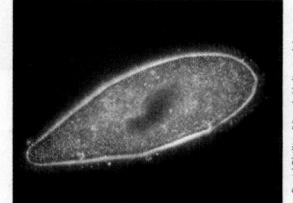 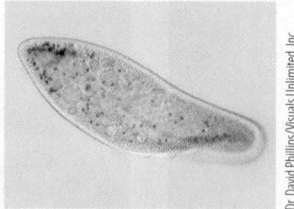

## Electron microscopy

Micrographs are of the green alga *Scenedesmus*.

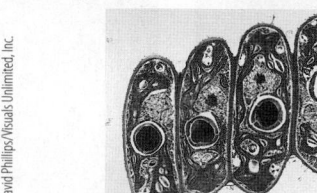

**Bright field microscopy:** Light passes directly through the specimen. Many cell structures have insufficient contrast to be discerned. Staining with a dye is used to enhance contrast in a specimen, as shown here, but this treatment usually fixes and kills the cells.

**Dark field microscopy:** Light illuminates the specimen at an angle, and only light scattered by the specimen reaches the viewing lens of the microscope. This gives a bright image of the cell against a black background.

**Phase-contrast microscopy:** Differences in refraction (the way light is bent) caused by variations in the density of the specimen are visualized as differences in contrast. Otherwise invisible structures are revealed with this technique, and living cells in action can be photographed or filmed.

**Transmission electron microscopy (TEM):** A beam of electrons is focused on a thin section of a specimen in a vacuum. Electrons that pass through form the image; structures that scatter electrons appear dark. TEM is used primarily to examine structures within cells. Various staining and fixing methods are used to highlight structures of interest.

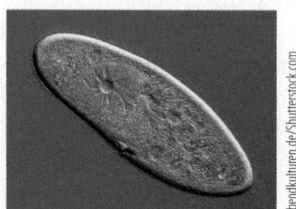 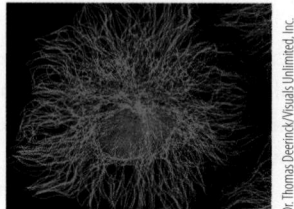

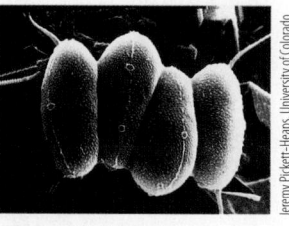

**Nomarski (differential interference contrast):** Similarly to phase-contrast microscopy, special lenses enhance differences in density, giving a cell a 3D appearance.

**Confocal laser scanning microscopy:** Lasers scan across a fluorescently stained specimen, and a computer focuses the light to show a single plane through the cell. This provides a sharper 3D image than other light microscopy techniques.

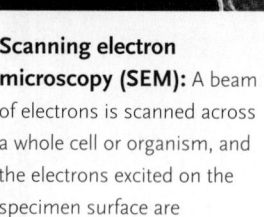

**Scanning electron microscopy (SEM):** A beam of electrons is scanned across a whole cell or organism, and the electrons excited on the specimen surface are converted to a 3D-appearing image.

**FIGURE 2.4 Different techniques of light and electron microscopy.** Each technique produces images that reveal different structures or functions of the specimen. A micrograph is a photograph of an image formed by a microscope.

---

through the transport proteins maintains the specialized internal ionic and molecular environments required for cellular life. (Membrane structure and functions are discussed further in Chapter 4.)

The central region of all cells contains DNA molecules, which store hereditary information. The hereditary information is organized in the form of **genes**—segments of DNA that code for individual proteins. The central region also contains proteins that help maintain the DNA structure and enzymes that duplicate DNA and copy its information into RNA.

All parts of the cell between the plasma membrane and the central region make up the **cytoplasm**. The cytoplasm contains the *organelles*, the *cytosol*, and the *cytoskeleton*. The **organelles** ("little organs") are small, organized structures important for cell function. The **cytosol** is an aqueous (water) solution containing ions and various **organic molecules**. The **cytoskeleton** is a protein-based framework of filamentous structures that, among other things, helps maintain proper cell shape and plays key roles in cell division and chromosome segregation from cell generation to cell generation. The cytoskeleton was once thought to be specific to eukaryotes, but recent research has shown that all major eukaryotic cytoskeletal proteins have functional equivalents in bacteria and archaeans.

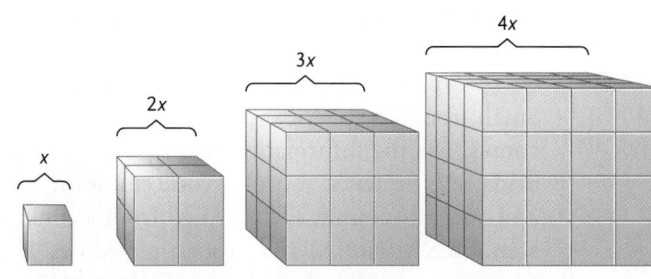

| | x | 2x | 3x | 4x |
|---|---|---|---|---|
| Total surface area | $6x^2$ | $6(2x)^2 = 24x^2$ | $6(3x)^2 = 54x^2$ | $6(4x)^2 = 96x^2$ |
| Total volume | $x^3$ | $(2x)^3 = 8x^3$ | $(3x)^3 = 27x^3$ | $(4x)^3 = 64x^3$ |
| Surface area/ volume ratio | 6:1 | 3:1 | 2:1 | 1.5:1 |

**FIGURE 2.5 Relationship between surface area and volume.** The surface area of an object increases as the square of the linear dimension, whereas the volume increases as the cube of that dimension.

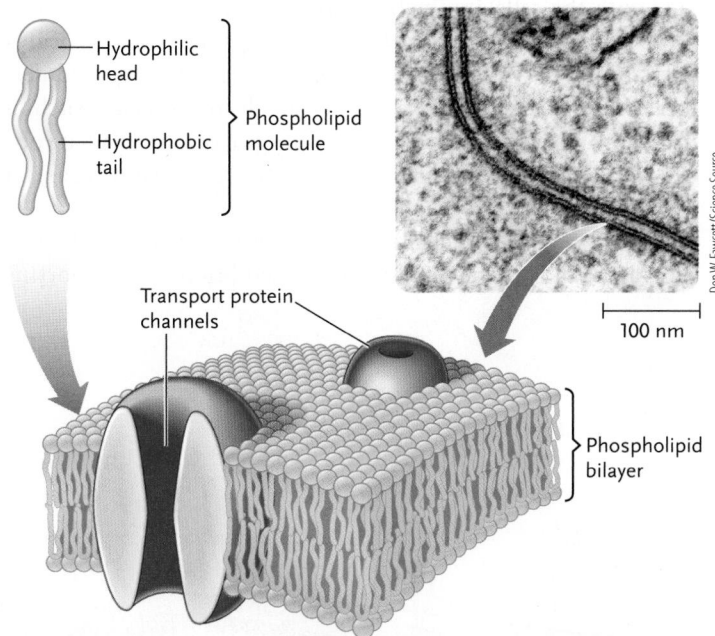

**FIGURE 2.6 The plasma membrane consists of a phospholipid bilayer, an arrangement of phospholipids two molecules thick, which provides the framework for all biological membranes.** Water-soluble substances cannot pass through the phospholipid part of the membrane. Instead, they pass through protein channels in the membrane; two proteins that transport substances across the membrane are shown. Other types of proteins are also associated with the plasma membrane. (Inset) Electron micrograph shows the plasma membranes of two adjacent animal cells.

Many of the cell's vital activities occur in the cytoplasm, including the synthesis and assembly of most of the molecules required for growth and reproduction and the conversion of chemical and light energy into forms that can be used by cells. The cytoplasm also conducts stimulatory signals from the outside into the cell interior, and carries out chemical reactions that respond to these signals.

## 2.1c Cells Occur in Prokaryotic and Eukaryotic Forms, Each with Distinctive Structures and Organization

**CONCEPT FIX** There are two fundamentally different types of cells: prokaryotic (*pro* = before; *karyon* = nucleus) and eukaryotic. Bacteria and archaea both have prokaryotic cell structure, and, until recently, it was because of this that they were grouped together as *prokaryotes*. Of course, this made perfect sense since basic cell structure between the two is similar, which suggested that bacteria and archaeans are evolutionarily closely related. However, more advanced biochemical and genetic techniques have revealed something surprising—archaeans are almost as different from bacteria as you are. So today, the term *prokaryote* to describe a unique group of evolutionarily related organisms has fallen out of use by microbiologists as Bacteria and Archaea are now viewed as being evolutionarily distinct. The term *prokaryotic cell* is still used as it refers to a particular cell architecture, that is, one lacking a nucleus, and not to a single group of organisms. ⬡

Within the prokaryotic cell that is a characteristic of both Bacteria and Archaea, the DNA-containing central region of the cell, the **nucleoid**, has no boundary membrane separating it from the cytoplasm. Many species of Archaea and Bacteria contain few if any internal membranes, but a number of other species of both groups contain extensive internal membranes.

The **eukaryotes** (*eu* = true) make up the domain Eukarya and are defined by having cells in which DNA is contained within a membrane-bound compartment called the **nucleus**. Typically, the cytoplasm of eukaryotic cells contains extensive membrane systems that form organelles with their own distinct environments and specialized functions. As in Archaea and Bacteria, a plasma membrane surrounds eukaryotic cells as the outer limit of the cytoplasm.

The remainder of this chapter surveys the components of prokaryotic and eukaryotic cells in more detail.

### STUDY BREAK QUESTIONS

1. What is the plasma membrane, and what are its main functions?
2. When a cell gets bigger, does its surface area-to-volume ratio go up or down? Explain.
3. What is the difference between the word *prokaryote* and the term *prokaryotic cell*?
4. In what way is scanning electron microscopy different than transmission electron microscopy?

## 2.2 Prokaryotic Cells

The cells of both Bacteria and archaeans are relatively small, usually not much more than a few micrometres in length and a micrometre or less in diameter. A typical human cell is about 10 times the diameter and over 8000 times the volume of an average prokaryotic cell. We discuss the structure, function and ecology of both Bacteria and Archaea in detail in Chapter 23.

### 2.2a Structure and Organization of Prokaryotic Cells

The three shapes most common among prokaryotes are spherical, rodlike, and spiral. *Escherichia coli* (*E. coli*), a normal inhabitant of the mammalian intestine that has been studied extensively as a model organism in genetics, molecular biology, and genomics research, is rodlike in shape. **Figure 2.7** shows an electron micrograph and a diagram of *E. coli* to illustrate the basic features of prokaryotic cell structure. More detail about prokaryotic cell structure and function, as well as about the diversity of prokaryotic organisms, is presented in Chapter 23.

The genetic material of archaea and bacteria is located in the nucleoid; in an electron micrograph, that region of the cell is seen to contain a highly folded mass of DNA (Figure 2.7). For most species, the DNA is a single, circular molecule that unfolds when released from the cell. This DNA molecule is the **prokaryotic chromosome**. (Chapters 12 and 13 discuss the organization and regulation of prokaryotic genes.)

Individual genes in the DNA molecule encode the information required to make proteins. This information is copied into a type of RNA molecule called *messenger RNA* (mRNA). Small, roughly spherical particles in the cytoplasm, the **ribosomes**, use the information in the mRNA to assemble **amino acids** into proteins. A prokaryotic ribosome consists of a large and a small subunit, each formed from a combination of **ribosomal RNA (rRNA)** and protein molecules. Each prokaryotic ribosome contains three types of rRNA molecules, which are also copied from the DNA, and more than 50 proteins.

In almost all prokaryotic cells, the plasma membrane is surrounded by a rigid external layer of material, the cell wall, which ranges in thickness from 15 to 100 nm or more (a nanometre is one millionth of a millimetre). The **cell wall** provides rigidity to prokaryotic cells and, with the capsule, protects the cell from physical damage. In many prokaryotic cells, the wall is coated with an external layer of **polysaccharides** called the **glycocalyx** (a "sugar coating" from *glykys* = sweet; *calyx* = cup or vessel). When the glycocalyx is diffuse and loosely associated with the cells, it is a **slime layer**; when it is gelatinous and more firmly attached to cells, it is a **capsule**. The glycocalyx helps protect prokaryotic cells from physical damage and desiccation, and may enable a cell to attach to a surface, such as other prokaryotic cells (as in forming a colony), eukaryotic cells (as in *Streptococcus pneumoniae* attaching to lung cells), or a nonliving substrate (such as a rock).

The plasma membrane itself performs several vital functions in both bacteria and archaea. In addition to transporting

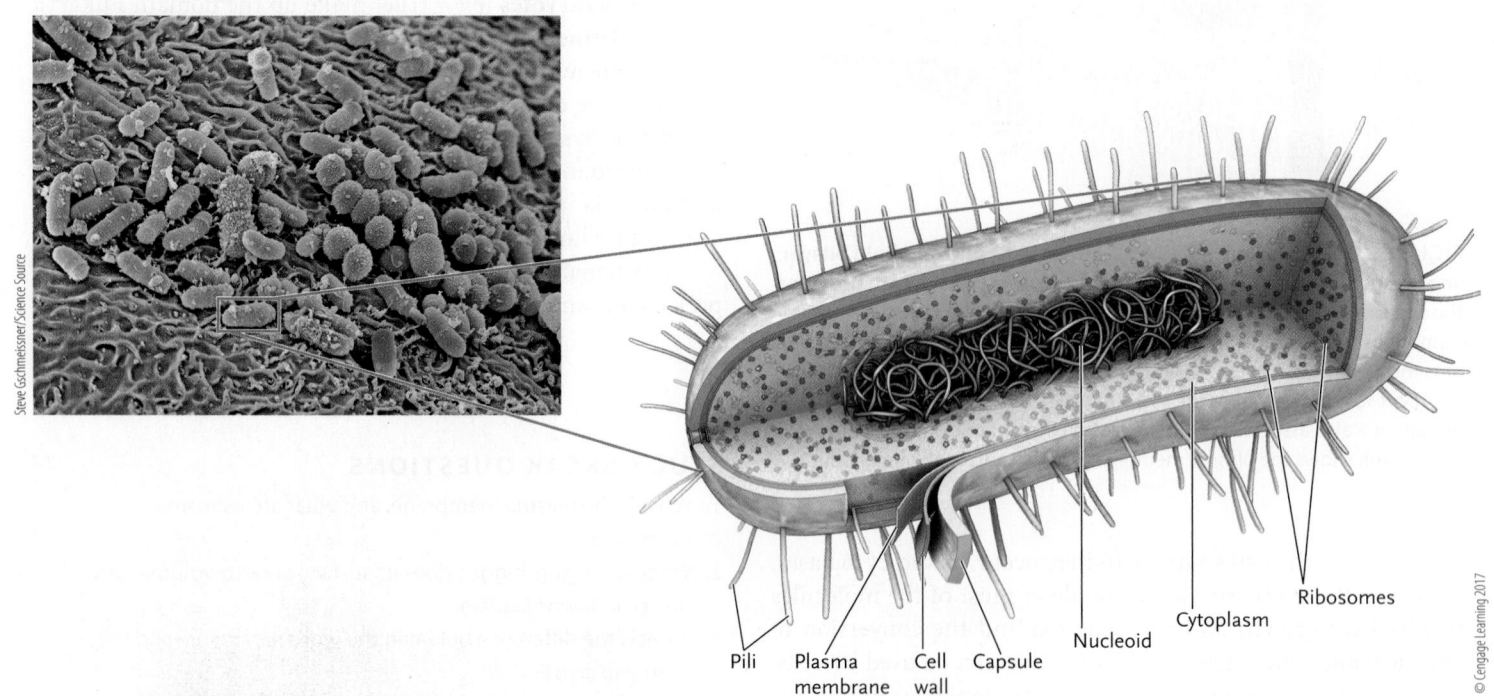

**FIGURE 2.7 Prokaryotic cell structure.** An electron micrograph (left) and a diagram (right) of the bacterium *Escherichia coli*. The pili extending from the cell wall attach bacterial cells to other cells of the same species or to eukaryotic cells as a part of infection. A typical *E. coli* has four flagella.

materials into and out of the cells, it contains most of the molecular systems that metabolize food molecules into the chemical energy of ATP. While most bacteria and archaea lack internal membranes, they do form in a small number of species. Derived from infolding of the plasma membrane, these internal membranes are most often the sites of photosynthetic and respiratory electron-transport chains.

As mentioned earlier, prokaryotic cells have filamentous cytoskeletal structures with functions similar to those in eukaryotes. Prokaryotic cytoskeletons play important roles in creating and maintaining the proper shape of cells; in cell division; and, for certain bacteria, in determining the polarity of the cells.

Many bacteria and archaea can move through liquids and across wet surfaces. Most commonly, they do so using long, threadlike, protein fibres called **flagella** (singular; *flagellum* = whip), which extend from the cell surface (see Figure 2.2a). The **bacterial flagellum**, which is helically shaped, rotates in a socket in the plasma membrane and cell wall to push the cell through a liquid medium (see Chapter 23). In *E. coli,* for instance, rotating bundles of flagella propel the bacterium. Archaeal flagella function similarly to bacterial flagella, but the two types differ significantly in their structures and mechanisms of action. Both types of prokaryotic flagella are also fundamentally different from the much larger and more complex flagella of eukaryotic cells, which are described in Section 2.3.

Some bacteria and archaea have hairlike shafts of protein called **pili** (singular, *pilus*) extending from their cell walls. The main function of pili is to attach the cell to surfaces or other cells. A special type of pilus, the *sex pilus*, attaches one bacterium to another during mating.

### STUDY BREAK QUESTIONS

1. What is a nucleoid?
2. Some bacteria and archaeans have internal membranes. How are these internal membranes formed?

## 2.3 Eukaryotic Cells

The domain of the eukaryotes, Eukarya, is divided into four major groups: the protists (see Chapter 24), fungi (see Chapter 25), plants (see Chapter 26), and animals (see Chapters 27 and 28). The rest of the chapter focuses on the cell components that are common to all large groups of eukaryotic organisms.

### 2.3a Eukaryotic Cells Have a Nucleus and Cytoplasmic Organelles Enclosed within a Plasma Membrane

The cells of all eukaryotes have a membrane-bound compartment called the *nucleus*. The cytoplasm surrounding the nucleus contains a remarkable system of membranous organelles that you don't find in prokaryotic cells. Each of these organelles is specialized to carry out one or more major functions of energy metabolism and molecular synthesis, storage, and transport. The cytosol, the cytoplasmic solution surrounding the organelles, participates in energy metabolism and molecular synthesis and performs specialized functions in support and motility. Our understanding of these various organelles has been aided by the technique of cell fractionation (**Figure 2.8**), which allows researchers to isolate specific organelles from the rest of the cell, making it easier to study their particular structure and function.

The eukaryotic plasma membrane carries out various functions through several types of embedded proteins. Some of these proteins form channels through the plasma membrane that transport substances into and out of the cell. Other proteins in the plasma membrane act as receptors; they recognize and bind specific signal molecules in the cellular environment and trigger internal responses. In some eukaryotes, particularly animals, plasma membrane proteins recognize and adhere to molecules on the surfaces of other cells. Yet other plasma membrane proteins are important markers in the immune system, labelling cells as "self," that is, belonging to the organism. Therefore, the immune system can identify cells without those markers as being foreign and most likely *pathogens* (disease-causing organisms or viruses).

A supportive cell wall surrounds the plasma membrane of fungal, plant, and many protist cells. Because the cell wall lies outside the plasma membrane, it is an *extracellular* structure (*extra* = outside). Although animal cells do not have cell walls, they also form extracellular material with supportive and other functions.

**Figure 2.9** presents a diagram of a representative animal cell, and **Figure 2.10** presents a diagram of a representative plant cell to show where the nucleus, cytoplasmic organelles, and other structures are located. The following sections discuss the structure and function of eukaryotic cell parts in more detail, beginning with the nucleus.

### 2.3b The Eukaryotic Nucleus Is More Complex Than the Nucleoid of the Prokaryotic Cell

The nucleus (see Figures 2.9 and 2.10) is separated from the cytoplasm by the **nuclear envelope**, which consists of two membranes, one layered just inside the other and separated by a narrow space (**Figure 2.11**). Embedded in the nuclear envelope are many hundreds of nuclear pore complexes. A **nuclear pore complex** is a large, cylindrical structure formed of many types of proteins, called the *nucleoporins*. Probably the largest protein complex in the cell, it exchanges molecules between the nucleus and the cytoplasm and prevents the transport of material not meant to cross the nuclear membrane. A channel through the nuclear pore complex, a **nuclear pore**, is the path for the assisted exchange of large molecules such as proteins and RNA molecules with the cytoplasm, whereas small molecules simply pass

FIGURE 2.8   **Research Method**

## Cell Fractionation

**Purpose:** Cell fractionation partitions cells into fractions containing a single cell component, such as mitochondria or ribosomes. Once isolated, the cell component can be disassembled by the same general techniques to analyze its structure and function.

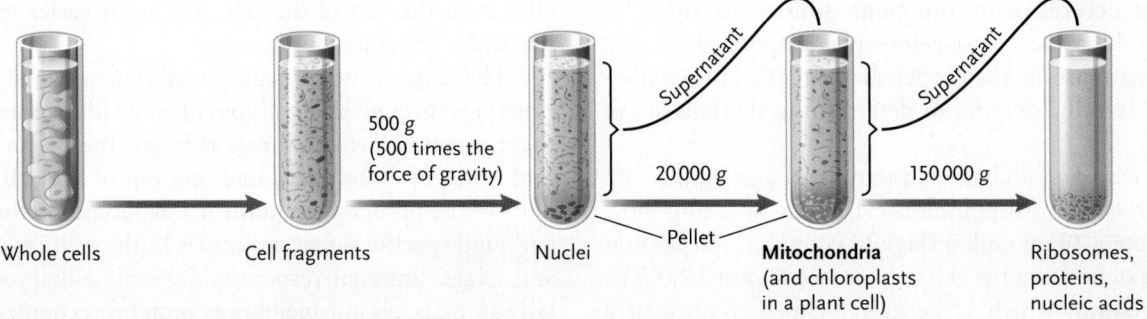

**Protocol:**

1. Break open intact cells by sonication (high-frequency sound waves), grinding in fine glass beads, or exposure to detergents that disrupt plasma membranes.

2. Use sequential centrifugations at increasing speeds to separate and purify cell structures. The spinning centrifuge drives cellular structures to the bottom of the tube at a rate that depends on their shape and density. With each centrifugation, the largest and densest components are isolated and concentrated into a pellet; the remaining solution, the supernatant, is drawn off and can be centrifuged again at higher speed.

3. Resuspend the pellet containing the isolated cell components and subfractionate using the same general techniques to examine the components of organelles.

**Interpreting the Results:** Many of the cell or organelle subfractions generated by cell fractionation retain their biological activity, making them useful in studies of various cellular processes. For example, cell fractionation is used to determine the cellular location of a protein or biological reaction, such as whether it is free in the cytosol or associated with a membrane.

through unassisted. Proteins including the enzymes for replicating and repairing DNA must be imported into the nucleus to carry out their functions after being synthesized in the cytosol.

Most of the space inside the nucleus is filled with **chromatin**, a combination of DNA and proteins. By contrast with most bacteria and archaea, most of the hereditary information of a eukaryote is distributed among several to many linear DNA molecules in the nucleus. Each DNA molecule with its associated proteins is a **eukaryotic chromosome**. The terms *chromatin* and *chromosome* are similar but have distinct meanings: *Chromatin* refers to any collection of eukaryotic DNA molecules with their associated proteins. *Chromosome* refers to one complete DNA molecule with its associated proteins.

A eukaryotic nucleus also contains one or more **nucleoli** (singular, *nucleolus*), which look like irregular masses of small fibres and granules (see Figures 2.9 and 2.10). These structures form around the genes coding for the rRNA molecules of ribosomes. Within the nucleolus, the information in rRNA genes is copied into rRNA molecules, which combine with proteins to form ribosomal subunits. The ribosomal subunits then leave the nucleoli and exit the nucleus through the nuclear pore complexes to enter the cytoplasm, where they join onto mRNAs to form complete ribosomes.

## 2.3c   Eukaryotic Ribosomes Are Either Free in the Cytosol Or Attached to Membranes

Like prokaryotic ribosomes, a eukaryotic ribosome consists of a large and a small subunit (**Figure 2.12**). However, the structures of bacterial, archaeal, and eukaryotic ribosomes, although similar, are not identical. In general, eukaryotic ribosomes are larger than bacterial and archaeal ribosomes; they contain 4 types of rRNA molecules and more than 80 proteins. Their function is identical to that of prokaryotic ribosomes: they use the information in mRNA to assemble amino acids into proteins.

Some eukaryotic ribosomes are freely suspended in the cytosol; others are attached to membranes. Proteins that are made on free ribosomes in the cytosol may remain in the

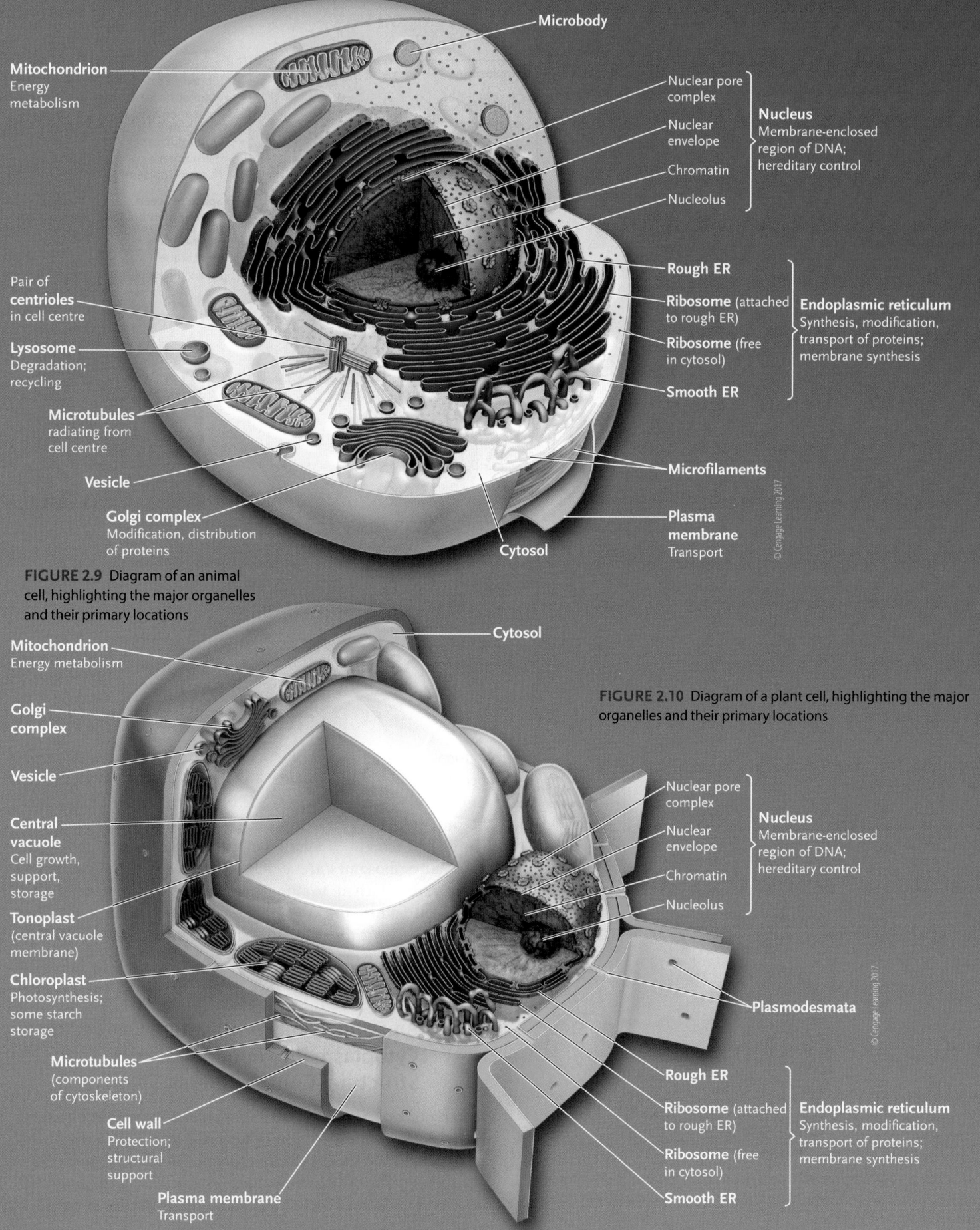

**Microbody**

**Mitochondrion**
Energy
metabolism

Nuclear pore
complex

Nuclear
envelope

Chromatin

Nucleolus

**Nucleus**
Membrane-enclosed
region of DNA;
hereditary control

**Rough ER**

**Ribosome** (attached
to rough ER)

**Endoplasmic reticulum**
Synthesis, modification,
transport of proteins;
membrane synthesis

Pair of
**centrioles**
in cell centre

**Ribosome** (free
in cytosol)

**Lysosome**
Degradation;
recycling

**Smooth ER**

**Microtubules**
radiating from
cell centre

**Vesicle**

**Microfilaments**

**Golgi complex**
Modification, distribution
of proteins

**Plasma
membrane**
Transport

**Cytosol**

© Cengage Learning 2017

**FIGURE 2.9** Diagram of an animal
cell, highlighting the major organelles
and their primary locations

**Cytosol**

**Mitochondrion**
Energy metabolism

**Golgi
complex**

**FIGURE 2.10** Diagram of a plant cell, highlighting the major
organelles and their primary locations

**Vesicle**

**Central
vacuole**
Cell growth,
support,
storage

Nuclear pore
complex

Nuclear
envelope

Chromatin

Nucleolus

**Nucleus**
Membrane-enclosed
region of DNA;
hereditary control

**Tonoplast**
(central vacuole
membrane)

**Chloroplast**
Photosynthesis;
some starch
storage

**Plasmodesmata**

**Microtubules**
(components
of cytoskeleton)

**Rough ER**

**Ribosome** (attached
to rough ER)

**Endoplasmic reticulum**
Synthesis, modification,
transport of proteins;
membrane synthesis

**Cell wall**
Protection;
structural
support

**Ribosome** (free
in cytosol)

**Plasma membrane**
Transport

**Smooth ER**

© Cengage Learning 2017

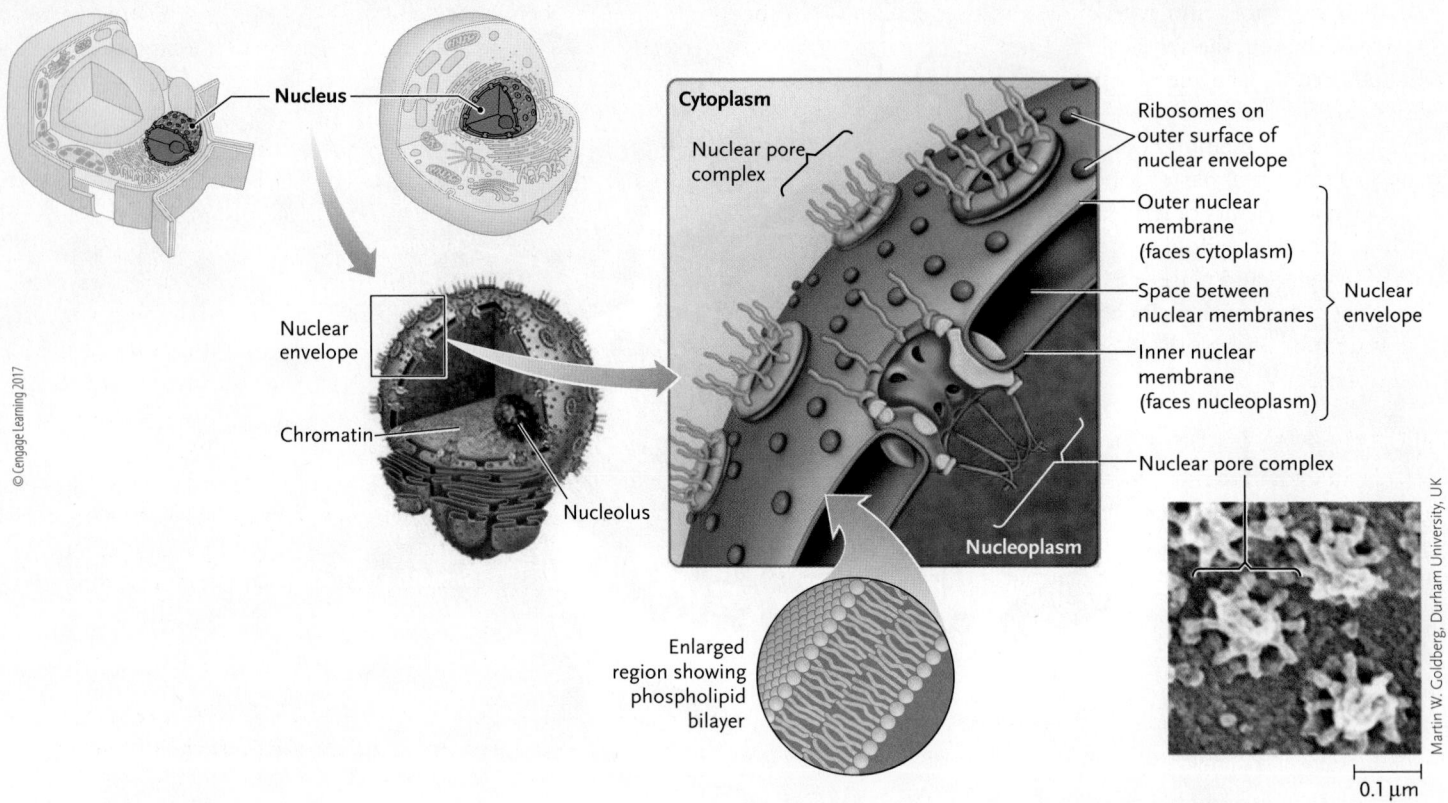

**FIGURE 2.11 The nuclear envelope, which consists of a system of two concentric membranes with nuclear pore complexes embedded.** Nuclear pore complexes are octagonally symmetrical protein structures with a channel, the nuclear pore, through the centre. They control the transport of molecules between the nucleus and the cytoplasm.

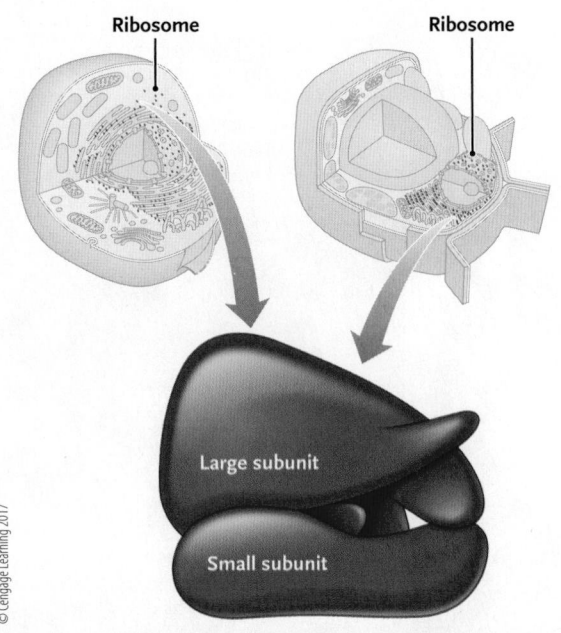

**FIGURE 2.12 A ribosome.** The diagram shows the structures of the two ribosomal subunits of mammalian ribosomes and how they come together to form the whole ribosome.

cytosol, or pass through the nuclear pores into the nucleus, or become parts of mitochondria, chloroplasts, the cytoskeleton, or other cytoplasmic structures. Proteins that enter the nucleus become part of chromatin, or line the nuclear envelope (the lamins), or remain in solution in the nucleoplasm.

Many ribosomes are attached to membranes. Some ribosomes are attached to the nuclear envelope, but most are attached to a network of membranes in the cytosol, called the *endoplasmic reticulum* (ER; described in more detail next). The proteins that are made on ribosomes attached to the ER follow a special path to other organelles within the cell.

### 2.3d An Endomembrane System Divides the Cytoplasm into Functional and Structural Compartments

Eukaryotic cells are characterized by an **endomembrane system** (*endo* = within), a collection of interrelated, internal, membranous sacs that divide the cell into functional and structural compartments. The endomembrane system has a number of functions, including the synthesis and modification of proteins and their transport into membranes and organelles or to the outside of the cell, the synthesis of lipids, and the detoxification of some toxins. The membranes of the system are connected either directly in the physical sense or indirectly by **vesicles**, which are small membrane-bound compartments that transfer substances between parts of the system.

The components of the endomembrane system include the nuclear envelope, endoplasmic reticulum, Golgi complex, lysosomes, vesicles, and plasma membrane. The plasma membrane and the nuclear envelope were discussed earlier in this chapter. The functions of the other organelles are described in the following sections.

**ENDOPLASMIC RETICULUM** The **endoplasmic reticulum (ER)** is an extensive interconnected network (*reticulum* = little net) of membranous channels and vesicles called **cisternae** (singular, *cisterna*). Each cisterna is formed by a single membrane that surrounds an enclosed space called the **ER lumen**

**(Figure 2.13).** The ER occurs in two forms, rough ER and smooth ER, each with a specialized structure and function.

The **rough ER** (see Figure 2.13a) gets its name from the many ribosomes that stud its outer surface. The proteins made on ribosomes attached to the ER enter the ER lumen, where they fold into their final form. Chemical modifications of these proteins, such as addition of carbohydrate groups to produce glycoproteins, occur in the lumen. The proteins are then delivered to other regions of the cell within small vesicles that pinch off from the ER, travel through the cytosol, and join with the organelle that performs the next steps in their modification and distribution. For most of the proteins made on the rough ER, the next destination is the Golgi complex, which packages and sorts them for delivery to their final destinations.

The outer membrane of the nuclear envelope is closely related in structure and function to the rough ER, to which it is connected. This membrane is also a rough membrane, studded with ribosomes attached to the surface facing the cytoplasm.

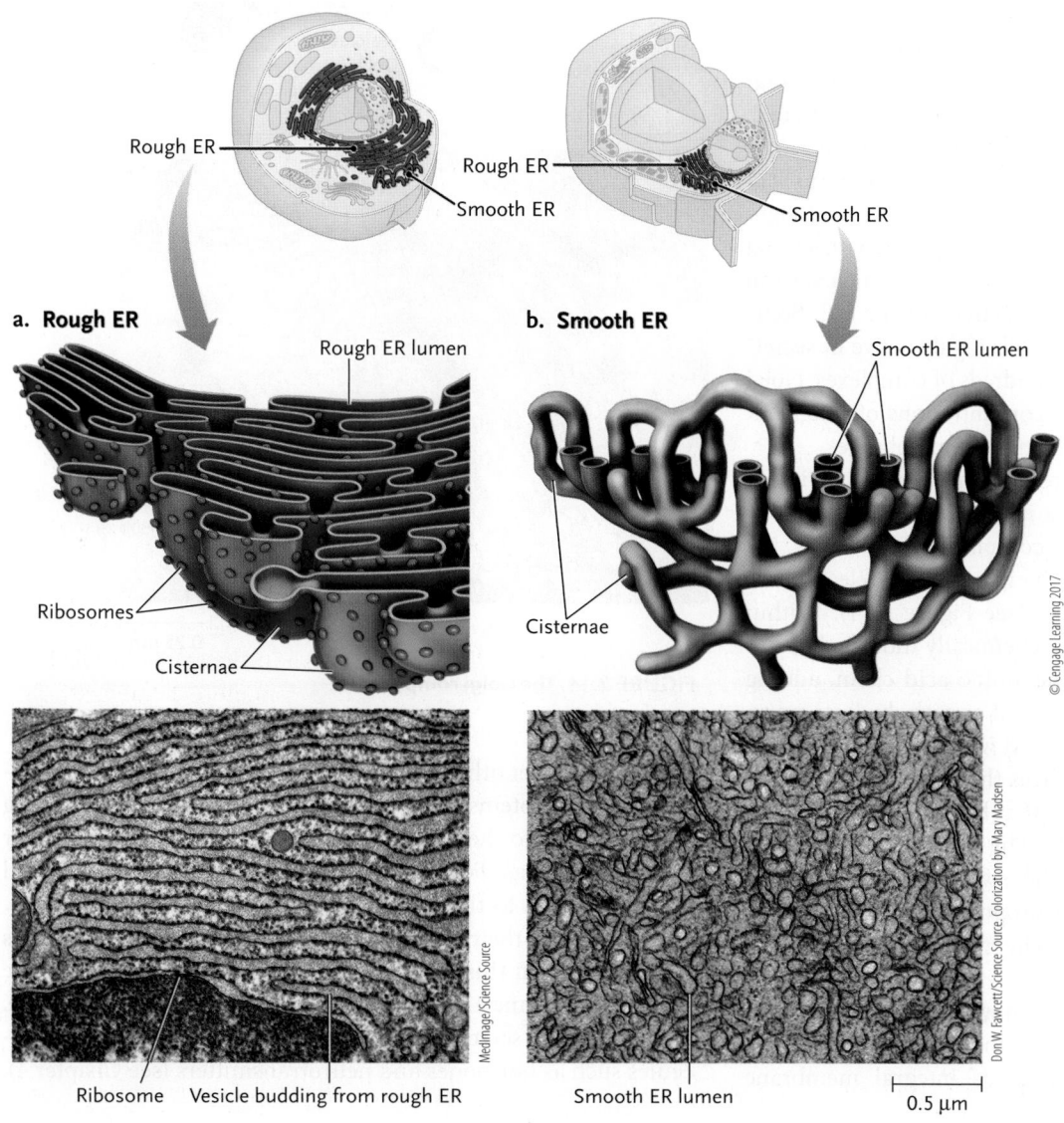

a. **Rough ER**

Rough ER lumen

Ribosomes

Cisternae

Ribosome    Vesicle budding from rough ER

b. **Smooth ER**

Smooth ER lumen

Cisternae

Smooth ER lumen

0.5 μm

**FIGURE 2.13 The endoplasmic reticulum. (a)** False-coloured TEM image of rough ER, showing the ribosomes that stud the membrane surfaces facing the cytoplasm. Proteins synthesized on these ribosomes enter the lumen of the rough ER, where they are modified chemically and then begin their path to their final destinations in the cell. **(b)** False-coloured TEM image of smooth ER membranes. Among their functions are the synthesis of lipids for cell membranes and enzymatic conversion of certain toxic molecules to safer molecules.

The proteins made on these ribosomes enter the space between the two nuclear envelope membranes. From there, the proteins can move into the ER and on to other cellular locations.

The **smooth ER** (see Figure 2.13b) is so called because its membranes have no ribosomes attached to their surfaces. The smooth ER has various functions in the cytoplasm, including synthesis of lipids that become part of cell membranes. In some cells, such as those of the liver, smooth ER membranes contain enzymes that convert drugs, poisons, and toxic by-products of cellular metabolism into substances that can be tolerated or more easily removed from the body.

The rough and smooth ER membranes are often connected, making the entire ER system a continuous network of interconnected channels in the cytoplasm. The relative proportions of rough and smooth ER reflect cellular activities in protein and lipid synthesis. Cells that are highly active in making proteins to be released outside the cell, such as pancreatic cells that make digestive enzymes, are packed with rough ER but have relatively little smooth ER. By contrast, cells that primarily synthesize lipids or break down toxic substances are packed with smooth ER but contain little rough ER.

**GOLGI COMPLEX** Camillo Golgi, a late-nineteenth-century Italian neuroscientist and Nobel laureate, discovered the **Golgi complex**. The Golgi complex consists of a stack of flattened, membranous sacs (without attached ribosomes) known as *cisternae* (**Figure 2.14**). In most cells, the complex looks like a stack of cupped pancakes. Typically there are between three and eight cisternae, but some organisms have Golgi complexes with several tens of cisternae. The number and size of Golgi complexes can vary with cell type and the metabolic activity of the cell. Some cells have a single complex, whereas cells highly active in secreting proteins from the cell can have hundreds of complexes. Golgi complexes are usually located near concentrations of rough ER membranes, between the ER and the plasma membrane.

The Golgi complex receives proteins that were made in the ER and transported to the complex in vesicles. When the vesicles contact the *cis* face of the complex (which faces the nucleus), they fuse with the Golgi membrane and release their contents directly into the cisternae (see Figure 2.14). Within the Golgi complex, the proteins are chemically modified by, for example, removing segments of the amino acid chain, adding small functional groups, or adding lipid or carbohydrate units. The modified proteins are transported within the Golgi to the *trans* face of the complex (which faces the plasma membrane), where they are sorted into vesicles that bud off from the margins of the Golgi (see Figure 2.14). The content of a vesicle is kept separate from the cytosol by the vesicle membrane. Three quite different models have been proposed for how proteins move through the Golgi complex. The mechanism is a subject of active current research.

The Golgi complex regulates the movement of several types of proteins. Some are secreted from the cell, others become embedded in the plasma membrane as integral membrane

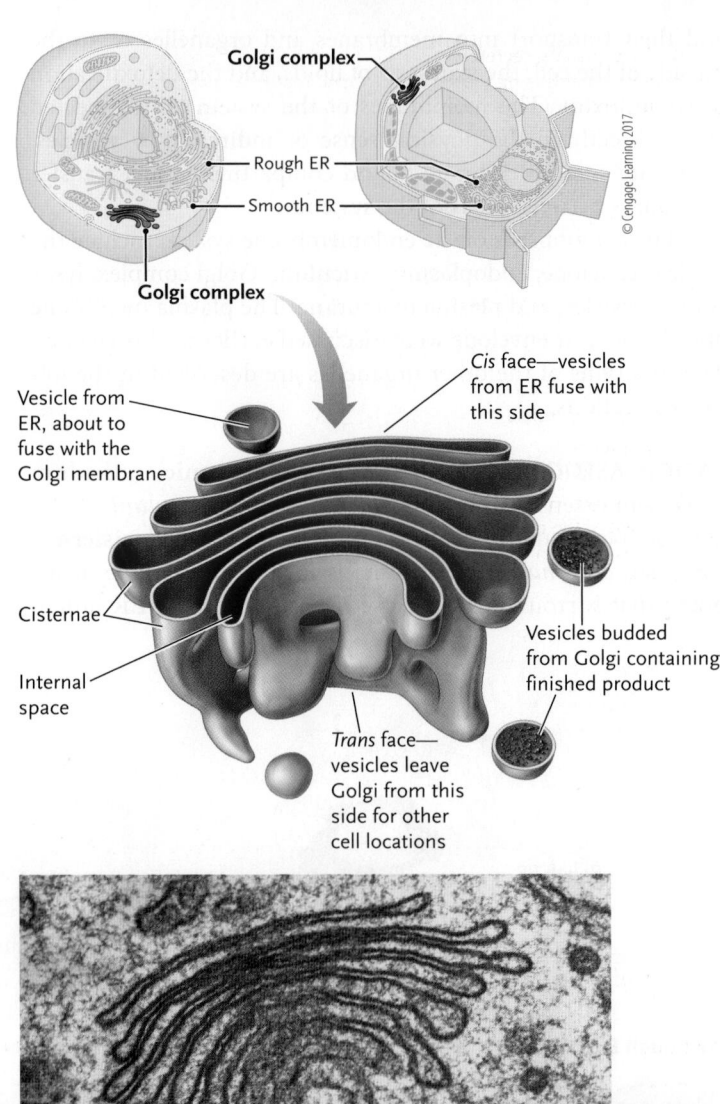

**FIGURE 2.14  The Golgi complex**

proteins, and yet others are placed in lysosomes. The modifications of the proteins within the Golgi complex include adding "postal codes" to the proteins, tagging them for sorting to their final destinations. For instance, proteins secreted from the cell are transported to the plasma membrane in **secretory vesicles**, which release their contents to the exterior by **exocytosis** (**Figure 2.15a**). In this process, a secretory vesicle fuses with the plasma membrane and spills the vesicle contents to the outside. The contents of secretory vesicles vary, including signalling molecules such as hormones and neurotransmitters (see Chapter 4),

**a. Exocytosis:** A secretory vesicle fuses with the plasma membrane, releasing the vesicle contents to the cell exterior. The vesicle membrane becomes part of the plasma membrane.

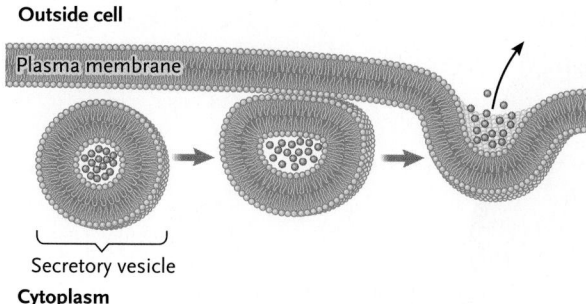

Outside cell

Plasma membrane

Secretory vesicle

Cytoplasm

**b. Endocytosis:** Materials from the cell exterior are enclosed in a segment of the plasma membrane that pockets inward and pinches off as an endocytic vesicle.

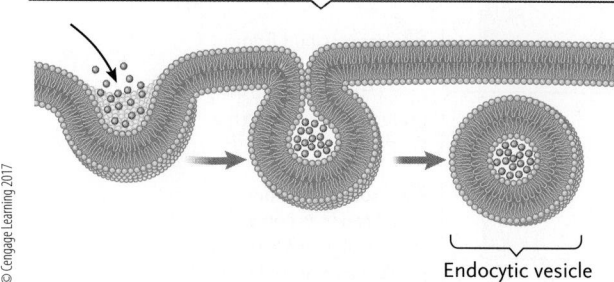

Endocytic vesicle

**FIGURE 2.15  Exocytosis and endocytosis**

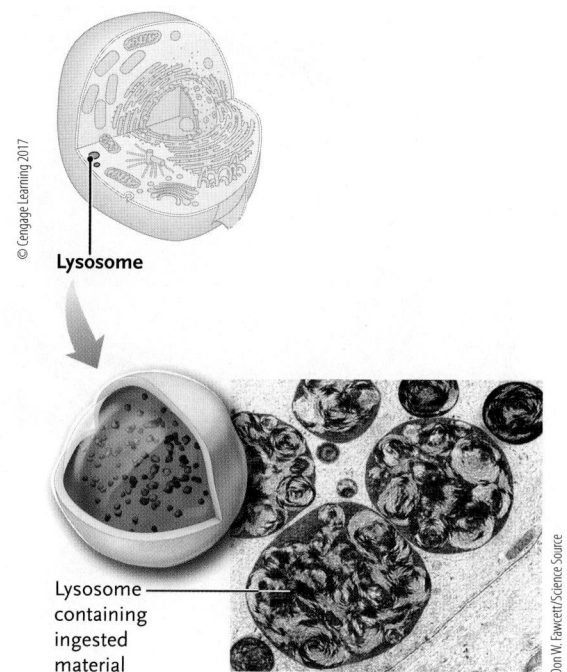

Lysosome

Lysosome

Lysosome containing ingested material

*Don W. Fawcett/Science Source*

**FIGURE 2.16  A lysosome**

waste products or toxic substances, and enzymes (such as from cells lining the intestine). The membrane of a vesicle that fuses with the plasma membrane becomes part of the plasma membrane. In fact, this process is used to expand the surface of the cell during cell growth.

Vesicles may also form by the reverse process, called **endocytosis**, which brings molecules into the cell from the exterior (Figure 2.15b). In this process, the plasma membrane forms a pocket, which then bulges inward and pinches off into the cytoplasm as an **endocytic vesicle**. Once in the cytoplasm, endocytic vesicles, which contain segments of the plasma membrane as well as proteins and other molecules, are carried to the Golgi complex or to other destinations such as lysosomes in animal cells. The substances carried to the Golgi complex are sorted and placed into vesicles for routing to other locations, which may include lysosomes. Those routed to lysosomes are digested into molecular subunits that may be recycled as building blocks for the biological molecules of the cell. Exocytosis and endocytosis are discussed in more detail in Chapters 43 and 45.

**LYSOSOMES Lysosomes** (*lys* = breakdown; *some* = body) are small, membrane-bound vesicles that contain more than 30 enzymes for the digestion of many complex molecules, including proteins, lipids, nucleic acids, and polysaccharides (**Figure 2.16**). The cell recycles the subunits of these molecules. Lysosomes are found in animal cells but not in plant cells. The functions of lysosomes in plant cells are carried out by the central vacuole (see

Section 2.4). Depending on the contents they are digesting, lysosomes assume a variety of sizes and shapes instead of a uniform structure as is characteristic of other organelles. Most commonly, lysosomes are small (0.1–0.5 μm in diameter) oval or spherical bodies. A human cell contains about 300 lysosomes.

Lysosomes are formed by budding from the Golgi complex. Their hydrolytic enzymes are synthesized in the rough ER, modified in the lumen of the ER to identify them as being bound for a lysosome, transported to the Golgi complex in a vesicle, and then packaged in the budding lysosome.

The pH within lysosomes is acidic (pH = 5) and is significantly lower than the pH of the cytosol (pH = 7.2). The hydrolytic enzymes in the lysosomes function optimally at the acidic pH within the organelle, but they do not function well at the pH of the cytosol; this difference reduces the risk to the viability of the cell should the enzymes be released from the vesicle. It also prevents the enzymes from becoming active before they reach the low pH of the lysosome, thereby protecting the organelles that the enzymes pass through on the way to their final destination.

Lysosomal enzymes can digest several types of materials. They digest food molecules entering the cell by endocytosis when an endocytic vesicle fuses with a lysosome. In a process called *autophagy,* they digest organelles that are not functioning correctly. A membrane surrounds the defective organelle, forming a large vesicle that fuses with one or more lysosomes; the organelle is then degraded by the hydrolytic enzymes. They also play a role in **phagocytosis**, a process in which some types of cells engulf bacteria or other cellular debris to break them down. These cells include the white blood cells known as *phagocytes,* which play an important role in the immune

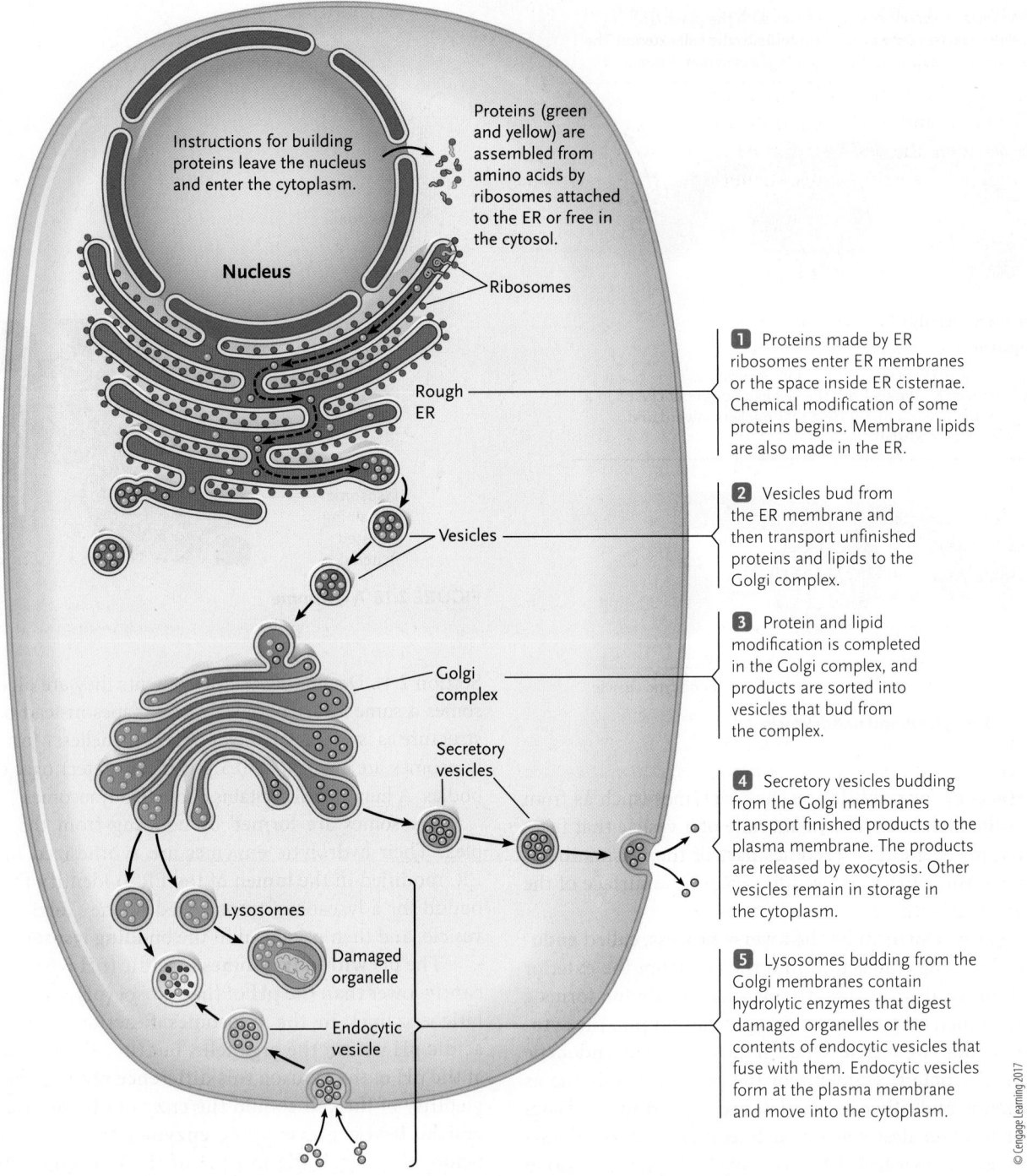

Instructions for building proteins leave the nucleus and enter the cytoplasm.

Proteins (green and yellow) are assembled from amino acids by ribosomes attached to the ER or free in the cytosol.

**Nucleus**

Ribosomes

Rough ER

Vesicles

Golgi complex

Secretory vesicles

Lysosomes

Damaged organelle

Endocytic vesicle

**1** Proteins made by ER ribosomes enter ER membranes or the space inside ER cisternae. Chemical modification of some proteins begins. Membrane lipids are also made in the ER.

**2** Vesicles bud from the ER membrane and then transport unfinished proteins and lipids to the Golgi complex.

**3** Protein and lipid modification is completed in the Golgi complex, and products are sorted into vesicles that bud from the complex.

**4** Secretory vesicles budding from the Golgi membranes transport finished products to the plasma membrane. The products are released by exocytosis. Other vesicles remain in storage in the cytoplasm.

**5** Lysosomes budding from the Golgi membranes contain hydrolytic enzymes that digest damaged organelles or the contents of endocytic vesicles that fuse with them. Endocytic vesicles form at the plasma membrane and move into the cytoplasm.

© Cengage Learning 2017

**FIGURE 2.17 Vesicle traffic in the cytoplasm.** The ER and Golgi complex are part of the endomembrane system, which releases proteins and other substances to the cell exterior and gathers materials from outside the cell.

system (see Chapter 4). Phagocytosis produces a large vesicle that contains the engulfed materials until lysosomes fuse with the vesicle and release the hydrolytic enzymes necessary for degrading them.

In certain human genetic diseases known as *lysosomal storage diseases,* one of the hydrolytic enzymes normally found in the lysosome is absent. As a result, the substrate of that enzyme accumulates in the lysosomes, and this accumulation eventually

interferes with normal cellular activities. An example is Tay–Sachs disease, a fatal disease of the central nervous system caused by the failure to synthesize the enzyme needed for hydrolysis of **fatty acid** derivatives found in brain and nerve cells.

In summary, the endomembrane system is a major traffic network for proteins and other substances within the cell. The Golgi complex in particular is a key distribution station for membranes and proteins **(Figure 2.17)**. From the Golgi complex, lipids and proteins may move to storage or secretory vesicles, and from the secretory vesicles, they may move to the cell exterior by exocytosis. Membranes and proteins may also move between the nuclear envelope and the endomembrane system. Proteins and other materials that enter cells by endocytosis also enter the endomembrane system to travel to the Golgi complex for sorting and distribution to other locations.

## 2.3e Mitochondria Are the Organelles in Which Cellular Respiration Occurs

**Mitochondria** (singular, *mitochondrion*) are the membrane-bound organelles in which cellular respiration occurs. *Cellular respiration* is the process by which energy-rich molecules such as sugars, fats, and other fuels are broken down to water and carbon dioxide by mitochondrial reactions, with the release of energy. Much of the energy released by the breakdown is captured in ATP. In fact, mitochondria generate most of the ATP of the cell. Mitochondria require oxygen for cellular respiration—when you breathe, you are taking in oxygen primarily for your mitochondrial reactions (see Chapter 5).

Mitochondria are enclosed by two membranes (**Figure 2.18**). The **outer mitochondrial membrane** is smooth and covers the outside of the organelle. The surface area of the **inner mitochondrial membrane** is expanded by folds called **cristae** (singular, *crista*). Both membranes surround the innermost compartment of the mitochondrion, called the **mitochondrial matrix**. The ATP-generating reactions of mitochondria occur in the cristae and matrix.

The mitochondrial matrix also contains DNA and ribosomes that resemble the equivalent structures in bacteria. These and other similarities suggest that mitochondria originated from ancient bacteria that became permanent residents of the cytoplasm during the evolution of eukaryotic cells. This is discussed in more detail in Chapter 21.

## 2.3f The Cytoskeleton Supports and Moves Cell Structures

The characteristic shape and internal organization of each type of cell is maintained in part by its cytoskeleton, the interconnected system of protein fibres and tubes that extends throughout the cytoplasm. The cytoskeleton also reinforces the plasma membrane and functions in movement, both of structures within the cell and of the cell as a whole. It is most highly developed in animal cells, in which it fills and supports the cytoplasm from the plasma membrane to the nuclear envelope (**Figure 2.19**). Although cytoskeletal structures are also present in plant cells, the fibres and tubes of the system are less prominent; much of cellular support in plants is provided by the cell wall and a large central vacuole (described in Section 2.4).

The cytoskeleton of animal cells contains structural elements of three major types: *microtubules, intermediate filaments,* and *microfilaments.* Plant cytoskeletons likewise contain the same three structural elements. Microtubules are the largest

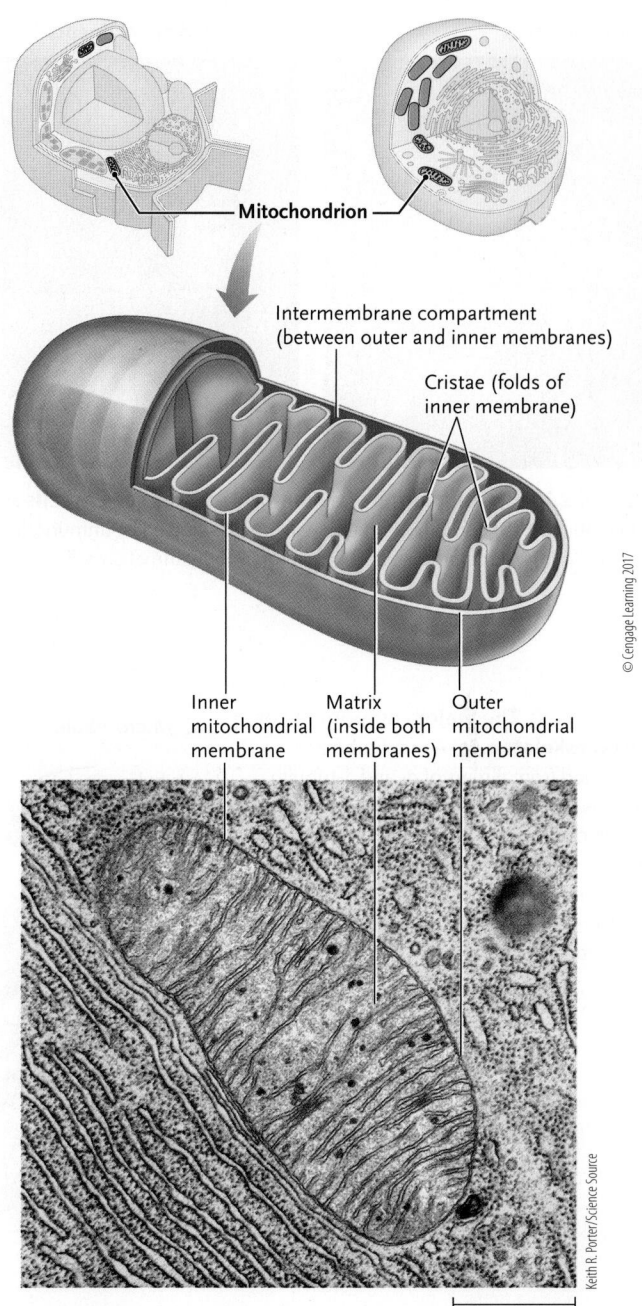

**Mitochondrion**

Intermembrane compartment (between outer and inner membranes)

Cristae (folds of inner membrane)

Inner mitochondrial membrane

Matrix (inside both membranes)

Outer mitochondrial membrane

© Cengage Learning 2017

Keith R. Porter/Science Source

0.5 µm

**FIGURE 2.18 Mitochondria.** The electron micrograph shows a mitochondrion from a bat pancreas, surrounded by cytoplasm containing rough ER. Cristae extend into the interior of the mitochondrion as folds from the inner mitochondrial membrane. The darkly stained granules inside the mitochondrion are probably lipid deposits.

cytoskeletal elements, and microfilaments are the smallest. Each cytoskeletal element is assembled from proteins: microtubules from *tubulins,* intermediate filaments from a large and varied group of *intermediate filament proteins,* and microfilaments from *actins* (**Figure 2.20**). The keratins of animal hair, nails, and claws contain a common form of intermediate filament proteins known as *cytokeratins;* for example, human hair consists of thick bundles of cytokeratin fibres extruded from hair follicle cells.

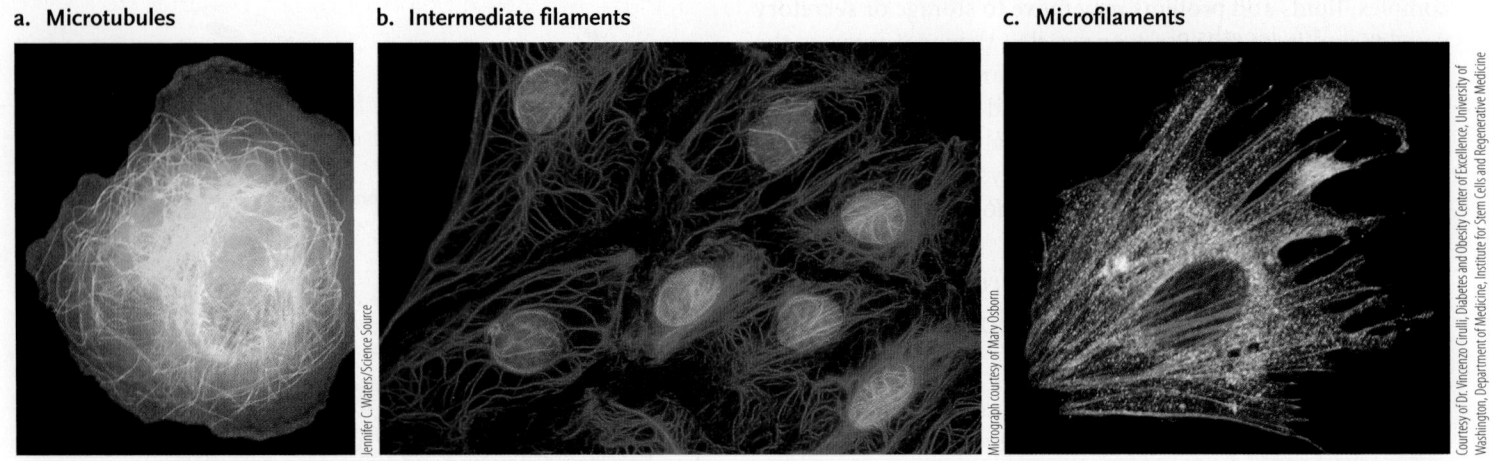

**a. Microtubules**  **b. Intermediate filaments**  **c. Microfilaments**

*Jennifer C. Waters/Science Source*

*Micrograph courtesy of Mary Osborn*

*Courtesy of Dr. Vincenzo Cirulli, Diabetes and Obesity Center of Excellence, University of Washington, Department of Medicine, Institute for Stem Cells and Regenerative Medicine*

**FIGURE 2.19 Cytoskeletons of eukaryotic cells, as seen in cells stained for light microscopy. (a)** Microtubules (yellow) and microfilaments (red) in a pancreatic cell. **(b)** Keratin intermediate filaments viewed by immunofluorescence microscopy in the rat kangaroo cell line PtK2. The nucleus is stained blue in these cells. **(c)** Microfilaments (red) in a migrating mammalian cell.

**FIGURE 2.20 The major components of the cytoskeleton. (a)** A microtubule, assembled from dimers of α- and β-tubulin proteins. **(b)** An intermediate filament. Eight protein chains wind together to form each subunit, shown as a green cylinder. **(c)** A microfilament, assembled from two linear polymers of actin proteins wound around each other into a helical spiral.

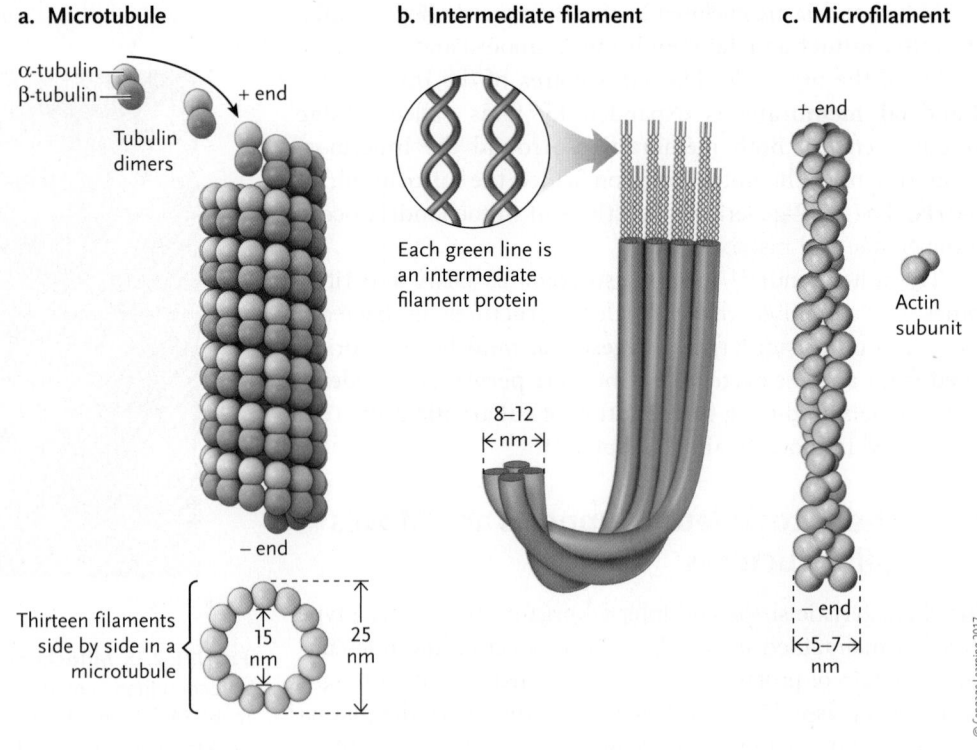

**a. Microtubule**

α-tubulin
β-tubulin
Tubulin dimers
+ end
− end
Thirteen filaments side by side in a microtubule
15 nm
25 nm

**b. Intermediate filament**

Each green line is an intermediate filament protein
8–12 nm

**c. Microfilament**

+ end
Actin subunit
− end
5–7 nm

© Cengage Learning 2017

**Microtubules** (Figure 2.20a) are microscopic tubes with an outer diameter of about 25 nm and an inner diameter of about 15 nm; they function much like the tubes used by human engineers to construct supportive structures. Microtubules vary widely in length, from less than 200 nm to several micrometres. The wall of the microtubule consists of 13 protein filaments arranged side by side. A filament is a linear polymer of tubulin dimers, each dimer consisting of one α-tubulin and one β-tubulin subunit bound noncovalently together. The dimers are organized head to tail in each filament, giving the microtubule a polarity, meaning that the two ends are different. One end, called the + (plus) end, has α-tubulin subunits at the ends of the filaments; the other end, called the − (minus) end, has β-tubulin subunits at the ends of the filaments. Microtubules are dynamic structures, changing their lengths as required by their functions. This is seen readily in animal cells that are changing shape. Microtubules change length by the addition or removal of tubulin dimers; this occurs asymmetrically, with dimers adding or detaching more rapidly at the $+$ end than at the $-$ end. The lengths of microtubules are tightly regulated in the cell.

Many of the cytoskeletal microtubules in animal cells are formed and radiate outward from a site near the nucleus, termed the **cell centre** or **centrosome** (see Figure 2.9). At its midpoint are two, short, barrel-shaped structures also formed from microtubules, called the **centrioles (Figure 2.21)**. Often, **intermediate filaments** also extend from the cell centre, apparently held in the same radiating pattern by linkage to microtubules. Microtubules that radiate from the cell centre anchor the ER, Golgi complex, lysosomes, secretory vesicles, and at least some mitochondria in position. The microtubules also provide tracks along which vesicles move from the cell interior to the plasma membrane and in the reverse direction.

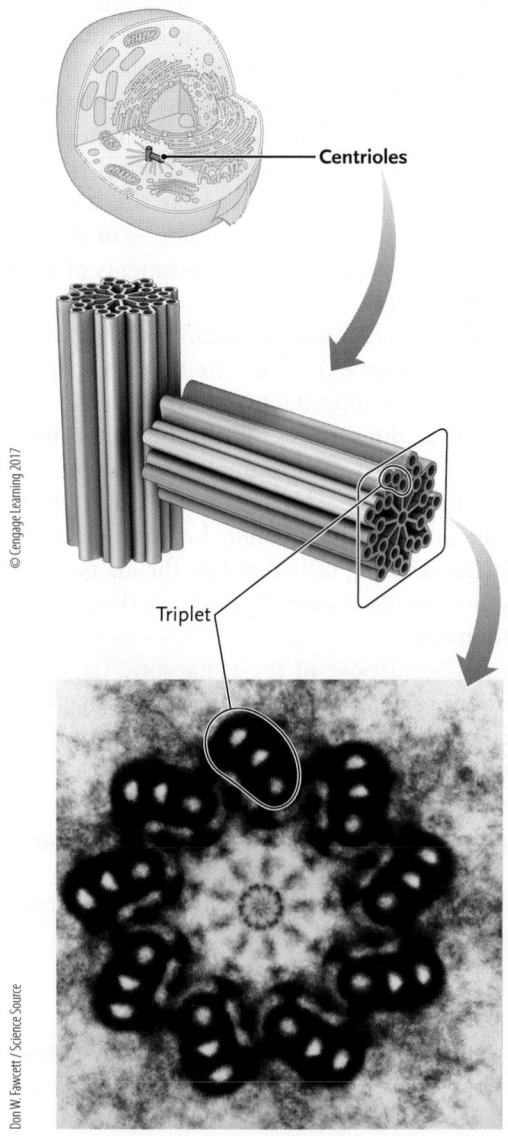

FIGURE 2.21 **Centrioles.** The two centrioles of the pair at the cell centre usually lie at right angles to each other as shown. The electron micrograph shows a centriole from a mouse cell in cross-section. A centriole gives rise to the 9 + 2 system of a flagellum and persists as the basal body at the inner end of the flagellum.

The intermediate filaments probably add support to the microtubule arrays.

Microtubules play other key roles, for instance, in separating and moving chromosomes during cell division, determining the orientation for growth of the new cell wall during plant cell division, maintaining the shape of animal cells, and moving animal cells themselves. Animal cell movements are generated by "motor" proteins that push or pull against microtubules or microfilaments, much as our muscles produce body movements by acting on bones of the skeleton. One end of a motor protein is firmly fixed to a cell structure such as a vesicle or to a microtubule or microfilament. The other end has reactive groups that "walk" along another microtubule or microfilament by making an attachment, forcefully swivelling a short distance, and then releasing (**Figure 2.22**). ATP supplies the energy for the walking movements. The motor proteins that walk along microfilaments are called *myosins,* and the ones that walk along microtubules are called *dyneins* and *kinesins.* Some cell movements, such as the whipping motions of sperm tails, depend entirely on microtubules and their motor proteins.

Intermediate filaments (Figure 2.20b) are fibres with diameters of about 8–12 nm. ("Intermediate" signifies, in fact, that these filaments are intermediate in size between microtubules and microfilaments.) These fibres occur singly, in parallel bundles, and in interlinked networks, either alone or in combination with microtubules, microfilaments, or both. Intermediate filaments are found only in multicellular organisms. Moreover, whereas microtubules and microfilaments are the same in all tissues, intermediate filaments are tissue specific in their protein composition. Despite the molecular diversity of intermediate filaments, however, they all play similar roles in the cell, providing structural support in many cells and tissues. For example, the nucleus in epithelial cells is held within the cell by a basketlike network of intermediate filaments made of keratins.

**Microfilaments** (Figure 2.20c) are thin protein fibres 5–7 nm in diameter that consist of two polymers of actin subunits wound around each other in a long helical spiral. The actin subunits are asymmetrical in shape, and they are all oriented in the same way in the polymer chains of a microfilament. Thus, as for microtubules, microfilaments have a polarity: the two ends are designated $+$ (plus) and $-$ (minus). And, as for microtubules, growth and disassembly occur more rapidly at the $+$ end than at the $-$ end.

Microfilaments occur in almost all eukaryotic cells and are involved in many processes, including a number of structural and locomotor functions. Microfilaments are best known as one of the two components of the contractile elements in muscle fibres of vertebrates (the roles of myosin and microfilaments in muscle contraction are discussed in Chapter 46). Microfilaments are involved in the actively flowing motion of cytoplasm, called **cytoplasmic streaming**, which can transport nutrients, proteins, and organelles in both animal and plant cells, and which is responsible for amoeboid movement. When animal

## a. "Walking" end of a kinesin molecule

Connects to a cell structure
such as a vesicle

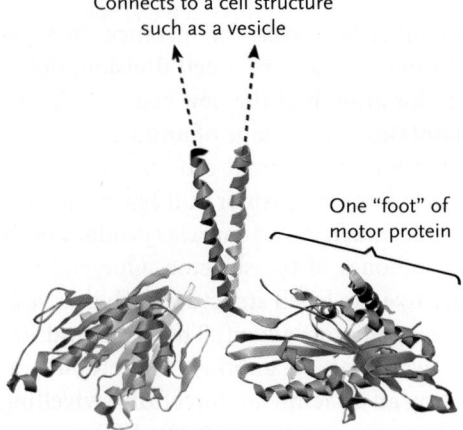

One "foot" of
motor protein

## b. How a kinesin molecule "walks"

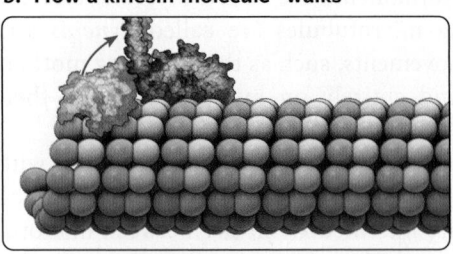

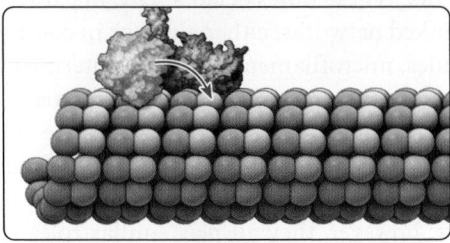

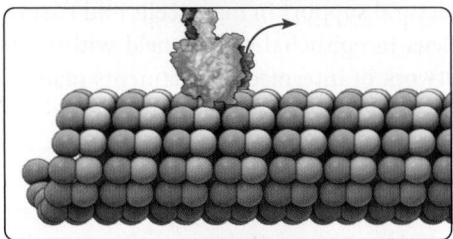

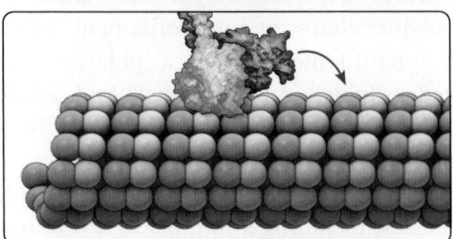

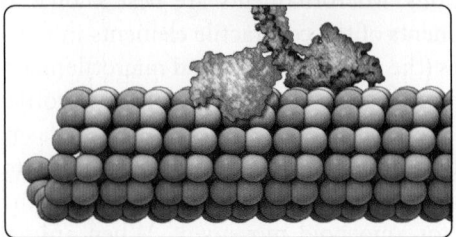

**FIGURE 2.22 The microtubule motor protein kinesin. (a)** Structure of the end of a kinesin molecule that "walks" along a microtubule, with α-helical segments shown as spirals and β strands as flat ribbons. **(b)** How a kinesin molecule walks along the surface of a molecule by alternately attaching and releasing its "feet"

cells divide, microfilaments are responsible for dividing the cytoplasm (see Chapter 8 for further discussion).

### 2.3g Flagella Propel Cells, and Cilia Move Materials over the Cell Surface

Flagella and **cilia** (singular, *cilium*) are elongated, slender, motile structures that extend from the cell surface. They are identical in structure except that cilia are usually shorter than flagella and occur on cells in greater numbers. The whiplike or oarlike movements of a flagellum propel a cell through a watery medium, and cilia move fluids over the cell surface.

A bundle of microtubules extends from the base to the tip of a flagellum or cilium (**Figure 2.23**). In the bundle, a circle of nine double microtubules surrounds a central pair of single microtubules, forming what is known as the *9 + 2 complex*. Dynein motor proteins slide the microtubules of the 9 + 2 complex over each other to produce the movements of a flagellum or a cilium (**Figure 2.24**).

Cilia and flagella are found in protozoa and algae, and many types of animal cells have flagella—the tail of a sperm cell is a flagellum—as do the reproductive cells of some plants. In humans, cilia cover the surfaces of cells lining cavities or tubes in some parts of the body. For example, cilia on cells lining the ventricles (cavities) of the brain circulate fluid through the brain, and cilia in the oviducts conduct eggs from the ovaries to the uterus. Cilia covering cells that line the air passages of the lungs sweep out mucus containing bacteria, dust particles, and other contaminants.

Although the purpose of the eukaryotic flagellum is the same as that of prokaryotic flagella, the genes that encode the components of the flagellar apparatus of cells of Bacteria, Archaea, and Eukarya are different in each case.

With a few exceptions, the cell structures described so far in this chapter occur in all eukaryotic cells. The major exception is lysosomes, which appear to be restricted to animal cells. The next section describes three additional structures that are characteristic of plant cells.

### STUDY BREAK QUESTIONS

1. Where in a eukaryotic cell is DNA found? How is that DNA organized?
2. What is the nucleolus, and what is its function?
3. Explain the structure and function of the endomembrane system.
4. What are the structure and function of a mitochondrion?
5. What are the structure and function of the cytoskeleton?

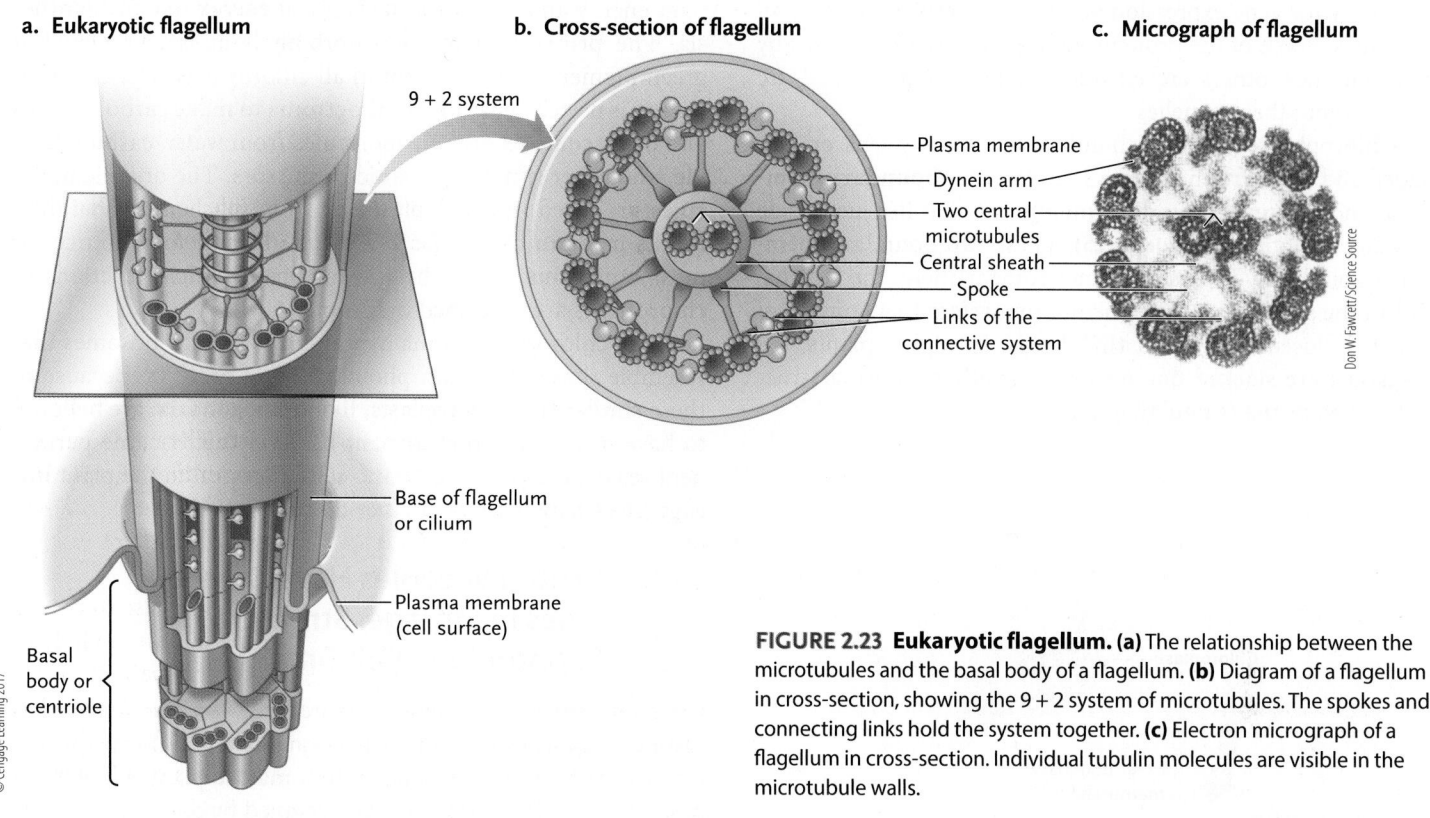

**a. Eukaryotic flagellum**

9 + 2 system

Base of flagellum or cilium

Plasma membrane (cell surface)

Basal body or centriole

© Cengage Learning 2017

**b. Cross-section of flagellum**

Plasma membrane
Dynein arm
Two central microtubules
Central sheath
Spoke
Links of the connective system

**c. Micrograph of flagellum**

Don W. Fawcett/Science Source

**FIGURE 2.23 Eukaryotic flagellum. (a)** The relationship between the microtubules and the basal body of a flagellum. **(b)** Diagram of a flagellum in cross-section, showing the 9 + 2 system of microtubules. The spokes and connecting links hold the system together. **(c)** Electron micrograph of a flagellum in cross-section. Individual tubulin molecules are visible in the microtubule walls.

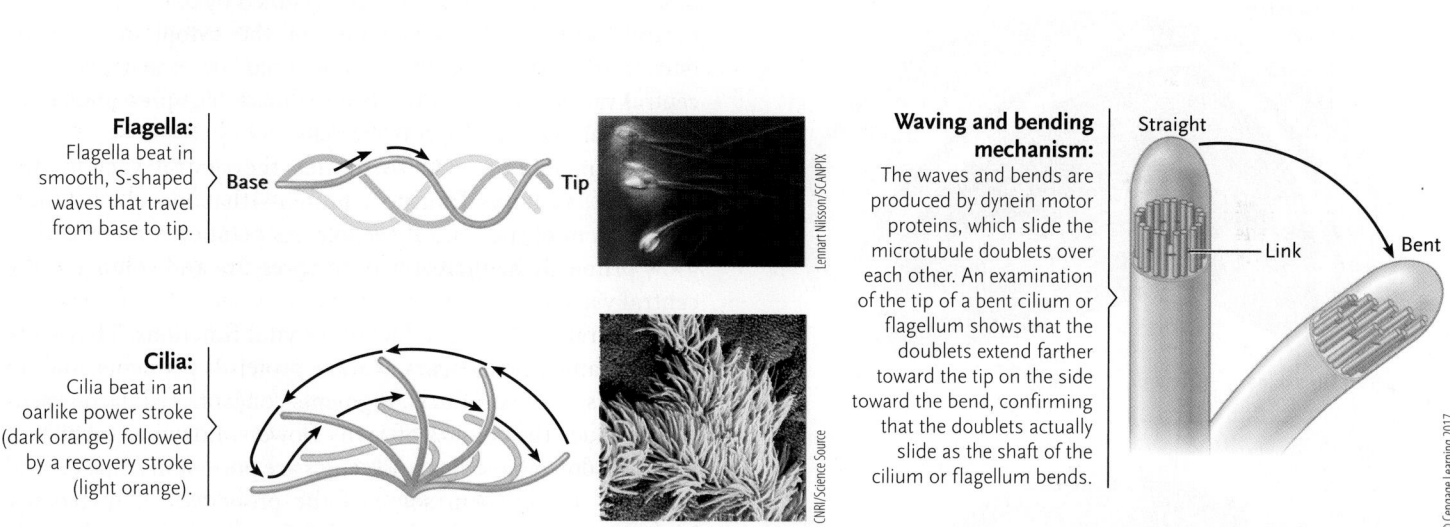

**Flagella:**
Flagella beat in smooth, S-shaped waves that travel from base to tip.

Base    Tip

Lennart Nilsson/SCANPIX

**Cilia:**
Cilia beat in an oarlike power stroke (dark orange) followed by a recovery stroke (light orange).

CNRI/Science Source

**Waving and bending mechanism:**
The waves and bends are produced by dynein motor proteins, which slide the microtubule doublets over each other. An examination of the tip of a bent cilium or flagellum shows that the doublets extend farther toward the tip on the side toward the bend, confirming that the doublets actually slide as the shaft of the cilium or flagellum bends.

Straight

Link

Bent

© Cengage Learning 2017

**FIGURE 2.24 Flagellar and ciliary beating patterns.** The micrographs show a few human sperm, each with a flagellum (top), and cilia from the lining of an airway in the lungs (bottom).

## 2.4 Specialized Structures of Plant Cells

Chloroplasts, large and highly specialized central vacuoles, and cell walls give plant cells their distinctive characteristics, but these structures also occur in some other eukaryotes, for example, in chloroplasts in algal protists and cell walls in algal protists and fungi.

### 2.4a Chloroplasts Are Biochemical Factories Powered by Sunlight

**Chloroplasts** (*chloro* = yellow-green), the sites of photosynthesis in plant cells, are members of a family of plant organelles known collectively as **plastids**. Other members of the family are colourless and store molecules, including starch. They occur in great numbers in the roots or tubers of some plants, such as the potato. All plastids contain DNA genomes and molecular machinery for gene expression and the synthesis of proteins on ribosomes. Some of the proteins within plastids are encoded by their genomes; others are encoded by nuclear genes and are imported into the organelles.

Chloroplasts, like mitochondria, are usually lens or disc shaped and are surrounded by a smooth **outer boundary membrane** and an **inner boundary membrane** that lies just inside the outer membrane (**Figure 2.25**). These two boundary membranes completely enclose an inner compartment, the **stroma**. Within the stroma is a third membrane system that consists of flattened closed sacs called **thylakoids**. In higher plants, the thylakoids are stacked one on top of another, forming structures called **grana** (singular, *granum*).

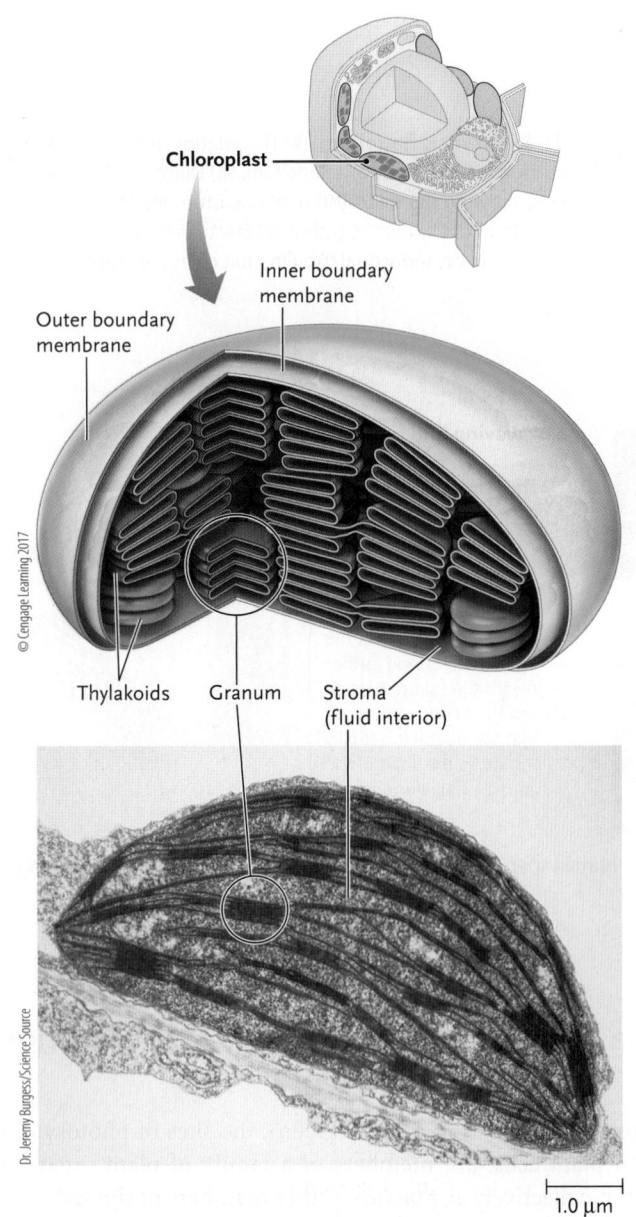

FIGURE 2.25 **Chloroplast structure.** This electron micrograph shows a maize (corn) chloroplast.

The thylakoid membranes contain molecules that absorb light energy and convert it to chemical energy in photosynthesis. The primary molecule absorbing light is *chlorophyll,* a green pigment that is present in all chloroplasts. The chemical energy is used by enzymes in the stroma to make carbohydrates and other complex organic molecules from water, carbon dioxide, and other simple inorganic precursors. The organic molecules produced in chloroplasts, or from biochemical building blocks made in chloroplasts, are the ultimate food source for most organisms. (The physical and biochemical reactions of chloroplasts are described in Chapter 6.)

The chloroplast stroma contains DNA and ribosomes that resemble those of certain photosynthetic bacteria. Because of these similarities, chloroplasts, like mitochondria, are believed to have originated from ancient bacteria that became permanent residents of the eukaryotic cells ancestral to the plant lineage (see Chapter 19 for further discussion).

## 2.4b Central Vacuoles Have Diverse Roles in Storage, Structural Support, and Cell Growth

**Central vacuoles** (see Figure 2.9) are large vesicles identified as distinct organelles of plant cells because they perform specialized functions unique to plants. In a mature plant cell, 90% or more of the cell's volume may be occupied by one or more large central vacuoles. The remainder of the cytoplasm and the nucleus of these cells is restricted to a narrow zone between the central vacuole and the plasma membrane. The pressure within the central vacuole supports the cells.

The membrane that surrounds the central vacuole, the **tonoplast**, contains transport proteins that move substances into and out of the central vacuole. As plant cells mature, they grow primarily by increases in the pressure and volume of the central vacuole.

Central vacuoles conduct other vital functions. They store salts, organic acids, sugars, storage proteins, pigments, and, in some cells, waste products. Pigments concentrated in the vacuoles produce the colours of many flowers. Enzymes capable of breaking down biological molecules are present in some central vacuoles, giving them some of the properties of lysosomes. Molecules that provide chemical defences against pathogenic organisms also occur in the central vacuoles of some plants.

## 2.4c Cell Walls Support and Protect Plant Cells

The cell walls of plants are extracellular structures because they are located outside the plasma membrane (**Figure 2.26**). Cell walls provide support to individual cells, contain the pressure produced in the central vacuole, and protect cells against invading bacteria and fungi. Cell walls consist of cellulose fibres, which give tensile strength to the walls and are embedded in a network of highly branched carbohydrates. Cell walls are perforated by minute channels, the plasmodesmata (singular,

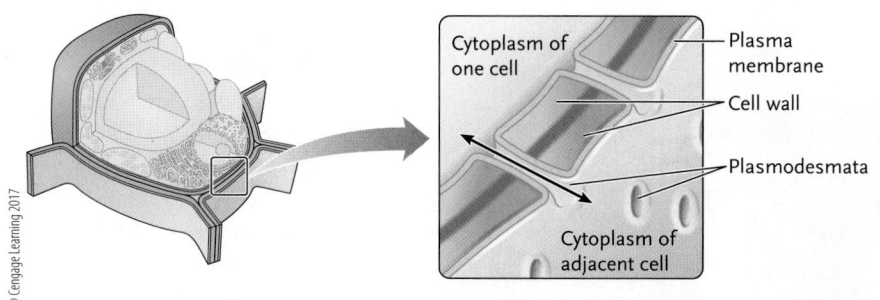

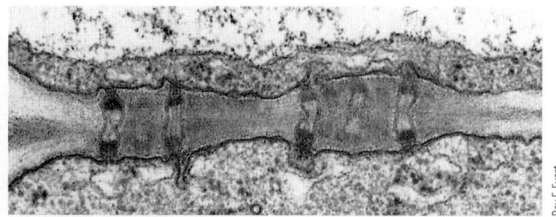

Section through five plasmodesmata that bridge the walls of two plant cells.

**FIGURE 2.26 Cell wall structure in plants.** The right diagram and electron micrograph show plasmodesmata, which form openings in the cell wall that directly connect the cytoplasm of adjacent cells.

*plasmodesma*; see Figure 2.26). A typical plant cell has between 1000 and 100 000 plasmodesmata connecting it to abutting cells. These cytosol-filled channels are lined by a plasma membrane, so that connected cells essentially all have one continuous surface membrane. Most plasmodesmata also contain a narrow tubelike structure derived from the smooth ER of the connected cells. Plasmodesmata allow ions and small molecules to move directly from one cell to another through the connecting cytosol, without having to penetrate the plasma membranes or cell walls. Proteins and nucleic acids move through some plasmodesmata using energy-dependent processes.

Cell walls also surround the cells of fungi and algal protists. Carbohydrate molecules form the major framework of cell walls in most of these organisms, as they do in plants. In some, the wall fibres contain **chitin** instead of cellulose. Details of cell wall structure in the algal protists and fungi, as well as in different subgroups of the plants, are presented in later chapters devoted to these organisms. As noted earlier, animal cells do not form rigid, external, layered structures equivalent to the walls of plant cells. However, most animal cells secrete extracellular material and have other structures at the cell surface that play vital roles in the support and organization of animal body structures. The next section describes these and other surface structures of animal cells.

**STUDY BREAK QUESTIONS**

1. In plant cells, what is the function of the vacuole?
2. What role do plasmodesmata serve in the plant cell wall?

## 2.5 The Animal Cell Surface

Animal cells have specialized structures that help hold cells together, produce avenues of communication between cells, and organize body structures. Molecular systems that perform these functions are organized at three levels: individual **cell adhesion molecules** bind cells together, more complex **cell junctions** seal the spaces between cells and provide direct communication between cells, and the **extracellular matrix (ECM)** supports

and protects cells and provides mechanical linkages, such as those between muscles and bone.

### 2.5a Cell Adhesion Molecules Organize Animal Cells into Tissues and Organs

Cell adhesion molecules are glycoproteins embedded in the plasma membrane. They help maintain body form and structure in animals ranging from sponges to the most complex invertebrates and vertebrates. Rather than acting as a generalized intercellular glue, cell adhesion molecules bind to specific molecules on other cells. Most cells in solid body tissues are held together by many different cell adhesion molecules.

Cell adhesion molecules make initial connections between cells early in embryonic development, but then attachments are broken and remade as individual cells or tissues change position in the developing **embryo**. As an embryo develops into an adult, the connections become permanent and are reinforced by cell junctions. Cancer cells typically lose these **adhesions**, allowing them to break loose from their original locations, migrate to new locations, and form additional tumours.

Some bacteria and viruses—such as the virus that causes the common cold—target cell adhesion molecules as attachment sites during infection. Cell adhesion molecules are also partially responsible for the ability of cells to recognize one another as being part of the same individual or foreign to that individual. For example, rejection of organ transplants in mammals results from an immune response triggered by the foreign cell surface molecules.

### 2.5b Cell Junctions Reinforce Cell Adhesions and Provide Avenues of Communication

Three types of cell junctions are common in animal tissues (**Figure 2.27**). **Anchoring junctions** form buttonlike spots, or belts, that run entirely around cells, "welding" adjacent cells together. For some anchoring junctions known as **desmosomes**, intermediate filaments anchor the junction in the underlying

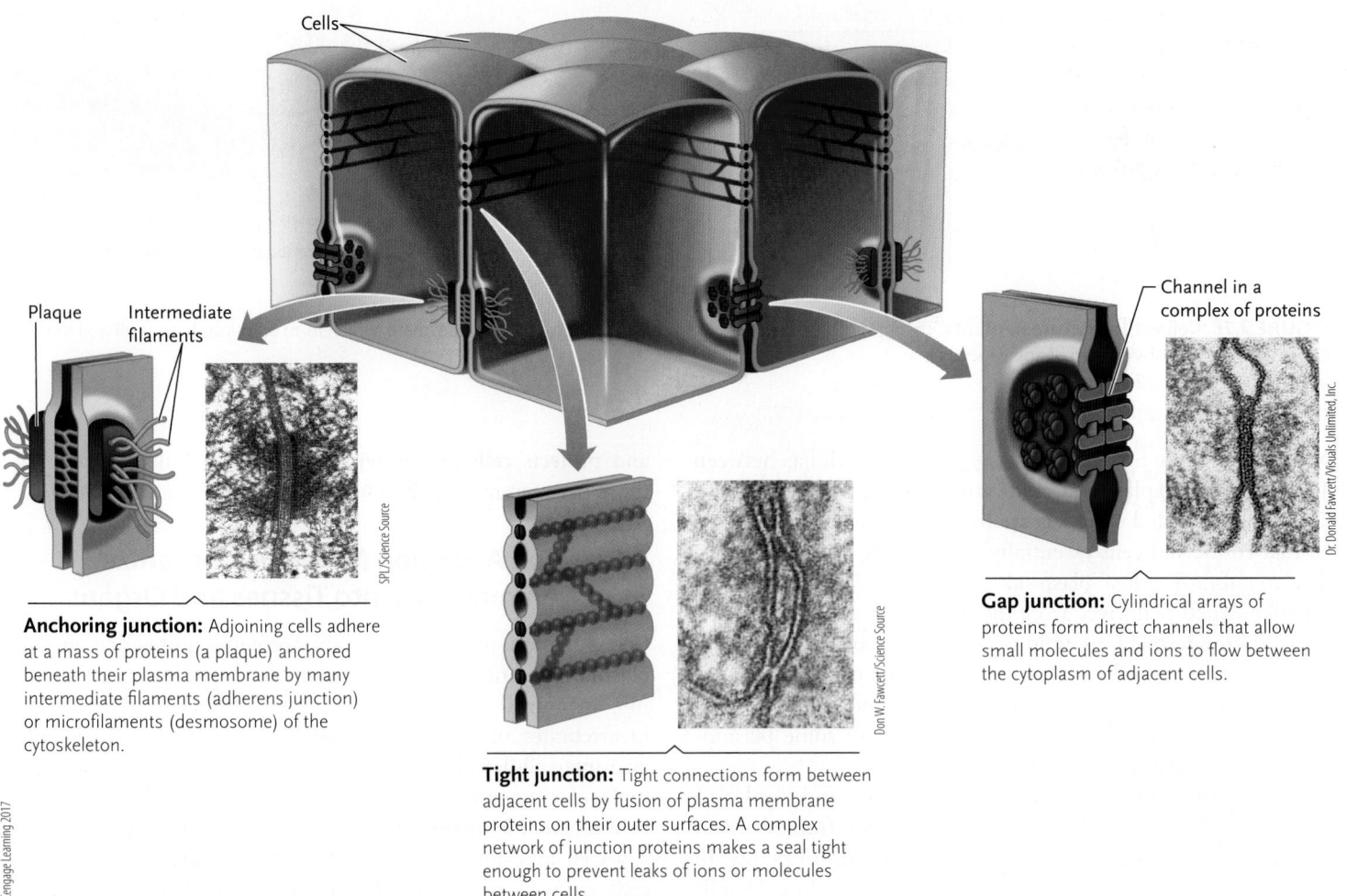

**Cells**

**Plaque** **Intermediate filaments**

*SPL/Science Source*

**Anchoring junction:** Adjoining cells adhere at a mass of proteins (a plaque) anchored beneath their plasma membrane by many intermediate filaments (adherens junction) or microfilaments (desmosome) of the cytoskeleton.

© Cengage Learning 2017

**Tight junction:** Tight connections form between adjacent cells by fusion of plasma membrane proteins on their outer surfaces. A complex network of junction proteins makes a seal tight enough to prevent leaks of ions or molecules between cells.

*Don W. Fawcett/Science Source*

**Channel in a complex of proteins**

*Dr. Donald Fawcett/Visuals Unlimited, Inc.*

**Gap junction:** Cylindrical arrays of proteins form direct channels that allow small molecules and ions to flow between the cytoplasm of adjacent cells.

**FIGURE 2.27 Anchoring junctions, tight junctions, and gap junctions, which connect cells in animal tissues.** Anchoring junctions reinforce the cell-to-cell connections made by cell adhesion molecules, tight junctions seal the spaces between cells, and gap junctions create direct channels of communication between animal cells.

cytoplasm; in other anchoring junctions, known as **adherens junctions**, microfilaments are the anchoring cytoskeletal component. Anchoring junctions are most common in tissues that are subject to stretching, shear, or other mechanical forces, for example, heart muscle, skin, and the cell layers that cover organs or line body cavities and ducts.

**Tight junctions**, as the name indicates, are regions of tight connections between membranes of adjacent cells (see Figure 2.27). The connection is so tight that it can keep particles as small as ions from moving between the cells in the layers.

Tight junctions seal the spaces between cells in the cell layers that cover internal organs and the outer surface of the body, or the layers that line internal cavities and ducts. For example, tight junctions between cells that line the **stomach**, intestine, and bladder keep the contents of these body cavities from leaking into surrounding tissues.

A tight junction is formed by direct fusion of proteins on the outer surfaces of the two plasma membranes of adjacent cells.

Strands of the tight junction proteins form a complex network that gives the appearance of stitch work holding the cells together. Within a tight junction, the plasma membrane is not joined continuously; instead, there are regions of intercellular space. Nonetheless, the network of junction proteins is sufficient to make the tight cell connections characteristic of these junctions.

**Gap junctions** open direct channels that allow ions and small molecules to pass directly from one cell to another (see Figure 2.27). Hollow protein cylinders embedded in the plasma membranes of adjacent cells line up and form a sort of pipeline that connects the cytoplasm of one cell with the cytoplasm of the next. The flow of ions and small molecules through the channels provides almost instantaneous communication between animal cells, similar to the communication that plasmodesmata provide between plant cells.

In vertebrates, gap junctions occur between cells within almost all body tissues, but not between cells of different tissues. These junctions are particularly important in heart muscle tissues and in the smooth muscle tissues that form the uterus, where their pathways of communication allow the cells of the organ to operate as a coordinated unit. Although most nerve tissues do not have gap junctions, nerve cells in dental pulp are connected by gap junctions; they are responsible for the discomfort you feel if your teeth are disturbed or damaged, or when a dentist pokes a probe into a cavity.

## 2.5c The Extracellular Matrix Organizes the Cell Exterior

Many types of animal cells are embedded in an ECM that consists of proteins and polysaccharides secreted by the cells themselves **(Figure 2.28)**. The primary function of the ECM is protection and support. The ECM forms the mass of skin, bones, and tendons; it also forms many highly specialized extracellular structures, such as the cornea of the eye and filtering networks in the kidney. The ECM also affects cell division, adhesion, motility, and embryonic development, and it takes part in reactions to wounds and disease.

Glycoproteins are the main component of the ECM. In most animals, the most abundant ECM glycoprotein is *collagen,* which forms fibres with great tensile strength and elasticity. In vertebrates, the collagens of tendons, cartilage, and bone are the most abundant proteins of the body, making up about half the total body protein by weight. (Collagens and their roles in body structures are described in further detail in Chapter 38.)

The consistency of the matrix, which may range from soft and jellylike to hard and elastic, depends on a network of proteoglycans that surrounds the collagen fibres. *Proteoglycans* are glycoproteins that consist of small proteins noncovalently attached to long polysaccharide molecules. Matrix consistency depends on the number of interlinks in this network, which determines how much water can be trapped in it; for example, cartilage, which contains a high proportion of interlinked glycoproteins, is relatively soft. Tendons, which are almost pure collagen, are tough and elastic. In bone, the glycoprotein network that surrounds collagen fibres is impregnated with mineral crystals, producing a dense and hard—but still elastic—structure that is about as strong as fibreglass or reinforced concrete.

Yet another class of glycoproteins is *fibronectins*, which aid in organizing the ECM and help cells attach to it. Fibronectins bind to **receptor proteins** called *integrins* that span the plasma membrane. On the cytoplasmic side of the plasma membrane, the integrins bind to microfilaments of the cytoskeleton. Integrins integrate changes outside and inside the cell by communicating changes in the ECM to the cytoskeleton.

Having laid the groundwork for cell structure and function in this chapter, we next take up further details of individual cell structures, beginning with the roles of cell membranes in transport in the next chapter.

### STUDY BREAK QUESTIONS

1. Distinguish between anchoring junctions, tight junctions, and gap junctions.
2. What is the structure and function of the ECM?

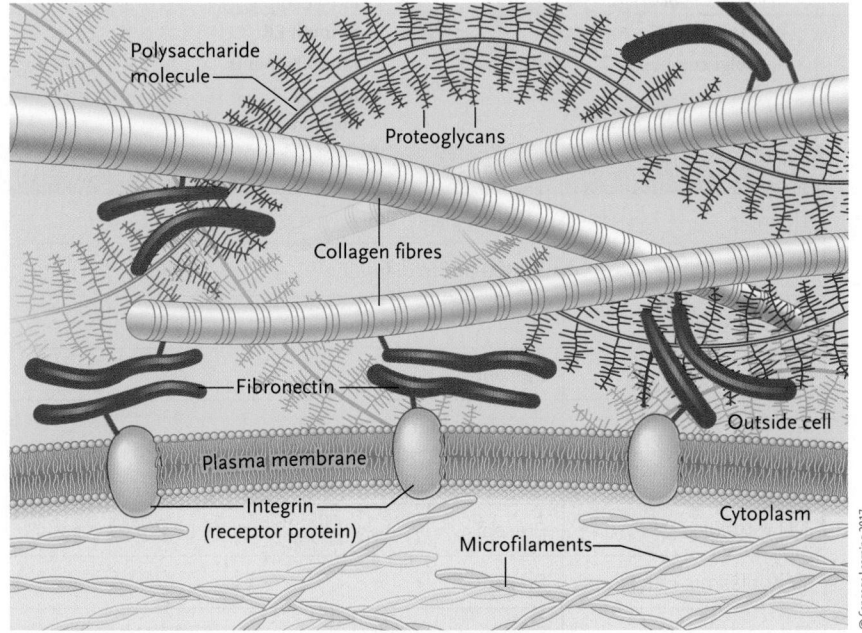

**FIGURE 2.28 Components of the ECM in an animal cell**

# Summary Illustration

The cell is the basic structural and functional unit of all living organisms. Cells carry out the essential processes of life and hold an organism's genetic information. They occur in prokaryotic and eukaryotic forms, each with distinctive structures and functions.

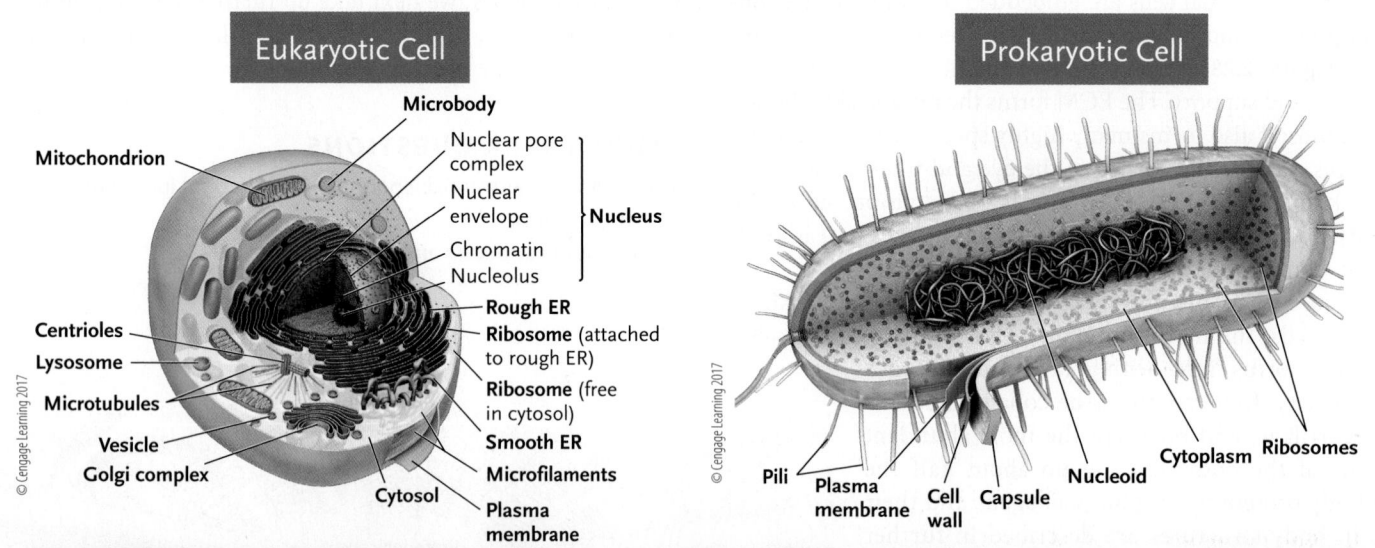

Eukaryotic Cell

Microbody
Nuclear pore complex
Mitochondrion
Nuclear envelope
Nucleus
Chromatin
Nucleolus
Rough ER
Centrioles
Ribosome (attached to rough ER)
Lysosome
Ribosome (free in cytosol)
Microtubules
Smooth ER
Vesicle
Microfilaments
Golgi complex
Cytosol
Plasma membrane

Prokaryotic Cell

Pili
Plasma membrane
Cell wall
Capsule
Nucleoid
Cytoplasm
Ribosomes

© Cengage Learning 2017

| | Eukaryotic Cell | Prokaryotic Cell |
|---|---|---|
| Example | Animals, plants, fungi | Bacteria, archae |
| Cell size | 10–100 µM in diameter | 0.2–2.0 µM in diameter |
| Cell number | Usually multicellular | Usually unicellular |
| Nucleus | Present | Absent |
| Cell wall | Only in plant cells and fungi | Present in all and usually complex |
| Genetic recombination | Meiosis and fusion of gametes | DNA transfer between organisms |
| Microtubules | Present | Absent |
| Endoplasmic reticulum | Present | Absent |
| Cytoskeleton | Extensive and complex | Minimal |
| Mitochondria | Present | Absent (but most bacteria carry out cellular respiration) |
| Ribosomes | Present | Present |
| Vesicles | Present | Absent |
| Golgi apparatus | Present | Absent |
| Chloroplasts | Present (in plants) | Absent (but some bacteria carry out photosynthesis) |
| Vacuoles | Present | Present |
| Flagella | Complex | Simple |

**Mitochondria** are membrane-bound organelles that are involved in cellular respiration.

The **nucleus** is a membrane-enclosed structure that contains DNA in the form of chromatin. The nuclear envelope consists of a system of two concentric membranes with nuclear pore complexes embedded. They control the transport of molecules between the nucleus and the cytoplasm.

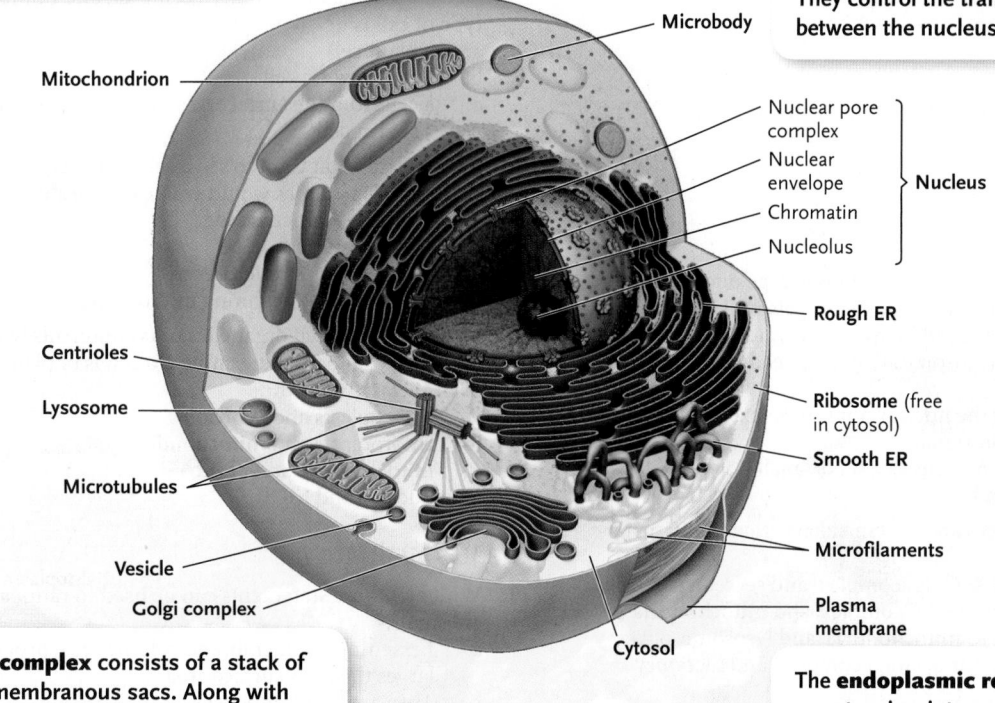

Mitochondrion

Microbody

Nuclear pore complex
Nuclear envelope
Chromatin
Nucleolus
} Nucleus

Rough ER

Centrioles

Lysosome

Ribosome (free in cytosol)

Smooth ER

Microtubules

Vesicle

Golgi complex

Microfilaments

Plasma membrane

Cytosol

The **Golgi complex** consists of a stack of flattened, membranous sacs. Along with the ER, the Golgi complex is involved in the transport of proteins to the cell surface.

The **endoplasmic reticulum (ER)** is an extensive, interconnected network of membranous channels and vesicles. Proteins synthesized on ribosomes of the rough ER enter the lumen, where they are modified and begin their path to the final destinations in the cell. Smooth ER membranes are involved in lipid synthesis and conversion of toxic molecules.

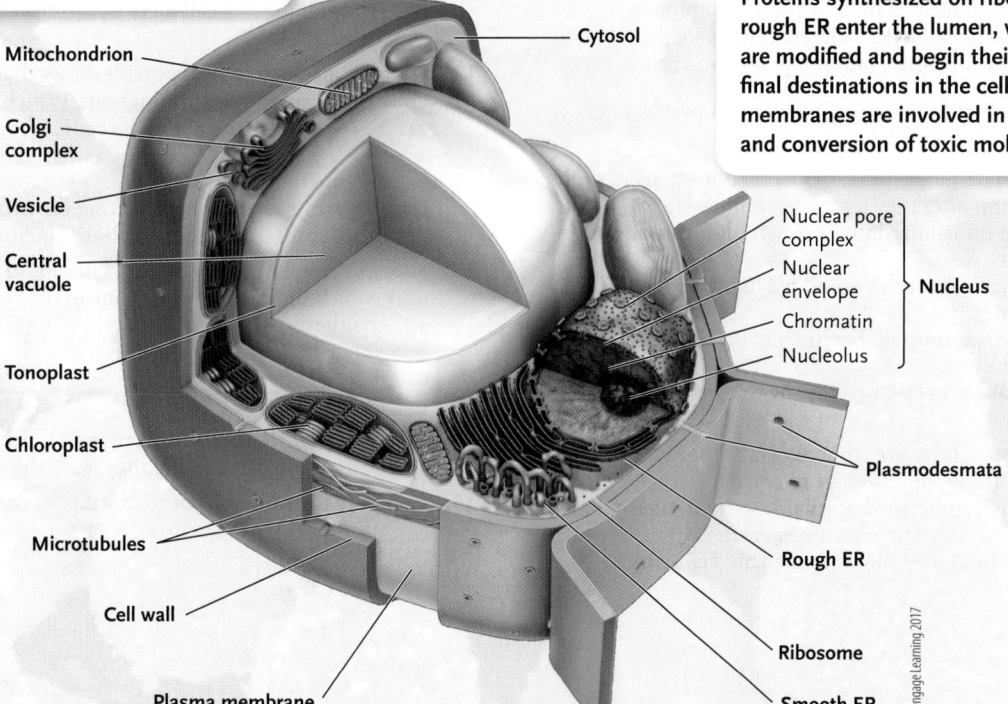

Cytosol

Mitochondrion

Golgi complex

Vesicle

Central vacuole

Tonoplast

Chloroplast

Microtubules

Cell wall

Plasma membrane

Nuclear pore complex
Nuclear envelope
Chromatin
Nucleolus
} Nucleus

Plasmodesmata

Rough ER

Ribosome

Smooth ER

© Cengage Learning 2017

Chloroplasts are the sites of photosynthesis in plant cells. They are members of a family of plant organelles known collectively as *plastids*.

**Ribosomes** each consist of a large subunit and a small subunit. They translate mRNA for protein synthesis.

# SELF-TEST QUESTIONS

## Recall/Understand

1. Some bacteria can convert food energy into the chemical energy of ATP using proteins that are found on what part of the cell?
   a. flagellum
   b. ribosome
   c. cell wall
   d. plasma membrane

2. Which of these structures is present in members of the domain Archaea?
   a. nuclear envelope
   b. microtubules
   c. ribosomes
   d. plasmodesmata

3. Which of these statements describes how a large nuclear-localized protein such as a transcription factor gets into the nucleus?
   a. It diffuses across the lipid bilayer of the nuclear envelope.
   b. It is translated on ribosomes that are already within the nucleus.
   c. It is recognized by the nuclear pore complex, as it contains a nuclear localization signal.
   d. It diffuses into the nucleus as a set of small polypeptides prior to their assembly.

4. Which of these structures are used in eukaryotic protein manufacture and secretion?
   a. ribosome, rough ER, Golgi complex, and secretory vesicles
   b. lysosome, ribosome, Golgi complex, and mitochondria
   c. ribosome, rough ER, mitochondria, and lysosome
   d. lysosome, mitochondria, Golgi complex, and secretory vesicles

5. Which of these structures contributes to sealing the lining of the digestive tract so that it can retain food?
   a. a tight junction formed by direct fusion of proteins
   b. a plasmodesma that helps cells communicate their activities
   c. a desmosome forming a buttonlike spot or a belt to keep cells joined
   d. a gap junction that communicates between cells of the stomach lining and its muscular wall

6. Which of these statements *best* explains what happens to some eukaryotic proteins after they have been synthesized?
   a. Proteins are transported to the rough ER for use within the cell.
   b. Lipids and carbohydrates are added to proteins by the Golgi complex.
   c. Proteins are transported directly into the cytosol for secretion from the cell.
   d. Proteins that are to be stored by the cell are moved to the rough ER.

7. Which of these structures are components of the cytoskeleton?
   a. cilia, flagella, and intermediate filaments
   b. microfilaments, intermediate filaments, and microtubules
   c. microtubules, cilia, and microfilaments
   d. flagella, microtubules, and intermediate filaments

## Apply/Analyze

8. Suppose that you are examining a cell from a crime scene using an electron microscope, and you find that it contains ribosomes, DNA, a plasma membrane, a cell wall, and mitochondria. What type of cell is it?
   a. a plant cell
   b. a prokaryotic cell
   c. a cell from the surface of a human fingernail
   d. a sperm cell

9. Suppose that you want to see a cell in its 3D appearance. Which of these microscopes would you use to be able to achieve this?
   a. bright field microscope
   b. dark field microscope
   c. phase-contrast microscope
   d. confocal laser scanning microscope

10. Which of these cell organelles or components would you search for if you wanted to determine if a cell is of plant or animal origin?
    a. chloroplasts and centrioles
    b. chloroplasts and mitochondria
    c. mitochondria and plasma membrane
    d. nucleus and ER

## Create/Evaluate

11. Which of these statements can be used to rationalize why cells are small?
    a. Lessening the membrane volume area, proportionally enlarges the cell's surface area.
    b. They are building blocks.
    c. The surface area of a cell increases as the cube of the linear dimension.
    d. The volume of a cell increases to the cube of the linear dimension.

12. Suppose an electron micrograph shows that a cell has extensive amounts of smooth ER throughout. Which of these deductions can be correctly made about the cell?
    a. It is synthesizing ATP.
    b. It is metabolically inactive.
    c. It is synthesizing and secreting proteins.
    d. It is synthesizing and metabolizing lipids.

13. Suppose you find a cell that has a flagellum. Based on this finding only, which of the following is one of the cell's abilities?
    a. synthesizing proteins
    b. reproducing
    c. moving
    d. growing

14. Trace the pathway of proteins in the cell from the place of their synthesis to the place where they leave the cell.

15. Compare the functions of anchoring, tight, and gap junctions.

# Chapter Roadmap

**Energy and Enzymes**

Life requires a constant supply of energy to maintain its highly ordered state. Life also requires enzymes, which are needed for reactions to proceed quickly at the relatively low temperatures conducive to life.

**3.1 Energy and the Laws of Thermodynamics**

Energy is required to do work and, while it can exist in different forms, it cannot be created or destroyed.

To Chapter 5

To Chapter 6

**3.2 Free Energy and Spontaneous Processes**

Spontaneous reactions are dependent upon the enthalpy change and entropy change of the reaction, and result in the products having less free energy than the reactants reactions: $\Delta G$ is negative.

**3.3 Thermodynamics and Life**

Living systems are characterized by a highly organized state that is maintained by a constant flow of energy and matter into cells.

**3.4 Overview of Metabolism**

Metabolism is built around two distinct types of pathways: catabolic, which break down molecules, converting trapped energy as ATP; and anabolic, which consume ATP in the synthesis of macromolecules.

**3.5 The Role of Enzymes in Biological Reactions**

As biological catalysts, enzymes increase the rate of reaction by lowering the activation energy required for reacting molecules to reach the transition state.

**3.6 Factors That Affect Enzyme Activity**

The activity of an enzyme is influenced by a wide range of factors, including substrate concentration and various compounds, as well as physical factors such as pH and temperature.

Energy

ADP + $P_i$    ATP/ADP cycle    ATP

Energy

© Cengage Learning 2017

Tony Campbell/Shutterstock.com

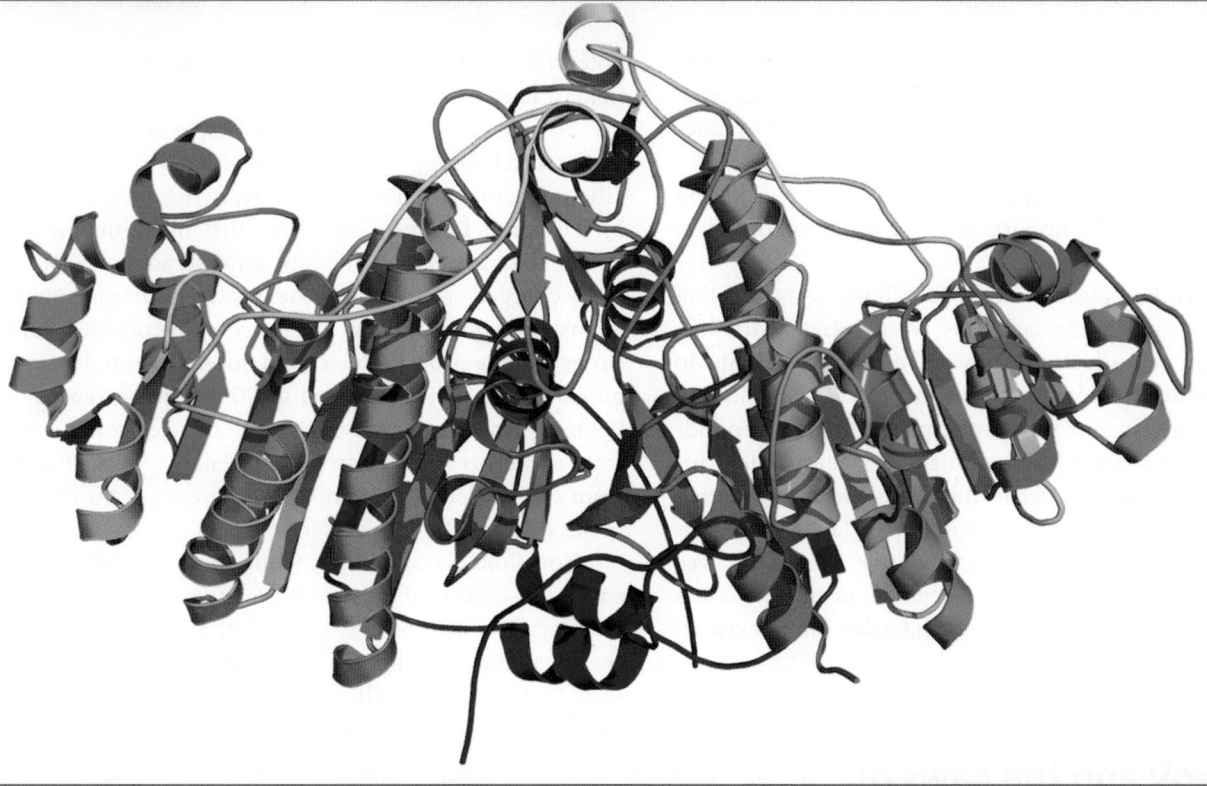

**Model of the enzyme alkaline phosphatase**

# Energy and Enzymes

# 3

**Why it matters . . .** Earth is a cold place—at least when it comes to chemical reactions. Life cannot survive at the high temperatures routinely used in industry for chemical synthesis. Instead, life relies on a group of catalysts called *enzymes* that speed up the rates of chemical reactions without the need for an increase in temperature.

Until recently, just how good enzymes are at speeding up reaction rates was not fully appreciated. Richard Wolfenden and his colleagues at the University of North Carolina experimentally measured the rates of a range of uncatalyzed and enzyme-catalyzed biochemical reactions. The prize for the greatest difference between the uncatalyzed rate and the enzyme-catalyzed rate goes to a reaction that simply removes a **phosphate group**. In the cell, a group of enzymes called *phosphatases* catalyze the removal of phosphate groups from a range of molecules, including proteins. The reversible addition and removal of a phosphate group from particular proteins is a central mechanism of intracellular communication in almost all cells (Chapter 4).

In the presence of the phosphatase enzyme, the removal of the phosphate takes approximately 10 milliseconds. Wolfenden's research group calculated that, in an aqueous environment such as within a cell, in the absence of an enzyme, the phosphate removal reaction would take over 1 trillion ($10^{12}$) years to occur. This exceeds the current estimate for the age of the universe!

This makes the difference between enzyme-catalyzed and uncatalyzed rates 21 orders of magnitude ($10^{21}$). For most reactions, the enzyme-catalyzed rate is many millions ($10^6$) of times faster than the uncatalyzed rate.

The high rates of catalysis brought about by the evolution of enzymes were critically important to the evolution of life on a relatively cold planet.

Enzymes are key players in the metabolic reactions that collectively accomplish the activities we associate with life, such as growth, reproduction, movement, and the ability to respond to stimuli. Central to these processes is the ability of organisms to harness and utilize energy from the surroundings, and thus this chapter starts with an overview of the principles of energy flow as governed by the laws of thermodynamics. This is followed by a focused discussion on the factors that govern chemical reactions and the central role played by **free energy**. We finish with an in-depth discussion of enzymes—the fundamental biological catalysts—which enable life to exist on this cold planet.

## 3.1 Energy and the Laws of Thermodynamics

Life, like all chemical and physical activities, is an energy-driven process. We define **energy** as the capacity to do work or be transferred as heat. It takes energy to move a car on a highway, and it takes energy to climb a mountain. It also takes energy to synthesize a protein from a group of amino acids and transport sucrose across a cell membrane.

### 3.1a Energy Exists in Different Forms

Energy can exist in many different forms, including chemical, electrical, and mechanical. Electromagnetic radiation, including visible light, is also a form of energy. While energy exists in many different forms, it can be transformed from one form into another. The chemical energy present in a flashlight battery, for example, is converted into electrical energy that passes through the flashlight bulb, where it is transformed into light and heat.

There are two major types of energy: kinetic and potential. **Kinetic energy** is the energy possessed by an object because it is in motion. Obvious examples of objects that possess kinetic energy are waves in the ocean, a falling rock, a kicked football. A less obvious example is the kinetic energy of electricity, which is a flow of electrons. Photons of light are also a form of kinetic energy. The movement associated with kinetic energy is of use because it can perform work by making other objects move. **Potential energy** is stored energy, the energy an object has because of its position or chemical structure. A boulder at the top of a cliff has potential energy because of its position in the gravitational field of Earth.

So what is it about certain molecules that make them high in potential energy? The potential energy possessed by a specific molecule, its chemical energy, is the energy that is stored in the bonds between the atoms that make up the molecule. Recall that covalent bonds are an interaction between negatively charged electrons and the positively charged nuclei of the atoms in the molecule. As an electron is attracted to and moves closer to one atomic nucleus, it loses potential energy. This potential energy is converted to other types of energy such as light or heat. Conversely, to move an electron further away from a nucleus requires an input of energy, as the further away from the nucleus the more potential energy an electron possesses (**Figure 3.1**).

You should realize that, while there are different kinds of energy, an object can possess more than one at a time. Consider a molecule of glucose. It has potential energy because of the energy stored in its bonds. But at temperatures above absolute zero ($-273°C$), like all molecules, it also possesses kinetic energy because it is constantly in motion.

### 3.1b The Laws of Thermodynamics Describe Energy and Its Transformation

The branch of science that concerns energy and how it changes during chemical and physical transformations is called **thermodynamics**. When discussing thermodynamics, it is important to define something called the *system*, which is the object(s) being studied. A system can be defined as anything, for example, a single atom, one cell, a planet. Everything outside the system is called the *surroundings*. The universe, in this context, is the total of the system and the surroundings. As well, it is important

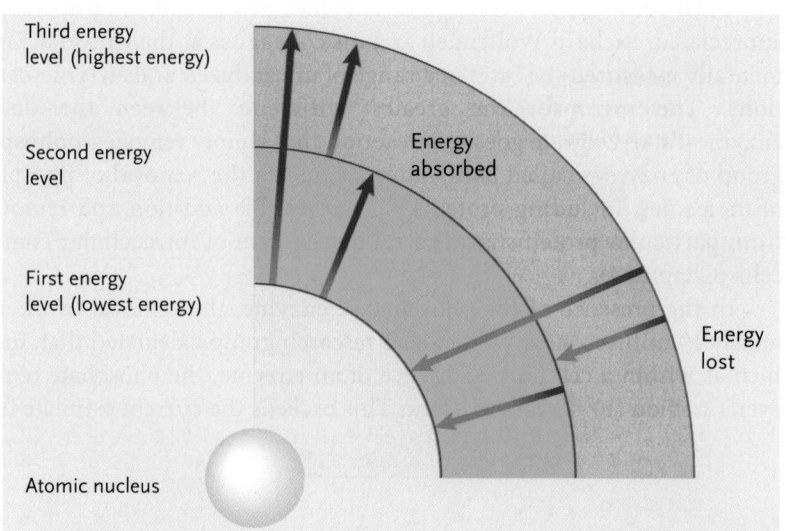

**FIGURE 3.1 Energy levels of the electrons of an atom.** Electrons can exist only in discrete energy states. When an electron gains energy, it moves to a higher energy level that is further away from the nucleus. When an electron loses energy, it moves to a lower energy level closer to the nucleus.

that we distinguish between three different types of systems: isolated, closed, and open (**Figure 3.2**).

- An *isolated system* is one that does not exchange matter or energy with its surroundings. The only truly isolated system is the universe itself. An insulated Thermos bottle is close to being an isolated system, as very little energy or matter is exchanged with the environment.
- A *closed system* can exchange energy, but not matter, with its surroundings. A saucepan of water with a lid heating on a stove is a good example of a closed system. Earth is also considered to be a closed system: it takes in an enormous amount of energy generated by the Sun and releases heat, but no matter is exchanged between Earth and the rest of the universe. Each year a few meteorites hit Earth, and a few gases escape, but essentially we can consider it a closed system.
- In an *open system*, both energy and matter can move freely between the system and the surroundings. An ocean is a great example of an open system: it absorbs and releases energy, and, as a component of the hydrological cycle, water is constantly being lost and gained by the ocean through evaporation and precipitation.

## 3.1c The First Law of Thermodynamics: Energy Can Be Transformed but Not Created or Destroyed

Research by physicists and chemists in the nineteenth century concerning energy flow between systems and the surroundings led to the formulation of two fundamental laws of thermodynamics that apply to all systems, both living and nonliving. According to the **first law of thermodynamics**, *energy can be transformed from one form into another or transferred from one place to another, but it cannot be created or destroyed.* The first law of thermodynamics is illustrated nicely by Niagara Falls (**Figure 3.3a**). Water at the top of the falls has high potential energy because of its location in Earth's gravitational field. As the water moves over the waterfall, its potential energy is converted into kinetic energy. The higher the waterfall, the more kinetic energy the water will possess. When the water reaches the bottom of the waterfall, its kinetic energy is transformed into other types of energy: heat, sound, and mechanical energy (causing weathering of the rocks). For thousands of years, the kinetic energy of waterfalls has been harnessed by people to do work. At Niagara Falls today, some of the kinetic energy of the moving water is converted into electricity through the use of hydroelectric turbines (Figure 3.3b) for the use of thousands of homes and businesses.

## 3.1d The Second Law of Thermodynamics: Energy Moves from Being Localized to Being Dispersed

Another important principle of thermodynamics is that the energy of a system tends to disperse, or spread out. Many everyday situations illustrate this. For example, let's say you heat a pan on a stove and then switch the stove off (**Figure 3.4**). At first the heat energy is concentrated very close to the pan, but slowly the heat energy disperses throughout the kitchen. This energy dispersal continues until no part of the room contains more energy than any other. This spreading out of energy is inevitable—it will happen. In thermodynamics, the tendency of energy to become dispersed or spread out is defined as **entropy**, which is abbreviated *S* (think *S* for *S*preading out). It is equally valid to consider entropy as a measure of disorder or randomness in a system because energy becomes more dispersed as matter

**a. Isolated system: does not exchange matter or energy with its surroundings**

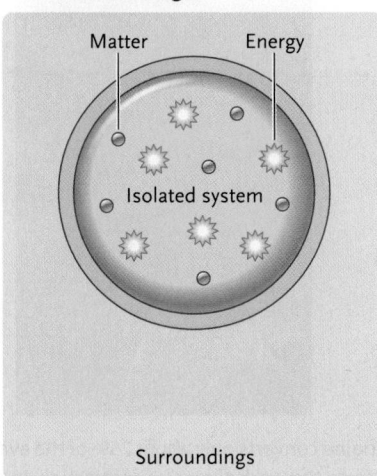

**b. Closed system: exchanges energy with its surroundings**

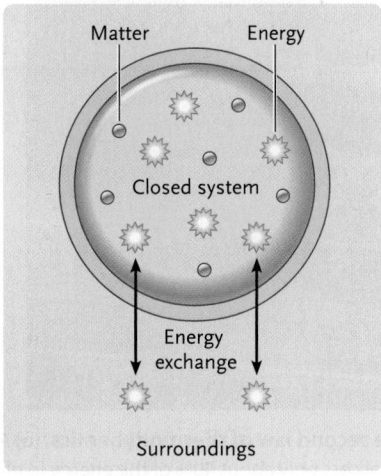

**c. Open system: exchanges both energy and matter with its surroundings**

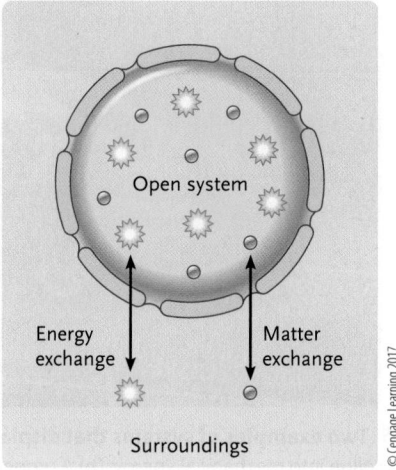

© Cengage Learning 2017

**FIGURE 3.2 Isolated, closed, and open systems in thermodynamics**

**a.**

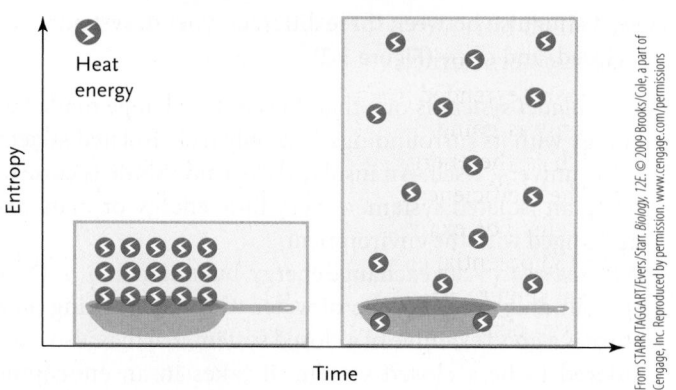

FIGURE 3.4 **Energy tends to spread out—to become more dispersed over time.** The thermodynamic measure of energy dispersal is called *entropy*.

becomes more dispersed. Consider, for example, a molecule of glucose ($C_6H_{12}O_6$). Glucose exhibits low entropy because the 24 atoms that make up the molecule are bonded to each other in a very precise way. There is more disorder in the molecules of $H_2O$ (a liquid) and $CO_2$ (a gas), from which glucose is synthesized.

The concept of entropy forms the basis of the **second law of thermodynamics**: *the entropy of a system and the surroundings will increase—energy and matter will always become more spread out.* Entropy is the measure of how much energy and matter has moved from being localized to becoming more widely dispersed.

The tendency of energy to spread out is the underlying reason why machines can never be 100% efficient. Although energy can be transformed from one form into another, a portion of the energy will always be lost to the surroundings by the tendency of energy to spread out. For example, the engine of a car only converts a portion of the potential energy in gasoline to the kinetic energy that powers the wheels (**Figure 3.5a**). Likewise, only a portion of the energy in a notebook computer

**b.**

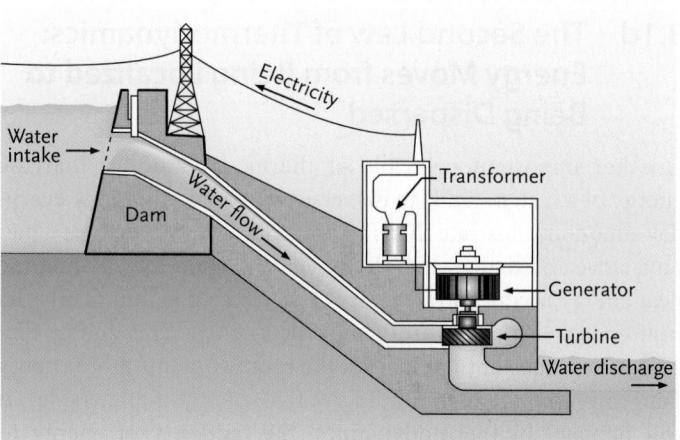

FIGURE 3.3 **Niagara Falls. (a)** The potential energy of the water is converted into kinetic energy as it moves over the falls. **(b)** A small portion of this kinetic energy is used to turn hydroelectric turbines, which convert the kinetic energy into electrical energy. In accordance with the first law of thermodynamics, energy hasn't been gained or lost but has changed form.

**a.**

**b.**

FIGURE 3.5 **Two examples of systems that display the second law of thermodynamics. (a)** A car engine converts only about 25% of the available energy in gasoline into mechanical energy. **(b)** A runner can access only about 40% of the energy in glucose to do the work of muscle contraction. In both cases, a significant portion of the energy localized in the fuel molecules is lost to the environment as heat and gases.

battery is used to run the computer. If you touch a car engine that has just been turned off or put a notebook computer on your lap for an extended period of time, it is obvious where a lot of the energy is going. It is being lost to the surroundings as *heat,* which is the energy associated with random molecular motion. The inefficiency of energy transformations also applies to living cells. For example, cellular respiration converts less than half the potential energy in glucose into a form usable for metabolism (Figure 3.5b). We will come back and reinforce the link between thermodynamics and life later in this chapter.

### STUDY BREAK QUESTIONS

1. What is the distinction between an isolated, a closed, and an open system?
2. Using the concept of energy spreading, why is a molecule of glucose considered to be low entropy?

## 3.2 Free Energy and Spontaneous Processes

The reaction between molecules of carbon dioxide and water that produces glucose and oxygen requires energy to occur, but the reverse reaction can take place all by itself. Why is that? Likewise, $O_2$ will readily diffuse into a region where its concentration is lower, but it will never diffuse into a region where its concentration is higher. Why not? In this section we tackle one of the basics of thermodynamics: the factors that determine if a given reaction will occur by itself or whether it needs a continual driving force. A process that can occur without a constant input of energy is referred to as a *spontaneous process.* We will refine this definition later on, but for now it is important to note that, in the context of thermodynamics, the term *spontaneous* does not refer to how fast a reaction will occur. As discussed in *Why It Matters,* some spontaneous reactions take a millisecond to occur, others a million years. As well, in our discussions we use the terms *transformation, process,* and *reaction* interchangeably to include both chemical reactions (where bonds break and form) and physical transformations, such as evaporation.

### 3.2a Enthalpy and Entropy Contribute to Making a Reaction Spontaneous

As the term *thermo*dynamics would suggest, heat is an important property of a system and needs to be considered. The heat content of a system is called its **enthalpy**, or $\Delta H$. In a molecule, enthalpy reflects the number and kinds of chemical bonds that exist between atoms. Transformations that result in a system taking up heat from its surroundings are termed **endothermic** and result in the products having more thermal energy than the initial state of the system. The overall change in enthalpy ($\Delta H = \Delta H_{\text{products}} - \Delta H_{\text{reactants}}$) of an endothermic process is positive.

The melting of ice is a simple example of an endothermic process. Compared to an endothermic process, a process that releases heat is called **exothermic**, as the products have less thermal energy than the starting molecules ($\Delta H$ is negative). The burning of wood is a simple example of an exothermic process. In your chemistry class you may have learned about measuring the change in enthalpy of a chemical reaction using the technique of calorimetry. It is used to measure the change in heat of a chemical reaction, and it's where the word calorie comes from.

The change in the enthalpy of a reaction is an important factor to evaluate whether or not a reaction will occur spontaneously; however, it is not the only factor. The change in entropy is also an important consideration. Here we consider how changes in both enthalpy and entropy influence the spontaneity of a reaction.

1. *Reactions tend to be spontaneous if they are exothermic, i.e., if the products have less thermal energy than the reactants.* In chemical reactions, the change in thermal energy between products and reactants reflects a change in how tightly electrons are held together, which is determined by the atoms making up the molecules involved.
2. *Reactions tend to be spontaneous when the entropy of the products is greater than the entropy of the reactants.* Transformations tend to occur spontaneously if the energy of the products is more spread out than the energy in the starting molecules.

As an example, let's look at the breakdown of glucose, a central molecule in cellular respiration:

$$C_6H_{12}O_6 \text{ (s)} + 6O_2 \text{ (g)} \rightarrow 6CO_2 \text{ (g)} + 6H_2O \quad (1)$$

The reaction is spontaneous in large part because it is exothermic: there is heat released as a result of bonds being broken and formed. Generally speaking, the electrons are more strongly held in the product molecules than in the reactant molecules, and the excess energy is released to the surroundings. However, the spontaneous nature of the reaction is also due to the entropy of the products being greater than the entropy of the reactants. But how do we know that the entropy increases simply by looking at the reaction?

As illustrated in **Figure 3.6**, whenever a chemical reaction results in an increase in the number of molecules, entropy increases. In the example of the breakdown of glucose, 7 reacting molecules are transformed into 12 molecules of product. The entropy has increased because the energy has spread out over a greater number of molecules. Entropy also increases when a solid is converted into a liquid, or a liquid into a gas. Energy spreads out more readily as matter undergoes these phase changes. In the example of the breakdown of glucose, six molecules of a gas and one molecule of a solid are converted into six molecules of a gas and six molecules of a liquid (Figure 3.6). A phase change in the other direction—gas to liquid or liquid to solid—decreases the entropy, as the energy becomes more localized.

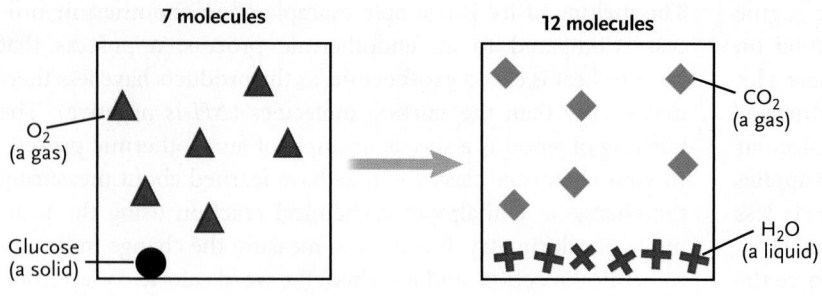

**7 molecules**

$O_2$
(a gas)

Glucose
(a solid)

**12 molecules**

$CO_2$
(a gas)

$H_2O$
(a liquid)

**FIGURE 3.6 The breakdown of glucose results in an increase in entropy.** This is because 1) the number of molecules increases, and 2) a phase change has occurred (e.g., solid → liquid → gas).

Source: Based on Lehninger Principles of Biochemistry (4th ed.) Nelson, D., and Cox, M.; W.H. Freeman and Company, New York, 2005.

## 3.2b The Change in Free Energy Indicates Whether a Process Is Spontaneous

From our previous discussion we know that both enthalpy and entropy need to be considered to determine if a reaction is spontaneous. It was the American physicist Josiah Gibbs who arrived at the mathematical relationship of how entropy and enthalpy interact to determine what is referred to as *Gibbs free energy* (*G*): the amount of energy that is actually available in a system to do work. The change in free energy ($\Delta G = G_{products} - G_{reactants}$) can be calculated for any specific transformation using the formula

$$\Delta G = \Delta H - T\Delta S$$

where $\Delta H$ is the change in the enthalpy, $\Delta S$ is the change in the entropy of the system over the course of the reaction, and $T$ is the temperature in Kelvin (K). $T$ is part of the entropy term because matter and energy spreading increases as temperature increases.

Recall from the start of Section 3.2 that we referred to a *spontaneous* process as one that will occur by itself without a continuous input of energy. Now that we have introduced the concept of free energy, we can be more precise with our definition: a **spontaneous reaction** is one in which the free energy of the products is less than the free energy of the reactants: $\Delta G$ is negative. A spontaneous process is also referred to as an **exergonic process**. Similarly, a nonspontaneous process is one in which the free energy of the products is greater than the free energy of the reactants: $\Delta G$ is positive. A nonspontaneous reaction is also referred to as an **endergonic process**.

To help in your understanding of the key differences between endergonic and exergonic reactions, take a look at **Figure 3.7**. Comparing the exergonic and the endergonic reactions you can clearly see it is the relationship between the free energy of the products compared to the reactants that defines the two reaction types. However,

you should also notice that, for both types of reactions, there is a requirement for an initial increase in free energy above that of the starting reactants. This "initial bump," or activation energy, is required for the reaction to proceed and may be very small or very large. What is important to remember, however, is that it is the overall change in free energy of products compared to the reactants that determines whether or not a reaction is exergonic or endergonic, which is unrelated to the energy required for activation. We will discuss this in greater detail later when we discuss enzymes.

The formula $\Delta G = \Delta H - T\Delta S$ tells us that both the change in enthalpy and the change in entropy can influence the overall $\Delta G$ of a reaction. In many processes, like the breakdown of glucose, the change in enthalpy of the system ($\Delta H$ is negative) and the change in entropy ($\Delta S$ is positive) both contribute to making the reaction exergonic. But this does not have to be the case. Let's consider a very interesting thermodynamic system, the ice cube. At room temperature, ice will spontaneously melt because the ice is absorbing energy from the surroundings. The melting of ice is an endothermic process ($\Delta H$ is positive): as the ice melts it is absorbing energy from the surroundings, resulting in the water having greater kinetic energy than the ice. But, even though the process is endothermic, what makes the melting of ice exergonic ($\Delta G$ is negative) is the very large increase in entropy as the solid ice changes into liquid water.

**a. Exergonic reaction:** Free energy is released, products have less free energy than reactants, and the reaction proceeds spontaneously.

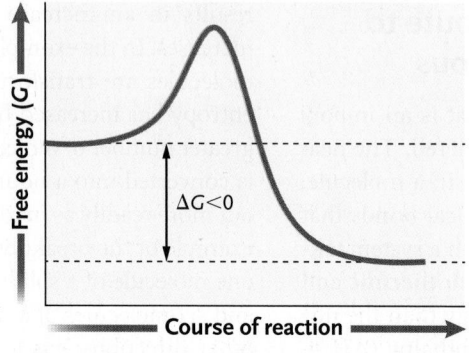

Free energy (*G*)

$\Delta G < 0$

Course of reaction

**b. Endergonic reaction:** Free energy is gained, products have more free energy than reactants, and the reaction is not spontaneous.

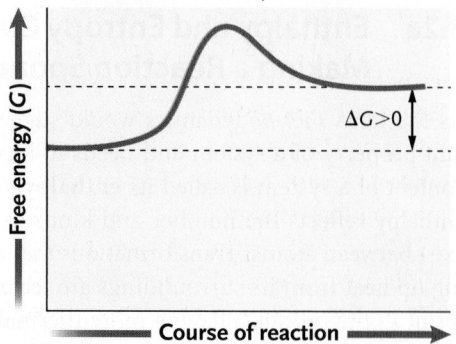

Free energy (*G*)

$\Delta G > 0$

Course of reaction

**FIGURE 3.7 Exergonic and endergonic reactions**

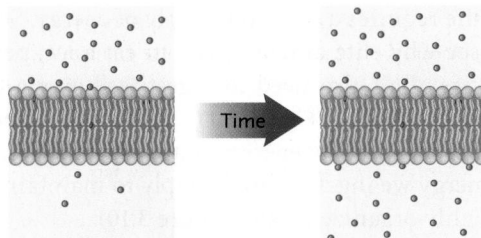

FIGURE 3.8 **Diffusion across a membrane is driven by an increase in entropy.** Molecules will move spontaneously across a membrane from a region of high concentration to a region of lower concentration because the energy associated with the molecules becomes more dispersed.

Let's look at one more example of a spontaneous process: diffusion of molecules across a membrane. As illustrated in **Figure 3.8**, any molecule that can cross a membrane will move spontaneously from a compartment where it is at a higher concentration to a compartment where its concentration is lower. The spontaneous nature of diffusion is explained completely by the increase in entropy as the molecules and their associated energy spread out. Although there is no change in enthalpy ($\Delta H$), the release of free energy during diffusion can be harnessed by the cell to do work. An elegant example of this is the generation of ATP using the proton gradient generated by electron transport (see Chapters 5 and 6).

## 3.2c Exergonic Reactions Move toward Equilibrium but Do Not Go to Completion

In the late nineteenth century, chemists were surprised to find that many chemical reactions never went to completion. The products were always "contaminated" with molecules of reactant. More shocking was the finding that, regardless of the amount of reactants and products in the initial mixture, the system reached the same state, in which the proportion of products to reactants was a constant. As an example, consider a chemical reaction in which glucose 1-phosphate is converted into glucose 6-phosphate (**Figure 3.9**). Starting with 0.02 M glucose 1-phosphate, the reaction will proceed spontaneously until there is 0.019 M of glucose 6-phosphate (product) and 0.001 M of glucose 1-phosphate (reactant) in the solution. In fact, regardless of the amounts of each that you start with, the reaction will reach a point at which there is 95% glucose 6-phosphate and 5% glucose 1-phosphate.

The point at which there is no longer any overall change in the concentration of products and reactants is called the *point of chemical equilibrium*. In this state, molecules do not stop reacting; rather, the rate of the forward reaction equals the rate of the backward reaction. As a system moves toward equilibrium, the free energy change of the system becomes progressively lower and reaches its lowest point when the system is at equilibrium. It is at this point that there is no tendency for spontaneous change in either the forward or the reverse direction. The system reaches a state of maximum stability, it has no capacity to do work, and $\Delta G = 0$.

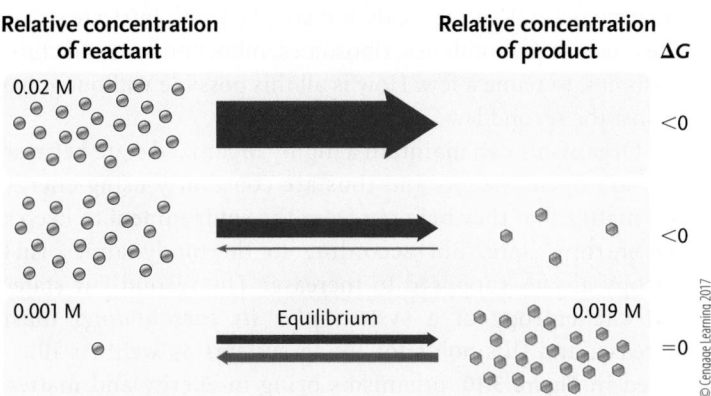

© Cengage Learning 2017

FIGURE 3.9 **Chemical reactions run to equilibrium.** No matter what quantities of glucose 1-phosphate and glucose 6-phosphate are dissolved in water, when equilibrium is attained, there will always be 95% glucose 6-phosphate and 5% glucose 1-phosphate. At equilibrium, the number of reactant molecules being converted to products equals the number of product molecules being converted back to reactants.

The point of equilibrium is related to $\Delta G$ for the reaction in that the more negative $\Delta G$, the further toward completion the reaction will move before equilibrium is established. Many reactions have a $\Delta G$ that is near zero and are thus readily **reversible** by adjusting the concentrations of products and reactants slightly.

**STUDY BREAK QUESTIONS**

1. What is the difference between a reaction that is exothermic and one that is exergonic?
2. What is the thermodynamic reason that molecules spontaneously diffuse across a membrane?
3. True or false: In a reaction that has a negative $\Delta G$, all the reactants are converted into products.

# 3.3 Thermodynamics and Life

One of the defining characteristics of life (see Chapter 22) is the ability to harness and utilize energy. In this section we focus on how living things abide by the laws of thermodynamics and yet are able to maintain a highly organized state. We expand our discussion to illustrate how energy flows through the biosphere—the regions of Earth occupied by life.

## 3.3a Life Does Not Go against the Second Law of Thermodynamics

At first glance, living systems seem to go against the second law of thermodynamics and its foundational concept that the entropy of a system and its surroundings must always increase. It is easy to think this because organisms are able to maintain themselves in a highly organized state with energy being concentrated in complex molecules. Cells can synthesize molecules like proteins and nucleic acids and are filled with intricate structures such as microtubules, ribosomes, mitochondria, and chromosomes, to name a few. How is all this possible without going against the second law?

Organisms can maintain a highly organized state because they are open systems and thus are constantly using energy and matter that they bring in from the environment to keep a low-entropy state. But according to thermodynamics isn't entropy always supposed to increase? The second law states that the entropy of a system *plus its surroundings* must increase, and this holds for living systems as well. As illustrated in **Figure 3.10**, organisms bring in energy and matter, but as a result of the thousands of chemical reactions that take place within cells, organisms also give off heat and by-products of metabolism, such as water and carbon dioxide, that spread out, increasing the entropy of the surroundings. The entropy of a system can be maintained in a low state but only because the entropy of its surroundings is constantly increasing.

But why do living systems have to keep consuming energy? Once all the proteins that are required to sustain life are synthesized, for example, why can't the energy-requiring process of protein synthesis stop? Once a human has fully developed and stopped growing, why can't we stop eating? Organisms need to constantly bring in energy and matter because, at a cellular level, the tendency of energy to spread out means that cellular components (molecules, organelles, etc.) are constantly breaking down (Figure 3.10). Just like a car that needs to be taken to a mechanic to have new parts installed and others repaired, the breakdown of cellular systems is an inevitable consequence of the second law and increasing entropy. New cells need to be made and old ones maintained by the continued synthesis of proteins, carbohydrates, and a myriad of other molecules. Metabolism can never stop, and living cells never reach chemical equilibrium

($\Delta G = 0$); life requires a constant supply of energy. So, while it is easy to see why elite athletes need to eat a lot, people who don't exercise at all also need to ingest well over a thousand kilocalories every day **(Figure 3.11)**. Although some of this food supplies us with the energy to use our muscles, much of the food energy we ingest is used simply to maintain our low-entropy, highly organized state (Figure 3.10).

## 3.3b The Flow of Energy through the Biosphere

Recall that Earth does not exchange matter with the rest of the universe, but it does exchange a huge amount of energy. Life exists on Earth because its position in the solar system allowed for heat from the Sun to maintain Earth at a temperature that allowed life to evolve. But it is not the heat from the Sun that the biosphere relies on as an energy source to maintain it organized state: it's the light, which is a very concentrated form of energy that exists in packets called *photons*.

Energy enters the biosphere when light energy from the Sun is transformed into chemical energy through the process of photosynthesis. By absorbing photons of light and using them to do work, photosynthetic organisms can transform molecules of $CO_2$ and water into high energy-containing molecules such as glucose. The energy in glucose in turn can drive the synthesis of a wide range of other organic molecules. As illustrated in **Figure 3.12**, the remainder of the biosphere (e.g., animals, fungi) is sustained by consuming the various forms of chemical energy produced by photosynthetic organisms.

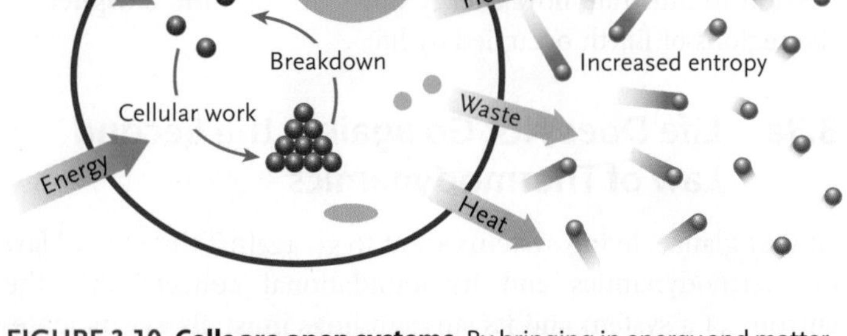

FIGURE 3.10 **Cells are open systems.** By bringing in energy and matter from their surroundings, cells can do work to maintain an ordered (low entropy) state. The release of heat and waste gases into the environment increases the entropy of the surroundings.

FIGURE 3.11 **Why do we need to eat?** The average person needs to ingest about 1500 kcal per day. A significant amount of this energy is needed to maintain the low entropy state of our cells.

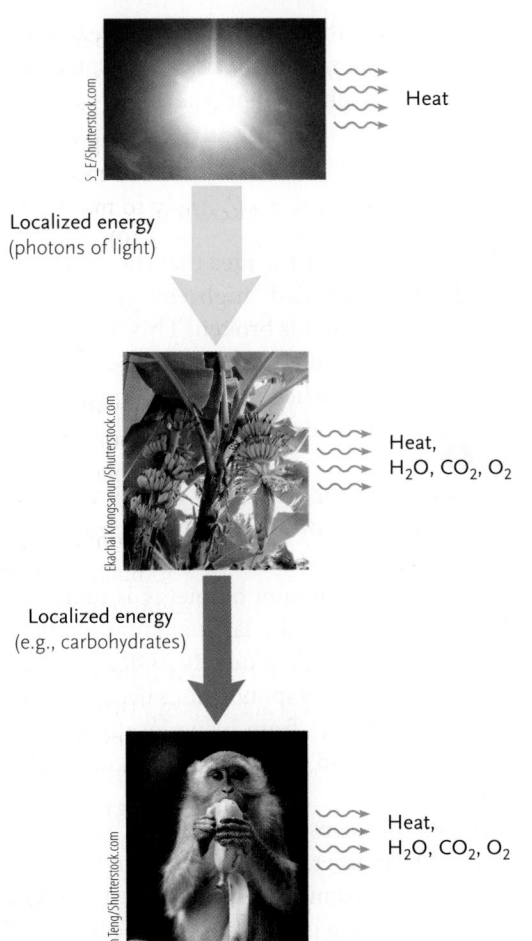

**FIGURE 3.12 Flow of energy from the Sun through the biosphere.** Living systems constantly bring in concentrated forms of energy and use them to do the work required to maintain a highly organized state. Organisms give off heat and gases (high-entropy energy).

## STUDY BREAK QUESTIONS

1. Why may someone think that life goes against the second law of thermodynamics?
2. Why can't we consume all the chemical energy produced by a plant through photosynthesis?
3. Explain in thermodynamic terms why, if you stopped eating, you would die.

# 3.4 Overview of Metabolism

The collection of all the chemical reactions present within a cell or organism is defined as **metabolism**. Many different metabolic reactions take place within a cell, resulting in the synthesis or breakdown of a huge variety of molecules. Most metabolic reactions fall into pathways, and there are two fundamental types of pathways: those that require energy to build molecules and those that release energy by breaking down molecules. A lot of the metabolism of the biosphere involves the energy transformation reactions of two metabolic pathways: respiration and

photosynthesis. The details of these processes, as well as others, such as protein synthesis, are the focus of later chapters. In this section, our attention is broader as we look at the central features of how energy is transformed during metabolism.

## 3.4a Metabolism Consists of Catabolic and Anabolic Pathways

The individual reactions that make up metabolism are grouped into *pathways*: starting molecules undergo stepwise transformation, one reaction at a time, generating one or more final products. For example, the hormone testosterone is the end-product of a five-reaction pathway that starts with the molecule cholesterol.

A series of chemical reactions that results in the breakdown of larger, more-complex molecules into smaller, less-complex ones is called a **catabolic pathway**. Energy is released in a catabolic pathway because, overall, the free energy of the final product(s) of the pathway is *less* than the free energy of the starting molecule(s) (**Figure 3.13**). Perhaps the best example of a catabolic pathway is cellular respiration: energy-rich food molecules are converted into simpler, lower-energy molecules such as $H_2O$ and $CO_2$. An **anabolic pathway**, on the other hand, is a series of reactions that results in the synthesis of larger, more-complex molecules from simpler starting molecules (Figure 3.13). Anabolic pathways, which are often called *biosynthetic pathways*, require energy because, overall, the free energy of the product(s) of the pathway is *greater* than the free energy of the starting molecule(s). The biosynthesis of specific carbohydrates, proteins, and nucleic acids are examples of anabolic pathways as is the process of photosynthesis (See Chapter 6).

A key feature of metabolism also shown in Figure 3.13 is that catabolic and anabolic pathways are linked through chemical energy. Because biosynthetic (anabolic) reactions result in

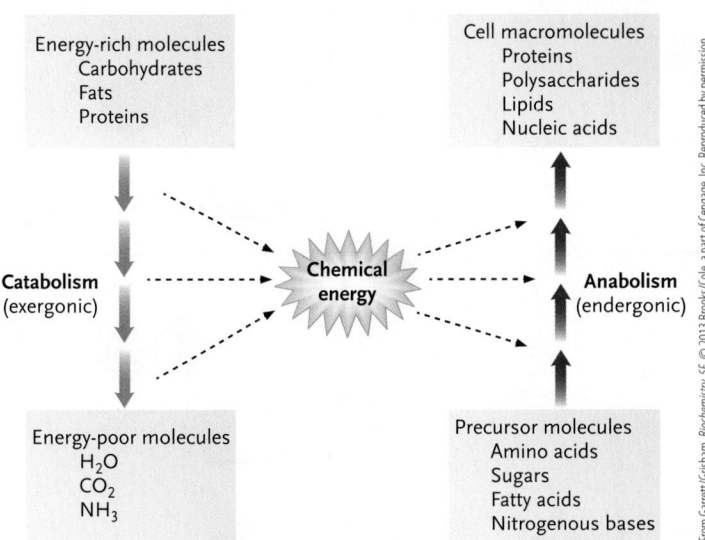

From Garrett/Grisham. Biochemistry, 5E. © 2013 Brooks/Cole, a part of Cengage, Inc. Reproduced by permission. www.cengage.com/permissions

**FIGURE 3.13 Energy relationship between the pathways of catabolism and anabolism.** Energy released from the breakdown of energy-rich molecules can be harnessed by anabolic reactions, which use the energy to generate macromolecules.

the formation of new covalent bonds, they require a source of chemical energy. The energy comes from the catabolic breakdown of high-energy molecules. The specific form of chemical energy that most often links the two types of pathways is the molecule adenosine triphosphate (ATP).

## 3.4b ATP Hydrolysis Provides Free Energy

All forms of life require a readily usable form of chemical energy. Like using dollars as an accepted currency to buy things, it would be advantageous to the cell if there were a single, widely accepted form of energy currency. Not only would this chemical currency be used for biosynthetic reactions, but ideally it could be readily transformed into mechanical energy required for muscle contraction or electrical energy required for the conduction of nerve impulses. The nucleotide ATP is that energy currency.

As shown in **Figure 3.14a**, ATP consists of a five-carbon sugar, ribose, linked to the **nitrogenous base** adenine joined to a chain of three phosphate groups. ATP is a source of free energy as a result of its reaction with water (Figure 3.14b). In

this *hydrolysis* reaction, the terminal phosphate bond is broken, resulting in the formation of adenosine diphosphate and a molecule of inorganic phosphate (abbreviated $P_i$):

$$ATP + H_2O \rightarrow ADP + P_i$$

$$\Delta G = -7.3 \text{ kcal/mol}$$

**CONCEPT FIX** You may have the idea that the energy associated with ATP is due to a so-called "high-energy phosphate bond" that releases energy when it is broken. This thinking, however, is incorrect. A foundational concept of chemistry is that energy is never released when bonds break; in fact, energy is required to break bonds. Energy is released when new bonds are formed. ⬢

So what is it about the chemistry of ATP that explains the negative $\Delta G$ when it is hydrolyzed? The electrostatic repulsion between the terminal phosphate and the rest of the molecule means a relatively small amount of energy is required to break that bond. Compare that to the large amount of energy that is released when the more stable products ADP and Pi are formed. The hydrolysis of ATP is also spontaneous because of an increase in entropy as energy moves from being localized on one molecule (ATP) to being spread out on two molecules (ADP and $P_i$) (Figure 3.14b).

The fact that all forms of life use ATP as their dominant energy currency is another piece of evidence that points to all forms of life sharing a common ancestor (see Chapter 21). This is because there is nothing particularly unique to ATP. There are a number of other phosphate-containing compounds, including the other nucleotide triphosphates, GTP, CTP, and TTP (see *The Purple Pages*) that liberate comparable free energy to ATP when they are hydrolyzed. Thus, the fact that life adopted ATP doesn't reflect a unique capability of ATP, but rather perhaps simply reflects a chance event that occurred as early as 3.5 billion years ago.

## 3.4c Energy Coupling Links the Energy of ATP Breakdown to Reactions

Although ATP releases free energy when it is hydrolyzed, this does not mean that it is an especially reactive molecule. In fact, the rate of ATP hydrolysis in an aqueous environment such as the cytosol of a cell is slow. If ATP were very reactive, it would be impossible for metabolism involving ATP to be tightly controlled. Its rapid hydrolysis would simply release heat, and not only can cells not use heat to do work, too much heat can cause damage and even cell death.

So how do cells harness the free energy available from ATP hydrolysis to do cellular work? To help answer this question, let's look at a very common anabolic reaction: the synthesis of glutamine. This amino acid is synthesized from glutamic acid and ammonia:

$$\text{glutamic acid} + NH_3 \rightarrow \text{glutamine} + H_2O$$

$$\Delta G = +3.4 \text{ kcal/mol}$$

**a. Chemical structure of ATP**

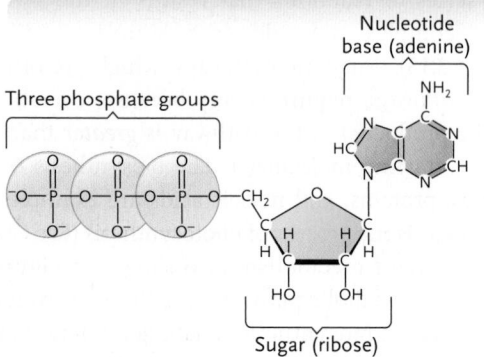

**b. Hydrolysis reaction**

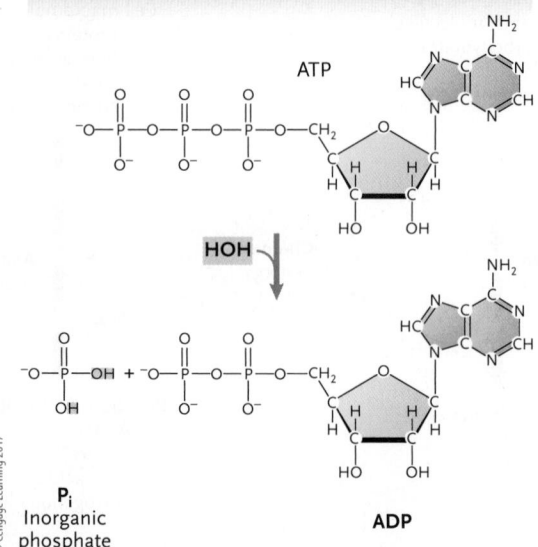

© Cengage Learning 2017

**FIGURE 3.14 ATP, the primary molecule used to supply the energy for biosynthetic reactions. (a)** Structure of one ATP molecule. **(b)** Reaction of ATP hydrolysis. Energy is released during the formation of ADP and $P_i$.

The positive $\Delta G$ shows that the reaction will not occur as written, and yet molecules of glutamine are synthesized within your cells all the time. How is that possible? During metabolism, glutamine is synthesized through a process called **energy coupling**: an endergonic reaction occurs by being coupled to an exergonic reaction (**Figure 3.15**). For the majority of energy coupling reactions, the energy is provided by the exergonic breakdown of ATP.

Looking at Figure 3.15a, it is easiest to think of energy coupling as the joining of two independent reactions, one spontaneous (exergonic) and the other nonspontaneous (endergonic). The free-energy changes of the two reactions can be added to yield the free-energy change of the **coupled reaction**. The sum of the two reaction free energies, ATP breakdown ($\Delta G = -7.3$ kcal/mol) and glutamine synthesis ($\Delta G = 3.4$ kcal/mol), yields $-3.9$ kcal/mol. This tells us that the coupled reaction will be spontaneous.

Within a cell, the actual reaction mechanism of the coupled reaction is distinctly different from the two independent reactions shown in Figure 3.15a although the overall $\Delta G$ remains simply the sum of the two reactions. Energy coupling during metabolism (Figure 3.15b) requires an enzyme that binds both a molecule of ATP and a molecule of substrate, and facilitates the transfer of the terminal phosphate group from ATP to the substrate. The addition of phosphate to the substrate increases its free energy and makes it more reactive, allowing the second reaction to occur spontaneously (Figure 3.15b). An important aspect of energy coupling is that the inclusion of an enzyme facilitates the movement of potential energy from a molecule of ATP to the substrate molecule through transfer of the terminal phosphate group. The energy-wasting hydrolysis of ATP is prevented in the first reaction shown in Figure 3.15b because water cannot access the site of catalysis on the enzyme. The hydrolysis of ATP is not complete until $P_i$ is released in the second reaction.

### 3.4d Cells Also Couple Reactions to Regenerate ATP

We have just seen how the hydrolysis of ATP is an exergonic reaction that can be harnessed through energy coupling reactions to make biosynthetic reactions proceed spontaneously. These coupling reactions occur continuously in living cells, consuming a tremendous amount of ATP. So where does the ATP for these processes come from? Some ATP is synthesized using a biosynthetic pathway that includes reactions that join ribose, adenine, and phosphate groups together; however, the vast majority of ATP is generated from recombining ADP and $P_i$.

If ATP breakdown is an exergonic process, then ATP synthesis from ADP and $P_i$ is an endergonic process. The free energy required for ATP synthesis comes from the catabolism of molecules that contain an abundance of energy. For animals, these molecules are food: carbohydrates, fats, and proteins, all abundant sources of energy. In photosynthetic organisms, the capture of light energy is also used to synthesize ATP from ADP and $P_i$.

The continuous breakdown and resynthesis of ATP is called the **ATP cycle (Figure 3.16)**. Approximately 10 million ATP molecules are broken down and resynthesized each second in a typical cell, illustrating that this cycle operates at an astonishing rate. In fact, if ATP were not regenerated from ADP and $P_i$, it is estimated that the average human would use an estimated 75 kg of ATP per day. It makes sense that cells should never be limited in their availability of ATP. In fact, a

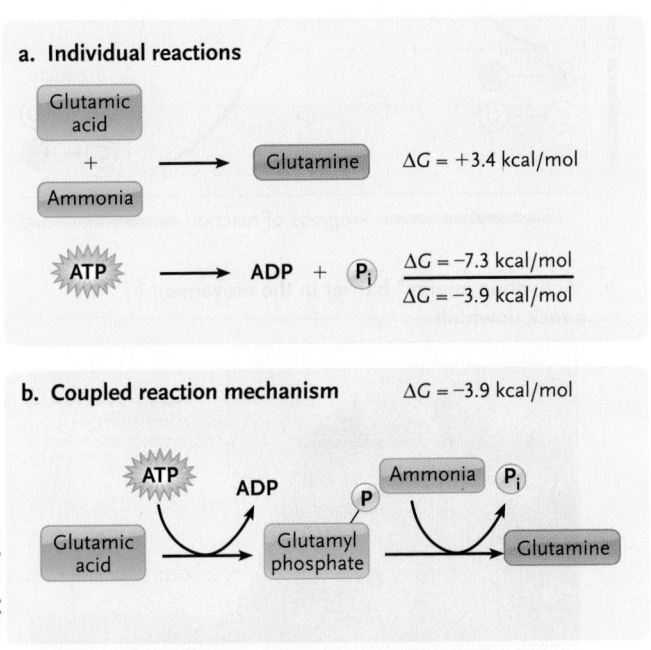

**FIGURE 3.15  An example of energy coupling.** The exergonic breakdown of ATP is linked to the endergonic biosynthesis of glutamine, a spontaneous process.

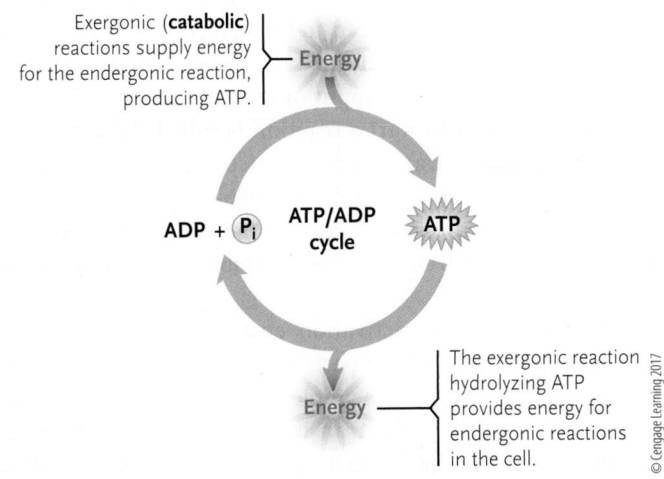

**FIGURE 3.16  The ATP/ADP cycle couples reactions releasing free energy and reactions requiring free energy**

typical cell maintains an ATP concentration that is about 1000 times greater than that of ADP.

**STUDY BREAK QUESTIONS**

1. In what ways do the end-products of catabolic pathways differ from their starting molecules?
2. In an energy coupling reaction, trace the fate of the terminal phosphate group of ATP.

## 3.5 The Role of Enzymes in Biological Reactions

So far in this chapter we have focused on the thermodynamics of energy transformation: exergonic and endergonic reactions and factors that determine whether a particular reaction will occur without an input of energy. We have avoided discussing anything about the rate of a reaction because, in fact, the laws of thermodynamics do not address how fast a process will occur, just whether or not it will occur. But the rate of a reaction is of fundamental importance to life, because most reactions must occur at very high rates for life to be sustained. In this section, we discuss the factors that control the rate of a chemical reaction and the central role played by enzymes in increasing reaction rates.

### 3.5a The Activation Energy of a Reaction Represents a Kinetic Barrier

The conversion of table sugar (sucrose) into the **monosaccharides** glucose and fructose is a spontaneous reaction, and yet a bag of sugar can sit around for decades without any detectable fructose or glucose being formed. So what is preventing this spontaneous reaction from occurring rapidly? Forget sugar, what about the planet? Given the large amounts of energy trapped in the wood of trees, and the coal and oil underground, why doesn't Earth just go up in flames?

For chemical reactions to occur, established bonds need to be broken and new bonds need to be formed. For bonds to be broken, they must first be strained or otherwise made less stable, which requires a small input of energy. The initial energy investment required to start a reaction is called the **activation energy** ($E_a$) **(Figure 3.17a)**. You will notice that Figure 3.17a is a more detailed version of Figure 3.7. Molecules that gain the necessary activation energy occupy what is called the **transition state**, in which bonds are unstable and ready to be broken.

What provides the activation energy for chemical reactions? The molecules taking part in chemical reactions are in constant motion, and reacting molecules may periodically gain enough energy to reach the transition state. But for the molecules of sucrose on the kitchen shelf, reaching the transition state is a very rare event. Supplying larger amounts of energy would allow more molecules to gain the activation energy

needed to get to the transition state and for the reaction to take place. Consider, for example, a propane torch **(Figure 3.18)**. Propane is a molecule that contains an abundance of free energy. In the presence of the $O_2$ in air, propane spontaneously decomposes into carbon dioxide and water. However, the reaction proceeds very slowly. This is because, if left undisturbed, it is a rare event for molecules of propane to acquire the energy needed in the presence of $O_2$ for combustion. Yet if you supply a stream of propane gas with a spark (see Figure 3.18b), then you provide the molecules with the energy necessary to reach the transition state, resulting in combustion. The heat released from the initial combustion event sustains the continuous burning of the propane stream.

### 3.5b Enzymes Accelerate Reactions by Reducing the Activation Energy

If you walk through a typical, undergraduate chemistry lab, you will find that the benches have Bunsen burners, which are

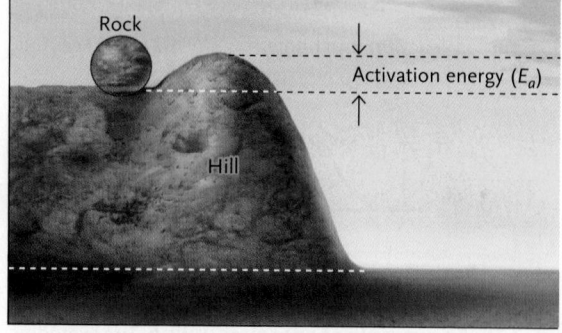

a.

b. "Activation energy" barrier in the movement of a rock downhill

**FIGURE 3.17 The concept of activation energy ($E_a$) for an exergonic reaction**

used to provide the heat for a range of chemical reactions. Chemists routinely use heat to provide the energy needed for reactant molecules to get to the transition state and thus speed up the rate of a reaction. In biology, using heat to speed up a reaction is problematic for two reasons: First, high temperatures destroy the structural components of cells, particularly proteins, and can result in cell death. Second, an increase in temperature would speed up all possible chemical reactions in a cell, and thus the precise regulation of metabolic pathways would be lost. So how can you increase the rate of specific reactions without raising the temperature? You can use a **catalyst**, which is a chemical agent that speeds up the rate of a reaction without itself being chemically altered. The most common biological catalyst is a group of proteins called **enzymes**.

Looking back at Figure 3.17, you can think of the transition state as a kinetic barrier: it is what prevents spontaneous

reactions from occurring rapidly because so few molecules at a given time acquire the energy necessary to get to the transition state. If you could lower this energy requirement, then many more molecules would react. This is exactly what enzymes do: they increase the rate of a reaction by decreasing the activation energy (**Figure 3.19**). Since the rate of a reaction (i.e., number of molecules of product made per second) is proportional to the number of reactant molecules that can get to the transition state, lowering the transition state results in a higher rate of reaction.

**CONCEPT FIX** There are two common misconceptions about the role of enzymes in biochemical reactions that we need to fix before moving on. First, although enzymes decrease the activation energy of a reaction, they do not alter the thermodynamics of a reaction. The change in the free energy ($\Delta G$) of a reaction is not altered by the presence of an enzyme. Second, enzymes do not supply energy to a reaction. Although enzymes are involved in energy coupling reactions (see Section 3.4c), the chemical energy is supplied by something else—usually ATP—not by the enzyme. ⬡

## 3.5c Enzymes Combine with Reactants and Are Released Unchanged

In biochemical reactions, an enzyme combines briefly with reacting molecules and is released unchanged when the reaction is complete. For example, the enzyme hexokinase (**Figure 3.20**) catalyzes the following reaction:

$$\text{glucose} + \text{ATP} \rightarrow \text{glucose 6-phosphate} + \text{ADP}$$

The reactant that an enzyme acts on is called the enzyme's *substrate*, or *substrates* if the enzyme binds two or more molecules. Each type of enzyme catalyzes the reaction of only a single type of molecule or a group of closely related molecules. This enzyme specificity explains why the metabolism of a typical cell involves thousands of different enzymes. Notice in Figure 3.20

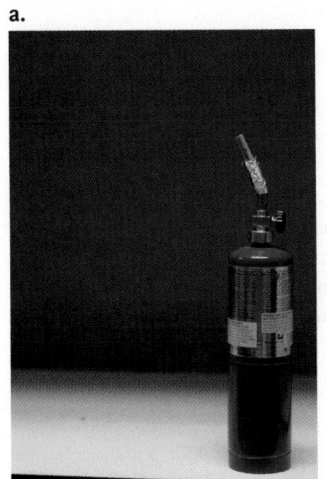
a.

b.

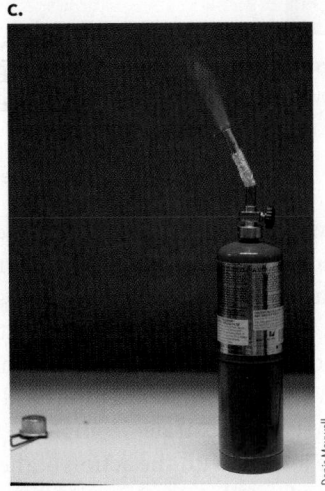
c.

Denis Maxwell

**FIGURE 3.18 Combustion of propane. (a)** The combustion of propane is a spontaneous reaction; however, the activation energy is a barrier that prevents its rapid breakdown. **(b)** When a spark is provided, propane obtains the energy required to attain the transition state. **(c)** The initial heat generated sustains continuous propane burning.

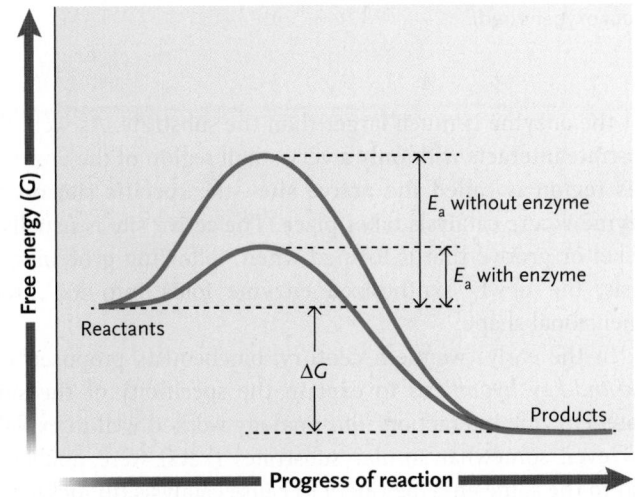

**FIGURE 3.19 Enzymes lower the activation energy ($E_a$) of a reaction**

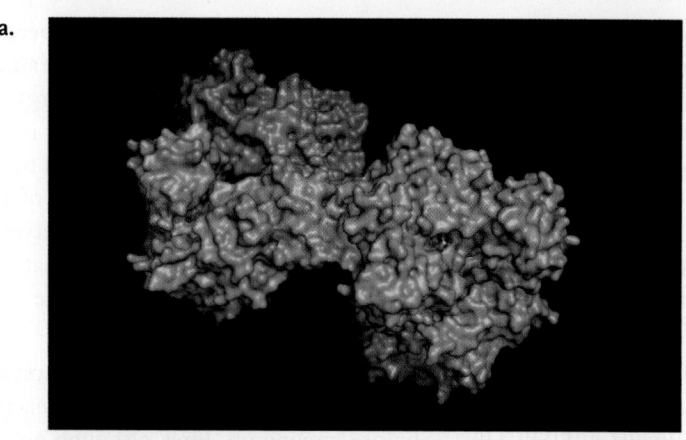

a.

Like other enzymes, hexokinase has an active site where specific substrates bind and where catalysis occurs. As shown by the boxed region, the active site is a very small part of the overall enzyme.

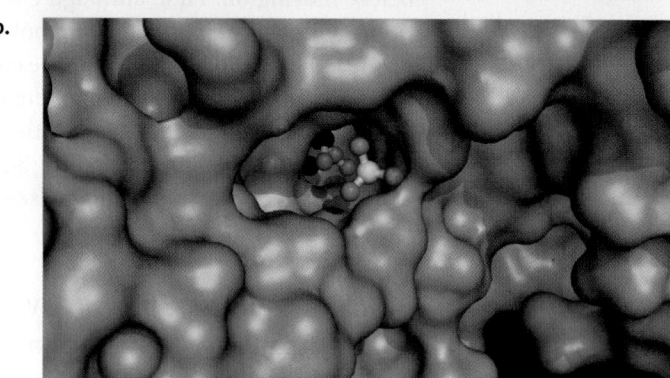

b.

A close-up showing glucose and phosphate within the active site.

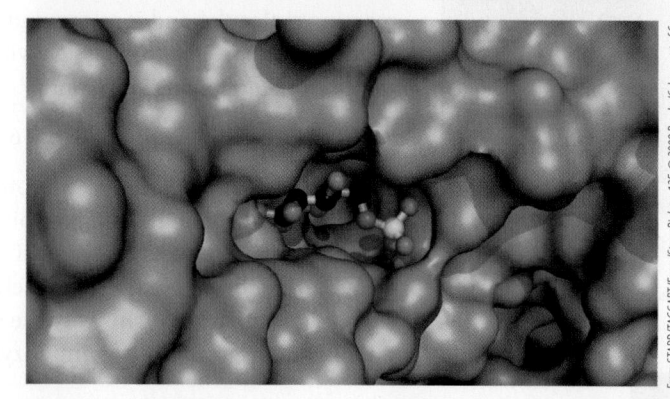

c.

The glucose has bonded with the phosphate. The product of the reaction, glucose 6-phosphate, is shown leaving the active site.

From STARR/TAGGART/Evers/Starr. *Biology, 12E.* © 2009 Brooks/Cole, a part of Cengage, Inc. Reproduced by permission. www.cengage.com/permissions

**FIGURE 3.20** **This model of the enzyme hexokinase shows the catalysis of glucose with phosphate, forming glucose 6-phosphate.** The glucose is represented by black (carbon) and red (oxygen) spheres, and the phosphate group is shown with the phosphorus atom (yellow sphere) bonded to four oxygens (red).

that the enzyme is much larger than the substrate. As well, the substrate interacts with only a very small region of the enzyme. This region is called the **active site**—the specific site on an enzyme where catalysis takes place. The active site is usually a pocket or groove that is formed when, following protein synthesis, the newly synthesized enzyme folds into its three-dimensional shape.

In the early twentieth century, biochemists proposed the *lock-and-key hypothesis* to explain the specificity of the substrate–enzyme interaction. The analogy worked well to explain how even somewhat similar substrates (keys) were unable to bind to the same enzyme (lock) to cause catalysis (unlocking of the door). However, more recently, this hypothesis has been superseded by what is known as the *induced-fit hypothesis*. Research has shown that unlike locks, enzymes are not rigid objects but instead are flexible. Just before substrate binding, the enzyme changes its shape (**conformation**) so that the active site becomes even more precise in its ability to bind the substrate.

As shown in **Figure 3.21**, the enzyme binds to the substrate, forming an enzyme–substrate complex. Catalysis occurs when the two are joined, with the action of the enzyme converting the substrate (or substrates) into one or more products. Because enzymes are released unchanged after a reaction, enzyme molecules can rapidly bind to other substrate molecules, catalyzing the same reaction again, repeating what is called the *enzyme cycle* (see Figure 3.21). The rate at which enzymes catalyze reactions varies widely depending on the specifics of the enzyme and substrates involved: typical rates vary from a low of about 100 reactions per second up to a high of 10 million reactions per second!

Many enzymes require a **cofactor**, a nonprotein group that binds very precisely to the enzyme. Cofactors are often metals, such as iron, copper, zinc, or manganese. Although most cells need very small amounts of these metals, they are absolutely essential for the catalytic activity of the enzyme to which they bind. Some cofactors, called **coenzymes,** are organic molecules that are often derived from vitamins.

### 3.5d Enzymes Reduce the Activation Energy by Inducing the Transition State

We know that enzymes reduce the activation energy of a reaction, but how do they do it? An enzyme uses at least one of three basic mechanisms to lower the energy required to get to the transition state. These mechanisms are shown in **Figure 3.22**.

Regardless of the mechanism used by a specific enzyme, the binding of the substrate to the active site results in the substrate attaining the transition state conformation—its bonds strained and ready to be broken. Without the enzyme, substrate molecules would also be able to acquire the transition state, it's just that for most reactions this would not occur very often.

**1.** *Bringing the reacting molecules together.* Reacting molecules can assume the transition state only when they collide with sufficient energy and in the correct orientation. Binding to an enzyme's active site brings the reactants together in the right orientation for catalysis to occur.

Bring reacting molecules close together

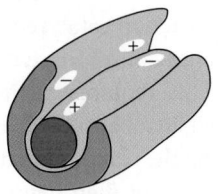

**2.** *Exposing the reactant molecule to altered charge environments that promote catalysis.* In some systems, the active site of the enzyme may contain ionic groups whose positive or negative charges alter the substrate in a way that favours catalysis.

Charge interactions

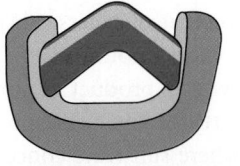

**3.** *Changing the shape of a substrate molecule.* The active site may strain or distort substrate molecules into a conformation that mimics the transition state.

Distort or strain substrate molecules

**FIGURE 3.22  The binding of substrate(s) to an active site results in the substrate acquiring the transition state conformation**

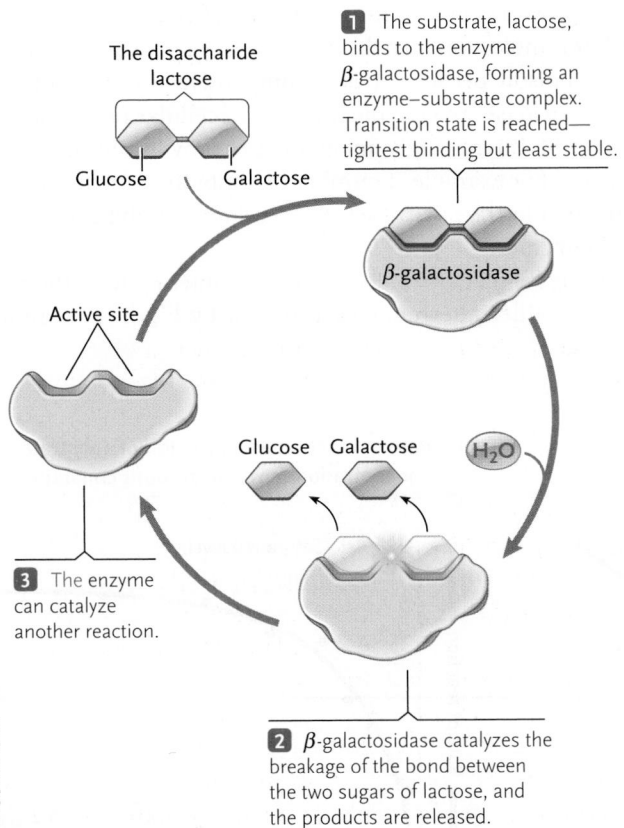

The disaccharide lactose

Glucose    Galactose

**1** The substrate, lactose, binds to the enzyme β-galactosidase, forming an enzyme–substrate complex. Transition state is reached—tightest binding but least stable.

β-galactosidase

Active site

Glucose    Galactose    H₂O

**3** The enzyme can catalyze another reaction.

**2** β-galactosidase catalyzes the breakage of the bond between the two sugars of lactose, and the products are released.

© Cengage Learning 2017

**FIGURE 3.21  The catalytic cycle of an enzyme.** Shown is the enzyme β-galactosidase, which cleaves the sugar lactose to produce glucose and galactose.

The addition of an enzyme simply enables many more molecules to reach the transition state. This is fundamentally why enzymes increase the rate of a reaction.

### STUDY BREAK QUESTIONS

1. Distinguish between the activation energy of a reaction and the transition state.
2. Which of the following aspects of a reaction is changed by the addition of an enzyme: free energy of products, $\Delta G$, requirement for energy, rate?
3. A mutation to the gene that codes for the enzyme hexokinase may result in the enzyme that is synthesized being unable to bind glucose. Why might this be the case?

## 3.6  Factors That Affect Enzyme Activity

Enzymes play a critical role in metabolism. Because of this, regulating how they operate is central to controlling metabolism. As you would expect, a number of factors can change the activity of a particular enzyme, including changes in the concentration of substrate and other molecules that bind to enzymes. As well, changes in environmental factors, including temperature and pH, can also effect enzyme activity.

## 3.6a Enzyme and Substrate Concentrations Can Change the Rate of Catalysis

Biochemists use a wide range of approaches to studying an enzyme. These span from using the tools of molecular biology and genetics to study the structure and regulation of the gene that encodes the enzyme to sophisticated computer programs for modelling the three-dimensional structure of the enzyme and its active site. The most fundamental and central approach has been to determine the rate of the specific reaction catalyzed by a particular enzyme and how the rate changes in response to altering certain experimental parameters. This requires purifying the enzyme from the remainder of the cell, incubating it in an appropriate buffered solution, and supplying the reaction mixture with substrate. With these constituents, one can then determine the rate of catalysis, which is most often done by measuring the rate at which product of the reaction is formed—so, for example, micromoles of product made per second.

As shown in **Figure 3.23a**, in the presence of excess substrate, the rate of catalysis is proportional to the amount of enzyme. Add more enzyme and the rate at which product is formed increases. As enzyme concentration increases, the rate of product formation increases. In this system, where substrate concentration is high, what is limiting the rate of the reaction is the amount of enzyme in the reaction mixture. Look at what happens if we instead keep the enzyme constant at some intermediate concentration and change the substrate concentration from low to high. At very low concentrations, substrate molecules collide so infrequently with enzyme molecules that the rate at which the product is formed is slow (Figure 3.23b). As the substrate concentration increases, the reaction rate initially increases linearly as enzyme and substrate molecules collide more frequently. But as the constant number of enzyme molecules approaches the maximum rate at which they can combine with reactants and release products, increasing the substrate concentration has a smaller and smaller effect, and the rate of reaction eventually levels off. When the catalytic cycle (see Figure 3.21) is turning as fast as possible,

further increases in substrate concentration have no effect on the reaction rate. At this point, the enzyme is said to be saturated with substrate.

## 3.6b Enzyme Activity Can Be Altered by Competitive and Noncompetitive Interactions

The rate of an enzyme-catalyzed reaction can be altered by a wide range of molecules that bind to the enzyme. A number of molecules that alter enzyme activity do so because they are structurally similar to the normal substrate of the enzyme and therefore can bind to the active site. Regulation of this type is called *competitive regulation* because the molecule competes with the substrate for the active site (**Figure 3.24a**). Competitive regulation is often referred to as **competitive inhibition** because the presence of the competitor decreases the rate of the normal substrate-dependent reaction.

Competitive regulators differ in how strongly they bind to the active site. Some molecules bind through covalent bonding, resulting in enzyme inhibition that is irreversible. However, many inhibitors bind to the active site weakly, through noncovalent interactions, resulting in inhibition that is readily reversible. As shown in Figure 3.24b, one trait of reversible competitive inhibition is that it can be overcome by a high substrate concentration.

Because of their ability to act on critical enzymes, many inhibitor molecules can be toxic. For example, cyanide is a potent poison because it is a competitive inhibitor of cytochrome oxidase, an enzyme involved in cellular respiration (see Chapter 5). Interestingly, many drugs act by inhibiting specific enzymes. For example, a number of antibiotics, including penicillin, are effective because they target and inhibit specific bacterial enzymes.

Some regulatory molecules do not interact with the active site, but rather alter enzyme function by binding to another

**FIGURE 3.23 Effect of increasing (a) enzyme concentration or (b) substrate concentration on the rate of an enzyme-catalyzed reaction**

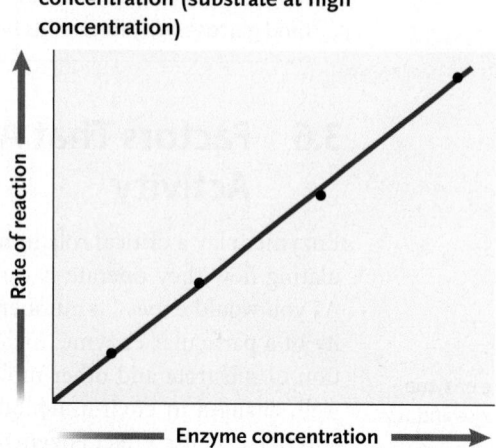

a. Rate of reaction as a function of enzyme concentration (substrate at high concentration)

Rate of reaction

Enzyme concentration ➡

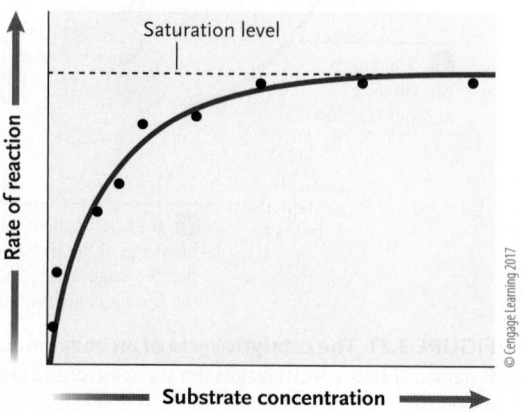

b. Rate of reaction as a function of substrate concentration (enzyme amount constant)

Saturation level

Rate of reaction

Substrate concentration ➡

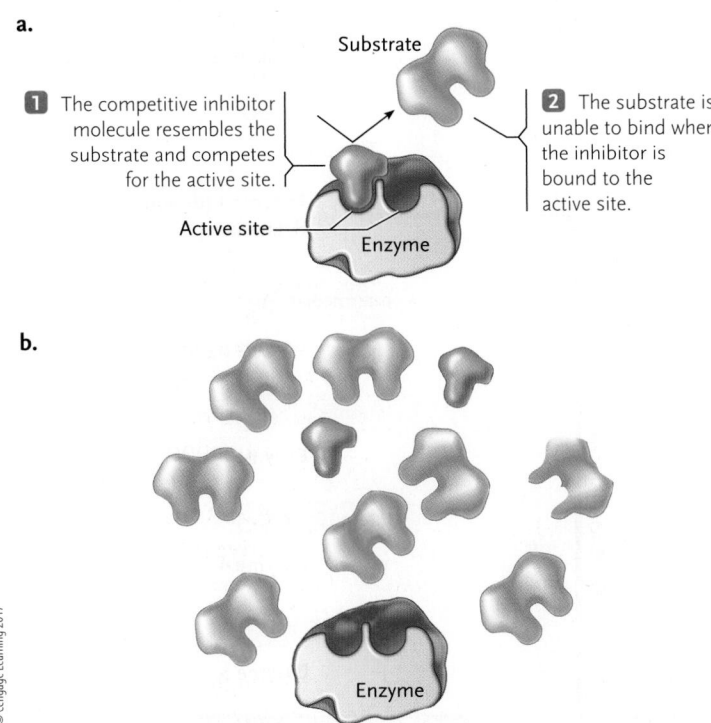

**a.**

Substrate

**1** The competitive inhibitor molecule resembles the substrate and competes for the active site.

**2** The substrate is unable to bind when the inhibitor is bound to the active site.

Active site

Enzyme

**b.**

Enzyme

© Cengage Learning 2017

**FIGURE 3.24** **(a)** Competitive regulation of enzyme activity. **(b)** The inhibition of enzyme activity by a competitive inhibitor can be overcome by increasing the amount of substrate relative to inhibitor.

location on the enzyme. These regulatory molecules do not compete with substrate molecules and result in what is referred to as *noncompetitive regulation* (**Figure 3.25**). Competitive regulation results in inhibition of normal enzyme function; in noncompetitive regulation, molecules that interact with the enzyme can cause an increase or decrease in enzyme function, depending upon the molecule and the enzyme.

In noncompetitive regulation, enzyme activity is controlled by the reversible binding of a regulatory molecule to what is often referred to as the **allosteric site**, a location on the enzyme outside the active site. Enzymes controlled by noncompetitive regulation are often referred to as allosteric enzymes and typically have two alternative conformations controlled from the allosteric site. In one conformation, called the *high-affinity state*, the enzyme binds strongly to its substrate; in the other conformation, the *low-affinity state*, the enzyme binds the substrate weakly or not at all. Binding with regulatory substances may induce either state: an **allosteric inhibitor** converts an enzyme from the high- to the low-affinity state, and an **allosteric activator** converts an enzyme from the low- to the high-affinity state (see Figure 3.25).

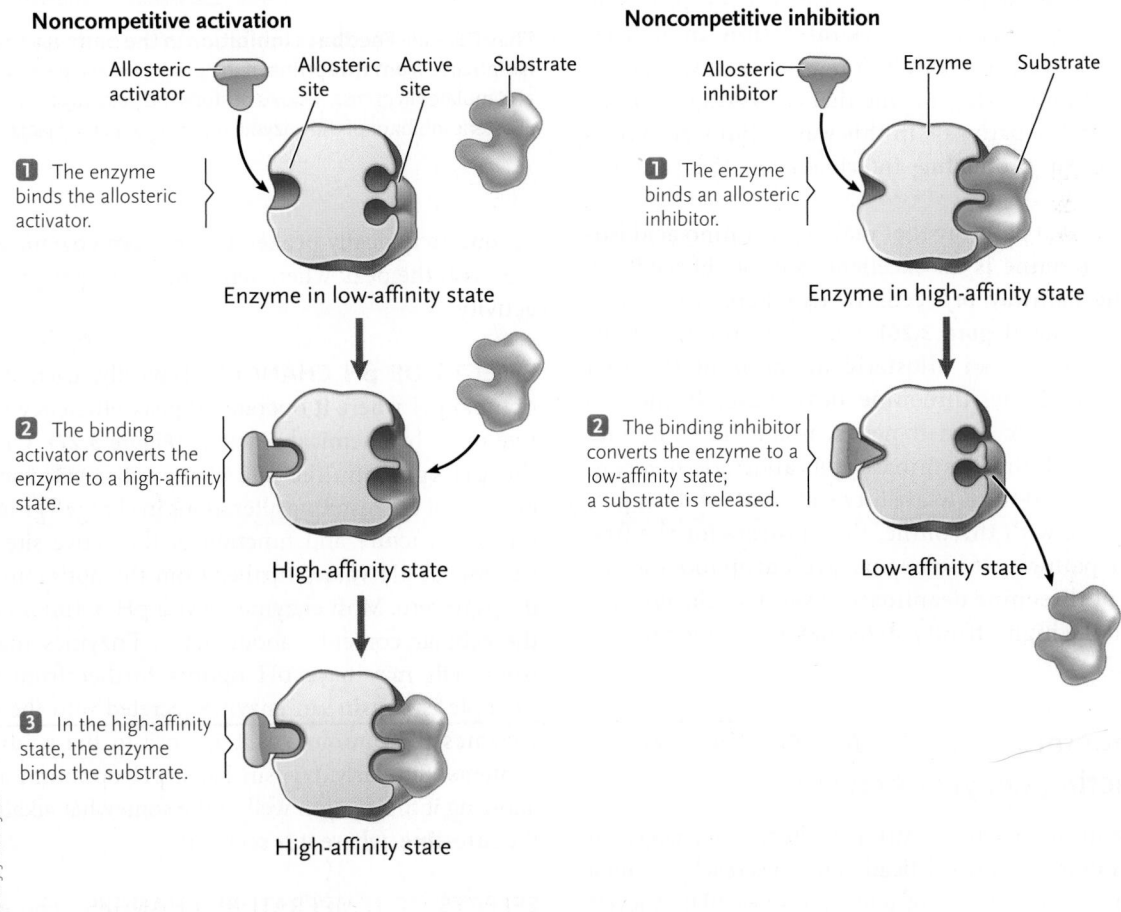

**Noncompetitive activation**

Allosteric activator — Allosteric site — Active site — Substrate

**1** The enzyme binds the allosteric activator.

Enzyme in low-affinity state

**2** The binding activator converts the enzyme to a high-affinity state.

High-affinity state

**3** In the high-affinity state, the enzyme binds the substrate.

High-affinity state

**Noncompetitive inhibition**

Allosteric inhibitor — Enzyme — Substrate

**1** The enzyme binds an allosteric inhibitor.

Enzyme in high-affinity state

**2** The binding inhibitor converts the enzyme to a low-affinity state; a substrate is released.

Low-affinity state

© Cengage Learning 2017

**FIGURE 3.25 Noncompetitive (allosteric) regulation**

## 3.6c Metabolism Is Finely Controlled by Noncompetitive Regulation

For metabolism to work efficiently, the activity of enzymes needs to be adjusted upward or downward so that the amount of product synthesized by any reaction matches the needs of the cell for the product. Considering that a typical cell contains thousands of enzymes that collectively catalyze a huge range of reactions, a key question to address is how enzyme activity is controlled to regulate overall metabolism. One mechanism of regulation is to control the abundance of specific enzymes. Since enzymes are proteins, this can be facilitated by regulating gene expression (transcription) and protein synthesis (translation). But this type of regulation lacks fine control: metabolic pathways are often adjusted in seconds, yet changes in enzyme abundance can take 30 minutes or more to occur. In addition to transcriptional and translational control, the cell is able to very rapidly regulate metabolic pathways by directly affecting enzyme activity. Two major mechanisms the cell uses to achieve this are allosteric control and covalent modification.

Frequently, allosteric inhibitors are a product of the metabolic pathway that they regulate. If the product accumulates in excess, its effect as an inhibitor automatically slows or stops the enzymatic reaction producing it. Accordingly, if the product becomes too scarce, the inhibition is reduced and the product begins to accumulate again. This type of metabolic regulation, in which the product of a reaction acts to inhibit its own synthesis, is termed **feedback inhibition**. In multireaction pathways, feedback inhibition usually involves the final product inhibiting the enzyme that catalyzes one of the early reactions in the pathway. In this way, cellular resources are not wasted in producing intermediates that are not needed.

The biochemical pathway that makes the amino acid isoleucine from threonine is an excellent example of feedback inhibition. The pathway proceeds in five steps, each catalyzed by an enzyme (**Figure 3.26**). The end-product of the pathway, isoleucine, is an allosteric inhibitor of the first enzyme of the pathway, threonine deaminase. If the cell makes more isoleucine than it needs, isoleucine combines reversibly with threonine deaminase at its allosteric site, converting the enzyme to the low-affinity state and inhibiting its ability to combine with threonine, the substrate for the first reaction in the pathway. If isoleucine levels drop too low, the allosteric site of threonine deaminase is vacated, the enzyme is converted to the high-affinity state, and isoleucine production increases.

## 3.6d Temperature and pH Are Key Factors Affecting Enzyme Activity

The activity of most enzymes is strongly altered by changes in pH and temperature. Characteristically, enzymes reach maximal activity within a narrow range of temperature or pH; at levels outside this range, enzyme activity drops off. These effects

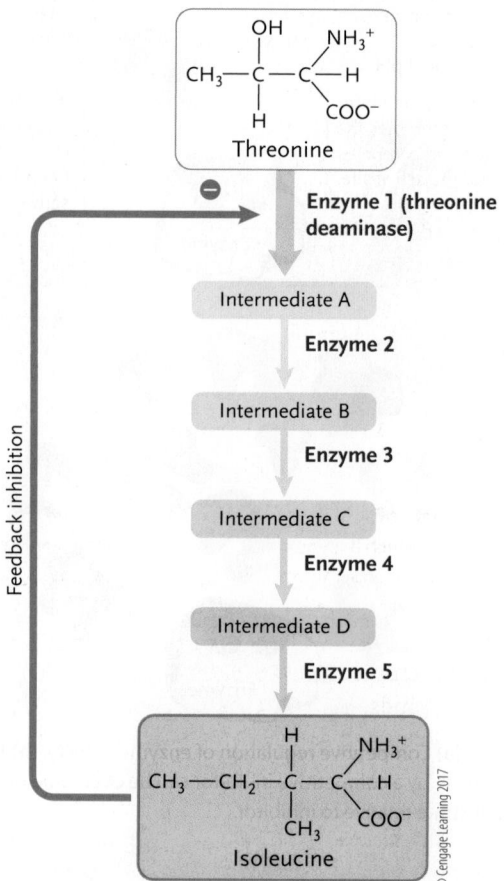

**FIGURE 3.26 Feedback inhibition in the pathway that produces isoleucine from threonine.** If the product of the pathway, isoleucine, accumulates in excess, it slows or stops the pathway by acting as an allosteric inhibitor of the enzyme that catalyzes the first step in the pathway.

produce a typically peaked curve when enzyme activity is plotted, with the peak where temperature or pH produces maximal activity.

**EFFECTS OF pH CHANGES.** Typically, each enzyme has an optimal pH where it operates at peak efficiency in speeding the rate of its biochemical reaction (**Figure 3.27**). On either side of this pH optimum, the rate of the catalyzed reaction decreases because of the resulting alterations in charged groups. The effects on the structure and function of the active site become more extreme at pH values further from the optimum, until the rate drops to zero. Most enzymes have a pH optimum near the pH of the cellular contents, about pH 7. Enzymes that are secreted from cells may have pH optima further from neutrality. An example is **pepsin**, an enzyme secreted into the stomach. This enzyme's pH optimum is 1.5, close to the **acidity** of stomach contents. Similarly, trypsin has a pH optimum at about pH 8, allowing it to function well in the somewhat alkaline contents of the **intestine**, where it is secreted.

**EFFECTS OF TEMPERATURE CHANGES.** The effects of temperature changes on enzyme activity reflect two distinct

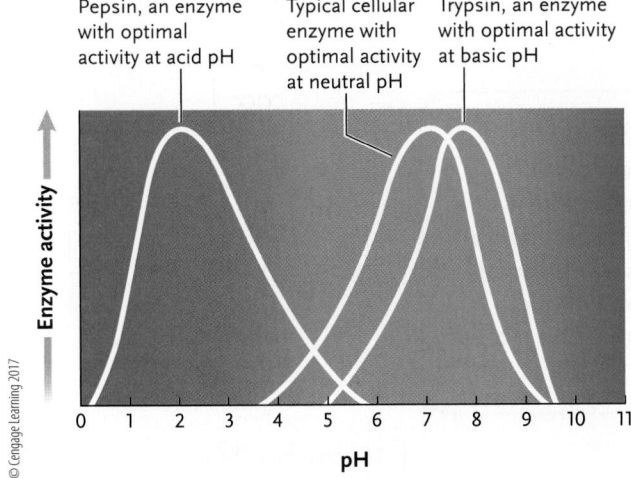

FIGURE 3.27 **Effects of pH on enzyme activity.** An enzyme typically has an optimal pH at which it is most active; at pH values above or below the optimum, the rate of enzyme activity drops off. At extreme pH values, the rate drops to zero.

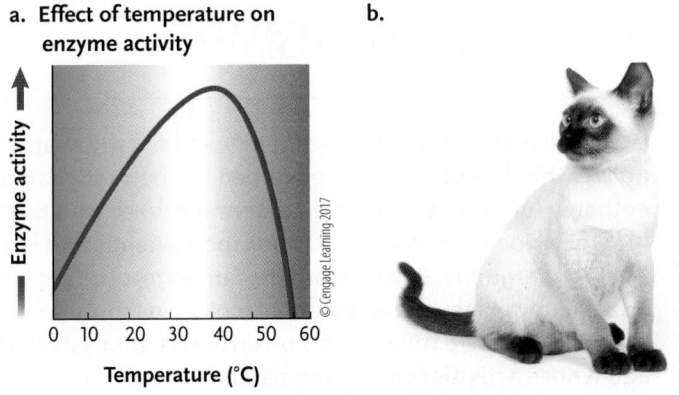

FIGURE 3.28 **Effect of temperature on enzyme activity. (a)** As the temperature rises, the rate of the catalyzed reaction increases proportionally until the temperature reaches the point at which the enzyme begins to denature. The rate drops off steeply as denaturation progresses and becomes complete. **(b)** Visible effects of environmental temperature on enzyme activity in Siamese cats. The fur on the extremities—ears, nose, paws, and tail—contains more dark brown pigment (melanin) than the rest of the body. A heat-sensitive enzyme controlling melanin production is denatured in warmer body regions, so dark pigment is not produced and fur colour is lighter.

processes. First, temperature has a general effect on chemical reactions of all kinds. As the temperature rises, the rates of chemical reactions typically increase. This effect reflects increases in the kinetic motion of all molecules, with more frequent and stronger collisions as the temperature rises, which allows more molecules to overcome the activation energy. Second, temperature has a more specific effect on all proteins, including enzymes. As the temperature rises, the kinetic motions of the amino acid chains of an enzyme increase, along with the strength and frequency of collisions between enzymes and surrounding molecules. At some point, these disturbances become strong enough to denature the enzyme: the hydrogen bonds and other forces that maintain its three-dimensional structure break, making the enzyme unfold and lose its function (see *The Purple Pages* for a more detailed description of protein denaturation). The two effects of temperature act in opposition to each other to produce characteristic changes in the rate of enzymatic catalysis **(Figure 3.28)**. In the range of 0°C to about 40°C, the reaction rate doubles for every 10°C increase in temperature. Above 40°C, the increasing kinetic motion begins to denature the enzyme, reducing the rate of increase in enzyme activity. As the temperature rises, at some point the denaturation of the enzyme causes the reaction rate to level off at a peak. Further increases cause such extensive unfolding that the reaction rate rapidly decreases to zero.

For most enzymes, the peak in activity lies between 40°C and 50°C; the drop-off becomes steep at 55°C and falls to zero at about 60°C. Thus, the rate of an enzyme-catalyzed reaction peaks at the temperature at which kinetic motion is greatest, but no significant unfolding of the enzyme has occurred. Although most enzymes have a temperature optimum between 40°C and 50°C, some have activity peaks below or above this range. For example, the enzymes of maize (corn) pollen function best near 30°C and undergo steep reductions in activity above 32°C. As a result, environmental temperatures above 32°C can seriously inhibit the growth of corn crops. Many animals living in cold regions have enzymes with much lower temperature optima than average. For example, the enzymes of arctic snow fleas are most active at 10°C. At the other extreme are the enzymes of archaeans that live in hot springs: these enzymes are so resistant to denaturation that they remain active at temperatures of 85°C or more.

## STUDY BREAK QUESTIONS

1. Why do enzyme-catalyzed reactions reach a saturation level when substrate concentration is increased?
2. Distinguish between competitive and noncompetitive inhibition.
3. Explain why the activity of an enzyme will eventually decrease to zero as the temperature rises.

# Summary Illustration

Living systems require a constant influx of energy, which they harness and utilize. This flow of energy is governed by thermodynamics. Both changes in enthalpy ($\Delta H$) and entropy ($\Delta S$) determine whether a process is spontaneous ($-\Delta G$, exergonic) or whether it is nonspontaneous and requires an input of energy ($+\Delta G$, endergonic). Energy from the Sun enters the biosphere and is transformed into chemical energy and essential molecules through reactions in metabolic pathways. These pathways rely on enzymes, catalysts that increase reaction rates and whose activities can be regulated.

What determines whether a reaction is exergonic or endergonic?

$$\Delta G = \Delta H - T\Delta S$$

The change in heat content ($\Delta H$) and entropy ($\Delta S$) can both influence the $\Delta G$ of a reaction.

$$C_3H_8\ (g) + 5O_2\ (g) \longrightarrow 3CO_2\ (g) + 4H_2O\ (g)$$

Combustion of propane, shown above, is exergonic. Why is that? (i) Energy released during bond formation in the products is greater than the energy needed to break the bonds in the reactants, and (ii) there is a greater number of product molecules than reacting molecules.

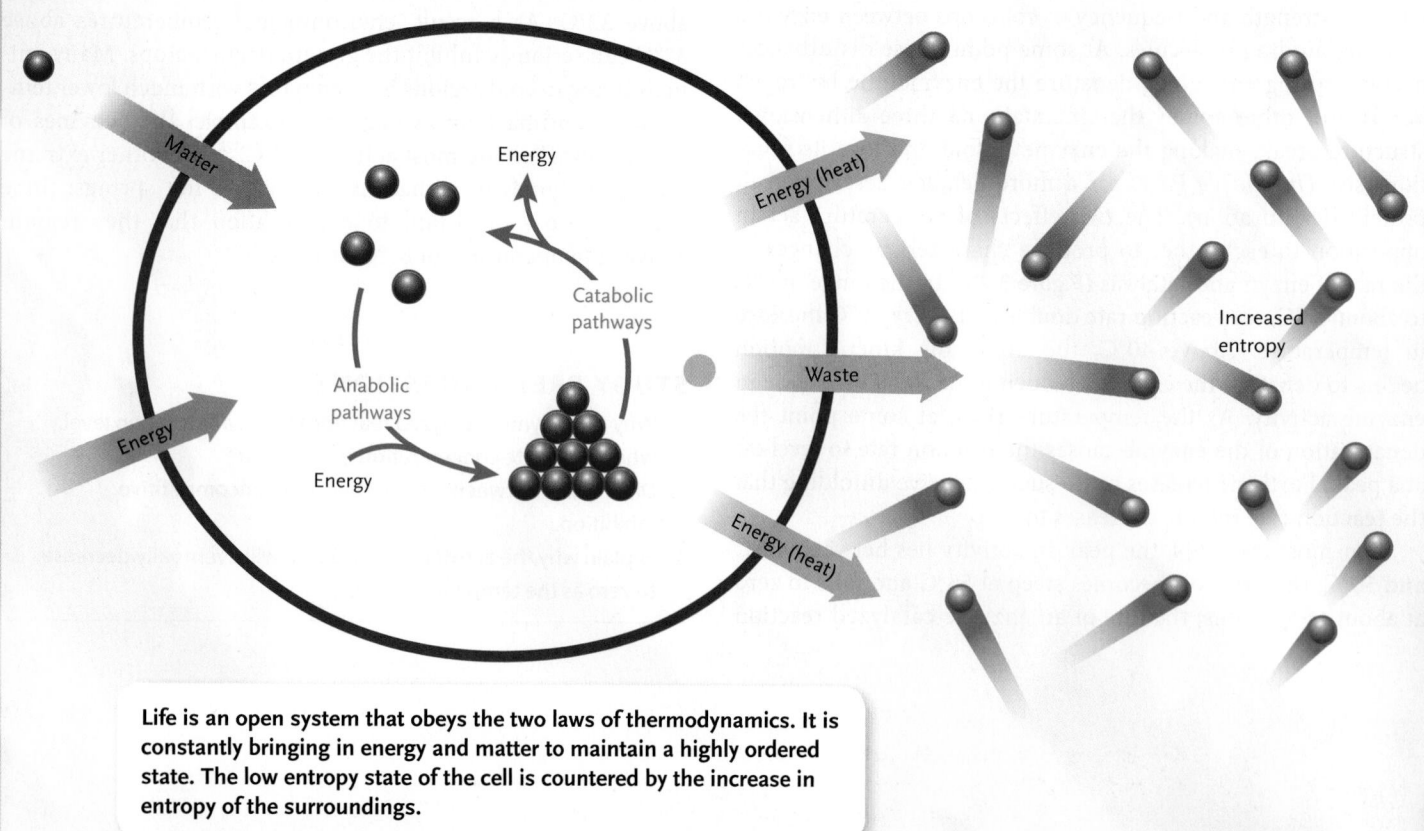

Life is an open system that obeys the two laws of thermodynamics. It is constantly bringing in energy and matter to maintain a highly ordered state. The low entropy state of the cell is countered by the increase in entropy of the surroundings.

## ATP links exergonic reactions to endergonic reactions

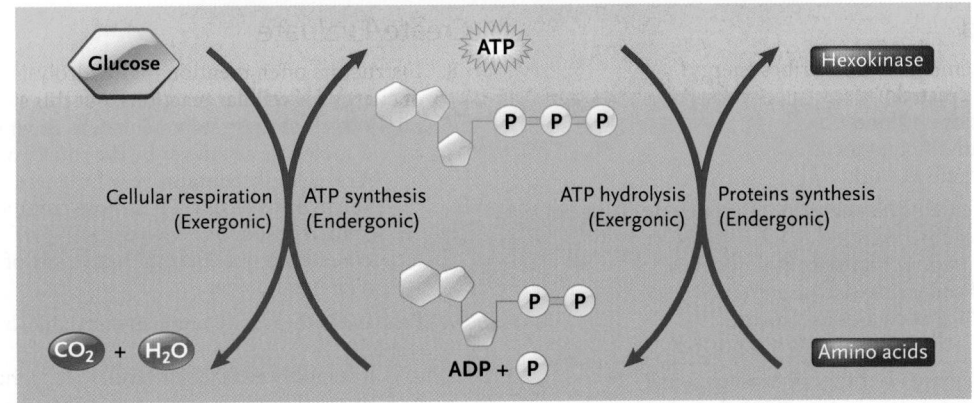

Glucose

ATP

Hexokinase

Cellular respiration (Exergonic)

ATP synthesis (Endergonic)

P—P—P

ATP hydrolysis (Exergonic)

Proteins synthesis (Endergonic)

$CO_2$ + $H_2O$

P—P

ADP + P

Amino acids

## Enzymes lower the activation energy for a reaction

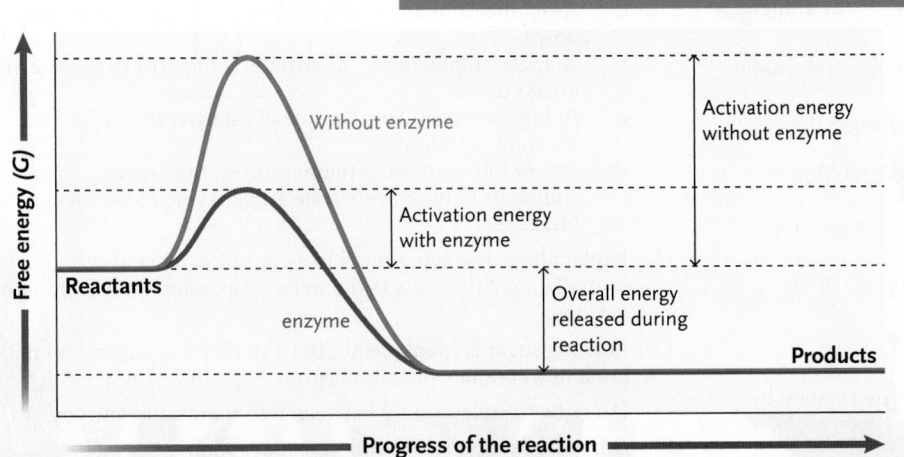

Free energy (*G*)

Without enzyme

Activation energy without enzyme

Activation energy with enzyme

Reactants

enzyme

Overall energy released during reaction

Products

Progress of the reaction

Look at this! By themselves, enzymes don't change the $\Delta G$ for a reaction. The path is different, but not the start or end points.

## Metabolism can be controlled by activating and inhibiting pathway enzymes

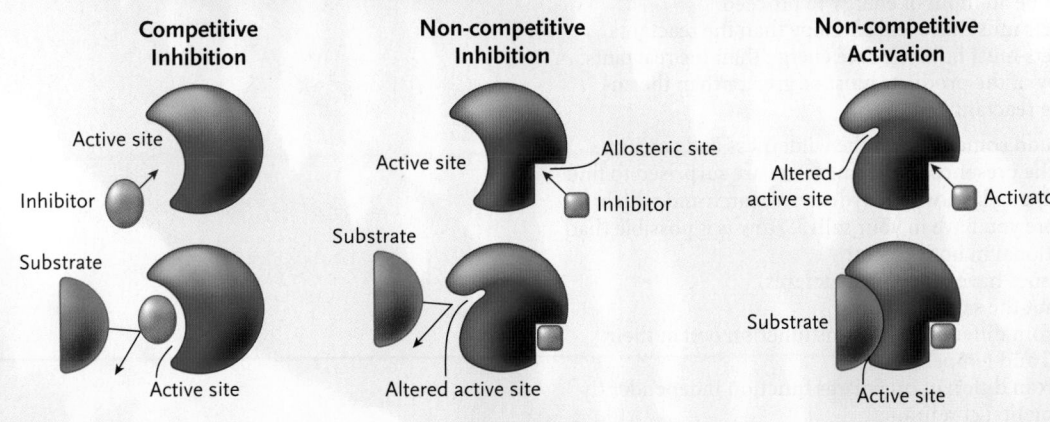

**Competitive Inhibition**

Active site

Inhibitor

Substrate

Active site

**Non-competitive Inhibition**

Active site

Allosteric site

Inhibitor

Substrate

Altered active site

**Non-competitive Activation**

Altered active site

Activator

Substrate

Active site

Factors that affect enzyme activity include environmental conditions (e.g., temperature, pH), concentration of enzyme and/or substrate, and (shown here) interactions with molecules that (i) compete with the substrate for active-site binding or (ii) bind to the enzyme and cause a change in its conformation.

# SELF-TEST QUESTIONS

## Recall/Understand

1. Which of these statements *best* describes energy?
   a. Energy can be created.
   b. Energy is the same as food.
   c. Energy exists in different forms.
   d. Energy is the same as work.

2. Which of these statements *best* describes the entropy change in specific matter?
   a. The entropy of vapour increases as it liquefies.
   b. The entropy of water increases as it freezes.
   c. The entropy of ice decreases as it melts.
   d. The entropy of water increases as it vaporizes.

3. Which of these statements *best* describes an enzyme?
   a. It is a protein that decreases the $\Delta G$ of an endergonic reaction.
   b. It is a protein that lowers the energy of activation.
   c. It is a protein that can make an endergonic reaction proceed spontaneously.
   d. It is a protein having a molecule that can bind only a single substrate molecule at any single time.

4. Which of these statements applies only to noncompetitive inhibition of an enzyme-catalyzed reaction?
   a. The process of noncompetitive inhibition changes the conformation of the enzyme.
   b. The inhibitory molecule in noncompetitive inhibition is similar to the normal substrate.
   c. Noncompetitive inhibition decreases the rate at which the product is made.
   d. The process of noncompetitive inhibition results in the enzyme becoming permanently inactive.

## Apply/Analyze

5. Which of the following is a good example of a closed system in thermodynamics?
   a. the universe itself
   b. a saucepan of water with a lid heating on a stove
   c. an ocean
   d. a dead organism

6. For a reaction to be exergonic, which of the following must occur?
   a. There must be an input of energy to proceed.
   b. The products must have less enthalpy than the reactants.
   c. The products must have less free energy than the reactants.
   d. The entropy of the products must be greater than the entropy of the reactants.

7. Suppose you found some fungi in the wilderness and you analyzed them for the presence of enzymes. You are surprised to find that they contain amylase, which hydrolyses starch and which you know for sure you have in your saliva. How is it possible that amylase is functional in both places?
   a. These enzymes have different structures.
   b. These are not the same enzymes.
   c. Enzymes from different organisms function best at their optimal pH and temperature.
   d. Enzymes from different organisms function independently of environmental conditions.

## Create/Evaluate

8. Instructors often mention the "hydrolysis of ATP" as the source of energy for cellular reactions, but this statement is NOT accurate. Which of these statements tells us why?
   a. A molecule can never be the source of energy.
   b. ATP actually contains very little free energy.
   c. The hydrolysis of GTP is more common than ATP in cellular reactions.
   d. Water does not enter the active site of enzymes linked to ATP breakdown.

9. Propane is thermodynamically unstable, but why is it kinetically stable?
   a. It is highly electronegative.
   b. Its breakdown is exergonic ($-\Delta G$).
   c. It has a high activation energy ($E_a$).
   d. It contains an abundance of oxygen and little hydrogen.

10. Which of these statements explains the shape of a curve that plots enzyme activity as a function of temperature?
   a. As temperature increases, the rate of all reactions slows down.
   b. At high temperatures, the structural integrity of the enzyme breaks down.
   c. At high temperatures, the rate of catalysis stays high and constant; it saturates.
   d. At low but increasing temperatures, the rate of collisions between substrate and enzyme molecules increases.

11. Explain how dissolving sugar in a glass of water, and subsequent crystalizing of the same as the water evaporates, is an example of entropy.

12. Burning sugar is spontaneous, but a spoonful of sugar does not burst into spontaneous combustion. Explain why not.

13. Describe the relationship between free energy and entropy.

14. Compare exergonic and endergonic reactions.

15. Having in mind the need for energy in cells, postulate how cells obtain enough energy for their endergonic reactions.

# Chapter Roadmap

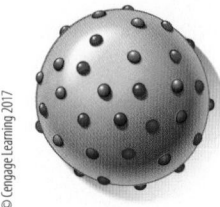

## Cell Membranes and Signalling

All cells have lipid membranes that serve to separate cells from the external environment as well as define distinct intracellular compartments. Transport and signalling across the membrane are facilitated by proteins that interact with the membrane.

### 4.1 An Overview of the Structure of Membranes

Membranes are composed of lipid molecules and a range of proteins that facilitate transport and signal transduction.

### 4.2 The Lipid Fabric of a Membrane

The foundation of a membrane is a collection of phospholipid molecules that self-organize into a bilayer.

**To Chapter 22** ▶

### 4.3 Membrane Proteins

The functional characteristics of a membrane are determined by the unique set of proteins that associate with it.

**To Chapters 24–27** ▶

### 4.4 Passive Membrane Transport

Many molecules move across membranes by diffusion: from high to low concentration.

**To Chapter 5** ▶

**To Chapter 6** ▶

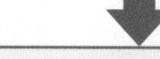

### 4.5 Active Membrane Transport

Maintaining concentrations of molecules at high concentration requires energy.

◀ **From Chapter 3**

### 4.6 Exocytosis and Endocytosis

The import and export of some macromolecules is achieved using plasma membrane vesicles.

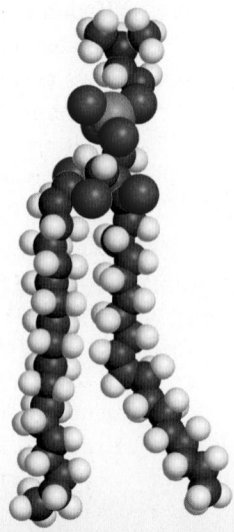

### 4.7 Role of Membranes in Cell Signalling

Binding of a signal molecule to a membrane receptor activates a signalling event that is transduced by molecules within the cell.

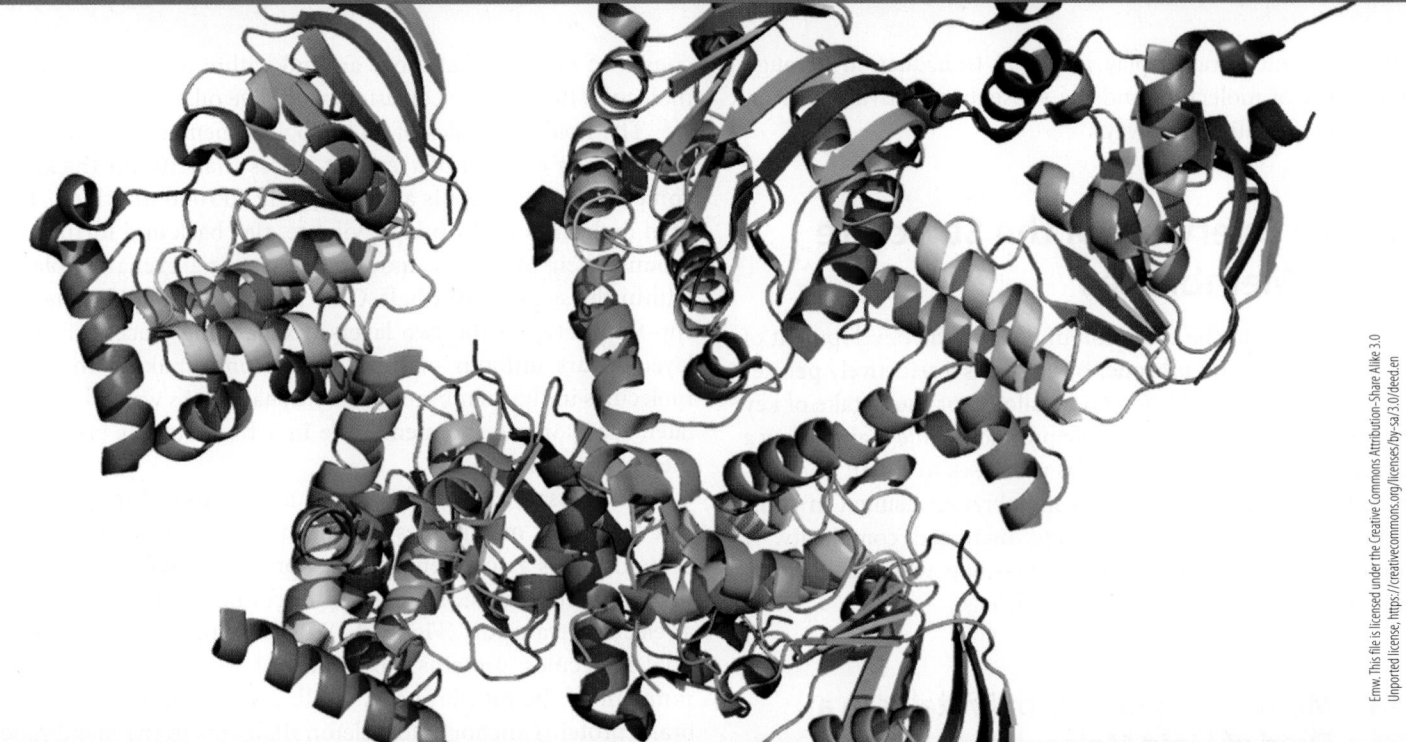

**The structure of the cystic fibrosis transmembrane conductance regulator (CFTR), a protein that acts as a chloride pump.** Mutations to the CFTR gene result in the pump being defective, causing cystic fibrosis.

# Cell Membranes and Signalling

# 4

**Why it matters . . .** Cystic fibrosis (CF) is one of the most common genetic diseases. It affects approximately 1 in 3900 children born in Canada. People with CF suffer from a progressive impairment of lung and gastrointestinal function, and although the treatments for CF are improving, the average lifespan for people with CF remains under 40 years. CF is caused by mutation to a gene that codes for a protein called the *cystic fibrosis transmembrane conductance regulator* (CFTR). In normal cells, CFTR acts as a membrane transport protein that pumps chloride ions ($Cl^-$) out of the cells that line the lungs and intestinal tract and into the overlying mucus lining. This produces an electrical gradient across the membrane and results in the movement of positively charged sodium ions ($Na^+$) into the mucus lining. Because of the high ion concentration ($Na^+$ and $Cl^-$), water moves by osmosis out into the mucus lining, keeping it moist. Keeping the lining of the lungs and intestinal tract wet is critical to their proper functioning. In individuals with CF, the $Cl^-$ channel CFTR does not function properly, which results in water being retained within cells, resulting in a buildup of thick, dry mucus that cannot effectively be removed by coughing. In addition to obstructing airways and preventing normal breathing, the buildup of mucus in the lungs makes CF patients very susceptible to bacterial infections.

Currently, there is no cure for CF. Although treatments for CF are steadily improving, as the disease progresses in young adults, invasive procedures, including lung transplants, are often necessary. Since CF is caused by a defect to a single gene, the greatest hope is in gene therapy (see Chapter 14), which would attempt to insert normal copies of the CFTR gene into affected cells. However, many technical and ethical hurdles need to be overcome before gene therapy becomes a viable treatment option.

The structure and the function of biological membranes are the focus of this chapter. We first consider the structure of membranes and then examine how membranes selectively transport substances in and out of cells and organelles. We close the chapter with a discussion of the critical role membranes play in signal transduction through the binding of molecules and the subsequent activation of intracellular signalling pathways.

# 4.1 An Overview of the Structure of Membranes

One of the keys to the evolution of life was the development of the cell or **plasma membrane**. By acting as a selectively permeable barrier, the plasma membrane allows for the uptake of key nutrients and elimination of waste products while maintaining a protected environment for cellular processes to occur. The subsequent development of internal membranes resulted in compartmentalization of processes and increased complexity. A good example of this is the nuclear envelope, which defines the hallmark of the eukaryotic cell: the nucleus.

## 4.1a Membrane Consists of Proteins In a Fluid of Lipid Molecules

Our current view of membrane structure is based on the **fluid mosaic model (Figure 4.1)**. The model proposes that membranes are not rigid with molecules locked into place, but rather consist of proteins that move around within a mixture of lipid molecules that has the consistency of olive oil.

The lipid molecules of all biological membranes exist in a double layer called a *bilayer* that is less than 10 nm thick. By comparison, this page is approximately 100 000 nm thick. The lipid molecules of the bilayer vibrate, flex back and forth, spin around their long axis, move sideways, and exchange places within the same bilayer half. Only rarely does a lipid molecule flip-flop between the two layers. Exchanging places within a layer occurs millions of times per second, making the lipid molecules in the membrane highly dynamic. As we will discuss later, maintaining the membrane in a fluid state is critical to membrane function.

The mosaic aspect of the fluid mosaic model refers to the fact that most membranes contain an assortment of types of proteins. This assortment includes proteins involved in transport and attachment, signal transduction, and processes such as electron transport (Figure 4.1). Because they are larger than lipid molecules, proteins move more slowly in the fluid environment of the membrane. As well, a small number of membrane proteins anchor cytoskeleton filaments to the membrane and do not move. As also shown in Figure 4.1, a number of the lipid and protein components of some membranes have carbohydrate groups linked to them, forming glycolipids and glycoproteins.

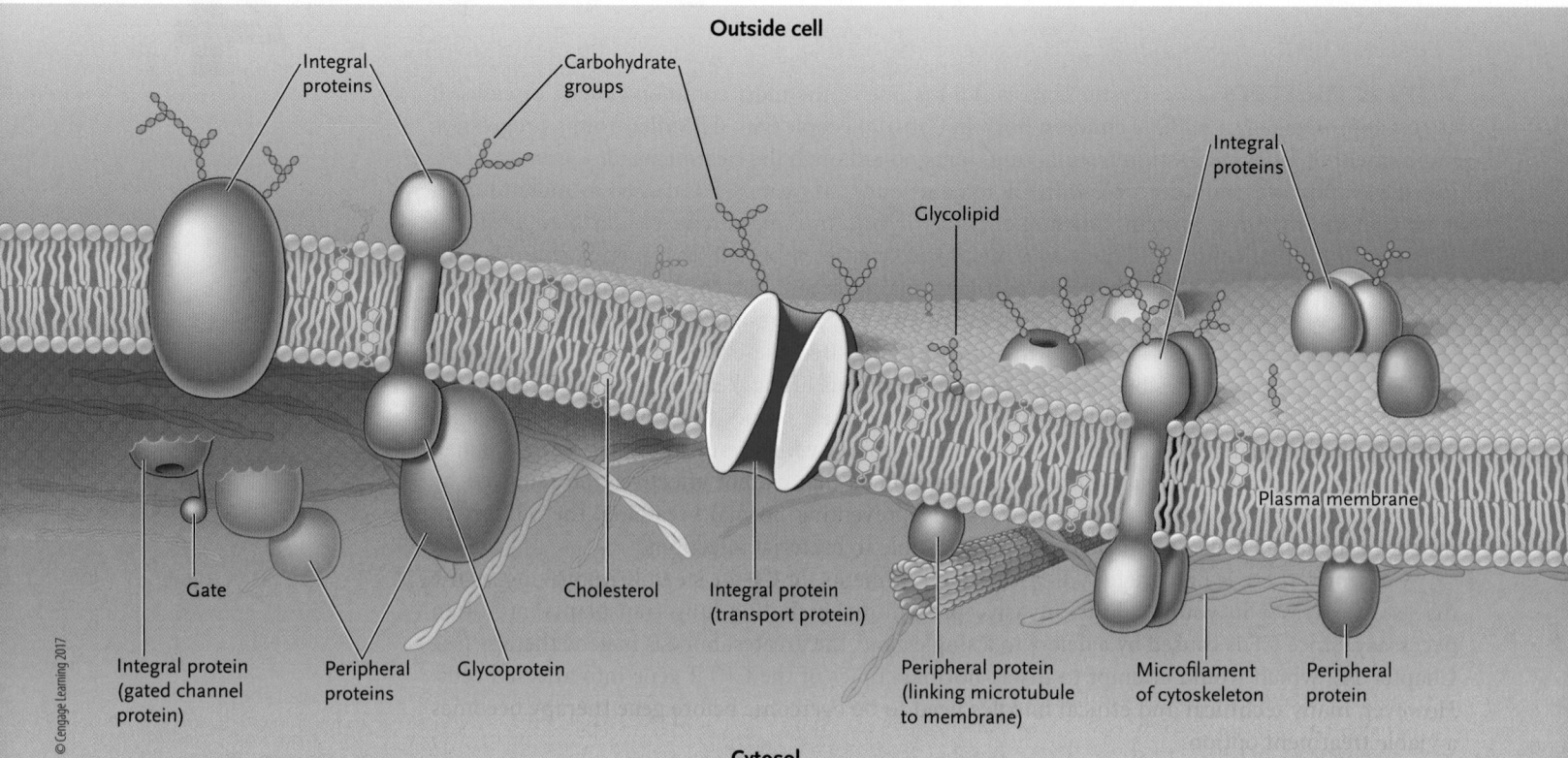

**FIGURE 4.1 Membrane structure according to the fluid mosaic model.** The model proposes that integral membrane proteins are suspended individually in a fluid lipid bilayer. Peripheral proteins are attached to integral proteins or membrane lipids mostly on the cytoplasmic side of the membrane (shown only on the inner surface in the figure). Carbohydrate groups of membrane glycoproteins and glycolipids face the cell exterior.

FIGURE 4.2   **Experimental Research**

## The Frye–Edidin Experiment Demonstrating That the Phospholipid Bilayer Is Fluid

**Question:** Is the phospholipid bilayer fluid?

**Experiment:** Frye and Edidin grew human cells and mouse cells separately in tissue culture. Then they added antibodies that bound to either human or mouse membrane proteins. The anti-human antibodies were attached to dye molecules that fluoresce red under ultraviolet light, and the anti-mouse antibodies to molecules that fluoresce green. The researchers fused the two cells and followed the pattern of fluorescence under a microscope.

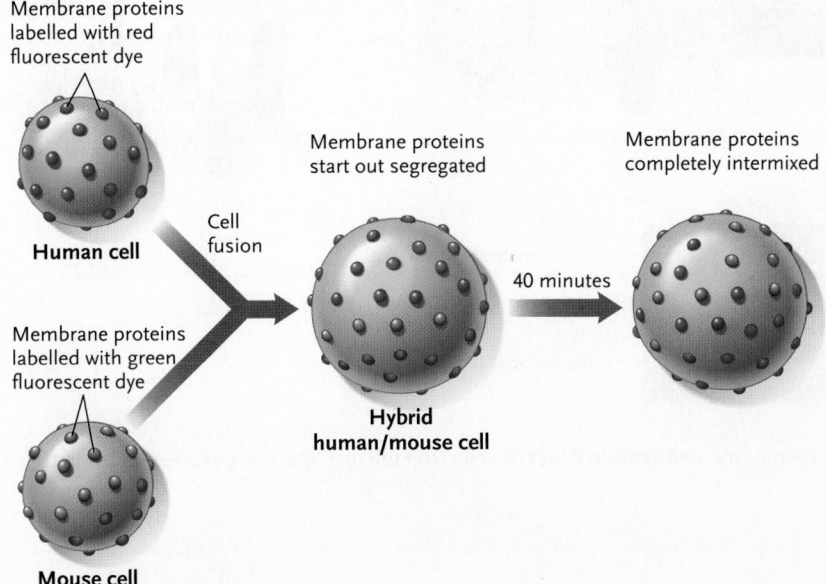

**Results:** After 40 minutes, the fluorescence pattern showed that the human and mouse membrane proteins had mixed completely.

**Conclusion:** The rapid mixing of membrane proteins in the fused human–mouse cells showed that membrane proteins move in the phospholipid bilayer, indicating that the membrane is fluid.

Source: © Cengage Learning 2017. Based on L. D. Frye and M. Edidin. 1970. The rapid intermixing of cell surface antigens after formation of mouse–human heterokaryons. *Journal of Cell Science* 7:319–335.

The relative proportions of lipid and protein within a membrane vary considerably depending on the type of membrane. For example, membranes that contain protein complexes involved in electron transport, such as the inner mitochondrial membrane, contain large amounts of protein (76% protein and only 24% lipid), whereas the plasma membrane contains nearly equal amounts of protein and lipid (49% and 51% respectively). Myelin, which is a cell layer that functions to insulate nerve fibres, has cell membranes composed mostly of lipids (18% protein and 82% lipid).

An important characteristic of membranes, illustrated in Figure 4.1, is that the proteins and other components of one half of the lipid bilayer are different from those that make up the other half of the bilayer. Referred to as *membrane asymmetry*, this reflects differences in the functions performed by each side of the membrane. For example, a range of glycolipids and carbohydrate groups are attached to proteins on the external side of the plasma membrane, whereas components of the cytoskeleton bind to proteins on the internal side of the plasma membrane. In addition, hormones and growth factors bind to receptor proteins that are found only on the external surface of the plasma membrane.

### 4.1b  Experimental Evidence In Support of the Fluid Mosaic Model

The fluid mosaic model of membrane structure is supported by two major pieces of experimental evidence.

**MEMBRANES ARE FLUID** In a now classic study carried out in 1970, David Frye and Michael A. Edidin grew human cells and mouse cells separately in tissue culture. They were able to tag the human or mouse membrane proteins (**Figure 4.2**) with dye molecules: the human proteins were linked to red dye molecules and the mouse proteins were linked to green. Frye and Edidin then fused the human and mouse cells. Within minutes, they found that the two distinctly coloured proteins began to mix. In less than an hour, the two colours had completely intermixed on the fused cells, indicating that the mouse and human proteins had moved around in the fused membranes.

Based on the measured rates at which molecules mix in biological membranes, the membrane bilayer appears to be about as fluid as olive oil or light machine oil.

**MEMBRANE ASYMMETRY** One of the key experiments revealing membrane asymmetry utilized the **freeze-fracture technique** in combination with electron microscopy (**Figure 4.3**). In this technique, a block of cells is rapidly frozen by dipping it in liquid nitrogen (−196°C). Then the block is fractured by hitting it with a microscopically sharp knife-edge. Often the fracture splits bilayers into inner and outer halves, exposing the membrane interior. Using electron microscopy, the split membranes appear as smooth layers in which individual particles the size of proteins are embedded (shown in Figure 4.3c). From these images, it is clear that the particles on either side of the membrane

FIGURE 4.3   **Research Method**

## Freeze Fracture

**Purpose:** Quick-frozen cells are fractured to split apart lipid bilayers for analysis of the membrane interior.

**Protocol:**

**1.** The specimen—a block of cells—is quickly frozen in liquid nitrogen, and then the block is fractured by a sharp blow from the sharp edge of a microscopic knife.

**2.** The fracture may travel over membrane surfaces as it passes through the specimen, or it may split membrane bilayers into inner and outer halves, thereby exposing the interior, as shown here.

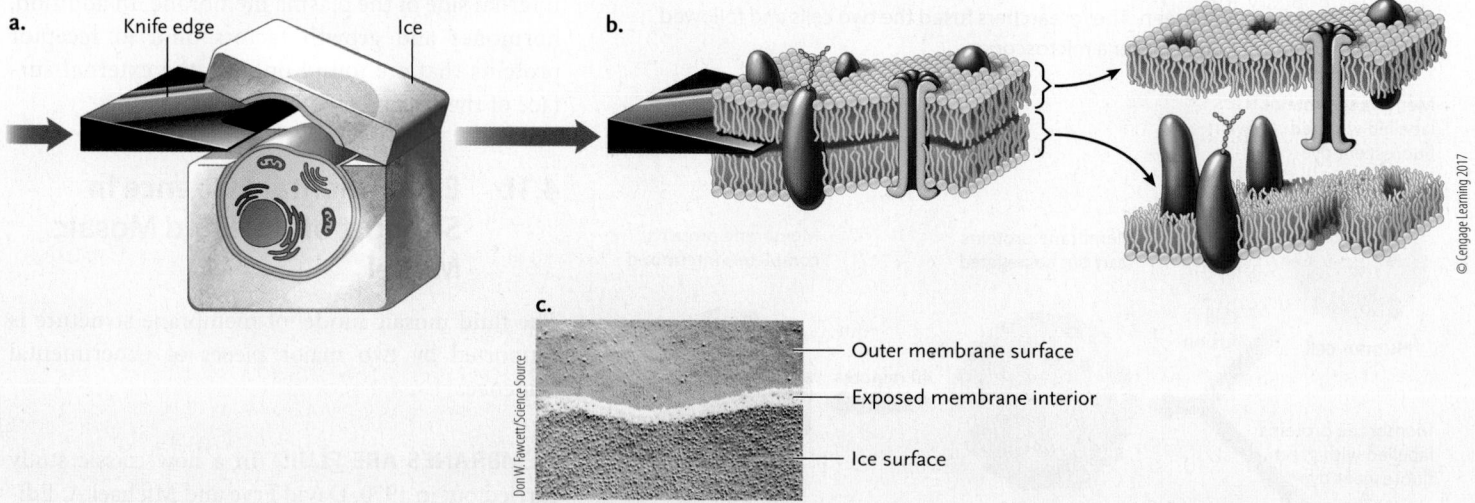

a.   Knife edge          Ice

b.

© Cengage Learning 2017

c.

Don W. Fawcett/Science Source

— Outer membrane surface

— Exposed membrane interior

— Ice surface

**Interpreting the Results:** The image of a freeze-fractured plasma membrane is visualized using the electron microscope. The particles visible in the exposed membrane interior are integral membrane proteins.

---

differ in size, number, and shape, providing evidence that the two sides are distinctly different.

### STUDY BREAK QUESTIONS

1. Describe the fluid mosaic model of membrane structure.
2. What is meant by the term *membrane asymmetry*?

## 4.2   The Lipid Fabric of a Membrane

Lipid molecules make up the underlying fabric of all biological membranes. Collectively, the term *lipid* refers to a diverse group of water-insoluble molecules that includes **fats**; **phospholipids**, which are the dominant lipids in membranes; and steroids. A structural overview of these molecules is found in *The Purple Pages*. As we discuss in this section, keeping membranes in a fluid state is important to overall membrane function. Many organisms can adjust the types of lipids in their membranes such that membranes do not become too rigid or overly fluid.

### 4.2a   Phospholipids Are the Dominant Lipids In Membranes

A lipid bilayer is formed of phospholipid molecules, each consisting of a head group attached to two long chains of carbon and hydrogen (a **hydrocarbon**) called *fatty acids* (**Figure 4.4a**). The head group consists of glycerol linked to one of several types of **alcohols** or amino acids by a phosphate group (see Figure 4.4a). A property that all phospholipids possess, which is critical to the structure and function of membranes, is that they are **amphipathic**—the molecule contains a region that is *hydrophobic* (water fearing) and a region that is *hydrophilic* (water loving). Whereas the fatty acid chains of a lipid are non-polar, the phosphate-containing head group is polar. Overall, polar molecules tend to be hydrophilic, and non-polar molecules hydrophobic. (For a review of molecular polarity, see *The Purple Pages*.) It is interesting to note that laundry detergents are a common type of amphipathic molecules—they are excellent at removing oil stains from clothing while also being soluble in water.

As illustrated in Figure 4.4a, phospholipids can differ in the degree of unsaturation of their fatty acids. Notice in Figure 4.4a that one of the fatty acids is fully saturated—all the carbons are bound to the maximum number of hydrogen atoms. The second fatty acid contains a carbon–carbon double bond (denoted by the arrow) and thus is **unsaturated**. As shown by the space-filling model, the presence of the C–C double bond imparts a kink or bend to the fatty acid tail (Figure 4.4b).

When added to water, phospholipids self-assemble into one of three structures: a **micelle**, a liposome, or a bilayer (**Figure 4.5**). Which structure forms depends mostly on the phospholipid concentration. Phospholipids spontaneously form these structures in an aqueous environment because of the *hydrophobic effect*—the tendency of polar molecules like water to exclude hydrophobic molecules such as fatty acids. This results in the aggregation of lipid molecules in structures in which the fatty acid tails interact with each other, and the polar head groups associate with water. These arrangements are favoured because they represent the lowest energy state and are more likely to occur over any other arrangement.

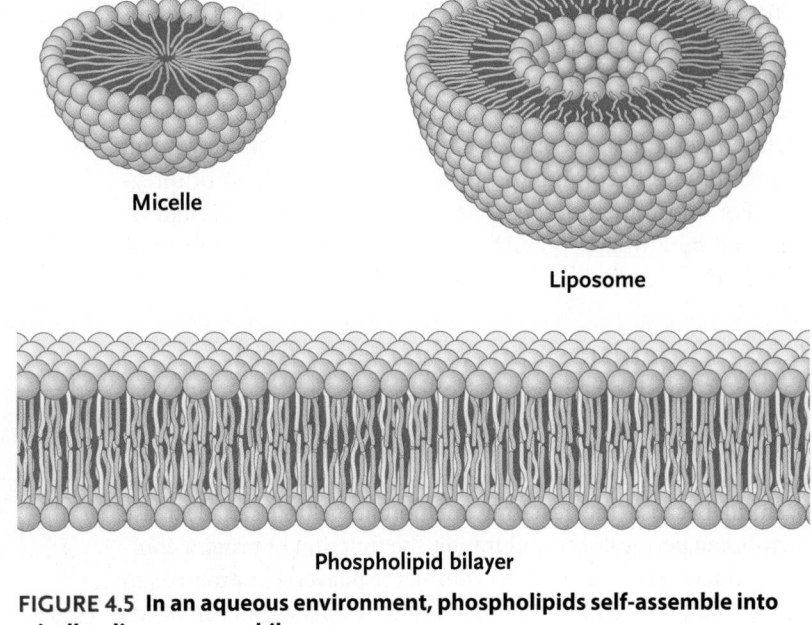

Micelle

Liposome

Phospholipid bilayer

**FIGURE 4.5  In an aqueous environment, phospholipids self-assemble into micelles, liposomes, or bilayers.**

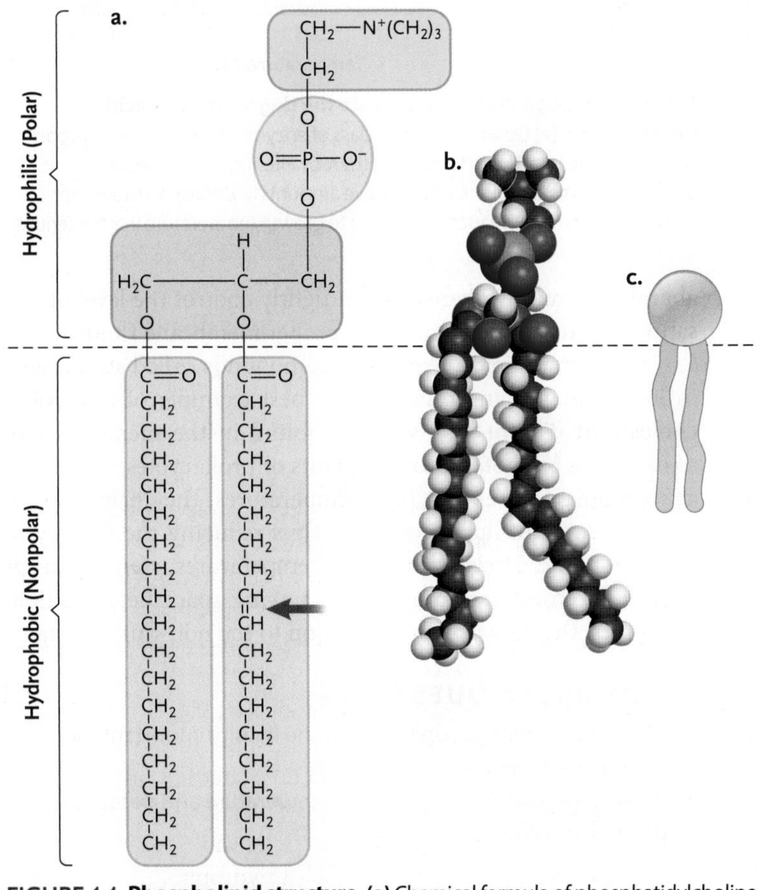

## 4.2b  Fatty Acid Composition and Temperature Affect Membrane Fluidity

The fluidity of the lipid bilayer is influenced primarily by two factors: the type of fatty acids that make up the lipid molecules and the temperature. Fully **saturated fatty acids** are linear, which allows lipid molecules to pack tightly together (**Figure 4.6a**). In contrast, lipid molecules with unsaturated fatty acids are prevented from packing closely together because the carbon–carbon double bonds in unsaturated fatty acids introduce kinks in the fatty acid structure (Figure 4.6b). As a result, the more unsaturated the fatty acids of the lipid molecules, the more fluid (less viscous) the membrane.

In addition to fatty acid composition, temperature can also dramatically affect membrane fluidity. As the temperature drops and the random molecular motion of lipid molecules slows down, a point is reached where fluidity is lost and the phospholipid molecules form a semisolid gel.

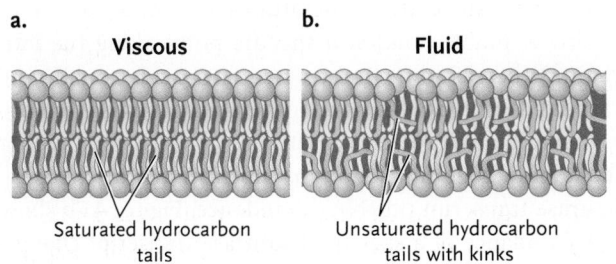

a.    **Viscous**

b.    **Fluid**

Saturated hydrocarbon tails

Unsaturated hydrocarbon tails with kinks

**FIGURE 4.6  Lipid molecule composition affects how closely the molecules interact.** Lipid molecules that contain saturated hydrocarbon tails are closely packed **(a)**, whereas unsaturated hydrocarbon tails have kinks that prevent lipid molecules from packing closely together **(b)**.

**FIGURE 4.4  Phospholipid structure. (a)** Chemical formula of phosphatidylcholine. The polar head group consists of glycerol (shown in pink) linked to the organic molecule choline (shown in blue) by a phosphate group (shown in yellow). In addition, the glycerol is linked to two fatty acids, each 18 carbons long. The structure of phospholipids is also often represented as space-filling models **(b)** and as an icon **(c)**. As shown in the space-filling model, the presence of a carbon–carbon double bond (denoted by the arrow in (a)) imparts a bend to one of the fatty acids.

This is exactly what happens when melted butter cools: at a certain temperature it turns from a liquid into a solid. The temperature at which gelling occurs depends upon the fatty acid composition. The more unsaturated a group of lipid molecules, the lower the temperature at which gelling occurs. Likewise, at high temperatures, the increased molecular motion may result in membranes becoming too fluid, resulting in a loss of integrity. For most membrane systems, the normal fluid state is achieved by a mixed population of saturated and unsaturated fatty acids.

## 4.2c Organisms Can Adjust Fatty Acid Composition

Keeping membranes in the optimal state of fluidity is absolutely essential to cell function. Exposure to low temperatures can be harmful because the resulting membrane gelling can decrease membrane permeability and inhibit the function of protein complexes attached to, or localized within, the bilayer. For example, to be functional these proteins often change shape, which can be inhibited if the membrane they are associated with is too rigid.

At high temperatures, the problem is the membrane may become too fluid. As a result of the increased molecular motion associated with higher temperatures, membranes may become leaky. The concentration of ions such as $K^+$, $Na^+$, and $Ca^{2+}$ on either side of a membrane is often strictly controlled. But if membranes become too fluid, these ions can start to freely diffuse across membrane, resulting in an irreversible disruption of cellular ion balance that can lead to cell death.

Unlike humans, the body temperature of most organisms closely matches that of the external environment. Examples of such organisms are plants, bacteria, protists, and insects. To live at a range of temperatures, these organisms are able to alter membrane fluidity by adjusting the relative proportions of saturated and unsaturated fatty acids.

Unsaturated fatty acids are produced during fatty acid biosynthesis through the action of a group of enzymes called *desaturases* (**Figure 4.7a**). All fatty acids are initially synthesized as fully saturated molecules without any carbon–carbon double bonds. Desaturases act on these saturated fatty acids by catalyzing a reaction that removes two hydrogen atoms from neighbouring carbon atoms and introducing a double bond. There are many different desaturase enzymes, each one introducing a double bond at a specific point along the fatty acid chain. Whereas some unsaturated fatty acids contain only one carbon–carbon double bond, others may contain two or more.

Like many proteins, desaturase abundance is regulated at the level of gene transcription, which results in changes to desaturase transcript (mRNA) abundance. Figure 4.7b shows how the abundance of a specific desaturase transcript changes with growth temperature in a bacterium. As growth temperature decreases, desaturase transcript abundance goes up, which results in an increase in synthesis of the desaturase enzyme. Higher amounts of the enzyme, in turn, result in an increase in the abundance of unsaturated fatty acids. By regulating desaturase

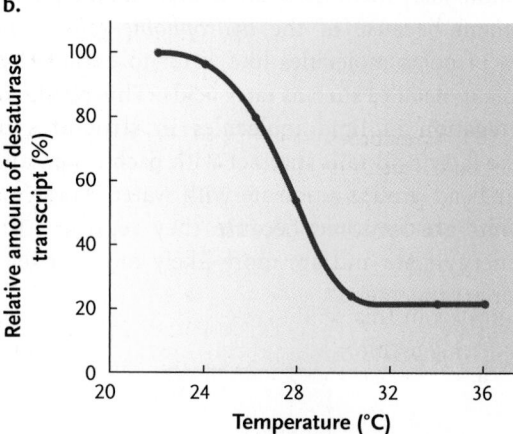

**a. Stearic acid, $CH_3(CH_2)_{16}COOH$**

desaturase

b.

FIGURE 4.7 **Organisms can regulate the degree of fatty acid unsaturation. (a)** Desaturases are a class of enzymes that introduce carbon–carbon double bonds into fatty acids, thereby altering the degree of unsaturation. **(b)** Graph showing relative amounts of desaturase transcript amounts (mRNA abundance) in relation to growth temperature in a bacterium.

abundance, many organisms can tightly control the level of unsaturation and thereby maintain proper membrane fluidity.

Apart from lipids, a group of compounds called **sterols** also influence membrane fluidity. The best example of a sterol is **cholesterol (Figure 4.8)**, which is found in the membranes of animal cells but not in those of plants or prokaryotes. Sterols act as membrane buffers: At high temperatures, they help restrain the movement of lipid molecules, thus reducing the fluidity of the membrane. However, at lower temperatures, sterols disrupt fatty acids from associating by occupying space between lipid molecules, thus slowing the transition to the non-fluid gel state.

### STUDY BREAK QUESTIONS

3. Why is maintaining proper membrane fluidity important for membrane function?
4. What is the relationship between temperature and desaturase gene expression?

## 4.3 Membrane Proteins

While the lipid molecules constitute the foundation of a membrane, the unique set of proteins associated with the membrane determines its function and makes each membrane unique. As

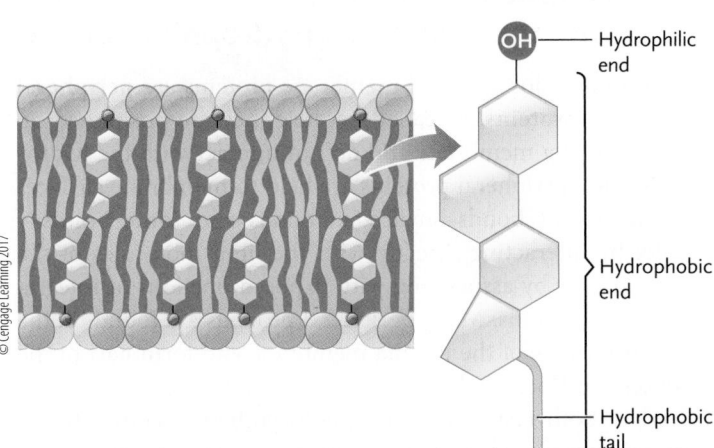

**Cholesterol**

Hydrophilic end

Hydrophobic end

Hydrophobic tail

© Cengage Learning 2017

**FIGURE 4.8 The position taken by cholesterol within a membrane.** The hydrophilic–OH group at one end of the molecule extends into the hydrophilic region of the bilayer; the ring structure extends into the hydrophobic membrane interior.

we will discuss in this section, two major types of proteins are associated with membranes: integral and peripheral membrane proteins.

## 4.3a The Key Functions of Membrane Proteins

Membrane proteins can be separated into four major functional categories, as shown in **Figure 4.9**. All these functions may exist in a single membrane, and one protein or protein complex may serve more than one of these functions:

1. **Transport.** Many substances cannot freely diffuse through the membrane. Instead, a protein may provide a channel that allows movement of a specific molecule. Alternatively, a membrane protein may change its shape and, in so doing, shuttle specific molecules from one side of a membrane to the other.

2. **Enzymatic activity.** A number of enzymes are membrane proteins; the best examples are the enzymes associated with the respiratory and photosynthetic electron transport chains.

3. **Signal transduction.** Membranes often contain receptor proteins on their outer surface that bind to specific chemicals such as hormones. On binding, these receptors trigger changes on the inside surface of the membrane that lead to transduction of the signal through the cell.

4. **Attachment/recognition.** Proteins exposed to both internal and external membrane surfaces act as attachment points for a range of cytoskeleton elements, as well as components involved in cell–cell recognition.

## 4.3b Integral Membrane Proteins Interact with the Membrane Hydrophobic Core

Proteins that are embedded in the phospholipid bilayer are called **integral membrane proteins**. These proteins traverse the entire lipid bilayer at least once, and are referred to as *transmembrane proteins*. Because they have to interact with both the aqueous environment on either side of the membrane and the hydrophobic core, transmembrane proteins have two distinct parts (called **domains**) that differ markedly in polarity. The domain that interacts with the lipid bilayer consists predominantly of non-polar amino acids, and domains that are exposed on either side of the membrane are composed primarily of polar amino acids. (The different classes of amino acids are presented in *The Purple Pages*.) In addition to being composed of mostly non-polar amino acids, the domain of a transmembrane protein that interacts with the hydrophobic core of a membrane forms a type of **secondary structure** termed an *alpha helix* (**Figure 4.10**; see *The Purple Pages* for an overview of protein structure).

Given the amino acid sequence (**primary structure**) of a protein, it is usually quite simple to determine if it is likely a transmembrane protein. What one looks for, usually with the aid of a computer program, are stretches of primarily non-polar

**a. Transport**

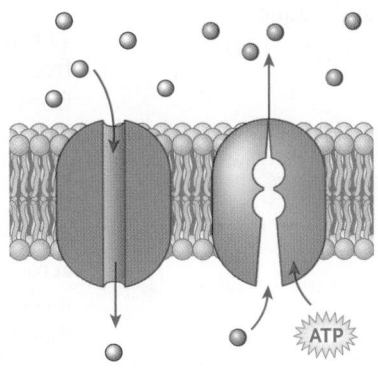

ATP

**b. Enzymatic activity**

Enzymes

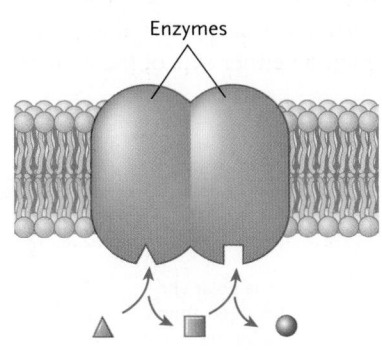

**c. Signal transduction**

Signal

Receptor

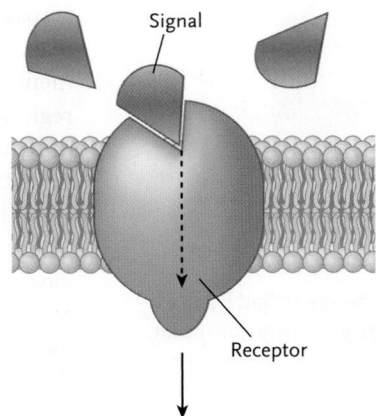

**d. Attachment/recognition**

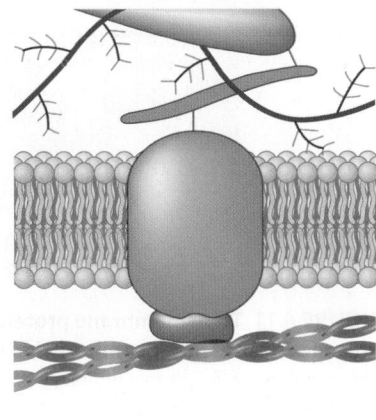

**FIGURE 4.9 The major functions of membrane proteins**

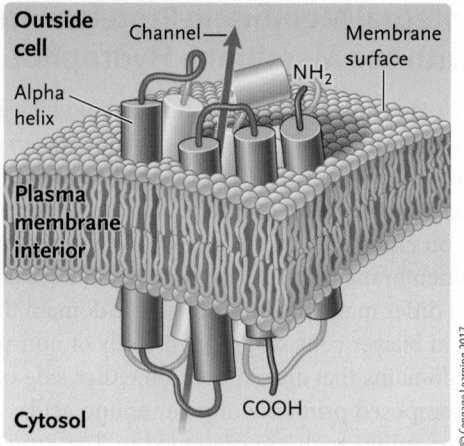

FIGURE 4.10 **The structure of membrane proteins.** A typical integral membrane protein shows the membrane-spanning, alpha-helical segments (blue cylinders) connected by flexible loops of the amino acid chain at the membrane surfaces.

amino acids. These stretches are about 17–20 amino acids in length, which matches the peptide length needed to span the lipid bilayer **(Figure 4.11)**. Most transmembrane proteins span the membrane more than once. So, for example, if a protein has three membrane-spanning domains, the primary sequence would show three distinct regions of predominantly non-polar amino acids linked by regions that are dominated by polar and charged amino acids. These polar amino acids are found in the portions of the protein that are exposed to the aqueous environment on either side of the membrane (see Figure 4.11).

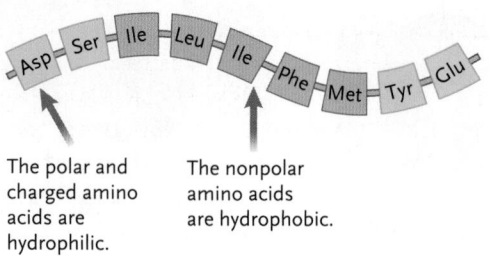

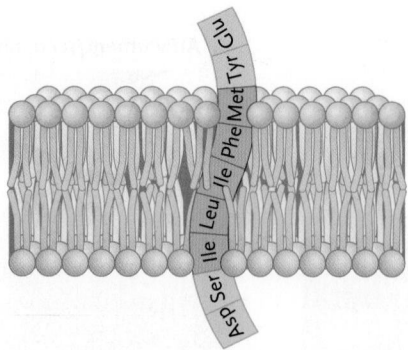

FIGURE 4.11 **Transmembrane proteins can be identified by the presence of stretches of amino acids that are primarily non-polar.** These regions of the protein interact with the hydrophobic regions of the membrane. Usually between 17 and 20 amino acids are needed to span the membrane once. For clarity, this model shows only five non-polar amino acids spanning the membrane.

### 4.3c Peripheral Membrane Proteins Interact with the Membrane Hydrophilic Surface

The second major group of membrane proteins are **peripheral membrane proteins**, so called because they are positioned on the surface of a membrane and do not interact with the hydrophobic core. Peripheral proteins are held to membrane surfaces by noncovalent bonds—hydrogen bonds and **ionic bonds**—usually by interacting directly with the lipid molecules of the membrane, or by associating with exposed portions of integral membrane proteins. Many peripheral proteins are found on the cytoplasmic side of the plasma membrane and form part of the cytoskeleton (look back at Figure 4.1). In addition, proteins involved in both respiratory and photosynthetic electron transport are peripheral membrane proteins. Because peripheral membrane proteins do not interact with the hydrophobic core of the membrane, they are made up of a mixture of polar and non-polar amino acids, similar to a protein found in the cytosol.

**STUDY BREAK QUESTIONS**

1. What roles are served by membrane proteins?
2. What are the two major classes of membrane proteins?

## 4.4 Passive Membrane Transport

The hydrophobic nature of membranes severely restricts the free movement of many molecules into and out of cells and from one compartment to another. Molecules such as $O_2$ and $CO_2$ diffuse very rapidly across membranes, which is important considering their vital role in cellular respiration and photosynthesis. However, a range of other molecules, including ions, charged molecules, and macromolecules, do not readily move across membranes. In this section, we consider the diffusion of molecules from one compartment to the other and the factors that influence the rate of their diffusion.

### 4.4a Passive Transport Is Based on Diffusion

**Passive transport** is defined as the movement of molecules across a membrane without the need to expend chemical energy (e.g., ATP). The molecules move by **diffusion**, the net movement of a substance from a region of higher concentration to a region of lower concentration. In addition to passive transport, diffusion is the primary mechanism of **solute** movement within any particular cell compartment.

The driving force of diffusion is an increase in entropy (see Chapter 3). When molecules are more concentrated in one region or on one side of a membrane, the molecules and their associated energy are localized. As diffusion occurs, and the molecules and energy spread out, this results in an increase in the system's entropy.

The rate of passive transport depends on the concentration difference (**concentration gradient**) that exists across the membrane. The larger the gradient, the faster the rate of diffusion. Diffusion in a particular direction will continue until the molecules are evenly distributed on both sides of the membrane; equilibrium is reached and the entropy reaches its maximum (**Figure 4.12**). Similar to chemical equilibrium (see Chapter 3), when diffusing molecules reach equilibrium, there is still movement of molecules from one space to another, but no net change in concentration (see Figure 4.12). The diffusion of molecules across a membrane releases free energy, which can be used to do work. We will see in Chapters 5 and 6 how proton gradients generated during cellular respiration and photosynthesis can be used to generate ATP.

## 4.4b There Are Two Types of Passive Transport: Simple and Facilitated

There are two types of passive transport: simple diffusion and facilitated diffusion. **Simple diffusion** is the movement of molecules directly across a membrane without the involvement of a transporter (e.g., protein channel or pore). The rate of simple diffusion of a molecule depends upon two factors: its molecular size and its lipid solubility. As shown in **Figure 4.13**, some molecules diffuse very rapidly across the membrane, and other molecules are essentially unable to transit the membrane.

Small non-polar molecules such as $O_2$ and $CO_2$ are readily soluble in the hydrophobic interior of a membrane and move very rapidly from one side to the other. As well, steroid hormones and many drugs that tend to be amphipathic can readily transit the lipid bilayer. Small uncharged molecules such as water and glycerol, even though they are polar, are still able to move quite rapidly across the membrane (see Figure 4.13). In contrast, the membrane is practically impermeable to charged molecules, including ions such as $Cl^-$, $Na^+$, and phosphate ($PO_4^{3-}$). What prevents these molecules from entering the hydrophobic core is their charge, combined with the fact that they are surrounded by a hydration shell of water ($H_2O$) molecules in solution.

The diffusion of molecules across a membrane through the aid of a transporter is called **facilitated diffusion**. The diffusion of many polar and charged molecules, such as water, amino acids, sugars, and ions, relies on specific transport

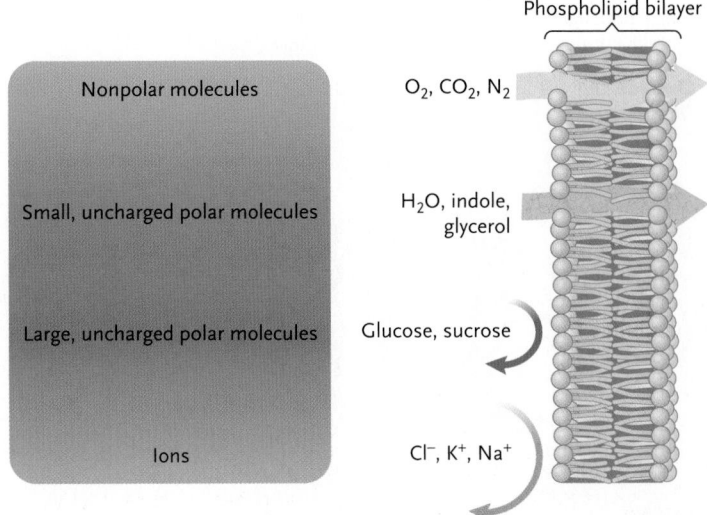

**FIGURE 4.13 The size and the charge of a molecule affect the rate of diffusion across a membrane.**

complexes for their rapid movement from one compartment to another. Although facilitated diffusion involves specific transporters, transport depends upon a concentration gradient across the membrane. Just like simple diffusion, when the concentration gradient falls to zero, facilitated diffusion stops.

## 4.4c Two Groups of Transport Proteins Carry Out Facilitated Diffusion

Facilitated diffusion is carried out by two types of transport proteins: channel proteins and carrier proteins, both of which are transmembrane proteins (**Figure 4.14**). **Channel proteins** form hydrophilic pathways in the membrane through which molecules can pass. The channel aids the diffusion of molecules by providing an avenue that is shielded from the hydrophobic core of the bilayer. Specific channel proteins are involved in the transport of certain ions and, most interestingly, the transport of water.

The diffusion of water is facilitated by water-specific transport proteins called *aquaporins* (Figure 4.14a). Aquaporins have been found in organisms as diverse as bacteria, plants, and humans. The aquaporin channel is very narrow and allows for the single-file movement of about a billion water molecules every second. Remarkably, the channel is very specific for water and does not allow for the diffusion of ions, including protons. Recent three-dimensional models of aquaporin show the presence of positive charges in the centre of the channel that are thought to specifically repel the transport of protons. For his discovery of aquaporins, Peter Agre at Johns Hopkins University received the Nobel Prize in Chemistry in 2003.

Another type of channel protein that is found in all eukaryotes is the **gated channel** (Figure 4.14a2). These transporters can switch between open, closed, and

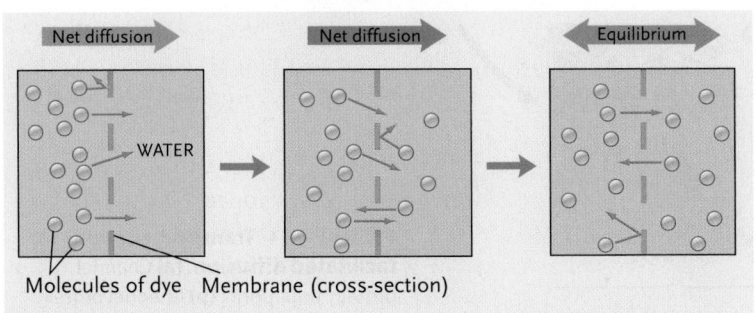

**FIGURE 4.12 Diffusion is the movement of molecules from regions of high concentration to areas of low concentration.** It is driven by the increase in entropy associated with energy becoming more dispersed.

## a. Channel protein: aquaporin

Channel proteins form hydrophilic channels in the membrane through which water and ions can move.

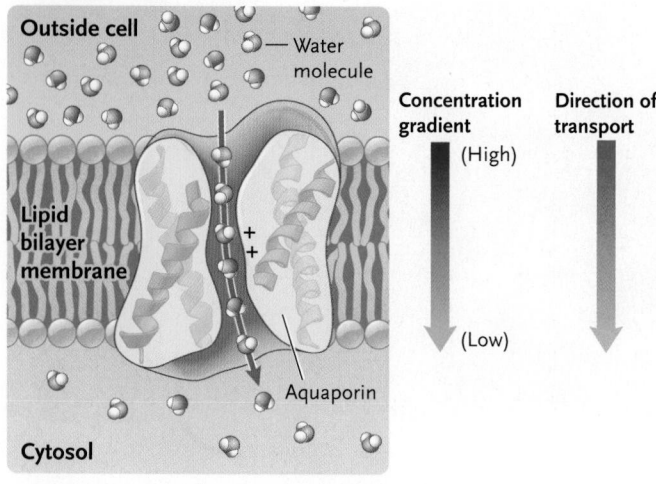

An aquaporin is a water channel. Water molecules move through the channel by being handed off to a succession of hydrogen-bonding sites on the channel in this protein.

## b. Channel protein: K⁺ voltage-gated channel

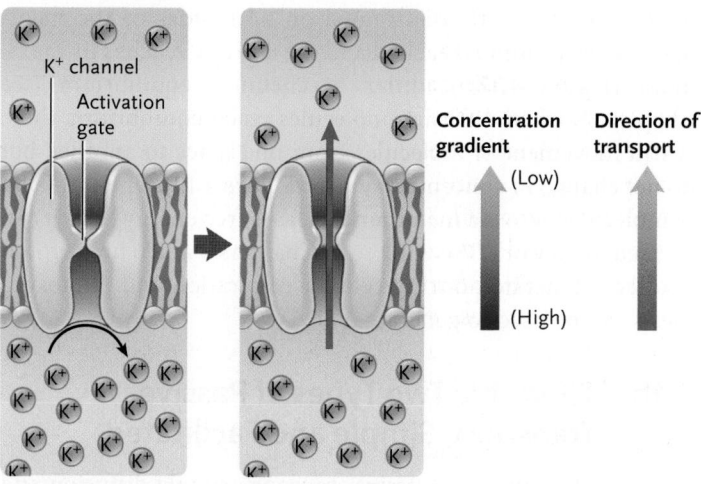

With normal voltage across the membrane, the activation gate of the K⁺ channel is closed and K⁺ cannot move across the membrane.

In response to a voltage change across the membrane, the activation gate of the K⁺ channel opens, and K⁺ moves with its concentration gradient from the cytoplasm to outside the cell.

## c. Carrier protein

Carrier proteins each bind a single solute and transport it across the lipid bilayer. During the transport step, the carrier protein undergoes conformational changes that move the solute-binding site progressively from one side of the membrane to the other, thereby transporting the solute. Shown is the transport of glucose.

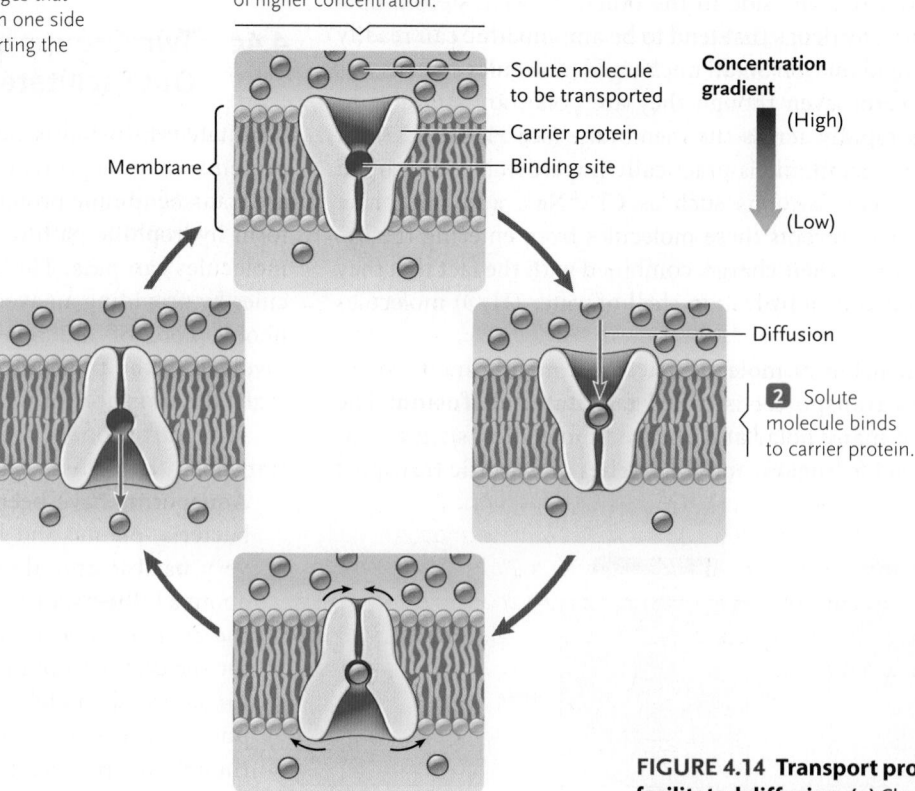

**1** Carrier protein is in conformation so that binding site is exposed toward region of higher concentration.

**2** Solute molecule binds to carrier protein.

**3** In response to binding, carrier protein changes conformation so that binding site is exposed to region of lower concentration.

**4** Transported solute is released and carrier protein returns to conformation in step 1.

**FIGURE 4.14 Transport proteins for facilitated diffusion. (a)** Channel protein: aquaporin. **(b)** Channel protein: K⁺ voltage-gated channel. **(c)** Carrier proteins: a model for how these proteins transport solutes such as glucose.

© Cengage Learning 2017

intermediate states and are critical to the movement of most ions, for example, sodium ($Na^+$), potassium ($K^+$), calcium ($Ca^{2+}$), and chlorine ($Cl^-$). The gates may be opened or closed by changes in voltage across the membrane for instance, or by binding signal molecules. The opening or closing involves changes in the protein's three-dimensional shape. In animals, voltage-gated ion channels are used in nerve conduction and the control of muscle contraction (see Chapters 45 and 46). As well, CFTR, the $Cl^-$ channel that is defective in individuals with cystic fibrosis, is a gated channel (see *Why It Matters*).

The second class of transport proteins that form passageways through the lipid bilayer are **carrier proteins** (Figure 4.14b). Each carrier protein binds a single specific solute, such as a sugar molecule or an amino acid, and transports it across the lipid bilayer. Because a single solute is transferred in this carrier-mediated fashion, the transfer is called *uniport transport*. In performing the transport step, the carrier protein undergoes conformational changes that progressively move the solute binding site from one side of the membrane to the other, thereby transporting the solute. This property distinguishes carrier protein function from channel protein function.

Most transport proteins display a high degree of substrate specificity, similar in a way to an enzyme. For example, transporters that carry glucose are unable to transport fructose, which is structurally similar. This specificity allows various cells and cellular compartments to tightly control what gets in and out. The kinds of transport proteins present in the plasma membrane or, for example, on the inner membrane of the mitochondrion, ultimately depend on the type of cell and growth conditions.

How can you experimentally determine if a molecule is transported by facilitated diffusion and not just simple diffusion? First, with facilitated diffusion, the rate of movement across the membrane is much faster than one would predict based just on the chemical structure of the molecule being transported **(Figure 4.15)**. Second, facilitated diffusion can be saturated in the same way that an enzyme can be saturated, by substrate (See Chapter 3). A membrane has a limited number of transporters for a particular molecule. If you measure the rate of transport at increasing concentration differences across a membrane, the rate of transport of a particular molecule (the substrate) reaches a plateau that represents a state when essentially all the transporters are occupied all the time by substrate (they are saturated). Increasing the concentration further has no effect on the rate of transport (see Figure 4.15). By comparison, in simple diffusion, the whole membrane surface is effectively the transporter; thus, the rate of transport, although usually slower, never reaches a plateau.

### 4.4d Osmosis Is the Passive Diffusion of Water

Like solutes, water can also move passively across membranes in a process called *osmosis*. The passive transport of water occurs constantly in living cells. Inward or outward movement of water by osmosis develops forces that can cause cells to swell or shrink.

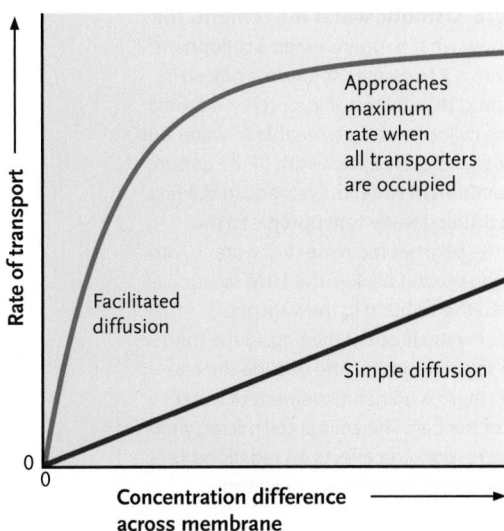

**FIGURE 4.15 Simple diffusion and facilitated diffusion display different transport kinetics.** Compared with simple diffusion, facilitated diffusion leads to higher rates of transport and displays saturation kinetics.

Formally, **osmosis** is defined as the diffusion of water molecules across a selectively permeable membrane from a solution of lower solute concentration to a solution of higher solute concentration. For osmosis to take place, the selectively permeable membrane must allow water molecules to pass but not molecules of the solute. Osmosis occurs in cells because they contain a solution of proteins and other molecules that are retained in the cytoplasm by a membrane impermeable to them but permeable to water. Osmosis can occur by simple diffusion through the lipid bilayer, or it can be facilitated by aquaporins (see Section 4.4c).

The movement of water by osmosis is dictated by solute concentration. If the solution surrounding a cell contains dissolved substances at lower concentrations than in the cell, the solution is said to be **hypotonic** to the cell (*hypo* = under or below; *tonos* = tension or tone). When a cell is in a hypotonic solution, water enters by osmosis, and the cell tends to swell **(Figure 4.16a)**. Animal cells, such as red blood cells, in a hypotonic solution may actually swell to the point of bursting. This is in contrast with plant cells, where the presence of the cell wall prevents the cells from bursting in a hypotonic solution. Instead the cell pushes against the cell wall, resulting in what is called *turgor pressure*. This is discussed in more detail in Chapter 34.

If the solution that surrounds a cell contains solutes at higher concentrations than that in the cell, then the outside solution is said to be **hypertonic** to the cell (*hyper* = over or above) (Figure 4.16b). When a cell is in a hypertonic solution, water leaves by osmosis. If the outward osmotic movement exceeds the capacity of cells to replace the lost water, both animal and plant cells will shrink (Figure 4.16b).

In animals, ions, proteins, and other molecules are concentrated in extracellular fluids, as well as inside cells so that the concentration of water inside and outside cells is usually equal, or **isotonic** (*iso* = the same), as shown in Figure 4.16c. However, this comes at an energetic cost of constantly having to pump

**FIGURE 4.16 Osmotic water movement.** The diagrams show what happens when a cellophane bag filled with a 2 M sucrose solution is placed in **(a)** a hypotonic, **(b)** a hypertonic, or **(c)** an isotonic solution. The cellophane is permeable to water but not to sucrose molecules. The width of the arrows shows the amount of water movement. In the first beaker, the distilled water is hypotonic to the solution in the bag; net movement of water is into the bag. In the second beaker, the 10 M solution is hypertonic to the solution in the bag; net movement of water is out of the bag. In the third beaker, the solutions inside and outside the bag are isotonic; there is no net movement of water into or out of the bag. The animal cell micrographs show the corresponding effects on red blood cells placed in hypotonic, hypertonic, or isotonic solutions.

Source: Micrographs, M. Sheetz, R. Painter, and S. Singer. *Journal of Cell Biology* 70:493, 1976. By permission of Rockefeller University Press.

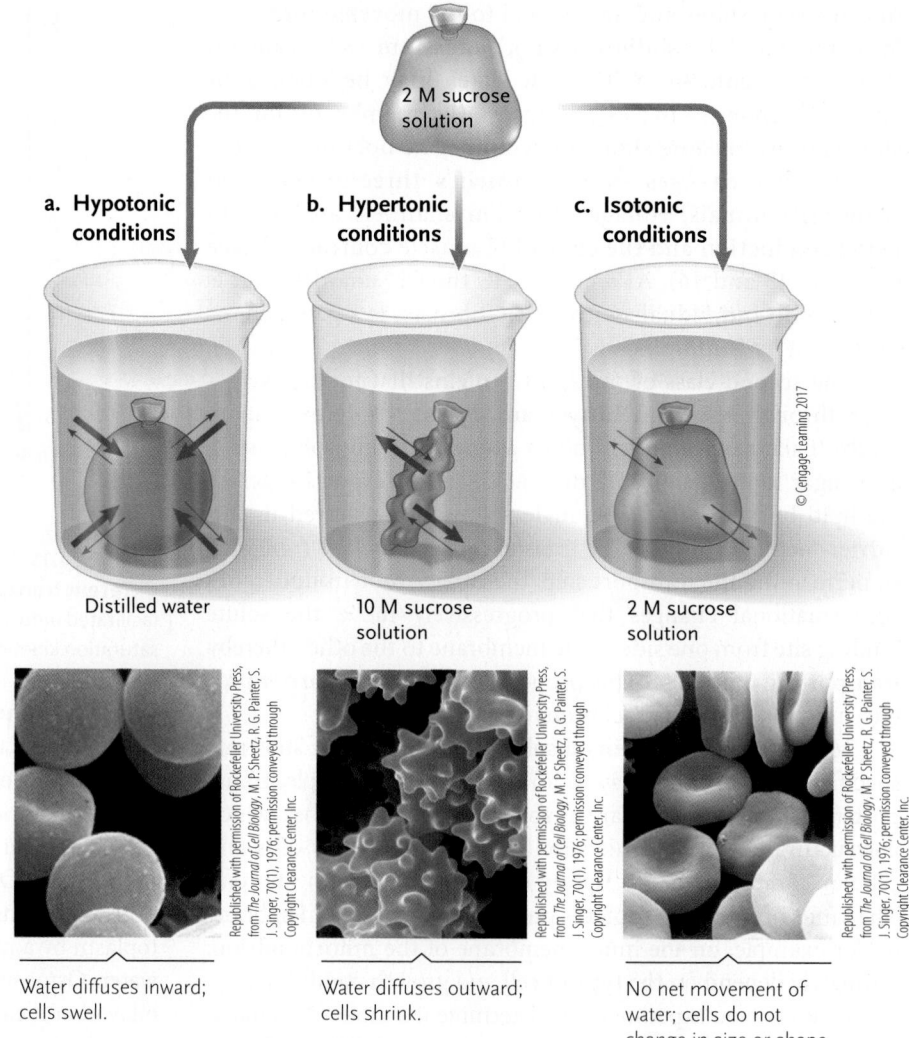

ions from one side to the other. For example, the ATP-dependent transport of $Na^+$ from inside to outside the cell is essential; otherwise, water would move inward by osmosis and cause the cells to burst. Osmotic movement in plant cells is discussed more in depth in Chapter 34, whereas the mechanisms by which animals balance their water content are discussed in Chapter 42.

### STUDY BREAK QUESTIONS

1. How do the size and charge of a molecule influence its transport across a membrane?
2. Explain how aquaporin functions to transport water.
3. What is the difference between passive transport and active transport?

## 4.5 Active Membrane Transport

Passive transport of molecules across membranes by either simple or facilitated diffusion is limited to movement down a concentration gradient. Yet many cellular processes require molecules to be maintained in cell compartments at higher concentrations than they are found outside that compartment.

The maintenance of this type of concentration difference is achieved by energy-dependent transport that moves molecules against a concentration gradient. That is, molecules are transported from a region of lower concentration to a region of higher concentration.

### 4.5a Active Transport Requires Energy

The transport of molecules across a membrane against a concentration gradient requires the expenditure of energy and is referred to as **active transport**. The energy is usually in the form of ATP, and it is estimated that about 25% of a cell's ATP requirements are for the active transport of molecules. Active transport concentrates molecules such as sugars and amino acids inside cells and pushes ions in or out of cells.

The three main functions of active transport in cells and organelles are (1) uptake of essential nutrients from the fluid surrounding cells, even when their concentrations are lower than in cells; (2) removal of secretory or waste materials from cells or organelles, even when the concentration of those materials is higher outside the cells or organelles; and (3) maintenance of essentially constant intracellular concentrations of $H^+$,

$Na^+$, $K^+$, and $Ca^{2+}$. Because ions are charged molecules, active transport of ions may contribute to voltage—an electrical potential difference—across the plasma membrane, called a **membrane potential**. This electrical difference across the plasma membrane is important in neurons and muscle cells, and is discussed in more detail in Chapters 44 and 46 respectively.

There are two classes of active transport: primary and secondary. In **primary active transport**, the same protein that transports the molecules also hydrolyzes ATP to directly power the transport. In **secondary active transport**, the transport is indirectly driven by ATP. That is, the transport proteins use a favourable concentration gradient of ions built up by primary active transport as the energy source to drive the transport of a different molecule.

Other features of active transport (listed in **Table 4.1**) resemble facilitated diffusion. Both processes depend on membrane transport proteins, both are specific, and the rate of both processes can plateau at high substrate concentrations.

## 4.5b Primary Active Transport Moves Positively Charged Ions

All primary active transport pumps move positively charged ions—$H^+$, $Ca^{2+}$, $Na^+$, and $K^+$—across membranes (**Figure 4.17**). The gradients of positive ions established by primary active transport pumps underlie functions that are absolutely essential for life. For example, the **proton pumps ($H^+$ pumps)** in plasma membranes push hydrogen ions from the cytoplasm to the cell exterior. These pumps (as in Figure 4.17) temporarily bind a phosphate group removed from ATP during the pumping cycle. Proton pumps have various functions. For example, in bacteria, archaea, and plants and fungi, proton pumps in the plasma membrane generate membrane potential. Proton pumps in lysosomes of animals and vacuoles of plants and fungi keep the pH within the organelle low, serving to activate the enzymes contained within them.

Another active transport system is the **calcium pump ($Ca^{2+}$ pump)**, which is widely distributed among eukaryotes. It pushes $Ca^{2+}$ from the cytoplasm to the cell exterior, and from the cytosol into the lumen of the endoplasmic reticulum (ER). As a result, $Ca^{2+}$ concentration is typically high outside cells and inside the ER, and low in the cytoplasmic solution. This $Ca^{2+}$ gradient is used universally among eukaryotes as a regulatory control of cellular activities as diverse as secretion, microtubule assembly, and muscle contraction. The latter is discussed further in Chapter 46.

The **sodium–potassium pump ($Na^+/K^+$ pump)**, located in the plasma membrane of all animal cells, pushes three $Na^+$ ions out of the cell and two $K^+$ ions into the cell in the same pumping cycle (**Figure 4.18**). As a result, positive charges accumulate in excess outside the membrane, and the inside of the cell becomes negatively charged with respect to the outside. Voltage—an electrical potential difference—across the plasma membrane results from this difference in charge as well as from the unequal distribution of ions across the membrane created by passive transport. The voltage across a membrane measures from about $-50$ to $-200$ millivolts (mV), with the minus sign indicating that the charge inside the cell is negative versus the outside. In sum, we have both a concentration difference (of the ions) and an electrical charge difference on the two sides of the membrane, constituting what is called an **electrochemical gradient**. Electrochemical gradients store energy that is used for other transport mechanisms. For instance, the electrochemical gradient across the membrane is involved with the movement of ions associated with nerve impulse transmission (described in Chapter 45). A membrane potential derived from a proton gradient across a membrane is the basis for ATP synthesis in mitochondria and chloroplasts, which will be discussed in Chapters 5 and 6 respectively.

## 4.5c Secondary Active Transport Moves Both Ions and Organic Molecules

As already noted, secondary active transport pumps use the concentration gradient of an ion established by a primary pump as their energy source. For example, the driving force for most secondary active transport in animal cells is the high outside/low inside $Na^+$ gradient set up by the sodium–potassium pump.

| **TABLE 4.1** | **Characteristics of Transport Mechanisms** | | |
|---|---|---|---|
| | Passive Transport | | |
| Characteristic | Simple Diffusion | Facilitated Diffusion | Active Transport |
| Membrane components responsible for transport | Lipids | Proteins | Proteins |
| Binding of transported substance | No | Yes | Yes |
| Energy source | Concentration gradients | Concentration gradients | ATP hydrolysis or concentration gradients |
| Direction of transport | With gradient of transported substance | With gradient of transported substance | Against gradient of transported substance |
| Specificity for molecules or molecular classes | Nonspecific | Specific | Specific |
| Saturation at high concentrations of transported molecules | No | Yes | Yes |

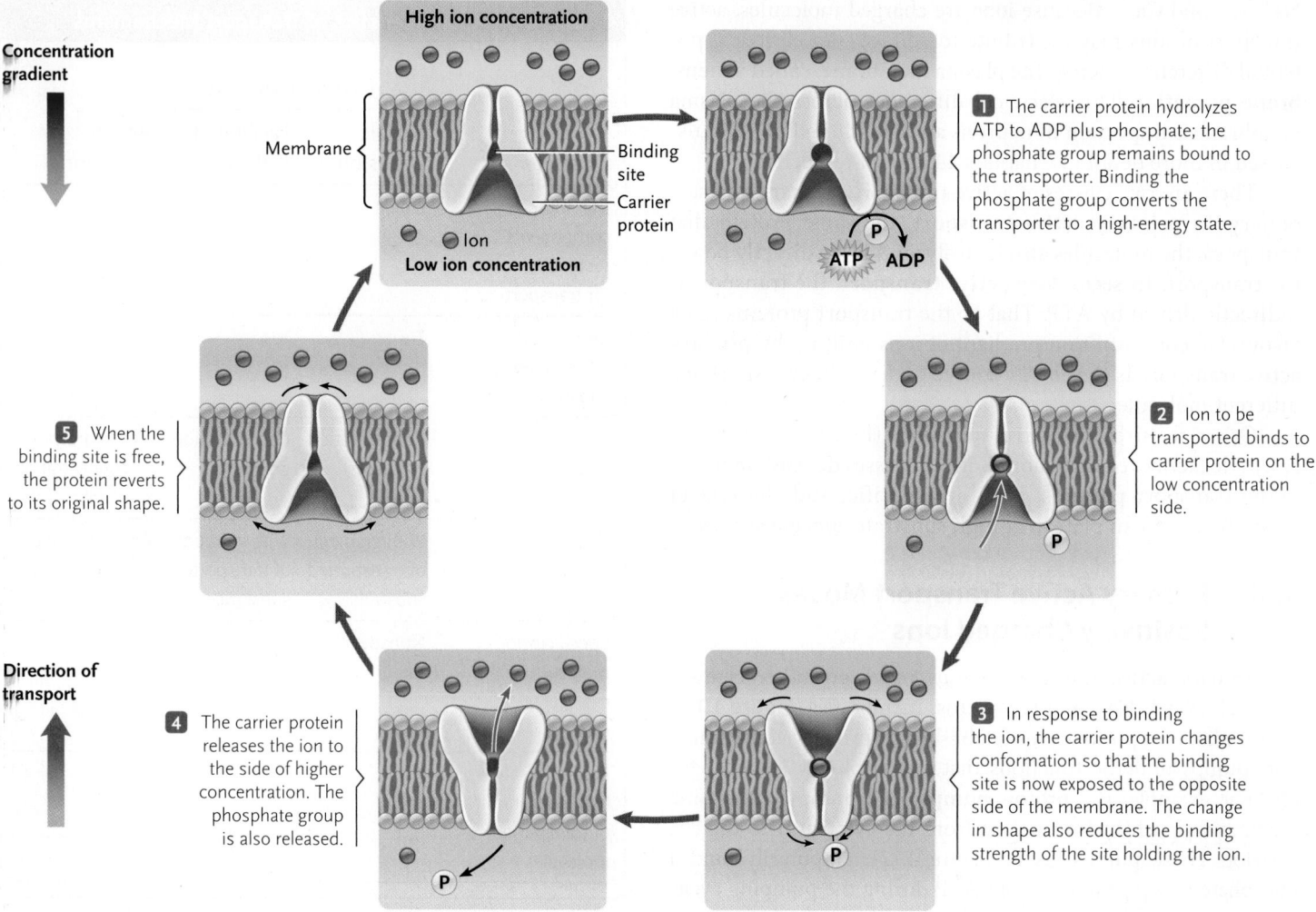

Concentration gradient

High ion concentration

Membrane

Binding site

Carrier protein

Ion

Low ion concentration

**1** The carrier protein hydrolyzes ATP to ADP plus phosphate; the phosphate group remains bound to the transporter. Binding the phosphate group converts the transporter to a high-energy state.

ATP    ADP

**2** Ion to be transported binds to carrier protein on the low concentration side.

**5** When the binding site is free, the protein reverts to its original shape.

Direction of transport

**4** The carrier protein releases the ion to the side of higher concentration. The phosphate group is also released.

**3** In response to binding the ion, the carrier protein changes conformation so that the binding site is now exposed to the opposite side of the membrane. The change in shape also reduces the binding strength of the site holding the ion.

**FIGURE 4.17 Model for how a primary active transport pump operates**

In secondary active transport, the transfer of the solute across the membrane is always coupled with the transfer of the ion supplying the driving force.

Secondary active transport occurs by two mechanisms, known as *symport* and *antiport* (**Figure 4.19**). In **symport**, the cotransported solute moves through the membrane channel in the same direction as the driving ion, a phenomenon known as **cotransport**. Sugars such as glucose and amino acids are examples of molecules actively transported into cells by symport. In **antiport**, the driving ion moves through the membrane channel in one direction, providing the energy for the active transport of another molecule in the opposite direction, a phenomenon known as **exchange diffusion**. In many cases, ions are exchanged by antiport. For example, antiport is the mechanism used in red blood cells for the coupled movement of chloride ions and bicarbonate ions through a membrane channel.

### STUDY BREAK QUESTIONS

1. What is the difference between primary active transport and secondary active transport?
2. How is a membrane potential generated?

## 4.6 Exocytosis and Endocytosis

The largest molecules transported through cellular membranes by passive and active transport are about the size of amino acids or monosaccharides such as glucose. Eukaryotic cells import and export larger molecules by endocytosis and exocytosis. The export of materials by exocytosis carries, primarily, secretory proteins and some waste materials from the cytoplasm to the cell exterior. Import by endocytosis may carry proteins, larger aggregates of molecules, or even whole cells from the outside into the cytoplasm. Exocytosis and endocytosis also contribute to the back-and-forth flow of membranes between the endomembrane system and the plasma membrane. Both exocytosis and endocytosis require energy; thus, both processes stop if a cell's ability to make ATP is inhibited.

### 4.6a Exocytosis Releases Molecules to the Outside By Means of Secretory Vesicles

In exocytosis, secretory vesicles move through the cytoplasm and contact the plasma membrane (**Figure 4.20a**). The vesicle membrane fuses with the plasma membrane, releasing the vesicle's contents to the cell exterior.

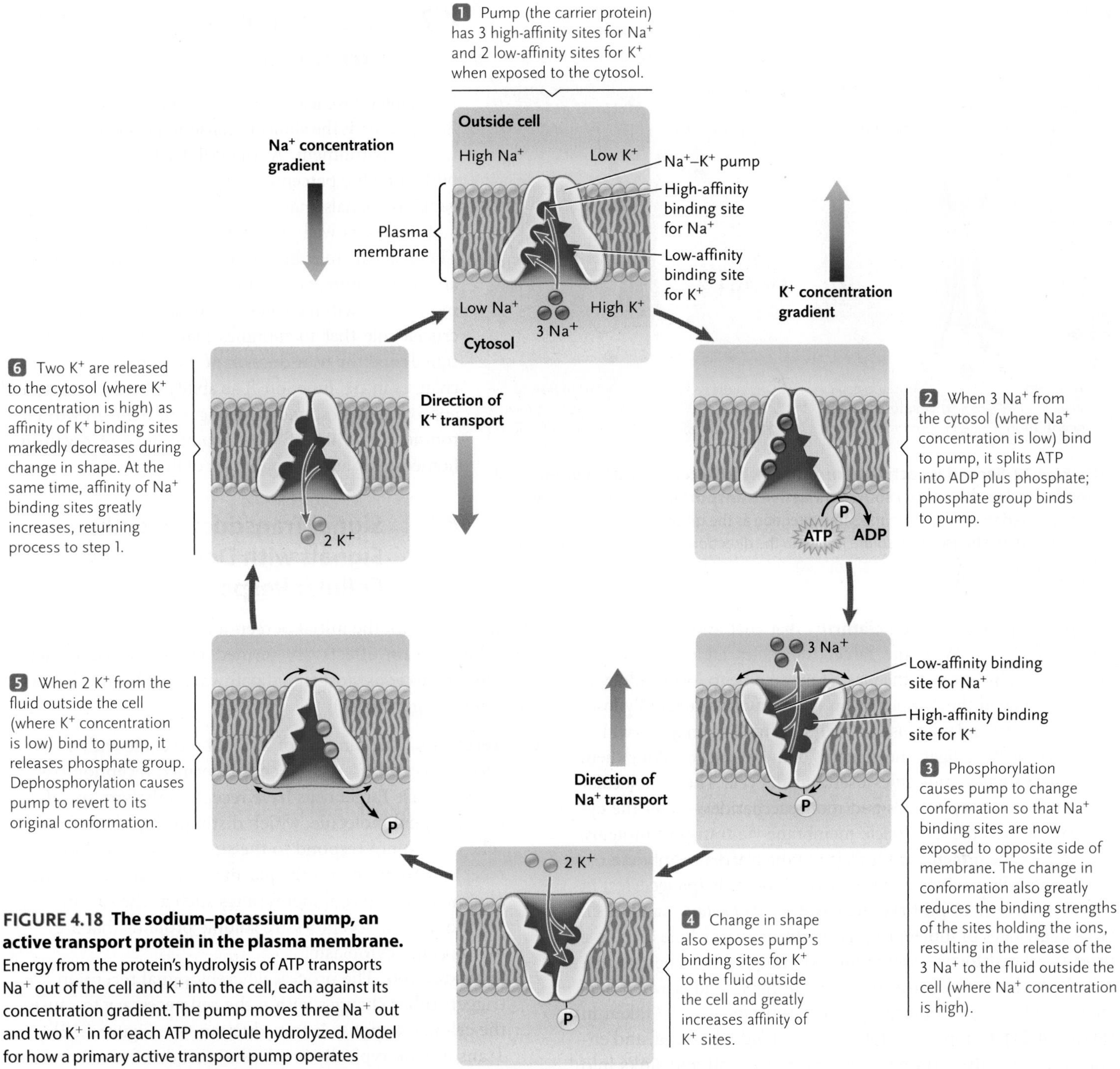

**1** Pump (the carrier protein) has 3 high-affinity sites for Na⁺ and 2 low-affinity sites for K⁺ when exposed to the cytosol.

Na⁺ concentration gradient

**Outside cell**

High Na⁺          Low K⁺

Plasma membrane

Na⁺–K⁺ pump

High-affinity binding site for Na⁺

Low-affinity binding site for K⁺

Low Na⁺          High K⁺

3 Na⁺

**Cytosol**

K⁺ concentration gradient

**6** Two K⁺ are released to the cytosol (where K⁺ concentration is high) as affinity of K⁺ binding sites markedly decreases during change in shape. At the same time, affinity of Na⁺ binding sites greatly increases, returning process to step 1.

Direction of K⁺ transport

2 K⁺

**2** When 3 Na⁺ from the cytosol (where Na⁺ concentration is low) bind to pump, it splits ATP into ADP plus phosphate; phosphate group binds to pump.

P
ATP → ADP

**5** When 2 K⁺ from the fluid outside the cell (where K⁺ concentration is low) bind to pump, it releases phosphate group. Dephosphorylation causes pump to revert to its original conformation.

P

Direction of Na⁺ transport

3 Na⁺

Low-affinity binding site for Na⁺

High-affinity binding site for K⁺

P

**3** Phosphorylation causes pump to change conformation so that Na⁺ binding sites are now exposed to opposite side of membrane. The change in conformation also greatly reduces the binding strengths of the sites holding the ions, resulting in the release of the 3 Na⁺ to the fluid outside the cell (where Na⁺ concentration is high).

2 K⁺

P

**4** Change in shape also exposes pump's binding sites for K⁺ to the fluid outside the cell and greatly increases affinity of K⁺ sites.

**FIGURE 4.18 The sodium–potassium pump, an active transport protein in the plasma membrane.** Energy from the protein's hydrolysis of ATP transports Na⁺ out of the cell and K⁺ into the cell, each against its concentration gradient. The pump moves three Na⁺ out and two K⁺ in for each ATP molecule hydrolyzed. Model for how a primary active transport pump operates

© Cengage Learning 2017

All eukaryotic cells secrete materials to the outside through exocytosis. For example, in animals, glandular cells secrete peptide hormones or milk proteins, and cells lining the digestive tract secrete mucus and digestive enzymes. Plant cells secrete carbohydrates by exocytosis to build a strong cell wall.

## 4.6b Endocytosis Brings Materials Into Cells In Endocytic Vesicles

In endocytosis, proteins and other substances are trapped in pitlike depressions that bulge inward from the plasma membrane. The depression then pinches off as an endocytic vesicle. Endocytosis takes place in most eukaryotic cells by one of two distinct but related pathways. In the simpler of these mechanisms, **bulk-phase endocytosis** (sometimes called **pinocytosis**, meaning "cell drinking"), extracellular water is taken in along with any molecules that happen to be in solution in the water (Figure 4.20b). No binding by surface receptors takes place.

In the second endocytic pathway, **receptor-mediated endocytosis**, the molecules to be taken in are bound to the outer cell surface by receptor proteins (Figure 4.20c). The receptors, which are integral proteins of the plasma membrane, recognize and bind only certain molecules—primarily proteins, or other molecules carried by proteins—from the solution surrounding the cell. After binding their target molecules, the receptors collect into a depression in the plasma membrane called a **coated pit** because of the

**a. Symport**
The transported solute moves in the same direction as the gradient of the driving ion.

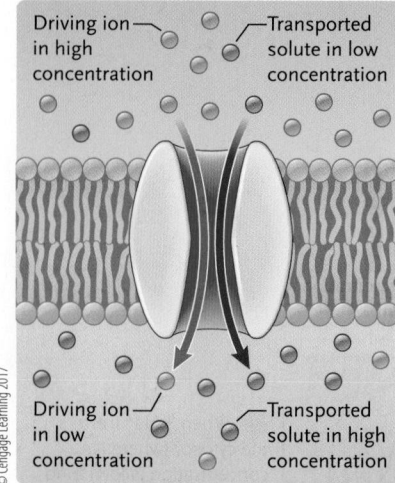

**b. Antiport**
The transported solute moves in the direction opposite from the gradient of the driving ion.

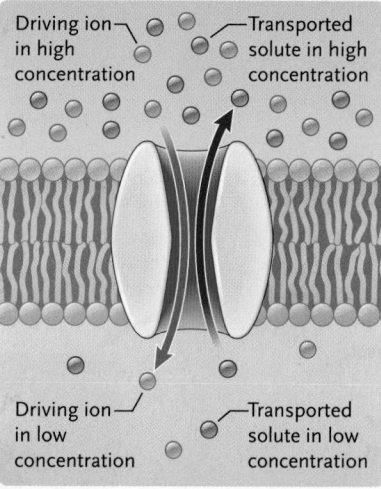

© Cengage Learning 2017

**FIGURE 4.19 Secondary active transport, in which a concentration gradient of an ion is used as the energy source for active transport of a solute. (a)** In symport, the transported solute moves in the same direction as the gradient of the driving ion. **(b)** In antiport, the transported solute moves in the direction opposite to the gradient of the driving ion.

network of proteins (called **clathrin**) that coat and reinforce the cytoplasmic side. With the target molecules attached, the pits deepen and pinch free of the plasma membrane to form endocytic vesicles. Once in the cytoplasm, an endocytic vesicle rapidly loses its clathrin coat and may fuse with a lysosome. The enzymes within the lysosome then digest the contents of the vesicle, breaking them down into smaller molecules useful to the cell. These molecular products—e.g., amino acids and monosaccharides—enter the cytoplasm by crossing the vesicle membrane via transport proteins. The membrane proteins are recycled to the plasma membrane.

Some cells, such as certain white blood cells (*phagocytes*) in the bloodstream, or protists, such as *Amoeba proteus,* can take in large aggregates of molecules, cell parts, or even whole cells by a process related to receptor-mediated endocytosis. The process, called **phagocytosis** (meaning "cell eating"), begins when surface receptors bind molecules on the substances to be taken in **(Figure 4.21)**. Cytoplasmic lobes then extend, surround, and engulf the materials, forming a pit that pinches off and sinks into the cytoplasm as a large endocytic vesicle. The materials are then digested within the cell as in receptor-mediated endocytosis, and any remaining residues are permanently sequestered into storage vesicles or are expelled from cells as waste by exocytosis.

The combined workings of exocytosis and endocytosis constantly cycle membrane segments between the internal cytoplasm and the cell surface. The balance of the two mechanisms maintains the surface area of the plasma membrane at controlled levels.

**STUDY BREAK QUESTIONS**

1. What is the mechanism of exocytosis?
2. What is the difference between bulk-phase endocytosis and receptor-mediated endocytosis?

## 4.7 Role of Membranes In Cell Signalling

In Chapter 2 we learn that one of the key attributes of all living things is the ability to sense and respond to changes to the environment. At the cellular level this is accomplished by the perception of signals. In multicellular organisms, signals may be derived from other cell types and tissues as well as factors external to the organism. These signals may be physical, such as changes in light and temperature, or they may be chemical, such as a hormone or growth regulator. In this section, we discuss the crucial role that membranes play in the perception of signals and the transduction of the signal to bring about changes in cell function. The ability of cells to sense and appropriately respond to changes in their growth environment is critical for the maintenance of organismal homeostasis, another hallmark of living systems.

### 4.7a Signal Transduction Links Signals with Downstream Cellular Responses

The steps that link the initial perception of a signal with its ultimate downstream effects are termed the signal transduction pathway, or cascade. Most signal pathways involve the following three steps **(Figure 4.22)**:

1. **Reception.** The binding of a signal molecule with a specific receptor on target cells is termed reception (see Figure 4.22). Target cells have receptors that are specific for the signal molecule, which distinguishes them from cells that do not respond to the signal molecule. Most receptors are found on the plasma membrane, but some are found on internal membranes such as the ER. In addition, other receptors are soluble proteins that are found in the cytoplasm.

2. **Transduction.** The process whereby signal reception triggers other changes within the cell necessary to cause the cellular response is transduction (see Figure 4.22). Transduction typically involves a cascade of reactions that include several different molecules, referred to as a *signalling cascade.*

3. **Response.** In the third and last stage, the transduced signal causes a specific cellular response (see Figure 4.22). Different signalling pathways lead to different downstream responses. For example, some signal transduction pathways lead to the direct activation of a specific enzyme; others often trigger changes in gene expression.

### 4.7b Membrane Surface Receptors

The membrane receptors that recognize and bind signal molecules are integral membrane proteins that extend through the entire membrane **(Figure 4.23a)**. Typically, the signal-binding

**a. Exocytosis: vesicle joins plasma membrane, releases contents**

FIGURE 4.20 **Exocytosis and endocytosis**

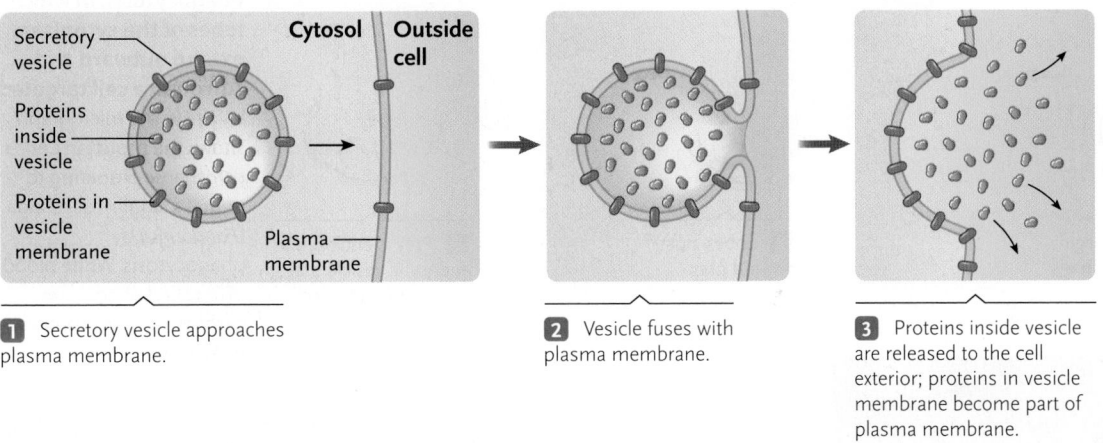

**1** Secretory vesicle approaches plasma membrane.

**2** Vesicle fuses with plasma membrane.

**3** Proteins inside vesicle are released to the cell exterior; proteins in vesicle membrane become part of plasma membrane.

**b. Bulk-phase endocytosis (pinocytosis): vesicle imports water and other substances from outside cell**

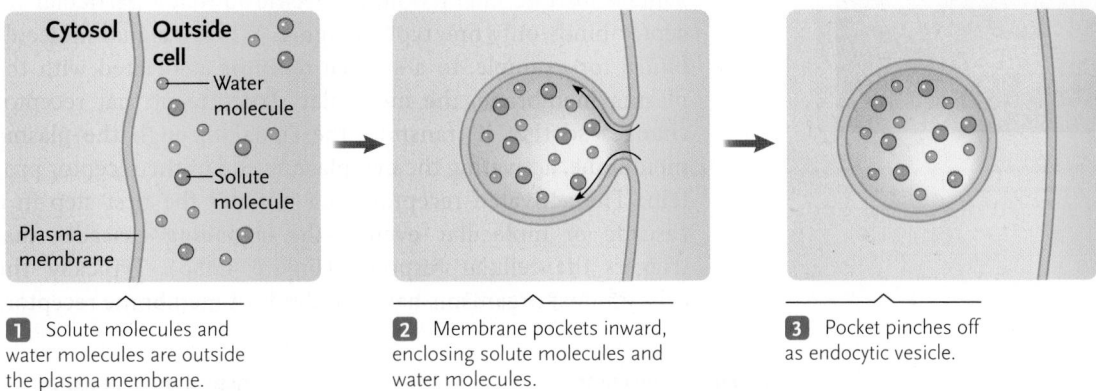

**1** Solute molecules and water molecules are outside the plasma membrane.

**2** Membrane pockets inward, enclosing solute molecules and water molecules.

**3** Pocket pinches off as endocytic vesicle.

**c. Receptor-mediated endocytosis: vesicle imports specific molecules**

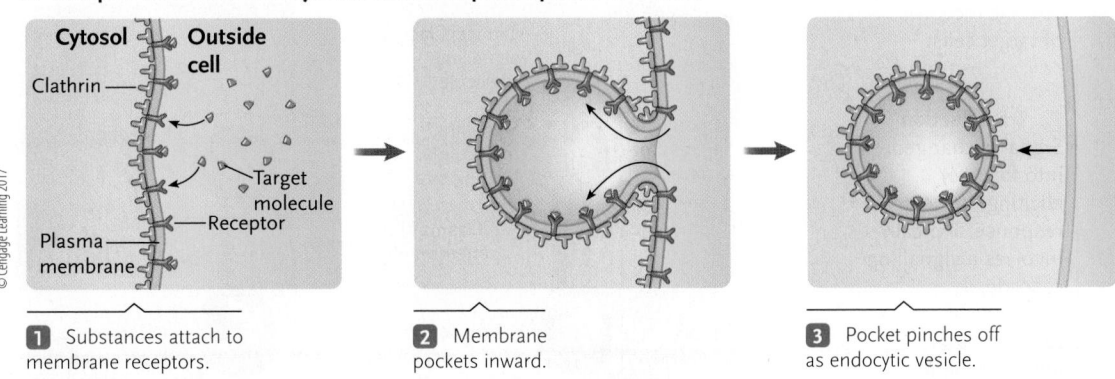

**1** Substances attach to membrane receptors.

**2** Membrane pockets inward.

**3** Pocket pinches off as endocytic vesicle.

**d. Micrographs of stages of receptor-mediated endocytosis shown in (c)**

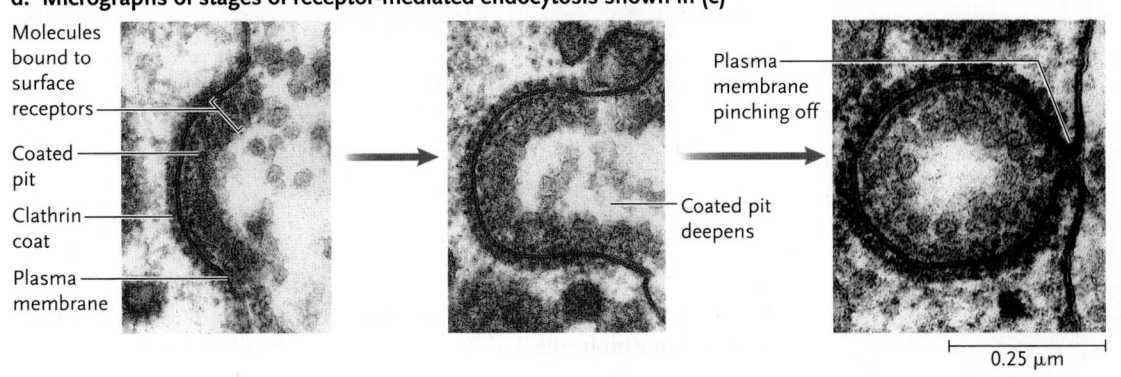

0.25 μm

jcs.biologists.org

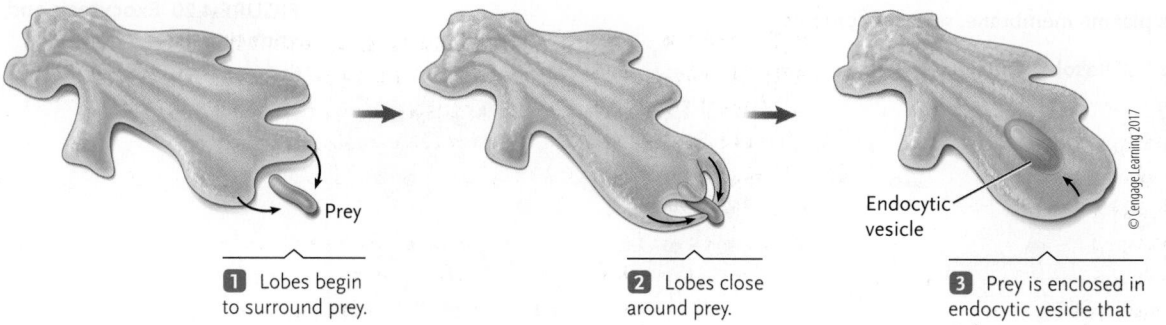

© Cengage Learning 2017

**1** Lobes begin to surround prey.

**2** Lobes close around prey.

**3** Prey is enclosed in endocytic vesicle that sinks into cytoplasm.

Endocytic vesicle

Prey

**FIGURE 4.21**
**Phagocytosis, in which lobes of the cytoplasm extend outward and surround a cell targeted as prey.** The micrograph shows the protistan *Chaos carolinense* preparing to engulf a single-celled alga (*Pandorina*) by phagocytosis. White blood cells called *phagocytes* carry out a similar process in mammals.

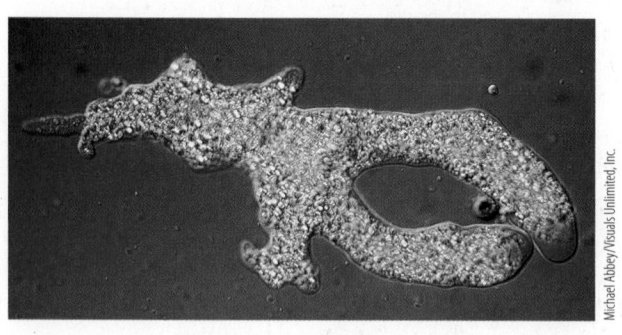

site of the receptor is the part of the protein that extends from the outer membrane surface and is folded in a way that closely fits the signal molecule. The fit, which is similar to an enzyme–substrate interaction, is specific so that a particular receptor binds only one type of signal. When a signal molecule binds, for example, to a surface receptor associated with the plasma membrane, the molecular structure of that receptor changes so that it transmits the signal through the plasma membrane, activating the cytoplasmic end of the receptor protein. The activated receptor then initiates the first step in a cascade of molecular events—the signalling cascade—that triggers the cellular response (Figure 4.23b). Typically, the cells of most organisms have hundreds of membrane receptors

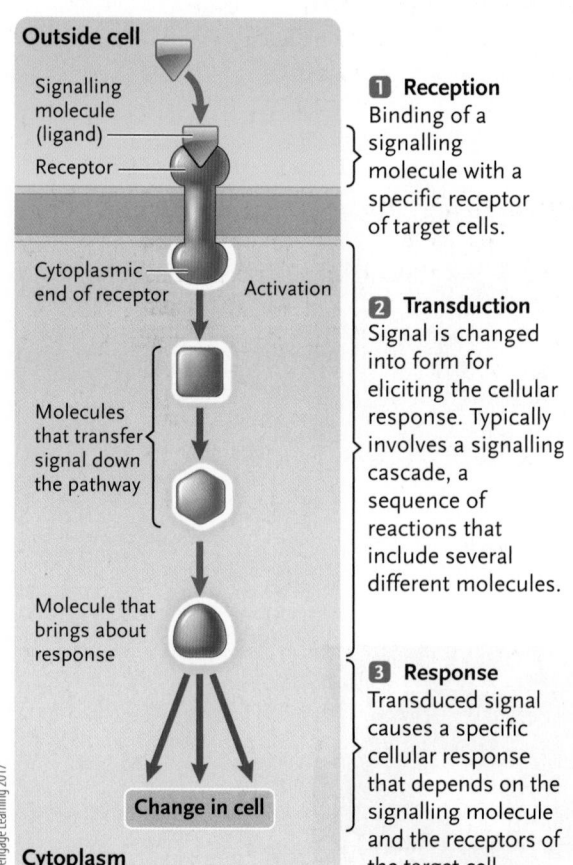

**1** **Reception**
Binding of a signalling molecule with a specific receptor of target cells.

**2** **Transduction**
Signal is changed into form for eliciting the cellular response. Typically involves a signalling cascade, a sequence of reactions that include several different molecules.

**3** **Response**
Transduced signal causes a specific cellular response that depends on the signalling molecule and the receptors of the target cell.

**FIGURE 4.22  The three stages of signal transduction: reception, transduction, and response (shown for a system using a surface receptor)**

**a. Surface receptor**

Outside cell

Extracellular signalling molecule

Extracellular segment of receptor

Signalling molecule-binding site

Transmembrane segment

Plasma membrane

Cytoplasmic segment

Site triggering cellular response, in inactive state

**Inactive receptor**

Cytoplasm

A surface receptor has an extracellular segment with a site that recognizes and binds a particular signalling molecule.

**b. Activation of receptor by binding of a specific signalling molecule**

Reception

Cytoplasmic site is activated and triggers cellular response.

**Active receptor**

When the signalling molecule is bound, a conformational change is transmitted through the transmembrane segment that activates a site on the cytoplasmic segment of receptor. The activation triggers a reaction pathway that results in the cellular response.

© Cengage Learning 2017

**FIGURE 4.23  The mechanism by which a surface receptor responds when it binds a signal molecule**

that represent many receptor types. Receptors for a specific animal peptide hormone, for example, may number from 500 to as many as 100 000 or more per cell. Different cell types contain distinct combinations of receptors, allowing them to react individually to a diversity of signal molecules.

### 4.7c Signal Reception Triggers Response Pathways Within the Cell

The binding of a signal molecule to a plasma membrane receptor, for example, is sufficient to trigger the activation of the signalling cascade. The signal molecule does not enter the cell. For example, experiments have shown that (1) a signal molecule produces no response if it is injected directly into the cytoplasm, and (2) unrelated molecules that mimic the structure of the normal extracellular signal molecule can trigger or block a full cellular response as long as they can bind to the recognition site of the receptor. In fact, many medical conditions are treated with drugs that are signal molecule mimics.

A common characteristic of signalling mechanisms is that the signal is relayed inside the cell by **protein kinases**, enzymes that transfer a phosphate group from ATP to one or more sites on particular proteins. As shown in **Figure 4.24**, protein kinases often act in a chain, catalyzing a series of phosphorylation reactions called a *phosphorylation cascade,* to pass along a signal. The first kinase catalyzes phosphorylation of the second, which then becomes active and phosphorylates the third

kinase, which then becomes active, and so on. The last protein in the cascade is the *target protein.* Phosphorylation of a target protein stimulates or inhibits its activity, depending on the particular protein. This change in activity brings about the cellular response. For example, phosphorylating a target protein may alter the activity of a transcription factor that regulates the expression of a suite of genes.

The effects of protein kinases in the signal transduction pathways are balanced or reversed by another group of enzymes called **protein phosphatases**, which remove phosphate groups from target proteins. Unlike the protein kinases, which are active only when a surface receptor binds a signal molecule, most of the protein phosphatases are continuously active in cells. By continually removing phosphate groups from target proteins, the protein phosphatases quickly shut off a signal transduction pathway if its signal molecule is no longer bound at the cell surface.

Another characteristic of signal transduction pathways is **amplification**—an increase in the magnitude of each step as a signal transduction pathway proceeds (**Figure 4.25**). Amplification occurs because many of the proteins that carry out individual steps in the pathways, including the protein kinases, are enzymes. Once activated, each enzyme can activate hundreds of proteins, including other enzymes that enter the next step in the pathway. Generally, the more enzyme-catalyzed steps in a response pathway, the greater the amplification. As a result, just a few extracellular signal molecules binding to their receptors can produce a full internal response.

This chapter has introduced you to the fundamentals of membrane structure and the role membranes serve in an array of functions, from transport through cellular signalling. Membranes and the compartments they define play a fundamental role in energy metabolism, which is the central theme of the next two chapters on respiration and photosynthesis.

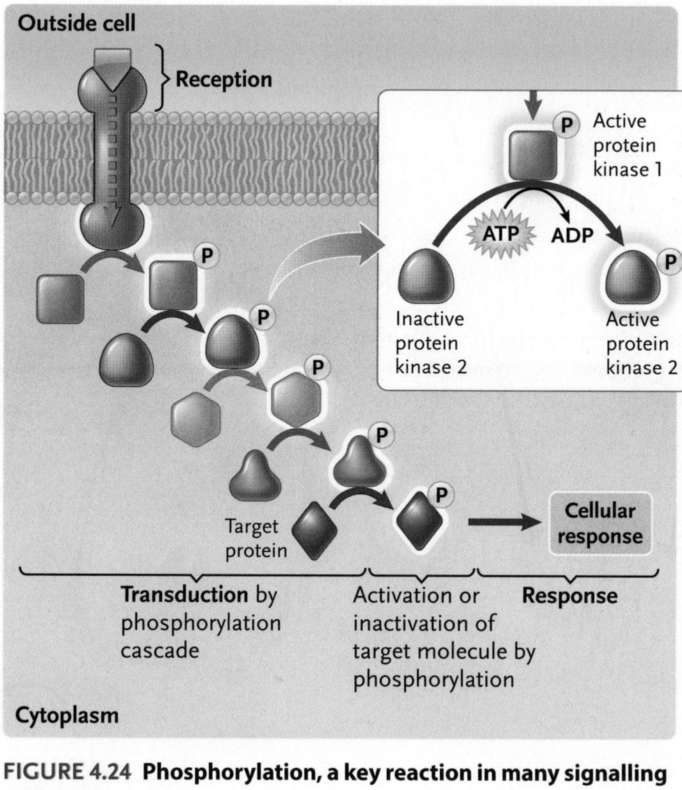

**FIGURE 4.24 Phosphorylation, a key reaction in many signalling pathways**

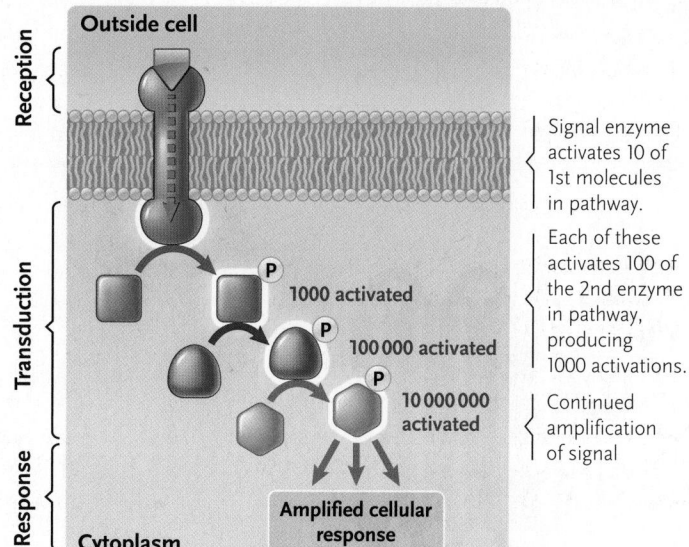

**FIGURE 4.25 Amplification in signal transduction**

# Summary Illustration

Biological membranes are selectively permeable barriers composed of a fluid phospholipid bilayer and proteins. The specific lipid molecules and proteins collectively determine the properties and unique functions of a membrane, which include mediating a cell's response to the environment via signal transduction pathways.

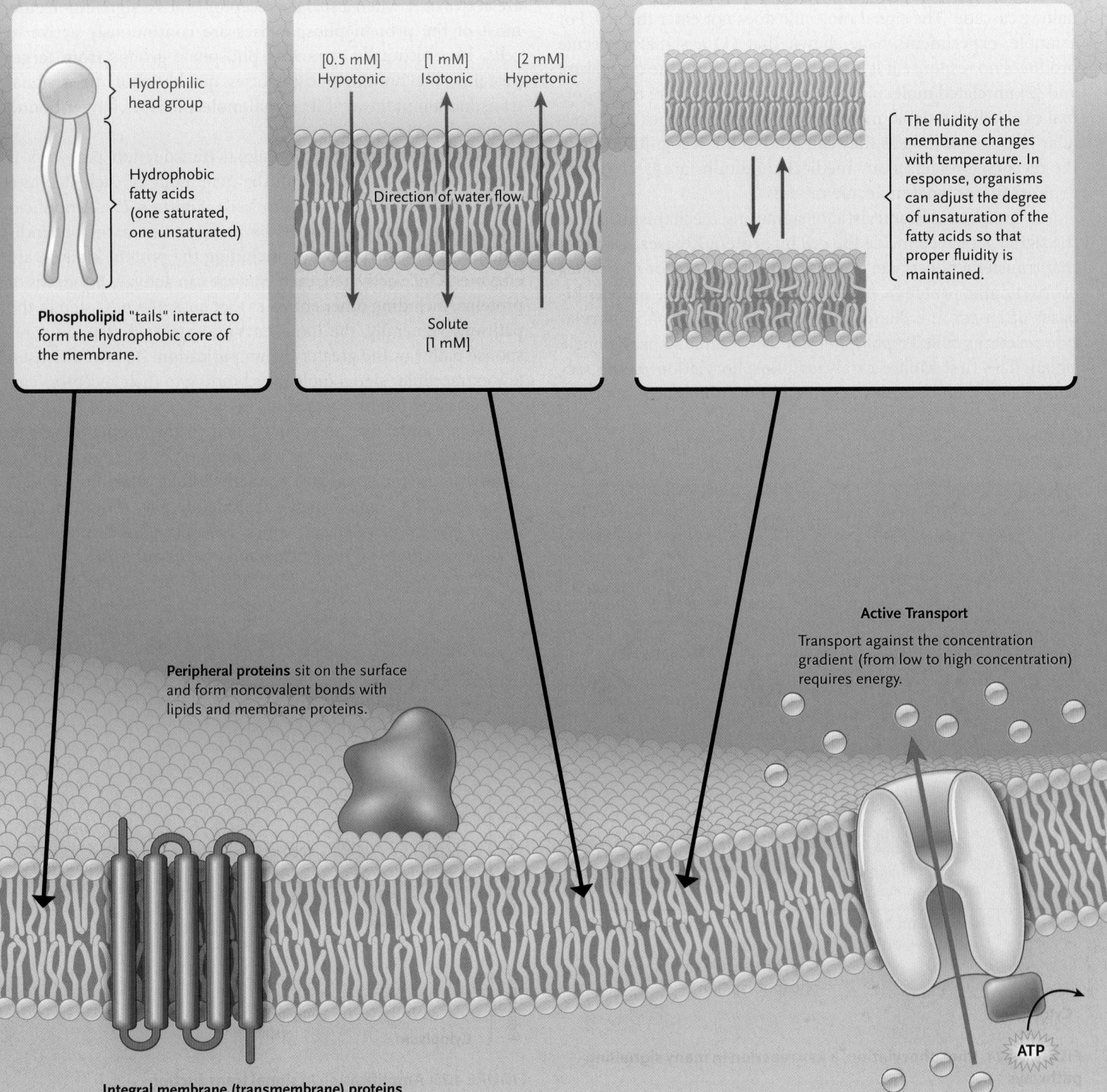

Hydrophilic head group

Hydrophobic fatty acids (one saturated, one unsaturated)

**Phospholipid** "tails" interact to form the hydrophobic core of the membrane.

[0.5 mM] Hypotonic

[1 mM] Isotonic

[2 mM] Hypertonic

Direction of water flow

Solute [1 mM]

The fluidity of the membrane changes with temperature. In response, organisms can adjust the degree of unsaturation of the fatty acids so that proper fluidity is maintained.

**Active Transport**

Transport against the concentration gradient (from low to high concentration) requires energy.

**Peripheral proteins** sit on the surface and form noncovalent bonds with lipids and membrane proteins.

**Integral membrane (transmembrane) proteins** contain hydrophobic domains that cross the bilayer.

ATP

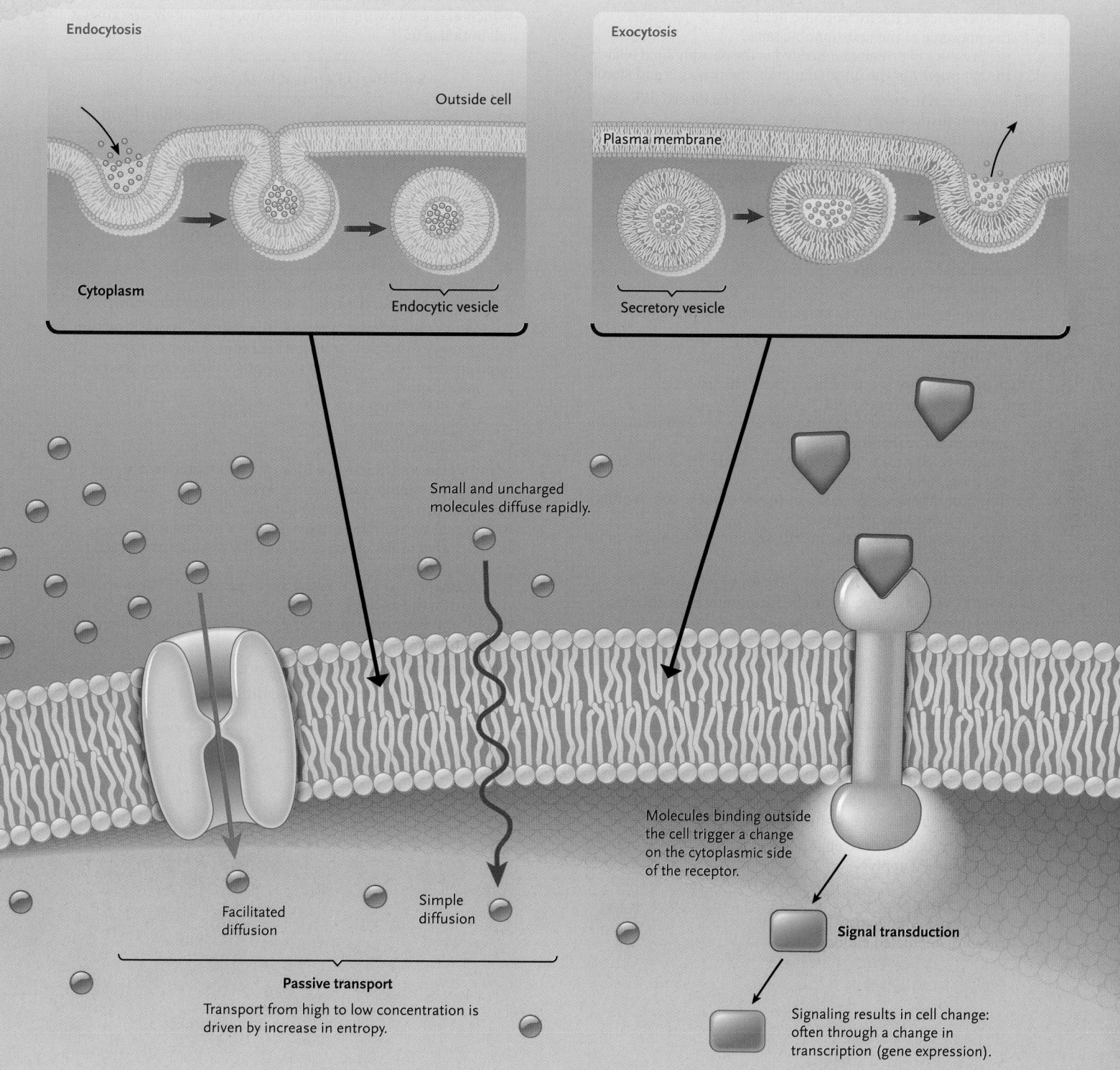

Larger molecules and cell components are transported into cells by endocytosis and out of cells by exocytosis.

Endocytosis

Outside cell

Cytoplasm

Endocytic vesicle

Exocytosis

Plasma membrane

Secretory vesicle

Small and uncharged molecules diffuse rapidly.

Facilitated diffusion

Simple diffusion

Passive transport

Transport from high to low concentration is driven by increase in entropy.

Molecules binding outside the cell trigger a change on the cytoplasmic side of the receptor.

Signal transduction

Signaling results in cell change: often through a change in transcription (gene expression).

# SELF-TEST QUESTIONS

## Recall/Understand

1. Cell membranes are modelled as a fluid mosaic. Which of the following does the "fluid" part of the model refer to?
   a. the constant movement of the phospholipids in the bilayer
   b. the presence of the phospholipid bilayer
   c. the presence of cholesterol
   d. the constant movement of the cytoskeleton attached to it

2. Cell membranes are modelled as a fluid mosaic. Which of the following does the "mosaic" part of the model refer to?
   a. the presence of the hydrophilic heads
   b. the presence of the hydrophobic tails
   c. the presence of proteins embedded in the phospholipid bilayer
   d. the symmetry of the internal membrane proteins and sterols

3. Which of these statements is a characteristic of facilitated diffusion?
   a. It can transport only hydrophobic molecules.
   b. It can be saturated by high substrate concentrations.
   c. It requires a source of chemical energy, such as ATP.
   d. It can transport molecules against a concentration gradient.

4. Aquaporin is an example of which of these proteins?
   a. non-gated channel protein
   b. voltage-gated channel protein
   c. gated channel protein
   d. carrier protein

5. What are the major functions of transmembrane proteins?

## Apply/Analyze

6. Which of the following would most likely characterize membranes that are more fluid?
   a. The more saturated the fatty acids of the lipid molecules, the more fluid the membrane.
   b. The more unsaturated the fatty acids of the lipid molecules, the more fluid the membrane.
   c. The more transport proteins in the membrane composition, the more fluid the membrane.
   d. The more enzymes in the membrane composition, the more fluid the membrane.

7. Suppose that you want to find out if the arrangement of membrane lipids and proteins in the membrane is symmetric. Which of these methods would you use?
   a. light microscopy
   b. scanning microscopy
   c. the freeze-fracture technique
   d. the Frye-Edidin experiment

8. Which one of these elements/molecules shows the slowest rate of membrane diffusion and why?
   a. $Na^+$, because it is small
   b. $K^+$, because it is charged
   c. glucose, because it is large
   d. $CO_2$, because it contains three atoms

9. Suppose that a cell needs to engulf lots of liquids. Which of these processes would it apply?
   a. exocytosis
   b. phagocytosis
   c. bulk-phase endocytosis
   d. receptor-mediated endocytosis

## Create/Evaluate

10. The integral membrane protein rhodopsin, which is used in light perception, is a protein that spans the membrane seven times. What does this tell you about rhodopsin's structure?
    a. It contains seven hydrophobic amino acids.
    b. It is composed only of hydrophobic amino acids.
    c. It contains both hydrophobic and hydrophilic domains.
    d. It contains one long stretch of hydrophobic amino acids.

11. Assume that the setup described by the table was left unattended. Which of the following statements most accurately describes a cell in that setup?

| Selectively Permeable Membrane | | | |
| --- | --- | --- | --- |
| Inside a Cell | | Extracellular Fluid | |
| Solvent | 95% | Solvent | 98% |
| Solute | 5% | Solute | 2% |

© Cengage Learning 2017

   a. The cell will soon shrink.
   b. The net flow of solvent is into the cell.
   c. The cell is in a hypertonic environment.
   d. The relation of the cell to its environment is isotonic.

12. An ion moving through a membrane channel in one direction gives energy to actively transport another molecule in the opposite direction. Which of these process does this describe?
    a. cotransport
    b. symport transport
    c. exchange diffusion
    d. facilitated diffusion

13. Many signal transduction pathways are initiated by a signal binding to a membrane receptor. Which of these statements describes this type of signalling mechanism?
    a. Signal transduction first activates a protein kinase.
    b. A signal molecule injected into the cytoplasm will activate the pathway.
    c. Signal transduction pathways never include components within the nucleus.
    d. A mutation in a single gene can disrupt an entire signalling pathway.

14. Compare passive and active transport.

15. Compare diffusion and facilitated diffusion.

**Cellular Respiration**

Cellular respiration is the collection of metabolic reactions that breaks down food molecules and uses the liberated free energy to synthesize ATP, the central energy currency of the cell.

**5.1 The Chemical Basis of Cellular Respiration**

Glucose and gasoline are both energy-rich molecules because they are composed primarily of carbon and hydrogen, and can be readily oxidized.

**5.2 Cellular Respiration: An Overview**

Cellular respiration can be split into three to four stages; pyruvate oxidation is sometimes split, and oxidative phosphorylation.

**5.3 Glycolysis: The Splitting of Glucose**

The first stage of cellular respiration is glycolysis, in which glucose is split into two three-carbon molecules.

**5.4 Pyruvate Oxidation and the Citric Acid Cycle**

The energy in pyruvate is further converted to synthesize NADH, FADH₂, and ATP.

**5.5 Oxidative Phosphorylation: Electron Transport and Chemiosmosis**

The electron transport chain oxidizes NADH and FADH₂, with the released energy conserved in a proton gradient, which in turn is used to generate ATP.

**5.6 The Efficiency and Regulation of Cellular Respiration**

Cellular respiration can vary in how it uses the total free energy of the molecule, and ATP synthesis is adjusted so that the ATP generated closely matches the cellular demand.

**5.7 Oxygen and Cellular Respiration**

Humans need a constant supply of oxygen, but many other organisms live where there is little, and can derive energy from it through glycolysis and fermentation.

# Chapter Roadmap

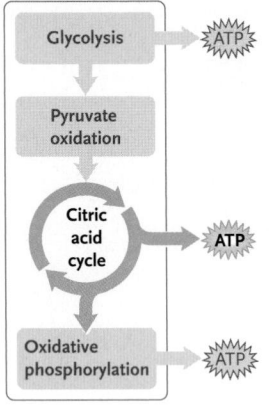

## Cellular Respiration

Cellular respiration is the collection of metabolic reactions that breaks down food molecules and uses the liberated free energy to synthesize ATP, the central energy currency of the cell.

**To Chapter 6**

### 5.1 The Chemical Basis of Cellular Respiration

Glucose and gasoline are both good fuel molecules because they are composed primarily of carbon and hydrogen and can be readily oxidized, liberating energy.

### 5.2 Cellular Respiration: An Overview

Cellular respiration can be divided into three distinct stages: glycolysis, pyruvate oxidation & the citric acid cycle, and oxidative phosphorylation.

### 5.3 Glycolysis: The Splitting of Glucose

The stage of cellular respiration that occurs in the cytosol is glycolysis, which generates NADH, ATP, and pyruvate.

### 5.4 Pyruvate Oxidation and the Citric Acid Cycle

The free energy in pyruvate is harnessed to synthesize NADH, FADH, and ATP.

### 5.5 Oxidative Phosphorylation: Electron Transport and Chemiosmosis

The electron transport chain oxidizes NADH and FADH, with the released energy conserved in a proton gradient, which in turn is used to generate ATP.

**To Chapter 6**

### 5.6 The Efficiency and Regulation of Cellular Respiration

Cellular respiration conserves about 25% of the total free energy of glucose in ATP and is tightly regulated so that the ATP generated closely matches cellular demand.

### 5.7 Oxygen and Cellular Respiration

Humans need a constant supply of oxygen, but other organisms are more flexible and can thrive relying solely on glycolysis and fermentation.

**To Chapter 40**

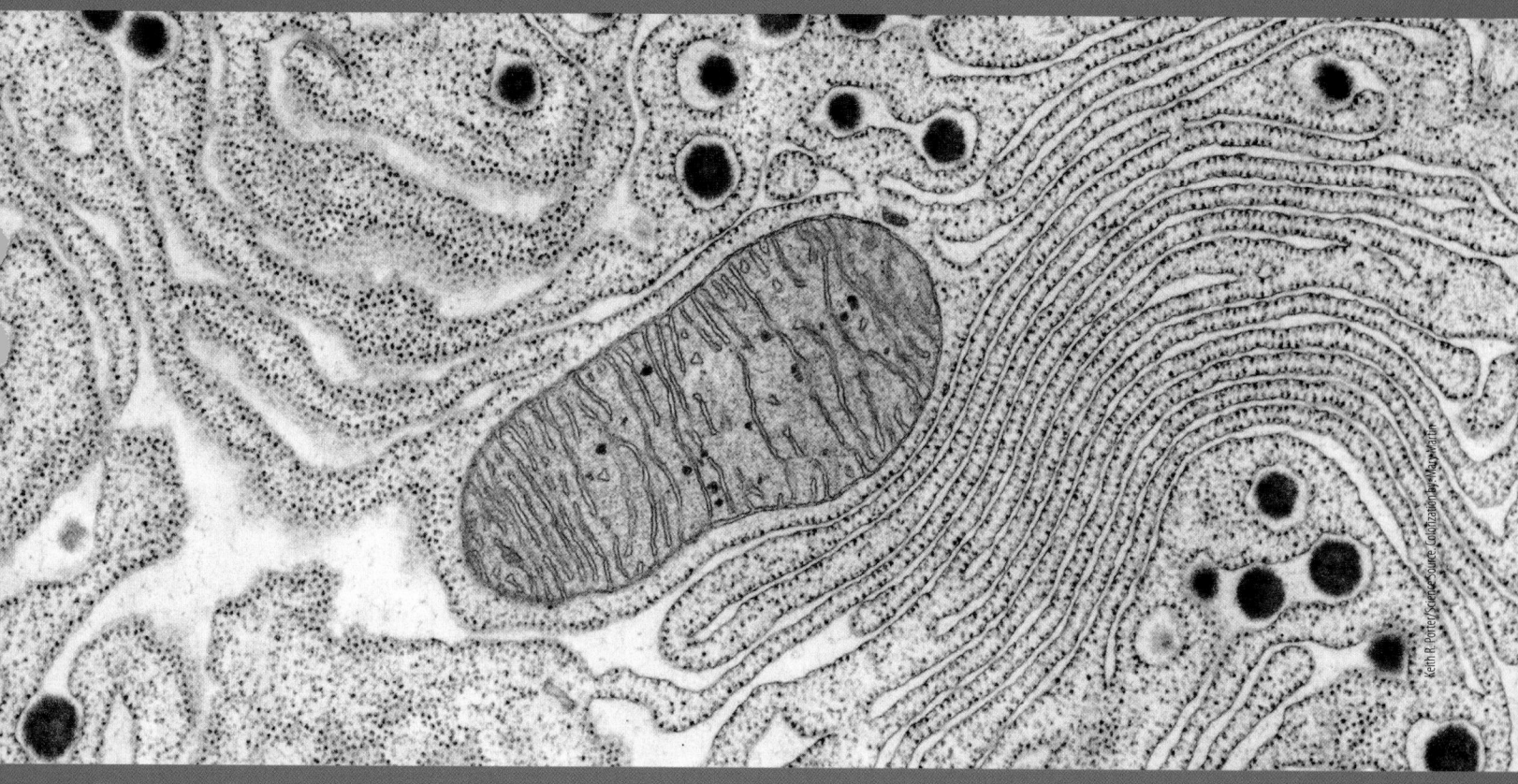

**Transmission electron micrograph of a mitochondrion.** Mitochondria are the sites of cellular respiration.

# Cellular Respiration

# 5

**Why it matters...** In the early 1960s, Swedish physician Rolf Luft mulled over some odd symptoms of a patient. The young woman was hot all the time. Even on the coldest winter days, she never stopped perspiring and her skin was always flushed. She also felt weak and was thin, despite a huge appetite.

Luft inferred that his patient's symptoms pointed to a metabolic disorder. Her cells seemed to be active, but much of their activity was being dissipated as metabolic heat. He decided to order tests to measure her metabolic rates. The patient's oxygen consumption was the highest ever recorded!

Luft also examined a tissue sample from the patient's skeletal muscles. Using a microscope, he found that her muscle cells contained many more mitochondria—the ATP-producing organelles of the cell—than normal; also, her mitochondria were abnormally shaped. Other studies showed that the mitochondria were engaged in cellular respiration—their prime function—but little ATP was being generated.

The disorder, now called *Luft syndrome*, was the first disorder to be linked directly to a defective cellular organelle. This syndrome is extremely rare and has now been shown to be due to a defect in one of the complexes of cellular respiration that links electron transport to proton pumping and subsequent ATP generation. With such a disorder, skeletal and heart muscles and the brain, the tissues with the highest energy demands, are affected the most. More than 100 mitochondrial disorders are now known. Defective mitochondria are now linked to a range of diseases and disorders, including amyotrophic lateral sclerosis (ALS; also called *Lou Gehrig's disease*) as well as Parkinson's, Alzheimer's, and Huntington diseases.

Clearly, human health depends on mitochondria that are structurally sound and functioning properly. But, of course, there is nothing unique to humans here; every animal, plant, and fungus requires correctly functioning mitochondria to live. In eukaryotes, this organelle is the site of key reactions of cellular respiration, the process whereby the energy present in food molecules is extracted and converted into a form usable by the cell. In this chapter, we explore the fundamentals of cellular respiration, starting by addressing what makes a good fuel molecule.

# 5.1 The Chemical Basis of Cellular Respiration

**Cellular respiration** is the collection of metabolic reactions within cells that break down food molecules (e.g., carbohydrates, fats, proteins) and use the liberated free energy to synthesize ATP. As we discussed in Chapter 3, it is ATP that is the form of chemical energy required for the thousands of biosynthetic reactions (**anabolic reactions**) that take place within a cell.

The ultimate source of the organic carbon used to synthesize carbohydrates, fats, and proteins is photosynthesis, which is the focus of the next chapter. In photosynthesis, light energy is used to convert carbon dioxide into glucose, a carbohydrate. Additional biosynthetic pathways can utilize carbohydrates in the synthesis of both amino acids (the building blocks of proteins) and fats. Thus, life of Earth is dependent upon a cycle of energy flow between photosynthesis and respiration (**Figure 5.1**).

## 5.1a Food Is Fuel

Looking at **Figure 5.2**, we can ask ourselves: What is it about glucose that makes it a source of free energy? (To review free energy see Chapter 3.) We could ask the same question of gasoline: What enables it to power a car? Both glucose and gasoline are good fuel molecules—both combust and burn in the presence of oxygen—because they contain an abundance of C—C and C—H covalent bonds. Recall from Chapter 3 that, for any atom, an electron that is further away from the nucleus contains more energy than an electron that is more closely held by the nucleus. The electrons that form the covalent C—C and C—H bonds are equidistant from both atomic nuclei and thus are high in energy.

In contrast to glucose and gasoline, molecules that contain more oxygen (e.g., carbon dioxide) contain less free energy because oxygen is strongly electronegative, and thus electrons are held closer to the nucleus of the oxygen atom. (To review the basics of electronegativity, see *The Purple Pages*.) This fundamental principle of chemistry has an everyday relevance: It explains why, compared to proteins and carbohydrates for example, fats contain more calories (energy) per unit of weight. A fat is almost entirely C—H bonds, while both proteins and carbohydrates contain varying amounts of other atoms, including oxygen.

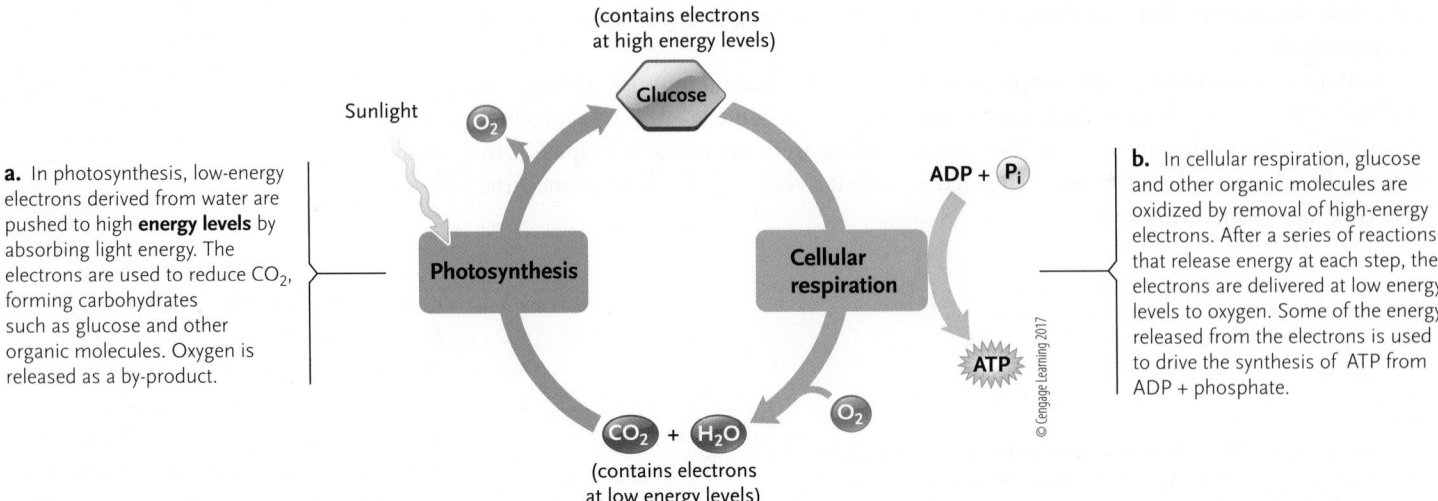

**a.** In photosynthesis, low-energy electrons derived from water are pushed to high **energy levels** by absorbing light energy. The electrons are used to reduce $CO_2$, forming carbohydrates such as glucose and other organic molecules. Oxygen is released as a by-product.

**b.** In cellular respiration, glucose and other organic molecules are oxidized by removal of high-energy electrons. After a series of reactions that release energy at each step, the electrons are delivered at low energy levels to oxygen. Some of the energy released from the electrons is used to drive the synthesis of ATP from ADP + phosphate.

(contains electrons at high energy levels)

Sunlight

$O_2$

Glucose

$ADP + P_i$

Photosynthesis

Cellular respiration

© Cengage Learning 2017

ATP

$CO_2$ + $H_2O$

$O_2$

(contains electrons at low energy levels)

**FIGURE 5.1 Flow of energy linking photosynthesis and respiration.** Photosynthesis uses light energy to convert carbon dioxide and water into energy-rich organic molecules, such as glucose, which in turn are oxidized by cellular respiration.

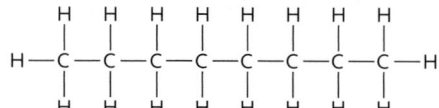

**a. Gasoline**

**b. Glucose**

**FIGURE 5.2 Fuel molecules.** Both gasoline (e.g., octane) and glucose are excellent fuels because electrons of the C—C and C—H bonds are far from the nucleus of the atoms.

The combustion of either glucose or gasoline in the presence of oxygen releases heat as the reactants are converted into the products carbon dioxide and water. Remember from Chapter 3 that *energy is required for bonds to break and is released only when bonds form*. So, the reason combustion reactions release heat is that the energy produced during the formation of the bonds in the products ($CO_2$ and $H_2O$) is greater than the energy required to break the bonds in the reactants (glucose or gasoline and $H_2O$).

### 5.1b Coupled Oxidation–Reduction Reactions Are Central to Energy Metabolism

Having discussed energy in a molecule of glucose, **Figure 5.3** shows the overall balanced equation for its complete breakdown during cellular respiration. What may not be obvious to you is that this reaction between glucose and oxygen producing carbon dioxide and water is an oxidation–reduction, or redox, reaction. The partial or full loss of electrons ($e^-$) from a substance is an **oxidation**, and the substance from which the electrons are lost—the *electron donor*—is said to be **oxidized**. The partial or full gain of electrons to a substance is a **reduction**, and the substance that gains the electrons—the *electron acceptor*—is said to be

**a.**

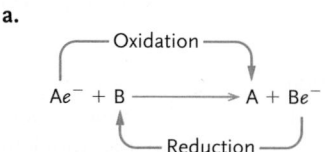

**b.**

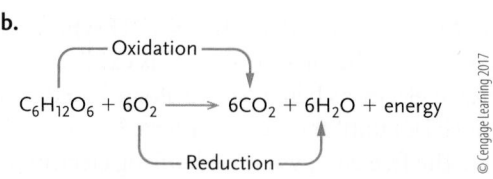

© Cengage Learning 2017

**FIGURE 5.3 Oxidation–reduction (redox) reactions result in the partial or complete transfer of electrons from one substance to another. (a)** Basic redox reaction where there is complete transfer of an electron. **(b)** The breakdown of glucose during cellular respiration is a redox reaction that results in the partial transfer of electrons.

**reduced**. Redox reactions are coupled reactions: the oxidation reaction and the reduction reaction occur simultaneously.

As mentioned above, while some redox reactions result in the complete loss of an electron from one molecule and its gain by another (shown in Figure 5.3a), many redox reactions, including the oxidation of glucose (Figure 5.3b), are the result of incomplete loss and gain of electrons. To understand why Figure 5.3b is a redox reaction, let's look at how the positions of the electrons change in the reactants and products. In the reaction, the glucose is being oxidized, forming carbon dioxide because in $CO_2$ the electrons have moved closer to the oxygen atom, which is more electronegative than carbon. We consider that carbon has partially lost electrons to oxygen; thus the glucose is oxidized. Along with the oxidation of glucose, Figure 5.3b shows that the reactant $O_2$ is being reduced to water. In $O_2$, electrons are shared equally between both oxygen atoms. However, in the product $H_2O$, the electron density is more closely associated with the oxygen atom; thus the oxygen is reduced.

As you have just learned, oxidation and reduction are defined with respect to the gain or loss of electrons. You will see in the reactions described later in this chapter that electron movement is associated with H atoms. Recall that a hydrogen atom, H, consists of a proton and an electron: $H = H^+ + e^-$. Therefore, the transfer of a hydrogen atom involves the transfer of an electron. As a result, when a molecule loses a hydrogen atom, it becomes oxidized.

### 5.1c Cellular Respiration Is Controlled Combustion

To get glucose to combust and burn, we can use a flame to provide the activation energy to get molecules to the transition state (**Figure 5.4a**). In contrast, within a cell, the oxidation of glucose occurs through a series of enzyme-catalyzed reactions (Figure 5.4b), each with a small activation energy. Thermodynamically, the two processes are identical: they are both exergonic, having the same change in free energy ($\Delta G$) of –686 kcal/mol. The big difference is that, if you simply burn glucose, the energy is released as heat and therefore not available to drive metabolic reactions. So a good way to think of the process of cellular respiration is controlled combustion, where the potential energy of glucose is not liberated suddenly, producing heat, but is slowly released in a stepwise fashion, with the energy being transferred to other molecules.

In cellular respiration, the oxidation of food molecules occurs in the presence of a group of enzymes called *dehydrogenases*, which facilitate the transfer of electrons from food to a molecule that acts as an energy carrier or shuttle. The most common energy carrier is the coenzyme nicotinamide adenine dinucleotide ($NAD^+$, oxidized; NADH, reduced; **Figure 5.5**). During respiration, the dehydrogenases remove two hydrogen atoms from a substrate molecule and transfer the two electrons—but only one of the protons—to $NAD^+$, reducing it to NADH. The efficiency of the enzyme-catalyzed transfer of

**FIGURE 5.4** A comparison of the oxidation of glucose by combustion and cellular respiration

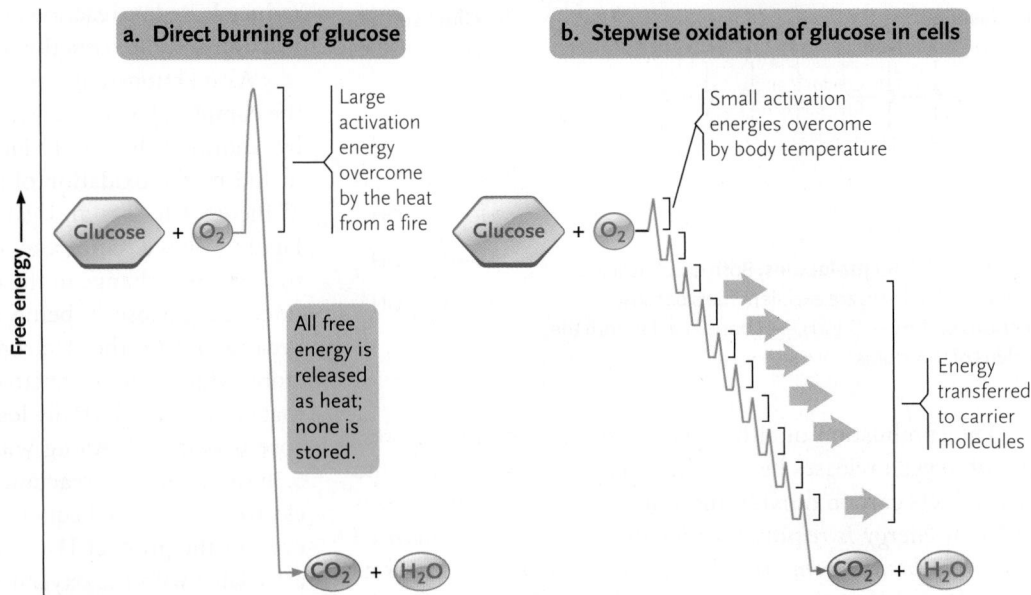

a. Direct burning of glucose

Free energy →

Large activation energy overcome by the heat from a fire

Glucose + $O_2$

All free energy is released as heat; none is stored.

$CO_2$ + $H_2O$

b. Stepwise oxidation of glucose in cells

Small activation energies overcome by body temperature

Glucose + $O_2$

Energy transferred to carrier molecules

$CO_2$ + $H_2O$

**FIGURE 5.5 Electron carrier NAD$^+$.** As the carrier is reduced to NADH, an electron is added at each of the two positions marked by a red arrow; a proton is also added at the position boxed in red. The nitrogenous base (blue) that adds and releases electrons and protons is nicotinamide, which is derived from the vitamin niacin (nicotinic acid).

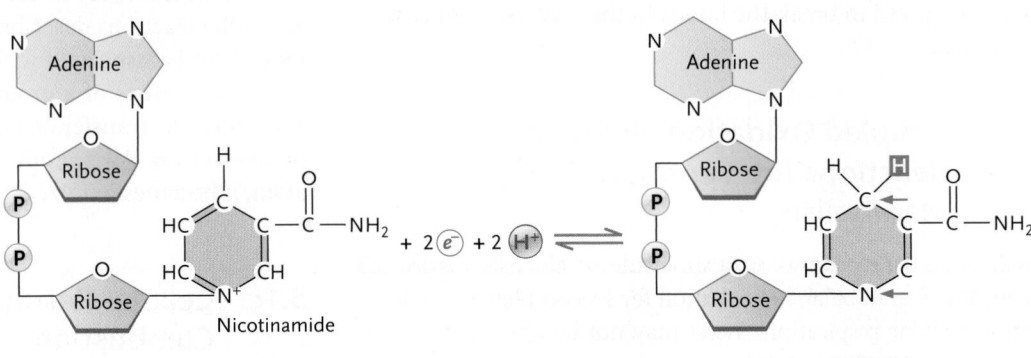

Adenine

Ribose

Nicotinamide

Oxidized (NAD$^+$)

$+ 2 \, e^- + 2 \, H^+ \rightleftharpoons$

Adenine

Ribose

Reduced (NADH)

energy between food molecules and NAD$^+$ is very high. As we will see later in this chapter, the potential energy carried in NADH is used to synthesize ATP.

**STUDY BREAK QUESTIONS**

1. What is it about the structure of gasoline and glucose that makes them both good fuels?
2. In the respiratory breakdown of glucose, what gets oxidized and what gets reduced?

# 5.2 Cellular Respiration: An Overview

At this point, let's step back and remind ourselves of the primary goal of cellular respiration: to transform the potential energy found in food molecules into ATP, the energy currency that is used for almost all energy-requiring metabolic processes. We will see later in this chapter that both proteins and lipids can be oxidized by the respiratory pathway and their potential energy harnessed; however, because the oxidation of glucose utilizes the entire respiratory pathway, it is the main focus of our discussion.

## 5.2a Cellular Respiration Can Be Divided into Three Phases

Cellular respiration can be divided into three phases (**Figure 5.6**):

1. *Glycolysis.* Enzymes break down a molecule of glucose into two molecules of pyruvate. Some ATP and NADH are synthesized.

2. *Pyruvate oxidation and the citric acid cycle.* Acetyl coenzyme A (acetyl-CoA), which is formed from the oxidation of pyruvate, enters a metabolic cycle, where it is completely oxidized to carbon dioxide. Some ATP and NADH are synthesized.

3. *Oxidative phosphorylation.* The NADH synthesized by both glycolysis and the citric acid cycle is oxidized, with the liberated electrons being passed along an electron transport chain (ETC) until they are transferred to oxygen, producing water. The free energy released during electron transport is used to generate a proton gradient across a membrane, which in turn is used to synthesize ATP. All three stages are required to extract the maximum amount of energy that is biologically possible from a molecule of glucose; however, not all organisms undergo all three stages.

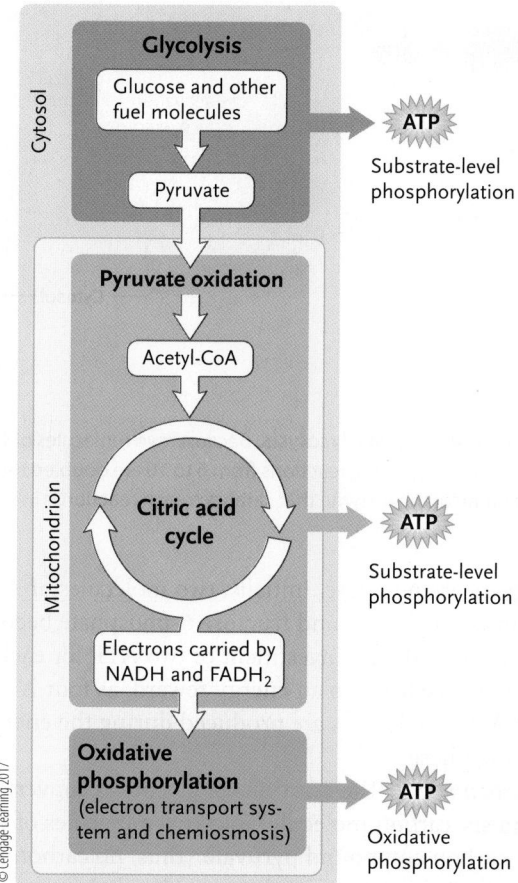

**FIGURE 5.6** The three stages of cellular respiration: glycolysis, pyruvate oxidation and the citric acid cycle, and oxidative phosphorylation

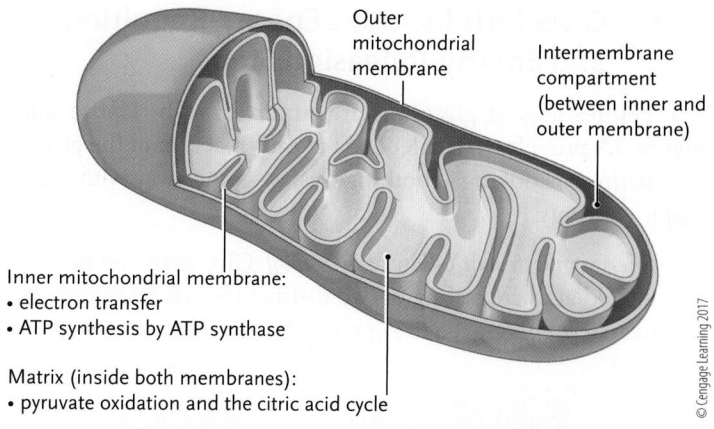

**FIGURE 5.7** **Membranes and compartments of mitochondria.** Label lines that end in a dot indicate a compartment enclosed by the membranes.

## STUDY BREAK QUESTIONS

1. What are the three stages of cellular respiration?
2. Outline the membranes and compartments of the mitochondrion.

## 5.2b The Mitochondrion Is the Site of Cellular Respiration in Eukaryotes

In eukaryotic cells, the citric acid cycle and oxidative phosphorylation occur in a specialized membrane-bound organelle called the *mitochondrion* (plural, *mitochondria*; **Figure 5.7**). The mitochondrion is often referred to as the *powerhouse of the cell* because it is the largest generator of ATP in the cell.

The mitochondrion is composed of two membranes, the outer membrane and the inner membrane, which together define two compartments (see Figure 5.7): the intermembrane space, which is found between the outer and inner membranes, and the matrix, which is the interior aqueous environment.

In the description of cellular respiration that follows, we often refer specifically to mitochondria and their various compartments, but it is important to realize that there is nothing uniquely eukaryotic about cellular respiration. Species of both bacteria and archaea possess the entire complement of reactions that make up cellular respiration, from glycolysis through oxidative phosphorylation. In prokaryotic cells, electron transport and oxidative phosphorylation occur on the plasma membrane or internalized membranes derived from the plasma membrane.

## 5.3 Glycolysis: The Splitting of Glucose

**Glycolysis** (*glykys* = sweet; *lysis* = breakdown) consists of 10 sequential enzyme-catalyzed reactions that lead to the oxidation of the six-carbon sugar glucose, producing two molecules of the three-carbon compound pyruvate. The potential energy released in the oxidation leads to the synthesis of both NADH and ATP.

### 5.3a Glycolysis Is a Universal and Ancient Metabolic Process

Glycolysis was one of the first metabolic pathways studied and is one of the best understood in terms of the enzymes involved, their mechanisms of action, and how the pathway is regulated to meet the energy needs of the cell. The first experiments investigating glycolysis took place over 100 years ago and were some of the first to show, using the extracts from yeast cells, that one could study biological reactions in an isolated, cell-free system. These experiments became the foundation of modern biochemistry.

Glycolysis is the most fundamental and probably most ancient of all metabolic pathways. This is supported by the following facts: (1) Glycolysis is universal, being found in all three domains of life: Archaea, Bacteria, and Eukarya. (2) Glycolysis does not depend upon the presence of $O_2$, which became abundant in Earth's atmosphere only about 2.5 billion years ago, about 1.5 billion years after scientists think life first evolved (see Chapter 21). (3) Glycolysis occurs in the cytosol of all cells using soluble enzymes and therefore does not require more sophisticated electron transport chains (ETCs) and internal membrane systems to function.

## 5.3b Glycolysis Includes Energy-Requiring and Energy-Releasing Steps

The key features of glycolysis are summarized in **Figure 5.8**; **Figure 5.9** provides a detailed look at each reaction of the glycolytic pathway. Looking at both figures, we come away with three major concepts:

1. *Energy investment followed by payoff.* Glycolysis can be looked at as consisting of two distinct phases: an initial five-step, energy-requiring phase followed by a five-step,

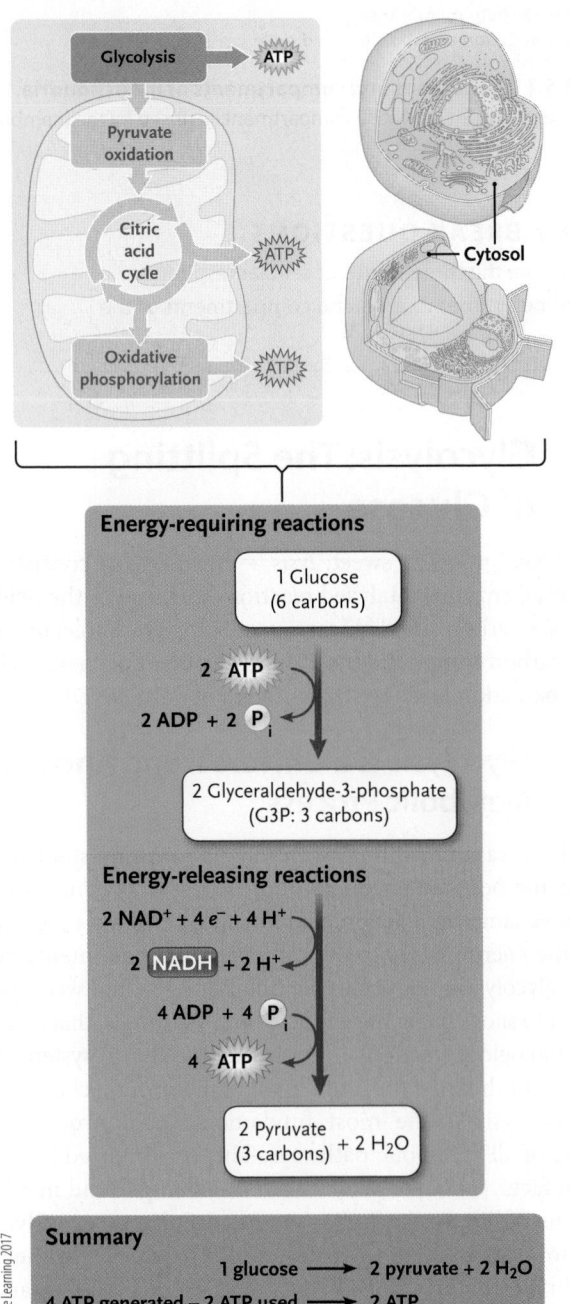

**FIGURE 5.8 Overall reactions of glycolysis.** Glycolysis, which occurs in the cytosol of all cells, splits glucose (six carbons) into pyruvate (three carbons) and yields ATP and NADH.

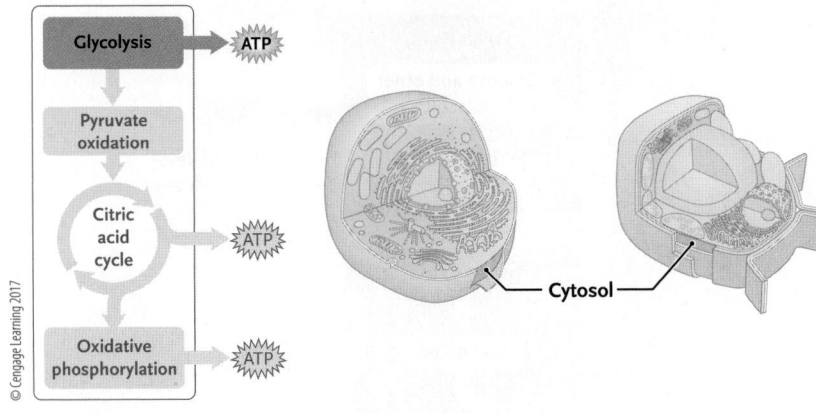

**FIGURE 5.9 Reactions of glycolysis.** Because two molecules of G3P are produced in reaction 5, all the reactions from 6 to 10 are doubled (not shown). The name of the enzyme that catalyzes each reaction is in red.

energy-releasing phase. Initially, two molecules of ATP are consumed as glucose and fructose 6-phosphate become phosphorylated. The investment of two ATP for each glucose molecule leads to an energy reward, as four ATP and two NADH molecules are produced during the energy-releasing phase.

2. *No carbon is lost.* The reactions of glycolysis convert glucose (a six-carbon molecule) into two molecules of the three-carbon compound pyruvate. Thus, no carbon is lost. However, since glucose has been oxidized, the potential energy in two molecules of pyruvate is less than that of one molecule of glucose.

3. *ATP is generated by substrate-level phosphorylation.* During glycolysis, ATP is generated by the process of **substrate-level phosphorylation**. This mode of ATP synthesis, shown in **Figure 5.10**, involves the transfer of a phosphate group from a high-energy substrate molecule to ADP, producing ATP. Substrate-level phosphorylation, which is mediated by a specific enzyme, is also the mode of ATP synthesis used in the citric acid cycle.

### STUDY BREAK QUESTIONS

1. What evidence suggests that glycolysis is an ancient metabolic pathway?
2. What accounts for the fact that two molecules of pyruvate have less free energy than one molecule of glucose?

## 5.4 Pyruvate Oxidation and the Citric Acid Cycle

The two molecules of pyruvate synthesized by glycolysis still contain usable free energy. The extraction of the remaining free energy in pyruvate and the trapping of this energy in the form of ATP and electron carriers such as NADH are the overarching goals of the series of reactions described in this section.

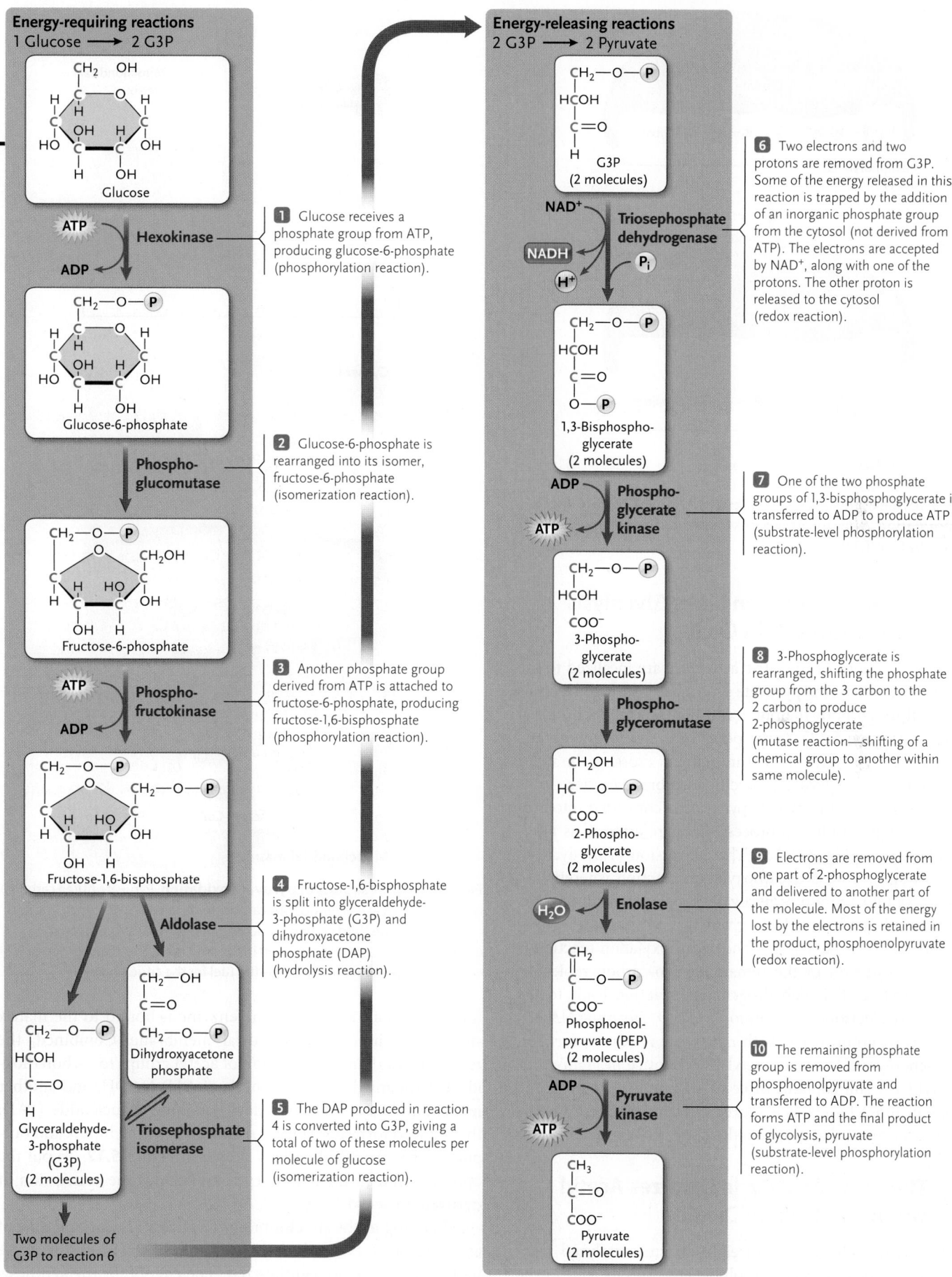

**Energy-requiring reactions**
1 Glucose → 2 G3P

Glucose

**1** Glucose receives a phosphate group from ATP, producing glucose-6-phosphate (phosphorylation reaction).

**Hexokinase**

Glucose-6-phosphate

**2** Glucose-6-phosphate is rearranged into its isomer, fructose-6-phosphate (isomerization reaction).

**Phospho-glucomutase**

Fructose-6-phosphate

**3** Another phosphate group derived from ATP is attached to fructose-6-phosphate, producing fructose-1,6-bisphosphate (phosphorylation reaction).

**Phospho-fructokinase**

Fructose-1,6-bisphosphate

**Aldolase**

**4** Fructose-1,6-bisphosphate is split into glyceraldehyde-3-phosphate (G3P) and dihydroxyacetone phosphate (DAP) (hydrolysis reaction).

Dihydroxyacetone phosphate

Glyceraldehyde-3-phosphate (G3P) (2 molecules)

**Triosephosphate isomerase**

**5** The DAP produced in reaction 4 is converted into G3P, giving a total of two of these molecules per molecule of glucose (isomerization reaction).

Two molecules of G3P to reaction 6

**Energy-releasing reactions**
2 G3P → 2 Pyruvate

G3P (2 molecules)

$NAD^+$

**Triosephosphate dehydrogenase**

NADH

$P_i$

$H^+$

**6** Two electrons and two protons are removed from G3P. Some of the energy released in this reaction is trapped by the addition of an inorganic phosphate group from the cytosol (not derived from ATP). The electrons are accepted by $NAD^+$, along with one of the protons. The other proton is released to the cytosol (redox reaction).

1,3-Bisphospho-glycerate (2 molecules)

ADP

**Phospho-glycerate kinase**

ATP

**7** One of the two phosphate groups of 1,3-bisphosphoglycerate is transferred to ADP to produce ATP (substrate-level phosphorylation reaction).

3-Phospho-glycerate (2 molecules)

**Phospho-glyceromutase**

**8** 3-Phosphoglycerate is rearranged, shifting the phosphate group from the 3 carbon to the 2 carbon to produce 2-phosphoglycerate (mutase reaction—shifting of a chemical group to another within same molecule).

2-Phospho-glycerate (2 molecules)

$H_2O$

**Enolase**

**9** Electrons are removed from one part of 2-phosphoglycerate and delivered to another part of the molecule. Most of the energy lost by the electrons is retained in the product, phosphoenolpyruvate (redox reaction).

Phosphoenol-pyruvate (PEP) (2 molecules)

ADP

**Pyruvate kinase**

ATP

**10** The remaining phosphate group is removed from phosphoenolpyruvate and transferred to ADP. The reaction forms ATP and the final product of glycolysis, pyruvate (substrate-level phosphorylation reaction).

Pyruvate (2 molecules)

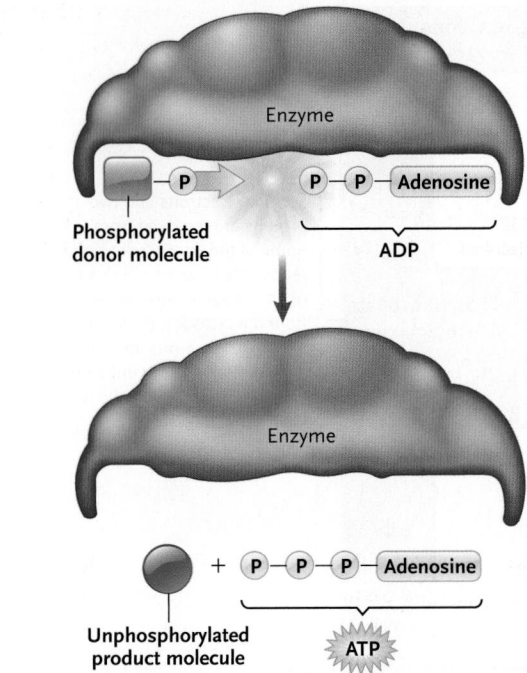

© Cengage Learning 2017

**FIGURE 5.10 Mechanism that synthesizes ATP by substrate-level phosphorylation.** A phosphate group is transferred from a high-energy donor directly to ADP, forming ATP.

## 5.4a Pyruvate Oxidation Links Glycolysis and the Citric Acid Cycle

Because the reactions of the citric acid cycle are localized to the mitochondrial matrix, the pyruvate synthesized during glycolysis must pass through both the outer and the inner mitochondrial membranes (**Figure 5.11**). Large pores in the outer membrane allow pyruvate to simply diffuse through, but crossing the inner membrane requires a pyruvate-specific membrane carrier.

Once it gets into the matrix, pyruvate is converted into acetyl-CoA through a multistep process that is referred to as *pyruvate oxidation* (see Figure 5.11). The conversion of pyruvate to acetyl-CoA starts with a decarboxylation reaction whereby the carboxyl ($-COO^-$) group of pyruvate is lost as carbon dioxide. This reaction is understandable given that the carboxyl group itself contains no usable energy. The decarboxylation reaction is followed by oxidation of the remaining two-carbon molecule, producing acetate. This dehydrogenation reaction leads to the transfer of two electrons and a proton to $NAD^+$, forming NADH. Last, the acetyl group reacts with coenzyme A (CoA), forming the high-energy intermediate acetyl-CoA. Notice in Figure 5.11 that acetyl-CoA still contains three C—H bonds. Liberating the electrons in those bonds as a source of chemical energy is the goal of the reactions that make up the citric acid cycle.

## 5.4b The Citric Acid Cycle Oxidizes Acetyl Groups to Carbon Dioxide

The **citric acid cycle** consists of eight enzyme-catalyzed reactions: seven of the enzymes are soluble enzymes located in the

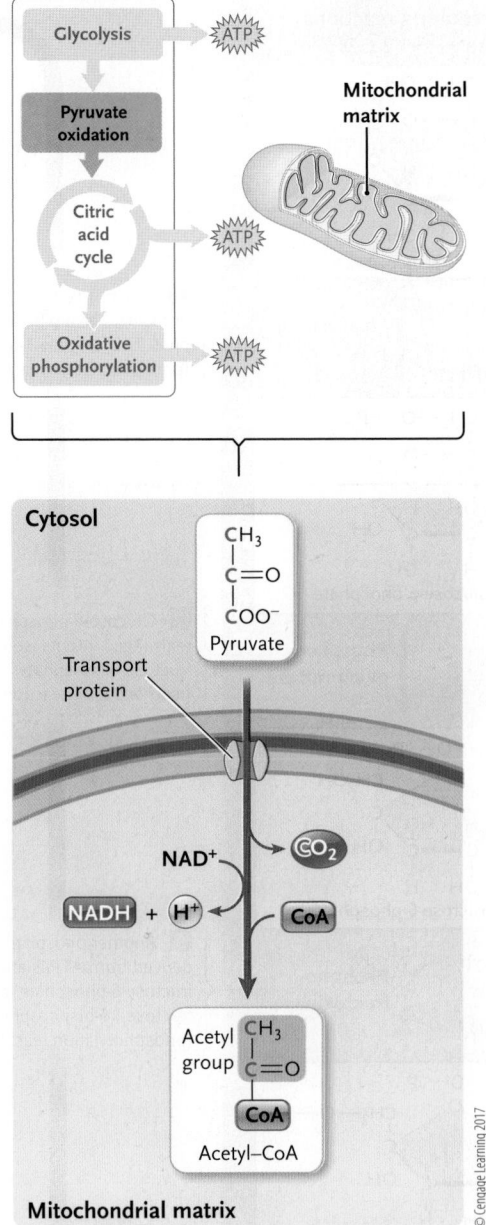

© Cengage Learning 2017

**FIGURE 5.11 Reactions of pyruvate oxidation.** Pyruvate (three carbons) is oxidized to an acetyl group (two carbons), which is carried to the citric acid cycle by CoA. The third carbon is released as $CO_2$. $NAD^+$ accepts two electrons and one proton removed in the oxidation. The acetyl group carried from the reaction by CoA is the fuel for the citric acid cycle.

mitochondrial matrix, and one enzyme is bound to the matrix side of the inner mitochondrial membrane. Combined, the reactions result in the oxidation of acetyl groups to carbon dioxide accompanied by the synthesis of ATP, NADH, and another nucleotide-based molecule, flavin adenine dinucleotide (FAD; the reduced form is $FADH_2$). A summary of the inputs and outputs of the citric acid cycle is shown in **Figure 5.12**. To put the cycle in context, the summary also includes the conversion of pyruvate to acetyl-CoA.

Looking at the stoichiometry (Figure 5.12), for one turn of the citric acid cycle, three NADH, one $FADH_2$, and a single molecule of ATP are synthesized. The energy for the synthesis

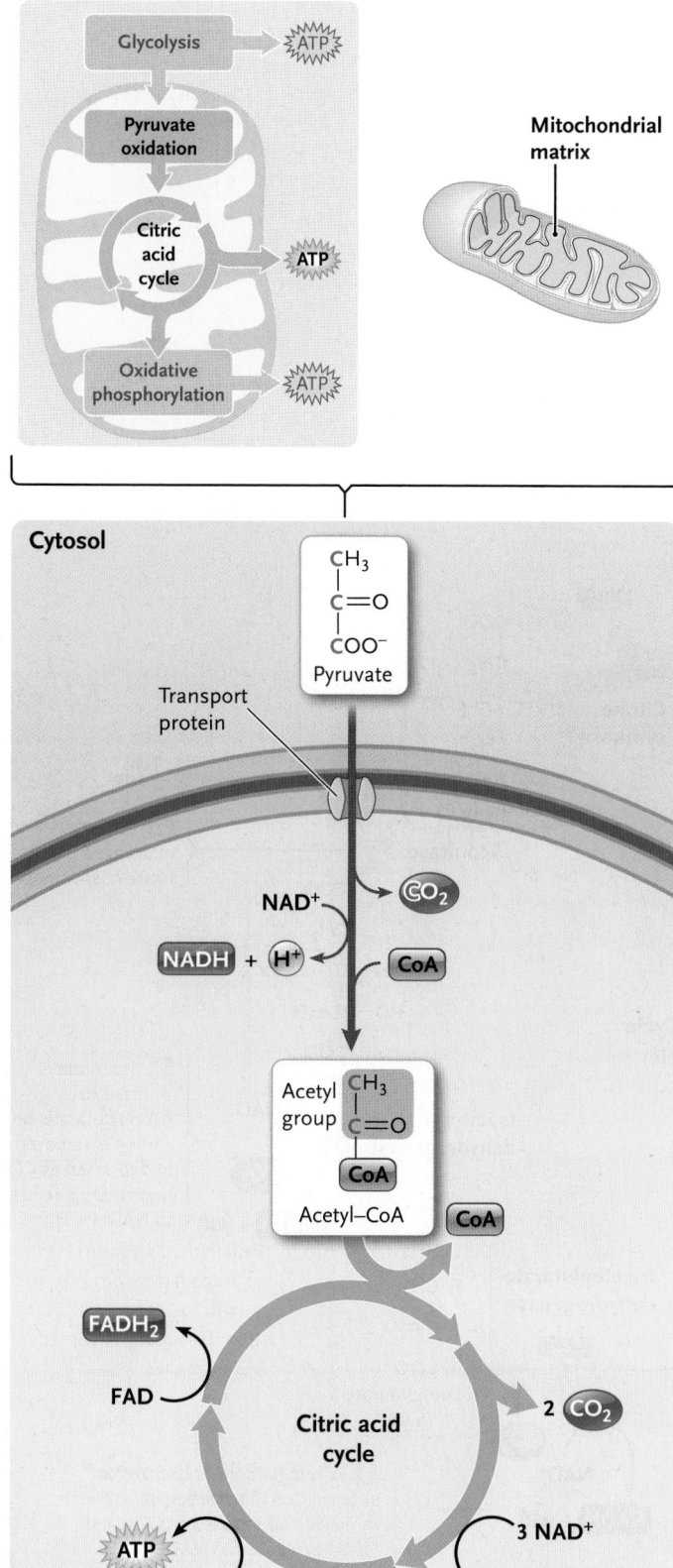

**FIGURE 5.12 The reactions of pyruvate oxidation and the citric acid cycle.** Each turn of the cycle oxidizes an acetyl group of acetyl-CoA to 2 $CO_2$. Acetyl-CoA, $NAD^+$, FAD, and ADP enter the cycle; CoA, NADH, $FADH_2$, ATP, and $CO_2$ are released as products.

of these molecules comes from the complete oxidation of one acetyl unit, resulting in the release of two molecules of carbon dioxide. The citric acid cycle is the stage of respiration where the remaining carbon atoms that were originally in glucose at the start of glycolysis are converted into carbon dioxide. The CoA molecule that carried the acetyl group to the site of the citric acid cycle is released and participates again in pyruvate oxidation. The net reactants and products of one turn of the citric acid cycle are

$$1 \text{ acetyl-CoA} + 3 \text{ NAD}^+ + 1 \text{ FAD} + 1 \text{ ADP} + 1 \text{ P}_i + 2 \text{ H}_2\text{O} \rightarrow$$

$$2 \text{ CO}_2 + 3 \text{ NADH} + 1 \text{ FADH}_2 + 1 \text{ ATP} + 3 \text{ H}^+ + 1 \text{ CoA}$$

Because one molecule of glucose is converted to two molecules of pyruvate by glycolysis, and each molecule of pyruvate is converted to one acetyl group, all the reactants and products in this equation should be doubled when the citric acid cycle is considered as a continuation of glycolysis and pyruvate oxidation. **Figure 5.13** presents a detailed view of the individual reactions of the citric acid cycle.

### STUDY BREAK QUESTIONS

1. What are the steps involved in converting pyruvate into acetyl-CoA?
2. What purpose is served by the citric acid cycle?

## 5.5 Oxidative Phosphorylation: Electron Transport and Chemiosmosis

Following the citric acid cycle, all the carbon atoms originally present in glucose have been completely oxidized and released as carbon dioxide. In addition to ATP formed by substrate-level phosphorylation, the potential energy originally present in glucose now exists in molecules of NADH and $FADH_2$. It is the role of the ETC coupled with the process of chemiosmosis to extract the potential energy in these molecules and synthesize additional ATP.

### 5.5a The Electron Transport Chain Converts the Potential Energy in NADH and $FADH_2$ into a Proton-Motive Force

The respiratory ETC (**Figure 5.14**) comprises a system of components that, in eukaryotes, is found on the inner mitochondrial membrane. The chain facilitates the transfer of electrons from $NADH_2$ and $FADH_2$ to oxygen. The chain consists of four protein complexes: **complex I**, NADH dehydrogenase; **complex II**, succinate dehydrogenase; **complex III**, cytochrome complex; and **complex IV**, cytochrome oxidase. Whereas complex II is a single peripheral membrane protein, the remaining complexes are composed of multiple proteins; for example, about 40 individual proteins make up complex I.

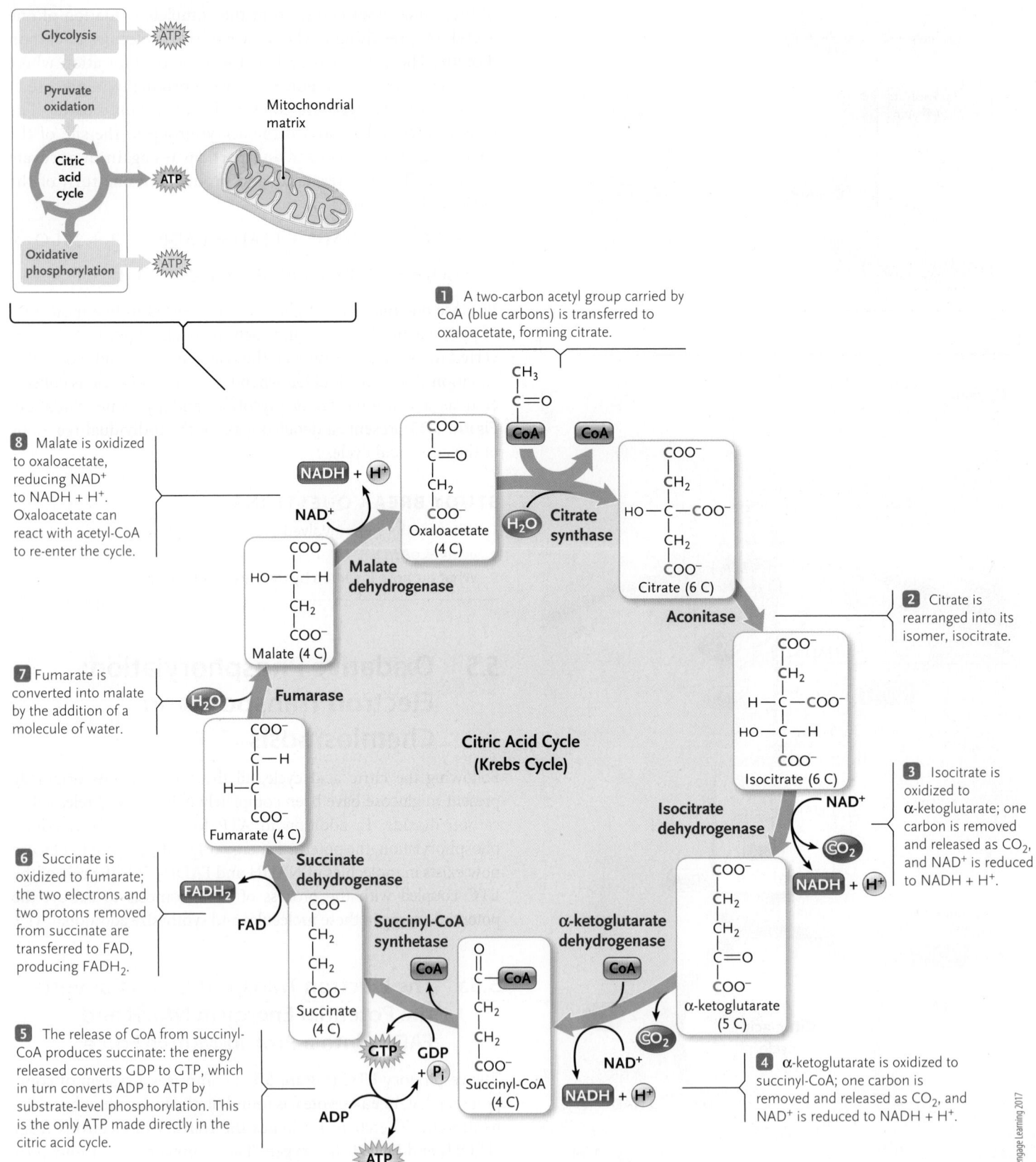

**1** A two-carbon acetyl group carried by CoA (blue carbons) is transferred to oxaloacetate, forming citrate.

**8** Malate is oxidized to oxaloacetate, reducing $NAD^+$ to $NADH + H^+$. Oxaloacetate can react with acetyl-CoA to re-enter the cycle.

**7** Fumarate is converted into malate by the addition of a molecule of water.

**6** Succinate is oxidized to fumarate; the two electrons and two protons removed from succinate are transferred to FAD, producing $FADH_2$.

**5** The release of CoA from succinyl-CoA produces succinate: the energy released converts GDP to GTP, which in turn converts ADP to ATP by substrate-level phosphorylation. This is the only ATP made directly in the citric acid cycle.

**2** Citrate is rearranged into its isomer, isocitrate.

**3** Isocitrate is oxidized to α-ketoglutarate; one carbon is removed and released as $CO_2$, and $NAD^+$ is reduced to $NADH + H^+$.

**4** α-ketoglutarate is oxidized to succinyl-CoA; one carbon is removed and released as $CO_2$, and $NAD^+$ is reduced to $NADH + H^+$.

Citric Acid Cycle (Krebs Cycle)

© Cengage Learning 2017

**FIGURE 5.13 Reactions of the citric acid cycle.** Acetyl-CoA, $NAD^+$, FAD, and ADP enter the cycle; CoA, NADH, $FADH_2$, ATP, and $CO_2$ are released as products. The CoA released in reaction 1 can cycle back for another turn of pyruvate oxidation. Enzyme names are in red.

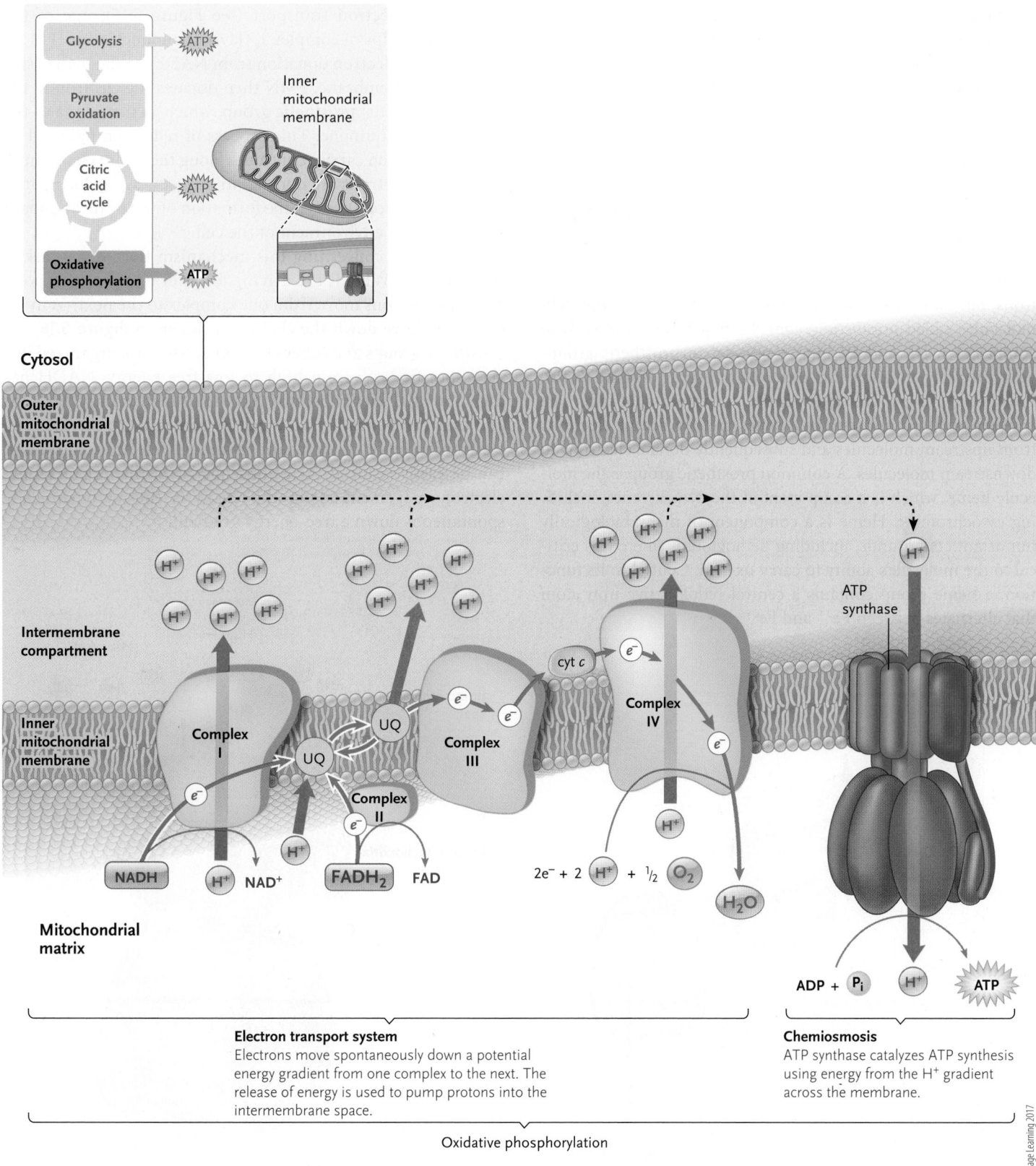

**FIGURE 5.14 Oxidative phosphorylation: the mitochondrial ETC and ATP synthase complex.** The electron transport system includes three major complexes, I, III, and IV. Two smaller electron carriers, ubiquinone (UQ) and cytochrome *c* (cyt *c*), act as shuttles between the major complexes; and succinate dehydrogenase (complex II) passes electrons to ubiquinone, bypassing complex I. Blue arrows indicate electron flow; red arrows indicate H⁺ movement. H⁺ is pumped from the matrix into the intermembrane space as electrons pass through complexes I and IV. H⁺ is also moved into the intermembrane space by the cyclic reduction/oxidation of ubiquinone. Chemiosmotic synthesis of ATP involves the ATP synthase complex, which uses the energy of the proton gradient to catalyze the synthesis of ATP.

Electron flow between the complexes is facilitated by two mobile electron shuttles. Ubiquinone, which is a hydrophobic molecule found in the core of the membrane, shuttles electrons from complexes I and II to complex III. A second shuttle, cytochrome *c*, is located on the intermembrane space side of the membrane and transfers electrons from complex III to complex IV, cytochrome oxidase.

## 5.5b Electrons Move Spontaneously along the Electron Transport Chain

In an ETC it is not the proteins themselves that transfer the electrons, but rather electron transport is facilitated by nonprotein molecules called *prosthetic groups*. Protein subunits of each of complexes I, III, and IV bind a number of prosthetic groups very precisely to allow for electron transport (**Figure 5.15**). Prosthetic groups are redox-active cofactors that alternate between reduced and oxidized states as they accept electrons from upstream molecules and subsequently donate electrons to downstream molecules. A common prosthetic group is the molecule heme, which is a component of the cytochromes, including cytochrome *c*. Heme is a component of many biologically important compounds, including hemoglobin, where it is critical to the molecule's ability to carry oxygen. Central to its function, a heme group contains a central redox-active iron atom that alternates between $Fe^{2+}$ and $Fe^{3+}$.

During electron transport (see Figure 5.15), one of the prosthetic groups of complex I, flavin mononucleotide (FMN), is reduced by electron donation from NADH on the matrix side of the inner membrane. FMN then donates the electron to the Fe/S (iron–sulfur) prosthetic group, which in turn donates the electron to ubiquinone. This process of reduction followed by oxidation of each carrier continues along the entire chain until, finally, the electrons are donated to oxygen ($O_2$), reducing it to water. The protons used in the formation of water are abundant in the aqueous environment of the cell.

Questions concerning this mechanism that we can ask at this stage are: What is the driving force for electron transport? Why do electrons move from one complex to the next? Why do electrons move down the chain? As shown in **Figure 5.16**, the prosthetic groups and other electron carriers are organized in a very specific way: from high to low free energy. NADH has high potential energy because it contains high-energy electrons and thus can be readily oxidized. By contrast, $O_2$, the terminal electron acceptor of the chain, is strongly electronegative and can be easily reduced. As a consequence of this organization, electron movement along the chain is thermodynamically spontaneous down a free-energy gradient.

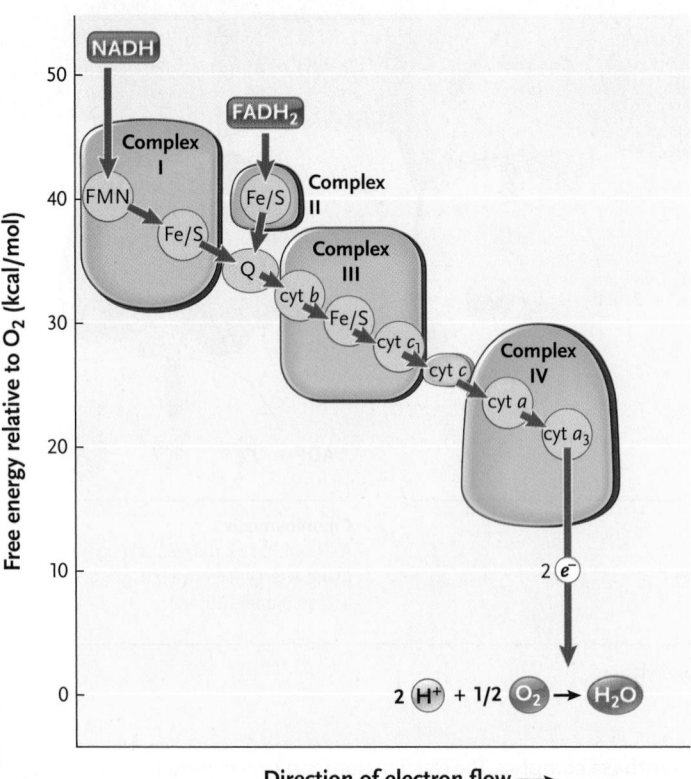

**FIGURE 5.15 Redox components of the ETC are organized from high to low potential energy.** Electron flow is spontaneous from high to low potential energy as electrons are passed from one redox molecule to the next.

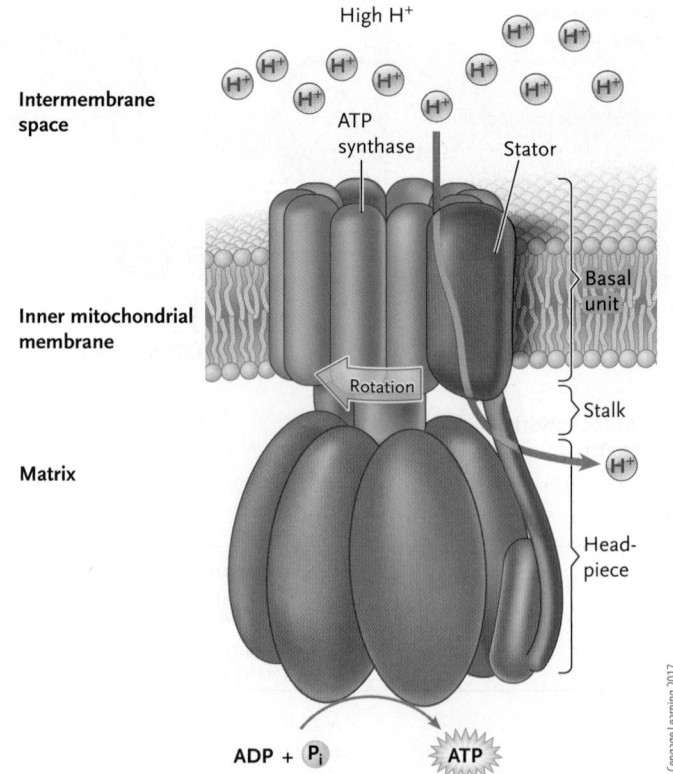

**FIGURE 5.16 Detailed structure of ATP synthase, a molecular motor.** The enzyme consists of a *basal unit* that is embedded in the inner mitochondrial membrane and connected to a *headpiece* by a *stalk*; a *stator* bridges the basal unit and the headpiece. Protons move through a channel between the basal unit and the stator, making the stalk and headpiece spin. This results in ATP synthesis.

## 5.5c Chemiosmosis Powers ATP Synthesis by a Proton Gradient

Although the goal of cellular respiration is the synthesis of ATP, electron transport from NADH (or $FADH_2$) to $O_2$ does not actually produce any ATP. Electrons are simply passed along a chain of electron carriers until they are donated to oxygen, producing water. To understand how ATP is formed let's go back and take another look at Figure 5.14. As we have already mentioned, NADH has more potential energy than $O_2$ has, so one can ask the question: Where does this energy go during electron transport? The energy that is released during electron transport is used to do work, specifically the work of transporting protons across the inner mitochondrial membrane, from the matrix to the intermembrane space. As a consequence of this proton pumping across the inner membrane, which is essentially impermeable to protons, the $H^+$ concentration becomes much higher (and the pH lower) in the intermembrane space than in the matrix.

Proton translocation occurs at distinct sites along the ETC (see Figure 5.14). Within complexes I and IV, specific protein components use the energy released from electron transport for proton pumping. In addition, as ubiquinone molecules accept electrons from complexes I and II, they pick up protons from the matrix. After migrating through the membrane and donating electrons to complex III, ubiquinone retains a neutral charge by releasing protons into the intermembrane space.

The situation in which one side of the inner mitochondrial membrane has a higher concentration of protons than the other side represents potential energy that can be harnessed to do work. The situation is somewhat analogous to water behind a dam. The potential energy possessed by a proton gradient is derived from two factors: First, a chemical gradient exists across the membrane because the concentration of protons is not equal on both sides. Second, because protons are charged, there is an electrical difference, with the intermembrane space more positively charged than the matrix. The combination of a concentration gradient and a voltage difference across the membrane produces stored energy known as the **proton-motive force**.

Harnessing the proton-motive force to do work is referred to as **chemiosmosis**. It was first proposed as a mechanism to generate ATP by the British biochemist Peter Mitchell, who was later awarded a Nobel Prize for Chemistry for his work in this area. Whereas in mitochondria, the energy for chemiosmosis comes from the oxidation of energy-rich molecules such as NADH by the ETC, chemiosmosis also applies to the generation of ATP by photosynthesis energy. The utility of chemiosmosis is shown by the fact that it is not used only for ATP synthesis, the proton-motive force is also used, for example, to pump substances across membranes (see Chapter 4) and to drive the rotation of flagella in bacteria.

The mode of ATP synthesis that is linked to the oxidation of energy-rich molecules by an ETC is called **oxidative phosphorylation**. Compared to the substrate-level phosphorylation that occurs during glycolysis and the citric acid cycle, oxidative phosphorylation relies on the action of a large multiprotein complex that spans the inner mitochondrial membrane, called **ATP synthase** (Figure 5.16).

## 5.5d ATP Synthase Is a Molecular Motor

ATP synthase is a lollipop-shaped complex consisting of a basal unit that is embedded in the inner mitochondrial membrane and connected to a headpiece by a stalk (see Figure 5.16). The headpiece extends into the mitochondrial matrix. The basal unit forms a channel through which $H^+$ can pass freely. The proton-motive force is what propels protons in the intermembrane space through the channel in the enzyme's basal unit, down their concentration gradient, and into the matrix. Evidence indicates that the binding of individual protons to sites in the headpiece causes it to rotate in a way that catalyzes the formation of ATP from ADP and $P_i$. The spinning of the headpiece of ATP synthase represents the smallest molecular rotary motor known in nature.

In Chapter 4, we described active transport pumps that use energy from ATP to transport ions across membranes against their concentration gradients (see Figure 4.17). An active transport pump is, in fact, an ATP synthase that is operating in reverse. It doesn't synthesize ATP but rather uses the free energy from the hydrolysis of ATP to provide the energy necessary to pump ions (such as protons) across a membrane.

Harnessing the potential energy that is present in a proton gradient to synthesize ATP is fundamental to almost all forms of life and developed early in the evolution of life. This is shown by the fact that the ATP synthase complex found in mitochondria is structurally very similar to the ATP synthase complexes found in the thylakoid membrane of the chloroplast and in the plasma membrane of many bacteria and archaea.

## 5.5e Electron Transport and Chemiosmosis Can Be Uncoupled

**CONCEPT FIX** Coming out of high school, many students think that ATP is a product of the respiratory ETC. This is a misconception that we need to fix. The generation of ATP by the ATP synthase complex is linked, or coupled, to electron transport by the proton gradient established across the inner mitochondrial membrane. But electron transport and the chemiosmotic generation of ATP are separate and distinct processes and are not always completely coupled (**Figure 5.17**). For example, it is possible to have high rates of electron transport (and thus high rates of oxygen consumption) and yet no ATP generated by chemiosmosis. This uncoupling of the two processes occurs when mechanisms prevent the formation of a proton-motive force. ⬣

A class of chemicals called *ionophores* form channels across membranes through which ions, including protons, can pass freely. As a consequence, in the presence of ionophores, proton pumping during electron transport is followed by the protons simply flowing back into the matrix through the ionophore channels. A proton gradient is prevented from becoming

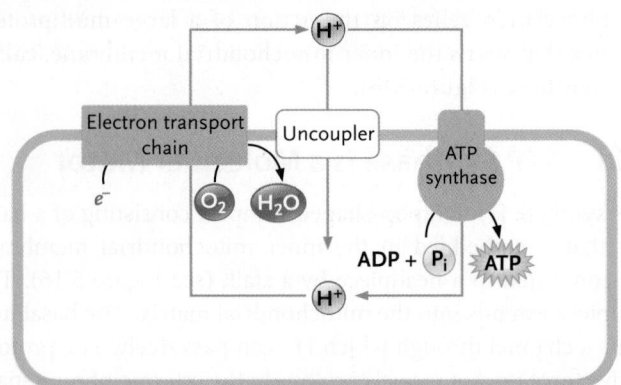

**FIGURE 5.17 Uncoupling of electron transport and ATP synthesis.** Respiratory electron transport results in the formation of a proton gradient across the membrane. Usually, this gradient is dissipated by protons flowing back to the matrix through the ATP synthase. Uncouplers, which may be specific chemicals or proteins, provide an alternative route for protons to flow back across the membrane. By circumventing the ATP synthase, no ATP is generated.

established. Often referred to as *uncouplers*, ionophores are very toxic because of their ability to inhibit oxidative phosphorylation. It is interesting to note that, in the 1930s, low concentrations of chemical uncouplers were commonly used as diet drugs. Although people did lose weight, overdoses resulting in death were not uncommon.

When electron transport is uncoupled from the chemiosmotic synthesis of ATP, the free energy released during electron transport is not conserved by the establishment of a proton-motive force, but instead is lost as heat. Many organisms take advantage of this as a means of regulating body temperature by altering the expression of a group of transmembrane proteins. These *uncoupling proteins* are localized to the inner mitochondrial membrane and, similar to chemical uncouplers, form channels through which protons can flow freely. This mechanism of regulating body temperature is especially important in animals. For example, in hibernating mammals and newborn infants, the activity of uncoupling proteins within mitochondria of brown adipose fat is an important mechanism of heat generation.

### STUDY BREAK QUESTIONS

1. Differentiate the terms *proton-motive force*, *chemiosmosis*, and *oxidative phosphorylation*.
2. What does it mean that electron transport and oxidative phosphorylation are coupled processes?

## 5.6 The Efficiency and Regulation of Cellular Respiration

In this section, we calculate the efficiency with which cellular respiration extracts energy from glucose. As well, we discuss how this entire multi-enzyme pathway is regulated so that it remains flexible in the face of changing cellular demands for ATP and changes in food supply.

### 5.6a What Are the ATP Yield and Efficiency of Cellular Respiration?

Determining the total number of ATP molecules synthesized for each molecule of glucose oxidized during cellular respiration is an important exercise that forces us to integrate all parts of the respiratory pathway. But before we look at the whole pathway, we first consider a question concerning oxidative phosphorylation: How many ATP molecules are produced by oxidative phosphorylation? Recent research suggests that, for each NADH that is oxidized, and thus for each pair of electrons that travels down the ETC, 10 $H^+$ are pumped into the inner membrane space. (*Note:* Don't try to figure out how you get 10 protons pumped from 2 electrons—it is not straightforward—wait until you take an advanced biochemistry course.) We also know that somewhere between 3 and 4 $H^+$ are needed to flow back through the ATP synthase for the synthesis of 1 molecule of ATP. So that gives between 2.5 and 3.3 molecules of ATP synthesized for every NADH oxidized by the ETC. To make life easier, let's round off and say that, for each NADH oxidized, 3 ATP are synthesized. Because the oxidation of $FADH_2$ skips the proton-pumping complex I (look back at Figure 5.14), only about 2 molecules of ATP are synthesized for each $FADH_2$ oxidized.

A detailed accounting of the ATP yield for each molecule of glucose oxidized is provided in **Figure 5.18**. Recall that the products of glycolysis include 2 molecules of ATP and 2 molecules of NADH. Next, the oxidation of the 2 molecules of pyruvate generated by glycolysis results in the synthesis of 2 NADH. During the citric acid cycle, the 2 molecules of acetyl-CoA that are oxidized result in the synthesis of 2 ATP along with 6 NADH and 2 $FADH_2$. That gives us a total of 10 NADH and 2 $FADH_2$ that can be oxidized by the ETC. Recall that about 3 ATP are produced by oxidative phosphorylation for each NADH oxidized by the ETC, and $FADH_2$ oxidation yields 2 ATP. So that gives a total of 34 ATP generated by oxidative phosphorylation as a result of the oxidation of 10 NADH and 2 $FADH_2$. So, adding up, we have 2 ATP from glycolysis, 2 ATP directly from the citric acid cycle, and 34 ATP from oxidative phosphorylation, yielding 38 molecules of ATP synthesized for each glucose oxidized!

The 38 ATP for each glucose oxidized is the maximum theoretical yield. There are three reasons, however, why this maximum is rarely achieved. First, while the maximum of 38 is true in bacteria, this is not the case in eukaryotic cells, where the theoretical maximum is only 36 ATP. This difference is due to the energy costs of transporting the NADH generated by glycolysis into the mitochondrion. The active transport system needed to move the electrons associated with NADH into the mitochondrion consumes 1 ATP for each molecule of NADH transported. Since 2 NADH are transported, the yield of ATP drops by 2. The second reason why the yield is less than 38 ATP is that electron transport and oxidative phosphorylation are rarely completely coupled to each other. Even under normal metabolic conditions, the inner mitochondrial membrane is somewhat leaky to protons, and thus not all the protons pumped across during electron transport pass back into the matrix through the ATP synthase. Some reenter the matrix by slowly

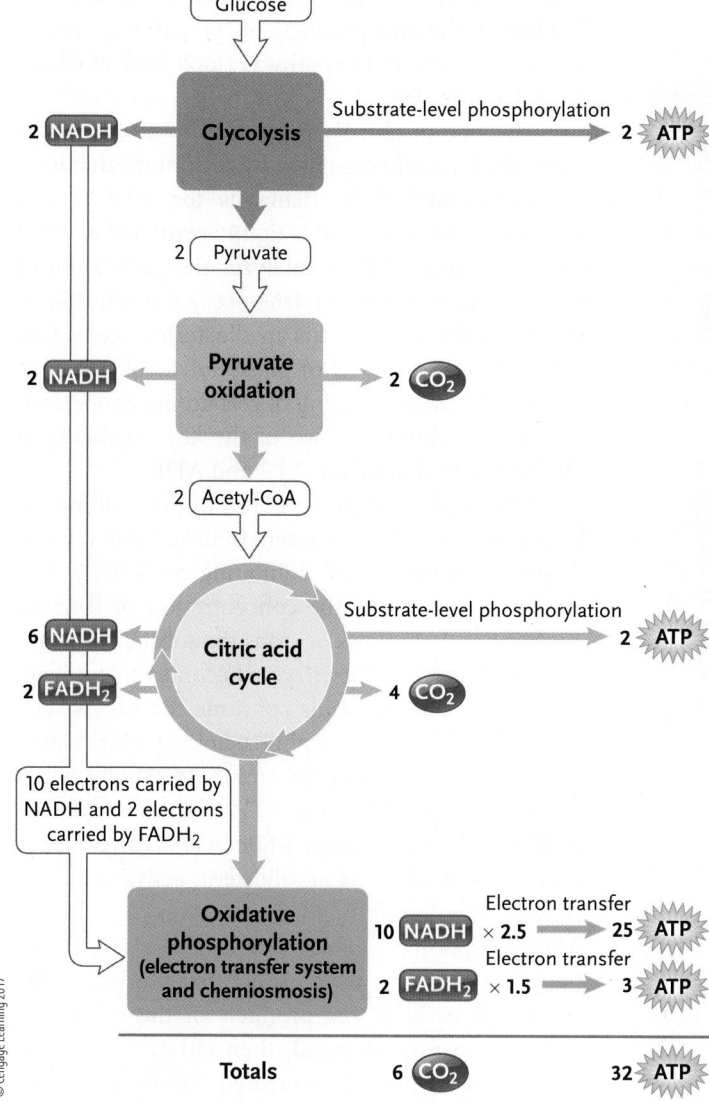

**FIGURE 5.18 ATP yield from the oxidation of glucose.** The maximum possible ATP yield from the oxidation of 1 molecule of glucose is 38. However, this yield is rarely achieved.

diffusing directly through the inner mitochondrial membrane. The third reason the theoretical maximum is not attained is that the proton-motive force generated by electron transport is used for other things than simply generating ATP. As a source of potential energy, the proton-motive force is used, for example, to transport the pyruvate synthesized by glycolysis into the matrix.

So how efficient is cellular respiration at extracting the energy from glucose and converting it into ATP? The phosphorylation of ADP to ATP requires about 7.3 kcal/mol. In eukaryotes, the theoretical maximum yield from that complete oxidation of a mole of glucose is 36 moles of ATP, so $36 \times 7.3$ gives a total of 263 kcal of energy. The complete oxidation of a mole of glucose releases exactly 686 kcal of energy. From these two numbers we can calculate the efficiency to be $263/686 \times 100 = 38\%$. In other words, 38% of the energy in glucose is converted into ATP. While this value of efficiency doesn't seem very high, it is greater than the energy transformations associated with most

machines engineers have developed. For example, an automobile extracts only about 25% of the energy in the fuel it burns. Recall from Chapter 3 that the second law of thermodynamics states that energy transformations can never be 100% efficient, as some of the energy is used to increase the entropy of the surroundings. We cannot forget that entropy plays a role in the energy transformations that occur during cellular respiration as well.

## 5.6b Fats, Proteins, and Carbohydrates Can Be Oxidized by Cellular Respiration

In addition to glucose and other six-carbon sugars, reactions leading from glycolysis through pyruvate oxidation also oxidize a range of other carbohydrates, as well as lipids and proteins, which enter the respiratory pathway at various points (**Figure 5.19**).

Carbohydrates such as sucrose and other disaccharides are easily broken down into monosaccharides such as glucose and fructose, which enter glycolysis in the early steps. Starch is hydrolyzed by digestive enzymes into individual glucose molecules, whereas **glycogen**, a more complex carbohydrate, is broken down and converted by enzymes into glucose 6-phosphate, an early substrate molecule in glycolysis.

Among the fats, the **triglycerides** are major sources of electrons for ATP synthesis. Before entering oxidative reactions, they are hydrolyzed into glycerol and individual fatty acids. The glycerol is converted to glyceraldehyde 3-phosphate before entering glycolysis. The fatty acids—and many other types of lipids—are split into two-carbon fragments, which enter the citric acid cycle as acetyl-CoA.

Proteins are hydrolyzed to amino acids before oxidation. The amino group ($2NH_2$) is removed, and the remainder of the molecule enters the respiratory pathway as pyruvate, acetyl units carried by coenzyme A, or intermediates of the citric acid cycle (see Figure 5.19). For example, the amino acid alanine is converted into pyruvate, leucine into acetyl units, and phenylalanine into fumarate, which enters the citric acid cycle.

## 5.6c Respiratory Intermediates Are Utilized for Anabolic Reactions

Organic molecules (carbohydrates, fats, proteins) are oxidized by cellular respiration, which is linked to the generation of ATP. Interestingly, these molecules are also the source of the carbon atoms found in a wide range of essential molecules. For example, the intermediates of glycolysis and the citric acid cycle are routinely diverted and used as the starting substrates required to synthesize amino acids, fats, and the pyrimidine and purine bases needed for nucleic acid synthesis. As well, respiratory intermediates supply the carbon backbones for the array of hormones, growth factors, prosthetic groups, and cofactors that are essential to cell function.

The metabolic flexibility of cellular respiration allows for reactions to be adjusted rapidly. For example, whereas fatty acids can be used as a source of energy by being oxidized to acetyl-CoA, excess acetyl-CoA can be removed from respiration and used to synthesize the fatty acids needed for a range of cellular processes.

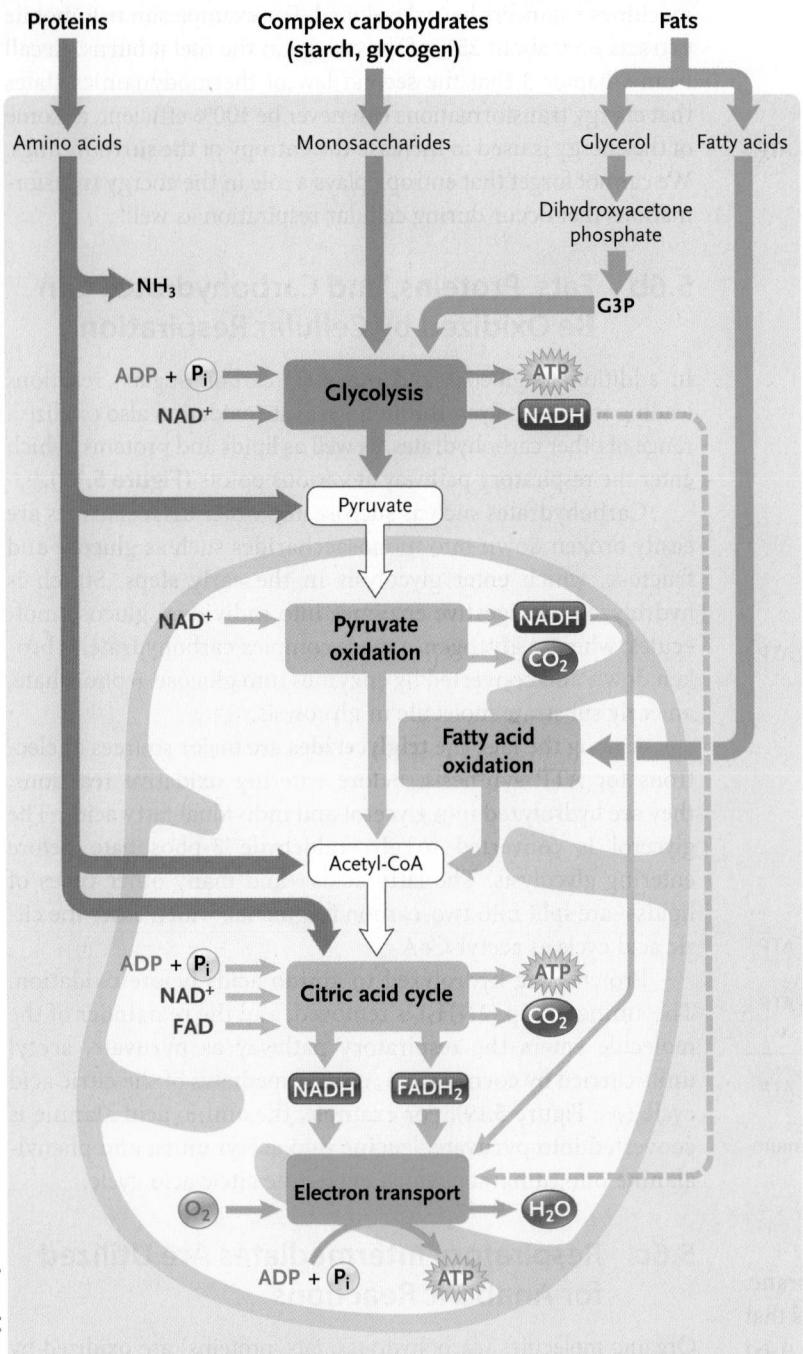

**FIGURE 5.19 Major pathways that oxidize carbohydrates, fats, and proteins.** Reactions that occur in the cytosol are shown against a tan background; reactions that occur in mitochondria are shown inside the organelle. CoA funnels the products of many oxidative pathways into the citric acid cycle.

### 5.6d Cellular Respiration Is Controlled by Supply and Demand

The rate at which food molecules (see Figure 5.19) are oxidized by cellular respiration is tightly controlled such that the rate of ATP generation matches the requirements of the cell for chemical energy. This illustrates the concept of supply and demand: the cell does not waste resources synthesizing molecules it already has in excess. Most metabolic pathways are regulated by supply and demand through the process of feedback inhibition: the end-products of the pathway inhibit an enzyme early in the pathway (look back at Chapter 3, Figure 3.26).

The rate of glucose oxidation by glycolysis for example, is closely regulated by several mechanisms to match the cellular demands for ATP. A key enzyme of glycolysis that is tightly regulated is phosphofructokinase, which catalyzes the conversion of fructose 6-phosphate to fructose 1,6-bisphosphate (**Figure 5.20**). Because it is an allosteric enzyme (see Chapter 3), the activity of phosphofructokinase can be adjusted by the binding of certain metabolic activators and inhibitors. Two of the key regulators of phosphofructokinase are ATP and ADP.

ATP is an allosteric inhibitor of phosphofructokinase: if excess ATP is present in the cytosol it binds to phosphofructokinase, inhibiting its activity. The resulting decrease in the concentration of fructose 1,6-bisphosphate slows or stops the subsequent reactions of glycolysis. The enzyme becomes active again when metabolic demands consume the excess ATP and the inhibition of phosphofructokinase is released. The increase in phosphofructokinase activity is not due solely to the release of ATP inhibition however, ADP, which accumulates when ATP is hydrolyzed during metabolism, is an allosteric activator of the enzyme (see Figure 5.20). In addition to ATP and ADP, phosphofructokinase activity is also sensitive to the levels of citrate, which is the first product of the citric acid cycle. If the products of the citric acid cycle are in high demand, then citrate should not accumulate in the cell. Increased citrate concentrations suggest that the demand for ATP is low, which may occur, for example, under conditions of limited oxygen when the rate of oxidative phosphorylation is restricted. Alternatively, it may indicate that citrate is not required as a carbon backbone for the products of biosynthetic reactions. Overall, through various metabolic activators and inhibitors altering phosphofructokinase activity, the functional state of glycolysis and the citric acid cycle can be kept balanced.

### STUDY BREAK QUESTIONS

1. Give an accounting of the total ATP yield from the oxidation of a molecule of glucose.
2. Explain how the activity of the enzyme phosphofructokinase is controlled.

## 5.7 Oxygen and Cellular Respiration

A constant supply of oxygen is required to maintain the high rates of oxidative phosphorylation necessary to supply cells with sufficient ATP. Although humans need an almost constant

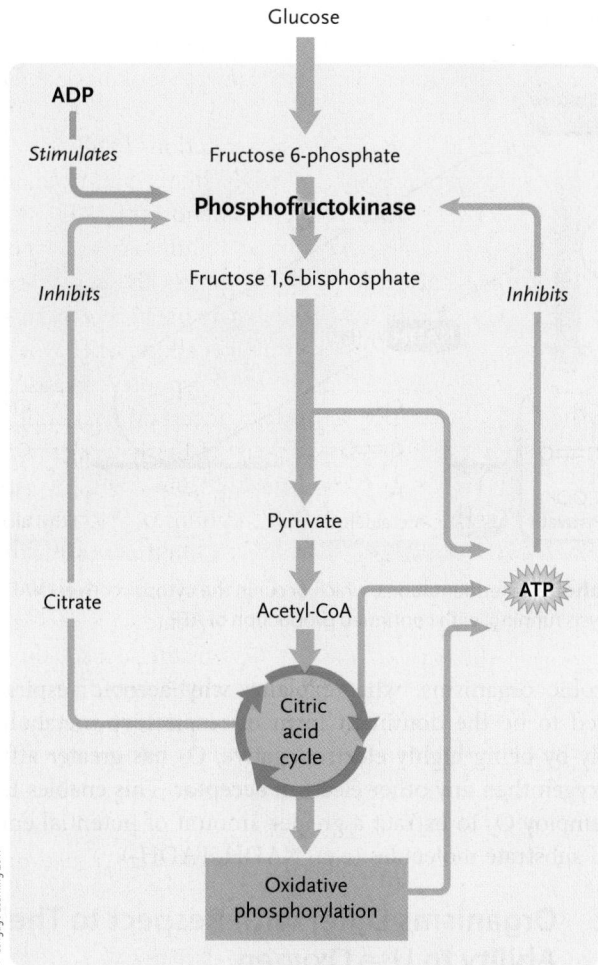

**FIGURE 5.20 The control of cellular respiration.** A major mechanism is allosteric control of the activity of the enzyme phosphofructokinase, which is found early in glycolysis. High levels of ATP and the citric acid cycle intermediate citrate allosterically inhibit phosphofructokinase. Alternatively, when ATP concentrations are low, the levels of ADP increase. ADP is an allosteric activator of the enzyme.

supply of oxygen, other organisms can survive and even thrive in the absence of oxygen.

There are two general mechanisms in which cellular respiration can occur in the absence of oxygen: fermentation and anaerobic respiration. The distinction between these two processes is that fermentation does not involve the citric acid cycle or electron transport, whereas anaerobic respiration uses a molecule other than oxygen as the terminal electron acceptor of electron transport.

## 5.7a In Eukaryotic Cells, Low Oxygen Levels Result in Fermentation

Following glycolysis, in eukaryotic cells cellular respiration can continue along one of two distinct pathways, depending on whether or not oxygen is present

(**Figure 5.21**). When oxygen is plentiful, the pyruvate and NADH produced by glycolysis are transported into mitochondria, where they are oxidized using the citric acid cycle and the ETC. If, instead, oxygen is absent or in short supply, the pyruvate remains in the cytosol, where it is reduced, consuming the NADH generated by glycolysis by a metabolic process called **fermentation**.

Two types of fermentation exist: lactate fermentation and alcohol fermentation. In **lactate fermentation**, which is found in many bacteria and some plant and animal tissues, pyruvate is converted into the three-carbon molecule lactate (**Figure 5.22a**). Lactate fermentation occurs, for example, when vigorous contraction of muscle cells calls for more oxygen than the circulating blood can supply. When the oxygen content of the muscle cells returns to normal levels, the reverse of the reaction in Figure 5.22a regenerates pyruvate and NADH. Lactate is also the fermentation product of some bacteria; the sour taste of buttermilk, yogurt, and dill pickles is a sign of their activity.

**Alcohol fermentation** (Figure 5.22b) occurs in microorganisms such as yeasts, which are single-celled fungi. In this reaction, pyruvate is reduced to ethyl alcohol as $CO_2$ is released and NADH is oxidized to $NAD^+$. Alcoholic fermentation by yeasts has widespread commercial applications. Bakers use the yeast *Saccharomyces cerevisiae* to make bread dough rise. They mix the yeast with a small amount of sugar and blend the mixture into the dough, where oxygen levels are low. As the yeast cells convert the sugar into ethyl alcohol and $CO_2$, the gaseous $CO_2$ expands and creates bubbles that cause the dough to rise. Oven heat evaporates the alcohol and causes further expansion of the bubbles, producing a light-textured product. Alcoholic fermentation is also the mainstay of beer and wine brewing. Fruits are a natural home to wild yeasts (**Figure 5.23**); for example, winemakers rely on a mixture of wild and cultivated yeasts to produce wine. Alcoholic fermentation also occurs naturally in the environment; for example, overripe or rotting fruit will frequently start to ferment, and birds that eat the fruit may become too drunk to fly.

Overall, the reactions of fermentation play a critical role whenever organisms are exposed to conditions in which the oxygen concentration is too low to support oxidative phosphorylation. By consuming the NADH generated by glycolysis,

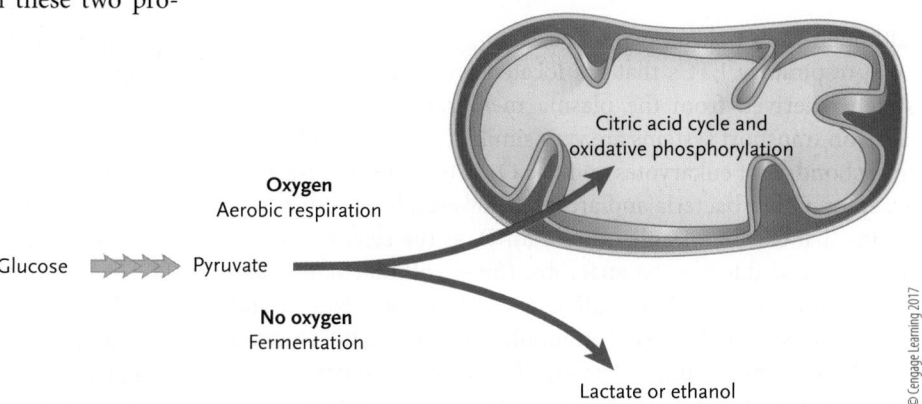

**FIGURE 5.21 The metabolic pathway of pyruvate oxidation depends upon the presence of oxygen.**

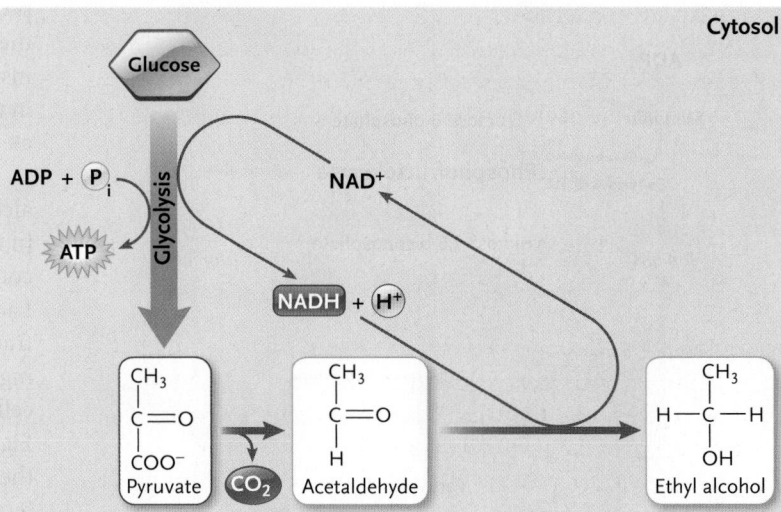

**a. Lactate fermentation**

Cytosol

Glucose

ADP + $P_i$

ATP

Glycolysis

NAD$^+$

NADH + H$^+$

$$\begin{array}{c} CH_3 \\ | \\ C=O \\ | \\ COO^- \end{array}$$
Pyruvate

$$\begin{array}{c} CH_3 \\ | \\ HO-C-H \\ | \\ COO^- \end{array}$$
Lactate

**b. Alcoholic fermentation**

Cytosol

Glucose

ADP + $P_i$

ATP

Glycolysis

NAD$^+$

NADH + H$^+$

$$\begin{array}{c} CH_3 \\ | \\ C=O \\ | \\ COO^- \end{array}$$
Pyruvate

$CO_2$

$$\begin{array}{c} CH_3 \\ | \\ C=O \\ | \\ H \end{array}$$
Acetaldehyde

$$\begin{array}{c} CH_3 \\ | \\ H-C-H \\ | \\ OH \end{array}$$
Ethyl alcohol

© Cengage Learning 2017

**FIGURE 5.22 Fermentation reactions that produce** (a) **lactate and** (b) **ethyl alcohol.** The fermentations, which occur in the cytosol, convert NADH to NAD$^+$, allowing the electron carrier to cycle back to glycolysis. This process keeps glycolysis running, with continued production of ATP.

Ed Reschke/Photolibrary/Getty Images

**FIGURE 5.23 Alcoholic fermentation in nature.** Wild yeast cells, visible as a dustlike coating on grapes

fermentation reactions keep cytosolic NAD$^+$ levels high. This is of critical metabolic importance because NAD$^+$ is required for glycolysis (look back at Figure 5.9, step 6). As long as there is sufficient NAD$^+$, glycolysis will continue to operate and generate ATP. Of course, the amount of ATP generated is small compared to oxidative phosphorylation, and thus fermentation is not sufficient to support the high ATP requirement of brain cells, for example.

## 5.7b   In Anaerobic Respiration, the Terminal Electron Acceptor Is Not Oxygen

Although they lack mitochondria, many bacteria and archaea have respiratory ETCs that are located on internal membrane systems derived from the plasma membrane. Some of these electron transport systems are very similar to those found in the mitochondria of eukaryotes and use O$_2$ as the terminal electron acceptor. Other bacteria and archaea, however, have respiratory chains that use a molecule other than O$_2$ as the electron acceptor and are said to possess anaerobic (*an* = without; *aero* = air) respiration. Instead of O$_2$, sulfate (SO$_4^{2-}$), nitrate (NO$_3^-$), and the ferric ion (Fe$^{3+}$) are commonly used terminal electron acceptors. There is a huge diversity of molecules that have a high affinity for electrons that are used as electron acceptors for electron transport and support ATP generation by oxidative phosphorylation. If oxidative phosphorylation can proceed in anaerobic organisms, what explains why aerobic respiration evolved to be the dominant form of respiratory metabolism? Simply by being highly electronegative, O$_2$ has greater affinity for oxygen than any other electron acceptor. This enables ETCs that employ O$_2$ to extract a greater amount of potential energy out of substrate molecules (e.g., NADH, FADH$_2$).

## 5.7c   Organisms Differ with Respect to Their Ability to Use Oxygen

We can differentiate three lifestyles depending on the requirements of an organism for oxygen strict aerobes, facultative anaerobes, and strict anaerobes. Many archaea and bacteria and most eukaryotes are **strict aerobes**; that is, they have an absolute requirement for oxygen for survival and are unable to live solely by fermentation. To understand why this is, look back at Figure 5.18. In the absence of oxygen, ATP is generated solely by substrate-level phosphorylation during glycolysis: 2 ATP are generated for every glucose oxidized. By comparison, in the presence of oxygen, up to 38 ATP can be generated; that's 19 times as much ATP for each glucose oxidized. As shown in Figure 5.19, the difference is explained by the huge ATP yield of oxidative phosphorylation. Humans and other animals are especially sensitive to low-oxygen environments because certain tissues, such as brain cells, have requirements for ATP that can be met only by constant and high rates of oxidative phosphorylation.

Other organisms, called **facultative anaerobes**, can switch between fermentation and aerobic respiration, depending on the oxygen supply. Facultative anaerobes include *Escherichia coli*, the bacterium that inhabits the digestive tract of humans; the *Lactobacillus* bacteria used to produce buttermilk and yogurt; and *S. cerevisiae*, the yeast used in brewing and baking. Many cell types in higher organisms, including vertebrate muscle cells, are also facultatively anaerobic. And last, some bacteria, some archaea, and a few fungi are classified as **strict**

**anaerobes** because they require an oxygen-free environment to survive. Strict anaerobes gain ATP from either fermentation or anaerobic respiration. Among these organisms are the bacteria that cause botulism, tetanus, and some other serious diseases. For example, the bacterium that causes botulism thrives in the oxygen-free environment of canned foods that prevents the growth of most other microorganisms.

## 5.7d The Paradox of Aerobic Life Is That Oxygen Is Essential and Toxic

As we mentioned above, some microbes are strict anaerobes: they cannot live in an oxygen environment. But why can't they? Lacking the ability to use $O_2$ as an electron acceptor is one thing, but actually dying in the presence of $O_2$? The reason that strict anaerobes die in an oxygen environment is related to what is often called *the paradox of aerobic life*: although oxygen is absolutely essential to the survival of many organisms, oxygen is also potentially toxic.

It takes four electrons to completely reduce a molecule of $O_2$ to water (**Figure 5.24**). Partially reduced forms of $O_2$ are formed when $O_2$ accepts fewer electrons, producing what are called *reactive oxygen species* (ROS). These molecules, which include the compounds superoxide and hydrogen peroxide (see Figure 5.24), are powerful oxidizing molecules and readily remove electrons from proteins, lipids, and DNA, resulting in oxidative damage. If ROS levels within a cell are excessive, their strong oxidizing nature can result in the destruction of many biological molecules and can be lethal. Because most cells contain an abundance of both $O_2$ and electron-rich molecules (e.g., proteins, lipids, nucleic acids) the formation of ROS is a consequence of aerobic life that cannot be avoided.

To survive in an oxygen-rich environment, aerobic organisms have evolved an antioxidant defence system that includes both enzymes and nonenzyme molecules that have the role of intercepting and inactivating reactive oxygen molecules as they are produced within cells. Two of the major ROS-scavenging enzymes are superoxide dismutase and catalase (see Figure 5.24). Working in concert, superoxide dismutase converts the superoxide anion to hydrogen peroxide, which in turn is reduced to water by the action of catalase. In addition to enzymes, many cells have a range of antioxidants, including vitamin C and vitamin E, which act as reducing agents, safely and rapidly reducing reactive oxygen compounds to water. In recent years, excessive

ROS formation has been implicated in a wide variety of degenerative diseases, including Parkinson's disease and Alzheimer's dementia. In fact, it is thought that the progressive buildup of oxidative damage may underlie the aging process itself. This, in part, explains the huge interest in the possible protective value of a wide variety of antioxidant compounds, particularly those from certain fruits and vegetables.

So why do strict anaerobes die in the presence of oxygen? For one group, their inability to live in an oxygen environment is because they lack one or both of the enzymes superoxide dismutase and catalase, which results in a buildup of toxic ROS within their cells if they are exposed to oxygen. Interestingly, some strict anaerobes do contain these enzymes, which are highly expressed when cells are placed in an oxygen environment. The inability of this second group of anaerobes to survive in an oxygen environment seems to be linked to $O_2$ itself binding to and inhibiting key metabolic enzymes.

As discussed in the previous section, oxidative phosphorylation generates much more ATP than the substrate-level phosphorylation that takes place during glycolysis and the citric acid cycle. From this it is clear that the evolution of the electron transport system with oxygen as the terminal electron acceptor enabled cells to extract far more energy from food molecules than other modes of metabolism. However, the evolution of the aerobic lifestyle required the development of antioxidants and enzymes such as catalase and superoxide dismutase to combat the harmful effects of oxygen, which include the inevitable formation of ROS. In addition, it required that cytochrome oxidase, the last enzyme of the mitochondrial ETC, develop a remarkable mode of catalysis. Looking back at Figure 5.14, notice that the cytochrome oxidase complex donates electrons from the electron carrier cytochrome $c$ to $O_2$. However, it does so in a way that, remarkably, leads to essentially no reactive oxygen generation. The enzyme is structurally quite complex, containing four redox centres (two hemes and two copper ions), each of which can store a single electron. When all centres are reduced, the enzyme simultaneously transfers all four electrons to $O_2$, producing two molecules of water. That cytochrome oxidase is the only enzyme that aerobic organisms, from bacterial to human, use as the terminal complex of electron transport indicates the chemical difficulty of carrying out the transfer of electrons to $O_2$ in a safe and controlled manner. Given that this single enzyme handles approximately 98% of the oxygen we metabolize, if the reaction resulted in significant amounts of partially reduced forms of oxygen (e.g., superoxide, hydrogen peroxide), aerobic life as we know it would have probably never evolved.

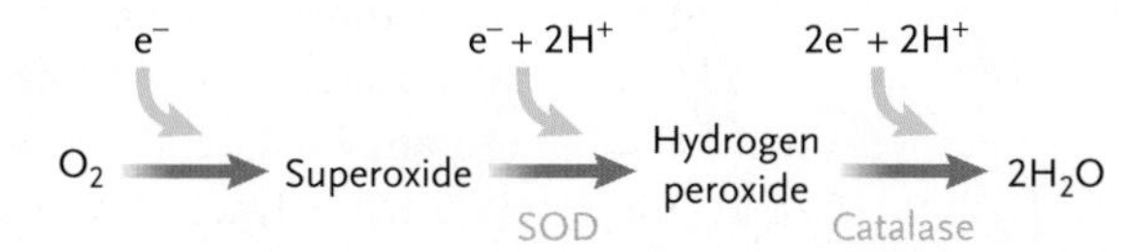

**FIGURE 5.24 The conversion of $O_2$ to water is a four-electron reduction.** If this occurs stepwise, it results in the formation of the intermediate ROS, which are potentially harmful. Aerobic cells contain the enzymes superoxide dismutase (SOD) and catalase, which together quickly convert superoxide and hydrogen peroxide to water.

## STUDY BREAK QUESTIONS

1. In what way does fermentative metabolism allow for continued generation of ATP under low oxygen conditions?
2. What is the underlying reason why some organisms die in the presence of $O_2$?

# Summary Illustration

Cellular respiration is a collection of reactions that converts the chemical energy present in carbohydrates, fats, and proteins into an energy currency, ATP, that is readily used by the cell. The phases of cellular respiration are: (i) glycolysis, (ii) pyruvate oxidation and the citric acid cycle, and (iii) oxidative phosphorylation. The overall process is represented by the chemical equation for the oxidation of glucose.

Cellular respiration is a redox process.
- The overall change in free energy ($\Delta G$) is negative.
- Energy released during the formation of the bonds in $CO_2$ and $H_2O$ is greater than the energy required to break the bonds in glucose and $O_2$.
- The goal is to couple the energy released to the synthesis of ATP!

$$C_6H_{12}O_6 + 6O_2 \longrightarrow 6CO_2 + 6H_2O$$

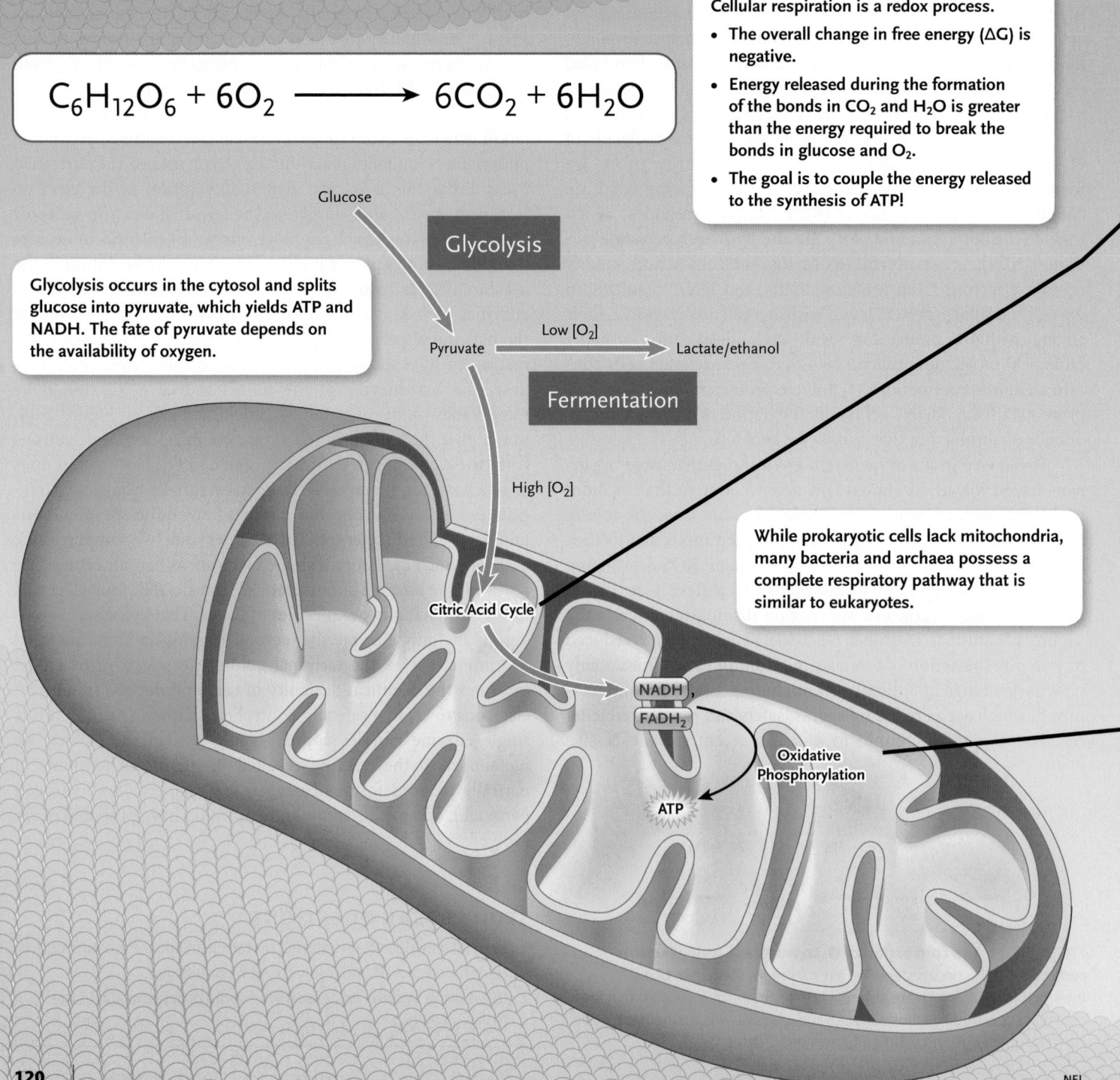

Glucose

**Glycolysis**

Glycolysis occurs in the cytosol and splits glucose into pyruvate, which yields ATP and NADH. The fate of pyruvate depends on the availability of oxygen.

Pyruvate    Low [$O_2$]    Lactate/ethanol

**Fermentation**

High [$O_2$]

While prokaryotic cells lack mitochondria, many bacteria and archaea possess a complete respiratory pathway that is similar to eukaryotes.

Citric Acid Cycle

NADH,
FADH$_2$

Oxidative Phosphorylation

ATP

## Citric Acid Cycle

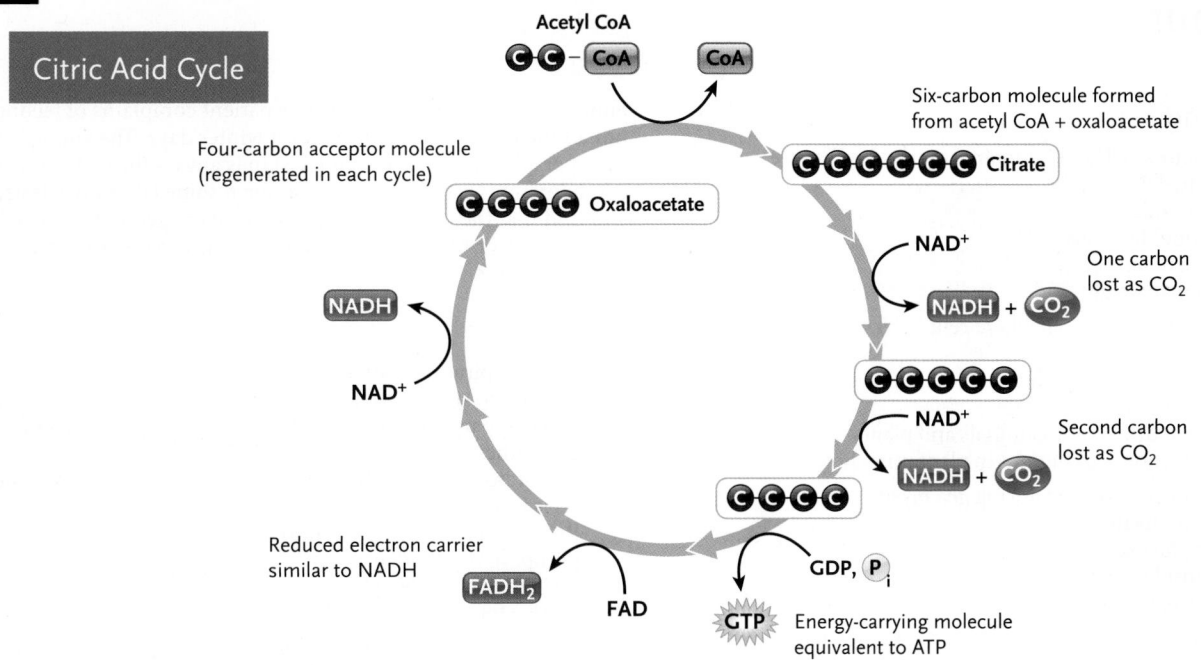

Acetyl CoA

C C – CoA    CoA

Four-carbon acceptor molecule
(regenerated in each cycle)

C C C C  Oxaloacetate

Six-carbon molecule formed
from acetyl CoA + oxaloacetate

C C C C C C  Citrate

$NAD^+$

NADH + $CO_2$

One carbon
lost as $CO_2$

NADH

$NAD^+$

C C C C C

$NAD^+$

NADH + $CO_2$

Second carbon
lost as $CO_2$

C C C C

Reduced electron carrier
similar to NADH

$FADH_2$    FAD

GDP, P$_i$

GTP    Energy-carrying molecule
equivalent to ATP

**Pyruvate is transported into the mitochondrial matrix and converted to acetyl-CoA, which enters the citric acid cycle and is oxidized. Notice the products formed.**

## Oxidative Phosphorylation

Cytosol

Outer mitochondrial membrane

Intermembrane compartment

Inner mitochondrial membrane

Complex I

Complex II

Complex III

cyt c

Complex IV

ATP synthase

$H^+$

UQ

$e^-$

NADH    $H^+$  $NAD^+$    $FADH_2$  FAD

$2e^- + 2 \ H^+ + \frac{1}{2} \ O_2$

$H_2O$

Mitochondrial matrix

ADP + P$_i$    $H^+$    ATP

Electron transport        Chemiosmosis

**Electrons from the oxidation of NADH and $FADH_2$ produced by glycolysis and the citric acid cycle are passed along an electron transport chain. Electron transport and chemiosmotic synthesis of ATP are coupled by a proton gradient.**

## Recall/Understand

1. Which of these factors is found in organic molecules that are considered good fuels?
   a. many C—H bonds
   b. many C=C double bonds
   c. an abundance of oxygen
   d. a high molecular weight

2. What is one of the places in a cell where cellular respiration occurs?
   a. in plant mitochondria, but not in animal mitochondria
   b. in plant chloroplasts
   c. in the mitochondria of both animals and plants
   d. in animal mitochondria, but not in plant mitochondria

3. Which of these processes occurs during glycolysis?
   a. oxidation of pyruvate
   b. reduction of glucose
   c. oxidative phosphorylation
   d. substrate-level phosphorylation

4. Which of these processes links glycolysis and the citric acid cycle?
   a. chemiosmosis
   b. formation of G3P
   c. reduction of $NAD^+$
   d. pyruvate oxidation

## Apply/Analyze

5. The breakdown of fats releases fatty acids. In what form do the carbon molecules enter the respiratory pathway?
   a. as NADH
   b. as acetyl-CoA
   c. a glucose
   d. as pyruvate

6. You are reading this text while breathing in oxygen and breathing out carbon dioxide. Which two processes are the sources of the carbon dioxide?
   a. glycolysis and pyruvate oxidation
   b. glycolysis and oxidative phosphorylation
   c. pyruvate oxidation and the citric acid cycle
   d. the citric acid cycle and oxidative phosphorylation

7. Under conditions of low oxygen, what key role is played by fermentation in overall metabolism?
   a. It regenerates the $NAD^+$ required for glycolysis.
   b. It synthesizes additional NADH for the citric acid cycle.
   c. It allows for pyruvate to be oxidized in mitochondria.
   d. By activating oxidative phosphorylation, it allows for the synthesis of extra ATP.

8. Suppose you are a doctor and your patient complains of feeling hot all the time, even on the coldest winter days. The young man perspires constantly and his skin is always flushed. He also eats a lot but is rather thin. You perform some laboratory tests, and find that the patient consumes lots of oxygen in his metabolic pathways. What would you suspect this patient suffers from and why?

## Create/Evaluate

9. In cellular respiration, which of the following does the term *uncoupled* refer to specifically?
   a. The two parts of glycolysis are running independently of each other.
   b. Respiratory electron transport is operating, but chemiosmosis is inhibited.
   c. Respiratory electron transport is operating, but proton pumping is inhibited.
   d. Oxidative phosphorylation is occurring, but the proton-motive force remains high.

10. Phosphofructokinase (PFK) is regulated by a number of metabolites. In addition to those mentioned in the text, which one of the following would also make sense?
    a. Pyruvate could function as an activator of PFK.
    b. Glucose could function as an inhibitor of PFK.
    c. ADP could function as an activator of PFK.
    d. Acetyl-CoA could act as an activator of PFK.

11. Which of these statements *best* describes the "paradox of aerobic life"?
    a. Humans are completely protected from the toxic effects of oxygen.
    b. Hydrogen peroxide is formed when a single electron is donated to $O_2$.
    c. Cytochrome oxidase is a major source of reactive oxygen species.
    d. Strict anaerobes often lack the enzyme(s) superoxide dismutase and/or catalase.

12. Compare direct burning of glucose and cellular respiration with reference to their progression.

13. Distinguish between reduction and oxidation during redox reactions.

14. Explain what happens with hydrogen and its bonding electrons during cellular respiration.

15. Cyanide is a strong toxin that reacts with the final protein in the electron transport chain (ETC). Explain why it can kill a human within a few minutes.

# Chapter Roadmap

## Photosynthesis
Photosynthesis is a process by which light energy is converted into chemical energy. This chemical energy sustains virtually all life on Earth.

### 6.1 Photosynthesis: An Overview
Photosynthesis is the light-dependent reduction of carbon dioxide into carbohydrate, and consists of two distinct stages: light reaction and the Calvin cycle.

**To Chapter 34**

### 6.2 The Photosynthetic Apparatus
Photosynthesis relies on a series of protein complexes in the thylakoid membrane that bind pigment molecules that facilitate light absorption and energy trapping.

**From Chapter 1**

### 6.3 The Light Reactions
Photons of light are used to drive photosynthetic electron transport, which generates NADPH and leads to the formation of ATP through chemiosmotic coupling.

**From Chapter 5**

### 6.4 The Calvin Cycle
The reduction of carbon dioxide to carbohydrate is carried out by a series of 11 enzyme-catalyzed reactions that occur in the stroma of the chloroplast.

**From Chapter 3**

### 6.5 Photorespiration and $CO_2$-Concentrating Mechanisms
Rubisco, the enzyme responsible for fixing carbon dioxide in the Calvin cycle, has an active site that can also bind $O_2$.

**From Chapter 3**

### 6.6 Photosynthesis and Cellular Respiration Compared
Photosynthesis and cellular respiration are similar in that they both rely on electron transport chains and the chemiosmotic generation of ATP; there are lots of differences as well.

**From Chapter 1**

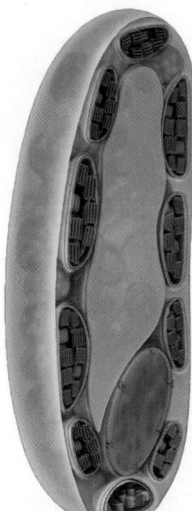

© Cengage Learning 2017

Photos.com

**Bioreactors of green algae.** Through the process of photosynthesis, atmospheric $CO_2$ is being converted by these algae into a wide range of organic compounds. Some of these compounds are being studied for their feasibility as alternative energy sources (so-called *biofuels*).

# Photosynthesis

# 6

**Why it matters . . .** Renewable sources of energy, including solar and wind power, are meeting an ever-increasing proportion of global energy demands. Although this is good news, well over 90% of the world's energy still comes from the burning of non-renewable reserves of coal, oil, and natural gas. The combustion of these sources of energy has been shown to be the major contributing factor to the increasing atmospheric $CO_2$ concentrations and the acceleration of global climate change over the past 100 years.

Coal, oil, and natural gas are referred to as "fossil fuels" because they are in fact the remnants of ancient forests formed by geological processes over millions of years. The organic carbon compounds that are burned were formed in these ancient plants through the process of photosynthesis.

In recent years, harnessing photosynthesis to generate renewable fuels has been a major aspect of the biofuel industry. Unlike coal and oil, biofuels are produced by living organisms through processes such as fermentation and photosynthesis. Biofuels include ethanol and a variety of oils that can be used, for example, to generate jet fuel.

One source of photosynthetically generated biofuels that is being intensively studied is single-celled algae grown in artificial lakes or bioreactors (small bioreactors are shown above). Culturing algae offers numerous advantages over crop plants, the traditional source of most oils. Algae grow very rapidly, and the extraction of oils is often easier than it is from plants. In addition, cultivating algae would preserve precious arable land that could be dedicated to growing food crops.

There remain a number of issues surrounding the wide implementation of algae and biofuel production. The costs associated with growing algae on a large scale are high, while the yield of oil needs to increase for it to be economically feasible. Such issues need to be addressed if biofuels are to make a serious dent in our current dependence on fossil fuels.

The focus of this chapter is photosynthesis, the process by which light energy is used to convert carbon dioxide into organic molecules. The chapter starts by laying out the basic chemistry of photosynthesis, focusing on the photophysical nature of light and light absorption. This adds to the more cursory treatment of light that is found in Chapter 1. Details of the two stages of photosynthesis (the light reactions and the Calvin cycle) follow, as does a discussion of how various photosynthetic organisms have evolved mechanisms to cope with a surprising attribute of the carbon-fixing enzyme Rubisco. The chapter ends with an important section on comparing photosynthesis with the topic of the previous chapter, cellular respiration.

# 6.1 Photosynthesis: An Overview

**Photosynthesis** is the use of light energy to convert carbon dioxide into organic compounds such as carbohydrates. We define an organic compound as one that contains one or more C—H bonds. Because they do not need to import already formed organic compounds from the environment, photosynthetic organisms are called **autotrophs** (*auto* = self; *trophos* = feeding). They are more narrowly defined as **photoautotrophs** because the energy to drive the conversion of carbon dioxide into an organic form comes from light. Some organisms are autotrophic but don't use light; instead they use compounds such as hydrogen sulfide ($H_2S$) and ferrous iron ($Fe^{2+}$) as a source of energy. This type of metabolism is found only in some bacteria and archaeans and is termed chemoautotrophy.

Photoautotrophic organisms are known as Earth's **primary producers (Figure 6.1)**, because they represent the organisms that generate the organic compounds that are used by other organisms: the consumers. Eventually, the bodies of both primary producers and consumers provide organic energy-rich molecules to support a range of **decomposers**, such as a range of bacteria and all fungi. Consumers and decomposers are classified as heterotrophs because they need to import carbon in the form of organic molecules to live.

Photosynthesis is an ancient process that evolved in bacteria perhaps as early as 2.5 billion years ago. Interestingly, today photosynthesis is found in the domains Bacteria and Eukarya but is not present in the Archaea. Some archaeans, such as the Halobacteria (see Chapter 1), do harvest light energy and convert it into chemical energy, but since this light energy is not used to convert carbon dioxide into an organic form, Halobacteria are not considered to be photosynthetic.

## 6.1a Photosynthesis Is an Oxidation–Reduction Process

In high school biology, one thing you probably memorized was the balanced chemical equation for the overall process of photosynthesis, which is

$$6\ CO_2 + 12\ H_2O \rightarrow C_6H_{12}O_6 + 6\ O_2 + 6\ H_2O \qquad (6.1)$$

As chemical equations go this seems pretty straightforward, but let's deconstruct it to see what's really going on. Taking the reaction as written, you could say that water is reacting with $CO_2$ (it's *hydrating* the carbon) to produce a six-carbon carbohydrate glucose, with $O_2$ and $H_2O$ produced as by-products. As we will discuss later in the chapter, glucose is technically not the direct product of the Calvin cycle but is made soon after, and so is used here for convenience. Notice from Equation 6.1 that equal molar amounts of the gases $CO_2$ and $O_2$ are consumed and produced respectively. This means that one can measure the rate of photosynthesis as either the rate at which $CO_2$ is consumed or the rate at which $O_2$ is produced.

What may not be clear to you yet is that Equation 6.1 is a classic example of an oxidation–reduction, or redox, reaction, which we introduced in the previous chapter. To make it easy to see its redox nature, let's put the equation in its simplest form by dividing through by 6, giving

$$CO_2 + 2\ H_2O \rightarrow (CH_2O) + O_2 + H_2O \qquad (6.2)$$

where the term ($CH_2O$) is the basic unit of a carbohydrate consisting of carbon, hydrogen, and oxygen atoms in the ratio 1C:2H:1O. A molecule of glucose is therefore six units, $(CH_2O)_6$.

Like all redox reactions, Equation 6.2 is actually two half-reactions: one oxidation reaction is coupled to a reduction reaction. In Equation 6.2 it is the water that is being oxidized (losing electrons) to $O_2$. Removing electrons from water is not easy; this is why photosynthesis requires the energy associated with photons of light:

$$2\ H_2O + light\ energy \rightarrow O_2 + 4\ H^+ + 4\ e^-$$

Looking back at Equation 6.2, it is the $CO_2$ that is being reduced (gaining electrons) to form carbohydrate:

$$CO_2 + 4\ H^+ + 4\ e^- \rightarrow (CH_2O) + H_2O$$

If you were to treat Equation 6.1 like a typical chemical reaction, you could easily assume that the water is reacting directly with the carbon dioxide to produce the carbohydrate and cause $O_2$ release. As we will see in the next section, the oxidation of $H_2O$

**FIGURE 6.1 Examples of photoautotrophs**

and the reduction of carbon dioxide are involved in distinctly different aspects of photosynthesis that are spatially separated within the chloroplast.

## 6.1b Photosynthesis Can Be Divided into the Light Reactions and the Calvin Cycle

The conversion of carbon dioxide into carbohydrates that defines photosynthesis requires the integration of two distinct processes (**Figure 6.2**): the light reactions and the Calvin cycle. The light reactions involve the capture of light energy by pigment molecules and the utilization of that energy to synthesize both NADPH (nicotinamide adenine dinucleotide phosphate) and ATP. The electrons needed to reduce NADP$^+$ to NADPH come from the oxidation of $H_2O$, resulting in the release of $O_2$ (Figure 6.2). In the Calvin cycle, the electrons and protons carried by NADPH and the energy of ATP hydrolysis are used to convert $CO_2$ into carbohydrate. This reduction reaction is often referred to as *carbon fixation*, or $CO_2$ fixation, as the gas carbon dioxide is being fixed into a solid (carbohydrate).

It is important to realize that the carbohydrate synthesized by the Calvin cycle ends up being used for a huge range of processes. In addition to sugars like glucose being a useful source of energy for cellular respiration, the carbohydrates also represent the source of the carbon skeletons used in the biosynthesis of other molecules, including lipids, amino acids, and nucleotides. In fact, one can consider all the organic molecules present in all organisms on Earth as direct or indirect products of photosynthesis.

## 6.1c In Eukaryotes, Photosynthesis Takes Place in Chloroplasts

In photosynthetic eukaryotes, both the light reactions and the Calvin cycle take place within the chloroplast, an organelle that is comprised of three membranes that define three distinct compartments (**Figure 6.3**). An *outer membrane* covers the entire surface of the organelle, and an *inner membrane* lies just inside the outer membrane. Between the outer and inner membranes is the *intermembrane space*. The aqueous environment within the inner membrane is the *stroma* of the chloroplast. Within the stroma is the third membrane system, the *thylakoid membranes*,

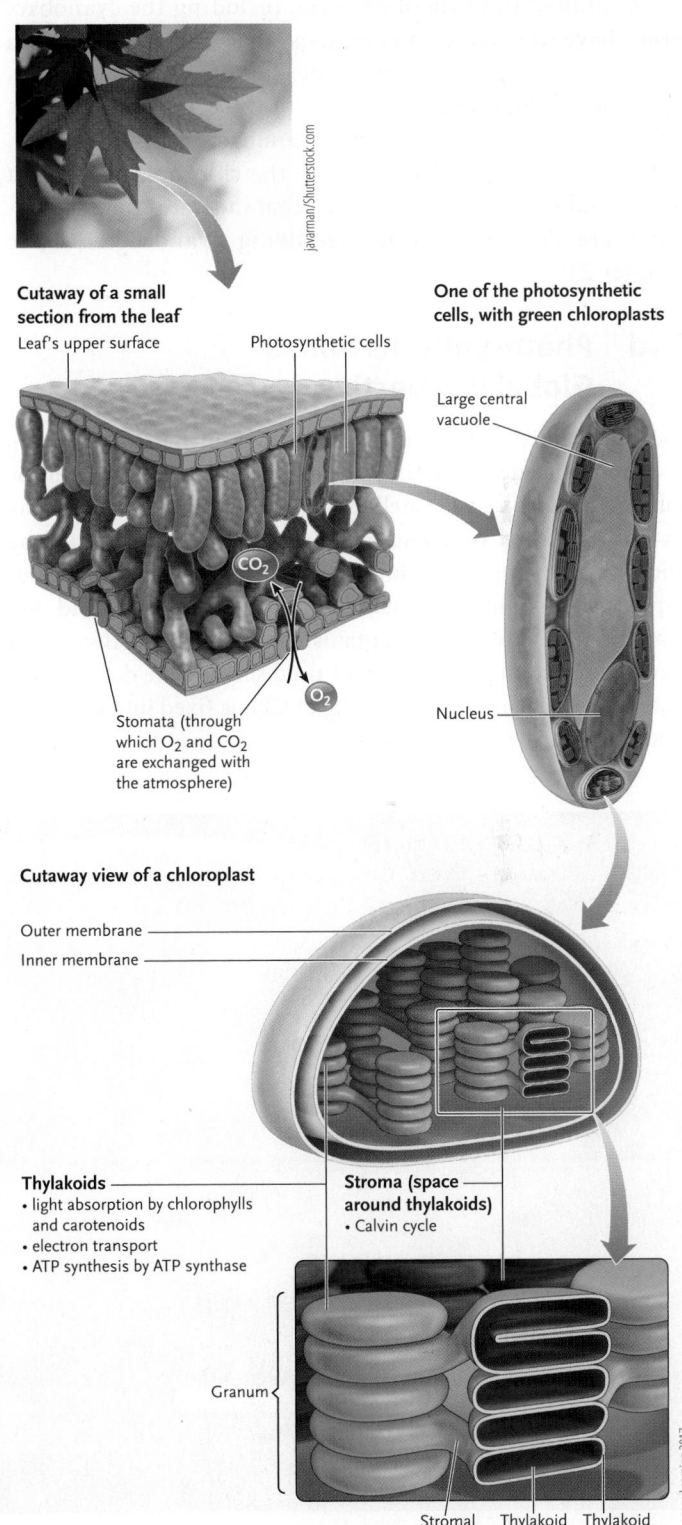

Cutaway of a small section from the leaf
Leaf's upper surface
Photosynthetic cells

$CO_2$
$O_2$

Stomata (through which $O_2$ and $CO_2$ are exchanged with the atmosphere)

One of the photosynthetic cells, with green chloroplasts

Large central vacuole

Nucleus

Cutaway view of a chloroplast

Outer membrane
Inner membrane

Thylakoids
• light absorption by chlorophylls and carotenoids
• electron transport
• ATP synthesis by ATP synthase

Stroma (space around thylakoids)
• Calvin cycle

Granum

Stromal lamella    Thylakoid lumen    Thylakoid membrane

**FIGURE 6.3 The membranes and compartments of chloroplasts**

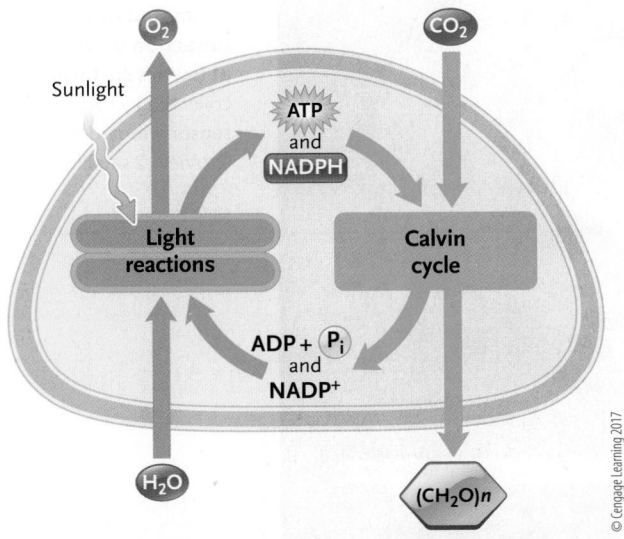

$O_2$    $CO_2$

Sunlight

ATP and NADPH

Light reactions

Calvin cycle

ADP + $P_i$ and NADP$^+$

$H_2O$    $(CH_2O)n$

**FIGURE 6.2 The light reactions and the Calvin cycle are the two stages of photosynthesis.** The two are linked by reactants and products. Both processes occur in the chloroplasts of photoautotrophic eukaryotes (plants and algae) as well as in photosynthetic bacteria.

or thylakoids, which often form flattened, closed sacs. The space enclosed by a thylakoid is called the *thylakoid lumen*.

Embedded within the thylakoid membrane are the components that carry out the light reactions of photosynthesis: proteins, pigments, electron transport carriers, and ATP synthase. The enzymes that catalyze the reactions of the Calvin cycle are found in the stroma of the chloroplast.

A number of phyla of bacteria, including the cyanobacteria, have thylakoid membranes that are formed from infolding of the plasma membrane. The enzymes of the Calvin cycle are found in the cytosol of the cell. In most ways, photosynthesis carried out in cyanobacteria is biochemically very similar to that found in the chloroplasts of plant leaves, and is part of the evidence that indicates that chloroplasts are descended from free-living cyanobacteria (see Chapter 21).

### 6.1d Photosynthesis from a Global Perspective

The importance of photosynthesis to life on Earth is perhaps best appreciated by getting a global perspective. A sensor onboard the OrbView-2 satellite can detect visible light at Earth's surface, including the green wavelengths that are reflected by chlorophyll, the primary photosynthetic pigment. This gives an unprecedented global estimate of both the abundance and distribution of photosynthetic organisms (**Figure 6.4**). Along with other information, scientists have used the satellite data to estimate that a staggering $11 \times 10^{13}$ kg of $CO_2$ is fixed into carbohydrate by photosynthesis each year.

While we often think about photosynthesis in terms of plants and trees, about half the carbon is fixed by unicellular, photosynthetic algae called *phytoplankton* that inhabit marine environments. Looking carefully at the global distribution in the oceans (Figure 6.4), notice that phytoplankton are more abundant around the poles than they are nearer the equator. This may seem odd because the oceans near the equator receive more sunlight and are warmer. In fact, the distribution of phytoplankton is explained by the abundance of nutrients: the oceans around the equator tend to be nutrient poor, while the cold waters around the Arctic and Antarctic are nutrient rich and thus can support large phytoplankton communities.

### STUDY BREAK QUESTIONS

1. Differentiate between autotroph and heterotroph; photoautotroph and chemoautotroph.
2. Define *carbon fixation*.
3. What explains the low chlorophyll concentration in the warm waters of the Pacific Ocean?

## 6.2 The Photosynthetic Apparatus

The photosynthetic apparatus is a series of large protein complexes imbedded in the thylakoid membrane that are responsible for light reactions. Central to these are two complexes built around proteins that bind pigment molecules involved in light absorption. These **photosystems** catalyze the conversion of light energy into chemical energy.

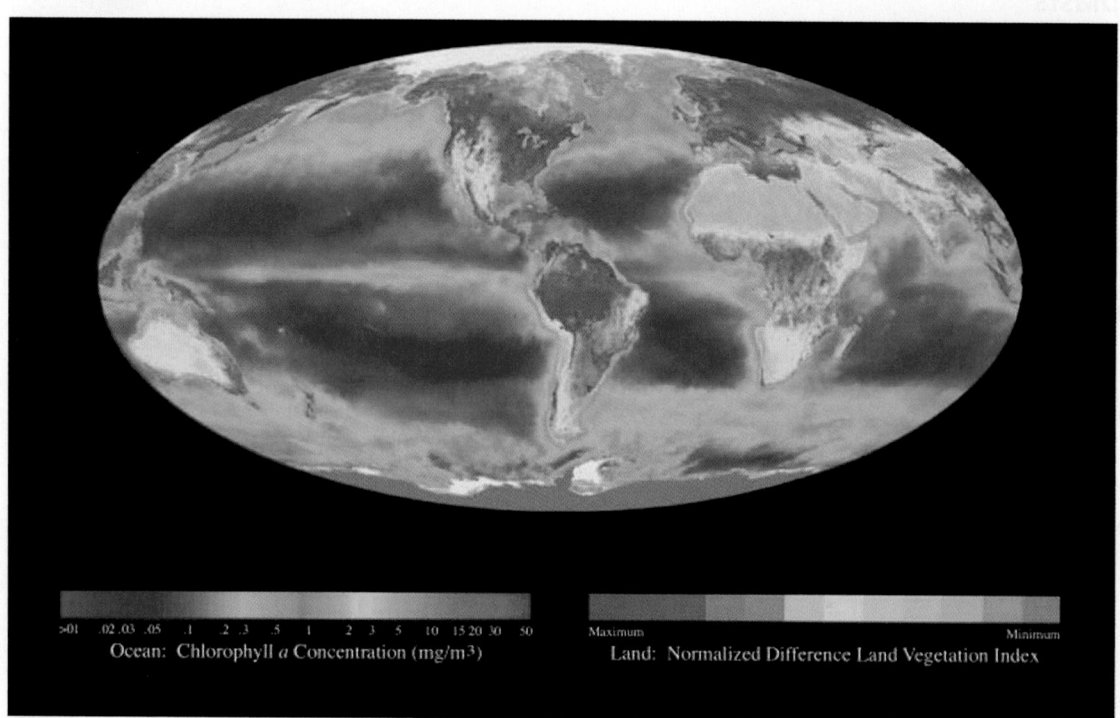

**FIGURE 6.4 Global oceanic and terrestrial photoautotroph abundance can be estimated by the satellite detection of chlorophyll at Earth's surface.** Data collected by NASA's SeaWiFS sensor onboard the OrbView-2 satellite.

NASA/Goddard Space Flight Center

Ocean: Chlorophyll *a* Concentration (mg/m³)
Land: Normalized Difference Land Vegetation Index

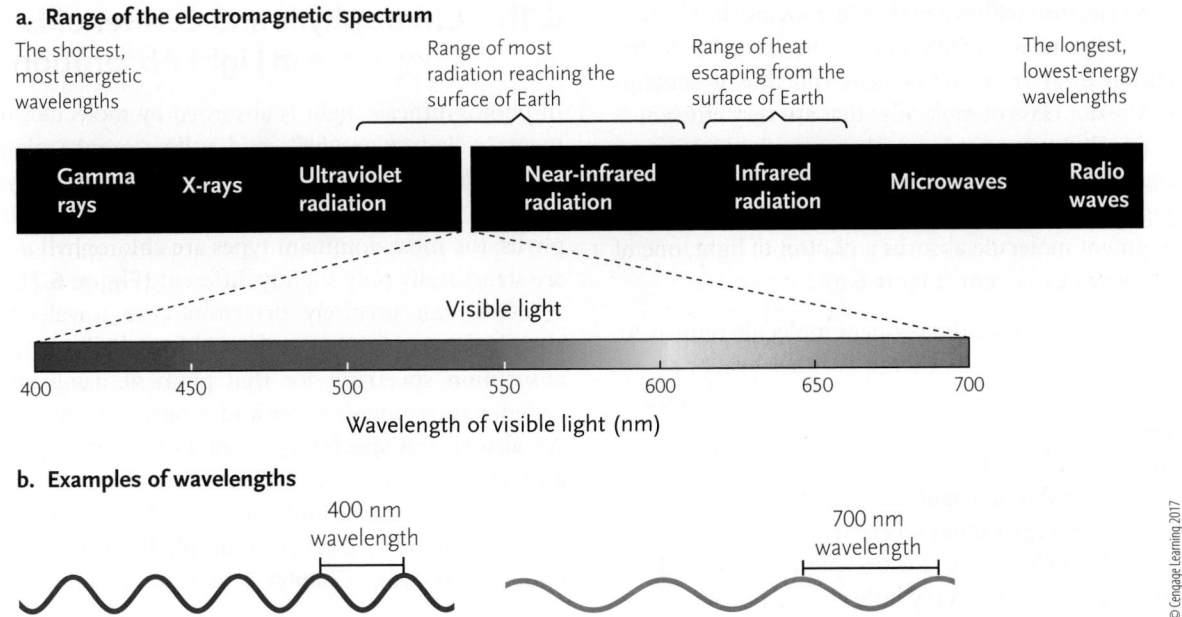

**a. Range of the electromagnetic spectrum**

The shortest, most energetic wavelengths

Range of most radiation reaching the surface of Earth

Range of heat escaping from the surface of Earth

The longest, lowest-energy wavelengths

| Gamma rays | X-rays | Ultraviolet radiation | Near-infrared radiation | Infrared radiation | Microwaves | Radio waves |

Visible light

400    450    500    550    600    650    700

Wavelength of visible light (nm)

**b. Examples of wavelengths**

400 nm wavelength

700 nm wavelength

© Cengage Learning 2017

**FIGURE 6.5 The electromagnetic spectrum. (a)** The electromagnetic spectrum ranges from gamma rays to radio waves. Visible light, which includes the wavelengths used for photosynthesis, occupies only a narrow band of the spectrum. **(b)** Examples of wavelengths that show the difference between the longest and shortest wavelengths of visible light.

## 6.2a Electrons in Pigment Molecules Absorb Light Energy

Photosynthesis requires the capture and utilization of light energy. As we did in Chapter 1, we can define light as that portion of the electromagnetic spectrum that humans can detect with their eyes (**Figure 6.5**). The various forms of radiation that make up the electromagnetic spectrum differ in wavelength, ranging from very long radio waves, which have wavelengths in the range of ten metres to hundreds of kilometres, to gamma rays, which have wavelengths in the range of one hundredth to one millionth of a nanometre. The electromagnetic radiation that humans can detect (light or visible light) has wavelengths between about 400 nm, seen as blue light, and 700 nm, seen as red light (see Figure 6.5).

Although light can be described using the concept of a wave moving through space, the interaction of light with matter is best understood in terms of discrete packets of energy called *photons* (also called *quanta*). A photon of light contains a fixed amount of energy that is inversely related to its wavelength: the shorter the wavelength, the greater the amount of energy that photons of that wavelength contain. So, for example, the energy of a photon of blue light is greater than the energy found in a red photon of light.

To be used as a source of energy, photons of light must be absorbed by a molecule (**Figure 6.6a**). Absorption occurs when the energy of a photon is

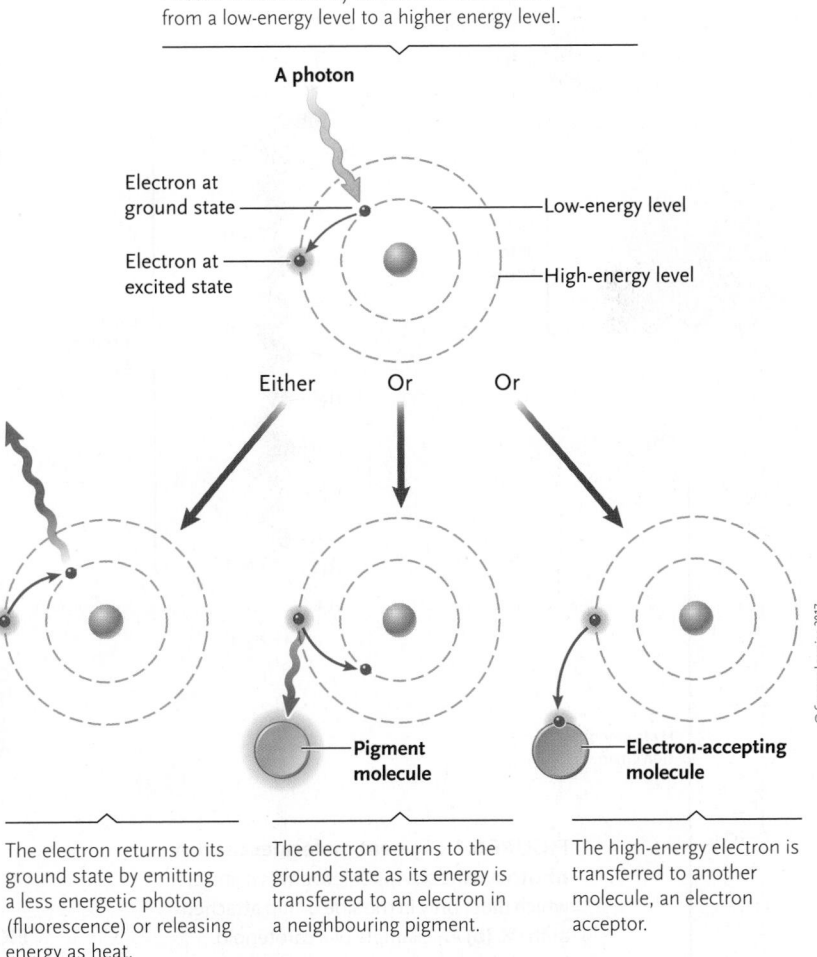

Photon is absorbed by an electron that moves from a low-energy level to a higher energy level.

**A photon**

Electron at ground state

Low-energy level

Electron at excited state

High-energy level

Either        Or        Or

**Pigment molecule**

**Electron-accepting molecule**

© Cengage Learning 2017

The electron returns to its ground state by emitting a less energetic photon (fluorescence) or releasing energy as heat.

The electron returns to the ground state as its energy is transferred to an electron in a neighbouring pigment.

The high-energy electron is transferred to another molecule, an electron acceptor.

**FIGURE 6.6 Three possible fates of an excited-state electron within a pigment molecule**

transferred to an electron within a molecule, moving the electron from the ground state to an excited state. In the excited state, the electron is farther away from the nucleus and thus it contains more energy. A major class of molecules that are very efficient at absorbing visible light are pigments because their structure results in a number of excitable electrons. The structures of a diversity of pigments are presented in Chapter 1, Figure 1.5.

After a pigment molecule absorbs a photon of light, one of three possible events can occur (Figure 6.6):

1. The excited electron from the pigment molecule returns to its ground state, releasing its energy as either heat or an emission of light of a longer wavelength, a process called *fluorescence.*

2. The energy of the excited electron (but not the electron itself) is transferred to a neighbouring pigment molecule. This transfer of energy excites an electron in the second molecule, and the electron in the first pigment molecule returns to its ground state. Very little energy is lost in this energy transfer.

3. The excited electron is transferred from the pigment molecule to a nearby electron-accepting molecule.

## 6.2b Chlorophylls and Carotenoids Cooperate in Light Absorption

In photosynthesis, light is absorbed by molecules of green pigments called *chlorophylls* and yellow-orange pigments called *carotenoids.* Chlorophylls are the major photosynthetic pigments in plants, green algae, and cyanobacteria. Of the chlorophylls, the most dominant types are chlorophyll *a* and *b*, which are structurally only slightly different (**Figure 6.7**).

One can precisely determine the wavelengths of light absorbed by a pigment such as chlorophyll *a* by producing an absorption spectrum for that pigment using an instrument called a *spectrophotometer* and a pure sample of the pigment. An **absorption spectrum** is a plot of the absorption of light as a function of wavelength. **Figure 6.8a** shows that chlorophyll *a* strongly absorbs blue and red light but does not absorb green or yellow light. Why doesn't chlorophyll absorb green or yellow light? Recall from Chapter 1 that, for a photon of light to be

**a.** The absorption spectra of chlorophylls *a* and *b* and carotenoids

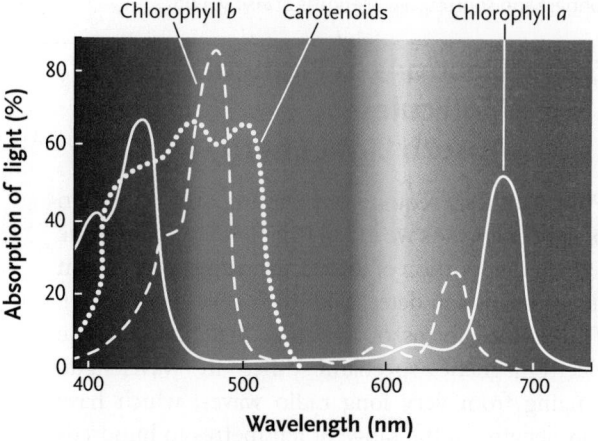

**b.** The action spectrum in higher plants, representing the combined effects of chlorophylls and carotenoids

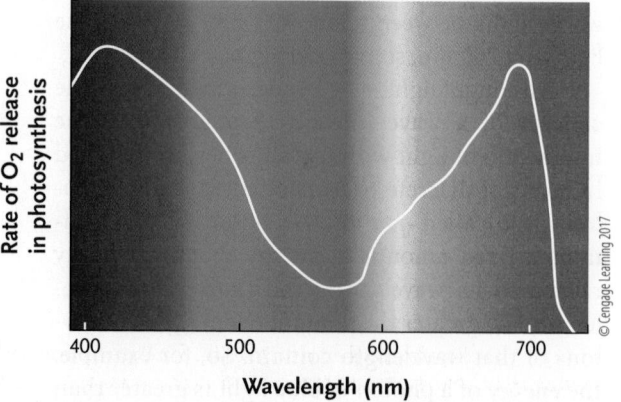

**a. Chlorophyll structure**

**b. Carotenoid structure**

**FIGURE 6.7 Pigment molecules used in photosynthesis. (a)** Chlorophylls *a* and *b*, which differ only in the side group attached at the X. **(b)** An example of a carotenoid. In both (a) and (b), the light-absorbing electrons are distributed among the bonds shaded in orange.

**FIGURE 6.8 The absorption spectra of three photosynthetic pigments** (a) **and the action spectrum of photosynthesis** (b) **in plants.** The absorption spectra in (a) were made from pigments that were extracted from cells and purified.

© Cengage Learning 2017

absorbed, the energy of that photon needs to match the amount of energy required to raise a pigment electron from the ground state to an excited state. If the energies do not match, then the photon is not absorbed. Chlorophyll has only two excited states: one that matches the energy of a blue photon and one that matches that of a red photon.

The absorption spectra of the accessory pigments (chlorophyll *b* and carotenoids; see Figure 6.8a) illustrate that these pigments expand the wavelengths of light that can be effectively captured and used for photosynthesis. Figure 6.8a illustrates that the slight differences in structure between chlorophyll *a* and chlorophyll *b* are reflected in differences in their absorption spectra.

Photosynthesis depends on the absorption of light by chlorophylls and carotenoids, acting in combination. This is supported by the **action spectrum** for photosynthesis. An action spectrum is a plot of the effectiveness of light of particular wavelengths in driving a process (Figure 6.8b). An action spectrum for photosynthesis is usually determined by using a suspension of chloroplasts or algal cells and measuring the amount of $O_2$ released by photosynthesis at different wavelengths of visible light.

One of the earliest action spectra was produced in 1883 by Theodor Engelmann, who used only a light microscope and a glass prism to determine which wavelengths of light were most effective for photosynthesis (**Figure 6.9**). Engelmann placed a strand of a green alga, *Spirogyra*, on a glass microscope slide, along with water containing aerobic bacteria. He adjusted the prism so that it split a beam of light into its separate colours, which spread like a rainbow across the strand (see Figure 6.9). After a short time, he noticed that the bacteria had begun to cluster around the algal strand in different locations. The

largest clusters were under the blue and violet light at one end of the strand and the red light at the other end. Very few bacteria were found in the green light.

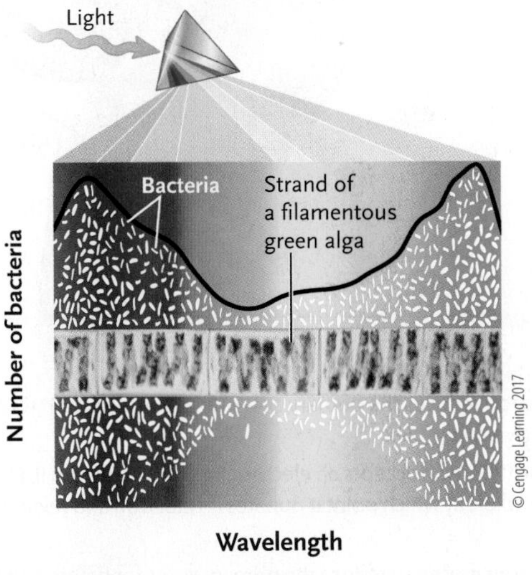

## 6.2c Photosynthetic Pigments Are Organized into Photosystems

Photosynthetic pigments are required not only to absorb photons of light but also to transfer the energy to neighbouring molecules. To do this efficiently, pigment molecules do not float freely within the thylakoid membrane but rather are bound very precisely to specific proteins. These pigment-proteins are organized within the thylakoid membrane into complexes called *photosystems* (**Figure 6.10**). Each photosystem is composed of a large **antenna complex** (also called a *light-harvesting complex*) of pigment-proteins that surrounds a central *reaction centre*. The reaction centre of a photosystem comprises a small number of proteins that bind a special chlorophyll *a* molecule and an electron-accepting molecule called the *primary electron acceptor* (Figure 6.10).

The function of a photosystem is to trap photons of light and use the energy to oxidize a reaction centre chlorophyll, with the electron being transferred to the primary electron acceptor. High rates of this oxidation–reduction reaction within the reaction centre are achieved by the large antenna complex of

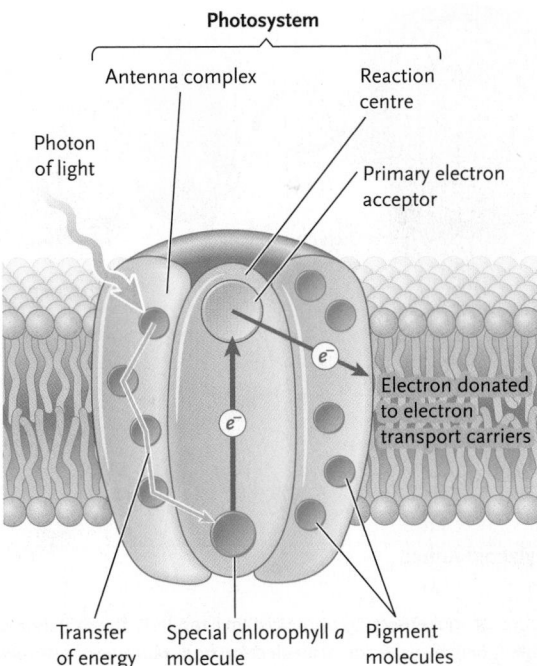

**FIGURE 6.9 Engelmann's experiment revealed the action spectrum of light used in photosynthesis by *Spirogyra*, a green alga.** The aerobic bacteria clustered along the algal strand in the regions where oxygen was released in greatest quantity, that is, the regions in which photosynthesis proceeded at the greatest rate. Those regions corresponded to the colours (wavelengths) of light being absorbed most effectively by the alga, in this case, blue and red.

**FIGURE 6.10 Major components of a photosystem.** A group of pigment-proteins form an antenna complex that surrounds a reaction centre. Light energy absorbed anywhere in the antenna complex is transferred to a special chlorophyll *a* molecule in the reaction centre. The absorbed light is converted to chemical energy when an excited electron from the chlorophyll *a* is transferred to a primary acceptor, also in the reaction centre. High-energy electrons are passed out of the photosystem to the electron transport system. The yellow arrow shows the migration of energy from one pigment to the other, and the blue arrows show movement of electrons.

pigments absorbing light of a range of wavelengths and efficiently transferring the energy to the **reaction centre**.

There are two different types of photosystems: photosystem I and photosystem II. The specialized chlorophyll *a* in the reaction centre of **photosystem I** is called *P700* (P = pigment) because its absorption maximum is at a wavelength of 700 nm. The reaction centre of **photosystem II** contains a specialized chlorophyll *a*, P680, which absorbs light maximally at 680 nm. Within a single chloroplast there are thousands of photosystems (both I and II), each containing about 500 chlorophyll molecules.

## STUDY BREAK QUESTIONS

1. What contains more energy, a photon of green light or a photon of orange light?
2. What are the three possible fates of an excited-state electron?
3. How is an absorption spectrum different from an action spectrum?

# 6.3 The Light Reactions

Photosystem I and photosystem II are the two light-trapping components involved in photosynthetic electron transport. In this section, we look in detail at how this particular electron transport chain operates and draw some analogies to respiratory electron transport.

## 6.3a Photosynthetic Electron Transport Synthesizes NADPH and Generates a Proton Gradient

**Figure 6.11** shows the components of photosynthetic electron transport and the ATP synthase complex within the thylakoid membrane. As in all electron transport systems, the electron carriers of the photosynthetic system consist of nonprotein cofactors that alternate between being oxidized and being reduced as electrons move through the system. The carriers,

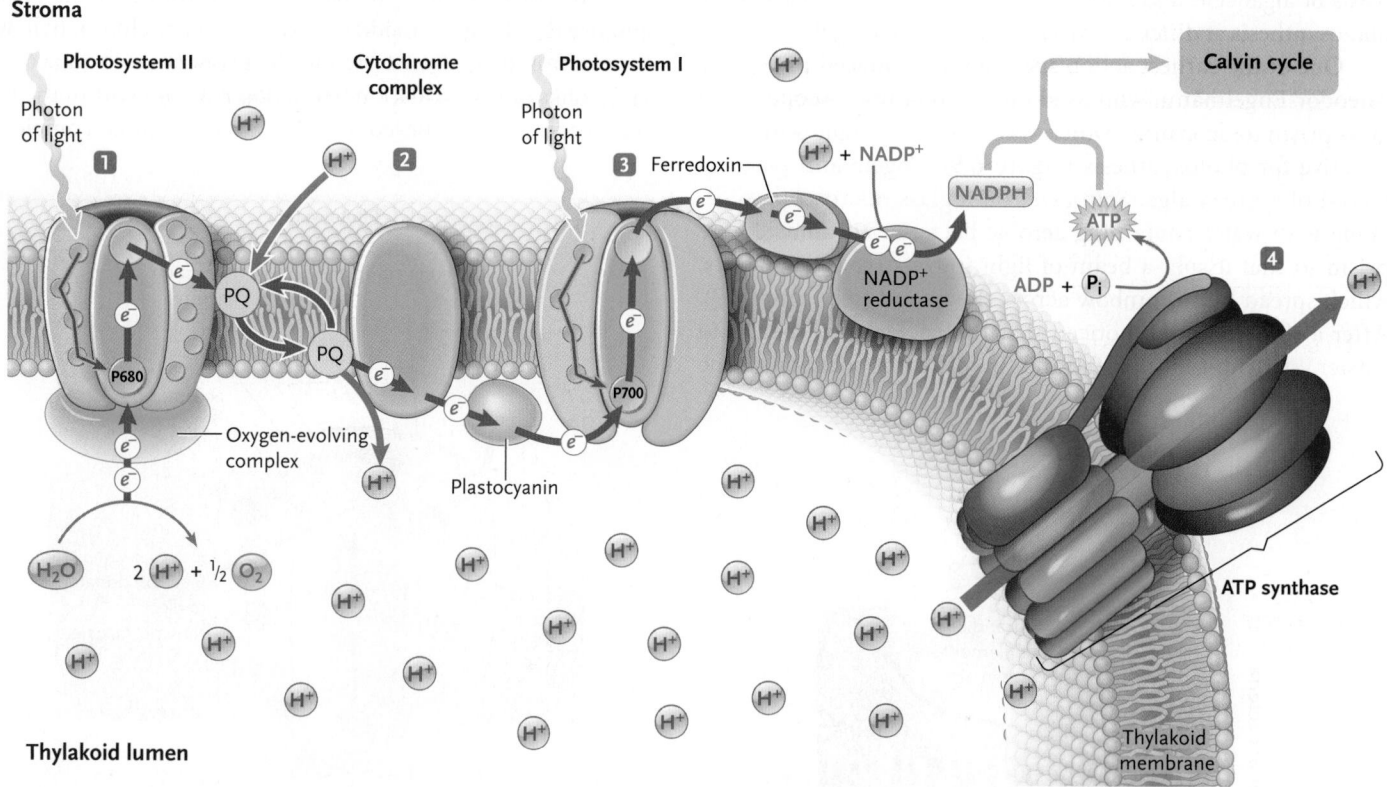

**1** Absorption of light energy by photosystem II results in the oxidation of P680. The released electron reduces the primary acceptor molecule. P680$^+$ is returned to the reduced state (P680) by donation of an electron from water, a process mediated by the oxygen-evolving complex.

**2** From the primary acceptor, the electron is passed to the mobile carrier molecule plastoquinone (PQ). As it accepts an electron from photosystem II, PQ picks up a proton from the stroma. PQ diffuses through the membrane before binding to the cytochrome complex, at which point it donates an electron and releases a proton into the thylakoid lumen. From the cytochrome complex the electron is donated to plastocyanin.

**3** Absorption of light energy by photosystem I results in the oxidation of P700. The liberated electron is used to reduce the primary acceptor before being passed to ferredoxin. This single electron is then held by the NADP$^+$ reductase complex. P700$^+$ is reduced back to P700 by the electron that is coming from plastocyanin. Once a second electron travels along the chain and reaches NADP$^+$ reductase complex, NADP$^+$ is reduced to NADPH.

**4** Proton movement by the reduction–oxidation of plastoquinone (red arrows) creates a concentration gradient of H$^+$ (a proton-motive force) across the thylakoid membrane. The gradient is dissipated as H$^+$ diffuses back into the stroma through the ATP synthase complex, which drives the synthesis of ATP from ADP and P$_i$.

**FIGURE 6.11  A model of the eukaryotic thylakoid membrane illustrating the major protein and redox cofactors required for photosynthetic electron transport and ATP synthesis**

many of which are bound precisely to proteins, include the same types that act in mitochondrial electron transfer: cytochromes, quinones, and iron–sulfur centres (see Chapter 5).

Most of the electron carriers are organized into three large complexes embedded in the thylakoid membrane: photosystem II, the cytochrome complex, and photosystem I. Electron flow between photosystem II and the cytochrome complex is facilitated by a pool of plastoquinone (PQ) molecules, which are similar in structure and function to the ubiquinone of respiratory electron transport. Electron flow from the cytochrome complex to photosystem I is linked by the mobile copper-containing protein plastocyanin.

From photosystem I, electrons are donated to an iron–sulfur protein called *ferredoxin*, which in turn donates electrons to the enzyme NADP$^+$ reductase found on the stromal side of the thylakoid membrane. The enzyme reduces NADP$^+$ to NADPH by using two electrons from electron transport and a proton from the surrounding aqueous environment.

## 6.3b Light Is Used Specifically to Oxidize Chlorophyll

Just like respiratory electron transport, photosynthetic electron transport operates with electrons flowing spontaneously from molecules that are easily oxidized to molecules that are progressively more easily reduced. In the case of mitochondrial electron transport, electron flow is from NADH, which is easy to remove electrons from, to O$_2$, which has a high affinity for electrons. In photosynthesis, electron transport occurs by the same principle; however, unlike NADH, the chlorophyll molecules in the reaction centres of photosystem II and photosystem I are not easily oxidized. So what process gets a chlorophyll molecule into a state in which it readily gives up an electron? Absorption of photons of light! The absorption of a photon of light within photosystem II and photosystem I and the funnelling of this high energy to the reaction centre is used to excite an electron within P680 or P700 (**Figure 6.12**). By raising an electron in P680 to a higher excited state (denoted as P680\*), the absorption of light energy produces a molecule that is easily oxidized by the electron transport chain, and electron flow is a spontaneous process from P680\* to photosystem I. A second photon of light absorbed by photosystem I results in the formation of P700\*, which is easily oxidized by the primary electron acceptor of photosystem I, and in turn ferredoxin, before the electron is finally donated to NADP$^+$ (see Figure 6.12). Oxidized P680 (P680$^+$) is reduced by electrons donated from water (Figure 6.11); P700$^+$ is reduced back to P700 by electrons coming from PSII.

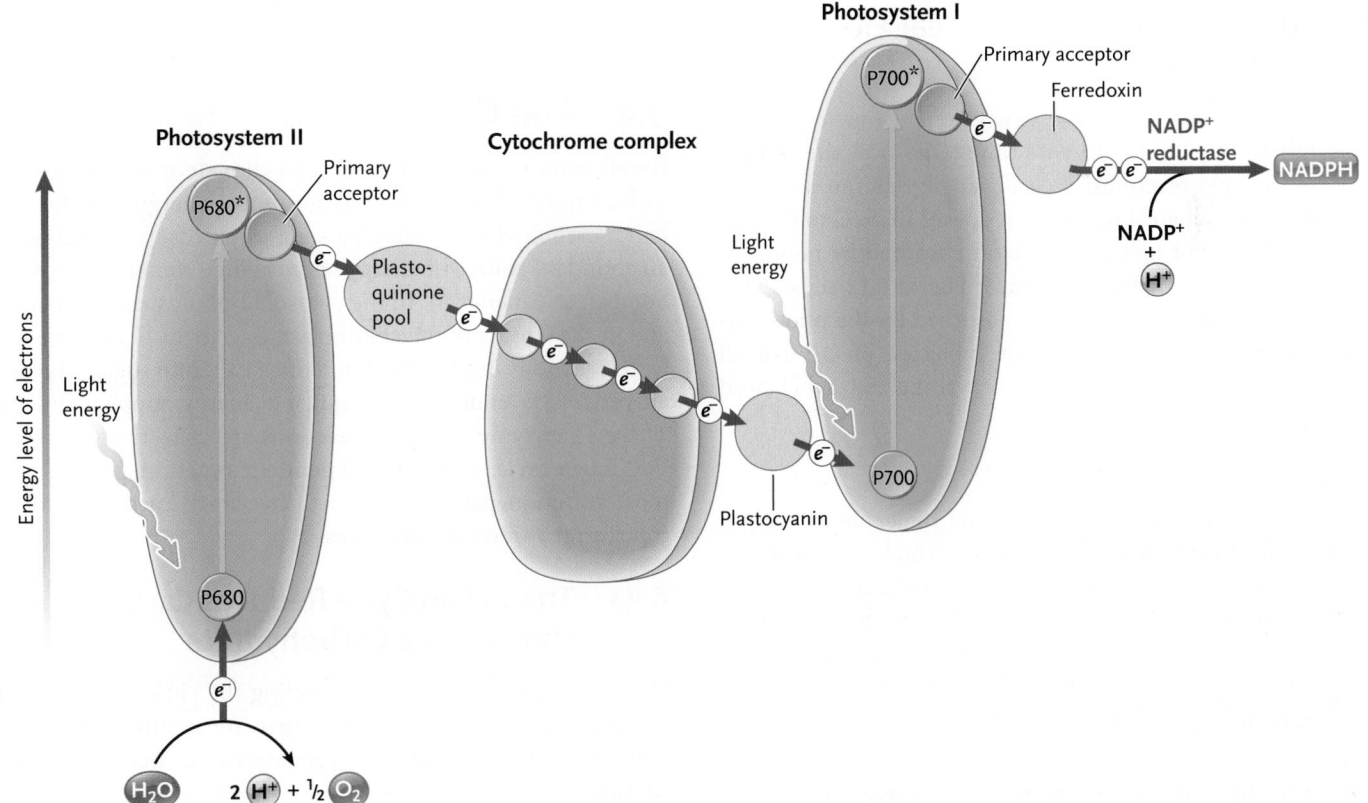

**FIGURE 6.12 The components of the thylakoid membrane organized according to their energy level.** This is also referred to as the *Z scheme*. When photosystem II absorbs a photon of light, an electron within the reaction centre chlorophyll of P680 gets excited to a higher energy level (P680\*). This results in spontaneous electron transport to photosystem I. However, the energy level of NADP$^+$ is greater than that of P700. This energy difference is overcome by photosystem I absorbing a photon of light, producing P700\*. Thus, two photons of light, one absorbed by photosystem II and another absorbed by photosystem I, are required to overcome the energy difference between H$_2$O and NADP$^+$.

## 6.3c In the Light Reactions, ATP Is Generated by Chemiosmosis

In a way analogous to respiratory electron transport, the flow of electrons along the photosynthetic ETC is coupled to ATP synthesis by the buildup of a proton gradient. In photosynthetic electron transport, the proton gradient across the thylakoid membrane is derived from three processes (see Figure 6.11). First, protons are translocated into the lumen by the cyclic reduction and oxidation of plastoquinone as it migrates from photosystem II to the cytochrome complex and back again. Second, the gradient is enhanced by the addition of two protons to the lumen from the oxidation of water, which occurs on the luminal side of photosystem II. Third, the removal of one proton from the stroma for each NADPH molecule synthesized further decreases the $H^+$ concentration in the stroma, thereby enhancing the gradient across the thylakoid membrane. The proton-motive force (see Section 5.5) established across the thylakoid membrane is used to synthesize ATP by chemiosmosis using the chloroplast ATP synthase. This multiprotein complex is structurally and functionally analogous to the ATP synthase used in oxidative phosphorylation in cellular respiration (see Figure 5.16, Chapter 5). Distinct from oxidative phosphorylation in cellular respiration, the process of using light to generate ATP is often referred to as **photophosphorylation.**

## 6.3d The Stoichiometry of Linear Electron Transport

We have described in detail the structure and function of the photosynthetic apparatus. Now it's time to go over the stoichiometry of the light reactions. To get a single electron down the ETC from photosystem II (or water, it doesn't matter) to NADP+ takes two photons of light, one photon absorbed by photosystem II and a second by photosystem I. Figure 6.12 shows this. But how many photons need to be absorbed by the photosynthetic apparatus to produce a single molecule of $O_2$? For all these types of questions, we start by writing out a balanced chemical reaction, such as

$$2\,H_2O \rightarrow 4\,H^+ + 4\,e^- + O_2$$

The reaction shows that to produce one molecule of $O_2$ you need to oxidize two molecules of water, which results in the release of four electrons. Now to move a single electron down the ETC requires the absorption of two photons. It follows then that to get four electrons from photosystem II to NADP+, the photosynthetic apparatus needs to absorb a total of eight photons of light, four by each photosystem.

## 6.3e Cyclic Electron Transport Generates ATP in the Absence of NADPH

The pathway of electron flow from photosystem II through photosystem I to synthesize NADPH is referred to as *linear electron transport*. Although this is the pathway of electron flow that occurs most often, photosystem I can function independently of photosystem II in what is called **cyclic electron transport (Figure 6.13)**. In this process, electron flow from photosystem I to ferredoxin is not followed by electron donation to the NADP+ reductase complex. Instead, reduced ferredoxin donates electrons back to the plastoquinone pool. In this manner, the plastoquinone pool gets continually reduced and oxidized and keeps moving protons across the thylakoid membrane without the involvement of electrons coming from photosystem II. Overall, cyclic electron transport only involves light absorption by photosystem I, with the energy being used to establish a proton-motive force and generate ATP. Unlike linear electron transport, NADPH is not formed during cyclic electron transport.

Cyclic electron transport plays an important role in overall photosynthesis. The reduction of carbon dioxide by the Calvin cycle requires more ATP than NADPH, and the additional ATP molecules are provided by cyclic electron transport. Other energy-requiring reactions in the chloroplast also depend on ATP produced by the cyclic pathway.

### STUDY BREAK QUESTIONS

1. In which compartment of the chloroplast is NADPH generated?
2. How is the proton gradient across the thylakoid membrane established during electron transport?
3. How many photons of light are required to generate one molecule of NADPH by linear electron transport?

## 6.4 The Calvin Cycle

Recall from Chapter 5 that carbon dioxide is a fully oxidized carbon molecule and contains no usable energy. On the other hand, carbohydrate molecules such as glucose and sucrose are an abundant source of energy because they contain many C—H bonds (see Chapter 5). In the cytosol of photosynthetic bacteria and in the stroma of the chloroplast, a series of 11 enzyme-catalyzed reactions use NADPH to reduce $CO_2$ into sugar. The overall process is endergonic, requiring energy supplied by ATP. These 11 enzyme-catalyzed reactions are collectively known as *the Calvin cycle*, or **light-independent reactions**, which is the most common pathway on Earth by which carbon dioxide is transformed into carbohydrates.

### 6.4a The Calvin Cycle Reduces Carbon Dioxide to a Carbohydrate

Like other metabolic cycles, including the citric acid cycle, the Calvin cycle generates products that are removed but it also requires that molecules be regenerated so that cycling can continue.

During each turn of the Calvin cycle, one molecule of $CO_2$ is converted into one reduced carbon—essentially, one $(CH_2O)$ unit of carbohydrate. To help you better understand the Calvin cycle, **Figure 6.14** represents a summary of what occurs following three turns of the cycle. It is only after three carbon dioxide

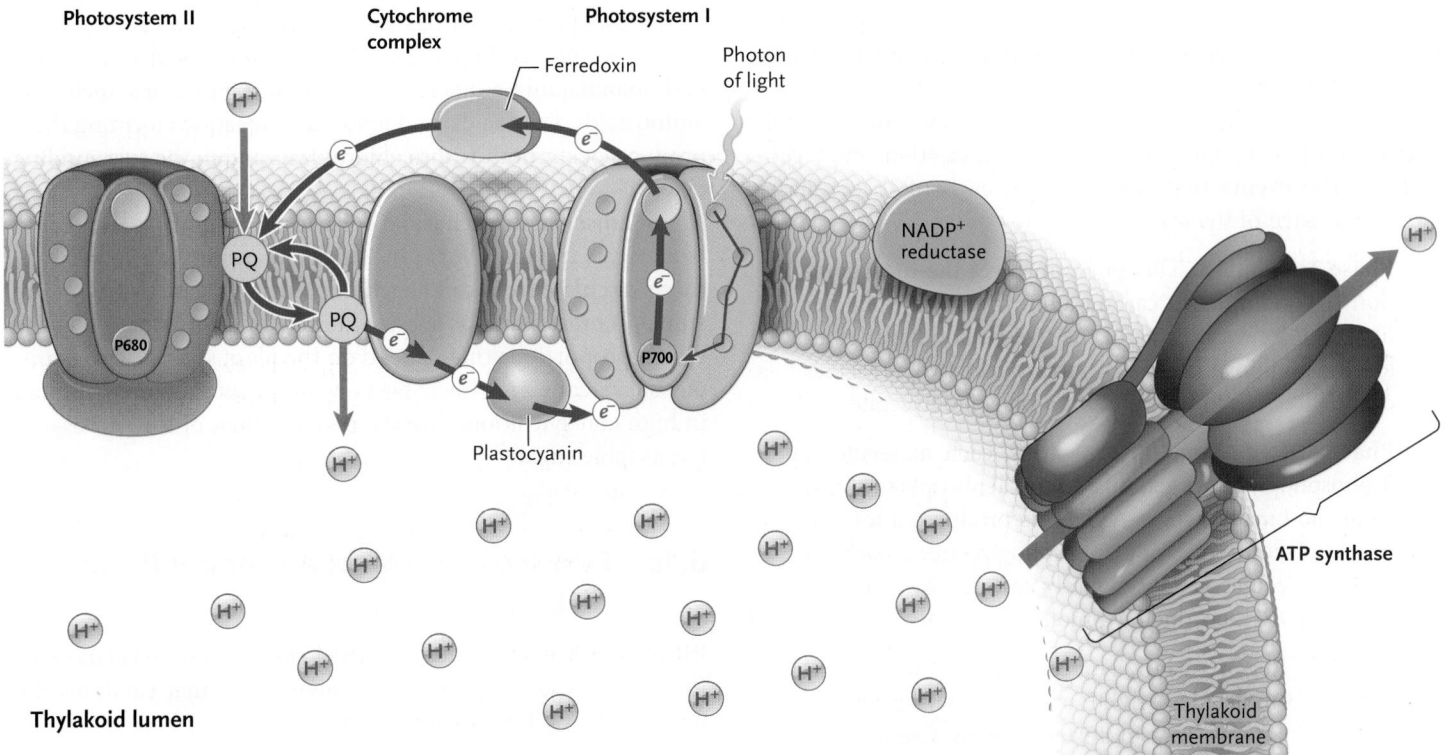

**FIGURE 6.13 Cyclic electron transport.** Electrons move in a circular pathway from photosystem I through ferredoxin back to the plastoquinone pool, through the cytochrome complex and plastocyanin, and then back to photosystem I. Photosystem II does not operate in cyclic electron transport. The pathway generates proton pumping and thus leads to ATP production but does not result in the synthesis of NADPH.

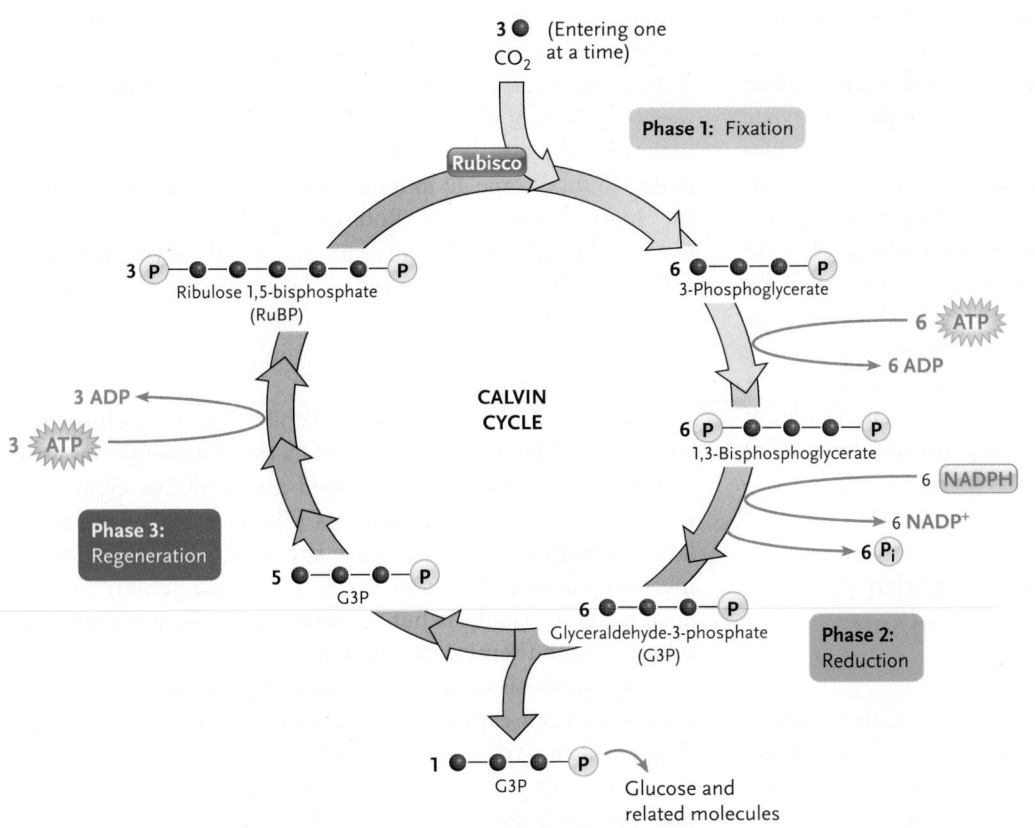

**FIGURE 6.14 The Calvin cycle.** An overview of the three phases of the Calvin cycle. The figure tracks the carbon atoms (dark grey balls) during three turns of the cycle. For every three molecules of $CO_2$ that are fixed, one molecule of the three-carbon sugar G3P is synthesized.

molecules get reduced that one actually generates a separate molecule, a three-carbon sugar, glyceraldehyde 3-phosphate (G3P). By a reaction that is not part of the Calvin cycle, two molecules of G3P can synthesize one molecule of the six-carbon sugar glucose.

As shown in Figure 6.14, the Calvin cycle can be subdivided into three distinct phases: fixation, reduction, and regeneration. The events that take place in each of these phases during *one* turn of the cycle are as follows:

**Phase 1: Fixation.** This phase involves the incorporation (i.e., fixing) of a carbon atom from $CO_2$ (one per turn) into one molecule of the five-carbon sugar ribulose 1,5-bisphosphate (RuBP) to produce two molecules of the three-carbon compound 3-phosphoglycerate.

**Phase 2: Reduction.** In this phase, each molecule of 3-phosphoglycerate gets an additional phosphate added from the breakdown of ATP. This produces a total of two molecules of 1,3-bisphosphoglycerate. Each of these molecules is subsequently reduced by electrons from NADPH, producing a molecule of G3P.

**Phase 3: Regeneration.** For each turn of the Calvin cycle, two molecules of G3P are produced—a total of six carbon atoms. In a multistep process, five of these carbons are rearranged to regenerate the single molecule of RuBP required for the next round of carbon fixation.

Let's work through Figure 6.14 (the key is to keep track of the carbons). In three turns of the Calvin cycle, 3 $CO_2$ (3 carbons) are incorporated into 3 molecules of RuBP (15 carbons), which produces 6 molecules of 3-phosphoglycerate (18 carbons). Each of these molecules is phosphorylated by a phosphate donated by ATP. In total, 6 ATP are consumed to phosphorylate the 6 molecules of 3-phosphoglycerate, generating 6 molecules of 1,3-bisphosphoglycerate. Six molecules of NADPH are consumed in converting the 6 molecules of 1,3-bisphosphoglycerate into 6 molecules of G3P (18 carbons). Five molecules of G3P (totalling 15 carbons) are used to regenerate 3 RuBP molecules (15 carbons), which requires 3 molecules of ATP. Thus, the cycle generates 1 surplus molecule of G3P (3 carbons) after every three turns. For the synthesis of this one extra G3P, the Calvin cycle requires a total of 9 molecules of ATP and 6 molecules of NADPH. Both ATP and NADPH are regenerated from ADP and $NADP^+$ respectively by the light reactions.

## 6.4b G3P Is the Starting Point for the Synthesis of Many Other Organic Molecules

The G3P molecule formed by three turns of the Calvin cycle is the starting point for the production of a wide variety of organic molecules. Carbohydrates such as glucose and other monosaccharides are made from G3P by reactions that, in effect, reverse the first half of glycolysis. Once produced, the monosaccharides may enter biochemical pathways that make disaccharides such as sucrose, polysaccharides such as starches and cellulose, and other complex carbohydrates. Other pathways that consume G3P manufacture a diverse array of other molecules, including amino acids, fatty acids, and lipids. The reactions forming these products occur both within chloroplasts and in the surrounding cytosol.

Sucrose, a disaccharide consisting of glucose linked to fructose, is the main form in which the products of photosynthesis circulate from cell to cell in plants. Organic nutrients are stored in most plants as sucrose, starch, or a combination of the two in proportions that depend on the plant species. For example, sugar cane and sugar beets, which contain stored sucrose in high concentrations, are the main sources of the sucrose we use as table sugar.

## 6.4c Rubisco Is the Most Abundant Protein on Earth

**Ribulose 1,5-bisphosphate (RuBP) carboxylase oxygenase**, or **Rubisco**, is the enzyme of the Calvin cycle that catalyzes the fixation of $CO_2$ into organic form:

$$\text{Ribulose 1,5-bisphosphate (RuBP)} + CO_2 \rightarrow$$
$$\text{2 3-phosphoglycerate}$$

Rubisco is considered the most important enzyme of the biosphere because, by catalyzing $CO_2$ fixation in all photoautotrophs, it provides the source of organic carbon for most of the world's organisms. The enzyme converts a staggering 100 billion tonnes of $CO_2$ into carbohydrates annually. There are so many Rubisco molecules in chloroplasts that this one enzyme accounts for about 50% of the total protein content of plant leaves. This makes Rubisco easily the planet's most abundant protein, estimated to total some 40 million tonnes worldwide. Interestingly, the high abundance of Rubisco in photosynthetic cells is explained by the fact that this very important enzyme is catalytically very slow. For most enzymes, one molecule of enzyme can react with hundreds to many thousands of molecules of substrate per second. Rubisco processes only about 3–10 molecules of carbon dioxide per second.

Isolation and purification of Rubisco from the chloroplast stroma has led to the elucidation of its three-dimensional structure. The molecule is cube shaped and contains eight small subunits and eight large subunits (**Figure 6.15a**). Each of the large subunits contains an active site, which has defined binding sites for both $CO_2$ and RuBP. The small subunits do not have a role in catalysis but do serve an important regulatory role, although their exact function remains unknown.

The synthesis of Rubisco is quite remarkable as it requires the coordinated expression of genes of two different genomes (Figure 6.15b). While the large subunit is encoded by a gene of the chloroplast genome, the small subunit is encoded by a gene that is found in the nucleus. After the small subunit polypeptide

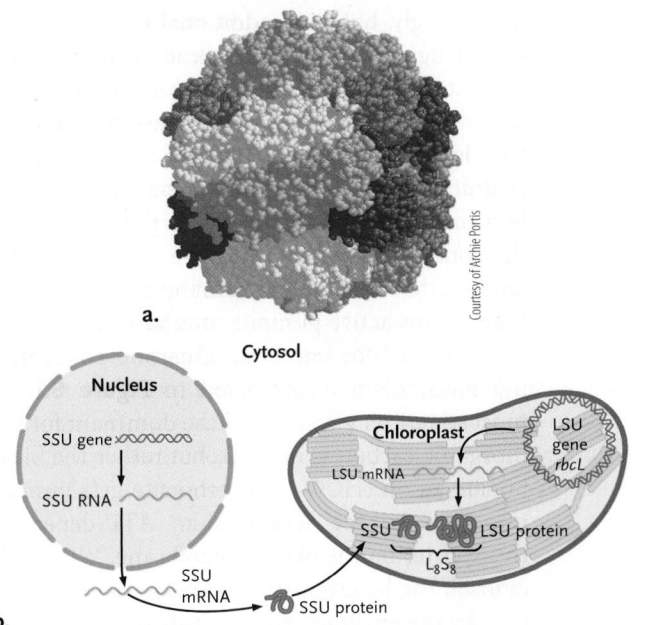

a.

**b.**

Cytosol

Nucleus

SSU gene

SSU RNA

SSU
mRNA

SSU protein

Chloroplast

LSU
gene
*rbcL*

LSU mRNA

SSU

LSU protein

$L_8S_8$

Courtesy of Archie Portis

**FIGURE 6.15 Model of Rubisco. (a)** The functional enzyme is composed of a total of 16 subunits: 8 large subunits (LSU) (shown in white and grey) and 8 small subunits (SSU) (shown in orange and blue). The synthesis of Rubisco **(b)** requires coordinated gene expression of two genomes. Each LSU is synthesized in the stroma of the chloroplast following the transcription of a gene coded by the chloroplast chromosome. The gene that encodes the SSU is found in the nucleus, with SSU monomers being synthesized by cytosolic ribosomes before being imported into the chloroplast.

is synthesized in the cytosol, it is imported into the chloroplast, where it associates with large subunit monomers to make the functional enzyme.

Interestingly, the vast majority of the proteins found in chloroplasts (and mitochondria) are in fact encoded by the nuclear genome and thus are synthesized on ribosomes in the cytosol (see Chapter 21 for further discussion on this).

### STUDY BREAK QUESTIONS

1. Glucose is not the actual product of the Calvin cycle. What is?
2. For the Calvin cycle to keep going, what compound needs to be constantly regenerated?
3. What role does the chloroplast genome play in the synthesis of Rubisco?

# 6.5 Photorespiration and CO$_2$-Concentrating Mechanisms

For being arguably the most important enzyme on the planet, Rubisco is surprisingly inefficient at fixing $CO_2$. The cause of this inefficiency is that the active site of Rubisco is not specific to $CO_2$: a molecule of $O_2$ can also bind to the active site and react with RuBP. When this occurs, one of the products is a two-carbon compound that is exported from the chloroplast and actually requires the cell to consume ATP to convert it

into carbon dioxide, which is simply lost. This wasteful process is called **photorespiration** because it occurs in the light and is similar to cellular respiration in that it consumes $O_2$ and releases $CO_2$. In this section, we present details on the biochemistry of the reactions that Rubisco catalyzes with $O_2$ and $CO_2$. As well, we discuss how photorespiration is exacerbated by certain environmental conditions and the key adaptations some plants and algae have evolved to minimize photorespiration.

## 6.5a Rubisco Is an Ancient Enzyme That Is Inhibited by Oxygen

Before we discuss the biochemistry of photorespiration, a key question we could ask is, Why would natural selection have led to the evolution of an enzyme that accepts a second substrate molecule that produces a wasteful product? Rubisco and Rubisco-like proteins evolved at least 3 billion years ago as the primary enzyme in the biosphere for reducing carbon dioxide into organic form. Support for this comes, in part, from Rubisco being found in a huge diversity of organisms, including many bacteria and archaea (while they don't carry out photosynthesis, some archaea do have Rubisco). As discussed in Chapter 21, the atmosphere 3 billion years ago contained only trace amounts of $O_2$ and much higher levels of $CO_2$ than today. Under such conditions, an early form of Rubisco that could bind $O_2$ as well as $CO_2$ would not have been detrimental to an organism. Photorespiration became a problem only as the levels of oxygen in the atmosphere increased. There is evidence that, over time, Rubisco has slowly evolved to be more specific for $CO_2$, but the inhibition by $O_2$ remains.

$O_2$ can directly compete with $CO_2$ for the active site of Rubisco, and as such is an excellent example of a competitive inhibitor of enzyme function (see Chapter 3). When oxygen binds to the active site of Rubisco, the enzyme acts as an *oxygenase* instead of a *carboxylase*. A comparison of the products of the carboxylation reaction and the oxygenation reaction of Rubisco is shown in **Figure 6.16**. The incorporation of a $CO_2$ molecule into the five-carbon compound RuBP leads to a net increase in carbon by producing two molecules of the three-carbon compound 3-phosphoglycerate. By comparison, the incorporation of $O_2$ into RuBP in the oxygenation reaction produces a single molecule of 3-phosphoglycerate and a single molecule of the two-carbon compound phosphoglycolate. There is no carbon gain: five carbons in and five carbons out. However, what makes photorespiration perhaps even more detrimental is that photoautotrophs cannot use phosphoglycolate. In the process of breaking it down to salvage the carbon, a toxic compound called *glycolate* is produced. The elimination of glycolate through its oxidation results in the release of carbon dioxide. Thus, whereas the carboxylation reaction leads to carbon gain, the oxygenation reaction actually results in the plant losing carbon.

If we compare the carboxylation and oxygenation reactions of Rubisco under laboratory conditions, where we can keep the

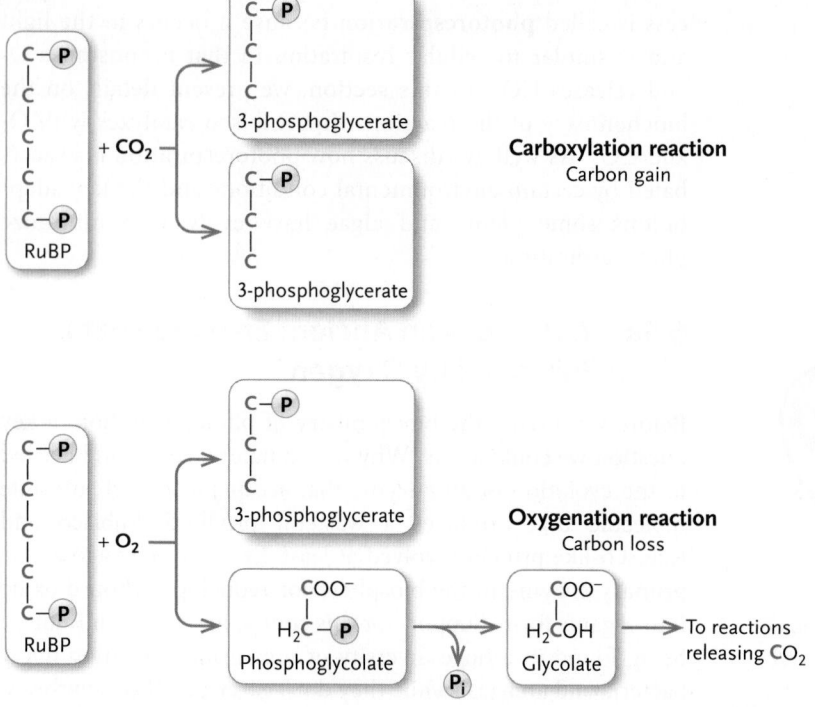

**FIGURE 6.16 The enzyme Rubisco possesses both a carboxylase and an oxygenase activity.** Compared with the usual carboxylase activity of the Calvin cycle, the oxygenase activity results in a net loss of carbon by the plant. Because oxygenase activity consumes $O_2$ and releases $CO_2$, it is also called *photorespiration*.

From Russell/Hertz/McMillan. *Biology, 2E.* © 2012 Brooks/Cole, a part of Cengage, Inc. Reproduced by permission. www.cengage.com/permissions

concentrations of both $O_2$ and $CO_2$ equal, then the carboxylation reaction will dominate because the active site of Rubisco has a greater affinity for $CO_2$ than $O_2$. In fact, the carboxylation reaction will occur about 80 times as fast as the oxygenation reaction. However, unlike in the laboratory, the atmosphere does not contain equal amounts of the two gases: it contains approximately 21% $O_2$ and only about 0.04% $CO_2$. Because of this, under normal atmospheric concentrations and at moderate temperatures, the oxygenation reaction can occur about once for every three times the carboxylation reaction occurs. This means that 25% of the time, the wasteful oxygenation reaction occurs, resulting in net carbon loss. To counter the extent to which the oxygenation reaction occurs, many species have evolved mechanisms to try to decrease the prevalence of the oxygenation reaction. The strategies involve using mechanisms that increase the $CO_2/O_2$ ratio at the site of Rubisco.

## 6.5b Algae Pump Carbon Dioxide into Their Cells

In aquatic environments, the concentration of $CO_2$ dissolved in the water is usually low, well below what is needed to saturate the active site of Rubisco. Yet,

interestingly, bubbling additional $CO_2$ into a culture of algae does not usually lead to an increase in the rate of photosynthesis, which is what you would expect. The lack of response to additional $CO_2$ is explained by the presence of a *carbon-concentrating mechanism* that pumps inorganic carbon into algal cells. This means that, even when the concentration of $CO_2$ in the water is low, the amount that is actually within the cells is kept very high by this active pumping mechanism.

A model for one type of carbon-concentrating mechanism is presented in **Figure 6.17**. In most aquatic environments, the dominant form of inorganic carbon is not $CO_2$ but rather the bicarbonate anion ($HCO_3^-$). Bicarbonate gets pumped into cells by the action of an ATP-dependent transporter on the plasma membrane. Within the cytosol, the bicarbonate is rapidly converted into $CO_2$ by the enzyme carbonic anhydrase. The $CO_2$ then diffuses into the chloroplast to the site of Rubisco. This system results in a concentration of $CO_2$ at the site of Rubisco that is sufficiently high to essentially out-compete the $O_2$ that is present for the active site of Rubisco.

## 6.5c High Temperatures Increase Photorespiration

Like algae, land plants also face the problem of photorespiration. However, many land plants face the additional problem of trying to conserve water. Interestingly, these two problems are linked.

The surface of a plant leaf consists of a waxy cuticle that prevents evaporation of water into the air. Because this waxy

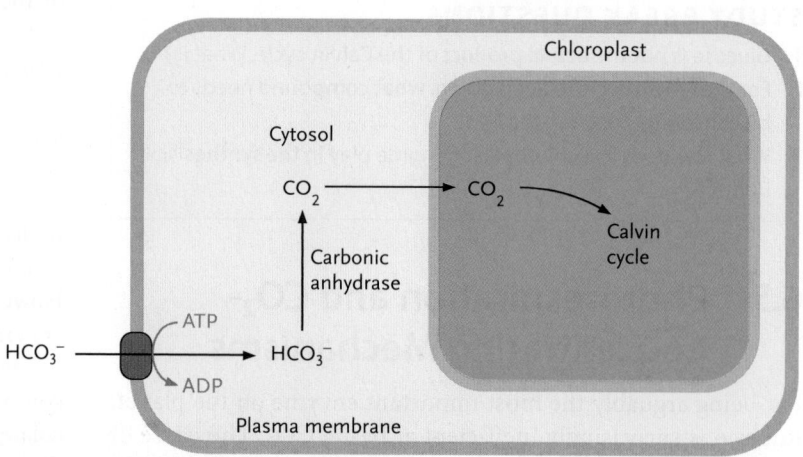

**FIGURE 6.17 $CO_2$ concentration mechanism.** Many aquatic photoautotrophs (e.g., algae) can increase their intracellular carbon dioxide concentrations through a mechanism that involves an ATP-dependent bicarbonate ($HCO_3^-$) pump on the plasma membrane. The bicarbonate is rapidly converted in the cytosol to $CO_2$ by the enzyme carbonic anhydrase.

cuticle also inhibits the flow of carbon dioxide, the leaf surface is covered by small pores called *stomata* (singular, *stoma*) that facilitate the movement of gases into and out of the leaf (**Figure 6.18**). What direction a gas moves through the stomata is governed by diffusion (movement from high to low concentration). As shown in Figure 6.18b, carbon dioxide diffuses into plant leaves. Its concentration is higher outside the leaf than inside because $CO_2$ is being consumed within the leaf by photosynthesis. Both $O_2$ and $H_2O$ (water vapour) diffuse out of the leaf because their concentrations are higher in the leaf than in the outside air; $O_2$ is being made during photosynthesis by

| TABLE 6.1 | Effect of Temperature on the Solubility of $O_2$ and $CO_2$ | | |
|---|---|---|---|
| Temperature (°C) | $[CO_2]$ (µM in solution) | $[O_2]$ (µM in solution) | $\dfrac{[CO_2]}{[O_2]}$ |
| 5 | 21.93 | 401.2 | 0.0547 |
| 15 | 15.69 | 319.8 | 0.0491 |
| 25 | 11.68 | 264.6 | 0.0441 |
| 35 | 9.11 | 228.2 | 0.0399 |

**a.**

**b.**

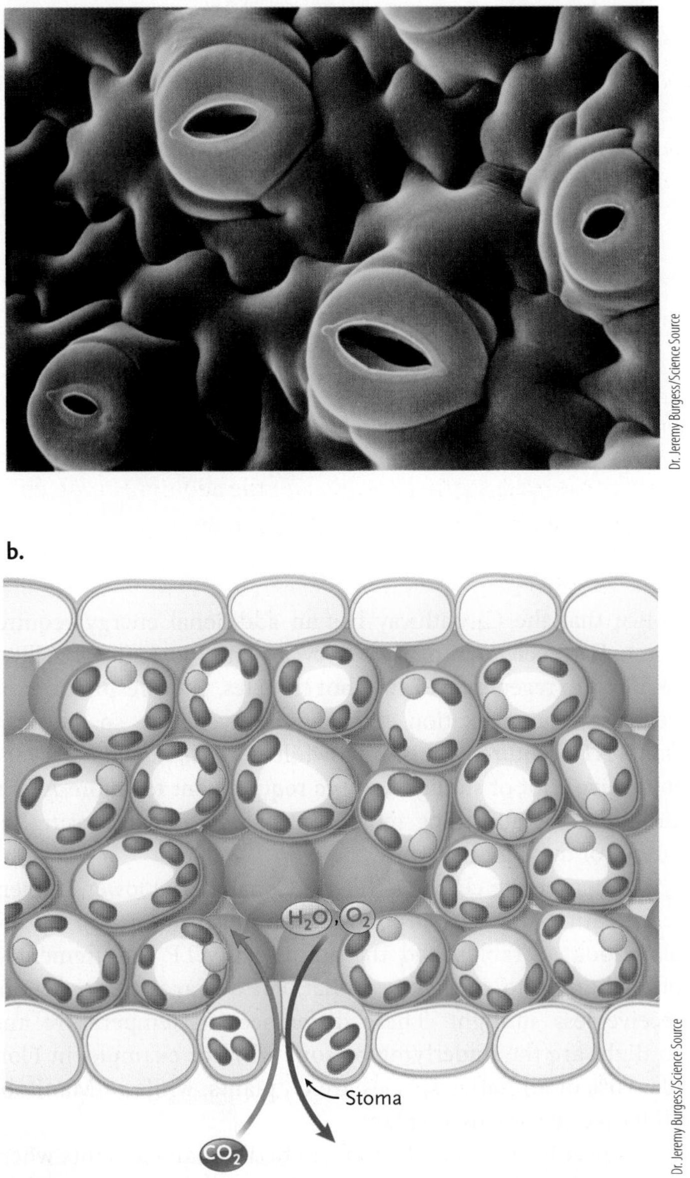

FIGURE 6.18 **Stomata. (a)** Micrograph of a leaf surface showing the presence of pores called *stomata* (singular, *stoma*). **(b)** Each stoma is formed from two guard cells that control the opening and closing of the pore. This controls the movement of gases into and out of the plant and water loss.

photosystem II, and water is moving through the plant following uptake by the roots.

Plants can regulate the size of their stomata from fully closed (to minimize water loss) to fully open (to maximize $CO_2$ uptake). This then illustrates the balancing act performed by plants, especially those living in dry **climates**: they need to open their stomata to let $CO_2$ in for photosynthesis, but to conserve water they need to keep their stomata closed. This balancing act is made more difficult in environments that are not only dry but hot as well. This is because photorespiration becomes a bigger problem the warmer the climate. The reason for this relates to the effect of temperature on the solubility of gases in solution. As shown in **Table 6.1**, the solubility of $O_2$ and $CO_2$ (in fact all gases) *decreases* as the temperature *increases*. However, the solubility of $CO_2$ decreases more rapidly than that of $O_2$ as the temperature rises. This means that, in the aqueous environment of the chloroplast stoma, the $CO_2/O_2$ ratio decreases as the temperature increases, and as a consequence the oxygenation reaction of Rubisco (photorespiration) becomes more common.

### 6.5d C$_4$ Plants Spatially Separate the C$_4$ Pathway and the Calvin Cycle

Some plant species that are adapted to hot, dry climates have evolved a mode of carbon fixation that minimizes photorespiration. In addition to the Calvin cycle, these plants have a second carbon-fixation pathway called the *C$_4$ cycle* (**Figure 6.19**). In this cycle, $CO_2$ initially combines with a three-carbon molecule, phosphoenolpyruvate (PEP), producing oxaloacetate, which in turn is reduced to malate. After being transported to the site of the Calvin cycle, the malate gets oxidized to pyruvate, releasing $CO_2$. To complete the cycle, pyruvate is converted back into PEP (for details see Figure 6.19). Because $CO_2$ is generated by the enzymatic conversion of malate to pyruvate, the levels of carbon dioxide at the site of the Calvin cycle are high, effectively inhibiting the oxygenation reaction of Rubisco, thereby minimizing photorespiration.

The C$_4$ cycle gets its name because its first product, oxaloacetate, is a four-carbon molecule rather than the three-carbon

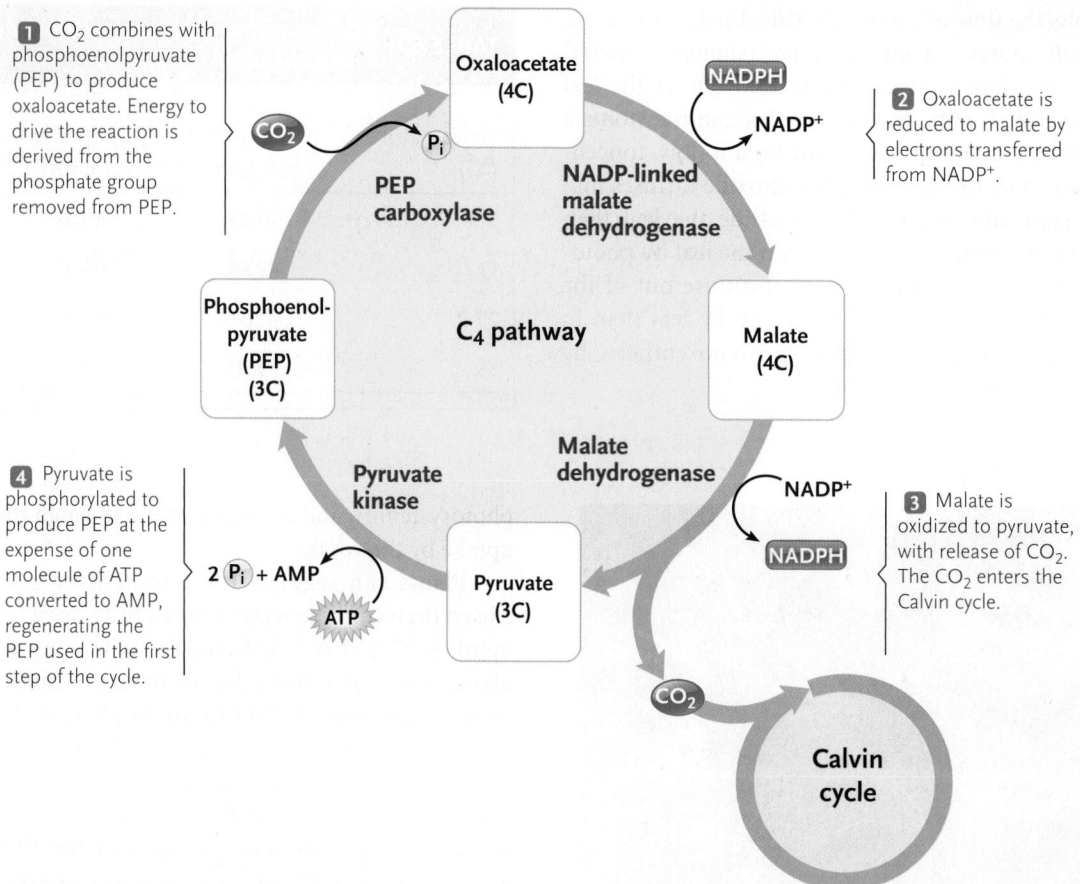

**1** $CO_2$ combines with phosphoenolpyruvate (PEP) to produce oxaloacetate. Energy to drive the reaction is derived from the phosphate group removed from PEP.

**2** Oxaloacetate is reduced to malate by electrons transferred from $NADP^+$.

**4** Pyruvate is phosphorylated to produce PEP at the expense of one molecule of ATP converted to AMP, regenerating the PEP used in the first step of the cycle.

**3** Malate is oxidized to pyruvate, with release of $CO_2$. The $CO_2$ enters the Calvin cycle.

Oxaloacetate (4C)

NADPH
NADP⁺

PEP carboxylase

NADP-linked malate dehydrogenase

Phosphoenol-pyruvate (PEP) (3C)

C₄ pathway

Malate (4C)

Pyruvate kinase

Malate dehydrogenase

NADP⁺

NADPH

2 Pᵢ + AMP

ATP

Pyruvate (3C)

CO₂

Calvin cycle

**FIGURE 6.19 The C4 cycle and its integration with the Calvin cycle.** Each turn of the cycle delivers one molecule of $CO_2$ to the Calvin cycle. This process is energy dependent, consuming ATP.

From Russell/Hertz/McMillan. *Biology, 2E.* © 2012 Brooks/Cole, a part of Cengage, Inc. Reproduced by permission. www.cengage.com/permissions

phosphoglycerate, the first product of the Calvin cycle. One often talks in terms of the $C_4$ pathway and the $C_3$ pathway when distinguishing between plants that have the $C_4$ cycle and those that possess only the Calvin cycle. A key distinction between $C_4$ and $C_3$ metabolism concerns the carboxylation reactions. In the $C_4$ cycle, the initial carboxylation reaction that incorporates $CO_2$ into PEP is catalyzed by the enzyme *PEP carboxylase* (Figure 6.19). Compared to Rubisco, PEP carboxylase has a rate of catalysis that is much faster and, more importantly, $O_2$ cannot compete with $CO_2$ for its active site. It can efficiently catalyze the carboxylation of PEP regardless of the $O_2$ concentration near the enzyme.

$C_4$ metabolism is found in many tropical plants and several temperate crop species, including corn and sugar cane. In these species, the $C_4$ cycle occurs in mesophyll cells, which lie close to the surface of leaves and stems, where $O_2$ from the air is abundant (see **Figure 6.20**). The malate intermediate of the $C_4$ cycle diffuses from the mesophyll cells to *bundle sheath cells,* located in deeper tissues, where $O_2$ concentrations are lower. In these cells, in which the Calvin cycle operates, the malate enters chloroplasts and is converted to pyruvate and $CO_2$.

You may ask: If $C_4$ metabolism is so good at preventing photorespiration, why don't all plants use it? Looking at Figure 6.19,

notice that the $C_4$ pathway has an additional energy requirement. For each turn of the $C_4$ cycle, one molecule of ATP is required to regenerate PEP. In hot climates, photorespiration can decrease carbon fixation efficiency by over 50%, so the additional ATP requirement is worthwhile. As well, hot climates tend to receive a lot of sunlight, so the requirement for more ATP is easily met by absorbing more light energy and increasing the output of the light reactions.

In temperate climates (like in Canada), the lower ambient temperatures mean that photorespiration is not as big a problem (look at Table), and the additional ATP requirement is often harder to meet given that, on average, these regions receive less sunlight. These differences in temperature and sunlight are the underlying reasons why, for example, in Florida, 70% of all native species are $C_4$ plants, while in Manitoba all native species are $C_3$ plants.

Not only do $C_4$ plants perform better than $C_3$ plants where it is hot, they also perform better where it is dry. Because of the competing oxygenation reaction, $C_3$ plants need to keep their stomata open longer to fix the same number of $CO_2$ molecules as $C_4$ plants. This means that $C_4$ plants lose less water and are thus much better suited to arid conditions.

## 6.5e CAM Plants Temporally Separate the C₄ Pathway and the Calvin Cycle

Instead of running the Calvin and $C_4$ cycles simultaneously in different locations (spatial separation), as is the case with $C_4$ plants, some plants, such as pineapple, run the cycles at different times (temporal separation). These plants are known as **CAM plants**, named for **crassulacean acid metabolism**, from the Crassulaceae family in which the adaptation was first observed. The plants in this group include many with thick, succulent leaves or stems, such cactus. A comparison of $C_4$ and CAM metabolism is illustrated in Figure 6.20.

Typically, CAM plants live in regions that are hot and dry during the day and cool at night. Their fleshy leaves or stems have a low surface-to-volume ratio, and their stomata are reduced in number. Further, the stomata open only at night,

### a. C₄—Spatial separation

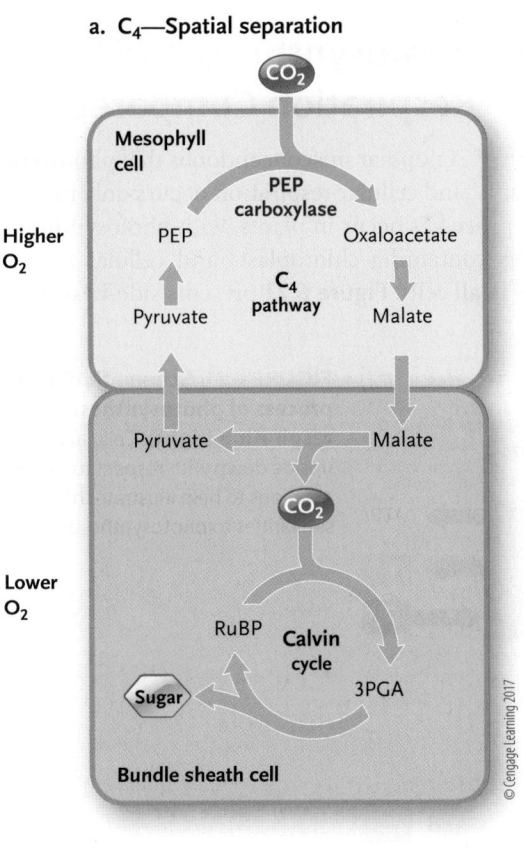

### b. CAM—Temporal separation

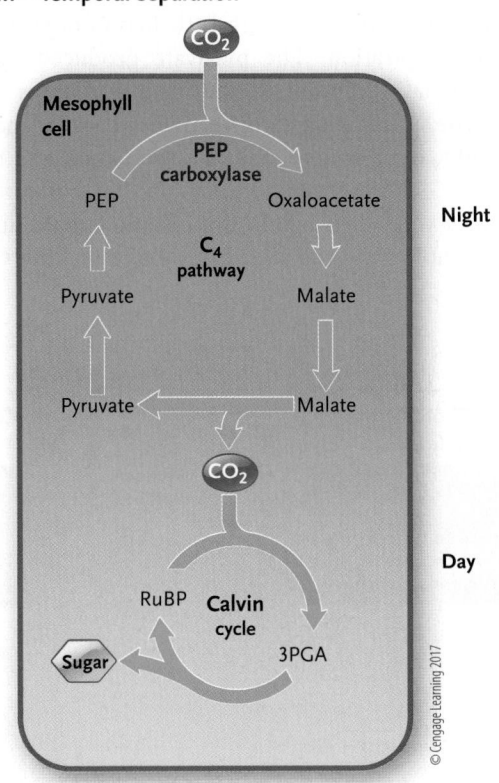

*Zea mays* (corn)

*Opuntia basilaris*
(beavertail cactus)

**FIGURE 6.20 Two alternative processes of carbon fixation to minimize photorespiration.** In each case, carbon fixation produces the four-carbon oxaloacetate, which is processed to generate the $CO_2$ that feeds into the Calvin ($C_3$) cycle. **(a)** In $C_4$ plants, carbon fixation and the Calvin cycle occur in different cell types: carbon fixation by the $C_4$ pathway takes place in mesophyll cells, while the Calvin cycle takes place in bundle sheath cells. **(b)** In CAM plants, carbon fixation and the Calvin cycle occur at different times in mesophyll cells: carbon fixation by the $C_4$ pathway takes place at night, and the Calvin cycle takes place during the day.

when they release $O_2$ that accumulates from photosynthesis during the day and allow $CO_2$ to enter the leaves. The entering $CO_2$ is fixed by the $C_4$ pathway into malate, which accumulates throughout the night and is stored in large cell vacuoles.

Daylight initiates the second phase of the strategy. As the Sun comes up and the temperature rises, the stomata close, reducing water loss and cutting off the exchange of gases with the atmosphere. Malate diffuses from cell vacuoles into the cytosol, where it is oxidized to pyruvate, and $CO_2$ is released in high concentration. The high $CO_2$ concentration favours the carboxylase activity of Rubisco, allowing the Calvin cycle to proceed at maximum efficiency with little loss of organic carbon from photorespiration. The pyruvate produced by the breakdown of malate accumulates during the day; as night falls, it enters the $C_4$ reactions, converting it back to malate. During the night, oxygen is released by the plants and more $CO_2$ enters.

Reduction of water loss by closure of the stomata during the hot daylight hours has the added benefit of making CAM plants highly resistant to dehydration. As a result, CAM species can tolerate extreme daytime heat and dryness.

## STUDY BREAK QUESTIONS

1. Explain how oxygenase activity suggests that Rubisco is an ancient enzyme.
2. Why is photorespiration thought to be a wasteful process?
3. What happens to the solubility of $O_2$ and $CO_2$ as the temperature is increased?

## 6.6 Photosynthesis and Cellular Respiration Compared

**CONCEPT FIX** A popular misconception is that photosynthesis occurs in plants, and cellular respiration occurs only in animals. In fact, both processes occur in plants, with photosynthesis confined to tissues containing chloroplasts and cellular respiration taking place in all cells. **Figure 6.21** presents side-by-side schematics of

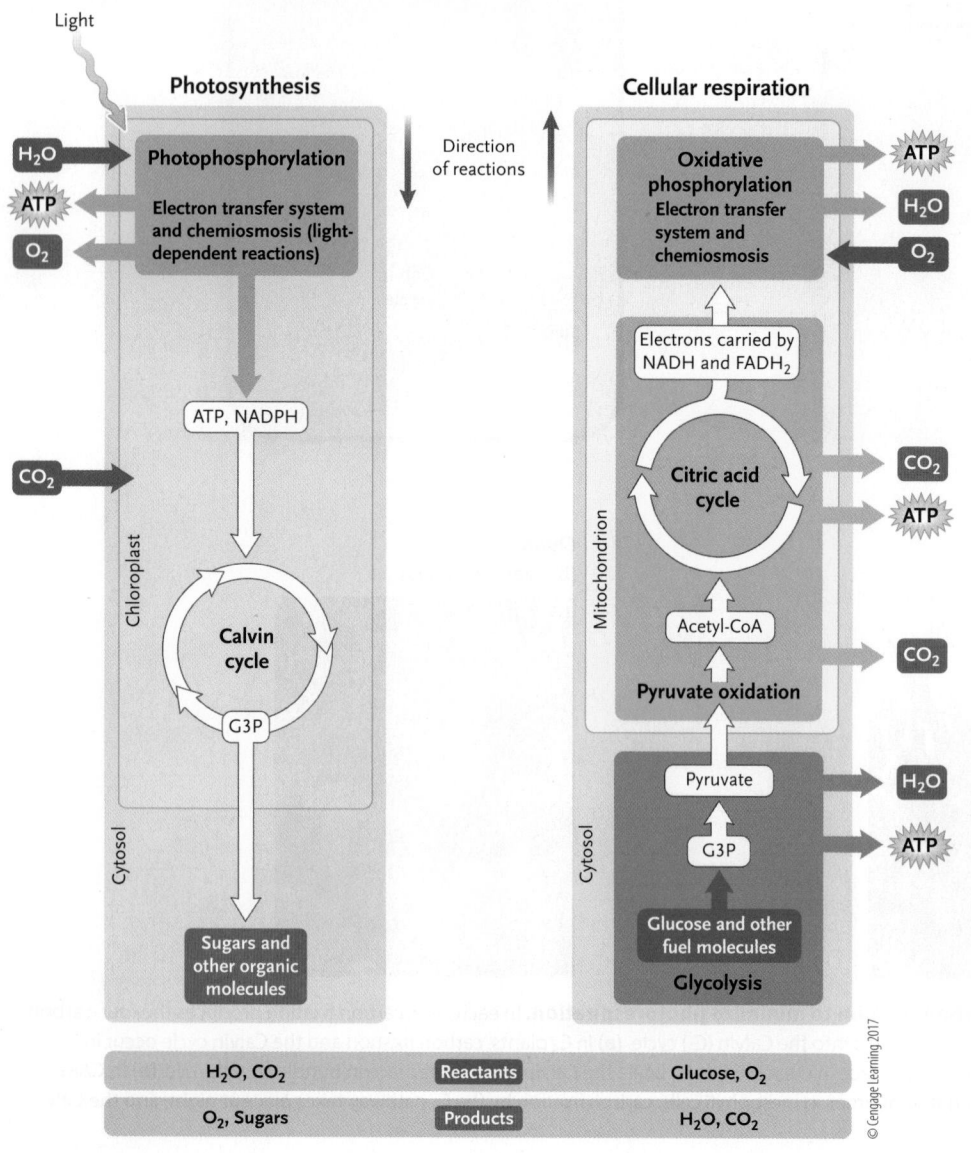

**FIGURE 6.21 Schematic diagrams of the process of photosynthesis (left) and cellular respiration (right).** Cellular respiration is shown upside down with respect to the direction of reactions to help illustrate the process's similarities to photosynthesis.

© Cengage Learning 2017

photosynthesis and cellular respiration to highlight their similarities and points of connection. Note that their overall reactions are basically the reverse of each other. That is, the reactants of photosynthesis, $CO_2$ and $H_2O$, are the products of cellular respiration, and the reactants of cellular respiration, glucose and $O_2$, are the products of photosynthesis. Both processes have key phosphorylation reactions involving an **electron transfer system**—photophosphorylation in photosynthesis and oxidative phosphorylation in cellular respiration—followed by the chemiosmotic synthesis of ATP. Further, G3P is found in the pathways of both processes. In photosynthesis, it is a product of the Calvin cycle and is used for the synthesis of sugars and other organic fuel molecules. In cellular respiration, it is an intermediate generated in glycolysis in the conversion of glucose to pyruvate. Thus, G3P is used by anabolic pathways when it is generated by photosynthesis, and it is a product of a catabolic pathway in cellular respiration. ⬡

In this chapter, you have seen how photosynthesis supplies the organic molecules used as fuels by almost all the organisms of the world. It is a story of electron flow: electrons, pushed to high energy levels by the absorption of light energy, are added to $CO_2$, which is fixed into carbohydrates and other fuel molecules. The high-energy electrons are then removed from the fuel molecules by the oxidative reactions of cellular respiration, which use the released energy to power the activities of life. Among the most significant of these activities are cell growth and division, the subjects of the next chapter.

## STUDY BREAK QUESTION

1. Explain how the products of photosynthesis are used in cellular respiration.

# Summary Illustration

Photosynthesis is the process by which light energy is used to convert carbon dioxide to organic molecules and is responsible for directly or indirectly sustaining virtually all life. In eukaryotes, it takes place within chloroplasts and consists of the light reactions and the Calvin cycle. The overall process can be represented by the following chemical equation:

$$6CO_2 + 6H_2O \longrightarrow C_6H_{12}O_6 + 6O_2$$

Photosynthesis is a redox process.

- The overall change in free energy ($\Delta G$) is positive.
- Energy released during the formation of the bonds in glucose and oxygen is less than the energy required to break the bonds in carbon dioxide and water.
- The goal is to harness the energy of light to reduce molecules of carbon dioxide to sugar using electrons from water.

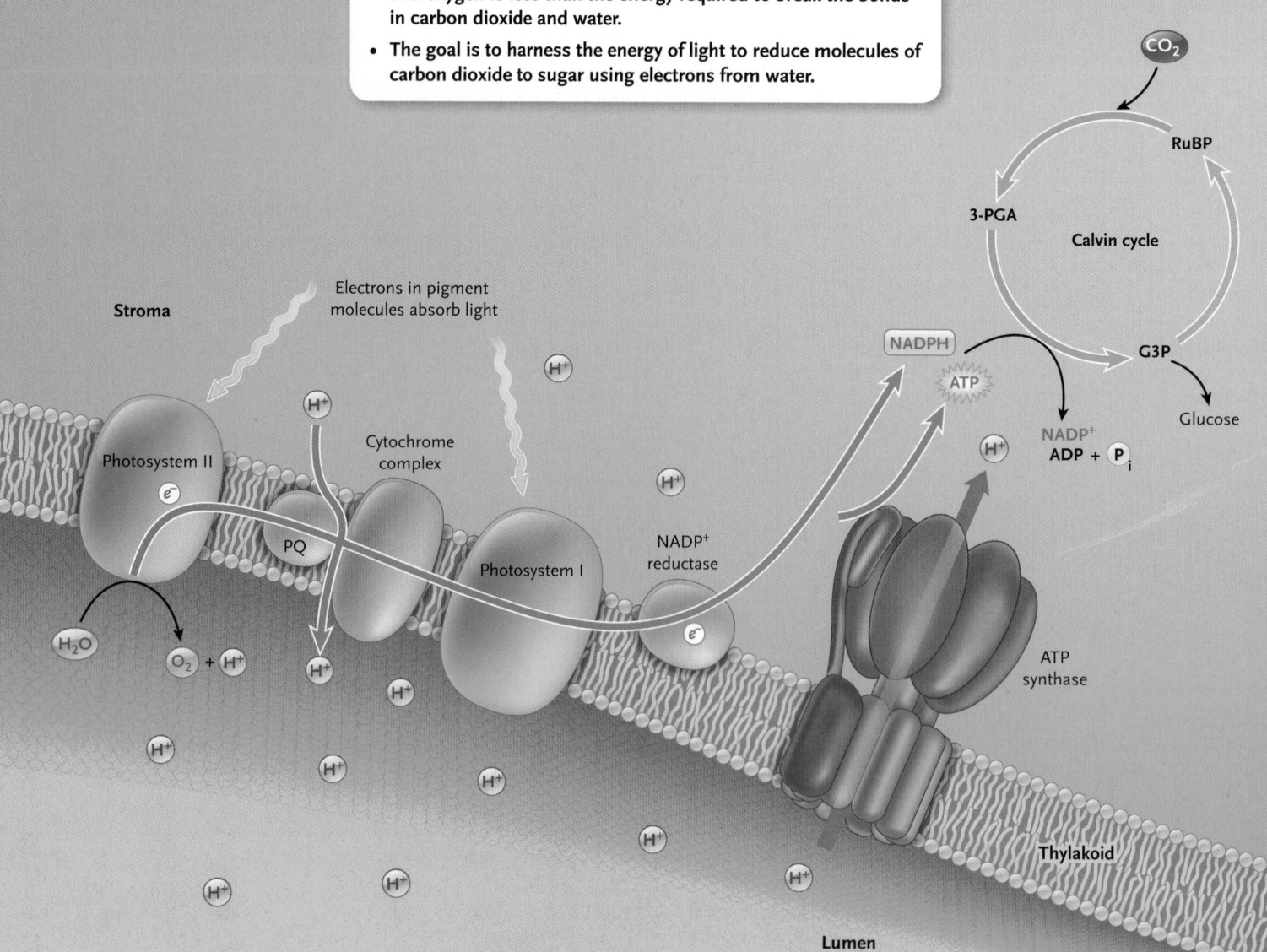

## Photorespiration: Rubisco can react with $O_2$ as well as $CO_2$

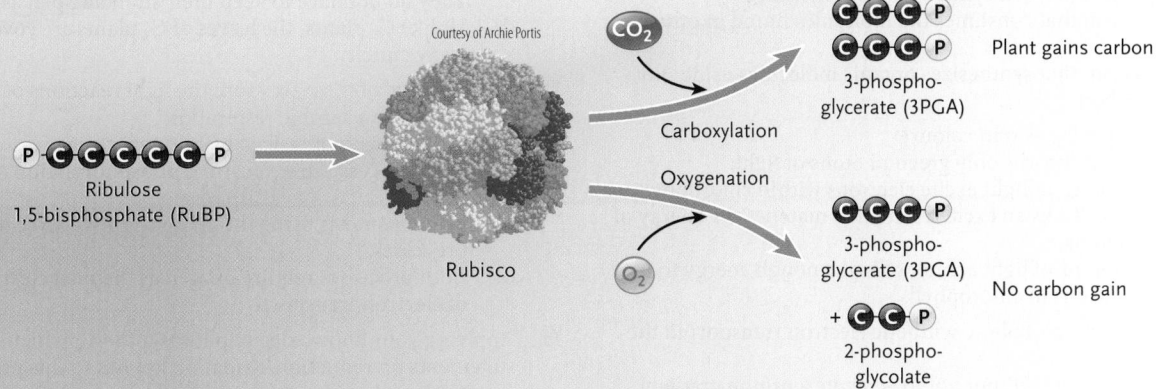

Courtesy of Archie Portis

Ribulose
1,5-bisphosphate (RuBP)

Rubisco

Carboxylation

Oxygenation

$CO_2$

$O_2$

3-phospho-
glycerate (3PGA)

Plant gains carbon

3-phospho-
glycerate (3PGA)

No carbon gain

2-phospho-
glycolate

- Rubisco preferentially binds $CO_2$, but there is 24x more $O_2$ in the atmosphere than $CO_2$. That's a problem.
- Organisms have developed mechanisms to increase the $\dfrac{[CO_2]}{[O_2]}$ ratio at the site of Rubisco (C4 pathway, $CO_2$ pumping)

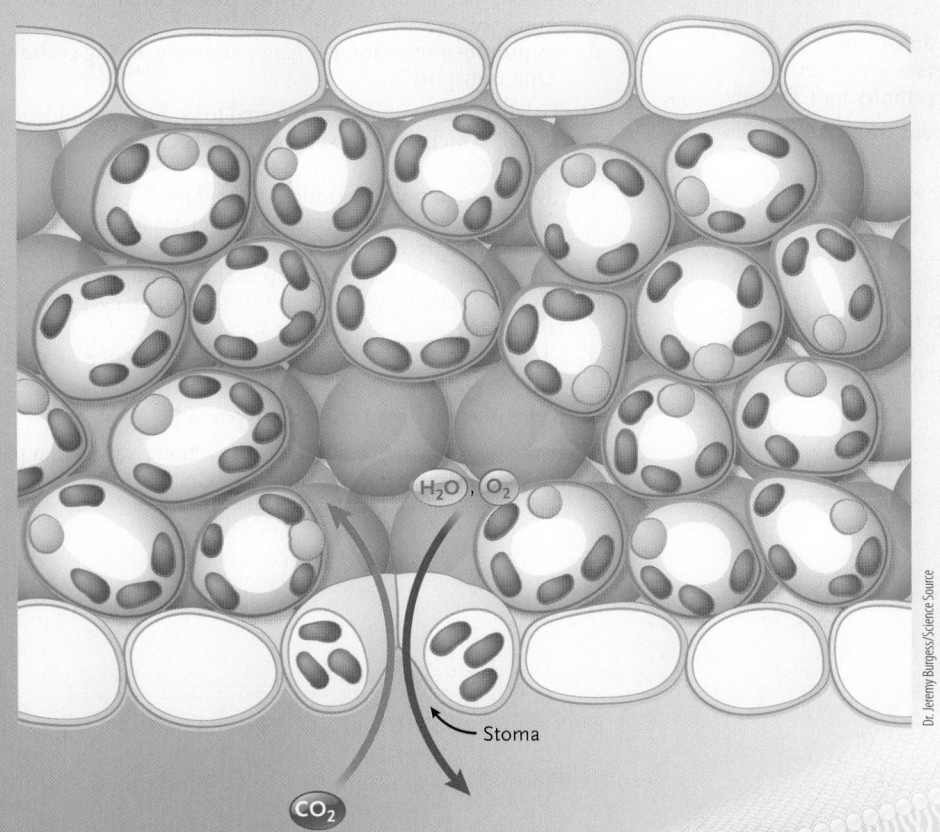

$H_2O$, $O_2$

Stoma

$CO_2$

Dr. Jeremy Burgess/Science Source

- Leaf stomata must open to allow $CO_2$ in. But when they open, water readily escapes into the atmosphere.
- Plants that grow in dryer climates tend to be more efficient at fixing carbon dioxide; their stomata can be open for less time. Alternatively, they open them during the night.

# SELF-TEST QUESTIONS

## Recall/Understand

1. Which of these organisms is an autotroph?
   a. an organism that uses light energy to live
   b. an organism that can synthesize carbohydrates
   c. an organism that consumes the molecules found in other organisms
   d. an organism that synthesizes organic molecules using inorganic carbon

2. Why is chlorophyll green in colour?
   a. Chlorophyll absorbs only green photons of light.
   b. Green photons of light excite electrons within chlorophyll.
   c. Chlorophyll lacks an excited state that matches the energy of green photons.
   d. Green photons of light are not of high enough energy to excite electrons in chlorophyll.

3. What is the function of photosynthetic electron transport in the light reactions?
   a. to synthesize NADP, but not to generate a proton gradient
   b. to synthesize NADPH, but not to generate a proton gradient
   c. to synthesize NADPH and to generate a proton gradient
   d. to synthesize NADP and to generate a proton gradient

4. Which of these statements *best* describes the Calvin cycle?
   a. The cycle stops if the regeneration of RuBP is prevented.
   b. After three turns, one molecule of glucose is synthesized.
   c. It takes three turns of the cycle to fix one molecule of $CO_2$.
   d. It takes nine molecules of ATP to fix one molecule of $CO_2$.

5. Which of these statements explains why photorespiration is low in $C_4$ plants?
   a. They lack mitochondria.
   b. They express high levels of carbonic anhydrase.
   c. The $CO_2/O_2$ ratio in their chloroplasts is very high.
   d. The Rubisco in their chloroplasts has affinity for $CO_2$ only.

6. Describe the photosystem and what happens when it traps photons of light.

7. Describe the movement of electrons in cyclic electron transport and state what this pathway generates.

## Apply/Analyze

8. What is the minimum number of photons that need to be absorbed by a photosystem to reduce three molecules of $NADP^+$ to NADPH by the photosynthetic electron transport chain?
   a. 3
   b. 6
   c. 12
   d. 18

9. Compared to $C_3$ plants, one more often finds $C_4$ plants in drier habitats. Which of these statements is the reason why?
   a. They have a larger root system.
   b. They can keep their stomata closed at all times.
   c. They do not have to keep their stomata open as long.
   d. Unlike $C_3$ plants, the leaves of $C_4$ plants are covered by a waxy cuticle.

10. In which one of these ways are the light reactions of photosynthesis similar to aerobic respiration?
    a. NADPH is synthesized by both processes.
    b. Both processes use substrate phosphorylation to synthesize ATP.
    c. Chemiosmosis using the proton-motive force occurs in both processes.
    d. Both processes require oxygen as the final electron acceptor of electron transport.

11. Applying your knowledge of photosynthesis, which of these statements on reduction/oxidation applies to this process?
    a. Carbon dioxide is reduced to glucose.
    b. Water is reduced to oxygen.
    c. Carbon dioxide is oxidized to glucose.
    d. Water is oxidized to glucose.

## Create/Evaluate

12. Which of these statements accurately distinguishes between linear electron transport and cyclic electron transport?
    a. NADH is generated only during linear electron transport.
    b. Photosystem I is used only during linear electron transport.
    c. Photosystem II is required only during cyclic electron transport.
    d. A proton-motive force is generated only during cyclic electron transport.

13. The Calvin cycle is sometimes referred to as the "light-independent reactions." Which of these statements tells us why this is misleading?
    a. Rubisco is rapidly degraded in the dark.
    b. $NAD^+$ generated by the light reactions is needed to activate 3-phosphoglycerate.
    c. In the dark, oxygen builds up in the chloroplast and inhibits Rubisco activity, which prevents the Calvin cycle from occurring.
    d. The Calvin cycle requires a constant supply of ATP generation by the light reactions.

14. Compare photosystem I and photosystem II.

15. There are two alternative processes of carbon fixation that plants evolved to minimize photorespiration. Compare them.

# Chapter Roadmap

## Cell Cycles

Expanding cell populations require coordination of DNA replication, chromosome segregation, and cell cycle control.

### 7.1 The Cycle of Cell Growth and Division: An Overview

New cells are needed for increasing the population of single-celled organisms, multicellular tissue growth and repair, as well as asexual reproduction.

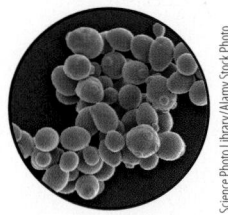

Science Photo Library/Alamy Stock Photo

### 7.2 The Cell Cycle in Prokaryotic Organisms

Two daughter chromosomes actively migrate to opposite ends of the cell undergoing binary fission. New cell wall material then partitions the cytoplasm.

### 7.3 Mitosis and the Eukaryotic Cell Cycle

Dividing cells cycle through interphase and the five phases of mitosis, followed by cytokinesis.

To Chapter 11

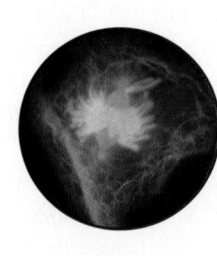

Photomicrograph by Dr. Conly L. Rieder, East Greenbush, New York

### 7.4 Formation and Action of the Mitotic Spindle

Microtubules stretch from opposite poles to interact with one another or with kinetochores. Motor proteins drive changes in cell shape and chromosome movement.

### 7.5 Cell Cycle Regulation

Progress through cell cycle checkpoints is controlled by complexes of cyclin and cyclin-dependent kinase (CDK). Some cells may divide out of control and give rise to cancer; others may be programmed to die.

To Chapter 13

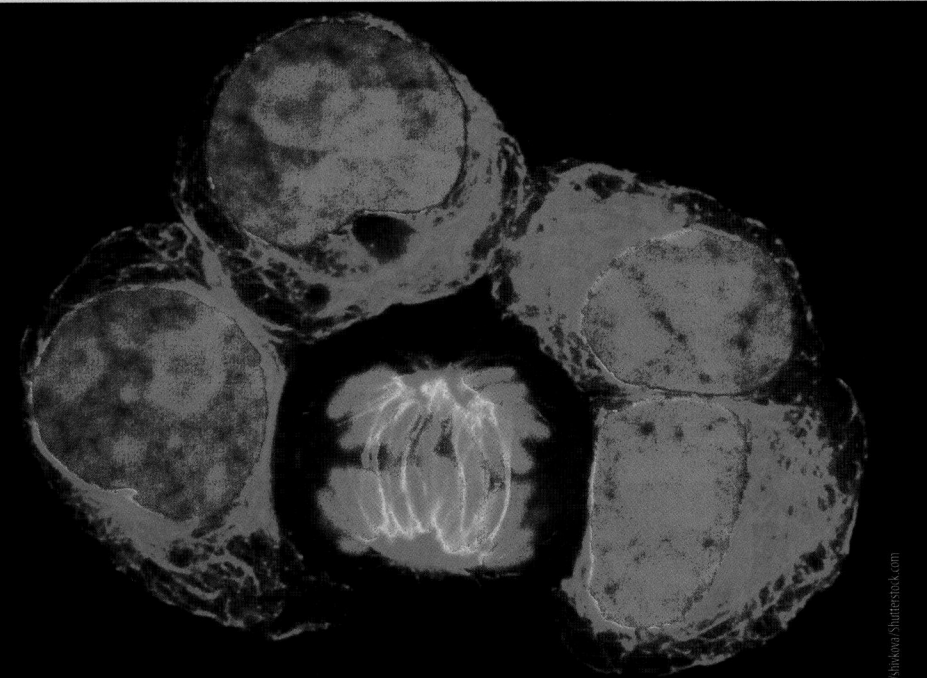

**Cells labelled with fluorescent dyes (fluorescent micrograph).** One of the cells is undergoing mitosis: the spindle in that cell (green) is separating copies of the cell's chromosomes (red) prior to cell division.

# Cell Cycles

# 7

**Why it matters . . .** Although single-celled organisms are invisible to the naked human eye, under favourable conditions for cell division, populations of certain microorganisms can become so astonishingly large that they are visible from space. **Figure 7.1** shows two views of an immense "bloom" of algae covering 5000 square kilometres of Lake Erie in 2011. Algal blooms occur across Canada in lakes, ponds, and rivers as well as coastal regions in British Columbia, the Atlantic region, and, surprisingly, under thinning Arctic sea ice. Blooms degrade water quality by reducing clarity, creating thick masses of cells, and consuming oxygen. A few of the organisms responsible for blooms are harmful, producing some of the most potent natural toxins known.

The recurring Lake Erie bloom results from exponentially increasing numbers of cells of a photosynthetic prokaryotic organism called *cyanobacteria*. Also known as *blue-green algae*, cyanobacteria are toxigenic; blooms often threaten drinking water supplies and commercial fisheries of shoreline communities.

On the coasts of Canada, populations of microscopic eukaryotic algae called *dinoflagellates* create thick blooms stretching along thousands of kilometres of coastline. Certain species produce neurotoxins that accumulate in shellfish, often to levels that are fatal if consumed by humans or wildlife. As a result, harmful algal blooms frequently threaten populations of marine mammals as well as commercial shellfish operations in coastal waters. In the Canadian Arctic, algal blooms may be absorbing sunlight and hastening the warming of this environment.

Cyanobacteria and dinoflagellates are natural members of their complex and constantly changing aquatic microbial communities. Their population size fluctuates seasonally but is usually kept in check by such factors as low water temperature, low levels of sunlight, predation, and viruses as well as low concentrations of essential nutrients in the environment. Phosphorus, needed for metabolism and DNA synthesis, often limits growth in natural aquatic environments. Although the causes of harmful algal blooms are complex and difficult to

**FIGURE 7.1 Massive numbers of cells in algal blooms as seen up close** (a) **and from a satellite image of Lake Erie in 2011** (b)

## 7.1 The Cycle of Cell Growth and Division: An Overview

Scientists have known since the early nineteenth century that all life on Earth is composed of cells and their products. All cells, in all organisms that have ever lived, are descended from previous cells in an unbroken chain of cell division stretching billions of years into the past. New progeny cells are needed for increasing the population of single-celled organisms (algal blooms), multicellular tissue growth (new leaves), asexual reproduction, and replacement of cells lost to wear and tear (shedding skin, virus infection; **Figure 7.2**).

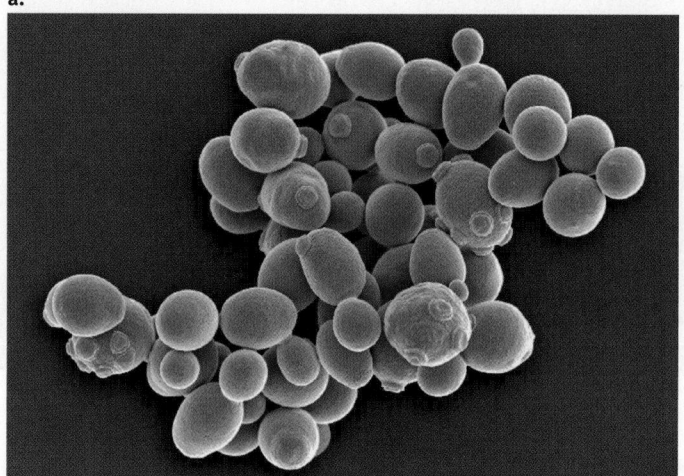

**FIGURE 7.2 Actively dividing cells provide for increased population size of yeast** (a), **growth of skin** (b), **and expansion of conifer needles** (c)

isolate, municipal sewage and runoff from intensive farming operations are believed to be major contributing factors through the release of phosphorus into the aquatic environment. Climate change may also aggravate the situation if water warms more quickly in summer, and heavy storms increase runoff. In spite of several provincial, national, and international policy agreements aimed at protecting Canada's fresh and marine water quality, the frequency and size of algal blooms continue to rise.

As problematic as algal blooms can be, the ability of single cells to generate such unimaginably large populations through cell division is astonishing and is the focus of this chapter. In particular, we intend for you to appreciate how this coordination is achieved in eukaryotic cells through the interplay of three cellular processes: (1) DNA replication, (2) a dynamically changing cytoskeleton, and (3) cell cycle "checkpoints." To provide a hint of what the ancestral cell division process may have been like, the chapter opens with a look at cell division in prokaryotic organisms and the simpler eukaryotes.

Although the cell division cycle is conceptually simple—grow larger, divide, grow larger, divide, and repeat for billions of years—the regulation of this process must be precise and complex. All dividing cells must meet the challenge of closely coordinating their increase in size, DNA replication, and cell division in the face of a changing environment.

Although this chapter highlights the characteristics of actively dividing cells, it is important for you to realize that most cells in the body of a multicellular organism are *not* destined to divide any time soon, if ever. In fact, some cells may even be programmed to die immediately! We will look at the mechanisms underlying these various fates of cells in more detail in the coming sections.

**STUDY BREAK QUESTION**

1. What are some functions or roles of actively dividing cells?

## 7.2 The Cell Cycle in Prokaryotic Organisms

A newly formed cell of a prokaryotic organism, such as the bacterium *Escherichia coli*, must increase in size, replicate its circular chromosome, and then move each of the resulting two daughter chromosomes into its own progeny cell during cell division. The entire mechanism of prokaryotic cell division, called **binary fission**—splitting or dividing into two parts—can be thought of in three periods as shown in **Figure 7.3**. Once daughter cells are formed, they may grow for some time (B period) before initiating DNA synthesis. Once the chromosomes are replicated and separated to opposite ends of the cell (C period), the membrane pinches together between them and two daughter cells are formed (D period).

### 7.2a Replication Occupies Most of the Cell Cycle in Rapidly Dividing Prokaryotic Cells

All bacteria and archaea use DNA as their hereditary information, and the vast majority of species package it all in a single, circular chromosome of double-stranded DNA (Figure 7.3, step 1). Although the chromosome is shown extended in Figure 7.3 for the purposes of illustration, it is actually compacted in a central region called the **nucleoid** throughout the cell cycle (see Chapter 2, Figure 2.7). When nutrients are abundant, prokaryotic cells have no need for a B period since they can grow quickly enough to divide their cytoplasm as soon as DNA replication is complete and chromosomes are separated. Under such optimal conditions, populations of *E. coli* cells can double every 20 minutes.

### 7.2b Replicated Chromosomes Are Distributed Actively to the Daughter Cells in Binary Fission

Although scientists first thought that the replicated chromosomes of prokaryotic cells were distributed to daughter cells through attachment to their membranes, current research indicates that bacterial chromosomes rapidly separate in an active way that is linked to DNA replication events and is independent of membrane dynamics. Replication of the bacterial chromosome begins at a specific region of DNA sequence called the **origin of replication** (*ori*). The *ori* region of the chromosome is in the middle of the cell, where the enzymes for DNA replication are located. Once the *ori* has been duplicated, the two new origins migrate toward the two opposite ends (poles) of the cell as replication continues for the rest of the chromosome (see Figure 7.3, step 3). The mechanism that propels the two replicated chromosomes to their respective ends of the cell is still unknown. Next, division of the cytoplasm is accomplished by an inward constriction of a ring of cytoskeletal proteins (see Figure 7.3, step 5).

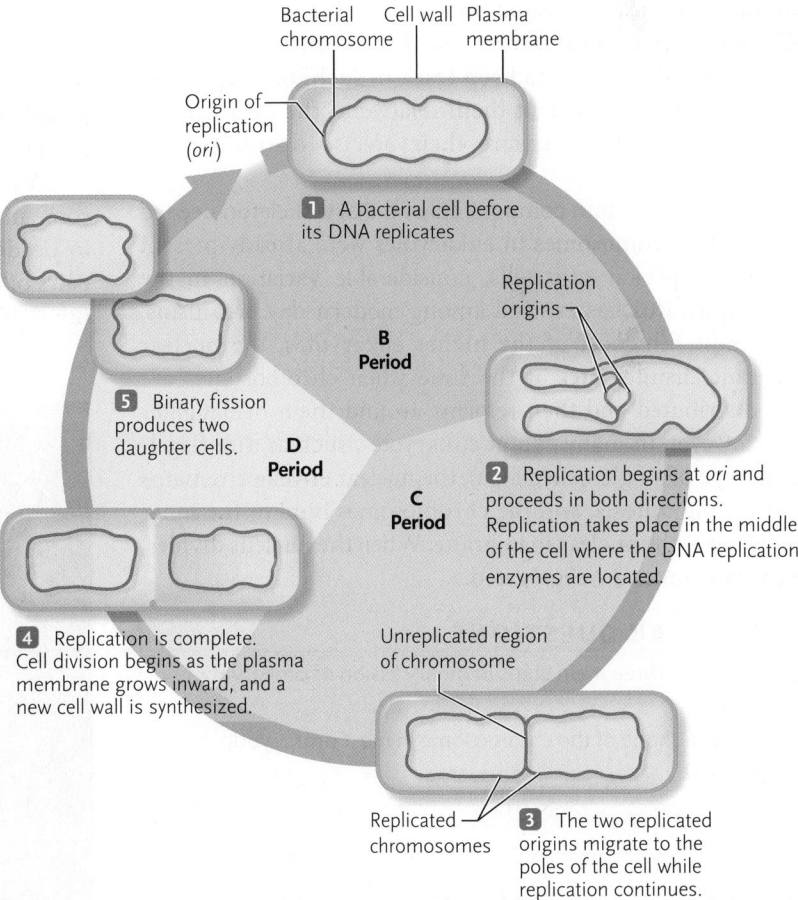

**FIGURE 7.3 The bacterial cell cycle.** During the B period, from birth to the initiation of DNA replication, the cell grows in size. The chromosome is replicated and the resulting daughter chromosomes move to opposite ends during the C period. Then the cell divides by binary fission during the D period. In very fast-growing cultures, the B period may be non-existent; daughter cells may be formed with chromosomes that are already partly replicated!

## 7.2c Mitosis Has Evolved from an Early Form of Binary Fission

The prokaryotic mechanism of cell division works effectively because most prokaryotic organisms have only a single chromosome. Thus, if a daughter cell receives at least one copy of the chromosome, its genetic information is complete. By contrast, the genetic information of typical eukaryotes is divided among several linear chromosomes, with each chromosome containing a much greater length of DNA than a prokaryotic chromosome contains. If a eukaryotic daughter cell fails to receive a copy of even one of the several chromosomes, the effects are usually lethal. It is also important to note that, during most of the cell cycle, eukaryotic chromosomes are contained within the nuclear membrane. Bacteria and archaea do not have an internal membrane around their nucleoid; therefore, eukaryotic cellular and chromosomal architecture demands a quite different mechanism for distributing chromosomes to daughter cells. Mitosis is that different mechanism, and we will examine this process in detail later in the chapter (see Figure 7.8). For now, just be aware that one of the central innovations of the evolution of mitosis is the ability to hold the two newly created molecules of double-stranded DNA (now called **chromatids**) together following DNA synthesis. This enables cells to keep track of such long replicated chromosomes and to orient them relative to the cytoskeleton at the proper time to ensure their precise distribution to daughter cells.

Although the main components of the cytoskeleton needed to segregate chromosomes in eukaryotes were already present in ancestral prokaryotic cells, considerable variation in the mitotic apparatus has evolved among modern-day organisms. For example, in most of the higher eukaryotes, the nuclear membrane disintegrates at the time when chromosomes are being distributed and then reforms around them in daughter cells. However, in many extant eukaryotes, such as dinoflagellates (a type of single-celled alga), the nuclear envelope remains intact during mitosis, and the chromosomes bind to the inner membrane of the nuclear membrane. When the nucleus divides, the chromosomes are segregated.

### STUDY BREAK QUESTIONS

1. What are the three main steps in binary fission of prokaryotic organisms?
2. What is the shape of the chromosome in most prokaryotic organisms?

# 7.3 Mitosis and the Eukaryotic Cell Cycle

As long as eukaryotes require their daughter cells to be genetic copies of the parental cell, **mitosis** serves very well to divide the replicated DNA equally and precisely.

This is the result of three elegantly interrelated systems:

1. An elaborate master program of molecular checks and balances ensures an orderly and timely progression through the cell cycle.
2. Within the overall regulation of the cell cycle, a process of DNA synthesis replicates each DNA chromosome into two nearly perfect copies (see Section 11.3).
3. A structural and mechanical web of interwoven "cables" and "motors" of the cytoskeleton separates the replicated DNA molecules precisely into the daughter cells.

We begin our discussion of mitosis with **chromosomes**, the nuclear units of genetic information divided and distributed by mitotic cell division.

## 7.3a Chromosomes Are the Genetic Units Divided by Mitosis

In typical eukaryotes, the hereditary information of the nucleus is distributed among several linear, double-stranded DNA molecules. These DNA molecules are combined with proteins that stabilize the DNA, assist in packaging DNA during cell division, and influence the expression of individual genes. Each chromosome (*chroma* = colour, when stained with dyes used in light microscopy; *soma* = body; **Figure 7.4**) in a cell is composed of one of these DNA molecules, along with its associated proteins.

Most eukaryotes have two copies of each type of chromosome in their nuclei, and their chromosome complement is said to be **diploid**, or $2n$. For example, humans have 23 different pairs of chromosomes for a diploid number of 46 chromosomes ($2n = 46$). Other eukaryotes, mostly microorganisms, may have

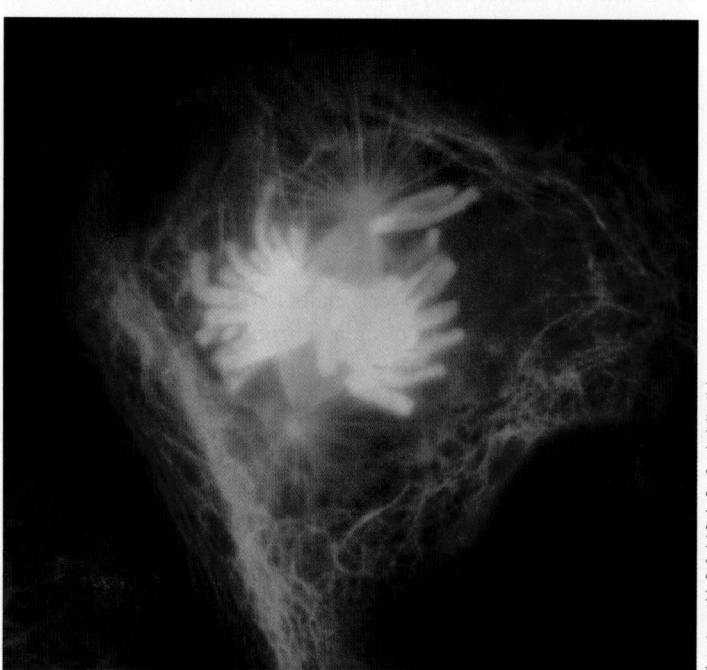

**FIGURE 7.4 Eukaryotic chromosomes (stained blue) during mitosis**

only one copy of each type of chromosome in their nucleus, so their chromosome complement is said to be **haploid**, or *n*. Baker's yeast (*Saccharomyces cerevisiae*) is an example of an organism that can grow as a diploid (2*n* = 32) and as a haploid (*n* = 16). Still others, such as many plant species, have three, four, or even more complete sets of chromosomes in each cell. The number of chromosome sets is called the **ploidy** of a cell or species. See Chapter 18 for a look at the role of ploidy in the formation of new species.

Before a cell divides in mitosis, replication of the DNA in a given chromosome produces two identical copies of that chromosome called **sister chromatids**. Newly formed sister chromatids are held together along their length by proteins called *cohesins*. During mitosis, the cohesins are removed and the sister chromatids are separated, with one of each pair going to each of the two daughter nuclei. As a result of this precise division, each daughter nucleus receives exactly the same number and types of chromosomes and contains the same genetic information as the parent cell that entered the division. The equal distribution of daughter chromosomes into each of the two daughter cells that result from cell division is called **chromosome segregation**.

The precision of chromosome replication and segregation in the mitotic cell cycle creates a group of cells called a **clone**. Rare mutations arising during replication make the cells of a clone genetically very similar but not strictly identical. Since all the diverse cell types of a complex multicellular organism arise by mitosis from a single cell (zygote), they all contain the same genetic information, with only rare variation in sequence. Forensic scientists rely on this common genetic information within organisms when, for instance, they match the genetic profile of a small amount of tissue (e.g., cells in dog saliva recovered from a bite victim) with that of a blood sample from the suspected animal.

## STUDY BREAK QUESTIONS

1. What are the three interrelated systems that contribute to the eukaryotic cell cycle?

2. What is a chromosome composed of?

3. When is a chromosome composed of two chromatids?

### 7.3b Interphase Extends from the End of One Mitosis to the Beginning of the Next Mitosis

If we set the formation of a new daughter cell as the beginning of the mitotic cell cycle, then the first and longest stage is **interphase** (**Figure 7.5**). Interphase comprises three phases of the cell cycle:

1. **$G_1$ phase**, in which the cell carries out its function and, in some cases, grows.

2. **S phase**, in which DNA replication and chromosome duplication occur (**Figure 7.6**).

3. **$G_2$ phase**, a brief gap in the cell cycle during which cell growth continues and the cell prepares for mitosis (the fourth phase of the cell cycle; also called *M phase*) and cytokinesis.

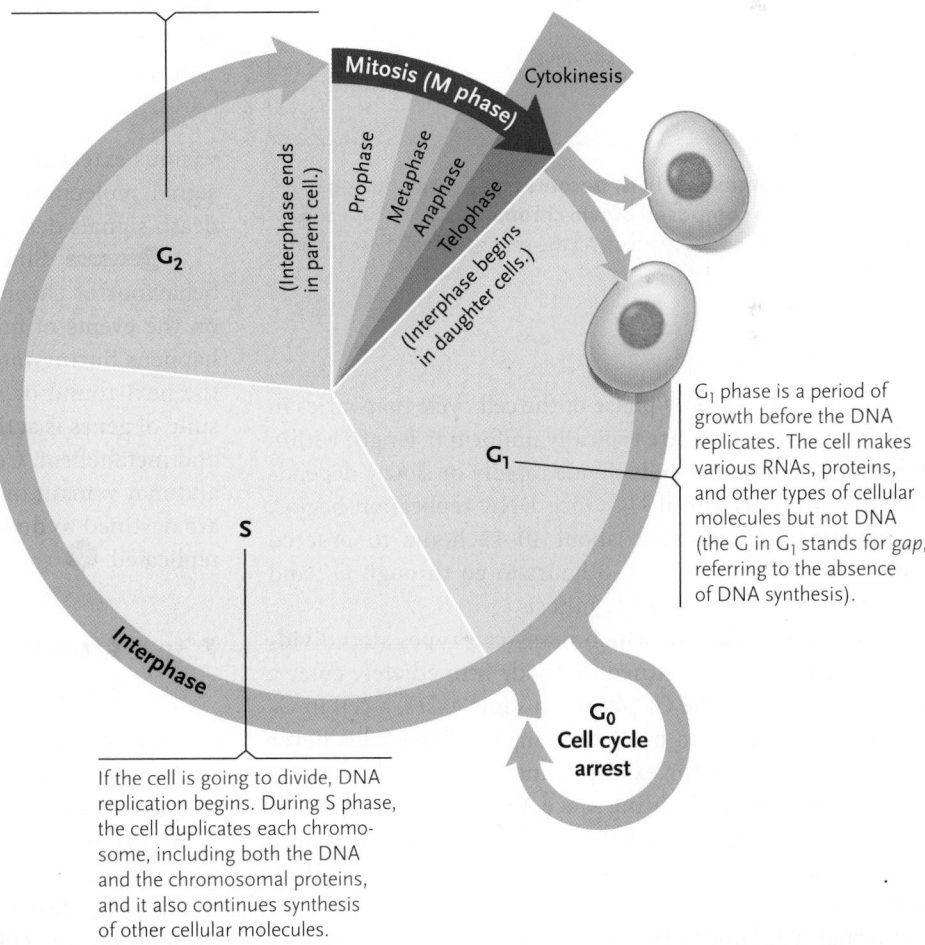

$G_2$ refers to the second gap in which there is no DNA synthesis. During $G_2$, the cell continues to synthesize RNAs and proteins, including those for mitosis, and it continues to grow. The end of $G_2$ marks the end of interphase; mitosis then begins.

$G_1$ phase is a period of growth before the DNA replicates. The cell makes various RNAs, proteins, and other types of cellular molecules but not DNA (the G in $G_1$ stands for *gap*, referring to the absence of DNA synthesis).

If the cell is going to divide, DNA replication begins. During S phase, the cell duplicates each chromosome, including both the DNA and the chromosomal proteins, and it also continues synthesis of other cellular molecules.

**FIGURE 7.5 The cell cycle.** The length of $G_1$ varies, but for a given cell type, the timing of S phase, $G_2$ phase, and mitosis is usually relatively uniform. Cytokinesis (red segment) usually begins while mitosis is in progress and reaches completion as mitosis ends. Cells in a state of division arrest are considered to enter a side loop (or shunt) from $G_1$ called "$G_0$ phase."

© Cengage Learning 2017

**Chromosomes and DNA molecules at different stages of the cell cycle**

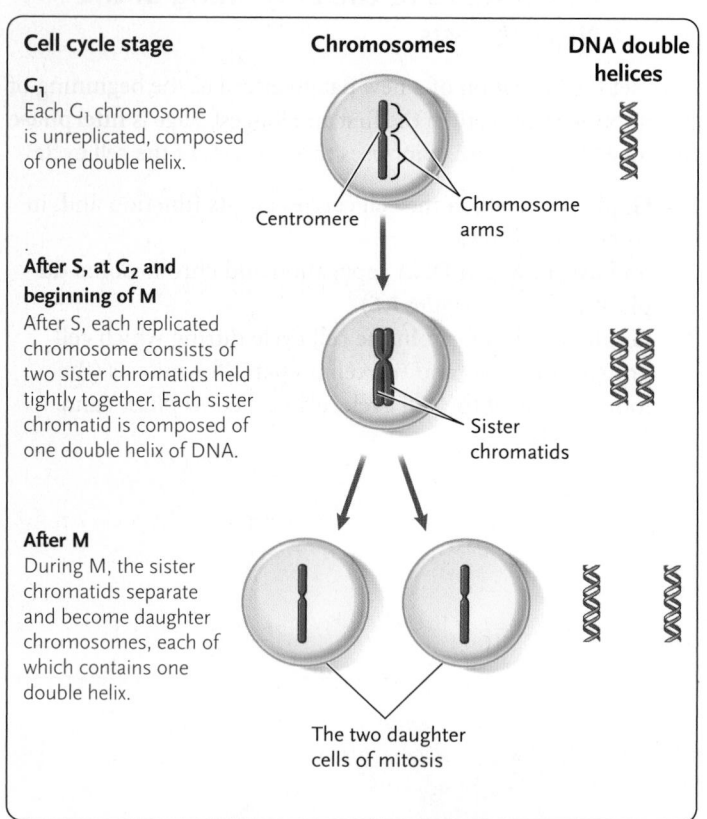

| Cell cycle stage | Chromosomes | DNA double helices |

**G₁**
Each $G_1$ chromosome is unreplicated, composed of one double helix.

Centromere

Chromosome arms

**After S, at G₂ and beginning of M**
After S, each replicated chromosome consists of two sister chromatids held tightly together. Each sister chromatid is composed of one double helix of DNA.

Sister chromatids

**After M**
During M, the sister chromatids separate and become daughter chromosomes, each of which contains one double helix.

The two daughter cells of mitosis

© Cengage Learning 2017

**FIGURE 7.6  A chromosome in G₁ becomes replicated during S phase and is then composed of two chromatids.** Anaphase pulls the two chromatids to opposite poles. All the cells shown above contain one chromosome.

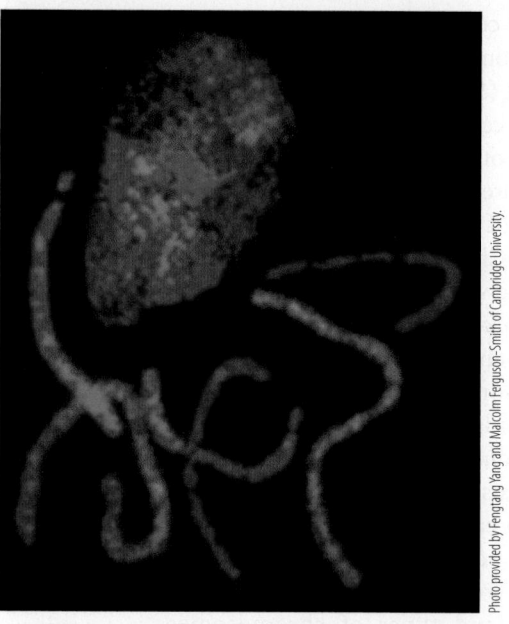

Photo provided by Fengtang Yang and Malcolm Ferguson-Smith of Cambridge University.

**FIGURE 7.7  Chromosomes from the muntjac deer are individually "painted" with fluorescent stain. Note that there are two cells in this picture.** The metaphase cell shows two copies of each of three long condensed chromosomes. The interphase nucleus shows the DNA of different chromosomes organized in close proximity rather than randomly distributed.

Usually, $G_1$ is the only phase of the cell cycle that varies in length. The other phases are typically uniform in length within a species. Thus, whether cells divide rapidly or slowly depends primarily on the length of $G_1$. Once DNA replication begins, most mammalian cells take about 10–12 hours to proceed through the S phase, about 4–6 hours to go through $G_2$, and about 1 hour or less to complete mitosis.

$G_1$ is also the stage in which many cell types stop dividing. Cells that are not destined to divide immediately enter a shunt from $G_1$ called the **G₀ phase**. In some cases, a cell in $G_0$ may start dividing again by re-entering $G_1$. Some cells never resume the cell cycle; for example, most cells of the human nervous system stop dividing once they are fully mature. During all the stages of interphase the chromosomes are organized but relatively loosely packaged within the nucleus **(Figure 7.7)**.

Internal regulatory controls trigger each phase of the cell cycle, ensuring that the processes of one phase are completed successfully before the next phase can begin. Various internal mechanisms also regulate the overall number of cycles that a cell goes through. These internal controls may be subject to various external influences, such as other cells or viruses and signal molecules, including hormones, growth factors, and death signals described later in this chapter.

🔵 **CONCEPT FIX**  Since the emphasis of this chapter is on the behaviour of chromosomes, your attention might get focused on the events of mitosis such that you assume nothing much happens during interphase. Cells are not just "resting up" for the next round of mitosis. During interphase, an appropriate suite of genes is actively expressed to support cell maintenance and metabolism. Cells are "doing their job" during interphase and may remain in this phase for the rest of their lives. If cells are destined to divide, it is also during interphase that DNA is replicated. ⬡

### 7.3c  After Interphase, Mitosis Proceeds in Five Stages

Mitosis involves both nuclear and cytoplasmic events. In the nucleus, normal gene expression decreases, DNA condenses, and kinetochores are built up. In the cytoplasm, the cytoskeleton that normally attends to cell shape, motility, and the movement of organelles now prepares to ensure accurate partitioning of chromosomes. If you were to watch a cell going through mitosis **(Figures 7.8 and 7.9)** you would notice several dramatic changes that signal the progression through different stages: prophase (*pro* = before), prometaphase (*meta* = between), metaphase, anaphase (*ana* = back), and telophase (*telo* = end).

**PROPHASE** During **prophase**, the greatly extended chromosomes that were replicated during interphase begin to condense into compact, rodlike structures. Each diploid human cell—although only about 40–50 μm in diameter—contains *2 m* of DNA distributed among 23 pairs of chromosomes. Condensation during prophase packs these long DNA molecules into units small enough to be divided successfully during mitosis.

DNA is compacted by winding the double helix twice around a complex of small positively charged proteins to form a **nucleosome**. The proteins in the nucleosome are called *histones*; two molecules of each of four different histones (H2A, H2B, H3, H4) make up the nucleosome core (**Figure 7.10**). A short segment of DNA, the **linker**, extends between one nucleosome and the next. Under the electron microscope, this structure looks like beads on a string. The diameter of the beads (the nucleosomes) gives this structure its name: the **10 nm chromatin fibre**.

The fifth histone, H1, brings about the next level of packing. One H1 molecule binds to both the nucleosomes and the linker DNA. This binding causes the nucleosomes to package into a coiled structure 30 nm in diameter, called the **30 nm chromatin fibre**, or **solenoid**. As they continue to fold and condense, the chromatin fibres become visible as the thin threadlike chromosomes that we see under the light microscope. The word *mitosis* (*mitos* = thread) is derived from this threadlike appearance.

While condensation is in progress, the nucleolus becomes smaller and, in most species, eventually disappears. This reflects a shutdown of all types of RNA synthesis, including the ribosomal RNA made in the nucleolus.

In the cytoplasm, the **mitotic spindle** (**Figure 7.11**; see also Figure 7.15) begins to form between the two centrosomes as they start migrating toward the opposite ends of the cell to form the **spindle poles**. The spindle develops as bundles of microtubules that radiate from the spindle poles.

**PROMETAPHASE** At the end of prophase, the nuclear envelope breaks down, heralding the beginning of **prometaphase**. Bundles of spindle microtubules grow from centrosomes at the opposing spindle poles toward the centre of the cell. Some of the developing spindle microtubules enter the former nuclear area and attach at the centromere of chromosomes.

Although replicated chromosomes are seldom visible as a double structure at this point, it is important for you to remember that each one is made up of two sister chromatids held together along their length by cohesin proteins. By this time, a complex of several proteins, called a **kinetochore**, has formed on each chromatid at the centromere. Microtubules bind to these kinetochores. These connections determine the outcome of mitosis because they attach the sister chromatids of each chromosome to microtubules leading to the opposite spindle poles (see Figure 7.11). Microtubules that do not attach to kinetochores overlap those from the opposite spindle pole.

**METAPHASE** During **metaphase**, the spindle reaches its final form and the chromosomes move into alignment at the spindle midpoint, also called the *metaphase plate*. The chromosomes complete their condensation in this stage and assume their characteristic shape as determined by the location of the centromere and the length and thickness of the chromatid arms.

Only when the chromosomes are all assembled at the spindle midpoint, with the two sister chromatids of each one attached to microtubules leading to opposite spindle poles, can metaphase give way to actual separation of chromatids.

**CONCEPT FIX** Although you probably think of chromosomes as X shapes, it is important to realize that few chromosomes ever actually look like this. Only chromosomes with their centromere near the middle could ever appear as an X. Chromosomes take on any visible shape at all only when they are highly condensed. ⬡

The complete collection of condensed chromosomes arranged according to size and shape forms the **karyotype** of a given species. In many cases, the karyotype is so distinctive that a species can be identified from this characteristic alone. **Figure 7.12** shows a human karyotype.

**CONCEPT FIX** Although the chromosomes shown in Figure 7.12 don't appear to be composed of two chromatids, this is just a result of the method of preparation. These chromosomes are replicated as is usual in metaphase. ⬡

**ANAPHASE** During **anaphase**, sister chromatids separate and move to opposite spindle poles. The first signs of chromosome movement can be seen at the centromeres as the kinetochores are the first sections to move toward opposite poles. The movement continues until the separated chromatids, now called *daughter chromosomes*, have reached the two poles. At this point, chromosome segregation has been completed.

**TELOPHASE** During **telophase**, the spindle disassembles and the chromosomes at each spindle pole decondense and return to the extended state typical of interphase. As decondensation proceeds, the nucleolus reappears, RNA transcription resumes, and a new nuclear envelope forms around the chromosomes at each pole, producing the two daughter nuclei. The cytoskeleton returns to normal interphase responsibilities. At this point, nuclear division is complete and the cell has two nuclei.

**CONCEPT FIX** The double-strandedness of DNA, the mechanism of cell division, and new vocabulary can lead to confusion about just how many chromosomes are in a particular cell at a particular time. Let's pick the fruit fly *Drosophila melanogaster* as an example organism because all of its genes are contained in only four different chromosomes. Every body cell in a fruit fly is diploid (*2n*) and therefore contains two of each of the four distinct *Drosophila* chromosomes—for a total of eight. Each of these eight chromosomes is composed of a pair of nucleic acid backbones that make up the DNA double helix of the type shown in Chapter 11, Figure 11.6. If the cell is preparing to divide, DNA synthesis, as shown in Chapter 11, Figure 11.7,

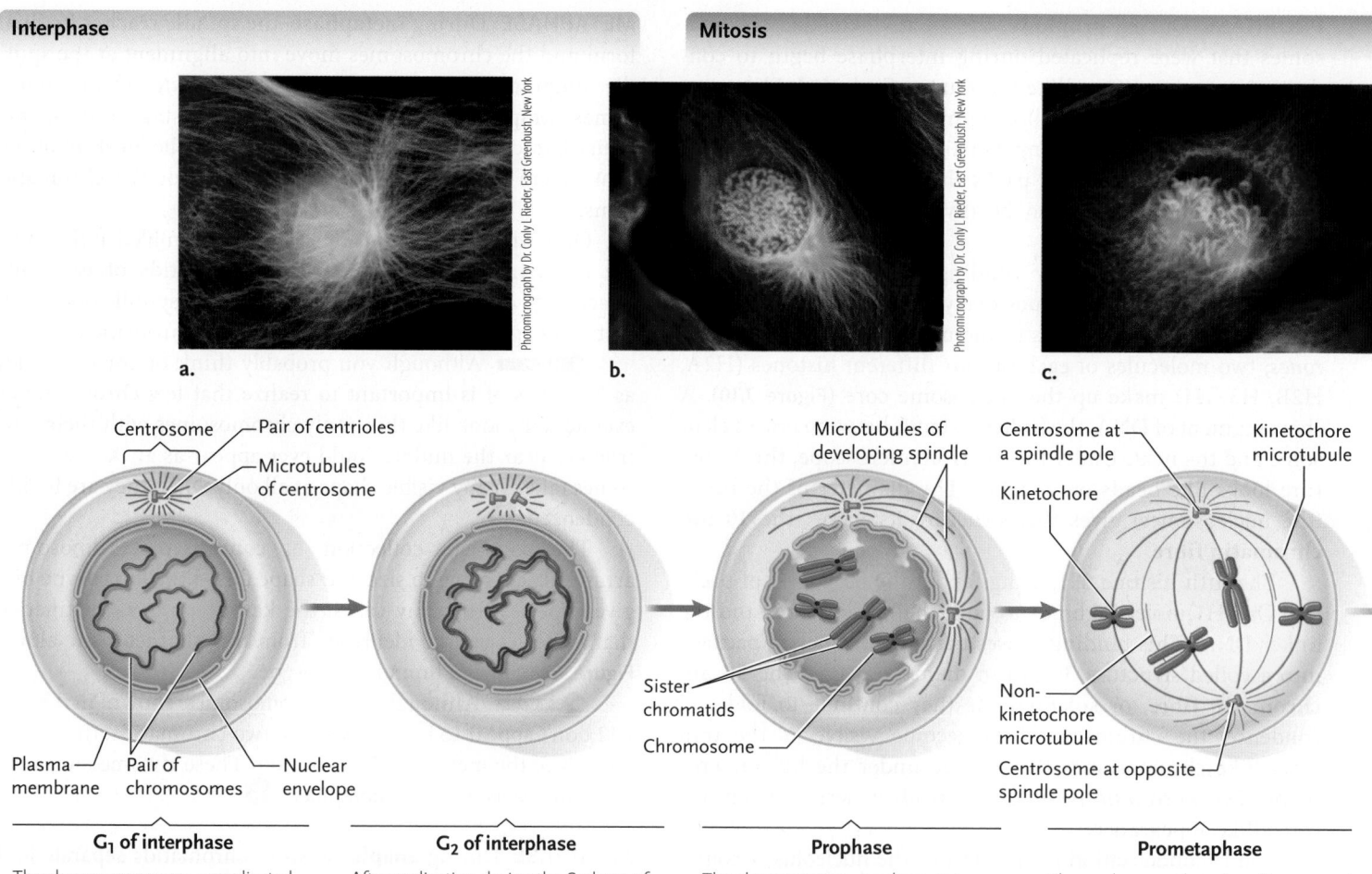

Photomicrograph by Dr. Conly L Rieder, East Greenbush, New York

a.

b.

c.

**Centrosome — Pair of centrioles**

Microtubules of centrosome

Microtubules of developing spindle

Centrosome at a spindle pole

Kinetochore microtubule

Kinetochore

Sister chromatids

Chromosome

Non-kinetochore microtubule

Centrosome at opposite spindle pole

Plasma membrane — Pair of chromosomes — Nuclear envelope

**G₁ of interphase**

The chromosomes are unreplicated and extend throughout the nucleus. For simplicity we show only two pairs of chromosomes. One of each pair was inherited from one parent, and the other was inherited from the other parent.

**G₂ of interphase**

After replication during the S phase of interphase, each chromosome is double at all points and now consists of two sister chromatids. Cohesins encircle each pair of sister chromatids along their lengths, aligning them tightly. The centrioles within the centrosome have also doubled into pairs.

**Prophase**

The chromosomes condense into threads that become visible under the light microscope. Each chromosome is double as a result of replication. The centrosome has divided into two parts, which are generating the spindle as they separate.

**Prometaphase**

The nuclear envelope has disappeared and the spindle enters the former nuclear area. Microtubules from opposite spindle poles attach to the two kinetochores of each chromosome.

**FIGURE 7.8** **The stages of mitosis.** Triple-stained immunofluorescent light micrographs show mitosis in an animal cell (salamander lung). The chromosomes are blue, the spindle and cytoplasmic microtubules are yellow–green, and the intermediate filaments are red. **(a)** Interphase. Microtubules focus on the centrosome, located adjacent to the nucleus. **(b)** Prophase. Chromosomes are well condensed, the nuclear envelope is intact, and the microtubules are organized into radial arrays. **(c)** Prometaphase. The nuclear envelope has broken down to allow the chromosomes to interact with the microtubules originating from two separate centrosomes. **(d)** Metaphase. All the replicated chromosomes are aligned on the equator of the mature mitotic spindle. **(e)** Anaphase/telophase. Chromosomes have been equally segregated and have decondensed to form two independent daughter nuclei. This cell has just begun cytokinesis. **(f)** The end result of mitosis: two genetically identical daughter cells

creates a complementary "copy" of each of the original backbones. The new DNA molecules created from each original chromosome remain attached to one another as sister chromatids. (A student once suggested that these two new molecules should be called *twin chromatids* because they are so similar.) Now here comes the confusing part. Since sister chromatids remain attached to each other following DNA synthesis, the pair of them is still referred to as just one chromosome. Before replication, one chromosome is composed of one DNA double helix; after replication, one chromosome is composed of two double helices. You should see that DNA replication increases the

amount of DNA in the nucleus but it does not increase the number of chromosomes. Our *Drosophila* cell has eight DNA double helices in the nucleus before DNA synthesis, and eight *pairs* of double helices afterward. There are eight chromosomes before DNA synthesis and eight *replicated* chromosomes after DNA synthesis. During cell division, each of the two daughter cells receives one of the two sister chromatids from each replicated chromosome. You should therefore agree to the rather counterintuitive claim that two daughter cells can each receive eight chromosomes even though there were only eight chromosomes in the original cell. ⬡

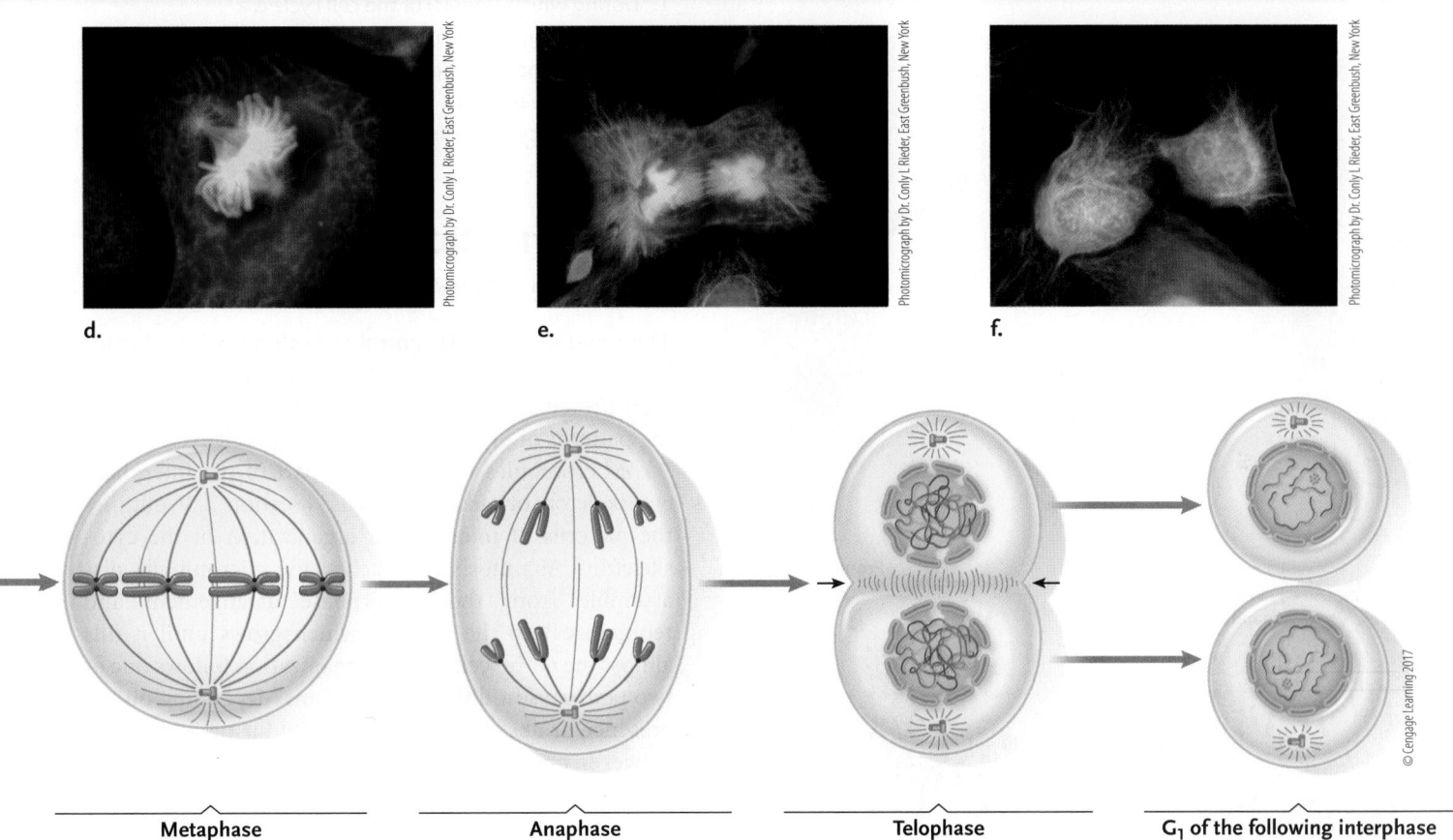

Photomicrograph by Dr. Conly L. Rieder, East Greenbush, New York

d.

e.

f.

© Cengage Learning 2017

**Metaphase**

The chromosomes become aligned at the spindle midpoint. Each sister chromatid pair is held in position by opposing forces: the kinetochore microtubules pulling to the poles and the cohesins binding the sister chromatids together.

**Anaphase**

Separase cleaves the cohesin ring holding sister chromatids together. The spindle separates the two sister chromatids of each chromosome and moves them to opposite spindle poles.

**Telophase**

The chromosomes unfold and return to the interphase state, and new nuclear envelopes form around the daughter nuclei. The cytoplasm is beginning to divide by furrowing at the points marked by arrows.

**G₁ of the following interphase**

The two daughter cells are genetic duplicates of the parental cell that entered mitotic division.

## 7.3d Cytokinesis Completes Cell Division by Dividing the Cytoplasm between Daughter Cells

**Cytokinesis**, the division of the cytoplasm, usually follows the nuclear division stage of mitosis and produces two daughter cells, each containing one of the daughter nuclei. In most cells, cytokinesis begins during telophase or even late anaphase. By the time cytokinesis is completed, the daughter nuclei have progressed to the interphase stage and entered the $G_1$ phase of the next cell cycle.

Cytokinesis proceeds by different pathways in the different kingdoms of eukaryotic organisms. In animals, protists, and many fungi, a groove, the **furrow**, girdles the cell and gradually deepens until it cuts the cytoplasm into two parts. In plants, a new cell wall, called the **cell plate**, forms between the daughter nuclei and grows laterally until it divides the cytoplasm. In both cases, the plane of cytoplasmic division is determined by the layer of microtubules that persist at the former spindle midpoint.

**FURROWING** In furrowing, the layer of microtubules that remains at the former spindle midpoint expands laterally until it stretches entirely across the dividing cell (**Figure 7.13**). As the layer develops, a band of microfilaments forms just inside the plasma membrane, forming a belt that follows the inside boundary of the cell in the plane of the microtubule layer (microfilaments are discussed in Section 2.3f). Powered by motor proteins, the microfilaments slide together, tightening the band and constricting the cell. The constriction forms a groove, the furrow, in the plasma membrane. The furrow gradually deepens, much like the tightening of a drawstring, until the daughter cells are completely separated. The cytoplasmic division isolates the daughter nuclei in the two cells and, at the same time, distributes the organelles and other structures (which have also doubled) approximately equally.

**CELL PLATE FORMATION** Since plant cells are walled, the plane of cell division is very important for growth and morphology of the plant. In cell plate formation, a layer of microtubules that persists at the former spindle midpoint serves as an

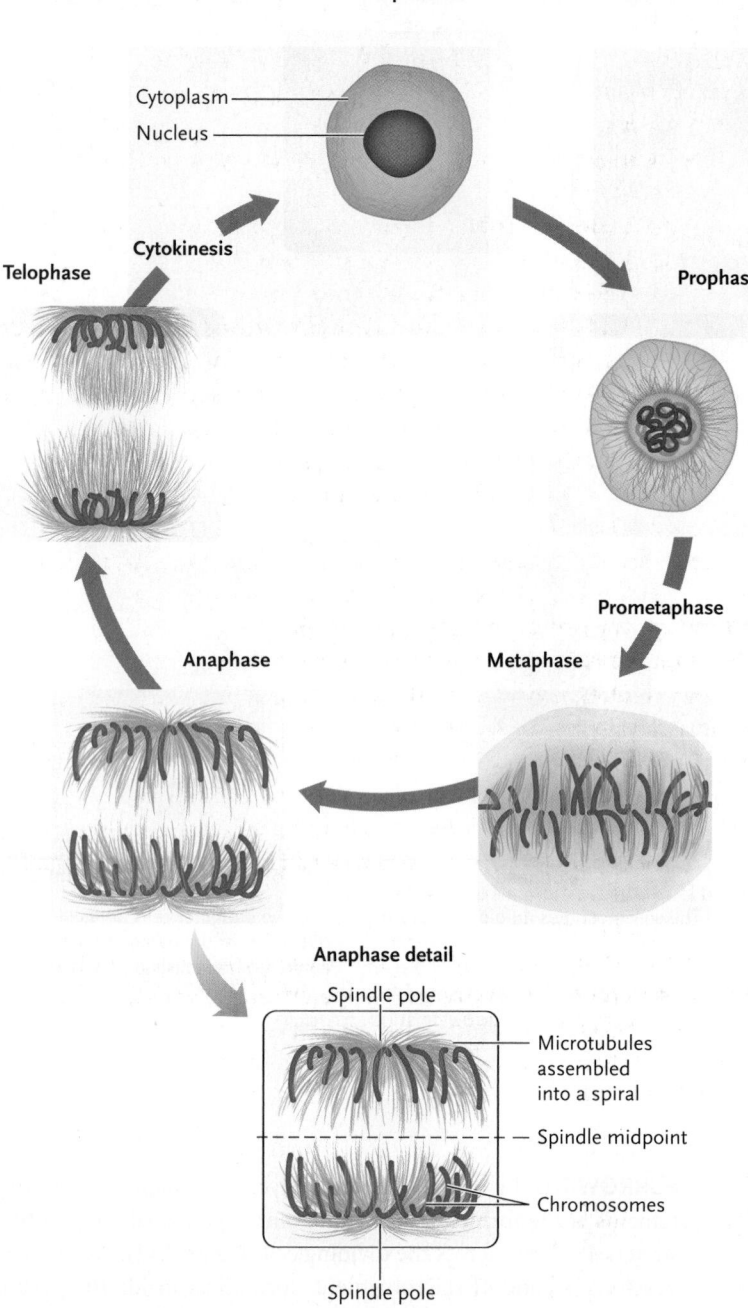

**FIGURE 7.9 Mitosis in the blood lily *Haemanthus*.** The chromosomes are shown in purple; the spindle microtubules are shown in pink.

Labels in figure:

Interphase
Cytoplasm
Nucleus
Cytokinesis
Telophase
Prophase
Anaphase
Prometaphase
Metaphase

Anaphase detail
Spindle pole
Microtubules assembled into a spiral
Spindle midpoint
Chromosomes
Spindle pole

**STUDY BREAK QUESTIONS**

1. During which stage(s) of the cell cycle is a chromosome composed of two chromatids?
2. What are the conditions under which a chromosome could appear as an X shape under the microscope?
3. How does cytokinesis differ in plant and animal cells?

## 7.4 Formation and Action of the Mitotic Spindle

The mitotic spindle is central to both mitosis and cytokinesis. The spindle is made up of microtubules and their proteins, and its activities depend on their changing patterns of organization during the cell cycle.

Microtubules form a major part of the interphase cytoskeleton of eukaryotic cells. (Section 2.3f outlines the patterns of microtubule organization in the cytoskeleton.) As mitosis approaches, the microtubules disassemble from their interphase arrangement and reorganize into the spindle, which grows until it fills almost the entire cell. This reorganization follows one of two pathways in different organisms, depending on the presence or absence of a *centrosome* during interphase. However, once organized, the basic function of the spindle is the same, regardless of whether a centrosome is present.

### 7.4a Animals and Plants Form Spindles in Different Ways

Animal cells and many protists have a **centrosome,** a site near the nucleus from which microtubules radiate outward in all directions (**Figure 7.15**, step 1). The centrosome is the main **microtubule organizing centre (MTOC)** of the cell, anchoring the microtubule cytoskeleton during interphase and positioning many of the cytoplasmic organelles. The centrosome contains a pair of **centrioles,** usually arranged at right angles to each other. Although centrioles originally appeared to be important in the construction of the mitotic spindle, it has now been shown that they can be removed with no ill effect. The primary function of centrioles is actually to generate the microtubules needed for flagella or cilia, the whiplike extensions that provide cell motility.

When DNA replicates during the S phase of the cell cycle, the centrioles within the centrosome also duplicate, producing two pairs of centrioles (see Figure 7.15, step 2). As prophase begins in the M phase, the centrosome separates into two parts (step 3). The duplicated centrosomes, with the centrioles inside them, continue to separate until they reach opposite ends of the

organizing site for vesicles produced by the endoplasmic reticulum (ER) and Golgi complex (**Figure 7.14**). These vesicles contain polysaccharides, cellulose, and other components of the cell wall. As the vesicles fuse together, their contents assemble into a new cell wall, the cell plate, stretching completely across the former spindle midpoint. Vesicle membranes become the inner plasma membrane of the daughter cells. This junction separates the cytoplasm and its organelles into two parts and isolates the daughter nuclei in separate cells.

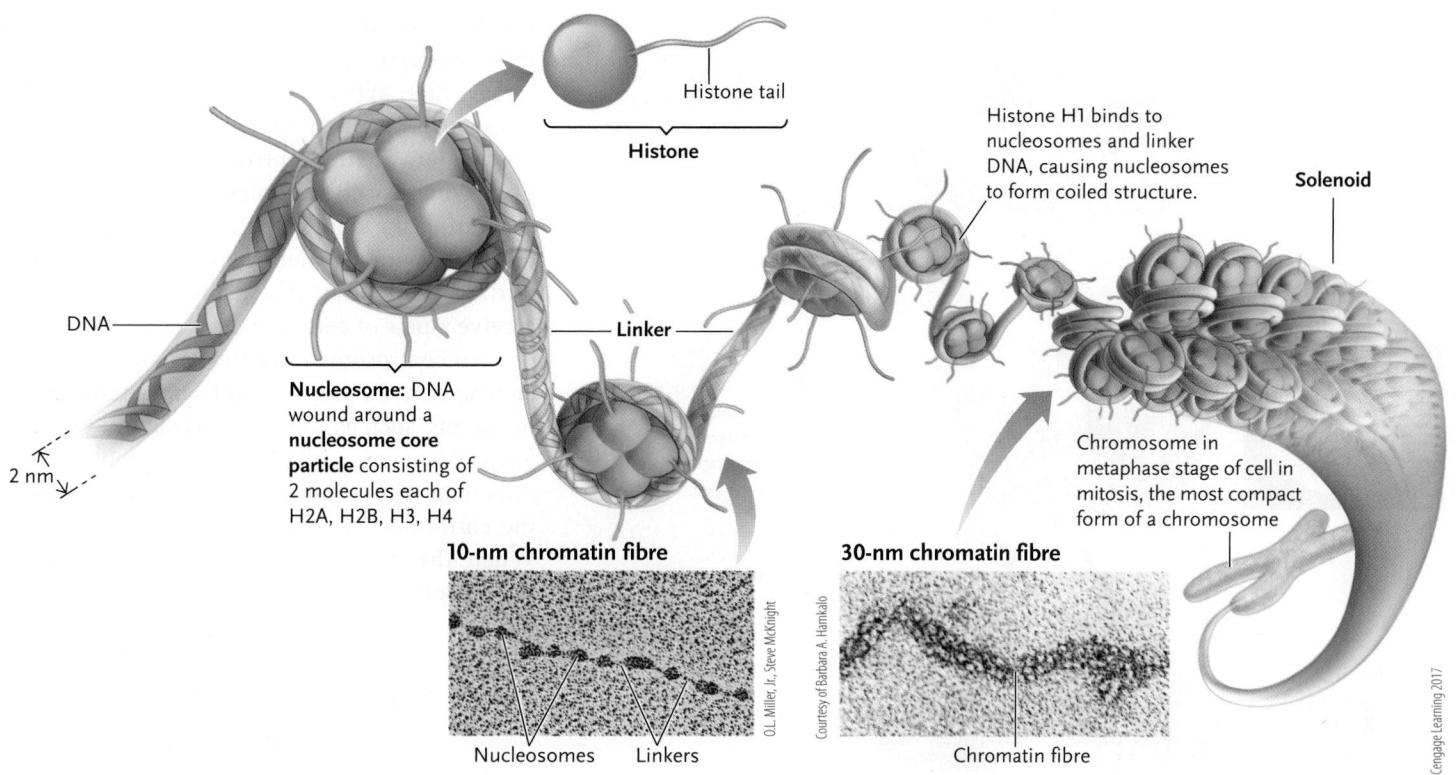

**FIGURE 7.10** **DNA packaging around histones in eukaryotic chromosomes**

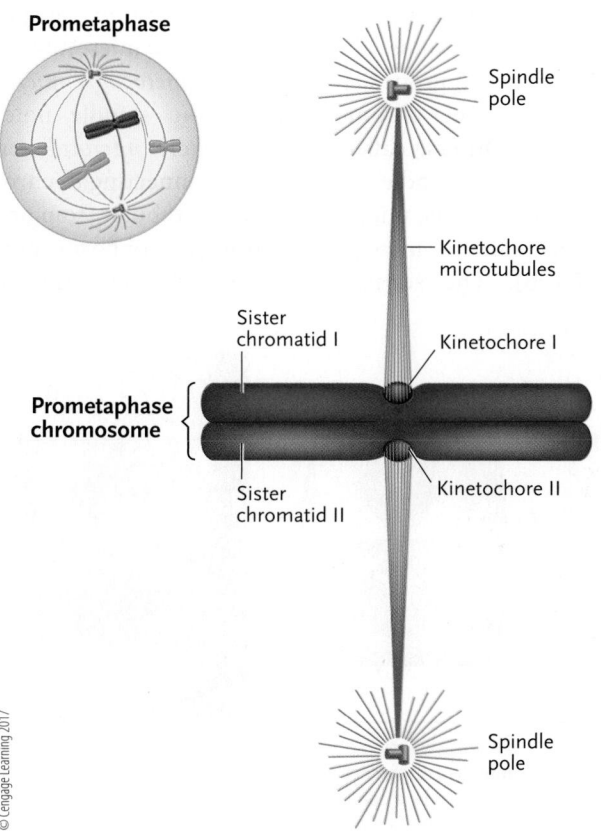

**Prometaphase**

Spindle pole

Kinetochore microtubules

Sister chromatid I

Kinetochore I

**Prometaphase chromosome**

Sister chromatid II

Kinetochore II

Spindle pole

**FIGURE 7.11** **Spindle connections made by chromosomes at mitotic metaphase in typical animal cells.** The two kinetochores of the chromosome connect to opposite spindle poles, ensuring that the chromatids are separated and moved to opposite spindle poles during anaphase.

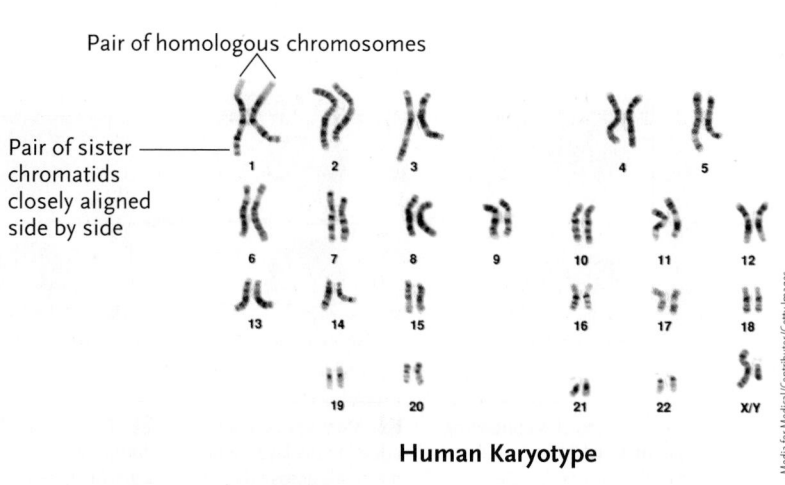

Pair of homologous chromosomes

Pair of sister chromatids closely aligned side by side

**Human Karyotype**

**FIGURE 7.12** **Karyotype of a human male.** Note the X and Y chromosomes.

CHAPTER 7 CELL CYCLES |

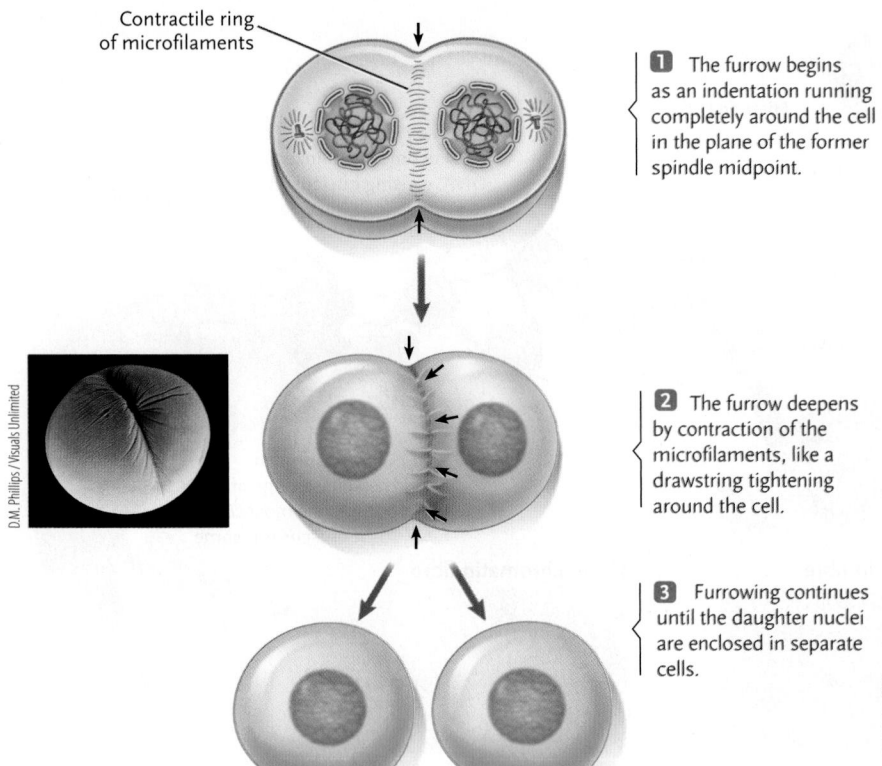

Contractile ring of microfilaments

**1** The furrow begins as an indentation running completely around the cell in the plane of the former spindle midpoint.

**2** The furrow deepens by contraction of the microfilaments, like a drawstring tightening around the cell.

**3** Furrowing continues until the daughter nuclei are enclosed in separate cells.

D.M. Phillips / Visuals Unlimited

© Cengage Learning 2017

**FIGURE 7.13 Cytokinesis by furrowing.** The micrograph shows a furrow developing in the first division of a fertilized egg cell.

nucleus (step 4). As the centrosomes move apart, the microtubules between them lengthen and increase in number.

By late prophase, when the centrosomes are fully separated, the microtubules that extend between them form a large mass around one side of the nucleus called the *early spindle*. When the nuclear envelope subsequently breaks down at the end of prophase, the spindle moves into the region formerly occupied by the nucleus and continues

growing until it fills the cytoplasm. The microtubules that extend from the centrosomes also grow in length and extent, producing radiating arrays that appear starlike under the light microscope. Initially named by early microscopists, **asters** are the centrosomes at the spindle tips, which form the poles of the spindle. By separating the duplicated centrioles, the spindle ensures that, when the cytoplasm divides during cytokinesis, the daughter cells each receive a pair of centrioles.

No centrosome or centrioles are present in angiosperms (flowering plants) or in most gymnosperms, such as conifers. Instead, the spindle forms from microtubules that assemble in all directions from multiple MTOCs surrounding the entire nucleus (see prophase in Figure 7.9). When the nuclear envelope breaks down at the end of prophase, the spindle moves into the former nuclear region, as in animals.

## 7.4b Mitotic Spindles Can Move Chromosomes by a Combination of Two Mechanisms

When fully formed at metaphase, the spindle may contain from hundreds to many thousands of microtubules, depending on the species (**Figure 7.16**). In almost all eukaryotes, these microtubules are divided into two groups. Some, called *kinetochore microtubules*, connect the chromosomes to the spindle poles (**Figure 7.17a**). Others, called *nonkinetochore microtubules*, extend between the spindle poles without connecting to chromosomes; at the spindle midpoint, the microtubules from one pole overlap with the microtubules from the opposite pole (Figure 7.17b). The separation of the chromosomes at

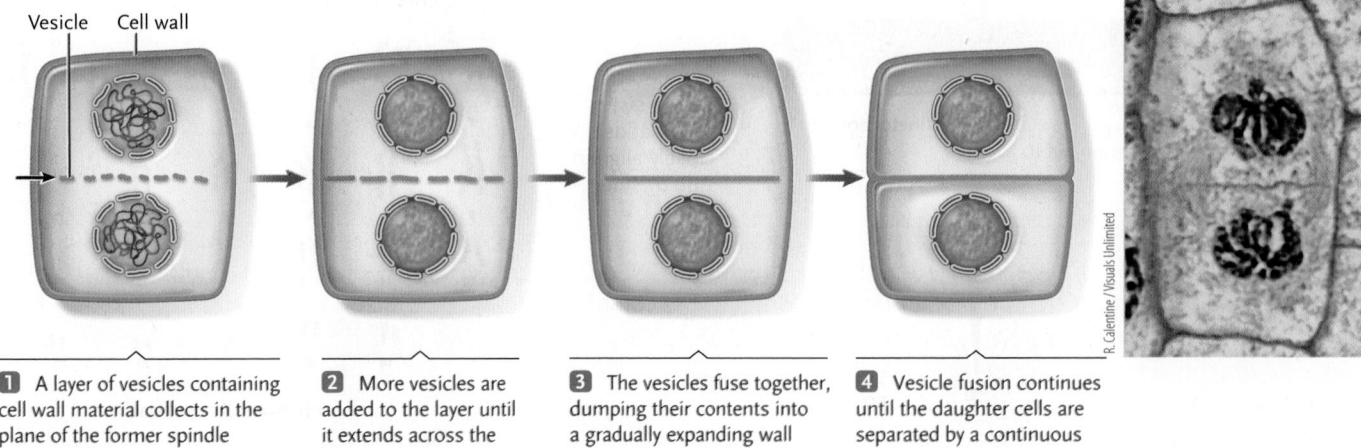

Vesicle    Cell wall

**1** A layer of vesicles containing cell wall material collects in the plane of the former spindle midpoint (arrow).

**2** More vesicles are added to the layer until it extends across the cell.

**3** The vesicles fuse together, dumping their contents into a gradually expanding wall between the daughter cells.

**4** Vesicle fusion continues until the daughter cells are separated by a continuous new wall, the cell plate.

R. Calentine / Visuals Unlimited

© Cengage Learning 2017

**FIGURE 7.14 Cytokinesis by cell plate formation in plant cells**

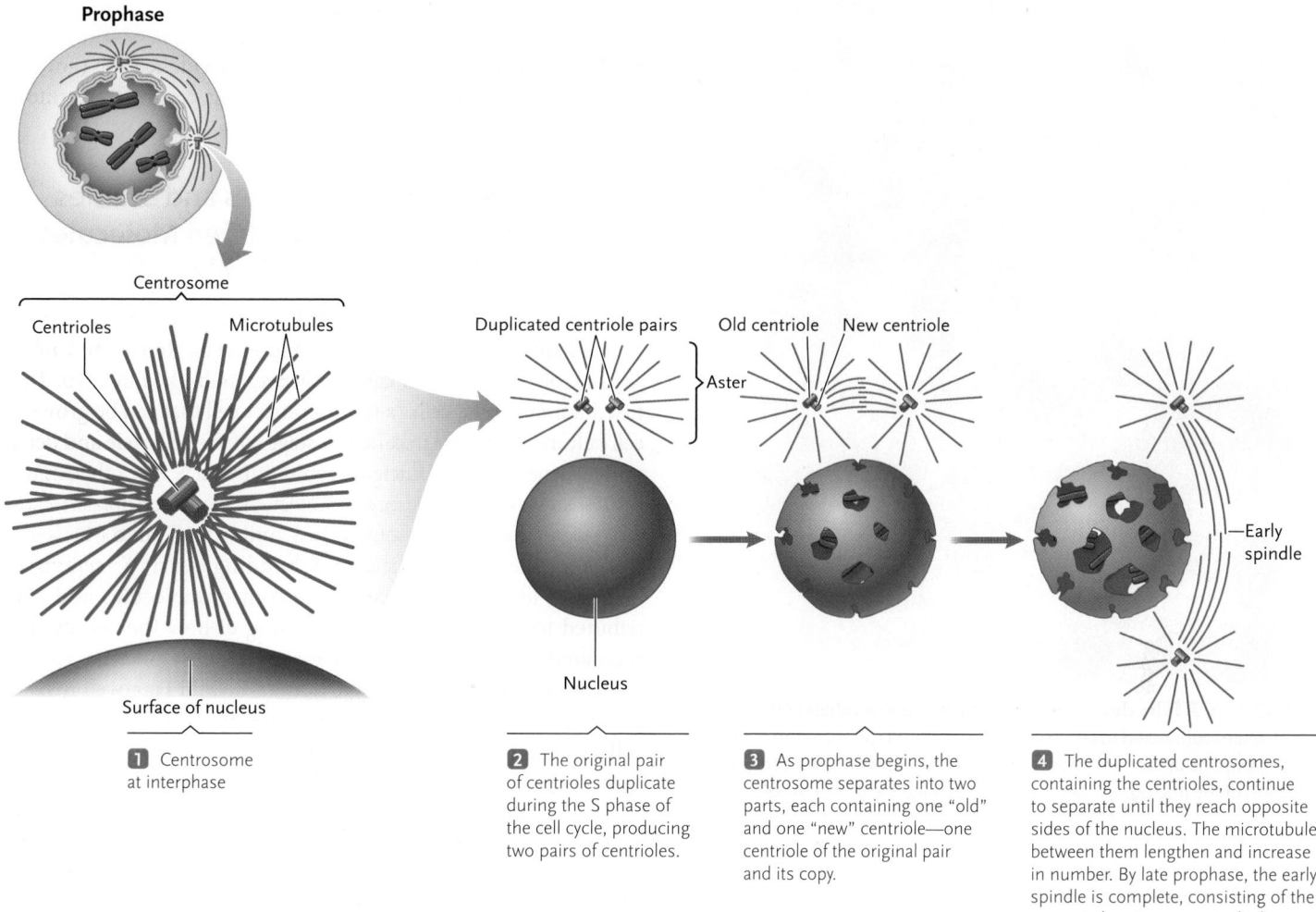

**FIGURE 7.15  The centrosome and its role in spindle formation**

Prophase

Centrosome

Centrioles    Microtubules

Surface of nucleus

**1** Centrosome at interphase

Duplicated centriole pairs    Old centriole    New centriole

Aster

Nucleus

**2** The original pair of centrioles duplicate during the S phase of the cell cycle, producing two pairs of centrioles.

**3** As prophase begins, the centrosome separates into two parts, each containing one "old" and one "new" centriole—one centriole of the original pair and its copy.

Early spindle

**4** The duplicated centrosomes, containing the centrioles, continue to separate until they reach opposite sides of the nucleus. The microtubules between them lengthen and increase in number. By late prophase, the early spindle is complete, consisting of the separated centrosomes and a large mass of microtubules between them.

© Cengage Learning 2017

anaphase appears to result from a combination of separate but coordinated movements produced by the two types of microtubules.

The exact mechanism by which chromosomes move is still uncertain. At one time, it was believed that microtubules pulled the chromosomes toward the poles of dividing cells; however, subsequent data suggested that chromosomes "climb" to the poles along stationary microtubules, using motor proteins in their kinetochores (**Figure 7.18**). The tubulin subunits of the kinetochore microtubules disassemble as the kinetochores pass along them; thus, the microtubules become shorter as the movement progresses (see Figure 7.17a). The movement is similar to you climbing a rope hand over hand as the rope disintegrates behind you. The most current hypotheses suggest that several different mechanisms combine efforts to ensure proper chromosome movement.

Evidence supporting kinetochore-based movement comes from experiments in which researchers tagged kinetochore microtubules with a microscopic beam of ultraviolet light, producing bleached sites that could be seen in the light microscope (**Figure 7.19**). As the chromosomes moved to the spindle poles, the bleached sites stayed in the same place. This result showed that the kinetochore microtubules do not move much with respect to the poles during the anaphase movement.

Chromosomes can also move toward the poles by a mechanism in which motor proteins at the spindle poles pull kinetochore microtubules poleward, disassembling those microtubules into tubulin subunits as that occurs. Both climbing and pulling mechanisms are used in mitosis, although the relative contributions of the two mechanisms to chromosome movement vary among species and cell types. (The cell type in the experiment of Figure 7.18 used predominantly climbing.) In nonkinetochore microtubule-based movement, the entire spindle is lengthened, elongating the cell in metaphase and anaphase (see Figure 7.17b). Presumably, the pushing movement is produced by microtubules sliding over one another in the zone of overlap, powered by proteins acting as microtubule motors. In many species, the nonkinetochore microtubules also push the poles apart by growing in length as they slide.

### STUDY BREAK QUESTIONS

1. What is the role of the centrosome?
2. What is the role of the kinetochore?

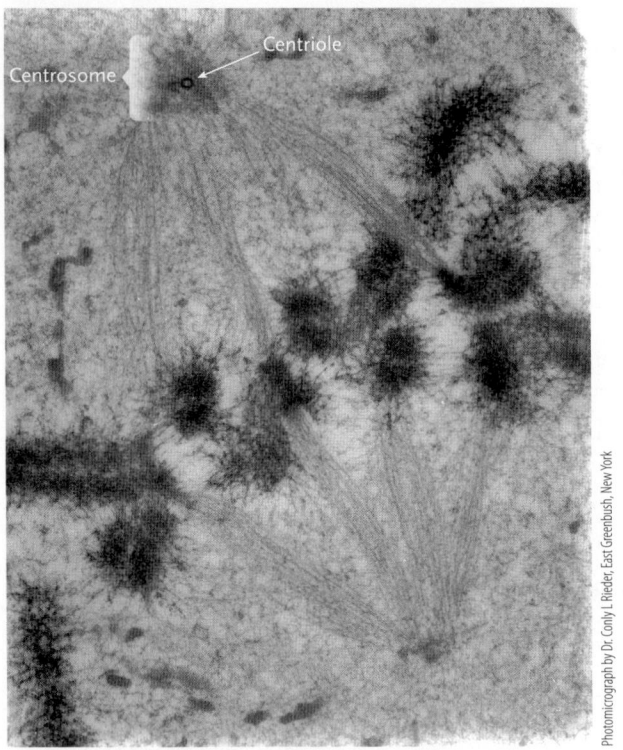

FIGURE 7.16 **A fully developed spindle in a mammalian cell.** Only microtubules connected to chromosomes have been caught in the plane of this section. One of the centrioles is visible in cross-section in the centrosome at the top of the micrograph (arrow). (Original magnification ×14 000.)

*Photomicrograph by Dr. Conly L Rieder, East Greenbush, New York*

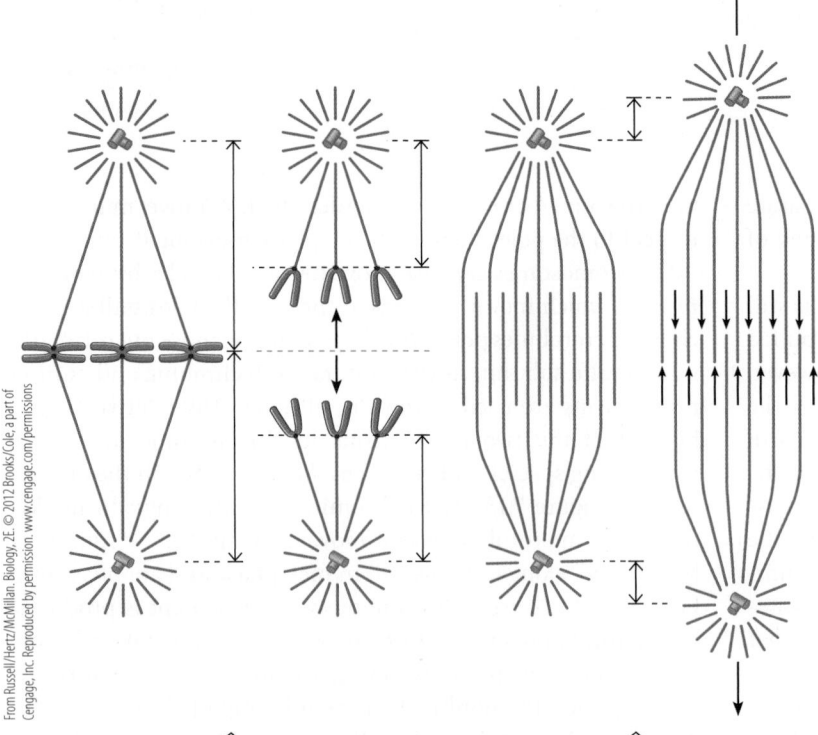

*From Russell/Hertz/McMillan. Biology, 2E. © 2012 Brooks/Cole, a part of Cengage, Inc. Reproduced by permission. www.cengage.com/permissions*

**a.** The kinetochore microtubules connected to the kinetochores of the chromosomes become shorter, lessening the distance from the chromosomes to the poles.

**b.** Sliding of the nonkinetochore microtubules in the zone of overlap at the spindle midpoint pushes poles farther apart and increases the total length of the spindle.

FIGURE 7.17 **The two microtubule-based movements of the anaphase spindle**

# 7.5 Cell Cycle Regulation

In this section, we discuss experimental evidence for (and the operation of) regulatory mechanisms that control the mitotic cell cycle.

## 7.5a Cell Fusion Experiments and Studies of Yeast Mutants Identified Molecules That Control the Cell Cycle

The first insights into how the cell cycle is regulated came from experiments by Robert T. Johnson and Potu N. Rao at the University of Colorado Medical Center, Denver, published in 1970. They fused human HeLa cells (a type of cancer cell that can be grown in cell culture) that were in different stages of the cell cycle and determined whether one nucleus could influence the other. Their results suggested that specific molecules in the cytoplasm cause the progression of cells from $G_1$ to S, and from $G_2$ into M.

Some key research using a budding yeast, *S. cerevisiae,* helped to identify these cell-cycle control molecules and contributed to our general understanding of how the cell cycle is regulated. (*The Purple Pages* describe yeast and its role in research in more detail.) In particular, Leland Hartwell investigated yeast mutants that become stuck at specific points in the cell cycle, but only when they are cultured at a high temperature. By growing the mutant cells at the standard temperature initially and then shifting the cells to the higher temperature, Hartwell was able to use time-lapse photomicroscopy to see if and when growth and division (budding) were affected. In this way, he isolated many cell division cycle, or *cdc,* mutants. Hartwell received a Nobel Prize in 2001 for his discovery.

Paul Nurse of the Imperial Cancer Research Fund, London, United Kingdom, made the breakthrough discovery that all eukaryotic cells studied have counterparts of a gene called *cdc2* that encodes a protein needed for yeast cells to progress from $G_2$ to M. This finding implies that this gene originated early during eukaryotic evolution and has played an essential role in cell-cycle regulation in all eukaryotes since that time. Paul Nurse received a Nobel Prize in 2001 for his discovery.

## 7.5b Cell-Cycle Checkpoints Ensure Accurate Cell Division

A cell has internal controls that monitor its progression through the cell cycle through the action of a particular set of control proteins called **cyclins**. Three key **checkpoints** ensure accurate cell division by preventing critical phases from beginning until the previous phases are completed correctly (**Figure 7.20**):

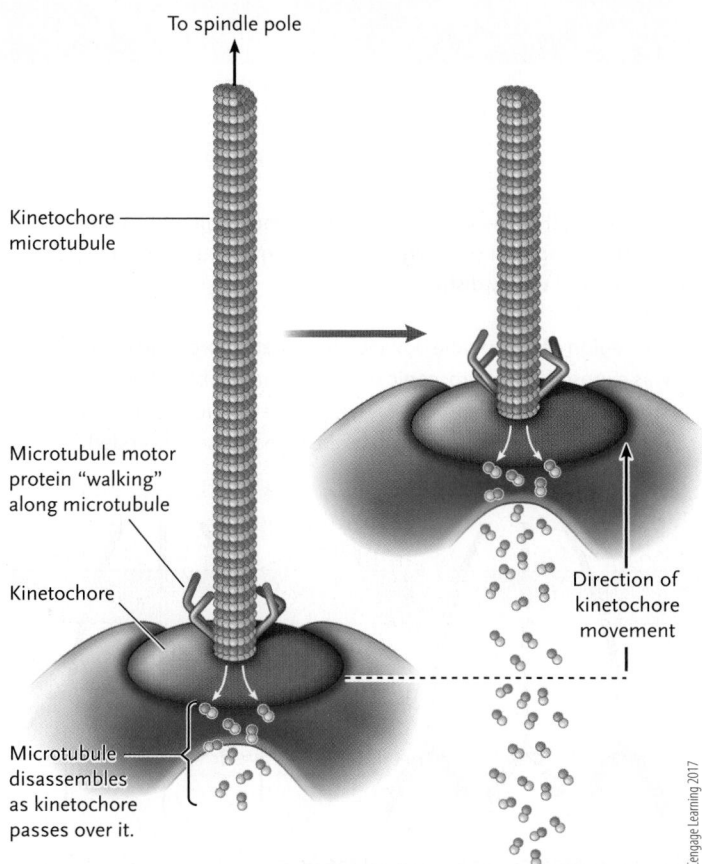

**To spindle pole**

Kinetochore
microtubule

Microtubule motor
protein "walking"
along microtubule

Kinetochore

Microtubule
disassembles
as kinetochore
passes over it.

Direction of
kinetochore
movement

© Cengage Learning 2017

**FIGURE 7.18 Microtubule motor proteins at the kinetochore allowing a chromosome to "climb" along a microtubule**

1. The *G₁/S checkpoint* is the main point in the cell cycle at which the mechanisms governing the cell cycle determine whether the cell will proceed through the rest of the cell cycle and divide. Once it passes this checkpoint, the cell is committed to continuing the cell cycle through to cell division in M. The cell cycle arrests (the cell stops proceeding through the cell cycle) at the $G_1/S$ checkpoint if, for example, the DNA is damaged by radiation or chemicals. The $G_1/S$ checkpoint is also the primary point at which cells "read" extracellular signals for cell growth and division. Therefore, if a hormone or growth factor required for stimulating cell growth is absent, the cells may arrest at this checkpoint. (Extracellular signals and their effects on the cell cycle are discussed in more detail later.)

2. The *G₂/M checkpoint* is at the junction between the $G_2$ and M phases. Passage through this checkpoint commits a cell to mitosis. Cells are arrested at the $G_2/M$ checkpoint if DNA was not replicated fully in S, or if the DNA has been damaged by radiation or chemicals. Complete DNA replication is essential for producing genetically complete daughter cells, highlighting the importance of this checkpoint.

3. The *mitotic spindle checkpoint* is within the M phase before metaphase. This checkpoint assesses whether chromo-

somes are attached properly to the mitotic spindle so that they will align correctly at the metaphase plate. This checkpoint is essential for production of daughter cells with the proper number of chromosomes, which depends on separation of daughter chromosomes in anaphase, which in turn depends on the correct alignment of the chromosomes on the spindle in metaphase. Once the cell begins anaphase, it is irreversibly committed to completing M, underlining the importance of the mitotic spindle checkpoint.

The control systems that operate at the checkpoints are signals to stop; basically, they are brakes. This becomes evident when a checkpoint is inactivated by mutation or chemical treatment, allowing the cell cycle to proceed even if DNA is damaged, DNA replication is incomplete, or the spindle did not assemble completely.

## 7.5c Cyclins and Cyclin-Dependent Kinases Are the Internal Controls That Directly Regulate Cell Division

The direct regulation of the cell cycle involves an internal control system consisting of protein cyclins and enzymes called **cyclin-dependent kinases (CDKs)** (see Figure 7.20). A CDK is a protein kinase that phosphorylates and thereby regulates the activity of target proteins. CDK enzymes are "cyclin dependent" because they are active *only* when bound to a cyclin molecule. Cyclins are named because their concentrations change as the cell cycle progresses. R. Timothy Hunt, of the Imperial Cancer Research Fund, received a Nobel Prize in 2001 for discovering cyclins. The basic control of the cell cycle by CDKs and cyclins is the same in all eukaryotes, but there are differences in the number and types of the molecules. We will focus on cell cycle regulation in vertebrates to explain how these proteins work.

The concentrations of the various CDKs remain constant throughout the cell cycle, while the concentrations of cyclins change as they are synthesized and degraded at specific stages of the cell cycle. Thus, a specific CDK becomes active when the cell synthesizes the cyclin that binds to it, and remains active until the cyclin is degraded. Each active CDK phosphorylates particular target proteins that play roles in initiating or regulating key events of the cell cycle. The phosphorylation regulates the activities of these proteins and keeps the cycle operating in an orderly way. These key events are DNA replication, mitosis, and cytokinesis. A succession of cyclin–CDK complexes, each of which has specific regulatory effects, ensures that these stages follow in sequence somewhat like a clock passing through the sequence of hours. Regulation of the activity of cyclin–CDK complexes is integrated with the regulatory events at the cell-cycle checkpoints to ensure that daughter cells do not inherit damaged DNA or abnormal numbers of chromosomes.

FIGURE 7.19 **Experimental Research**

## Movement of Chromosomes during Anaphase of Mitosis

**Question:** How do chromosomes move during anaphase of mitosis?

**Experiment:** One hypothesis for how chromosomes move during anaphase of mitosis was that the kinetochore microtubules moved, pulling chromosomes to the poles. An alternative hypothesis was that chromosomes move by sliding over or along kinetochore microtubules. To test the hypotheses, G. J. Gorbsky and his colleagues made regions of the kinetochore microtubules visibly distinct.

1.  Kinetochore microtubules were combined with a dye molecule that bleaches when it is exposed to light.

2.  The region of the spindle between the kinetochores and the poles was exposed to a microscopic beam of light that bleached a narrow stripe across the microtubules. The bleached region could be seen with a light microscope and analyzed as anaphase proceeded.

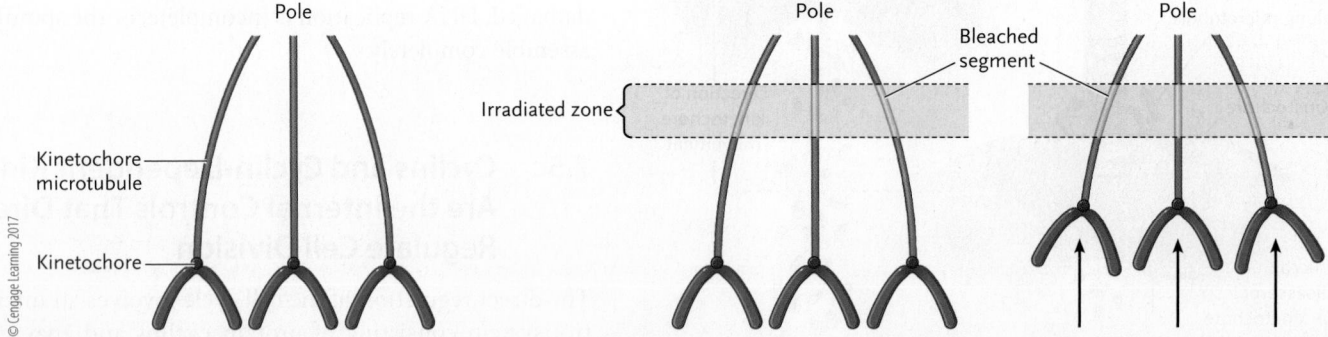

**Results:** The bleached region remained at the same distance from the pole as the chromosomes moved toward the pole.

**Conclusion:** The results support the hypothesis that chromosomes move by sliding over or along kinetochore microtubules.

© Cengage Learning 2017

## 7.5d External Controls Coordinate the Mitotic Cell Cycle of Individual Cells with the Overall Activities of the Organism

The internal controls that regulate the cell cycle can respond to signal molecules that originate from outside the dividing cells. In animals, these signal molecules include the peptide hormones and similar proteins called *growth* or *death factors*. In plants, growth hormones such as cytokinin and auxin affect cell cycling in special growth centres called *meristems* (described further in Chapter 33).

Many of these external factors bind to receptors at the cell surface, which respond by triggering reactions inside the cell. These reactions often include steps that add phosphate groups to the cyclin–CDK complexes, thereby affecting their function. The overall effect is to speed, slow, or stop the progress of cell division, depending on the particular hormone or factor and the internal pathway that is stimulated. Some growth factors are even able to break the arrest of cells shunted into the $G_0$ stage and return them to active division. (Hormones, growth factors, and other signal molecules are part of the cell communication system, as discussed in Chapter 4.)

Cell surface receptors in animal cells also recognize contact with other cells or with molecules of the **extracellular matrix (ECM)**. The contact triggers internal reaction pathways that inhibit division by arresting the cell cycle, usually in the $G_1$ phase. The response, called **contact inhibition**, stabilizes cell growth in fully developed organs and tissues. As long as the cells of most tissues are in contact with one another or with the ECM, they are shunted into the $G_0$ phase and prevented from dividing.

Contact inhibition is easily observed in cultured mammalian cells grown on a glass or plastic surface. In such cultures, division proceeds until all the cells are in contact with their neighbours in a continuous, unbroken, single layer. At this point, division stops. If a researcher then scrapes some of the cells from the surface, cells at the edges of the "wound" are released from inhibition and divide until they form a continuous layer, and all the cells are again in contact with their neighbours.

## 7.5e Stem Cells Exhibit Asymmetric Cell Division

The mitotic mechanism described so far in this chapter is symmetric in that it produces two daughter cells of roughly the same

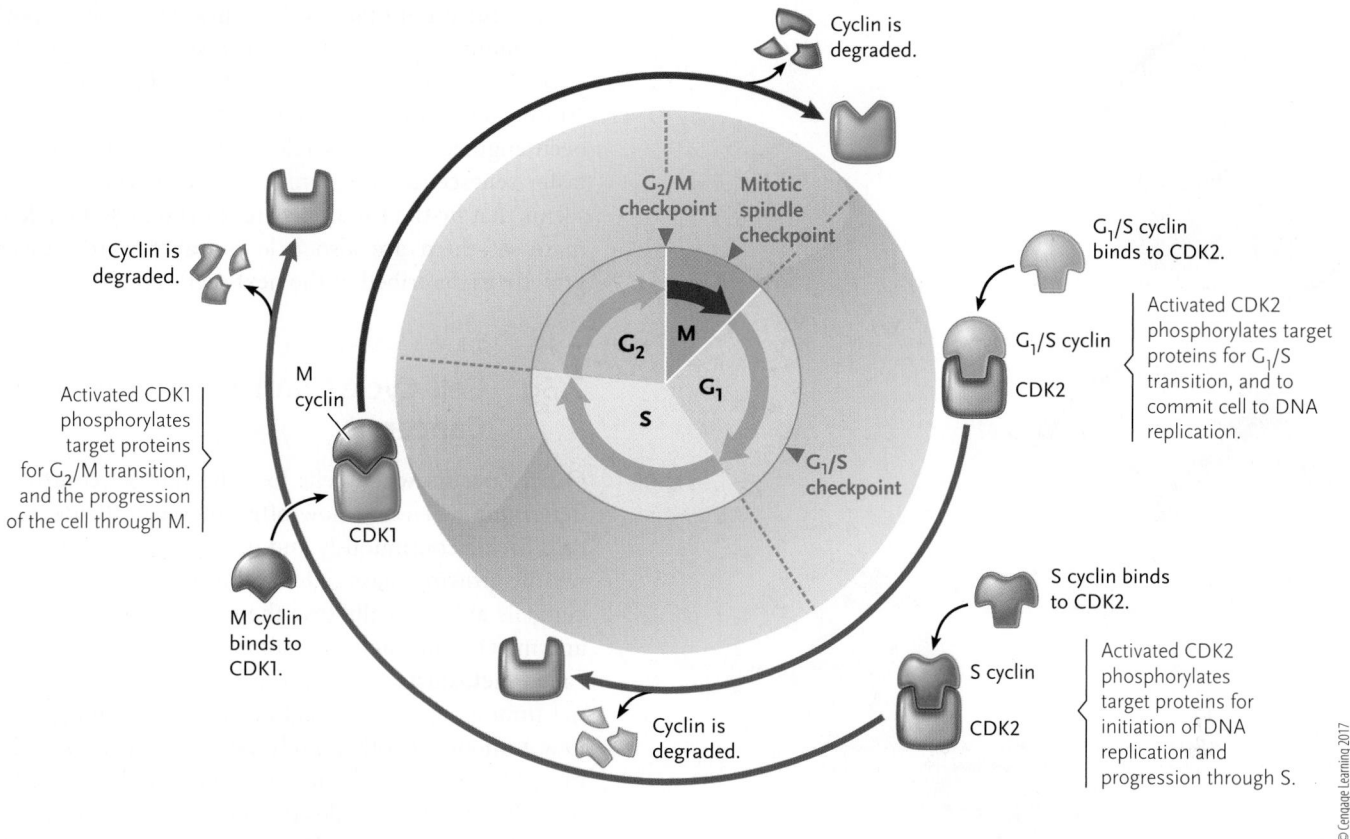

**FIGURE 7.20  Regulation of the mitotic cell cycle by internal controls.** Three key checkpoints for the G1/S transition, for the G2/M transition, and for the attachment of chromosomes to the mitotic spindle monitor cell-cycle events to prevent crucial phases of the cell cycle from starting until previous phases are completed correctly. Complexes of cyclins and cyclin-dependent kinases (CDKs) regulate the progression of the cell through the cell cycle. The three cyclin–CDKs present in all eukaryotes are shown. The CDKs are present throughout the cell cycle, but they are active only when complexed with a cyclin (shown by the broad arrows in the figure). Each cyclin is synthesized and degraded in a regulated way so that it is present only for a particular phase of the cell cycle. During that phase, the CDK to which it is bound phosphorylates and thereby regulates the activity of target proteins in the cell that are involved in initiating or regulating key events of the cell cycle.

size, shape, and function whose genomes are essentially identical. However, asymmetric cell division (producing daughter cells that are decidedly different in some characteristic or other) is an essential feature of multicellular organisms, particularly during growth and development. One of the most striking examples of asymmetric cell division is found in the populations of stem cells present in plant meristems and various animal tissues (**Figure 7.21**).

Asymmetric cell division of stem cells provides new cells for growth and maintenance while at the same time maintaining the pool of stem cells. Stem cell division is asymmetric in that the two daughter cells each have a different fate. One daughter cell remains a stem cell and therefore contributes to a pool of self-renewing relatively undifferentiated cells that are capable of multiple cell divisions. The other daughter cell, called a *progenitor cell*, divides a limited number of times while undergoing subsequent differentiation into a specialized cell type needed for growth.

This asymmetry in cell fate arises from the ability of stem cells to specify the location of certain cytoplasmic components during cell division. Although mitosis divides the DNA and distributes cytoplasmic organelles relatively equally to each daughter cell, specific regulatory proteins and mRNAs (e.g., cyclins and transcription factors) are localized at only one pole or the other in the dividing cell. Therefore, the two resulting daughter cells each receive a different array of regulatory proteins that will, in turn, influence gene expression toward different cell fates.

Regulation of asymmetric division ensures the important balance between maintaining the stem cell pool and producing specialized somatic tissue. The local area where stem cells are dividing is called a *niche*. Signalling proteins produced by cells surrounding the niche maintain external regulation of stem cell division. Loss of this regulation is associated with cancer in brain and other tissues.

## 7.5f  Most Cells in a Multicellular Body Cannot Divide Indefinitely

In 1961, Leonard Hayflick and Paul Moorhead reported that normal human skin cells eventually stopped dividing when

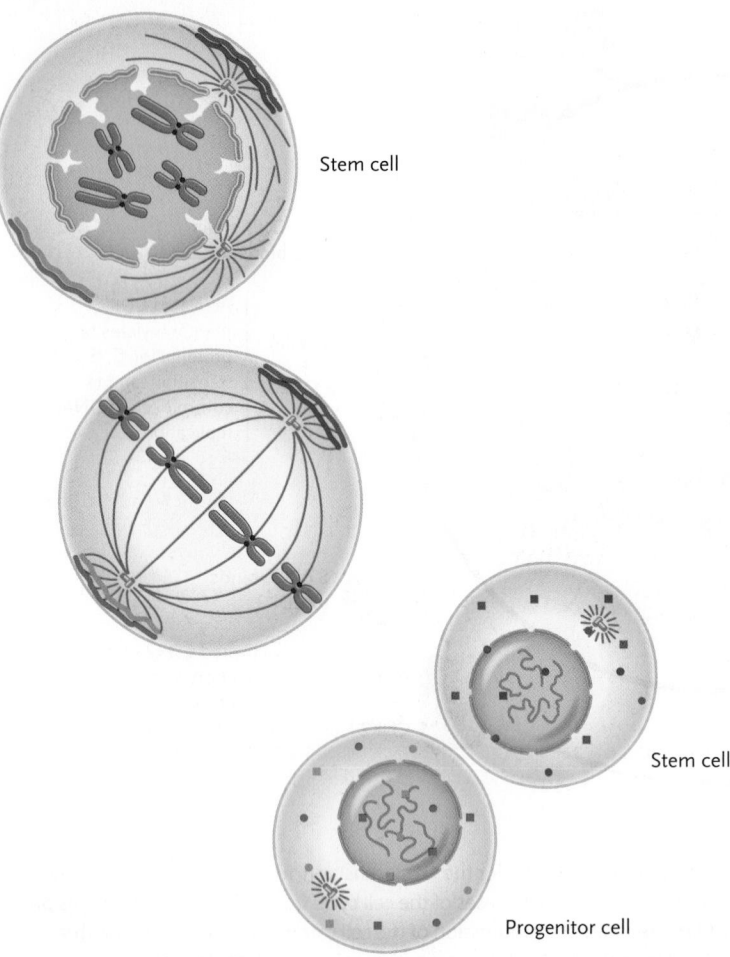

Stem cell

Stem cell

Progenitor cell

**FIGURE 7.21 Asymmetric fate of dividing stem cells.** The localization of different gene regulatory proteins and mRNA at the two poles during early mitosis anchors the mitotic spindle and ensures that the two daughter cells inherit a different array of regulatory elements. One cell remains a stem cell; the other becomes a differentiating progenitor cell.

grown in artificial culture. This loss of proliferative ability over time is called **cellular senescence**, and scientists have been searching for the *Hayflick factors* that are responsible for it. We consider two candidates: DNA damage and telomere shortening.

The progressive accumulation of damage to a cell's DNA sequence, or its chromosome structure, or even the genes coding for the enzyme machinery needed to repair such damage, is perhaps the most intuitive Hayflick factor. One would expect "older" cells to have diminished function if they have suffered mutations in genes controlling critical activities.

Telomeres are repetitive DNA sequences that are added to the ends of chromosomes by the enzyme telomerase. Since DNA replication machinery is unable to replicate the entire ends of linear chromosomes, telomere sequence is lost at each round of replication (see Chapter 11, Figure 11.20). Once telomeres diminish to a certain minimum length, cells stop dividing (senesce) and may die.

You might wonder why we do not just take a pill to stimulate our telomerase, rejuvenate our cells, and extend our life span. It turns out that cellular senescence is an important antitumour mechanism. Some researchers have stimulated the telomerase of cultured cells: they become "immortal" and divide out of control. Mice that have been engineered to lack telomerase, and therefore suffer faster senescence, are significantly *resistant* to cancer. It seems that by the time cells are short on telomere length, many of them are also a long way toward cancerous growth, as described in the next section.

## 7.5g Cell-Cycle Controls Are Lost in Cancer

Cancer occurs when cells lose the normal controls that determine when and how often they will divide. Cancer cells divide continuously and uncontrollably, producing a rapidly growing mass called a *tumour* (**Figure 7.22**). Cancer cells also typically lose their adhesions to other cells and may become actively mobile. As a result, in a process called **metastasis**, they tend to break loose from an original tumour, spread throughout the body, and grow into new tumours in other body regions. Metastasis is promoted by changes that defeat contact inhibition and alter the cell surface molecules that link cells together.

Growing tumours damage surrounding normal tissues by compressing them and interfering with blood supply and nerve function. Tumours may also break through barriers such as the outer skin, internal cell layers, or the gut wall. The breakthroughs cause bleeding, open the body to infection by microorganisms, and destroy the separation of body compartments necessary

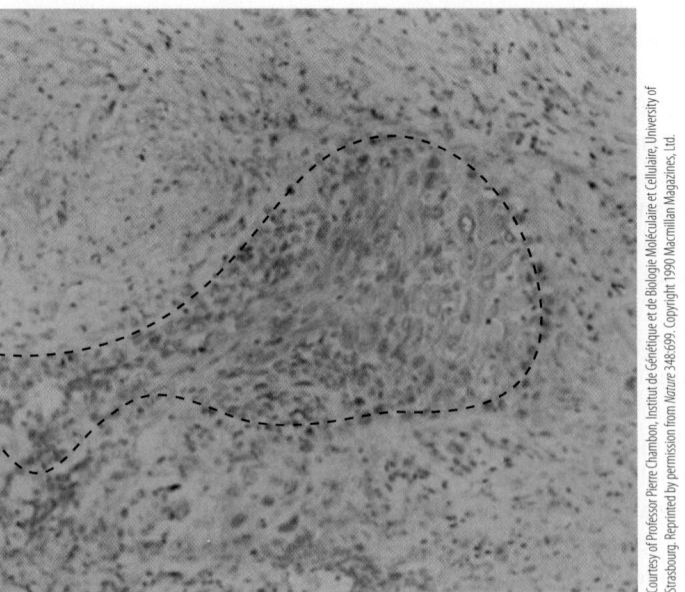

Courtesy of Professor Pierre Chambon, Institut de Génétique et de Biologie Moléculaire et Cellulaire, University of Strasbourg. Reprinted by permission from *Nature* 348:699. Copyright 1990 Macmillan Magazines, Ltd.

**FIGURE 7.22 A mass of tumour cells (dashed line) embedded in normal tissue.** As is typical, the tumour cells appear to be more densely packed because they have less cytoplasmic volume than normal cells. (Original magnification × 270.)

for normal function. Both compression and breakthroughs can cause pain that, in advanced cases, may become extreme. As tumours increase in mass, the actively growing and dividing cancer cells may deprive normal cells of their required nutrients, leading to generally impaired body functions, muscular weakness, fatigue, and weight loss.

Cancer cells have typically accumulated mutations in a variety of genes. Many of these genes code for components of the cyclin–CDK system that regulates cell division; others encode proteins that regulate gene expression, form cell surface receptors, or make up elements of the signalling pathways controlled by the receptors. When mutated, the genes, called **oncogenes,** encode altered versions of these products, which then promote uncontrolled growth or metastasis.

For example, a mutation in a gene that codes for a surface receptor might result in a protein that is constantly active, even without binding the intended extracellular signal molecule. As a result, the internal reaction pathways triggered by the receptor, which induce cell division, are continually stimulated. Another mutation, this time in a cyclin gene, could result in increased cyclin–CDK binding that triggers DNA replication and the rest of the cell cycle. Cancer, oncogenes, and the alterations that convert normal genes to oncogenes are discussed in further detail in Chapter 13.

## 7.5h  Some Cells Are Programmed to Die

Although normal development of multicellular organisms creates many tens to thousands of millions of cells, not all of them are needed. Development is actually a highly regulated balance between cell division and cell death. Programmed cell death, called **apoptosis**, is a very ancient mechanism common to all multicellular eukaryotes in which normal gene expression in a cell can lead to its own death.

The nematode *Caenorhabditis elegans* is one useful model organism to study this signalling because all adult animals have exactly the same number of cells. In addition, the fate of each of these cells, from the zygote to the adult, can be tracked with a light microscope. Detailed studies of the 1090 cells that are generated to form an adult reveal that 131 of them not only stop dividing, they stop living.

The apoptosis machinery in *C. elegans* is available in all of its cells, waiting in an inactive state for the right trigger. The main "executioner" enzyme is one of a family of normally inactive proteases called **caspases**. Once activated, caspases activate other enzymes in a cascade of destruction that results in nuclear DNA degradation and disrupted mitochondrial function. The corpses of dead cells are engulfed and eaten by neighbouring cells. The 2002 Nobel Prize in Physiology or Medicine was awarded jointly to Sydney Brenner, Robert Horvitz, and John Sulston for their discoveries concerning "genetic regulation of organ development and programmed cell death" in *C. elegans*. The Model Research Organisms section of *The Purple Pages* describes *C. elegans* and its role in research in more detail.

Removing cells that are surplus for development is one function of apoptosis, but why are other cells programmed to die? We hope you will agree that it would be beneficial for an organism to invoke apoptosis in cells suffering severe DNA damage, viral infection, or mutations leading to uncontrolled division. Sometimes perfectly normal and healthy cells die by apoptosis. For instance, the cells that make up xylem elements in the vascular tissue of woody plants actually function as "skeletons." They must die to fulfill their function as hollow, water-conducting pipes as described further in Chapter 33. Your fingers became separate digits due to apoptosis in the paddle-shaped hand you had when you were an embryo.

The overview of the cell cycle and its regulation presented in this chapter only hints at the complexity of cell growth and division among the wildly diverse life forms on Earth. The likelihood of any given cell dividing is determined by weighing a variety of internal signals in the context of external cues from the environment. If a cell is destined to divide, then the problem of accurately replicating and partitioning its DNA requires a highly regulated, intricately interrelated series of mechanisms involving nuclear replication machinery, a cytoplasmic cytoskeleton, as well as myriad cell-cycle regulatory proteins. Male Australian Jack Jumper ants (*Myrmecia pilosula*) have only one chromosome to deal with; think of the challenge faced by the fern *Ophioglossum pycnostichum*, which has 1260 chromosomes in each cell!

This chapter looked at the mechanisms underlying cell division. Whether the purpose is to grow a multicellular body, or repair a wound, or create a massive algal bloom, cell division creates daughter cells with essentially the same DNA as the parent cell. However, the following chapter introduces meiosis, a kind of cell division that evolved from mitosis to create diverse specialized cells with only half the DNA of parent cells.

## STUDY BREAK QUESTIONS

1. Explain how the *activity* of CDKs can rise and fall with each turn of the cell cycle, whereas the *concentration* of these enzymes remains constant.
2. What observation do Hayflick factors explain?
3. What is metastasis?

All cells arise from division of previous cells through the action of three elegantly interrelated systems: (i) a master system of molecular checkpoints regulates progression through the cell cycle, (ii) DNA synthesis replicates the cellular genome, and (iii) the structural web of interconnected cables and motors of the cytoskeleton separates DNA copies into daughter cells.

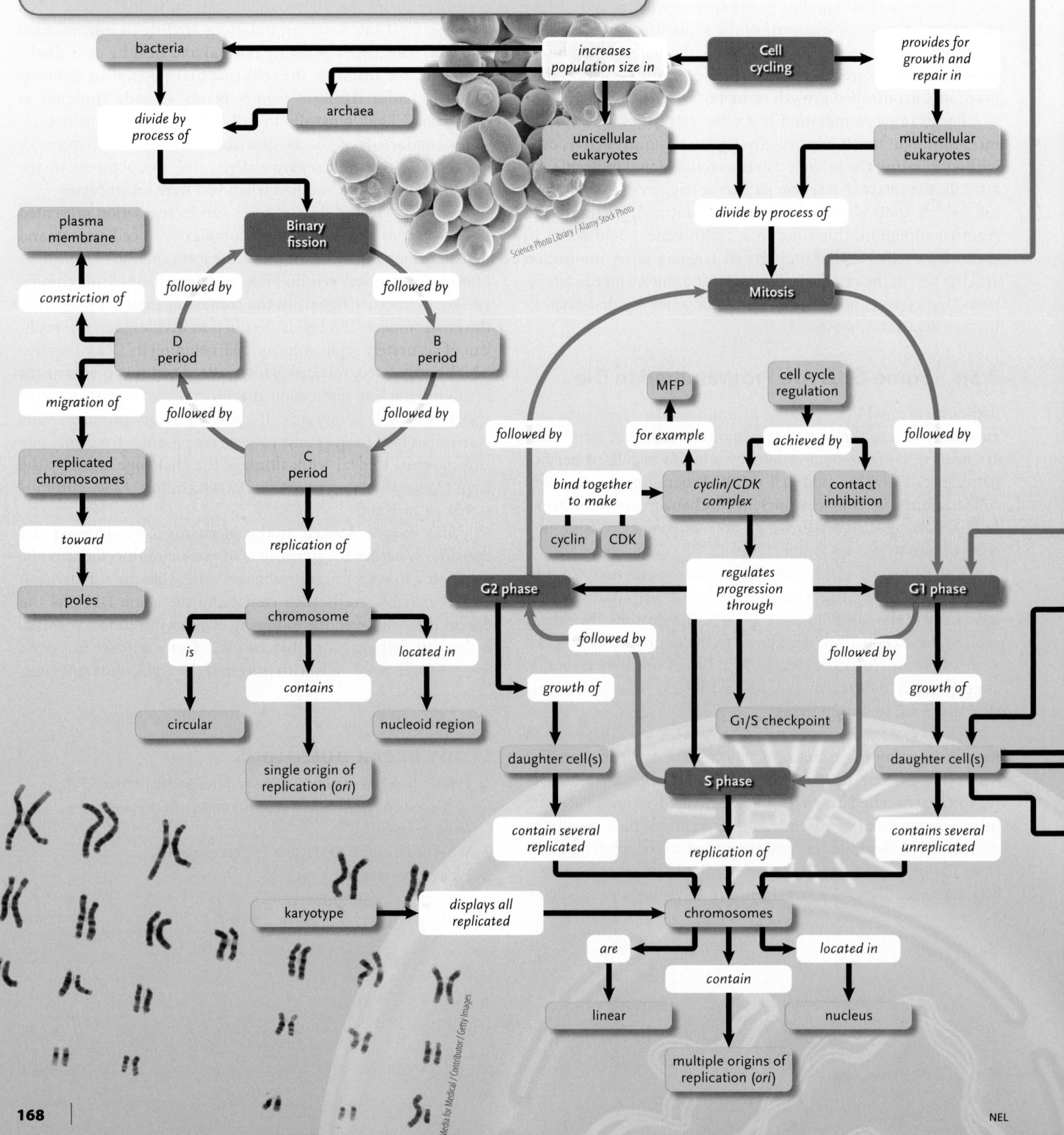

Science Photo Library / Alamy Stock Photo

Media for Medical / Contributor / Getty Images

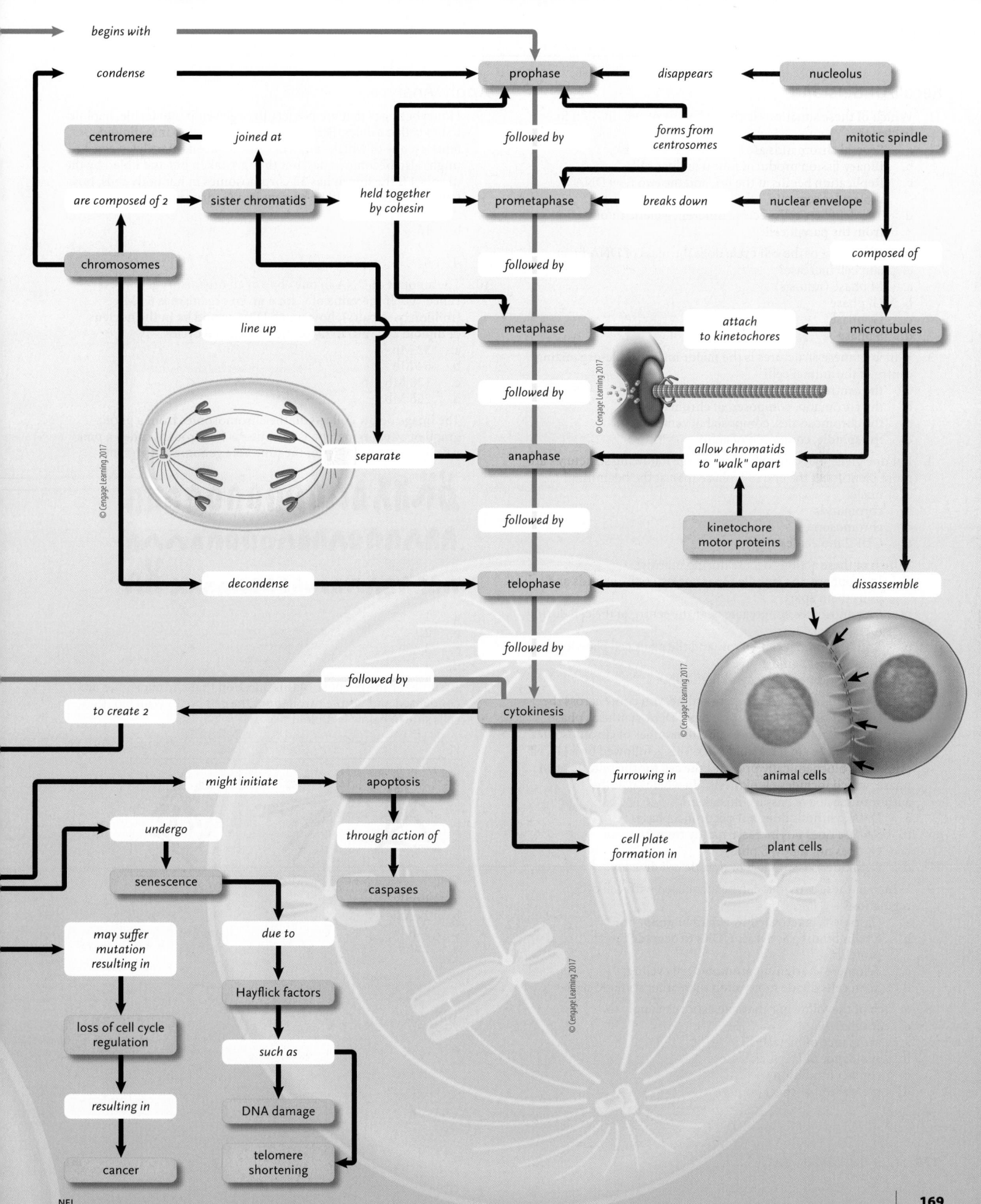

begins with

condense → prophase ← disappears ← nucleolus

centromere ← joined at

forms from centrosomes ← mitotic spindle

are composed of 2 → sister chromatids → held together by cohesin → prometaphase ← breaks down ← nuclear envelope

followed by

chromosomes

composed of

line up → metaphase ← attach to kinetochores ← microtubules

followed by

separate → anaphase ← allow chromatids to "walk" apart

kinetochore motor proteins

followed by

decondense → telophase ← dissassemble

followed by

followed by

to create 2 ← cytokinesis

might initiate → apoptosis

furrowing in → animal cells

undergo

through action of

cell plate formation in → plant cells

senescence

caspases

may suffer mutation resulting in

due to

loss of cell cycle regulation

Hayflick factors

resulting in

such as

cancer

DNA damage

telomere shortening

# SELF-TEST QUESTIONS

## Recall/Understand

1. Which of these situations is characteristic of cell division in bacteria?
   a. Several chromatids are separated at anaphase.
   b. Binary fission produces four daughter cells.
   c. Replication begins at the *ori*, and the two new DNA molecules separate.
   d. The daughter cells receive different genetic information from the parent cell.

2. In which phase of the cell cycle does the mass of DNA in an elephant cell increase?
   a. M phase (mitosis)
   b. $G_1$ phase
   c. $G_2$ phase
   d. S phase

3. Which of these structures is the major microtubule-organizing centre of the animal cell?
   a. the centrosome, composed of centrioles
   b. the chromatin, composed of chromatids
   c. the chromosomes, composed of centromeres
   d. the spindle, composed of actin

4. For one given oak tree cell, which of the following structures are more plentiful at the end of S phase than at the beginning?
   a. nuclei
   b. chromatids
   c. chromosomes
   d. CDK2 molecules

5. Which of these actions occurs during mitosis?
   a. In prophase, the spindle separates sister chromatids and pulls them apart.
   b. Chromosomes congregate near the centre of the cell during metaphase.
   c. Both the animal cell furrow and the plant cell plate form at their former spindle poles.
   d. Chromosomes move cytokinetically.

6. While researching an assignment online, you come across the following passage: "The cell cycle has a DNA synthesis phase (S phase) that doubles the normal full number of chromosomes from diploid ($2n$) to tetraploid ($4n$). This is followed by a $G_2$ cell phase that biochemically prepares the cell for the mitotic or M phase, which includes cytokinesis." In what way is the author of the above passage mistaken?
   a. DNA synthesis does not occur in S phase.
   b. S phase does not increase ploidy from $2n$ to $4n$.
   c. $G_2$ does not follow S phase.
   d. Cytokinesis is not part of mitotic cell division.

7. Which of these activities can be associated with cell cycle regulation?
   a. Caspase is inactivated by cyclin binding.
   b. Cyclin binding activates CDKs to degrade target proteins.
   c. Telomere shortening promotes cell cycling.
   d. Stem cells divide more often than other somatic cells.

8. Which of the following characteristics can apply to cancer cells?
   a. avoidance of metastasis
   b. avoidance of Hayflick factors
   c. contact inhibition
   d. cycle arrest at checkpoints

## Apply/Analyze

9. Honeybee eggs that are not fertilized develop into fertile, haploid males called *drones*. Fertilized eggs can develop into diploid females, one of which might become a queen. (Fertilized eggs might also become males, but they are taken out and killed by the drones.) If the queen has 32 chromosomes in her body cells, how many chromatids will be present in a $G_2$ drone cell?
   a. 8
   b. 16
   c. 32
   d. 64

10. The amount of DNA in one copy of an organism's genome is called "C." If the value of C for a given organism is 64 Mb (million base pairs), how much DNA would be in the nucleus of diploid cell ($2n$) in $G_2$ of the mitotic cell cycle?
    a. 32 Mb
    b. 64 Mb
    c. 128 Mb
    d. 256 Mb

11. The image below collects all the chromosomes from a photograph of a cell in metaphase of mitosis for a rodent called a *pine vole*. How many copies of the pine vole genome are present?

    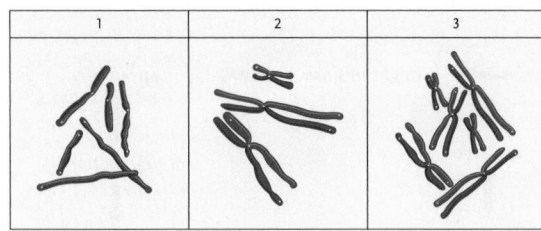

    a. 1
    b. 2
    c. 3
    d. 4

12. Assume for the purpose of this question that chromosomes are condensed and visible throughout the cell cycle. Which of the cells shown below is diploid?

    |   1   |   2   |   3   |
    |-------|-------|-------|

    a. 1 only
    b. 2 only
    c. 3 only
    d. 1 and 3

## Create/Evaluate

13. Imagine that you are in a job interview for a pharmaceutical company and are asked to suggest a good mechanism for an anti-cancer drug. Which of the following mechanisms would you suggest?
    a. decreased apoptosis
    b. decreased binding of cyclin to CDK
    c. increased CDK activity
    d. increased telomerase

14. A cell has 38 chromosomes. After mitosis and cell division, 1 daughter cell has 39 chromosomes and the other has 37. Suggest a hypothesis to explain what might have caused these abnormal chromosome numbers.

15. Many chemicals in the food we eat potentially have effects on cancer cells. Chocolate, for example, contains a number of flavonoid compounds, which act as natural antioxidants. Design an experiment to determine whether any of the flavonoids in chocolate inhibit the cell cycle of breast cancer cells growing in culture.

# Chapter Roadmap

## Genetic Recombination

The recombination of backbones from different DNA double helices is a powerful mechanism for the generation of genetic diversity in all domains of life.

### 8.1 Mechanism of Genetic Recombination

The mechanism of recombination involves enzymatic cutting, exchanging, and re-attaching of sugar phosphate backbones of two different DNA double helices. This can result in progeny cells with different collections of alleles than their parents.

### 8.2 Genetic Recombination in Bacteria

Bacteria recombine their chromosomes following any of several mechanisms that bring DNA from two different cells into close proximity.

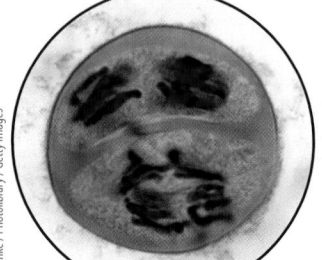

### 8.3 Genetic Recombination Occurs in Eukaryotes During Meiosis

Meiotic cell division is the central mechanism in sexual life cycles, reducing chromosome number and creating novel combinations of alleles that result in highly diverse zygotes following fertilization.

**To Chapter 9**

**To Chapter 10**

Ed Reschke / Photolibrary / Getty Images

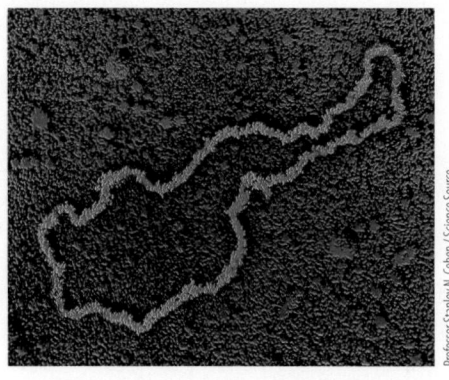

Professor Stanley N. Cohen / Science Source

**Mating octopuses**

# Genetic Recombination

**8**

**Why it matters...** Why do many plants and animals go to all the trouble of reproducing sexually? Imagine that a couple clearly shows mutual interest. First, he caresses her with one arm, then another, then another, and another, and another. She reciprocates. This interaction goes on for hours; a hug here, a squeeze there. At the climactic moment, the male reaches deftly under his mantle and removes a packet of sperm, which he inserts under the mantle of the female. For every one of his sperm that successfully performs its function, a fertilized egg can develop into a new octopus.

For the octopus, sex is an occasional event, preceded by a courtship ritual that involves intermingled tentacles. For another marine animal, the slipper limpet, sex is a lifelong group activity. Slipper limpets are relatives of snails. Like many other animals, a slipper limpet passes through a free-living immature stage before it becomes a sexually mature adult. When the time comes for an immature limpet to transform into an adult, it settles onto a rock or other firm surface. If the limpet settles by itself, it develops into a female. If instead it settles on top of a female, it develops into a male. If another slipper limpet settles down on that male, it too becomes a male. Adult slipper limpets almost always live in such piles, with the one on the bottom always being a female. All the male limpets continually contribute sperm that fertilize eggs shed by the female. If the one female dies, the surviving male at the bottom of the pile changes into a female and reproduction continues.

The life history of these octopuses and slipper limpets illustrates a tension in biology between sameness and difference. On the one hand, the growth and repair of their multicellular tissues depend on faithful replication of DNA during mitotic cell division, as described in Chapters 7 and 11. At the level of the organism, it is important that the individual cells in the body of a slipper limpet, for example, are genetically alike. However, on the other hand, at the level of the population, it is important that the individual limpets are genetically *different* from one another. If populations have genetic variability, they have the potential to evolve. Evolutionary forces can act on this variability such that certain variants leave more offspring than others. Over time, the relative proportion of different variants will change. This is evolution in action.

The ultimate source of genetic diversity is mutation of the DNA sequence, often resulting from errors during DNA replication. Since mutations are relatively rare, diversity is amplified through various mechanisms that shuffle existing mutations into novel combinations. This process of literally cutting and pasting DNA backbones into new combinations is called **genetic recombination** and is very widespread in nature. Genetic recombination allows "jumping genes" to move, inserts some viruses into a chromosome of their hosts, underlies the spread of antibiotic resistance among bacteria and archaea, and is at the heart of meiosis in eukaryotic organisms. Genetic recombination puts the "sexual" in sexual reproduction; without genetic recombination, reproduction is asexual, and offspring are simply identical clones of their parent. We begin this chapter with a look at the basic mechanism of DNA recombination.

## 8.1 Mechanism of Genetic Recombination

In its most general sense, recombination requires the following: two DNA double helices, a mechanism for bringing the DNA into close proximity, and a collection of enzymes to "cut," "exchange," and "paste" the DNA back together. While biologists who study genetic recombination have developed several models to precisely explain the process, **Figure 8.1** conveys the basic concept of genetic recombination without showing the specific molecular details.

The elegant double helix of DNA represented in Figure 8.1 is one of the most widely recognized molecular structures; you should be able to discern the "backbones" of the helix winding around the interior "steps" of paired bases. Each sugar–phosphate backbone is held together by strong covalent bonds, making each of the two strands of DNA a single molecule—the double helix being formed from two molecules. In the centre of the double helix, the bases pair with their partners through relatively weak hydrogen bonds. (If these ideas are new to you, see Chapter 11 and *The Purple Pages* for a more comprehensive look at DNA structure.) As you'll see later in this chapter, the hydrogen bonds can be broken to separate the

DNA molecules, forming templates to allow precise replication of genetic material for cell division.

Figure 8.1a shows two similar double helixes lying close together as the first step in recombination. Most of the recombination discussed in this chapter occurs between regions of DNA that are very similar, but not identical, in their sequences of bases. These regions, which may be as short as a few base pairs or as long as an entire chromosome, are called **homologous.** Homology allows different DNA molecules to line up and recombine precisely. Homologous regions of DNA are paired by using enzymes that separate hydrogen bonds of one double-helix and allow the bases to reassociate with complementary bases in a homologous (nonsister) chromatid. This also involves cutting the sugar–phosphate backbones of DNA molecules and then linking those of nonsister chromatids. Figure 8.1b shows the general mechanism of lining up homologous regions, and cutting and reattaching two DNA backbones. Figure 8.1c shows the result of cutting the remaining two DNA molecules. Although the actual recombination mechanism is somewhat more complicated than depicted here, the overall result is two recombined double helixes in which the original red DNA is now covalently bound to the blue DNA, and vice versa. In this chapter, we consider all the steps shown in Figure 8.1 to make

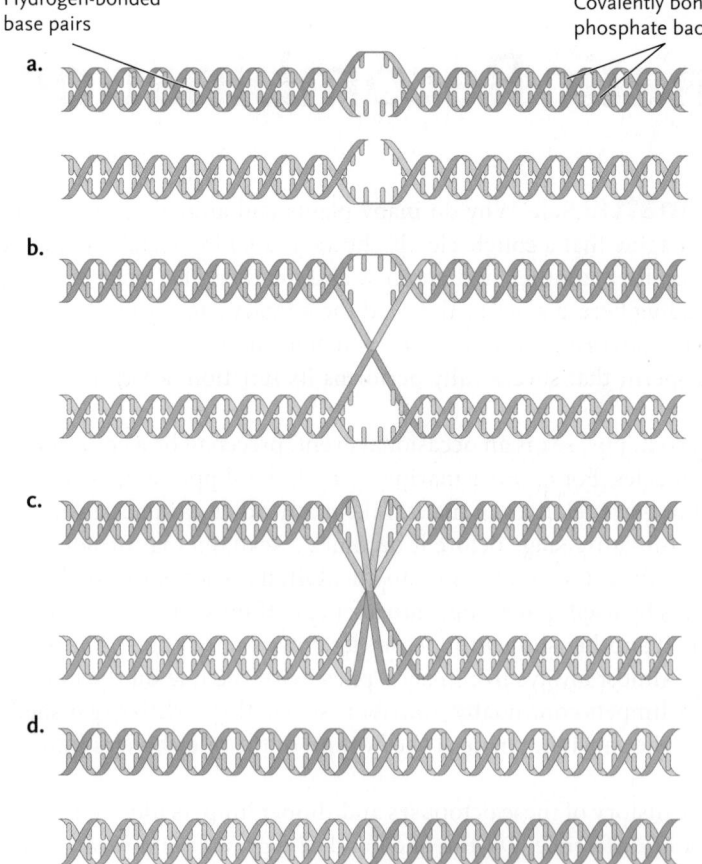

Hydrogen-bonded base pairs

Covalently bonded sugar–phosphate backbones

a.

b.

c.

d.

**FIGURE 8.1  A conceptual model of genetic recombination. (a)** Two molecules of DNA in close proximity have their backbones nicked by nuclease enzymes. **(b)** and **(c)** Recombination enzymes exchange the free backbone ends and reattach them. **(d)** The final result is two recombined chromosome arms.

up a single recombination event. This idea is worth restating: cutting and pasting *four* DNA backbones results in *one* recombination event.

As we move through examples of recombination in this chapter, from plasmids in bacteria to meiotic crossing-over in eukaryotes, the characteristics of the participating DNA molecules will be different, the enzymes will change, and the results of recombination will have quite different consequences for the organism in question. However, you can always return to Figure 8.1 to remind yourself of the basic underlying mechanism.

## STUDY BREAK QUESTION

1. In what way(s) are the two participating double helices changed as a result of genetic recombination?

## 8.2 Genetic Recombination in Bacteria

Historically, genetic recombination was first associated with meiosis in sexually reproducing eukaryotes. Genetic and microscopic research in the early decades of the twentieth century characterized recombination and culminated in the construction of the first genetic maps of chromosomes. However, by the middle of that century, improved techniques for studying the genetics of prokaryotic organisms (and their viruses) enabled researchers to look for evidence of genetic recombination, even though these organisms do not reproduce sexually by meiosis. The data showed that, for particular bacteria, there are mechanisms to bring DNA from different cells together, and that this DNA recombines to create offspring that are different from either parent cell. Bacteria clearly have a type of sex in their lives. It may be surprising for you to learn that, in some types of bacterial recombination, one of the participating cells is dead.

*Escherichia coli*, the most extensively studied prokaryotic organism, is named in honour of its discoverer, a Viennese pediatrician named Theodor Escherich, who isolated it from dirty diapers during an outbreak of diarrhea in 1885. Ready availability and ease of growth in the laboratory have made *E. coli* a workhorse of bacterial genetics that has helped lay the foundations for our understanding of the role of DNA as the genetic material, as well as the molecular structure, expression, and recombination of genes. (See more information about *E. coli* as a model research organism in *The Purple Pages*.)

### 8.2a Genetic Recombination Occurs in Bacteria

In 1946, two scientists at Yale University, Joshua Lederberg and Edward L. Tatum, set out to determine if genetic recombination occurs in bacteria, using *E. coli* as their experimental organism. In essence, they were testing whether bacteria have a kind of sexuality in their reproduction process. In order to understand Lederberg and Tatum's work, you first need to know how bacteria are grown in the laboratory.

*Escherichia coli* and many other bacteria can be grown in a **minimal medium** containing water, an organic carbon source such as glucose, and a selection of inorganic salts, including one, such as ammonium chloride, that provides nitrogen. The growth medium can be in liquid form or in the form of a gel made by adding agar to the liquid medium. (Agar is a polysaccharide material, indigestible by most bacteria, that is extracted from algae.) Since it is not practical to study a single bacterium for most experiments, researchers developed techniques for starting bacterial cultures from a single cell, thereby generating cultures with a large number of genetically identical cells. Cultures of this type are called **clones**. To start bacterial clones, the scientist spreads a drop of a bacterial culture over a sterile agar gel in a culture dish. The culture is diluted enough to ensure that cells will be widely separated on the agar surface. Each cell divides many times to produce a clump of identical cells called a *colony*. Cells can be removed from a colony and introduced into liquid media or spread on agar and grown in essentially any quantity.

Now, for Lederberg and Tatum to detect genetic recombination, they needed some sort of detectable differences that could be shown to occur in changing combinations. The difference that proved most useful was related to nutrition. Cells require various amino acids for synthesis of proteins. Strains that are able to synthesize the necessary amino acids are called **prototrophs**. Mutant strains that are unable to synthesize amino acids are called **auxotrophs**; they can grow only if the required amino acid is provided for them in the growth medium. A strain that cannot manufacture its own arginine is represented by the genetic shorthand *argA*⁻. In this shorthand, *argA* refers to one of the genes that govern a cell's ability to synthesize arginine from simple inorganic molecules. A given strain of bacteria might carry this gene in its normal form, *argA*⁺, or its mutant form, *argA*⁻. These alternative forms of the gene are called **alleles** and might differ by as little as one base pair in their respective DNA sequences. Prokaryotic cells typically have one circular chromosome that carries one particular allele for each of their genes.

Using mutagens such as X-rays or ultraviolet light, Lederberg and Tatum isolated two different strains of *E. coli* carrying distinctive combinations of alleles for various metabolic genes. (See **Figure 8.2** to understand how **replica plating** could isolate these auxotrophic strains.) One particular strain could grow only if the vitamin biotin and the amino acid methionine were added to the culture medium. A second mutant strain did not need biotin or methionine, but could grow only if the amino acids leucine and threonine were added along with the vitamin thiamine. These two multiple-mutant strains of *E. coli* were represented in genetic notation as follows:

Strain 1: bio⁻ met⁻ leu⁺ thr⁺ thi⁺

Strain 2: bio⁺ met⁺ leu⁻ thr⁻ thi⁻

FIGURE 8.2 **Research Method**

## Replica Plating

**Purpose:** Replica plating is used to identify different strains of bacteria with respect to their growth requirements in a heterogeneous mixture of strains.

**Protocol:**

1. Press sterile velveteen gently onto the master plate of solid growth medium with bacterial colonies on it. Some of each colony transfers to the velveteen in the same pattern as the colonies on the plate. In the example, a mixture of colonies of normal and auxotrophic strains is on a plate of complete medium.

2. Press the velveteen gently onto a sterile replica plate to transfer some of each strain. In the example, the replica plate contains minimal medium. Incubate to allow colonies to grow, and compare the pattern of colonies on the replica plate with that on the master plate.

**Interpreting the Results:** A colony present on the master plate but not on the replica plate indicates that the strain requires some substance missing from the minimal medium in order to grow. In other words, the strain is an auxotroph. In actual experiments, the compositions of the master plate and replica plate media are chosen to be appropriate for the goals of the experiment.

Based on J. Lederberg and E. M. Lederberg. 1952. Replica plating and indirect selection of bacterial mutants. *Journal of Bacteriology* 63:399–406.

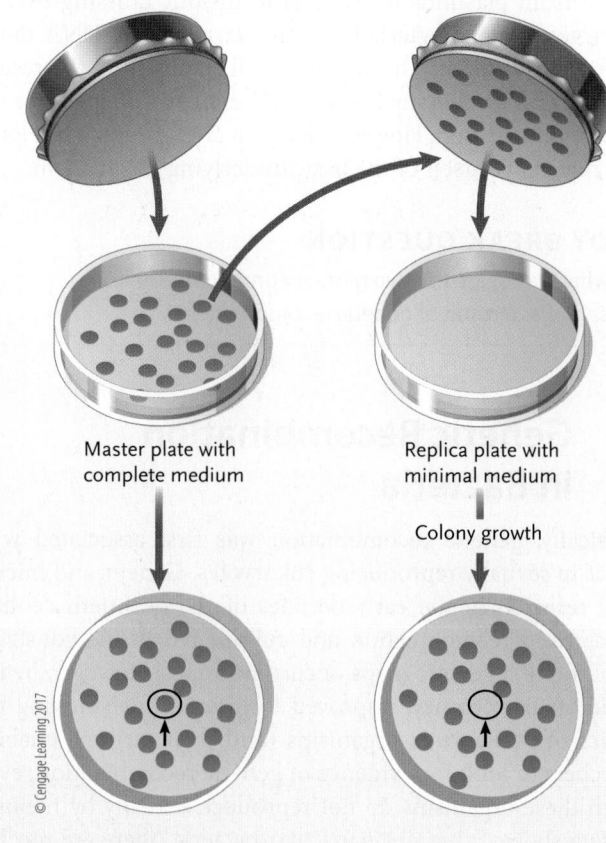

Master plate with complete medium

Replica plate with minimal medium

Colony growth

© Cengage Learning 2017

---

Lederberg and Tatum mixed about 100 million cells of the two mutant strains together and placed them on a minimal medium (**Figure 8.3**). Several hundred colonies grew, even though, individually, none of the original cells carried all the normal alleles needed for growth. You might be thinking, "They are mutants. Maybe some of the originally mutated alleles went back to normal." This possibility was easily discounted by plating large numbers of cells from each original strain onto minimal medium separately. If mutation were responsible for the initial results with mixed cultures, then colonies should have also appeared when strains were plated separately. There were none. Some form of recombination between the DNA molecules of the two parental types must have produced the necessary combination with normal alleles for each of the five genes:

$$bio^+ \; met^+ \; leu^+ \; thr^+ \; thi^+$$

## 8.2b Bacterial Conjugation Brings DNA of Two Cells into Close Proximity

How was DNA from two different bacterial cells able to recombine? We will see in Section 8.3 that genetic recombination in eukaryotes occurs in diploid cells by an exchange of segments between pairs of chromosomes. However, bacteria are haploid organisms: each cell typically has its own single, circular chromosome. So how do the chromosomes from two different strains come together? Although bacterial cells were first thought to bring their DNA together by fusing two cells together, it was later established that transfer of genetic information is unidirectional, from one donor cell to a recipient cell. Instead of fusing, bacterial cells *conjugate*. That is, cells contact each other by a long tubular structure called a *sex pilus*, which draws the bacteria together so they can form a cytoplasmic bridge (**Figure 8.4a and b**). During conjugation, a copy of part of the DNA of one cell moves through the cytoplasmic bridge into the other cell. Once DNA from one cell enters the other, genetic recombination can occur. Through this unidirectional transfer of a part of the chromosome, conjugation facilitates a kind of sexual reproduction in prokaryotic organisms.

**THE F PLASMID AND CONJUGATION** Conjugation is initiated by a bacterial cell that contains a small circle of DNA in addition to the main circular chromosomal DNA (**Figures 8.5 and 8.6**). Such small circles are called *plasmids*, and this particular one is

FIGURE 8.3    **Experimental Research**

## Genetic Recombination in Bacteria

**Question:** Does genetic recombination occur in bacteria?

**Experiment:** To answer the question, Lederberg and Tatum used two mutant strains of *E. coli*: Mutant strain 1's genotype was *bio– met– leu+ thr+ thi+*, where the "+" means a normal allele and the "–" means a mutant allele. This strain required biotin and methionine to grow. Mutant strain 2's genotype was *bio+ met+ leu– thr– thi–*; it required leucine, threonine, and thiamine to grow.

Lederberg and Tatum plated about 100 million cells of a mixture of the two mutant strains on minimal medium, which lacked any of the nutrients the strains needed for growth. As controls, they also plated large numbers of the two mutant strains individually on minimal medium.

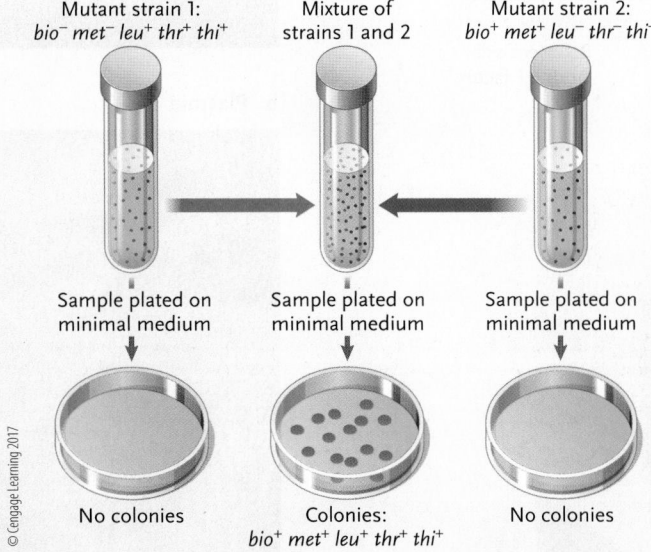

**Results:** No colonies grew on the control plates, meaning that the mutant alleles in the strains had not mutated back to normal alleles. However, for the mixture of mutant strain 1 and mutant strain 2, several hundred colonies grew on the minimal medium.

**Conclusion:** To grow on minimal medium, the bacteria must have been able to make biotin, methionine, leucine, threonine, and thiamine, meaning that they had the genotype *bio+ met+ leu+ thr+ thi+*. Lederberg and Tatum concluded that the colonies on the plate must have resulted from genetic recombination between mutant strains 1 and 2.

Based on J. Lederberg and E. Tatum. 1946. Gene recombination in Escherichia coli. Nature 158:558.

known as the *fertility plasmid*, or the *F plasmid*. Like all plasmids, the F plasmid carries several genes as well as a replication origin that permits a copy to be passed on to each daughter cell during the usual process of bacterial cell division. This is an example of vertical inheritance from one generation to the next, which you should be familiar with. However, during conjugation, the F plasmid can also be copied and passed directly from the donor cell to the recipient cell. This is an example of horizontal inheritance.

Donor cells are called **F⁺ cells** because they contain the F plasmid. They are able to mate with recipient cells but not with other donor cells. Recipient cells lack the F plasmid and therefore are called **F⁻ cells**. The F plasmid carries about 20 genes. Several of them encode proteins of the **sex pilus**, also called the **F pilus** (plural, *pili*; see Figures 8.4 and 8.6a, step 1).

During conjugation, the F plasmid replicates using a special type of DNA replication called *rolling circle*. To understand this mechanism, first picture a site, called the *origin of transfer*, on the F plasmid. Then imagine a break in just one strand of the double helix at this site. Now, imagine gently pulling the free end of the single strand of DNA away from the F plasmid, through the cytoplasmic bridge, and into the recipient cell. As the single strand is pulled, the remaining strand—still a circle—"rolls" like the spool on a tape dispenser. DNA synthesis fills in the complementary bases to ensure that the F plasmid is double stranded in both the donor and the recipient cells. When the entire F plasmid strand has transferred and replicated, it circularizes again (see Figure 8.6a, step 4). It is important to understand that, although the recipient cell becomes F⁺, no chromosomal DNA

## a. Attachment by sex pilus

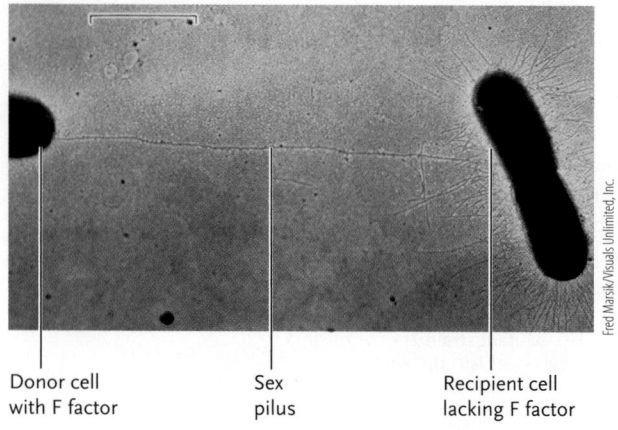

Donor cell
with F factor

Sex
pilus

Recipient cell
lacking F factor

*Fred Marsik/Visuals Unlimited, Inc.*

## b. Cytoplasmic bridge formed

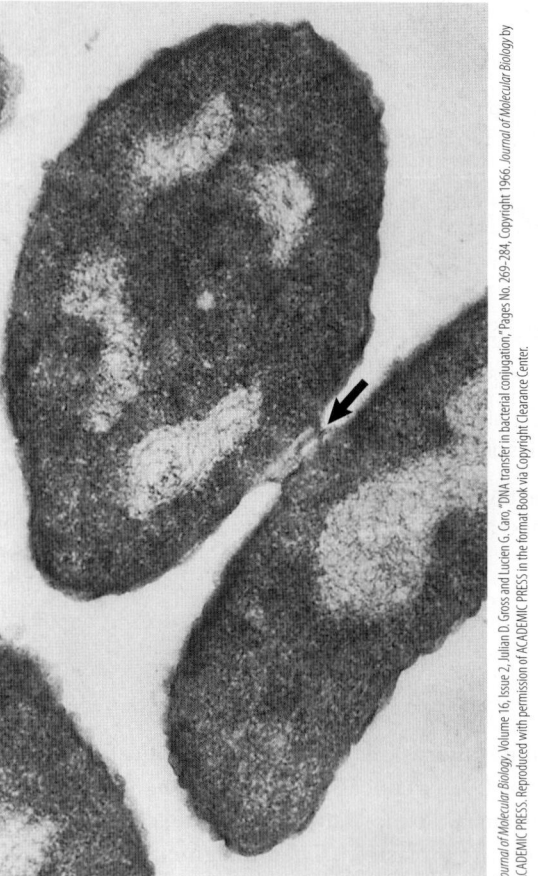

*Journal of Molecular Biology, Volume 16, Issue 2, Julian D. Gross and Lucien G. Caro, "DNA transfer in bacterial conjugation," Pages No. 269-284, Copyright 1966. Journal of Molecular Biology by ACADEMIC PRESS. Reproduced with permission of ACADEMIC PRESS in the format Book via Copyright Clearance Center.*

**FIGURE 8.4 Conjugating *E. coli* cells.** **(a)** Initial attachment of two cells by the sex pilus. **(b)** A cytoplasmic bridge (arrow) has formed between the cells, through which DNA moves from one cell to the other.

is transferred between cells in this process. *That is, no genetic recombination occurs between the DNA of two different cells in such a mating.*

So why are we including F plasmid conjugation in this chapter if it does not recombine DNA of different cells? The answer lies in the Hfr cells described in the next section.

## a. Bacterial DNA released from cell

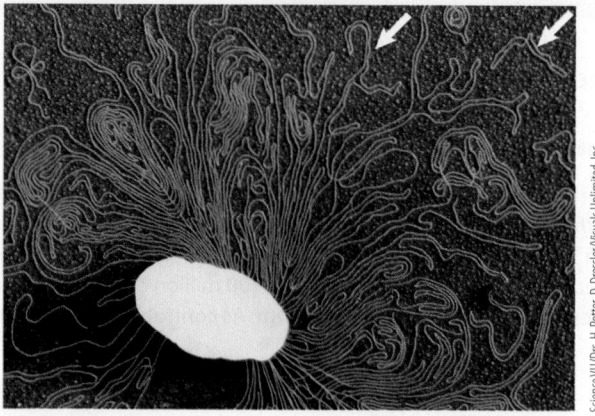

*Science VU/Drs. H. Potter–D. Dressler/Visuals Unlimited, Inc.*

## b. Plasmid

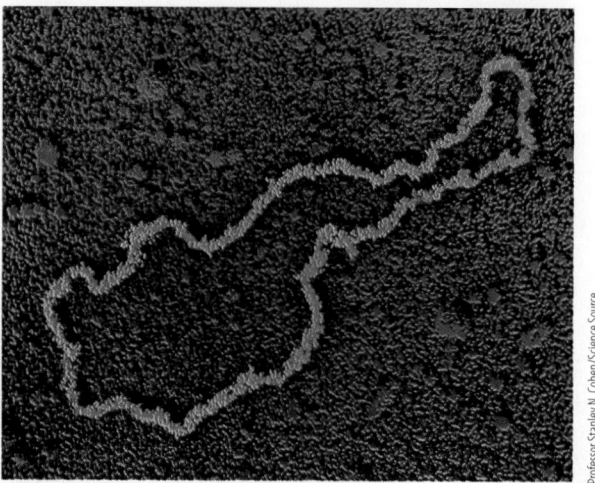

*Professor Stanley N. Cohen/Science Source*

**FIGURE 8.5 Electron micrographs of DNA released from a disrupted bacterial cell. (a)** Plasmids (arrows) near the mass of chromosomal DNA. **(b)** A single plasmid at higher magnification (colourized)

**HFR CELLS AND GENETIC RECOMBINATION** In some F$^+$ cells, the F plasmid comes into close proximity with the main chromosome and, lining up in a short region of homology, undergoes a recombination event. When two circular DNA molecules recombine (by the mechanism shown in Figure 8.1), they simply fuse into one larger circle. In this way, the F plasmid actually becomes a part of the main bacterial chromosome (see Figure 8.6b, step 2). These special donor cells are known as **Hfr cells** (*Hfr* = high-frequency recombination). It is important not to be confused at this point: although a recombination event integrated the F plasmid into the host chromosome, this is recombination within one cell, not between the chromosomes of different cells. Hfr cells are called "high-frequency recombination" because they can promote recombination of DNA between different cells by "exporting" copies of chromosomal genes to another cell, as described below.

When the F plasmid is integrated into the bacterial chromosome, its genes are still available for expression. Therefore, these Hfr cells make sex pili and can conjugate with an F$^-$ cell. Figure 8.6b, step 3, shows an Hfr × F$^-$ mating where the two cell

## a. Transfer of the F factor

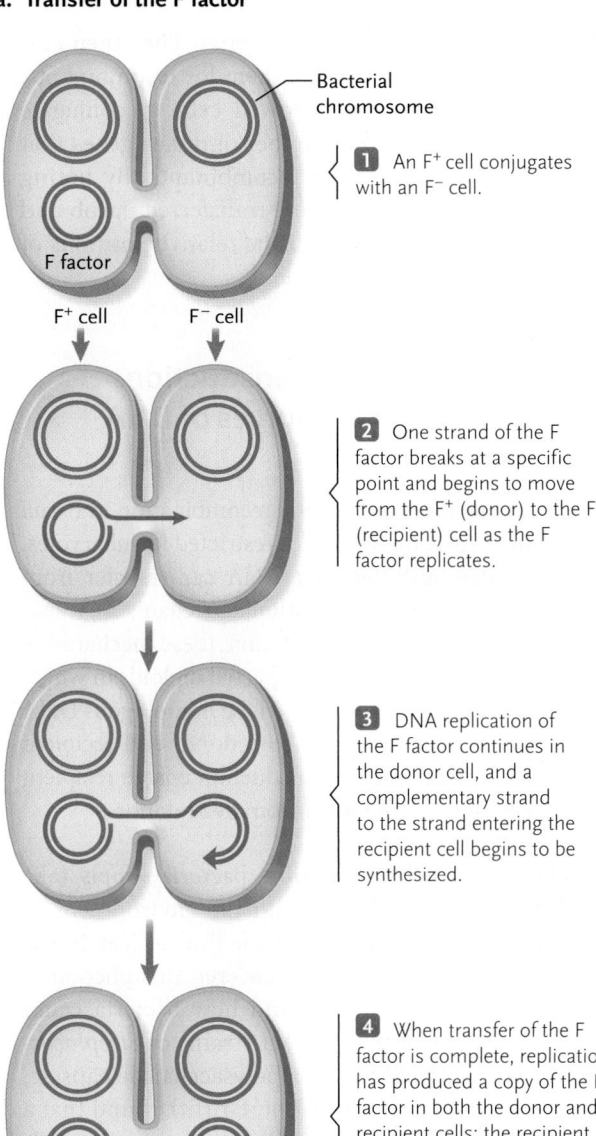

**Bacterial chromosome**

**F factor**

F⁺ cell    F⁻ cell

**1** An F⁺ cell conjugates with an F⁻ cell.

**2** One strand of the F factor breaks at a specific point and begins to move from the F⁺ (donor) to the F⁻ (recipient) cell as the F factor replicates.

**3** DNA replication of the F factor continues in the donor cell, and a complementary strand to the strand entering the recipient cell begins to be synthesized.

**4** When transfer of the F factor is complete, replication has produced a copy of the F factor in both the donor and recipient cells; the recipient has become an F⁺. No chromosomal DNA is transferred in this mating.

F⁺ cell    F⁺ cell

## b. Transfer of bacterial genes

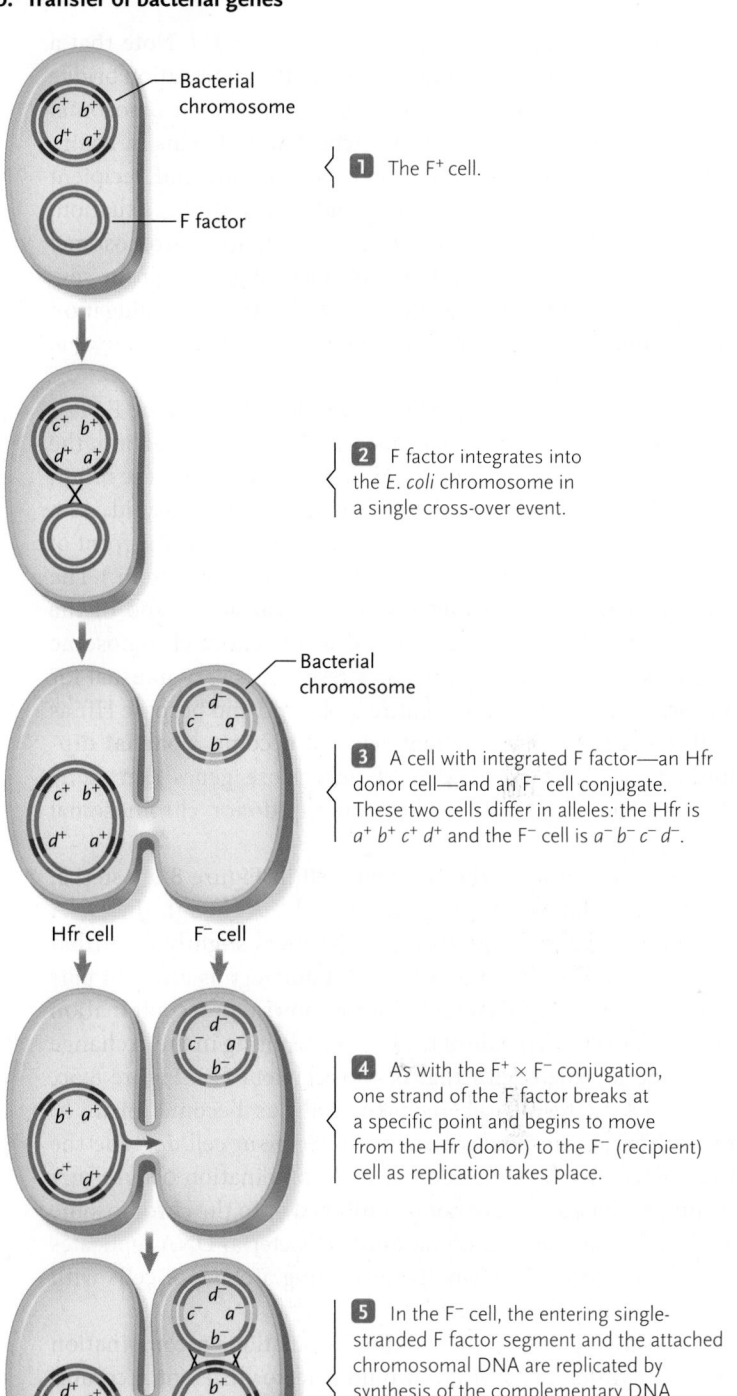

**Bacterial chromosome**

$c^+$ $b^+$
$d^+$ $a^+$

**F factor**

**1** The F⁺ cell.

**2** F factor integrates into the *E. coli* chromosome in a single cross-over event.

**Bacterial chromosome**

Hfr cell    F⁻ cell

**3** A cell with integrated F factor—an Hfr donor cell—and an F⁻ cell conjugate. These two cells differ in alleles: the Hfr is $a^+ b^+ c^+ d^+$ and the F⁻ cell is $a^- b^- c^- d^-$.

**4** As with the F⁺ × F⁻ conjugation, one strand of the F factor breaks at a specific point and begins to move from the Hfr (donor) to the F⁻ (recipient) cell as replication takes place.

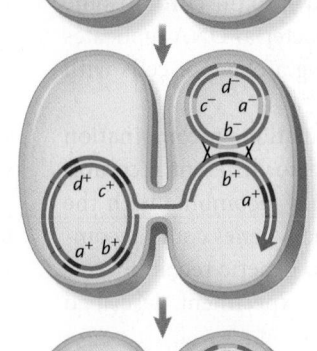

**5** In the F⁻ cell, the entering single-stranded F factor segment and the attached chromosomal DNA are replicated by synthesis of the complementary DNA strand. Recombination occurs between the entering donor chromosomal DNA and the recipient's chromosome.

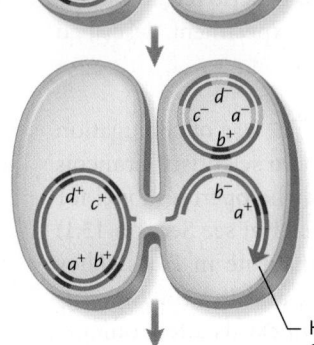

**6** Here, as a result of recombination, two cross-overs produce a $b^+$ recombinant. When the conjugating pair breaks apart, the linear piece of donor DNA is degraded and all descendants of the recipient will be $b^+$. The recipient remains F⁻ because not all the F factor has been transferred.

Hfr chromosome (part of F factor, followed by bacterial genes)

Conjugation bridge breaks.
F⁻ is a $b^+$ recombinant.

**FIGURE 8.6  Transfer of genetic material during conjugation between E. coli cells. (a)** Transfer of the F plasmid during conjugation between F⁺ and F⁻ cells. **(b)** Transfer of bacterial genes and the production of recombinants during conjugation between Hfr and F⁻ cells

types differ in alleles for the genes *a, b, c,* and *d*. Note that a segment of the F plasmid moves through the conjugation bridge into the recipient, bringing the single-stranded, chromosomal DNA behind it (see Figure 8.6b, steps 4 and 5). This is, again, rolling circle replication, in which both donor and recipient cells restore the DNA to double strandedness. In this situation, the circle that rolls is the entire Hfr donor chromosome! Although DNA transfer often continues long enough for several genes to enter the recipient cell, the fragile conjugation bridge soon breaks. It is rare for the entire donor chromosome to be transferred.

At this point, it is important to recall that, when the F plasmid transfers by itself, as described in the previous section, the recipient cells often become F⁺. However, in Hfr cells, the origin of transfer is near the middle of the integrated F plasmid. As a result, only half the F plasmid DNA is transferred at the front of the chromosomal DNA. (Think of the engine of a train.) The other half of the F plasmid (the dining car at the end of the train) can follow only after the rest of the entire chromosome (see Figure 8.6b, steps 4 to 6). As a result, it is very unusual for a recipient cell to obtain the entire F plasmid and become Hfr as well. Most likely, the recipient cell will become a **partial diploid:** it will have two copies of only those genes that came through the conjugation bridge on the donor chromosomal DNA segment.

For our example, the recipient cell in Figure 8.6b, step 5, has become, for the moment, $a^+ b^+/a^- b^-$. Although the DNA carrying + alleles for genes *a* and *b* differs slightly from that carrying − alleles, these regions are homologous and can pair for recombination. In fact, Figure 8.6 shows two recombination events, one on either side of the b gene, resulting in the exchange of the donor allele with that of the recipient (see Figure 8.6b, step 5). As a result, the recipient cell has become an $a^- b^+$ **recombinant**. Since enzymes in the recipient cell degrade the linear Hfr chromosome soon after recombination occurs, any incoming alleles that are not recombined onto the chromosome are lost. Following recombination, the bacterial DNA replicates and the cell divides normally, producing a clone of cells with the new combination of alleles.

In other pairs in the mating population, recombination events at different locations would lead to different recombinant recipients: perhaps the *a* gene could recombine with the homologous recipient gene, or both a and b genes could recombine to give $a^+ b^+$ recipients. The various genetic recombinants observed in the Lederberg and Tatum experiment described earlier were produced in this general way.

**MAPPING GENES BY CONJUGATION** The use of conjugation for genetic mapping was discovered by two scientists, François Jacob (the same scientist who proposed the operon model for the regulation of gene expression in bacteria; see Section 13.1) and Elie L. Wollman, at the Pasteur Institute in Paris. They began their experiments by mating Hfr and F- cells that differed in a number of alleles. At regular intervals after conjugation commenced, they removed some of the cells and agitated them in a blender to break apart mating pairs. They then cultured the separated cells and analyzed them for recombinants. They found that the longer they allowed cells to conjugate before separation, the greater the number of donor genes that entered the recipient and produced recombinants. By noting the order and time at which genes were transferred, Jacob and Wollman were able to map and assign the relative positions of several genes in the *E. coli* chromosome.

## 8.2c Transformation and Transduction Provide Additional Sources of DNA for Recombination

The discovery of conjugation and genetic recombination in *E. coli* showed that genetic recombination is not restricted to eukaryotes. Further discoveries demonstrated that DNA can transfer from one bacterial cell to another by two additional mechanisms, transformation and transduction. Like conjugation, these mechanisms transfer DNA in one direction and create partial diploids in which recombination can occur between alleles in the homologous DNA regions. Unlike conjugation, in which both donor and recipient cells are living, transformation and transduction enable recipient cells to recombine with DNA obtained from dead donors.

**TRANSFORMATION** In **transformation**, bacteria simply take up pieces of DNA that are released into the environment as other cells disintegrate. Fred Griffith, a medical officer in the British Ministry of Health, London, discovered this phenomenon in 1928 while trying to understand how bacteria cause pneumonia in mice. Cells of the virulent strains of *Streptococcus pneumoniae* were surrounded by a polysaccharide capsule, whereas the nonvirulent strains were not. Griffith found that a mixture of heat-killed virulent cells and living nonvirulent cells still caused pneumonia. One interpretation of this observation was that the living nonvirulent cells had been transformed to virulence by something released from the dead cells. In 1944, Oswald Avery and his colleagues at New York University found that the substance derived from the killed virulent cells, the substance capable of transforming nonvirulent bacteria to the virulent form, was DNA (discussed in Section 11.1).

Subsequently, geneticists established that, in the transformation of *Streptococcus*, the chromosomal DNA of the nonvirulent cells recombines with the linear DNA fragments taken up from disrupted virulent cells in much the same way as it does during conjugation. In this case, recombination introduces the normal allele for capsule formation into the DNA of the nonvirulent cells; expression of that normal allele generates a capsule around the cell and its descendants, making them virulent.

Only some species of bacteria can take up DNA from the surrounding medium by natural mechanisms, and *E. coli* is not one of them. Fortunately for molecular biologists, *E. coli* cells can be induced to take up DNA in the laboratory by a variety of artificial transformation techniques involving exposure to calcium ions and/or pulses of electric current. Artificial transformation is often used to insert recombinant DNA plasmids into *E. coli* cells as part of cloning or genetic engineering techniques. (DNA cloning and genetic engineering are discussed further in Chapter 14.)

**TRANSDUCTION** In **transduction**, DNA is transferred from donor to recipient cells inside the head of an infecting bacterial virus. The infection cycles of viruses that infect bacteria, called **bacteriophages** (or just *phages*), are described in Chapter 22. The basic details of phage infection are shown in **Figures 8.7** and **8.8**. In general, transduction begins when new phages

assemble within an infected bacterial cell; they sometimes incorporate fragments of the host cell DNA along with, or instead of, the viral DNA. After the host cell is killed, the new phages that are released may then attach to another cell and inject the bacterial DNA (and the viral DNA if it is present) into that recipient cell. The introduction of this DNA, as in conjugation and transformation, makes the recipient cell a partial diploid and allows recombination to take place. Recipients are not killed because they have received bacterial DNA rather than infective viral DNA. Lederberg and his graduate student, Norton Zinder, then at the University of Wisconsin at Madison, discovered transduction in 1952 in experiments with the

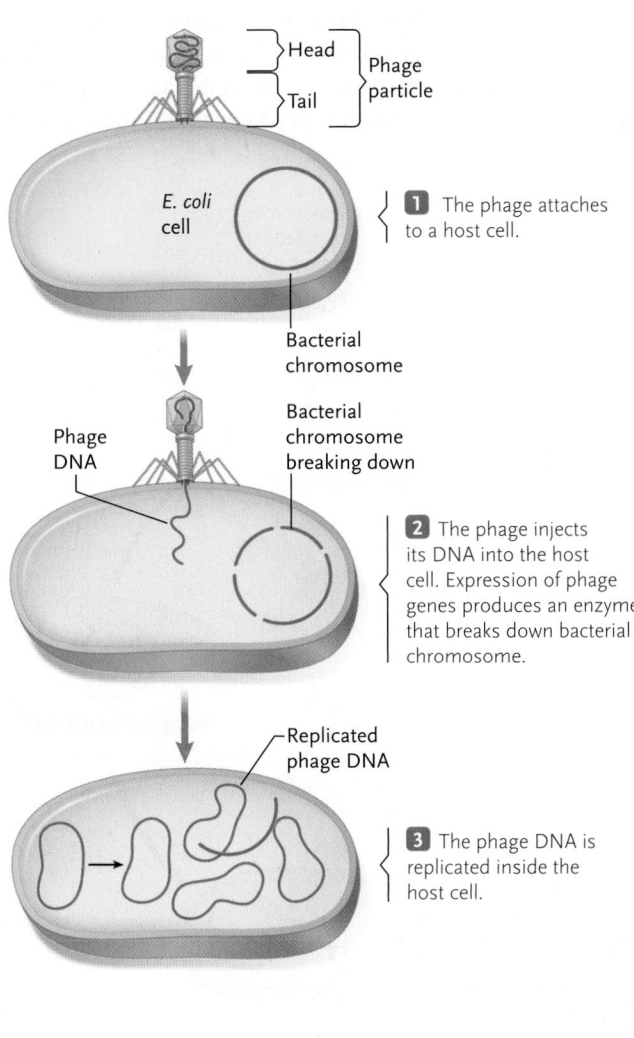

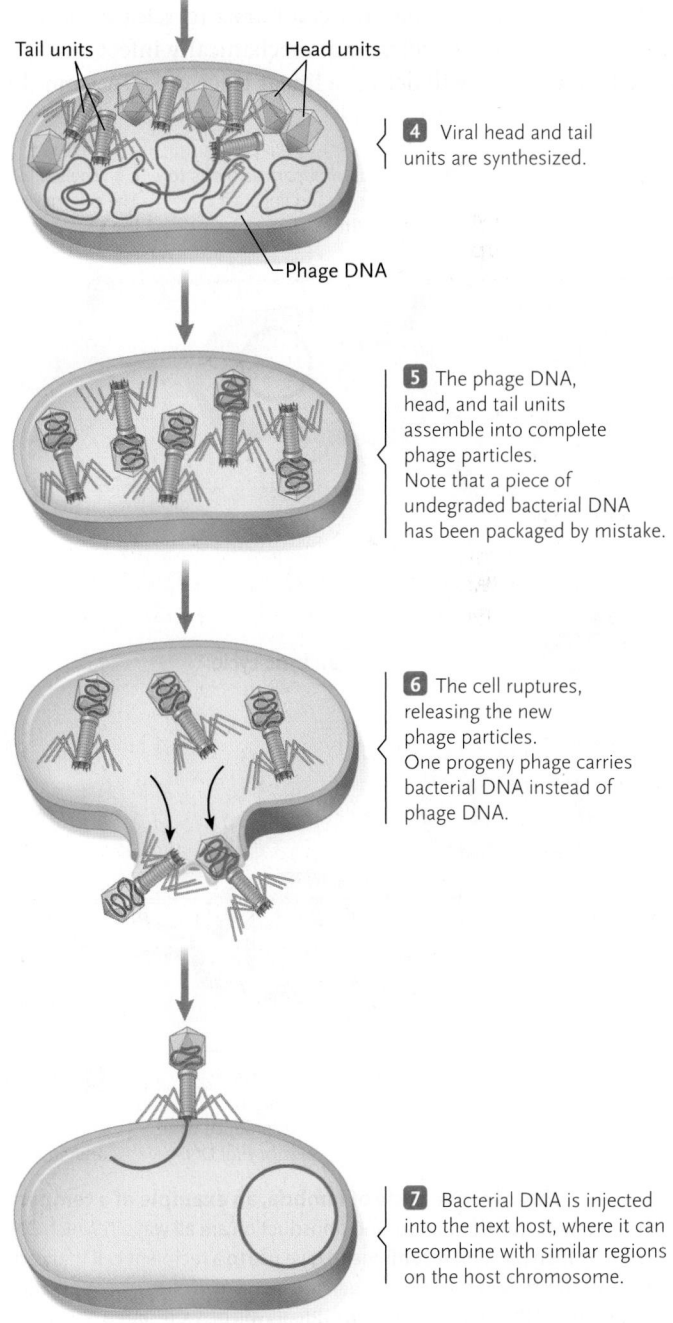

**FIGURE 8.7 Generalized transduction.** Movement of bacterial DNA from one cell to another inside the head of a lytic bacteriophage

bacterium *Salmonella typhimurium* and phage P22. Lederberg received a Nobel Prize in 1958 for his discovery of conjugation and transduction in bacteria.

There are two different types of transduction, generalized and specialized, arising from the different infection cycles of the phage involved. **Generalized transduction**, in which all donor genes are equally likely to be transferred, is associated with some virulent bacteriophages, those that kill their host cells during each cycle of infection (the **lytic cycle**). Notice in Figure 8.7 that, during infection by the virulent phage, the host bacterial chromosome is degraded to provide raw material for synthesis of new phage chromosomes. However, sometimes a fragment of host chromosome avoids degradation and is packed into the head of a new phage *by mistake*. This particular phage now contains a small random sample of bacterial genes *instead* of phage genes. When the host cell bursts to release the new phage, this *transducing phage* can mechanically infect a recipient cell. However, it will deliver a linear piece of DNA from the donor cell rather than an infectious phage chromosome. The newly infected (and incredibly lucky) recipient cell will survive; incoming DNA may then pair, and recombine, with homologous regions on the recipient chromosome.

One of the most extensively studied bacteriophages is phage lambda, which infects *E. coli*. Again, a mistake in the infection cycle can result in the transfer of bacterial genes from a donor to a recipient cell. However, in this case, a different type of mistake, in a different infection cycle, gives rise to a different type of transduction, **specialized transduction** (shown in **Figure 8.8**). Lambda is a **temperate bacteriophage**. That is, when lambda first infects a new host, it determines whether this cell is likely to be a robust and long-lived host. Is it starving? Is it suffering from DNA damage? If the host cell passes this molecular health checkup, then the lambda chromosome lines up with a small region of homology on the bacterial chromosome, and a phage-coded enzyme catalyzes a single recombination event. The phage is thus integrated into the host chromosomal DNA and,

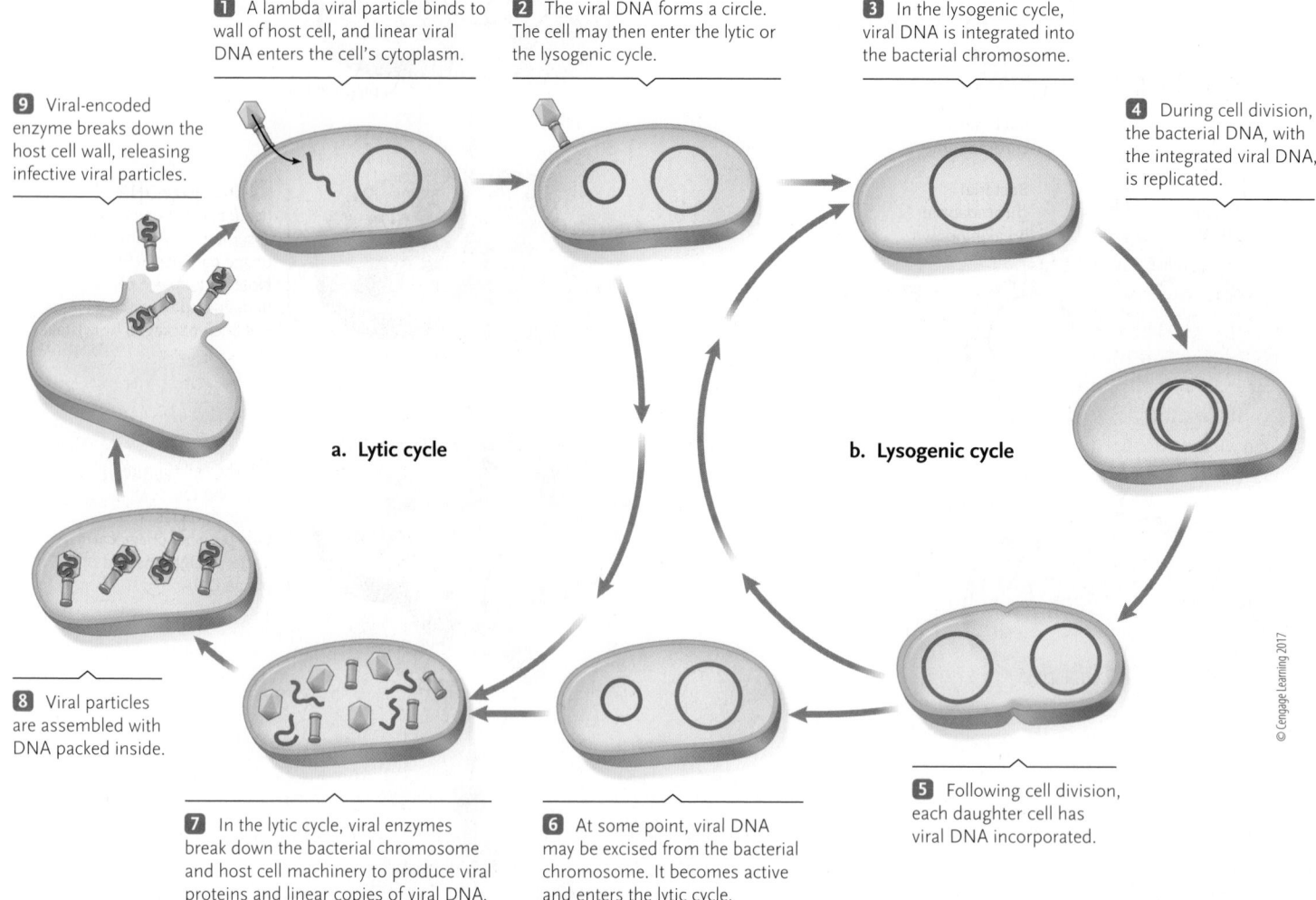

**1** A lambda viral particle binds to wall of host cell, and linear viral DNA enters the cell's cytoplasm.

**2** The viral DNA forms a circle. The cell may then enter the lytic or the lysogenic cycle.

**3** In the lysogenic cycle, viral DNA is integrated into the bacterial chromosome.

**4** During cell division, the bacterial DNA, with the integrated viral DNA, is replicated.

**9** Viral-encoded enzyme breaks down the host cell wall, releasing infective viral particles.

a. Lytic cycle

b. Lysogenic cycle

**5** Following cell division, each daughter cell has viral DNA incorporated.

**6** At some point, viral DNA may be excised from the bacterial chromosome. It becomes active and enters the lytic cycle.

**7** In the lytic cycle, viral enzymes break down the bacterial chromosome and host cell machinery to produce viral proteins and linear copies of viral DNA.

**8** Viral particles are assembled with DNA packed inside.

© Cengage Learning 2017

**FIGURE 8.8 The infective cycle of lambda, an example of a temperate phage, which can go through the lytic cycle** (a) **or the lysogenic cycle** (b)**.** Conjugation, transformation, and transduction are all ways in which DNA from two different bacterial cells is brought into close proximity. Homologous regions may then pair and recombine to give rise to a recipient cell that carries a different collection of alleles than it had previously. Overall, these processes create more diversity in the DNA sequence among members of a population than would arise by mutation and binary fission alone. More diversity leads to a higher likelihood that at least some individuals will be well-suited to survival in a changing environment.

in this state, is called a **prophage**. (Overall, this mechanism is very similar to the integration of the F plasmid discussed previously.) The prophage is then replicated and passed to daughter cells along with the rest of the bacterial chromosome as long as conditions remain favourable (the **lysogenic cycle** in Figure 8.8).

If, however, the host cell becomes inhospitable (perhaps as a result of ultraviolet-induced DNA damage), the prophage activates several genes, releases itself from the chromosome by a recombination event, and proceeds to manufacture new phages, which are released as the cell bursts as a result of lytic growth.

In specialized transduction, the "mistake" occurs when the prophage is excised from the chromosome. Sometimes this recombination event is imprecise: bacterial DNA is removed from the host chromosome and some prophage DNA is left behind. As a result, this bacterial DNA is packaged into new phages and carried to recipient cells. Since the transducing phage is defective, having left some of its genes behind in the host, it does not kill its new host. You should be able to see that, in the case of specialized transduction, only bacterial genes that are close to the integration site of the phage will likely be incorporated into the phage chromosome by the recombination mistake. Typically, only genes coding for galactose and biotin metabolism are transferred at high frequency by phage lambda.

These basic principles also apply to single-celled and multicellular eukaryotes. The next section of this chapter introduces genetic recombination in eukaryotes as it occurs within the overall process of meiosis. Notice how DNA from two different individuals is brought close together in the same cell following fertilization. Also watch for extensive similarity of the DNA sequence (homology) that now extends the full length of large linear chromosomes. Finally, notice the genetic recombination at the centre of this process, which generates novel chromosomes with new combinations of alleles.

### STUDY BREAK QUESTIONS

1. Contrast the characteristics of F⁻, F⁺, and Hfr cells.
2. Contrast specialized vs. generalized transduction.

# 8.3 Genetic Recombination Occurs in Eukaryotes during Meiosis

The octopuses and slipper limpets described at the opening of this chapter are engaged in forms of **sexual reproduction**, the production of offspring through the union of male and female **gametes**; for example, eggs and sperm cells in animals. Sexual reproduction depends on **meiosis**, a specialized process of cell division that recombines DNA sequences and produces cells with half the number of chromosomes present in the **somatic cells** (body cells) of a species. The derivation of the word *meiosis*

(*meioun* = to diminish) reflects this reduction. At **fertilization** the nuclei of an egg and a sperm cell fuse, producing a cell called the **zygote**, in which the diploid chromosome number is restored. Without the halving of chromosome number by the meiotic divisions, fertilization would double the number of chromosomes in each subsequent generation.

Both meiosis and fertilization also mix genetic information into new combinations; thus, none of the offspring of a mating pair are likely to be genetically identical to either their parents or their siblings. This genetic variability is the raw material for the process of evolution, as described in Chapter 16.

The biological foundations of sexual reproduction are the mixing of genetic information into new combinations and the halving of the chromosome number, both of which occur through meiosis, as well as the restoration of the original chromosome number by fertilization. Intermingled tentacles in octopuses, communal sex among limpets, clouds of pollen in the wind, and the courting and mating rituals of humans are nothing more or less than variations of the means for achieving fertilization, thus bringing DNA together for recombination.

## 8.3a Meiosis Occurs at Different Times in Different Organismal Life Cycles

Although the life cycle of nearly all eukaryotes alternates between a stage with one basic set of chromosomes (haploid) and a stage with two basic sets of chromosomes (diploid), **Figure 8.9** shows that evolution has produced wide variety in the relative timing of mitosis, meiosis, and fertilization among different species.

**CONCEPT FIX** The life cycles of plants, algae, and fungi may be unfamiliar to you and can be better understood by focusing your attention on the function of the cells that are the immediate products of meiosis. You might assume that gametes are made by meiosis. This assumption is true, but only for yourself and most other animals. In the life cycle of houseplants and some of the fungi living in the soil in the park, the haploid products of meiosis are spores, not gametes. These spores divide by mitosis to form multicellular bodies that, in turn, make gametes by mitosis. That idea is worth repeating: many organisms make gametes by mitosis. ⬡

**ANIMALS Animals** typically follow the pattern in which the diploid phase dominates the life cycle (see Figure 8.9a), the haploid phase is reduced, and meiosis is followed directly by gamete formation. (You could think of this as the "diploid life cycle" since the diploid stage is multicellular.) In male animals, each of the four nuclei produced by meiosis is enclosed in a separate cell by cytoplasmic divisions, and each of the four cells differentiates into a functional sperm cell. In female animals, only one of the four nuclei becomes functional as an egg cell nucleus. Eggs are usually defined as the less motile gamete, and are this way because they are loaded with cytoplasm. Unequal partitioning of cytoplasm during cell division gives one cell those

### a. Animal life cycles

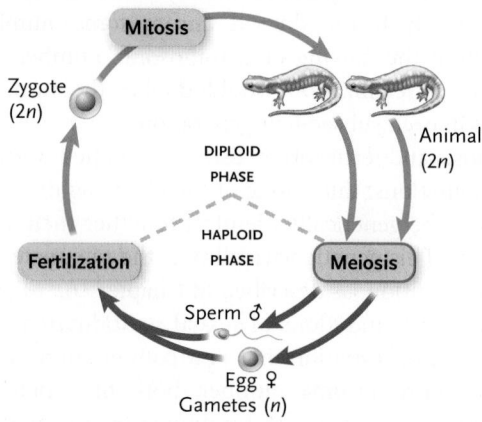

### b. All land plants and some fungi and algae (fern shown; relative length of the two phases varies widely in plants)

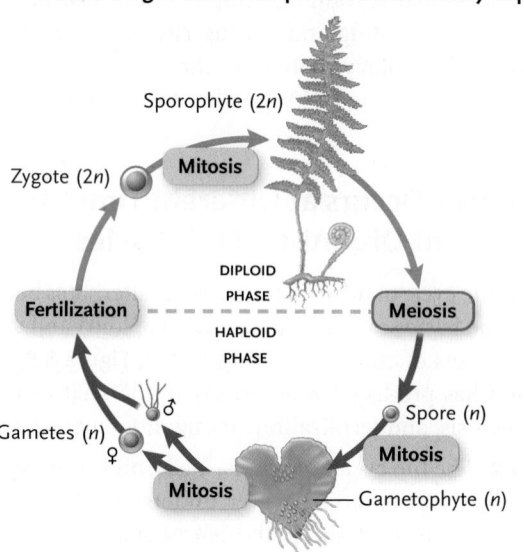

### c. Other fungi and algae

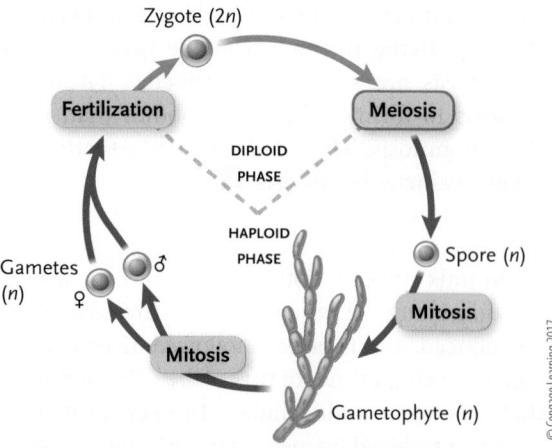

© Cengage Learning 2017

**FIGURE 8.9 Variations in the time and place of meiosis and mitosis in the life cycle of eukaryotes.** The diploid phase of the life cycles is shown in red; the haploid phase is shown in blue. *n* refers to the haploid number of chromosomes; 2*n* refers to the diploid number. **(a)** Meiosis typical of animal life cycles. Zygotes divide by mitosis. **(b)** Meiosis in most plants and some fungi and algae. Spores and zygotes divide by mitosis. **(c)** Meiosis in other fungi and algae. Spores divide by mitosis.

materials it needs to start a zygote off on its developmental journey.

Fertilization restores the diploid phase of the life cycle. Thus, animals are haploids only as sperm or eggs, and no mitotic divisions occur during the haploid phase of the life cycle.

**MOST PLANTS AND SOME FUNGI** Most plants and some algae and fungi follow the life cycle pattern shown in Figure 8.9b. These organisms alternate between haploid and diploid generations in which, depending on the organism, either generation may dominate the life cycle; mitotic divisions occur in both phases. (You could think of this as the "alternating-generations life cycle" since both the diploid and the haploid stages can be multicellular.) In these organisms, fertilization produces the diploid generation, in which the individuals are called *sporophytes* (*spora* = seed; *phyta* = plant). After the sporophytes grow to maturity by mitotic divisions, some of their cells undergo meiosis, producing haploid, genetically different, reproductive cells called *spores*. The spores are not gametes; they germinate and grow directly by mitotic divisions into a generation of haploid individuals called *gametophytes* (*gameta* = gamete). At maturity, the nuclei of some cells in gametophytes develop into egg or sperm nuclei. All the egg or sperm nuclei produced by a particular gametophyte are genetically identical because they arise through mitosis; meiosis does not occur in gametophytes. Fusion of a haploid egg and sperm nucleus produces a diploid zygote nucleus that divides by mitosis to produce the diploid sporophyte generation again.

**CONCEPT FIX** A trick to remember which phase is a gametophyte and which is a sporophyte is to remember what each phase produces: haploid gametophytes make gametes through mitosis; diploid sporophytes use meiosis to make spores. ⬣

In all plants (except bryophytes), the diploid sporophyte generation is the most visible part of the plant. The gametophyte generation is reduced to an almost microscopic stage that develops in the reproductive parts of the sporophytes—in flowering plants, in the structures of the flower. The female gametophyte remains in the flower; the male gametophyte is released from flowers as microscopic pollen grains. When pollen contacts a flower of the same species, it releases a haploid nucleus that fertilizes a haploid egg cell of a female gametophyte in the flower. The resulting cell, the zygote, reproduces by mitosis to form a sporophyte.

*Sphagnum* moss (commonly known as *peat moss*) is a good example of a plant in which the gametophyte is the most visible and familiar stage of the life cycle. In this case, the sporophyte is reduced and develops from a zygote within the body of the gametophyte. Vast peatlands of *Sphagnum* gametophytes are industrially harvested in many parts of the world for fuel and horticultural use.

**MOST FUNGI** The life cycle of most fungi and algae follows the third life cycle pattern (see Figure 8.9c). In these organisms, the diploid phase is limited to a single cell, the zygote, produced by fertilization. Immediately after fertilization, the diploid zygote undergoes meiosis to produce the haploid phase. Mitotic divisions occur only in the haploid phase. (You could think of this as the "haploid life cycle" since the haploid stage is multicellular.)

During fertilization, two haploid gametes, usually designated simply as positive (+) and negative (–) because they are similar in structure, fuse to form a diploid nucleus. This nucleus immediately enters meiosis, producing four haploid cells. These cells develop either directly or, after one or more mitotic divisions, into haploid spores. These spores germinate to produce haploid individuals, which grow or increase in number by mitotic divisions. Eventually, positive and negative gametes are formed in these individuals by differentiation of some of the cells produced by the mitotic divisions. Because the gametes are produced by mitosis, all the gametes of an individual are genetically identical.

Why might these different life cycle strategies have arisen? They have different advantages. A diploid multicellular organism can have a variety of alleles to call upon to increase its chances of survival, but lethal recessive alleles are maintained in the gene pool, being "protected" in heterozygous individuals. A haploid multicellular organism will weed out these lethal alleles when the haploid spores germinate and grow; they are not protected by having another allele that masks the lethal one.

**CONCEPT FIX** We are emphasizing that zygotes arising from fertilization contain DNA from two different parents in close proximity so that recombination may occur. However, note carefully that, in the life cycles of the animals and plants you are likely familiar with, it is not this single-celled fertilized zygote that undergoes recombination. It is only after many rounds of replication by mitosis that specific cells in the resulting multicellular body are destined to divide by meiosis. That is when and where recombination occurs. ⬡

## 8.3b Meiosis Changes Both Chromosome Number and DNA Sequence

In order to understand the mechanism of meiosis, it is helpful to keep the big picture in mind. Chapter 7 made the point that the essence of mitotic cell division is *sameness*. That is, chromosomes are replicated and partitioned to ensure that cells produced by the process have the same number of chromosomes, with the same DNA sequence, as the cell that began the process. In this way, somatic cells accumulate to form multicellular organisms. However, the essence of meiosis is *difference*, actually two kinds of difference: halved chromosome number and new combinations of alleles arising from recombined DNA sequences. The products of meiosis are not intended to contribute to the body of the organisms that make them. In multicellular animals and plants, you would find that meiosis occurs only in specialized tissues that produce gametes and spores respectively.

Both types of difference mentioned above arise from the very different behaviour of chromosomes in meiosis relative to

mitosis. If you understand the significance of the chromosome pairs in diploid organisms as described below, then the differences in chromosome behaviour in meiosis and mitosis will more easily make sense.

As discussed in Section 8.1, the two representatives of each chromosome in a diploid cell constitute a *homologous pair* (*homo* = same; *logos* = information): they have the same genes, arranged in the same order, in the DNA of the chromosomes. One chromosome of each homologous pair, the **paternal chromosome**, is derived from the male parent of the organism, and the other chromosome, the **maternal chromosome**, is derived from its female parent. Although two homologous chromosomes carry the same genes arranged in the same order, different *versions* of these genes, alleles, may be present on either chromosome. Recall from the bacterial conjugation material at the beginning of this chapter that different alleles of a given gene have similar, but distinct, DNA sequences. They therefore likely encode variations of the given RNA or protein gene product, which may then have a different structure, or a different biochemistry, or both.

For example, all the different breeds of dogs normally have 78 chromosomes in their cells, made up of 39 homologous pairs. However, each individual has a unique combination of the alleles carried by the two chromosomes of each homologous pair. The distinct set of alleles, arising from the mixing mechanisms of meiosis and fertilization in the parents, gives an individual offspring its own unique combination of inherited traits, including attributes such as size, coat colour, susceptibility to certain diseases and disorders, and aspects of behaviour and intelligence.

One of the more dramatic accomplishments of meiosis in an organism like a dog is the separation of the members of each homologous pair into different cells, thereby reducing the diploid, or 2*n*, number of chromosomes to the haploid, or *n*, number. Each cell produced by meiosis carries only one member of each homologous pair. An egg or a sperm cell contains 39 chromosomes, one of each pair. When the egg and sperm combine in sexual reproduction to produce the zygote—the first cell of the new puppy—the diploid number of 78 chromosomes (39 pairs) is regenerated. The processes of DNA replication and mitotic cell division ensure that this diploid number is maintained in the body cells as the zygote divides and develops (see Chapter 7).

**CONCEPT FIX** Students often get confused by "chromatid," "chromosome," "centromere," and "chromatin," and a whole host of terminology starting with "c." Chromatin refers to the stuff chromosomes are made from: nucleic acid and proteins. The centromere is a structure that helps a chromosome to get oriented during cell division and holds sister chromatids together. Sister chromatids are evident after the chromosome replicates its DNA, but they are held together at the centromere. Joined sister chromatids are part of *one* chromosome. To determine how many chromosomes a cell has, count the centromeres. If two of each type of chromosome are found in a cell, it is diploid; if each chromosome is distinct from all the others, it is haploid. ⬡

The second significant consequence of meiotic cell division is, of course, genetic recombination of the actual DNA sequence on chromosomes. Referring back to Figure 8.1, recall that recombination involves the precise breaking of covalently bonded DNA backbones, exchanging the "ends" with those of the other homologue and reforming the bonds. As a result, each chromosome passed on to offspring is composed of a novel mixture of both maternal and paternal DNA sequences.

The following sections describe how the ability of homologues to find their respective partners, and pair intimately along their length, allows both the partitioning of homologues into separate cells and the process of recombination to occur during the first part of the two-step process of meiosis.

## 8.3c Meiosis Produces Four Genetically Different Daughter Cells

Cells that are destined to divide by meiosis (called **meiocytes**) move through their last turn of the cell cycle as usual, replicating DNA and making more chromosomal proteins during S phase. (See Chapter 11 for details of DNA replication.) The resulting G2 cells carry replicated chromosomes, each composed of two sister chromatids (**Figure 8.10**). Following this premeiotic interphase, cells enter the first of the two meiotic divisions: meiosis I and meiosis II. During **meiosis I**, chromosomes behave dramatically differently than they do during mitosis. That is, early in meiosis I, homologous chromosomes find their partners and pair lengthwise, gene for gene, in a process called **synapsis**. During this intimate pairing, recombination occurs, and chromosomal segments are exchanged. As the meiocyte continues through to the end of the first division, the members of each homologous pair are moved into one or the other of the two daughter cells. These daughter cells still contain replicated chromosomes (composed of two chromatids each); however, the number of such chromosomes is only half that of the original meiocyte. That is, the cells now have the haploid number of chromosomes but each chromosome still has two sister chromatids.

During the second meiotic division, **meiosis II**, these sister chromatids are separated into different cells, further reducing the amount of DNA in each product of meiosis. A total of four cells, each with the haploid number of chromosomes and a novel collection of alleles, is the final result of the two meiotic divisions.

**CONCEPT FIX** Notice that the chromosome in the cells at the right of Figure 8.10 is an unreplicated, single structure. Since

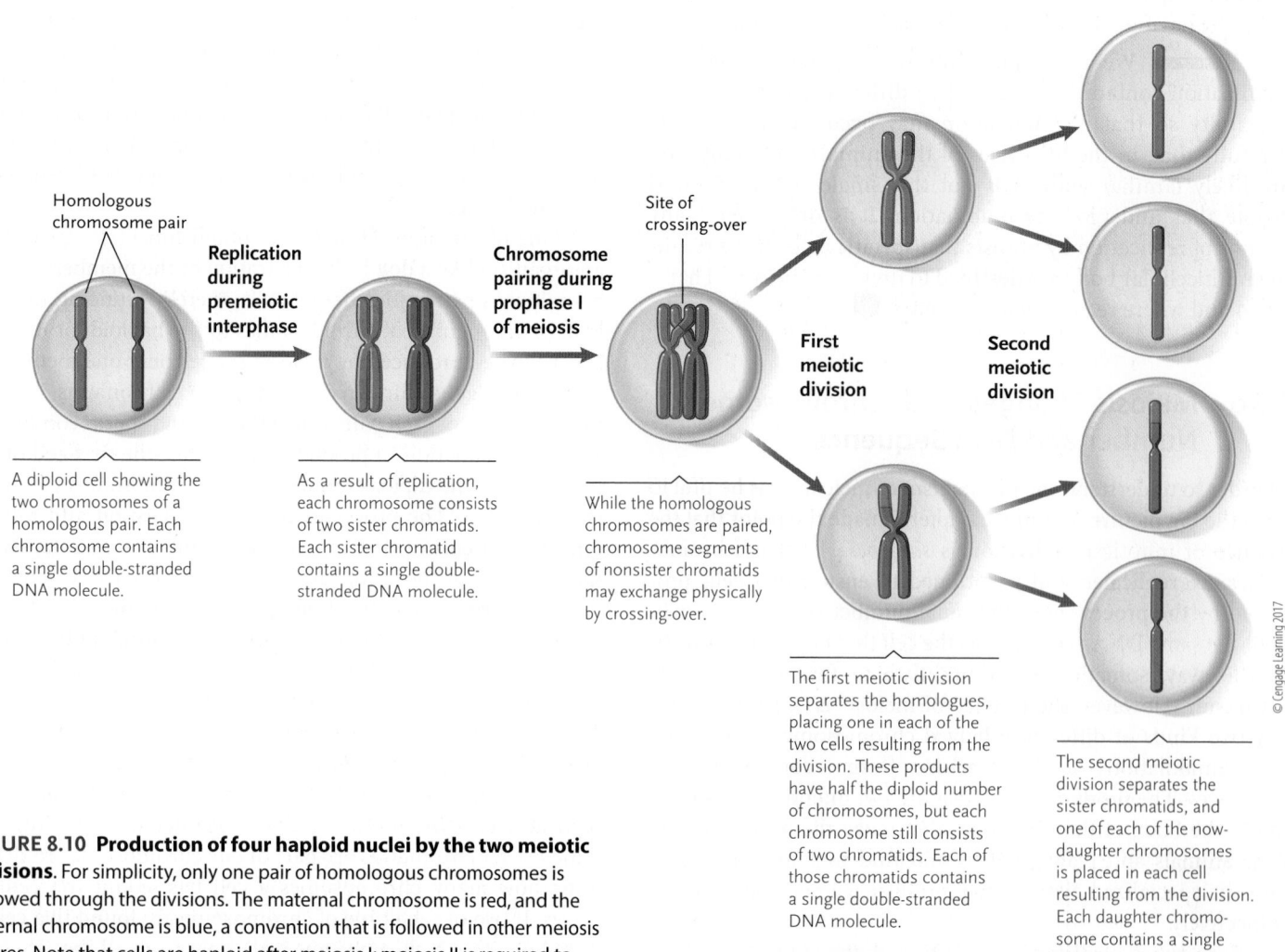

Homologous chromosome pair

**Replication during premeiotic interphase**

**Chromosome pairing during prophase I of meiosis**

Site of crossing-over

**First meiotic division**

**Second meiotic division**

A diploid cell showing the two chromosomes of a homologous pair. Each chromosome contains a single double-stranded DNA molecule.

As a result of replication, each chromosome consists of two sister chromatids. Each sister chromatid contains a single double-stranded DNA molecule.

While the homologous chromosomes are paired, chromosome segments of nonsister chromatids may exchange physically by crossing-over.

The first meiotic division separates the homologues, placing one in each of the two cells resulting from the division. These products have half the diploid number of chromosomes, but each chromosome still consists of two chromatids. Each of those chromatids contains a single double-stranded DNA molecule.

The second meiotic division separates the sister chromatids, and one of each of the now-daughter chromosomes is placed in each cell resulting from the division. Each daughter chromosome contains a single double-stranded DNA molecule.

© Cengage Learning 2017

**FIGURE 8.10 Production of four haploid nuclei by the two meiotic divisions.** For simplicity, only one pair of homologous chromosomes is followed through the divisions. The maternal chromosome is red, and the paternal chromosome is blue, a convention that is followed in other meiosis figures. Note that cells are haploid after meiosis I; meiosis II is required to separate the sister chromatids.

these cells are haploid, sometimes people come to believe that all chromosomes in haploid cells are unreplicated, single structures, and that all chromosomes in diploid cells are double structures with two chromatids each. However, Figure 8.10 clearly shows that the left cell is diploid, even though its two chromosomes are unreplicated. Following meiosis I, the cells are haploid, even though their single chromosome is replicated. Ploidy is determined only by the number of chromosomes; it is not influenced by whether the chromosomes are replicated or not. ⬡

For convenience, biologists separate each meiotic division into the same key stages as mitosis: prophase, prometaphase, metaphase, anaphase, and telophase. The stages are identified as belonging to the two divisions, meiosis I and meiosis II, by "I" or "II" put after the stage, as in "prophase I" and "prophase II." A brief interphase called **interkinesis** separates the two meiotic divisions, but no DNA replication occurs during interkinesis.

**PROPHASE I** At the beginning of prophase I, the replicated chromosomes (as a result of the S phase preceding it), each consisting of two sister chromatids, begin to fold and condense into threadlike structures in the nucleus (**Figure 8.11**, step 1). The two chromosomes of each homologous pair then come together and line up side by side in a zipperlike way in synapsis (step 2). The fully paired homologues are called *tetrads*, referring to the fact that each homologous pair consists of a total of four chromatids. Note that chromosomes do not normally pair up during mitosis.

While they are paired, the chromatids of homologous chromosomes physically exchange segments (step 3). This physical exchange, genetic recombination, is the step that mixes the alleles of the homologous chromosomes into new combinations, and is one of the mechanisms contributing to the generation of genetic variability during sexual reproduction. (This is the process that underlies recombination frequency mapping described in Chapter 10.) As prophase I finishes, a spindle forms in the cytoplasm by the same basic mechanisms described in Chapter 7.

**PROMETAPHASE I** In prometaphase I, the nuclear envelope breaks down and the spindle enters the former nuclear area (see Figure 8.11, step 4). The two chromosomes of each pair attach to kinetochore microtubules that are anchored to opposite spindle poles. That is, both sister chromatids of one homologue attach to microtubules leading to one spindle pole, whereas both sister chromatids of the other homologue attach to microtubules leading to the opposite pole. Notice, again, how this is different from the spindle attachments during mitosis.

**METAPHASE I AND ANAPHASE I** At metaphase I, movements of the spindle microtubules have aligned the recombined tetrads on the equatorial plane—the **metaphase plate**—between the two spindle poles (see Figure 8.11, step 5). Then the two chromosomes of each homologous pair separate and move to opposite spindle poles during anaphase I (step 6). The movement segregates homologous pairs, delivering a haploid set of chromosomes to each pole of the spindle. However, all the chromosomes at the poles are still double structures composed of two sister chromatids joined at their centromeres.

**TELOPHASE I AND INTERKINESIS** Telophase I is a brief, transitory stage in which there is little or no change in the chromosomes (see Figure 8.11, step 7). Cell division (cytokinesis) in telophase I creates truly haploid cells. During interkinesis the spindle of the first meiotic division disassembles and the microtubules reassemble into new spindles for the second division. Recall that there is no DNA replication between the first and the second division.

**PROPHASE II, PROMETAPHASE II, AND METAPHASE II** During prophase of meiosis II, the chromosomes condense (see Figure 8.11, step 8). During prometaphase II, the nuclear envelope breaks down, the spindle enters the former nuclear area, and spindle microtubules leading to opposite spindle poles attach to the two kinetochores of each chromosome. At metaphase II, movements of the chromosomes within the spindle bring them to rest at the metaphase plate (step 9).

🔴 **CONCEPT FIX** Although the separation of chromatids during meiosis II is superficially similar to that in a mitotic division, it is important to remember that these two processes are quite distinct. Meiosis II is not "just like mitosis." Meiosis II produces reproductive cells, there is no immediately preceding DNA replication phase, and the resulting daughter cells are not genetically identical (see Figure 8.16). ⬡

**ANAPHASE II AND TELOPHASE II** Anaphase II begins as the sister chromatids of each chromosome separate from each other and move to opposite spindle poles (see Figure 8.11, step 10). At the completion of anaphase II, the separated chromatids—now themselves each called a *chromosome*—have been segregated to the two poles. During telophase II, the chromatids decondense to the extended interphase state, the spindles disassemble, and new nuclear envelopes form around the masses of chromatin and the cells divide (step 11). The result is four haploid cells, each with a nucleus containing half the number of chromosomes present in the meiocyte that began meiotic division. These chromosomes all carry various new combinations of maternal and paternal alleles.

**FAILURE IN CHROMOSOME SEGREGATION** Rarely, chromosome segregation fails at either meiosis I or II. For example, during meiosis I, both chromosomes of a homologous pair may connect to the same spindle pole in anaphase I. In the resulting *nondisjunction*, as it is called, the spindle fails to separate the homologous chromosomes of the tetrad. As a result, one pole receives both chromosomes of the homologous pair, whereas the other pole has no copies of that chromosome. Meiosis II will proceed to separate the chromatids of the extra chromosome as usual, with the result that gametes will have two copies of this chromosome (instead of one). A failure at meiosis II, in which chromatids do not separate to opposite poles, also results in gametes with abnormal numbers of chromosomes. Zygotes that receive an extra

**Prophase I**

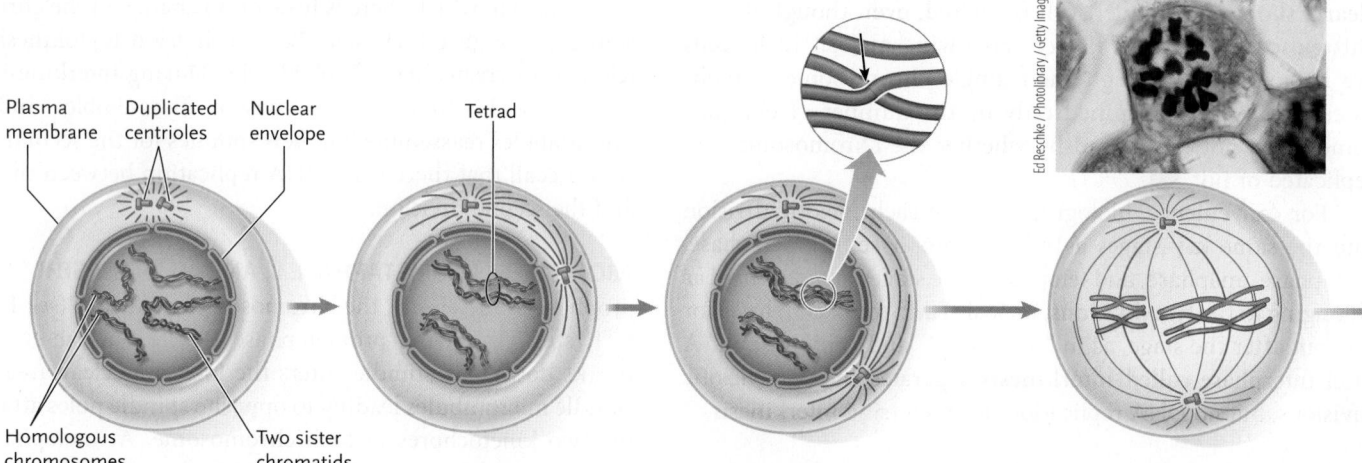

Plasma membrane | Duplicated centrioles | Nuclear envelope

Tetrad

Homologous chromosomes | Two sister chromatids

### Condensation of chromosomes

**1** At the beginning of prophase I, the chromosomes begin to condense into threadlike structures. Each consists of two sister chromatids, as a result of DNA replication during premeiotic interphase. The chromosomes of two homologous pairs, one long and one short, are shown.

### Synapsis

**2** Homologous chromosomes come together and pair.

### Recombination

**3** While they are paired, the chromatids of homologous chromosomes undergo recombination by exchanging segments. The enlarged circle shows a site undergoing recombination (arrow).

### Prometaphase I

**4** In prometaphase I, the nuclear envelope breaks down, and the spindle moves into the former nuclear area. Kinetochore microtubules connect to the chromosomes—kinetochore microtubules from one pole attach to both sister kinetochores of one duplicated chromosome, and kinetochore microtubules from the other pole attach to both sister kinetochores of the other duplicated chromosome.

Ed Reschke / Photolibrary / Getty Images

### Second meiotic division

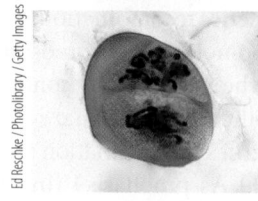

Ed Reschke / Photolibrary / Getty Images

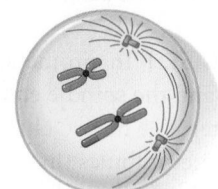

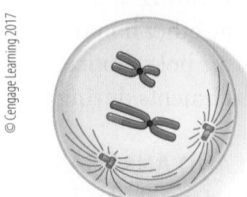

© Cengage Learning 2017

### Prophase II

**8** The chromosomes condense and a spindle forms.

**FIGURE 8.11  The meiotic divisions.** The artwork summarizes the behaviour of chromosomes in a hypothetical animal cell having two homologous pairs of chromosomes ($2n = 4$). Photomicrographs show comparable stages in the anther cells of a lily plant.

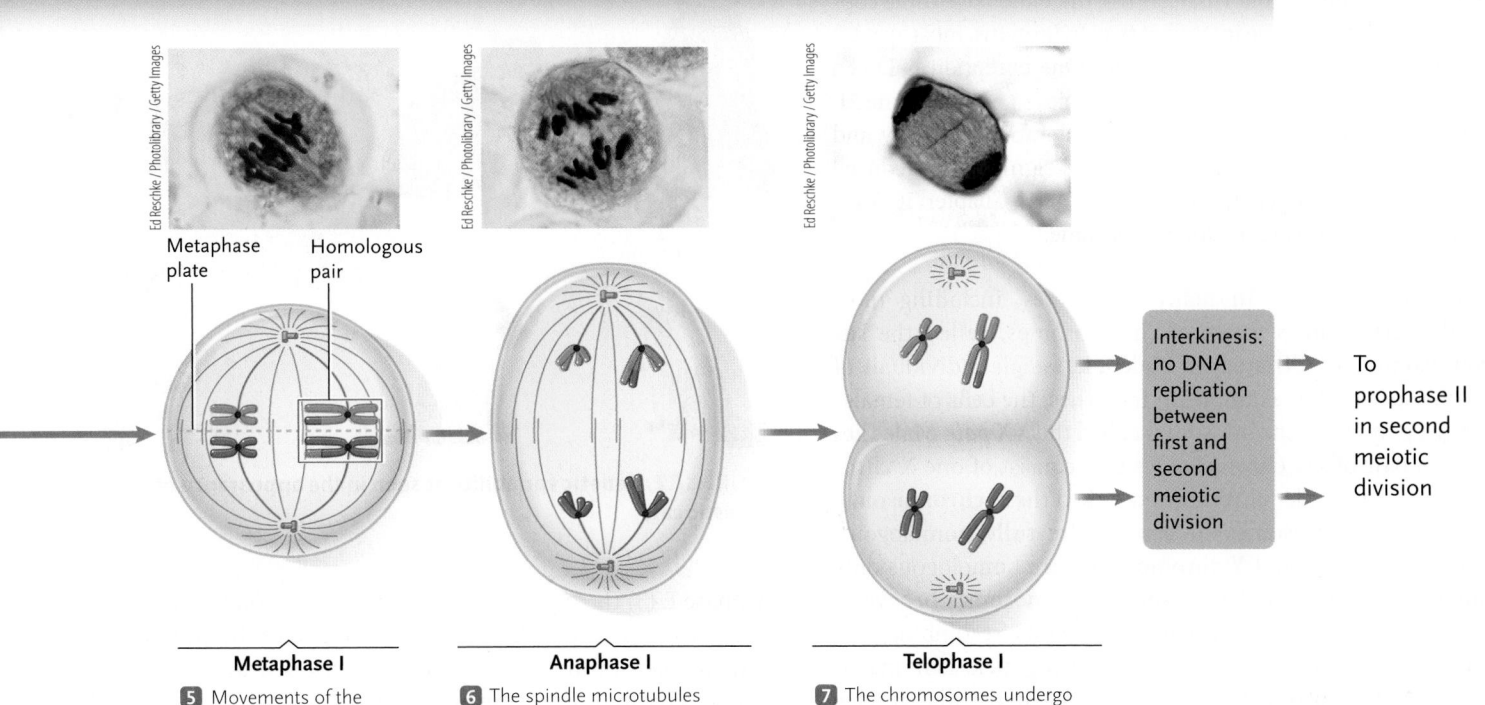

**Metaphase I**

**5** Movements of the spindle microtubules align the tetrads in the equatorial plane—metaphase plate—between the two spindle poles.

**Anaphase I**

**6** The spindle microtubules separate the two chromosomes of each homologous pair and move them to opposite spindle poles. The poles now contain the haploid number of chromosomes. However, each chromosome at the poles still contains two chromatids.

**Telophase I**

**7** The chromosomes undergo little or no change except for limited decondensation or unfolding in some species. Cells divide. The spindle of the first meiotic division disassembles, and two new spindles form for the second division.

Interkinesis: no DNA replication between first and second meiotic division

To prophase II in second meiotic division

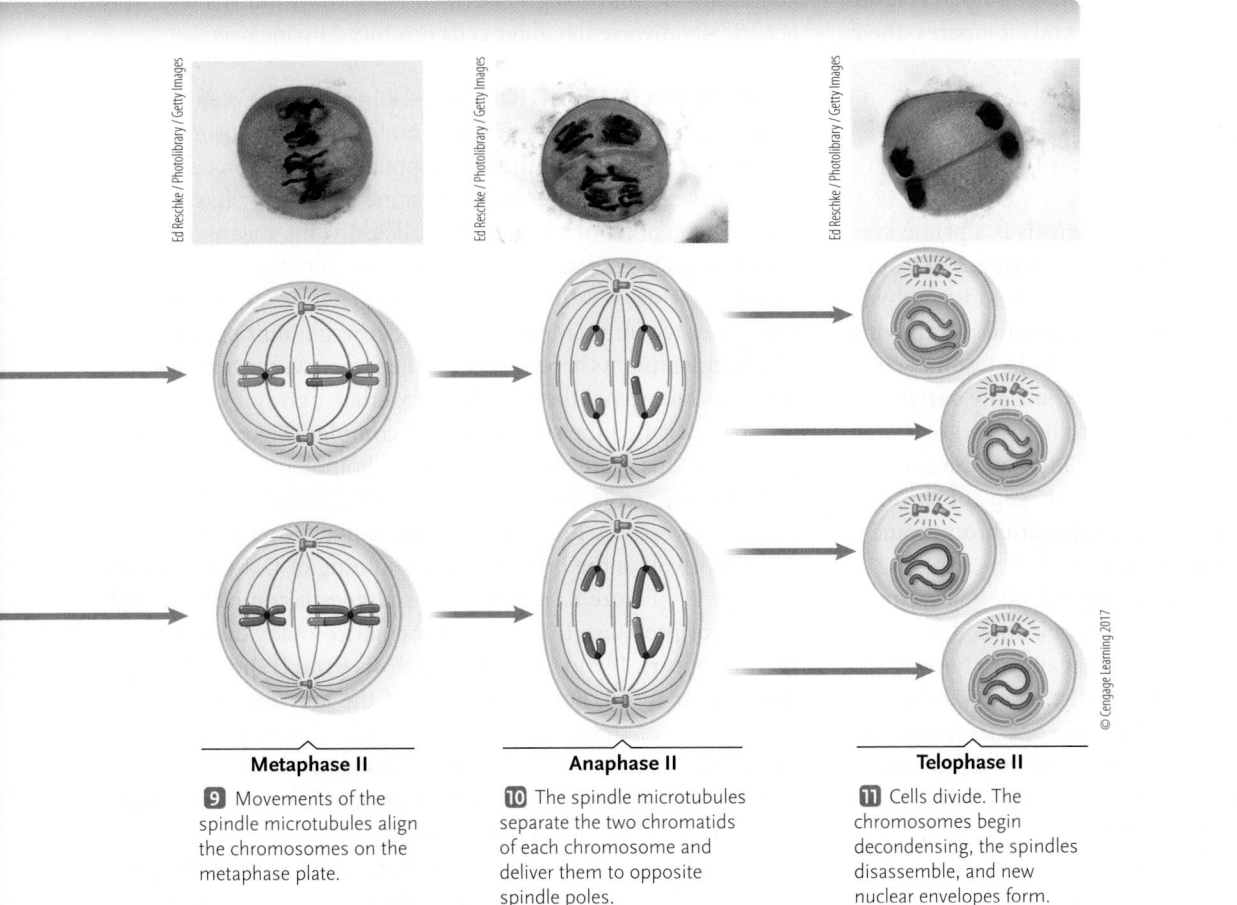

**Metaphase II**

**9** Movements of the spindle microtubules align the chromosomes on the metaphase plate.

**Anaphase II**

**10** The spindle microtubules separate the two chromatids of each chromosome and deliver them to opposite spindle poles.

**Telophase II**

**11** Cells divide. The chromosomes begin decondensing, the spindles disassemble, and new nuclear envelopes form.

chromosome from an abnormal gamete therefore have three copies of a given chromosome instead of two. In humans, most zygotes of this kind do not result in live births. One exception is Down syndrome, which can result from three copies of chromosome 21. Down syndrome involves characteristic alterations in body and facial structure, developmental delays, and significantly reduced fertility due to extra genetic information. (See Chapter 10 for a more detailed discussion of Down syndrome.)

**SEX CHROMOSOMES** In many eukaryotes, including most animals, one or more pairs of chromosomes, called the **sex chromosomes**, are different in male and female individuals of the same species. For example, in fruit flies, the cells of females contain a pair of sex chromosomes called the *XX pair*. Male flies contain a pair of sex chromosomes that consist of one X chromosome and a smaller chromosome called the **Y chromosome**. The two X chromosomes in females are fully homologous, whereas the male X and Y chromosomes are homologous only through a short region. The X and Y chromosomes behave as homologues (i.e., they pair where homologous, recombine, and move together to the metaphase plate) during meiosis in males. As a result of meiosis, a gamete formed by females may receive either member of the XX pair. A gamete formed by males receives either an X or a Y chromosome. (See Chapter 10 for a discussion of the inheritance of genes on sex chromosomes.)

The sequence of steps in the two meiotic divisions accomplishes the major outcomes of meiosis: the generation of genetic variability and the reduction in chromosome number. (Figure 8.16, reviews the two meiotic divisions and compares them with the single division of mitosis.)

## 8.3d Several Mechanisms Contribute to Genetic Diversity

The generation of genetic variability by meiosis is a prime evolutionary advantage of sexual reproduction (**Figure 8.12**). Such variability increases the chance that at least some offspring will have combinations of alleles that will be successful in surviving and reproducing in changing environments. In fact, some scientists argue that meiosis exists not to create just any variability, but to generate "repaired" chromosomes to be passed on to the next generation. As you work through the ideas in this section, try to envision how you could pass a "perfect" copy of chromosome 6 to your children even if both copies of chromosome 6 you inherited from your parents are damaged.

The variability produced by sexual reproduction is apparent all around us, particularly in the human population. Except for identical twins, no two humans look alike, act alike, or have identical biochemical and physiological characteristics, even if they are members of the same immediate family. Other species that reproduce sexually show equivalent variability arising from meiosis.

During meiosis and fertilization, genetic variability arises from four sources: (1) genetic recombination between homologous chromosomes, (2) the differing combinations of maternal and paternal chromosomes segregated to the poles during

**FIGURE 8.12 Genetic variability as seen in the appearance of domestic cats**

anaphase I, (3) the differing combinations of recombinant chromatids segregated to the poles during anaphase II, and (4) the particular sets of male and female gametes that unite in fertilization. The four mechanisms, working together, produce so much total variability that no two products of meiosis produced by the same or different individuals and no two zygotes produced by union of the gametes are likely to have the same genetic makeup. Each of these sources of variability is discussed in further detail in the following sections. **Figure 8.13** contrasts the genetically similar daughter cells arising from mitosis with the genetically diverse daughter cells produced by meiosis.

**GENETIC RECOMBINATION** Recombination, the key genetic event of prophase I, starts when homologous chromosomes pair (**Figure 8.14**, step 1). Recall that, although homologous chromosomes have the same genes in the same order, they likely carry different versions of those genes (alleles). This means that the underlying DNA sequence is similar enough to form the basis of meiotic pairing, yet different enough to generate novel combinations after recombination. (Recall Lederberg's multiple auxotrophic E. coli mutants here; the idea is the same.) As the homologous chromosomes pair, they are held together tightly by a protein framework called the **synaptonemal complex (Figure 8.15)**. Supported by this framework, regions of homologous chromatids exchange segments, producing new combinations of alleles (see Figure 8.14, step 2). Recall that the exchange process is very precise and involves the breakage and rejoining of DNA molecules by enzymes (Figure 8.1). When the exchange is complete toward the end of prophase I, the synaptonemal complex disassembles and disappears. If you now follow meiosis I and II through to the end in your mind, notice that each of the four resulting nuclei receives one of these four chromatids (see Figure 8.14, step 3): two receive unchanged "parental" chromatids and two receive chromatids that have new combinations of alleles due to recombination; these are called *recombinants*.

The physical effect of recombination can be seen later in prophase I, when increased condensation of the chromosomes

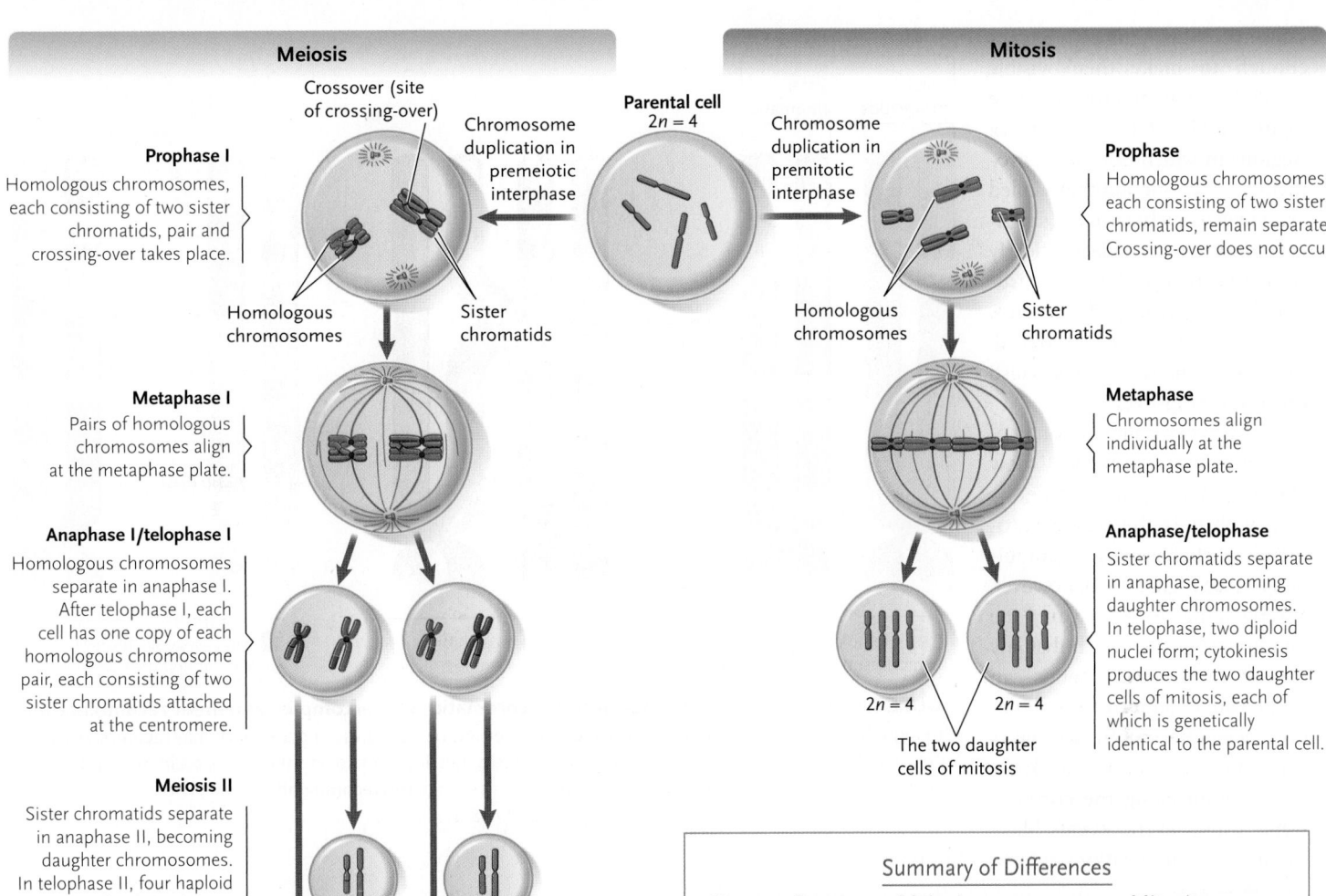

**Prophase I**
Homologous chromosomes, each consisting of two sister chromatids, pair and crossing-over takes place.

Crossover (site of crossing-over)

Chromosome duplication in premeiotic interphase

Parental cell
$2n = 4$

Chromosome duplication in premitotic interphase

**Prophase**
Homologous chromosomes, each consisting of two sister chromatids, remain separate. Crossing-over does not occur.

Homologous chromosomes

Sister chromatids

Homologous chromosomes

Sister chromatids

**Metaphase I**
Pairs of homologous chromosomes align at the metaphase plate.

**Metaphase**
Chromosomes align individually at the metaphase plate.

**Anaphase I/telophase I**
Homologous chromosomes separate in anaphase I. After telophase I, each cell has one copy of each homologous chromosome pair, each consisting of two sister chromatids attached at the centromere.

**Anaphase/telophase**
Sister chromatids separate in anaphase, becoming daughter chromosomes. In telophase, two diploid nuclei form; cytokinesis produces the two daughter cells of mitosis, each of which is genetically identical to the parental cell.

$2n = 4$     $2n = 4$
The two daughter cells of mitosis

**Meiosis II**
Sister chromatids separate in anaphase II, becoming daughter chromosomes. In telophase II, four haploid nuclei form; cytokinesis produces four haploid cells, each containing one-half as many chromosomes as the parental cell. Each cell is genetically different from the parental cell and from each other.

$n = 2$     $n = 2$

$n = 2$     $n = 2$

© Cengage Learning 2017

| Summary of Differences | | |
|---|---|---|
| Event or Feature | Meiosis | Mitosis |
| Number of daughter cells | Four. Each cell has one-half the number of chromosomes vs. the parental cell. The chromosomes are genetically different from the parent cell, with various combinations of paternal and maternal chromosomes, and mixtures of paternal and maternal segments within chromosomes due to crossing-over. | Two. Genetically identical to parental cell, with the same number of chromosomes |
| Role in life cycle | Halving chromosome number in animal cells that produce gametes, in plant cells that produce spores, and in fungi and algae to produce spores; generates genetic variability in gametes or spores | Cell division for growth; asexual reproduction in some eukaryotes |

| Summary of Differences | | |
|---|---|---|
| Event or Feature | Meiosis | Mitosis |
| Cell divisions | Two; occurs only in diploid cells | One; occurs in both haploid and diploid cells |
| Synapsis of homologous chromosomes | Yes | No |
| Crossing-over | Yes | No |

**FIGURE 8.13 Meiosis and mitosis compared.** Comparison of key steps in meiosis and mitosis. Both diagrams use an animal cell as an example. Maternal chromosomes are shown in red and paternal chromosomes are shown in blue.

thickens the chromosomes enough to make them visible under the light microscope (see Figure 8.11, steps 3 and 4). Regions in which nonsister chromatids cross one another, called **crossovers** or **chiasmata** (singular, *chiasma* = crosspiece), clearly show that two of the four chromatids have exchanged segments. Because of the shape produced, the recombination process is also called **crossing-over**.

Note that illustrations of recombination usually show chromosomes "paired" side by side, with only the closest chromatids participating in recombination (see Figure 8.14); however, chromosomes actually pair "one on top of the other" such that any two of the four chromatids can participate in a given recombination event. Recombination takes place largely at random, at almost any position along the chromosome arms. Several events likely occur at various locations along all chromatids.

**CONCEPT FIX** Notice in Figure 8.14 that a recombination event does not just "switch" the alleles of a given gene in a localized area. Rather, all the DNA sequence stretching from the site of recombination to the ends of the participating chromatids is exchanged. ⬡

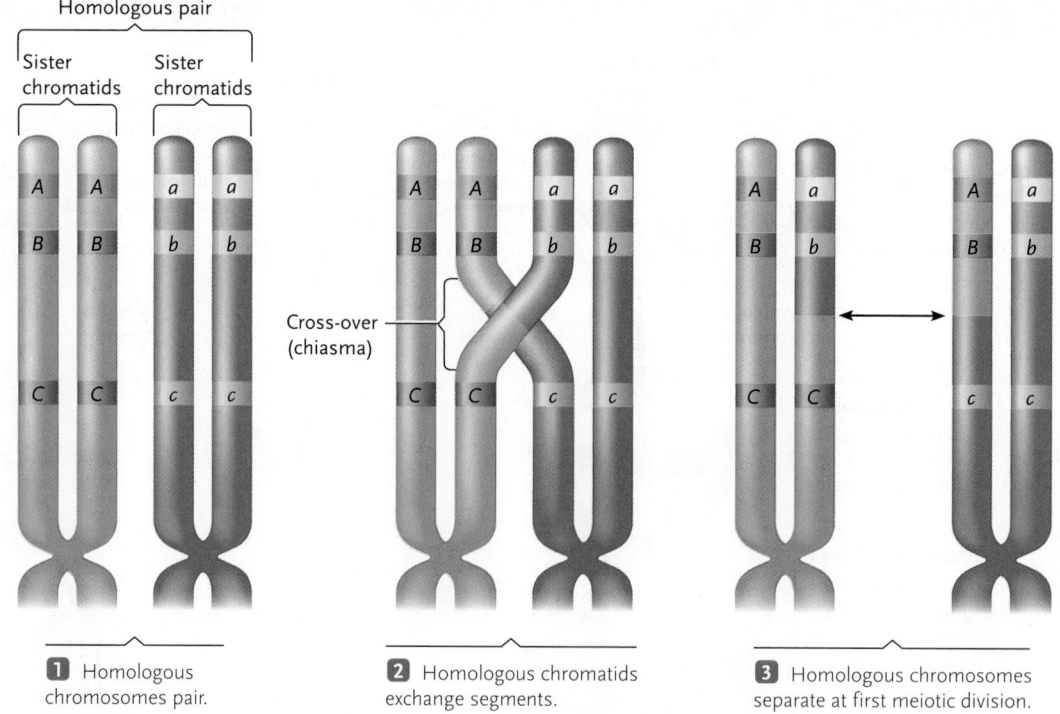

1 Homologous chromosomes pair.

2 Homologous chromatids exchange segments.

3 Homologous chromosomes separate at first meiotic division.

© Cengage Learning 2017

**FIGURE 8.14** **Effects of the exchange between chromatids that accomplishes genetic recombination**. Although the closest chromatids are shown crossing over, any pair of nonsister chromatids may recombine. The letters indicate two alleles (e.g., A and a) for each of three genes. In the meiocyte, the alleles are in the combination of *A–B–C* and *a–b–c* on their respective homologues. As a result of this recombination event, two of the chromatids, the recombinants, have a new combination: *a–b–C* and *A–B–c*.

**RANDOM SEGREGATION** Random segregation of chromosomes of maternal and paternal origin accounts for the second major source of genetic variability in meiosis. Recall that the maternal and paternal members of each homologous pair are different in that they typically carry different alleles of many of the genes on that chromosome. During prometaphase I, spindle microtubules make connections to kinetochores. For each homologous pair, one chromosome makes spindle connections leading to one pole, and the other chromosome connects to the opposite pole in a random choice. In making these connections, all the maternal chromosomes may connect to one pole, and all the paternal chromosomes may connect to the opposite pole. Or, as is much more likely, a random combination of maternal and paternal chromosomes will be segregated to a given spindle pole (**Figure 8.16**).

The number of possible random combinations depends on the number of chromosome pairs in a species. For example, the 39 chromosome pairs in dogs allow 2³⁹ different combinations of maternal and paternal chromosomes to be delivered to the poles, producing potentially 550 billion genetically different gametes from this source of variability alone. Note that this

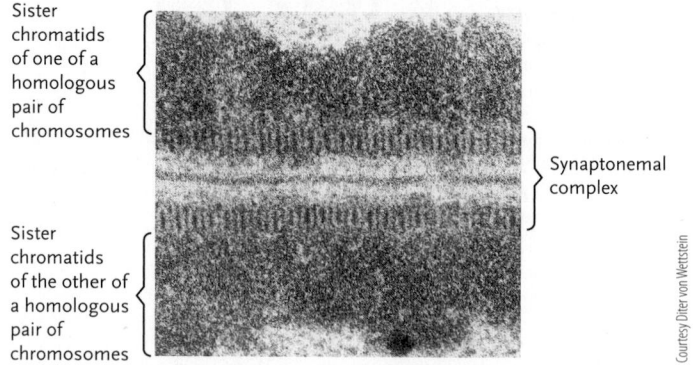

Synaptonemal complex

Sister chromatids of one of a homologous pair of chromosomes

Sister chromatids of the other of a homologous pair of chromosomes

Courtesy Diter von Wettstein

**FIGURE 8.15** **The synaptonemal complex as seen in a meiotic cell of the fungus *Neotiella***

random partitioning of maternal and paternal chromosomes is responsible for the independent assortment of the alleles of two genes in Mendel's experiments with garden peas described in Chapter 9.

**ALTERNATIVE COMBINATIONS AT MEIOSIS II** If you look carefully at the cells drawn in metaphase II in Figure 8.11, you will see that the chromosomes are still replicated and, as a result of recombination in prophase I, each chromosome carries one recombinant chromatid and one nonrecombinant chromatid. Notice that, in the case shown in the figure, the chromosomes have aligned at metaphase II with both recombinant chromatids

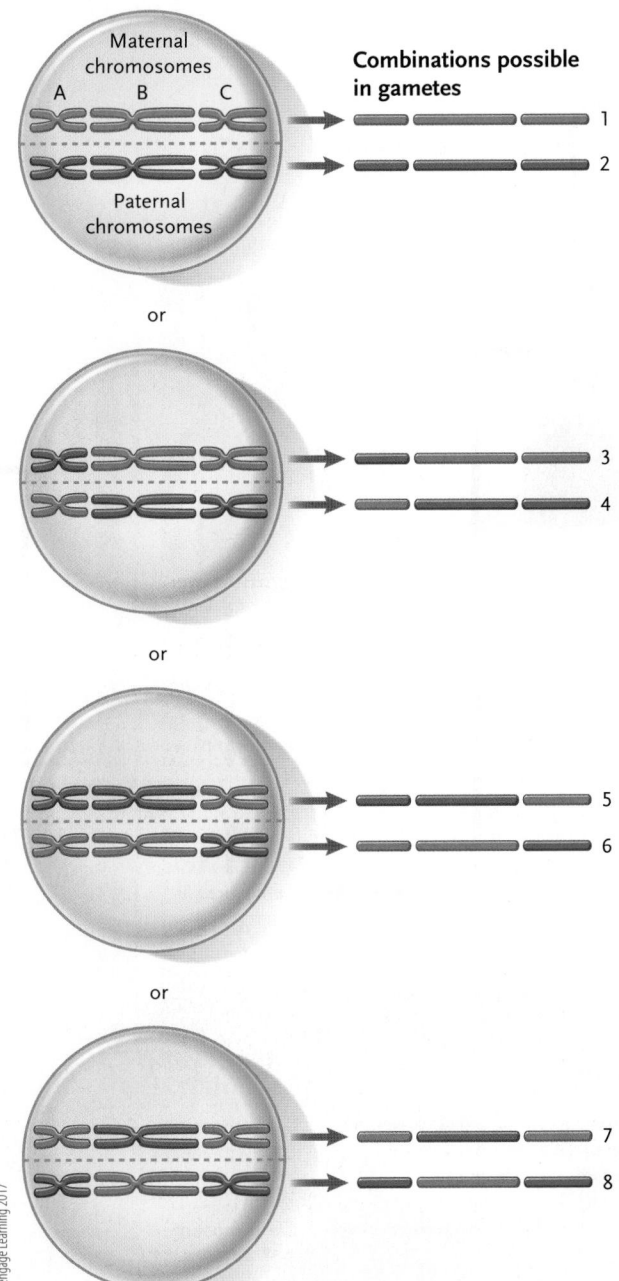

**Combinations possible in gametes**

Maternal chromosomes

A B C

1
2

Paternal chromosomes

or

3
4

or

5
6

or

7
8

© Cengage Learning 2017

**FIGURE 8.16 Possible outcomes of the random spindle connections of three pairs of chromosomes at metaphase I of meiosis.** The three types of chromosomes are labelled A, B, and C, and for simplification, crossing-over is not considered. Maternal chromosomes are red; paternal chromosomes are blue. There are four possible patterns of connections, giving eight possible combinations of maternal and paternal chromosomes in gametes (labelled 1–8).

attached to the same spindle pole. However, since the attachment of spindles to kinetochores is random at this stage, you should be able to see that it is just as likely that these chromosomes *could* have lined up, with the smaller chromosome sending its recombinant chromatid to one pole and the larger chromosome sending its recombinant chromatid to the opposite pole. The resulting daughter cells will be genetically different, depending on how the chromosomes align in metaphase II.

**RANDOM FERTILIZATION** The haploid products of meiosis are genetically diverse. The random combination of these cells (or their descendants) during fertilization is a matter of chance, which amplifies the variability of sexual reproduction. For example, if we consider only the variability available from random separation of homologous chromosomes at meiosis I along with that from random fertilization, the possibility that two children of the same human parents could receive the same combination of maternal and paternal chromosomes is 1 chance out of $(2^{23})^2$, or 1 in about 70 trillion, a number that far exceeds the number of humans who have ever lived. The further variability introduced by recombination and shuffling at meiosis II makes it practically impossible for humans and most other sexually reproducing organisms to produce genetically identical gametes or offspring. The only exception is identical twins (or identical triplets, identical quadruplets, and so forth), which arise not from the combination of identical gametes during fertilization, but from mitotic division of a single fertilized egg into separate cells that give rise to genetically identical individuals.

## STUDY BREAK QUESTIONS

1. Which phase, diploid or haploid, dominates the respective life cycles of animals, plants, and fungi?
2. What are the two functions of meiosis?
3. What are the four sources of genetic variability in sexually reproducing organisms?
4. What is nondisjunction, and how does it occur?

This has been a long chapter. We hope that, taken together, all these ideas will help you understand the balance that life must strike between the stability and the plasticity of its genetic material. On the one hand, DNA must be faithfully replicated and passed to the next generation. Lack of quality control at this step would allow widespread random mutations to undermine the selection and preservation of beneficial combinations of alleles. On the other hand, any system that made only perfectly "photocopied" DNA available for the next generation would be doomed as well. A wide repertoire of diverse genetic "solutions" are needed for a population to survive in constantly changing environments that are impossible to anticipate.

For octopuses, limpets, and a whole cast of other plants, fungi, algae, and animals, sexual reproduction is a stage upon which various mechanisms create new diversity through meiosis. We have seen that meiosis has three outcomes that are vital to sexual reproduction. This process reduces the chromosomes to the haploid number so that they can be brought together with those of another individual without doubling the usual chromosome number during fertilization. Through genetic recombination and random separation of maternal and paternal chromosomes, meiosis produces genetic variability in gametes; further variability is provided by the random combination of gametes in fertilization. These ideas form the "mechanics" that underlie the patterns of inheritance of traits in sexually reproducing organisms discovered by Mendel and described in Chapter 9.

# Summary Illustration

Genetic recombination, the enzymatic cutting of DNA backbones and pasting in new combinations, is a widespread and powerful mechanism for increasing genetic diversity. Recombination during meiosis is one of the hallmarks of eukaryotic sexual life cycles.

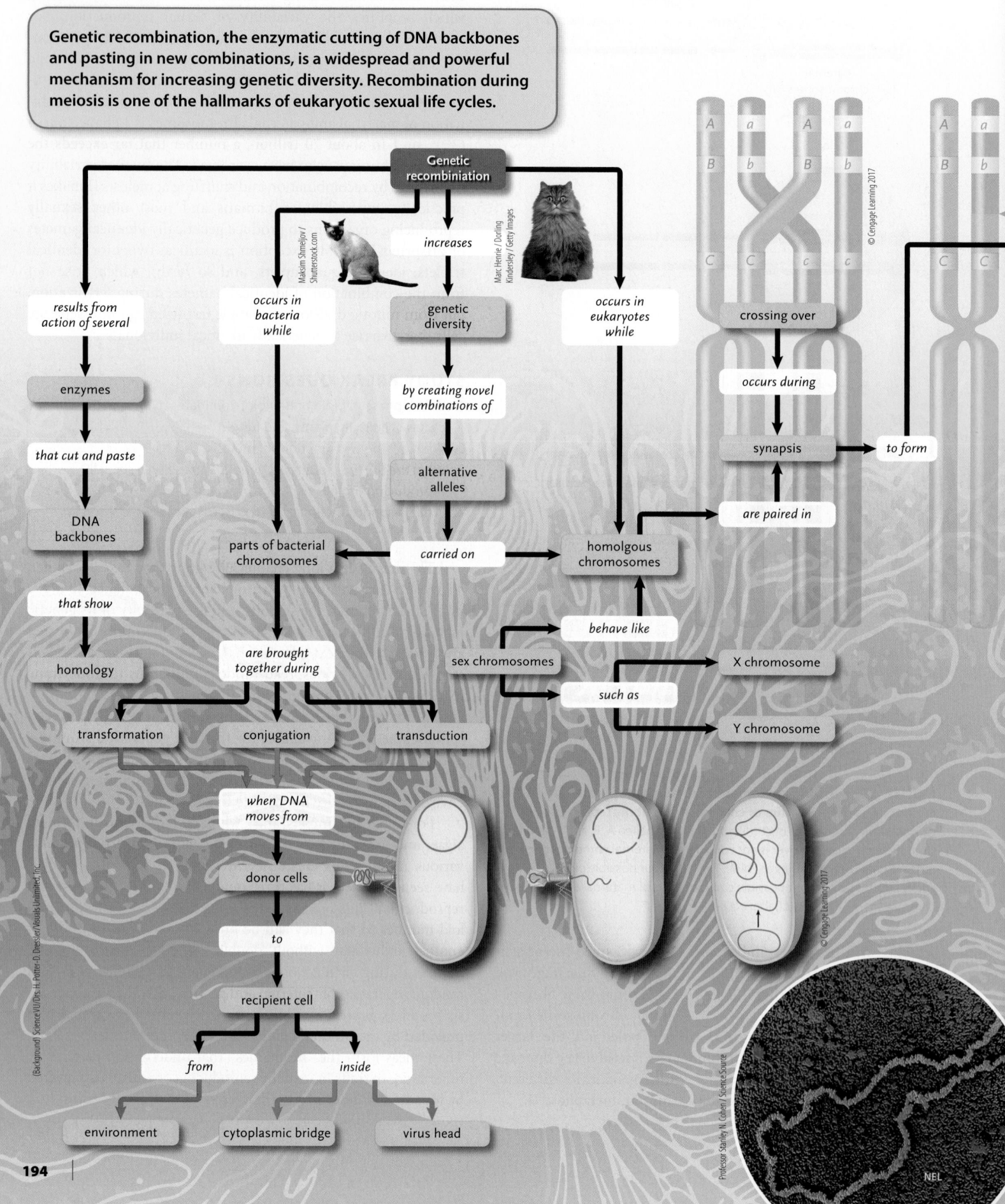

NEL

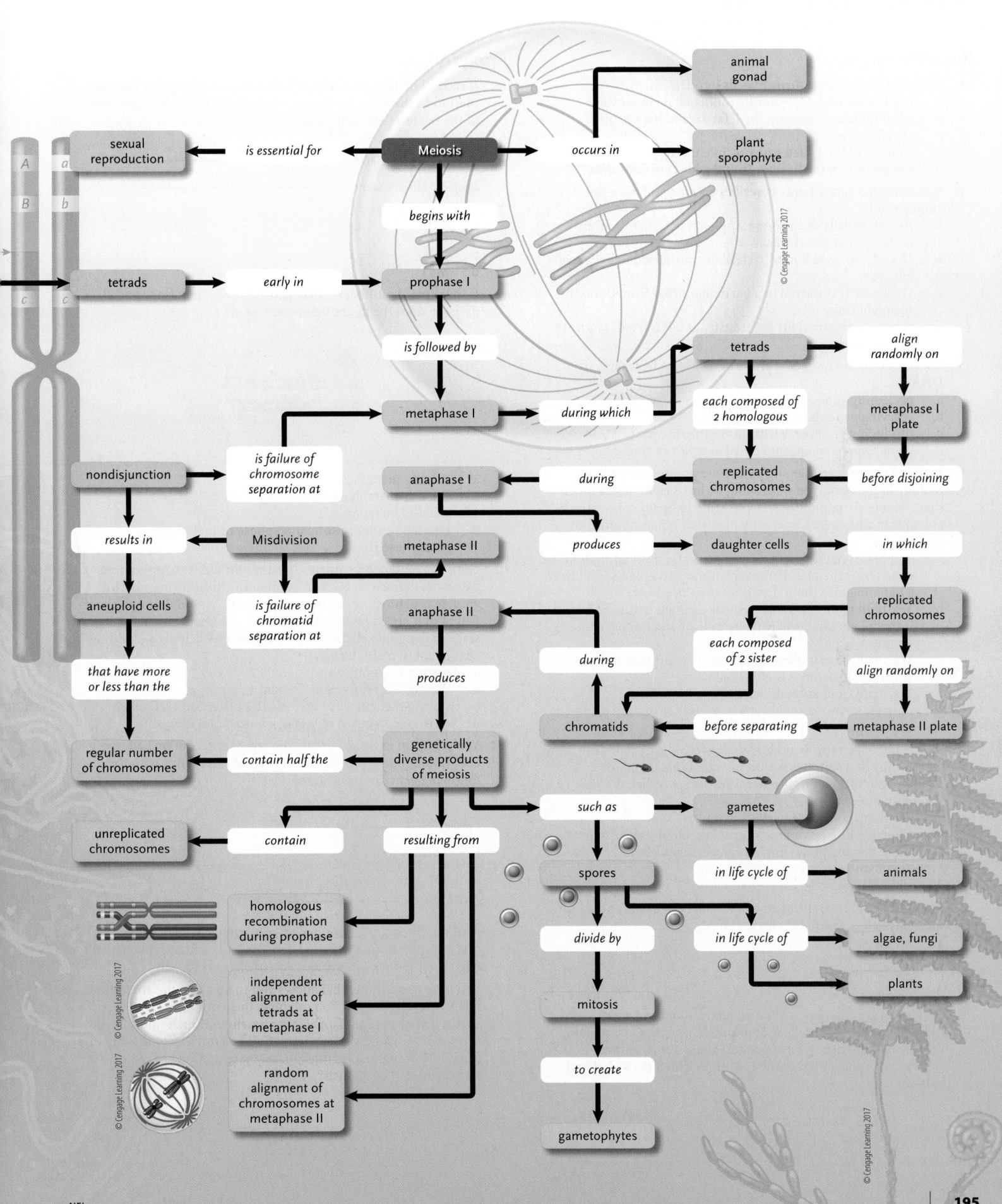

sexual reproduction ← *is essential for* ← **Meiosis** → *occurs in* → animal gonad

**Meiosis** → *occurs in* → plant sporophyte

**Meiosis** → *begins with* → prophase I

tetrads → *early in* → prophase I

prophase I → *is followed by* → metaphase I

metaphase I → *during which* → tetrads

tetrads → *align randomly on* → metaphase I plate

tetrads → each composed of 2 homologous → replicated chromosomes

metaphase I plate → *before disjoining* → replicated chromosomes

nondisjunction → *is failure of chromosome separation at* → metaphase I

replicated chromosomes → *during* → anaphase I

nondisjunction → *results in* → aneuploid cells

Misdivision → *results in*

Misdivision → *is failure of chromatid separation at* → metaphase II

anaphase I → *produces* → daughter cells

daughter cells → *in which* → replicated chromosomes

aneuploid cells → *that have more or less than the* → regular number of chromosomes

metaphase II → anaphase II

anaphase II → *during* → chromatids

replicated chromosomes → each composed of 2 sister → chromatids

replicated chromosomes → *align randomly on* → metaphase II plate

metaphase II plate → *before separating* → chromatids

genetically diverse products of meiosis → *contain half the* → regular number of chromosomes

anaphase II → *produces* → genetically diverse products of meiosis

unreplicated chromosomes ← *contain*

genetically diverse products of meiosis → *such as* → gametes

genetically diverse products of meiosis → *resulting from* → homologous recombination during prophase

*resulting from* → independent alignment of tetrads at metaphase I

*resulting from* → random alignment of chromosomes at metaphase II

gametes → *in life cycle of* → animals

spores → *divide by* → mitosis

mitosis → *to create* → gametophytes

gametes → *in life cycle of* → algae, fungi

*in life cycle of* → plants

## Recall/Understand

1. Which of these events turns F⁺ cells into Hfr cells?
   a. replication of the F factor by rolling circle replication
   b. recombination between the F factor and the recipient chromosome
   c. transfer of the F factor to a recipient cell
   d. integration of the F factor into the host chromosome

2. Which of these statements describes an aspect of bacterial conjugation?
   a. Recipient cells incorporate single-stranded DNA from donors into their chromosome.
   b. DNA from dead donor bacteria is transferred to live recipient cells.
   c. Genes are transferred in a particular order from donor to recipient cells.
   d. A virus is required for the transfer of DNA from donors to recipient cells.

3. If a virus is in the lysogenic phase of its life cycle, what is its DNA doing?
   a. packaging genes into the viral protein coat
   b. carrying genes into a bacterial cell
   c. producing viral particles that rupture the host cell
   d. being expressed and/or copied as a part of the host DNA

4. Imagine that you are helping your younger brother with his biology homework. You notice that he has written in his notes that, "Plants are haploid and make gametes by mitosis. Animals are diploid and make gametes by meiosis." What should your response be?
   a. Yes, plants make gametes by mitosis and most animals make gametes by meiosis. However, animals and plants both have a haploid and a diploid stage of their life cycle.
   b. Yes, both plants and animals make gametes. The difference is that plant gametes divide by mitosis and animal gametes do not.
   c. Yes, plants are simpler organisms than animals and have fewer chromosomes in their cells.
   d. Yes, plants and animals use meiosis for different purposes. Animals make gametes by meiosis and plants make zygotes.

5. As a result of genetic recombination, each of the chromosomes of your family dog contains a different combination of alleles compared to those of its brothers and sisters. When did this recombination occur?
   a. when the dog's parents made gametes
   b. when the dog was a newly fertilized, single-celled zygote
   c. when the dog grew from a zygote to a multicellular organism
   d. when the dog reached sexual maturity

6. The number of human chromosomes in a cell in prophase I of meiosis is _____ and in telophase II it is _____.
   a. 92; 46
   b. 46; 23
   c. 23; 23
   d. 23; 46

7. Mutations are changes in DNA sequences that can create new alleles. In which cells of an individual, somatic or meiotic cells, would mutations be of greatest significance to that individual? What about to the species to which the individual belongs?

## Apply/Analyze

8. If recombination occurred in a bacterium undergoing transformation as shown in the figure, what would be the final genotype of the bacterial chromosome?

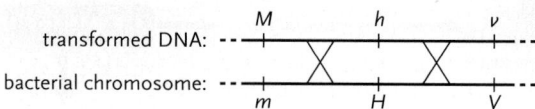

   a. *Mhv*
   b. *MHv*
   c. *mHV*
   d. *mhV*

9. If the diploid number of an organism is 6, which stage of cell division does the figure below represent?

   a. mitotic metaphase
   b. meiotic metaphase I
   c. meiotic metaphase II
   d. could be either mitotic metaphase or meiotic metaphase II

10. Consider a penguin gamete. The amount of DNA (pg) in this gamete is defined as 1*C*. The number of chromosomes in this gamete is defined as 1n. That is, the coefficient of *C* and the coefficient of n are equal in a penguin gamete. During which other stage of penguin cell division would the coefficient of *C* and the coefficient of n also be equal?
    a. during G1; both *n* and C equal 2
    b. during G2; both *n* and C equal 4
    c. during metaphase of meiosis II; both *n* and *C* equal 1
    d. during metaphase of mitosis; both n and *C* equal 2

11. You set up an experiment like the one carried out by Lederberg and Tatum, mixing millions of *E. coli* of two strains with the following genetic constitutions.

    Strain 1:  bio⁻ met⁻ thr⁺ leu⁺

    Strain 2:  bio⁺ met⁺ thr⁻ leu⁻

    Among the bacteria obtained after mixing, you find some cells that do not require threonine, leucine, or biotin to grow but still need methionine. How might you explain this result?

12. You have a technique that allows you to measure the amount of DNA in a cell nucleus. You establish the amount of DNA in a sperm cell of an organism as your baseline. Which multiple of this amount would you expect to find in a nucleus of this organism at G2 of premeiotic interphase? At telophase I of meiosis? At telophase II of meiosis?

## Create/Evaluate

13. A "zonkey" is a hybrid between a zebra and a donkey. Zebras are $2n = 46$; donkeys are $2n = 62$. Zonkeys are usually infertile. Which of the following explanations for zonkey infertility is most likely?

    a. Genes coding for donkey and zebra ovaries and testes are not properly expressed in zonkey hybrids.

    b. Zonkey gametes will all have an odd number of chromosomes (27), causing them to be non-functional.

    c. When zebra and donkey chromosomes recombine at meiosis, the resulting recombinant chromosomes will be partly zebra and partly donkey; therefore, the resulting gametes are non-functional.

    d. The zebra and donkey chromosomes will fail to form proper homologous pairs during meiosis I, resulting in unbalanced gametes following meiosis II.

14. Sometimes pieces of chromosomes can be exchanged in a kind of rearrangement called a *reciprocal translocation*. Imagine the case in a diploid organism in which the end of one chromosome 4 was exchanged for the end of a chromosome 12. The other chromosomes 4 and 12 remained uninvolved and normal in structure. What shape might these four chromosomes take as they try to pair during meiosis I?

15. What would happen if two circular DNA molecules were involved in a single recombination event?

# Chapter Roadmap

**The Chromosomal Basis of Mendelian Inheritance**

The mechanism of meiosis underlies the Mendelian "Laws" of Random Segregation and Independent Assortment

From Chapter 8 →

**9.1 The Beginnings of Genetics: Mendel's Garden Peas**

The basic patterns of inheritance of single character traits in eukaryotes were discovered by Mendel. The underlying mechanism is chromosome segregation during meiosis and random fertilization of gametes.

To Chapter 10 →

To Chapter 35 →

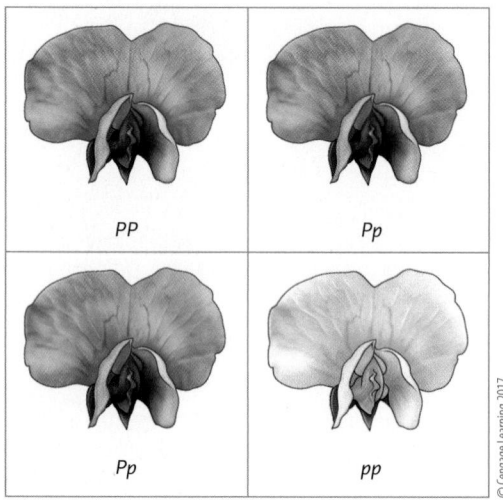

PP Pp

Pp pp

© Cengage Learning 2017

From Mendel's *Principles of Heredity: A Defence*

From Chapter 8 →

**9.2 Later Modifications and Additions to Mendel's Hypotheses**

Most traits follow inheritance patterns that are more complex than those found by Mendel.

To Chapter 10 →

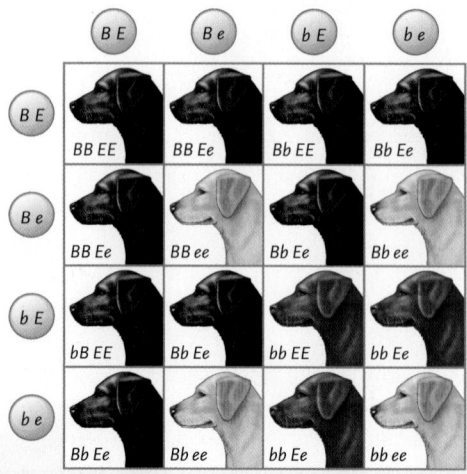

The White Bear, known to the Kitasoo First Nation as "moskgm'ol," in the Great Bear Rainforest of Northern British Columbia

# The Chromosomal Basis of Mendelian Inheritance

# 9

**Why it matters...** Your body is so peppered with bites that it is now pointless to resist your personal cloud of buzzing mosquitos. After five days of soggy slogging through one of the largest temperate rainforests on Earth, you have arrived here, hidden behind a fallen tree and transfixed by the scene in front of you. A small family is fishing in a cascading mountain stream, their claws swiping at wriggling salmon. You can't believe your luck as you slowly reach for your camera.

This area of snowy mountains, deep fjords, and coastal islands of Northern British Columbia is called the Great Bear Rainforest and is the ancestral home of First Nations communities including the Gitga'at, Kitasoo Xai'xais, Haisla, Heiltsuk, Henaaksiala, and Tsimshian. The area is very rich in biodiversity, including hemlock, grizzly bears, wolverines, humpback whales, sea lions, Sitka spruce, grey wolves, dolphins, orcas, bald eagles, salmon, and ancient red cedars. A Kitasoo guide named Charlie has led your group to this hidden valley in search of an animal that can be found only in this part of the world. Charlie smiles broadly as he watches the mother black bear coach her cub in snatching salmon from the water. The cub is the colour of champagne. It is the "moskgm'ol," or White Bear.

Important symbols in West Coast First Nations' culture for centuries, about 500 white bears are believed to inhabit the nearby islands and valleys today. Neither polar bear nor albino, the White Bear is actually a blonde version of the more commonly black Kermode bear. That is, the mutation that gives rise to its strikingly light coloured fur occurs in the MC1R gene, the same gene that can code for blonde hair in otherwise dark-haired humans and other animals.

Even this small family sample provides enough data for us to make a good guess that the white coat version of the MC1R gene must be recessive. That is, the white cub must be carrying two copies of the light version, while the mother has one copy of black and one copy of the light colour.

We can draw these types of preliminary conclusions about inheritance patterns thanks largely to the pioneering work of a nineteenth century scholarly monk named Gregor Mendel (**Figure 9.1**), who used garden peas to study patterns of inheritance. To test his hypotheses about inheritance, Mendel bred generation after generation of pea plants and carefully observed the patterns by which parents transmit traits to their offspring. Through his experiments and observations, Mendel discovered the fundamental rules that govern inheritance. His discoveries and conclusions founded the science of genetics and still have the power to explain many of the puzzling and sometimes devastating aspects of inheritance that continue to occupy our attention.

## 9.1 The Beginnings of Genetics: Mendel's Garden Peas

Until about 1900, scientists and the general public believed in the **blending theory of inheritance**, which suggested that hereditary traits blend evenly in offspring through mixing of the parents' blood, much like the effect of mixing coffee and cream. Even today, many people assume that parental characteristics such as skin colour, body size, and facial features blend evenly in their offspring, with the traits of the children appearing about halfway between those of their parents. Yet if blending takes place, why don't extremes—such as very tall and very short individuals—gradually disappear over generations as repeated blending takes place? Also, why do children with blue eyes keep turning up among the offspring of brown-eyed parents?

Gregor Mendel's experiments with garden peas, performed in the 1860s, provided the first answers to these questions and many more. Mendel was an Augustinian monk who lived in a monastery in Brünn, now part of the Czech Republic. But he had an unusual education for a monk in the mid-nineteenth century. He had studied mathematics, chemistry, zoology, and botany at the University of Vienna under some of the foremost scientists of his day. He grew up on a farm and was well aware of agricultural principles and their application. He kept abreast of breeding experiments published in scientific journals. Mendel also won several awards for developing improved varieties of fruits and vegetables.

In his work with peas, Mendel studied a variety of heritable characteristics called **characters**, such as flower colour or seed shape. A variation in a character, such as purple or white flower colour, is called a **trait**. Mendel established that characters are passed to offspring in the form of discrete hereditary factors, which are now known as *genes*. Mendel observed that, rather than blending evenly, many parental traits appear unchanged in offspring, whereas others disappear in one generation and reappear unchanged in the next. Although Mendel did not know it, the inheritance patterns he observed are the result of the segregation of chromosomes, on which the genes are located, to gametes in meiosis (see Chapter 8). Mendel's methods illustrate, perhaps as well as any experiments in the history of science, how rigorous scientific work is conducted: through observation, making hypotheses, and testing the hypotheses with experiments. Although others had studied inheritance patterns before him, Mendel's most important innovation was his quantitative approach to science, specifically his rigour and statistical analysis in an era when qualitative, purely descriptive science was the accepted practice. In this chapter, we will pay particular attention to the experimental aspect of Mendel's approach to explaining inheritance.

### 9.1a Mendel Chose True-Breeding Garden Peas for His Experiments

Mendel chose the garden pea (*Pisum sativum*) for his research because the plant could be grown easily in the monastery garden, without elaborate equipment. As in other flowering plants, gametes are produced in structures of the flowers (**Figure 9.2**). The male gametes are sperm nuclei contained in the pollen, which is produced in the *anthers* of the flower. The female gametes are egg cells, produced in the *carpel* of the flowers. Normally, pea plants **self-fertilize** (also known as **self-pollinate** or, more simply, *self*): sperm nuclei in pollen produced by anthers fertilize egg cells housed in the carpel of the same flower. However, for his experiments, Mendel prevented self-fertilization by cutting off the anthers. Pollen to fertilize these flowers then had to come from a different plant. This technique is called **cross-pollination** or, more simply, a *cross*. This technique allowed Mendel to test the effects of mating pea plants of different parental types.

*From Mendel's Principles of Heredity: A Defence*

**FIGURE 9.1 Gregor Mendel (1822–1884), the founder of genetics**

FIGURE 9.2   **Research Method**

## Making a Genetic Cross between Two Pea Plants

**Purpose:** Mendel used the garden pea, *Pisum sativum,* for his genetic experiments. The goal of the experiments was to test various hypotheses about the patterns of inheritance by cross-breeding plants with easily observable characters, such as flower colour and seed shape. He could then analyze whether the characters he observed and counted in the offspring supported the predictions made by a particular hypothesis.

In cross-breeding, the sperm and the egg must come from different plants. However, this type of flowering plant has both male and female structures within the same flower and is capable of self-fertilization, also called "selfing." The figure to the left shows a pea flower sectioned to show the location of the reproductive structures. (Details of plant fertilization are presented in Chapter 35).

The figure below shows how Mendel designed his experiments to prevent selfing and perform his crosses.

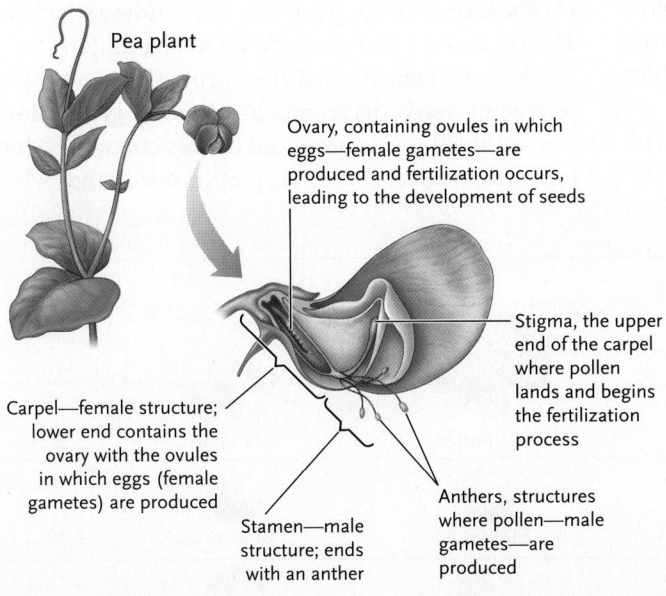

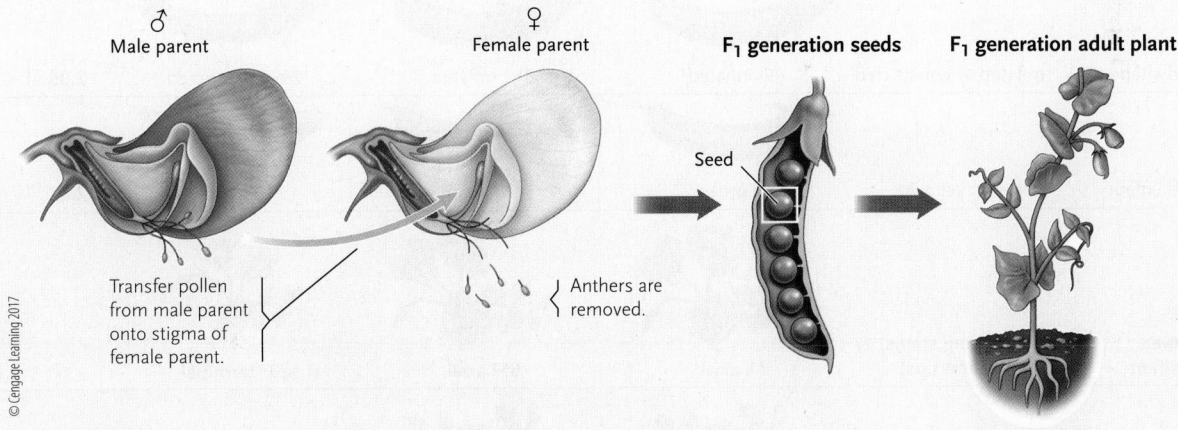

## Protocol:

1.  Remove the anthers from one of the parents (the white-flowered plant) to prevent self-fertilization. Transfer pollen from the male parent (the purple-flowered plant) onto the stigma of the white flower (the female parent). This results in cross-fertilization, the fertilization of one plant with pollen from another.

2.  The cross-fertilized plant produces seeds. Seeds may be scored for seed traits, such as round vs. wrinkled shape. Seeds are grown into adult plants. Plants may be scored for adult traits, such as purple vs. white flower colour.

To begin his experiments, Mendel chose pea plants that were known to be **true-breeding** (also called *pure-breeding*); that is, when self-fertilized or, more simply, *selfed*, they passed traits without change from one generation to the next.

## 9.1b Mendel First Worked with Crosses of Plants Differing in One Character

Mendel selected seven characters for study (**Figure 9.3**). The alternative forms of each character could be readily seen visually. Although Mendel knew nothing about the molecular bases of character differences, keep in mind as you learn about his experiments that the visual differences result from underlying molecular differences.

Flower colour was among the seven characters Mendel chose for study: one true-breeding variety of peas had purple flowers, and the other true-breeding variety had white flowers (see Figure 9.2). Would these traits blend evenly if plants with purple flowers were cross-pollinated with plants with white flowers?

To answer this question, Mendel took pollen from the anthers of plants with purple flowers and placed it in the flowers of white-flowered plants. He placed the pollen on the *stigma,* the part of the carpel that receives pollen in flowers (see Figure 9.2). He also performed the reciprocal experiment by placing pollen from white-flowered plants on the stigmas of purple-flowered plants. Seeds were the result of the crosses; each seed contains a zygote, or embryo, that will develop into a new pea plant. The plants that develop from the seeds produced by the cross—the first generation of offspring from the cross—are the $F_1$ **generation** (F stands for *filial; filius* = son). The plants used in the initial cross are called the *parental* or **P generation**. The plants that grew from the $F_1$ seeds all formed purple flowers, as if the trait for white flowers had disappeared. The flowers showed no evidence of blending.

Mendel then allowed the purple-flowered $F_1$ plants to self, producing seeds that represented the $F_2$ **generation**. When he planted the $F_2$ seeds produced by this cross, the white-flowered trait reappeared: both purple-flowered and white-flowered

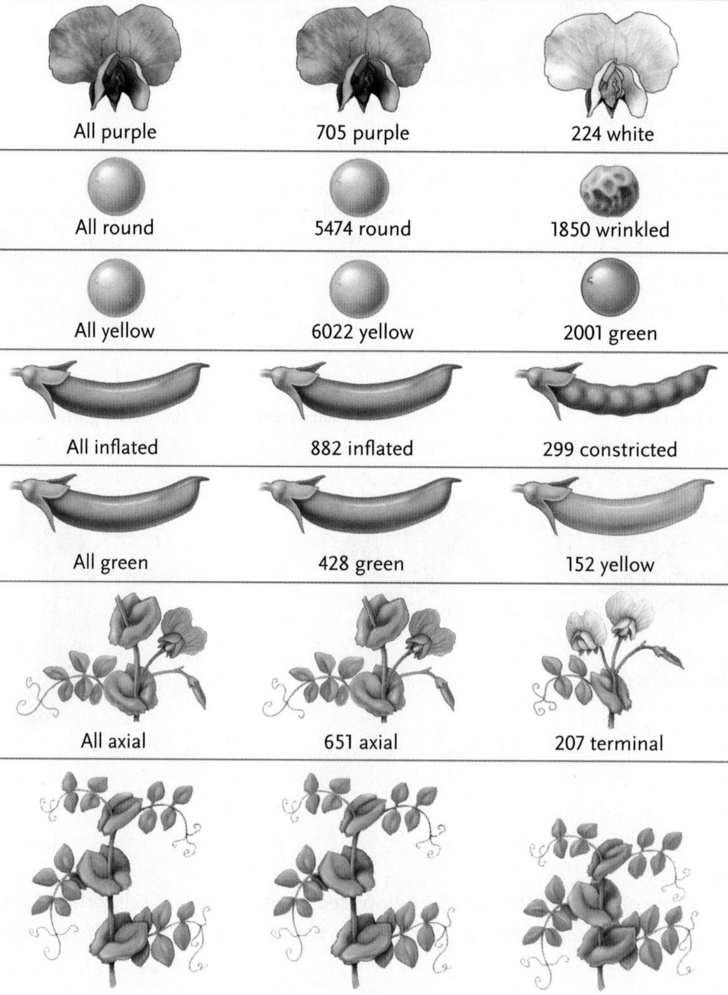

| Character | Traits crossed | $F_1$ | $F_2$ | | Ratio |
|---|---|---|---|---|---|
| Flower colour | Purple × white | All purple | 705 purple | 224 white | 3.15 : 1 |
| Seed shape | Round × wrinkled | All round | 5474 round | 1850 wrinkled | 2.96 : 1 |
| Seed colour | Yellow × green | All yellow | 6022 yellow | 2001 green | 3.01 : 1 |
| Pod shape | Inflated × constricted | All inflated | 882 inflated | 299 constricted | 2.95 : 1 |
| Pod colour | Green × yellow | All green | 428 green | 152 yellow | 2.82 : 1 |
| Flower position | Axial (along stems) × terminal (at tips) | All axial | 651 axial | 207 terminal | 3.14 : 1 |
| Stem length | Tall × dwarf | All tall | 787 tall | 277 dwarf | 2.84 : 1 |

**FIGURE 9.3** Mendel's crosses with seven characters in peas, including his results and the calculated ratios of offspring

© Cengage Learning 2017

plants were produced. Mendel counted 705 plants with purple flowers and 224 with white flowers. He noted that this ratio was close to 3:1, or about 75% purple-flowered plants and 25% white-flowered plants. Statistical tools developed since Mendel's time confirm that his data are indeed consistent with a 3:1 ratio.

Mendel made similar crosses that involved six other characters, each with pairs of traits (Figure 9.3); for example, the character of seed colour has the traits yellow and green. In all cases, he observed a uniform $F_1$ generation, in which only one of the two traits was present. In the $F_2$ generation, the missing trait reappeared, and both traits were present among the offspring. Moreover, the trait present in the $F_1$ generation was present in a definite, predictable proportion among the $F_2$ offspring.

## 9.1c Single-Character Crosses Led Mendel to Propose the Principle of Segregation

Using his knowledge of mathematics, Mendel developed a set of hypotheses to explain the results of his crosses. His first hypothesis was that *adult plants carry a pair of factors that govern the inheritance of each character*. He correctly deduced that, for each character, an organism inherits one factor from each parent.

In modern terminology, Mendel's factors are called *genes* and are located on chromosomes. The different versions of a gene, which have different DNA sequences and may produce different traits of a character, are called **alleles**. Thus, there are two alleles of the gene that govern flower colour in garden peas: one allele for purple flowers and the other allele for white flowers. Organisms with two copies of each gene are now known as *diploids*; the two alleles of a gene in a diploid individual may be identical or different.

How can the disappearance of one of the traits, such as white flowers, in the $F_1$ generation and its reappearance in the $F_2$ generation be explained? Mendel deduced that the trait that had seemed to disappear in the $F_1$ generation was actually present but was masked in some way by the "stronger" allele. Mendel called the masking effect **dominance**. Accordingly, Mendel's second hypothesis stated that *if an individual's pair of genes consists of different alleles, one allele is dominant over the other, recessive, allele.*

**CONCEPT FIX** What makes an allele **dominant**? In the case of flower colour in Mendel's peas, the purple allele is declared to be dominant simply because, when both alleles are present, the flowers are purple rather than white. More generally, when an organism carries two different alleles, the dominant allele is simply the one that determines the appearance of the organism. In the years since Mendel's work, various mechanisms underlying dominance have been discovered. For example, notice the round versus wrinkled pea seed shape character shown in Figure 9.3. We now know that round seeds contain a branched form of starch called *amylopectin*, and wrinkled seeds do not. In the DNA of pea plants there is a gene that codes for an enzyme that produces amylopectin. At some time

in the past, a mutation in this gene created an alternative, mutant, version. This mutant allele codes for an enzyme that is nonfunctional and produces no amylopectin. Therefore, plants that contain both alleles produce both the functional and the nonfunctional enzymes. Although 50% of the enzymes are likely nonfunctional, the functional enzymes create enough amylopectin to result in round seeds. Since the allele coding the functional enzyme determines the appearance of the seeds in such plants, it is called the *dominant allele. Notice that dominant alleles do not directly inhibit recessive alleles.* ⬣

As a third hypothesis, Mendel proposed the following: the pairs of alleles that control a character **segregate** (separate) as gametes are formed; half the gametes carry one allele, and the other half carry the other allele. This hypothesis is now known as Mendel's **principle of segregation**. During fertilization, fusion of the haploid maternal and paternal gametes produces a diploid nucleus called the *zygote nucleus*. The zygote nucleus receives one allele for the character from the male gamete and one allele for the same character from the female gamete, reuniting the pairs.

Mendel's three hypotheses explained the results of the crosses, as summarized in **Figure 9.4**. Both alleles of the flower colour gene in the true-breeding parent plant with purple flowers are the same. The symbol *P* is used here to designate this allele, with the capital letter indicating that it is dominant, which gives this true-breeding parent the *PP* combination of alleles. Such an individual is called a **homozygote** (*homo* = same) and is said to be **homozygous** for the *P* allele. Therefore, when the individual produces gametes and the paired alleles separate during meiosis, all the gametes from this individual will receive a *P* allele (steps 1 and 2 in Figure 9.4).

In the original true-breeding parent with white flowers, both alleles of the flower colour gene are also the same. Here the symbol *p* is used to designate this allele, with the lowercase letter indicating that it is recessive, which gives this true-breeding plant the homozygous *pp* combination of alleles. These alleles also separate during meiosis, leading to gametes that all contain one *p* allele.

All the $F_1$ plants produced by crossing purple-flowered and white-flowered plants—the cross *PP* × *pp*—received the same combination of alleles: *P* from one parent and *p* from the other (step 3 in Figure 9.4). An individual of this type, with two different alleles of a gene, is called a **heterozygote** (*hetero* = different) and is said to be **heterozygous** for the trait. Because *P* is dominant over *p*, all the *Pp* plants have purple flowers, even though they also carry the allele for white flowers. An $F_1$ heterozygote produced from a cross that involves a single character is called a **monohybrid** (*mono* = one; *hybrid* = an offspring of parents with different traits).

According to Mendel's hypotheses, all the *Pp* plants in the $F_1$ generation produce two kinds of gametes. Because the heterozygous *Pp* pair separates during meiosis I, half the gametes receive the *P* allele and half receive the *p* allele (steps 4 and 5 of Figure 9.4). Step 5 of Figure 9.4 shows how these gametes can combine during selfing of $F_1$ plants. Generally, a cross between

FIGURE 9.4   **Experimental Research**

## The Principle of Segregation: Inheritance of Flower Colour in Garden Peas

**Question:** How is flower colour in garden peas inherited?

**Experiment:** Mendel crossed a true-breeding, purple-flowered plant with a true-breeding, white-flowered plant and analyzed the progeny through the $F_1$ and $F_2$ generations. We explain this cross here in modern terms.

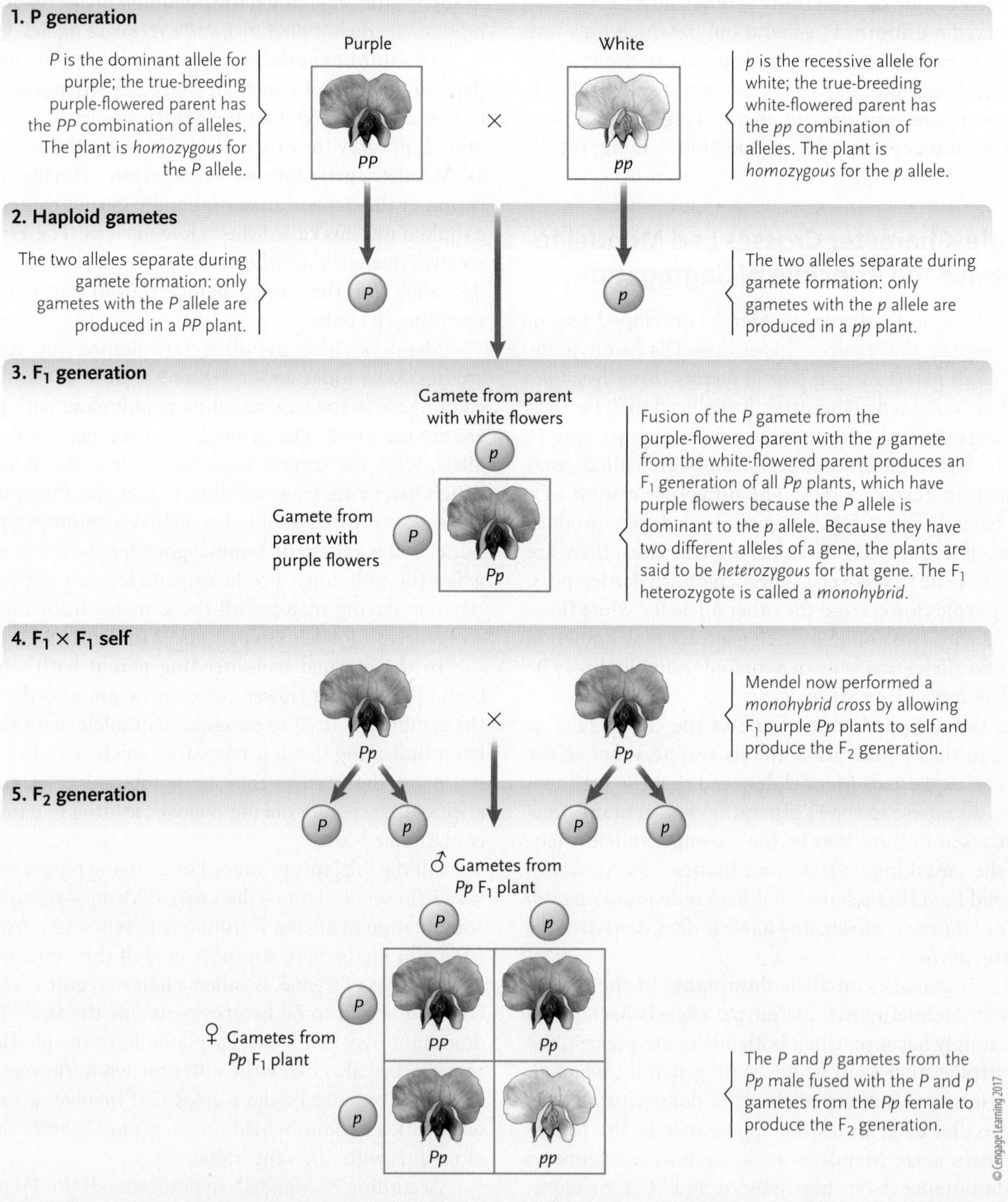

### 1. P generation

*P* is the dominant allele for purple; the true-breeding purple-flowered parent has the *PP* combination of alleles. The plant is *homozygous* for the *P* allele.

Purple

White

$\times$

*PP*

*pp*

*p* is the recessive allele for white; the true-breeding white-flowered parent has the *pp* combination of alleles. The plant is *homozygous* for the *p* allele.

### 2. Haploid gametes

The two alleles separate during gamete formation: only gametes with the *P* allele are produced in a *PP* plant.

*P*

*p*

The two alleles separate during gamete formation: only gametes with the *p* allele are produced in a *pp* plant.

### 3. $F_1$ generation

Gamete from parent with white flowers

*p*

Gamete from parent with purple flowers

*P*

*Pp*

Fusion of the *P* gamete from the purple-flowered parent with the *p* gamete from the white-flowered parent produces an $F_1$ generation of all *Pp* plants, which have purple flowers because the *P* allele is dominant to the *p* allele. Because they have two different alleles of a gene, the plants are said to be *heterozygous* for that gene. The $F_1$ heterozygote is called a *monohybrid*.

### 4. $F_1 \times F_1$ self

*Pp*

$\times$

*Pp*

Mendel now performed a *monohybrid cross* by allowing $F_1$ purple *Pp* plants to self and produce the $F_2$ generation.

### 5. $F_2$ generation

*P*   *p*      *P*   *p*

♂ Gametes from *Pp* $F_1$ plant

*P*   *p*

♀ Gametes from *Pp* $F_1$ plant

*P*

*p*

|  | *PP* | *Pp* |
|---|---|---|
|  | *Pp* | *pp* |

The *P* and *p* gametes from the *Pp* male fused with the *P* and *p* gametes from the *Pp* female to produce the $F_2$ generation.

© Cengage Learning 2017

**Results:** Mendel's selfing of the $F_1$ purple-flowered plants produced an $F_2$ generation consisting of 3/4 purple-flowered and 1/4 white-flowered plants. White flowers were inherited as a recessive trait, disappearing in the $F_1$ and reappearing in the $F_2$.

**Conclusion:** The results supported Mendel's principle of segregation hypothesis that the pairs of alleles that control a character segregate as gametes are formed, with half the gametes carrying one allele, and the other half carrying the other allele.

two individuals that are each heterozygous for the same pair of alleles—*Pp* × *Pp* here—is called a **monohybrid cross**. The gametes are entered in both the rows and the columns in Figure 9.4; the cells show the possible combinations. Combining two gametes that both carry the *P* allele produces a *PP* F₂ plant; combining *P* from one parent and *p* from the other produces a *Pp* plant; and combining *p* from both F₁ parents produces a *pp* F₂ plant. The homozygous *PP* and heterozygous *Pp* plants in the F₂ generation have purple flowers, the dominant trait; the homozygous *pp* offspring have white flowers, the recessive trait.

Mendel's hypotheses explain how individuals may differ genetically but still look the same. The *PP* and *Pp* plants, although genetically different, both have purple flowers. In modern terminology, **genotype** refers to the *genetic constitution of an organism*, and **phenotype** (Greek *phainein* = to show) refers to its *outward appearance*. In this case, the two different genotypes *PP* and *Pp* produce the same purple-flower phenotype.

Thus, the results of Mendel's crosses support his three hypotheses:

1. The genes that govern genetic characters are present in two copies in individuals.
2. If different alleles are present in an individual's pair of genes, one allele is dominant over the other.
3. The two alleles of a gene segregate and enter gametes singly.

## 9.1d Mendel Could Predict Both Classes and Proportions of Offspring from His Hypotheses

Mendel could predict both classes and proportions of offspring from his hypotheses. To understand how Mendel's hypotheses allowed him to predict the proportions of offspring resulting from a genetic cross, let's review the mathematical rules that govern **probability**, that is, the possibility that an outcome will occur if it is a matter of chance, as in the random fertilization of an egg by a sperm cell that contains one allele or another.

In the mathematics of probability, the likelihood of an outcome is predicted on a scale of 0 to 1. An outcome that is certain to occur has a probability of 1 (100%), and an outcome that cannot possibly happen has a probability of 0. The standard game die, a cube with one of the numbers 1 through 6 on each face, is a familiar model to demonstrate working with probability. In general, we determine the probability of any given outcome (e.g., rolling a 4) by dividing that outcome by the total number of possible outcomes. For obtaining 4 in rolling a die, the probability is 1 divided by 6, or 1/6. The likelihood of rolling an even number (2 or 4 or 6) is 3/6 = 1/2. The probabilities of all the possible outcomes, when added together, must equal 1.

**THE PRODUCT RULE IN PROBABILITY** If you roll two dice together, what is the chance of rolling double fours? Because the outcome of one die has no effect on the outcome of the

other one, the two rolls are independent. When two or more events are independent, the probability that they will both occur is calculated using the **product rule**: their individual probabilities are multiplied. That is, the probability that events A and B *both* will occur equals the probability of event A *multiplied* by the probability of event B. For example, the probability of getting a 4 on the first die is 1/6; the probability of a 4 on the second die is also 1/6 (**Figure 9.5**). Because the events are independent, the probability of getting a 4 on both dice is 1/6 × 1/6 = 1/36. Applying this principle to human families, the sex of one child has no effect on the sex of the next child; therefore, the probability of having four girls in a row is the product of their individual probabilities (very close to 1/2 for each birth): 1/2 × 1/2 × 1/2 × 1/2 = 1/16.

**THE SUM RULE IN PROBABILITY** Another relationship, the **sum rule**, applies when several different events all give the same outcome; that is, the probability that *either* event A *or* event B *or* event C will occur equals the probability of event A *plus* the probability of event B *plus* the probability of event C. Returning to the two dice example, what is the probability of rolling a 7? Several different events all give the same total. One could make a total of 7 from a 1 on the first die and a 6 on the second, or a 5 on the first and a 2 on the second, or a 4 on the first and a 3 on the second. Each of these three combinations would be expected to occur at a frequency of 1/6 × 1/6 = 1/36. You should be able to see three more possible combinations that are just the opposite of the first three, that is, 6 on the first die and 1 on the second,

**a. Likelihood of rolling a double four**

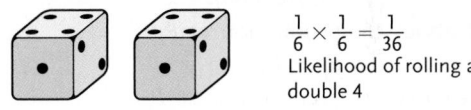

$$\frac{1}{6} \times \frac{1}{6} = \frac{1}{36}$$
Likelihood of rolling a double 4

**b. Likelihood of rolling a seven in any combination**

**FIGURE 9.5 Rules of probability. (a)** For each die, the probability of a 4 is 1/6. Because the outcome of one die is independent of that of the other, the combined probability of rolling a 4 on both dice at the same time is calculated by multiplying the individual probabilities (product rule).
**(b)** There are six different possible outcomes for rolling two dice that add up to 7. The total likelihood of rolling a 7 is calculated by adding the individual probabilities (sum rule).

and so on, for a total of six different ways to roll a 7; that is, there are six ways of obtaining the same outcome. Therefore, for the probability of rolling a 7, we sum the individual probabilities to get the final probability: $1/36 + 1/36 + 1/36 + 1/36 + 1/36 + 1/36 = 6/36 = 1/6$. On average, you could expect to roll a combination of numbers totalling 7 once in every six attempts.

**PROBABILITY IN MENDEL'S CROSSES** Since the randomness inherent in meiosis is comparable to the randomness inherent in rolling dice, the same rules of probability just discussed apply to genes carried on chromosomes in Mendel's crosses. For example, in the crosses that involve the purple-flowered and white-flowered traits, half the gametes of the $F_1$ generation contain the *P* allele of the gene and half contain the *p* allele (see Figure 9.4). To produce a *PP* zygote, two *P* gametes must combine. The probability of selecting a *P* gamete from one $F_1$ parent is 1/2, and the probability of selecting a *P* gamete from the other $F_1$ parent is also 1/2. Therefore, the probability of producing a *PP* zygote from this monohybrid cross is $1/2 \times 1/2 = 1/4$. That is, by the product rule, one-fourth of the offspring of the $F_1$ cross *Pp* × *Pp* are expected to be *PP*, which have purple flowers **(Figure 9.6a)**. By the same line of reasoning, one-fourth of the $F_2$ offspring are expected to be *pp*, which have white flowers (Figure 9.6b).

What about the production of *Pp* offspring? The cross *Pp* × *Pp* can produce *Pp* in two different ways. A *P* gamete from the first parent can combine with a *p* gamete from the second parent (*Pp*), or a *p* gamete from the first parent can combine with a *P* gamete from the second parent (*pP*) (Figure 9.6c). Because there are two different ways to get the same outcome, we apply the sum rule to obtain the combined probability. Each of the ways to get *Pp* has an individual probability of 1/4; when we add these individual probabilities, we have $1/4 + 1/4 = 1/2$. Therefore, half the offspring are expected to be *Pp*, which have purple flowers. We could get the same result from the requirement that all the individual probabilities must add up to 1. If the probability of *PP* is 1/4 and the probability of *pp* is 1/4, then the probability of the remaining possibility, *Pp*, must

be 1/2 because the total of the individual probabilities must add up to 1: $1/4 + 1/4 + 1/2 = 1$.

What if we want to know the probability of obtaining purple flowers in the cross *Pp* × *Pp*? In this case, the rule of addition applies, because there are two ways to get purple flowers: genotypes *PP* and *Pp*. Adding the individual probabilities of these combinations, 1/4 *PP* + 1/2 *Pp*, gives a total of 3/4, indicating that three-fourths of the $F_2$ offspring are expected to have purple flowers. Because the total probabilities must add up to 1, the remaining one-fourth of the offspring are expected to have white flowers (1/4 *pp*). These proportions give the ratio 3:1, which is close to the ratio Mendel obtained in his cross.

**Gametes from $F_1$
purple *Pp* plant**

**Gametes from $F_1$ purple *Pp* plant**

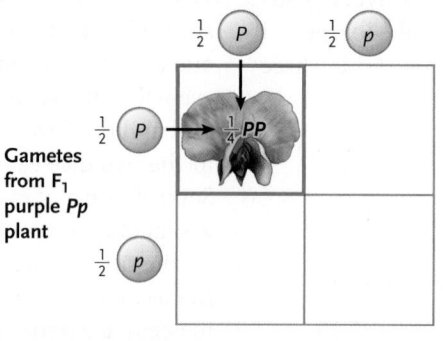

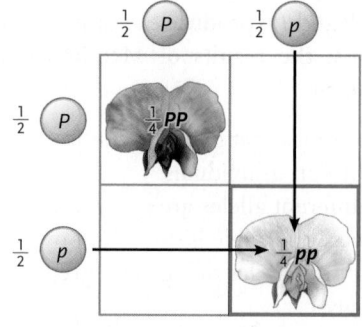

**a.** To produce an $F_2$ plant with the *PP* genotype, two *P* gametes must combine. The probability of selecting a *P* gamete from one $F_1$ parent is $\frac{1}{2}$, and the probability of selecting a *P* gamete from the other $F_1$ parent is also $\frac{1}{2}$. Using the product rule, the probability of producing purple-flowered *PP* plant from a *Pp* × *Pp* cross is $\frac{1}{2} \times \frac{1}{2} = \frac{1}{4}$.

**b.** To produce an $F_2$ plant with the *pp* genotype, two *p* gametes must combine. The probability of selecting a *p* gamete from one $F_1$ parent is $\frac{1}{2}$, and the probability of selecting a *p* gamete from the other $F_1$ parent is also $\frac{1}{2}$. Using the product rule, the probability of producing a white-flowered *pp* plant from a *Pp* × *Pp* cross is $\frac{1}{2} \times \frac{1}{2} = \frac{1}{4}$.

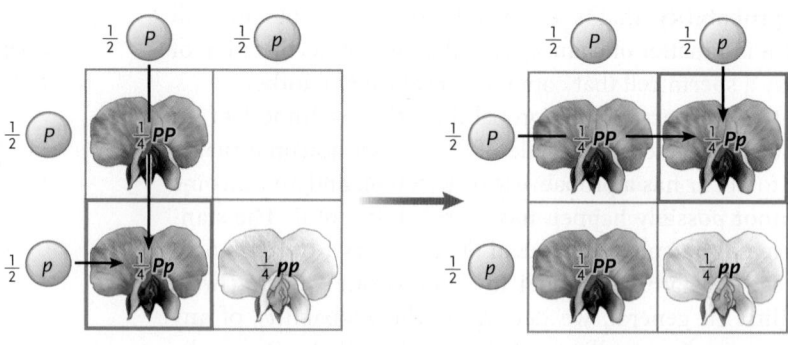

**c.** To produce an $F_2$ plant with the *Pp* genotype, a *P* gamete must combine with a *p* gamete. The cross *Pp* × *Pp* can produce *Pp* offspring in two different ways: (1) a *P* gamete from the first parent can combine with a *p* gamete from the second parent or (2) a *p* gamete from the first parent can combine with a *P* gamete from the second parent. We apply the sum rule to obtain the combined probability: each of the ways to get *Pp* has an individual probability of $\frac{1}{4}$, so the probability of *Pp*, purple-flowered offspring, is $\frac{1}{4} + \frac{1}{4} = \frac{1}{2}$.

**FIGURE 9.6 Punnett square method for predicting offspring and their ratios in genetic crosses.** The example is the $F_1 \times F_1$ cross of purple-flowered plants from Figure 9.5. Each cell shows the genotype and proportion of one type of $F_2$ plant.

In Figure 9.6 we have just stepped through the **Punnett square** method for determining the genotypes of offspring and their expected proportions. To use the Punnett square, write the probability that meiosis will produce gametes with each type of allele from one parent at the top of the diagram and write the chance of obtaining each type of allele from the other parent on the left side. Then fill in the cells by combining the alleles from the top and from the left and multiplying their individual probabilities.

### 9.1e Mendel Used a Testcross to Check the Validity of His Hypotheses

Mendel realized that he could assess the validity of his hypotheses by determining whether they could be used successfully to *predict* the outcome of a cross of a different type than he had tried so far. Accordingly, he crossed an $F_1$ plant with purple flowers, assumed to have the heterozygous genotype *Pp*, with a true-breeding white-flowered plant, with the homozygous genotype *pp* (**Figure 9.7**, Experiment 1). There are two expected classes of offspring, *Pp* and *pp*, both with a probability of 1/2. Thus, the phenotypes of the offspring are expected to be 1 purple-flowered : 1 white-flowered. Mendel's actual results closely approach the expected 1:1 ratio. Mendel also made the same type of cross with all the other traits used in his study, including those traits affecting seed shape, seed colour, and plant height, and found the same 1:1 ratio.

A cross between an individual with the dominant phenotype and a homozygous recessive individual, such as the one described, is called a **testcross**. Geneticists use a testcross as a standard test to determine whether an individual with a dominant trait is a heterozygote or a homozygote, because these cannot be distinguished phenotypically. If the offspring of the testcross are of two types, with half displaying the dominant trait and half the recessive trait, then the individual in question must be a heterozygote (see Figure 9.7, Experiment 1). If all the offspring display the dominant trait, the individual in question must be a homozygote. For example, the cross *PP* × *pp* gives all *Pp* progeny, which shows the dominant purple phenotype (see Figure 9.7, Experiment 2).

While the principle of a testcross holds for humans, it is obviously ethically unacceptable to conduct such controlled matings. However, the concept can still be useful in reverse by noting the traits that are inherited in families over several generations and working backward to deduce whether a parent must have been a homozygote or a heterozygote (see also Chapter 10).

### 9.1f Mendel Tested the Independence of Different Genes in Crosses

Mendel next asked what happens in crosses when more than one character is involved. Would the alleles of different characters be inherited independently, or would they interact to alter their expected proportions in offspring?

To answer these questions, Mendel crossed parental stocks that had differences in two of the hereditary characters he was studying: seed shape and seed colour. His single-character crosses had shown that each was controlled by a pair of alleles.

For seed shape, the *RR* or *Rr* genotype produces round seeds and the *rr* genotype produces wrinkled seeds. For seed colour, yellow is dominant. The homozygous *YY* and heterozygous *Yy* genotypes produce yellow seeds; the homozygous *yy* genotype produces green seeds.

**Figure 9.8** shows how Mendel crossed plants that bred true for the production of round and yellow seeds (*RR YY*) with plants that bred true for the production of wrinkled and green seeds (*rr yy*). The cross, *RR YY* × *rr yy*, yielded an $F_1$ generation that consisted of all round yellow seeds, with the genotype *Rr Yy*. A zygote produced from a cross that involves two characters is called a **dihybrid** (*di* = two).

Mendel then planted the $F_1$ seeds, grew the plants to maturity, and selfed them; that is, he crossed the $F_1$ plants to themselves. A cross between two individuals that are heterozygous for two pairs of alleles—here *Rr Yy* × *Rr Yy*—is called a **dihybrid cross** (see Figure 9.8). The seeds produced by these plants, representing the $F_2$ generation, included 315 round yellow seeds, 101 wrinkled yellow seeds, 108 round green seeds, and 32 wrinkled green seeds. Mendel noted that these numbers were close to a 9:3:3:1 ratio (3:1 for round: wrinkled, and 3:1 for yellow: green).

This 9:3:3:1 ratio was consistent with Mendel's previous findings if he added one further hypothesis: *The alleles of the genes that govern the two characters segregate independently during formation of gametes.* That is, the allele for seed shape that the gamete receives (*R* or *r*) has no influence on which allele for seed colour it receives (*Y* or *y*), and vice versa. The two events are completely independent. Mendel termed this assumption **independent assortment**; it is now known as Mendel's **principle of independent assortment**.

To understand the effect of independent assortment in the cross, assume that the *RR YY* parent produces only *R Y* gametes, and that the *rr yy* parent produces only *r y* gametes. In the $F_1$ generation, all possible combinations of these gametes produce only one genotype, *Rr Yy,* in the offspring. As observed, all the $F_1$ will be round yellow seeds.

If the alleles that control seed shape and seed colour assort independently in gamete formation, each $F_1$ plant grown from the seeds will produce four types of gametes. As shown in **Figure 9.9**, the random alignment of homologous chromosome pairs in meiosis I ensures that the *R* allele for seed shape can be delivered independently to a gamete with either the *Y* or the *y* allele for seed colour, and similarly, the *r* allele can be delivered to a gamete with either the *Y* or the *y* allele. Thus, the independent assortment of genes from the *Rr Yy* parents allows the organism to produce, overall, four types of gametes with equal probability: 1/4 *R Y*, 1/4 *R y*, 1/4 *r Y*, and 1/4 *r y*. These gametes and their probabilities are entered as the row and column headings of the Punnett square in Figure 9.9.

Filling in the cells of the diagram (see Figure 9.8) gives 16 combinations of alleles, all with an equal probability of 1 in every 16 offspring. Of these, the genotypes *RR YY*, *RR Yy*, *Rr YY*, and *Rr Yy* all have the same phenotype: round yellow seeds. These combinations occur in 9 of the 16 cells in the diagram, giving a total probability of 9/16. The genotypes *rr YY* and *rr Yy*,

FIGURE 9.7    **Experimental Research**

## Testing the Predicted Outcomes of Genetic Crosses

**Question:** How can it be determined whether a plant with the dominant phenotype is a heterozygote or a homozygote?

**Experiment 1:** Mendel crossed an F₁ plant with purple flowers, predicted to have a $Pp$ genotype, with a true-breeding, white-flowered plant and analyzed the flower colour phenotypes in the offspring.

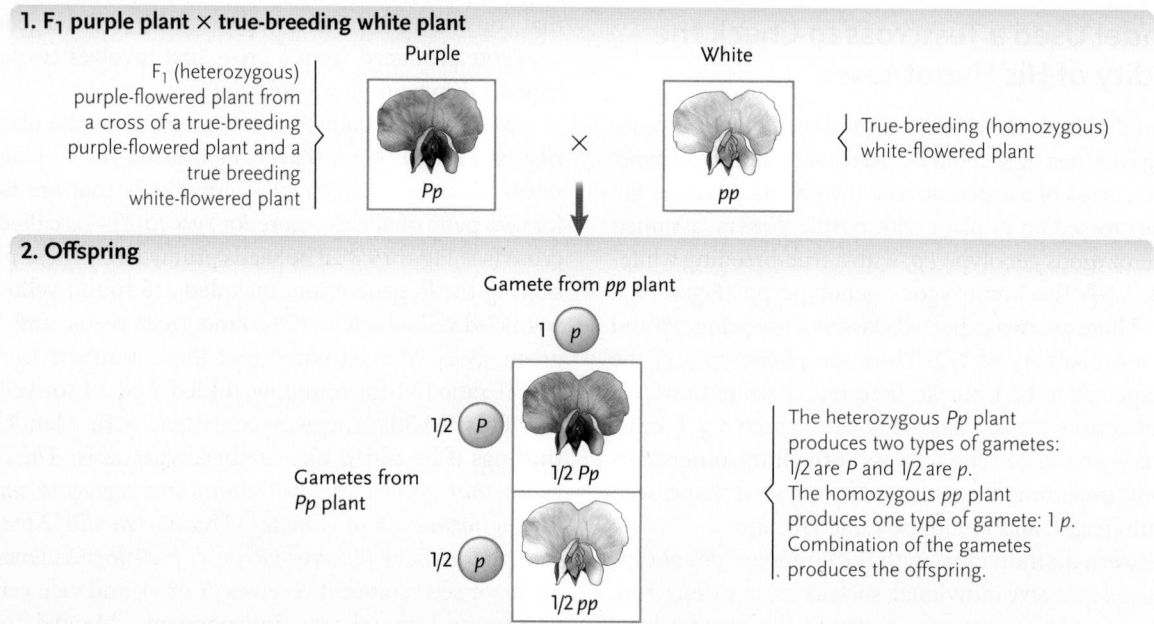

**1. F₁ purple plant × true-breeding white plant**

F₁ (heterozygous) purple-flowered plant from a cross of a true-breeding purple-flowered plant and a true breeding white-flowered plant

Purple

$Pp$

×

White

$pp$

True-breeding (homozygous) white-flowered plant

**2. Offspring**

Gamete from $pp$ plant

1  $p$

1/2  $P$

Gametes from $Pp$ plant

1/2 $Pp$

1/2  $p$

1/2 $pp$

The heterozygous $Pp$ plant produces two types of gametes: 1/2 are $P$ and 1/2 are $p$. The homozygous $pp$ plant produces one type of gamete: 1 $p$. Combination of the gametes produces the offspring.

**Results:** Predicted progeny from a cross of a purple-flowered heterozygote with a true-breeding, white-flowered plant is 1 $Pp$ purple-flowered and 1 $pp$ white-flowered. Mendel observed 85 purple-flowered and 81 white-flowered plants, close to the prediction.

**Experiment 2:** Mendel crossed a true-breeding plant with purple flowers, predicted to have a $PP$ genotype, with a true-breeding, white-flowered plant and analyzed the flower colour phenotypes in the offspring.

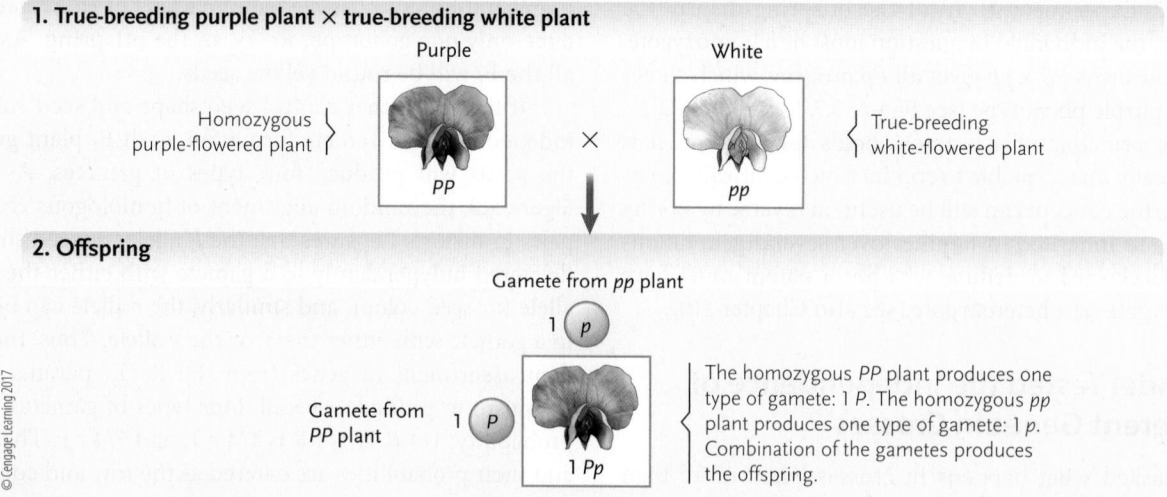

**1. True-breeding purple plant × true-breeding white plant**

Homozygous purple-flowered plant

Purple

$PP$

×

White

$pp$

True-breeding white-flowered plant

**2. Offspring**

Gamete from $pp$ plant

1  $p$

Gamete from $PP$ plant

1  $P$

1 $Pp$

The homozygous $PP$ plant produces one type of gamete: 1 $P$. The homozygous $pp$ plant produces one type of gamete: 1 $p$. Combination of the gametes produces the offspring.

**Results:** The outcome of crossing a purple-flowered homozygote with a true-breeding, white-flowered plant is all $Pp$ plants, which have purple flowers.

**Conclusion:** The outcome of a cross between (here) a plant with a dominant phenotype and a plant with a recessive phenotype—a testcross—gives a different result depending on whether the plant with the dominant phenotype is a homozygote or a heterozygote. Therefore, a testcross is a useful way to determine the genotype for an individual with a dominant phenotype.

© Cengage Learning 2017

FIGURE 9.8 **Experimental Research**

## The Principle of Independent Assortment

**Question:** Do alleles of genes for two different characters in garden peas assort independently in a cross?

**Experiment:** Mendel crossed a true-breeding plant with round and yellow seeds with a true-breeding plant with wrinkled and green seeds and analyzed the progeny through the $F_1$ and $F_2$ generations. We explain this cross here in modern terms.

**1. P generation**

The genotype of the true-breeding round, yellow parent is *RR YY*, where *R* is the dominant allele for round, and *Y* is the dominant allele for yellow.

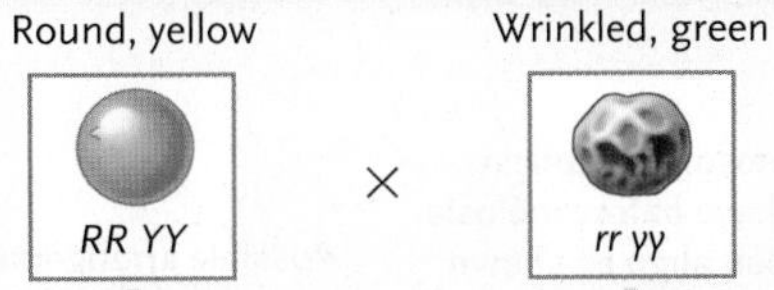

Round, yellow
*RR YY*

×

Wrinkled, green
*rr yy*

The genotype of the true-breeding wrinkled, green parent is *rr yy*, where *r* is the recessive allele for wrinkled, and *y* is the recessive allele for green.

**2. Haploid gametes**

Only gametes with the *R* and *Y* alleles are produced in an *RR YY* plant.

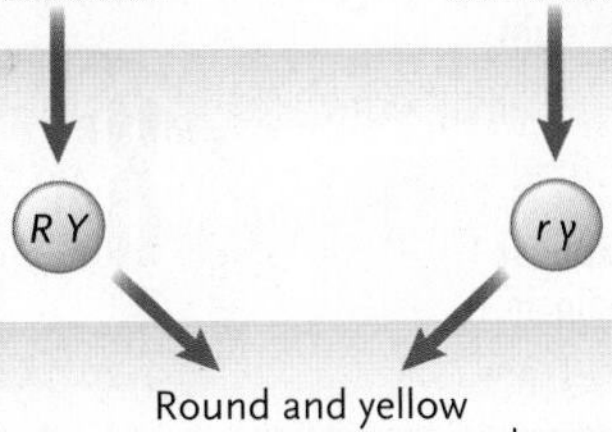

*R Y*

*r y*

Only gametes with the *r* and *y* alleles are produced in an *rr yy* plant.

**3. $F_1$ generation**

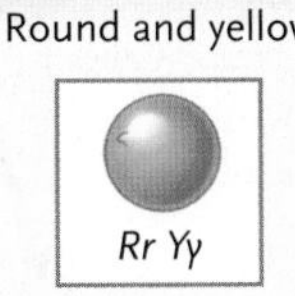

Round and yellow

*Rr Yy*

Fusion of an *R Y* gamete from the round, yellow parent with an *r y* gamete from the wrinkled, green parent produces an $F_1$ generation all of which have the genotype *Rr Yy*, phenotype round, yellow seeds. The doubly heterozygous individual is called a *dihybrid*. The seeds are round because the *R* allele is dominant to the *r* allele, and yellow because the *Y* allele is dominant to the *y* allele.

**4. $F_1$ × $F_1$ self**

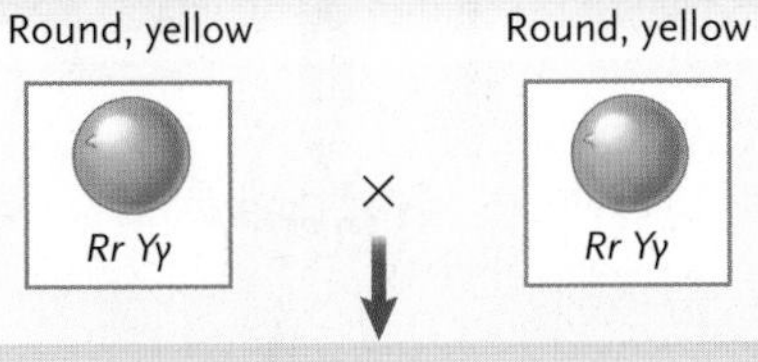

Round, yellow
*Rr Yy*

×

Round, yellow
*Rr Yy*

Mendel then planted the $F_1$ seeds, grew the plants to maturity, and selfed them; that is, he crossed the $F_1$ to themselves. A cross such as this of two double heterozygotes is called a *dihybrid cross*.

**5. $F_2$ generation**

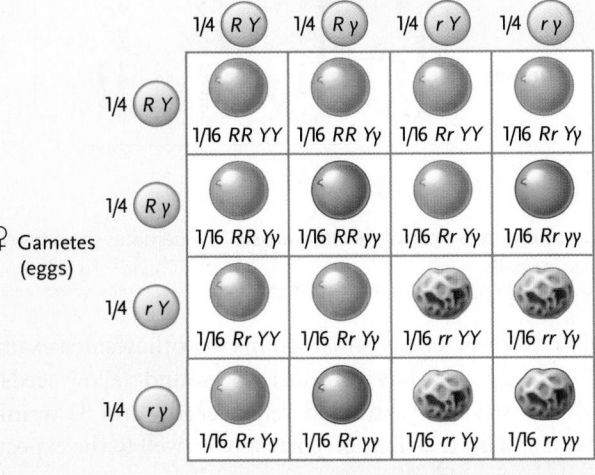

♂ Gametes

If the alleles that control seed shape and seed colour assort independently, each $F_1$ plant grown from the seeds would produce four types of gametes: the *R* allele for seed shape would go to a gamete with either the *Y* or *y* allele for seed colour, and similarly, the *r* allele would go to a gamete with either the *Y* or *y* allele. Thus, independent assortment of genes from the *Rr Yy* parents is expected to produce four types of gametes with equal probability: 1/4 *R Y*, 1/4 *R y*, 1/4 *r Y*, and 1/4 *r y*. Random fusion of the four different male gametes with the four different female gametes produces the $F_2$ generation.

**Results:** Filling in the cells of the Punnett square gives 16 combinations, each with an equal probability of 1 in every 16 offspring if the alleles of the two genes assort independently. The 16 combinations resulting from independent assortment give an expected $F_2$ phenotypic ratio of 9 round yellow, 3 round green, 3 wrinkled yellow, 1 wrinkled green. Mendel's selfing of the $F_1$ *Rr Yy* round yellow plants produced an $F_2$ generation with 315 round yellow: 108 round green: 101 wrinkled yellow: 32 wrinkled green, which is close to a 9:3:3:1 ratio (3:1 for round: wrinkled, and 3:1 for yellow: green).

**Conclusion:** The results indicate that the alleles of the genes for the two characters assort independently during the formation of gametes.

**Behaviour of chromosomes in meiosis**

**Meiosis in male or female diploid parent**

**Behaviour of genes and alleles in meiosis and their correspondence to Mendel's principles**

Chromosomes occur in pairs in diploid individuals.

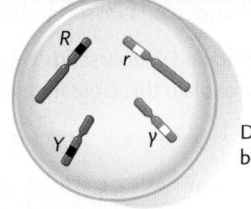

Diploid nucleus before replication

Alleles of genes occur in pairs in diploid individuals. (*R r* is a pair of alleles and *Y y* is another.)

Chromosomes replicate in S phase before meiosis and then align as shown at left OR at right

Possible arrangement 1

Possible arrangement 2

Metaphase I of meiosis

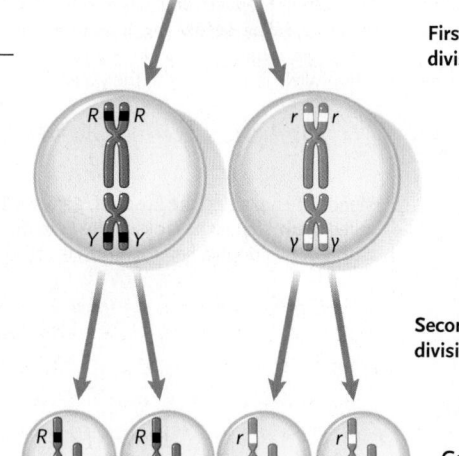

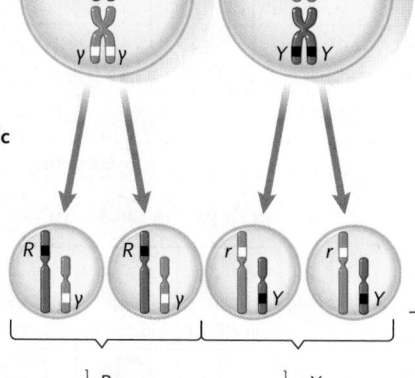

First meiotic division

During chromosome separation, the chromosomes of different pairs segregate independently.

The two meiotic divisions separate chromosome pairs and deliver them singly to gametes.

Second meiotic division

Gametes

$\frac{1}{4}RY$     $\frac{1}{4}ry$     $\frac{1}{4}Ry$     $\frac{1}{4}rY$

**Principle of segregation.** The two alleles of a gene segregate from each other during gamete formation. (*R* and *r* enter gametes singly, as do *Y* and *y*.)

**Principle of independent assortment.** During the segregation of alleles into gametes, the alleles of different pairs assort independently. (*R r* and *Y y* alleles give four combinations in gametes in equal proportion.)

© Cengage Learning 2017

**FIGURE 9.9** **The parallels between the behaviour of chromosomes and genes and alleles in meiosis.** The gametes show four different combinations of alleles produced by independent segregation of chromosome pairs.

which produce wrinkled yellow seeds, are found in three cells, giving a probability of 3/16 for this phenotype. Similarly, the genotypes *RR yy* and *Rr yy*, which yield round green seeds, occur in three cells, giving a probability of 3/16. Finally, the genotype *rr yy*, which produces wrinkled green seeds, is found in only one cell and therefore has a probability of 1/16.

These probabilities of round yellow seeds, wrinkled yellow seeds, round green seeds, and wrinkled green seeds, in a 9:3:3:1 ratio, closely approximate the actual results of 315:101:108:32 obtained by Mendel. Thus, Mendel's first three hypotheses, with the added hypothesis of independent assortment, explain the observed results of his dihybrid cross. Mendel's testcrosses

completely confirmed his hypotheses: for example, the testcross *Rr Yy × rr yy* produced 55 round yellow seeds, 51 round green seeds, 49 wrinkled yellow seeds, and 53 wrinkled green seeds. This distribution corresponds well to the expected 1:1:1:1 ratio in the offspring. (Try to set up a Punnett square for this cross and predict the expected classes of offspring and their frequencies.)

Mendel's first three hypotheses provided a coherent explanation of the pattern of inheritance for alternative traits of the same character, such as purple and white for flower colour. His fourth hypothesis, independent assortment, addressed the inheritance of traits for different characters, such as seed shape, seed colour, and flower colour, and showed that, instead of being inherited together, the traits of different characters were distributed independently to offspring.

## 9.1g Mendel's Research Founded the Field of Genetics

Mendel's techniques and conclusions were so advanced for his time that their significance was not immediately appreciated. Mendel's success was based partly on a good choice of experimental organism. He was also lucky. The characters he chose all segregate independently; that is, none of them are physically near each other on the chromosomes, a condition that would have given ratios other than 9:3:3:1, showing that they do not assort independently.

We now know that Mendel's findings demonstrated the patterns by which genes and chromosomes determine inheritance. Yet, when Mendel first reported his findings during the nineteenth century, the structure and function of chromosomes and the patterns by which they are separated and distributed to gametes were unknown; meiosis remained to be discovered. In addition, his use of mathematical analysis was a new and radical departure from the usual biological techniques of his day.

Mendel reported his results to a small group of fellow intellectuals in Brünn and presented his results in 1866 in a natural history journal published in the city. His article received little notice outside of Brünn, and those who read it were unable to appreciate the significance of his findings. His work was overlooked until the turn of the century, when three investigators, Hugo de Vries in Holland, Carl Correns in Germany, and Erich von Tschermak in Austria, independently performed a series of breeding experiments similar to Mendel's and reached the same conclusions. These investigators, in searching through previously published scientific articles, were surprised to discover Mendel's article about his experiments conducted three decades earlier. Each gave credit to Mendel's discoveries, and the quality and far-reaching implications of his work were at last realized. Mendel died in 1884, less than 20 years before the rediscovery of his experiments and conclusions; thus, he never received the recognition that he so richly deserved during his lifetime.

Mendel was unable to relate the behaviour of his "factors" (genes) to cell structures because the critical information he required was not obtained until later, through the discovery of meiosis during the 1890s. The next section describes how a genetics student familiar with meiosis was able to make the connection between Mendel's factors and chromosomes.

## 9.1h Sutton's Chromosome Theory of Inheritance Related Mendel's Genes to Chromosomes

By the time Mendel's results were rediscovered in the early 1900s, critical information from studies of meiosis was available. It was not long before a genetics student, Walter Sutton, recognized the similarities between the inheritance of the genes discovered by Mendel and the behaviour of chromosomes in meiosis and fertilization (Figure 9.9).

In a historic article published in 1903, Sutton, then a graduate student at Columbia University in New York, drew all the necessary parallels between genes and chromosomes:

- Chromosomes occur in pairs in sexually reproducing, diploid organisms, as do the alleles of each gene.
- The chromosomes of each pair are separated and delivered singly to gametes, as are the alleles of a gene.
- The separation of any pair of chromosomes in meiosis and gamete formation is independent of the separation of other pairs (see Figure 9.9), as in the independent assortment of the alleles of different genes in Mendel's dihybrid crosses.
- Finally, one member of each chromosome pair is derived in fertilization from the male parent, and the other member is derived from the female parent, in an exact parallel with the two alleles of a gene.

From these similarities in behaviour, Sutton correctly concluded that genes and their alleles are carried on the chromosomes, a conclusion known today as the **chromosome theory of inheritance**.

The exact parallel between the principles set forth by Mendel and the behaviour of chromosomes and genes during meiosis is shown in Figure 9.9 for an $Rr\ Yy$ diploid. For a cross of $Rr\ Yy \times Rr\ Yy$, when the gametes fuse randomly the progeny will show a phenotypic ratio of 9:3:3:1. This mechanism explains the same ratio of gametes and progeny as the $Rr\ Yy \times Rr\ Yy$ cross in Figure 9.8.

The particular site on a chromosome at which a gene is located is called the **locus** (plural, *loci*) of the gene. The locus is a particular DNA sequence that usually encodes a protein or RNA product responsible for the phenotype controlled by the gene. A locus for a gene with two alleles, *A* and *a*, on a homologous pair of chromosomes is shown in **Figure 9.10**. At the molecular level, different alleles consist of small differences in the DNA sequence of a gene, which may result in functional differences in the

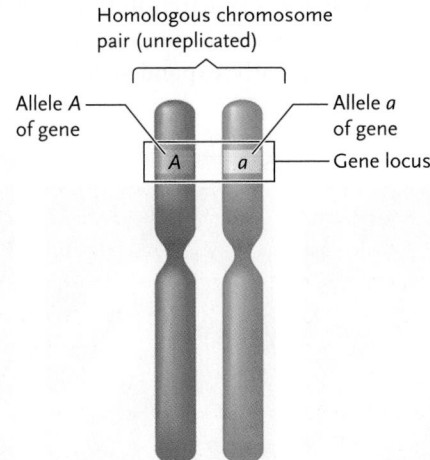

**FIGURE 9.10 A locus, the site occupied by a gene on a pair of homologous chromosomes.** Two alleles, *A* and *a*, of the gene are present at this locus in the homologous pair. These alleles have differences in the DNA sequence of the gene.

protein or RNA product encoded by the gene. These differences are detected as distinct phenotypes in the offspring of a cross.

All the genetics research conducted since the early 1900s has confirmed Mendel's basic hypotheses about inheritance. This research has shown that Mendel's conclusions apply to all types of organisms, from yeast and fruit flies to humans, and has led to the rapidly growing field of human genetics. In humans, a number of easily seen traits show inheritance patterns that follow Mendelian principles (**Figure 9.11**); for example, albinism, the lack of normal skin colour, is recessive to normal skin colour, and fingers with webs between them are recessive to normally separated fingers. Similarly, achondroplasia, the most frequent form of short-limb dwarfism, is a recessive trait that involves abnormal bone growth. Many human disorders that cannot be seen easily also show simple inheritance patterns. For instance, cystic fibrosis, in which a defect in the membrane transport of chloride ions leads to pulmonary and digestive dysfunctions and reduced life span, is a recessive trait.

The post-Mendel research has demonstrated additional patterns of inheritance (see the next section) that were not anticipated by Mendel and, in some circumstances, require modifications or additions to his hypotheses.

### STUDY BREAK QUESTIONS

1. What characteristics of the garden pea made this organism a good model system for Mendel?
2. How does independent assortment explain Mendel's dihybrid cross data?
3. How is an allele related to a locus?

## 9.2 Later Modifications and Additions to Mendel's Hypotheses

The rediscovery of Mendel's research in the early 1900s produced an immediate burst of interest in genetics. The research that followed greatly expanded our understanding of genes and their inheritance. That research fully supported Mendel's hypotheses, but also revealed many variations on the basic principles he had outlined. The following sections discuss each of these extensions of Mendel's fundamental principles.

### 9.2a In Incomplete Dominance, Products of Dominant Alleles Do Not Completely Compensate for those of Recessive Alleles

**Incomplete dominance** occurs when the effects of recessive alleles can be detected to some extent in heterozygotes. Flower colour in snapdragons can show incomplete dominance (**Figure 9.12**). If true-breeding, red-flowered and white-flowered snapdragon plants are crossed, all the $F_1$ offspring have pink flowers (see Figure 9.12). The pink colour might make it appear that the pure red and white colours have blended—mixing red and white makes pink. However, when two $F_1$ plants are crossed, the red and white traits both reappear in the $F_2$ generation, which has red, pink, and white flowers in numbers approximating a 1:2:1 ratio. This shows that the alleles themselves are not altered in the next generation, something that was unknown in Mendel's time (see Section 9.1).

This outcome can be explained by incomplete dominance between a $C^R$ allele for red colour and a $C^W$ allele for white colour. When one allele is not completely dominant to the other, we use a superscript to signify the character. In this case, $C$ signifies the character for flower colour and the superscripts indicate the alleles (R for red and W for white). Therefore, the initial cross is $C^R C^R$ (red) $\times$ $C^W C^W$ (white), which produces $C^R C^W$ $F_1$ (pink) plants. The $C^R$ allele encodes an enzyme that produces a red pigment, but two alleles ($C^R C^R$) are necessary to produce enough of the active form of the enzyme to produce fully red flowers. The enzyme is completely inactive in $C^W C^W$ plants, which produce colourless flowers that appear white because of the scattering of light by cell walls and other

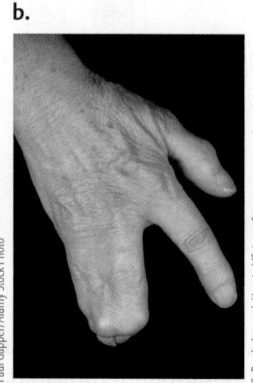

**a.**
**b.**
**c.**

**FIGURE 9.11 Human traits showing inheritance patterns that follow Mendelian principles. (a)** Lack of normal skin colour (albinism), **(b)** webbed fingers, **(c)** achondroplasia or short-limb dwarfism

FIGURE 9.12 **Experimental Research**

## Experiment Showing Incomplete Dominance of a Trait

**Question:** How is flower colour in snapdragons inherited?

**Experiment:** Cross a true-breeding, red-flowered snapdragon with a true-breeding, white-flowered snapdragon and analyze the progeny through the $F_1$ and $F_2$ generations.

### 1. P generation

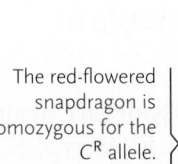
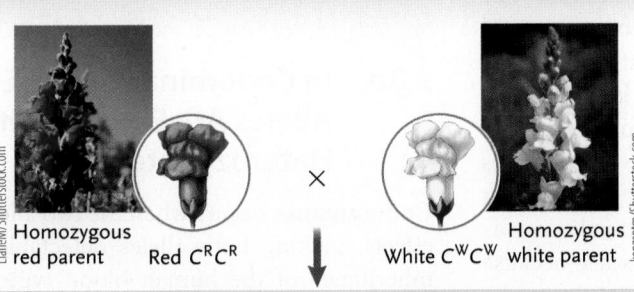

The red-flowered snapdragon is homozygous for the $C^R$ allele.

Homozygous red parent — Red $C^RC^R$

×

White $C^WC^W$ — Homozygous white parent

The white-flowered snapdragon is homozygous for the $C^W$ allele.

### 2. $F_1$ generation

$F_1$ offspring all pink — Pink $C^RC^W$

Fusion of $C^R$ gametes from the red-flowered plant and $C^W$ gametes from the white-flowered plant produces $C^RC^W$ heterozygotes in the $F_1$. These plants have pink flowers, an intermediate phenotype between red and white. This phenotype is not that expected if one of the alleles shows complete dominance to the other allele. This phenotype is, however, consistent with incomplete dominance.

### 3. $F_1 \times F_1$ cross

Pink $C^RC^W$ × Pink $C^RC^W$

$F_1$ pink-flowered plants are crossed to produce the $F_2$ generation.

### 4. $F_2$ generation

Gametes from one $C^RC^W$ $F_1$ pink-flowered plant

 $C^R$     $C^W$

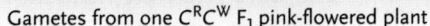

Gametes from another $C^RC^W$ $F_1$ pink-flowered plant

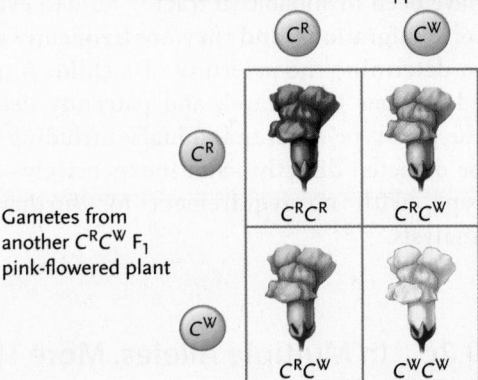

$C^R$

$C^W$

$C^RC^R$    $C^RC^W$

$C^RC^W$    $C^WC^W$

Each parent plant produces two types of gametes, $C^R$ and $C^W$. Random fusion of the gametes from the two parents produces the $F_2$ generation.

**Results:** The $F_2$ phenotypic ratio is 1 red: 2 pink: 1 white. Each phenotype results from a distinct genotype, $C^RC^R$ for red flowers, $C^RC^W$ for pink flowers, and $C^WC^W$ for white flowers. The 1:2:1 phenotypic ratio is consistent with incomplete dominance.

**Conclusion:** In incomplete dominance, each genotype has a distinct phenotype. From a cross of two heterozygotes, the outcome is a phenotypic ratio of 1:2:1 rather than the 3:1 ratio characteristic of complete dominance.

structures. With their single $C^R$ allele, the $C^RC^W$ heterozygotes of the $F_1$ generation can produce only enough pigment to give the flowers a pink colour. When the pink $C^RC^W$ $F_1$ plants are crossed, the fully red and white colours reappear, together with the pink colour, in the $F_2$ generation, in a ratio of 1/4 $C^RC^R$ (red), 1/2 $C^RC^W$ (pink), and 1/4 $C^WC^W$ (white). This ratio is exactly the same as the ratio of genotypes produced from a cross of two heterozygotes in Mendel's experiments (e.g., see Figure 9.6).

Some human disorders show incomplete dominance. For example, sickle cell (see Section 9.2f) disease is characterized by an alteration in the hemoglobin molecule that changes the shape of red blood cells when oxygen levels are low. An individual with sickle cell disease is homozygous for a recessive allele that encodes a defective form of one of the polypeptides of the hemoglobin molecule. Individuals heterozygous for that recessive allele and the normal allele have a condition known as *sickle cell trait,* which is a milder form of the disease because the individuals still produce normal polypeptides from the normal allele.

Familial hypercholesterolemia is another example of incomplete dominance. The gene involved encodes the low-density lipoprotein (LDL) receptor, a cell membrane protein responsible for removing excess cholesterol from the blood. Individuals with familial hypercholesterolemia are homozygous for a defective LDL receptor gene, produce no LDL receptors, and have a severe form of the disease. These individuals have six times the normal level of cholesterol in the blood and therefore are very prone to atherosclerosis (hardening of the arteries). Many individuals with familial hypercholesterolemia have heart attacks as children. Heterozygous individuals have half the normal number of receptors, which results in a milder form of the disease. Their symptoms are twice the normal blood cholesterol level, an unusually high risk of atherosclerosis, and a high risk of heart attacks before age 35.

Many alleles that appear to be completely dominant are actually incomplete in their effects when analyzed at the biochemical or molecular level. For example, for pigments that produce fur or flower colours, biochemical studies often show that even though heterozygotes may produce enough pigment to make them look the same externally as homozygous dominants, a difference in the amount of pigment is measurable at the biochemical level. Thus, whether dominance between alleles is complete or incomplete often depends on the level at which the effects of the alleles are examined.

A similar situation occurs in humans who carry the recessive allele that causes Tay–Sachs disease. Children who are homozygous for the recessive allele do not have a functional version of an enzyme that breaks down gangliosides, a type of membrane lipid. As a result, gangliosides accumulate in the brain, leading to mental impairment and eventually to death. Heterozygotes are without symptoms of the disease, even though they have one copy of the recessive allele. However, at the biochemical level, reduced breakdown of gangliosides can be detected in heterozygotes, evidently due to a reduced quantity of the active enzyme.

**CONCEPT FIX** Since all of Mendel's traits show "simple" or "complete" dominance, you might get the idea that most traits in nature are governed by one dominant and one recessive allele. However, the above examples illustrate that only a minority of human genetic disorders show such simple dominance. ⬡

## 9.2b In Codominance, the Effects of Different Alleles Are Equally Detectable in Heterozygotes

**Codominance** occurs when the two alleles both have significant effects, making both alleles detectable in heterozygotes. The inheritance of the human blood types M, MN, and N is an example of codominance. These are different blood types from the familiar blood types of the ABO blood group. The $L^M$ and $L^N$ alleles of the MN blood group gene that control this character encode different forms of a glycoprotein molecule located on the surface of red blood cells. If the genotype is $L^ML^M$, only the M form of the glycoprotein is present and the blood type is M; if it is $L^NL^N$, only the N form is present and the blood type is N. In heterozygotes with the $L^ML^N$ genotype, both glycoprotein types are present and can be detected, producing the blood type MN. Because each genotype has a different phenotype, the inheritance pattern for the MN blood group alleles is generally the same as for incompletely dominant alleles. That is, you would not be able to distinguish between codominance and incomplete dominance just by comparing the ratio of offspring from crosses.

The MN blood types do not affect blood transfusions and have relatively little medical importance. However, they have been invaluable in tracing human evolution and prehistoric migrations, and they are frequently used in initial tests to determine the paternity of a child. Among their primary advantages in research and paternity determination is that the genotype of all individuals, including heterozygotes, can be detected directly—and inexpensively—from their phenotype, with no requirement for further genetic tests or analysis.

## 9.2c In Multiple Alleles, More Than Two Alleles of a Gene Are Present in a Population

One of Mendel's major and most fundamental assumptions was that alleles occur in pairs in individuals; in the pairs, the alleles may be the same or different. After the rediscovery of

Mendel's principles, it soon became apparent that, although alleles do indeed occur in pairs in individuals, **multiple alleles** (more than two different alleles of a gene) may be present if all the individuals of a population are taken into account. For example, for a gene B, there could be several alleles with alterations in the gene named, for example, b1, b2, b3, and so on. Some individuals in a population may have the b1 and b2 alleles of the gene; others, the b2 and b3 alleles; still others, the b3 and b5 alleles; and so on, for all possible combinations. Thus, although any one individual can carry only two alleles of the gene, there are more than two alleles in the population as a whole. One of the genes that plays a part in the acceptance or rejection of organ transplants in humans has more than 200 different alleles!

The multiple alleles of a gene each contain nucleotide differences at one or more locations in their DNA sequences (**Figure 9.13**), and these often cause detectable alterations in the structure and function of gene products encoded by the alleles. Despite the presence of multiple alleles at the population level, each diploid individual still has only two of the alleles, allowing gametes to be predicted and traced through crosses by the usual methods.

**HUMAN ABO BLOOD GROUP** The human ABO blood group provides a real example of multiple alleles in a system that also exhibits both dominance and codominance. Karl Landsteiner, an Austrian biochemist, discovered the ABO blood group in 1901 while investigating the fact that attempts to transfer whole blood from one person to another were sometimes fatal. Landsteiner found that only certain combinations of four blood types, designated A, B, AB, and O, can be mixed safely in transfusions (**Table 9.1**).

Landsteiner determined that, in certain combinations, red blood cells from one blood type are agglutinated or clumped by

| TABLE 9.1 | Blood Types of the Human ABO Blood Group | | |
|---|---|---|---|
| Blood Type | Antigens | Antibodies | Blood Types Accepted in a Transfusion |
| A | A | Anti-B | A or O |
| B | B | Anti-A | B or O |
| AB | A and B | None | A, B, AB, or O |
| O | None | Anti-A, anti-B | O |

an agent in the serum of another type (the serum is the fluid in which the blood cells are suspended). The clumping was later found to depend on the action of an **antibody** in the blood serum. (Antibodies are protein molecules that interact with specific substances called *antigens*).

The antigens responsible for the blood types of the ABO blood group are the carbohydrate parts of glycoproteins located on the surfaces of red blood cells (these are unrelated to the glycoprotein carbohydrates responsible for the blood types of the MN blood group). People with type A blood produce an enzyme that creates *antigen A* on their red blood cells, and people with type B blood produce a different enzyme that creates *antigen B* on their red blood cells. At the same time, people with type A blood have antibodies against antigen B, and people with type B blood have antibodies against antigen A. People with type O blood do not produce enzymes that create antigen A or antigen B on their red blood cells, but they have antibodies against both of these antigens. People with type AB blood have neither anti-A nor anti-B antibodies, but they have both the A and B antigens, and their red blood cells are clumped by antibodies in the blood of all the other groups.

The four blood types—A, B, AB, and O—are produced by different combinations of multiple (three) alleles of a single gene I (**Figure 9.14**). The three alleles, designated $I^A$, $I^B$, and $i$, produce the following blood types:

$$I^A I^A = \text{type A blood}$$

$$I^A i = \text{type A blood}$$

$$I^A I^B = \text{type AB blood}$$

$$I^B I^B = \text{type B blood}$$

$$I^B i = \text{type B blood}$$

$$ii = \text{type O blood}$$

In addition to being codominant to each other, $I^A$ and $I^B$ alleles are each dominant to the $i$ allele.

*B* allele    5′...ATGCAGATACCGATTACAGACCATAGG...3′
             3′...TACGTCTATGGCTAATGTCTGGTATCC...5′

*b₁* allele    5′...ATGCAGAGACCGATTACAGACCATAGG...3′
             3′...TACGTCTCTGGCTAATGTCTGGTATCC...5′

*b₂* allele    5′...ATGCAGATACCGACTACAGACCATAGG...3′
             3′...TACGTCTATGGCTGATGTCTGGTATCC...5′

*b₃* allele    5′...ATGCAGATACCGATTACAGTCCATAGG...3′
             3′...TACGTCTATGGCTAATGTCAGGTATCC...5′

**FIGURE 9.13 Multiple alleles.** Multiple alleles consist of small differences in the DNA sequence of a gene at one or more points that result in detectable differences in the structure of the protein encoded by the gene. The *B* allele is the normal allele, which encodes a protein with normal function. The three *b* alleles each have alterations of the normal protein-coding DNA sequence that may adversely affect the function of that protein.

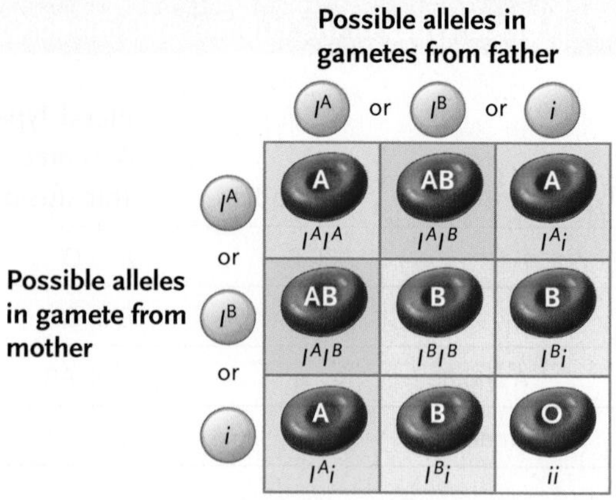

**Possible alleles in gametes from father**

**FIGURE 9.14 Inheritance of the blood types of the human ABO blood group.** Note that, although there are three possible alleles in the population, each parent carries only two.

## 9.2d In Epistasis, Genes Interact, with the Activity of One Gene Influencing the Activity of Another Gene

The genetic characters discussed so far in this chapter, such as flower colour, seed shape, and the blood types of the ABO group, are all produced by the alleles of single genes, with each gene functioning on its own. This is not the case for every trait. In **epistasis** (*epi* = on or over; *stasis* = standing or stopping), genes interact, with one or more alleles of a gene at one locus inhibiting or masking the effects of one or more alleles of a gene at a different locus. The result of epistasis is that some expected phenotypes do not appear among offspring.

Labrador retrievers may have black, chocolate brown, or yellow fur (**Figure 9.15**). The different colours result from variations in the amount and distribution in hairs of a brownish-black pigment called *melanin*. One gene coding for an enzyme involved in melanin production determines how much melanin is produced. The dominant *B* allele of this gene produces black fur colour in *BB* or *Bb* Labs; less pigment is produced in *bb* dogs, which are chocolate brown. However, another gene at a different locus determines whether the black or chocolate colour appears at all by controlling the deposition of pigment in hairs. The dominant *E* allele of this second gene permits pigment deposition, so that the black colour in *BB* or *Bb* individuals or the chocolate colour in *bb* individuals actually appears in the fur. Pigment deposition is almost completely blocked in homozygous recessive *ee* individuals, so the fur lacks melanin and has a yellow colour, whether the genotype for the *B* gene is *BB*, *Bb*, or *bb*. Thus, the *E* gene is said to be epistatic to the *B* gene.

Epistasis by the *E* gene eliminates some of the expected classes from crosses among Labs. Rather than two separate classes, as would be expected from a dihybrid cross without epistasis, the *BB ee*, *Bb ee*, *bB ee*, and *bb ee* genotypes produce a single yellow phenotype, giving the distribution 9/16 black,

3/16 chocolate, and 4/16 yellow; that is, the ratio is 9:3:4 instead of the expected 9:3:3:1 ratio. Many other dihybrid crosses that involve epistatic interactions produce distributions that differ from the expected 9:3:3:1 ratio.

In human biology, researchers believe that gene interactions and epistasis are common. The current thinking is that epistasis is an important factor in determining an individual's susceptibility to common human diseases. That is, the different degrees of susceptibility are the result of different gene interactions in the individuals. A specific example is insulin resistance, a disorder in which muscle, fat, and liver cells do not use insulin correctly, with the result that glucose and insulin levels become high in the blood. This disorder is believed to be determined by several genes often interacting with one another.

## 9.2e In Polygenic Inheritance, a Character Is Controlled by the Common Effects of Several Genes

Some characters follow a pattern of inheritance in which there is a more or less even gradation of types, forming a continuous distribution rather than "on" or "off" (discontinuous) effects such as the production of only purple or white flowers in pea plants. For example, human adults range from short to tall in a continuous distribution of height between limits of about 1 and 2 m. Typically, a continuous distribution of this type is the result of **polygenic inheritance**, in which several to many different genes contribute to the same character. Other characters that undertake a similar continuous distribution include skin colour and body weight in humans, ear length in corn, seed colour in wheat, and colour spotting in mice. These characters are also known as **quantitative traits**.

Polygenic inheritance can be detected by defining classes of variation, such as human body height of 180 cm in one class, 181 cm in the next class, 182 cm in the next class, and so on. The number of individuals in each class is then plotted as a graph. If the plot produces a bell-shaped curve, with fewer individuals at the extremes and the greatest numbers clustered around the midpoint, it is a good indication that the trait is quantitative (**Figure 9.16**).

The expression of a genetic phenotype can be influenced by the environment; this is particularly common with quantitative traits like body size. For example, poor nutrition during infancy and childhood is one environmental factor that can limit growth and prevent individuals from reaching the height expected from purely genetic contributions; good nutrition can have the opposite effect. Thus, the average young adult in Japan today is several inches taller than the average adult in the 1930s, when nutrition was poorer.

🔵 **CONCEPT FIX** At first glance, the wide variation shown in a quantitative trait might appear to support the old idea that the characteristics of parents are blended in their offspring. Commonly, people believe that the children in a family with one tall and one short parent will be of intermediate height. Although the children of such parents are indeed most likely to be of intermediate height, careful genetic analysis of hundreds of such families shows that their offspring actually range over a continuum from short to tall, forming a typical bell-shaped curve. Some children are not intermediate relative to their parents: they are either taller or shorter than both parents. Careful analysis of the inheritance of skin colour produces the same result. Although the skin colour of children is most often intermediate between that of their parents, a typical bell-shaped distribution is obtained in which some children at the extremes are lighter or darker than either parent. Thus, genetic analysis does not support the idea of blending or even mixing of parental traits in quantitative characteristics such as body size or skin colour. ⬡

**FIGURE 9.15  An example of epistasis.** The inheritance of coat colour in Labrador retrievers

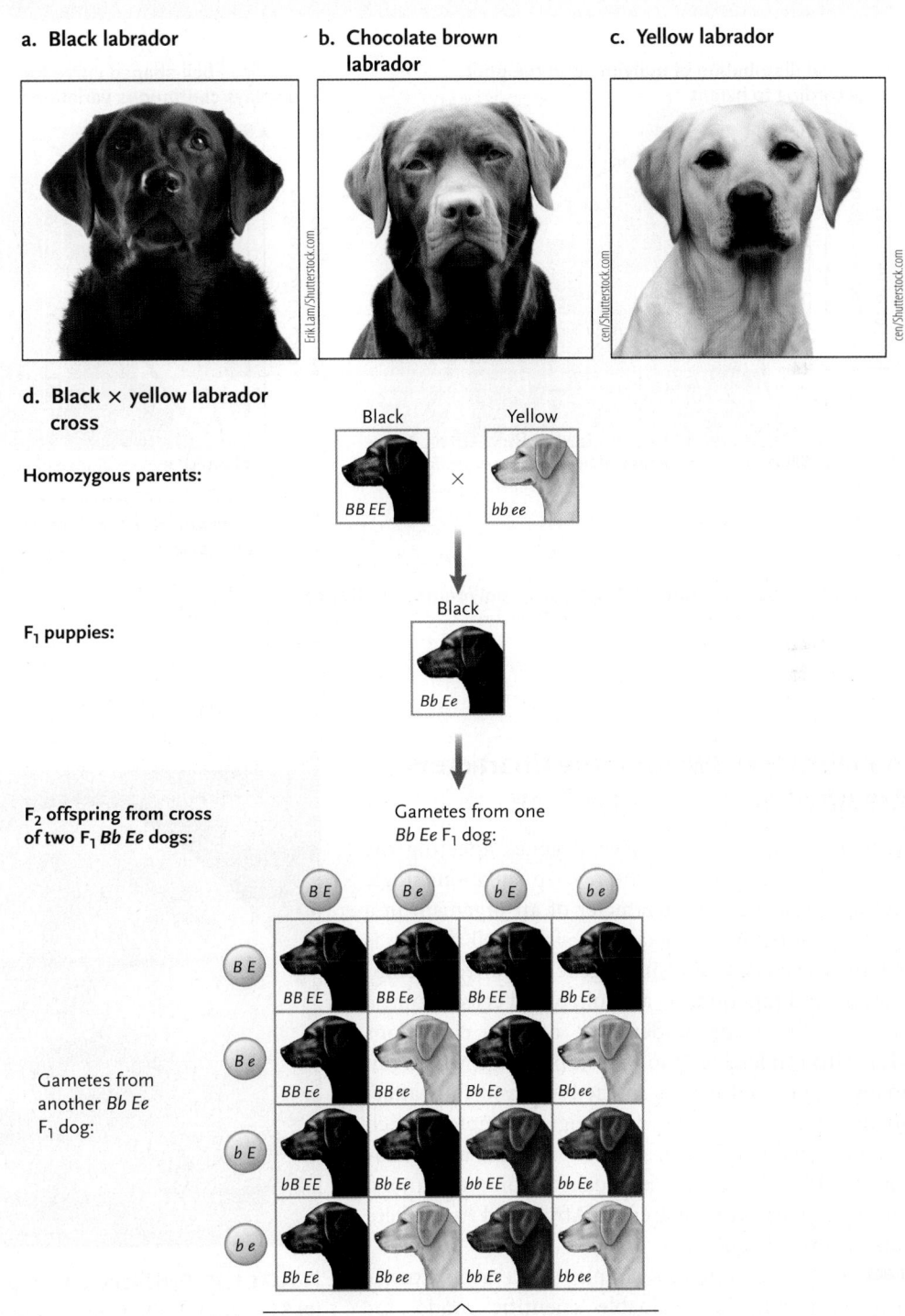

a. Black labrador

b. Chocolate brown labrador

c. Yellow labrador

d. Black × yellow labrador cross

Homozygous parents:

Black  *BB EE*  ×  Yellow  *bb ee*

F₁ puppies:

Black  *Bb Ee*

F₂ offspring from cross of two F₁ *Bb Ee* dogs:

Gametes from one *Bb Ee* F₁ dog:

Gametes from another *Bb Ee* F₁ dog:

F₂ phenotypic ratio is 9 black : 3 chocolate : 4 yellow

**a. Students at Brigham Young University, arranged according to height**

**b. Actual distribution of individuals in the photo according to height**

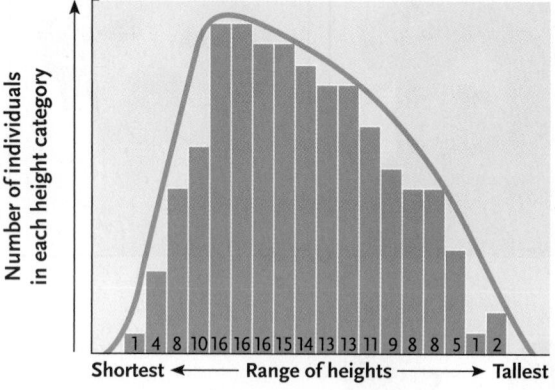

Number of individuals in each height category

1  4  8  10  16  16  16  15  14  13  13  11  9  8  8  5  1  2

Shortest ←——— Range of heights ———→ Tallest

**c. Idealized bell-shaped curve for a population that displays continuous variation in a trait**

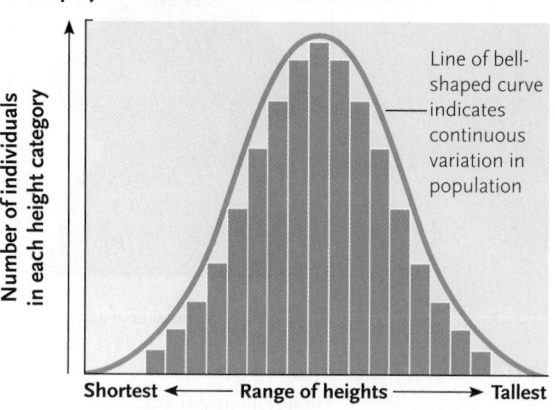

Number of individuals in each height category

Line of bell-shaped curve indicates continuous variation in population

Shortest ←——— Range of heights ———→ Tallest

If the sample in the photo included more individuals, the distribution would more closely approach this ideal.

**FIGURE 9.16  Continuous variation in height due to polygenic inheritance**

## 9.2f    In Pleiotropy, Two or More Characters Are Affected by a Single Gene

In the previous section, we saw several genes affecting the same trait. In this section we see the reverse situation: single genes affecting more than one character of an organism in a process called **pleiotropy**. For example, sickle cell disease is caused by a recessive allele of a single gene that affects hemoglobin structure and function. As a result, blood cells assume a characteristic sickle shape under low oxygen conditions (**Figure 9.17**). This can lead to blood vessel blockage, which can damage many tissues and organs in the body and thus affect many body functions, producing wide-ranging symptoms such as fatigue, abdominal pain, heart failure, paralysis, and pneumonia (**Figure 9.18**). This trait is particularly common among people whose ancestors lived in areas of Africa and Asia where malaria was historically endemic.

**CONCEPT FIX** Although Mendel's simple, single-gene experiments in peas provided a valuable scientific model for

**a.**                                          **b.**

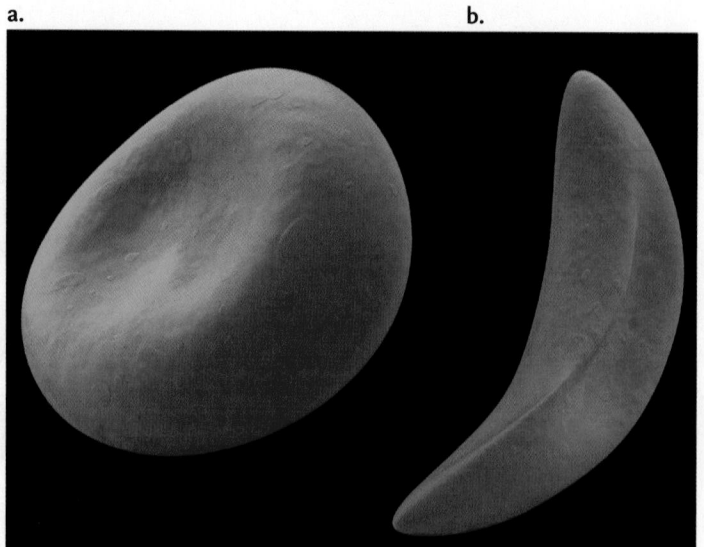

**FIGURE 9.17  Red blood cell shape in sickle cell disease.**
**(a)** A healthy cell. **(b)** A sickle-shaped, diseased cell

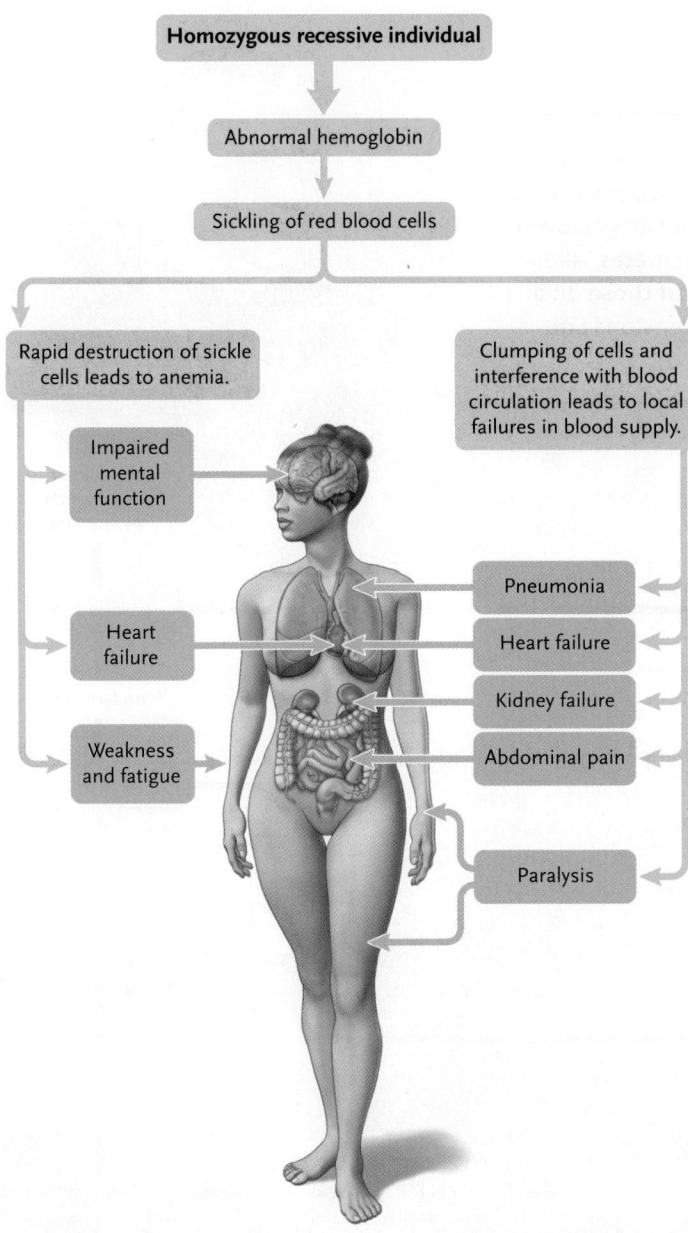

**FIGURE 9.18 Pleiotropy, as demonstrated by the wide-ranging, multiple effects of the single mutant allele responsible for sickle cell disease.** (Not all effects are shown.)

understanding inheritance, modern analyses in a wide variety of organisms are finding that many traits are quantitative, and that most genes have some pleiotropic effects. ⬡

The next chapter describes additional patterns of inheritance that were not anticipated by Mendel, including the effects of recombination during meiosis. These additional patterns also extend, rather than contradict, Mendel's fundamental principles.

## STUDY BREAK QUESTIONS

1. Distinguish between alleles that are incompletely dominant and those that are codominant.
2. How might you know that a trait is polygenic?

# Summary Illustration

With no knowledge of the function of DNA or chromosomes, Gregor Mendel used meticulous quantitative analyses of controlled crosses to deduce the basic mechanism of inheritance. He discovered that diploid organisms carry two alleles for any given trait. These alleles are distributed randomly into gametes. Alleles of genes carried on a given chromosome assort independently of those on a different chromosome. Subsequent research revealed many extensions and variations of Mendel's basic mechanisms.

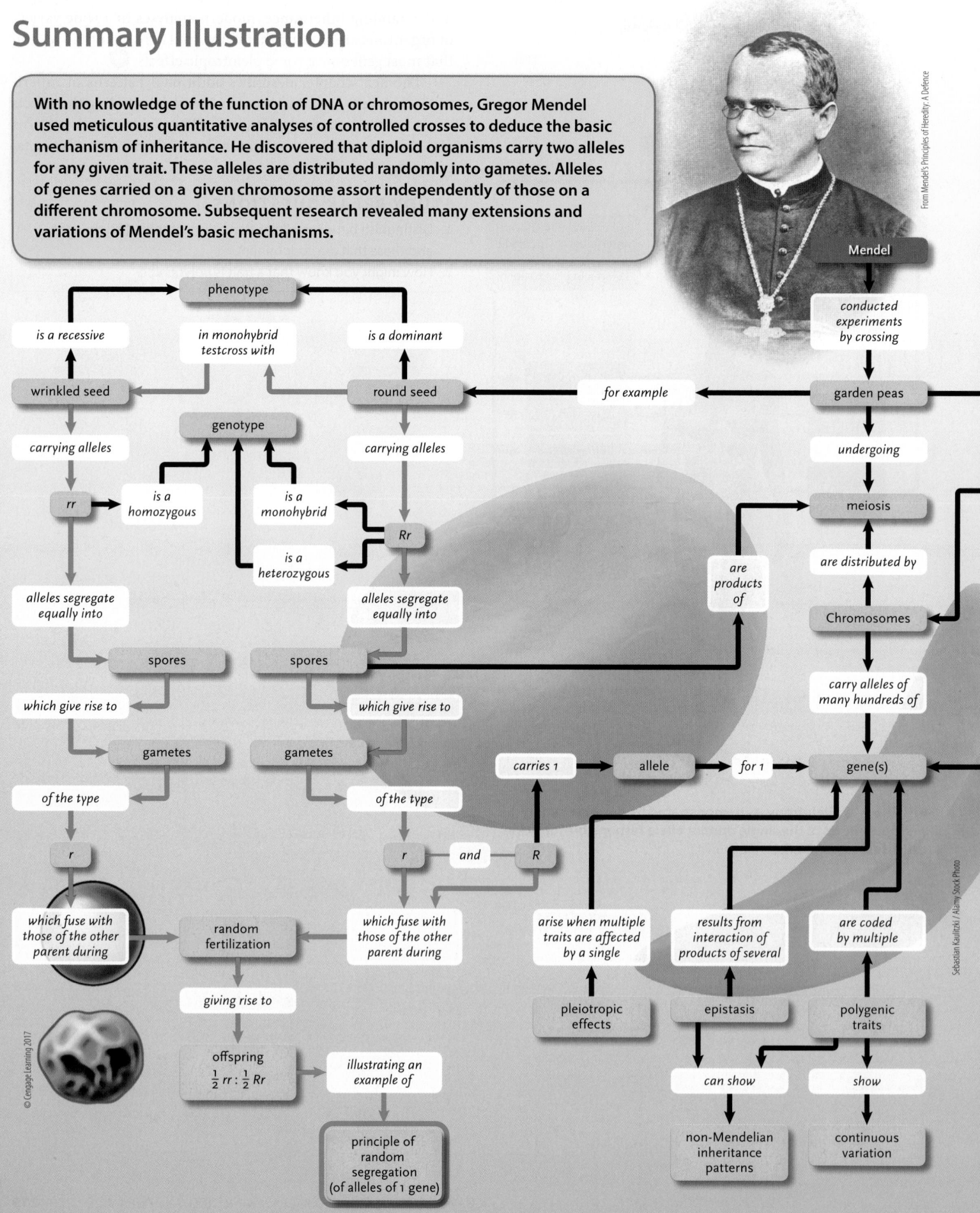

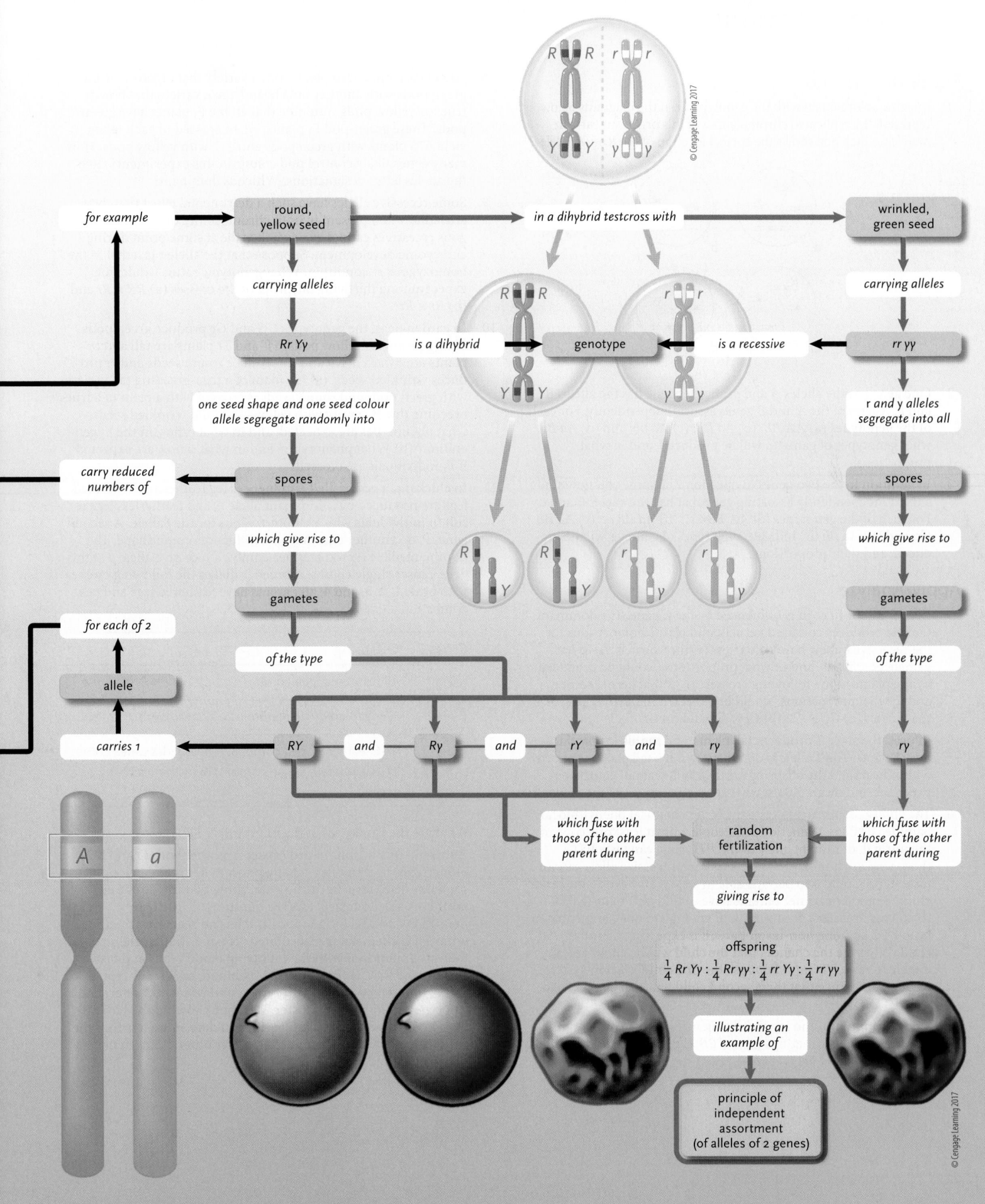

# SELF-TEST QUESTIONS

## Recall/Understand

1. Imagine an organism with the genotype *Rr*. If the diagrams below represent the replicated chromosomes of this organism early in meiosis, which one shows the correct location of the *R* and *r* alleles?

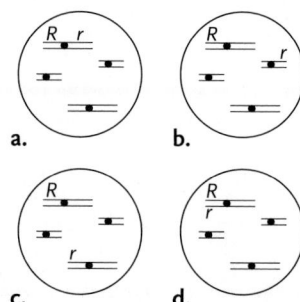

2. One gene has the alleles *A* and *a*; another gene has the alleles *B* and *b*. Alleles of the *A* and *B* genes assort independently. For each of the genotypes (a) *AA BB*; (b) *Aa BB*; (c) *Aa bb*; and (d) *Aa Bb*, what genotypes of gametes will be produced, and in what proportions?

3. In addition to the two genes in question 2, assume you now study a third independently assorting gene that has the alleles *C* and *c*. For each of the genotypes (a) *AA BB CC*; (b) *Aa BB cc*; (c) *Aa BB Cc*; and (d) *Aa Bb Cc*, indicate what types of gametes will be produced, and their proportions.

## Apply/Analyze

4. Kernel colour in corn is influenced by the *C* gene. The dominant *C* allele produces coloured kernels, and plants homozygous for the recessive *c* allele have colourless (white) kernels. (i) What gamete genotypes, and in what proportions, would be produced by the plants in the following crosses? (ii) What kernel colour, and in what proportions, would be expected in the offspring of the crosses (a) *CC × Cc*; (b) *Cc × Cc*; and (c) *Cc × cc*?

5. In peas, the allele *T* produces tall plants, and the allele *t* produces dwarf plants. The *T* allele is dominant to *t*. If a tall plant is crossed with a dwarf and the offspring are distributed about equally between tall and dwarf plants, what are the genotypes of the parents?

6. The ability of humans to taste the bitter chemical phenylthiocarbamide (PTC) is a genetic trait. People with at least one copy of the normal, dominant allele of the *PTC* gene can taste PTC; those who are homozygous for a mutant, recessive allele cannot taste it. (a) Could two parents able to taste PTC have a non-taster child? Could non-taster parents have a child able to taste PTC? (b) A pair of taster parents, both of whom had one parent able to taste PTC and one non-taster parent, is expecting their first child. What are the chances that the child will be either able or unable to taste PTC? (c) Suppose the first child is a non-taster, what is the chance that their second child will also be unable to taste PTC?

7. Which genotypes, and in what frequencies, will be present in the offspring from the matings (a) *AA BB × aa BB*; (b) *Aa Bb × Aa Bb*; (c) *Aa Bb × aa bb*; and (d) *Aa BB × AA Bb*?

8. You cross a lima bean plant from a variety that breeds true for green pods with another lima bean from a variety that breeds true for yellow pods. You note that all the $F_1$ plants have green pods. These green-pod $F_1$ plants, when crossed to each other, yield 675 plants with green pods and 217 with yellow pods. How many genes likely control pod colour in this experiment? Give the alleles letter designations. Which is dominant?

9. Some recessive alleles have such a detrimental effect that they are lethal when present in both chromosomes of a pair. Homozygous recessives cannot survive; they die at some point during embryonic development. Suppose that the allele *r* is lethal in the homozygous *rr* condition. What genotypic ratios would you expect among the living offspring of the crosses (a) *RR × Rr* and (b) *Rr × Rr*?

10. In garden peas, the genotypes *GG* and *Gg* produce green pods and *gg* produces yellow pods; *TT* and *Tt* plants are tall and *tt* plants are dwarfed; *RR* and *Rr* produce round seeds and *rr* produces wrinkled seeds. (a) If a plant of a true-breeding tall variety with green pods and round seeds is crossed with a plant of a true-breeding dwarf variety with yellow pods and wrinkled seeds, what phenotypes are expected, and in what ratios, in the $F_1$ generation? (b) What phenotypes, and in what ratios, are expected if $F_1$ individuals are crossed?

11. In chickens, a gene called *F* influences leg feathering. Feathered legs are produced by a dominant allele *F*, and featherless legs result in individuals who are homozygous for the *f* allele. A second gene, *P*, on another chromosome influences comb shape. The dominant allele *P* produces pea combs; a recessive allele *p* of this gene causes single combs. A breeder makes the following crosses with birds 1, 2, 3, and 4; all parents have feathered legs and pea combs.

| Cross | Offspring |
|---|---|
| 1 × 2 | All feathered, pea comb |
| 1 × 3 | 3/4 feathered, 1/4 featherless, all pea comb |
| 1 × 4 | 9/16 feathered, pea comb; 3/16 featherless, pea comb; 3/16 feathered, single comb; 1/16 featherless, single comb |

What are the genotypes of the four birds?

12. A mix-up in a hospital ward causes a mother with O and MN blood types to think that a baby given to her really belongs to someone else. Tests in the hospital show that the doubting mother is able to taste PTC (see question 6). The baby given to her has O and MN blood types and has no reaction when the bitter PTC chemical is placed on its tongue. The mother has four other children with the following blood types and tasting abilities for PTC (i) type A and MN blood, taster; (ii) type B and N blood, non-taster; (iii) type A and M blood, taster; and (iv) type A and N blood, taster. Without knowing the father's blood types and tasting ability, can you determine whether the child is really hers? (Assume that all her other children have the same father.)

13. In cats, the genotype *AA* produces tabby fur colour; *Aa* is also a tabby, and *aa* is black. Another independently assorting gene at a different locus is epistatic to the gene for fur colour. When present in its dominant *W* form (*WW* or *Ww*), this gene blocks the formation of fur colour and all the offspring are white; *ww* individuals develop normal fur colour. What fur colours, and in what proportions, would you expect from the cross *Aa Ww* × *Aa Ww*?

14. Having malformed hands with shortened fingers is a dominant trait controlled by a single gene; people who are homozygous for the recessive allele have normal hands and fingers. Having woolly hair is a dominant trait controlled by a different, independently assorting gene; homozygous recessive individuals have normal, non-woolly hair. Suppose a woman with normal hands and non-woolly hair marries a man who has malformed hands and woolly hair. Their first child has normal hands and non-woolly hair. (a) What are the genotypes of the mother, the father, and the child? (b) If this couple has a second child, what is the probability that it will have normal hands and woolly hair?

## Create/Evaluate

15. Imagine that you are helping a friend with genetics problems. He has drawn the Punnett square below to answer questions about a dihybrid cross: *Mm Hh* × *Mm Hh*. Use the principles of meiosis to explain why this diagram is incorrect.

|   | M | H | h | m |
|---|---|---|---|---|
| M |   |   |   |   |
| h |   |   |   |   |
| H |   |   |   |   |
| m |   |   |   |   |

16. A man is homozygous dominant for alleles at 10 different genes that assort independently. (a) How many genotypically different types of sperm cells can he produce? A woman is homozygous recessive for the alleles of 8 of these 10 genes, but she is heterozygous for the other 2 genes. (b) How many genotypically different types of eggs can she produce? (c) What mathematical expression can you suggest to describe the relationship between the number of different possible gametes and the number of heterozygous and homozygous genes that are present?

17. In guinea pigs, an allele for rough fur (*R*) is dominant over an allele for smooth fur (*r*); an allele for a black coat (*B*) is dominant over that for white (*b*). You have an animal with rough black fur. (a) What cross would you use to determine whether the animal is homozygous for these traits? (b) What phenotype would you expect in the offspring if the animal were homozygous?

18. The eyes of brown-eyed people are not alike but rather vary considerably in shade and pattern. What hypothesis can you suggest to explain these differences?

# Chapter Roadmap

**Genetic Linkage, Sex Linkage, and Other Non-Mendelian Inheritance Mechanisms**

There are many examples of traits that are not inherited in the fashion discovered by Mendel.

**From Chapter 8** →

**10.1 Genetic Linkage and Recombination**

If several genes of interest are present on the same chromosome, their traits will not be inherited independently as shown by Mendel.

**10.2 Sex-Linked Genes**

Some genes are carried on sex chromosomes; these traits have characteristic inheritance patterns.

Martin Shields/Science Source

**From Chapter 8** →

**10.3 Chromosomal Mutations that Affect Inheritance**

Changes in chromosome structure or number affect the inheritance of traits.

Martin Shields/Science Source

**10.4 Human Genetic Traits, Pedigree Analysis, and Genetic Counselling**

Inheritance patterns can reveal the underlying mechanisms of disease.

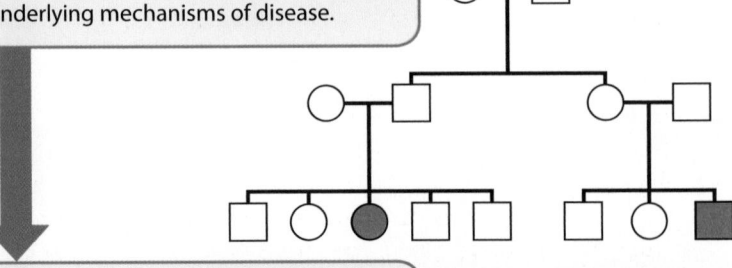

© Cengage Learning 2017

**10.5 Additional Non-Mendelian Patterns of Inheritance**

Some genes are carried on organelle chromosomes; some genes are imprinted.

**To Chapter 12** →

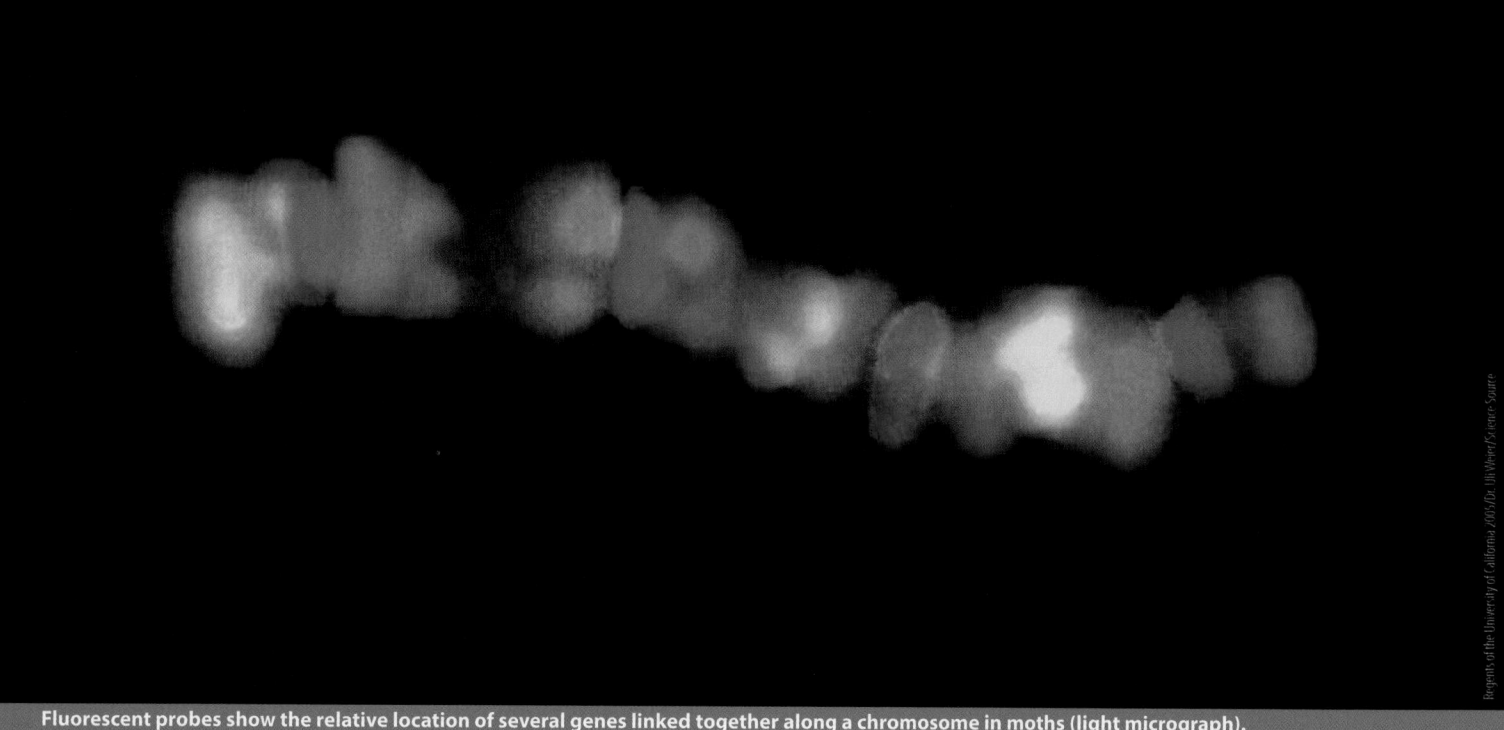

**Fluorescent probes show the relative location of several genes linked together along a chromosome in moths (light micrograph).**
New ways of mapping chromosome structure yield insights into the inheritance of normal and abnormal traits.

# Genetic Linkage, Sex Linkage, and Other Non-Mendelian Inheritance Mechanisms

# 10

**Why it matters...** Sometime during the summer after his first year in music at Université du Québec à Montréal, Julien noticed some blurry vision in one eye. By the start of classes in the fall he was relying almost entirely on his one good eye to read music during ensemble practice.

Walking out of his appointment with an ophthalmologist, Julien texted his sister, Madeleine. "We need to talk." Madeleine was a veterinarian and had always been the family biologist.

"They said I have Leber's hereditary optic neuropathy," he explained to Madeleine over coffee in his apartment. "The bad news is that it will also likely affect my other eye. I may start twitching in my muscles and there is no treatment. The only good news is that the mutation I have—here look in the report; it's called T14484C—is the best one to have since it often shows some improvement over time. They said it is unusually common in Quebec."

Madeleine flipped through screens on her phone and reported, "Wikipedia says that T14484C is a single base-pair change of a T to a C. The change reduces energy production by electron transport, so I guess that is what causes trouble in optic nerves and muscles. The mutation is not on regular chromosomes but on your mitochondrial chromosome instead."

"Yeah, they said that I inherited this from mom. Men don't pass it on."

"If this is mitochondrial then, yes, you inherited it from Mom's egg cell." Madeleine took breath before adding, "And so did I."

"I thought so, Maddy. But the doctors said that women have a much lower chance of being affected, even though they have the same mutation as men. No one knows why."

"This means mom has it and she must have got it from her mother, and she from her mother, and she from her mother, all the way back...." Madeleine started searching online again.

"Back to what...?" Julien asked.

"Wow. Look at this article. All the way back to the Filles du Roi. It says that this disease in most modern Quebec families can be traced back 12 generations to one woman who came to New France in the 1600s."

Madeleine read aloud, "At that time, New France was a struggling colony in North America. In order to entice young soldiers and contract workers to stay and settle, Louis the XIV provided an allowance, transportation, clothing, and a marriage dowry for hundreds of young single women who agreed to travel to the colony from Paris and surrounding areas. Many of them orphans, all of them poor, these 'daughters of the King' married in New France, and their children are the ancestors of a significant fraction of Quebecers today."

Madeleine sat quietly for a moment. "So, it seems that our 10-times great grandmother carried this mutation to North America in her mitochondria and passed it to her children. Daughters passed it to their daughters, who passed it to their daughters for 400 years before it arrived at us."

"So now it stops at me because I'm male but Maddy, you are one of those daughters. Are you going to pass it along to your kids?"

The story of Julien and Madeleine draws attention to the complex genetic inheritance that is passed down to each of us from our ancestors. In particular, this case shows that traits may follow a distinctly non-Mendelian pattern of inheritance and may have unexpected patterns of expression, depending on the sex of the individual or a host of other environmental factors. Although the powerful insights of Gregor Mendel outlined in previous chapters revolutionized our understanding of the basic mechanisms of inheritance, we now know there is more. There are many traits that follow inheritance mechanisms not observed, nor even imagined, by Mendel. This chapter introduces several non-Mendelian mechanisms of inheritance in plants and animals with an emphasis on human genetics.

## 10.1 Genetic Linkage and Recombination

In the historic experiments described in previous chapters, Gregor Mendel carried out crosses with seven different characters in garden peas, controlled by seven different genes. He found that his observations from crosses were consistent with the hypothesis that each of the genes assorted independently of all of the others. If Mendel had extended his study to additional characters, he would soon have found exceptions to this principle. This should not be surprising because an organism has many more genes than chromosomes. Conceptually, then, chromosomes contain many

**FIGURE 10.1 Filles du roi are welcomed to New France in the mid-1600s.**
Painting by Eleanor Fortescue-Brickdale

genes, with each gene at a particular location, or locus. Genes located on different chromosomes assort independently during meiosis because the two chromosomes behave independently of one another as they line up on the metaphase plate (see Chapter 8 for a review of chromosome behaviour during meiosis). Genes located on the same chromosome may be inherited together in genetic crosses (i.e., they do not assort independently) because the chromosome is inherited as a single unit in meiosis. Genes on the same chromosome are known as **linked genes**, and the phenomenon is called **linkage**.

## 10.1a Linked Genes Show a Different Pattern of Inheritance Than Independently Assorting Genes

In the early part of the twentieth century, Thomas H. Morgan and co-workers at Columbia University used the fruit fly, *Drosophila melanogaster*, as a model organism to investigate Mendel's principles in animals. (For more information about *Drosophila* as a model research organism, see *The Purple Pages*.) Groups of genes that tended to assort together in crosses were believed to be carried on the same chromosome. It was an undergraduate student named Alfred Sturtevant, working in Morgan's lab, who developed the insight that resulted in the construction of the first genetic map showing the relative order of genes on a chromosome. This map also estimated the distance separating the genes. These brilliant and far-reaching hypotheses were typical of Morgan's group, which founded genetics research in the United States, developed *Drosophila* as a research organism, and made discoveries that were likely as significant to the development of genetics as those of Mendel.

Although it is tempting to assume that genetic maps could be made by simply looking down a microscope, finding the genes, and measuring the distance between them, the technology to do this was not available. Instead, Morgan's group used an indirect measure of distance. They reasoned that genes sitting relatively far apart on a chromosome would be more likely to be separated from one another during meiotic crossing-over than genes lying closer together. Figure 8.14, Chapter 8, illustrates this process of recombination occurring in the space separating two genes as they appear on chromosomes paired during meiosis. Obviously, if recombination is to be used as a measure of the distance separating genes, it must be detectable. That is why the organism used in Figure 8.14, Chapter 8, is heterozygous for all genes; the chromatids resulting from recombination are then different from the original, nonrecombinant, ones and can be identified. Following meiosis I and II, each of the four different chromatids will become a chromosome in a separate gamete (review the basic mechanisms of meiosis in Figure 8.10, Chapter 8). Which chromosome, recombinant or not, is carried by a given gamete is most clearly revealed only in offspring resulting from fertilization with a homozygous recessive gamete. This is called a *testcross*

(Section 9.1e). All offspring are guaranteed to have one recessive allele from each locus, so the identity of the allele that was inherited by crossover is clearly revealed. That is why, in the cross originally done by Morgan in 1911, you will notice that one parent is heterozygous and the other is homozygous recessive (**Figure 10.2**).

To understand the following crosses, you need to learn to work with the genetic symbolism developed by Morgan instead of the *A/a* system used in Chapter 9. Although *Drosophila* notation might appear counterintuitive at first, understanding a few basic principles will help you see the logic behind it. First, note that geneticists working with fruit flies have all agreed on a "normal," or "**wild-type**," genotype; any change from wild type is, by definition, a mutant. Mutant alleles are named based on the altered phenotype of the organism that expresses them. The names for dominant mutant alleles are written with the first letter in uppercase, whereas those for recessive mutant alleles are written with the first letter in lowercase. For example, a dominant mutant allele transforming an antenna into a leg is called *Antennapedia* (*Antp*), whereas a recessive mutant allele altering eye colour is called *vermilion* (*v*). The notation for a wild-type allele is always made by simply adding a superscripted plus + sign to the mutant allele notation. You know you understand this system if you agree that $Antp^+$ refers to a *recessive* allele giving a normal phenotype when homozygous.

Morgan began a specific breeding program using true-breeding fruit flies with normal red eyes and normal wing length (genotype $pr^+ pr^+ vg^+ vg^+$), along with a true-breeding fly with the recessive traits of purple eyes and vestigial (i.e., short and crumpled) wings (genotype *prpr vgvg*) (Figure 10.2, step 1).

**CONCEPT FIX** You can see that the two flies used in the P generation cross illustrated in Figure 10.2 are different in several features. The differences in body size and coloration pattern are the natural differences between female and male fruit flies. The two types of difference that were studied by Morgan in this cross were eye colour and wing shape. ⬡

The $F_1$ (first-generation) offspring were all dihybrid $pr^+pr$ $vg^+vg$, and because of the dominance of the wild-type alleles, they all had red eyes and normal wings (see Figure 10.2, step 2). Morgan then selected these wild-type $F_1$ females as the dihybrid parent and mated them to homozygous recessive males (with purple eyes and vestigial wings) as the testcross parent. If the purple and vestigial genes were carried on different chromosomes, Mendel's principle of independent assortment (see Section 9.1) would predict four classes of phenotypes in the offspring, in the approximate 1:1:1:1 ratio of red eyes, normal wings : purple, vestigial : red, vestigial : purple, normal. Given over 2800 offspring from several females, about 700 should have been in each class. However, Morgan observed two types of progeny in which the counts were much higher than 700 (red, normal and purple, vestigial) and two types with counts that were much lower (red, vestigial, and purple, normal) (see Figure 10.2, step 4).

FIGURE 10.2    **Experimental Research**

## Evidence for Gene Linkage

**Question:** Do the purple-eye and vestigial-wing genes of *Drosophila* assort independently?

**Experiment:** Morgan crossed true-breeding, wild-type flies having red eyes and normal wings with purple-eyed, vestigial-winged flies. The F1 dihybrids were all wild type in phenotype. Next he crossed the F1 dihybrid flies with purple-eyed, vestigial-winged flies (this is a testcross) and analyzed the phenotypes of the progeny.

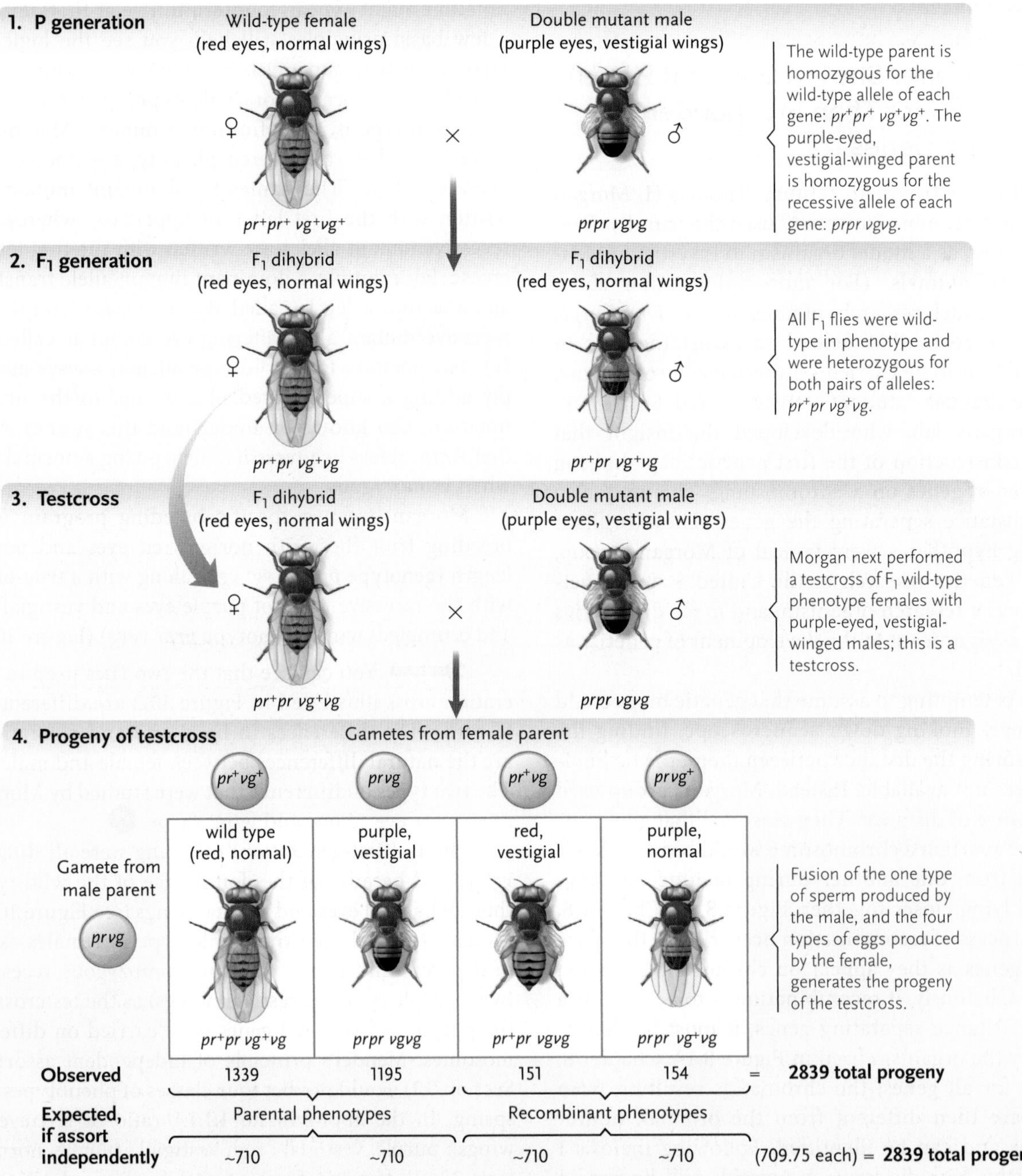

**1. P generation**

Wild-type female
(red eyes, normal wings)

♀    ×    ♂

$pr^+pr^+ vg^+vg^+$

Double mutant male
(purple eyes, vestigial wings)

$prpr\ vgvg$

The wild-type parent is homozygous for the wild-type allele of each gene: $pr^+pr^+ vg^+vg^+$. The purple-eyed, vestigial-winged parent is homozygous for the recessive allele of each gene: $prpr\ vgvg$.

**2. F₁ generation**

F₁ dihybrid
(red eyes, normal wings)

♀

$pr^+pr\ vg^+vg$

F₁ dihybrid
(red eyes, normal wings)

♂

$pr^+pr\ vg^+vg$

All F₁ flies were wild-type in phenotype and were heterozygous for both pairs of alleles: $pr^+pr\ vg^+vg$.

**3. Testcross**

F₁ dihybrid
(red eyes, normal wings)

♀    ×    ♂

$pr^+pr\ vg^+vg$

Double mutant male
(purple eyes, vestigial wings)

$prpr\ vgvg$

Morgan next performed a testcross of F₁ wild-type phenotype females with purple-eyed, vestigial-winged males; this is a testcross.

**4. Progeny of testcross**

Gametes from female parent

$pr^+vg^+$    $prvg$    $pr^+vg$    $prvg^+$

Gamete from male parent

$prvg$

| wild type (red, normal) | purple, vestigial | red, vestigial | purple, normal |
|---|---|---|---|
| $pr^+pr\ vg^+vg$ | $prpr\ vgvg$ | $pr^+pr\ vgvg$ | $prpr\ vg^+vg$ |

Fusion of the one type of sperm produced by the male, and the four types of eggs produced by the female, generates the progeny of the testcross.

| Observed | 1339 | 1195 | 151 | 154 | = | **2839 total progeny** |
|---|---|---|---|---|---|---|

| | Parental phenotypes | | Recombinant phenotypes | | | |
|---|---|---|---|---|---|---|
| Expected, if assort independently | ~710 | ~710 | ~710 | ~710 | (709.75 each) = | **2839 total progeny** |

© Cengage Learning 2017

**Results:** 2534 of the testcross progeny flies were parental—wild-type or purple, vestigial—while 305 of the progeny were recombinant—red, vestigial or purple, normal. If the genes assorted independently, the expectation is for a 1:1:1:1 ratio for testcross progeny: approximately 1420 of both parental and recombinant progeny.

**Conclusion:** The purple-eye and vestigial-wing genes do not assort independently. The simplest alternative is that the two genes are linked on the same chromosome. The small number of flies with recombinant phenotypes is explained by crossing-over.

Morgan's hypothesis to explain this non-Mendelian distribution is illustrated in **Figure 10.3**. He suggested that the two genes are linked genetically—physically associated on the same chromosome—that is, *pr* and *vg* are linked genes. He further hypothesized that the behaviour of these linked genes is explained by *chromosome recombination* during meiosis. Furthermore, he proposed that the frequency of this recombination is a function of the distance between linked genes.

The $pr^+pr$ $vg^+vg$ F$_1$ dihybrid parents produce four types of gametes (see Figure 10.3). The two parental gametes, $pr^+$ $vg^+$ and *pr vg*, are generated by simple segregation of the chromosomes during meiosis without any crossing-over (recombination) between the genes. The two recombinant gametes, $pr^+$ *vg* and *pr* $vg^+$, result from crossing-over between the homologous chromatids when they are paired in prophase I of meiosis (see Figures 8.10 and 8.13, Chapter 8). The offspring of the cross are produced by fusion of each of these with a pr vg gamete produced by the homozygous recessive (*prpr vgvg*) male parent. The phenotypes of the offspring directly reflect the genotypes of the gametes produced by the dihybrid parent.

**CONCEPT FIX** Students of genetics sometimes assume that the wild-type and purple vestigial offspring in the above cross are called "parental" because they *look like* the F$_1$ parents. However, the term *parental* actually refers to the original genotypes involved in the cross; 'parental' F$_2$ offspring are the ones that *inherit chromosomes that were NOT involved in recombination in the dihybrid parent.* Parental offspring, therefore, do not always resemble the F1 parents of the cross. ⬡

Although Morgan could not look down a microscope and measure the distance between genes directly, he could look down a microscope and identify the phenotypes of recombinant offspring from dihybrid, fruit fly testcrosses. Thus, the relative frequency of recombinant progeny became his "measure" of the distance separating genes. The example in Figure 10.3 reveals that purple eyes and vestigial wings are on the same chromosome and are separated by a recombinant offspring frequency distance of 10.7%: 10.7% of the progeny are recombinant. The smaller the number of recombinants between two loci, the closer the loci are to each other.

## 10.1b The Frequency of Recombinant Offspring Can Be Used to Map Chromosomes

The recombinant offspring frequency of 10.7% for the *pr* and vg genes of Drosophila means that 10.7% of the gametes originating from the $pr^+pr$ $vg^+vg$ parent contained recombined chromosomes (i.e., either $pr^+$ *vg* or *pr* $vg^+$). That recombinant offspring frequency is characteristic for those two genes. In other crosses that involve linked genes, Morgan found that the recombinant offspring frequency was characteristic of the two particular genes involved, and varied from less than 1% up to a maximum of 50% (see the next section).

From these observations, Alfred Sturtevant realized that the variation in recombinant offspring frequencies could be

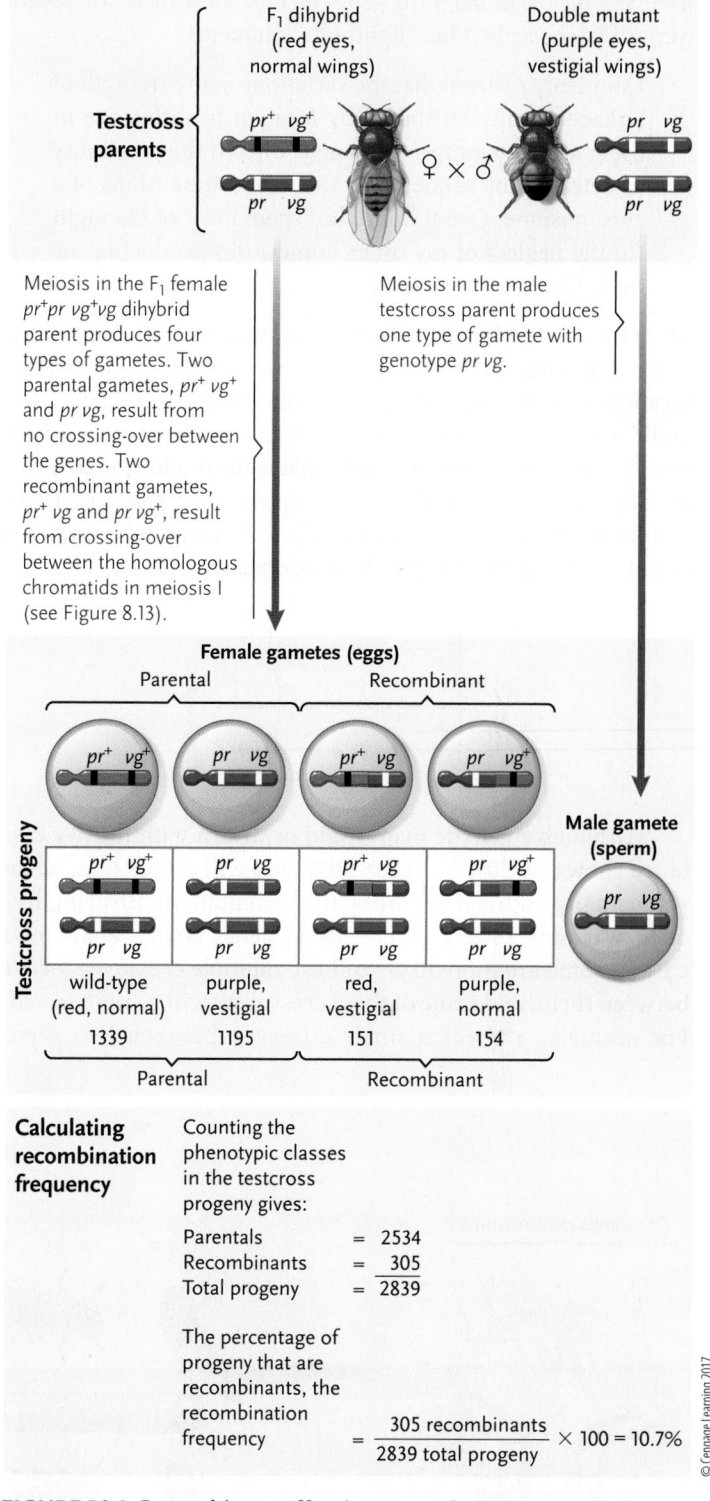

**FIGURE 10.3 Recombinant offspring carry chromosomes that result from recombination during meiosis in the dihybrid female parent.** The testcross of Figure 10.2 is redrawn here to show the inheritance of the two linked genes on chromosomes. The two homologues in the dihybrid parent (female, on the left) are coloured differently to allow us to follow them during the cross. The arrangement of alleles on these chromosomes is called "parental." Offspring showing the parental phenotype have inherited a chromosome from the dihybrid parent that was unchanged during meiosis. The recombinant offspring inherit a chromosome that was changed by recombination from the dihybrid parent.

used as a means of mapping genes on chromosomes. Sturtevant himself later recalled his "lightbulb" moment:

> I suddenly realized that the variations in the strength of linkage already attributed by Morgan to difference in the spatial separation of the gene offered the possibility of determining sequence in the linear dimensions of a chromosome. I went home and spent most of the night (to the neglect of my other homework) producing the first chromosome map.

Therefore, recombinant offspring frequencies can be used to make a **linkage map** of a chromosome, showing the relative locations of genes. For example, assume that the three genes d, e, and *f* are carried together on the same chromosome. Crosses reveal a 28% frequency of recombinants for d and *e*, *a* 20% frequency for *d* and *f*, and a 10% frequency for *f* and *e*. These recombinant offspring frequencies allow the genes to be arranged in only one sequence on the chromosomes as follows:

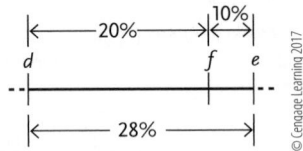

Although a genetic map would be drawn with the *d–e* distance shown as 20% + 10% = 30%, you will notice that, when you actually do the *d* × *e* cross, the recombinant offspring frequency is only 28%. This is because genes farther apart on a chromosome are more likely to have multiple crossovers occur between them, and some of these crossovers will go undetected. For example, whereas a single crossover between two genes

gives recombinant chromatids, a *double* crossover (two single crossovers occurring in the same meiosis) between two genes gives the parental arrangement of alleles (and therefore these chromatids would not give rise to recombinant offspring and would not be counted in the recombination frequency). You can see this simply by drawing out single versus double crossovers between two genes on a piece of paper. In our example, the undetectable double crossovers that occur between d and e have slightly decreased the estimate of the overall recombinant offspring frequency between these two genes.

Using this method, Sturtevant created the first linkage map showing the arrangement of six genes on the *Drosophila* X chromosome. (A partial linkage map of a *Drosophila* chromosome is shown in **Figure 10.4**.)

Since the time of Morgan, many *Drosophila* genes and those of other eukaryotic organisms widely used for genetic research, including *Neurospora* (a fungus), yeast, maize (corn), and the mouse, have been mapped using the same approach. Recombinant offspring frequencies, together with the results of other techniques, have been used to create linkage maps of the locations of genes in the DNA of prokaryotic organisms such as *Escherichia coli*.

The unit of a linkage map, called a **map unit** (abbreviated mu), is equivalent to a recombinant offspring frequency of 1%. The map unit is also called the **centimorgan** (cM) in honour of Morgan's discoveries of linkage and recombination. It is very important to understand that map units are not absolute physical distances such as micrometres or nanometres; rather, they are *relative*, showing the positions of genes with respect to each other based on relative recombinant offspring frequencies. One of the reasons that the units are relative and not absolute distances is that the frequency of crossing-over giving rise to

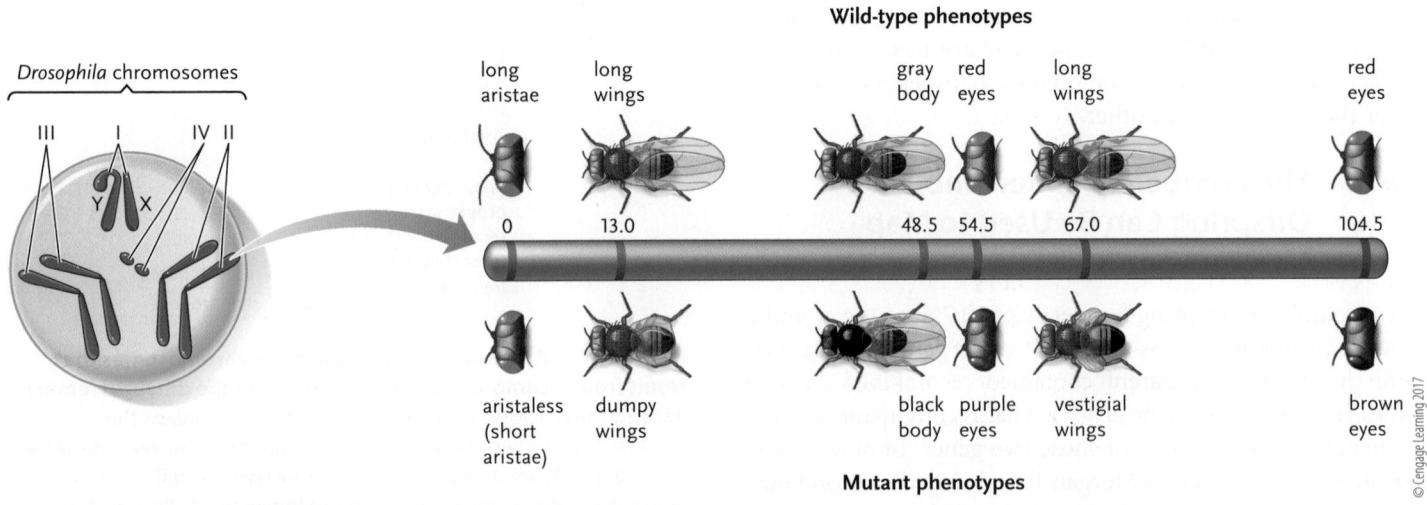

**FIGURE 10.4 Relative map locations of several genes on chromosome 2 of *Drosophila*, as determined by frequencies of recombinant offspring from dihybrid testcrosses.** For each gene, the diagram shows the normal, or wild-type, phenotype on the top and the mutant phenotype on the bottom. Mutant alleles at two different locations alter wing structure, one producing the *dumpy-wing* phenotype and the other the *vestigial-wing* phenotype; the normal allele at these locations results in normal long-wing structure. Mutant alleles at two different locations also alter eye colour.

recombinant offspring varies to some extent from one position to another along chromosomes.

In recent years, DNA sequencing of whole genomes has supplemented the linkage maps of a number of species. DNA sequencing shows the precise physical locations of genes, right down to the number of base pairs separating them.

### 10.1c Widely Separated Linked Genes Assort Independently

Figure 10.4 shows that chromosome 2 in *Drosophila* has a linkage map stretching over 100 mu from one end to the other. This map was created by adding together the recombinant offspring frequencies arising from crosses of closely linked genes. However, genes can be so widely separated on a chromosome that recombination is almost certain to occur at some point between them in every cell undergoing meiosis. When this is the case, alleles of these genes assort independently even though they are on the same chromosome. The map distance separating them will be 50 mu. (Fifty map units reflects 50% recombinant offspring. This is the same proportion of recombinant offspring observed when genes are on different chromosomes.)

To understand this apparent paradox, first recall Figure 8.13, Chapter 8, showing that a recombination event in a given cell creates two recombinant and two nonrecombinant chromatids. Next, imagine 100 meiocytes going through meiosis as usual to yield 400 gametes. If a recombination event occurred in the space separating 2 given genes in 10 of those cells, then 20 recombinant chromatids would be produced during prophase I. Twenty gametes would eventually receive recombinant chromosomes, and 20/400 = 5% of the total testcross progeny would be recombinant. We would conclude that these genes are 5 mu apart. Now assume that a recombination event occurs along the chromosome in the space separating the two genes in *every one of the 100 cells* going through meiosis. Two hundred recombinant offspring would result from the total of 400; 50% would be recombinants; 50 mu would separate the genes.

Linkage between such widely separated genes can still be detected, however, by testing their linkage to one or more genes that lie between them. For example, the genes *a* and *c* in **Figure 10.5** are located so far apart that they assort independently and show no linkage in crosses. However, crosses that show a and b are 23 mu apart (recombinant offspring frequency of 23%), and other crosses show b and c are 34 mu apart. Therefore, *a* and *c* must also be linked and carried on the same chromosome at 23 mu + 34 mu = 57 mu apart. Obviously, we could *not* see a recombinant offspring frequency of 57% in testcross progeny because the maximum frequency of recombinant chromatids is 50%, as described above.

We now know that some of the genes Mendel studied are actually on the same chromosome in pea plants. For example, although the genes for flower colour and seed colour are located on the same chromosome, they are so far apart that frequent

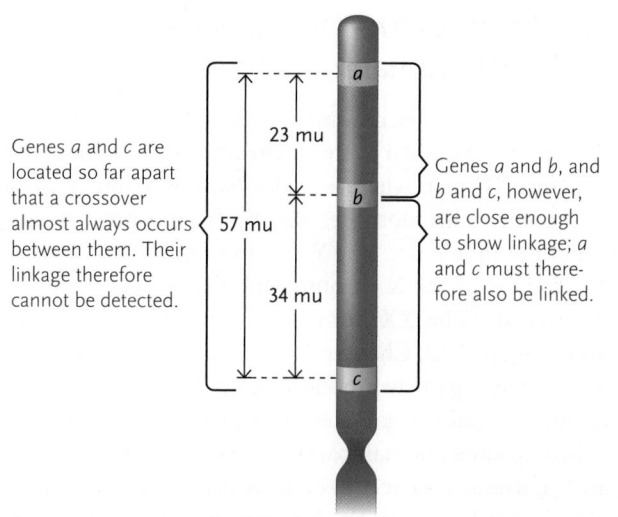

**FIGURE 10.5 Genes far apart on the same chromosome.** Genes *a* and *c* are far apart and will not show linkage in crosses, suggesting that they are on different chromosomes. However, linkage between such genes can be established by noting their linkage to another gene or genes located between them, that is, gene *b* in this example.

recombination between them made them assort independently in Mendel's dihybrid cross analysis.

### STUDY BREAK QUESTIONS

1. What type of cross is typically used to discover whether two genes are linked or not?
2. How can two genes be on the same chromosome and yet assort independently (as if they were on separate chromosomes)?
3. If two genes assort independently, how would you know if they are on the same chromosome or not?

## 10.2 Sex-Linked Genes

In many organisms, one or more pairs of chromosomes are different in males from those in females. Genes located on these chromosomes, the sex *chromosomes*, are called **sex-linked genes**; they are inherited differently in males and females.

**CONCEPT FIX** Note that the word "linked" in the phrase "sex-linked gene" means only that the gene is on a sex chromosome. The use of the word "linked" when considering two or more genes refers to genetic linkage and means that the genes in question are on the same chromosome. Linked genes might be on a sex chromosome or an autosome. ⬢

Chromosomes other than the sex chromosomes are called **autosomes**; genes on these chromosomes have the same patterns of inheritance in both sexes. In humans, chromosomes 1 to 22 are the autosomes.

## 10.2a Females Are XX and Males Are XY In Both Humans and Fruit Flies

In most species with sex chromosomes, females have two copies of a chromosome known as the **X chromosome**, forming a fully homologous XX pair, whereas males have only one X chromosome. Another chromosome, the Y chromosome, occurs in males but not in females. The Y chromosome has a short region of homology with the X chromosome that allows them to pair during meiosis. The XX human chromosome complement is shown in Figure 7.12, Chapter 7.

Each normal gamete produced by an XX female carries an X chromosome. Half the gametes produced by an XY male carry an X chromosome and half carry a Y. When a sperm cell carrying an X chromosome fertilizes an X-bearing egg cell, the new individual develops into an XX female. Conversely, when a sperm cell carrying a Y chromosome fertilizes an X-bearing egg cell, the combination produces an XY male. The Punnett square (see **Figure 10.6**) shows that fertilization is expected to produce females and males with an equal probability of 1/2. This expectation is closely matched in human and *Drosophila* populations.

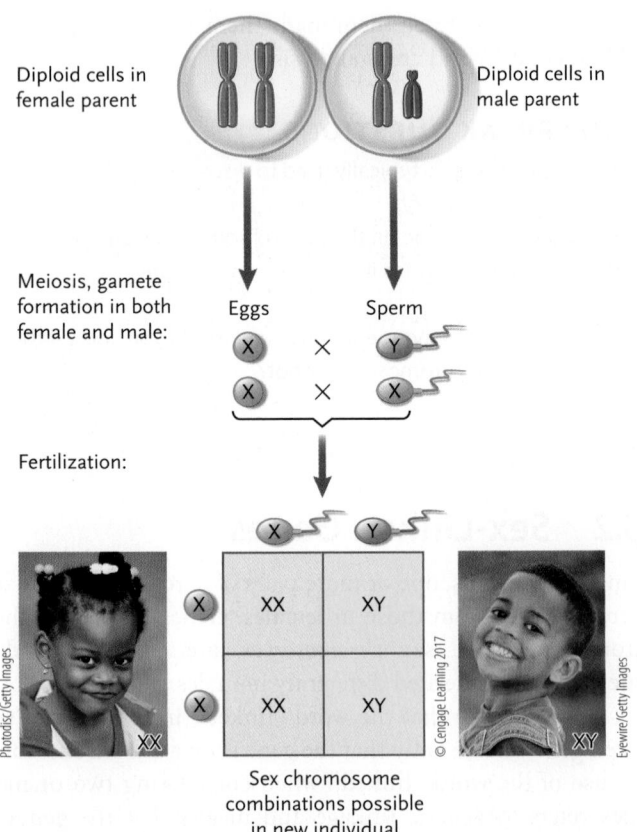

**FIGURE 10.6 Sex chromosomes and the chromosomal basis of sex determination in humans.** Females have two X chromosomes and therefore all gametes (eggs) have the X sex chromosome. Males have one X and one Y chromosome and therefore produce equal numbers of gametes containing an X chromosome versus a Y chromosome. Males transmit their Y chromosome to their sons, but not to their daughters. Males receive their X chromosome only from their mother.

Other sex chromosome arrangements have been found, as in some insects with XX females and XO males (the O means there is no Y chromosome). In birds, butterflies, and some reptiles, the situation is reversed: males have a homologous pair of sex chromosomes (ZZ instead of XX), and females have the equivalent of an XY combination (ZW).

## 10.2b Human Sex Determination Depends on the *SRY* Gene

One gene carried on the Y chromosome, *SRY* (for sex-determining region of the Y), appears to be the master switch that directs development toward maleness at an early point in embryonic development.

For the first month or so of embryonic development in humans and other mammals, the rudimentary structures that give rise to reproductive organs and tissues are the same in XX and XY embryos. After six to eight weeks, the *SRY* gene becomes active in XY embryos, producing a protein that regulates the expression of other genes, thereby stimulating part of these structures to develop as testes. As a part of stimulation by hormones secreted in the developing testes and elsewhere, tissues degenerate that would otherwise develop into female structures such as the vagina and oviducts. The remaining structures develop into the penis and scrotum. In XX embryos, which do not have a copy of the SRY gene, development proceeds toward female reproductive structures. The rudimentary male structures degenerate in XX embryos because the hormones released by the developing testes in XY embryos are not present.

**CONCEPT FIX** Although the X and Y *chromosomes* are called *sex chromosomes*, only a few genes they carry have any influence on sex determination or sexual function. For instance, most of the roughly 2400 known genes on the human X chromosome code for phenotypes needed by both sexes, such as colour perception, blood clotting, and DNA replication. Conversely, genes governing structures needed by only one sex or the other, such as breast development, penis structure, and facial hair, are coded on autosomes. If you are male, you have inherited the genes needed for uterine development and you will pass them along to your offspring to be used by daughters. You do not express these genes in your body. If you are female, a comparable situation is the case for genes coding for penis structure, and so on. You inherited these genes but you don't express them. ⬡

## 10.2c Sex-Linked Genes Show a Different Pattern of Inheritance from Autosomal Genes

Since males and females have different sets of sex chromosomes, the genes carried on these chromosomes can be inherited in a distinctly non-Mendelian pattern called **sex linkage**. Sex linkage arises from two differences between males and females: (1) males have one X chromosome and therefore one allele for each gene on this chromosome (males are hemizygous for X-linked genes, *hemi* = half); females have two copies of the X chromosome and therefore two alleles for all genes on the X chromosome; (2) males also have one copy of the Y chromosome and one allele for each gene on this chromosome; females have no Y chromosome and therefore no Y alleles at all. Y chromosomes are present in males but not females.

Morgan discovered sex-linked genes and their pattern of sex linkage in 1910. The story of his discovery started when he found a male fly in his stocks with white eyes instead of the normal red eyes (**Figure 10.7**). He crossed the white-eyed male with a true-breeding female with red eyes and observed that all the F1 flies had red eyes (**Figure 10.8a**). He concluded that the white-eye trait was recessive. Next, he allowed the F1 flies to interbreed. Based on Mendel's principles, he expected that both male and female F2 flies would show a 3:1 ratio of red-eyed flies to white-eyed flies. Morgan was surprised to find that all the F2 females had red eyes, *but half the* $F_2$ *males had red eyes and half had white eyes* (Figure 10.8b).

Morgan hypothesized that the alleles segregating in the cross were of a gene located on the X chromosome, now termed a sex-linked gene. The white-eyed male parent in the cross had the genotype $X^WY$—an X chromosome with a white ($X^W$) allele—and no other allele of that gene on the Y chromosome. The red-eyed, female parent in the cross had the genotype $X^{W+}X^{W+}$—each X chromosome carries the dominant normal allele for red eyes, $X^{W+}$.

We can follow the alleles in this cross (see Figure 10.8a). The $F_1$ flies of a cross $X^{W+}X_w \times X^WY$ are produced as follows. The X chromosome of each male comes from his mother; therefore, his genotype is $Xw^+Y$, and his phenotype is red eyes. Each female receives one X from each parent; therefore, her genotype is $X^{W+}X^W$, and her phenotype is red eyes due to the dominance of the $X^{W+}$ allele.

In the $F_2$ generation, each female receives an $X^{W+}$ allele from her father ($F_1$) and either an $X^{W+}$ or $X^W$ allele from her mother ($F_1$); these genotypes result in red eyes (see Figure 10.8a). Each male receives his one X chromosome from his mother ($F_1$),

who has the genotype $X^{W+}X^W$. Therefore, F2 males are half $X^{W+}Y$ (red eyes) and half $X^WY$ (white eyes).

Morgan also made a *reciprocal cross* of the one just described; that is, the phenotypes were switched between the parents. The reciprocal cross here was a white-eyed female ($X^WX^W$) with a red-eyed male ($X^{W+}Y$) (see Figure 10.8b). All F1 males had white eyes because they received the $X^W$-bearing chromosome from their mother; thus, their genotype is $X^WY$. The F1 females have red eyes; they are all heterozygous $X^{W+}X^W$. *This result is clearly different from the reciprocal cross shown in Figure 10.8a.*

In the $F_2$ generation of this second cross, both male and female flies showed a 1:1 ratio of red eyes to white eyes (see Figure 10.8b). Again, this result differs markedly from that of the cross in Figure 10.8a.

In summary, Morgan's work showed that there is a distinctive pattern in the phenotypic ratios for reciprocal crosses in which the gene involved is on the X chromosome. A key indicator of this sex linkage is when all male offspring of a cross between a true-breeding mutant female and a wild-type male have the mutant phenotype. As we have seen, this occurs because a male receives his X chromosome from his female parent. In humans, as in fruit flies, sex-linked recessive traits appear more frequently among males than females because males need to receive only one copy of the allele on the X chromosome inherited from their mothers to develop the trait. Females must receive two copies of the recessive allele, one from each parent, to express the trait. An example of this inheritance pattern can be seen in Figure 10.15c. Two examples of human sex-linked traits are red–green colour blindness, a recessive trait in which the affected individual is unable to distinguish between the colours red and green because of a defect in light-sensing cells in the retina; and hemophilia, a recessive trait in which affected individuals have a defect in blood clotting.

**CONCEPT FIX** Colour-blindness does not mean that people see only black and white. The inability to see any colour at all is very rare. As shown in Figure 10.16, colour-blindness reduces the variety of colours that can be distinguished. ⬡

## 10.2d Inactivation of One X Chromosome Evens Out Gene Effects in Mammalian Females

Although mammalian females have twice as many copies of genes carried on the X chromosome as males, it is unlikely that they require twice as much of the products of those genes. Theoretically, products from genes on the X chromosome could be equalized in males and females if (1) expression of genes on the single male X chromosome were doubled, or (2) expression of genes on both female X chromosomes were halved, or (3) one X chromosome were "turned off" in females. All these **dosage compensation** mechanisms are known in nature, but mammals use the latter; females with two X chromosomes inactivate most of the genes on one X chromosome or the other in most body cells.

a.                    b.

Martin Shields/Science Source

**FIGURE 10.7  Eye colour phenotypes in *Drosophila*. (a)** Normal red wild-type eye colour; **(b)** mutant white eye colour caused by a recessive allele of a sex-linked gene carried on the X chromosome

FIGURE 10.8   **Experimental Research**

## Evidence for Sex-Linked Genes

**Question:** How is the white-eye gene of *Drosophila* inherited?

**Experiment:** Morgan crossed a white-eyed male *Drosophila* with a true-breeding female with red eyes and then crossed the F1 flies to produce the F$_2$ generation. He also performed the reciprocal cross in which the phenotypes were switched in the parental flies: true-breeding white-eyed female × red-eyed male.

**a. True-breeding red-eyed female × white-eyed male**

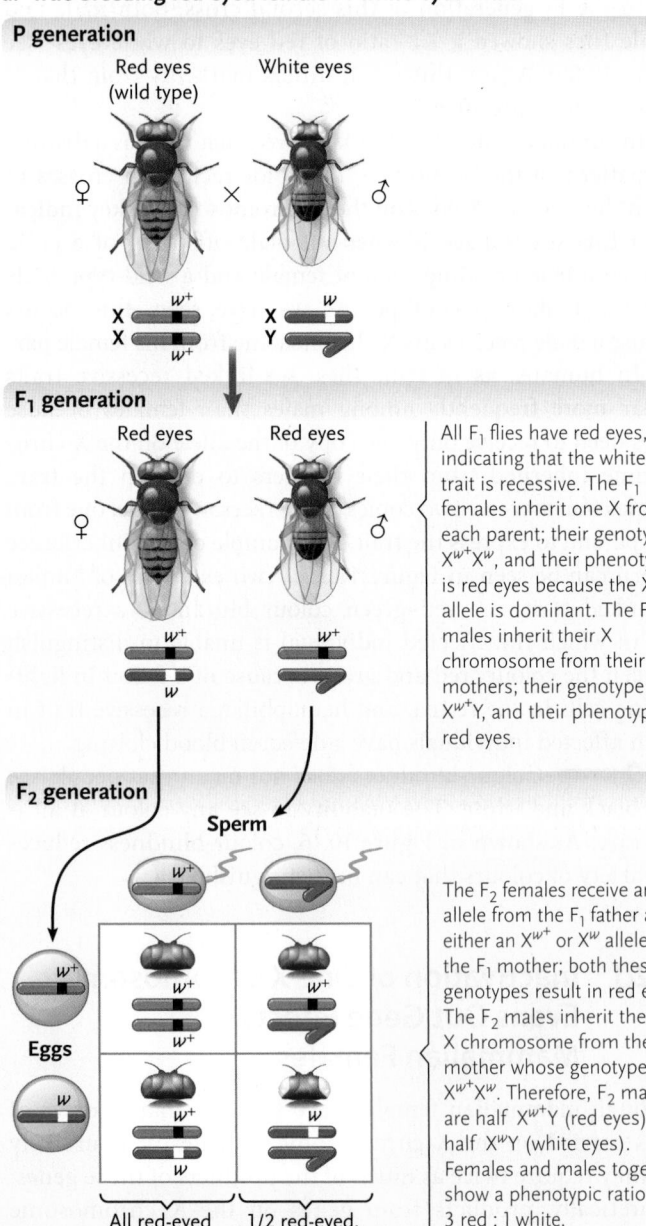

All F$_1$ flies have red eyes, indicating that the white-eye trait is recessive. The F$_1$ females inherit one X from each parent; their genotype is $X^{w^+}X^w$, and their phenotype is red eyes because the $X^{w^+}$ allele is dominant. The F$_1$ males inherit their X chromosome from their mothers; their genotype is $X^{w^+}Y$, and their phenotype is red eyes.

The F$_2$ females receive an $X^{w^+}$ allele from the F$_1$ father and either an $X^{w^+}$ or $X^w$ allele from the F$_1$ mother; both these genotypes result in red eyes. The F$_2$ males inherit their one X chromosome from the F$_1$ mother whose genotype is $X^{w^+}X^w$. Therefore, F$_2$ males are half $X^{w^+}Y$ (red eyes) and half $X^wY$ (white eyes). Females and males together show a phenotypic ratio of 3 red : 1 white.

**b. White-eyed female × red-eyed male**

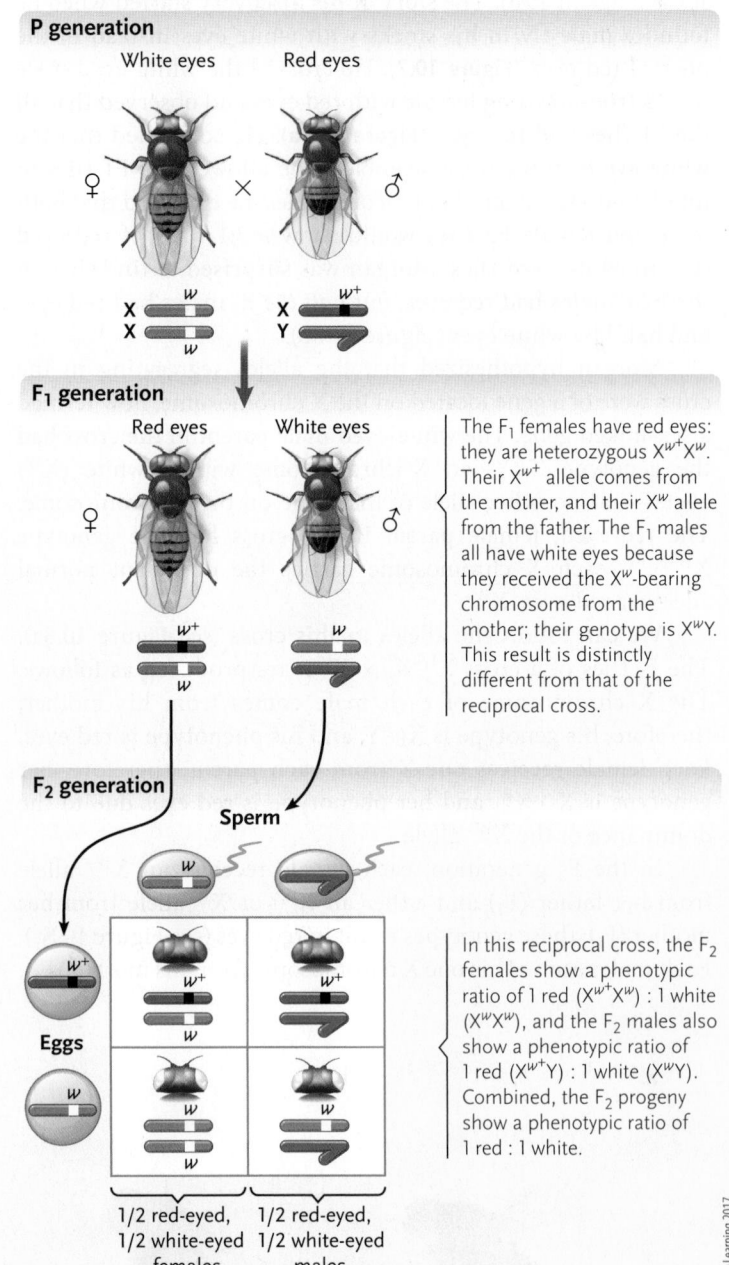

The F$_1$ females have red eyes: they are heterozygous $X^{w^+}X^w$. Their $X^{w^+}$ allele comes from the mother, and their $X^w$ allele from the father. The F$_1$ males all have white eyes because they received the $X^w$-bearing chromosome from the mother; their genotype is $X^wY$. This result is distinctly different from that of the reciprocal cross.

In this reciprocal cross, the F$_2$ females show a phenotypic ratio of 1 red ($X^{w^+}X^w$) : 1 white ($X^wX^w$), and the F$_2$ males also show a phenotypic ratio of 1 red ($X^{w^+}Y$) : 1 white ($X^wY$). Combined, the F$_2$ progeny show a phenotypic ratio of 1 red : 1 white.

© Cengage Learning 2017

**Results:** Differences were seen in both the F1 and F2 generations for the red ♀ × white ♂ and white ♀ × red ♂ crosses.

**Conclusion:** The segregation pattern for the white-eye trait showed that the white-eye gene is a sex-linked gene located on the X chromosome.

As a result of the equalizing mechanism, the activity of most genes carried on the X chromosome is essentially the same in the cells of males and females. The inactivation occurs by a condensation process that folds and packs the chromatin of one of the two X chromosomes into a tightly coiled state similar to the condensed state of chromosomes during cell division. The inactive, condensed X chromosome can be seen within the nucleus in cells of females as a dense mass of chromatin, called the **Barr body.**

The inactivation occurs during embryonic development. Which of the two X chromosomes becomes inactive in a particular embryonic cell line is a random event. But once one of the X chromosomes is inactivated in a cell, that same X is inactivated in all descendants of the cell. Thus, within one female, one of the X chromosomes is active in particular cells and inactive in others, and vice versa.

If the two X chromosomes carry different alleles of a gene, one allele will be active in cell lines in which one X chromosome is active, and the other allele will be active in cell lines in which the other X chromosome is active. For many sex-linked alleles, such as the recessive allele that causes hemophilia, random inactivation of either X chromosome has little overall whole-body effect in heterozygous females because the dominant allele is active in enough of the critical cells to produce a normal phenotype. However, for some genes, the inactivation of either X chromosome in heterozygotes produces recognizably different effects in distinct regions of the body.

For example, the orange and black patches of fur in calico cats result from inactivation of one of the two X chromosomes in regions of the skin of heterozygous females (**Figure 10.9**). Males, which get only one of the two alleles, normally have either black or orange fur. Similarly, in humans, females who are heterozygous for an allele on the X chromosome that blocks development of sweat glands may have a patchy distribution of skin areas with and without the glands. Females with the patchy distribution are not seriously affected and may be unaware of the condition.

As we have seen, the discovery of genetic linkage, recombination, and sex-linked genes led to the elaboration and expansion of Mendel's principles of inheritance. Next, we examine what happens when patterns of inheritance are modified by changes in the chromosomes.

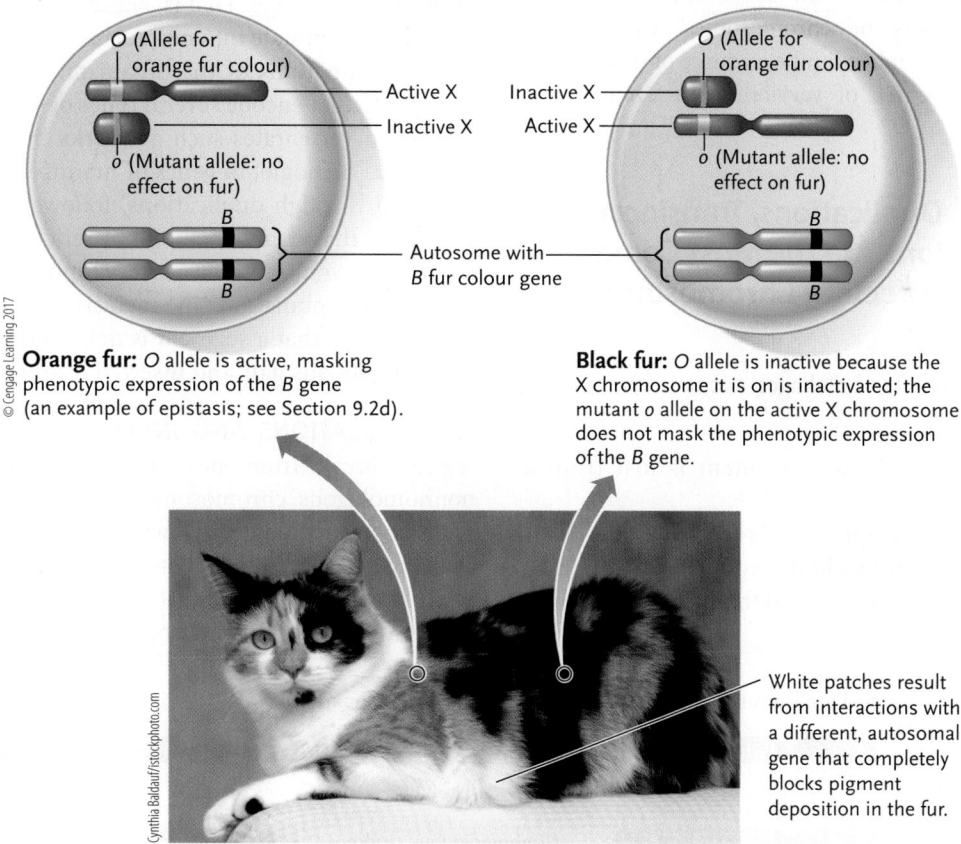

**Orange fur:** *O* allele is active, masking phenotypic expression of the *B* gene (an example of epistasis; see Section 9.2d).

**Black fur:** *O* allele is inactive because the X chromosome it is on is inactivated; the mutant *o* allele on the active X chromosome does not mask the phenotypic expression of the *B* gene.

White patches result from interactions with a different, autosomal gene that completely blocks pigment deposition in the fur.

**FIGURE 10.9 The patchy black, orange, and white coat coloration known as "calico" arises from two main genetic mechanisms: epistatic interaction (see Section 9.2d) and X inactivation.** An autosomal gene, *B*, codes for dark pigmentation (*B_* is black; *bb* is chocolate brown). However, a second gene, *O*, is sex-linked and, through epistasis, the dominant allele results in orange pigmentation rather than black or chocolate. The recessive allele has no effect. Assuming the calico cat above has the genotype *Oo BB*, random X inactivation will determine whether or not this epistatic interaction occurs in any given patch of skin. An orange patch results when the inactivated X chromosome carries the recessive o allele; the remaining, dominant *O* allele results in orange rather than black. A black patch results whenever the dominant *O* allele is inactivated; the recessive *o* allele has no effect on the black pigmentation. White patches result from yet another epistatic interaction with a third autosomal gene, *S*: the dominant allele prevents deposition of any pigment and the recessive allele has no effect. For reasons that are poorly understood, expression of this white spotting allele over the body is highly variable.

## 10.3 Chromosomal Mutations That Affect Inheritance

A chromosomal mutation is any change from the normal structure or number of chromosomes in a cell. Although chromosomes are relatively stable structures, they are sometimes altered by breaks in the DNA, which can be generated by agents such as radiation or certain chemicals, or by enzymes encoded in some infecting viruses. The broken chromosome fragments may be lost or they may reattach to the same or different chromosomes. The resulting changes in chromosome structure may have genetic consequences if alleles are eliminated, mixed in new combinations, duplicated, or placed in new locations by the alterations in cell lines that lead to the formation of gametes.

Genetic changes may also occur through changes in chromosome number, including addition or loss of one or more chromosomes or even entire sets of chromosomes. Changes in chromosome structure or number can be a source of disease and disability, as well as a source of variability for evolutionary processes.

### 10.3a Deletions, Duplications, Translocations, and Inversions Are the Most Common Mutations Affecting Chromosome Structure

Chromosomal alterations after breakages occur in four major forms (**Figure 10.10**):

- A **deletion** occurs if a broken segment is lost from a chromosome.
- A **duplication** occurs if a segment is broken from one chromosome and inserted into its homologue. In the receiving homologue, the alleles in the inserted fragment are added to the ones already there.
- A **translocation** occurs if a broken segment is attached to a different, nonhomologous chromosome.
- An inversion occurs if a broken segment reattaches to the same chromosome from which it was lost, but in reversed orientation so that the order of genes is reversed.

In order to be inherited by offspring, chromosomal alterations must occur in cells of the germ line leading to development of eggs or sperm.

**DELETIONS AND DUPLICATIONS** A deletion (see Figure 10.10a) may cause severe problems if the missing segment contains genes that are essential for normal development or cellular functions. For example, one deletion from human chromosome 5 typically leads to severe cognitive impairment and a malformed larynx. The cries of an affected infant sound more like a meow than a human cry—hence the name of the disorder, *cri-du-chat* (meaning "cat's cry").

A duplication (see Figure 10.10b) may have effects that vary from harmful to beneficial, depending on the genes and alleles contained in the duplicated region. Although most duplications are likely to be detrimental due to disturbance of the normal gene product levels, some have been important sources of evolutionary change. That is, because there are duplicate genes, one copy can mutate into new forms without seriously affecting the basic functions of the organism. For example, mammals have genes that encode several types of hemoglobin that are not present in vertebrates such as sharks that evolved earlier; the additional hemoglobin genes of mammals are believed to have appeared through duplications, followed by mutations in the duplicates that created new and beneficial forms of hemoglobin as further evolution took place. Duplications sometimes arise during recombination in meiosis if crossing-over occurs unequally, so that a segment is deleted from one chromosome of a homologous pair and inserted into the other.

**TRANSLOCATIONS AND INVERSIONS** In a translocation, a segment breaks from one chromosome and attaches to another, nonhomologous, chromosome. In many cases, a translocation is reciprocal, meaning that two nonhomologous chromosomes exchange segments (see Figure 10.10c). Reciprocal translocations resemble genetic recombination, except that the two chromosomes involved in the exchange do not contain the same genes.

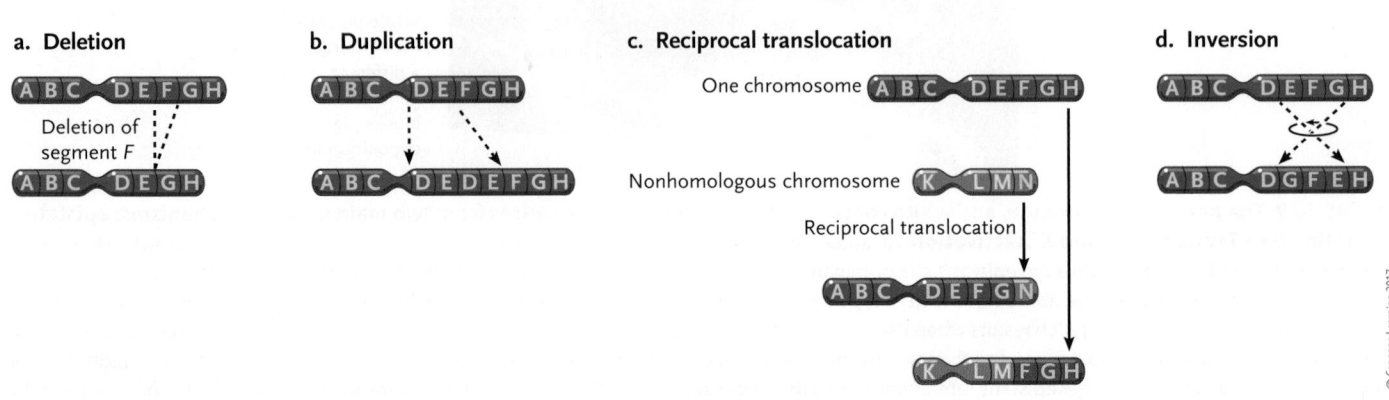

**FIGURE 10.10** Chromosome **(a)** deletion, **(b)** duplication, **(c)** translocation (a reciprocal translocation is shown), and **(d)** inversion

In an inversion, a chromosome segment breaks and then reattaches to the same chromosome, but in reverse order (see Figure 10.10d). Inversions have essentially the same effects as translocations: genes may be broken internally by the inversion, with loss of function, or they may be transferred intact to a new location within the same chromosome, producing effects that range from beneficial to harmful.

Many cancers have chromosomal mutations, and the most common type of chromosomal mutation involved is a translocation. For example, 90% of patients with chronic myelogenous leukemia (CML) have a chromosomal mutation called the *Philadelphia chromosome*. CML is a type of cancer of the blood involving the uncontrolled division of stem cells for white blood cells. The Philadelphia chromosome arises from a reciprocal translocation event involving chromosomes 9 and 22 (**Figure 10.11**). A segment of chromosome 9 moves to chromosome 22 and they fuse together on the resulting Philadelphia chromosome: the *ABL* gene from 9 fuses with the *BCR* gene on 22. The *ABL* gene is one of many genes that control cell growth and division. (Cell division control is described in Chapter 7.)

Its product is a tyrosine kinase, an enzyme that adds phosphate to tyrosine amino acids in target proteins. In its new location on the Philadelphia chromosome, the *ABL* gene becomes much more active because of its fusion with the *BCR* gene, and much more of its tyrosine kinase product is made than normal. As a result of its overactivity, normal cell-cycle control breaks down and the cells are stimulated to grow and they divide uncontrollably, becoming cancer cells. The drug Gleevec is used to treat CML patients. It works by inhibiting the tyrosine kinase enzyme so that the body stops, or at least reduces, the production of too many white blood cells.

Chromosome structure mutations have played a role in the evolution of genomes. For instance, many new genes and gene families evolved as a result of duplication. Also, inversions and translocations have been important factors in the evolution of the genomes of plants and some animals, including insects and primates. As an example, nine of the human chromosome pairs show evidence of translocations and inversions that differ between humans and chimpanzees, and therefore must have occurred after the ancestral lineages leading to chimpanzees and humans split. (Genome evolution is discussed further in Chapter 16.)

## 10.3b Some Chromosomal Mutations Involve Changes In the Number of Entire Chromosomes

At times, whole single chromosomes are lost or gained from cells entering or undergoing meiosis, resulting in a change of chromosome number. Most often, these changes occur through **nondisjunction**, the failure of homologous pairs to separate during the first meiotic division, or through misdivision, the failure of chromatids to separate during the second meiotic division (see Chapter 8 and **Figure 10.12**). As a result, products of meiosis are produced that lack one or more chromosomes or contain extra copies of the chromosomes. *Note that failure of homologues to disjoin in meiosis I does not affect meiosis II; chromatids will most likely separate normally in meiosis II.* Fertilization by such gametes produces an individual with extra or missing chromosomes. Such individuals are called *aneuploids*, whereas individuals with a normal set of chromosomes are called *euploids.*

Changes in chromosome number can also occur through duplication of entire sets, meaning individuals may receive one or more extra copies of the entire haploid complement of chromosomes. Such individuals are called **polyploids**. *Triploids* have three copies of each chromosome instead of two; *tetraploids* have four copies of each chromosome. Multiples higher than tetraploid also occur.

**ANEUPLOIDS** The effects of addition or loss of whole chromosomes vary depending on the chromosome and the species. In animals, aneuploidy of autosomes usually produces debilitating or lethal developmental abnormalities. These abnormalities also occur in humans; addition or loss of an autosomal chromosome

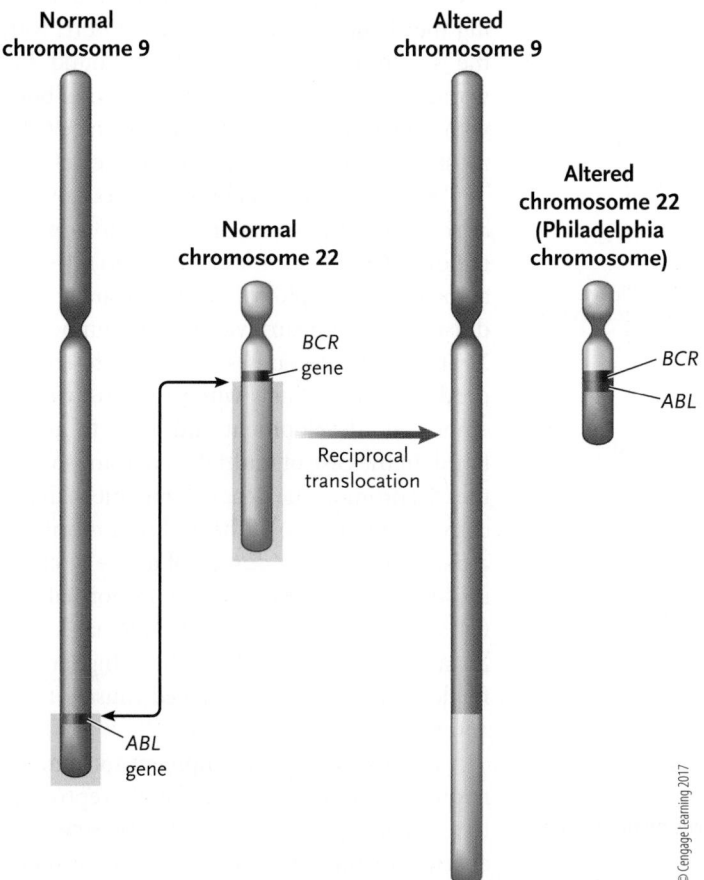

**FIGURE 10.11 Translocation is found in many patients with a form of blood cancer called *chronic myelogenous leukemia* (CML).** A reciprocal translocation involving chromosomes 9 and 22 produces a short chromosome named the *Philadelphia* chromosome. On this chromosome, the chromosome 9 *ABL* gene has become fused to the chromosome 22 *BCR*. The resulting overactivity of the *ABL* gene, which normally helps control cell division, causes the cell to convert to a cancer cell.

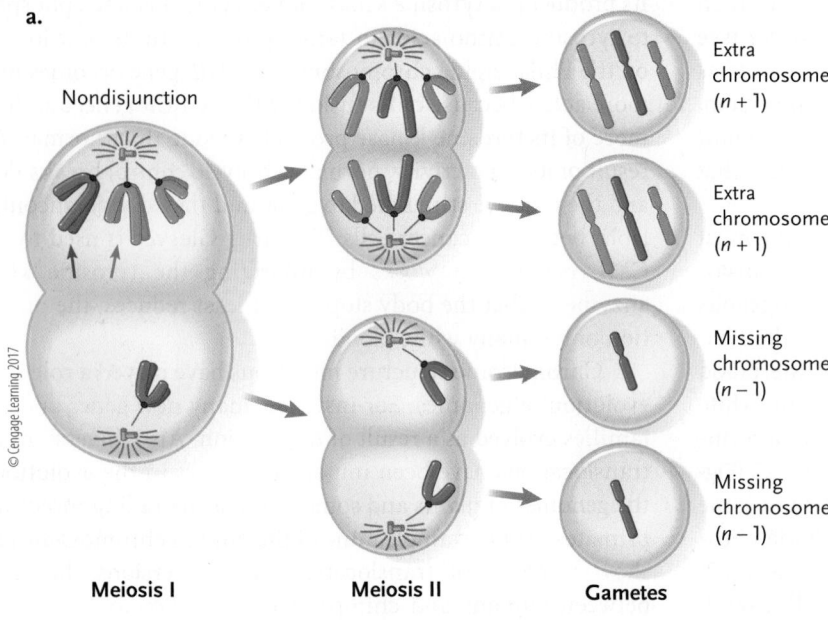

a.

Nondisjunction

Meiosis I | Meiosis II | Gametes

Extra chromosome (n + 1)

Extra chromosome (n + 1)

Missing chromosome (n − 1)

Missing chromosome (n − 1)

© Cengage Learning 2017

Nondisjunction during the first meiotic division causes both chromosomes of one pair to be delivered to the same pole of the spindle. The nondisjunction produces two gametes with an extra chromosome and two with a missing chromosome.

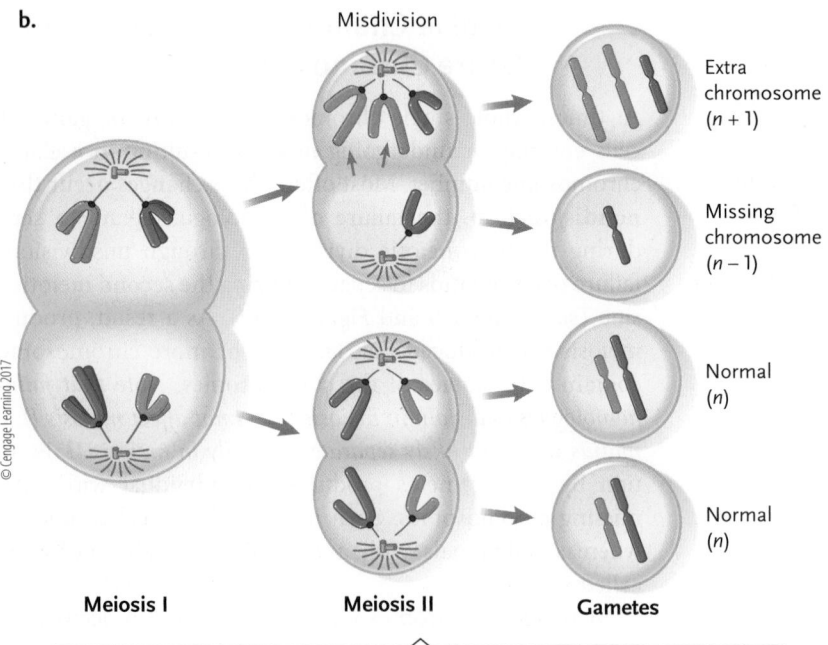

b.

Misdivision

Meiosis I | Meiosis II | Gametes

Extra chromosome (n + 1)

Missing chromosome (n − 1)

Normal (n)

Normal (n)

© Cengage Learning 2017

Misdivision during the second meiotic division produces two normal gametes, one gamete with an extra chromosome, and one gamete with a missing chromosome.

**FIGURE 10.12** **(a)** Nondisjunction during the first meiotic division and **(b)** misdivision during the second meiotic division.

causes embryos to develop so abnormally that they are aborted naturally. For reasons that are not understood, aneuploidy is as much as 10 times as frequent in humans as in other mammals. Of human embryos that have been miscarried and examined, about 70% are aneuploids.

In some cases, autosomal aneuploids survive. This is the case with humans who receive an extra copy of chromosome 21, one of the smallest chromosomes (**Figure 10.13a**). Many of these individuals survive well into adulthood. The condition produced by the extra chromosome, called *Down syndrome or trisomy 21*, is characterized by short stature and some degree of cognitive impairment. About 40% of individuals with Down syndrome have heart defects, and skeletal development is slower than normal. Most do not mature sexually and remain sterile. However, with attentive care and appropriate educational opportunities, individuals with Down syndrome can successfully participate in many activities.

Most Down syndrome cases arise from nondisjunction or misdivision of chromosome 21 during meiosis, primarily in women (about 5% of nondisjunctions that lead to Down syndrome occur in men). The nondisjunction occurs more frequently as women age, increasing the chance that a child may be born with the syndrome (Figure 10.13b). Around the world, about 1 in every 800 children is born with Down syndrome, making it one of the most common serious human genetic defects.

Aneuploidy of sex chromosomes can also arise by nondisjunction or misdivision during meiosis (**Figure 10.14** and **Table 10.1**). Unlike autosomal aneuploidy, which usually has drastic effects on survival, altered numbers of X and Y chromosomes are often tolerated, producing individuals who progress through embryonic development and grow to adulthood. In the case of multiple X chromosomes, the X-chromosome inactivation mechanism converts all but one of the X chromosomes to a Barr body, so the dosage of active X-chromosome genes is the same as in normal XX females and XY males. Triple X females may be taller than usual and may be at higher risk for learning disability, reduced muscle tone, and menstrual irregularities.

Because sexual development in humans is pushed toward male or female reproductive organs primarily by the presence or absence of the *SRY* gene on the Y chromosome, people with a Y chromosome are externally malelike, no matter how many X chromosomes are present. If no Y chromosome is present, X chromosomes in various numbers give rise to femalelike individuals. (Table 10.1 lists the effects of some alterations in sex chromosome number.) Extra Y chromosomes, due to their small complement of genes, do not have a significant phenotypic effect on men who are

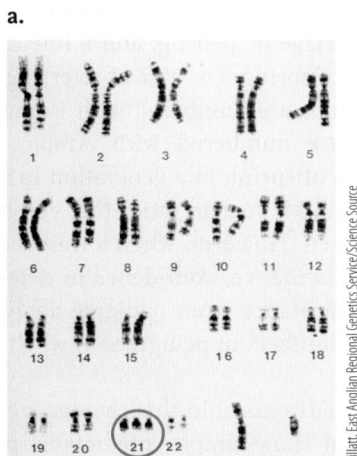

**a.**

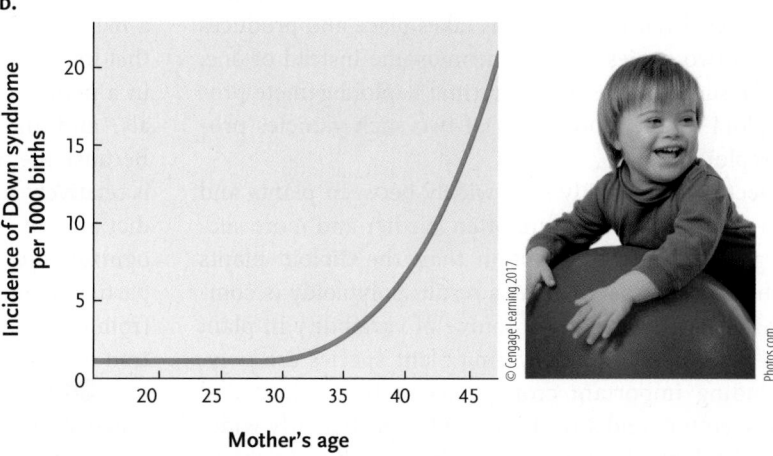

**b.**

**FIGURE 10.13 Down syndrome. (a)** The chromosomes of a human female with Down syndrome showing three copies of chromosome 21 (circled in red). **(b)** The incidence of Down syndrome increases with the age of the mother, as determined in a study conducted in Victoria, Australia, between 1942 and 1957.

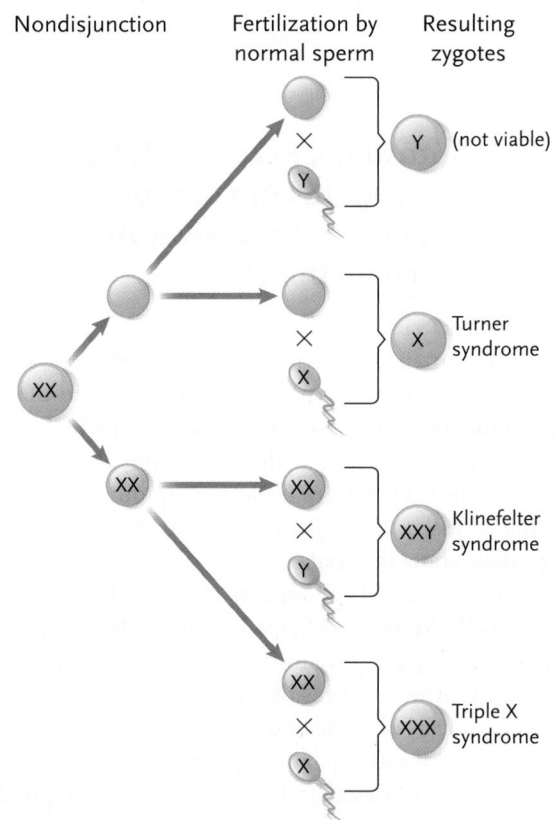

**FIGURE 10.14 Some abnormal combinations of sex chromosomes in fertilized zygotes resulting from nondisjunction of X chromosomes during meiosis in females**

aneuploidy for their Y. Similar abnormal combinations of sex chromosomes also occur in other animals, including *Drosophila*, with varying effects on viability.

**POLYPLOIDS** Polyploidy often originates from failure of the spindle to function normally during mitosis in cell lines leading to germ-line cells. In these divisions, the spindle fails to separate the duplicated chromosomes, which are therefore

| TABLE 10.1 | Effects of Unusual Combinations of Sex Chromosomes in Humans | |
|---|---|---|
| Combination of Sex Chromosomes | Approximate Frequency | Effects |
| XO* | 1 in 5000 births | Turner syndrome: females with underdeveloped ovaries; sterile; intelligence and external genitalia are normal; typically, individuals are short in stature with underdeveloped breasts |
| XXY | 1 in 2000 births | Klinefelter syndrome: male external genitalia with very small and underdeveloped testes; sterile; intelligence usually normal; sparse body hair and some development of the breasts; similar characteristics in XXXY and XXXXY individuals |
| XYY | 1 in 1000 births | XYY syndrome: apparently normal males but often taller than average |
| XXX | 1 in 1000 births | Triple-X syndrome: apparently normal female with normal or slightly delayed mental development |

*When one sex chromosome is missing, the notation "O" is added; therefore, females with a single X chromosome are designated "XO."

incorporated into a single nucleus with twice the usual number of chromosomes. Eventually, meiosis takes place and produces products with two copies of each chromosome instead of one. Fusion of one such gamete with a normal haploid gamete produces a triploid zygote, and fusion of two such gametes produces a tetraploid zygote.

The effects of polyploidy vary widely between plants and animals. In plants, polyploids are often hardier and more successful in growth and reproduction than the diploid plants from which they were derived. As a result, polyploidy is common and has been an important source of variability in plant evolution. About half of all flowering plant species are polyploids, including important crop plants such as wheat and other cereals, cotton, and strawberries. One particularly widespread use of polyploids is in seedless fruits such as bananas, grapes, and watermelon. These triploid plants have difficulty disjoining homologues properly in meiosis so they are often sterile or, in these cases, seedless.

By contrast, polyploidy is less common among animals. In vertebrate animals, polyploidy is found, for instance, in some fish species and in several amphibians. Polyploidy is more common among invertebrates, an example being flatworms. In humans, only about 1% of polyploids survive until birth, and these people die within a month. The lethality is probably due to disturbance of animal developmental pathways, which are typically much more complex than those of plants.

We now turn to a description of the effects of altered alleles on human health and development.

**STUDY BREAK QUESTIONS**

What mechanisms are responsible for

(a)  duplication of a chromosome segment?
(b)  generation of a Down syndrome individual?
(c)  a chromosome translocation?
(d)  polyploidy?

# 10.4 Human Genetic Traits, Pedigree Analysis, and Genetic Counselling

The study of human genetics is complicated because controlled genetic matings of humans are not possible for ethical reasons. Instead, the inheritance patterns of human genetic traits can sometimes be identified by examining the way a trait of interest occurs in family trees of individuals who exhibit the trait. The selected trait is usually a mutation responsible for a genetic disease, or it could be a specific trait of interest, like hair pigment. Typically, these trees include several generations of phenotypes, and the associated genotypes must then be determined by interpretation. The family tree is called a **pedigree**, and the study of the pedigree is called **pedigree analysis.** Pedigree analysis has its own set of symbols: females are designated by a circle and males by a square; a solid circle or square indicates

the presence of the trait; a horizontal line between a female and a male indicates a marriage or pairing; and a line down from that line leads to their offspring. For ease of referring to people in a pedigree, generations are numbered with Roman numerals, and individuals are numbered with Arabic numerals. Because the number of offspring in a generation in a pedigree is relatively small, typical Mendelian ratios that you might predict are not typically seen. However, when a trait shows a recognizable *pattern* of inheritance, confidence in determining a particular mode of inheritance from pedigree analysis comes from examining large numbers of pedigrees in which the same trait is found.

**CONCEPT FIX** The traits discussed in this chapter are each governed by one gene and show simple, predictable patterns of inheritance in pedigrees. Although such traits do illustrate fundamental features of inheritance in humans, most traits that are important to the health of human populations (e.g., obesity, heart disease, cancer, dementia, diabetes, asthma, autism spectrum disorder) are influenced by many genes and do not show such simple inheritance patterns. ⬡

## 10.4a  In Autosomal Recessive Inheritance, Heterozygotes Are Carriers and Homozygous Recessives Are Affected By the Trait

Phenylketonuria, sickle cell anemia, and cystic fibrosis are examples of human disorders caused by recessive alleles on autosomes. These traits are passed on according to the pattern known as **autosomal recessive inheritance**, in which individuals who are homozygous for the dominant allele are free of symptoms. Heterozygotes are usually symptom free but are carriers of the recessive allele. People who are homozygous for the recessive allele show the trait.

*Phenylketonuria* (PKU) appears in about 1 of every 12 000 births in North America. Affected individuals cannot produce an enzyme that converts the amino acid phenylalanine to another amino acid, tyrosine. As a result, phenylalanine builds up in the blood and is converted in the body into other products, including phenylpyruvate. Elevations in both phenylalanine and phenylpyruvate damage brain tissue and can lead to severe mental retardation. All newborns in Canada are tested for PKU because, if diagnosed early enough, an affected infant can be placed on a phenylalanine-controlled diet and develop normally.

**Figure 10.15a** shows part of a pedigree for PKU. Analysis of the pedigree illustrates the general characteristics of autosomal recessive inheritance for a rare human genetic trait such as this.

- Most affected individuals have two normal parents, both of whom are heterozygotes. For example, III.3 and III.8 both have PKU, so their parents II.1 and II.2, and II.3 and II.4, respectively, all must have been heterozygotes.
- From a marriage of two heterozygotes, 1/4 of the offspring are expected to have the trait. From one pedigree, there are

### a. Phenylketonuria (PKU)

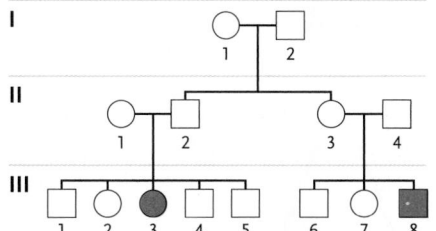

### b. Achondroplasia

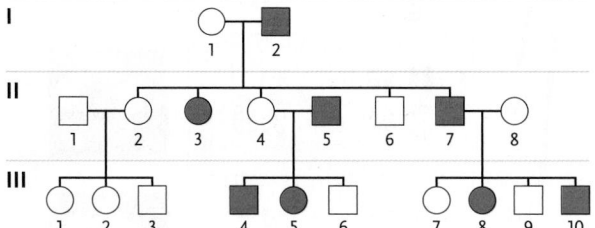

### c. Duchenne muscular dystrophy

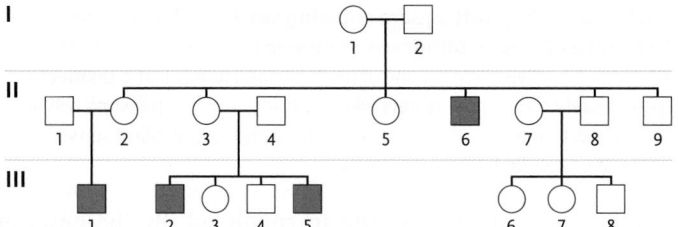

### d. Hereditary enamel hypoplasia

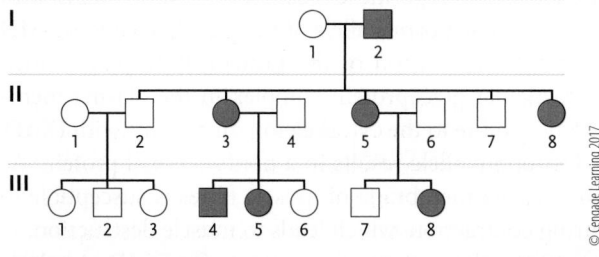

© Cengage Learning 2017

**FIGURE 10.15 Pedigrees of human genetics traits showing different modes of inheritance. (a)** Part of a pedigree for phenylketonuria (PKU), an autosomal recessive trait. **(b)** Part of a pedigree for achondroplasia, an autosomal dominant trait. **(c)** Part of a pedigree for Duchenne muscular dystrophy (DMD), an X-linked recessive trait. **(d)** Part of a pedigree for hereditary enamel hypoplasia, an X-linked dominant trait

rarely enough individuals to see that ratio. However, the ratio would likely be seen when a large number of pedigrees are looked at together.

In sickle cell anemia, an amino acid change in hemoglobin causes red blood cells to assume a sickle shape (see Section 9.2f). The problems the sickled red blood cells have in passing through capillaries cause the wide ranging symptoms of sickle cell anemia. Between 10% and 15% of people of African descent in North

America are carriers for this disorder. Although carriers make enough normal hemoglobin through the activity of the normal allele to be essentially unaffected, the mutant, sickle cell form of the hemoglobin molecule is also present in their red blood cells. Carriers can be identified by a molecular test for the mutant hemoglobin. Carriers are less susceptible to malaria, which helps explain the increased proportions of the mutant allele in populations whose ancestors originated in some areas of Africa and other parts of the world where the malarial parasite is common.

Cystic fibrosis (CF), one of the most common genetic disorders among persons of Northern European descent, is another autosomal recessive trait. About 1 in every 25 people from this line of descent is an unaffected carrier with one copy of the recessive allele. Approximately 1 per 4000 children born in Canada has CF. Affected individuals have a mutated form of the transport protein called *cystic fibrosis transmembrane conductance regulator* (CFTR). CFTR is embedded in the plasma membrane of epithelial cells, such as those of the passageways and ducts of the lungs, pancreas, and digestive tract. The mutant CFTR protein does not reach the plasma membrane and cannot transport $Cl^-$ (chloride ions) out of the cells and into the extracellular fluids. This reduction in chloride transport results in thick, sticky mucus that collects in the airways of the lungs, in the ducts of glands such as the pancreas, and in the digestive tract. The accumulated mucus impairs body functions and, in the lungs, promotes pneumonia and other infections.

## 10.4b In Autosomal Dominant Inheritance, Only Homozygous Recessives Are Unaffected

Some human traits follow a pattern of **autosomal dominant inheritance**. In this case, the allele underlying the trait of interest is dominant, and people who are either homozygous or heterozygous for this allele are affected. Individuals homozygous for the recessive allele are unaffected.

*Achondroplasia* (see Figure 10.15c), a type of dwarfing that occurs in about 1 in 25 000 births worldwide, is caused by an autosomal dominant allele of a gene on chromosome 4. Of individuals with the dominant allele, only heterozygotes survive embryonic development; homozygous dominants are usually stillborn. When limb bones develop in heterozygous children, cartilage formation is defective, leading to disproportionately short arms and legs. They also have a relatively large head, but the trunk and torso are of normal size. Affected adults are usually not much more than 4 feet tall.

The mutation responsible for achondroplasia maps to the *FGFR3* (fibroblast growth factor receptor 3) gene, which encodes a receptor tyrosine kinase enzyme. The normal role of *FGFR3* is to repress the maturation of chondrocytes in the formation of bone in response to the signalling molecule that binds to the receptor. (Chondrocytes are cells that form cartilage and bone.) This negative effect on bone formation is regulated by opposing positive effects on bone growth by other pathways so that, in individuals homozygous for the normal

*FGFR3* gene, bones of normal length are produced. In heterozygotes with the dominant mutation in *FGFR3*, the receptor is overly active all the time, resulting in a long-term, negative effect on bone growth, hence the dwarfing symptoms of achondroplasia.

Figure 10.15b shows part of a pedigree for achondroplasia. Analysis of the pedigree illustrates the general characteristics of autosomal dominant inheritance for a rare trait:

- Every affected person in a pedigree has at least one affected parent.
- The trait does not skip generations. Here, you can see that affected individuals are present in each generation of the pedigree. In contrast, for the autosomal recessive pedigree shown in Figure 10.15a, affected individuals appeared only in generation III.
- On average, an affected individual (who would typically be heterozygous for the mutant allele of a rare autosomal dominant trait) will transmit the mutant allele to half his or her offspring. That is, if the dominant mutant allele is designated *A*, and the normal recessive allele is *a*, then most pairings will be *Aa* × *aa*. From Mendelian principles, 1/2 of the offspring should be *Aa* (have the trait) and 1/2 should be *aa* (normal). Again, with small pedigrees there are usually insufficient numbers of individuals to see such ratios.

## 10.4c  In X-Linked Recessive Inheritance, Males Are More Commonly Affected

Red–green colour-blindness (**Figure 10.16**) and hemophilia have already been mentioned as examples of human traits that demonstrate **X-linked recessive inheritance**, that is, traits due to inheritance of recessive alleles carried on the X chromosome. People with hemophilia bleed uncontrollably if they are injured because a protein required for forming blood clots is not produced in functional form. With luck and good care, affected people can reach maturity, but their lives are tightly circumscribed by the necessity to avoid injury. Even internal bleeding from slight bruises can be fatal. The disease, which affects about 1 in 7000 males, can be treated by injection of the required clotting protein.

Hemophilia has had effects reaching far beyond individuals who inherit the disease. The most famous cases occurred in the royal families of Europe descended from Queen Victoria of England. At one time, 18 of Queen Victoria's 69 descendants were affected males or female carriers. In Russia, Crown Prince Alexis was one of Victoria's descendants with hemophilia. His affliction drew together his parents, Czar Nicholas II and Czarina Alexandra (a granddaughter of Victoria and a carrier), and the hypnotic monk Rasputin, who manipulated the family to his advantage by convincing them that only he could control the boy's bleeding. The situation escalated and contributed to the onset of the Russian Revolution of 1917, which ended the Russian monarchy and led to the establishment of a Communist government in the former Soviet Union.

Another X-linked recessive human disease trait is Duchenne muscular dystrophy (DMD). In affected individuals, muscle

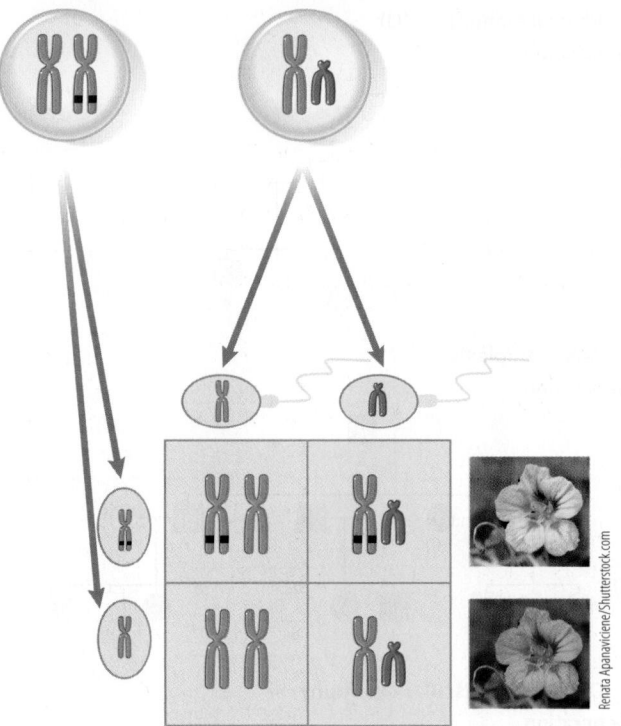

**FIGURE 10.16 Punnett square showing sex-linked recessive inheritance of colour-blindness in humans.** Note that the mother carries the defective allele on one of her X chromosomes but is unaffected. Approximately half her daughters will be carriers and half her sons will be colour-blind. Images indicate how the normal and colour-blind sons perceive a particular flower and leaves.

tissue begins to degenerate late in childhood. By the onset of puberty, most individuals with this disease are unable to walk. Muscular weakness progresses, with later involvement of the heart muscle. The average life expectancy for individuals with DMD is 25 years. The normal allele of the gene that causes DMD encodes a functional version of the protein dystrophin, which anchors a particular glycoprotein complex in the plasma membrane of a muscle fibre to the cytoskeleton. In patients with DMD, a mutant dystrophin allele results in a nonfunctional protein. As a result, the plasma membrane of muscle fibres is susceptible to tearing during contraction, which leads to muscle destruction.

Figure 10.15c shows part of a pedigree for DMD. Analysis of the pedigree illustrates some general characteristics of X-linked recessive inheritance:

- Many more males than females should exhibit the trait due to the different number of X chromosomes in the two sexes. We can see that property here in this pedigree, with only males showing the trait.
- All sons of an affected (homozygous mutant) mother should show the trait because males receive their only X chromosome from their mothers. (There is no case of that in this pedigree.)
- The sons of heterozygous (carrier) mothers should show an approximately 1:1 ratio of normal individuals to individuals expressing the trait; that is, $X^{a+}X^a \times X^{a+}Y$ gives 1/2 $X^{a+}Y$ and 1/2 $X^aY$ sons.

- From a pairing of a carrier female with a normal male, all daughters will be normal phenotypically, but 1/2 will be carriers; that is, $X^{a+}X^a \times X^{a+}Y$ gives 1/2 $X^{a+}X^{a+}$ and 1/2 $X^{a+}X^a$ females. In turn, 1/2 the sons of these carrier females will exhibit the trait. In the pedigree shown, the I.1 female must be a carrier because offspring II.6 has the trait. I.2 is a normal male because he does not show the trait. We see three female offspring, two of whom must be carriers because they produce some male offspring with the trait.
- A male expressing the trait, when paired with a homozygous normal female, will produce all normal children. But all the female progeny will be carriers; that is, $X^{a+}X^{a+} \times X^aY$ gives $X^{a+}X^a$ females and $X^{a+}Y$ (normal) males.

## 10.4d  X-Linked Dominant Traits Are Rare

Only a few X-linked dominant traits have been identified in humans. One example is hereditary faulty enamel and dental discoloration, technical name *hereditary enamel hypoplasia*. Another is a severe bleeding anomaly called *constitutional thrombopathy*.

Figure 10.15d shows part of a pedigree for hereditary enamel hypoplasia. Analysis of the pedigree illustrates some characteristics of X-linked dominant inheritance. Generally, X-linked dominant traits follow the same inheritance rules as do X-linked recessives, except that heterozygous females express the trait.

- Because females have twice the number of X chromosomes as males, X-linked dominant traits are more frequent in females than in males, and we see that in the pedigree.
- Males with an X-linked dominant trait pass on the trait to all their daughters and none of their sons. We see that in the pedigree where male I.2 with the trait passes on his X chromosome to each of his female offspring II.2, II.5, and II.8, and so they show the trait. However, the two male offspring, II.2 and II.4, received their X chromosomes from their mother who was normal; hence they do not show the trait.

Theoretically, those females could have passed their X chromosome with the dominant mutant allele to male or female offspring, who then would show the trait. In fact, we see that, if the trait is rare, as is the case here, females with the trait are likely to be heterozygous. These females pass on the trait to 1/2 their male progeny and 1/2 their female progeny. We see this roughly in the pedigree where female II.3 produced both a male (III.4) and a female (III.5) child with the trait, plus a normal child (III.6).

## 10.4e  Human Genetic Disorders Can Be Predicted and Many Can Be Treated

Each year, roughly 8 million children around the world are born with a severe disease or disability with a significant genetic component. The rate of such births in middle- and low-income countries is double that for high-income countries. Why might this be? One contributing factor has already been mentioned: in areas where malaria is endemic, the frequency of the sickle cell allele tends to be higher and the incidence of newborn sickle cell

disease is higher. Nutritional deficiencies, consanguineous (blood relative) marriage practices, and higher numbers of children born to older mothers may also elevate birth defect rates in certain societies. In addition to improvements in basic financial, health, and nutritional standards, programs offering genetic counselling, prenatal diagnosis, and genetic screening can help reduce the suffering associated with genetic disorders.

**Genetic counselling** allows prospective parents to assess the possibility that they might have an affected child. For example, parents may seek counselling if they, a close relative, or one of their existing children has a genetic disorder. Genetic counselling begins with identification of parental genotypes through pedigrees or direct testing for an altered protein or DNA sequence. With this information in hand, counsellors can often predict the chances of having a child with the trait in question. Couples can then make an informed decision about whether to have a child.

Genetic counselling is often combined with techniques of **prenatal diagnosis**, in which cells derived from a developing embryo or its surrounding tissues or fluids are tested for the presence of mutant alleles or chromosomal alterations. In **amniocentesis**, cells are obtained from the amniotic fluid—the watery fluid surrounding the embryo in the mother's uterus (**Figure 10.17**). In **chorionic villus sampling**, cells are obtained from portions of the placenta that develop from tissues of the embryo. More than 100 genetic disorders can now be detected by these tests. If prenatal diagnosis detects a serious genetic defect, the prospective parents can reach an informed decision about whether to continue the pregnancy, including religious and moral considerations, as well as genetic and medical advice.

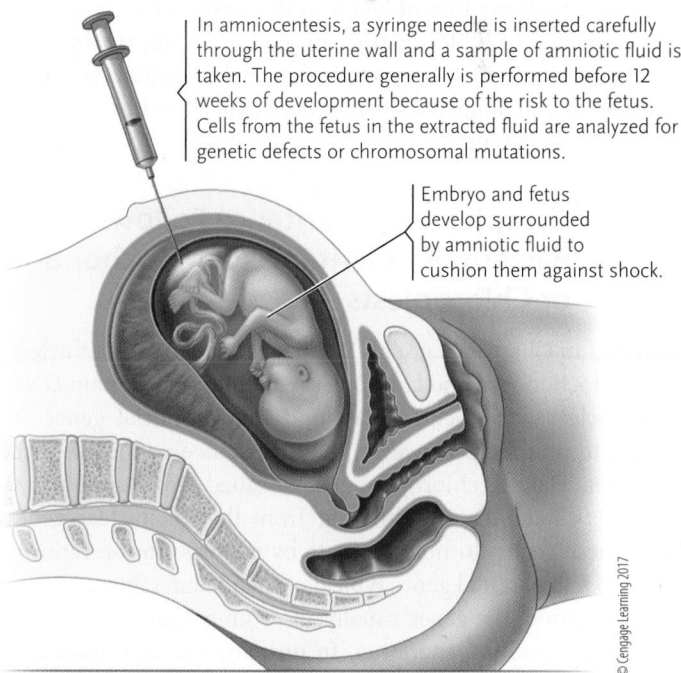

In amniocentesis, a syringe needle is inserted carefully through the uterine wall and a sample of amniotic fluid is taken. The procedure generally is performed before 12 weeks of development because of the risk to the fetus. Cells from the fetus in the extracted fluid are analyzed for genetic defects or chromosomal mutations.

Embryo and fetus develop surrounded by amniotic fluid to cushion them against shock.

© Cengage Learning 2017

**FIGURE 10.17 Amniocentesis, a procedure used for prenatal diagnosis of genetic defects.** The procedure is complicated and costly, and, therefore, it is used primarily in high-risk cases.

Once a child is born, inherited disorders are identified by genetic screening, in which biochemical or molecular tests for disorders are routinely applied to children and adults or to newborn infants in hospitals. The tests can detect inherited disorders early enough to start any available preventive measures before symptoms develop. As mentioned previously, worldwide newborn screening for PKU identifies affected children in time for them to avoid the debilitating symptoms of this disease. The first generation of people to survive childhood with PKU are now adults and having families of their own.

Although the traits discussed in this chapter so far are all coded by genes carried by nuclear chromosomes, some situations, such as linkage and sex linkage, did not follow the traditional patterns shown by the traits studied by Mendel. The following section looks at additional examples of non-Mendelian inheritance arising when genes are either located on DNA in mitochondria and chloroplasts, or are expressed differently depending on which parent they are inherited from.

### STUDY BREAK QUESTIONS

1. What inheritance pattern would suggest that a trait is dominant and carried on an autosome?
2. How are inherited disorders detected before symptoms arise?

## 10.5 Additional Non-Mendelian Patterns of Inheritance

We consider two examples of non-traditional patterns of inheritance in this section. In **cytoplasmic inheritance**, the pattern of inheritance follows that of genes in the cytoplasmic organelles: mitochondria or chloroplasts. In **genomic imprinting**, the expression of an allele of a particular nuclear gene is based on whether an individual organism inherits the allele from the male or the female parent.

### 10.5a Cytoplasmic Inheritance Follows the Pattern of Inheritance of Mitochondria or Chloroplasts

As noted in Chapter 2, not all DNA is contained in the nucleus; both mitochondrial and chloroplast genomes also contain DNA. Like nuclear genes, chloroplast and mitochondrial genes are subject to mutation. However, the inheritance pattern of these mitochondrial and chloroplast genes—called *cytoplasmic inheritance*—is fundamentally different from that of nuclear genes. First, these genes do not segregate by meiosis, so the ratios of mutated and parental genes typical of Mendelian segregation are absent. Second, the genes usually show uniparental inheritance from generation to generation. In **uniparental inheritance**, all progeny (both males and females) have the phenotype of only one of the parents. For most multicellular eukaryotes, offspring inherit only the mother's phenotype, a phenomenon called **maternal inheritance.** In sexual reproduction, both the male

and the female gamete provide nuclear DNA, but the female provides most of the cytoplasm in the fertilized cell. Maternal inheritance occurs because, in animals, a zygote receives most of its cytoplasm, including mitochondria and (in plants) chloroplasts, from the female parent and little from the male parent. In plants, cytoplasmic inheritance varies depending on the species and the organelle (mitochondrion or chloroplast).

The first example of cytoplasmic inheritance of a mutant trait was found in 1909 by the German scientist Carl Correns. Correns studied variegated four-o'clock plants, *Mirabilis jalapa*. Variegation means that there are areas of pale green or white in otherwise normal green leaves. In some cases, whole branches may have green leaves, whereas others may have entirely pale green or white leaves. Correns made crosses of all combinations between these different types of branches on different plants. His results showed that the progeny always resembled the maternal parent (the parent producing the seed from which the offspring grew) and not the plant providing the pollen (the male parent). Correns was observing maternal inheritance. The explanation here is that the leaf colours are due to the plastids they contain. For example, green leaves contain normal chloroplasts, and white leaves contain chloroplasts that carry a mutation for the production of the green pigment chlorophyll (see Chapter 6). The maternal parent contributes essentially all plastids to the progeny, hence the progeny had the chloroplast phenotype of that parent and not the male parent.

Maternal inheritance of mutant traits involving the mitochondria have also been characterized in many eukaryotic species, including animals, plants, protists, and fungi. Similar to the mutant traits of chloroplasts, each mutant trait results from an alteration of a gene in the mitochondrial genome.

In humans, several inherited diseases have been traced to mutations in mitochondrial genes. Recall that the mitochondrion plays a critical role in synthesizing ATP, the energy source for many cellular reactions. Several maternally inherited diseases in humans involve mutations in mitochondrial genes that encode components of the ATP-generating system of the organelle. The resulting mitochondrial defects are especially destructive to the organ systems most dependent on mitochondrial reactions for energy: the central nervous system, skeletal and cardiac muscle, the liver, and the kidneys. Leber's hereditary optic neuropathy (LHON), as described in *Why It Matters* at the opening of this chapter, is one example of such a maternally inherited human disease.

The maternal inheritance of mitochondria in humans has some useful experimental applications, including genealogical studies to trace a maternal lineage back in time, and in forensics. For example, mitochondrial DNA testing has proved to be a valuable tool in missing persons investigations and in identifying remains in mass disasters.

⬢ CONCEPT FIX Many people believe that they inherit half their DNA from each of their parents. Although this idea is roughly true for nuclear DNA, recall that mitochondria also contain DNA and they are inherited exclusively from mothers. You have considerably more of your mother's DNA than your father's. ⬢

## 10.5b  In Gene Imprinting, the Allele Inherited from One of the Parents Is Expressed Whereas the Other Allele Is Silent

Throughout our discussions of Mendelian inheritance, we have assumed that a particular allele has the same effect in an individual whether it was inherited from the mother or the father. For the vast majority of genes, the assumption is correct. However, researchers have identified a number of genes whose effects do, in fact, depend on whether an allele is inherited from the mother or the father. For some of these genes, only the paternal, sperm-derived allele is expressed. For others, only the maternal, egg-derived allele is expressed. The phenomenon in which the expression of an allele of a gene depends on the parent that contributed it is called *genomic imprinting*. The gene involved is called an *imprinted gene*. The silent allele—the inherited allele that is not expressed—is called the *imprinted allele*. In humans and mice, nearly 100 imprinted genes have been identified.

The first imprinted gene identified was *Igf2* in mice. *Igf2* encodes insulin-like growth factor 2, a protein that stimulates cell growth and division. The growth factor is needed for early embryos to develop normally. Researchers studying mice heterozygous for a deletion of the entire *Igf2* gene from the genome observed that if mice inherited the mutated chromosome from the father they were small, but if they had inherited the mutated chromosome from the mother they were normal size (**Figure 10.18a**). It appeared that only the paternally inherited gene had an effect on size. The maternally inherited gene, whether normal or not, had no effect. The researchers reasoned that, in normal mice homozygous for *Igf2*, the active form of the gene is the copy on the paternal chromosome, whereas the maternal copy of the gene is imprinted (silent) (Figure 10.18b). So, if a heterozygote inherits the deletion from the father, that copy of the gene is inactive because of the deletion. Even if the maternal copy is nonmutant, it is not expressed because it is silenced by imprinting. As a result, normal development does not occur and the adult mouse produced is small.

Genomic imprinting occurs in the germ cells that develop into gametes. In those germ cells, the allele destined to be inactive in the new embryo after fertilization is methylated. That is, in the production of sperm, alleles for paternally imprinted genes are methylated, and in the production of eggs, alleles for maternally imprinted genes are methylated. That methylated (silenced) state of a gene is passed on cell generation to cell generation as the cells grow and divide to produce the somatic (body) cells of the organism. The mechanism of genomic imprinting involves modification of the DNA in the region that controls the expression of an allele by the addition of methyl (—CH$_3$) groups to cytosine (C) nucleotides. The methylation of the control region of a gene prevents it from being expressed. (You will learn more about the regulation of gene expression by methylation of DNA in Chapter 13.)

Inherited imprints must first be erased in the germ cells before new imprinting occurs in the production of gametes. Consider a gene that is maternally imprinted, for example: In the adult, the maternal chromosome has an imprinted allele of that gene, whereas the paternal chromosome has an active allele. When that adult produces gametes, it needs to imprint all alleles in a way appropriate to its sex; for example, if it is male, it must erase the imprint from the maternally inherited gene so that sperm the male produces has a nonimprinted copy of the gene.

**CONCEPT FIX**  Although imprinted traits can show a *parent of origin effect*, imprinting is not the same as sex linkage. Imprinted traits are not necessarily carried on sex chromosomes, and any given sex-linked allele can be inherited from either a mother or a father. ⬢

This chapter finishes our look at the inheritance of genes and the role of chromosomes in Mendelian versus non-Mendelian inheritance mechanisms. In the next chapter, you will learn about the molecular structure and function of the genetic material that makes up genes and about the molecular mechanism by which DNA is replicated.

### STUDY BREAK QUESTIONS

1.  Which inheritance pattern would suggest that a trait is coded by the mitochondrial genome?
2.  Is imprinting a permanent change in gene expression?

**a. Phenotypes of mice heterozygous for a deletion of gene *Igf2***

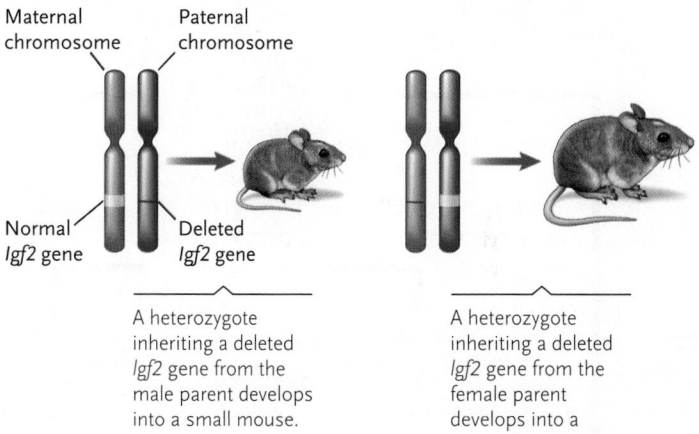

A heterozygote inheriting a deleted *Igf2* gene from the male parent develops into a small mouse.

A heterozygote inheriting a deleted *Igf2* gene from the female parent develops into a normal-sized mouse.

**b. Phenotype of mice homozygous for the normal allele of *Igf2***

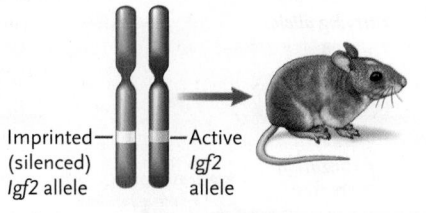

In a mouse heterozygous for the normal allele of *Igf2*, the paternal allele is active, and the maternal allele is imprinted (silenced). As long as a normal allele is inherited from the male parent, the mouse develops into a normal-sized adult.

© Cengage Learning 2017

**FIGURE 10.18  Imprinting of the mouse *Igf2* (insulin-like growth factor 2) gene**

# Summary Illustration

Genetic linkage, sex-linkage and organelle chromosomes, and changes in nuclear chromosome structure or number can all result in inheritance patterns that are distinctly different from those originally observed by Mendel. Noting inheritance patterns in human families can reveal underlying mechanisms of disease.

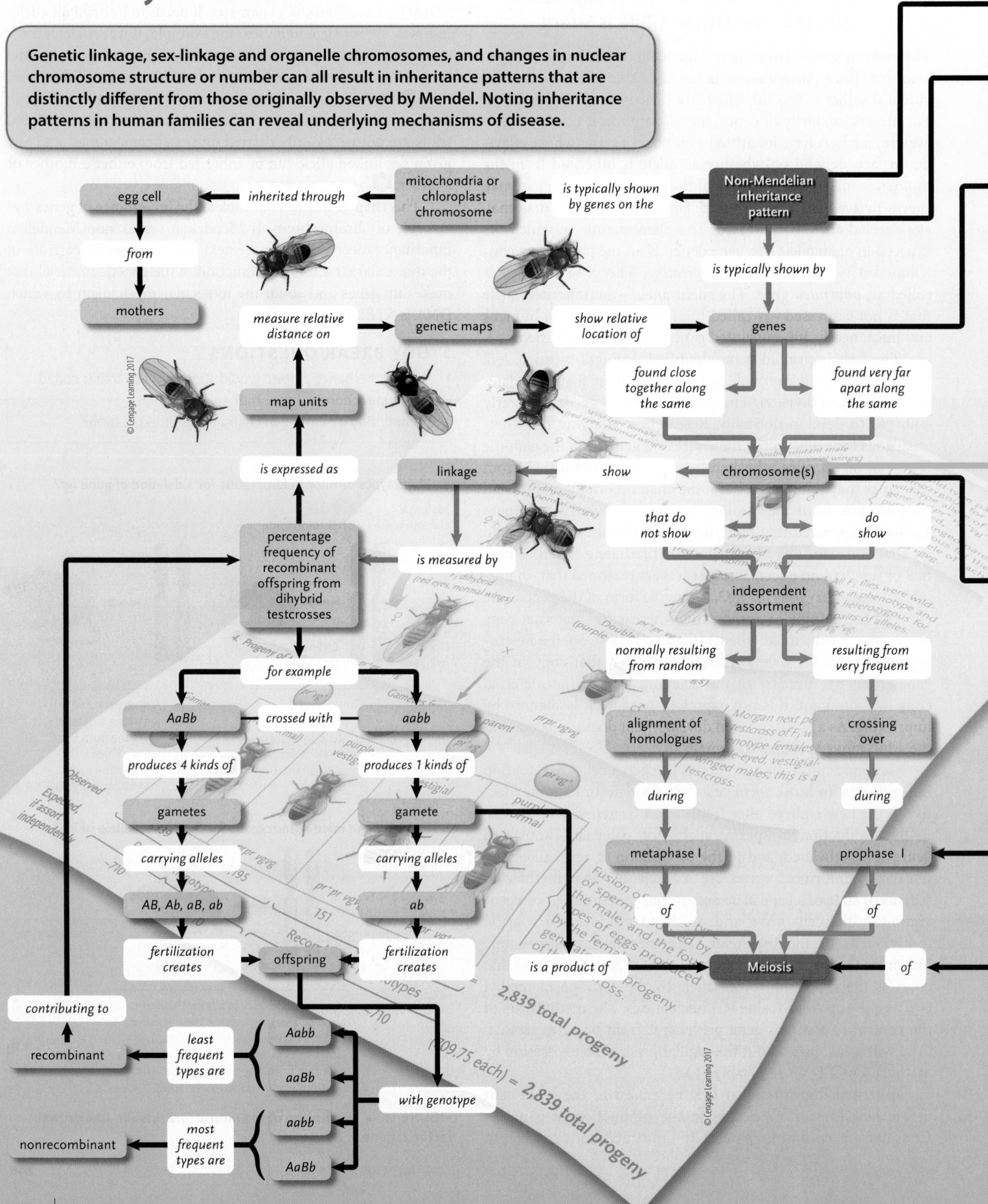

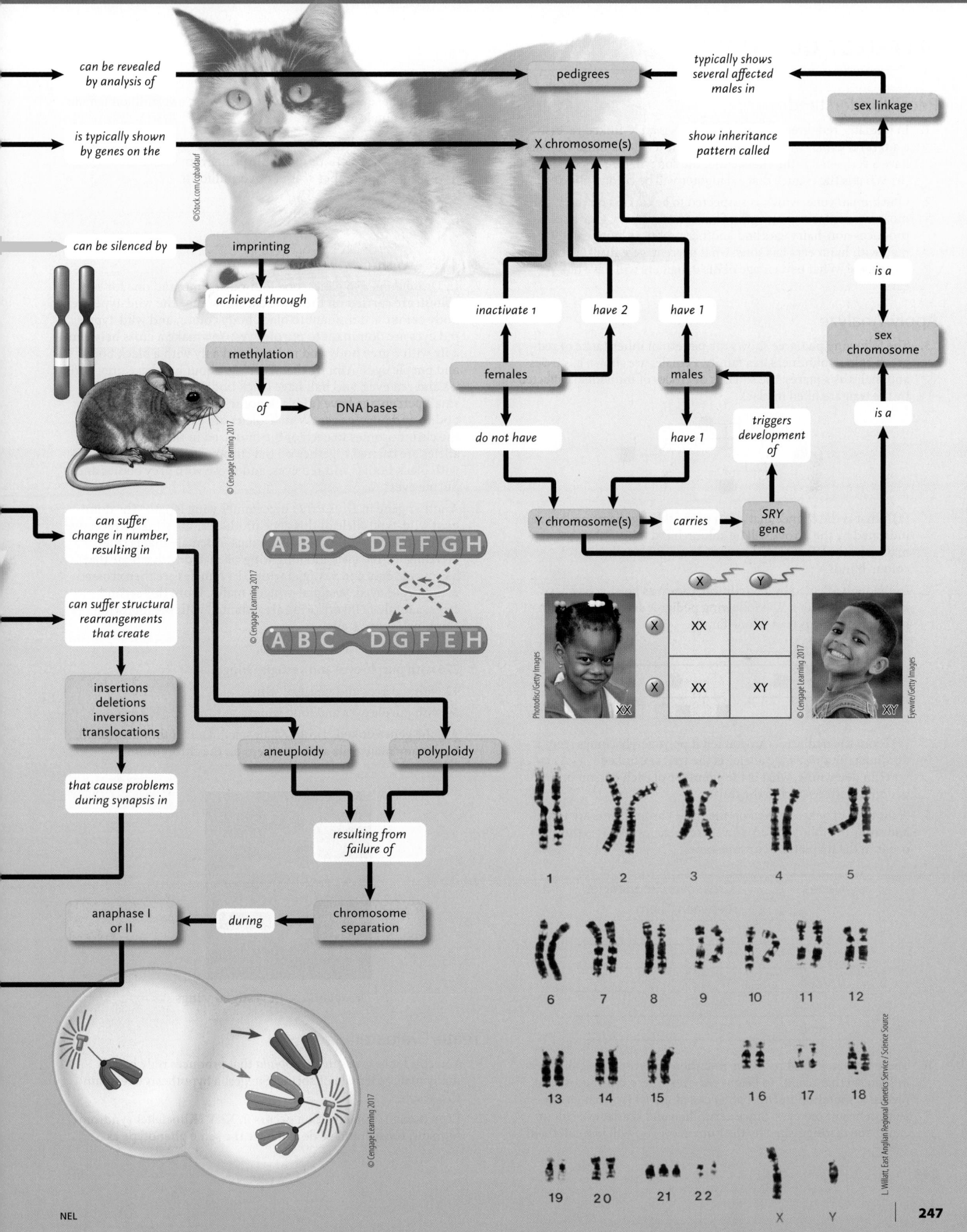

- can be revealed by analysis of → pedigrees ← typically shows several affected males in
- sex linkage
- is typically shown by genes on the → X chromosome(s) → show inheritance pattern called → sex linkage
- can be silenced by → imprinting → achieved through → methylation → of → DNA bases
- inactivate 1 · have 2 · have 1
- females → do not have
- males → have 1
- females / males → Y chromosome(s) → carries → SRY gene → triggers development of → males
- is a → sex chromosome
- is a → sex chromosome
- can suffer change in number, resulting in → aneuploidy · polyploidy
- can suffer structural rearrangements that create → insertions deletions inversions translocations → that cause problems during synapsis in
- A B C • D E F G H → A B C • D G F E H
- aneuploidy · polyploidy → resulting from failure of → chromosome separation → during → anaphase I or II

X · Y

| | X | Y |
|---|---|---|
| X | XX | XY |
| X | XX | XY |

XX · XY

1 2 3 4 5
6 7 8 9 10 11 12
13 14 15 16 17 18
19 20 21 22 X Y

©iStock.com/cgbaldauf
© Cengage Learning 2017
Photodisc/Getty Images
Eyewire/Getty Images
L. Willatt, East Anglian Regional Genetics Service / Science Source

# SELF-TEST QUESTIONS

## Recall/Understand

1. In humans, red–green colour-blindness is an X-linked recessive trait. (a) If a man with normal vision and a colour-blind woman have a son, what is the chance that the son will be colour-blind? (b) What is the chance that a daughter will be colour-blind?

2. One human gene, which is suspected to be carried on the Y chromosome, controls the length of hair on men's ears. One allele produces non-hairy ears and another produces hairy ears. If a man with hairy ears has sons, what percentage will also have hairy ears? What percentage of his daughters will have hairy ears?

## Apply/Analyze

3. The following pedigree shows the pattern of inheritance of red–green colour-blindness in a family. Females are shown as circles and males as squares; the squares or circles of individuals affected by the trait are filled in black.

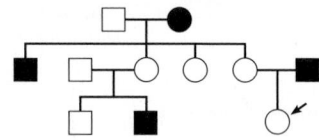

(a) What is the chance that a son of the third-generation female, indicated by the arrow, will be colour-blind if his father is a normal man? (b) What would be the chance if his father is colour-blind?

4. Individuals affected by a condition known as *polydactyly* have extra fingers or toes. The following pedigree shows the pattern of inheritance of this trait in one family.

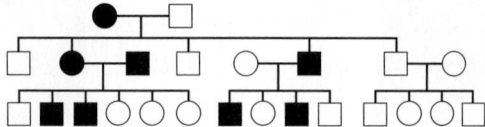

(a) From the pedigree, can you tell if polydactyly comes from a dominant or a recessive allele? Is the trait sex linked? (b) As far as you can determine, what is the genotype of each person in the pedigree with respect to the trait?

5. A number of genes carried on the same chromosome are tested and show the following crossover frequencies. What is their order in the map of the chromosome?

| Genes | Crossover Frequencies between Them |
|---|---|
| C and A | 7% |
| B and D | 3% |
| B and A | 4% |
| C and D | 6% |
| C and B | 3% |

6. There is a sex-linked recessive mutation in *Drosophila* called *vermillion* (*v*) that results in bright red eyes. There is an autosomal recessive mutation in *Drosophila* called *scarlet* (*sc*) that also results in bright red eyes. Since vermillion and scarlet eye colour cannot be distinguished by the human eye, we will just call them both "bright" eyes. Consider a cross between a vermillion female and scarlet male as below:

$$v\,v\,;\,sc^+\,sc^+\quad \times\quad v^+\,Y\,;\,sc\,sc$$

Which of these fractions of the offspring from such a cross would have bright eyes (either scarlet or vermillion)?

a. None

b. ¼

c. ½

d. ¾

7. In *Drosophila*, two genes, one for body colour and one for eye colour, are carried on the same chromosome. The wild-type grey body colour is dominant to black body colour, and wild-type red eyes are dominant to purple eyes. You make a cross between a fly with a grey body and red eyes and a fly with a black body and purple eyes. Among the offspring, about half have grey bodies and red eyes, and half have black bodies and purple eyes. A small percentage have (a) black bodies and red eyes or (b) grey bodies and purple eyes. Which alleles are carried together on the chromosomes in each of the flies used in the cross? Which alleles are carried together on the chromosomes of the F1 flies with black bodies and red eyes, and those with grey bodies and purple eyes?

8. Another gene in *Drosophila* determines wing length. The dominant wild-type allele of this gene produces long wings; a recessive allele produces vestigial (short) wings. A female that is true-breeding for red eyes and long wings is mated with a male that has purple eyes and vestigial wings. F1 females are then crossed with purple-eyed, vestigial-winged males. From this second cross, a total of 600 offspring are obtained with the following combinations of traits:

252 with red eyes and long wings,

276 with purple eyes and vestigial wings,

42 with red eyes and vestigial wings,

30 with purple eyes and long wings.

Are the genes linked, unlinked, or sex linked? If they are linked, how many map units separate them on the chromosome?

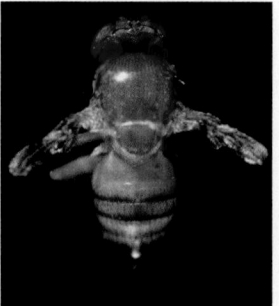

***Drosophila* with vestigial wings**

## Create/Evaluate

9. You conduct a cross in *Drosophila* that produces only half as many male as female offspring. Suggest a hypothesis to explain this result.

10. Even though X inactivation occurs in XXY (Klinefelter syndrome) humans, those humans do not have the same phenotype as

normal XY males. Similarly, even though X inactivation occurs in XX individuals, they do not have the same phenotype as XO (Turner syndrome) humans. Suggest a hypothesis to explain these observations.

11. Assume that genes *a*, *b*, *c*, *d*, *e*, and *f* are linked. Explain how you would construct a linkage map that shows the order of these six genes and the map units between them.

12. Roughly one in every 5000 children is born with Edward's syndrome, a severe condition characterized by slow growth, heart defects, intellectual impairment, and short life span. Affected individuals have three copies of chromosome 18 (trisomy 18). In humans, chromosome 18 carries the dymeclin gene, DYM, which has been associated with schizophrenia and dyslexia. Imagine a baby, Kinshoo, with trisomy 18. Her parents have normal karyotypes. One of Kinshoo's three copies of the DYM gene is clearly the same as one of her father's two copies of this gene. Assuming that Kinshoo's triple 18 karyotype resulted from a single error in chromosome partitioning, propose a hypothesis to explain in which division of meiosis (I or II) and in which parent the error could have occurred.

# Chapter Roadmap

## DNA Structure, Replication, and Repair

The basic structure and the mechanism of replication of deoxyribonucleic acid (DNA) are shared by all life forms on Earth.

**From Chapter 9**

### 11.1 Establishing DNA as the Hereditary Molecule

A series of classic experiments led to the unexpected identification of DNA as the hereditary material of cells.

**To Chapter 22**

### 11.2 DNA Structure

The elegant double helix of DNA is one of the most iconic molecular structures known.

**To Chapter 13**

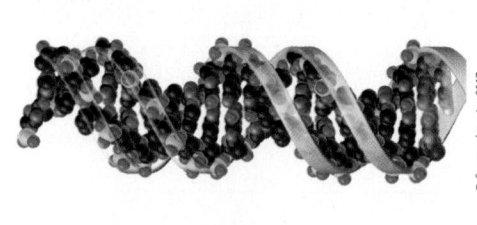

© Cengage Learning 2017

**From Chapter 8**

### 11.3 DNA Replication

Many enzymes and other proteins coordinate their activities in a DNA replication machine called the *replisome*.

### 11.4 Repair of Damage in DNA

A variety of mechanisms prevent damage to DNA from becoming a mutation.

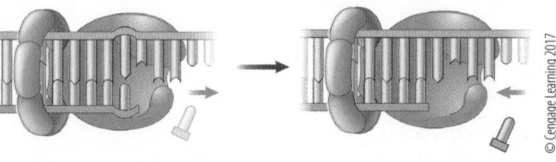

© Cengage Learning 2017

**An artist's depiction of woolly mammoths**

# DNA Structure, Replication, and Repair

# 11

**Why it matters . . .** Although it is hard to imagine anything resembling an elephant grazing in New Brunswick today, fossil bones and teeth as well as soft tissue from specimens recovered from permafrost indicate that at least two species of early mammoths entered North America over the Bering land bridge, starting about 1.5 million years ago. The populations thrived in this new environment, diverging into new species and spreading to nearly every habitable region. The well-known woolly mammoth ranged as far south as the Great Lakes and the Atlantic region. Despite hundreds of thousands of years of success, all mammoth species were extinct in North America by about 10 000 years ago.

While fossils and preserved specimens provide useful morphological data for understanding the flourishing and rather abrupt extinction of these creatures, modern facilities in several Canadian universities now enable scientists to recover and characterize samples of ancient DNA (aDNA) preserved in the bodies of these animals.

Characterization of aDNA sequences promises to enhance our understanding of the likely physical appearance of these animals as well as their evolutionary genetic history and the dynamics of their populations. Some people even hope that we might someday see the de-extinction of mammoths if they can be cloned from aDNA sequence. However, the ancient DNA field is currently overshadowed by two significant problems: DNA degradation and contamination. The double helix of DNA is subject to breakages in one or both strands, in addition to inappropriate cross-linking and chemical modification of individual bases. As this chapter shows, living cells very successfully prevent or repair most of this DNA damage, but post-mortem degradation can be extensive after tens of thousands of years. Sustained cold temperatures preserve aDNA relatively well, facilitating successful recovery of sequences from frozen mammoths in **permafrost**, penguins in ice, and the human "Ice Man" frozen in a glacier. Ancient bacterial DNA sequences have been recovered from 500 000-year-old sections of ice cores, and the complete genome has been sequenced from a 700 000-year-old horse bone recovered from permafrost.

The natural degradation of DNA over time usually means that aDNA sequences remaining in a given tissue sample are very rare and therefore prone to contamination by DNA from modern or ancient sources; hence the need for ultraclean laboratories, decontamination procedures, and authentication protocols.

As the future brings better techniques for the recovery and characterization of authentic aDNA sequences on Earth, we will undoubtedly turn these skills toward the search for evidence of past or present life on other planets. The Martian polar ice caps are very cold and very persistent, providing ideal conditions for preservation of DNA from any organisms that may have inhabited the Red Planet in the past.

# 11.1 Establishing DNA as the Hereditary Molecule

Our current ability to find, characterize, and manipulate DNA arises ultimately from the work of a Swiss physician and physiological chemist, Johann Friedrich Miescher. In 1868, Miescher was engaged in a study of the composition of the cell nucleus. He collected pus cells from discarded bandages and extracted large quantities of an acidic substance with a high phosphorus content. He called the unusual substance *nuclein*. Nuclein is now known by its modern name, **deoxyribonucleic acid**, or **DNA**, the molecule that we now know is the genetic material of all living organisms and, as indicated by ancient DNA studies, all extinct organisms as well.

At the time of Miescher's discovery, scientists knew nothing about the molecular basis of heredity, and very little about genetics. Although Mendel had already published the results of his genetic experiments with garden peas, the significance of his findings was not widely known or appreciated. It was not known which chemical substance in cells actually carries the instructions for reproducing parental traits in offspring. Not until 1952, more than 80 years after Miescher's discovery, did scientists fully recognize that the hereditary molecule was DNA.

In the first half of the twentieth century, many scientists believed that proteins were the most likely candidates for hereditary molecules because they appeared to offer greater opportunities for information coding than did nucleic acids. That is, proteins contain 20 types of amino acids, whereas nucleic acids have only 4 different nitrogenous bases available for coding. Other scientists believed that nucleic acids were the hereditary molecules. In this section, we describe the experiments showing that DNA, not protein, is the genetic material.

## 11.1a Experiments Began When Griffith Found a Substance That Could Genetically Transform Pneumonia Bacteria

In 1928, Frederick Griffith, a British medical officer, observed an interesting phenomenon in his experiments with the bacterium *Streptococcus pneumoniae,* which causes a severe form of pneumonia in mammals. Griffith was trying to make a vaccine to prevent pneumonia infections in the epidemics that occurred after World War I. He used two strains of the bacterium in his attempts. The smooth strain, S, has a polysaccharide capsule surrounding each cell and forms colonies that appear smooth and glossy when grown on a culture plate. When he injected the S strain into mice, it was virulent (highly infective, or pathogenic), causing pneumonia and killing the mice in a day or two (**Figure 11.1**, step 1). The rough strain, R, does not have a polysaccharide capsule and forms colonies with a non-shiny, rough appearance. When Griffith injected the R strain into mice, it was avirulent (not infective, or non-pathogenic); the mice lived (step 2). Evidently, the capsule was responsible for the virulence of the S strain. We now know that the capsule hinders the ability of the host's immune system to detect the *Streptococcus* cells. The smooth strain could therefore live long enough to multiply and cause fatal pneumonia.

If Griffith killed the S bacteria by heating before injecting them into the mice, the mice remained healthy (step 3). However, quite unexpectedly, Griffith found that if he injected living R bacteria along with the heat-killed S bacteria, many of the mice died (step 4). Also, he was able to isolate living S bacteria with polysaccharide capsules from the infected mice. In some way, living R bacteria had acquired the ability to make the polysaccharide capsule from the dead S bacteria, and they had changed (transformed) into virulent S cells. The transformed bacteria were altered permanently; the smooth, infective trait was stably inherited by the descendants of the transformed bacteria. Griffith called the conversion of R bacteria to S bacteria *transformation,* and the agent responsible the *transforming principle.* What was the nature of the molecule responsible for the transformation? Carbohydrates, lipids, proteins, and nucleic acids are the four main types of biological macromolecules. The structure of carbohydrates and lipids tends to be highly repetitive and therefore not very likely to carry information. However, proteins and nucleic acids are built of various combinations of different amino acids and nucleotides respectively. This gives them a complexity of structure that makes them likely candidates for carrying the information needed for transformation. A good deal was known about protein structure at the time, so the favoured hypothesis was that only proteins were complex enough to carry genetic information. Data from later experiments that didn't support this assumption surprised the scientific community and challenged it to discard ideas thought to be "common sense"; that is, that DNA was far too simple to contain genetic information.

FIGURE 11.1 **Experimental Research**

## Griffith's Experiment with Virulent and Nonvirulent Strains of *Streptococcus pneumoniae*

**Question:** What is the nature of the genetic material?

**Experiment:** Frederick Griffith studied the conversion of a nonvirulent (non-infective) *R* form of the bacterium *Streptococcus pneumoniae* to a virulent (infective) *S* form. The *S* form has a capsule surrounding the cell, giving colonies of it on a laboratory dish a smooth, shiny appearance. The *R* form has no capsule, so the colonies have a rough, non-shiny appearance. Griffith injected the bacteria into mice and determined how the mice were infected.

**1.** Mice injected with live *S* cells (control to show effect of *S* cells)

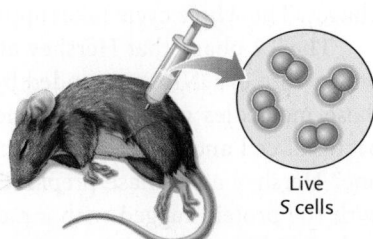

Live
S cells

**Result:** Mice die. Live *S* cells in their blood; shows that *S* cells are virulent.

**2.** Mice injected with live *R* cells (control to show effect of *R* cells)

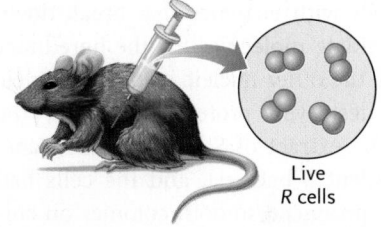

Live
R cells

**Result:** Mice live. No live *R* cells in their blood; shows that *R* cells are nonvirulent. Evidently the capsule is responsible for virulence of the *S* strain.

**3.** Mice injected with heat-killed *S* cells (control to show effect of dead *S* cells)

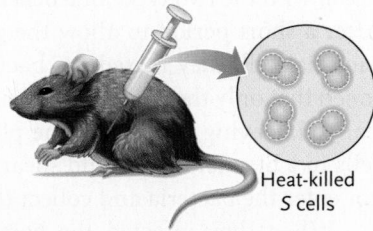

Heat-killed
S cells

**Result:** Mice live. No live *S* cells in their blood; shows that live *S* cells are necessary to be virulent to mice.

**4.** Mice injected with heat-killed *S* cells plus live *R* cells

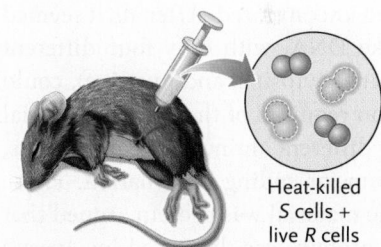

Heat-killed
S cells +
live R cells

**Result:** Mice die. Live *S* cells in their blood; shows that living *R* cells can be converted to virulent *S* cells with some factor from dead *S* cells.

© Cengage Learning 2017

**Conclusion:** Griffith concluded that some molecules released when *S* cells were killed could change living nonvirulent *R* cells genetically to the virulent *S* form. He called the molecule the *transforming principle* and the process of genetic change *transformation*.

## 11.1b Avery and His Co-workers Identified DNA as the Molecule That Transforms the Avirulent Rough *Streptococcus* to the Virulent Smooth Form

In the 1940s, Oswald Avery, a Canadian-born physician and medical researcher at the hospital at the Rockefeller Institute for Medical Research in New York, and his co-workers, Colin MacLeod (also a Canadian) and Maclyn McCarty, performed an experiment designed to identify the chemical nature of the transforming principle that can change the avirulent *rough* form of *Streptococcus* bacteria into the infective *smooth* form. Rather than working with mice, they attempted to reproduce the transformation using bacteria growing in culture tubes. They used heat to kill virulent *S* bacteria and then treated the macromolecules extracted from the cells with enzymes that break down each of the three main candidate molecules for the hereditary material: protein, DNA, and the other nucleic acid, ribonucleic acid (RNA). When they destroyed proteins or RNA, the researchers saw no effect: the extract of *S* bacteria still transformed *R* bacteria into virulent *S* bacteria, and the cells had polysaccharide capsules and produced smooth colonies on culture plates. When they destroyed DNA, however, no transformation occurred: no smooth colonies were seen on culture plates.

In 1944, Avery and his colleagues published their discovery that the transforming principle was DNA. Remember, at this time, many scientists firmly believed that the genetic material was protein. So although their findings were clearly revolutionary, Avery and his colleagues presented their conclusions in the paper cautiously, offering several interpretations of their results. Although some scientists accepted these data almost immediately, others remained unconvinced. After all, it seemed unlikely that a molecule like DNA, with only four different components (adenine, thymine, cytosine, and guanine), could hold the complex information required of the genetic material in a cell. Protein, with its 20 different amino acid components, seemed a far superior medium for coding information. Those who believed that the genetic material was protein argued that it was possible that not all protein was destroyed by Avery's enzyme treatments, and, as contaminants in their DNA transformation reaction, these remaining proteins were in fact responsible for the transformation. Further experiments were needed to convince all scientists that DNA is the hereditary molecule.

## 11.1c Hershey and Chase Found the Final Evidence Establishing DNA as the Hereditary Molecule

A final series of elegant experiments conducted in 1952 by bacteriologist Alfred D. Hershey and his laboratory assistant Martha Chase at the Cold Spring Harbor Laboratory removed any remaining doubts that DNA is the hereditary molecule.

Hershey and Chase studied the infection of the bacterium *Escherichia coli* by bacteriophage T2. *Escherichia coli* is a bacterium normally found in the intestines of mammals. **Bacteriophages** (or simply **phages**; see Chapters 8 and 22) are viruses that infect bacteria. A **virus** is an infectious agent that contains either DNA or RNA surrounded by a protein coat. Viruses cannot reproduce except in a host cell. When a virus infects a cell, it can use the cell's resources to produce more virus particles.

The phage replication cycle begins when a phage attaches to the surface of a bacterium. For phages such as T2, the infected cell quickly stops producing its own molecules and instead starts making progeny phages. After about 100 to 200 phages are assembled inside the bacterial cell, a viral enzyme breaks down the cell wall, killing the cell and releasing the new phages. The whole cycle takes approximately 90 minutes.

The T2 phage that Hershey and Chase studied consists of only a core of DNA surrounded by proteins. Therefore, one of these molecules must be the genetic material that enters the bacterial cell and directs the infective cycle within. But which one? Hershey and Chase prepared two batches of phages, one with the protein tagged with a radioactive label and the other with the DNA tagged with a radioactive label. To obtain labelled phages, they added T2 to *E. coli* growing in the presence of *either* the radioactive isotope of sulfur ($^{35}$S) *or* the radioactive isotope of phosphorus ($^{32}$P; **Figure 11.2**, step 1). The progeny phages produced in the $^{35}$S medium had labelled proteins and unlabelled DNA because sulfur is a component of proteins but not of DNA. The phages produced in the $^{32}$P medium had labelled DNA and unlabelled proteins because phosphorus is a component of DNA but not of proteins.

Hershey and Chase then infected separate cultures of *E. coli* with the two types of labelled phages (Figure 11.2, step 2). After a short period to allow the genetic material to enter the bacterial cell, they mixed the bacteria in a blender. They reasoned that only the genetic material was injected into the bacterial cell, leaving the rest of the phage outside. By mixing the cells in a blender, they could shear off the phage parts that did not enter the bacteria and collect them separately for analysis.

When they infected the bacteria with phages that contained labelled protein coats, they found no **radioactivity** in the bacterial cells, but could easily measure it in the material removed by the blender (Figure 11.2, step 3, top). They also found no radioactivity in the progeny phages (Figure 11.2, step 4, top). However, if the infecting phages contained radioactive DNA, they found radioactivity inside the infected bacteria but none in the phage coats removed by the blender (Figure 11.2, step 3, bottom). In addition, radioactivity *was* seen in the progeny phages (Figure 11.2, step 4, bottom). The results were unequivocal: the genetic material of the phage was DNA, not protein.

When taken together, the experiments of Griffith, Avery and his co-workers, and Hershey and Chase established that DNA, not proteins, carries genetic information. Their research also established the term *transformation,* which is still used in

FIGURE 11.2    **Experimental Research**

**The Hershey and Chase Experiment Demonstrating That DNA Is the Hereditary Molecule**

**Question:** Is DNA or protein the genetic material?

**Experiment:** Hershey and Chase performed a definitive experiment to show whether DNA or protein is the genetic material. They used phage T2 for their experiment; it consists only of DNA and protein. Because DNA contains phosphorus and not sulfur, they could label DNA selectively with radioactive $^{32}P$. And, because protein contains sulfur and not phosphorus, they could label protein selectively with radioactive $^{35}S$.

1. They infected *E. coli* growing in the presence of radioactive $^{32}P$ or $^{35}S$ with phage T2. The progeny phages were labelled in either their protein with $^{35}S$ (top) or their DNA with $^{32}P$ (bottom).

2. Separate cultures of *E. coli* were infected with the radioactively labelled phages.

3. After a short period of time to allow the genetic material to enter the bacterial cell, the bacteria were mixed in a blender. The blending sheared from the cell surface the phage coats that did not enter the bacteria. The components were analyzed for radioactivity.

4. Progeny phages analyzed for radioactivity.

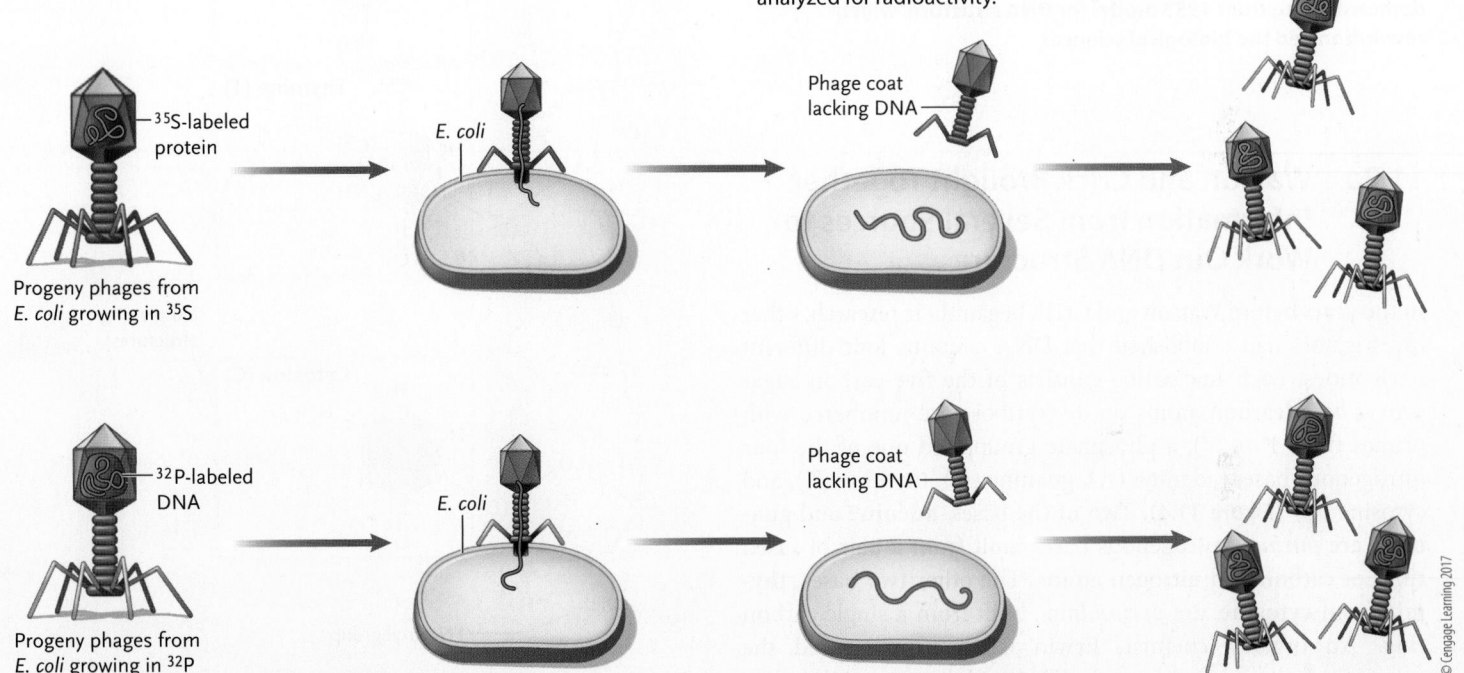

**Conclusion:** A significant amount of $^{32}P$, the isotope used to label DNA, was found within phage-infected cells and in progeny phages, indicating that DNA is the genetic material. A significant amount of $^{35}S$, the radioisotope used to label proteins, was found in phage coats after infection, but little was found in the infected cell or in progeny phages, showing that protein is not the genetic material.

molecular biology. **Transformation** is the conversion of a cell's hereditary type by the uptake of DNA released by the breakdown of another cell, as in the Griffith and Avery experiments. Having identified DNA as the hereditary molecule, scientists turned next to determining its structure.

**STUDY BREAK QUESTION**

1. How did Hershey and Chase exploit the reproductive cycle of a phage to gain evidence for DNA as the hereditary material?

## 11.2   DNA Structure

The experiments that established DNA as the hereditary molecule were followed by a highly competitive scientific race to discover the structure of DNA. The race ended in 1953 when an American post-doctoral student named James Watson and an English graduate student named Francis Crick elucidated the structure of DNA at Cambridge University, ushering in a new era of understanding of genetics and molecular biology **(Figure 11.3)**.

**FIGURE 11.3** James D. Watson and Francis H. C. Crick demonstrating their 1953 model for DNA structure, which revolutionized the biological sciences

## 11.2a Watson and Crick Brought Together Information from Several Sources to Work Out DNA Structure

In the years before Watson and Crick began their research, other investigators had established that DNA contains four different nucleotides. Each nucleotide consists of the five-carbon sugar *deoxyribose* (carbon atoms on deoxyribose are numbered with primes from 1′ to 5′); a phosphate group; and one of the four nitrogenous bases, adenine (A), guanine (G), thymine (T), and cytosine (C) (**Figure 11.4**). Two of the bases, **adenine** and **guanine**, are *purines,* nitrogenous bases built from a pair of fused rings of carbon and nitrogen atoms. The other two bases, **thymine** and **cytosine**, are *pyrimidines*, built from a single carbon ring. An organic chemist, Erwin Chargaff, measured the amounts of nitrogenous bases in DNA and discovered that they occur in definite ratios. He observed that the number of purines equals the number of pyrimidines, but, more specifically, the amount of adenine equals the amount of thymine, and the amount of guanine equals the amount of cytosine; these relationships are known as *Chargaff's rules.*

Researchers had also determined that DNA contains nucleotides joined to form a *polynucleotide chain.* In a polynucleotide chain, the deoxyribose sugars are linked by phosphate groups in an alternating sugar–phosphate–sugar–phosphate pattern, forming a **sugar–phosphate backbone** (highlighted in grey in Figure 11.4). Each phosphate group is a "bridge" between the 3′ carbon of one sugar and the 5′ carbon of the next sugar; the entire linkage, including the bridging phosphate group, is called a **phosphodiester bond**.

The polynucleotide chain of DNA has polarity, or directionality. That is, the two ends of the chain are not the same: at

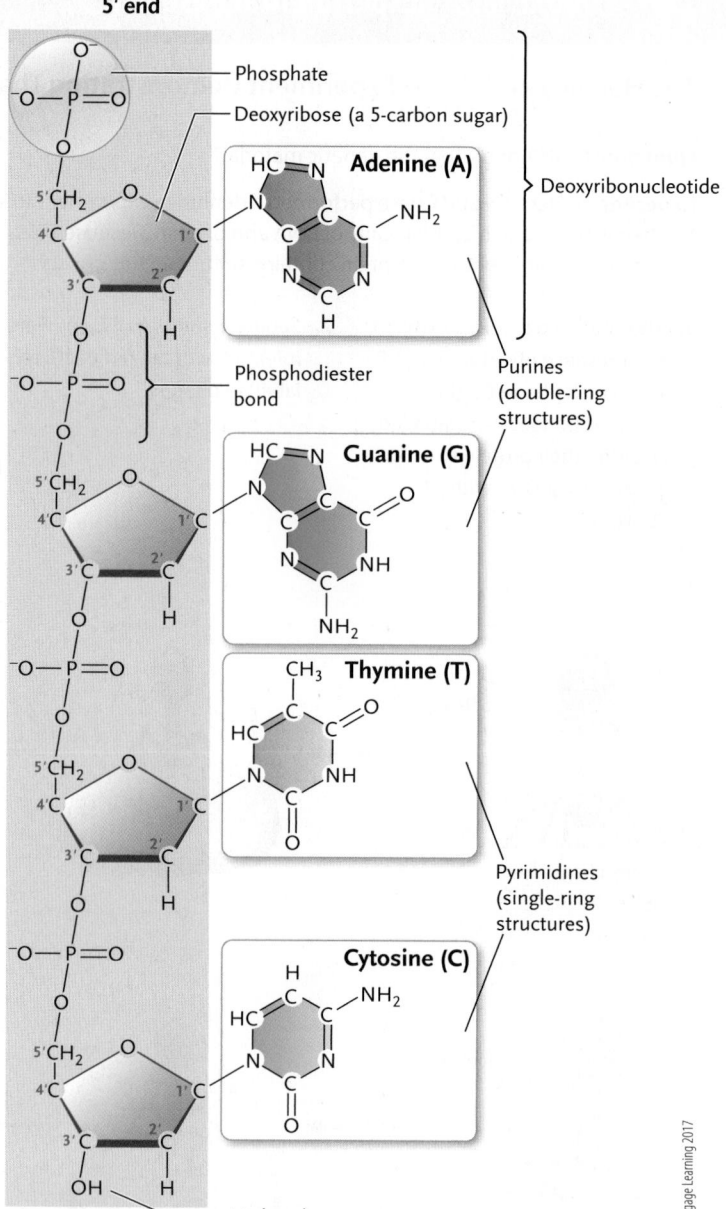

**FIGURE 11.4 The four nucleotide subunits of DNA, linked into a polynucleotide chain.** The sugar–phosphate backbone of the chain is highlighted in grey. The connection between adjacent deoxyribose sugars is a phosphodiester bond. The polynucleotide chain has polarity: at one end (5′), a phosphate group is bound to the 5′ carbon of a deoxyribose sugar; at the other end (3′), a hydroxyl group is bound to the 3′ carbon of a deoxyribose sugar.

one end, a phosphate group is bound to the 5′ carbon of a deoxyribose sugar, whereas at the other end, a **hydroxyl group** is bonded to the 3′ carbon of a deoxyribose sugar (see Figure 11.4 and see Nucleic Acids in *The Purple Pages*). Consequently, the two ends are called the **5′ end** and the **3′ end** respectively.

These were the known facts when Watson and Crick began their collaboration in the early 1950s. However, the number of polynucleotide chains in a DNA molecule and the manner in which they fold or twist in DNA were unknown. Watson and Crick themselves did not conduct experiments to study the structure of DNA; instead, they used the research data of others for their analysis, relying heavily on data gathered by physicist Maurice H.F. Wilkins and research associate Rosalind Franklin (**Figure 11.5a**) at King's College, London. These researchers were using **X-ray diffraction** to study the structure of DNA (Figure 11.5b). In X-ray diffraction, an X-ray beam is directed at a molecule in the form of a regular solid, ideally in the form of a crystal. Within the crystal, regularly arranged atoms bend and reflect the X-rays into smaller beams that exit the crystal at definite angles determined by the arrangement of atoms in the structure of the crystal. If a photographic film is placed behind the crystal, the exiting beams produce a pattern of exposed spots. From that pattern, researchers can deduce the positions of the atoms in the crystal.

Wilkins and Franklin did not have DNA crystals to work with, but they were able to obtain X-ray diffraction patterns from a sample of DNA that had been pulled out into a fibre (see Figure 11.5). The patterns indicated that DNA within the fibre was cylindrical and about 2 nm in diameter. Separations between the spots showed that major patterns of atoms repeat at intervals of 0.34 nm and 3.4 nm within the DNA. Franklin correctly interpreted an X-shaped distribution of spots in the diffraction pattern (see dashed lines in Figure 11.5) to mean that DNA has a helical structure.

## 11.2b The New Model Proposed That Two Polynucleotide Chains Wind into a DNA Double Helix

Watson and Crick constructed scale models of the four DNA nucleotides and fitted them together in different ways until they arrived at an arrangement that satisfied both Wilkins's and Franklin's X-ray data and Chargaff's chemical analysis. Watson and Crick's trials led them to a double-stranded model for DNA structure in which two polynucleotide chains twist around each other in a right-handed way, like a double-spiral staircase

(**Figure 11.6**). They were the first to propose the famous double-helix model for DNA.

In the **double-helix model**, the two sugar–phosphate backbones are separated from each other by a regular distance. The bases extend into and fill this central space. A purine and a pyrimidine, if paired together, are exactly wide enough to fill the space between the backbone chains in the double helix. However, a purine–purine base pair is too wide to fit the space exactly, and a pyrimidine–pyrimidine pair is too narrow. From Chargaff's data, Watson and Crick proposed that the purine–pyrimidine base pairs in DNA are A-T and G-C pairs. That is, wherever an A occurs in one strand, a T must be opposite it in the other strand; and wherever a G occurs in one strand, a C must be opposite it. This feature of DNA is called **complementary base-pairing**, and one strand is said to be *complementary* to the other. The base pairs, which fit together like pieces of a jigsaw puzzle, are stabilized by hydrogen bonds: two between A and T, and three between G and C (see Figure 11.6; hydrogen bonds are discussed in *The Purple Pages*). The hydrogen bonds between the paired bases, repeated along the double helix, hold the two strands together in the helix.

**CONCEPT FIX** Although the generally common convention refers to the DNA double helix as a *DNA molecule*, this terminology is, strictly speaking, inaccurate. If a molecule is defined as a collection of atoms connected by covalent bonds, then *each* of the two sugar–phosphate backbones of the double helix qualifies as a molecule. The double helix is composed of *two* polynucleotide molecules held together by hydrogen bonds. ⬡

The base pairs lie in flat planes almost perpendicular to the long axis of the DNA helix. In this state, each base pair occupies a length of 0.34 nm along the long axis of the double helix (see Figure 11.6). This spacing accounts for the repeating 0.34 nm pattern noted in the X-ray diffraction patterns. The larger 3.4 nm repeat pattern was interpreted to mean that each full turn of the double helix takes up 3.4 nm along the length of the molecule; therefore, 10 base pairs are packed into a full turn.

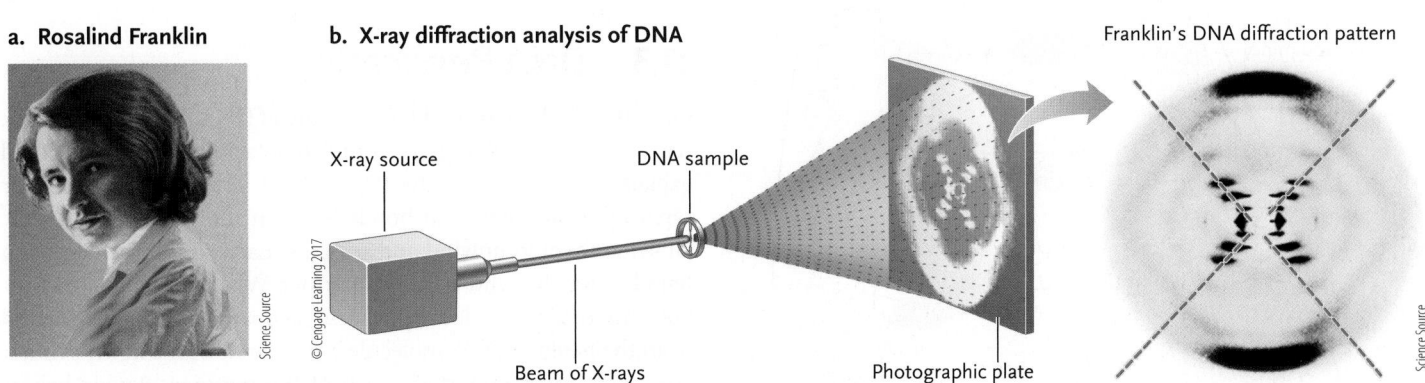

### a. Rosalind Franklin
### b. X-ray diffraction analysis of DNA

X-ray source

DNA sample

Beam of X-rays

Photographic plate

Franklin's DNA diffraction pattern

**FIGURE 11.5 X-ray diffraction analysis of DNA. (a)** Rosalind Franklin. **(b)** The X-ray diffraction method to study DNA, and the diffraction pattern Rosalind Franklin obtained. The X-shaped pattern of spots (dashed lines) was correctly interpreted by Franklin to indicate that DNA has a helical structure similar to a spiral staircase.

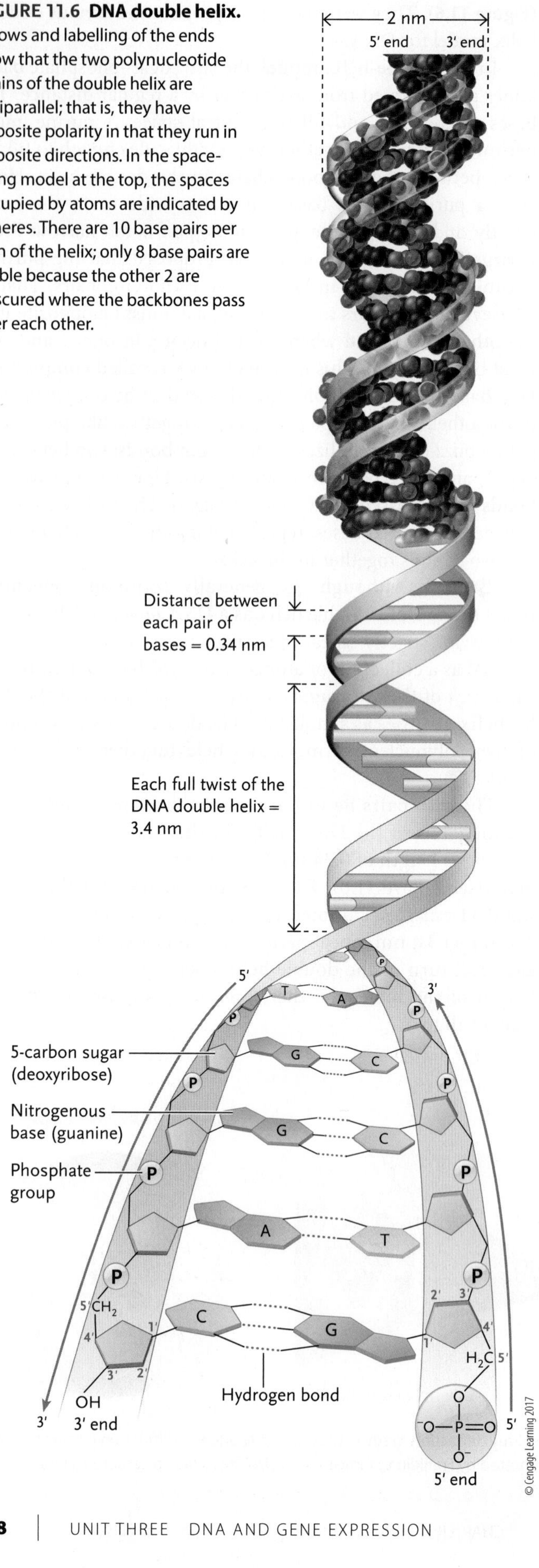

**FIGURE 11.6 DNA double helix.**
Arrows and labelling of the ends show that the two polynucleotide chains of the double helix are antiparallel; that is, they have opposite polarity in that they run in opposite directions. In the space-filling model at the top, the spaces occupied by atoms are indicated by spheres. There are 10 base pairs per turn of the helix; only 8 base pairs are visible because the other 2 are obscured where the backbones pass over each other.

2 nm

5′ end    3′ end

Distance between each pair of bases = 0.34 nm

Each full twist of the DNA double helix = 3.4 nm

5′

3′

5-carbon sugar (deoxyribose)

Nitrogenous base (guanine)

Phosphate group

Hydrogen bond

OH

3′    3′ end

5′ end

Watson and Crick also realized that the two strands of a double helix fit together in a stable chemical way only if they are **antiparallel**, that is, only if they run in opposite directions (see Figure 11.6, arrows). In other words, the *3′ end* of one strand is opposite the *5′ end* of its complementary strand. This antiparallel arrangement is highly significant for the process of replication, which is discussed in the next section.

As hereditary material, DNA must faithfully store and transmit genetic information for the entire life cycle of an organism. Watson and Crick recognized that this information is coded into the DNA by the particular sequence of the four nucleotides. This sequence is preserved by robust covalent bonds between the molecules in a DNA double helix. Although only four different kinds of nucleotides exist, combining them in groups allows an essentially infinite number of different sequences to be "written," just as the 26 letters of the alphabet can be combined in groups to write a virtually unlimited number of words. Chapter 12 shows how taking the four nucleotides in groups of three forms enough "words" to spell out the structure of any conceivable protein.

Watson and Crick announced their model for DNA structure in a brief but monumental paper published in the journal *Nature* in 1953. Watson and Crick shared a Nobel Prize with Wilkins in 1962 for their discovery of the molecular structure of DNA. Rosalind Franklin might have been a candidate for a Nobel Prize had she not died of cancer at age 38 in 1958. (The Nobel Prize is normally given only to living investigators.) Unquestionably, Watson and Crick's discovery of DNA structure opened the way to molecular studies of genetics and heredity, leading to our modern understanding of gene structure and action at the molecular level.

**STUDY BREAK QUESTIONS**

1. Which bases in DNA are purines? Which are pyrimidines?
2. What bonds form between complementary base pairs? Between a base and the deoxyribose sugar?
3. Which features of the DNA molecule did Watson and Crick describe?

## 11.3 DNA Replication

Once they had discovered the structure of DNA, Watson and Crick realized immediately that complementary base-pairing could explain how DNA replicates (**Figure 11.7**). They imagined that, for replication, the hydrogen bonds between the two strands break, allowing them to unwind and separate. Each strand then acts as a template for the synthesis of its partner. When replication is complete, there are two double helices, each with one strand derived from the parental DNA molecule base-paired with a newly synthesized one. Most important, each of the two new double helices consists of the identical base-pair sequences as the parental DNA.

The model of replication that Watson and Crick proposed is termed **semiconservative replication** (**Figure 11.8a**). Other

© Cengage Learning 2017

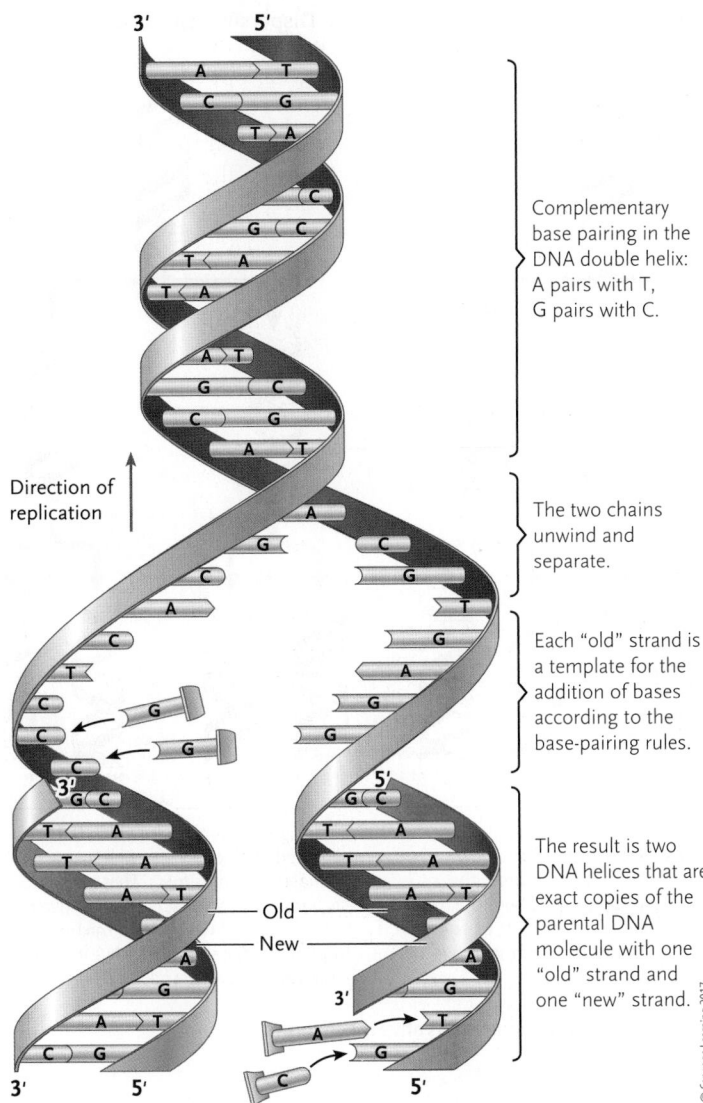

Direction of replication

Complementary base pairing in the DNA double helix: A pairs with T, G pairs with C.

The two chains unwind and separate.

Each "old" strand is a template for the addition of bases according to the base-pairing rules.

The result is two DNA helices that are exact copies of the parental DNA molecule with one "old" strand and one "new" strand.

Old
New

© Cengage Learning 2017

**FIGURE 11.7 Watson and Crick's model for DNA replication.** The original DNA is shown in grey. A new polynucleotide chain (red) is assembled on each original chain as they unwind. The template and complementary copy chains remain together when replication is complete, producing DNA double helices that are half old and half new. The model is known as the *semiconservative model* for DNA replication.

scientists proposed two other models for replication. In the *conservative replication model*, each of the two strands of original DNA serves as a template for a new DNA double helix (Figure 11.8b). After the two complementary copies separate from their templates, they wind together into an all "new" DNA double helix. In the *dispersive replication model*, neither parental molecule remains intact; both chains of each replicated double helix contain old and new segments (Figure 11.8c).

## 11.3a Meselson and Stahl Showed That DNA Replication Is Semiconservative

A definitive experiment published in 1958 by Matthew Meselson and Franklin Stahl of the California Institute of Technology

demonstrated that DNA replication is semiconservative (**Figure 11.9**). In their experiment, Meselson and Stahl had to be able to distinguish parental DNA molecules from newly synthesized DNA. To do this, they used a nonradioactive "heavy" nitrogen isotope to tag the parental DNA. The heavy isotope, $^{15}N$, has one more neutron in its nucleus than the normal $^{14}N$ isotope. Molecules containing $^{15}N$ are measurably heavier (denser) than molecules of the same type containing $^{14}N$.

As the first step in their experiment, Meselson and Stahl grew *E. coli* bacteria in a culture medium containing the heavy $^{15}N$ isotope (see Figure 11.9, step 1). The heavy isotope was incorporated into the nitrogenous bases of DNA, resulting in the entire DNA being labelled with $^{15}N$. Then they transferred the bacteria to a culture medium containing the light $^{14}N$ isotope (step 2). All new DNA synthesized after the transfer contained the light isotope. Just before the transfer to the medium with the $^{14}N$ isotope, and after each round of replication following the transfer, they took a sample of the cells and extracted the DNA (step 3).

Meselson and Stahl then mixed the DNA samples with cesium chloride (CsCl) and centrifuged the mixture at very high speed (step 3). During centrifugation, the CsCl forms a density gradient and DNA double helices move to a position in the gradient where their density matches that of the CsCl. Therefore, DNA of different densities is separated into bands, with the densest DNA settling closer to the bottom of the tube. In Figure 11.9 "Results" shows the outcome of these experiments, and "Conclusion" shows why the results were compatible with only the semiconservative replication model.

## 11.3b DNA Polymerases Are the Primary Enzymes of DNA Replication

During replication, complementary polynucleotide chains are assembled from individual deoxyribonucleotides by enzymes known as **DNA polymerases**. More than one kind of DNA polymerase is required for DNA replication in all cells. *Deoxyribonucleoside triphosphates* are the substrates for the polymerization reaction catalyzed by DNA polymerases (**Figure 11.10**). A nucleoside triphosphate is a nitrogenous base linked to a sugar, which in turn is linked to a chain of three phosphate groups. You have encountered a nucleoside triphosphate before, namely the ATP produced in cellular respiration (see Chapter 6). In that case, the sugar is ribose, making ATP a ribonucleoside triphosphate. The deoxyribonucleoside triphosphates used in DNA replication have the sugar *deoxyribose* rather than the sugar *ribose*. Because four different bases are found in DNA—adenine (A), guanine (G), cytosine (C), and thymine (T)—four different deoxyribonucleoside triphosphates are used for DNA replication. In keeping with the ATP naming convention, the deoxyribonucleoside triphosphates for DNA replication are given the short names dATP, dGTP, dCTP, and dTTP, where the "d" stands for deoxyribose.

Figure 11.10 presents a section of a DNA polynucleotide chain being replicated, showing how DNA polymerase catalyzes the assembly of a new DNA strand that is complementary to the template strand. To understand Figure 11.10, remember

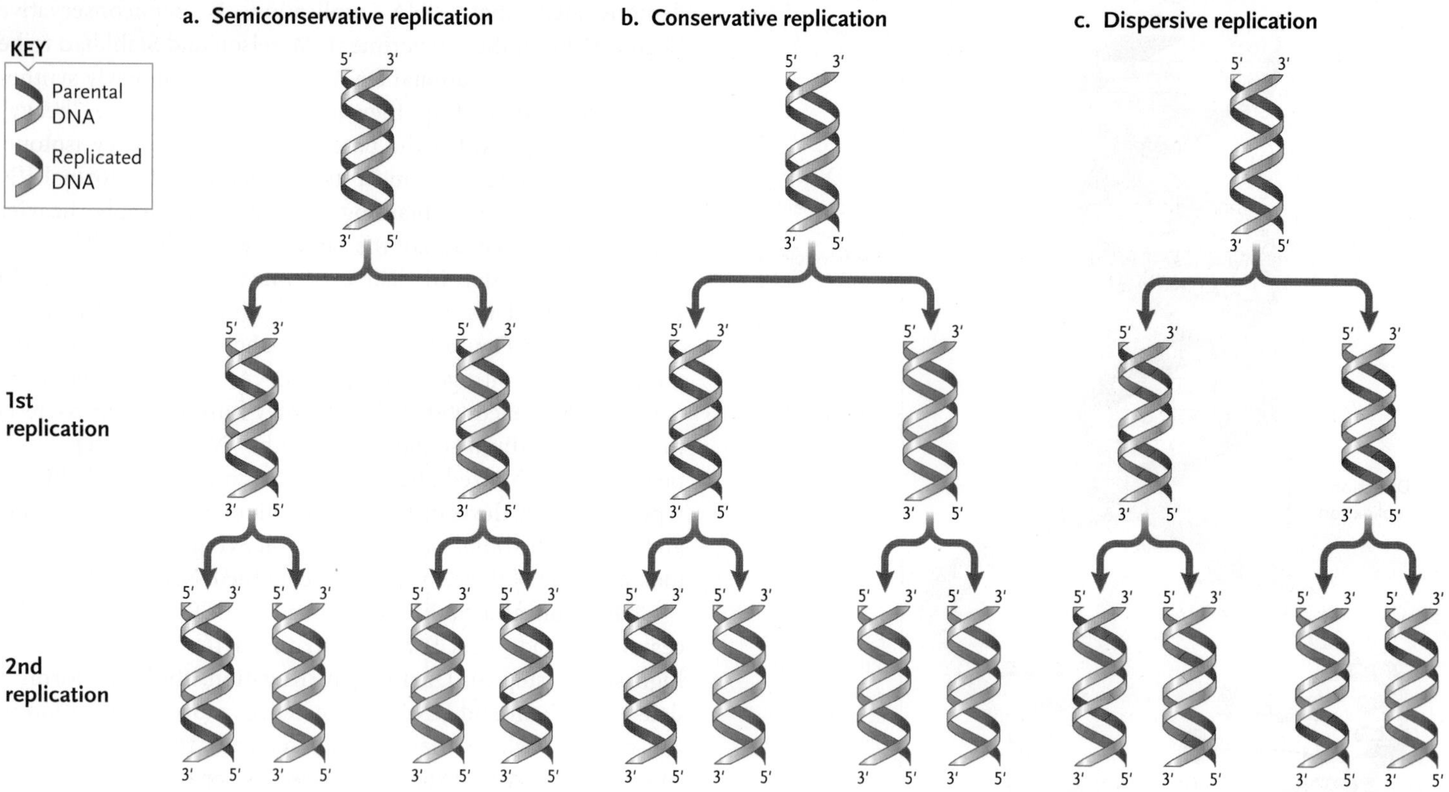

**a. Semiconservative replication**

**b. Conservative replication**

**c. Dispersive replication**

1st replication

2nd replication

The two parental strands of DNA unwind, and each is a template for synthesis of a new strand. After replication has occurred, each double helix has one old strand paired with one new strand. This model was the one proposed by Watson and Crick themselves.

The parental strands of DNA unwind, and each is a template for synthesis of a new strand. After replication has occurred, the parental strands pair up again. Therefore, the two resulting double helices consist of one with two old strands and the other with two new strands.

The original double helix splits into double-stranded segments onto which new double-stranded segments form. These newly formed sections somehow assemble into two double helices, both of which are a mixture of the original double-stranded DNA interspersed with new double-stranded DNA.

© Cengage Learning 2017

**FIGURE 11.8 Three theoretical models for DNA replication.** Experimental data support the semiconservative mechanism.

that the carbons in the deoxyriboses of nucleotides are numbered with primes. Each DNA strand has two distinct ends: the 5′ end has an exposed phosphate group attached to the 5′ carbon of the sugar, and the 3′ end has an exposed hydroxyl group attached to the 3′ carbon of the sugar. As you learned earlier, because of the antiparallel nature of the DNA strands within a double helix, the 5′ end of one strand is opposite the 3′ end of the other. DNA polymerase can add a nucleotide *only* to the 3′ end of an existing nucleotide chain. As a new DNA strand is assembled, a 3′ –OH group is always exposed at its "newest" end; the "oldest" end of the new chain has an exposed 5′ phosphate. DNA polymerases are therefore said to assemble nucleotide chains in the 5′ → 3′ direction.

Because of the antiparallel nature of DNA, the template strand is "read" in the 3′ → 5′ direction for this new synthesis. DNA polymerases of bacteria, archaeans, and eukaryotes all consist of several polypeptide subunits arranged to form different domains (see Polypeptides in *The Purple Pages*). The polymerases share a shape that is said to resemble a partially closed human right hand in which the template DNA lies over the "palm" in a groove formed by the "fingers" and "thumb"

(Figure 11.11a). The palm domain is evolutionarily related among the polymerases of bacteria, archaea, and eukaryotes, while the finger and thumb domains are different sequences in each of these three types of organisms. The template strand does not pass through the tunnel formed by the thumb and finger domains, however. Instead, the template strand and the 3′ –OH of the new strand meet at the active site for the polymerization reaction of DNA synthesis, located in the palm domain. A nucleotide is added to the new strand when an incoming dNTP enters the active site carrying a base complementary to the template strand base positioned in the active site. By moving along the template strand, one nucleotide at a time, DNA polymerase extends the new DNA strand, as we saw in Figure 11.10.

Figure 11.11b shows the representation of DNA polymerase used in the following DNA replication figures, and it also shows a sliding DNA clamp. The **sliding DNA clamp** is a protein that encircles the DNA and binds to the rear of the DNA polymerase in terms of the enzyme's forward movement during replication. The function of the sliding DNA clamp is to tether the DNA polymerase to the template strand. Tethering

FIGURE 11.9  **Experimental Research**

## The Meselson and Stahl Experiment Demonstrating the Semiconservative Model for DNA Replication to Be Correct

**Question:** Does DNA replicate semiconservatively?

**Experiment:** Matthew Meselson and Franklin Stahl proved that the semiconservative model of DNA replication is correct and that the conservative and dispersive models are incorrect.

1. Bacteria were grown in $^{15}N$ (heavy) medium. The heavy isotope was incorporated into the bases of DNA, resulting in all the DNA being heavy, that is, labelled with $^{15}N$.

2. Bacteria were transferred to $^{14}N$ (light) medium and allowed to grow and divide for several generations. All new DNA was light.

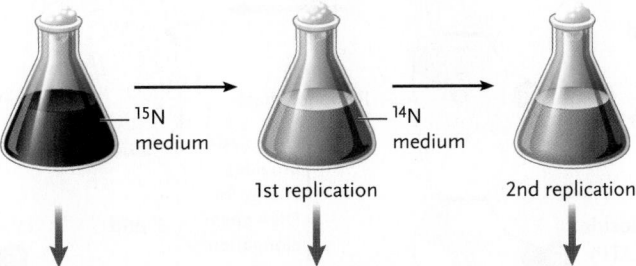

3. DNA was extracted from bacteria cultured in $^{15}N$ medium and after each generation in $^{14}N$ medium. Extracted DNA was centrifuged in a special solution to separate DNA of different densities.

**Results:** Meselson and Stahl obtained the following results:

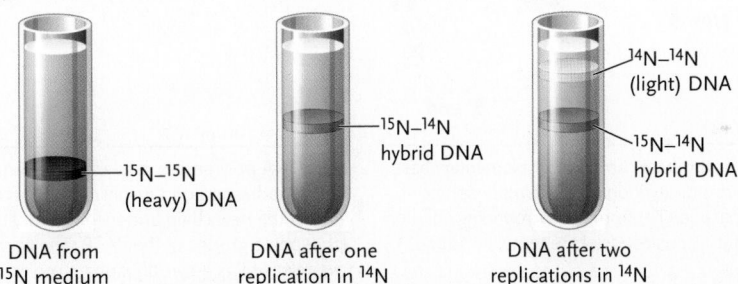

**Conclusion:** The predicted DNA banding patterns for the three DNA replication models shown in Figure 11.8 were:

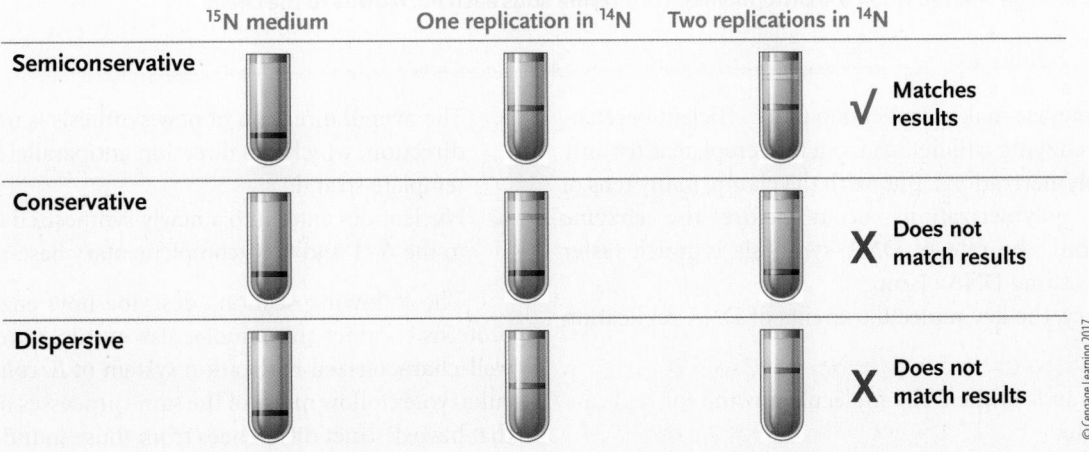

The results support the semiconservative model.

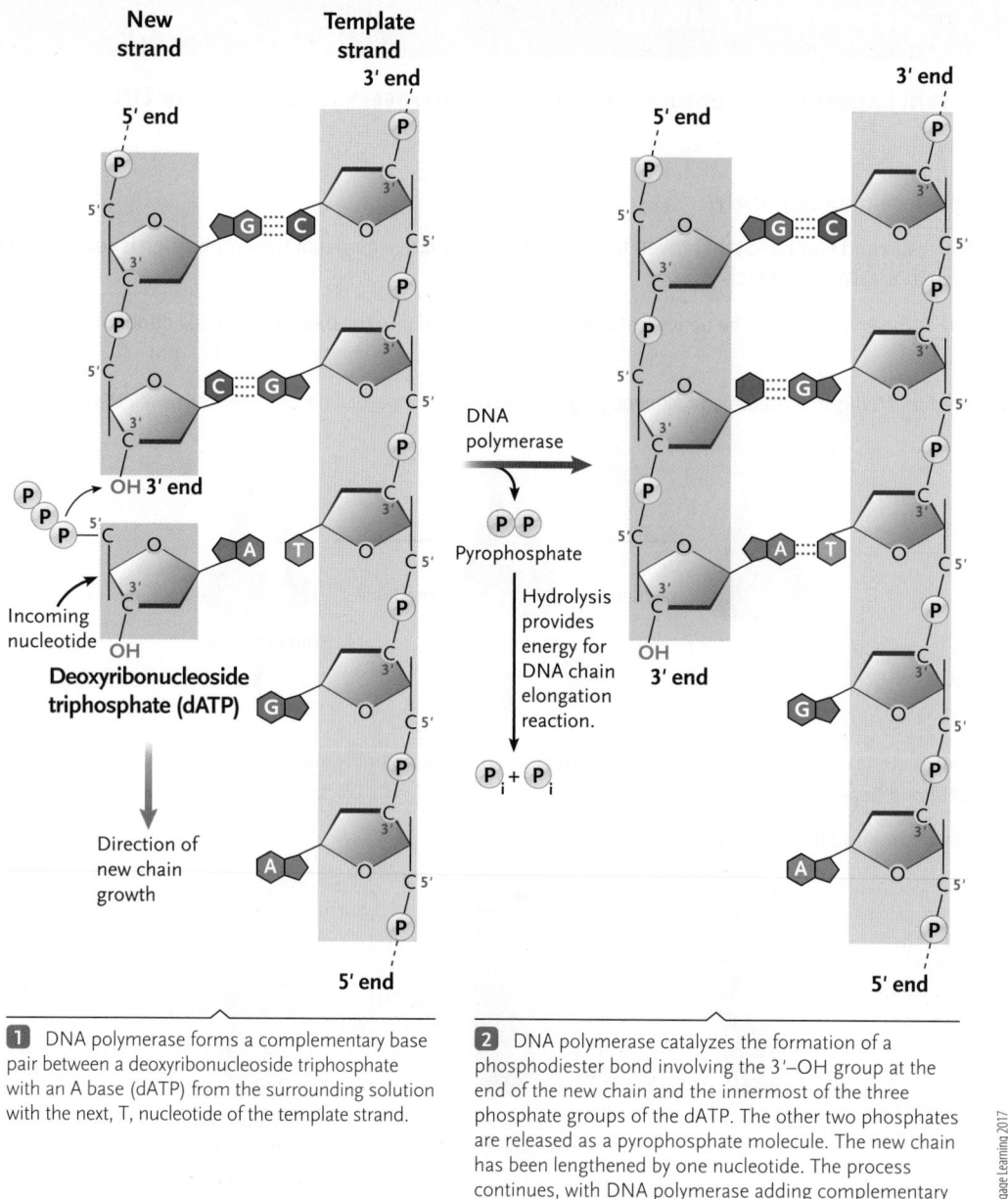

**New strand**

**Template strand**

**1** DNA polymerase forms a complementary base pair between a deoxyribonucleoside triphosphate with an A base (dATP) from the surrounding solution with the next, T, nucleotide of the template strand.

**2** DNA polymerase catalyzes the formation of a phosphodiester bond involving the 3'–OH group at the end of the new chain and the innermost of the three phosphate groups of the dATP. The other two phosphates are released as a pyrophosphate molecule. The new chain has been lengthened by one nucleotide. The process continues, with DNA polymerase adding complementary nucleotides one by one to the growing DNA chain.

© Cengage Learning 2017

**FIGURE 11.10  Reactions assembling a complementary chain in the 5′ → 3′ direction on a template DNA strand, showing the phosphodiester linkage created when the DNA polymerase enzyme adds each nucleotide to the chain**

the DNA polymerase makes replication more efficient because, without it, the enzyme will detach from the template after only a few dozen polymerizations. But, with the clamp, many tens of thousands of polymerizations occur before the enzyme detaches. Overall, the rate of DNA synthesis is much faster because of the sliding DNA clamp.

In summary, the key molecular events of DNA replication are as follows:

1. The two strands of the DNA molecule unwind for replication to occur.
2. DNA polymerase can add nucleotides only to an existing chain.

3. The overall direction of new synthesis is in the 5′ → 3′ direction, which is a direction antiparallel to that of the template strand.
4. Nucleotides enter into a newly synthesized chain according to the A–T and G–C complementary base-pairing rules.

The following sections describe how enzymes and other proteins conduct these molecular events. Our focus is on the well-characterized replication system of *E. coli*. Archaeans and eukaryotes follow many of the same processes but with enzymes that have distinct differences from those found in bacteria. Due to evolutionary relatedness (Chapter 19), Archaea and Eukarya are more similar to each other than either one is to Bacteria.

**a. Bacterial DNA polymerase**

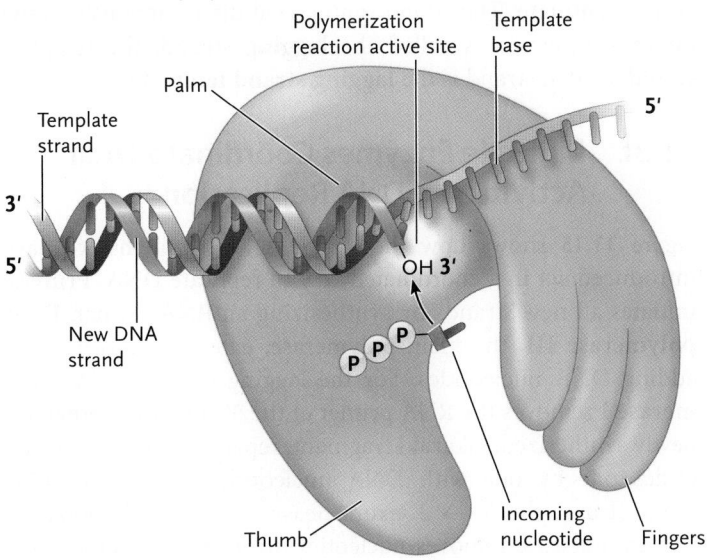

**b. How a DNA polymerase and sliding clamp are shown in the book**

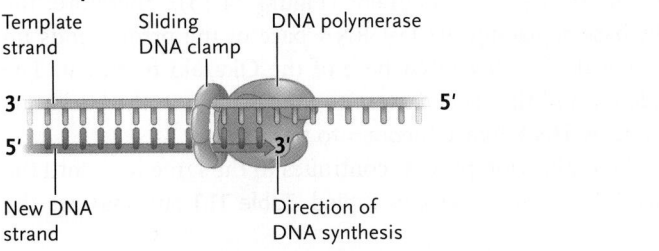

© Cengage Learning 2017

**FIGURE 11.11  DNA polymerase structure. (a)** Stylized drawing of a bacterial DNA polymerase. The enzyme viewed from the side resembles a human right hand. The polymerization reaction site lies on the palm. When the incoming nucleotide is added, the thumb and fingers close over the site to facilitate the reaction. **(b)** How DNA polymerase is shown in subsequent figures of DNA replication. The figure also shows a sliding DNA clamp tethering the DNA polymerase to the template strand.

## 11.3c  Helicases Unwind DNA for New DNA Synthesis, and Other Proteins Stabilize the DNA at the Replication Fork

In semiconservative replication, the two strands of the parental DNA molecule unwind and separate to expose the template strands for new DNA synthesis (**Figure 11.12**). Unwinding of the DNA for replication occurs at a small, specific sequence in the bacterial chromosome known as the **origin of replication (ori)**. Specific proteins bind to an *ori* sequence and, in turn, promote binding of **DNA helicase**, which unwinds the DNA strands. The unwinding produces a Y-shaped structure called a **replication fork**, which consists of the two unwound template strands transitioning to double-helical DNA.

**Single-stranded binding proteins (SSBs)** coat the exposed single-stranded DNA segments, stabilizing the DNA and keeping the two strands from pairing back together (see Figure 11.12). The SSBs are displaced as the replication enzymes make the

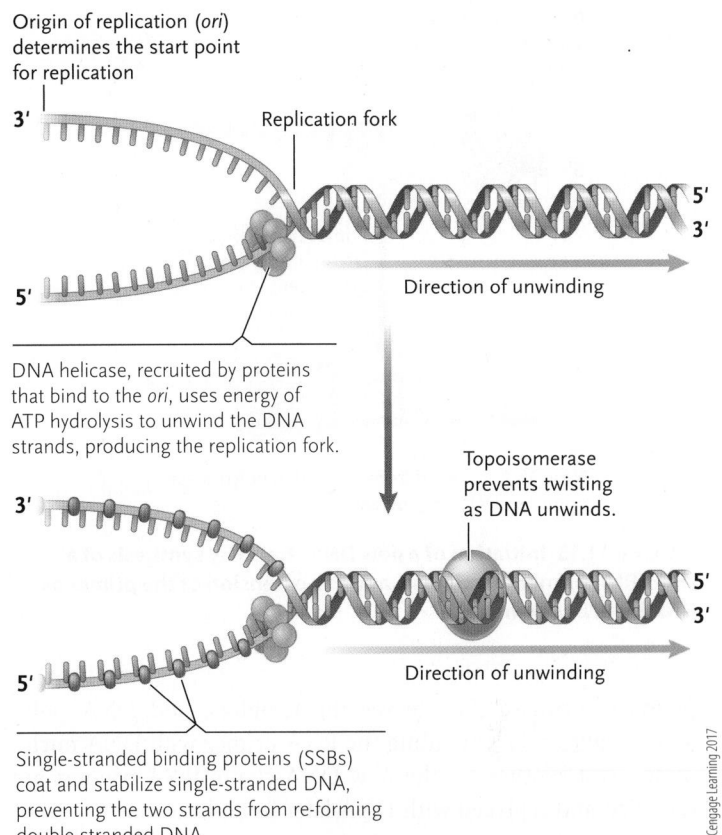

© Cengage Learning 2017

**FIGURE 11.12  The roles of DNA helicase, single-stranded binding proteins (SSBs), and topoisomerase in DNA replication**

new polynucleotide chain on the template strands. For circular chromosomes, such as the genomes of most bacteria, unwinding the DNA will eventually cause the still-wound DNA ahead of the unwinding to become highly twisted. You can visualize this phenomenon with some string. Take two equal lengths of string and twist them around each other. Now tie the two ends of each string together. You have created a model of a circular DNA double helix. Pick anywhere in the circle and pull apart the two pieces of string. The more you pull, the more the region where the two strings are still together becomes highly twisted. In the cell, the twisting of DNA during replication is relieved by **topoisomerase**. This enzyme cuts the DNA ahead of the replication fork, turns the DNA on one side of the break in the opposite direction of the twisting force, and rejoins the two strands (see Figure 11.12).

## 11.3d  RNA Primers Provide the Starting Point for DNA Polymerase to Begin Synthesizing a New DNA Chain

If DNA polymerases can add nucleotides only to the 3′ end of an existing strand, how can a new strand begin when there is no existing strand in place? The answer lies in a short chain a few nucleotides long called a **primer**, which is made of RNA instead of DNA (**Figure 11.13**). The primer is synthesized by the enzyme

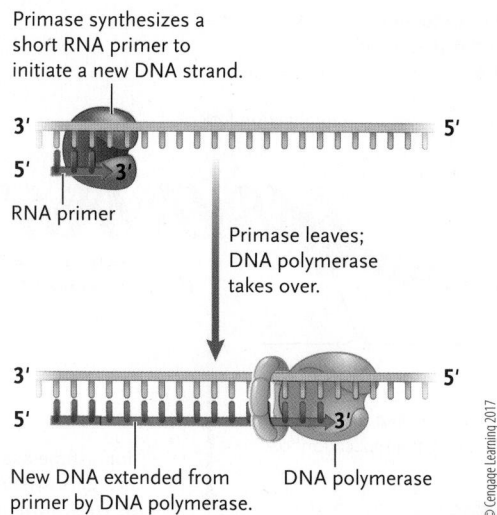

Primase synthesizes a short RNA primer to initiate a new DNA strand.

RNA primer

Primase leaves; DNA polymerase takes over.

New DNA extended from primer by DNA polymerase.

DNA polymerase

© Cengage Learning 2017

**FIGURE 11.13 Initiation of a new DNA strand by synthesis of a short RNA primer by primase, and the extension of the primer as DNA by DNA polymerase**

primase. Primase then leaves the template, and DNA polymerase takes over, extending the RNA primer with DNA nucleotides as it synthesizes the new DNA chain. RNA primers are removed and replaced with DNA later in replication.

## 11.3e One New DNA Strand Is Synthesized Continuously; the Other, Discontinuously

DNA polymerases elongate growing DNA backbones by adding nucleotides onto the 3′ hydroxyl. That means polymerase moves along the template strand toward its 5′ end. Because the two strands of a DNA double helix are antiparallel, only one of them runs in a direction that allows DNA polymerase to make a 5′ → 3′ complementary copy in the direction of unwinding. That is, on this template strand—top strand in **Figure 11.14**—new DNA is synthesized continuously in the direction of unwinding of the double helix. However, the other template strand—bottom strand in Figure 11.14—runs in the opposite direction; this means DNA polymerase has to copy it in the direction opposite to the unwinding direction. How is new DNA polymerized in the direction opposite to the unwinding? The polymerases make this strand in short lengths that are synthesized in the direction opposite to that of DNA unwinding (see Figure 11.14). The short lengths produced by this **discontinuous replication** are then covalently linked into a single continuous polynucleotide chain. The short lengths are called **Okazaki fragments**, after Reiji Okazaki, the scientist who first detected them. The new DNA strand synthesized in the direction of DNA unwinding is called the **leading strand**

of DNA replication; the template for that strand is the **leading strand template**. The strand synthesized discontinuously in the opposite direction is called the **lagging strand**; the template strand for that strand is the **lagging strand template**.

## 11.3f Multiple Enzymes Coordinate Their Activities in DNA Replication

**Figure 11.15** shows how the enzymes and proteins we have introduced act in a coordinated way to replicate DNA. Primase initiates all new strands by synthesizing an RNA primer. **DNA polymerase III**, the main polymerase, extends the primer by adding DNA nucleotides. For the lagging strand, **DNA polymerase I** removes the RNA primer at the 5′ end of the previous, newly synthesized, Okazaki fragment, replacing the RNA nucleotides one by one with DNA nucleotides. RNA nucleotide removal uses the 5′ → 3′ exonuclease activity of the enzyme. (An exonuclease removes nucleotides from the end of a molecule; the primer is digested from its 5′ end toward its 3′ end.) DNA polymerase I stops replacing RNA and leaves the template when it encounters the first DNA nucleotide that was synthesized in the Okazaki fragment (Figure 11.15). Therefore, the DNA base replacing the last RNA base of the primer ends up right beside the first DNA base of the Okazaki fragment. The covalent bond that is necessary to join the gap in the backbone is made by **DNA ligase** (*ligare* = to tie).

The replication process continues in the same way until the entire DNA double helix is copied. **Table 11.1** summarizes the

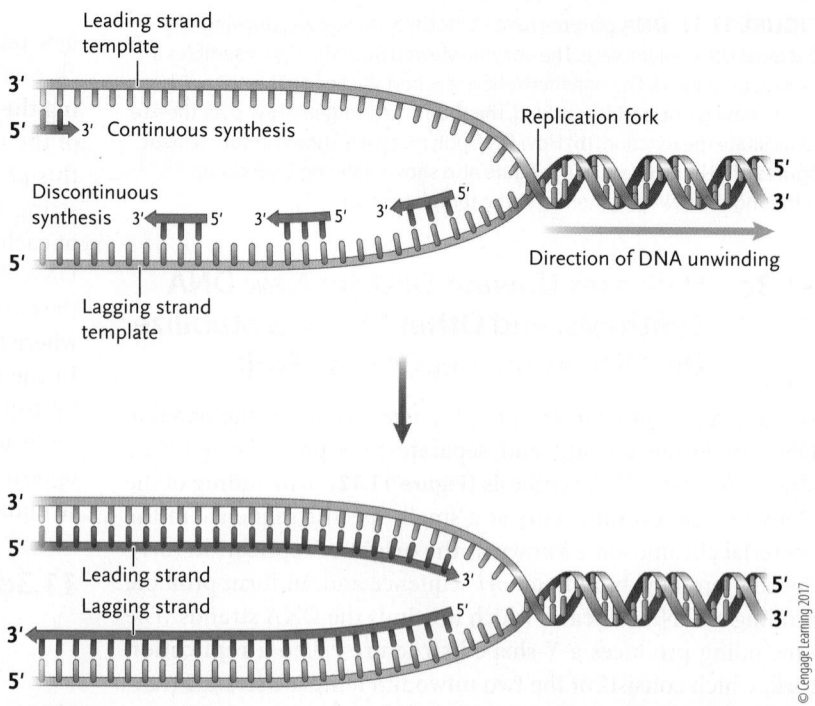

**FIGURE 11.14 Replication of antiparallel template strands at a replication fork.** Synthesis of the new DNA strand on the top template strand is continuous. Synthesis on the new DNA strand on the bottom template strand is discontinuous. Short lengths of DNA are made, which are then joined into a continuous chain. The overall effect is synthesis of both strands in the direction of replication fork movement.

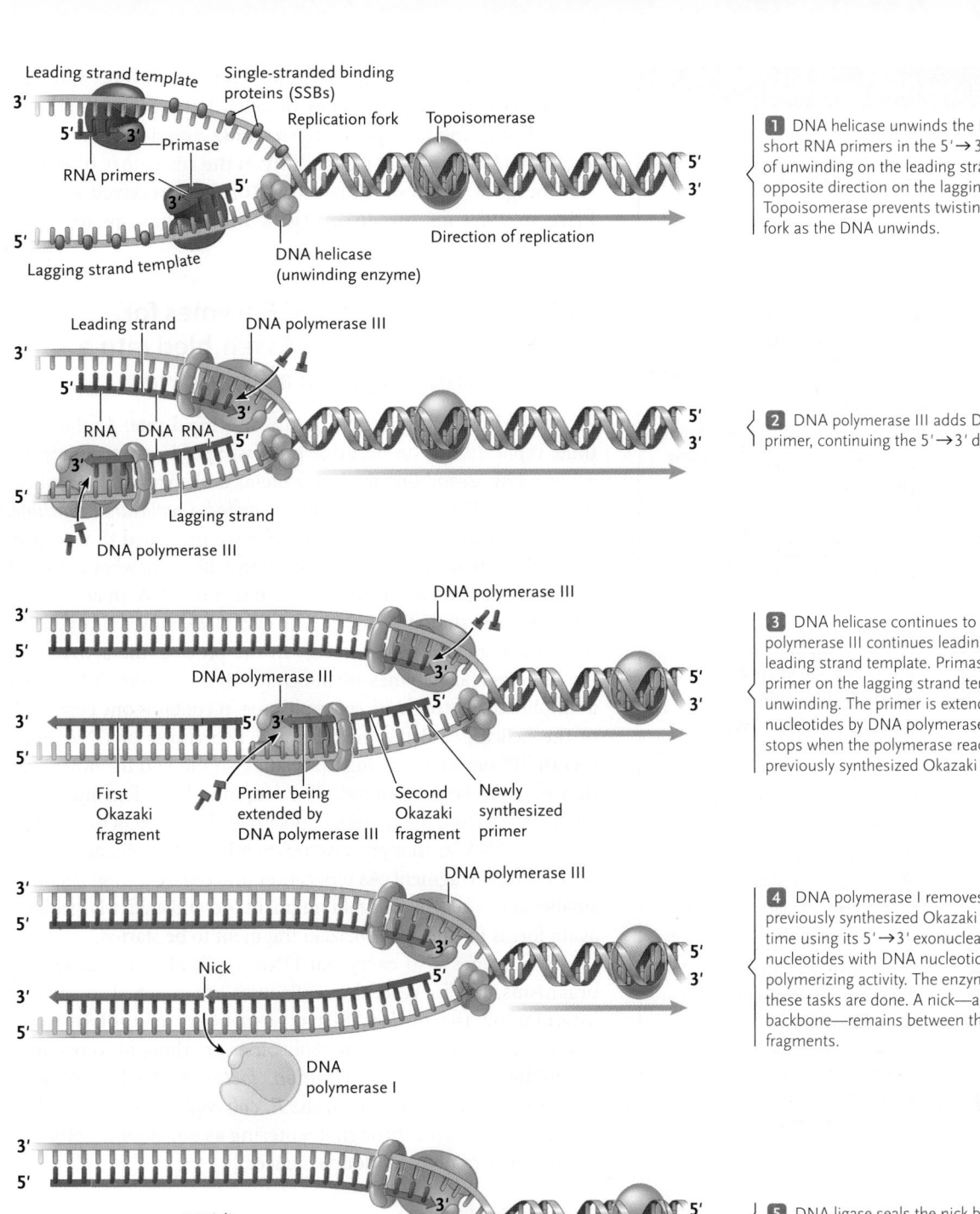

**1** DNA helicase unwinds the DNA. Primases synthesize short RNA primers in the 5'→3' direction—in the direction of unwinding on the leading strand template, and in the opposite direction on the lagging strand template. Topoisomerase prevents twisting ahead of the replication fork as the DNA unwinds.

**2** DNA polymerase III adds DNA nucleotides to the RNA primer, continuing the 5'→3' direction of synthesis.

**3** DNA helicase continues to unwind the DNA. DNA polymerase III continues leading strand synthesis on the leading strand template. Primase synthesizes a new RNA primer on the lagging strand template near the point of unwinding. The primer is extended by the addition of DNA nucleotides by DNA polymerase III. New DNA synthesis stops when the polymerase reaches the 5' end of the previously synthesized Okazaki fragment.

**4** DNA polymerase I removes the RNA primer of the previously synthesized Okazaki fragment one nucleotide at a time using its 5'→3' exonuclease activity. It replaces the RNA nucleotides with DNA nucleotides using its 5'→3' polymerizing activity. The enzyme leaves the template when these tasks are done. A nick—a break in the sugar–phosphate backbone—remains between the adjacent newly synthesized fragments.

**5** DNA ligase seals the nick between the two lagging strand fragments.

**6** DNA helicase continues to unwind the DNA, and synthesis proceeds as before: continuous synthesis of the leading strand, and synthesis of a new fragment to be added to the lagging strand.

© Cengage Learning 2017

**FIGURE 11.15 Molecular model of DNA replication. The drawings simplify the process.** In reality, the enzymes assemble at the fork, replicating both strands from that position as the template strands fold and pass through the assembly.

TABLE 11.1 | Major Proteins of DNA Replication

| Protein | Symbol | Function |
|---------|--------|----------|
| Helicase | | Unwinds DNA helix |
| Single-stranded binding proteins | | Stabilize single-stranded DNA and prevent the two strands at the replication fork from reforming double-stranded DNA |
| Topoisomerase | | Avoids twisting of the DNA ahead of replication fork (in circular DNA) by cutting the DNA, turning the DNA on one side of the break in the direction opposite to that of the twisting force, and rejoining the two strands again |
| Primase | | Synthesizes RNA primer in the $5' \rightarrow 3'$ direction to initiate a new DNA strand |
| DNA polymerase III | | Main replication enzyme in *E. coli*. Extends the RNA primer by adding DNA nucleotides to it |
| DNA polymerase I | | *E. coli* enzyme that uses its $5' \rightarrow 3'$ exonuclease activity to remove the RNA of the previously synthesized Okazaki fragment, and uses its $5' \rightarrow 3'$ polymerization activity to replace the RNA nucleotides with DNA nucleotides |
| Sliding clamp | | Tethers DNA polymerase III to the DNA template, making replication more efficient |
| DNA ligase | | Seals nick left between adjacent fragments after RNA primers replaced with DNA |

© Cengage Learning 2017

experiments with a variety of bacteria and eukaryotes and with viruses that infect both types of cells. Experiments with the bacterium *E. coli* have provided the most complete information about DNA replication, particularly in the laboratory of Arthur Kornberg, at Stanford University. Kornberg received a Nobel Prize in 1959 for his discovery of the mechanism for DNA synthesis.

### 11.3g Key Proteins and Enzymes for Replication Are Assembled into a Complex Called a *Replisome*

As just indicated, replication occurs at a rapid rate. At the same time, replication is an accurate process. Speed and accuracy are achieved by assembling the key proteins and enzymes for replication into a DNA replication complex called a *replication machine*, or a **replisome**. That is, whereas we have presented drawings of the molecular steps of DNA replication with somewhat scattered enzymes and proteins moving along tracks of DNA, in actuality, a replisome sits stationary at the fork and DNA moves through the machine as replication proceeds. In the process, the activities of the proteins and enzymes are integrated tightly. **Figure 11.16** shows a simplified view of the *E. coli* replisome. It contains one copy each of the helicase and the primase, and two copies of DNA polymerase III, one synthesizing the leading strand and the other synthesizing the lagging strand. The looping of the lagging strand template out from the replisome positions the 3' end of that single-stranded DNA so that primase can synthesize the primer for the next Okazaki fragment. As replication proceeds, the loop becomes smaller and, after the Okazaki fragment is completed, a larger loop again forms for the next Okazaki fragment to be started.

Replisomes also carry out DNA replication in eukaryotic organisms. In this case, the replisomes are attached to specific locations on the nuclear matrix, a network of protein fibres within the nucleus. Multiple replisomes are thought to occur in assemblies known as *replication factories*. Each replisome remains stationary and, as in the *E. coli* replisome, the DNA to be replicated moves through it, entering as one double helix and leaving as two identical double helices.

activities of the major enzymes replicating DNA. Replication advances at a rate of about 500–1000 nucleotides per second in *E. coli* and other bacteria, and at a rate of about 50–100 per second in eukaryotes. The entire process is so rapid that the RNA primers and nicks left by discontinuous synthesis persist for only seconds or fractions of a second. A short distance behind the fork, the new DNA chains are fully continuous and wound into complete DNA double helices. Each helix consists of one "old" and one "new" polynucleotide. Researchers identified the enzymes that replicate DNA through

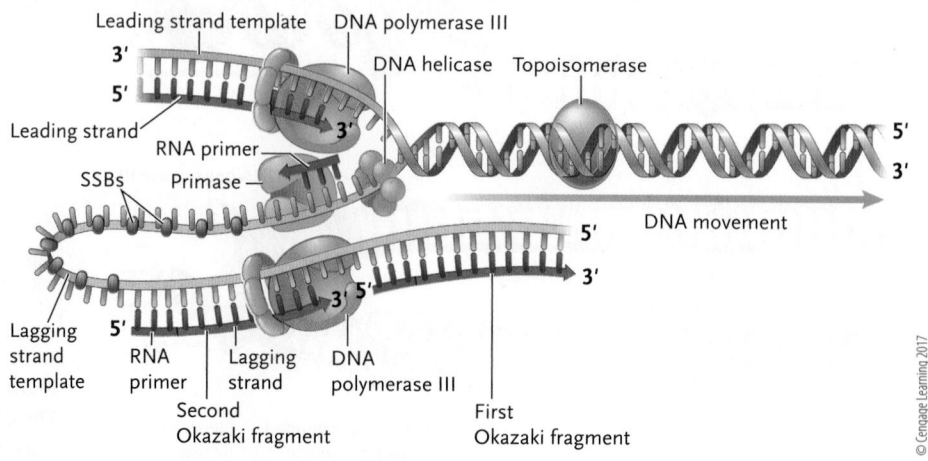

FIGURE 11.16 **Simplified depiction of the *E. coli* replisome**

© Cengage Learning 2017

## 11.3h Bacterial Chromosomes Have a Single Replication Origin; Eukaryotic Chromosomes Have Multiple Replication Origins

Unwinding at an *ori* within a DNA helix actually produces two replication forks: two Ys joined together at their tops to form a **replication bubble**. Typically, each of the replication forks moves away from the *ori* as DNA replication proceeds, with the events at each fork mirroring those in the other (**Figure 11.17**). In this way, DNA replication is bidirectional.

For small circular genomes, such as those found in *E. coli* and in many bacteria and archaea, there is a single *ori*. DNA replication begins from a single origin in the DNA circle, forming two forks that travel around the circle in opposite directions. Eventually, the forks meet at the opposite side from the origin to complete replication (**Figure 11.18**). The replicated

chromosomes are distributed actively to the two halves of the bacterial cell. Subsequent binary fission of the cell produces two daughter bacterial cells, each with a copy of the chromosome (discussed in Chapter 8).

Eukaryotic genomes, by contrast, are distributed among several linear chromosomes, each of which can be very long. The average human chromosome, for instance, is about 25 times longer than the *E. coli* chromosome. Nonetheless, replication of long eukaryotic chromosomes is relatively rapid—sometimes faster than the *E. coli* chromosome—because there are many, sometimes hundreds of origins of replications along eukaryotic chromosomes. Replication initiates at each origin, forming a replication bubble at each (**Figure 11.19**). Movement of the two forks in opposite directions from each origin extends the replication bubbles until the forks eventually meet along the chromosomes to produce fully replicated chromosomes.

**FIGURE 11.17**
**Synthesis of leading and lagging strands in the two replication forks of a replication bubble formed at an origin of replication**

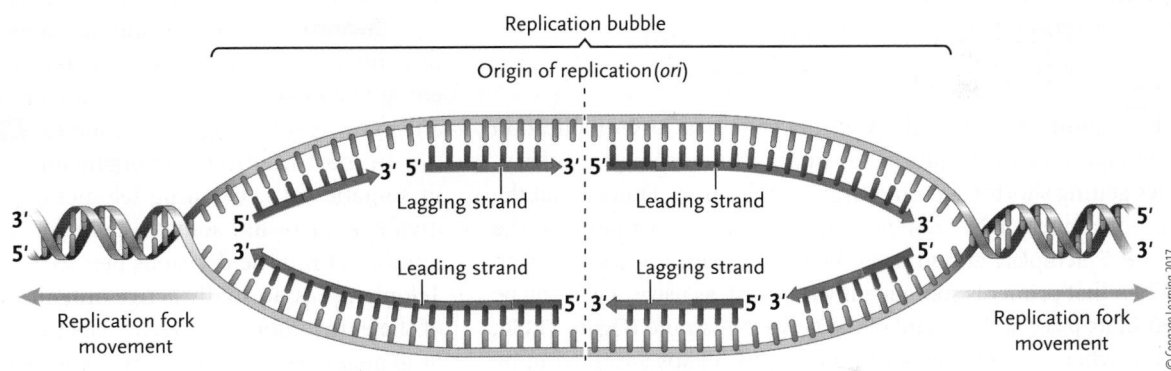

Replication bubble

Origin of replication (*ori*)

3′ 5′  3′ 5′
Lagging strand    Leading strand

Leading strand    Lagging strand
5′ 3′    5′ 3′

3′
5′

5′
3′

Replication fork movement

Replication fork movement

© Cengage Learning 2017

**FIGURE 11.18**
**Replication from a single origin of replication in a circular bacterial chromosome**

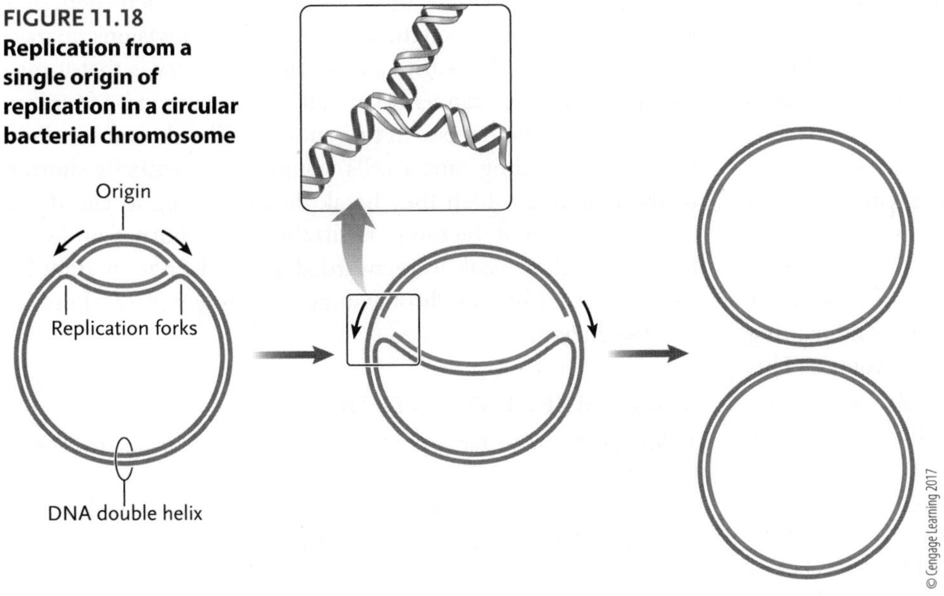

Origin

Replication forks

DNA double helix

© Cengage Learning 2017

Normally, a replication origin is activated only once during the S phase of a eukaryotic cell cycle, so no portion of the DNA is replicated more than once.

**CONCEPT FIX** Figures 11.14, 11.15, and 11.16 show that one strand of DNA is replicated continuously (leading strand), and the other is replicated discontinuously (lagging strand). This might lead you to believe that any one particular strand of DNA on a chromosome is replicated either continuously or discontinuously along its entire length. However, if you look carefully at the replication bubble in Figure 11.17, you will see that a bubble consists of two replication forks replicating in opposite directions. You will see that any one particular strand of DNA on a chromosome is replicated continuously at one fork but discontinuously at the other fork. ⬡

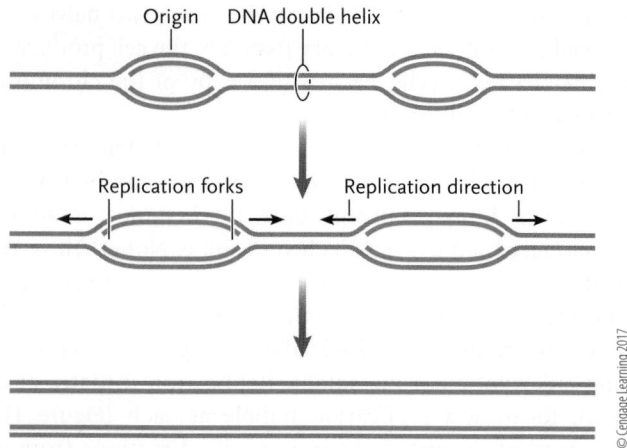

Origin    DNA double helix

Replication forks    Replication direction

© Cengage Learning 2017

**FIGURE 11.19  Replication from multiple origins in the linear chromosomes of eukaryotes**

## 11.3i  Telomerases Solve a Special Replication Problem at the Ends of Linear Chromosomes in Eukaryotes

The requirement for an RNA primer to initiate DNA replication (see Figure 11.13) results in the linear chromosomes of eukaryotes getting shorter at each round of replication. Think about the end of a linear DNA double helix. New DNA synthesis on the $3' \rightarrow 5'$ template strand must be started with an RNA primer. When that primer is subsequently removed, as usual, a gap will be left in its place at the 5′ end of the new DNA strand (**Figure 11.20**). Everywhere else on the chromosome, such gaps are filled in by DNA polymerase by elongating the 3′ end of a neighbouring nucleotide. However, at the very ends of chromosomes, there is no existing nucleotide chain that can be elongated. Therefore, DNA polymerase cannot fill in the gap with the required DNA nucleotides, and the resulting newly synthesized strand will be too short. (You should agree that this problem occurs on both ends of the chromosome, just on opposite strands of the double helix.) When these new, now shortened, DNA strands are used as a template for the next round of DNA replication, the resulting chromosomes will be shorter still. Indeed, when most somatic cells go through the cell cycle, their chromosomes shorten with each division. Such loss of DNA sequences can eventually have lethal consequences for the cell.

Most eukaryotic chromosomes can afford to lose some DNA sequence because a buffer of highly repetitive noncoding DNA protects genes near the ends of chromosomes. This region of noncoding DNA is called the **telomere** (*telo* = end; *mere* = segment). A telomere consists of a short DNA sequence that is repeated hundreds to thousands of times. In humans, the repeated sequence, the *telomere repeat,* is 5′-TTAGGG-3′ on the template strand (the top strand in Figure 11.20, step 1). With each replication, a fraction of the telomere repeats is lost by the mechanism described above, but the genes are unaffected. The buffering fails only when the entire telomere is lost.

The length of telomeres can be maintained by the action of an unusual enzyme, called **telomerase**, which adds DNA to the ends of chromosomes. Since telomerase makes DNA, it is a type of DNA polymerase. Recall that DNA polymerases require a free 3′ OH to extend, a supply of dNTPs, and a template strand. If you look closely at Figure 11.20, you might predict that telomerase elongates the 5′ end of the bottom strand to fill in the gap. Although this solution appears easiest, it is impossible since *there are no known polymerases capable of elongating a 5′ end.* So, instead, telomerase must elongate the available 3′ end of the top strand. But now there is a different problem: what to use for a template strand? The lack of a template on the chromosome is solved by *telomerase carrying its own template* in the form of a single-stranded RNA molecule. Telomerase adds a telomere repeat to the 3′ end of the DNA using the RNA as a template (see Figure 11.20). Then it shifts toward the end of the chromosome and adds another, and another. Once several hundred repeats are added to the top strand, it is primed and used as a template as usual. When the RNA primer is removed, there will be a single-stranded region at the end of the chromosome as before.

**CONCEPT FIX** It is important to understand that telomerase does not directly prevent the mechanism that causes the shortening of chromosomes. Telomerase just acts against this mechanism by lengthening chromosomes. ⬡

In most multicellular organisms, telomerase is not active in somatic cells, meaning telomeres shorten when such cells divide. As a result, somatic cells are capable of only a certain number of mitotic divisions before they stop dividing and die. Telomerase is normally active only in the rapidly dividing cells of the early embryo, in germ cells to ensure that chromosomes of gametes have telomeres restored before passing to the next generation, and in stem cells.

Telomerase explains how cancer cells can divide indefinitely and not be limited to a certain number of divisions as a result of telomere shortening. For many cancers, as normal cells develop into cancer cells, their telomerases are reactivated, preserving chromosome length during the rapid divisions characteristic of cancer. A positive side of this discovery is that it may lead to an effective cancer treatment if a means can be found to switch off the telomerases in tumour cells. The chromosomes in the rapidly dividing cancer cells would then eventually shorten to the length at which they break down, leading to cell death and elimination of the tumour. Elizabeth Blackburn, Carol Greider, and Jack Szostak were awarded a Nobel Prize in 2009 for their discovery of how chromosomes are protected by telomeres and the enzyme telomerase.

### STUDY BREAK QUESTIONS

1. What is the importance of complementary base-pairing to DNA replication?
2. Why is a primer needed for DNA replication on both strands?
3. Two DNA polymerases are used in DNA replication. What are their roles?
4. Why are telomeres important?

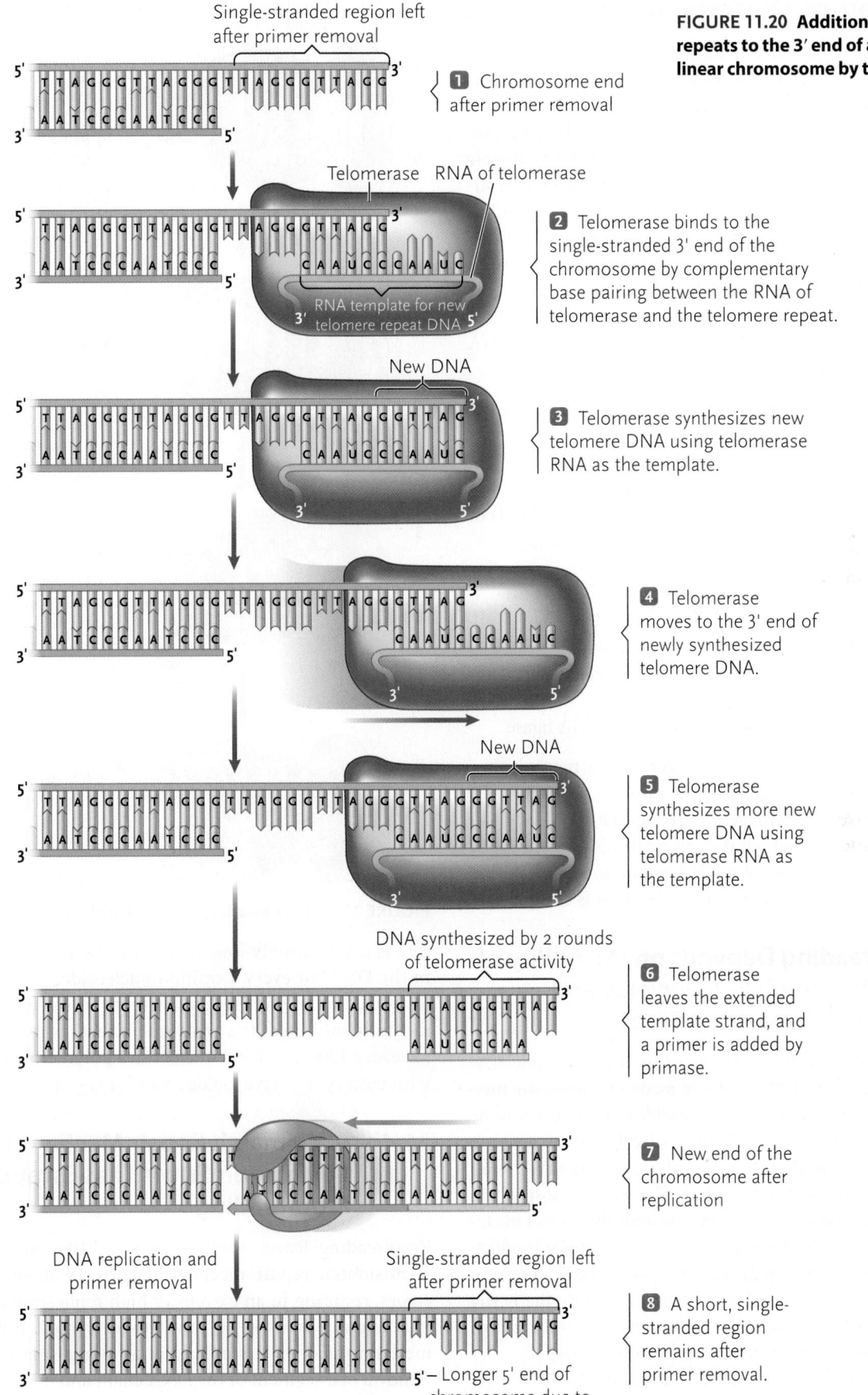

Single-stranded region left after primer removal

5′ TTAGGGTTAGGGTTAGGGTTAGG 3′
3′ AATCCCAATCCC 5′

**FIGURE 11.20 Addition of telomere repeats to the 3′ end of a eukaryotic linear chromosome by telomerase**

**1** Chromosome end after primer removal

Telomerase    RNA of telomerase

5′ TTAGGGTTAGGGTTAGGGTTAGG 3′
3′ AATCCCAATCCC 5′
CAAUCCCAAUC

RNA template for new telomere repeat DNA

3′                    5′

**2** Telomerase binds to the single-stranded 3′ end of the chromosome by complementary base pairing between the RNA of telomerase and the telomere repeat.

New DNA

5′ TTAGGGTTAGGGTTAGGGTTAGGGTTAG 3′
3′ AATCCCAATCCC 5′
CAAUCCCAAUC
3′                    5′

**3** Telomerase synthesizes new telomere DNA using telomerase RNA as the template.

5′ TTAGGGTTAGGGTTAGGGTTAGGGTTAG 3′
3′ AATCCCAATCCC 5′
CAAUCCCAAUC
3′                    5′

**4** Telomerase moves to the 3′ end of newly synthesized telomere DNA.

New DNA

5′ TTAGGGTTAGGGTTAGGGTTAGGGTTAGGGTTAG 3′
3′ AATCCCAATCCC 5′
CAAUCCCAAUC
3′                    5′

**5** Telomerase synthesizes more new telomere DNA using telomerase RNA as the template.

DNA synthesized by 2 rounds of telomerase activity

5′ TTAGGGTTAGGGTTAGGGTTAGGGTTAGGGTTAG 3′
3′ AATCCCAATCCC 5′
AAUCCCAA

**6** Telomerase leaves the extended template strand, and a primer is added by primase.

5′ TTAGGGTTAGGGT GGTTAGGGTTAGGGTTAG 3′
3′ AATCCCAATCCC AUCCCAATCCCAAUCCCAA 5′

**7** New end of the chromosome after replication

DNA replication and primer removal

Single-stranded region left after primer removal

5′ TTAGGGTTAGGGTTAGGGTTAGGGTTAGGGTTAG 3′
3′ AATCCCAATCCCCAATCCCCAATCCC 5′

5′ — Longer 5′ end of chromosome due to telomerase activity

**8** A short, single-stranded region remains after primer removal.

© Cengage Learning 2017

# 11.4 Repair of Damage in DNA

Although you may consider any change to DNA structure as a mutation, this is not actually the case. For the purposes of this discussion, we will define a mutation as a double-stranded change in the base sequence of a region of DNA. Therefore, we will refer to changes that affect only one strand of the double helix as DNA damage rather than mutation. For example, replication errors that result in improperly paired bases or chemical reactions that add chemical groups to bases both create DNA damage. Repair of such damage is very important because, if damage is allowed to persist, it may then promote changes in the remaining DNA strand and give rise to a heritable mutation.

Three types of repair mechanisms operate to correct DNA damage:

1. **Proofreading**, a mechanism for correcting errors made by DNA polymerase during replication
2. **Mismatch repair**, a mechanism for correcting errors made during replication that escape proofreading
3. **Excision repair**, mechanisms for correcting various kinds of DNA damage, such as those caused by chemicals and radiation

Errors in DNA are corrected following three basic steps:

1. Recognition of the DNA error and its removal
2. Replacing the removed DNA by new DNA synthesis using a repair DNA polymerase
3. Sealing the new DNA to the old DNA using DNA ligase

Step 1 varies with the different error correction mechanisms, whereas steps 2 and 3 are essentially the same.

Base-pair mismatch damage is corrected either by a proofreading mechanism carried out during replication by the DNA polymerases themselves, or by a DNA repair mechanism that corrects mismatched base pairs after replication is complete.

## 11.4a Proofreading Depends on the Ability of DNA Polymerases to Reverse and Remove Mismatched Bases

DNA polymerases make very few errors as they assemble new nucleotide chains. Most of the mistakes made are **base-pair mismatches**, in which the new inserted nucleotide has a base that is the incorrect one to pair with the base of the nucleotide on the template strand. A **proofreading** mechanism functions during DNA replication to correct base-pair mismatches. That is, for most of the polymerization reactions, DNA polymerase adds the correct nucleotide to the growing chain (**Figure 11.21**, step 1). If a newly added nucleotide is mismatched (step 2), the DNA polymerase can reverse using a built-in $3' \rightarrow 5'$ exonuclease activity to remove the newly added incorrect nucleotide (step 3). The enzyme then resumes forward synthesis, now inserting the correct nucleotide (step 4).

Several experiments showed that the major DNA polymerases of replication proofread their work. For example, when the *E. coli* DNA polymerase III is fully functional, its overall error

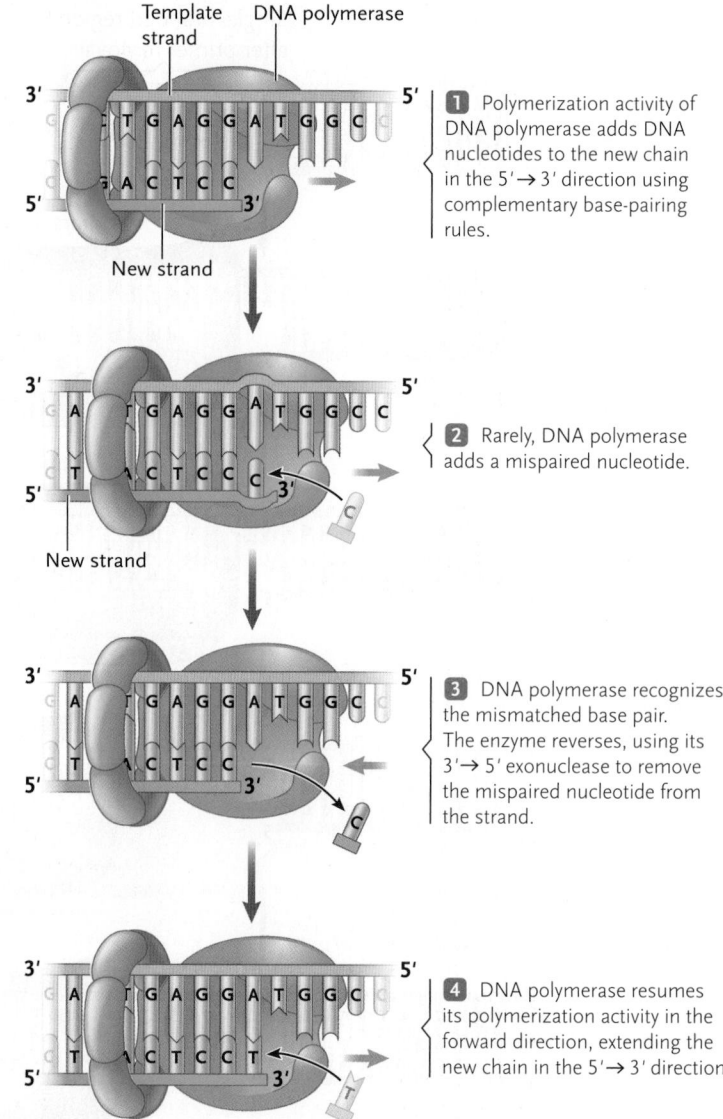

**1** Polymerization activity of DNA polymerase adds DNA nucleotides to the new chain in the $5' \rightarrow 3'$ direction using complementary base-pairing rules.

**2** Rarely, DNA polymerase adds a mispaired nucleotide.

**3** DNA polymerase recognizes the mismatched base pair. The enzyme reverses, using its $3' \rightarrow 5'$ exonuclease to remove the mispaired nucleotide from the strand.

**4** DNA polymerase resumes its polymerization activity in the forward direction, extending the new chain in the $5' \rightarrow 3'$ direction.

Template strand — DNA polymerase

New strand

New strand

© Cengage Learning 2017

**FIGURE 11.21 Proofreading by a DNA polymerase**

rate is astonishingly low, with only about 1 mispair surviving in the DNA for every 1 million nucleotides polymerized in the test tube. If the proofreading activity of the enzyme is experimentally inhibited, the error rate increases to about 1 mistake for every 1000 to 10 000 nucleotides polymerized. Experiments with eukaryotes have yielded similar results.

## 11.4b A Mismatch Repair Mechanism Corrects Replication Errors That Escape Proofreading

Proofreading leaves about 1 error in $10^7$ nucleotides copied. A **mismatch repair** mechanism corrects about 99% of those errors, resulting in an extremely high replication accuracy, with only about 1 error in $10^9$ nucleotides copied. Mismatch repair mechanisms operate similarly in all organisms and involve the removal of a segment of the DNA chain and its replacement with a newly synthesized segment complementary to the template strand. Evolutionary conservation of many of the mismatch

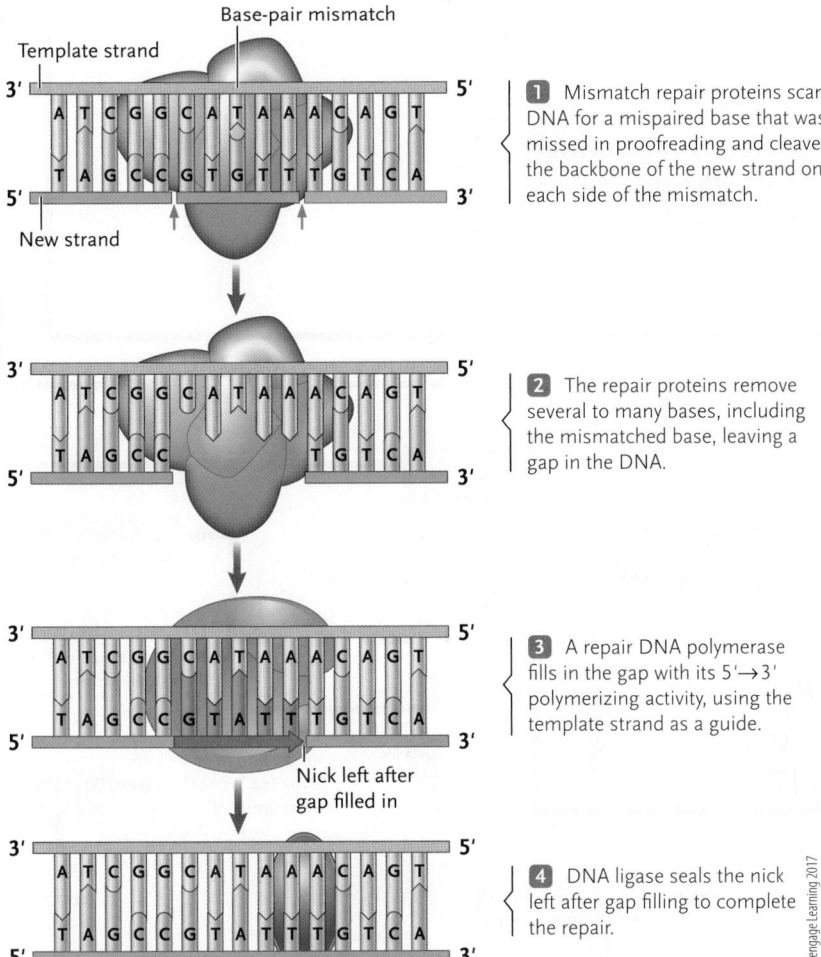

① Mismatch repair proteins scan DNA for a mispaired base that was missed in proofreading and cleave the backbone of the new strand on each side of the mismatch.

② The repair proteins remove several to many bases, including the mismatched base, leaving a gap in the DNA.

③ A repair DNA polymerase fills in the gap with its $5' \rightarrow 3'$ polymerizing activity, using the template strand as a guide.

④ DNA ligase seals the nick left after gap filling to complete the repair.

**FIGURE 11.22** **Repair of mismatched bases in replicated DNA**

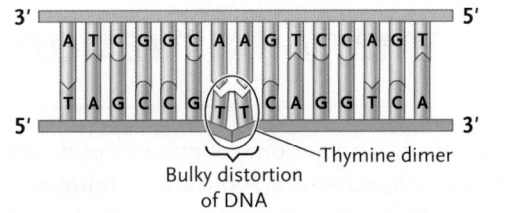

**FIGURE 11.23** **A thymine dimer in DNA, caused by UV light irradiation**

repair proteins from bacteria to yeast to humans indicates that this mechanism is both ancient and vital to all living organisms.

To correct postreplication mismatch damage, mismatch repair proteins detect the mispaired base, cut the new DNA strand on each side of the mismatch, and remove a portion of the chain (**Figure 11.22**). A repair DNA polymerase (DNA polymerase I in *E. coli*) fills in the gap with new DNA. The repair is completed by DNA ligase, which seals the nucleotide chain into a continuous DNA backbone.

Mismatch repair is important in the prevention of cancer. One type of colon cancer, for instance, is caused in part by a mutation in a gene that encodes a mismatch repair protein.

## 11.4c Excision Repair Mechanisms Correct Various Kinds of DNA Damage

DNA damage occurs all the time in cells as a result of chemical events that result in nonbulky damage to bases, such as the chemical modification of bases, or the loss of purine bases from the DNA. "Nonbulky" here means that there is significant distortion of the helix, called *bulging*.

Repair of nonbulky damage to bases occurs by a **base-excision repair** mechanism that operates to remove the erroneous base and replace it with the correct one complementary to the

base on the other DNA strand. Conceptually, this repair mechanism takes place similarly to mismatch repair (see Figure 11.22), with different proteins involved in the recognition step. After proofreading, base-excision repair is the most important mechanism to fix incorrect or damaged bases.

Some DNA damage is more extensive, causing bulky distortions in the DNA. For example, ultraviolet (UV) light causes thymine dimers to form in DNA in which adjacent thymine bases on one strand of the DNA form chemical bonds with each other (**Figure 11.23**). If unrepaired, bulky DNA distortions such as thymine dimers have serious consequences because DNA polymerase cannot continue DNA synthesis past the distortion. As a result, replication stops, and a blocked replication fork can cause cell death. **Nucleotide-excision repair** is a mechanism that can repair DNA damage such as thymine dimers. This mechanism is similar to the others we have discussed (such as the mechanism shown in Figure 11.22), differing primarily in the recognition step. That is, proteins specific for nucleotide-excision repair recognize the bulky distortion in the DNA and remove a segment of the DNA strand containing the thymine dimer. Repair DNA polymerase and DNA ligase then replace the removed DNA with new DNA and seal it to the rest of the DNA strand.

## 11.4d Replication Errors and Other DNA Damage That Remain Unrepaired Give Rise to Mutations

Although very few mismatches remain in DNA after proofreading and DNA repair, those that do will give rise to double-stranded changes in DNA (mutation) following the next round of replication. The many other kinds of bulky and nonbulky DNA damage also are repaired routinely by the scavenging DNA repair systems. Again, some damage persists and can lead to double-stranded changes following the next round of replication. When a mutation occurs in a gene, it can alter the property of the protein encoded by the gene, which in turn may alter how the organism functions. Hence, mutations are very important to the evolutionary process as the ultimate source of the variability in offspring acted on by natural selection.

### STUDY BREAK QUESTION

1. Why is a proofreading mechanism important for DNA replication, and what are the mechanisms that correct errors?

# Summary Illustration

All cells carry a genome composed of deoxyribonucleic acid (DNA). Discovery of the role, structure, replication, mutation, and repair of DNA has unleashed a revolution in our understanding of information flow in living systems.

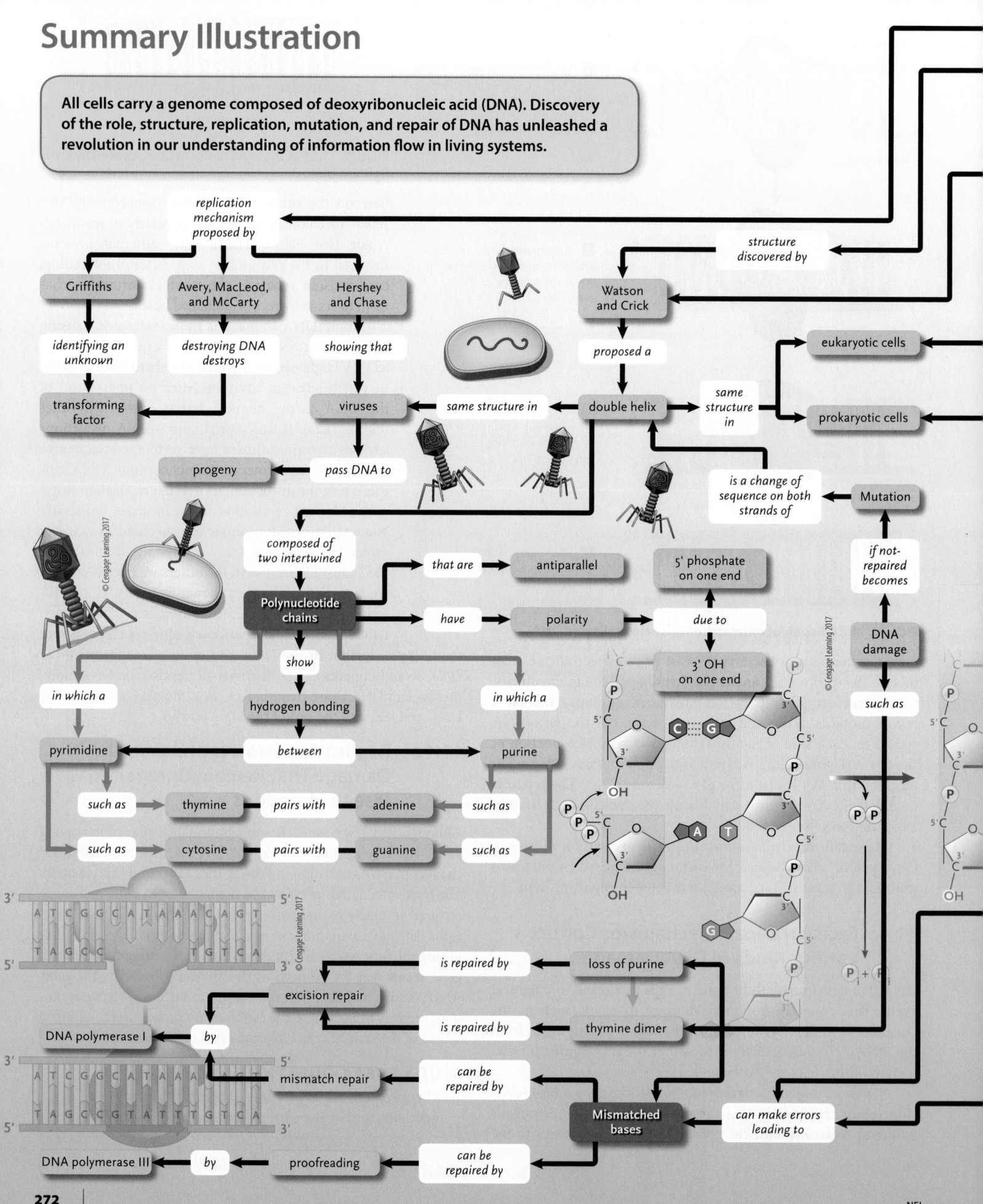

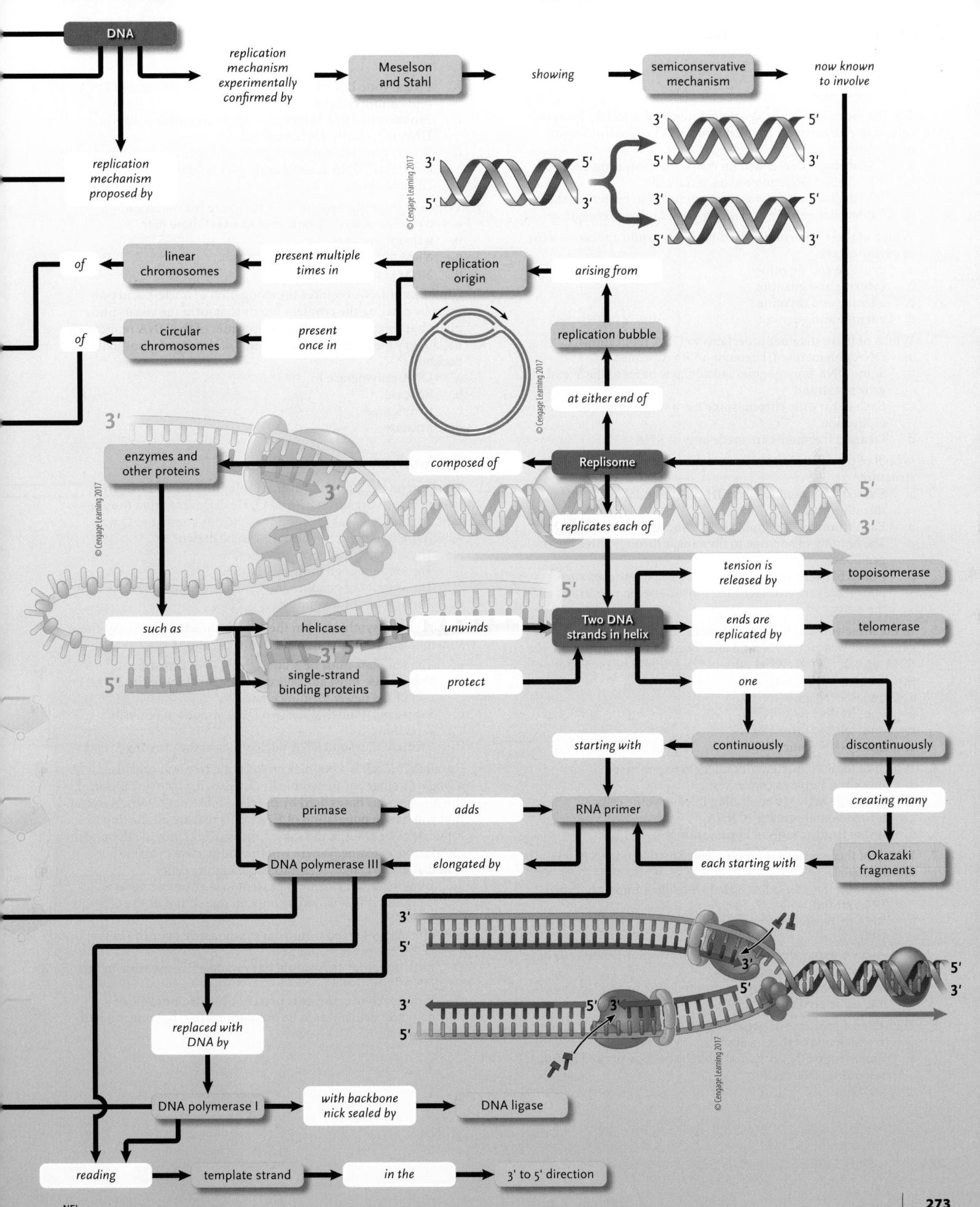

DNA

replication mechanism experimentally confirmed by → Meselson and Stahl → showing → semiconservative mechanism → now known to involve

replication mechanism proposed by

of ← linear chromosomes ← present multiple times in ← replication origin ← arising from

of ← circular chromosomes ← present once in

replication bubble

at either end of

enzymes and other proteins ← composed of ← **Replisome**

replicates each of

such as → helicase → unwinds → **Two DNA strands in helix**

tension is released by → topoisomerase

ends are replicated by → telomerase

single-strand binding proteins → protect

one

starting with ← continuously

discontinuously

creating many

primase → adds → RNA primer

DNA polymerase III ← elongated by

each starting with ← Okazaki fragments

replaced with DNA by

DNA polymerase I → with backbone nick sealed by → DNA ligase

reading → template strand → in the → 3' to 5' direction

# SELF-TEST QUESTIONS

## Recall/Understand

1. The Hershey and Chase experiment involved infecting bacterial cells with radioactively labelled viruses. What did this experiment show?
   a. $^{35}S$-labelled DNA ended up inside the virus progeny.
   b. $^{32}P$-labelled DNA entered bacterial cells.
   c. $^{35}S$-labelled protein was incorporated into bacterial cells.
   d. $^{32}P$-labelled protein was incorporated into virus coats.

2. Which of these pairs of nitrogenous bases would appear on a list of pyrimidines?
   a. cytosine and thymine
   b. cytosine and guanine
   c. adenine and thymine
   d. adenine and guanine

3. Which of these statements pertains to DNA replication?
   a. DNA polymerase III extends an RNA primer.
   b. Some DNA polymerases can add new bases to the 5′ end of a growing strand.
   c. Each eukaryotic chromosome has a single origin of replication.
   d. Okazaki fragments are made only of RNA.

4. Which of the following statements describes an aspect of DNA structure?
   a. Each DNA strand has a 3′ OH on one end and a 5′ OH on the other end.
   b. Each strand of the double helix runs parallel to the other.
   c. The binding of adenine to thymine is through three hydrogen bonds.
   d. Bonds between components of the backbone (i.e., sugar–phosphate) are stronger than those between one strand and the other.

5. In the Meselson and Stahl experiment, the DNA in the parental generation was all $^{15}N^{15}N$; and after one round of replication, the DNA was all $^{15}N^{14}N$. What ratio of DNA would be seen after three rounds of replication?
   a. one $^{15}N^{14}N$ : one $^{14}N^{14}N$
   b. one $^{15}N^{14}N$ : two $^{14}N^{14}N$
   c. one $^{15}N^{14}N$ : three $^{14}N^{14}N$
   d. one $^{15}N^{14}N$ : four $^{14}N^{14}N$

6. Which of these characteristics refers to telomerase?
   a. It is often active in cancer cells.
   b. It is more active in adult than in embryonic cells.
   c. It has telomeres made of RNA.
   d. It shortens the ends of chromosomes.

7. Which of these actions is accomplished by the process of mismatch repair?
   a. Okazaki fragments are sealed with ligase into a continual DNA strand.
   b. RNA primers are removed and replaced with the correct DNA.
   c. A DNA sequence lost during the replication of the ends of chromosomes is restored.
   d. Incorrect bases that escape proofreading by DNA polymerase are replaced.

8. The DNA of prokaryotic organisms differs from that of eukaryotes in which one of these ways?
   a. Prokaryotic DNA is surrounded by densely packed histones; eukaryotic DNA is not.
   b. Prokaryotic DNA has many sites for the initiation of DNA replication; eukaryotic DNA does not.
   c. Prokaryotic DNA is typically single stranded; eukaryotic DNA is typically double stranded.
   d. Prokaryotic DNA is rarely packaged in linear chromosomes; eukaryotic DNA is commonly packaged in linear chromosomes.

9. Which of these changes to DNA structure is a mutation?
   a. a change of an A–T base pair to a G–C base pair
   b. a thymine dimer
   c. a lost purine base
   d. an A–G mismatch

10. Synthesis of DNA requires the elongation of nucleic acid polymers by creating the covalent bonds that form the sugar–phosphate backbone. Which of these enzymes of the DNA replication machinery *breaks* the covalent bonds of the sugar–phosphate backbone?
    a. DNA polymerase I
    b. helicase
    c. telomerase
    d. primase

## Apply/Analyze

11. Working on the Amazon River, a biologist isolated DNA from two unknown organisms, P and Q. He discovered that the adenine content of P was 15% and the cytosine content of Q was 42%. Which of these conclusions can be drawn?
    a. The amount of adenine in Q is 42%.
    b. The amount of guanine in P is 15%.
    c. The amount of guanine and cytosine combined in P is 70%.
    d. The amount of thymine in Q is 21%.

12. Since DNA is synthesized in the 5′ → 3′ direction, which of these statements applies to a step in DNA replication?
    a. The template must be read in the 5′ → 3′ direction.
    b. Polymerase must add successive nucleotides to the 3′ –OH end of the newly forming chain.
    c. Ligase must unwind the two DNA strands in opposite directions.
    d. Primase must add RNA nucleotides to the growing 5′ end.

13. Recall that *E.coli* is a popular prokaryotic research organism with a single circular chromosome. Recall also that cytosine is one of the nitrogenous bases used by *E. coli* to make new DNA. Assume that you have a population of *E.coli* cells that are all starting to replicate their DNA at the same time, and you provide them with radioactive cytosine. Where will the radioactive cytosine be found after the cell divides into two daughter cells?
    a. If radioactive cytosine is present in a chromosome of a daughter cell, it would be only on one strand or the other, not both.
    b. One daughter cell would have radioactive cytosine in its DNA; the other would not.
    c. Both daughter cells would have radioactive cytosine in their DNA.
    d. If radioactive cytosine is present in a chromosome of a daughter cell, it would be on both strands, but only on half the circle.

## Create/Evaluate

14. During replication, an error uncorrected by proofreading or mismatch repair produces a DNA molecule with the wrong base paired with a G at the indicated position:

    AATTCCGACTCCTATGG
    TTAAGGTTGAGGATACC
            ↑

    This DNA molecule is received by one of the two daughter cells produced by mitosis. In the next round of replication and division, a mutation appears in only one of the two daughter cells. Explain this observation.

15. Strains of bacteria that are resistant to an antibiotic sometimes appear spontaneously among other bacteria of the same type that are killed by the antibiotic. In view of the information in this chapter about DNA replication, what might account for the appearance of this resistance?

# Chapter Roadmap

## Gene Structure, Expression, and Mutation

The information encoded in the DNA sequence of genes is accessed by all cells through the process of transcription, which, for protein-coding genes, is then followed by translation. Changes in the DNA sequence of genes can result in alterations of gene products.

**From Chapter 9**

**From Chapter 11**

### 12.1 The Connection between DNA, RNA, and Protein

A series of classic experiments revealed the flow of information from DNA to RNA to protein, and "cracked" the genetic code.

**To Chapter 13**

### 12.2 Transcription: DNA-Directed RNA Synthesis

Many types of RNA are produced from a DNA template by the process of transcription.

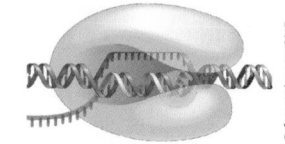

© Cengage Learning 2017

### 12.3 Processing of mRNAs in Eukaryotes

mRNAs produced in eukaryotes are altered within the nucleus to modify their ends and remove intervening sequences (introns).

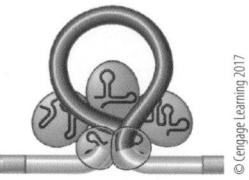

© Cengage Learning 2017

### 12.4 Translation: mRNA-Directed Polypeptide Synthesis

The sequence of bases in mRNA dictates the sequence of amino acids in proteins through a process involving ribosomes and tRNA.

© Cengage Learning 2017

**From Chapter 8**

**From Chapter 11**

### 12.5 Mutations Can Affect Protein Structure and Function

Various types of changes in the DNA sequence of genes can have effects on protein function, ranging from severe to nothing at all.

**To Chapter 15**

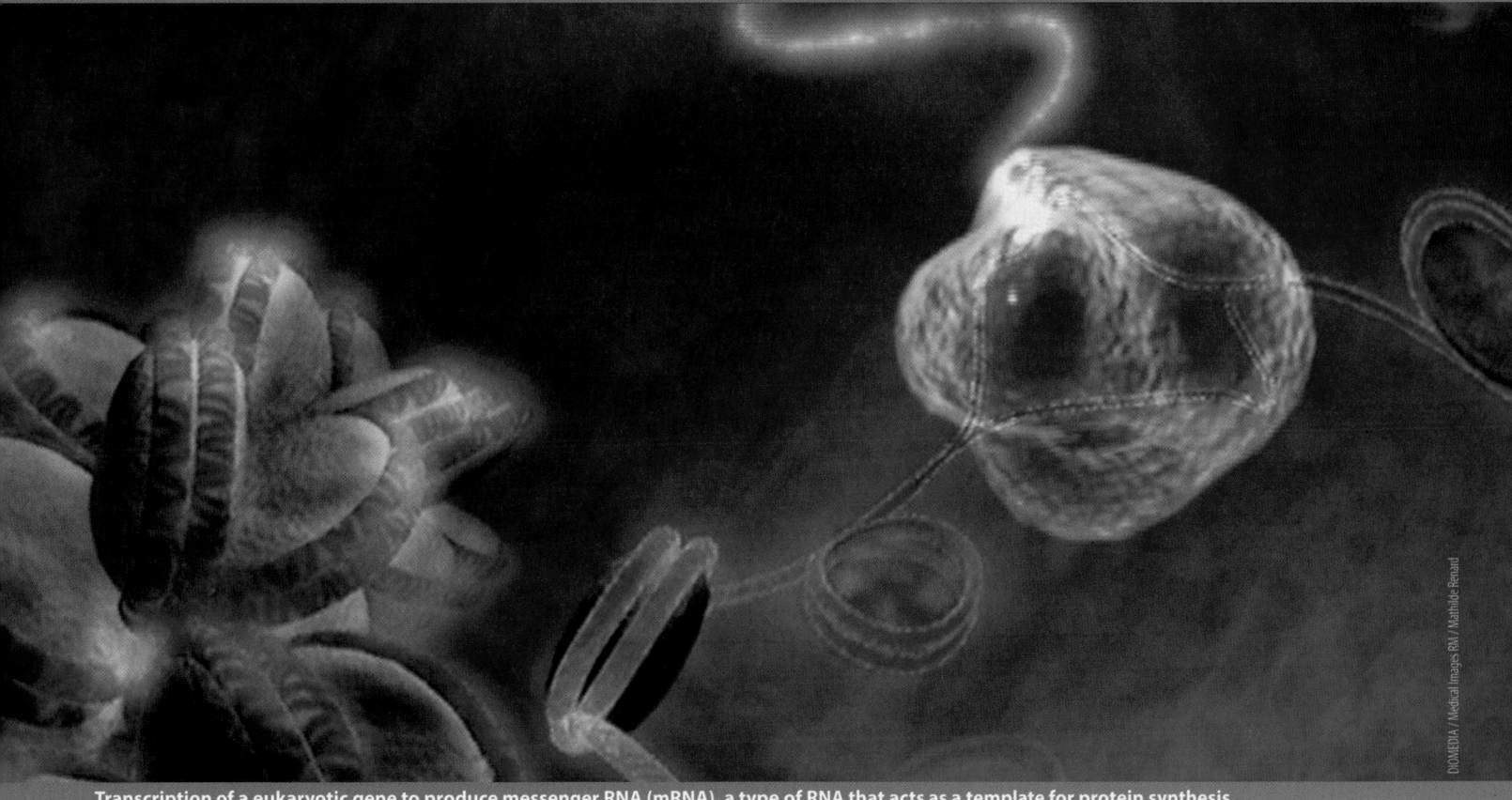

**Transcription of a eukaryotic gene to produce messenger RNA (mRNA), a type of RNA that acts as a template for protein synthesis.** The DNA of the gene unwinds from the nucleosome (left side) and is copied by an RNA polymerase (centre) into mRNA (exiting the top).

# Gene Structure, Expression, and Mutation

# 12

**Why it matters . . .** Raveena stared into the glass in her hand and wondered what could possibly be so black. Many hours of abdominal pain, vomiting, and diarrhea had left her muscles weak and her thoughts foggy. "Drink it up," urged the nurse, thinly disguising her concern with forced encouragement. "If you have toxin in your system, the charcoal will adsorb it." Raveena drank dutifully but her stomach didn't tolerate the foul-tasting mud for very long.

A few moments later, Raveena's friend Tony came into her hospital room. His eyes were moist. "They are transferring Yan to Vancouver General Hospital; he may need a liver transplant."

"What! A liver transplant? I thought we just had food poisoning from that stir fry he cooked for us."

"It isn't food poisoning. It's the mushrooms. I didn't like the smell of that dish so I just ate the rice. I didn't get sick. You must have eaten some of the mushrooms."

"Yeah, I ate a few bites because I was trying to be polite. But what about the mushrooms? Yan was so excited to find them on our hike. He said he and his parents collected them all the time back home in Vietnam. Why is that a problem now?"

"An Emergency Room doctor said that every year a few people make this mistake around here in Victoria. She said that there is a mushroom called *paddy straw* that is common in Southeast Asia and looks similar to the ones that Yan found on Sunday. Paddy straw mushrooms have pinkish gills and are edible. But the mushrooms Yan picked for his meal had white gills. I found some pieces in our kitchen garbage and brought them in to the hospital for identification."

a.

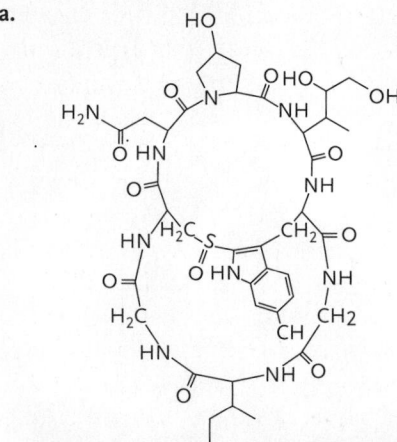

b.

FIGURE 12.1 (a) The very striking double circular structure of amanitin; (b) *Amanita phalloides*

Tony stopped speaking, biting his lip.

"So who cares what colour the gills are?" Raveena was feeling nauseated again.

"The mushrooms with white gills are *Amanita;* they are very toxic. You only ate a bit and are likely going to be OK. Yan ate a lot of it; he was so proud of making a Vietnamese meal." Tony paused. "If he doesn't get a liver transplant soon, he may die."

On the bus ride home, Tony searched for more information on his phone and discovered that Raveena and Yan's symptoms were caused by a compound called *alpha-amanitin.* This complex toxin stops the expression of genes by blocking RNA polymerase, resulting in extensive and frequently fatal damage to liver and kidney tissue. (See **Figure 12.1.**)

In this chapter, we explore one of life's few universal truths: *Every protein is assembled on ribosomes according to instructions dictated by genes coded in genetic material.* We will trace the basic process that produces proteins in cells of all organisms, beginning with the instructions encoded in DNA and leading through RNA to the sequence of amino acids in a protein. Many enzymes and other proteins are players as well as products in this story, as are several kinds of RNA and the cell's protein-making machines, the ribosomes. You will come to understand why blocking RNA polymerase by amanitin has such devastating effects on cells. As your understanding of the fundamental elements of all protein production grows, be sure to notice the differences in the kinds of information coded in

DNA, differences in the mechanisms in prokaryotic cells versus eukaryotes, and differences in the structure of genes that code for protein versus those that code for RNA.

# 12.1 The Connection between DNA, RNA, and Protein

Although the relationship between proteins and nucleic acids was once uncertain, it is now common knowledge that proteins are encoded by genes made of DNA. In this section, you will learn how that connection was discovered. We also present an overview of the molecular steps needed to go from gene to protein: transcription and translation.

## 12.1a Genes Specify Either Protein or RNA Products

How do we know that genes encode—that is, specify the amino acid sequence of—proteins? Two key pieces of research involving defects in metabolism illustrated this connection unequivocally. The first began in 1896 with Archibald Garrod, an English physician. He studied *alkaptonuria,* a human disease that does little harm but is detected easily by the fact that a patient's urine turns black when exposed to oxygen. Garrod and William Bateson, a geneticist, studied families of patients with the disease and concluded that it is an inherited trait. Garrod also found that people with alkaptonuria excrete a particular compound, homogentisic acid, in their urine. Garrod concluded that normal people are able to metabolize the homogentisic acid, whereas people with alkaptonuria cannot. By 1908, Garrod had concluded that the disease was an inborn error of metabolism. Garrod's work was the first to show a specific relationship between genes and metabolism.

In the second piece of research, George Beadle and Edward Tatum, working in the 1940s with the orange bread mould *Neurospora crassa,* collected data showing a direct relationship between genes and enzymes. Beadle and Tatum chose *Neurospora* for their work because it is a haploid fungus with simple nutritional needs. That is, wild-type *Neurospora*—the form of the mould found in nature—grows readily on a minimal medium (MM) consisting of a number of inorganic salts, sucrose, and a vitamin. The researchers reasoned that the fungus uses only simple chemicals in the medium to synthesize all the more complex molecules needed for growth and reproduction, including amino acids for proteins and nucleotides for DNA and RNA.

Beadle and Tatum exposed spores of wild-type *Neurospora* to X-rays that caused mutations. They found that some of the treated spores would not germinate and grow unless MM was supplemented with additional nutrients, such as amino acids or vitamins. Mutant strains that are unable to grow on MM are called *auxotrophs* (*auxo* = increased; *troph* = eater), or nutritional mutants. Beadle and Tatum hypothesized that each auxotrophic strain had a defect in a gene coding for an enzyme needed to synthesize a nutrient that now had to be added to the MM. The wild-type strain could make the nutrient for itself from raw materials in the MM, but the mutant strain could grow only if the researchers supplied the nutrient. By testing to see if each mutant strain would grow on MM supplemented with a given nutrient, Beadle and Tatum discovered which specific nutrient each mutant needed to grow and, therefore, which gene defect it had. For example, a mutant that required the addition of the amino acid arginine to grow had a defect in a gene for an enzyme involved in the synthesis of arginine. Such arginine auxotrophs are known as *arg* mutants. The assembly of arginine from raw materials is a multi-step "assembly-line" process, with a different enzyme catalyzing each step. Therefore, different *arg* mutants might have defects in different enzymes and therefore have blocks at different steps in the assembly line. (This is conceptually similar to Lederberg's work with auxotrophic bacteria, described in Chapter 8.)

Beadle and Tatum determined where in the arginine synthesis pathway each of four mutants (*argE*, *argF*, *argG*, and *argH*) was blocked. They tested whether each mutant could grow on MM or on MM supplemented with one of ornithine, citrulline, argininosuccinate (three compounds known to be involved in the synthesis of arginine), and arginine itself (**Figure 12.2**). While none of the four mutants could grow on MM because it was lacking arginine, they all grew well on MM with arginine. Each of the *arg* mutants showed a different pattern of growth on the supplemented MM (see Figure 12.2). Beadle and Tatum deduced that the biosynthesis of arginine occurred in a number of steps, with each step controlled by a gene that encoded the enzyme for the step (see Figure 12.2). For example, the *argH* mutant grows on MM with arginine but not on MM containing any of the other three compounds; this means that the mutant is blocked at the last step in the pathway that produces arginine. Similarly, the *argG* mutant grows on MM with arginine or argininosuccinate but not on MM containing any of the other supplements; this means that *argG* is blocked in the pathway before argininosuccinate is made (see Figure 12.2). With similar analysis, the researchers deduced the whole pathway from precursor to arginine and showed which gene encoded the enzyme that carried out each step. In sum, Beadle and Tatum had shown the direct relationship between genes and enzymes, which they put forward as the **one gene–one enzyme hypothesis**. Their experiment was a keystone in the development of molecular biology. As a result of their work, they were awarded a Nobel Prize in 1958.

It is important to understand that protein structure and function are now known to be more complex than suggested by the work of Beadle and Tatum. Many proteins consist of more than one subunit. Each of these subunits is a separate molecule, called a *polypeptide*, that is coded by a separate gene. Polypeptides can assemble to create a functional cluster of molecules called a *protein*. For instance, the protein hemoglobin is made up of four polypeptides, two each of an α-subunit and a β-subunit; this composition gives the protein its functional property of transporting oxygen rather than catalyzing a chemical reaction. Two different genes are needed to encode the hemoglobin protein: one for the α-polypeptide and one for the β-polypeptide. Beadle and Tatum's hypothesis was therefore later restated as the **one gene–one polypeptide hypothesis**. It is important to keep the distinction between protein, the functional collection of polypeptides (quaternary structure), and the polypeptide, the molecule encoded by a gene (tertiary structure), clear in your mind as we discuss transcription and translation in the rest of this chapter. *The Purple Pages* elaborate on these levels of structure.

## 12.1b The Pathway from Gene to Polypeptide Involves Transcription and Translation

The pathway from gene to polypeptide has two major steps, transcription and translation. **Transcription** is the mechanism by which the information encoded in DNA is made into a complementary RNA copy. It is called *transcription* because the information in one nucleic acid type is transferred to another nucleic acid type. **Translation** is the use of the information encoded in the RNA to assemble amino acids into a polypeptide. It is called *translation* because the information in a nucleic acid, in the form of nucleotides, is converted into a different kind of molecule, an amino acid. In 1956, Francis Crick gave the name "Central Dogma" to the flow of information from DNA to RNA to protein.

In transcription, the enzyme **RNA polymerase** creates an RNA sequence that is complementary to the DNA sequence of a given gene. The process follows the same basic rules of complementary base-pairing and nucleic acid chemistry that we first encountered in DNA replication (see Chapter 11). For each of the several thousand genes that will be expressed in a given cell, one DNA strand or the other is the **template strand** and is read by the RNA polymerase. The RNA transcribed from a gene encoding a polypeptide is called **messenger RNA (mRNA)**. RNA polymerase is the enzyme that is blocked by amanitin as described in *Why It Matters*.

In translation, an mRNA associates with a **ribosome**, a particle on which amino acids are linked into polypeptide chains. As the ribosome moves along the mRNA, the amino acids specified by the mRNA are joined one by one to form the polypeptide encoded by the gene.

The processes of transcription and translation are similar in prokaryotic and eukaryotic cells (**Figure 12.3**). One key difference is that, whereas prokaryotic cells can transcribe and translate a given gene simultaneously, eukaryotic cells transcribe and process mRNA in the nucleus before exporting it to the cytoplasm for translation on ribosomes.

FIGURE 12.2 **Experimental Research**

## The Gene–Enzyme Relationship

**Question:** What is the relationship between genes and enzymes?

**Experiment:** Adrian Srb and Norman Horowitz studied three *arg* auxotrophic mutants of *Neurospora crassa*. The mutants had been isolated because they did not grow on MM (minimal medium), but they did grow on MM with arginine. The researchers determined how each mutant grew in MM with and without ornithine and citrulline intermediates involved in the arginine biosynthesis pathway in other organisms.

**Results:**

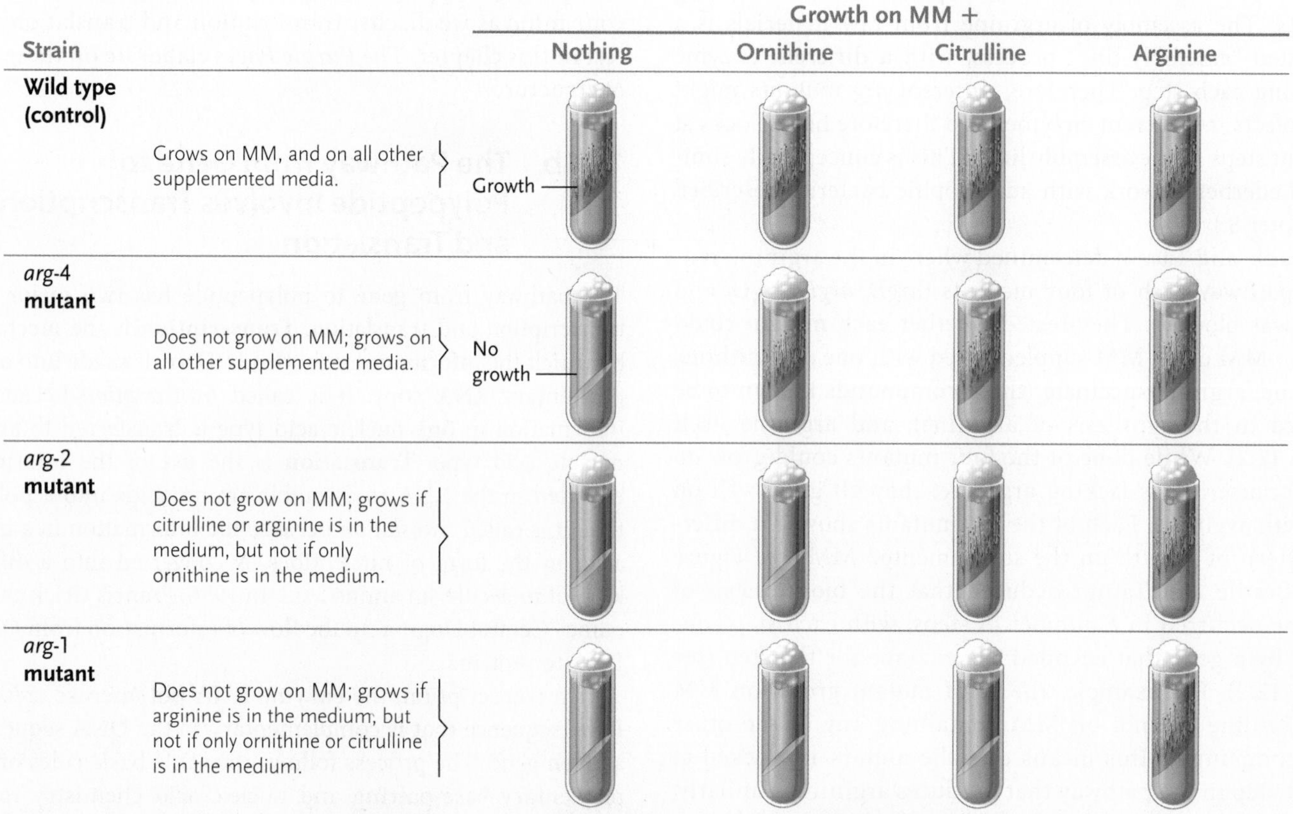

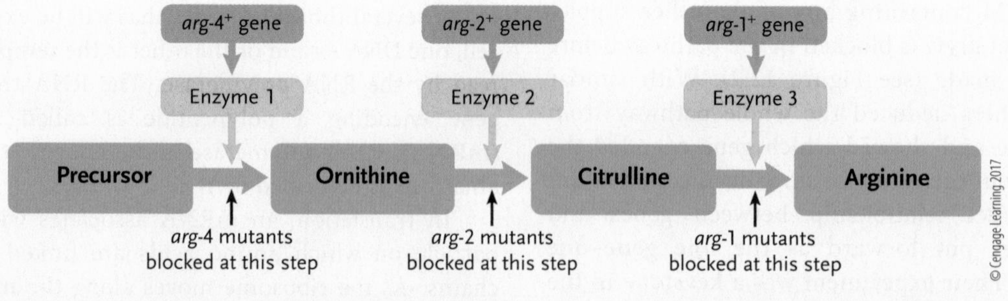

|  | Growth on MM + | | | |
|---|---|---|---|---|
| **Strain** | Nothing | Ornithine | Citrulline | Arginine |
| **Wild type (control)** <br> Grows on MM, and on all other supplemented media. | Growth | Growth | Growth | Growth |
| *arg*-4 **mutant** <br> Does not grow on MM; grows on all other supplemented media. | No growth | Growth | Growth | Growth |
| *arg*-2 **mutant** <br> Does not grow on MM; grows if citrulline or arginine is in the medium, but not if only ornithine is in the medium. | No growth | No growth | Growth | Growth |
| *arg*-1 **mutant** <br> Does not grow on MM; grows if arginine is in the medium; but not if only ornithine or citrulline is in the medium. | No growth | No growth | No growth | Growth |

*arg*-4⁺ gene → Enzyme 1
*arg*-2⁺ gene → Enzyme 2
*arg*-1⁺ gene → Enzyme 3

Precursor → Ornithine → Citrulline → Arginine

*arg*-4 mutants blocked at this step
*arg*-2 mutants blocked at this step
*arg*-1 mutants blocked at this step

© Cengage Learning 2017

**Conclusion:** Each of the three *arg* mutants showed a different pattern of growth on the supplemented MM. Srb and Horowitz concluded that the biosynthesis of arginine occurs in a series of steps, with each step controlled by a gene that encodes the enzyme for the step.

The logic is as follows, working from the end of the pathway back to its beginning:

- The *arg*-1 mutant grows on MM with arginine, but not on MM with citrulline or ornithine; this means that the mutant is blocked at the last step in the pathway that produces arginine.

- The *arg*-2 mutant grows on MM with arginine or citrulline, but not on MM with ornithine; this means that *arg*-2 is blocked in the pathway between ornithine and citrulline.

- The *arg*-4 mutant grows on MM with arginine, citrulline, or ornithine; this means that *arg*-1 is blocked in the pathway before ornithine is made.

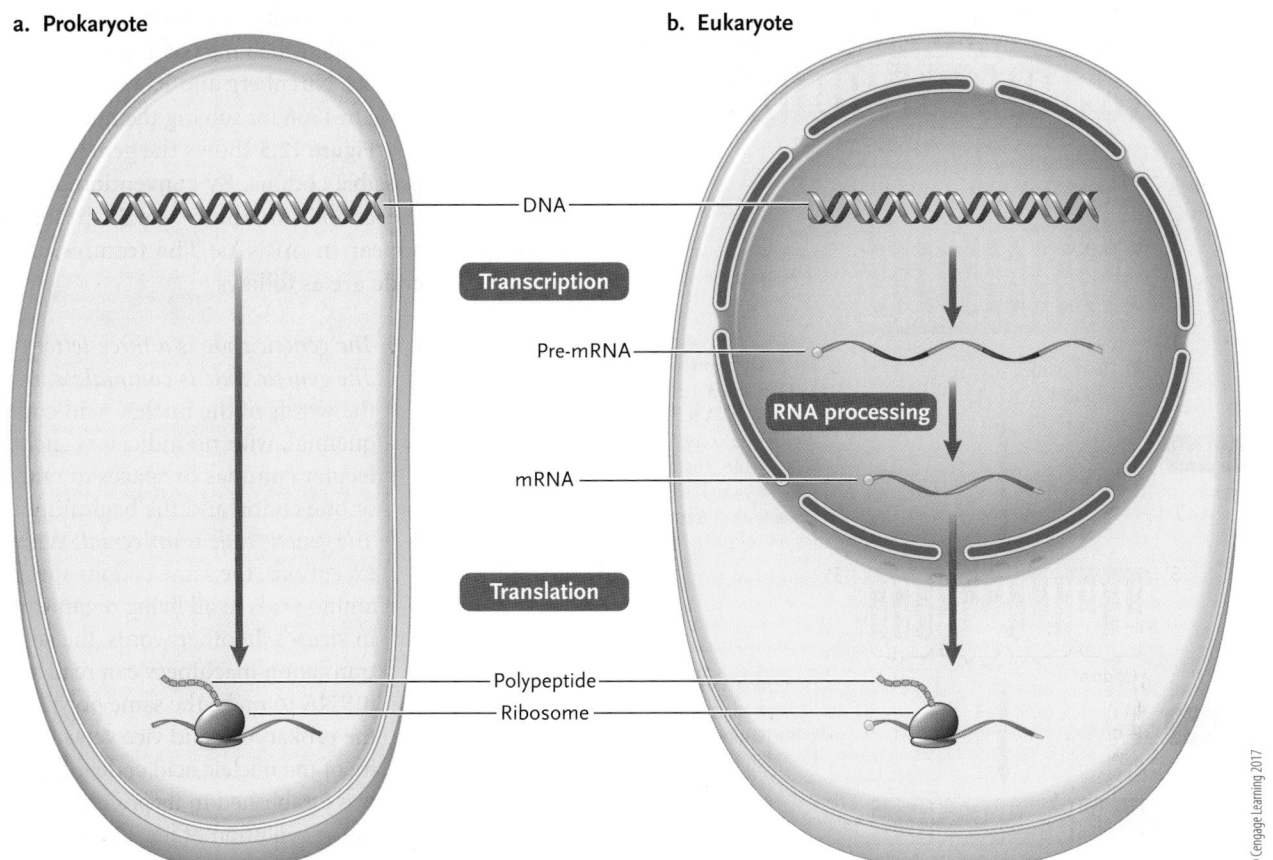

**a. Prokaryote**

**b. Eukaryote**

DNA

Transcription

Pre-mRNA

RNA processing

mRNA

Translation

Polypeptide

Ribosome

© Cengage Learning 2017

**FIGURE 12.3  Transcription and translation in** (a) **prokaryotic and** (b) **eukaryotic cells.** In prokaryotic cells, RNA polymerase synthesizes an mRNA molecule that is immediately available for translation on ribosomes. In eukaryotes, RNA polymerase synthesizes a precursor-mRNA (pre-mRNA molecule) containing extra segments that are removed by RNA processing to produce a translatable mRNA. That mRNA exits the nucleus through a nuclear pore and is translated on ribosomes in the cytoplasm. Note that only a small segment of DNA is shown. In prokaryotic cells the chromosome is circular.

## 12.1c  The Genetic Code Is Written in Three-Letter Words Using a Four-Letter Alphabet

Conceptually, the transcription of DNA into RNA is straightforward. The DNA "alphabet" consists of the four letters A, T, G, and C, representing the four DNA nucleotide bases, adenine, thymine, guanine, and cytosine, and the RNA alphabet consists of the four letters A, U, G, and C, representing the four RNA bases, adenine, uracil, guanine, and cytosine. In other words, both nucleic acids share three of the four bases but differ in the other one: T in DNA is equivalent to U in RNA. But whereas there are 4 RNA bases, there are 20 amino acids. How is nucleotide information in an mRNA translated into the amino acid sequence of a polypeptide?

**BREAKING THE GENETIC CODE** The nucleotide information that specifies the amino acid sequence of a polypeptide is called the **genetic code**. Scientists hypothesized that the 4 bases in an mRNA (A, U, G, C) would have to be used in combinations of at least 3 to provide the capacity to code for 20 amino acids. One- and 2-letter words were eliminated because if the code used 1-letter words, only 4 different amino acids could be specified (i.e., $4^1$); if 2-letter words were used, only 16 different

amino acids could be specified (i.e., $4^2$). But if the code used 3-letter words, 64 different amino acids could be specified (i.e., $4^3$), more than enough to specify 20 amino acids. We know now that the genetic code is indeed a three-letter code; each three-letter word (triplet) is called a **codon. Figure 12.4** illustrates the relationship among a gene, codons in an mRNA, and the amino acid sequence of a polypeptide. Genetic information in DNA is first transcribed into complementary three-letter RNA codons (the RNA complement to adenine (A) in the template strand is uracil (U) instead of thymine (T)).

▶ **CONCEPT FIX**  Because nucleic acids can be extended only by adding nucleotides to the 3′ end, and because nucleic acids pair up in opposite directions (antiparallel), the template strand for a given gene is always *read* from 3′ to 5′. For gene *a* in Figure 12.4, the bottom strand is the template and is therefore read left to right. However, the template for gene *b* might be the top strand; RNA polymerase would then have to be read right to left. ⬡

How do the codons correspond to the amino acids? Marshall Nirenberg and Philip Leder of the National Institutes of Health (NIH) in the United States established the identity of most of the codons in 1964. These researchers found that short artificial mRNAs of codon length—three nucleotides—could

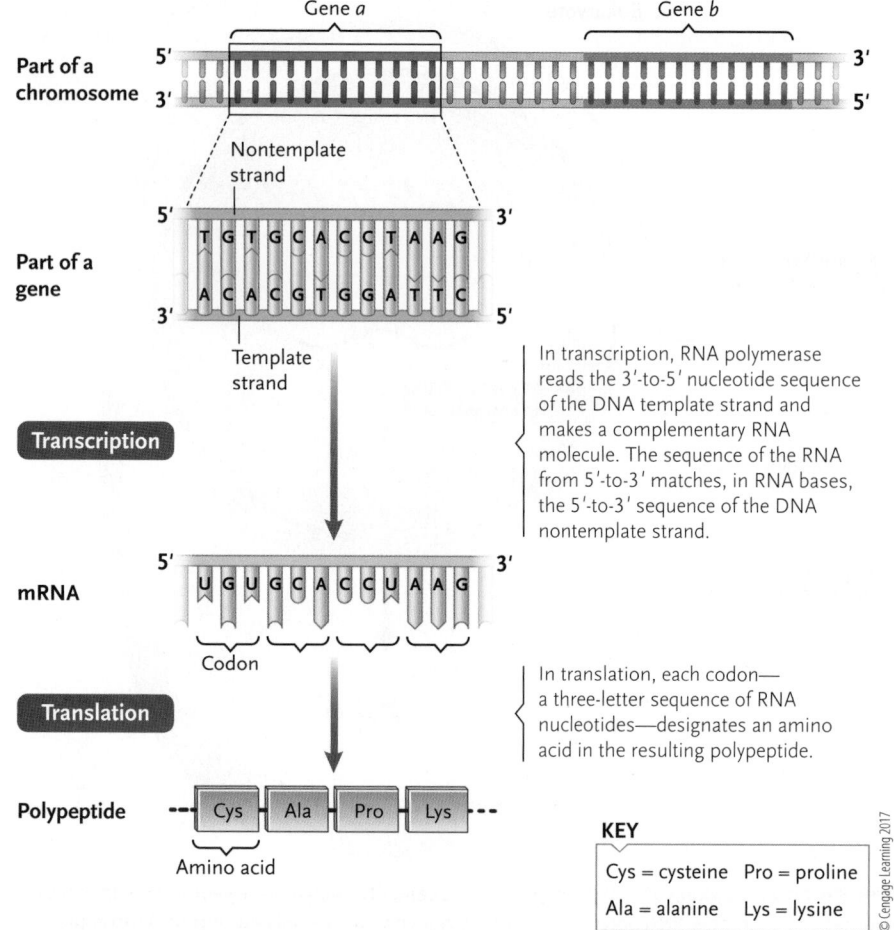

In transcription, RNA polymerase reads the 3′-to-5′ nucleotide sequence of the DNA template strand and makes a complementary RNA molecule. The sequence of the RNA from 5′-to-3′ matches, in RNA bases, the 5′-to-3′ sequence of the DNA nontemplate strand.

In translation, each codon—a three-letter sequence of RNA nucleotides—designates an amino acid in the resulting polypeptide.

**KEY**

Cys = cysteine   Pro = proline

Ala = alanine   Lys = lysine

© Cengage Learning 2017

**FIGURE 12.4 Relationship between a gene, codons in an mRNA, and the amino acid sequence of a polypeptide**

bind to ribosomes in a test tube and cause a single transfer RNA (tRNA), with its linked amino acid, to bind to the ribosome. (As we will discuss in Section 12.4, tRNAs are a special class of RNA molecules that bring amino acids to the ribosome for assembly into the polypeptide chain.) Nirenberg and Leder then made 64 of the short mRNAs, each consisting of a different single codon. They added the mRNAs, one at a time, to a mixture in a test tube containing ribosomes and all the different tRNAs, each linked to its own amino acid. The idea was that, from the mixture of tRNAs, each single-codon mRNA would link to the tRNA carrying the amino acid corresponding to the codon. The experiment worked for 50 of the 64 codons, allowing those codons to be assigned to amino acids definitively.

Another approach, carried out in 1966 by H. Gobind Khorana and his co-workers, used long, artificial mRNA molecules containing only one nucleotide repeated continuously or different nucleotides in repeating patterns. Each artificial mRNA was added to ribosomes in a test tube, and the sequence of amino acids in the polypeptide chain made by the ribosomes was analyzed. For example, an artificial mRNA containing only uracil nucleotides in the sequence UUUUUU… resulted in a polypeptide containing only the amino acid phenylalanine; they deduced that UUU must be the codon for phenylalanine. Khorana's approach, combined with the results of Nirenberg and Leder's experiments, identified the coding assignments of all the codons. Nirenberg and Khorana received a Nobel Prize in 1968 for solving the nucleic acid code.

**Figure 12.5** shows the genetic code of the 64 possible codons. By convention, scientists write the codons in the 5′ → 3′ direction, as they appear in mRNAs. The features of the genetic code are as follows:

1. *The genetic code is a three-letter code.*
2. *The genetic code is **commaless**,* meaning that the words of the nucleic acid code are sequential, with no indicators such as molecular commas or spaces to mark the end of one codon and the beginning of the next.
3. *The genetic code is **universal**.* With a few exceptions, the same codons specify the same amino acids in all living organisms, and also in viruses. In other words, the eukaryotic translation machinery can read a prokaryotic mRNA to make the same polypeptide as in the prokaryote, and vice versa. The universality of the nucleic acid code indicates that it was established in its present form very early in the evolution of life, and has remained virtually unchanged since then. Minor exceptions to the universality of the genetic code have been found in a few organisms, including a yeast, some protists, a prokaryote, and in the genetic systems of mitochondria and chloroplasts.
4. *The genetic code is degenerate.* Only two amino acids, methionine and tryptophan, are specified by a single codon. All the rest are each represented by more than one codon, some by as many as six, a feature known as **degeneracy** (also called *redundancy*). For example, UGU and UGC both specify cysteine, and CCU, CCC, CCA, and CCG all specify proline. There are also particular patterns in the degeneracy. For instance, when the first two letters in a codon are identical and the third letter is U or C, the codon always codes for the same amino acid. For example, UUU and UUC code for phenylalanine, and the cysteine and proline codons mentioned above. Also, when the first two letters in a codon are identical and the third letter is A or G, the codon often codes for the same amino acid. For example, CAA and CAG code for glutamine, and the proline codons mentioned above.
5. *The genetic code has start and stop signals.* Of the 64 codons, 61 specify amino acids. These are known as **sense codons**. One sense codon, AUG, specifying the amino acid methionine, is the first codon read in an mRNA in translation in both prokaryotes and eukaryotes. In that position, AUG is called a **start codon** or **initiator codon**. The three codons that do not specify amino acids—UAA, UAG, and UGA—are **stop codons** (also called **nonsense codons** and **termination codons**) that act as "periods" indicating the end of a

## Second base of codon

**FIGURE 12.5 The genetic code, written in the form in which the codons appear in mRNA.** The AUG initiator codon, which codes for methionine, is shown in green; the three terminator codons are boxed in red. The key shows both the three-letter and one-letter abbreviations for each amino acid.

**KEY**

| | |
|---|---|
| Ala (A) | = alanine |
| Arg (R) | = arginine |
| Asn (N) | = asparagine |
| Asp (D) | = aspartic acid |
| Cys (C) | = cysteine |
| Gln (Q) | = glutamine |
| Glu (E) | = glutamic acid |
| Gly (G) | = glycine |
| His (H) | = histidine |
| Ile (I) | = isoleucine |
| Leu (L) | = leucine |
| Lys (K) | = lysine |
| Met (M) | = methionine |
| Phe (F) | = phenylalanine |
| Pro (P) | = proline |
| Ser (S) | = serine |
| Thr (T) | = threonine |
| Trp (W) | = tryptophan |
| Tyr (Y) | = tyrosine |
| Val (V) | = valine |

© Cengage Learning 2017

polypeptide-encoding "sentence." When a ribosome reaches one of the stop codons, polypeptide synthesis stops and the new polypeptide chain is released from the ribosome.

The genetic code can be read correctly only by starting at the right place—at the first base of the first three-letter codon at the beginning of a coded message—and reading three nucleotides at a time from this beginning codon. In other words, for each mRNA, there is only one correct **reading frame**, the linear sequence of codons in mRNA that specify amino acids during translation, beginning at a particular start codon. By analogy, if you read the message SADMOMHASMOPCUT-OFFBOYTOT three letters at a time, starting with the first letter of the first "codon," you would find that a mother reluctantly had her small child's hair cut. However, if you start incorrectly at the second letter of the first codon, you read the gibberish message ADM OMH ASM OPC UTO FFB OYT OT.

### STUDY BREAK QUESTIONS

1. On the basis of their work with auxotrophic mutants of the fungus *Neurospora crassa*, Beadle and Tatum proposed the one gene–one enzyme hypothesis. Why was this hypothesis updated subsequently to the one gene–one polypeptide hypothesis?
2. Why is the sequence of bases in the mRNA different from that in the DNA of a given gene?

## 12.2 Transcription: DNA-Directed RNA Synthesis

Transcription is the process by which information coded in sequential DNA bases is transferred to a complementary RNA strand. Although certain aspects of this mechanism (**Figure 12.6**) are similar to those of DNA replication (see Figure 12.15), it is important for you to understand how these processes are different. In transcription,

- the machinery is used for making an RNA transcript of a gene to be used in gene expression, not for cell division as in DNA replication;
- for a given gene, *only one of the two DNA nucleotide strands acts as a template* for synthesis of a complementary copy, instead of both, as in replication;
- only a relatively small part of a DNA molecule—the sequence encoding a single gene—serves as a template, rather than all of both strands, as in DNA replication;
- RNA polymerases catalyze the assembly of nucleotides into an RNA strand, rather than the DNA polymerases that catalyze replication;
- the RNA molecules resulting from transcription are single polynucleotide chains, not double ones, as in DNA replication;
- wherever adenine appears in the DNA template chain, a uracil is matched to it in the RNA transcript instead of thymine, as in DNA replication.

Although the mechanism of transcription is similar in prokaryotic cells and eukaryotes, watch for the important differences pointed out in this section.

### 12.2a Transcription Proceeds in Three Steps

Figure 12.6 illustrates the general structure of a eukaryotic protein-coding gene and shows how it is transcribed. The gene consists of two main parts, a **promoter**, which is a control sequence for transcription, and a **transcription unit**, the section of the gene that is copied into an RNA molecule.

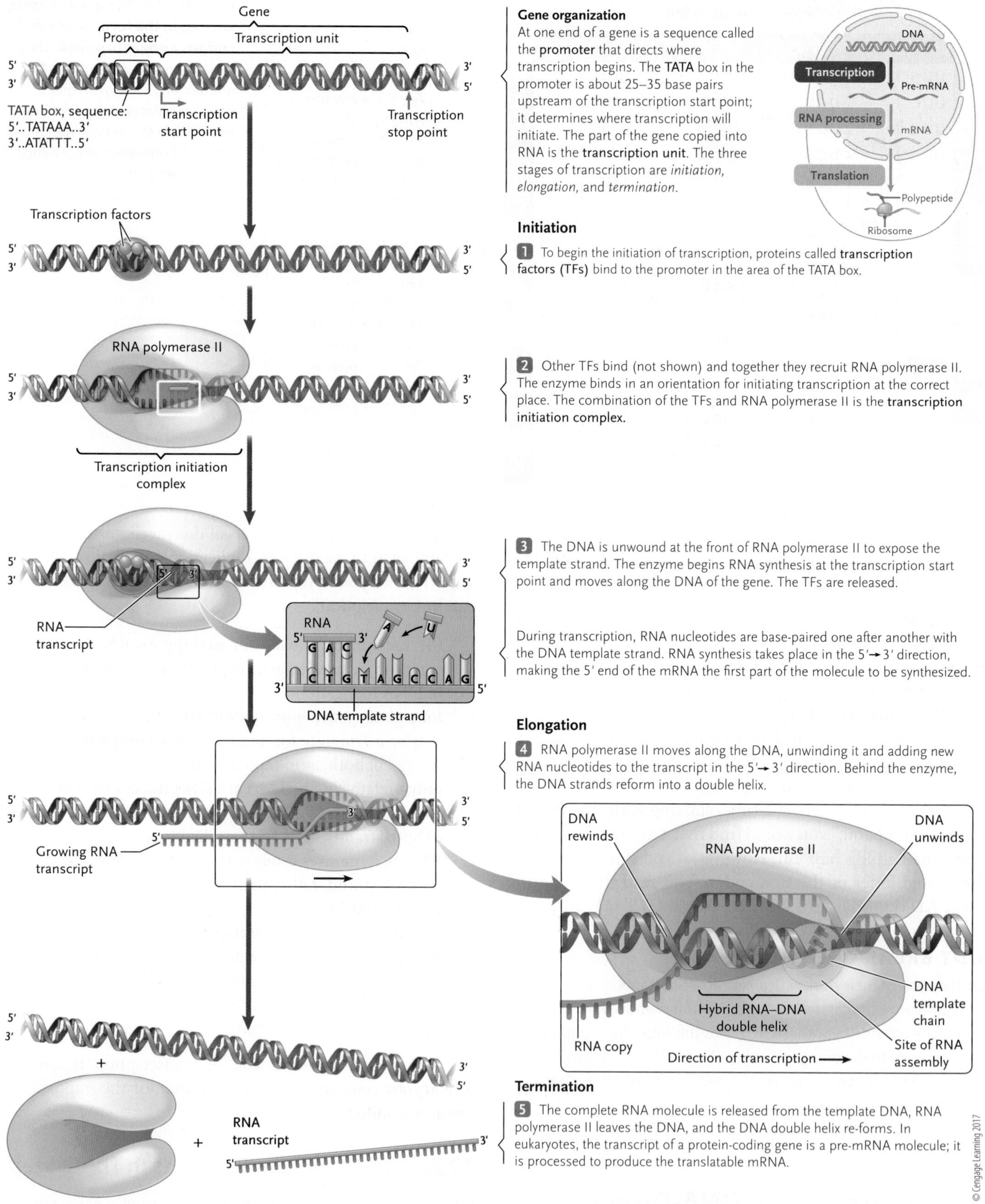

**Gene organization**

At one end of a gene is a sequence called the **promoter** that directs where transcription begins. The **TATA** box in the promoter is about 25–35 base pairs upstream of the transcription start point; it determines where transcription will initiate. The part of the gene copied into RNA is the **transcription unit**. The three stages of transcription are *initiation*, *elongation*, and *termination*.

**Initiation**

**1** To begin the initiation of transcription, proteins called **transcription factors (TFs)** bind to the promoter in the area of the TATA box.

**2** Other TFs bind (not shown) and together they recruit RNA polymerase II. The enzyme binds in an orientation for initiating transcription at the correct place. The combination of the TFs and RNA polymerase II is the **transcription initiation complex**.

**3** The DNA is unwound at the front of RNA polymerase II to expose the template strand. The enzyme begins RNA synthesis at the transcription start point and moves along the DNA of the gene. The TFs are released.

During transcription, RNA nucleotides are base-paired one after another with the DNA template strand. RNA synthesis takes place in the 5′→3′ direction, making the 5′ end of the mRNA the first part of the molecule to be synthesized.

**Elongation**

**4** RNA polymerase II moves along the DNA, unwinding it and adding new RNA nucleotides to the transcript in the 5′→3′ direction. Behind the enzyme, the DNA strands reform into a double helix.

**Termination**

**5** The complete RNA molecule is released from the template DNA, RNA polymerase II leaves the DNA, and the DNA double helix re-forms. In eukaryotes, the transcript of a protein-coding gene is a pre-mRNA molecule; it is processed to produce the translatable mRNA.

© Cengage Learning 2017

**FIGURE 12.6  Transcription of a eukaryotic protein-coding gene.** Transcription has three stages: initiation, elongation, and termination. RNA polymerase moves along the gene, separating the two DNA strands to allow RNA synthesis in the 5′ → 3′ direction using the 3′ → 5′ DNA strand as template.

Transcription takes place in three steps: (1) initiation, in which the molecular machinery that carries out transcription assembles at the promoter and begins synthesizing an RNA copy of the gene; (2) elongation, in which the RNA polymerase moves along the gene extending the RNA chain; and (3) termination, in which transcription ends and the RNA molecule—the transcript—and the RNA polymerase are released from the DNA template. Roger Kornberg of Stanford University in California received a Nobel Prize in 2006 for describing the molecular structure of the eukaryotic transcription apparatus and how it acts in transcription.

Similarities and differences in transcription of eukaryotic and bacterial protein-coding genes are as follows:

- Gene organization is the same, although the specific sequences in the promoter where the transcription apparatus assembles differ.
- In eukaryotes, RNA polymerase II, the enzyme that transcribes protein-coding genes, cannot bind directly to DNA; it is recruited to the promoter after proteins called **transcription factors** have bound. In bacteria, RNA polymerase binds directly to DNA; it is directed to the promoter by a protein factor that is then released once transcription begins. Binding to a promoter region automatically orients the RNA polymerase in the proper direction on the DNA. When the region unwinds, the polymerase reads whichever strand is running 3′ to 5′. This is the template strand.
- Elongation is essentially identical in the two types of organisms.
- In prokaryotic cells, there are two types of specific DNA sequences, called **terminators**, that signal the end of transcription of the gene. Both types of terminator sequences act *after they are transcribed*. In the first case, the terminator sequence on the mRNA uses complementary base-pairing with itself to form a "hairpin." In the second case, a protein binds to a particular terminator sequence on the mRNA. Both of these mechanisms trigger the termination of transcription and the release of the RNA and RNA polymerase from the template. In eukaryotes, there are no equivalent "transcription terminator" sequences. Instead, the 3′ end of the mRNA is specified by a different process, which is discussed in a later section.

Once an RNA polymerase molecule has started transcription and progressed past the beginning of a gene, another molecule of RNA polymerase may start transcribing as soon as there is room at the promoter. In most genes this process continues until there are many RNA polymerase molecules spaced closely along a gene, each making an RNA transcript.

## 12.2b Transcription of Non-protein-coding Genes Occurs in a Similar Way

Non-protein-coding genes include, for example, those for tRNAs and rRNAs. In eukaryotes, RNA polymerase II

transcribes protein-coding genes, RNA polymerase III transcribes tRNA genes and the gene for one of the four rRNAs, and RNA polymerase I transcribes the genes for the three other rRNAs. The promoters for these non-protein-coding genes are different from those of protein-coding genes, being specialized for the assembly of the transcription machinery that involves the correct RNA polymerase type. In bacteria, a single type of RNA polymerase transcribes all types of genes. The promoters for bacterial non-protein-coding genes are essentially the same as those of protein-coding genes.

**CONCEPT FIX** Genes are typically drawn, and their sequence is usually written, left to right, 5′ to 3′. This reflects the direction of synthesis of mRNA. Sequences that are more toward the 5′ end are referred to as "upstream," and sequences more toward the 3′ end are "downstream." Using this logic, the promoters shown in this chapter are therefore upstream of the gene to be transcribed. ⬡

### STUDY BREAK QUESTIONS

1. If the DNA template strand has the sequence 3′-CAAATTGGCTTATTACCGGATG-5′, what is the sequence of an RNA transcribed from it?
2. What is the role of the promoter in transcription?

# 12.3 Processing of mRNAs in Eukaryotes

Although mRNAs obviously contain regions that code for protein, they also contain noncoding regions that, although not specifying an amino acid, nevertheless play key roles in the process of protein synthesis. For instance, in prokaryotic mRNAs the coding region is flanked by untranslated ends, the 5′ untranslated region (5′ UTR) and a 3′ untranslated region (3′ UTR). These same elements are present in eukaryotic mRNAs along with additional types of noncoding elements. The following section looks at the structure and function of genes, with particular focus on the synthesis of mRNA in eukaryotes.

## 12.3a Eukaryotic Protein-Coding Genes Are Transcribed into Precursor mRNAs That Are Modified in the Nucleus

A eukaryotic protein-coding gene is typically transcribed into a **precursor mRNA (pre-mRNA)** that must be processed in the nucleus to produce translatable mRNA (see Figures 12.3, **12.7**, and **12.8**). The mature mRNA exits the nucleus and is translated by ribosomes in the cytoplasm.

**MODIFICATIONS OF PRE-MRNA AND MRNA ENDS** At the 5′ end of the pre-mRNA is the 5′ guanine cap, consisting of a guanine-containing nucleotide that is reversed so that its 3′ –OH group faces the beginning rather than the end of the molecule. A capping

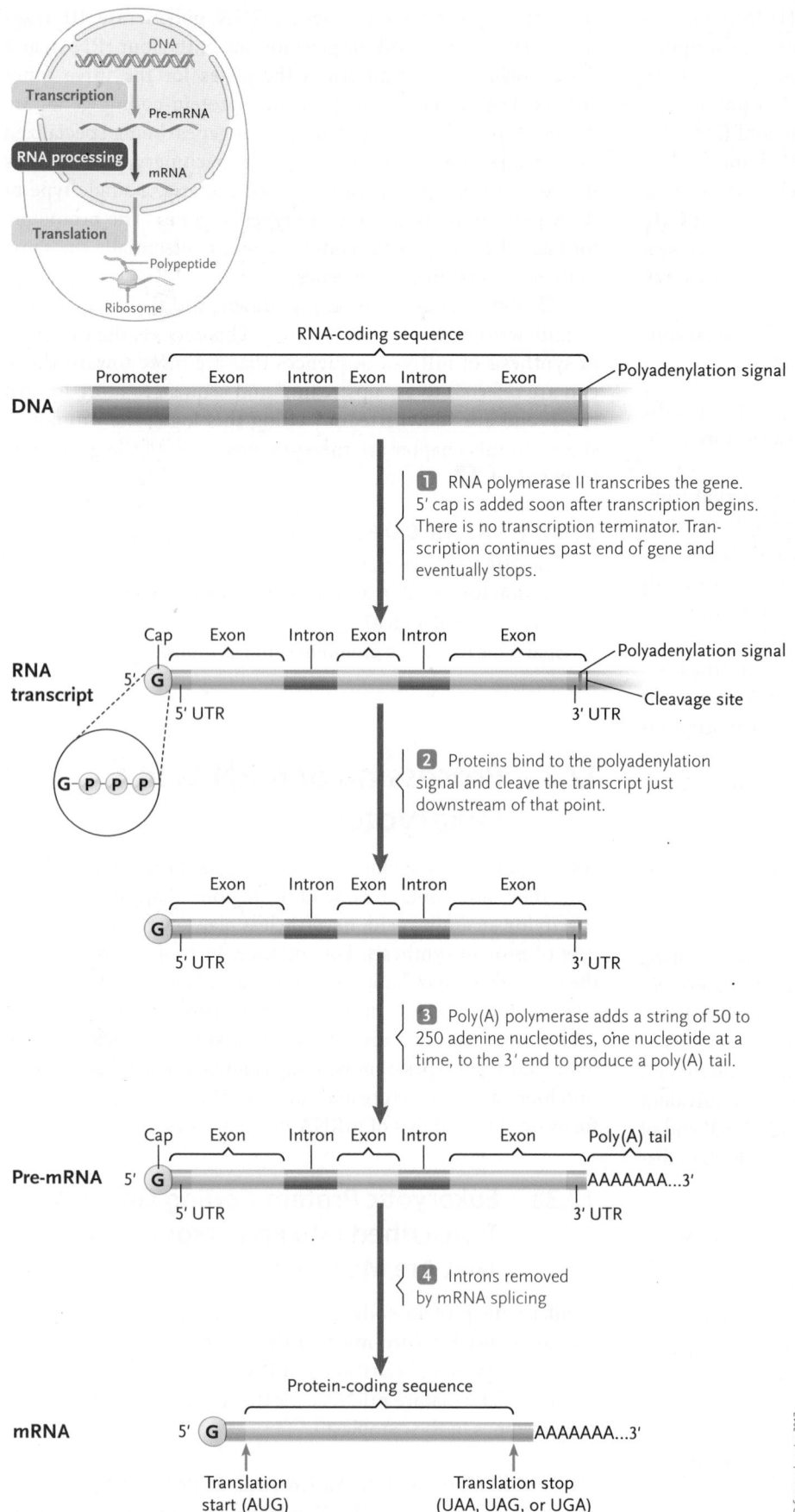

**FIGURE 12.7 Relationship between a eukaryotic protein-coding gene, the pre-mRNA transcribed from it, and the mRNA processed from the pre-mRNA**

Labels within the figure:

DNA / Transcription / Pre-mRNA / RNA processing / mRNA / Translation / Polypeptide / Ribosome

RNA-coding sequence

Promoter | Exon | Intron | Exon | Intron | Exon — Polyadenylation signal
**DNA**

**1** RNA polymerase II transcribes the gene. 5′ cap is added soon after transcription begins. There is no transcription terminator. Transcription continues past end of gene and eventually stops.

Cap | Exon | Intron | Exon | Intron | Exon — Polyadenylation signal
**RNA transcript** 5′ G — 5′ UTR — 3′ UTR — Cleavage site

G–P–P–P

**2** Proteins bind to the polyadenylation signal and cleave the transcript just downstream of that point.

Exon | Intron | Exon | Intron | Exon
G — 5′ UTR — 3′ UTR

**3** Poly(A) polymerase adds a string of 50 to 250 adenine nucleotides, one nucleotide at a time, to the 3′ end to produce a poly(A) tail.

Cap | Exon | Intron | Exon | Intron | Exon | Poly(A) tail
**Pre-mRNA** 5′ G — 5′ UTR — 3′ UTR — AAAAAAA...3′

**4** Introns removed by mRNA splicing

Protein-coding sequence
**mRNA** 5′ G — AAAAAAA...3′
Translation start (AUG) — Translation stop (UAA, UAG, or UGA)

enzyme adds this **5′ cap** to the pre-mRNA (without the need for complementary base-pairing) soon after RNA polymerase II begins transcription. The cap, which is connected to the rest of the chain by three phosphate groups, remains when pre-mRNA is processed to mRNA. The cap protects the mRNA from degradation and is the site where ribosomes attach at the start of translation.

Transcription of a eukaryotic protein-coding gene is terminated differently from that of a prokaryotic gene (Figure 12.7). The eukaryotic gene has no terminator sequence in the DNA that, after transcription into RNA, signals RNA polymerase to stop transcribing. Instead, near the 3′ end of the gene is a DNA sequence that is transcribed into the pre-mRNA. Proteins bind to this *polyadenylation signal* in the RNA and cleave it just downstream. This signals the RNA polymerase to stop transcription. Then the enzyme poly(A) polymerase adds a chain of 50–250 adenine nucleotides, one nucleotide at a time, to the newly created 3′ end of the pre-mRNA.

**CONCEPT FIX** No complementary base-pairing with a template is needed for poly(A) synthesis on mRNA. There is no "poly(T)" sequence in the DNA corresponding to the poly(A) sequence in the pre-mRNA.

The string of adenine nucleotides, called the **poly(A) tail**, enables the mRNA produced from the pre-mRNA to be translated efficiently, and protects it from attack by RNA-digesting enzymes in the cytoplasm.

**SEQUENCES INTERRUPTING THE PROTEIN-CODING SEQUENCE** The transcription unit of a protein-coding gene—the RNA-coding sequence—also contains non-protein-coding *intervening* sequences called **introns** that interrupt the protein-coding sequence (shown in Figure 12.8). The introns are transcribed into pre-mRNAs but are removed from pre-mRNAs during processing in the nucleus. The amino acid–coding sequences that are retained in finished mRNAs are *expressed* and therefore called **exons.** The mechanisms by which introns originated in genes remain a mystery.

© Cengage Learning 2017

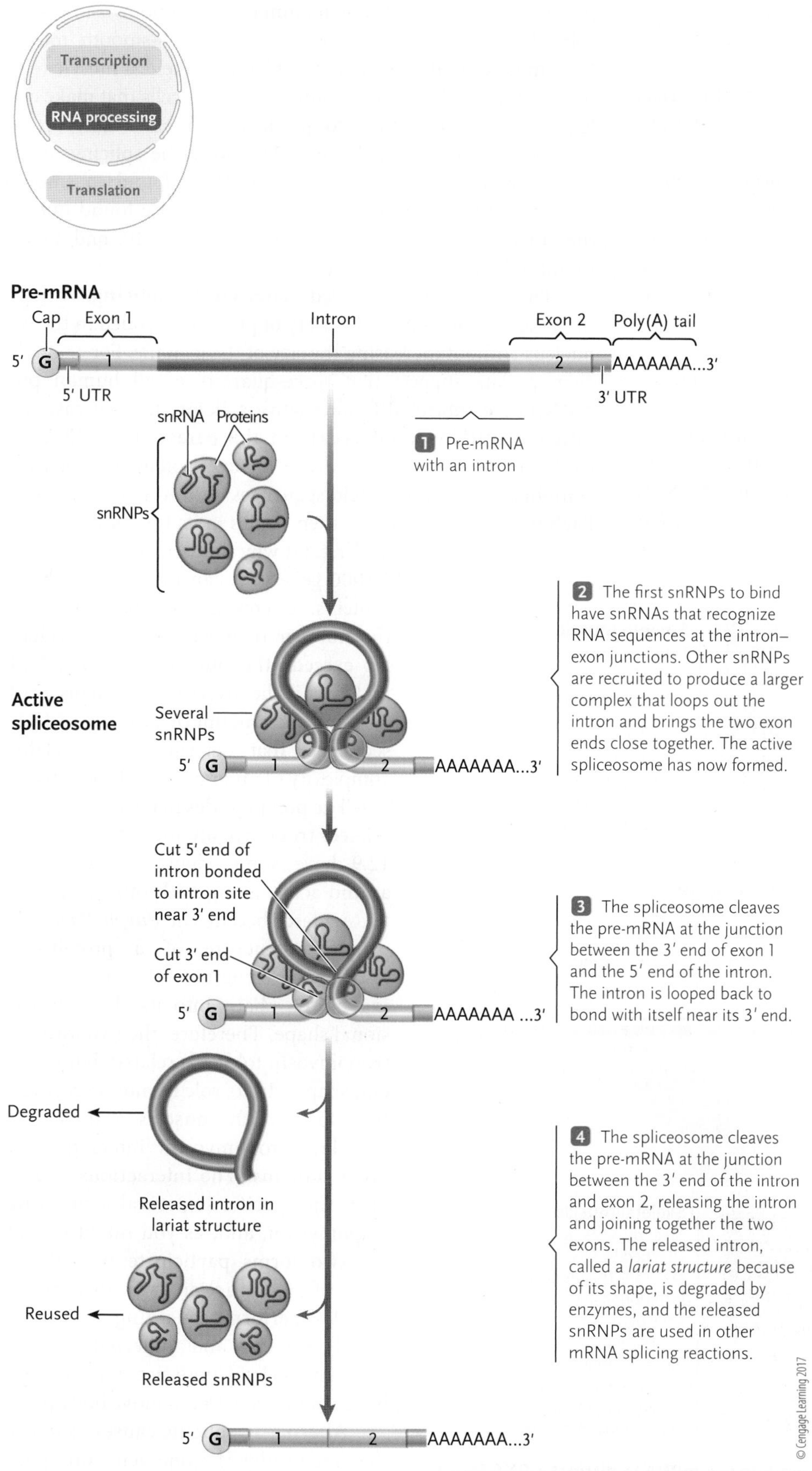

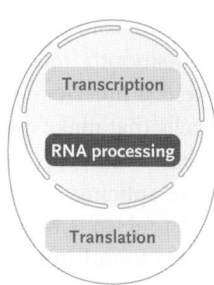

## Pre-mRNA

Cap  Exon 1                          Intron                     Exon 2   Poly(A) tail

5′ **G** | 1 |                                              | 2 | AAAAAAA...3′

5′ UTR                                                              3′ UTR

snRNA  Proteins

snRNPs

**1** Pre-mRNA
with an intron

**Active spliceosome**

Several — snRNPs

5′ **G** 1 2 AAAAAAA...3′

**2** The first snRNPs to bind have snRNAs that recognize RNA sequences at the intron–exon junctions. Other snRNPs are recruited to produce a larger complex that loops out the intron and brings the two exon ends close together. The active spliceosome has now formed.

Cut 5′ end of intron bonded to intron site near 3′ end

Cut 3′ end of exon 1

5′ **G** 1 2 AAAAAAA ...3′

**3** The spliceosome cleaves the pre-mRNA at the junction between the 3′ end of exon 1 and the 5′ end of the intron. The intron is looped back to bond with itself near its 3′ end.

Degraded ←

Released intron in lariat structure

Reused ←

Released snRNPs

**4** The spliceosome cleaves the pre-mRNA at the junction between the 3′ end of the intron and exon 2, releasing the intron and joining together the two exons. The released intron, called a *lariat structure* because of its shape, is degraded by enzymes, and the released snRNPs are used in other mRNA splicing reactions.

5′ **G** 1 2 AAAAAAA...3′

© Cengage Learning 2017

**FIGURE 12.8  mRNA splicing: the removal from pre-mRNA of introns and the joining of exons in the spliceosome**

Introns were discovered by several methods, including direct comparisons between the nucleotide sequences of mature mRNAs and either pre-mRNAs or the genes encoding them. Although many eukaryotic genes do not contain introns, most have at least one, and some contain more than 60. In humans, introns are, on average, 6 times the length of exons. The discoverers of introns, Richard Roberts and Phillip Sharp, received a Nobel Prize in 1993 for their findings.

## 12.3b Introns Are Removed during Pre-mRNA Processing to Produce Translatable mRNA

A process called **mRNA splicing**, which occurs in the nucleus, removes introns from pre-mRNAs and joins exons together. As an illustration of one type of mRNA splicing, Figure 12.8 shows the processing of a pre-mRNA with a single intron to produce a mature mRNA. mRNA splicing takes place in a **spliceosome**, a complex formed between the pre-mRNA and a handful of **small ribonucleoprotein particles**. A ribonucleoprotein particle is a complex of RNA and proteins. The small ribonucleoprotein particles involved in mRNA splicing are located in the nucleus; each consists of a relatively short *small nuclear RNA* (snRNA) bound to a number of proteins. The particles are therefore known as *snRNPs*—pronounced "snurps." The snRNPs bind in a particular order to an intron in the pre-mRNA and form the active spliceosome. The spliceosome cleaves the pre-mRNA to release the intron, and joins the flanking exons.

Complementary base-pairing between regions of snRNA and mRNA ensures that the cutting and splicing are so exact that not a single base of an intron is retained in the finished mRNA, nor is a single base removed from the exons. Without this precision, removing introns would change the reading frame of the coding portion of the mRNA, producing the wrong codons from the point of a mistake onward.

## 12.3c Introns Contribute to Protein Variability

Introns seem wasteful in terms of the energy and raw materials required to replicate and transcribe them and the elaborate cellular machinery required to remove them during pre-mRNA processing. Why are they present in mRNA-encoding genes? Among a number of possibilities, introns may provide a selective advantage to organisms by increasing the coding capacity of existing genes through a process called *alternative splicing* and provide an evolutionary mechanism to generate new proteins called *exon shuffling*.

**ALTERNATIVE SPLICING** The removal of introns from a given pre-mRNA is not absolute. That is, in particular tissues or sexes, or under certain environmental conditions, different regions of a given pre-mRNA may be identified as introns and removed in different combinations to produce different mature mRNAs. *Regions that are an exon in one situation may well be removed as an intron in another situation* (**Figure 12.9**). For example, the pre-mRNA transcript of the mammalian α-tropomyosin gene is spliced in various ways in different tissues—smooth muscle (e.g., muscles of the intestine and bladder), skeletal muscle (e.g., biceps, glutes), fibroblasts (connective tissue cells that make collagen), liver, and brain—to produce different forms of the α-tropomyosin protein. Figure 12.9 shows the splicing of the α-tropomyosin pre-mRNA to the mRNAs found in smooth muscle and skeletal muscle. Exons 2 and 12 are found only in the smooth muscle mRNA, whereas exons 3, 10, and 11 are found only in the skeletal muscle mRNA.

The mechanism, called **alternative splicing**, greatly increases the number and variety of proteins encoded in the cell nucleus without increasing the size of the genome. For example, current data suggest that three-quarters of all human pre-mRNAs are subjected to alternative splicing. In each case, the different mRNAs produced from the parent pre-mRNA are translated to produce a family of related proteins with various combinations of amino acid sequences derived from the exons. Each protein in the family, then, varies in its function. Alternative splicing helps us understand why humans have only about 20 000 genes but can make over 100 000 proteins. As a result of alternative splicing, the number of diverse protein products far exceeds the number of genes. Ultimately, it is the diversity of proteins available, not the amount or diversity of DNA sequence, that determines the relative complexity of an organism's functions.

The polypeptides made from the two related tropomyosin mRNAs in Figure 12.9 have some identical stretches of amino acids, along with others that differ. As described in *The Purple Pages*, the primary structure of a protein—its amino acid structure—directs the folding of the chain into its three-dimensional shape. Therefore, the two forms of tropomyosin fold into related, but different, shapes. In its role in muscle contraction in smooth muscles and skeletal muscles, tropomyosin interacts with other proteins. The interactions depend upon the specific structural form of the tropomyosin, and, as you might expect, the two forms participate in different types of muscle action; typically, smooth muscles perform squeezing actions in blood vessels and internal organs, whereas skeletal muscles pull on the bones of the skeleton to move body parts.

Alternative splicing causes us to further reconsider the one gene–one polypeptide hypothesis introduced earlier in this chapter. We must now accept the fact that, for some genes at least, one

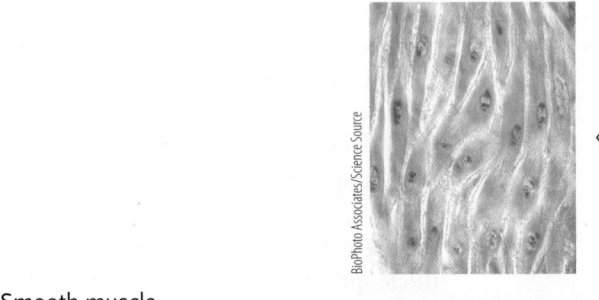

**Smooth muscle**
Found in walls of tubes and cavities of the body, including blood vessels, the stomach and intestine, the bladder, and the uterus. Contraction of smooth muscles typically produces a squeezing motion.

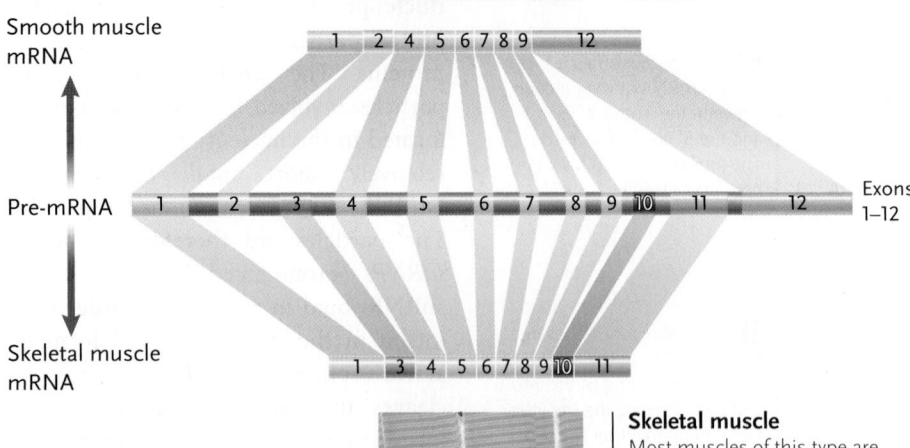

**Skeletal muscle**
Most muscles of this type are attached by tendons to the skeleton. Their function is locomotion and movement of body parts. The human body has more than 600 skeletal muscles, ranging in size from the small muscles that move the eyeballs, to the large muscles that move the legs.

**FIGURE 12.9 Alternative splicing of the α-tropomyosin pre-mRNA to distinct mRNA forms found in smooth muscle and skeletal muscle.** All the introns are removed in both mRNA splicing pathways, but exons 3, 10, and 11 are also removed to produce the smooth muscle mRNA, and exons 2 and 12 are also removed to produce the skeletal muscle mRNA.

gene may specify a number of polypeptides, each of which has a related function.

**EXON SHUFFLING** Intron–exon junctions often fall at points dividing major functional regions in encoded proteins, as they do in the genes for antibody proteins, blood hemoglobin proteins, and the peptide hormone insulin. The functional divisions may have allowed new proteins to evolve by exon shuffling, a process by which existing protein regions or domains, already selected for due to their useful functions, are mixed into novel combinations to create new proteins. Evolution of new proteins by this mechanism would produce new proteins with novel functions. Recombining stretches of polypeptides with established functions contribute to new protein activity much more quickly than by undirected changes in individual amino acids.

**GENOME-WIDE ANALYSIS HAS REVEALED UNEXPECTED DETAILS OF THE HUMAN TRANSCRIPTOME** The entire collection of transcripts made by an organism is called its **transcriptome**. Study of the transcriptome can provide new insights into how genes are structured, expressed, and regulated. Many students of biology are surprised to learn that only about 1.2% of the human genome is ever transcribed into mRNAs coding for proteins used in the function of human cells (see Chapter 15). Other sequences that are transcribed but not translated, including introns and various RNA genes (e.g., tRNA, rRNA, snRNA, etc.), account for another small percentage of the genome. This leaves the vast majority of the genome composed of regulatory sequences (e.g., promoters and enhancers described in Chapter 13), nonhuman genes such as viruses and mobile elements (Chapter 15), non-functional genes (called *pseudogenes*), repetitive sequences at centromeres and telomeres, and a considerable amount of sequence of unknown function. The term "junk DNA" has been used in the literature to describe sequences that are present in the genome but do not make a direct contribution to human cell function. Although new technologies have enabled detailed genome-wide analysis of transcription, the role of junk DNA remains uncertain.

An example of one such genome-wide analysis is research done as part of the ENCODE project. ENCODE (Encyclopedia of DNA Elements) is a worldwide consortium of research groups with the goal of examining the human genome sequence in great depth. In a research paper published in 2013, ENCODE researchers reported the most complete information to date about the human transcriptome.

With the goal of obtaining a genome-wide catalogue of human transcripts and to identify their subcellular locations, the ENCODE researchers studied the RNAs expressed in 15 different human cell lines. Two key findings were,

- *Pervasive transcription:* Combining data from the 15 cell lines, three-quarters of the genome was shown to be transcribed. However, the functional significance of such transcripts remains a matter of considerable debate. While some of the transcripts are clearly non-coding RNAs that have a role in gene regulation, others may be rarely expressed, non-functional, transcriptional "noise."

- *Variable expression of isoforms of protein-coding genes:* About three-quarters of protein-coding genes were found to be transcribed to produce different forms of their mRNAs, called **gene isoforms**. You have already learned that alternative splicing is a mechanism that produces different mRNAs for a given gene. Those mRNAs are examples of gene isoforms. Other mechanisms that produce different mRNAs from a gene include the use of different transcription start sites and the generation of different 3′ ends. Although transcription of several different isoforms of a given gene represents a large amount of potential variation in gene expression, again, the functional significance of this variable transcription is still an active research question.

**STUDY BREAK QUESTIONS**

1. What are the similarities and differences between pre-mRNAs and mRNAs?
2. What is the role of base-pairing in mRNA splicing?
3. How is it possible for an organism to produce more proteins than it has genes for?

## 12.4 Translation: mRNA-Directed Polypeptide Synthesis

Translation is the assembly of amino acids into polypeptides on ribosomes. In prokaryotic organisms, translation takes place throughout the cell, whereas in eukaryotes it occurs in the cytoplasm. (However, a few specialized genes are transcribed and translated in mitochondria or chloroplasts.)

**Figure 12.10** summarizes the translation process. In prokaryotic cells, the mRNA produced by transcription is not confined within a nucleus, and is therefore available immediately for translation. However, for eukaryotes the mRNA produced by splicing of the pre-mRNA first exits the nucleus and is then translated in the cytoplasm. In translation, the mRNA associates with a ribosome and another type of RNA, transfer RNA (tRNA), which brings amino acids to the complex to be joined, one by one, into the polypeptide chain. The sequence of amino acids in the polypeptide chain is determined by the sequence of codons in the mRNA. The mRNA is read from the 5′ end to the 3′ end; the polypeptide is assembled from the **N-terminal end** to the **C-terminal end**.

In this section, we will start by discussing the key players in the process, the tRNAs and ribosomes, and then walk through the translation process from a start codon to a stop codon.

### 12.4a tRNAs Are Small RNAs of a Highly Distinctive Structure That Bring Amino Acids to the Ribosome

Transfer RNAs (tRNAs) bring amino acids to the ribosome for addition to the polypeptide chain.

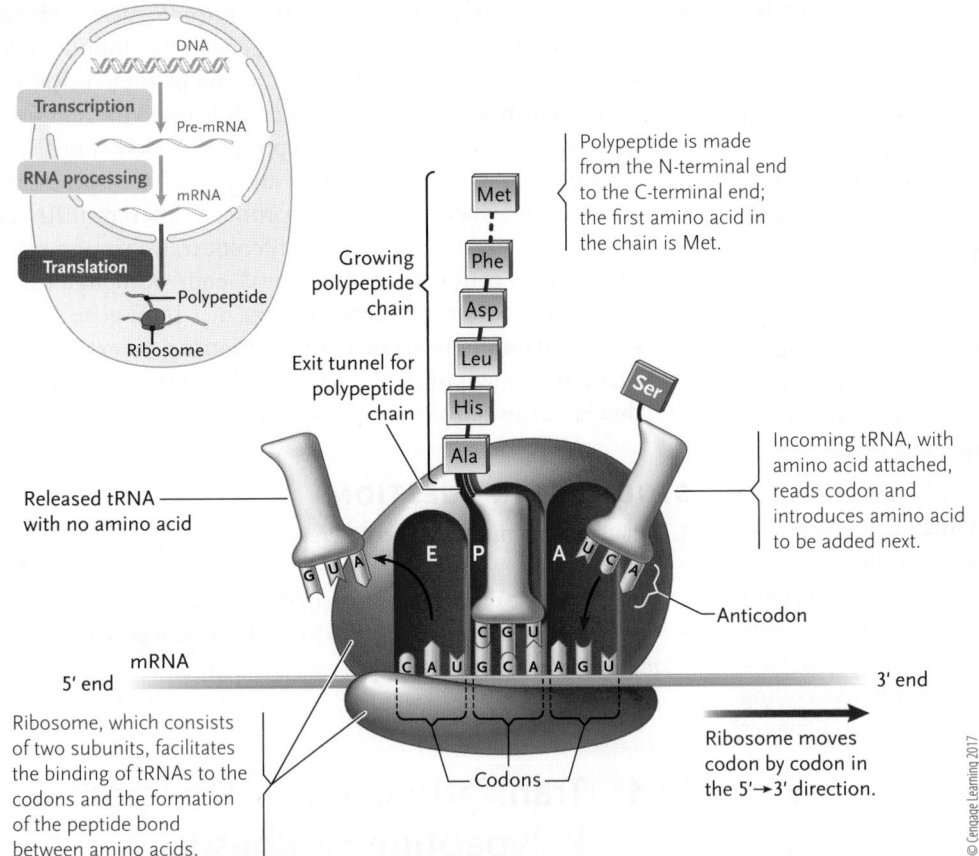

Polypeptide is made from the N-terminal end to the C-terminal end; the first amino acid in the chain is Met.

Growing polypeptide chain

Met
Phe
Asp
Leu
His
Ala

Exit tunnel for polypeptide chain

Ser

Incoming tRNA, with amino acid attached, reads codon and introduces amino acid to be added next.

Released tRNA with no amino acid

E  P  A

Anticodon

mRNA
5′ end                                                              3′ end

Ribosome, which consists of two subunits, facilitates the binding of tRNAs to the codons and the formation of the peptide bond between amino acids.

Codons

Ribosome moves codon by codon in the 5′→3′ direction.

© Cengage Learning 2017

**FIGURE 12.10  An overview of translation, in which ribosomes assemble amino acids into a polypeptide chain.** The figure shows a ribosome in the process of translation. A tRNA molecule with an amino acid bound to it is entering the ribosome on the right. The anticodon on the tRNA will pair with the codon in the mRNA. Its amino acid will then be added to the growing polypeptide that is currently attached to the tRNA in the middle of the ribosome. As it assembles a polypeptide chain, the ribosome moves from one codon to the next along the mRNA in the 5′ → 3′ direction.

**tRNA STRUCTURE** tRNAs are small RNAs, about 75–90 nucleotides long (mRNAs are typically hundreds of nucleotides long), with a highly distinctive structure that accomplishes their role in translation (**Figure 12.11**). All tRNAs can base-pair with themselves to wind into four double-helical segments, forming a cloverleaf pattern when flattened into two dimensions. At the tip of one of the double-helical segments is the **anticodon**, the three-nucleotide segment that base-pairs with a codon in mRNAs. At the other end of the cloverleaf, opposite the anticodon, is a free 3′ end of the molecule that links to the amino acid corresponding to the anticodon. For example, a tRNA that is linked to serine (Ser) pairs with the codon 5′-AGU-3′ in mRNA (see Figure 12.11). The anticodon of the tRNA that pairs with this codon is 3′-UCA-5′.

**CONCEPT FIX** The anticodon and codon pair in an antiparallel manner, as do the two strands in the DNA helix. We will therefore write anticodons in the 3′ → 5′ direction to make it easy to see how they pair with codons, which are normally written 5′ → 3′.

**a. A tRNA molecule in two dimensions (yeast alanine tRNA) with amino acid attached**

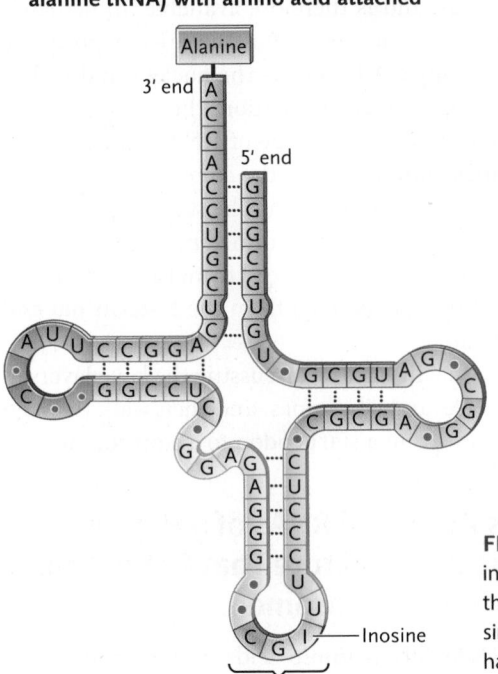

Alanine
3′ end
5′ end
Anticodon
Inosine

**b. A tRNA molecule in three dimensions**

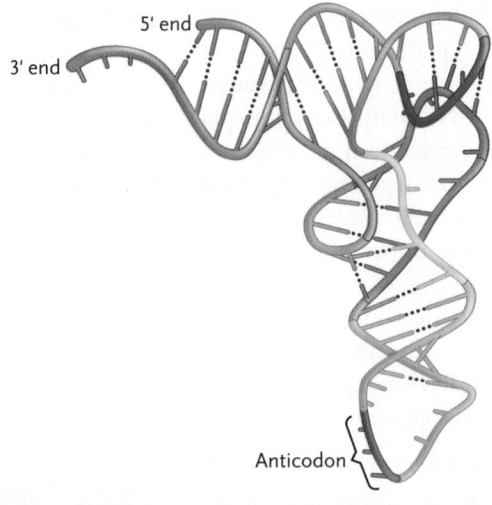

5′ end
3′ end
Anticodon

**c. How a tRNA is shown in this book**

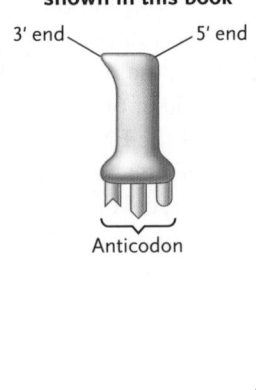

3′ end          5′ end
Anticodon

© Cengage Learning 2017

**FIGURE 12.11  tRNA structure.** In (a) the red dots show sites where bases are chemically modified into other forms; chemical modification of certain bases is typical of tRNAs. This yeast alanine tRNA has the purine inosine (I) in the anticodon, which has relatively loose base-pairing ability, allowing this single tRNA to pair with each of three alanine codons 5′-GCU-3′, 5′-GCC-3′, and 5′-GCA-3′. This tRNA also has the unusual base pair G–U. Unusual base pairs, allowed by the greater flexibility of short RNA chains, are common in tRNAs. The amino acid, in this case alanine, binds to the 3′ end of a tRNA molecule.

The tRNA cloverleaf folds into a three dimensional, L-shaped structure as shown in Figure 12.11b. This slender, bent cylinder fits into the ribosome's large subunit where it encounters an mRNA. The anticodon and the segment binding the amino acid are located at the opposite ends of the L structure.

Recall that 61 of the 64 codons of the genetic code specify an amino acid. Does this mean that 61 different tRNAs read the **sense codons**? The answer is no. Francis Crick's **wobble hypothesis** proposed that the complete set of 61 sense codons can be read by fewer than 61 distinct tRNAs because of the particular pairing properties of the bases in the anticodons. That is, the pairing of the anticodon with the first two nucleotides of the codon is always precise, but the anticodon has more flexibility in pairing with the third nucleotide of the codon. In many cases, the same tRNA's anticodon can read codons that have either U or C in the third position; for example, a tRNA carrying phenylalanine can read both codons 5′-UUU-3′ and 5′-UUC-3′. Similarly, the same tRNA's anticodon can read two codons that have A or G in the third position; for example, a tRNA carrying glutamine can pair with both 5′-CAA-3′ and 5′-CAG-3′ codons. The special purine called *inosine* in the alanine tRNA shown in Figure 12.11a allows even more extensive wobble by allowing the tRNA to pair with codons that have one of U, C, and A in the third position.

**ADDITION OF AMINO ACIDS TO THEIR CORRESPONDING TRNAS** The correct amino acid must be present on a tRNA if translation is to be accurate. The process of adding an amino acid to a tRNA is called **aminoacylation** (literally, the addition of an amino acid) or **charging** (because the process adds free energy as the amino acid–tRNA combinations are formed).

The finished product of charging, a tRNA linked to its "correct" amino acid, is called an **aminoacyl–tRNA**. A collection of different enzymes called **aminoacyl–tRNA synthetases** catalyze aminoacylation, as shown in **Figure 12.12**. This energy in the aminoacyl–tRNA eventually drives the formation of the **peptide bond** that links amino acids during translation.

With the tRNA attached to its corresponding amino acid, our attention moves to the ribosome, where each tRNA has its amino acid removed and linked onto a growing polypeptide chain.

## 12.4b Ribosomes Are rRNA–Protein Complexes That Work as Automated Protein Assembly Machines

**Ribosomes** are ribonucleoprotein particles that carry out protein synthesis by translating mRNA into chains of amino acids. Like some automated machines, such as those forming complicated metal parts by a series of machining steps, ribosomes use an information tape—an mRNA molecule—as the directions required to accomplish a task. For ribosomes, the task is to join amino acids into ordered sequences to make a polypeptide chain.

In prokaryotic cells, ribosomes carry out their assembly functions throughout the cell. In eukaryotes, ribosomes function only in the cytoplasm, either suspended freely in the cytoplasmic solution or attached to the membranes of the endoplasmic reticulum (ER), the system of membrane-bound tubular or flattened sacs in the cytoplasm. A finished ribosome is made up of two parts of dissimilar size called the *large* and *small ribosomal subunits* (**Figure 12.13**). Each subunit is made up of a combination of ribosomal RNA (rRNA) and ribosomal proteins.

**CONCEPT FIX** The endosymbiotic origin of chloroplasts and mitochondria in eukaryotic cells is reflected by the fact that these organelles still code for their own "bacterial" ribosomes that are distinct from those in the cytoplasm. ⬡

Prokaryotic and eukaryotic ribosomes are similar in structure and function. However, the differences in their molecular structure, particularly in the ribosomal proteins, give them distinct properties. For example, the antibiotics streptomycin and erythromycin are effective antibacterial agents because they inhibit bacterial, but not eukaryotic, ribosomes.

To fulfill its role in translation, the ribosome has special binding sites active in bringing together mRNA with aminoacyl–tRNAs (see Figure 12.13, and refer also to Figure 12.10). One such site is where the mRNA threads a bent path through the ribosome. The **A site** (aminoacyl site) is where the incoming aminoacyl–tRNA (carrying the next amino acid to be added to the polypeptide chain) binds to the mRNA. The **P site** (peptidyl site) is where the tRNA carrying the growing polypeptide chain is bound. The **E site** (exit site) is where an exiting tRNA binds as it leaves the ribosome.

## 12.4c Translation Initiation Brings the Ribosomal Subunits, an mRNA, and the First Aminoacyl–tRNA Together

There are three major stages of translation: *initiation, elongation,* and *termination*. During initiation, the translation components assemble on the start codon of the mRNA. In elongation, the assembled complex reads the string of codons in the mRNA one at a time while joining the specified amino acids into the polypeptide. Termination completes the translation process when the complex disassembles after the last amino acid of the polypeptide specified by the mRNA has been added to the polypeptide.

**Figure 12.14** illustrates the steps of translation initiation in eukaryotes. In bacteria, translation initiation is similar in using a special initiator Met–tRNA and GTP, but the way in which the ribosome assembles at the start codon is different than in eukaryotes. Rather than scanning from the 5′ end of the mRNA—the small ribosomal subunit—the initiator Met–tRNA and GTP bind directly to the region of the mRNA with the AUG start codon. This initiation complex is then guided by the **ribosome binding site**—a short, specific RNA sequence—just upstream of the start codon on the mRNA that base-pairs with a complementary sequence of rRNA in the small ribosomal subunit. The large ribosomal subunit then binds to the small

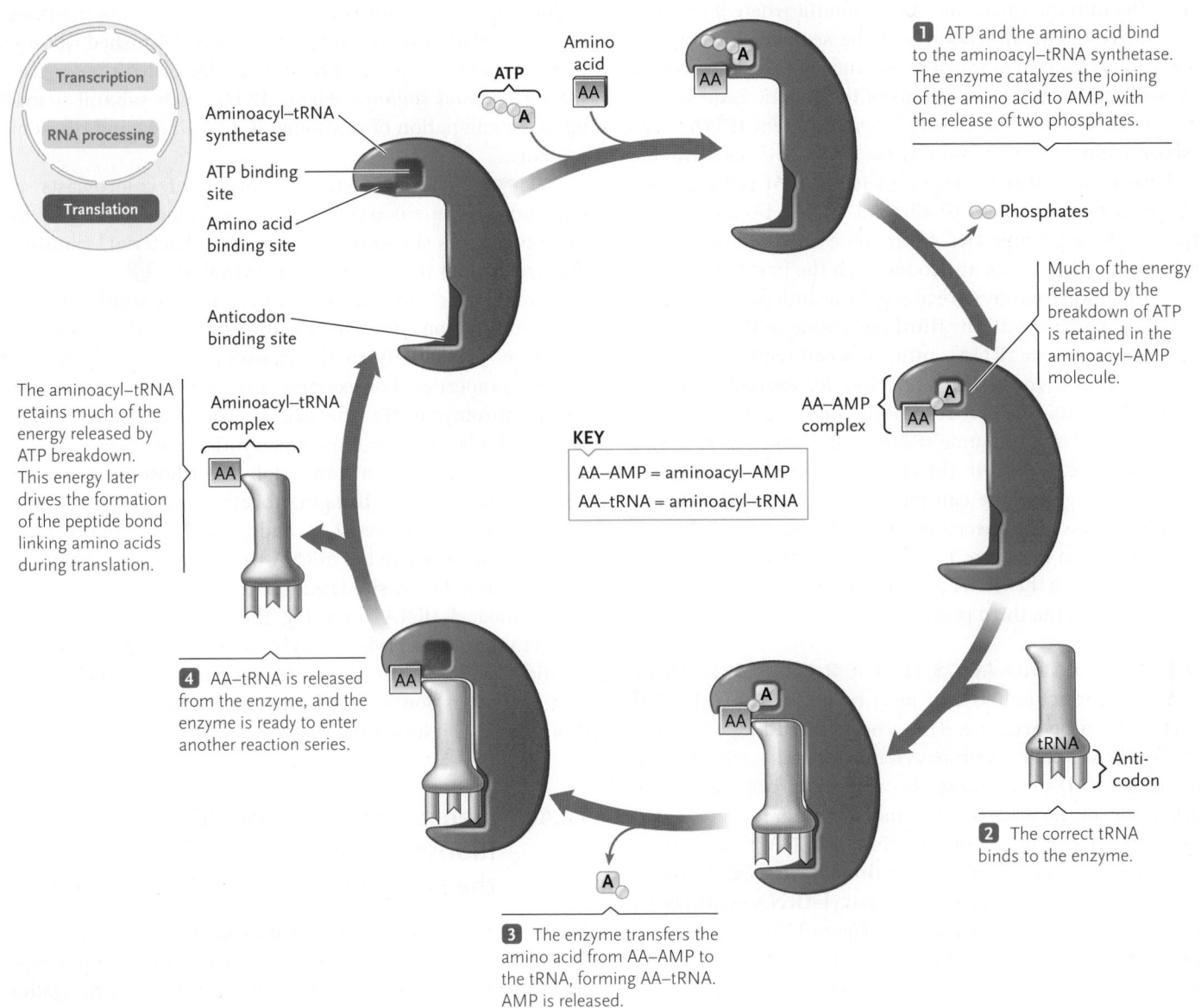

The figure contains the following labels:

- Transcription
- RNA processing
- Translation

Aminoacyl–tRNA synthetase
ATP binding site
Amino acid binding site
Anticodon binding site

ATP
Amino acid
AA

**1** ATP and the amino acid bind to the aminoacyl–tRNA synthetase. The enzyme catalyzes the joining of the amino acid to AMP, with the release of two phosphates.

Phosphates

Much of the energy released by the breakdown of ATP is retained in the aminoacyl–AMP molecule.

AA–AMP complex

**KEY**

AA–AMP = aminoacyl–AMP
AA–tRNA = aminoacyl–tRNA

The aminoacyl–tRNA retains much of the energy released by ATP breakdown. This energy later drives the formation of the peptide bond linking amino acids during translation.

Aminoacyl–tRNA complex

**4** AA–tRNA is released from the enzyme, and the enzyme is ready to enter another reaction series.

tRNA
Anti-codon

**2** The correct tRNA binds to the enzyme.

**3** The enzyme transfers the amino acid from AA–AMP to the tRNA, forming AA–tRNA. AMP is released.

© Cengage Learning 2017

**FIGURE 12.12 Aminoacylation or charging: the addition of an amino acid to a tRNA**

subunit to complete the ribosome. GTP hydrolysis then begins translation.

After the initiator tRNA pairs with the AUG initiator codon, the subsequent stages of translation simply read the codons one at a time on the mRNA. The initiator tRNA–AUG pairing thus establishes the correct **reading frame**—the series of codons for the polypeptide encoded by the mRNA. This is often referred to as the *open reading frame.*

## 12.4d Polypeptide Chains Grow during the Elongation Stage of Translation

The central reactions of translation take place in the elongation stage, which adds amino acids one at a time to a growing

polypeptide chain. The individual steps of elongation depend on the binding properties of the P, A, and E sites of the ribosome. The P site, with one exception, can bind only to a **peptidyl–tRNA**, that is, a tRNA linked to a growing polypeptide chain containing two or more amino acids. The exception is the initiator tRNA, which is recognized by the P site as a peptidyl–tRNA even though it carries only a single amino acid, methionine. The A site can bind only to an aminoacyl–tRNA. The tRNA that was previously in the P site is shifted to the E site and then leaves the ribosome.

**Figure 12.15** shows the elongation cycle of translation. The cycle begins at the point when an initiator tRNA with its attached methionine is bound to the P site, and the A site is empty (top of figure). The first step in each round of the cycle

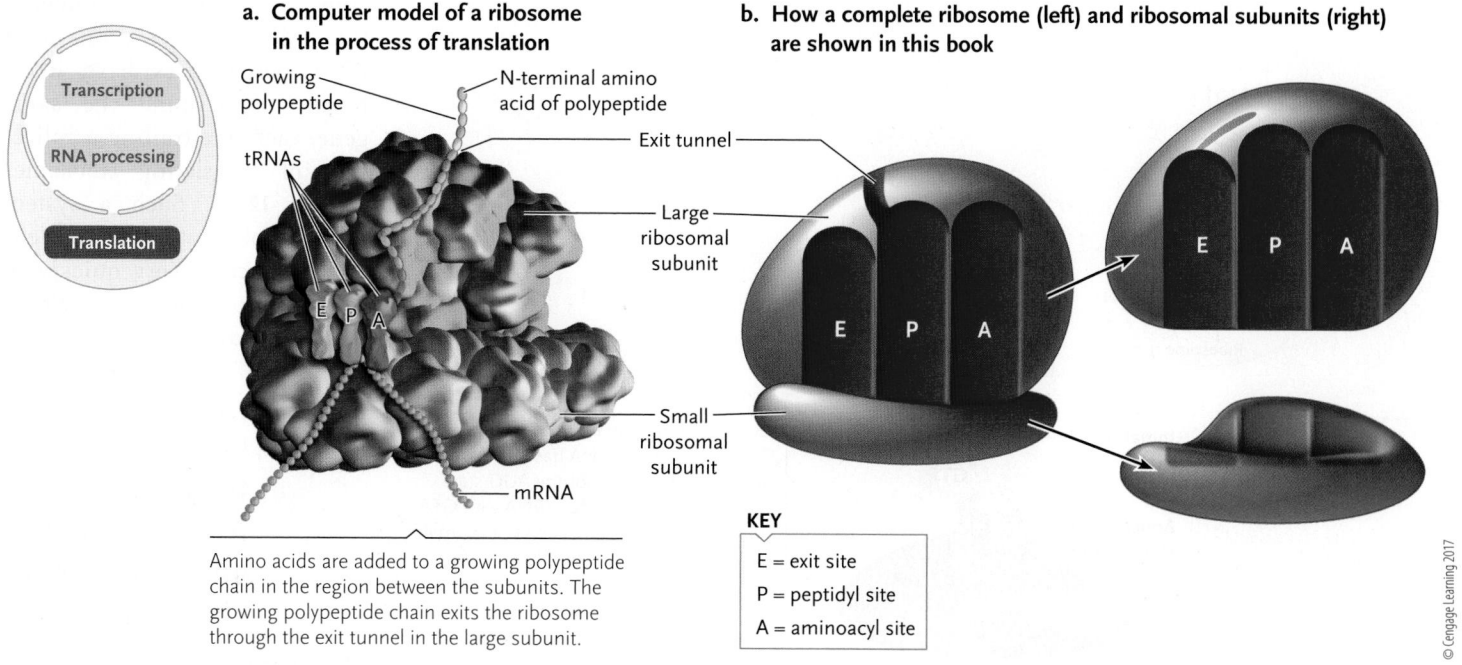

**a. Computer model of a ribosome in the process of translation**

Transcription

RNA processing

Translation

Growing polypeptide

N-terminal amino acid of polypeptide

tRNAs

Exit tunnel

Large ribosomal subunit

E P A

Small ribosomal subunit

mRNA

Amino acids are added to a growing polypeptide chain in the region between the subunits. The growing polypeptide chain exits the ribosome through the exit tunnel in the large subunit.

**b. How a complete ribosome (left) and ribosomal subunits (right) are shown in this book**

E P A

E P A

**KEY**
E = exit site
P = peptidyl site
A = aminoacyl site

© Cengage Learning 2017

**FIGURE 12.13 Ribosome structure. (a)** Computer model of a ribosome in the process of translation. **(b)** The ribosome during translation as we will show it in this book

is the binding of the appropriate aminoacyl–tRNA to the codon in the A site of the ribosome (step 1). This binding is facilitated by a protein **elongation factor (EF)** that is bound to the amino-acyl–tRNA and that is released once the tRNA binds to the codon. Another EF is used when the ribosome translocates along the mRNA to the next codon (step 3). Each EF is released after its job is completed. GTP hydrolysis is used to power the ribosome along the mRNA. In elongation, a peptide bond is formed between the C-terminal end of the growing polypep-tide on the P site tRNA and the amino acid on the A site tRNA (step 2). **Peptidyl transferase** catalyzes this reaction. As we noted in an earlier example of the splicing reaction, researchers have demonstrated that the enzyme activity in the large ribo-somal subunit is not a protein but a ribozyme (catalytic RNA) within the large subunit.

The elongation cycle is quite similar in prokaryotic cells and eukaryotes, turning at the rate of about 1–3 times per sec-ond in eukaryotes versus 15–20 times per second in bacteria.

## 12.4e Termination Releases a Completed Polypeptide from the Ribosome

Translation termination is similar in prokaryotic and eukary-otic cells; it takes place when one of the stop codons on the mRNA—UAG, UAA, or UGA—arrives in the A site of a ribo-some **(Figure 12.16)**. A protein **release factor** (**RF**; also called a **termination factor**) binds in the A site and causes the ribosome to disassemble into its subunits.

**CONCEPT FIX** Since the termination factor is a protein and not a tRNA, it cannot base-pair with the stop codon. It has a shape similar to tRNA and simply wins the competition to occupy the A site of the ribosome since there are no competing tRNAs that recognize termination codons.

## 12.4f Multiple Ribosomes Simultaneously Translate a Single mRNA

Once the first ribosome has begun translation, another one can assemble with an initiator tRNA as soon as there is room at the 5′ UTR of the mRNA. Ribosomes continue to attach as translation continues and become spaced along the mRNA like beads on a string. The entire structure of an mRNA molecule and the multiple ribosomes attached to it is known as a **poly-some** (a contraction of *polyribosome*; **Figure 12.17**). The mul-tiple ribosomes greatly increase the overall rate of polypeptide synthesis from a single mRNA. The total number of ribosomes in a polysome depends on the length of the coding region of its mRNA molecule, ranging from a minimum of one or two ribo-somes on the smallest mRNAs to as many as 100 on the longest mRNAs.

In prokaryotic cells, because of the absence of a nuclear envelope, transcription and translation are typically coupled. As soon as the 5′ end of a new mRNA emerges from the RNA polymerase, ribosomal subunits attach and initiate transla-tion. By the time the mRNA is completely transcribed, it is covered with ribosomes from end to end, each assembling a

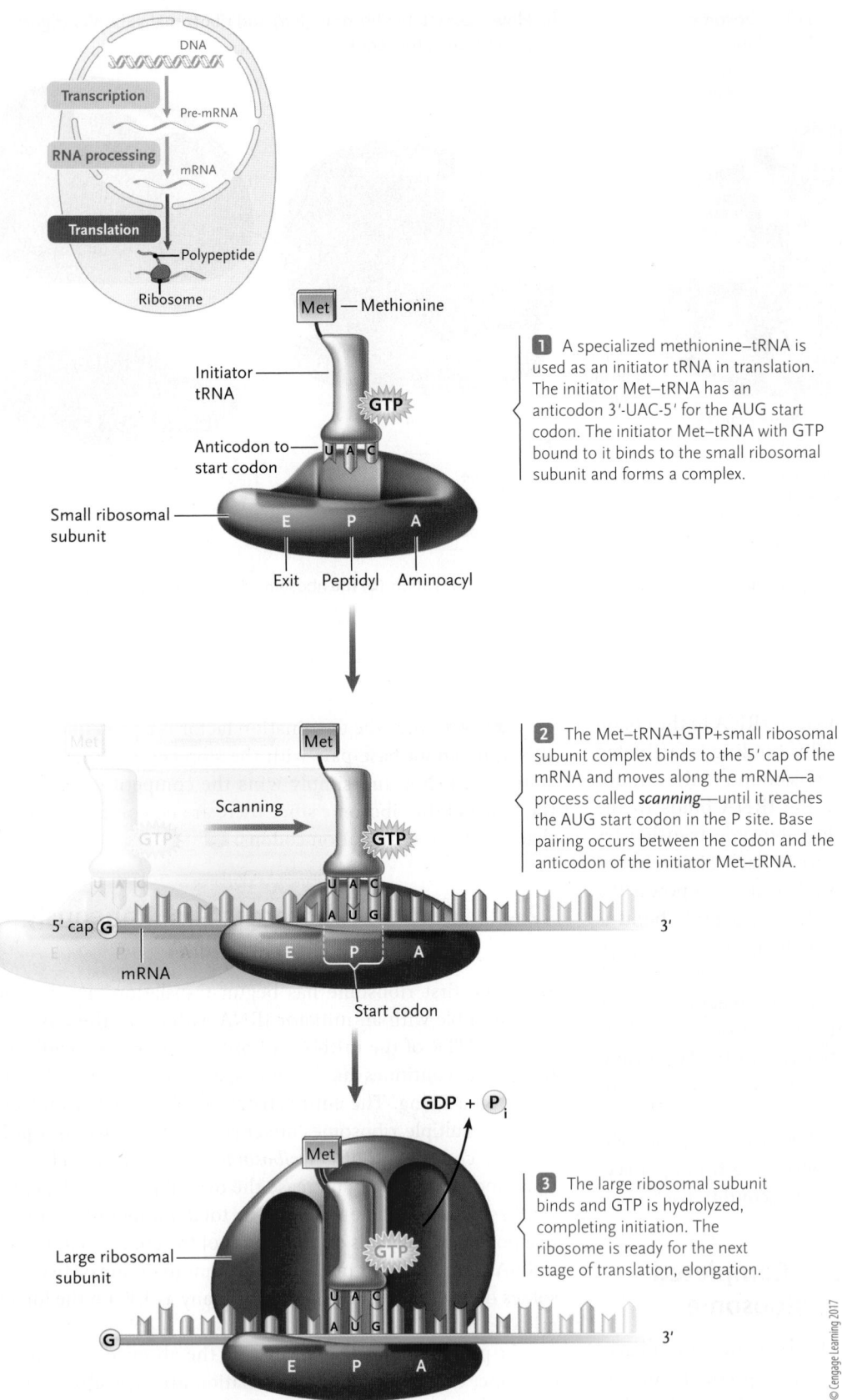

**1** A specialized methionine–tRNA is used as an initiator tRNA in translation. The initiator Met–tRNA has an anticodon 3'-UAC-5' for the AUG start codon. The initiator Met–tRNA with GTP bound to it binds to the small ribosomal subunit and forms a complex.

**2** The Met–tRNA+GTP+small ribosomal subunit complex binds to the 5' cap of the mRNA and moves along the mRNA—a process called *scanning*—until it reaches the AUG start codon in the P site. Base pairing occurs between the codon and the anticodon of the initiator Met–tRNA.

**3** The large ribosomal subunit binds and GTP is hydrolyzed, completing initiation. The ribosome is ready for the next stage of translation, elongation.

© Cengage Learning 2017

**FIGURE 12.14 Translation initiation in eukaryotes.** Protein initiation factors (IFs) participate in the event but, for simplicity, they are not shown in the figure. The IFs are released when the large ribosomal subunit binds and GTP is hydrolyzed.

copy of the encoded polypeptide. Meanwhile, several other RNA polymerases have likely begun transcribing the same gene, each one trailing a collection of translating ribosomes (**Figure 12.18**). Such a system allows prokaryotic cells to regulate production very quickly in response to changing environmental conditions.

### 12.4g Newly Synthesized Polypeptides Are Processed and Folded into Finished Form

Most eukaryotic proteins are in an inactive, unfinished form when ribosomes release them. Processing reactions that convert the new proteins into the finished form include the removal of amino acids from the ends or interior of the polypeptide chain and the addition of larger organic groups, including carbohydrate or lipid structures.

Proteins fold into their final three-dimensional shapes as the processing reactions take place. For many proteins, helper proteins called *chaperones* or *chaperonins* assist the folding process by combining with the folding protein, promoting correct three-dimensional structures and inhibiting incorrect ones.

In some cases, the same initial polypeptide may be processed by alternative pathways that produce different mature polypeptides, usually by removing different long stretches of amino acids from the interior of the polypeptide chain. Alternative processing is another mechanism—distinct from alternative splicing of mRNA—that increases the number of proteins encoded by a single gene.

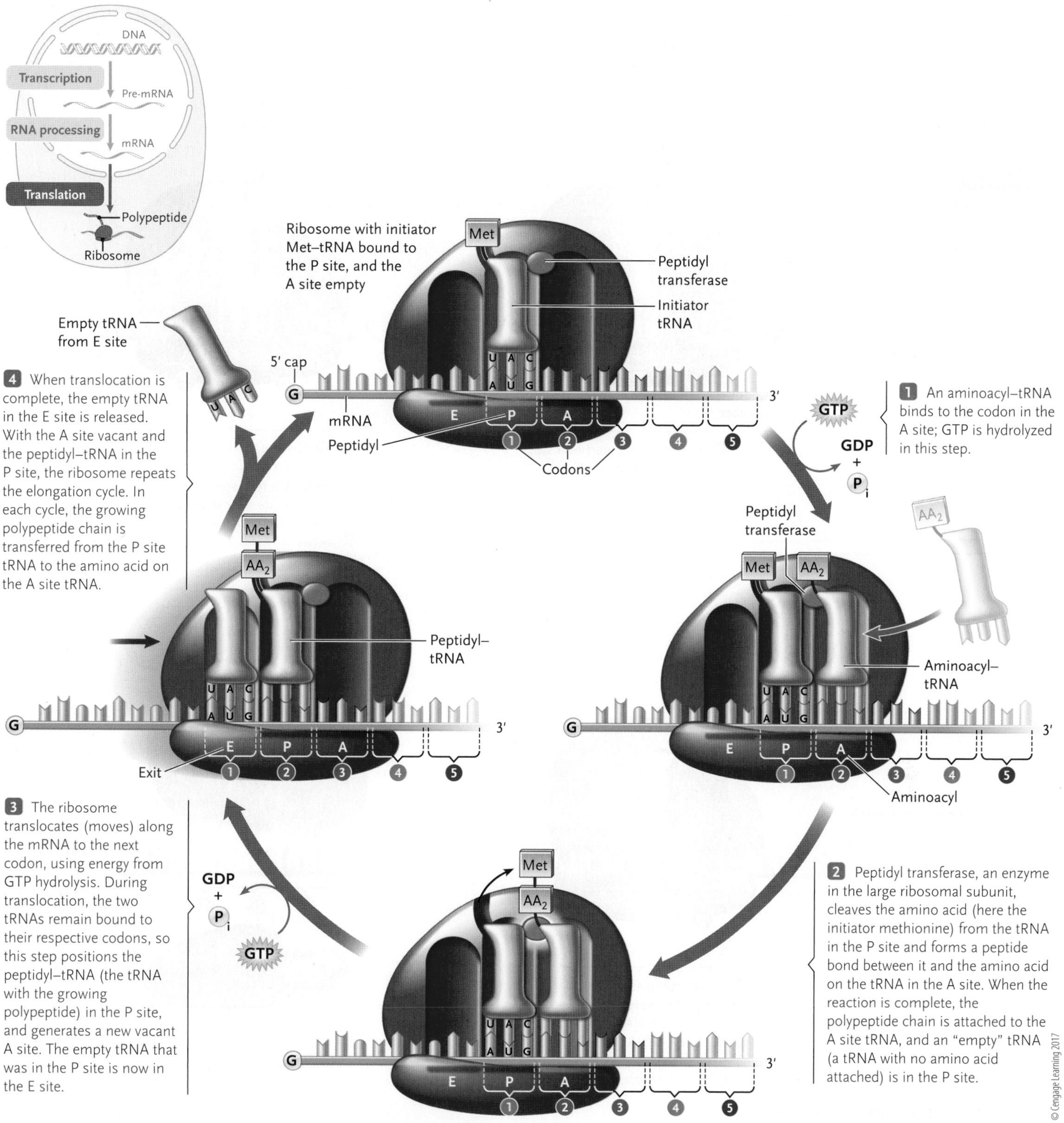
DNA
Transcription
Pre-mRNA
RNA processing
mRNA
Translation
Polypeptide
Ribosome
Ribosome with initiator Met–tRNA bound to the P site, and the A site empty
Met
Peptidyl transferase
Initiator tRNA
5′ cap
G
3′
mRNA
Peptidyl
E
P
A
Codons
Empty tRNA from E site
4 When translocation is complete, the empty tRNA in the E site is released. With the A site vacant and the peptidyl–tRNA in the P site, the ribosome repeats the elongation cycle. In each cycle, the growing polypeptide chain is transferred from the P site tRNA to the amino acid on the A site tRNA.
GTP
GDP
+
P
1 An aminoacyl–tRNA binds to the codon in the A site; GTP is hydrolyzed in this step.
Peptidyl transferase
AA2
Peptidyl–tRNA
Aminoacyl–tRNA
Aminoacyl
Exit
3 The ribosome translocates (moves) along the mRNA to the next codon, using energy from GTP hydrolysis. During translocation, the two tRNAs remain bound to their respective codons, so this step positions the peptidyl–tRNA (the tRNA with the growing polypeptide) in the P site, and generates a new vacant A site. The empty tRNA that was in the P site is now in the E site.
2 Peptidyl transferase, an enzyme in the large ribosomal subunit, cleaves the amino acid (here the initiator methionine) from the tRNA in the P site and forms a peptide bond between it and the amino acid on the tRNA in the A site. When the reaction is complete, the polypeptide chain is attached to the A site tRNA, and an "empty" tRNA (a tRNA with no amino acid attached) is in the P site.
© Cengage Learning 2017

**FIGURE 12.15 Translation elongation.** A protein elongation factor (EF) complexes with the aminoacyl–tRNA to bring it to the ribosome, and another EF is needed for ribosome translocation. For simplicity, the EFs are not shown in the figure.

Other proteins are processed into an initial inactive form that is later activated at a particular time or location by removal of a covering segment of the amino acid chain. The digestive enzyme pepsin, for example, is made by cells lining the stomach in an inactive form called **pepsinogen**. When the cells secrete pepsinogen into the stomach, the high acidity of that organ triggers removal of a segment of amino acids, thus converting the enzyme into an active form that rapidly degrades food proteins. The initial production of the protein as inactive pepsinogen protects the cells that make it from having their own proteins degraded by the enzyme.

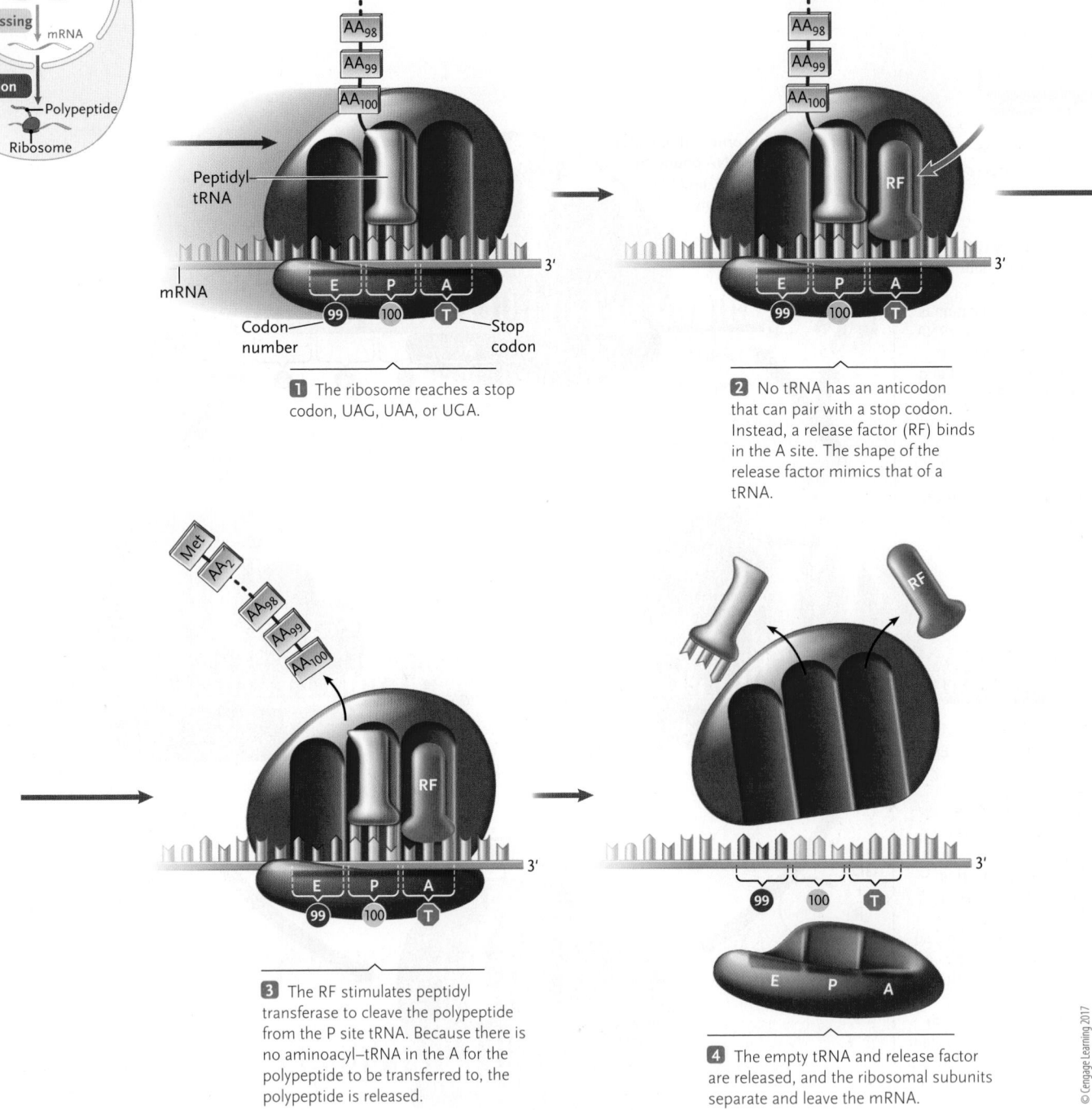

**1** The ribosome reaches a stop codon, UAG, UAA, or UGA.

**2** No tRNA has an anticodon that can pair with a stop codon. Instead, a release factor (RF) binds in the A site. The shape of the release factor mimics that of a tRNA.

**3** The RF stimulates peptidyl transferase to cleave the polypeptide from the P site tRNA. Because there is no aminoacyl–tRNA in the A for the polypeptide to be transferred to, the polypeptide is released.

**4** The empty tRNA and release factor are released, and the ribosomal subunits separate and leave the mRNA.

© Cengage Learning 2017

**FIGURE 12.16  Translation termination**

## 12.4h  Finished Proteins Are Sorted to the Cellular Locations Where They Function

Eukaryotic cells are structurally compartmentalized, with various organelles performing specialized functions. Therefore, every protein that is made must be delivered to its appropriate compartment. Without a sorting and delivery system, cells would wind up as a jumble of proteins floating about in the cytoplasm, with none of the spatial organization that makes cellular life possible.

Although translation of all proteins begins on free ribosomes in the cytosol, there are three types of final destination compartments where the final products may be needed: (1) the

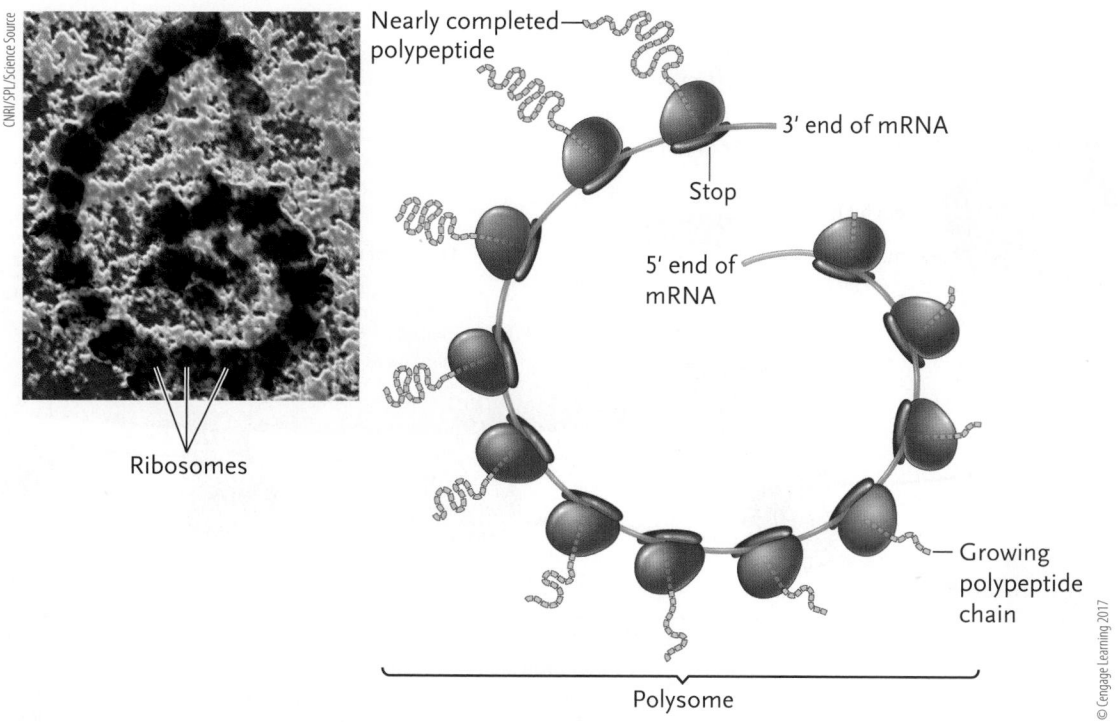

**Nearly completed** polypeptide

3' end of mRNA

Stop

5' end of mRNA

Ribosomes

Growing polypeptide chain

Polysome

FIGURE 12.17 **Polysomes, consisting of a series of ribosomes reading the same mRNA**

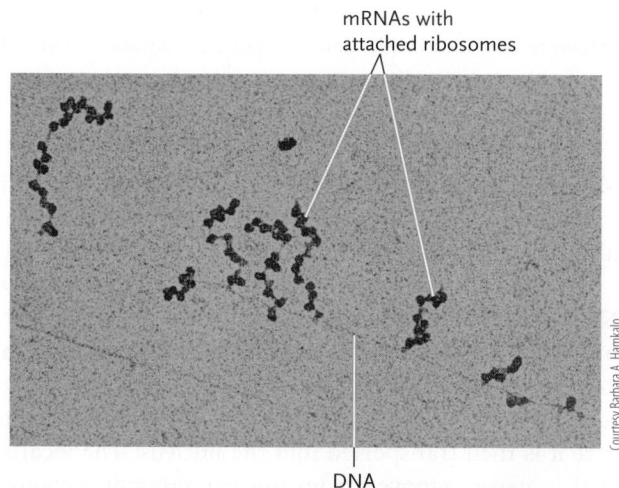

mRNAs with attached ribosomes

DNA

FIGURE 12.18 **Simultaneous transcription and translation in progress in an electron microscope preparation extracted from *E. coli* (× 57 000)**

cytosol; (2) the endomembrane system, which includes the Golgi complex, lysosomes, secretory vesicles, the nuclear envelope, and the plasma membrane; and (3) other membrane-bound organelles distinct from the endomembrane system, including the nucleus, mitochondria, chloroplasts, and microbodies (e.g., **peroxisomes**).

**PROTEIN SORTING TO THE CYTOPLASM** Proteins that function in the cytosol are simply released from ribosomes once translation is completed. Examples of proteins that function in the cytoplasm are cytoskeleton proteins (e.g., tubulin and keratin) and the enzymes that carry out glycolysis (see Section 5.3).

**PROTEIN SORTING TO THE ENDOMEMBRANE SYSTEM** The endomembrane system is a major traffic network for proteins. Polypeptides that sort to the endomembrane system begin their synthesis on free ribosomes in the cytosol and produce a short segment of amino acids called a **signal sequence** (also called a **signal peptide**) near their N-terminal ends. As **Figure 12.19** shows, the signal sequence is recognized by a signal recognition particle that initiates a series of steps that ultimately result in the polypeptide entering the lumen (interior) of the rough ER. This mechanism is called **cotranslational import** because import of the polypeptide into the ER occurs simultaneously with translation of the mRNA encoding the polypeptide.

**CONCEPT FIX** Ribosomes engaged in cotranslational import stud the surface of the ER and give rise to the term *rough*. Note that ribosomes do not sit on the rough ER waiting for mRNA to translate. Rather, they only associate with the ER *after* they have begun translation as free ribosomes in the cytosol. ⬡

The signal sequence was discovered in 1975 by Günter Blobel, B. Dobberstein, and colleagues at Rockefeller University in New York when they observed that proteins sorted through the endomembrane system initially contain extra amino acids at their N-terminal ends. Blobel received a Nobel Prize in 1999 for his work with the mechanism of sorting proteins in cells.

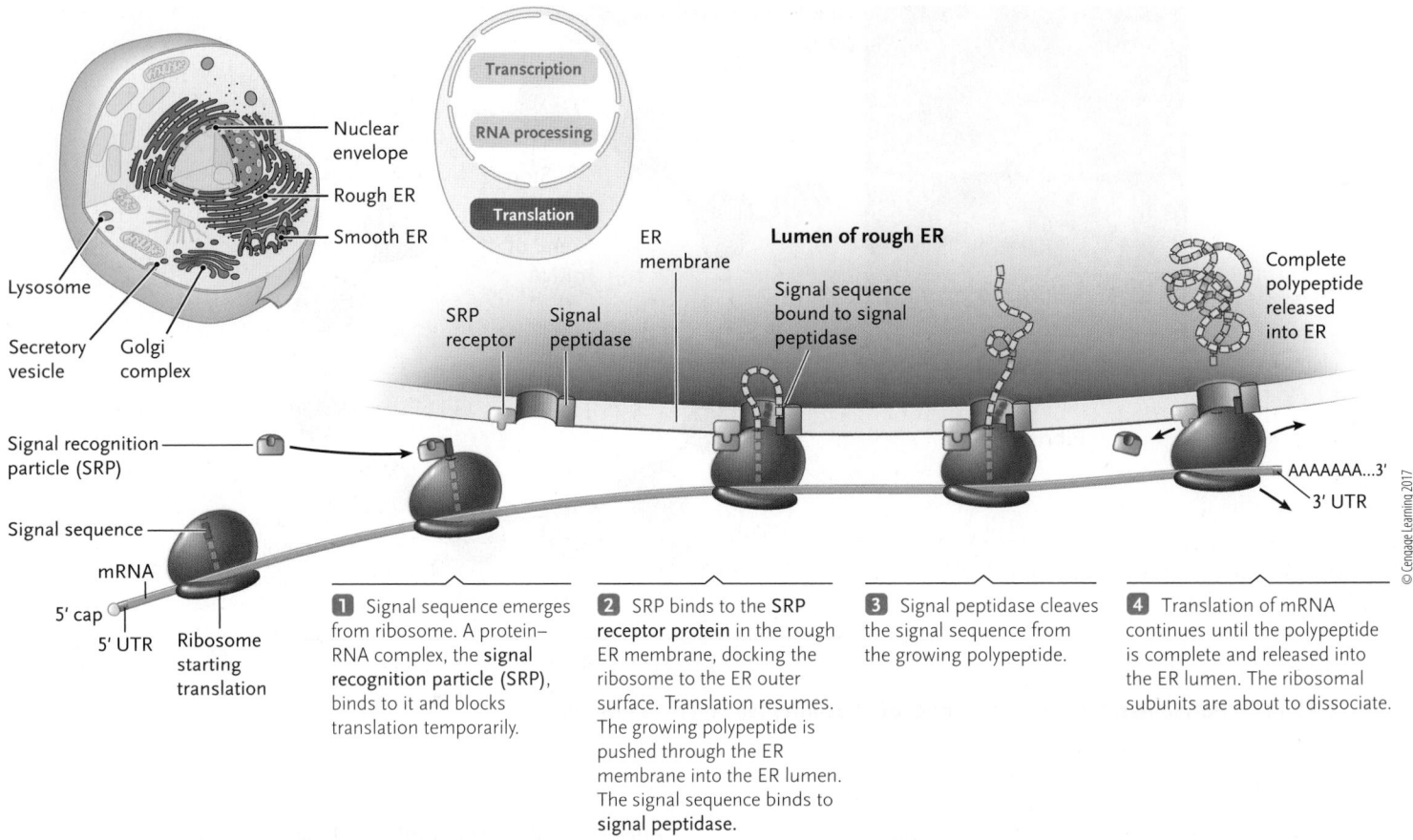

**FIGURE 12.19 The signal mechanism directing proteins to the ER.** The figure shows several ribosomes at different stages of translation of the mRNA.

Labels in figure:

Nuclear envelope
Rough ER
Smooth ER
Lysosome
Secretory vesicle
Golgi complex
Transcription
RNA processing
Translation
ER membrane
**Lumen of rough ER**
SRP receptor
Signal peptidase
Signal sequence bound to signal peptidase
Complete polypeptide released into ER
Signal recognition particle (SRP)
Signal sequence
mRNA
5' cap
5' UTR
Ribosome starting translation
AAAAAAA...3'
3' UTR
© Cengage Learning 2017

**1** Signal sequence emerges from ribosome. A protein–RNA complex, the **signal recognition particle (SRP)**, binds to it and blocks translation temporarily.

**2** SRP binds to the **SRP receptor protein** in the rough ER membrane, docking the ribosome to the ER outer surface. Translation resumes. The growing polypeptide is pushed through the ER membrane into the ER lumen. The signal sequence binds to signal peptidase.

**3** Signal peptidase cleaves the signal sequence from the growing polypeptide.

**4** Translation of mRNA continues until the polypeptide is complete and released into the ER lumen. The ribosomal subunits are about to dissociate.

Once inside the lumen of the rough ER, proteins fold into their final form. They also have, or obtain, a type of tag—a postal code if you will—that targets each protein for sorting to its final destination. Depending on the protein and its destination, the tag may be an amino acid sequence already coded in the protein, or a functional group or short sugar chain added to the protein in the lumen. Some proteins remain in the ER, whereas others are transported to the Golgi complex, where they may be modified further. From the Golgi complex, proteins are packaged into vesicles, which may deliver them to lysosomes, secrete them from the cell (e.g., digestive enzymes), or deposit them in the plasma membrane (e.g., cell surface receptors).

**PROTEIN SORTING TO THE MITOCHONDRIA, CHLORO-PLASTS, MICROBODIES, AND THE NUCLEUS** Proteins are sorted to the nucleus, mitochondria, chloroplasts, and micro-bodies after they have been made on free ribosomes in the cytosol. This mechanism of sorting is called **posttranslational import**. Proteins destined for the mitochondria, chloroplasts, and microbodies have short amino acid sequences called **transit sequences** at their N-terminal ends that target them to the appropriate organelle. The protein is taken up into the correct organelle by interactions between its transit sequences and organelle-specific transport complexes in the membrane of the appropriate organelle. A transit peptidase enzyme within the organelle then removes the transit sequence.

Proteins sorted to the nucleus, such as the enzymes for DNA replication and RNA transcription, each have a short amino acid sequence called a **nuclear localization signal**. A cytosolic transport protein binds to the signal and moves the nuclear protein to the nuclear pore complex (see Chapter 2), where it is then transported into the nucleus. The localization signal is never removed from nuclear proteins because they need to reenter the nucleus each time the nuclear envelope breaks down and re-forms during the cell division cycle.

Although prokaryotic cells are structurally simpler than eukaryotes, the same basic system of molecular sorting signals distributes proteins throughout prokaryotic cells. In prokaryotic organisms, signals similar to the ER-directing signals of eukaryotes direct newly synthesized bacterial proteins to the plasma membrane (bacteria do not have ER membranes); further information built into the proteins keeps them in the plasma membrane or allows them to enter the cell wall or to be secreted outside the cell. Proteins without sorting signals remain in the cytoplasm. The similarity of mechanisms across all cells suggests that protein sorting is a very ancient evolutionary innovation.

1. How does translation initiation occur in eukaryotes versus prokaryotic cells?

2. Distinguish between the E, P, and A sites of the ribosome.

3. How are proteins directed to different parts of a eukaryotic cell?

## 12.5 Mutations Can Affect Protein Structure and Function

To this point in the chapter, we have been building an understanding of how the sequence of DNA bases in protein-coding genes is directly related to the structure and function of the polypeptides that they encode. We will close the chapter with consideration of how various types of small changes in the DNA sequence might affect protein structure. (Contrast these small changes with the rather large-scale changes associated with the movement of mobile genetic elements described in

Chapter 15 and the chromosomal rearrangements shown in Chapter 8.)

**Mutations** are changes in the double-stranded sequence of bases in genetic material. Such changes contribute to the genetic variability among individuals that is the raw material acted upon by evolutionary forces. How will mutations affect protein structure and function? Your understanding of this chapter should lead you to respond, "It depends." Consider a theoretical stretch of normal (nonmutated) DNA encoding a string of amino acids in a polypeptide (**Figure 12.20a**). Four types of base-pair mutations affecting a protein-coding gene are as follows:

1. **Missense mutation:** (Figure 12.20b) A sense codon is changed to a different sense codon that specifies a different amino acid. Whether the function of a polypeptide is altered significantly depends on the amino acid change that occurs. (Missense mutations to amino acids with similar properties or in parts of the protein far away from critical active, binding, or functional domains may have little to no effect on protein function.) Individuals homozygous for a missense mutation in the gene for one of the two polypeptide types found in the oxygen-carrying protein hemoglobin (**Figure 12.21**)

**a. Normal**

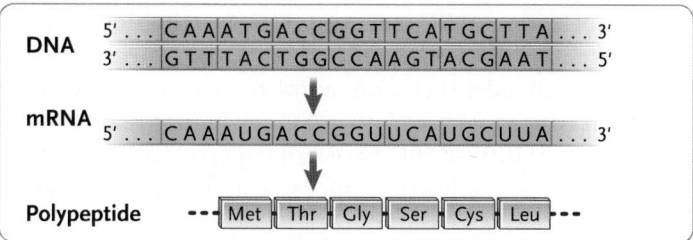

**b. Missense mutation.** Changes sense codon to a sense codon for a different amino acid

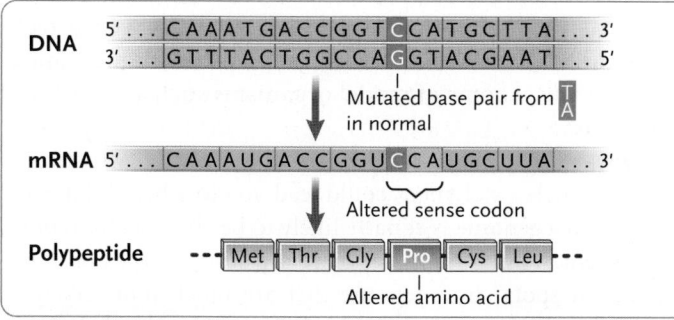

**c. Nonsense mutation.** Changes sense codon to a stop codon

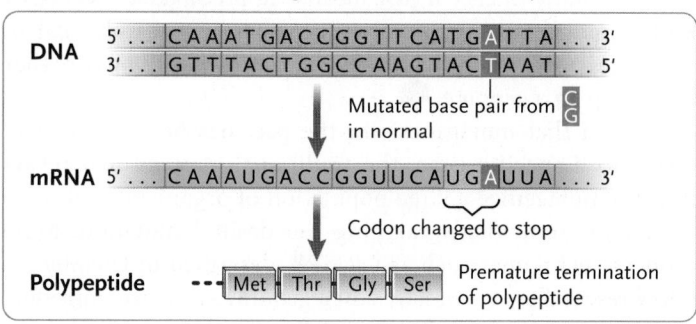

**d. Silent mutation.** Changes sense codon to another codon for the same amino acid

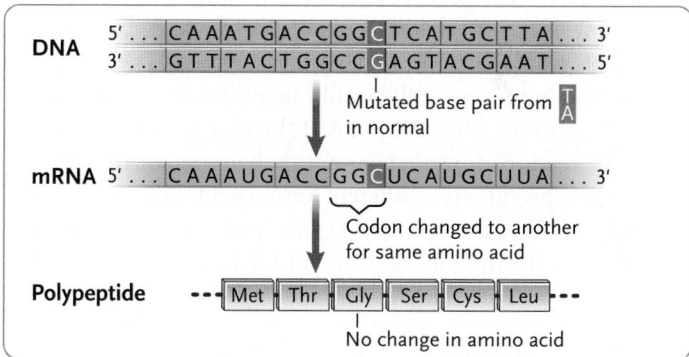

**e. Frameshift mutation.** Changes reading frame after mutation

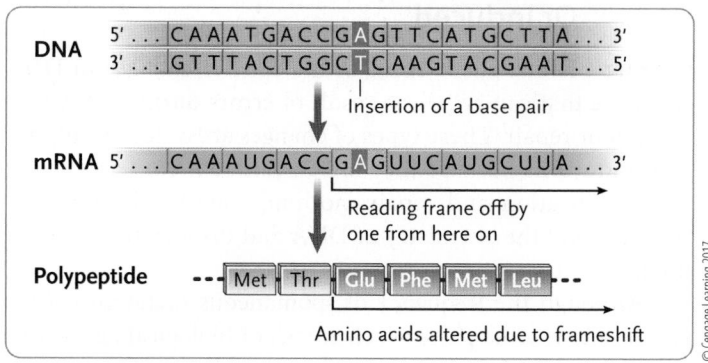

© Cengage Learning 2017

**FIGURE 12.20 Effects of base-pair mutations in protein-coding genes on the amino acid sequence of the encoded polypeptide**

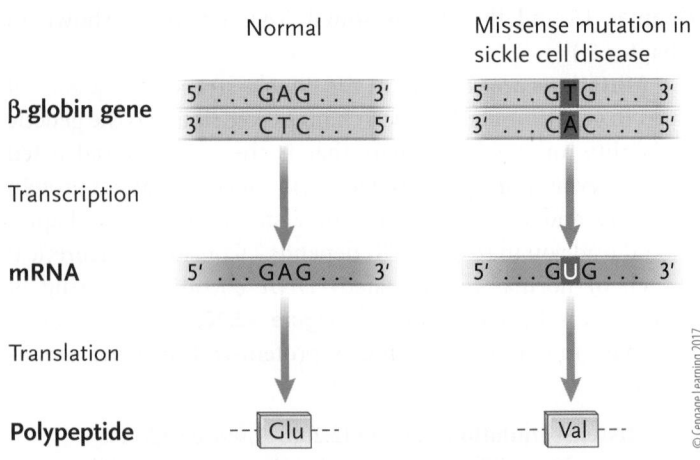

**FIGURE 12.21 Missense mutation in a gene for one of the two polypeptides of hemoglobin that is the cause of sickle cell disease**

have the genetic disease sickle cell anemia (described in Chapter 9). Many other human genetic diseases are caused by missense mutations, including albinism, hemophilia, and achondroplasia.

2. **Nonsense mutation:** (Figure 12.20c) A sense codon is changed to a nonsense (stop) codon. Translation of an mRNA containing a nonsense mutation results in a shorter-than-normal polypeptide that, in many cases, will be only partially functional at best.

3. **Silent mutation:** (Figure 12.20d) A sense codon is changed to a different sense codon, but that codon specifies the same amino acid as in the normal polypeptide, so the function of the polypeptide is unchanged.

4. **Frameshift mutation:** (Figure 12.20e) A single base-pair deletion or insertion in the coding region of a gene alters the reading frame of the resulting mRNA (the figure shows an insertion). After the point of the mutation, the ribosome reads codons that are not the same as for the normal mRNA, producing a different amino acid sequence in the polypeptide from then on. Typically, the resulting polypeptide is non-functional because of the significantly altered amino acid sequence.

## 12.5a Mutations Can Be Spontaneous Or Induced

Chapter 11 introduced some of the smaller changes in DNA sequence that can arise as a result of errors during DNA replication or repair. These types of changes are called **spontaneous mutations** because they are an inherent consequence of DNA replication and repair: nothing "causes" these alterations beyond the chemistry of DNA and the enzymes that act upon it.

Although the frequency of spontaneous mutation is usually very low, some physical, chemical, or biological agents can generate **induced mutations** at a much higher frequency. Such agents are called **mutagens**. Production of mutations in a laboratory by exposure to a mutagen is called **mutagenesis**, and the treated organism is said to be *mutagenized*.

One of the first mutagens used in research was high-energy ionizing radiation such as X-rays. Exposure to this type of radiation creates reactive oxygen species (ROS) in cells, causing double-stranded breaks in chromosomes. Repair of such breaks can be imperfect, resulting in mutation. Lower-energy, nonionizing radiation such as UV light causes a particular type of DNA damage called **thymine dimers**. Thymine bases that are side by side in a chromosome become linked together covalently. Attempts by the cell to repair or replicate dimers can lead to mutation.

There is a wide variety of natural and synthetic chemical mutagens with a respectively wide variety of mechanisms of action. The one example we will choose is that of 5-bromouracil (5BU). You will notice in **Figure 12.22a** that 5BU and thymine have similar shapes; 5BU has a bromine atom where thymine has a methyl group. 5BU is called a **base analogue** because it is so similar to thymine that it is incorporated into DNA by polymerases as if it were thymine. If 5BU always behaved like thymine, always presenting two hydrogen bonds to always pair with adenine, there would be no problem. However, 5BU is quite unstable, switching between two alternative forms: one that presents two hydrogen bonds (pairing with adenine) and another that presents three hydrogen bonds (pairing with guanine). Figure 12.22b shows how the instability of 5BU base pairing can lead to substitution mutation following successive rounds of DNA replication.

Chapter 15 describes sequences of mobile DNA, such as transposons and retrotransposons, that are able to replicate themselves and insert at a new location in the genome. These biological agents have been used by researchers in a technique called **insertional mutagenesis** to introduce mutations into the genome of model organisms such as *E. coli* and *Drosophila*.

**CONCEPT FIX** You have likely heard the phrase, "Mutation is random." Such a statement could lead you to a belief that each base pair in a genome is equally likely to be changed by a mutational event. This is not true; there are several types of mutational "hot spots" in a genome that are much more likely to change than other regions. So, in this case, "random" does not mean "equally likely," it just means "unpredictable." Whether mutations are spontaneous or induced by chemical, physical, or biological agents, it is not possible to predict exactly where they will occur in a genome. ⬢

Given that mutagenesis in the past has been difficult to target to a specific gene, the traditional strategy has always been to mutagenize a large population of organisms, and then screen for individuals carrying the desired mutation. More modern techniques such as CRISPR, described in Chapter 14, allow researchers to directly edit a genome sequence, introducing precise changes at exact locations.

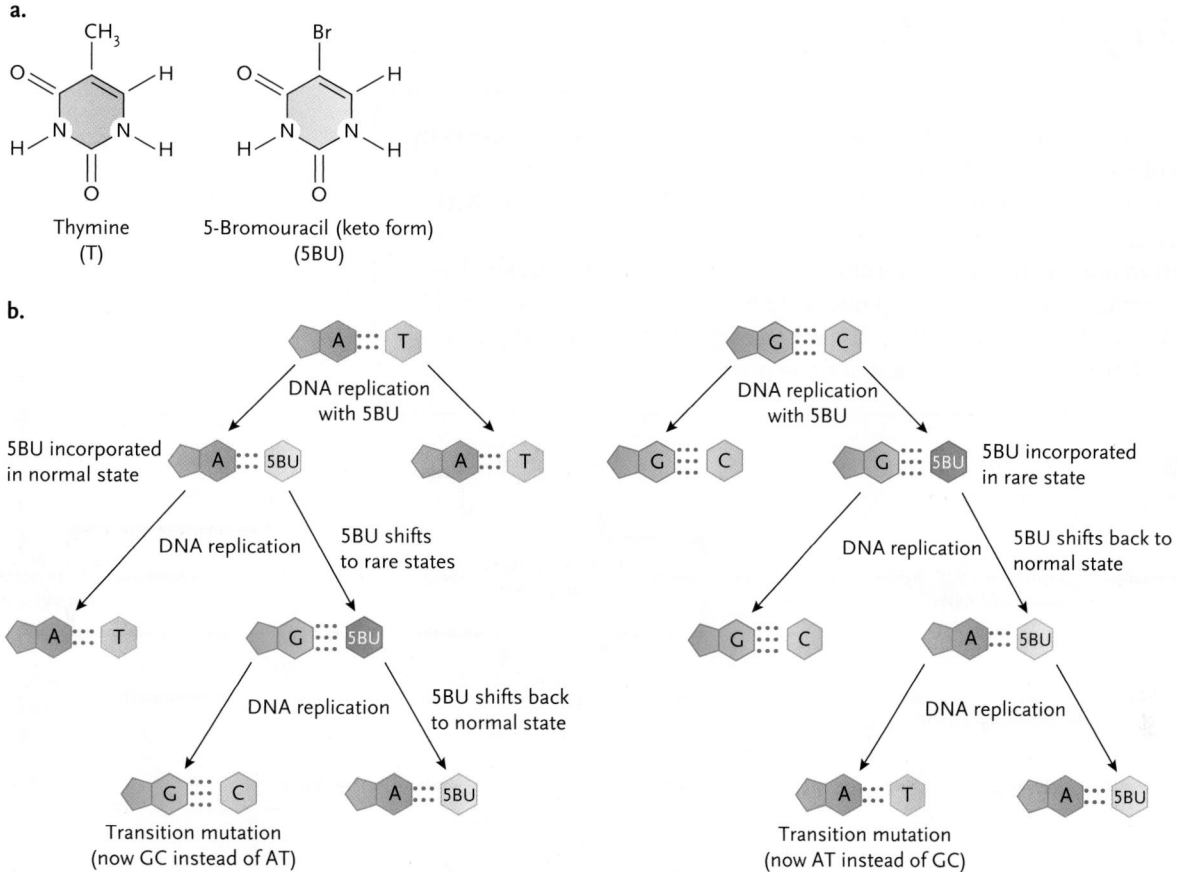

**FIGURE 12.22** **(a)** 5-bromouracil (5BU) is an analogue of thymine. **(b)** 5BU can give rise to substitution mutations following multiple rounds of DNA replication.

## STUDY BREAK QUESTIONS

1. Which type of mutation results in a change in a codon?
2. What are the three types of mutagenic agents?
3. Why is a base analogue, such as 5BU, mutagenic?

As we saw with the work of Beadle and Tatum early in this chapter, the study of mutants has been a very powerful tool for understanding the relationship between gene structure and function. Hopefully you now understand why agents that inhibit RNA polymerase could cause extensive cellular damage, as seen in *Why It Matters* for this chapter. In the next chapter we will note that gene expression is regulated by several interrelated mechanisms to ensure the production of needed products in the right amounts, in the right places, at the right times.

# Summary Illustration

In all cells, the expression of genes coded in DNA gives rise to RNA products by the process of transcription. The RNA products of some genes have structural or catalytic roles (i.e., rRNA, tRNA, snRNA), while other products (i.e., mRNA) carry the genetic code to ribosomes for translation into proteins. Separation of transcription (inside the nucleus) from translation (outside the nucleus) in eukaryotes provides opportunity and necessity for more complex processing of RNA products. Changes in the base sequence of genes may have any of a wide variety of effects on the function of gene products.

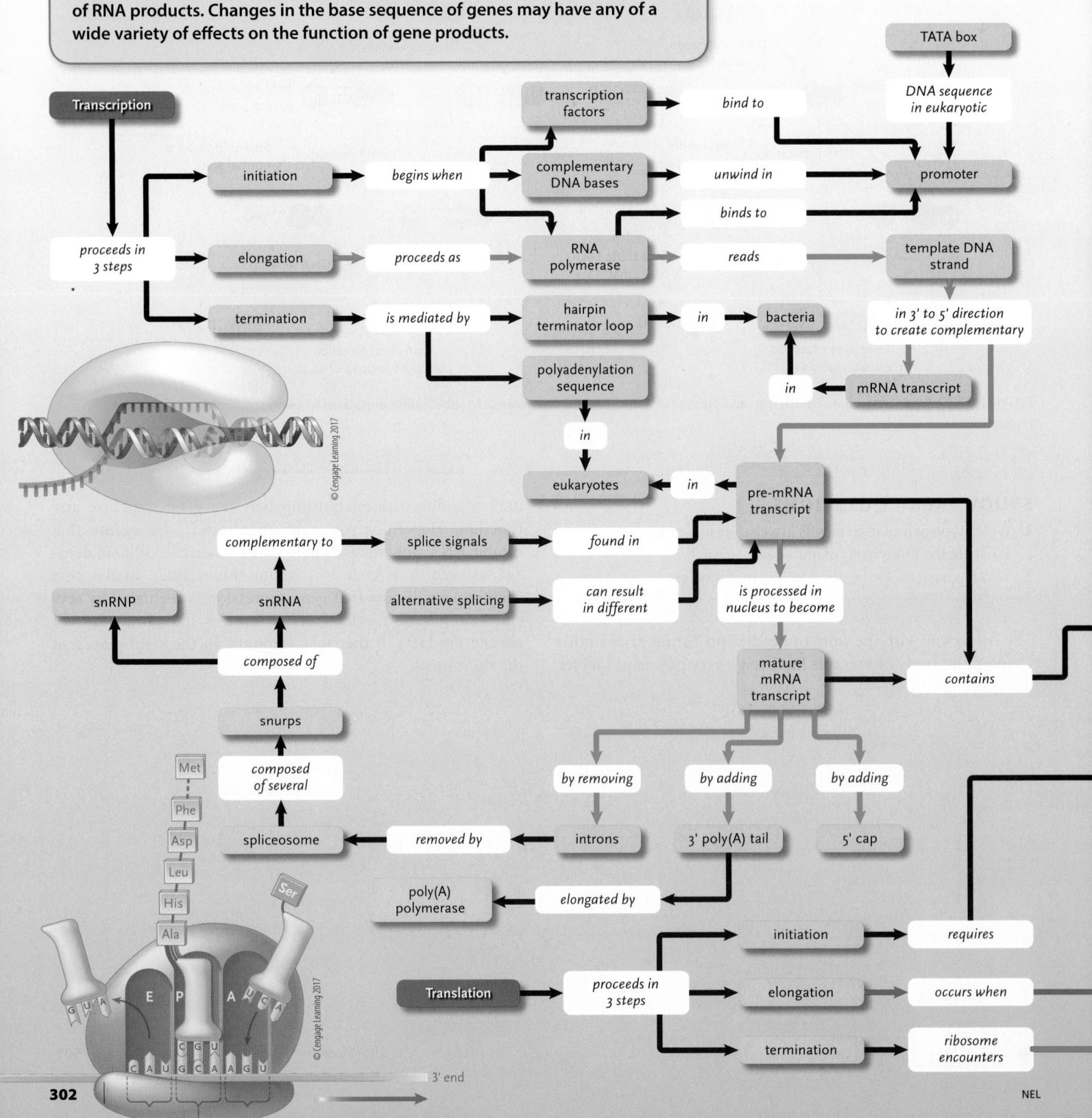

NEL

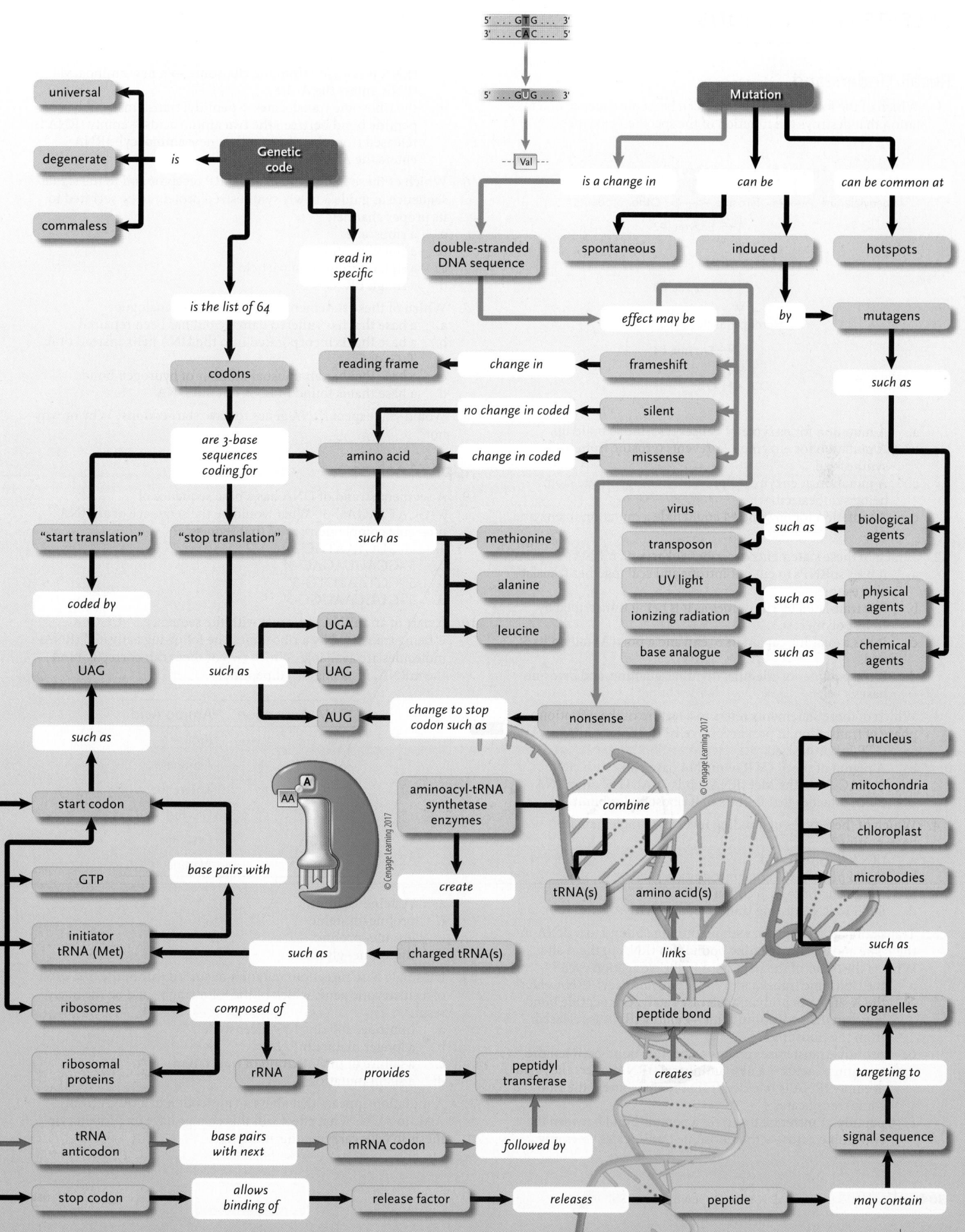

5' . . . G T G . . . 3'
3' . . . C A C . . . 5'

5' . . . G U G . . . 3'

-- Val --

**Mutation**

universal

degenerate ← *is* ← **Genetic code**

commaless

Genetic code → *read in specific*

Genetic code → *is the list of 64*

*read in specific* → reading frame

*is the list of 64* → codons

codons → *are 3-base sequences coding for*

*are 3-base sequences coding for* → amino acid

Mutation → *is a change in*

Mutation → *can be*

Mutation → *can be common at*

*is a change in* → spontaneous

*can be* → induced

*can be common at* → hotspots

double-stranded DNA sequence

*effect may be*

*induced* → *by* → mutagens

*effect may be* → frameshift → *change in* → reading frame

silent → *no change in coded* → amino acid

missense → *change in coded* → amino acid

mutagens → *such as*

amino acid → *such as* → methionine

alanine

leucine

"start translation"

"stop translation"

"start translation" → *coded by* → UAG → *such as* → start codon

"stop translation" → *such as* → UGA

UAG

AUG

*such as* → UGA / UAG / AUG

AUG ← *change to stop codon such as* ← nonsense

virus

transposon → *such as* → biological agents

UV light

ionizing radiation → *such as* → physical agents

base analogue → *such as* → chemical agents

biological agents
physical agents
chemical agents

aminoacyl-tRNA synthetase enzymes → *combine*

*combine* → tRNA(s) / amino acid(s)

aminoacyl-tRNA synthetase enzymes → *create* → charged tRNA(s)

charged tRNA(s) → *such as* → initiator tRNA (Met)

GTP → *base pairs with* → initiator tRNA (Met)

start codon

initiator tRNA (Met)

ribosomes → *composed of*

*composed of* → ribosomal proteins / rRNA

rRNA → *provides* → peptidyl transferase

tRNA anticodon → *base pairs with next* → mRNA codon → *followed by* → peptidyl transferase

stop codon → *allows binding of* → release factor → *releases* → peptide

peptidyl transferase → *creates*

tRNA(s) / amino acid(s) → *links* → peptide bond → *creates*

peptide → *may contain* → signal sequence → *targeting to* → organelles → *such as*

nucleus
mitochondria
chloroplast
microbodies

© Cengage Learning 2017

NEL

**303**

# SELF-TEST QUESTIONS

## Recall/Understand

1. Which of the following statements can be a consequence of a mutation that destroys the function of the specified enzyme?

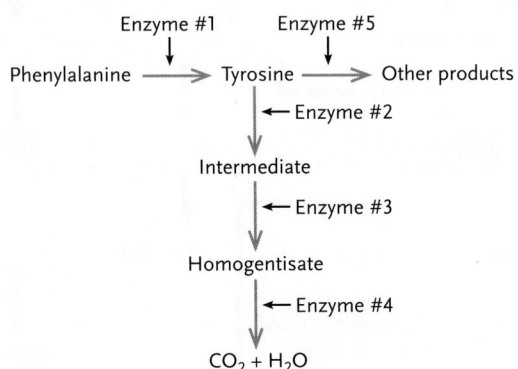

   a. A mutation for enzyme #1 causes tyrosine to build up.
   b. A mutation for enzyme #2 prevents tyrosine from being synthesized.
   c. A mutation at enzyme #3 prevents homogentisate from being synthesized.
   d. A mutation for enzyme #4 could hide a mutation in enzyme #1.

2. Which of these statements describes eukaryotic mRNA?
   a. It uses snRNPs to cut out introns and seal together translatable exons.
   b. It is translated by ribosomes as it is being transcribed by RNA polymerase.
   c. It has a guanine cap on its 3′ end and a poly(A) tail on its 5′ end.
   d. It is a polymer of adenine, thymine, guanine, and cytosine bases.

3. Which of these statements refers to a feature of the initiation phase of translation in prokaryotic cells?
   a. GTP is synthesized.
   b. A region of the 5′ UTR of mRNA base pairs with rRNA.
   c. 5′-UAC-3′ on the Met tRNA binds 3′-AUG-5′ on mRNA.
   d. tRNA attaches first to the small ribosomal subunit.

4. Which of these types of bonding involves complementary base-pairing?
   a. tRNA to amino acid
   b. signal peptide to signal recognition particle
   c. release factor to stop codon
   d. DNA to RNA during transcription of rRNA gene

5. Translation is in progress, with methionine bound to a tRNA in the P site and a phenylalanine bound to a tRNA in the A site. What is the order of the next steps in the elongation cycle?
   a. the ribosome translocates → a new aminoacyl-tRNA enters the A site → peptidyl transferase catalyzes a peptide bond between the two amino acids → empty tRNA is released from the ribosome
   b. peptidyl transferase catalyzes a peptide bond between the two amino acids → a new aminoacyl–tRNA enters the A site → empty tRNA is released from the ribosome → the ribosome translocates
   c. peptidyl transferase catalyzes a peptide bond between the two amino acids → the ribosome translocates → empty tRNA is released from the ribosome → a new aminoacyl–tRNA enters the A site
   d. the ribosome translocates → peptidyl transferase catalyzes a peptide bond between the two amino acids → empty tRNA is released from the ribosome → a new aminoacyl–tRNA enters the A site

6. Which of these items binds to the SRP receptor and to the signal sequence to guide a newly synthesized protein to be secreted to its proper channel?
   a. a ribosome
   b. a signal peptidase
   c. a signal recognition particle
   d. a rough ER

7. Which of these statements describes a base analogue?
   a. a base that has suffered damage but has been repaired
   b. a base that is incorporated into the DNA helix instead of A, T, G, or C
   c. a base that has an unusual number of hydrogen bonds
   d. a base that is found in RNA but not DNA

8. Would you expect rRNA genes to have start codons? Why or why not?

## Apply/Analyze

9. A segment strand of DNA has a base sequence of 5′-GCATTAGAC-3′. What would be the sequence of an RNA molecule complementary to that sequence?
   a. 5′-GUCTAATGC-3′
   b. 5′-GCAUUAGAC-3′
   c. 5′-CGTAATCTG-3′
   d. 5′-GUCUAAUGC-3′

10. A part of an mRNA molecule with the sequence 5′-UGCGCA-3′ is being translated by a ribosome. The following activated tRNA molecules are available. Which two of them can correctly bind the mRNA, resulting in a dipeptide?

| tRNA Anticodon | Amino Acid |
| --- | --- |
| 3′-GGC-5′ | Proline |
| 3′-CGU-5′ | Alanine |
| 3′-UGC-5′ | Threonine |
| 3′-CCG-5′ | Glycine |
| 3′-ACG-5′ | Cysteine |
| 3′-CGG-5′ | Alanine |

   a. cysteine–alanine
   b. proline–cysteine
   c. glycine–proline
   d. threonine–glycine

11. If a single base insertion mutation occurred within the first exon of a eukaryotic gene, which of the following would be the likely result?
   a. improper splicing by spliceosome
   b. a longer mature mRNA
   c. a failure of the initiation of translation
   d. a silent mutation

12. A mutation appears that alters an anticodon in a tRNA from AAU to AUU. What effect will this change have on protein synthesis in cells carrying this mutation?

## Create/Evaluate

13. A geneticist is attempting to isolate mutations in the genes for four enzymes acting in a metabolic pathway in the bacterium *Escherichia coli*. The end product, E, of the pathway is absolutely essential for life:

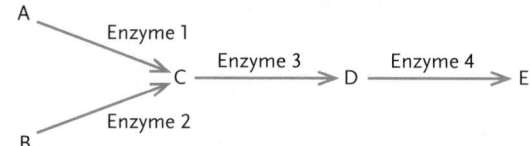

The geneticist has been able to isolate mutations in the genes for enzymes 1 and 2, but not for enzymes 3 and 4. Develop a hypothesis to explain why.

14. How could we show experimentally that the genetic code is universal, namely, that it is the same in bacteria as it is in eukaryotes such as fungi, plants, and animals?

15. Experimental systems have been developed in which transposable elements (TE) can be induced to move under the control of a researcher. Following the induced transposition of a yeast TE, two mutants were identified with altered activities of enzyme X. One of the mutants lacked enzyme activity completely, whereas the other had five times as much enzyme activity as normal cells did. Both mutants were found to have the TE inserted in the vicinity of the gene for enzyme X. Propose hypotheses for how the two different mutant phenotypes were produced.

# Chapter Roadmap

### Regulation of Gene Expression

Many layers and mechanisms of control regulate the expression of genes in order to ensure that the right product is available at the right time in the right amount.

**From Chapter 12**

### 13.1 Regulation of Gene Expression in Prokaryotic Cells

Studies of the expression of the *lac* and *trp* operons have provided insight into how genes can be arranged and regulated in prokaryotic cells.

### 13.2 Regulation of Transcription in Eukaryotes

Eukaryotes employ several mechanisms to modify the interactions between genes and the transcriptional machinery.

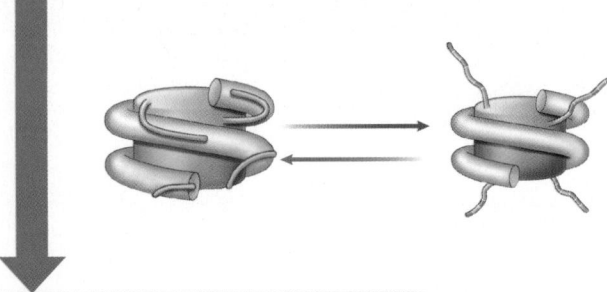

© Cengage Learning 2017

### 13.3 Posttranscriptional, Translational, and Posttranslational Regulation

Eukaryotes take advantage of myriad opportunities to influence the fate of mRNA, the process of translation, as well as the location and functionality of gene products.

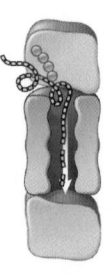

© Cengage Learning 2017

**From Chapter 7**

**From Chapter 11**

### 13.4 The Loss of Regulatory Controls in Cancer

The uncontrolled growth of cancer cells highlights the role of gene regulation in normal cell functioning.

**To Chapter 46**

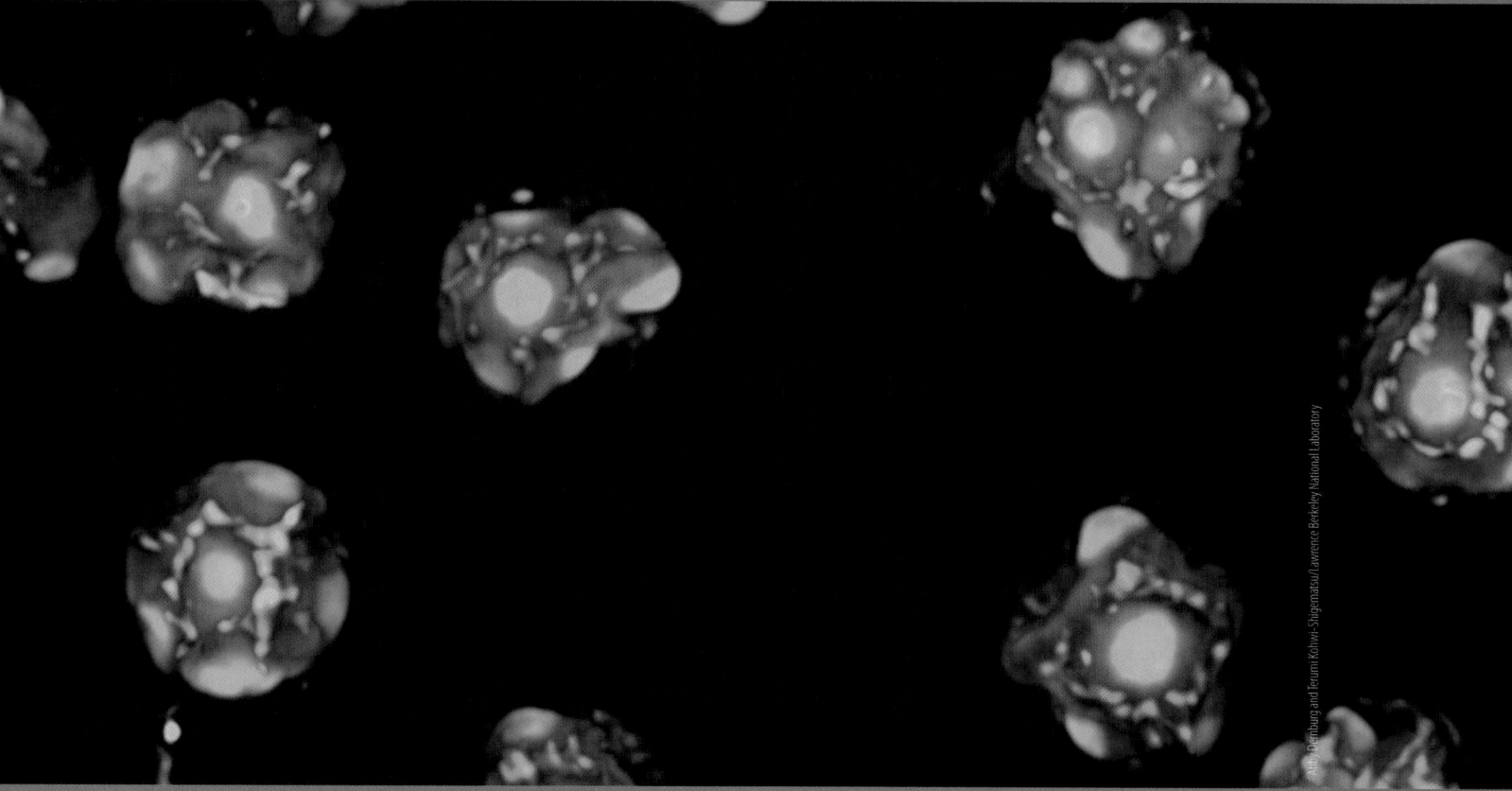

**Chromatin remodelling proteins (gold) binding to chromatin (blue).** Chromatin remodelling, a change in chromosome structure in the region of a gene, is a key step in the activation of genes in eukaryotes.

# Regulation of Gene Expression

# 13

**Why it matters . . .** The Honey Council of Canada reports that commercial and hobbyist apiarists raise tens of billions of honeybees (*Apis mellifera*) each year, producing millions of kilograms of honey and pollinating up to one-third of the country's crop plants.

Each honeybee hive is a highly structured insect society with over 50000 members. Although all members of a hive carry the same genes, a finely tuned program of regulated gene expression maintains three distinct castes: queen, worker, and drone **(Figure 13.1)**. The queen bee is relatively large and lays all the eggs for the entire hive. All the other females in the hive are smaller, sterile workers who forage for nectar and pollen, tend the queen, feed developing larvae, as well as clean and defend the hive. The main function of drones, the only males in the society, is to mate with queens to produce more workers. Whether an individual honeybee develops as a queen, or a worker, or a drone depends on when, where, and how much certain genes are expressed.

While fertilized eggs are diploid and develop as females, males result from the development of unfertilized haploid eggs. This is one example of genes being expressed differently under different conditions, in this case differences in ploidy. However, the most dramatic example of differential gene expression in honeybees is the development of female larvae as queens rather than workers, depending on their diet. All larvae are initially fed royal jelly, a glandular secretion; those larvae destined to become workers are switched to a diet rich in honey and beebread (processed pollen). A variety of compounds in these different diets change the expression of well over half of all honeybee genes; some genes are turned up and others are turned down. In another dramatic example of gene regulation, workers remain sterile throughout their lifetime because the genetic program needed for them to produce eggs is turned off by a chemical signal, a pheromone, produced by the queen.

**FIGURE 13.1** **The three honeybee castes: queen** (a)**, drone** (b)**, and worker** (c)

a.

b.

c.

WILDLIFE GmbH/Alamy Stock Photo

If you think of a honeybee colony as a kind of "superorganism," you may realize that you are also a colony of sorts in which different cell types, like honeybee castes, express different genes. You might think it most efficient for the cells in each differentiated tissue to retain only those genes needed to carry out its specific function; that is, liver cells might be expected to have a different collection of genes than bone cells. However, biochemical and cytogenetic analyses do not support this model and have in fact demonstrated that all nucleated cells of a developing embryo retain essentially the same set of genes that was created in the original single-celled zygote at fertilization. Structural and functional differences in cell types result from the presence or absence of the *products resulting from expression of genes* rather than the presence or absence of the genes themselves. As you saw in the previous chapter, all gene expression initially results in ribonucleic acid (RNA) products made by transcription. One type of RNA product, mRNA, further directs the synthesis of protein products by translation. But what determines when the product is produced, where, and how much? For example, the products of some genes, known as *housekeeping genes*, are expressed in nearly all cells, whereas the products of other genes may be found only in certain cell types, at specific times, and under particular environmental conditions. To illustrate this point, consider that all cells contain genes coding for the rRNA molecules needed for ribosome function as well as genes coding for various hemoglobin polypeptides. While rRNA gene products are abundant in all cells, particular hemoglobins are found only in those cells that give rise to red blood cells.

The material on transcription and translation in the previous chapter hinted at possible regulatory mechanisms of gene expression. Usually, when we say that a gene is "turned on," we mean that it is more likely to be transcribed actively. Beyond transcription, the expression of gene products is subject to further controls affecting the processing of RNA, possible translation into protein, and the activity and "life span" of the product itself.

You saw in the previous chapter that transcription and translation are coincident in prokaryotic cells. This enables a rapid response to environmental conditions through regulation of transcription initiation. Eukaryotes, particularly multicellular organisms, exhibit a variety of regulatory mechanisms not used by prokaryotic organisms. In this chapter, we examine the mechanisms of transcriptional regulation and its fine-tuning by additional controls at the posttranscriptional, translational, and posttranslational levels. Our discussion begins with bacterial systems, where researchers first discovered a mechanism for transcriptional regulation, and then moves to eukaryotic systems, where the regulation of gene activity is more complex. The chapter closes with a look at the loss of regulatory controls in cancer cells.

## 13.1 Regulation of Gene Expression in Prokaryotic Cells

Prokaryotic organisms tend to be single celled and relatively simple, with generation times measured in minutes. Rather than the complex patterns of long-term cell differentiation and development typical of multicellular eukaryotes, prokaryotic cells typically undergo rapid and reversible alterations in biochemical pathways that allow them to adapt quickly to changes in their environment. These alterations are the result of regulatory mechanisms affecting gene expression.

The bacterium *Escherichia coli,* for example, can find itself in the intestinal tract of a cow one minute and then in a treated municipal water supply soon after. Sugars such as lactose might be more available in the aquatic environment, and genes coding for enzymes needed to metabolize this energy source must be turned on. Other nutrients, such as the amino acid tryptophan, may be abundant in the intestinal tract environment. Therefore, genes coding for enzymes needed to manufacture the amino acid from scratch must be turned off. A versatile and responsive control system allows the bacterium to make the most efficient use of the particular array of nutrients and energy sources available at any given time.

## 13.1a Some Regulated Genes Occur in Clusters Called *Operons*

Some regulated genes in the prokaryotic genome occur singly, meaning that the gene is transcribed by RNA polymerase to produce an mRNA molecule that is translated to produce a single polypeptide. A useful term to introduce here is the **transcription unit**, which means the segment of DNA from the initiation point of transcription to the termination point of transcription (see Chapter 12). The transcription unit for a protein-coding gene that occurs singly in a genome corresponds to the mRNA-coding sequence of that gene.

Other regulated genes occur in clusters. Each cluster constitutes one transcription unit, meaning that the set of genes in the cluster is transcribed into a *single* mRNA molecule. Translation of the mRNA produces polypeptides corresponding to each of the genes in the transcription unit. The organization of genes in a cluster provides a means for efficient coordinated regulation of those genes, called the *operon model,* for the control of gene expression. In 1961, François Jacob and Jacques Monod of the Pasteur Institute in Paris proposed this model for the control of the expression of genes for lactose metabolism in *E. coli.* Subsequently, data have shown the operon model to be widely applicable to the regulation of gene expression in bacteria and their viruses. Jacob and Monod received the Nobel Prize in 1965 for their explanation of bacterial operons and their regulation by repressors.

An **operon** is a cluster of prokaryotic genes and the DNA sequences involved in their regulation. The promoter, as we saw in the previous chapter, is a region where the RNA polymerase begins transcription. Another regulatory DNA sequence in the operon is the **operator**, a short segment that is a binding sequence for a **regulatory protein**. A gene that is separate from the operon encodes the regulatory protein. Some operons are controlled by a regulatory protein termed a **repressor**, which, when bound to the DNA, reduces the likelihood that genes will be transcribed. Other operons are controlled by a regulatory protein termed an **activator**, which, when bound to the DNA, increases the likelihood that genes will be transcribed. Many operons are controlled by more than one regulatory mechanism, and several of the repressors or activators control more than one operon. The result is a complex network of superimposed controls that provides regulation of transcription, allowing almost instantaneous global responses to changing environmental conditions.

Each operon, which can contain several to many genes, is transcribed as a unit from the promoter into a single messenger RNA (mRNA), and, as a result, the mRNA contains codes for several proteins. The cluster of genes transcribed into a single mRNA is called a **transcription unit**. A ribosome translates the entire mRNA from one end to the other, sequentially making each protein that is encoded in the mRNA. Typically, the proteins encoded by genes in the same operon catalyze steps in the same process, such as enzymes acting in sequence in a biochemical pathway.

## 13.1b The *lac* Operon for Lactose Metabolism Is Transcribed When an Inducer Inactivates a Repressor

Jacob and Monod researched the genetic control of lactose metabolism in *E. coli* through a series of brilliantly creative genetic and biochemical approaches. Their studies showed that metabolism of lactose as an energy source involves three genes: *lacZ, lacY,* and *lacA* (**Figure 13.2**). These three genes are adjacent to one another on the chromosome in the order *Z-Y-A.* The genes are transcribed as a unit into a single mRNA starting with the *lacZ* gene; the promoter for the transcription unit is upstream of *lacZ.* The *lacZ* gene encodes the enzyme β-galactosidase, which catalyzes the conversion of the disaccharide sugar lactose

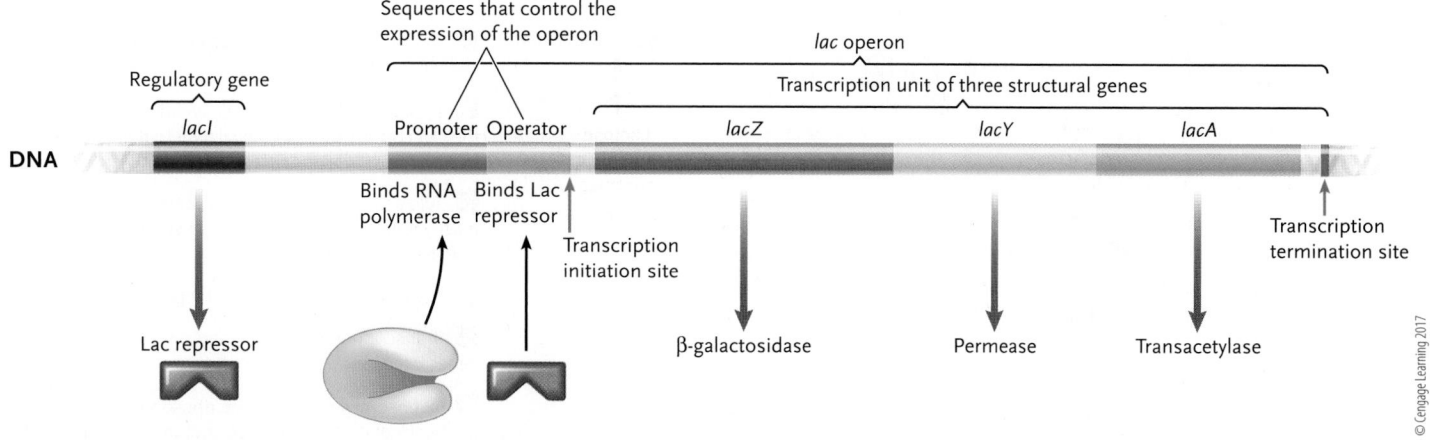

**FIGURE 13.2 The *E. coli lac* operon.** The *lacZ, lacY,* and *lacA* genes encode the proteins taking part in lactose metabolism. A separate regulatory gene, *lacI,* encodes the Lac repressor, which plays a pivotal role in the control of the operon. The promoter binds RNA polymerase, and the operator binds activated Lac repressor. The transcription unit, which extends from the transcription initiation site to the transcription termination site, contains the structural genes.

into the monosaccharide sugars glucose and galactose. It also can convert lactose into an isomer called *allolactose*, which is important for regulating the operon. Glucose and galactose are further metabolized by other enzymes, producing energy for the cell by glycolysis and the citric acid cycle (see Chapter 5). The *lacY* gene encodes a permease enzyme that transports lactose actively into the cell, and the *lacA* gene encodes a transacetylase enzyme, the function of which is more relevant to metabolism of compounds other than lactose.

Jacob and Monod called the cluster of genes and adjacent sequences that control their expression the *lac operon* (see Figure 13.2). They coined the name *operon* from the key DNA sequence they discovered for regulating transcription of the operon, the operator. The operator was named because it controls the operation of the genes adjacent to it. For the *lac* operon,

the operator is a short DNA sequence between the promoter and the *lacZ* gene.

These two investigators showed that the *lac* operon was controlled by a regulatory protein that they termed the *Lac repressor*. The Lac repressor is encoded by the regulatory gene *lacI*, which is nearby but separate from the *lac* operon (see Figure 13.2), and is synthesized in active form. When lactose is absent from the medium, the Lac repressor binds to the operator, thereby blocking the RNA polymerase from binding to the promoter **(Figure 13.3a)**. Repressor binding is a kind of equilibrium: while it is bound to the operator most of the time, it occasionally comes off. In moments when the repressor is not bound, polymerase can successfully transcribe. As a result, *there is always a low concentration of* lac *operon gene products in the cell.*

**a. Lactose absent from medium: structural genes not transcribed**

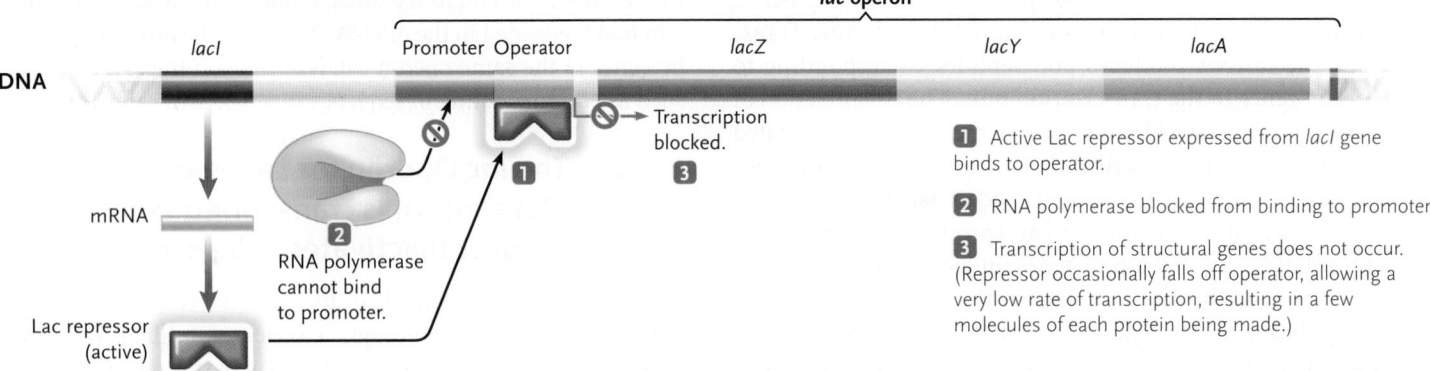

**b. Lactose present in medium: structural genes transcribed**

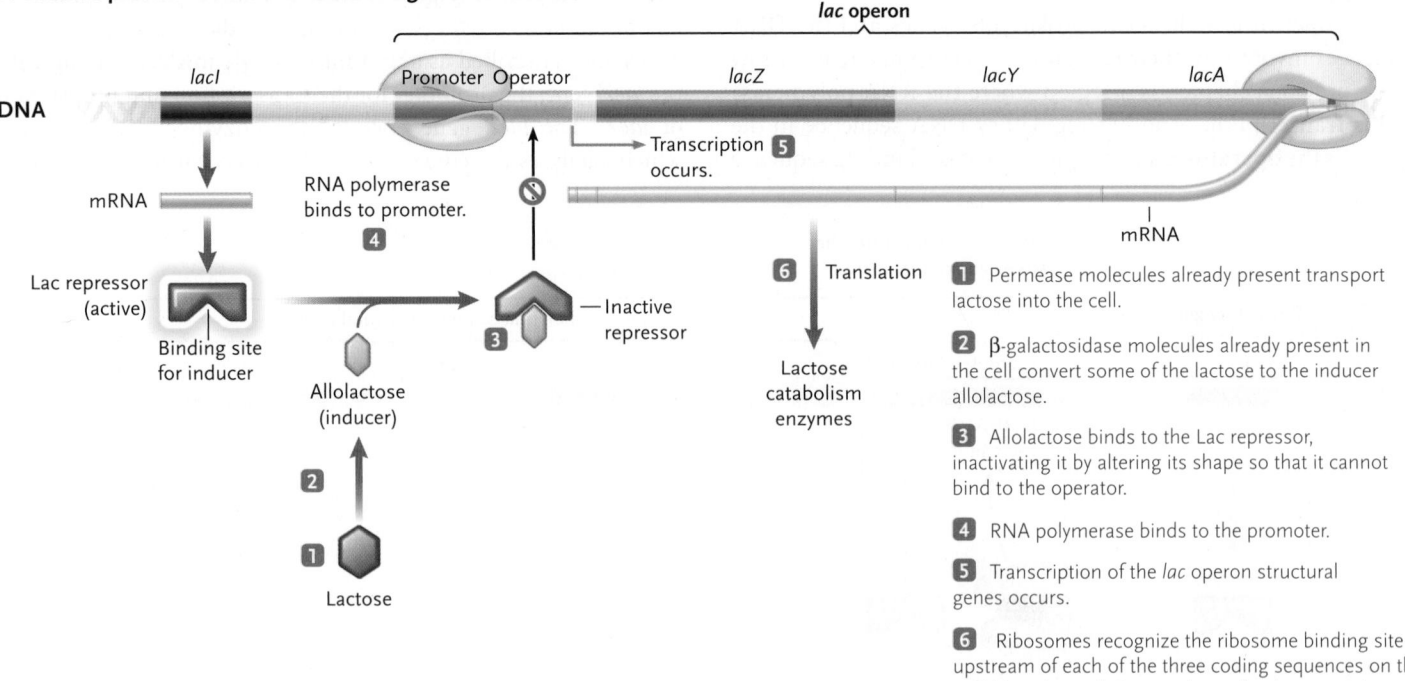

**FIGURE 13.3 Regulation of the inducible *lac* operon by the Lac repressor in the absence (a) and presence (b) of lactose**

When lactose is added to the medium, the *lac* operon is turned on and all three enzymes are synthesized rapidly (Figure 13.3b). How does this occur? Lactose enters the cell and the low levels of β-galactosidase molecules already present convert some of it to *allolactose*, an isomer of lactose. Allolactose is an **inducer** for the *lac* operon. It binds to the Lac repressor, altering its shape so that the repressor can no longer bind to the operator DNA. With the repressor out of the way, RNA polymerase is then able to bind freely to the promoter and transcribe the three genes at a dramatically elevated rate. Because an inducer molecule increases its expression, the *lac* operon is called an **inducible operon**.

As the lactose is used up, the regulatory system switches the *lac* operon off. That is, the absence of lactose means that there are no allolactose inducer molecules to inactivate the repressor; the repressor binds to the operator, reducing transcription of the operon. These controls are aided by the fact that bacterial mRNAs are very short lived, about three minutes on average. This quick turnover permits the cytoplasm to be cleared quickly of the mRNAs transcribed from an operon. The enzymes themselves also have short lifetimes and are quickly degraded.

### 13.1c Transcription of the *lac* Operon Is Also Controlled by a Positive Regulatory System

Several years after Jacob and Monod proposed their negatively regulated operon model for the lactose metabolism genes, researchers found a *positive gene regulation* system that makes expression of the *lac* operon responsive to the availability of glucose. Glucose can be used directly in the glycolysis pathway to produce energy for the cell (see Chapter 5). However, lactose must first be converted into glucose by biochemical reactions that require energy. The net yield of energy from other sugars is therefore less than that for glucose, and cells will grow best if they ensure the preferential metabolism of glucose whenever it is available.

**Figure 13.4** shows that the *lac* operon is sensitive to the availability of glucose through the binding of an activator protein called *CAP* (catabolite activator protein). The CAP binding site is on the DNA, just upstream of the *lac* promoter. When bound at this site, CAP bends the DNA in ways that make the promoter *more* accessible to RNA polymerase, and transcription increases. To understand how CAP binding is related to the availability of glucose, you need to know (1) that CAP is synthesized in an inactive form that can bind to DNA only *after* it is activated by binding with **cyclic AMP** (**cAMP**; a nucleotide that plays a role in regulating cellular processes in both prokaryotic and eukaryotic cells; see Chapter 7), and (2) that cAMP levels are inversely related to the uptake of glucose from the growth medium: when glucose is abundant, cAMP levels tend to be low (meaning CAP is mostly inactive), and when glucose is absent from the environment, cAMP concentration tends to be high inside the cell, leading to an increased level of activated CAP.

Taken together, the negative control by the Lac repressor and the positive control by CAP/cAMP ensure that cells express the *lac* operon most strongly only when lactose is present and glucose is not. Let's walk through one illustrative example to emphasize the interrelationships among the various players. Imagine cells growing on glucose only. In the presence of glucose, very little cAMP is available to bind to CAP. Therefore, CAP/cAMP binding will be rare and there will be very little stimulation of expression. In the absence of lactose, the Lac repressor will be bound to the operator site most of the time and very little synthesis of the *lac* genes will occur. For these two reasons, expression of the *lac* operon will be at its lowest level. If we then add lactose to the environment, it will be metabolized to the inducer, allolactose, which will bind to and inactivate the Lac repressor. RNA polymerase will then bind to the promoter and transcribe the *lac* operon genes at a low level. Expression will increase further as glucose is metabolized from the surrounding medium, allowing cAMP levels to rise, activated CAP to bind, and the *lac* promoter to become even more available to RNA polymerase.

**CONCEPT FIX** Inducing *lac* operon expression through negative control and repressing expression through positive control may sound confusing. How can negative control make expression increase? The answer to this apparent paradox lies in focusing your attention on the DNA-binding proteins: Lac repressor and CAP. In general, if the binding of a protein to DNA results in decreased gene expression, that is negative control. If the binding of a protein results in increased gene expression, that is positive control. Therefore, the binding of the Lac repressor is a clear example of negative control. When this repression is *released*, the *lac* operon is induced and expression increases. *Whether gene expression is under negative or positive control depends on the impact of the respective DNA-binding proteins, not on the impact of the available substrates such as glucose or lactose.* ◼

The same positive gene regulation system using CAP and cAMP regulates many other operons that control the metabolism of many sugars. In each case, the system functions so that glucose, if it is present in the growth medium, is metabolized first. This type of regulatory system, in which several operons are under the control of a common regulator, is called a *regulon*.

### 13.1d Transcription of the *trp* Operon Genes for Tryptophan Biosynthesis Is Repressed When Tryptophan Activates a Repressor

Tryptophan is an essential amino acid used in the synthesis of proteins. If tryptophan is absent from the medium, *E. coli* must manufacture it; if tryptophan is present in the medium, then the cell will use that source rather than make its own.

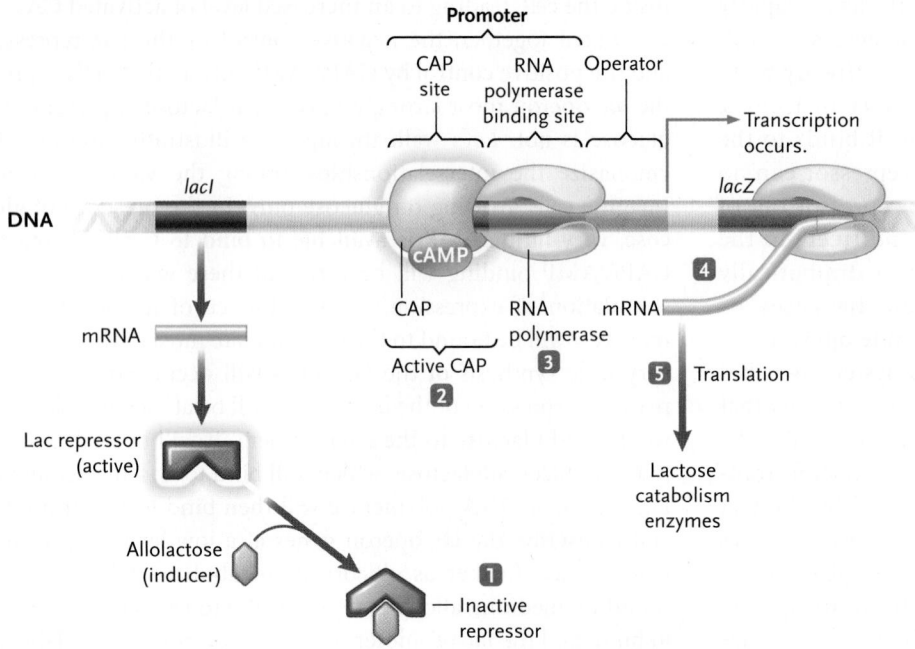

**a. Lactose present and glucose low or absent: structural genes expressed at high levels**

**Promoter**

CAP site

RNA polymerase binding site

Operator

*lacI*

DNA

cAMP

Transcription occurs.

*lacZ*

CAP

RNA polymerase

mRNA

Active CAP

mRNA

Lac repressor (active)

Translation

Lactose catabolism enzymes

Allolactose (inducer)

Inactive repressor

1. Lactose converted to the inducer, allolactose, which inactivates Lac repressor.

2. Active adenylyl cyclase synthesizes cAMP to high levels. cAMP binds to activator CAP, activating it. Activated CAP binds to CAP site in the promoter.

3. RNA polymerase binds efficiently to the promoter.

4. Genes of operon transcribed to high levels.

5. Translation produces high amounts of proteins.

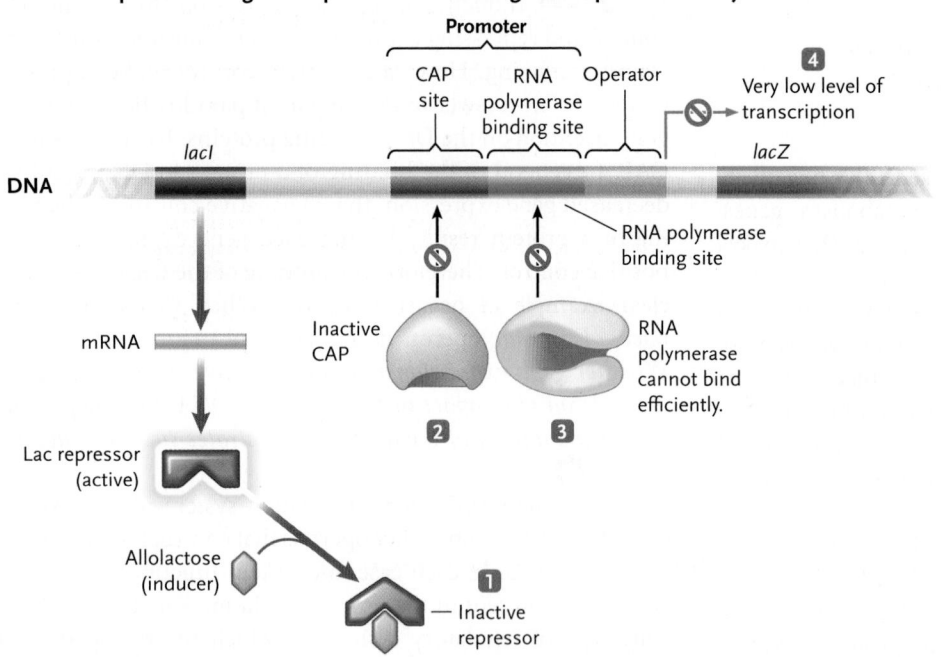

**b. Lactose present and glucose present: structural genes expressed at very low levels**

**Promoter**

CAP site

RNA polymerase binding site

Operator

Very low level of transcription

*lacI*

DNA

*lacZ*

RNA polymerase binding site

mRNA

Inactive CAP

RNA polymerase cannot bind efficiently.

Lac repressor (active)

Allolactose (inducer)

Inactive repressor

1. Lactose converted to the inducer, allolactose, which inactivates Lac repressor.

2. Catabolism of incoming glucose leads to inactivation of adenylyl cyclase, which causes the amount of cAMP in the cell to drop to a level too low to activate CAP. Inactive CAP cannot bind to the CAP site.

3. RNA polymerase is unable to bind to the promoter efficiently.

4. Transcription occurs at a very low level: Because the Lac repressor is not present to block RNA polymerase from binding to the promoter, the level of transcription is higher than when lactose is absent, but far lower than when lactose is present and glucose is absent.

© Cengage Learning 2017

**FIGURE 13.4 Positive regulation of the *lac* operon by the CAP activator**

The genes involved in tryptophan biosynthesis are coordinately controlled in an operon called the *trp* operon (**Figure 13.5**). The five genes in this operon, *trpA* to *trpE*, encode the enzymes for the steps in the tryptophan biosynthesis pathway. Upstream of the *trpE* gene are the operon's promoter and operator sequences. Expression of the *trp* operon is controlled by the Trp repressor, a regulatory protein encoded by the *trpR* gene, which is located elsewhere in the genome. In contrast to the Lac repressor, the Trp repressor is synthesized in an inactive form in which it cannot bind to the operator.

When tryptophan is absent from the medium and must be made by the cell, the *trp* operon genes are expressed (see Figure 13.5a). This is the default state. Since the Trp repressor is inactive and cannot bind to the operator, RNA polymerase can bind to the promoter and transcribe the operon. The resulting mRNA is translated to produce the five tryptophan biosynthetic enzymes that catalyze the reactions for tryptophan synthesis.

If tryptophan is present, there is no need for the cell to make it, so the *trp* operon is shut off (see Figure 13.5b). This occurs because the tryptophan entering the cell binds to the Trp

**a. Tryptophan absent from medium: tryptophan must be made by the cell—structural genes transcribed**

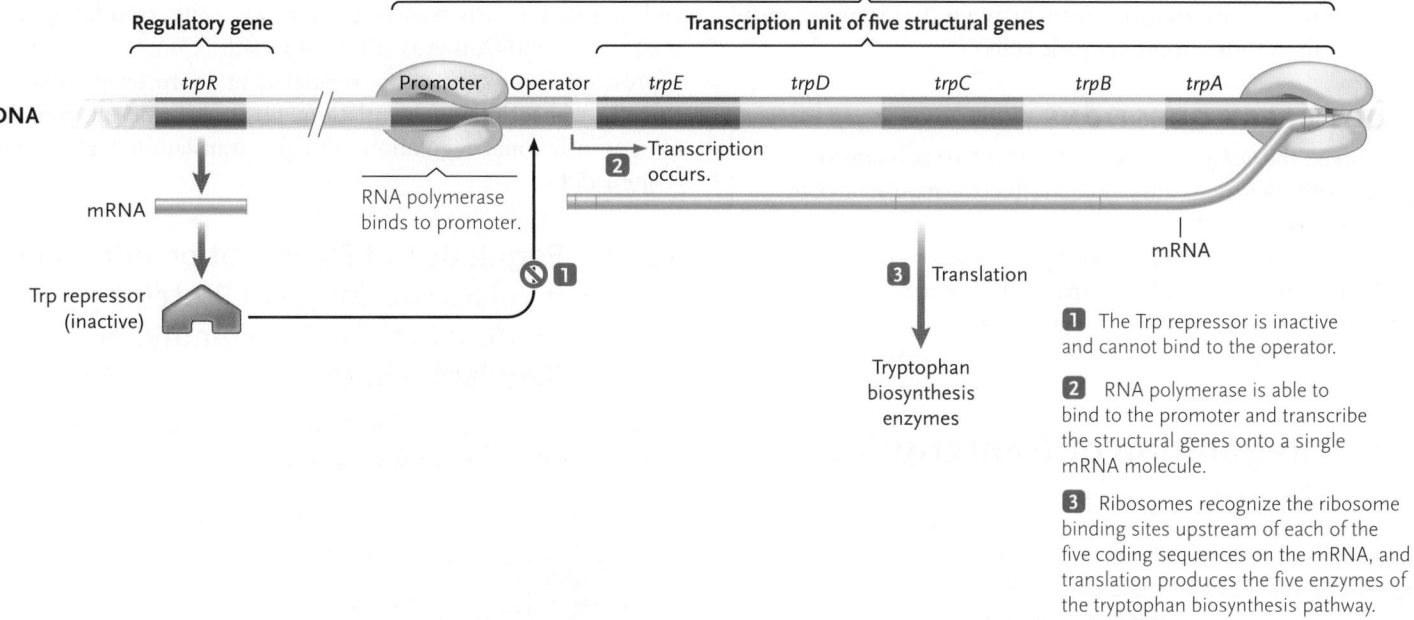

1. The Trp repressor is inactive and cannot bind to the operator.

2. RNA polymerase is able to bind to the promoter and transcribe the structural genes onto a single mRNA molecule.

3. Ribosomes recognize the ribosome binding sites upstream of each of the five coding sequences on the mRNA, and translation produces the five enzymes of the tryptophan biosynthesis pathway.

**b. Tryptophan present in medium: cell uses tryptophan in medium rather than synthesizing it—structural genes not transcribed**

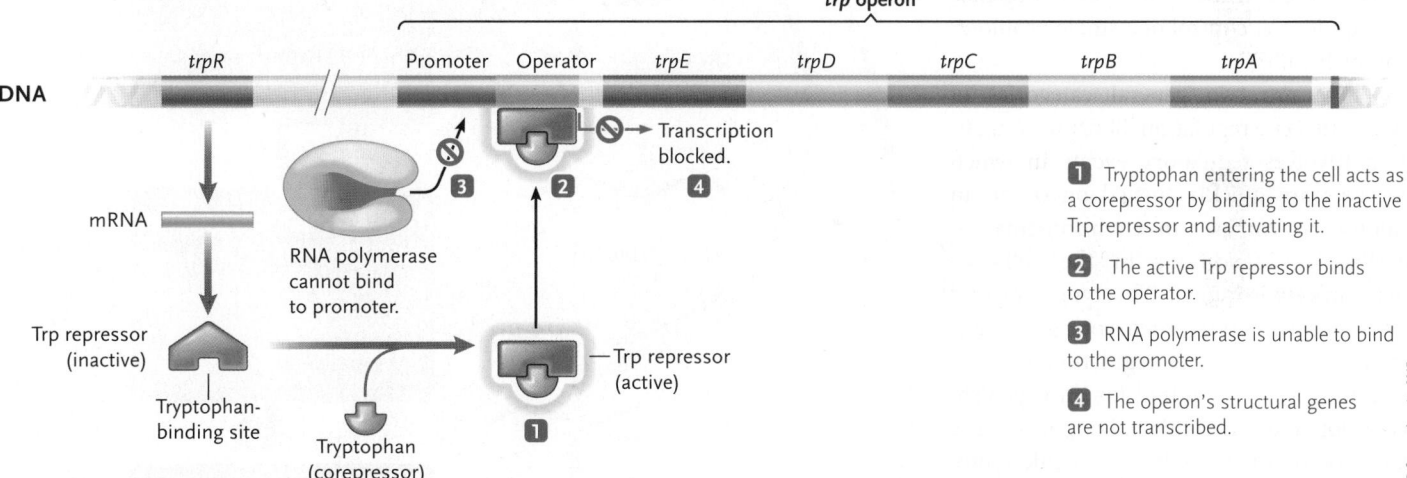

1. Tryptophan entering the cell acts as a corepressor by binding to the inactive Trp repressor and activating it.

2. The active Trp repressor binds to the operator.

3. RNA polymerase is unable to bind to the promoter.

4. The operon's structural genes are not transcribed.

© Cengage Learning 2017

**FIGURE 13.5 Regulation of the repressible *trp* operon by the Trp repressor protein in the absence** (a) **and presence** (b) **of the amino acid tryptophan**

repressor and activates it. The active Trp repressor then binds to the operator of the *trp* operon and blocks RNA polymerase from binding to the promoter: the operon cannot be transcribed.

For the *trp* operon, then, the presence of tryptophan represses the expression of the tryptophan biosynthesis genes; hence, this operon is an example of a **repressible operon**. Here, tryptophan acts as a **corepressor**, a regulatory molecule that combines with a repressor to activate it and thus shut off the operon.

Let's compare the two operons we have discussed: (1) In the *lac* operon, the repressor is synthesized in an active form. When the inducer (allolactose) is present, it binds to the repressor and inactivates it. The operon is then transcribed. (2) In the *trp* operon, the repressor is synthesized in an inactive form.

When the corepressor (tryptophan) is present, it binds to the repressor and activates it. The active repressor blocks transcription of the operon.

**CONCEPT FIX** Both inducible and repressible operons illustrate *negative gene regulation* because both are regulated by a repressor that turns off gene expression when it binds DNA.

In summary, regulation of gene expression in prokaryotic cells occurs primarily at the transcription level. There are also, however, some examples of regulation at the translation level. For example, some proteins can bind to the mRNAs in unfertilized eggs, preventing translation until fertilization. This serves as a feedback mechanism to fine-tune the amounts of the proteins in the cell. In the remainder of the chapter, we discuss the regulation of gene expression in eukaryotes. You will see that regulation occurs at several points in the gene expression pathway and that regulatory mechanisms are more complex than those in prokaryotic cells.

# 13.2 Regulation of Transcription in Eukaryotes

The molecular mechanisms in prokaryotic operon function are a simple means of coordinating synthesis of proteins with related functions. In eukaryotes, the coordinated synthesis of proteins with related functions also occurs, but without the need to organize genes under the control of a single promoter in an operon.

There are two general categories of eukaryotic gene regulation. Short-term regulation involves regulatory events in which gene sets are quickly turned on or off in response to changes in environmental or physiological conditions in the cell's or organism's environment. This type of regulation is most similar to prokaryotic gene regulation. Long-term gene regulation involves regulatory events required for an organism to develop and differentiate. Long-term gene regulation occurs in multicellular eukaryotes and not in simpler, unicellular eukaryotes. The mechanisms we discuss in this and the next section are applicable to both short-term and long-term regulation.

## 13.2a In Eukaryotes, Regulation of Gene Expression Occurs at Several Levels

The regulation of gene expression is more complicated in eukaryotes than in prokaryotic cells because eukaryotic cells are more complex, because the nuclear DNA is organized with histones into chromatin, and because multicellular eukaryotes produce

large numbers and different types of cells. Further, the eukaryotic nuclear envelope separates the processes of transcription and translation, whereas in prokaryotic cells, translation can start on an mRNA that is still being made. Consequently, gene expression in eukaryotes is regulated at more levels; that is, there is transcriptional regulation, posttranscriptional regulation, translational regulation, and posttranslational regulation (**Figure 13.6**).

## 13.2b Regulation of Transcription Initiation Involves the Effects of Proteins Binding to a Gene's Promoter and Regulatory Sites

Transcription initiation is the most common level at which the regulation of gene expression takes place.

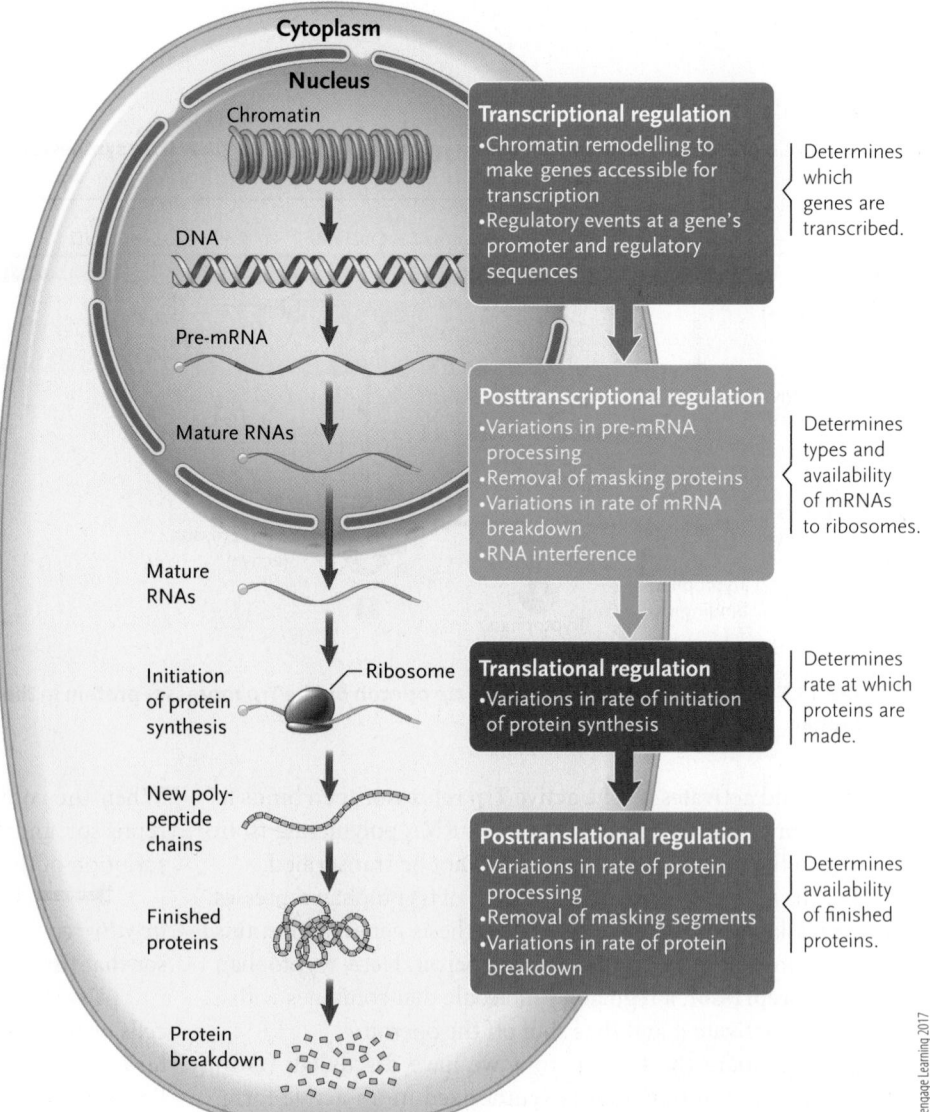

**FIGURE 13.6 Steps in transcriptional, posttranscriptional, translational, and posttranslational regulation of gene expression in eukaryotes**

© Cengage Learning 2017

## ORGANIZATION OF A EUKARYOTIC PROTEIN-CODING GENE Figure 13.7 shows a eukaryotic gene, emphasizing the regulatory sites involved in its expression. Immediately upstream of the transcription unit is the promoter. The promoter in the figure contains a **TATA box**, a sequence about 25 base pairs (bp) upstream of the start point for transcription that, as we will shortly see, plays an important role in transcription initiation in many promoters. The TATA box has the 7 bp consensus sequence

5′-TATAAAA-3′

3′-ATATTTT-5′

Promoters without TATA boxes have other sequence elements that play a similar role. In the following discussions, we describe transcription initiation involving a TATA box-containing promoter.

RNA polymerase II itself cannot recognize the promoter sequence. Instead, proteins called **transcription factors** recognize and bind to the TATA box and then recruit the polymerase. Once the RNA polymerase II–transcription factor complex forms, the polymerase unwinds the DNA and transcription begins. Adjacent to the promoter, farther upstream, is the **promoter proximal region** (*proximus* is Latin for "nearby"), which contains regulatory sequences called **promoter proximal elements**. Regulatory proteins that bind to promoter proximal elements may stimulate or inhibit the rate of transcription initiation. More distant from the beginning of the gene is the **enhancer**. Regulatory proteins binding to regulatory sequences

within an enhancer also stimulate or inhibit the rate of transcription initiation. Next we see more specifically how these regulatory sequences are involved in transcription initiation.

## ACTIVATION OF TRANSCRIPTION To initiate transcription, proteins called **general transcription factors** (also called *basal transcription factors*) bind to the promoter in the area of the TATA box (**Figure 13.8**). These factors recruit the enzyme RNA polymerase II (which alone cannot bind to the promoter) and orient the enzyme to start transcription at the correct place. The combination of general transcription factors with RNA polymerase II is the **transcription initiation complex**. On its own, this complex brings about only a low rate of transcription initiation, which leads to just a few mRNA transcripts.

**Activators** are regulatory proteins that play a role in a positive regulatory system that controls the expression of one or more genes. Activators that bind to the promoter proximal elements interact directly with the general transcription factors at the promoter to stimulate transcription initiation, so many more transcripts are synthesized over a given time. Housekeeping genes (genes that are expressed in all cell types for basic cellular functions such as glucose metabolism) have promoter proximal elements that are recognized by activators present in all cell types. By contrast, genes expressed only in particular cell types or at particular times have promoter proximal elements that are recognized by activators found only in those cell types, or at those times when transcription of these genes needs to be activated. To turn this around, the particular set of activators present within a cell at a given time are responsible for determining which genes in that cell are expressed to a significant level.

The DNA-binding and activation functions of activators are properties of two distinct domains in the proteins. (Protein domains are introduced in *The Purple Pages*.) The three-dimensional arrangement of amino acid chains within and between domains also produces highly specialized regions called **motifs**. Several types of motifs, each with a specialized

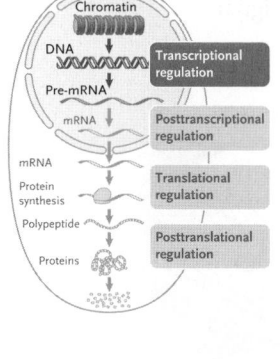

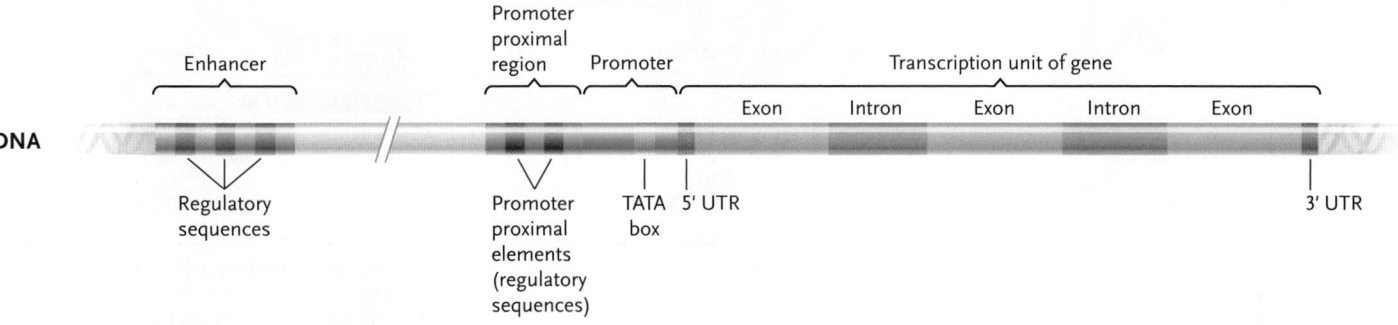

**FIGURE 13.7 Organization of a eukaryotic gene.** The transcription unit is the segment that is transcribed into the pre-mRNA; it contains the 5′ UTR (untranslated region), exons, introns, and 3′ UTR. Immediately upstream of the transcription unit is the promoter, which often contains the TATA box. Adjacent to the promoter and farther upstream of the transcription unit is the promoter proximal region, which contains regulatory sequences called *promoter proximal elements*. More distant from the gene is the enhancer, which contains regulatory sequences that control the rate of transcription of the gene. Transcription of the gene produces a pre-mRNA molecule with a 5′ cap and 3′ poly(A) tail; processing of the pre-mRNA to remove introns generates the functional mRNA (see Chapter 12).

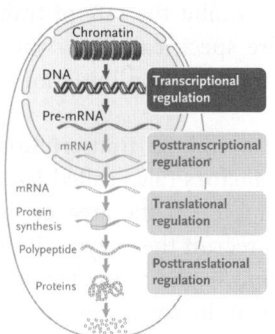

**FIGURE 13.8 Formation of the transcription complex on the promoter of a protein-coding gene by the combination of general transcription factors with RNA polymerase.** General transcription factors are needed for RNA polymerase to bind and initiate transcription at the correct place.

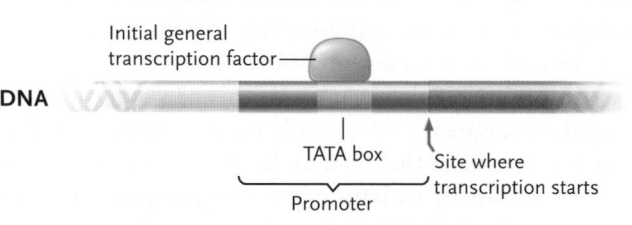

**1** The first general transcription factor recognizes and binds to the TATA box of a protein-coding gene's promoter.

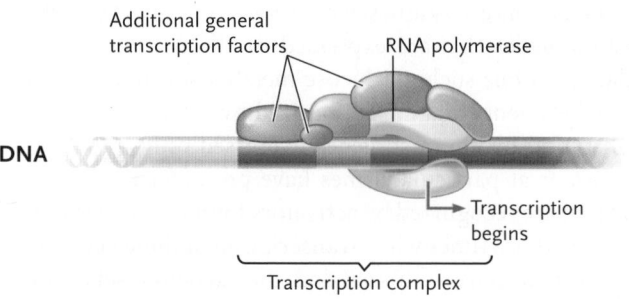

**2** Additional general transcription factors and then RNA polymerase add to the complex. A general transcription factor unwinds the promoter DNA, and then transcription begins.

© Cengage Learning 2017

function, are found in proteins, including motifs that insert into the DNA double helix. Motifs found in the DNA-binding domains of regulatory proteins, such as activators, include the helix-turn-helix, the zinc finger, and the leucine zipper (**Figure 13.9**).

Activators binding at the enhancer greatly increase transcription rates (**Figure 13.10**). The enhancers of different genes have different sets of regulatory sequences, which bind particular activators. A **coactivator** (also called a *mediator*) is a large multiprotein complex that forms a bridge between the activators at the enhancer and the proteins at the promoter and promoter proximal region, causing the DNA to form a loop. The interactions between the activators at the enhancer, the coactivator, the proteins at the promoter, and the RNA polymerase greatly stimulate transcription up to its maximal rate.

**REPRESSION OF TRANSCRIPTION** In some genes, repressors oppose the effect of activators, thereby blocking or reducing the rate of transcription. The final rate of transcription then depends on the "battle" between the activation signal and the repression signal.

**a. Helix-turn-helix**

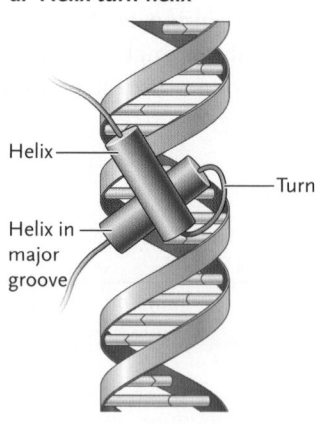

A helix-turn-helix motif is part of a protein bound to DNA. One of the α-helices binds to base pairs in the major groove of the DNA. A looped region of the protein—the turn—connects to a second α-helix, which helps hold the first helix in place.

**b. Zinc finger**

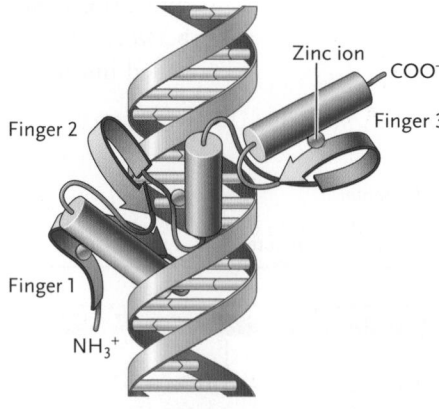

Zinc finger motifs are parts of proteins named for their resemblance to fingers projecting from a protein and the presence of a bound zinc atom. Zinc fingers bind to specific base pairs in the grooves of DNA.

**c. Leucine zipper**

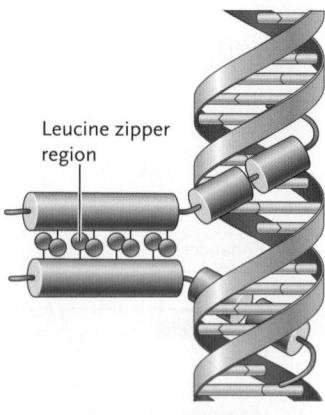

Leucine zipper proteins are dimers, with each monomer consisting of α-helical segments. Hydrophobic interactions between leucine residues within the leucine zipper motif hold the two monomers together. Other α-helices bind to DNA base pairs in the major groove.

**FIGURE 13.9 Three DNA-binding motifs found in activators and other regulatory proteins**

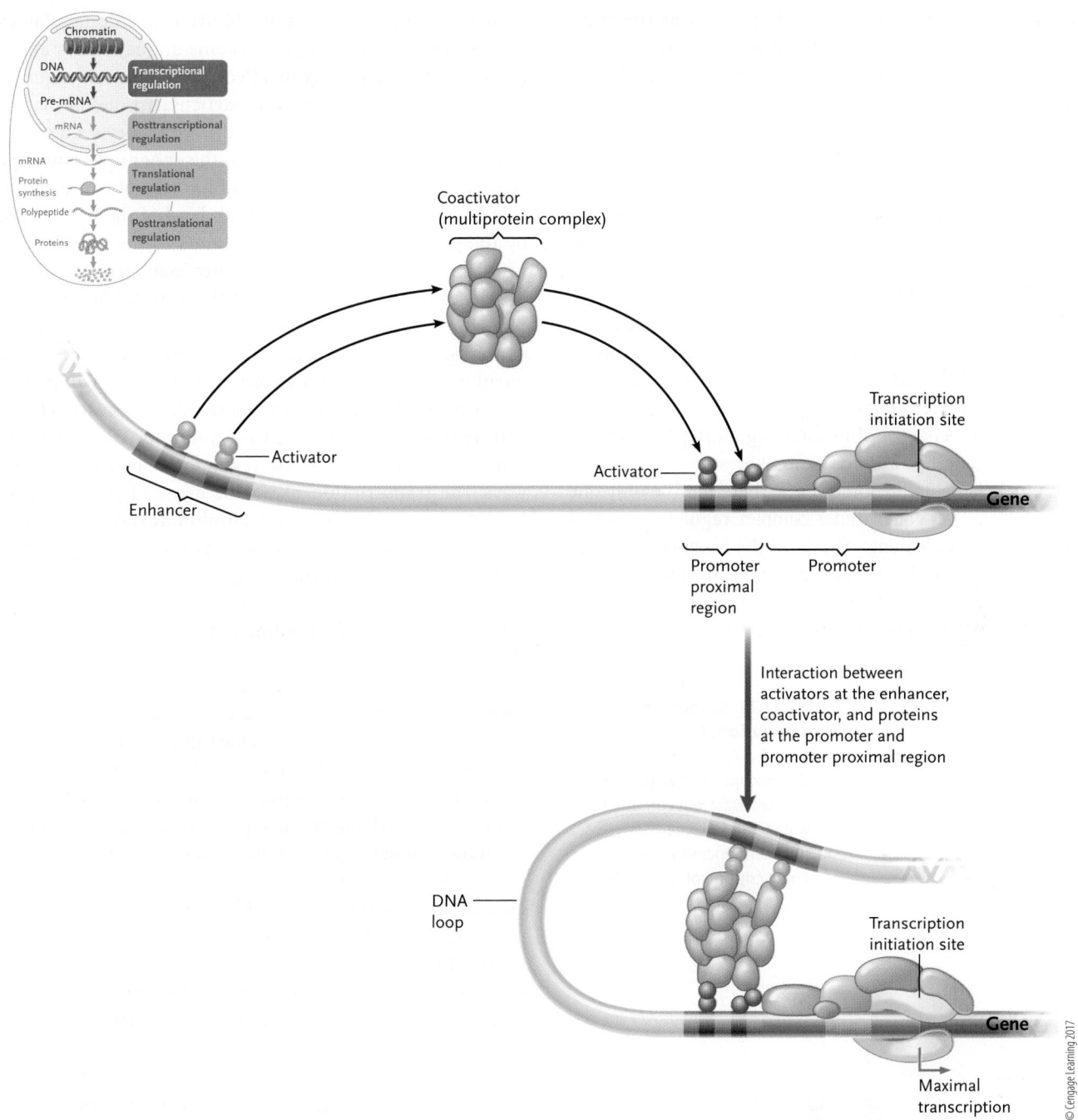

**FIGURE 13.10 Interactions between activators at the enhancer, a coactivator, and general transcription factors at the promoter lead to maximal transcription of the gene**

Repressors in eukaryotes work in various ways. Some repressors bind to the same regulatory sequence to which activators bind (often in the enhancer), thereby preventing activators from binding to that site. Other repressors bind to their own specific site in the DNA near where the activator binds and interact with the activator so that it cannot interact with the coactivator. Yet other repressors bind to specific sites in the DNA and recruit corepressors, inhibiting transcription initiation. (Corepressors are multiprotein complexes analogous to coactivators except that they are negative regulators.)

One new area of research in gene regulation is the influence of various RNA molecules on the transcription of target genes.

You learned in Chapter 12 that the human genome is transcribed pervasively. Most transcripts are noncoding RNAs (ncRNAs), RNAs that are not translated into proteins. In humans, the largest class of ncRNAs consists of long noncoding RNAs (lncRNAs; pronounced "link" RNAs). lncRNAs are like mRNAs: they are transcribed by RNA polymerase II and have 5′ caps and 3′ poly(A) tails. Primary lncRNA transcripts contain introns that often are removed by splicing. However, like other ncRNAs, and unlike mRNAs, they are not translated to produce proteins.

Although most lncRNAs appear be non-functional products of accidental transcription, accumulating evidence indicates that particular lncRNAs can negatively or positively regulate the expression of protein-coding genes at the transcriptional level. Diverse mechanisms of gene expression regulation have been seen, including guiding chromatin remodelling complexes to specific genomic loci so they can exert their effects, and binding to transcription factors to prevent them from binding to their target DNA sequence.

**COMBINATORIAL GENE REGULATION** Let's review the key elements of transcription regulation for a protein-coding gene. General transcription factors bind to certain promoter sequences, such as the TATA box, and recruit RNA polymerase II; this results in a basal level of transcription. Specific activators bind to promoter proximal elements and stimulate the rate of transcription initiation. Activators also bind to the enhancer to greatly stimulate transcription of the gene.

How are these events coordinated in regulating gene expression? Any given gene has a specific number and types of promoter proximal elements. In some genes, there may be only one regulatory element, but genes under complex regulatory control have many regulatory elements. Similarly, the number and types of regulatory sequences in the enhancer are specific for each gene.

Both promoter proximal regions and enhancers are important in regulating the transcription of a gene. Each regulatory

sequence in these two regions binds a specific regulatory protein. Since some regulatory proteins are activators and others are repressors, the overall effect of regulatory sequences on transcription depends on the particular proteins that bind to them. If activators bind both to the regulatory sequences in the promoter proximal region and to the enhancer, transcription is activated maximally, meaning a high rate of transcription and therefore the production of a high level of the mRNA encoded by the gene. But, if a repressor binds to the enhancer and an activator binds to the promoter proximal element, the amount of gene expression depends upon the relative effects of these two regulatory proteins. For example, if the repressor is strong, gene expression, in terms of the rate of transcription and the consequent level of the mRNA encoded by the gene, will be reduced.

A relatively small number of regulatory proteins (activators and repressors) control transcription of all protein-coding genes. By combining a few regulatory proteins in particular ways, the transcription of a wide array of genes can be controlled. The process is called **combinatorial gene regulation**. Consider a theoretical example of two genes, each with activators already bound to their respective promoter proximal elements **(Figure 13.11)**. Maximal transcription of gene A requires activators 2, 5, 7, and 8 binding to their regulatory sequences in the enhancer, whereas maximal transcription of gene B requires activators 1, 5, 8, and 11 binding to its enhancer. Looked at another way, both genes require activators 5 and 8 combined with other different activators for full activation.

This operating principle solves a basic dilemma in gene regulation: if each gene were regulated by a single distinct protein, the number of genes encoding regulatory proteins would have to equal the number of genes to be regulated. Regulating the regulators would require another set of genes of equal number, and so on until the coding capacity of any chromosome set, no matter how large, would be exhausted. But because different genes require different combinations of regulatory proteins, the number of genes encoding regulatory proteins can be much lower than the number of genes the regulatory proteins control. Another advantage is that a small set of regulatory proteins can modulate several genes required for a single type of response.

**COORDINATED REGULATION OF TRANSCRIPTION OF GENES WITH RELATED FUNCTIONS** In the discussion of prokaryotic operons, you learned that genes with related function are often clustered *and* they are transcribed from one promoter onto a single mRNA. That mRNA is translated to produce the several proteins encoded by the genes. There are no operons in eukaryotes, yet

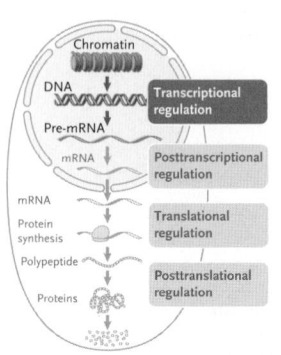

**FIGURE 13.11 Combinatorial gene regulation.** A relatively small number of regulatory proteins control transcription of all protein-coding genes. Different combinations of activators bind to enhancer regulatory sequences to control the rate of transcription of each gene.

a. **A unique combination of activators controls gene A.**

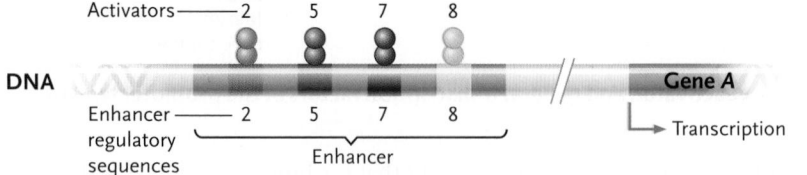

Gene A, controlled by activators 2, 5, 7, and 8 binding to regulatory sequences in its enhancer

b. **A different combination of activators controls gene B.**

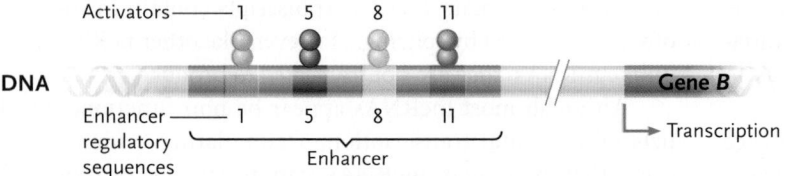

Gene B, controlled by activators 1, 5, 8, and 11 binding to regulatory sequences in its enhancer

© Cengage Learning 2017

the transcription of genes with related function is coordinately controlled. The preceding discussion of regulatory sequences and binding proteins gives an indication of how coordinated control is accomplished in eukaryotes.

All genes that are coordinately regulated have the same regulatory sequences associated with them. Therefore, with one signal, the transcription of all the genes can be controlled simultaneously. Consider the control of gene expression by steroid hormones in mammals. A **hormone** is a molecule produced by one tissue and transported to a target tissue or tissues to alter physiological activity. A **steroid** is a type of lipid derived from cholesterol (see *The Purple Pages*). Examples of steroid hormones are testosterone and glucocorticoid. Testosterone regulates the expression of many genes associated with the maintenance of primary and secondary male characteristics (see Section 10.2b). Glucocorticoid, among other actions, regulates the expression of genes involved in the maintenance of the concentration of glucose and other fuel molecules in the blood. **Figure 13.12** illustrates how a steroid hormone, when it enters a cell, activates gene transcription.

**FIGURE 13.12  Steroid hormone regulation of gene expression.**
A steroid hormone enters the cell and forms a complex in the cytoplasm with a steroid hormone receptor that is specific to the hormone. Steroid hormone–receptor complexes migrate to the nucleus, bind to the steroid hormone response element next to each gene they control (one such gene is shown in the figure), and affect the transcription of those genes.

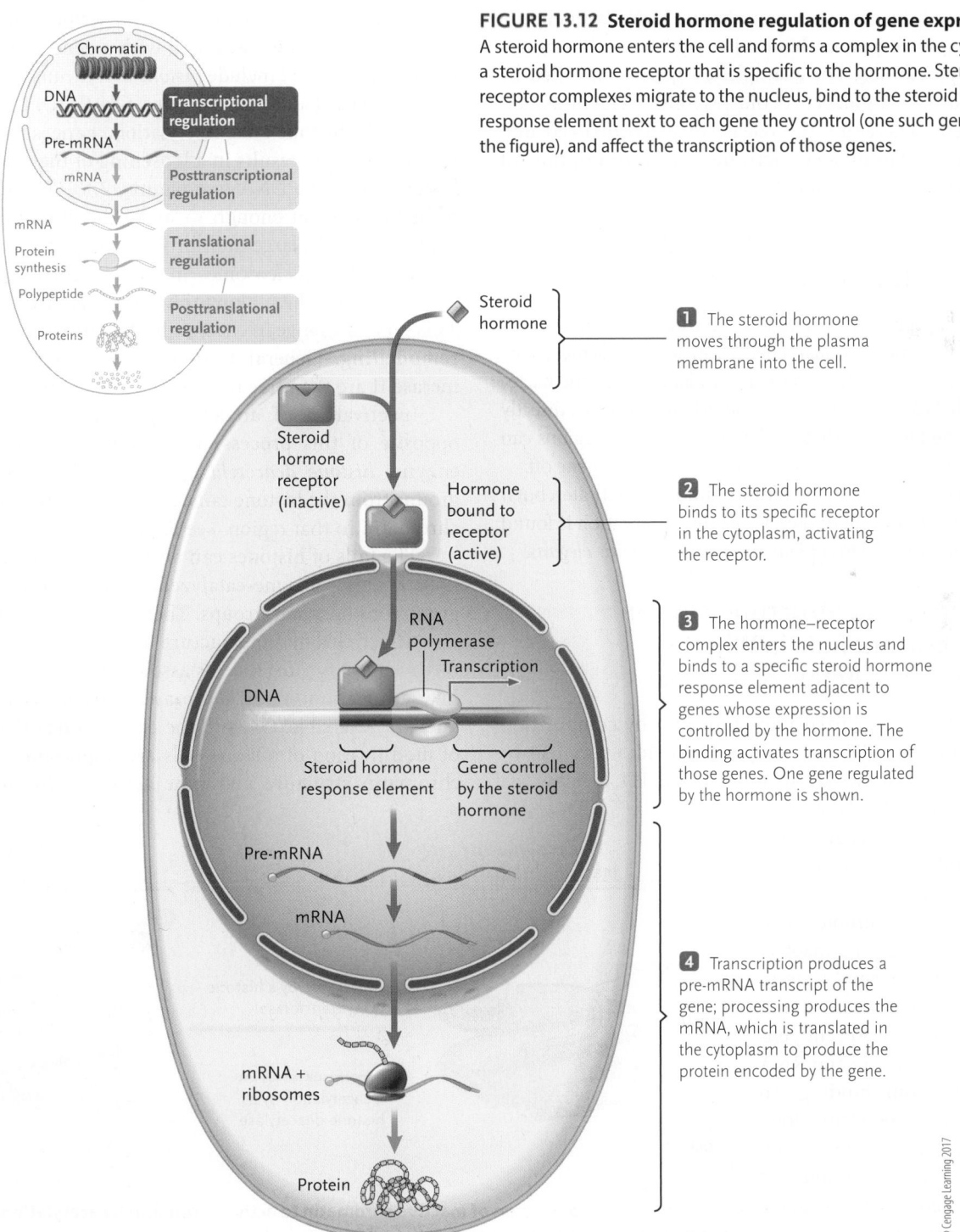

1  The steroid hormone moves through the plasma membrane into the cell.

2  The steroid hormone binds to its specific receptor in the cytoplasm, activating the receptor.

3  The hormone–receptor complex enters the nucleus and binds to a specific steroid hormone response element adjacent to genes whose expression is controlled by the hormone. The binding activates transcription of those genes. One gene regulated by the hormone is shown.

4  Transcription produces a pre-mRNA transcript of the gene; processing produces the mRNA, which is translated in the cytoplasm to produce the protein encoded by the gene.

© Cengage Learning 2017

A steroid hormone acts on specific target tissues in the body because only cells in those tissues have **steroid hormone receptors** in their cytoplasm that recognize and bind the hormone (see Chapter 4). The steroid hormone moves through the plasma membrane into the cytoplasm and the receptor binds to it (Figure 13.12). The hormone–receptor complex then enters the nucleus and binds to specific regulatory sequences that are adjacent to the genes whose expression is controlled by the hormone. This binding activates transcription of those genes, and proteins encoded by the genes are synthesized rapidly.

A single steroid hormone can regulate many different genes because all the genes have an identical DNA sequence (a **steroid hormone response element**) to which the hormone–receptor complex binds. For example, all genes controlled by glucocorticoid have a glucocorticoid response element associated with them. Therefore, the release of glucocorticoid into the bloodstream coordinately activates the transcription of genes with that response element.

## 13.2c Methylation of DNA Can Control Gene Transcription

Although binding proteins to DNA is a common mechanism for regulating transcription, similar effects can also be achieved by modifying the DNA directly. In vertebrates, plants, fungi, and bacteria, **DNA methylation** enzymes add a methyl group (–CH$_3$) directly onto bases in the DNA. Methylated bases in promoter regions can prevent the binding of transcription factors, turning the gene off.

**Silencing** by methylation is common among vertebrates, but it is not universal among eukaryotes; very little methylation is found in the model organisms *Drosophila* and *Caenorhabditis elegans*.

## 13.2d Chromatin Structure Plays an Important Role in Whether a Gene Is Active or Inactive

Eukaryotic DNA is organized into chromatin by combination with histone proteins. DNA is wrapped around a core of two molecules each of histones H2A, H2B, H3, and H4, forming the nucleosome. Higher levels of chromatin organization occur when histone H1 links adjacent nucleosomes (see Figure 7.10).

A eukaryotic promoter can exist in two states. In the inactive state, which is the normal state in eukaryotic cells, the nucleosomes in normal chromatin prevent general transcription factors and RNA polymerase II from binding, so transcription does not occur. However, regulatory transcription factors can bind to the DNA and lead to a change in chromatin to make it active so transcription can occur.

In the active state, general transcription factors and RNA polymerase II bind to the promoter and, controlled by the molecular events already discussed, transcription regulation can occur. A key regulatory event for regulating transcription initiation, then, is controlling the transition between the inactive and active states of chromatin in the region of a promoter.

Acetylation of histone tails is one mechanism that plays an important role in determining whether chromatin is inactive or active. In inactive chromatin, the histone tails are not acetylated and, in this form, the tails form a tight association with the DNA wrapped around the histone octamer of a nucleosome **(Figure 13.13)**. When a regulatory transcription factor binds to a regulatory sequence associated with a gene, it can recruit protein complexes that include *histone acetyltransferase*, an enzyme that acetylates (adds acetyl groups; CH$_3$COO) to specific amino acids of the histone tails. Acetylation changes the charge of the histone tails and results in a loosening of the association of the histones with the DNA (see Figure 13.13). Usually, acetylation of histones is not enough to make the chromatin completely active. Typically, large multiprotein complexes bind to displace the acetylated nucleosomes in the promoter region from the DNA, or move them along the DNA away from the promoter. This type of change in chromatin structure is called **chromatin remodelling**. General transcription factors and RNA polymerase II are then free to bind and initiate transcription.

Inactivation of an active gene involves essentially the opposite of this process. With respect to the histones, the enzyme *histone deacetylase* catalyzes the removal of acetyl groups from the histone tails, restoring the inactive state of the chromatin in that region (see Figure 13.13).

The tails of histones can also be modified at specific positions by the enzyme-catalyzed covalent addition of methyl groups or phosphate groups. These chemical modifications can also affect chromatin structure and gene expression. Histone methylation, for instance, is associated with gene inactivation. Like acetylation, methylation and phosphorylation of histone tails are reversible. Overall, the conclusion is that the patterns of modification of histone tails are important in determining chromatin structure and gene activity. This has led to the

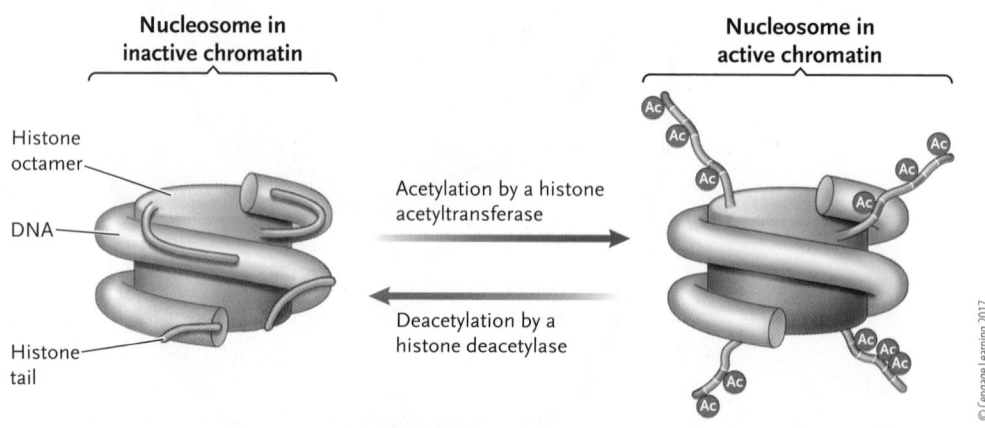

**FIGURE 13.13 Conversion of inactive chromatin to active chromatin by acetylation of histone tails, and the reverse by deacetylation of histone tails**

concept of the **histone code**, which is a regulatory mechanism for altering chromatin structure, and therefore gene activity based on signals in histone tails represented by chemical modification patterns.

Once mRNAs are transcribed from active genes, further regulation occurs at each of the major steps in the pathway from genes to proteins: during pre-mRNA processing and the movement of finished mRNAs to the cytoplasm (posttranscriptional regulation), during protein synthesis (translational regulation), and after translation is complete (posttranslational regulation). The next section takes up the regulatory mechanisms operating at each of these steps.

## STUDY BREAK QUESTIONS

1. What is the role of histones in gene expression? How does acetylation of the histones affect gene expression?
2. What are the roles of general transcription factors, activators, and coactivators in transcription of a protein-coding gene?

# 13.3   Posttranscriptional, Translational, and Posttranslational Regulation

The previous sections describe several mechanisms that determine which mRNAs are produced under various conditions. The following sections illustrate that, once a given mRNA is made, there are several opportunities to fine-tune expression through posttranscriptional, translational, and posttranslational controls (refer again to Figure 13.6).

## 13.3a   Posttranscriptional Regulation Controls mRNA Availability

Posttranscriptional regulation directs translation by controlling the availability of mRNAs to ribosomes. The controls work by several mechanisms, including changes in pre-mRNA processing and the rate at which mRNAs are degraded.

**VARIATIONS IN PRE-mRNA PROCESSING** In Chapter 12 we noted that mRNAs are transcribed initially as pre-mRNA molecules. These pre-mRNAs are variously processed to produce the finished mRNAs, which then enter protein synthesis. Variations in pre-mRNA processing can regulate *which* proteins are made in cells. As described in Section 12.3, pre-mRNAs can be processed by *alternative splicing*. Alternative splicing produces different mRNAs from the same pre-mRNA by removing different combinations of exons (the amino acid–coding segments) along with the introns (the noncoding spacers). The resulting mRNAs are translated to produce a family of related proteins with various combinations of amino acid sequences derived from the exons. Alternative splicing itself is under regulatory control. Regulatory proteins specific to the type of cell control which exons are removed from pre-mRNA molecules by binding to regulatory sequences within those molecules. The outcome of alternative splicing is that appropriate proteins within a family are synthesized in cell types or tissues in which they function optimally. Perhaps three-quarters of human genes are alternatively spliced at the pre-mRNA level.

**POSTTRANSCRIPTIONAL CONTROL BY MASKING PROTEINS** Some posttranscriptional controls operate by means of *masking* proteins that bind to mRNAs and make them unavailable for protein synthesis. These controls are important in many animal eggs, keeping mRNAs in an inactive form until the egg has been fertilized and embryonic development is under way. When an mRNA is to become active, other factors—other proteins, made as part of the developmental pathway—remove the masking proteins and allow the mRNA to enter protein synthesis.

**VARIATIONS IN THE RATE OF mRNA BREAKDOWN** The rate at which eukaryotic mRNAs break down can also be controlled posttranscriptionally. The mechanism involves a regulatory molecule, such as a steroid hormone, directly or indirectly affecting the mRNA breakdown steps, by either slowing or increasing the rate of those steps. For example, in the mammary gland of rats, the mRNA for casein (a milk protein) has a half-life of about 5 hours (meaning that it takes 5 hours for half of the mRNA present at a given time to break down). The half-life of casein mRNA changes to about 92 hours when the peptide hormone prolactin is present. Prolactin is synthesized in the brain and in other tissues, including the breast. The most important effect of prolactin is to stimulate the **mammary glands** to produce milk (i.e., it stimulates lactation). During milk production, a large amount of casein must be synthesized, and this is accomplished in part by radically decreasing the rate of breakdown of the casein mRNA.

Nucleotide sequences in the 5′ UTR (untranslated region; see Section 12.3) also appear to be important in determining mRNA half-life. If the 5′ UTR is transferred experimentally from one mRNA to another, the half-life of the receiving mRNA becomes the same as that of the donor mRNA. The controlling sequences in the 5′ UTR of an mRNA might be recognized by proteins that regulate its stability.

**REGULATION OF GENE EXPRESSION BY SMALL NONCODING RNAs** You saw earlier in this chapter that lncRNA can affect gene expression at the level of transcription initiation. Another role for RNA in regulation of gene expression, this time occurring after the transcripts are made, is described below.

In 1998, Andrew Fire of the Stanford University School of Medicine and Craig Mello of the University of Massachusetts Medical School were among those who showed that RNA silenced the expression of a particular gene in the nematode worm, *C. elegans*. They called the phenomenon **RNA interference (RNAi)**. Their discovery revolutionized the way scientists thought about and studied gene regulation in eukaryotes. They now understand that posttranscriptional regulation may be carried out, not only by regulatory proteins but also by noncoding, single-stranded RNAs that can bind to mRNAs and affect their translation. We now know that RNAi is widespread among eukaryotes. Fire and Mello received a Nobel Prize in 2006 for their discovery of RNA interference.

Two major groups of small regulatory RNAs are involved in RNAi: **microRNAs (miRNAs)** and **short interfering RNAs (siRNAs)**. The transcription of an miRNA gene and the processing of the transcript to produce the functional miRNA molecule are shown in **Figure 13.14**. The miRNA, in a protein complex called the **miRNA-induced silencing complex (miRISC)**, binds to sequences in the 3′ UTRs of target mRNAs. If the miRNA and mRNA pair imperfectly, the double-stranded segment formed between the miRNA and the mRNA blocks ribosomes from translating the mRNA (shown in Figure 13.14). In this case, the target mRNA is not destroyed, but its expression is silenced. If the miRNA and mRNA pair perfectly, an enzyme in the protein complex cleaves the target mRNA where the miRNA is bound to it, destroying the mRNA and silencing its expression. RNAi by imperfect pairing and translation inhibition is the most common mechanism in animals. RNAi by perfect pairing and RNA degradation is the most common mechanism in plants.

Analysis of genome sequences has identified over 17 000 miRNAs in 142 species, including more than 1900 in humans. Interestingly, many miRNAs have been implicated in common human diseases, including cancer (see later in this chapter). Sequence comparisons show that miRNAs are conserved across species, and that they are expressed in different cell types. It is estimated that more than half of all mRNAs are targets of miRNAs, and that each miRNA may regulate hundreds of target mRNAs.

The other major type of small regulatory RNAs is the siRNA. Whereas miRNA is produced from RNA that is encoded in the cell's genome, siRNA is produced from double-stranded RNA that is *not* encoded by nuclear genes. For example, the replication cycle of many viruses with RNA genomes involves a double-stranded RNA stage. Cells attacked by such a virus can defend themselves using siRNA that they produce from the virus's own RNA. The viral double-stranded RNA enters the cell's RNAi process in a way very similar to that described for miRNAs: double-stranded RNA is cut by Dicer (see Figure 13.14) into short, double-stranded RNA molecules, and then a protein complex binds to the molecules and degrades one of the RNA strands to produce single-stranded siRNA. The protein complex is similar to one that acts on the double-stranded RNA precursors of miRNAs. The siRNA with the protein complex in this case is the **siRNA-induced silencing complex (siRISC)**. In the RNAi process, the siRNA in the siRISC acts like the miRNA in the miRISC: single-stranded RNAs complementary to the siRNA are targeted and, in this case, the target RNA is cleaved and the pieces are then degraded. In our viral example, the targeted RNAs would be viral mRNAs for proteins that the virus uses to replicate itself, or a single-stranded RNA that is the viral genome itself, or that is produced from the viral genome during replication.

The expression of any gene can be knocked down to low levels, or knocked out completely, in experiments involving RNAi with siRNA. To silence a gene, researchers introduce into the cell

a double-stranded RNA that can be processed by Dicer and the protein complex into an siRNA complementary to the mRNA transcribed from that gene. Knocking down or knocking out the function of a gene is equivalent to creating a mutated version of

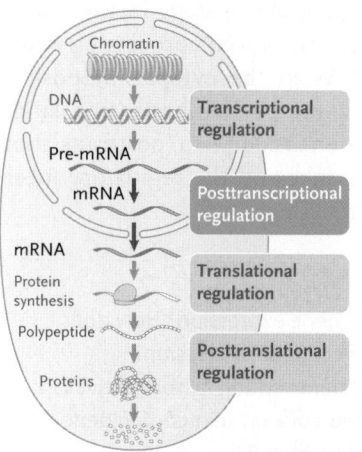

**FIGURE 13.14 RNA interference.** Regulation of gene expression by microRNAs (miRNAs).

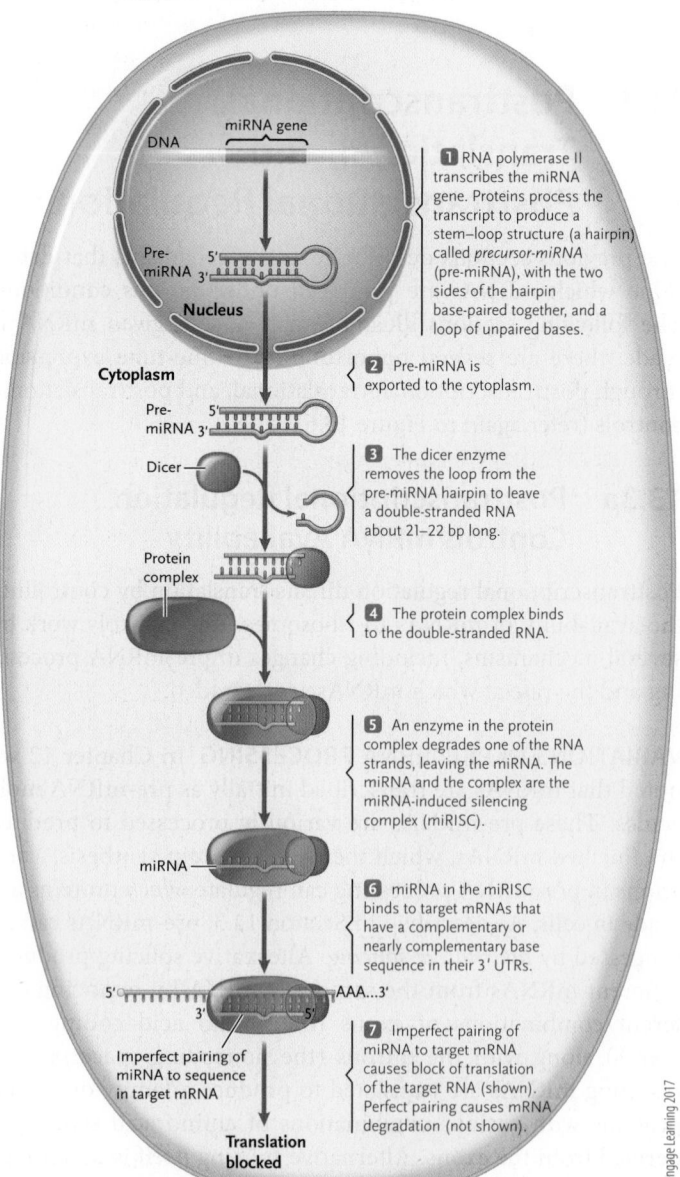

1 RNA polymerase II transcribes the miRNA gene. Proteins process the transcript to produce a stem–loop structure (a hairpin) called *precursor-miRNA* (pre-miRNA), with the two sides of the hairpin base-paired together, and a loop of unpaired bases.

2 Pre-miRNA is exported to the cytoplasm.

3 The dicer enzyme removes the loop from the pre-miRNA hairpin to leave a double-stranded RNA about 21–22 bp long.

4 The protein complex binds to the double-stranded RNA.

5 An enzyme in the protein complex degrades one of the RNA strands, leaving the miRNA. The miRNA and the complex are the miRNA-induced silencing complex (miRISC).

6 miRNA in the miRISC binds to target mRNAs that have a complementary or nearly complementary base sequence in their 3′ UTRs.

7 Imperfect pairing of miRNA to target mRNA causes block of translation of the target RNA (shown). Perfect pairing causes mRNA degradation (not shown).

© Cengage Learning 2017

that gene, but without changing the gene's DNA sequence. Researchers use this experimental approach to identify the functions of genes whose presence has been detected by sequencing complete genomes, but whose function is completely unknown. After an siRNA specific to a gene of interest is introduced into the cell, researchers look for a change in phenotype, such as properties relating to growth or metabolism. If such a change is seen, the researchers now have some insight into the gene's function, and they can investigate the gene with more focus. RNAi using siRNAs may also have some applications in medicine, perhaps to regulate the expression of genes associated with human diseases.

## 13.3b Translational Regulation Controls the Rate of Protein Synthesis

At the next regulatory level, translational regulation controls the rate at which mRNAs are used in protein synthesis. Translational regulation occurs in essentially all cell types and species. For example, translational regulation is involved in cell cycle control in all eukaryotes and in many processes during development in multicellular eukaryotes, such as red blood cell differentiation in animals. Significantly, many viruses exploit translational regulation to control their infection of cells and to shut off the host cell's own genes.

Let's consider the general role of translational regulation in animal development. During early development of most animals, little transcription occurs. The changes in protein synthesis patterns seen in developing cell types and tissues instead derive from the activation, repression, or degradation of maternal mRNAs—the mRNAs that were present in the mother's egg before fertilization. One important mechanism for translational regulation involves adjusting the length of the poly(A) tail of the mRNA. (Recall from Section 12.3 that the poly(A) tail—a string of adenine-containing nucleotides—is added to the 3′ end of the pre-mRNA and is retained on the mRNA produced from the pre-mRNA after introns are removed.) That is, enzymes can change the length of the poly(A) tail on an mRNA in the cytoplasm in either direction by shortening it or lengthening it. Increases in poly(A) tail length result in increased translation; decreases in length result in decreased translation. For example, during embryogenesis (the formation of the embryo) of the fruit fly, *Drosophila*, key proteins are synthesized when the poly(A) tails on the mRNAs for those proteins are lengthened in a regulated way. Evidence for this came from experiments in which poly(A) tail lengthening was blocked; the result was that embryogenesis was inhibited. But although researchers know that the length of poly(A) tails is regulated in the cytoplasm, how this process occurs is not completely understood.

## 13.3c Posttranslational Regulation Controls the Availability of Functional Proteins

Posttranslational regulation controls the availability of functional proteins in three primary ways: chemical modification, processing, and degradation. Chemical modification involves the addition or removal of chemical groups, a process that reversibly alters the activity of the protein. For example, you saw in Section 4.7 how the addition of phosphate groups to proteins involved in signal transduction pathways either stimulates or inhibits the activity of those proteins. Further, in Section 7.5, you learned how the addition of phosphate groups to target proteins plays a crucial role in regulating how a cell progresses through the cell division cycle. And in Section 13.3d, you saw how acetylation of histones altered the properties of the nucleosome, loosening its association with DNA in chromatin.

In processing, proteins are synthesized as inactive precursors, which are converted to an active form under regulatory control. For example, you saw in Section 12.4 that the digestive enzyme pepsin is synthesized as pepsinogen, an inactive precursor that activates by removal of a segment of amino acids. Similarly, the glucose-regulating hormone insulin is synthesized as a precursor called *proinsulin;* processing of the precursor removes a central segment but leaves the insulin molecule, which consists of two polypeptide chains linked by disulfide bridges.

The rate of degradation of proteins is also under regulatory control. Some proteins in eukaryotic cells last for the lifetime of the individual, whereas others persist only for minutes. Proteins with relatively short cellular lives include many of the proteins regulating transcription. Typically, these short-lived proteins are marked for breakdown by enzymes that attach a "doom tag" consisting of a small protein called *ubiquitin* (**Figure 13.15**, step 1). The protein is given this name because it is indeed ubiquitous—present in almost the same form in essentially all eukaryotes. The ubiquitin tag labels the doomed proteins so that they are recognized and attacked by a *proteasome,* a large cytoplasmic complex of several different proteins (step 2). The proteasome unfolds the protein, and protein-digesting enzymes within the core digest the protein into small peptides. The peptides are released from the proteasome, and cytosolic enzymes further digest the peptides into individual amino acids, which are recycled for use in protein synthesis or oxidized as an energy source (step 3). The ubiquitin protein and proteasome are also recycled. Aaron Ciechanover and Avram Hershko, both of the Israel Institute of Technology in Haifa, Israel, and Irwin Rose of the University of California, Irvine, received a Nobel Prize in 2004 for the discovery of ubiquitin-mediated protein degradation.

## 13.3d Epigenetic Regulation Persists through Cell Division

The previous sections of this chapter outline several mechanisms for regulating changes in gene expression that are readily reversible and usually transient. *Lac* operon expression increases when lactose is present but decreases when lactose is absent. Certain genes are turned on when testosterone is present but then shut off again when hormone levels fall. However, there are many situations in which an established pattern of gene expression persists into the next cell or even organismal generation. For example, genes encoding the blood protein hemoglobin are

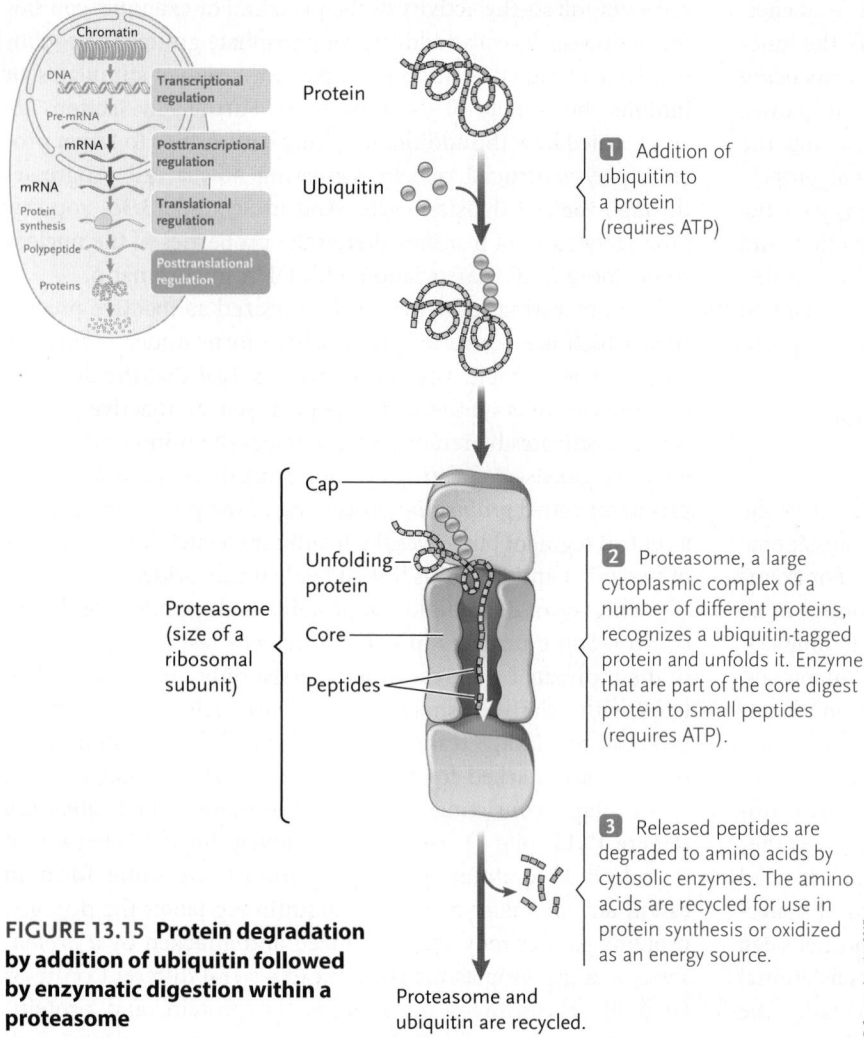

**FIGURE 13.15 Protein degradation by addition of ubiquitin followed by enzymatic digestion within a proteasome**

1 Addition of ubiquitin to a protein (requires ATP)

2 Proteasome, a large cytoplasmic complex of a number of different proteins, recognizes a ubiquitin-tagged protein and unfolds it. Enzymes that are part of the core digest protein to small peptides (requires ATP).

3 Released peptides are degraded to amino acids by cytosolic enzymes. The amino acids are recycled for use in protein synthesis or oxidized as an energy source.

Proteasome and ubiquitin are recycled.

© Cengage Learning 2017

associates with its own promoter and stimulates its own transcription. A classic example of this comes from studies of phage lambda (λ), which can remain dormant in the chromosome of infected *E. coli* cells for several generations (Figure 22.5). Early in the infection cycle of this phage, the lambda repressor protein (cI) shuts down expression of other phage genes, but stimulates expression of its own gene. As a result, high levels of repressor protein are maintained, even as the host cell divides, replicating the phage DNA along with the rest of its chromosome.

Comparable feedback loops are important in the differentiation of multicellular tissue types, and figure prominently in the dramatic dedifferentiation of mouse adult fibroblast cells into stem cells. The creation of these induced stem cells, resulting from the introduction of only four transcription factors, won a share of the 2012 Nobel Prize in Medicine and Physiology for Shinya Yamanaka from Tokyo University, Japan.

**CHROMATIN PACKAGING** Another strategy to achieve longer-term control of gene expression is to regulate the packaging of DNA and its associated proteins, known as *chromatin*. Figure 13.13 shows that this packaging is affected by chemical modifications of the histone proteins that make up nucleosomes. Densely compacted regions are called *heterochromatin*, and (most) genes in these regions are silenced. The specific genomic regions to be compacted into heterochromatin in a given cell are identified by DNA-binding proteins or small RNAs that, in turn, recruit additional protein complexes responsible for modifying histones and/or DNA. Histones may be modified by acetylation, methylation, or phosphorylation. DNA modification is typically methylation of cytosine in vertebrates or adenine in bacteria (Section 13.2c).

One dramatic example of regulation that is maintained through many cell divisions is the inactivation of specific X chromosomes in mammalian females, as described in Section 10.2d. Although the detailed mechanism is still being discovered, it is now certain that silencing of this entire chromosome involves tightly compacting chromatin in concert with DNA methylation, histone modification, and the association of a noncoding RNA called *Xist*. Mechanisms to explain how epigenetic modifications are maintained through mitosis, binary fission, and meiosis are the subject of active research.

We now describe cancer, a collection of diseases in which the control of gene expression goes awry.

present but inactive in most lines of vertebrate body cells. In the cell lines giving rise to red blood cells, hemoglobin genes are activated. In certain pathogenic strains of *E. coli,* genes for cell surface structures associated with virulence are turned off in most cells. Cells that happen to be involved in an active infection maintain expression of virulence genes in subsequent generations. In the case of genomic imprinting in mice (Section 10.5), an allele of a given gene is silenced during gametogenesis. This allele remains turned off in the fertilized zygote and resulting offspring. In all these diverse examples, the appropriate pattern of gene expression is inherited from parent cells rather than having to be independently determined anew by each daughter cell.

This type of gene regulation is called **epigenetic** in that it persists through cell or organismal generations but does not result from changes in the DNA sequence. Although the notion of epigenetic regulation is not new, a wide variety of potential underlying mechanisms is still being actively investigated and debated. Two of the most well-documented epigenetic mechanisms are feedback loops and chromatin packaging.

**FEEDBACK LOOPS** One way that control of gene expression can be maintained over cell generations is by a self-sustaining regulatory loop. Such a loop arises when the product of a particular gene

**STUDY BREAK QUESTIONS**

1. How does miRNA silence gene expression?
2. If the poly(A) tail on an mRNA were removed, what would likely be the effect on the translation of that mRNA?

## 13.4 The Loss of Regulatory Controls in Cancer

Chapter 7 showed that the cell division cycle in all eukaryotes is carefully regulated by genes (see Section 7.5 and Figure 7.20). For normal cells, it is the balance between internal or external factors that stimulate cell division and corresponding factors that inhibit cell division that governs whether the cell remains in a nondividing state or grows and divides.

Occasionally, differentiated cells of complex multicellular organisms deviate from their normal genetic program and begin to grow and divide inappropriately, giving rise to tissue masses called *tumours* (see Figure 7.22). Such cells have lost their normal regulatory controls and have reverted toward an embryonic developmental state in a process called *dedifferentiation* (**Figure 13.16**). If the altered cells stay together in a single mass, the tumour is *benign*. Benign tumours are usually not life-threatening, and their surgical removal generally results in a complete cure.

If, however, the cells of a tumour invade and disrupt surrounding tissues, the tumour is *malignant* and is called a *cancer*. Sometimes cells from malignant tumours break off and move through the blood system or the lymphatic system, forming new tumours at other locations in the body. The spreading of a malignant tumour is called *metastasis* (meaning "change of state"). Malignant tumours can result in debilitation and death in various ways, including damage to critical organs, metabolic imbalances, hemorrhage, and secondary malignancies. In some cases, malignant tumours can be eliminated from the body by surgery or destroyed by chemicals (*chemotherapy*) or radiation.

### 13.4a Cancers Are Genetic Diseases

Experimental evidence of various kinds shows that cancers are genetic diseases:

1. Particular cancers can have a high incidence in some human families. Cancers that run in families are known as **familial (hereditary) cancers**. Cancers that do not appear to be inherited are known as **sporadic (nonhereditary) cancers**. Familial cancers are less frequent than sporadic cancers.

2. Descendants of cancer cells are all cancer cells. In fact, it is the cloned descendants of certain cancer cells that form a tumour.

3. The incidence of cancers increases upon exposure to mutagens, agents that cause mutations in DNA. Particular chemicals and certain kinds of radiation are effective mutagens.

4. Particular chromosomal mutations are associated with specific forms of cancer (see Section 10.3). In these cases, chromosomal breakage affects the expression of genes associated with the regulation of cell division.

5. Some viruses can induce cancer. Some viruses carry "cancer genes" with them, and others contain viral genes that disrupt normal cell cycle control of host cells.

All the characteristics of cancer cells that have been mentioned—dedifferentiation, uncontrolled division, and metastasis—reflect changes in gene expression.

### 13.4b Cancer Driver Genes: Oncogenes and Tumour Suppressor Genes

A normal cell becomes a tumour cell when a particular mutation provides a selective growth advantage over surrounding cells. That growth advantage typically is very small, but large enough for the original mutated cell to grow and divide and produce a clone: the benign tumour. Benign tumours can then progress to being malignant by the accumulation over time of a series of mutations that increase the selective growth advantage of the cells. Even though, like the original mutation, each subsequent mutation provides only a small selective growth advantage, collectively and over time the results can be a tumour mass containing billions of cells.

A mutation that confers a selective growth advantage to the cell is called a **driver mutation**—it "drives" tumour formation. A gene that contains a driver mutation or that is expressed abnormally so as to confer a selective growth advantage is called a **driver gene**. In a paper published in 2014, 168 driver genes were identified among the genomes of thousands of human tumours. A typical tumour contains between two and eight mutations in driver genes, although some cancer types can have many more driver gene mutations. A typical tumour also contains many additional mutations—often more than 100—in other genes that do not have any effect on cancer progression. These mutations are called **passenger mutations**. Most tumours also have dozens of translocations (movements of chromosome segments to other locations in the genome; see Section 10.3), most of which are also passengers rather than drivers of tumour formation.

Known driver genes fall into two major groups based on the role of the normal version of the gene in cell growth and

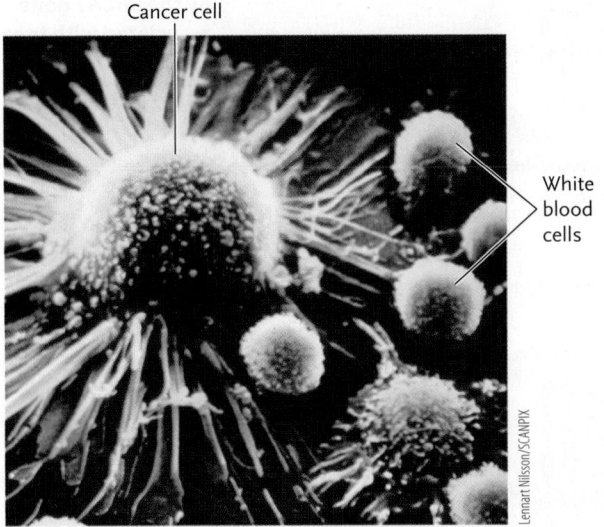

Cancer cell

White blood cells

Lennart Nilsson/SCANPIX

**FIGURE 13.16 A scanning electron micrograph of a cancer cell surrounded by several white blood cells**

division: approximately 40% of the potential driver genes are *oncogenes*, and the others are *tumour suppressor genes*. An **onco-gene** (*onkos* = bulk or mass; cancer formation is also called *onco-genesis*) is a gene that, when *activated* by a mutation or when altered to increase its expression, confers a selective growth advantage on the cell. Alterations that increase expression of the gene include amplification of the number of copies of the gene, a mutation in the gene's promoter or other regulatory sequence that increases transcription rate, or a translocation event that moves the gene under the control of a stronger promoter or enhancer.

A nonmutated version of an oncogene in a normal cell is called a **proto-oncogene**. The products of proto-oncogenes stimulate growth and cell division; examples are growth factors and receptors on target cells that are activated by growth factors.

A **tumour suppressor gene** is a gene that, when *inactivated* by mutation or otherwise downregulated, results in a selective growth advantage to the cell. The normal alleles of tumour suppressor genes encode, for example, growth-inhibiting factors—proteins that inhibit cell growth and division. Tumour suppressor gene mutations are recessive; that is, both alleles of a tumour suppressor gene must be inactivated for inhibitory activity of the gene's product to be lost in cancer cells. **Figure 13.17** illustrates inactivation of the tumour suppressor gene *BRCA1* (i.e., *breast cancer 1*) in sporadic and familial forms of breast cancer. Inactivating both alleles of *BRCA1* is not by itself sufficient for the development of breast cancer, but is one of the gene changes typically involved. Since sporadic breast cancer requires the mutational inactivation of two normal alleles of *BRCA1*, this form of the disease typically occurs later in life than the familial form. For familial breast cancer and other familial cancers, the term *predisposition* for the cancer is used. This term relates to the inactivation mechanism just described. That is, individuals are predisposed to develop a particular cancer if they inherit one mutant allele of an associated tumour suppressor disease because then a mutation inactivating the other allele is all that is needed to lose the growth inhibitory properties of the tumour suppressor gene's product.

**CONCEPT FIX** This section shows that *cancer genes* are just mutated, or otherwise deregulated, versions of the genes that are normally essential for the controlled growth of all cells. ⬡

In terms of specific functions, the identified driver genes fall into 1 or more of 12 signalling pathways that regulate 3 core cellular processes:

- *Cell survival.* Cell survival genes include genes that promote cell division such as growth factors, the genes for which in normal cells are proto-oncogenes. They also include genes that inhibit the normal death of damaged cells by apoptosis (programmed cell death; see Chapter 42); mutations of these genes allow damaged—mutated—cells to continue dividing.
- *Cell fate.* Cell fate genes determine how a cell will differentiate. Typically, differentiated cells do not grow and divide. Mutations in particular driver genes can perturb differentiation and allow continued cell division.
- *Genome maintenance.* Genome maintenance genes maintain the integrity of the genome. They include genes for the components of the DNA repair systems (see Section 11.4). An example is the tumour suppressor gene, TP53, so called because its encoded protein, p53, has a molecular weight of 53 000 daltons. The p53 protein is a transcription factor that turns on the expression of cell division-inhibiting proteins. While p53 activity is important as part of the checks and balances involved in cell

**a. Sporadic breast cancer**
Two independent mutations of the *BRCA1* tumour suppressor

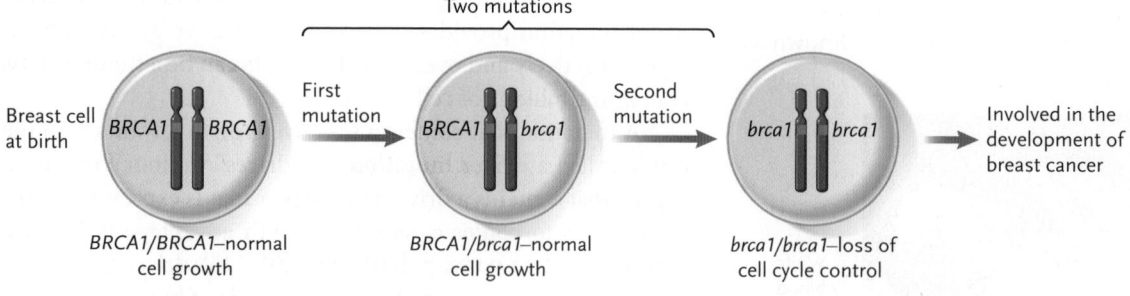

**b. Familial breast cancer**
An individual has a predisposition for breast cancer because of inheriting one mutated *brca1* allele; mutation of the other normal *BRCA1* allele then occurs.

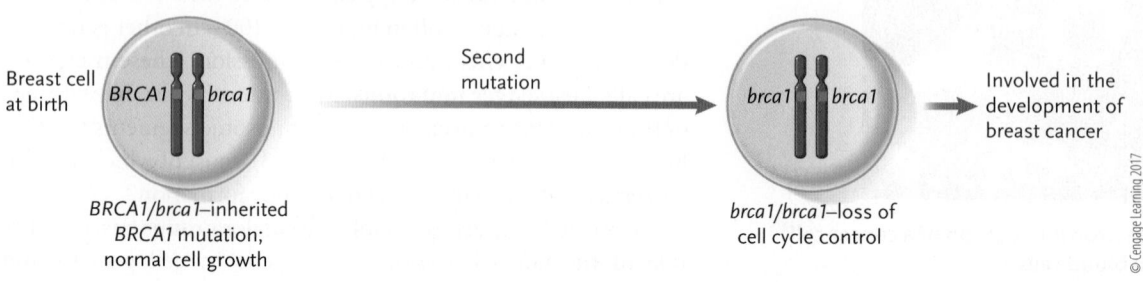

**FIGURE 13.17 Mutational inactivation of tumour suppressor gene alleles in sporadic (a) and familial (b) cancers as exemplified by the *BRCA1* gene associated with breast cancer**

© Cengage Learning 2017

division of normal cells, it is also important if the cell has sustained genomic DNA damage. In normal cells, p53, along with other tumour suppressor gene-encoded proteins, arrests the cell cycle to give the cell time to repair the damage or, if the damage cannot be repaired, trigger the cell to undergo apoptosis. However, if both copies of the *TP53* gene are mutated so that the p53 protein is not produced or is produced in an inactive form, this may allow a damaged cell to continue through the cell cycle, passing its mutations on to progeny cells. The importance of p53 to the control of cell division is shown by the fact that inactive *TP53* genes are found in at least 50% of all cancers.

Gaining a better understanding of the 12 pathways is currently a major goal of cancer research.

**miRNA GENES** You learned earlier in this chapter about the role of microRNAs (miRNAs) in regulating the expression of target mRNAs. In human cancers, many miRNA genes show altered, cancer-specific, expression patterns. Some miRNAs are found to be overexpressed in various tumours, directly stimulating tumour formation by their activity on target mRNAs. These miRNAs are acting as oncogenes. Some other miRNAs are tumour suppressors; they are found at abnormally low levels in, or are absent from, tumours. Rather than having defects in individual miRNAs, many tumours have deficiencies in many miRNAs, caused by the cell having diminished ability to process miRNA precursors to the mature molecules (see Figure 13.15).

## 13.4c Cancer Develops Gradually by Multiple Steps

Cancer rarely develops by alteration of a single proto-oncogene to an oncogene, or inactivation of a single tumour suppressor gene. Rather, in almost all cancers, successive alterations in several-to-many genes gradually accumulate to transform normal cells into cancer cells. This gradual mechanism is called the *multistep progression of cancer*. One example of the steps that can occur, in this case for a form of colorectal cancer, is shown in **Figure 13.18**.

The ravages of cancer, probably more than any other example, bring home the critical extent to which humans and all other multicellular organisms depend on the mechanisms controlling gene expression to develop and live normally. Coming back to a honeybee colony as a superorganism, you might have a deeper understanding of how the same genes, turned on and off at different times, might give rise to different castes.

### STUDY BREAK QUESTIONS

1. What is the normal function of a tumour suppressor gene? How do mutations in tumour suppressor genes contribute to the onset of cancer?
2. What is the normal function of a proto-oncogene? How can mutations in proto-oncogenes contribute to the onset of cancer?
3. How can changes in expression of miRNA genes contribute to the onset of cancer?

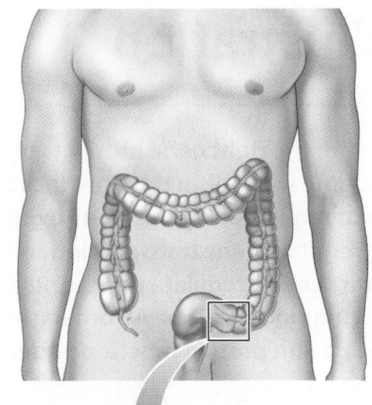

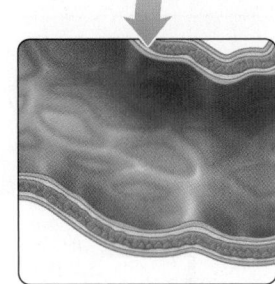

Normal colon cells

Loss of the *APC* tumour suppressor gene activity, and other DNA changes

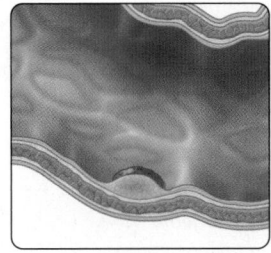

Small adenoma (benign growth)

*ras* oncogene activation; loss of *DCC* tumour suppressor gene

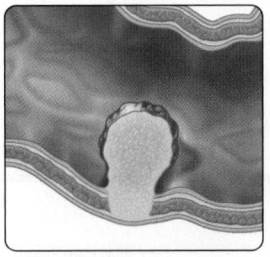

Large adenoma (benign growth)

Loss of *TP53* tumour suppressor gene activity and other mutations

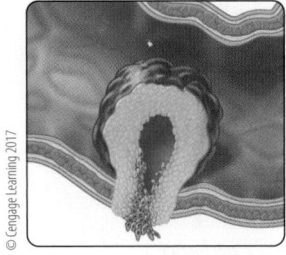

Carcinoma (malignant tumour with metastasis)

© Cengage Learning 2017

**FIGURE 13.18  A multistep model for the development of a type of colorectal cancer**

# Summary Illustration

Living organisms require the right gene products to be produced in the right amounts, at the right time interval, in the right location. This precision is achieved through many levels of regulation during gene expression. Prokaryotic cells tend to coordinately regulate gene transcription by clustering genes together in operons. Eukaryotes tend to regulate transcription of related genes through combinations of DNA binding proteins. All organisms show additional layers of regulation of translation and protein function or degradation. Unregulated cell growth can lead to cancer.

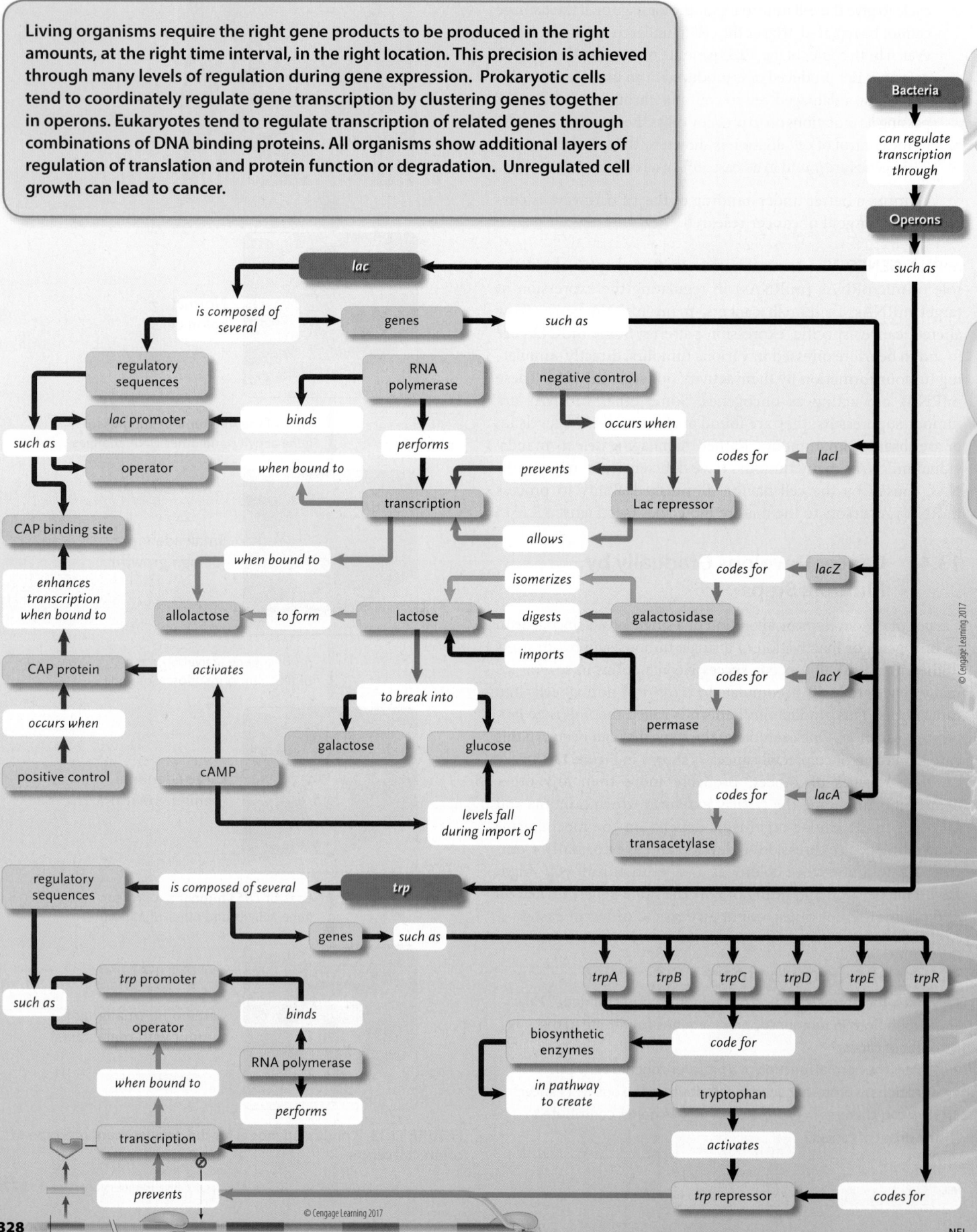

© Cengage Learning 2017

NEL

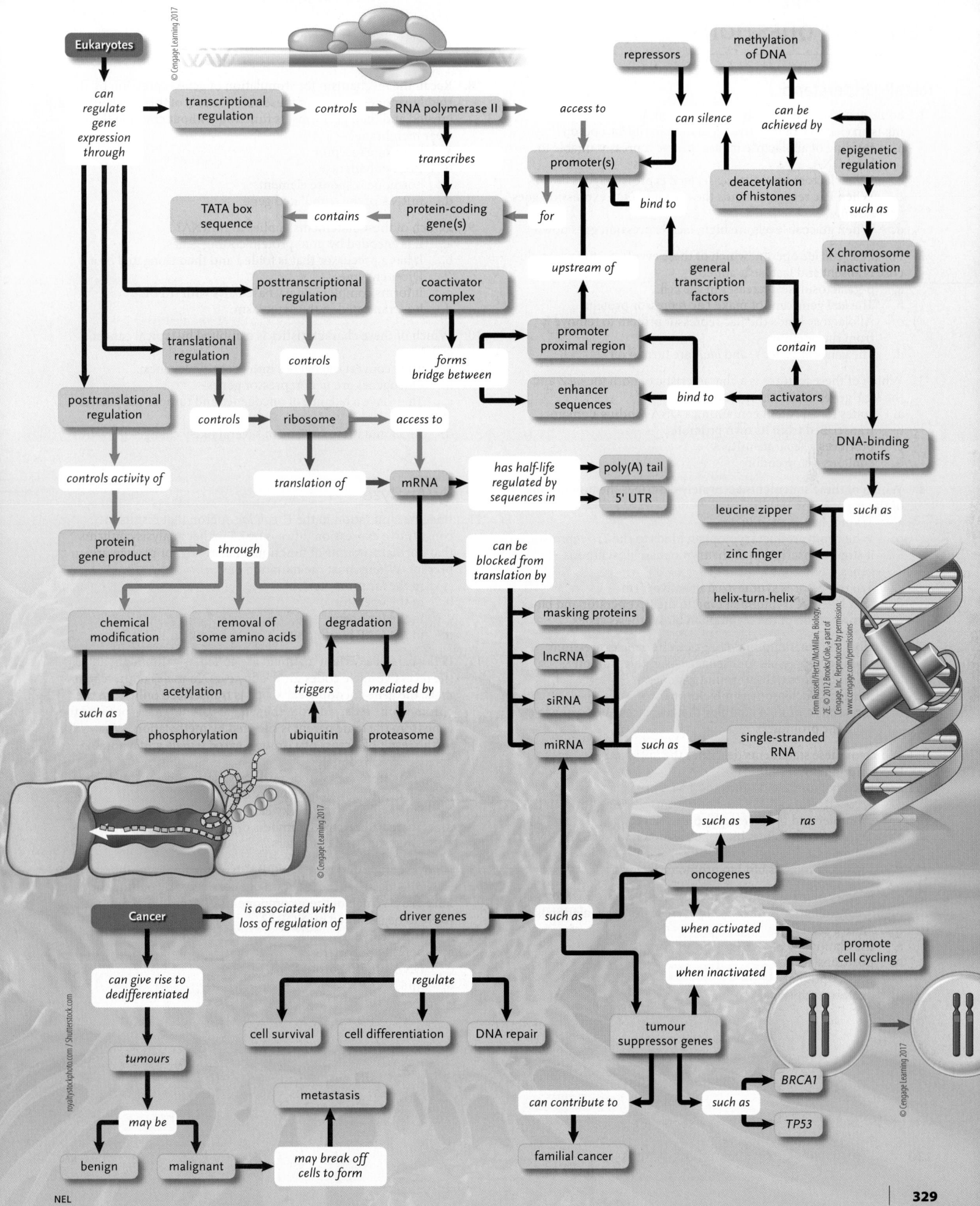

**Eukaryotes**

*can regulate gene expression through*

**transcriptional regulation** → *controls* → **RNA polymerase II**

RNA polymerase II → *transcribes* → **protein-coding gene(s)**

protein-coding gene(s) → *contains* → **TATA box sequence**

protein-coding gene(s) → *for* → **promoter(s)**

*access to* → promoter(s)

**repressors** → *can silence* → promoter(s)

**methylation of DNA** → *can be achieved by* → **epigenetic regulation**

epigenetic regulation → *such as* → **X chromosome inactivation**

*can be achieved by* → **deacetylation of histones**

**posttranscriptional regulation** → *controls* → **ribosome**

**translational regulation** → *controls* → ribosome

**posttranslational regulation** → *controls activity of* → **protein gene product**

**coactivator complex** → *forms bridge between* → **promoter proximal region** / **enhancer sequences**

**general transcription factors** → promoter proximal region

general transcription factors → *contain* → **activators**

activators → *bind to* → enhancer sequences

activators → **DNA-binding motifs**

*upstream of* → promoter proximal region

*bind to* → promoter(s)

DNA-binding motifs → *such as* → **leucine zipper** / **zinc finger** / **helix-turn-helix**

ribosome → *access to* → **mRNA**

ribosome → **translation of** → mRNA

protein gene product → *through* → **chemical modification** / **removal of some amino acids** / **degradation**

chemical modification → *such as* → **acetylation** / **phosphorylation**

degradation → *triggers* ← **ubiquitin**

degradation → *mediated by* → **proteasome**

mRNA → **has half-life regulated by sequences in** → **poly(A) tail** / **5' UTR**

mRNA → **can be blocked from translation by** → **masking proteins** / **lncRNA** / **siRNA** / **miRNA**

**single-stranded RNA** → *such as* → miRNA

lncRNA / siRNA / miRNA

**Cancer** → *is associated with loss of regulation of* → **driver genes**

driver genes → *such as* → *such as*

driver genes → *regulate* → **cell survival** / **cell differentiation** / **DNA repair**

*such as* → **oncogenes** / **tumour suppressor genes**

oncogenes → *such as* → **ras**

oncogenes → *when activated* → **promote cell cycling**

tumour suppressor genes → *when inactivated* → promote cell cycling

tumour suppressor genes → *can contribute to* → **familial cancer**

tumour suppressor genes → *such as* → **BRCA1** / **TP53**

Cancer → *can give rise to dedifferentiated* → **tumours**

tumours → *may be* → **benign** / **malignant**

malignant → **may break off cells to form** → **metastasis**

oncogenes → miRNA

# SELF-TEST QUESTIONS

## Recall/Understand

1. Some genes are under negative regulation. Which of the following is an example of negative regulation in the *lac* operon?
   a. Binding of allolactose makes the Lac repressor unable to bind DNA.
   b. When lactose levels decrease, *lacZ* expression goes down.
   c. When Lac repressor binds the operator, *lacZ* expression goes down.
   d. When glucose levels are high, *lacZ* expression goes down.

2. For the *E. coli lac* operon, which of these events occurs when glucose is absent and lactose is added?
   a. β-galactosidase decreases in the cell.
   b. The *lacI* gene cannot make Lac repressor protein.
   c. Allolactose binds the Lac repressor protein to remove it from the operator.
   d. The genes *lacZ*, *lacY*, and *lacA* are turned off.

3. Which of these features is a characteristic of both the *lacZ* and the *lacY* genes of the *lac* operon?
   a. codes for a protein containing a DNA binding domain
   b. transcribed from its own promoter
   c. produces a separate mRNA
   d. contains a stop codon

4. Which of these statements accurately describes the functioning of the *trp* operon?
   a. Tryptophan is an inducer.
   b. When end-product tryptophan binds to the Trp repressor, it stops transcription of the tryptophan biosynthesis genes.
   c. Trp repressor is synthesized in active form.
   d. Low levels of tryptophan bind to the *trp* operator and block transcription of the tryptophan biosynthesis genes.

5. How does chromatin remodelling activate gene expression?
   a. It allows repressors to disengage from the promoter.
   b. It winds genes tightly around histones.
   c. It inserts nucleosomes into chromatin.
   d. It recruits a protein complex that displaces nucleosomes from the promoter.

6. Which of these statements describes the initiation of transcription?
   a. RNA polymerase II binds the TATA box.
   b. A coactivator called a *mediator* forms a bridge between the promoter and the gene to be transcribed.
   c. Transcription factors bind the promoter, followed by RNA polymerase.
   d. Enhancer regions bind to promoter regions.

7. The delivery of mature mRNA to the cytoplasm in eukaryotes is highly controlled. At which one of these levels of regulation is this control achieved?
   a. translational
   b. posttranslational
   c. transcriptional
   d. posttranscriptional

8. Recall the mechanism for stimulation of gene expression by steroid hormones. Which of these components of this mechanism is created and then performs its function without crossing the nuclear membrane?
   a. hormone receptor
   b. RNA polymerase
   c. hormone response element
   d. mRNA of the stimulated gene

9. Which of these statements applies to miRNA?
   a. It is encoded by non–protein coding genes.
   b. It has a precursor that is folded and then elongated by a Dicer enzyme.
   c. It forms complementary base pairs with tRNA.
   d. It is translated in the cytoplasm.

10. Which of these characteristics is exhibited by typical cancer cells?
    a. They convert oncogenes into proto-oncogenes.
    b. Oncogenes are near repressor genes.
    c. They have a balance of oncogenes and tumour suppressor genes.
    d. *TP53* mutations are one of several likely changes in DNA.

## Apply/Analyze

11. Imagine a mutation in the *E. coli lac* operon that results in constitutive expression (always on). Further analysis confirms that normal amounts of functional Lac repressor protein are present. Where must the mutation be?
    a. in the *lac* promoter
    b. in the operator
    c. in the *lacZ* gene
    d. in the CAP binding site

12. Perky ears in a certain mammal are coded by a dominant allele; the recessive allele codes for droopy ears. In males of these mammals, the gene encoding ear shape is transcribed only from the chromosome received from the female parent. This is because the gene from the male parent is silenced by methylation. What will be the result of a cross of a droopy-eared female and a homozygous perky-eared male?
    a. Daughters' ears will be perky and sons' ears will be droopy.
    b. All offspring will have perky ears.
    c. Sons will have one perky ear and one droopy ear.
    d. There will be equal numbers of perky-eared and droopy-eared sons and daughters.

13. A novel compound called "NOBA" is a zinc finger inhibitor. That is, NOBA destroys the function of zinc fingers by pulling the zinc ions away. Which of these components of gene expression is most likely to be inhibited by NOBA?
    a. enhancer
    b. poly(A) polymerase
    c. DNA-binding protein
    d. miRNA

## Create/Evaluate

14. In a mutant strain of *E. coli*, the CAP protein is unable to combine with its target region of the *lac* operon. Compare and contrast transcription of the *lac* operon in this mutant strain versus a normal strain under the following conditions.
    a. Both lactose and glucose are available.
    b. Lactose is available but glucose is not.
    c. Both lactose and glucose are unavailable.

15. Duchenne muscular dystrophy, an inherited genetic disorder, affects boys almost exclusively. Early in childhood, muscle tissue begins to break down in affected individuals, who typically die in their teens or early 20s due to respiratory failure. Muscle samples from women who carry the mutation reveal some regions of degenerating muscle tissue adjacent to other regions that are normal. Develop a hypothesis explaining these observations.

# Chapter Roadmap

### DNA Technologies

The various techniques called genetic engineering allow researchers to make new combinations of DNA sequences and introduce them into microbes, plants, and animals. The field of synthetic biology is moving rapidly toward designing living systems for specific purposes.

From Chapter 11

### 14.1 DNA Cloning

A variety of techniques enable researchers to isolate, amplify, and recombine novel DNA sequences.

### 14.2 Applications of DNA Technologies

Several methods provide scientists with powerful tools to add, remove, or edit the genes of a wide variety of organisms.

To Chapter 15

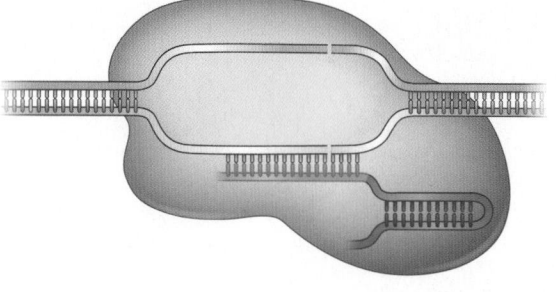

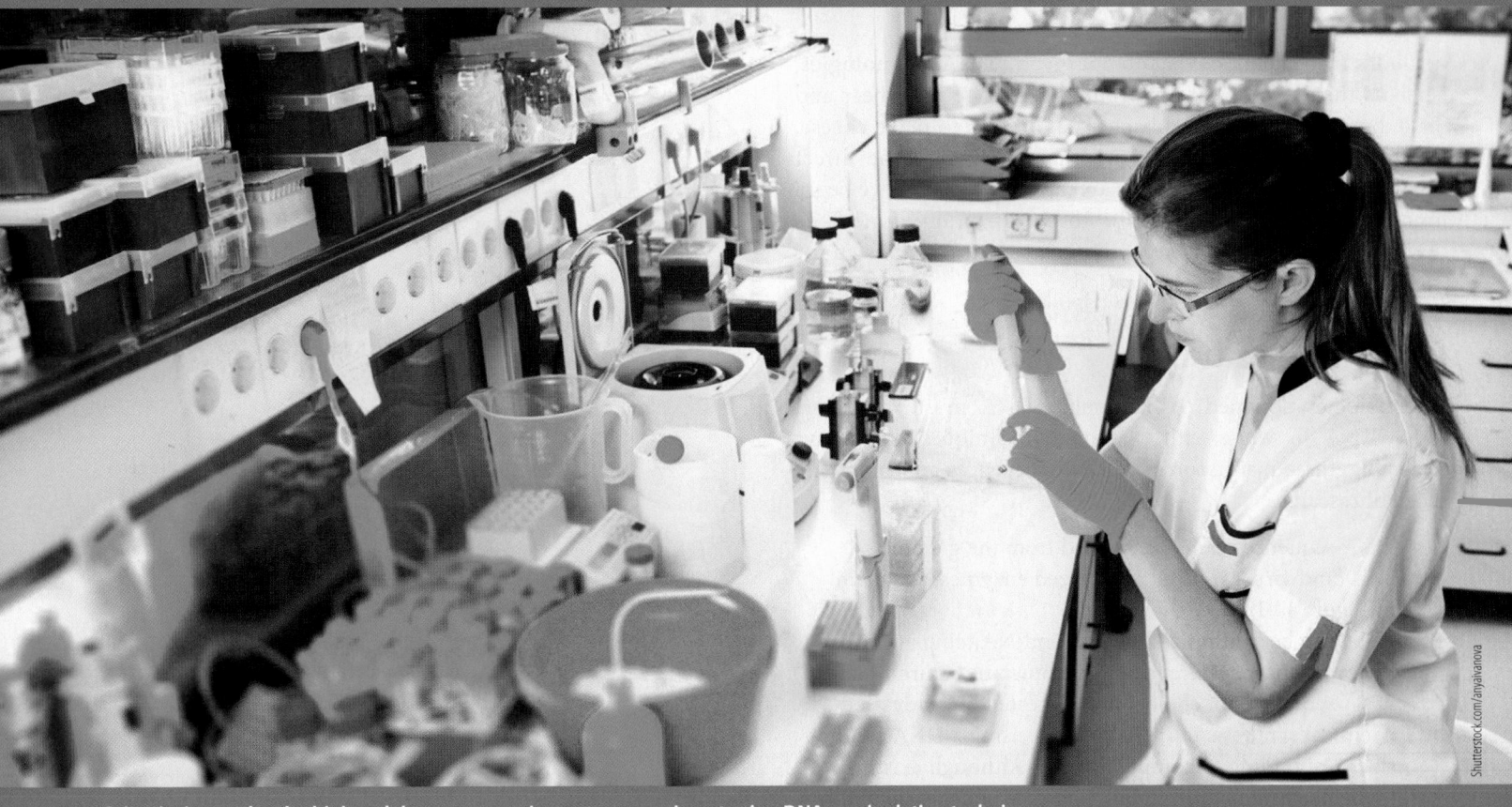

Scientist in a molecular biology laboratory carrying out an experiment using DNA manipulation techniques

# DNA Technologies

# 14

**Why it matters . . .** Have you ever wished you could create a new organism that would solve a real-world problem? Maybe you would create a fungus that converts toxic waste into fuel. Artificial blood requires some sort of cell to carry the oxygen; could you design such a cell? What if you could program the bacteria that normally make yogurt to produce different flavours on demand? Or maybe you could invent a multicellular organism that could measure and report the concentration of specific compounds in air.

The age of do-it-yourself (DIY) biology has arrived, and the basic tools of genetic engineering developed since the 1970s are now in the hands of undergraduates like you. Teams of students are collaborating with scientists and engineers in classrooms, labs, and informal makerspaces all over the world to develop innovative entries in the annual International Genetically Engineered Machine Competition (iGEM). In an open-source spirit of creating and sharing, teams of passionate students start with over a thousand standardized interchangeable BioBrick DNA sequences, plasmid backbones, and living cells. Adding their own custom-created parts, teams assemble parts into devices that, in turn, are combined to create innovative pathways and systems—all housed in living cells. Each year, teams present their novel living machines to address issues in categories such as art, energy, environment, food, health, measurement, and manufacturing.

The competition also highlights and promotes consideration of the broad range of risks and controversies surrounding genetic engineering, as well as the scientific, social, and ethical questions related to its rapidly expanding role in society.

In this chapter we look at the topic of **genetic engineering** as the latest addition to the broad area known as **biotechnology**, which is any technique applied to biological systems or living organisms to make or modify products or processes for a specific purpose. Thus, biotechnology includes manipulations that do not involve **DNA technologies**, such as the use of naturally occurring yeast to brew beer and bake bread, and the use of bacteria and fungi to make cheese. With respect to biotechnologies that do involve the direct manipulation of genes for basic and applied research, we begin our discussion in this chapter with a description of methods used to obtain genes in large quantities, an essential step for their analysis or further application.

## 14.1 DNA Cloning

Technologies designed to manipulate DNA must, of course, have DNA to work with. Although techniques are always changing, three main sources of DNA sequences are commonly used in research:

1. DNA sequences can be extracted from the genome of cells (and viruses) using specialized enzymes, as shown in Figure 14.1.
2. DNA can be synthesized from an mRNA template by the reverse transcriptase enzyme, as shown in Figure 14.4.
3. DNA sequences of choice can be created by automated chemical synthesis in the laboratory using a DNA synthesizer responding to computer input. Although existing "gene machines" can create specified sequences up to a few thousand base pairs, this capacity is expanding rapidly.

Once a DNA sequence of choice has been obtained from nature or created artificially, the number of copies of the sequence can be increased dramatically, as described in the following sections.

A *clone* is a line of genetically identical cells or individuals derived from a single ancestor. By similar reasoning, DNA cloning is a method for producing many copies of a given piece of DNA; the piece of DNA is referred to as a *gene of interest,* which is a gene that a researcher wants to study or manipulate.

An overview of one common method for cloning a gene of interest from a genome is shown in **Figure 14.1**; the method uses bacteria (commonly *Escherichia coli*) and plasmids, the small circular DNA molecules that replicate separately from the bacterial chromosome. The researcher first extracts DNA from cells containing the gene of interest and then cuts the DNA into fragments. One of these fragments will likely carry the desired gene. Each of the fragments is inserted into a plasmid, thus producing a collection of separate *recombinant DNA molecules*—**recombinant DNA** is DNA from two or more different sources that are joined together. These recombinant plasmids are then introduced into bacteria; each bacterium receives a different plasmid. The bacterium continues growing and dividing, and as it does, the recombinant plasmid DNA is also replicated. The final step is to identify which bacterium contains the plasmid carrying the gene of interest and then isolate the gene for further study.

Cloned genes and other cloned DNA sequences from genomes are used in both basic research and applied research. In **basic research**, a researcher might want to study a cloned gene to learn about its structure, including its DNA sequence

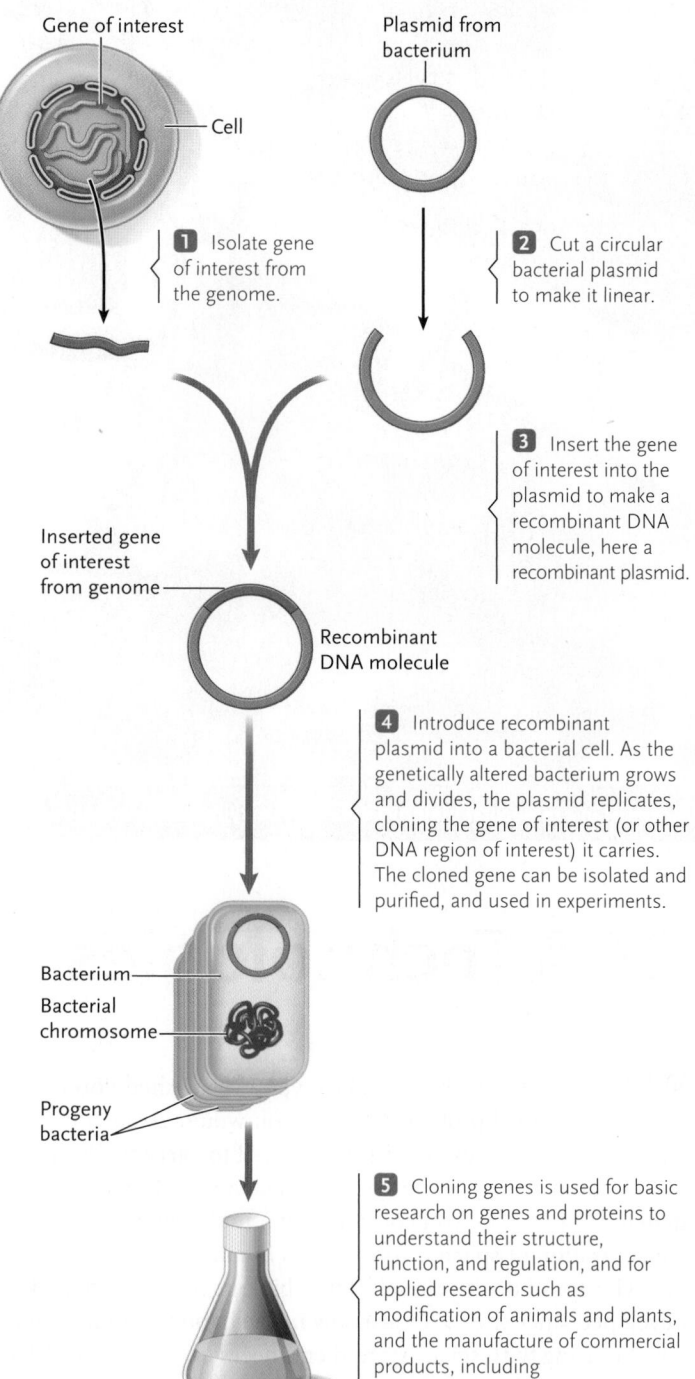

**1** Isolate gene of interest from the genome.

**2** Cut a circular bacterial plasmid to make it linear.

**3** Insert the gene of interest into the plasmid to make a recombinant DNA molecule, here a recombinant plasmid.

**4** Introduce recombinant plasmid into a bacterial cell. As the genetically altered bacterium grows and divides, the plasmid replicates, cloning the gene of interest (or other DNA region of interest) it carries. The cloned gene can be isolated and purified, and used in experiments.

**5** Cloning genes is used for basic research on genes and proteins to understand their structure, function, and regulation, and for applied research such as modification of animals and plants, and the manufacture of commercial products, including pharmaceuticals.

© Cengage Learning 2017

**FIGURE 14.1 Overview of cloning DNA fragments in a bacterial plasmid**

and sequences that regulate its expression. A researcher might also want to study the gene's function, including how its expression is regulated and the nature of the gene's product. For protein-coding genes, for instance, the cloned gene could be used to produce the protein product in large quantities in a microorganism host to facilitate study of that protein's structure and function. As part of this research, the cloned gene could be manipulated in the laboratory to help dissect a gene's function.

In **applied research**, the interest in cloned genes or other cloned DNA sequences is not in the structure and function of a gene or sequence; that typically is understood at the beginning of research projects. Rather, cloned genes or cloned DNA sequences are used, for instance, for medical, forensic, agricultural, or commercial applications. Some examples are

- Gene therapy to correct or treat genetic diseases
- Diagnosis of genetic diseases, such as sickle cell disease;
- DNA fingerprinting in forensics;
- Production of pharmaceuticals, such as *Humulin*, human insulin to treat diabetes, and tissue plasminogen activator to break down blood clots;
- Generation of genetically modified animals and plants, including animals that synthesize pharmaceuticals, and plants that are nutritionally enriched, insect resistant, or herbicide resistant;
- Modification of bacteria to use in cleanup of oil spills or toxic waste.

## 14.1a Bacterial Enzymes Called Restriction Endonucleases Form the Basis of DNA Cloning

The key to DNA cloning is the specific cutting and joining of two DNA molecules from different sources, such as a genomic DNA fragment and a bacterial plasmid (see Figure 14.1). Precise cutting of DNA is made possible by using bacterial enzymes called **restriction endonucleases** (also called **restriction enzymes**). Restriction enzymes recognize short, specific DNA sequences called *restriction sites*, typically four to eight base pairs long, and cut the DNA at specific locations within those sequences. The DNA fragments produced by cutting a long DNA molecule with a restriction enzyme are known as **restriction fragments**.

The *restriction* in the name of the enzymes refers to their normal role inside bacteria, in which the enzymes defend against viral attack by breaking down (restricting) the DNA molecules of infecting viruses. Why don't such enzymes break down the cell's own DNA? The bacterium "hides" the restriction sites in its own DNA by attaching methyl groups to bases in those sites, thereby blocking the binding of its restriction enzyme.

Hundreds of different restriction enzymes have been identified, each one cutting DNA at a specific restriction site. As illustrated by the restriction site of *Eco*RI (**Figure 14.2**), most restriction sites are symmetrical in that the sequence of nucleotides read in the 5′ → 3′ direction on one strand is the same as the sequence read in the 5′ → 3′ direction on the complementary strand. A given enzyme always recognizes the same short DNA sequence as its cut site, and always

cuts at the same place within the sequence. The restriction enzymes most used in cloning—such as *Eco*RI—cleave the sugar–phosphate backbones of DNA to produce DNA fragments with single-stranded ends (Figure 14.2, step 1). The ends are called **sticky ends** because the short, single-stranded regions

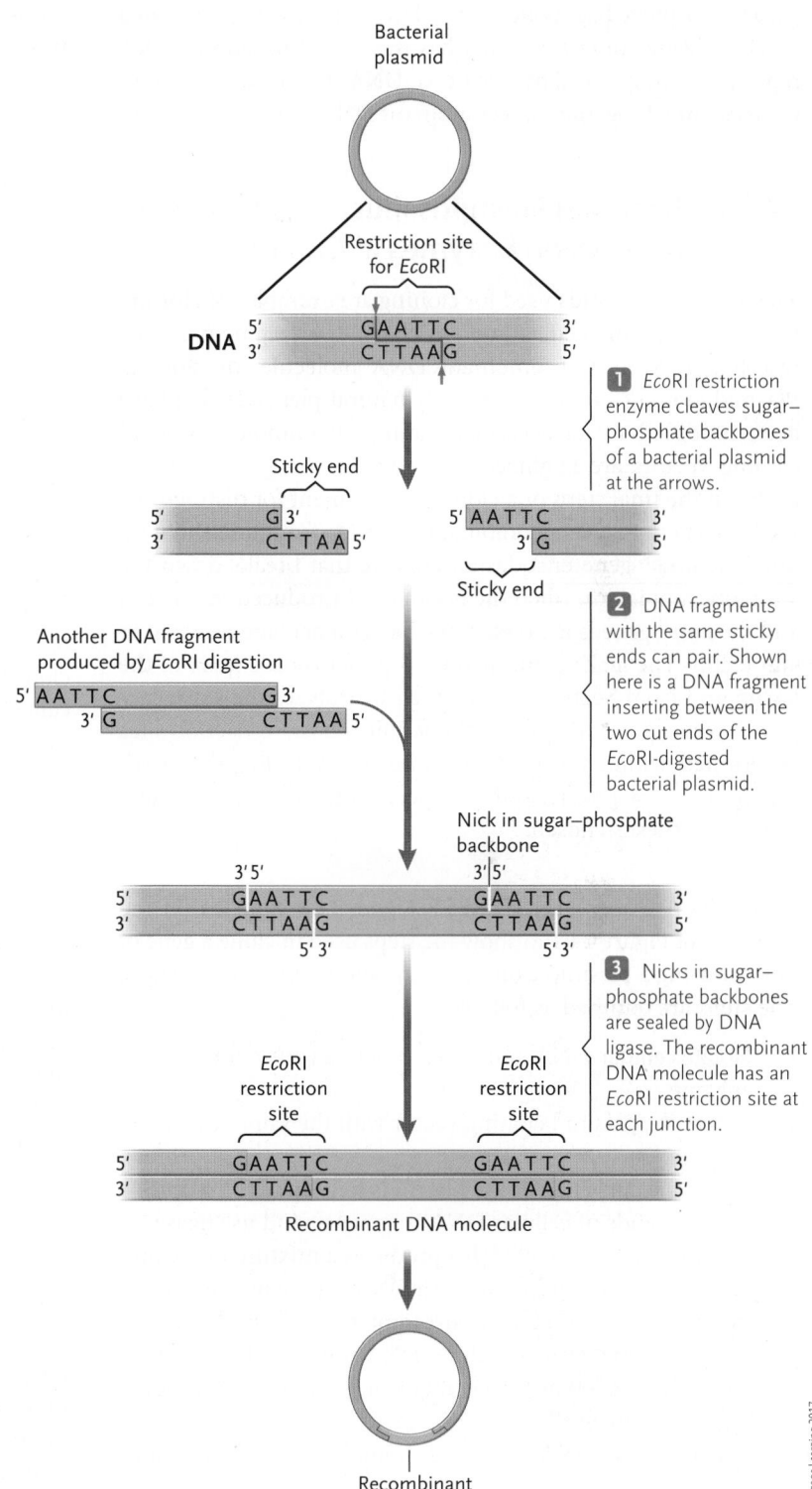

FIGURE 14.2 **A bacterial plasmid (gray) and DNA to be cloned (blue) are each cut with EcoRI at the GAATTC site.** The sticky ends of the restriction sites join using hydrogen bonds between complementary bases. Their backbones are joined covalently to make a recombinant plasmid.

can form hydrogen bonds with complementary sticky ends on any other DNA molecules cut with the same enzyme. For example, step 2 shows the insertion of a DNA molecule with sticky ends produced by *Eco*RI between two other DNA molecules with the same sticky ends. The pairings leave nicks in the sugar–phosphate backbones of the DNA strands that are sealed by *DNA ligase,* an enzyme that has the same function in DNA replication (step 3). The result is DNA from two different sources joined together: a recombinant DNA molecule.

## 14.1b    Bacterial Plasmids Illustrate the Use of Restriction Enzymes in Cloning

The bacterial plasmids used for cloning are examples of **cloning vectors**—DNA molecules into which a DNA fragment can be inserted to form a recombinant DNA molecule for cloning. Plasmid cloning vectors are usually natural plasmids that have been modified to have special features. Commonly, plasmid cloning vectors are engineered to contain two genes that are useful in the final steps of a cloning experiment for distinguishing bacteria that have recombinant plasmids from those that do not. The *amp*^R gene encodes an enzyme that breaks down the antibiotic ampicillin; when the plasmid is introduced into *E. coli* and the *amp*^R gene is expressed, the bacteria become resistant to ampicillin. The *lacZ*^+ gene encodes β-galactosidase (part of the *lac* operon from Section 13.1), which hydrolyzes the sugar lactose as well as a number of synthetic substrates. Restriction sites are located within the *lacZ*^+ gene but do not alter the gene's function. For a given cloning experiment, only one of these restriction sites is chosen.

**CLONING A GENE OF INTEREST** **Figure 14.3** expands on the overview of Figure 14.1 to show the steps used to clone a gene of interest using a plasmid cloning vector and restriction enzymes. The steps are outlined as follows:

1.  Isolate cellular DNA and digest it with a restriction enzyme.
2.  Digest the plasmid cloning vector with the same restriction enzyme.
3.  Allow the cuts ends of the plasmids to bind with complementary ends of cellular DNA fragments, and use ligase to join them permanently. This produces a mixture of recombinant plasmids (plasmids with DNA fragments inserted into the cloning vector), nonrecombinant plasmids (resealed cloning vectors with no DNA fragment inserted), and joined-together pieces of genomic DNA with no cloning vector involved.
4.  Transform the DNA into *E. coli*. Some bacteria will take up a plasmid, whereas others will not.

*Selection:* Spread the bacterial cells on growth medium containing ampicillin and X-gal and incubate to allow colonies to grow. Bacteria containing plasmids are selected for (i.e., they are allowed to live) because they are resistant to the ampicillin in

the growth medium. Within each cell of a colony, the plasmids replicate until approximately 100 copies are present.

*Screening:* Distinguishing recombinant plasmids carrying cellular DNA from those plasmids that did not accept cellular DNA is possible using *blue–white screening* because X-gal activity is present only in nonrecombinants (see Interpreting the Results). White colonies contain recombinant plasmids (*lacZ*^+, in which the restriction sites are located, now have cellular DNA), whereas blue colonies contain nonrecombinant plasmids (their *lacZ*^+ is intact). X-gal (colourless) is cleaved by the *lacZ*^+ protein, causing it to turn blue. Among the white colonies are a very few with a recombinant plasmid that contains the gene of interest. We will see a little later how we can identify that particular plasmid.

In 1973, three researchers, Paul Berg, Stanley N. Cohen, and Herbert Boyer, pioneered the development of DNA cloning techniques using restriction enzymes and bacterial plasmids. Berg received a Nobel Prize in 1980 for his research.

## 14.1c    DNA Libraries Contain Collections of Cloned DNA Fragments

In the previous example, the starting point for cloning a gene of interest was a large set of plasmid clones carrying fragments representing the entire DNA of an organism. A collection of clones that contains a copy of every DNA sequence in a cell is called a **genomic library**. Just as for a book library, where you can search through the same set of books on various occasions to find different passages of interest, you can search through the same genomic library on various occasions to find and isolate different genes or other DNA sequences.

Researchers also commonly use another kind of DNA library that is made starting with mRNA molecules isolated from a cell (**Figure 14.4**). To convert single-stranded mRNA to double-stranded DNA for cloning (RNA cannot be cloned directly), first the researchers use the enzyme *reverse transcriptase* (made by retroviruses) to make a single-stranded DNA that is complementary to the mRNA. Then they degrade the mRNA strand with an enzyme and use DNA polymerase to make a second DNA strand that is complementary to the first. The result is **complementary DNA (cDNA)**. After adding restriction sites to each end, the researchers insert the cDNA into a cloning vector as described for the genomic library. The entire collection of cloned cDNAs made from the mRNAs isolated from a cell is a **cDNA library**.

Not all genes are active in every cell. Therefore, a cDNA library is limited in that it includes copies of only the genes that were active in the cells used as the starting point for creation of the library. This limitation can be an advantage, however, in identifying genes active in one cell type and not another. cDNA libraries are useful, therefore, for providing clues to the changes in gene activity that are responsible for cell differentiation and specialization. An ingenious method for comparing the cDNA libraries produced by different cell types—the DNA chip—is described in the next chapter.

FIGURE 14.3    **Research Method**

## Identifying a Recombinant Plasmid Containing a Gene of Interest

**Protocol:**

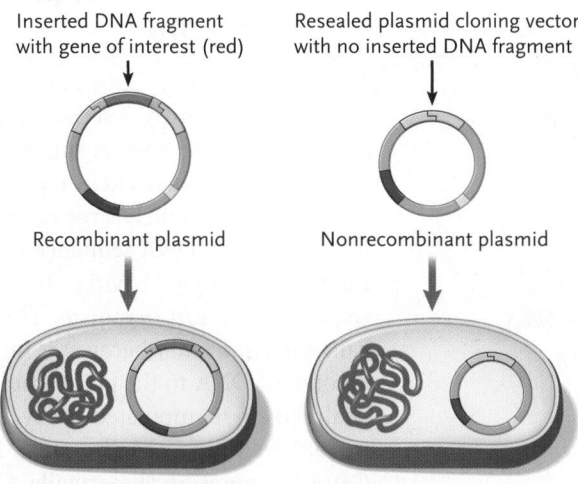

Inserted DNA fragment with gene of interest (red)

Resealed plasmid cloning vector with no inserted DNA fragment

Recombinant plasmid

Nonrecombinant plasmid

Bacteria transformed with plasmids

Bacteria not transformed with a plasmid or transformed with gene fragments

**Purpose:** To identify a recombinant plasmid containing a gene of interest from a ligation reaction mixture containing a bacterial cloning vector and a DNA fragment containing the gene of interest, each digested with the same restriction enzyme

1.  The ligation reaction produces recombinant plasmids (the only products that might contain the gene of interest), nonrecombinant plasmids, and joined pieces of genomic DNA (not shown).

2.  Transform ampicillin-sensitive, *lacZ⁻* *E. coli* (which cannot make β-galactosidase) with a sample of the ligation reaction. In this step, some bacteria will take up DNA, whereas others will not.

**Selection:**
Bacteria transformed with plasmids grow on medium containing ampicillin because of *amp*ᴿ gene on plasmid.

**Screening:**
Blue colony contains bacteria with a nonrecombinant plasmid; that is, the *lacZ⁺* gene is intact.

White colony contains bacteria with a recombinant plasmid, that is, the vector with an inserted DNA fragment, in this case the gene of interest.

© Cengage Learning 2017

Untransformed bacteria or bacteria transformed with gene fragments cannot grow on medium containing ampicillin.

Plate of growth medium containing ampicillin and X-gal

3.  Spread the bacterial cells on a plate of growth medium containing ampicillin and X-gal, and incubate the plate until colonies appear.

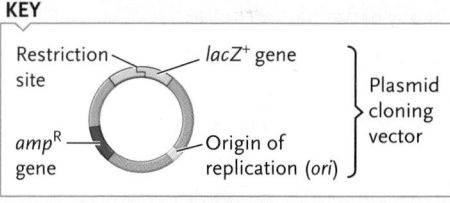

**KEY**

Restriction site

*lacZ⁺* gene

*amp*ᴿ gene

Origin of replication (*ori*)

Plasmid cloning vector

**Interpreting the Results:** All the colonies on the plate contain plasmids because the bacteria that form the colonies are resistant to the ampicillin present in the growth medium. Blue–white screening distinguishes bacterial colonies with nonrecombinant plasmids from those with recombinant plasmids. Bacteria making up blue colonies contain nonrecombinant plasmids. These plasmids have intact *lacZ⁺* genes and produce β-galactosidase, which changes X-gal to a blue product. Bacteria that form the white colonies contain recombinant plasmids. Each recombinant plasmid has a DNA fragment (in this example, the gene of interest) inserted into the *lacZ⁺* gene, so β-galactosidase cannot be produced. As a result, bacteria with recombinant plasmids cannot convert X-gal to the blue product and the colonies are white. Culturing a white colony produces large quantities of the recombinant plasmid that can be isolated and purified for analysis and/or manipulation of the gene = "gene of interest".

FIGURE 14.4    **Research Method**

## Synthesis of DNA from mRNA Using Reverse Transcriptase

**Purpose:** To produce double-stranded, complementary DNA (cDNA) copies of mRNA molecules isolated from cells

**Protocol:**

1.  Isolate mRNAs from cells. One mRNA is shown.

2.  Add primer of a short sequence of T DNA nucleotides (oligo(dT)). Primer base-pairs to poly(A) tail of mRNA.

3.  Reverse transcriptase uses DNA precursors to synthesize a DNA copy of the mRNA in the 5′ → 3′ direction. The result is a hybrid nucleic acid molecule consisting of the mRNA base-paired with a DNA strand.

4.  An RNase enzyme degrades the mRNA strand, leaving a single strand of DNA.

5.  A complementary strand of DNA is created on the DNA template, resulting in a double-stranded complementary DNA (cDNA) copy of the starting mRNA.

**Outcome:** The outcome is a population of double-stranded, cDNA molecules that have base-pair sequences corresponding to the base sequences of the mRNA molecules isolated from the cell.

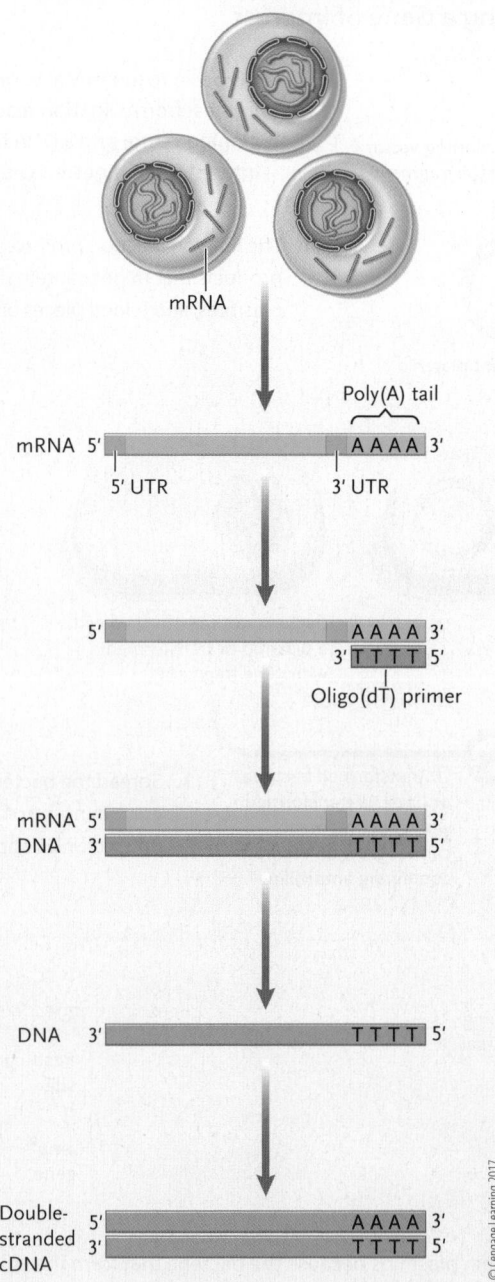

cDNA libraries provide a critical advantage to synthetic biologists who wish to insert eukaryotic genes into bacteria, particularly when the bacteria are to be used as "factories" for making the protein encoded in the gene. The genes in eukaryotic nuclear DNA typically contain many *introns,* spacer sequences that interrupt the amino acid-coding sequence of a gene (see Section 12.3). Because bacterial DNA does not contain introns, bacteria are not equipped to process eukaryotic genes correctly. However, the cDNA copy of a eukaryotic mRNA already has the introns removed, so bacteria can transcribe and translate it accurately to make eukaryotic proteins.

## 14.1d The Polymerase Chain Reaction Amplifies DNA *In Vitro*

Producing multiple DNA copies by cloning in bacteria requires a series of techniques and considerable time. A much more rapid process, **polymerase chain reaction (PCR)**, produces an extremely large number of copies of a specific DNA sequence from a DNA mixture without having to clone the sequence in a host organism. The process is called *amplification* because it increases the amount of DNA to the point where it can be analyzed or manipulated easily. Developed in 1983 by Kary B. Mullis and F. Faloona at Cetus Corporation (Emeryville, California), PCR has become one of the most important tools in modern molecular biology, finding wide application in all areas of biology. Mullis received a Nobel Prize in 1993 for his role in the development of PCR.

**Figure 14.5** shows that PCR is essentially a special case of DNA replication in which a DNA polymerase replicates just a portion of a DNA molecule rather than the whole molecule. PCR takes advantage of a characteristic common to all DNA polymerases: these enzymes add nucleotides only to the 3′ end of an existing chain called the *primer* (see Section 11.3). For replication to begin, a primer base-paired to the template chain must be available. By cycling 20 to 30 times through a series of priming and replication steps, PCR amplifies the target sequence, producing billions of copies.

**CONCEPT FIX** Careful attention to Figure 14.6 can help you avoid the common pitfalls in understanding PCR. Notice that

1.  the primers are made of DNA, not RNA as in natural DNA replication;

2.  the left primer binds to one strand while the right primer binds to the opposite strand of the original DNA;

3.  of all the DNA sequences put into the PCR reaction tube, only the *target sequence,* the sequence between the primers, is amplified exponentially; and

4.  although the diagram shows DNA being synthesized left to right on the bottom strand, and right to left on the top strand, the DNA polymerase is reading the template 3′ → 5′ in both cases. ⬢

FIGURE 14.5 **Research Method**

## The Polymerase Chain Reaction (PCR)

**Purpose:** To amplify—produce large numbers of copies of—a target DNA sequence (e.g., a gene of interest) in the test tube without cloning in bacteria

**Protocol:** A polymerase chain reaction mixture has four key elements: (1) the DNA with the target sequence to be amplified; (2) a pair of DNA primers, one complementary to one end of the target sequence on one strand of the double helix and the other complementary to the other end of the target sequence (on the other strand of the helix); (3) the four nucleoside triphosphate precursors for DNA synthesis (dATP, dTTP, dGTP, and dCTP); and (4) DNA polymerase. Since PCR uses high temperatures that would break down normal DNA polymerases, a heat-stable DNA polymerase is used.

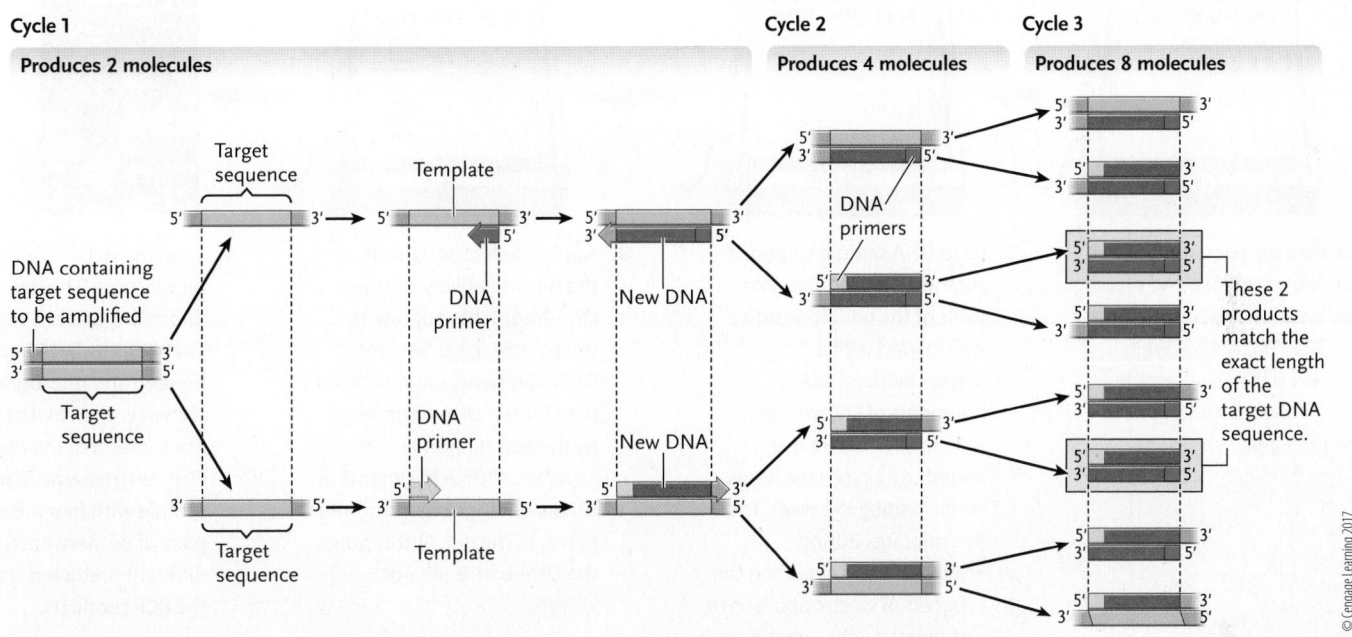

1. **Denaturation:** Heat DNA containing target sequence to 95°C to denature it to single strands.

2. **Annealing:** Cool the mixture to 55°C to 65°C (depending on the primers) to allow the two primers to anneal their complementary sequences at the two ends of the target sequence.

3. **Extension:** Heat to 72°C, the optimal temperature for DNA polymerase to extend the primers, using the four nucleoside triphosphate precursors to make complementary copies of the two template strands. This completes cycle 1 of PCR; the end result is two new molecules.

4. Repeat the same steps of denaturation, annealing of primers, and extension in cycle 2, producing a total of four molecules.

5. Repeat the same steps in cycle 3, producing a total of eight molecules. Two of the eight match the exact length of the target DNA sequence (highlighted in yellow).

**Interpreting the Results:** After three cycles, PCR produces a pair of molecules matching the target sequence. Subsequent cycles amplify these molecules to the point where they outnumber all other molecules in the reaction by many orders of magnitude.

Since the primers used in PCR are designed to bracket only the sequence of interest, the cycles exponentially amplify only this sequence from a mixture of essentially any DNA molecules. Thus, PCR not only finds the "needle in the haystack" among all the sequences in a mixture, but also makes millions of copies of the "needle"—the DNA sequence of interest.

FIGURE 14.6  **Research Method**

## Separation of DNA Fragments by Agarose Gel Electrophoresis

**Purpose:** To separate DNA fragments using gel electrophoresis. Gel electrophoresis separates DNA molecules, RNA molecules, or proteins according to their sizes, electrical charges, or other properties through a gel in an electric field. Different gel types and conditions are used for different molecules and types of applications. A common gel for separating large DNA fragments is made of agarose.

**Protocol:**

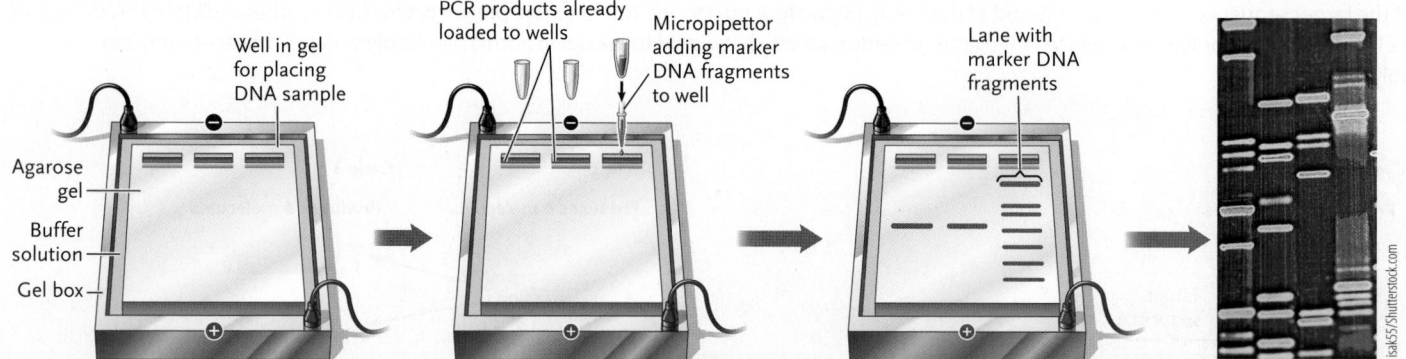

1. Prepare a gel consisting of a thin slab of agarose and place it between two electrodes in a gel box. The gel has wells for placing the DNA samples to be analyzed. Add buffer to cover the gels.

2. Load DNA sample solutions, such as PCR products, into wells of the gel, alongside a well loaded with a DNA marker ladder (DNA fragments of known sizes). (All samples have a dye added to help see the liquid when loading the wells. The dye migrates during electrophoresis, enabling the progress of electrophoresis to be followed although it does not show where the DNA is.)

3. Apply an electric current to the gel; negatively charged DNA fragments migrate to the positive pole. Shorter DNA fragments migrate faster than longer DNA fragments. By the completion of separation, DNA fragments of the same length have formed bands in the gel. At this point, the DNA bands are not visible.

4. Stain the gel with a DNA-binding dye. The dye fluoresces under UV light, enabling the DNA bands to be seen and photographed. Shown is an actual gel photograph of the results of PCRs on the same DNA sample with four different pairs of primers, each with a different predicted size for the PCR products.

© Cengage Learning 2017

**Interpreting the Results:** Agarose gel electrophoresis separates DNA fragments according to their length. The lengths of the DNA fragments being analyzed are determined by measuring their migration distances and comparing those distances to a calibration curve of the migration distances of the bands of the DNA marker ladder, which have known lengths. For PCR, agarose gel electrophoresis shows whether DNA of the correct length was amplified. For restriction enzyme digests, this technique shows whether fragments are produced as expected.

The characteristics of PCR allow extremely small DNA samples to be amplified to concentrations high enough for analysis. PCR is used, for example, to produce enough DNA for analysis from the root of a single human hair, or from a small amount of blood, semen, or saliva, such as the traces left at the scene of a crime. It is also used to extract and multiply DNA sequences from skeletal remains; ancient sources such as mammoths, Neanderthals, and Egyptian mummies; and, in rare cases, amber-entombed fossils, fossil bones, and fossil plant remains.

A successful outcome of PCR is shown by analyzing a sample of the amplified DNA using **agarose gel electrophoresis** to see if the copies are the same length as the target (**Figure 14.6**). Gel electrophoresis is a technique by which DNA, RNA, or protein molecules are separated in a gel subjected to an electric field. The type of gel and the conditions used vary with the aim of the experiment, but in each case, the gel functions as a molecular sieve to separate the macromolecules based on size, electrical charge, or other properties. To separate large DNA molecules such as those typically produced by PCR, a gel made of agarose—a natural molecule isolated from seaweed—is used because of its large pore size.

The basic mechanism of PCR has been developed and refined in several specialized applications. One of these is quantitative PCR (qPCR) used in gene expression studies. For example, researchers can rapidly and accurately determine the relative amount of a given mRNA transcript produced from a given gene in a cell in real time. This technique uses reverse transcriptase to make cDNA and then labels the resulting PCR products with a fluorescent dye. The dye is detected directly by the qPCR machine, thus eliminating the need for electrophoresis.

**REVIEW OF SOME OF THE MATERIALS, CONCEPTS, AND TECHNIQUES INTRODUCED IN THIS SECTION** In this chapter so far, we have discussed many research methods—so there are a lot of new terms and techniques to learn! Here is a collection of some of these terms and techniques and what they are or what they do:

- *Genetic engineering.* The use of DNA technologies to alter genes for practical purposes
- *DNA cloning.* A method for producing many copies of a piece of DNA
- *Gene cloning.* DNA cloning that involves a gene
- *Recombinant DNA.* DNA fragments from two or more sources that have joined together
- *Restriction enzyme (restriction endonuclease).* An enzyme that recognizes a specific DNA sequence and cuts the DNA within that sequence. Fragments produced by cutting DNA with a restriction enzyme are *restriction fragments.*
- *Ligation.* The process of joining two or more DNA fragments together to make one DNA molecule
- *DNA ligase.* The enzyme that seals together DNA fragments generated by restriction enzyme digestion to produce a recombinant DNA molecule
- *Cloning vector.* A DNA carrier into which DNA of interest can be inserted to form recombinant DNA as a product. The product can be replicated in a host organism for the purpose of cloning and the DNA of interest excised from the vector.
- *Genomic DNA library.* A set of clones that collectively contain a copy of every DNA sequence in a genome
- *cDNA (complementary DNA).* A double-stranded DNA copy of a single-stranded mRNA molecule
- *cDNA library.* A collection of cloned cDNAs made from the mRNAs isolated from a cell
- *Polymerase chain reaction (PCR).* A DNA replication-based technique for amplifying DNA sequences without cloning in bacteria
- *Agarose gel electrophoresis.* A technique in which an electric field passing through an agarose gel is used to separate DNA or RNA molecules on the basis of size

**STUDY BREAK QUESTIONS**

1. What features do restriction enzymes have in common? How do they differ?
2. Plasmid cloning vectors are one type of cloning vector that can be used with *E. coli* as a host organism. What features of a plasmid cloning vector make it useful for constructing and cloning recombinant DNA molecules?
3. What is a cDNA library, and from what cellular material is it derived? How does a cDNA library differ from a genomic library?
4. What information and materials are needed to amplify a region of DNA using PCR?

## 14.2 Applications of DNA Technologies

The ability to clone pieces of DNA—genes, especially—and to amplify specific segments of DNA by PCR has revolutionized biology. These and other DNA technologies are now used for research in all areas of biology, including cloning genes to determine their structure, function, and regulation of expression; manipulating genes to determine how their products function in cellular or developmental processes; and identifying differences in DNA sequences among individuals in ecological studies. The same DNA technologies also have practical applications, including medical and forensic detection, modification of animals and plants, and the manufacture of commercial products. In this section, we provide examples of how the techniques are used to answer questions and solve problems.

### 14.2a DNA Technologies Are Used in Molecular Testing for Many Human Genetic Diseases

Many human genetic diseases are caused by defects in enzymes or other proteins that result from mutations at the DNA level. Once scientists have identified the specific mutations responsible for human genetic diseases, they can often use DNA technologies to develop molecular tests for those diseases. One example is sickle cell disease (Section 9.2f and Section 10.4a). People with this disease are homozygous for a DNA mutation that affects hemoglobin, the oxygen-carrying molecule of the blood. The mutation, which is in the β-globin gene, alters one amino acid in the polypeptide. As a consequence, the function of hemoglobin is significantly impaired in individuals homozygous for the mutation (who have sickle cell disease), and mildly impaired in individuals heterozygous for the mutation (who have sickle cell trait).

The change in DNA sequence that results in the sickle cell mutation also happens to change a restriction site in the DNA **(Figure 14.7)**. Three restriction sites for *Mst*II are associated with the normal β-globin gene: two within the coding sequence of the gene and one upstream of the gene. The sickle cell mutation eliminates the middle site of the three. Therefore, cutting

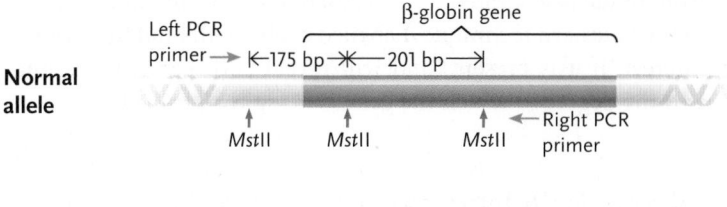

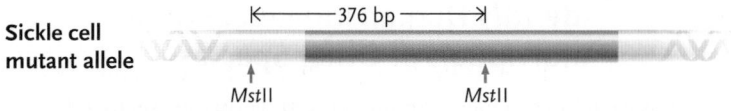

**FIGURE 14.7 Restriction site differences between the normal and sickle cell mutant alleles of the β-globin gene**

the β-globin gene with *Mst*II produces two DNA fragments from the normal gene and one fragment from the mutated gene (see Figure 14.8). Restriction enzyme-generated DNA fragments of different lengths from the same region of the genome, such as in this example, are known as **restriction fragment length polymorphisms** (RFLPs; pronounced "riff-lips").

RFLPs are typically analyzed using **Southern blot analysis**, named after its inventor, researcher Edward Southern (**Figure 14.8**). In this technique, genomic DNA is digested with a restriction enzyme, and the DNA fragments are separated using agarose gel electrophoresis. The fragments are then transferred—blotted—to a filter paper. A labelled piece of DNA that is complementary to the DNA of interest, called a probe, is used to identify a DNA sequence of interest from among the many thousands of fragments on the filter paper.

Analyzing DNA for the sickle cell mutation by *Mst*II digestion and Southern blot analysis is straightforward (see Figure 14.8). An individual with sickle cell disease will have one DNA band of 376 bp detected by the probe (lane A), a healthy individual will have two DNA bands of 175 and 201 bp (lane B), and an individual heterozygous for normal and mutant alleles will have three DNA bands of 376 bp (mutant allele) and 201 and 175 bp (normal allele) (lane C). The same probe detects all three RFLP fragments by binding to all or part of the sequence.

Restriction enzyme digestion and Southern blot analysis may be used to test for a number of other human genetic diseases, including phenylketonuria and Duchenne muscular dystrophy. In some cases, restriction enzyme digestion is combined with PCR for a quicker, easier analysis. The gene or region of the gene with the restriction enzyme variation is first amplified using PCR, and the amplified DNA is then cut with the diagnostic restriction enzyme. Amplification produces enough DNA so that separation by size on an agarose gel produces clearly visible bands positioned according to fragment length. Researchers can then determine whether the fragment lengths match a normal or an abnormal RFLP pattern. This method eliminates the need for a probe or for Southern blotting.

An interesting modification of the Southern blot is the northern blot (the word "northern" is wordplay and not named after an individual, and hence not capitalized). RNA taken from tissue is separated in a gel and blotted in a method similar to the Southern technique. Labelled probes will bind to RNA of interest, if it is present, and will reveal both gene expression and the degree to which the gene is being transcribed.

## 14.2b DNA Fingerprinting Is Used to Identify Human Individuals and Individuals of Other Species

Just as each human has a unique set of fingerprints, each also has unique combinations and variations of DNA sequences (with the exception of identical twins) known as *DNA fingerprints*. **DNA**

fingerprinting is a technique used to distinguish between individuals of the same species using DNA samples. Invented by Sir Alec Jeffreys in 1985, DNA fingerprinting has become a mainstream technique for distinguishing human individuals, notably in forensics and paternity testing. Although the technique can be applied to all kinds of animals and plants, in this chapter we focus on humans.

**DNA Fingerprinting Principles** In DNA fingerprinting, scientists use molecular techniques, most typically PCR, to analyze DNA variations at various loci in the genome. Several loci in noncoding regions of the genome are used for analysis. Each locus is an example of a *short tandem repeat* (STR) sequence, meaning that it has a short sequence of DNA repeated in series, with each repeat about 3–5 bp. Each locus has a different repeated sequence, and the number of repeats varies among individuals in a population. For example, one STR locus has the sequence AGAT repeated between 8 and 20 times. As a further source of variation, a given individual is either homozygous or heterozygous for an STR allele; perhaps you are homozygous for the 11-repeat allele or heterozygous for a 9-repeat allele and a 14-repeat allele. Likely, your DNA fingerprint for this locus is different from most of the others in your class. Because every individual has an essentially unique combination of alleles (identical twins are the exception), analysis of multiple STR loci can discriminate between DNA of different individuals.

**Figure 14.9** illustrates how PCR is used to obtain a DNA fingerprint for a theoretical STR locus with three alleles of 9, 11, and 14 tandem repeats (see Figure 14.9a). Using primers that flank the STR locus, the locus is amplified from genomic DNA using PCR, and the PCR products are analyzed by gel electrophoresis (see Figure 14.9b).

**CONCEPT FIX** Notice in Figure 14.9b that the first lane has only one band, even though the cell that was the source of DNA was diploid and had two copies of all alleles. In this case, both alleles produce the same size fragment by PCR analysis. Therefore, fragments from both alleles migrate the same distance in the gel. Notice how this band is more prominent than the others, indicating more DNA. ⬢

**DNA Fingerprinting in Forensics** DNA fingerprints are routinely used to identify criminals or eliminate innocent people as suspects in legal proceedings. For example, a DNA fingerprint prepared from a hair found at the scene of a crime or from a semen sample might be compared with the DNA fingerprint of a suspect. Or a DNA fingerprint of blood found on a suspect's clothing or possessions might be compared with the DNA fingerprint of a victim. The evidence is typically presented in terms of the unlikelihood that the particular DNA sample could have come from a random individual, or it can be used to exclude a suspect if the DNA fingerprints don't match. Hence, the media report probability values, such as one in several million, or in several billion, that a person other than the accused could have left his or her DNA at the crime scene.

FIGURE 14.8   **Research Method**

## Southern Blot Analysis

**Purpose:** To identify DNA fragments of interest after separating DNA fragments on a gel, using the Southern blot technique. One application is to compare different samples of genomic DNA cut with a restriction enzyme to detect specific RFLPs. Here the technique is used to distinguish between individuals with sickle cell disease, individuals with sickle cell trait, and normal individuals.

**Protocol:**

**1.** Isolate genomic DNA and digest with a restriction enzyme. Here genomic DNA is isolated from three individuals: A, sickle cell disease (homozygous for the sickle cell mutant allele); B, normal (homozygous for the normal allele); and C, sickle cell trait (heterozygous for sickle cell mutant allele). Digest the DNA with *Mst*II.

**2.** Separate the DNA fragments by agarose gel electrophoresis. The thousands of differently sized DNA fragments produce a smear of DNA down the length of each lane in the gel, which can be seen after staining the DNA. (Gel electrophoresis and gel staining are shown in Figure 14.6.)

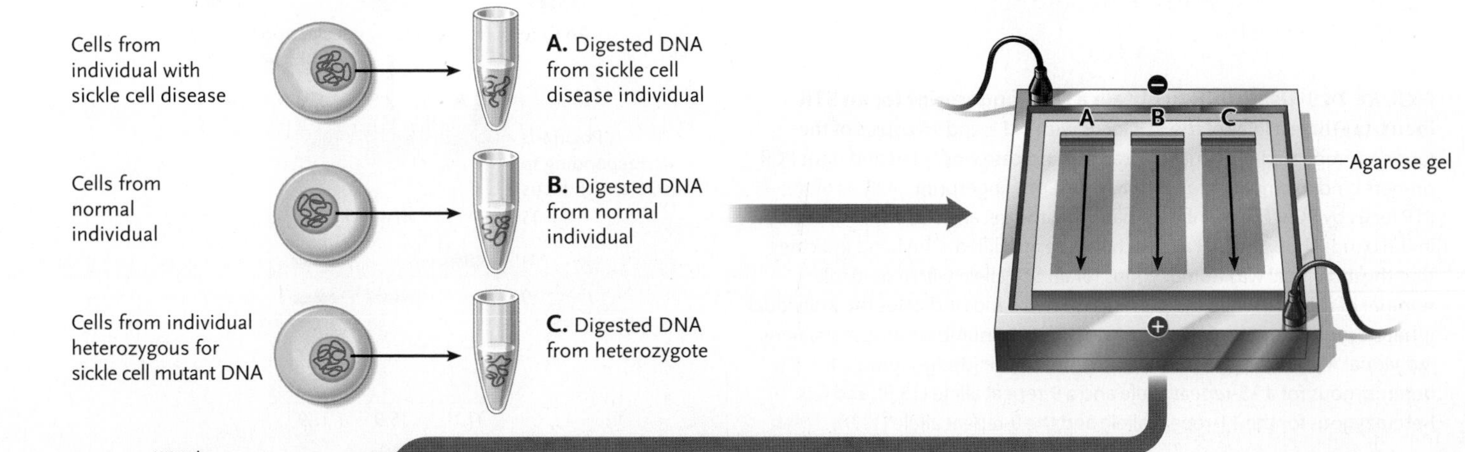

Cells from individual with sickle cell disease → **A.** Digested DNA from sickle cell disease individual

Cells from normal individual → **B.** Digested DNA from normal individual

Cells from individual heterozygous for sickle cell mutant DNA → **C.** Digested DNA from heterozygote

A  B  C — Agarose gel

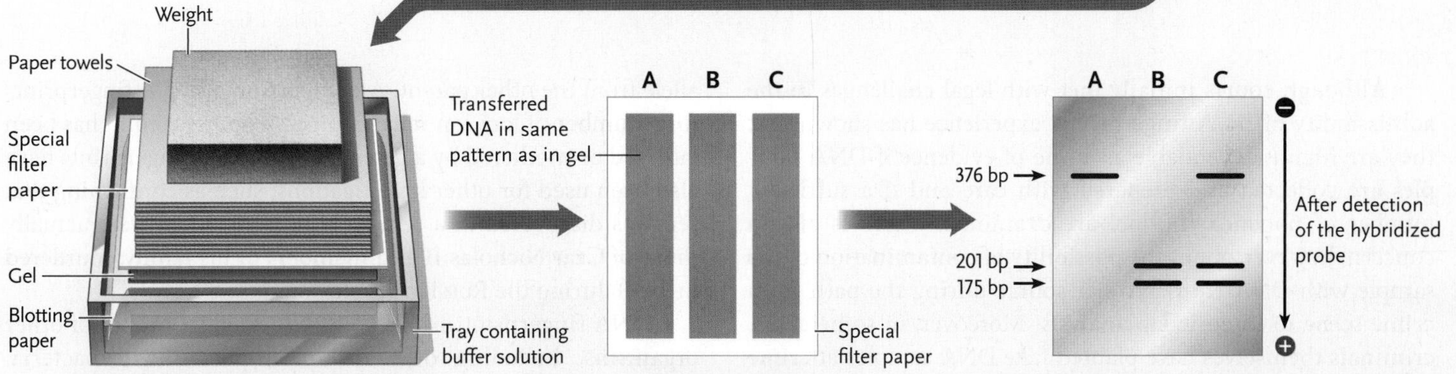

Weight

Paper towels

Special filter paper

Gel

Blotting paper

Tray containing buffer solution

Transferred DNA in same pattern as in gel

A  B  C — Special filter paper

A  B  C

376 bp →
201 bp →
175 bp →

After detection of the hybridized probe

**3.** Hybridization with a labelled DNA probe to identify DNA fragments of interest cannot be done directly with an agarose gel. Edward Southern devised a method to transfer the DNA fragments from a gel to a special filter paper. First, treat the gel with a solution to denature the DNA into single strands. Next, place the gel on a piece of blotting paper with the ends of the paper in the buffer solution and place the special filter paper on top of the gel. Capillary action wicks the buffer solution in the tray up the blotting paper, through the gel and special filter paper, and into the weighted stack of paper towels on top of the gel. The movement of the solution transfers—blots—the single-stranded DNA fragments to the filter paper, where they stick. The pattern of DNA fragments is the same as it was in the gel.

**4.** To focus on a particular region of the genome, use DNA hybridization with a labelled probe. That is, incubate a labelled, single-stranded probe with the filter and, after washing off excess probe, detect hybridization of the probe with DNA fragments on the filter. For a radioactive probe, place the filter against photographic film, which, after development, will show a band or bands where the probe hybridized. In this experiment, the probe is a cloned piece of DNA from the area shown in Figure 14.7 (the β-globin gene) that can bind to all three of the *Mst*II fragments of interest.

© Cengage Learning 2017

**Interpreting the Results:** The hybridization result indicates that the probe has identified a very specific DNA fragment or fragments in the digested genomic DNA. The RFLPs for the β-globin gene can be seen in Figure 14.7. DNA from the sickle cell disease individual cut with *Mst*II results in a single band of 376 bp detected by the probe, while DNA from the normal individual results in two bands, 201 bp and 175 bp. DNA from a sickle cell trait heterozygote results in three bands, 376 bp (from the sickle cell mutant allele) and 201 bp and 175 bp (both from the normal allele). This type of analysis in general is useful for distinguishing normal and mutant alleles of genes where the mutation involved alters a restriction site.

**a. Alleles at an STR locus**

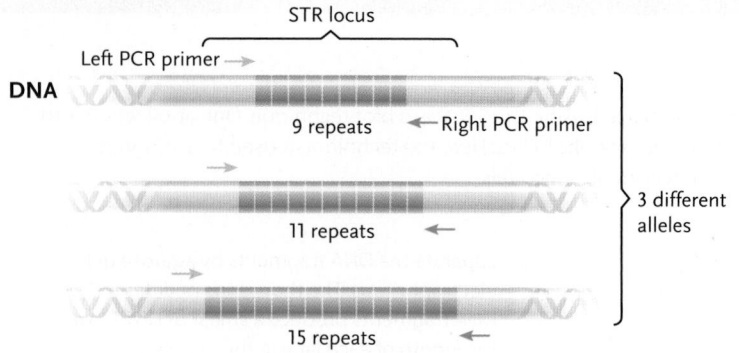

**b. DNA fingerprint analysis of the STR locus by PCR**

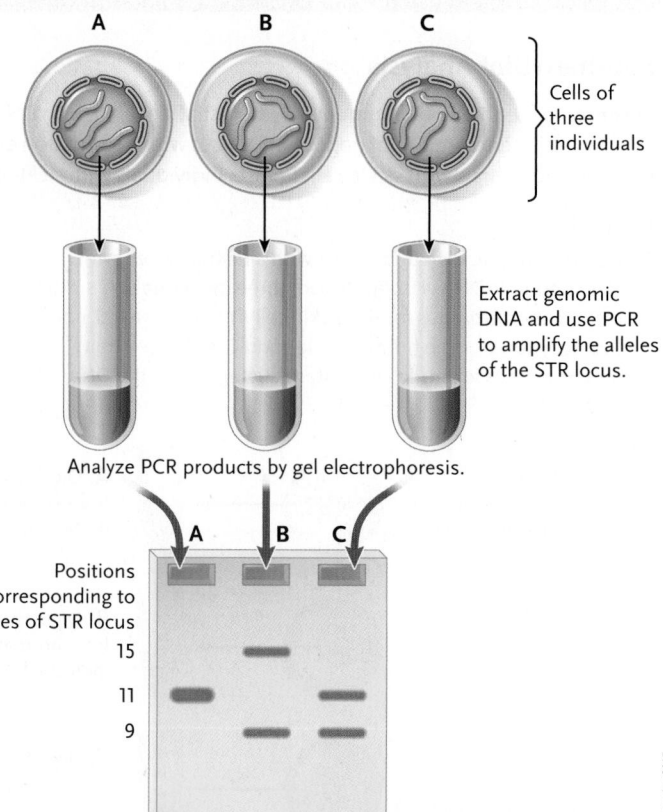

Analyze PCR products by gel electrophoresis.

**FIGURE 14.9 Using PCR to obtain a DNA fingerprint for an STR locus. (a)** Three alleles of the STR locus with 9, 11, and 15 copies of the tandemly repeated sequence. The arrows indicate where left and right PCR primers bind to amplify the STR locus. **(b)** DNA fingerprint analysis of the STR locus by PCR. The number of bands on the gel and the sizes of the DNA in the bands show the STR alleles that were amplified. One band indicates that the individual was homozygous for an STR allele with a particular number of repeats, while the presence of two bands indicates the individual is heterozygous for two STR alleles with different numbers of repeats. Here, individual A is homozygous for an 11-repeat allele (designated 11,11), B is heterozygous for a 15-repeat allele and a 9-repeat allele (15,9), and C is heterozygous for the 11-repeat allele and the 9-repeat allele (11,9).

Although courts initially met with legal challenges to the admissibility of DNA fingerprints, experience has shown that they are highly dependable as a line of evidence if DNA samples are collected and prepared with care and if a sufficient number of polymorphic loci are examined. There is always concern, however, about the possibility of contamination of the sample with DNA from another source during the path from crime scene to forensic lab analysis. Moreover, in some cases, criminals themselves have planted fake DNA samples at crime scenes to confuse the investigation.

There are many examples of the use of DNA fingerprinting to identify a criminal. For example, in a case in England, the DNA fingerprints of more than 4000 men were made during an investigation of the rape and murder of two teenage girls. The results led to the release of a man wrongly imprisoned for the crimes and to the confession and conviction of the actual killer. And the application of DNA fingerprinting techniques to stored forensic samples has led to the release of a number of people wrongly convicted for rape or murder.

**DNA FINGERPRINTING IN TESTING PATERNITY AND ESTABLISHING ANCESTRY** DNA fingerprints are also widely used as evidence of paternity because parents and their children share common alleles in their DNA fingerprints. That is, each child receives one allele of each locus from one parent and the other allele from the other parent. A comparison of DNA fingerprints for a number of loci can reliably prove whether a child has been fathered or mothered by a given person. DNA fingerprints have also been used for other investigations, such as confirming that remains discovered in a remote region of Russia were actually those of Czar Nicholas II and members of his family, murdered in 1918 during the Russian revolution.

DNA fingerprinting is also widely used in studies of other organisms, including other animals, plants, and bacteria. Examples include testing for pathogenic *E. coli* in food sources such as hamburger meat, investigating cases of wildlife poaching, detecting genetically modified organisms among living organisms or in food, and comparing the DNA of ancient organisms with that of present-day descendants.

## 14.2c Genetic Engineering Uses DNA Technologies to Alter the Genes of a Cell or Organism

We have seen the many ways scientists use DNA technologies to ask and answer questions that were once completely inaccessible. Genetic engineering goes beyond gathering information; it is the use of DNA technologies to modify genes of a cell or organism. The goals of genetic engineering include using prokaryotic cells, fungi, animals, and plants as factories for the production of proteins needed in medicine and scientific research; correcting hereditary disorders; and improving animals and crop plants of agricultural importance. In many of these areas, genetic engineering has already been spectacularly successful. The successes and potential benefits of genetic engineering, however, are tempered by ethical and social concerns about its use, along with the fear that the methods may produce toxic or damaging foods or release dangerous and uncontrollable organisms to the environment.

Genetic engineering uses DNA technologies of the kind already discussed in this chapter. DNA—perhaps a modified gene—is introduced into target cells of an organism. Organisms that have undergone a gene transfer are called **transgenic**, meaning that they have been modified to contain genetic information—the *transgene*—from an external source.

The following sections discuss examples of applications of genetic engineering to bacteria, animals, and plants and assess major controversies arising from these projects.

**GENETIC ENGINEERING OF BACTERIA TO PRODUCE PROTEINS** Transgenic bacteria have been made, for example, to synthesize proteins for medical applications, break down toxic wastes such as oil spills, produce industrial chemicals such as alcohols, and process minerals. *E. coli* is the organism of choice for many of these applications of DNA technologies.

Using *E. coli* to make a protein from a foreign source is conceptually straightforward (**Figure 14.10**). First, the gene for the protein is cloned from the appropriate organism. Then the gene is inserted into an **expression vector** that, in addition to the usual features of a cloning vector, contains the regulatory sequences that allow transcription and translation of the gene. For a bacterial expression vector, this means having a promoter and a transcription terminator that are recognized by the *E. coli* transcriptional machinery, and having the ribosome binding site needed for the bacterial ribosome to recognize the start codon of the transgene (see Section 12.1). The regulatory sequences flank the cluster of restriction sites of the expression vector that are used for cloning so that the inserted gene is correctly placed for transcription and translation when the recombinant plasmid is transformed into *E. coli*.

As we mentioned earlier while discussing DNA libraries, a cDNA copy of a eukaryotic gene is used when we want to use bacteria to express the protein encoded by the gene (see Figure 14.4). This is because the gene itself typically contains introns, which bacteria cannot remove when they transcribe a eukaryotic gene. However, the eukaryotic mRNA that is copied by reverse transcriptase to synthesize cDNA has had its introns removed; thus, when that cDNA is expressed in bacteria, it can be transcribed and translated to make the encoded eukaryotic protein. That protein is either extracted from the bacterial cells and purified, or, if the protein is secreted from the cells, purified from the culture medium.

Expression vectors are available for a number of organisms. They vary in the regulatory sequences they contain and the selectable marker they carry so that the host organism

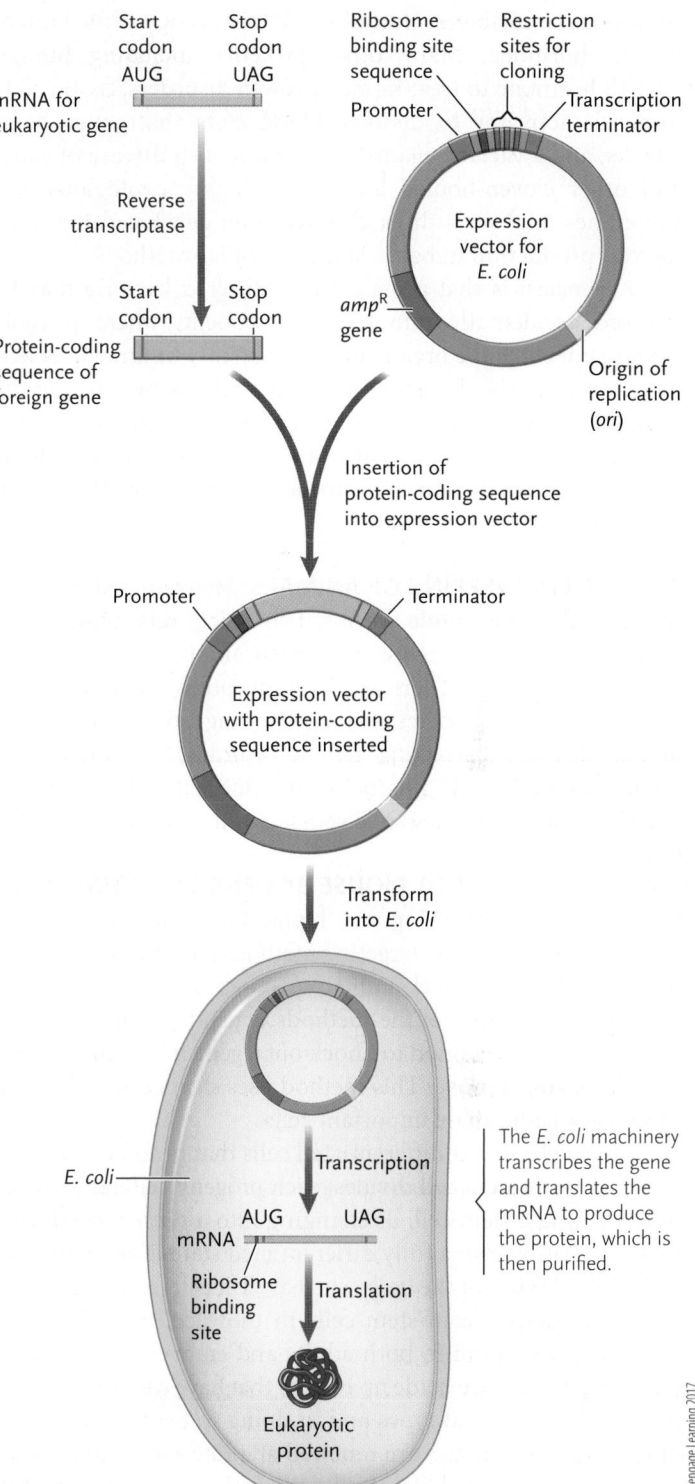

**FIGURE 14.10 Using an expression vector to synthesize a foreign protein in *E. coli*.** The *E. coli* machinery transcribes the coding sequence for the foreign protein and translates the mRNA to produce the protein, which is then purified.

transformed with the vector carrying a gene of interest can be detected and the host can express that gene.

For example, *E. coli* bacteria have been genetically engineered to make the human hormone insulin; the commercial product is called Humulin. Insulin is required by people with some forms of diabetes. Humulin is a perfect copy of the human insulin hormone. Many other proteins, including human growth hormone to treat human growth disorders, tissue plasminogen activator to dissolve blood clots that cause heart attacks, and a vaccine against foot-and-mouth disease of cattle and other cloven-hoofed animals (a highly contagious and sometimes fatal viral disease), have been developed for commercial production in bacteria using similar methods.

A concern is that genetically engineered bacteria may be released accidentally into the environment, where possible adverse effects of the organisms are currently unknown. Scientists minimize the danger of accidental release by growing the bacteria in laboratories that follow appropriate biosafety protocols. In addition, the bacterial strains typically used are genetic mutants that cannot survive outside the growth media used in the laboratory.

**GENETIC ENGINEERING OF ANIMALS** Many animals, including fruit flies, nematode worms, fish, mice, rats, pigs, sheep, goats, monkeys, and cows, have been altered successfully by genetic engineering. There are many purposes for these alterations, including basic research, generating animal models of human diseases, correcting genetic disorders in humans and other mammals, and producing pharmaceutically important proteins. Some examples are discussed in this section.

**MAKING A KNOCKOUT MOUSE BY GENE TARGETING** Gene targeting is the knocking out, replacement, or addition of a gene in a genome. Gene targeting methods have been developed for a number of model animals (as well as yeast and some plants). The specifics of the methods depend on the organism. Let us consider a method to knock out a gene in a mouse to create a **knockout mouse**. This method uses *stem cells,* so first we must learn about these important cells.

**Stem cells** are undifferentiated cells that proliferate indefinitely. When a stem cell divides, each progeny cell has a choice of remaining a stem cell, or changing into a *precursor cell* that follows a pathway to a fully differentiated state. The many specialized cell types of the body, such as skin cells and cells of the intestines, derive from stem cells in those cell types' tissues. Stem cells are found in both adults and embryos. In an adult mammal, tissues are made up of cells that have differentiated to be specific functional types and in doing so become incapable of cell division. Tissues are renewed at a rate that is tissue specific; for example, red blood cells are replaced about every 120 days, and intestinal epithelial cells are replaced every 3–6 days. Small numbers of stem cells in the tissues divide to produce the precursor cells that differentiate into the cells needed for tissue renewal. Control mechanisms involving extracellular signalling molecules that regulate specific intracellular pathways (see Chapter 4) ensure that new cells are produced in the right places and in the right numbers. Stem cells not only are important for the normal replacement of cells in adult tissues, they are also used to repair damaged tissues.

Stem cells in adult tissues—*adult stem cells*—that are used for normal replacement, or tissue cells, or repairing damaged tissues are specialized for the tissues in which they are located. Hence, skin cell stem cells are responsible only for replacing the various cell types of the skin, and bone marrow stem cells are responsible only for replacing the various cell types of the blood. Stem cells like this are said to be *multipotent,* meaning that they have a restricted ability to produce cell types, specifically only those cell types in the tissues in which they are located. Another type of stem cell in mammals is the **embryonic stem cell** (ES cell), which is a *pluripotent* cell, meaning that it is capable of differentiating into many of the different cell types of the body, but not all of them. Embryonic stem cells are found in a mass of cells inside an early-stage embryo (the blastocyst; see Figure 50.11). Embryonic stem cells can be isolated from early mouse embryos and, under appropriate conditions, they can be proliferated using cell culture methods and still remain pluripotent. That is, if some of these cells are injected back into an early embryo, they can give rise to many of the tissues and cell types of the body, including germline cells. The cells can also be induced in culture to differentiate into different cell types.

**Figure 14.11** shows a method using ES cells to make a knockout mouse. To make the method efficient, researchers use strains of mice that differ in coat colour and a selectable marker in the DNA construct used to replace the normal gene in the genome. Mice in which both alleles of the normal gene are knocked out are confirmed by DNA testing. In 2007, Mario Capecchi, Sir Martin Evans, and Oliver Smithies were awarded a Nobel Prize "for their discoveries of principles for introducing specific gene modifications in mice by the use of embryonic stem cells."

Because humans share many genes with yeast, knockout mice have proved to be a useful system for studying and modelling human diseases, including several different kinds of cancer, heart disease, arthritis, diabetes, Parkinson's disease, and obesity. Knockout mice are also useful for testing pharmaceutical treatments and other therapies that might have efficacy in humans.

Making mice in which genes are replaced with mutated versions rather than being knocked out is also a valuable tool for research. That is, a gene can be isolated and cloned from a mouse, manipulated in the laboratory to introduce a specific mutation or mutations, and then used to replace the normal copies of the gene in the mouse. A mouse model for cystic fibrosis (CF) was made in this way. Cystic fibrosis is caused by particular mutations in the gene for the cystic fibrosis transmembrane conductance regulator (CFTR) transport protein. Researchers cloned the mouse homologue of the human CFTR gene, mutated it in the laboratory to introduce the mutations known to cause CF, and replaced the normal mouse CFTR genes with the mutated form. The mouse CF model is being used to study the disease in detail and for developing effective treatments.

FIGURE 14.11 **Research Method**

## Making a Knockout Mouse

**Purpose:** To make a transgenic mouse in which a specific gene has been knocked out (deleted) so that the function of that gene is lost

**Protocol:**

1. Extract ES cells from blastocyst of an agouti (mottled, greyish brown fur colour) mouse and grow them in cell culture.

2a. Transform the ES cells with a DNA construct consisting of a selectable marker, here the neomycin-resistance ($neo^R$) gene (red), flanked by end sequences of the mouse gene of interest. The construct migrates to the nucleus and the mouse gene sequences align with the homologous sequences of a genomic copy of the mouse gene, allowing crossing-over to occur …

2b. … The outcome of crossing-over is the replacement of the genomic copy of the gene with the $neo^R$-containing DNA sequence. The chromosomal allele of the mouse gene is now nonfunctional.

3. Select for the ES cells in which a normal gene has been replaced by the $neo^R$-containing DNA sequence by growing cells in media containing neomycin.

4. Inject genetically engineered ES cells into blastocysts from white mice.

5. Implant the blastocysts into white, surrogate (foster) mother.

6. Some progeny mice will be white; others will be chimeric mice with patches of agouti fur. (Agouti fur is genetically dominant to white.) Chimeric mice have many cells derived from the original white mouse blastocyst, but some cells derived from the agouti mouse-derived, genetically engineered, ES cells that were introduced into the blastocyst in step 4.

7. Mate chimeric mice with white mice. If the chimeric mouse parent has gonads derived from the genetically engineered stem cells, all offspring will have agouti fur. The agouti offspring are heterozygous for the gene knockout.

8. Interbreed the heterozygous knockout mice. Perform DNA testing on agouti progeny to identify those homozygous for the gene knockout.

**Outcome:** The result is a mouse in which both chromosomal alleles of a specific gene of interest have been knocked out. The effects of the loss of function of that gene can then be studied.

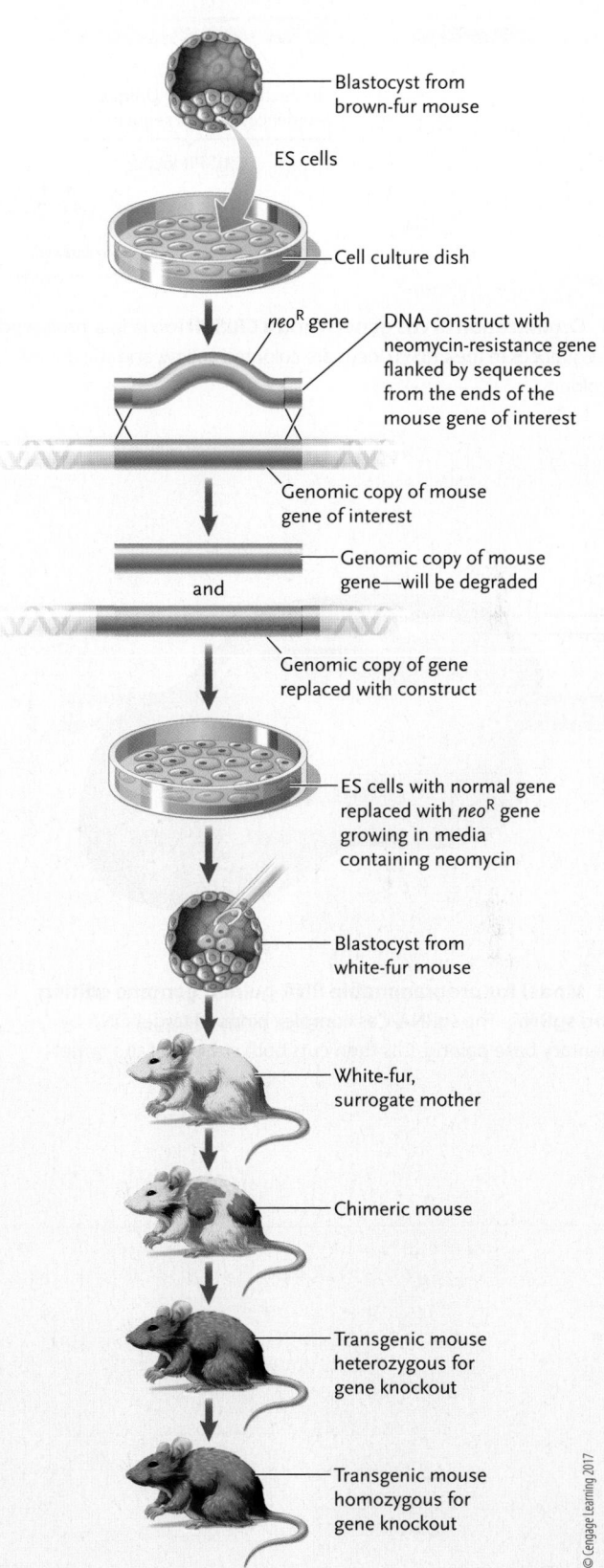

Blastocyst from brown-fur mouse

ES cells

Cell culture dish

$neo^R$ gene

DNA construct with neomycin-resistance gene flanked by sequences from the ends of the mouse gene of interest

Genomic copy of mouse gene of interest

Genomic copy of mouse gene—will be degraded

and

Genomic copy of gene replaced with construct

ES cells with normal gene replaced with $neo^R$ gene growing in media containing neomycin

Blastocyst from white-fur mouse

White-fur, surrogate mother

Chimeric mouse

Transgenic mouse heterozygous for gene knockout

Transgenic mouse homozygous for gene knockout

© Cengage Learning 2017

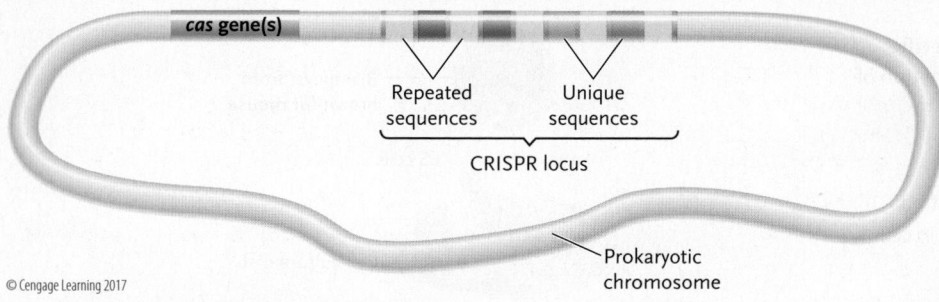

© Cengage Learning 2017

**Figure 1** **Organization of *cas* gene(s) and a CRISPR locus in a prokaryotic chromosome.** The repeated sequences in the CRISPR locus are coloured yellow, and the unique sequences each have a different colour.

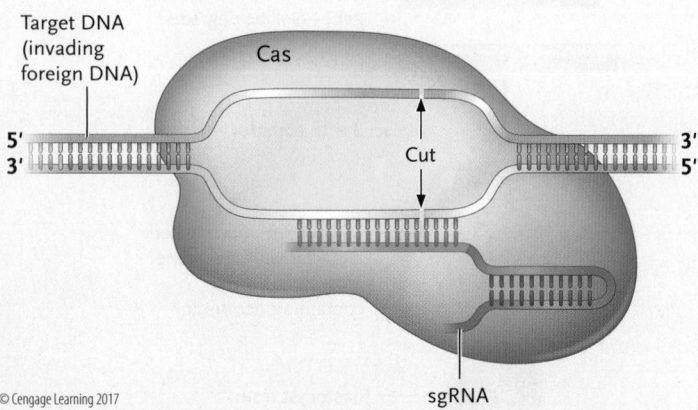

© Cengage Learning 2017

**Figure 2** **Model for programmable RNA-guided genome editing by Cas and sgRNA.** The sgRNA/Cas complex binds to target DNA by complementary base pairing. Cas then cuts both strands of the target DNA.

## CRISPR: A Programmable RNA-Guided Genome Editing System

In the first decade of the 2000s, converging areas of research revealed that prokaryotic cells have an elegant molecular machinery that confers immunity from infection by viruses and plasmids. In a remarkably short time, scientists turned this discovery in basic research into one of the most powerful tools of applied research in biology.

Approximately 70% of sequenced bacterial genomes and 90% of sequenced archaeal genomes have CRISPR (pronounced "crisper") loci and *cas* genes that, together, encode a kind of immune system against invading foreign bacteriophages and plasmids. In brief, the system works as follows: One or more **CRISPR (*C*lusters of *R*egularly *I*nterspersed *S*hort *P*alindromic *R*epeats)** loci are found in the bacterial genome. **(Figure 1)**. Each CRISPR locus consists of repeated sequences about 40 bp long that are interspersed with unique sequences of about the same length. The unique sequences have been "captured" from the genomes of bacteriophages and plasmids during previous infections. Near each CRISPR locus are *cas* genes encoding DNA endonucleases (see Figure 1). Transcription and translation of the region containing the *cas* genes and the CRISPR locus generates two products, a Cas endonuclease enzyme and an RNA called *crisprRNA (crRNA)*, that bind to each other to form the crRNA/Cas complex.

In the event of an infection by a bacteriophage or plasmid, the regions of the crRNA that are complementary to regions of the foreign DNA guide the crRNA/Cas complex to the invading DNA. The Cas endonuclease then cleaves both strands of the foreign DNA, thereby inactivating the infecting DNA.

In this elegant natural immune system, the key to inactivating foreign DNA is expressing an RNA molecule containing a sequence that can base pair with that target DNA. Collaborators Jennifer Doudna (University of California, Berkeley) and Emmanuelle Charpentier (Helmholtz Centre for Infection Research, Germany) hypothesized that the natural system could be adapted to cutting within any DNA sequence by using custom-designed crRNA molecules. Support for their hypothesis came from *in vitro* experiments in which purified Cas protein and custom-designed crRNA molecules—called *single guide RNAs (sgRNAs)*—cut plasmid DNA to produce fragment sizes predicted by the crRNA sequences. Thus, the natural CRISPR–Cas system had been modified to be a **programmable RNA-guided genome editing system (Figure 2)**. The CRISPR–Cas system can be targeted to cut any given sequence of DNA simply by customizing a complementary crRNA sequence. The system has been modified to introduce very specific nucleotide changes in target DNA.

The technique described in Figure 14.11 for modifying the genome of an animal is rather laborious and expensive. An exciting new technology called CRISPR (described in the Research in Biology box) now enables much faster, simpler, and accurate editing of specific sequences. Through various engineered modifications of the system, a wide range of programmed genome editing is possible, including gene knockouts, gene insertion, gene replacement, and altering specific sequences. This tool is the most important advance in molecular biology since the invention of PCR, and promises significant impacts in a wide variety of basic and applied research. The work will almost certainly attract a Nobel Prize in the coming years. Researchers at Sichuan University in China have already used CRISPR technology to treat human lung cancer.

**GENE THERAPY: CORRECTING GENETIC DISORDERS** The path to **gene therapy**—correcting genetic disorders—in humans began with experiments using mice. In 1982, Richard Palmiter at the University of Washington, Ralph Brinster of the University of Pennsylvania, and their colleagues injected a growth hormone gene from rats into fertilized mouse eggs and implanted the eggs into a surrogate mother. She gave birth to some normal-sized mouse pups that grew more quickly than normal and became about twice the size of their normal litter mates. These *giant mice* (**Figure 14.12**) attracted extensive media attention from around the world.

Palmiter and Brinster next attempted to cure a genetic disorder by gene therapy. In this experiment, they were able to correct a genetic growth hormone deficiency that produces dwarf mice. They introduced a normal copy of the growth hormone gene into fertilized eggs taken from mutant dwarf mice and implanted the eggs into a surrogate mother. The transgenic mouse pups grew to slightly larger than normal, demonstrating that the genetic defect in these mice had been corrected.

**FIGURE 14.12 A genetically engineered giant mouse (right) produced by the introduction of a rat growth hormone gene into the animal.** A mouse of normal size is on the left.

This sort of experiment, in which a gene is introduced into germ-line cells of an animal to correct a genetic disorder, is called **germ-line gene therapy**. For ethical reasons, germ-line gene therapy is not permitted with humans. Instead, humans are treated with **somatic gene therapy**, in which genes are introduced into somatic cells (as described in the previous section).

The first successful use of somatic gene therapy with a human subject who had a genetic disorder was carried out in the 1990s by W. French Anderson and his colleagues at the National Institutes of Health (NIH) in the United States. The subject was a young girl with *adenosine deaminase deficiency (ADA)*. Without the adenosine deaminase enzyme, white blood cells cannot mature; without normally functioning white blood cells, the body's immune response is so deficient that most children with ADA die of infections before reaching puberty. The researchers successfully introduced a functional ADA gene into mature white blood cells isolated from the patient. Those cells were reintroduced into the girl, and expression of the ADA gene provided a temporary cure for her ADA deficiency. The cure was not permanent because mature white blood cells, produced by differentiation of stem cells in the bone marrow, are nondividing cells with a finite lifetime. Therefore, the somatic gene therapy procedure has to be repeated every few months. Indeed, the subject of this example still receives periodic gene therapy to maintain the necessary levels of the ADA enzyme in her blood. In addition, she receives direct doses of the normal enzyme. More recent improved protocols have resulted in successful treatment of over 30 ADA patients worldwide without adverse effects or the need for ongoing therapy.

Successful somatic gene therapy has also been achieved for sickle cell disease. In December 1998, a 13-year-old boy's bone marrow cells were replaced with stem cells from the **umbilical cord** of an unrelated infant. The hope was that the stem cells would produce healthy bone marrow cells, the source of blood cells. The procedure worked, and the patient has been declared cured of the disease.

However, despite enormous efforts, human somatic gene therapy has not been the panacea people expected. Relatively little progress has been made since the first gene therapy clinical trial for ADA deficiency was described, and, in fact, there have been major setbacks. In 1999, for example, a teenage patient in a somatic gene therapy trial died as a result of a severe immune response to the viral vector being used to introduce a normal gene to correct his genetic deficiency. Furthermore, some children in gene therapy trials involving the use of retrovirus vectors to introduce genes into blood stem cells have developed a leukemia-like condition. In short, somatic gene therapy is not yet an effective treatment for human genetic disease, even though the approach has been successful in a number of cases to correct models of human genetic disorders in experimental mammals. Although no commercial human gene therapy product has been approved for use, roughly 100 new clinical trials are approved worldwide each year, focusing on improved therapies for a long list of conditions, including cancer, congenital blindness, Parkinson's disease, malaria, multiple sclerosis, arthritis, Type I diabetes, cystic fibrosis, and muscular dystrophy, as well as various blood and immunological disorders. The development of CRISPR technology, described previously, may soon lead to advances in gene therapy for humans.

**TURNING DOMESTIC ANIMALS INTO PROTEIN FACTORIES** Another successful application of genetic engineering turns animals into protein factories for the production of proteins used to treat human diseases, or to harvest novel biomaterials such as spider silk. Most of these *pharming* projects, as they are called, engineer the animals to produce the desired proteins in milk, making the production, extraction, and purification of the proteins harmless to the animals.

One of the first successful applications of this approach was carried out with sheep engineered to produce a protein required for normal blood clotting in humans. The protein, called a *clotting factor*, is deficient in people with one form of hemophilia, who require frequent injections of the factor to avoid bleeding to death from even minor injuries. Using DNA-cloning techniques, researchers joined the gene encoding the normal form of the clotting factor to the promoter sequences of the β-lactoglobin gene, which encodes a protein secreted in milk, and introduced it into fertilized eggs. These cells were implanted into a surrogate mother, and the transgenic sheep born were allowed to mature. The β-lactoglobin promoter controlling the clotting factor gene became activated in mammary gland cells of females, resulting in the production of clotting factor. The clotting factor was then secreted into the milk. Production in the milk is harmless to the sheep and yields the protein in a form that can be obtained and purified easily.

Other similar projects are under development to produce particular proteins in transgenic mammals. These include a protein to treat cystic fibrosis, collagen to correct scars and wrinkles, human milk proteins to be added to infant formulas, and normal hemoglobin for use as an additive to blood transfusions.

**PRODUCING ANIMAL CLONES** Making transgenic mammals is expensive and inefficient. And because only one copy of the transgene typically becomes incorporated into the treated cell, not all progeny of a transgenic animal inherit that gene. Scientists reasoned that an alternative to breeding a valuable transgenic mammal to produce progeny with the transgene would be to clone the mammal. Each clone would be identical to the original, including the expression of the transgene. This was shown to be possible in 1997 when two scientists, Ian Wilmut and Keith H. S. Campbell of the Roslin Institute, Edinburgh, Scotland, announced that they had successfully cloned a sheep from a single somatic cell derived from an adult sheep (**Figure 14.13**)—the first cloned mammal.

Since the successful cloning experiment producing Dolly, many additional mammals have been cloned, including mice, goats, pigs, monkeys, rabbits, dogs, a male calf appropriately named Gene, and a domestic cat called CC (for *Copy Cat*).

Cloning farm animals has been so successful that several commercial enterprises now provide cloned copies of champion animals. One example is a clone of an American Holstein cow, Zita, who was the U.S. national champion milk producer for many years. Animal breeders estimate that there are now more than 100 cloned animals on U.S. farms, and breeders plan to produce entire herds if government approval is granted.

The cloning of domestic animals has its drawbacks. Many cloning attempts fail, leading to the death of the transplanted embryos. Cloned animals often suffer from conditions such as birth defects and poor lung development. Molecular studies have shown that the expression of perhaps hundreds of genes in the genomes of clones is regulated abnormally due to epigenetic effects.

**CONCEPT FIX** In studying Figures 14.11 and 14.13, both related to manipulating animal embryos, it may be tempting to see Dolly as an advance in stem cell research. However, Dolly resulted from the transfer of a somatic cell nucleus to an egg cell that was lacking a nucleus. This cloning technique, called somatic cell nuclear transfer (SCNT), doesn't involve stem cells.

**GENETIC ENGINEERING OF PLANTS** Genetic engineering of plants has led to increased resistance to pests and disease; greater tolerance to heat, drought, and salinity; greater crop yields; faster growth; and resistance to herbicides. Another aim is to produce seeds with higher levels of amino acids. The essential amino acid lysine, for example, is present only in limited quantities in cereal grains such as wheat, rice, oats, barley, and corn; the seeds of legumes such as beans, peas, lentils, soybeans, and peanuts are deficient in the essential amino acid methionine or cysteine. Increasing the amounts of the deficient amino acids in plant seeds by genetic engineering would greatly improve the diet of domestic animals and human populations that rely on seeds as a primary food source. Efforts are also under way to increase the content of vitamins and minerals in crop plants.

Another possibility for plant genetic engineering is plant pharming to produce pharmaceutical products. Plants are ideal for this purpose because they are primary producers at the bottom rung of the food chain, and can be grown in huge numbers with maximum conservation of the Sun's energy captured in photosynthesis.

Some plants, such as *Arabidopsis*, tobacco, potato, cabbage, and carrot, have special advantages for genetic engineering because individual cells can be removed from an adult, altered by the introduction of a desired gene, and then grown in cultures into a multicellular mass of cloned cells called a *callus*. Subsequently, roots, stems, and leaves develop in the callus, forming a young plant that can then be grown in containers or fields by the usual methods. In the plant, each cell contains the introduced gene. The gametes produced by the transgenic plants can then be used in crosses to produce offspring, some of which will have the transgene, as in the similar experiments with animals.

**METHODS USED TO INSERT GENES INTO PLANTS** Genes are inserted into plant cells by several techniques. One commonly used method takes advantage of a natural process that causes

FIGURE 14.13 **Experimental Research**

## The First Cloning of a Mammal

**Question:** Does the nucleus of an adult mammal contain all the genetic information to specify a new organism? In other words, can mammals be cloned starting with adult cells?

**Experiment:** Ian Wilmut, Keith Campbell, and their colleagues fused a mammary gland cell from an adult sheep with an unfertilized egg cell from which the nucleus had been removed, and tested whether that fused cell could produce a lamb.

1. A diploid cell was isolated from a mammary gland of an adult, white-faced ewe and propagated in tissue culture.

2. The nucleus was removed from an unfertilized egg of a black-faced ewe.

3. The mammary gland cell was fused with the enucleated egg cell.

4. Cells were cultured to produce a cluster that was implanted into the uterus of an adult, black-faced ewe.

5. An embryo was developed in a surrogate mother.

**Result:** Dolly was born and grew normally. She was white-faced—a clone of the donor ewe. DNA fingerprinting using STR loci showed her DNA matched only that of the donor ewe, and neither the ewe who donated the egg nor the ewe who was the surrogate mother.

**Conclusion:** An adult nucleus of a mammal contains all the genetic material necessary to direct the development of a normal new organism, a clone of the original. Dolly was the first cloned mammal. The success rate for Wilmut and Campbell's experiment was very low—Dolly represented less than 0.4% of the fused cells they made—but its significance was huge.

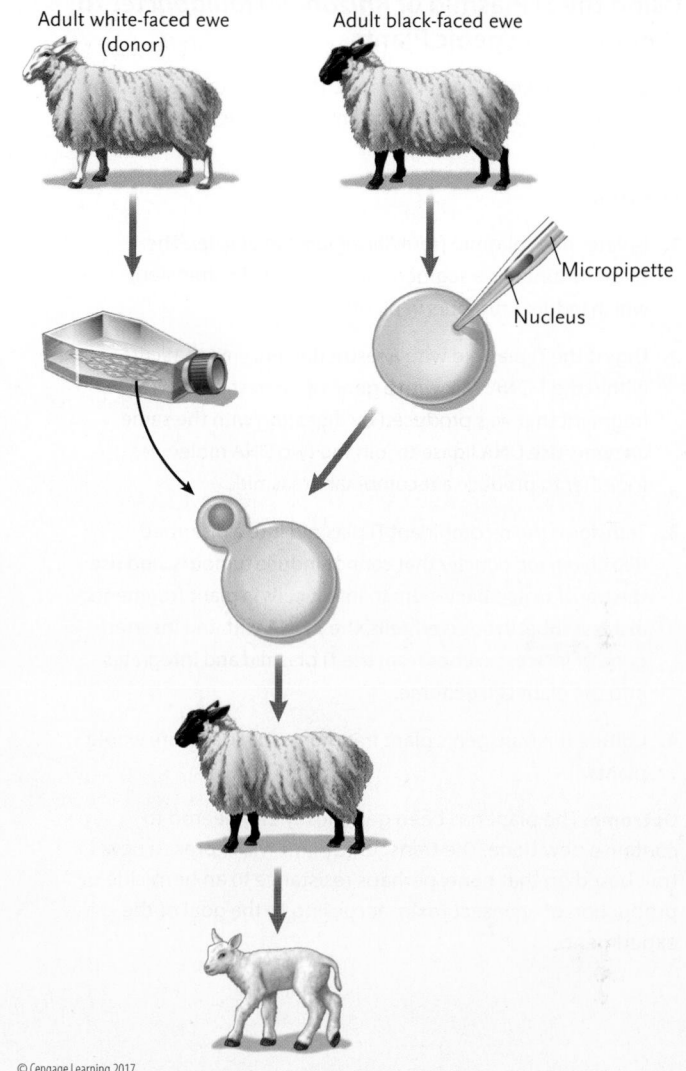

© Cengage Learning 2017

crown gall disease, which is characterized by bulbous, irregular growths—tumours, essentially—that can develop at wound sites on the trunks and limbs of deciduous trees (**Figure 14.14**). Crown gall disease is caused by the bacterium *Rhizobium radiobacter* (formerly *Agrobacterium tumefaciens*, recently reclassified on the basis of genome analysis). This bacterium contains a large, circular plasmid called the **Ti (tumour-inducing) plasmid**. The interaction between the bacterium and the plant cell it infects stimulates the excision of a segment of the Ti plasmid called *T DNA* (for "transfer DNA"), which then integrates into the plant cell's genome. Genes on the T DNA are then expressed; the products stimulate the transformed cell to grow and divide and therefore to produce a tumour. The tumours provide essential nutrients for the bacterium. The Ti plasmid is used as a vector for making transgenic plants in much the same way as bacterial plasmids are used as vectors to introduce genes into bacteria (**Figure 14.15**).

**FIGURE 14.14 A crown gall tumour on the trunk of a California pepper tree.** The tumour, stimulated by genes introduced from the bacterium *Rhizobium radiobacter*, is the bulbous, irregular growth extending from the trunk.

FIGURE 14.15    **Research Method**

## Using the Ti Plasmid of *Rhizobium radiobacter* to Produce Transgenic Plants

**Purpose:** To make transgenic plants. This technique is one way to introduce a transgene into a plant for genetic engineering purposes.

**Protocol:**

1. Isolate the Ti plasmid from *Rhizobium radiobacter*. The plasmid contains a segment called *T DNA* (*T* = transfer), which induces tumours in plants.

2. Digest the Ti plasmid with a restriction enzyme that cuts within the T DNA. Mix with a gene of interest on a DNA fragment that was produced by digesting with the same enzyme. Use DNA ligase to join the two DNA molecules together to produce a recombinant plasmid.

3. Transform the recombinant Ti plasmid into a disarmed *Rhizobium radiobacter* that cannot induce tumours, and use the transformed bacterium to infect cells in plant fragments in a test tube. In infected cells, the T DNA with the inserted gene of interest excises from the Ti plasmid and integrates into the plant cell genome.

4. Culture the transgenic plant fragments to regenerate whole plants.

**Outcome:** The plant has been genetically engineered to contain a new gene. The transgenic plant will express a new trait based on that gene, perhaps resistance to an herbicide or production of an insect toxin, according to the goal of the experiment.

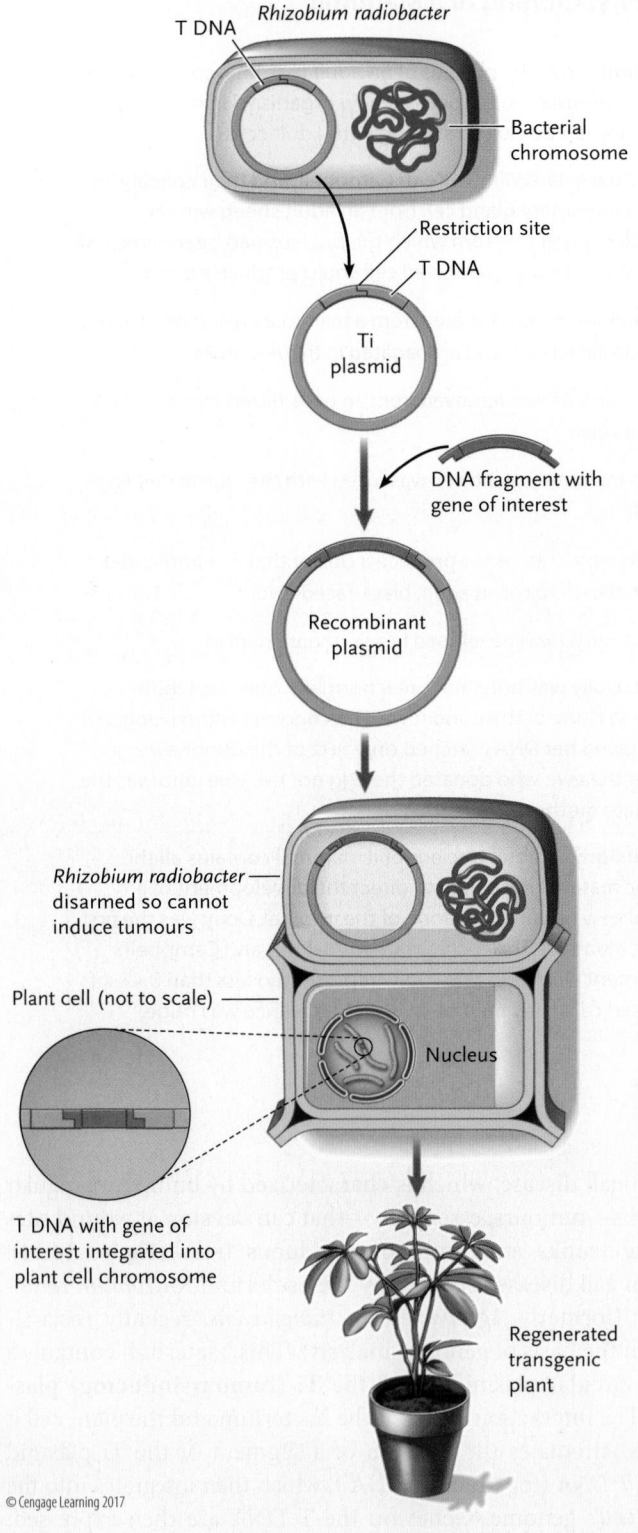

© Cengage Learning 2017

**PLANT GENETIC ENGINEERING PROJECTS** An early visual demonstration of the successful use of genetic engineering techniques to produce a transgenic plant is the glowing tobacco plant (**Figure 14.16**). The transgenic plant contained luciferase, the gene for the firefly enzyme. When the plant was soaked in the substrate for the enzyme, it became luminescent.

The most widespread application of genetic engineering of plants involves the production of transgenic crops. Thousands of such crops have been developed and field tested, and many have been approved for commercial use. If you analyze the processed plant-based foods at a national supermarket chain, you will likely find that at least two-thirds contain products made from transgenic plants.

In many cases, plants are modified to make them resistant to insect pests, viruses, or herbicides. Crops modified for insect resistance include corn, cotton, and potatoes. The most common approach to making plants resistant to insects is to introduce the gene from the bacterium *Bacillus thuringiensis* that encodes the *Bt* toxin, an organic pesticide. This toxin has been used in powder form to kill insects in agriculture for many years, and now transgenic plants making their own *Bt* toxin are resistant to specific groups of insects that feed on them. Millions of acres of crop plants planted in the United States and Canada are *Bt*-engineered varieties.

Virus infections cause enormous crop losses worldwide. Transgenic crops that are virus resistant would be highly valuable to the agricultural community. There is some promise in this area. By some unknown process, transgenic plants expressing certain viral proteins become resistant to infections by whole viruses that contain these same proteins. Two virus-resistant, genetically modified crops made so far are papaya and squash.

Several crops in Canada have also been engineered to become resistant to herbicides. For example, *glyphosate* (commonly known by its brand name, Roundup) is a highly potent herbicide that is widely used in weed control. The herbicide works by inhibiting a particular enzyme in the chloroplast. Unfortunately, it kills crop species along with the undesirable weeds. But transgenic crops have been made in which a bacterial form of the chloroplast enzyme has been added to the plants. The bacteria-derived enzyme is not affected by Roundup, and farmers who use these herbicide-resistant crops can spray fields of crops to kill weeds without killing the crops. Most of the corn, soybean, canola, and cotton plants grown in North America are now the genetically engineered, glyphosate-resistant ("Roundup-Ready") varieties.

Crop plants are also being engineered as a way to alter their nutritional qualities. For example, a strain of rice plants has been produced with seeds rich in β-carotene, a precursor of vitamin A, as well as iron (**Figure 14.17**). The new rice, which is given a yellow or golden colour by the carotene (hence its name, "golden rice"), may provide improved nutrition for the billions of people who depend on rice as a diet staple. In particular, the rice may help improve the nutrition of children younger than age 5 in Southeast Asia, 70% of whom are at risk of suffering from impaired vision because of vitamin A deficiency.

Plant pharming is also an active area both in university research labs and at biotechnology companies. Plant pharming involves the engineering of transgenic plants to produce medically valuable products. The approach is one described earlier: The gene for the product is cloned into a cloning vector adjacent to a promoter, in this case one active in plants, and the recombinant DNA molecule is introduced into plants. Products under development include vaccines for various bacterial and viral diseases, protease inhibitors to treat or prevent virus infections, collagen to treat scars and wrinkles, and aprotinin to reduce bleeding and clotting during heart surgery.

In contrast to animal genetic engineering, genetically altered plants have been widely developed and widely adopted by the agricultural community. But, as the next section discusses, both animal and plant genetic engineering have not proceeded without concerns.

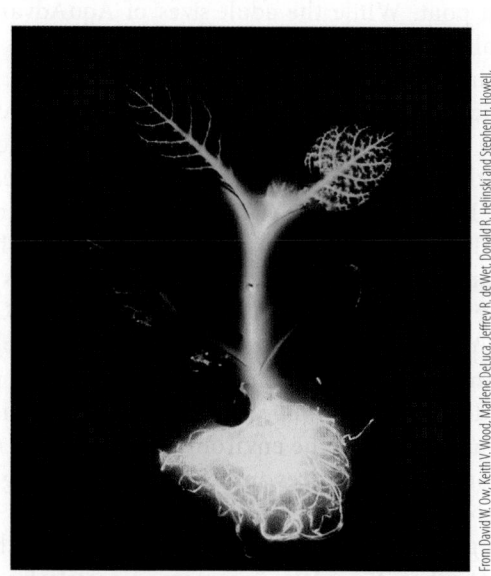

From David W. Ow, Keith V. Wood, Marlene DeLuca, Jeffrey R. de Wet, Donald R. Helinski and Stephen H. Howell, "Transient and stable expression of the firefly luciferase gene in plant cells and transgenic plants." *Science* 14 November 1986, Vol. 234 no. 4778 pp. 856–859. *Science* by American Association for the Advancement of Science Reproduced with permission of AMERICAN ASSOCIATION FOR THE ADVANCEMENT OF SCIENCE in the format Republish in a book via Copyright Clearance Center.

**FIGURE 14.16** **A genetically engineered tobacco plant was made capable of luminescence by the introduction of a firefly gene coding for the enzyme luciferase**

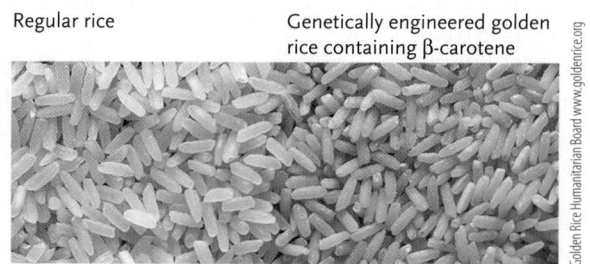

Regular rice    Genetically engineered golden rice containing β-carotene

Golden Rice Humanitarian Board www.goldenrice.org

**FIGURE 14.17** **Rice genetically engineered to contain β-carotene**

## 14.2d DNA Technologies and Genetic Engineering Are a Subject of Public Concern

When recombinant DNA technology was developed in the early 1970s, researchers quickly recognized that, in addition to the many anticipated benefits, there might be deleterious outcomes. One key concern at the time was that a bacterium carrying a recombinant DNA molecule might escape into the environment. Perhaps it could transfer that molecule to other bacteria and produce new, potentially harmful strains. To address these concerns, the U.S. scientists who developed the technology drew up safety guidelines for recombinant DNA research in the United States. Adopted by the NIH, the guidelines listed the precautions to be used in the laboratory when constructing recombinant DNA molecules, and included the design and use of host organisms that could survive only in growth media in the laboratory. Since that time, countless experiments involving recombinant DNA molecules have been done in laboratories around the world. These experiments have shown that recombinant DNA manipulations can be done safely. Over time, therefore, the recombinant DNA guidelines have become more relaxed. Nonetheless, stringent regulations still exist for certain areas of recombinant DNA research that pose significant risk, such as cloning genes from highly pathogenic bacteria or viruses, or gene therapy experiments. In essence, as the risk increases, the research facility must increase its security and must obtain higher levels of approval by peer scientist groups and government regulators.

Guidelines for genetic engineering also extend to research in several areas that have been the subject of public concern and debate. Although the public does not seem to be very concerned about genetically engineered microorganisms, for example, those cleaning up oil spills and hazardous chemicals, it is concerned about possible problems with **genetically modified organisms (GMOs)** used as food. A GMO is a transgenic organism; the majority of GMOs are crop plants. Issues are the safety of GMO-containing food and the possible adverse effects of the GMOs to the environment, such as by interbreeding with natural species or by harming beneficial insect species. For example, introduced genes providing herbicide or insect resistance can move from crop plants into related weed species through cross-pollination, producing "superweeds" that are difficult to control. *Bt*-expressing corn was originally thought to have adverse effects on monarch butterflies who fed on the pollen. The most recent of a series of independent studies investigating this possibility has indicated that the risk to the butterflies is extremely low.

More broadly, different countries have reacted to GMOs in different ways. Health Canada defines a genetically modified food as, "*one derived from an organism that has had some of its heritable traits changed. This can involve:*

- *Traditional techniques of crossbreeding.*
- *Using chemicals or radiation to alter the genetic make-up of the organism's cells in a process called mutagenesis.*

- *Applying recombinant DNA or genetic engineering techniques—for instance, introducing a gene from one species into another species."*

Although Health Canada refers to conventional breeding and mutagenesis, as well as recombinant DNA techniques, in the definition of GM food, most consumers consider "genetically modified" to mean "genetically engineered by recombinant DNA technologies." The considerable majority of the corn, soybean, canola, and sugar beet grown and consumed in Canada is from genetically engineered varieties. These crops are widely used in processed foods and as animal feed. Four additional engineered GM organisms, papaya, squash, alfalfa, and cotton, are routinely imported into Canadian markets. While a small fraction of the fresh produce available in Canada is genetically engineered, a large proportion of processed food contains some ingredients from genetically engineered crop plants.

A GM crop grown in or imported into Canada has to be deemed safe by a regulatory process led by Health Canada, Environment Canada, and Agriculture and Agri-Food Canada that relies on data provided by the applicant. The scientific literature on GM food safety is inconsistent and suffers from a lack of independent long-term studies on the effects of GM food on human health.

In 2015, Health Canada approved the sale of the GM "non-browning" Arctic Apple variety, produced by the British Columbia company Okanagan Specialty Fruits. The apple is genetically engineered to suppress the expression of the polyphenol oxidase enzyme, which dramatically delays browning when the apple is sliced.

In 2016, Health Canada approved the sale of the first GM food animal, a fast-growing salmon called AquAdvantage. This fish is engineered to contain the protein-coding domain of a growth hormone gene from Chinook salmon and the regulatory sequences of an antifreeze protein gene from a third fish, the ocean pout. While the adult sizes of AquAdvantage and normal salmon are similar, the genetic modifications allow the AquAdvantage salmon to reach market weight faster.

Political opposition to GMOs has been particularly strong in Europe, dampening the use of transgenic crop plants in the fields and GMOs in food until quite recently. In 1999, the European Union (EU) imposed a six-year moratorium on all GMOs, leading to a bitter dispute with the United States, Canada, and Argentina, the leading growers of transgenic crops. More recently, the EU has revised the GMO regulations in all member states, deciding that using genetic engineering in agriculture and food production is permissible provided that the GMO or food containing it is safe for humans, animals, and the environment. All use of GMOs in the field or in food requires authorization following a careful review process.

On a global level, an international agreement, the **Cartagena Protocol on Biosafety**, "promotes biosafety by establishing practical rules and procedures for the safe transfer [between countries], handling and use of GMOs." Separate procedures have been set up for GMOs that are to be introduced into the environment and those that are to be used as food or feed or for processing. Although 167 countries have signed and implemented the Protocol, several others, mainly GMO exporters such as Canada, the United States, and Argentina, have not.

In summary, the use of DNA technologies in biotechnology has the potential for tremendous benefits to humankind. However, researchers, regulators, and commercial producers have yet to devise a robust system for long-term health and environmental risk assessment as GM organisms and their products become increasingly common.

## 14.2e Synthetic Biologists Engineer New Systems in Living Cells

Although the technologies for manipulation and transfer of genes into new hosts, as described at the beginning of this chapter, have long been known as genetic engineering, the influence of fundamental ideas and approaches of formal engineering on the design of living systems dates to the late 1990s, when engineers, physicists, and software designers began working with molecular biologists. This collaboration gave rise to the new interdisciplinary field of **synthetic biology**. Synthetic biologists combine standardized parts (DNA sequences) to design and build modified regulatory networks to study the organization of natural systems in living cells, and to create novel networks with potential benefits in a wide range of biotechnologies. (The iGEM competition described in Why it Matters is a good example of the approaches and potential of the field of synthetic biology.)

Using genes "mined" from organisms in the environment, or sequences created from scratch by DNA synthesizers, scientists in this field can insert new enzymes into biosynthetic pathways, resulting in cells that produce novel products such as biodiesel, gasoline, and bioplastics. This work has culminated in the creation of a yeast strain containing an engineered biochemical pathway producing artemisinin (an antimalarial drug normally produced by the wormwood plant) on an industrial scale.

The logical end point of synthetic biology is the creation of artificial life, that is, the assembly of living systems entirely from nonliving parts. Such studies would provide a powerful model for understanding the possible origin of life, as well as the dynamics of basic cellular functioning. Synthetic cells, designed entirely from off-the-shelf parts in a laboratory, could be customized to serve a staggering array of applications in biotechnology.

Since synthetic cells would require a genome, one avenue of research toward the goal of artificial life is the top-down approach, which asks, "What is the minimum collection of genes required by a living cell?" Insights into the answer to this question come from characterizing organisms that have very small genomes, as well as studies that note the effect of inactivating every gene of an organism's genome one at a time. Although the true minimal genome has yet to be established, it is likely in the range of about 300 genes for a free-living prokaryotic cell. In 2010, Craig Venter's group published an account of a replicating strain of a bacterium, *Mycoplasma mycoides*, they had engineered to contain a 1-million-base-pair synthetic genome. The genome was synthesized in 1000-base-pair segments from digitized sequence information, and then the segments were assembled in yeast before being transferred to the *Mycoplasma*. This was the first known life form that did not obtain its genome from a parent cell, proving the concept that a cell could be "booted up" by synthesized DNA.

A complementary approach to creating synthetic life is the bottom-up interest in building a functional cell, and its various components, from nonliving parts. Early research is well under way toward the creation of various types of primitive protocells that contain simple metabolism and nucleic acid biochemistry. The rapid advance of synthetic biology has led many researchers to predict that the first truly artificial living cells will be created in the near future.

In this chapter you have learned about how individual genes are being isolated and manipulated by students and researchers using various DNA technologies. But a gene is just a part of a genome. Researchers also want to know about the set of genes in a complete genome, and how genes and their gene products work together in networks to control life. They also want to know more generally about the organization of the genome with respect to both genes and nongene sequences. Genomes, transcriptomes (the complete set of transcripts expressed by a genome), and proteomes (the complete set of proteins expressed by a genome) are the subjects of the next chapter.

### STUDY BREAK QUESTIONS

1. What are the principles of DNA fingerprinting?
2. What is a transgenic organism?
3. What is the difference between using germ-line cells and somatic cells for gene therapy?

# Summary Illustration

DNA technologies, such as gene cloning and PCR, have a vast number of applications that include determining the functions of genes, producing plants with desirable traits, and developing medically relevant products and protocols for treating diseases. While these technologies have provided numerous benefits, the many unknowns require a robust system for long-term risk assessment.

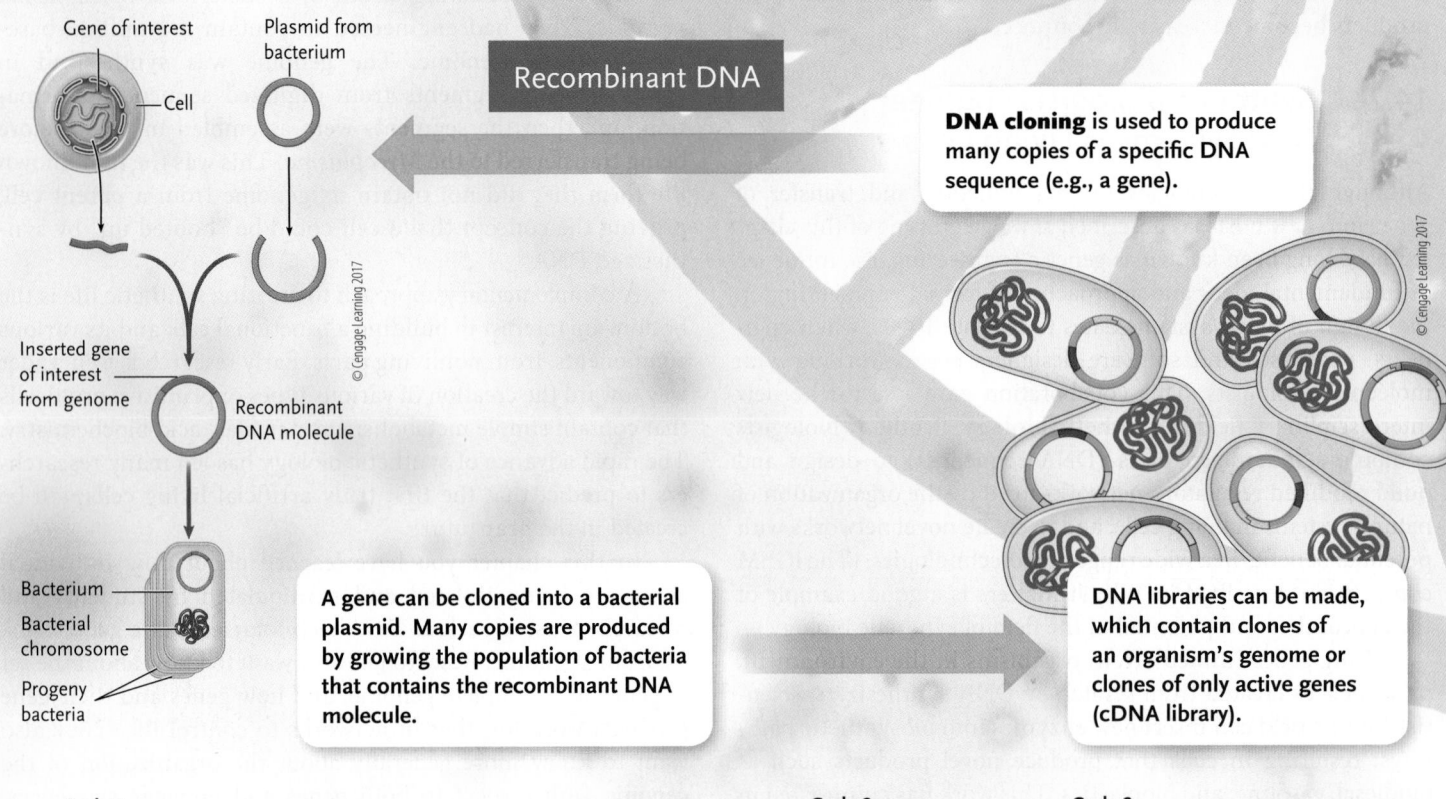

Gene of interest

Plasmid from bacterium

Cell

## Recombinant DNA

**DNA cloning** is used to produce many copies of a specific DNA sequence (e.g., a gene).

Inserted gene of interest from genome

Recombinant DNA molecule

Bacterium

Bacterial chromosome

Progeny bacteria

A gene can be cloned into a bacterial plasmid. Many copies are produced by growing the population of bacteria that contains the recombinant DNA molecule.

DNA libraries can be made, which contain clones of an organism's genome or clones of only active genes (cDNA library).

© Cengage Learning 2017

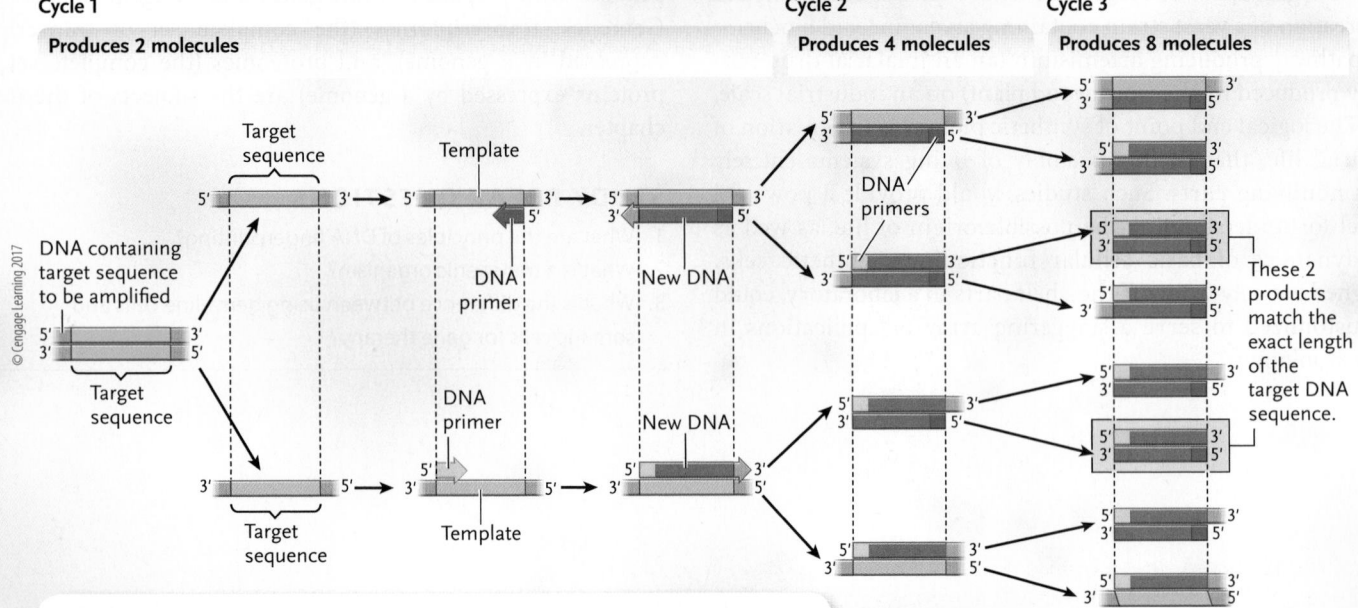

| Cycle 1 | Cycle 2 | Cycle 3 |
|---|---|---|
| Produces 2 molecules | Produces 4 molecules | Produces 8 molecules |

Target sequence

Template

DNA containing target sequence to be amplified

DNA primer

New DNA

DNA primers

These 2 products match the exact length of the target DNA sequence.

Target sequence

Template

DNA primer

New DNA

PCR can be used to produce large amounts of a specific DNA sequence without having to clone it into bacteria. DNA polymerase synthesizes many copies of target DNA that is between two annealed primers.

(Background) paulista/Shutterstock.com

## DNA Analysis

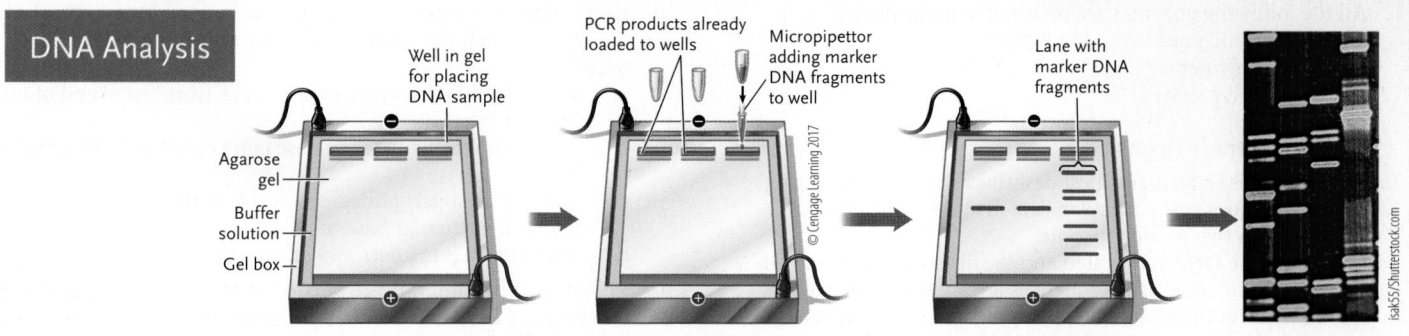

DNA can be separated for analysis using gel electrophoresis. Changes to DNA sequences that result in genetic diseases can be identified. Also, a person's DNA fingerprint (unique DNA sequence) can be determined and used in forensics and paternity testing.

## Genetic Engineering

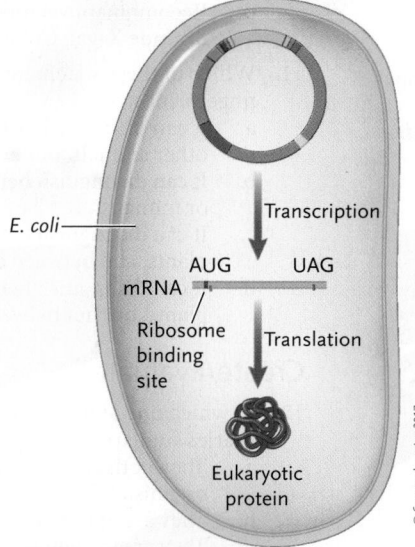

Transgenic bacteria can synthesize medicinal proteins, such as insulin. Recombinant DNA containing the gene is introduced into bacteria, whose transcription and translation machinery produce the protein that is then isolated from the cells and purified.

Regular rice

Genetically engineered golden rice containing β-carotene

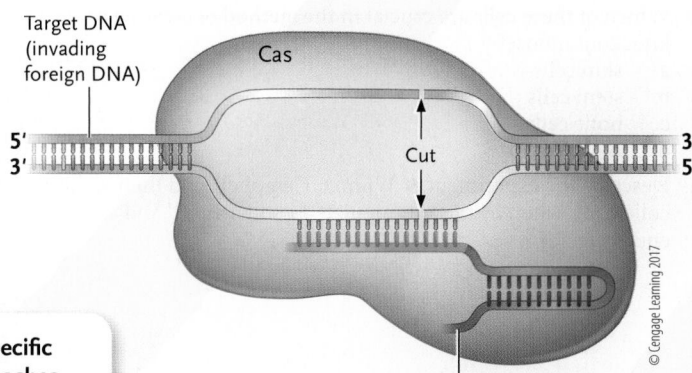

Genetically modifying plants and animals has helped to produce specific types of crops, and to study and treat human diseases. Many approaches have been used to modify an organism's genome. However, one of the most powerful tools now available is CRISPR. This programmable RNA-guided genome editing system can introduce very specific nucleotide changes.

# SELF-TEST QUESTIONS

## Recall/Understand

1. All the following enzymes are required to make nucleic acid polymers. Which one is used in PCR?
   a. DNA polymerase
   b. RNA polymerase
   c. primase
   d. reverse transcriptase

2. Which of these statements best describes DNA fingerprinting?
   a. It compares one particular stretch of the same DNA between two or more people.
   b. Genomic DNA is digested and the different lengths of DNA containing repeating sequences are separated by size.
   c. It requires the several DNA fragments to separate on a gel, with the longest lengths running the greatest distance.
   d. It can easily differentiate DNA between identical twins.

3. Dolly, a sheep, was an example of reproductive (germ-line) cloning. Which of these examples of cell fusion was required to perform this process?
   a. the fusion of a somatic cell from one organism with an enucleated egg of another
   b. the fusion of an egg from one organism with the egg of a different one
   c. the fusion of an embryonic diploid cell of one organism with an adult haploid cell (gamete) from another
   d. the fusion of two enucleated mammary cells from two different organisms

4. Which of these statements applies to somatic cell gene therapy?
   a. Red blood cells can be used as a target tissue.
   b. The technique is potentially useful for all types of genetic diseases.
   c. The inserted genes are passed on to the offspring.
   d. The desired DNA can be introduced to somatic cells cultured outside the body.

5. Which of these characteristics of the Ti plasmid makes this vector particularly useful in genetic engineering?
   a. It is circular.
   b. It carries antibiotic resistance.
   c. Its natural host cells are plant cells.
   d. It has sites that are cut by restriction endonucleases.

6. What is the minimum number of genes that a free-living, prokaryotic cell likely requires?
   a. about 50
   b. about 300
   c. about 10 000
   d. about 1 000 000

7. Which of these cells are crucial in the method of creating a knockout mouse?
   a. skin cells
   b. stem cells
   c. bone cells
   d. muscle cells

8. Describe the experiment of Wilmut, Campbell, and their colleagues whereby they manipulated a somatic cell and an enucleated egg.

## Apply/Analyze

9. Restriction enzymes are used in genetic engineering to precisely cut DNA. Which one of these methods tells us how they are used?
   a. They digest DNA, one base at a time, from the 3′ end of the DNA of interest.
   b. They remove mismatched base pairs resulting from errors in ligation.
   c. They break sugar–phosphate bonds in the DNA backbone between particular bases.
   d. They cut PCR primers away from the template DNA.

10. Vectors in a ligation mix are of two varieties: recombinant (those carrying the DNA of interest) and nonrecombinant (the original vector without new DNA). Suppose these are transformed into bacterial hosts for replication (see Figure 14.3). Which of the following characteristics can be used to identify colonies of bacteria transformed with nonrecombinant vectors relative to those colonies of bacteria transformed with recombinant vectors?
    a. Recombinant vectors carry DNA that interrupts and inactivates the *lacZ* gene. Colonies are white.
    b. Recombinant vectors make their hosts more antibiotic resistant. Colonies are larger.
    c. Recombinant vectors make their hosts replicate more slowly. Colonies are smaller.
    d. Recombinant vectors have more restriction enzymes to degrade X-gal. Colonies are blue.

11. Which of these statements describes the value of DNA fingerprinting?
    a. It can distinguish between human individuals, and between other animals, but not between plants.
    b. It can distinguish between plants, but not between animals or humans.
    c. It can distinguish between human individuals, between plants, and between animals.
    d. It can distinguish between human individuals, and between plants, but not between animals.

## Create/Evaluate

12. In which one of these ways are genomic libraries and cDNA libraries similar?
    a. They both carry just the expressed gene sequences from an organism.
    b. They are of the same size.
    c. They are the whole genome of an organism.
    d. They both contain start and stop codons.

13. Which of these statements accurately describes the separation of DNA fragments by gel electrophoresis?
    a. Smaller fragments travel more quickly than larger fragments.
    b. Smaller fragments travel in the opposite direction of larger fragments.
    c. Smaller fragments float to the top of the gel; larger fragments sink to the bottom.
    d. Smaller fragments are visible under UV illumination; larger fragments are not.

14. Suppose that you work in an institution that uses DNA technologies to distinguish between individuals who have sickle cell disease and those who have sickle cell trait or are sickle cell free. Which of these techniques would be the most applicable one in this situation?
    a. cloning technique
    b. transgenic technique
    c. DNA fingerprinting technique
    d. Southern blot technique

15. Suggest a valid scenario of how DNA fingerprinting may be used in forensics, and explain the limitations of using fingerprinting; for example, how might a criminal anticipate the use fingerprinting and commit the crime to make the case harder to prove in court?

# Chapter Roadmap

## Genomes

Genomics is an emerging field that extends traditional studies of individual gene structure, expression and evolution to include all of the sequences in an organism. DNA structure, gene expression, and evolution inform and are informed by genomics science.

**From Chapter 11** →

### 15.1 Genomics: An Overview

Genomics is the characterization of whole genomes, including their structures, sequences, functions, and evolution.

### 15.2 Genome Sequencing

- Nucleotide order is the basis of sequencing.
- Mechanisms of natural DNA synthesis are exploited in sequencing methods.

**To Chapter 18** →

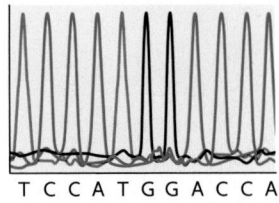

T C C A T G G A C C A

**From Chapter 12** →
**From Chapter 13** →

### 15.3 Annotation Identifies Genes

- DNA sequences from related species tend to be very similar.
- Comparing sequences between known and unknown genes, especially from different organisms, can reveal their function.

| | |
|---|---|
| HumanB-hemo | AATGCCCTGGCCCACAAGTATCACTAAGCTCGCTTTCTTGC |
| ChimpB-hemo | AATGCCCTGGCCCACAAGTATCACTAAGCTCGCTTTCTTGC |
| ChickenB-hemo | CATGCCCTGGCTCGCAAGTACCACTAAGCACCAG······C |
| PufferfishB-hemo | TCTGCTCTGGGAAGACAGTACCACTAAGATGTCCCCCAAGA |
| | *** **** **** ******* |

### 15.4 Comparative Genomics Can Reveal How Genes and Genomes Evolved

- Gene organization can be traced back through common ancestors.
- Eukaryotic and prokaryotic genomes are distinct in their organization.

**To Chapter 16** →
**To Chapter 17** →
**To Chapter 18** →

AristoKrates/Shutterstock.com

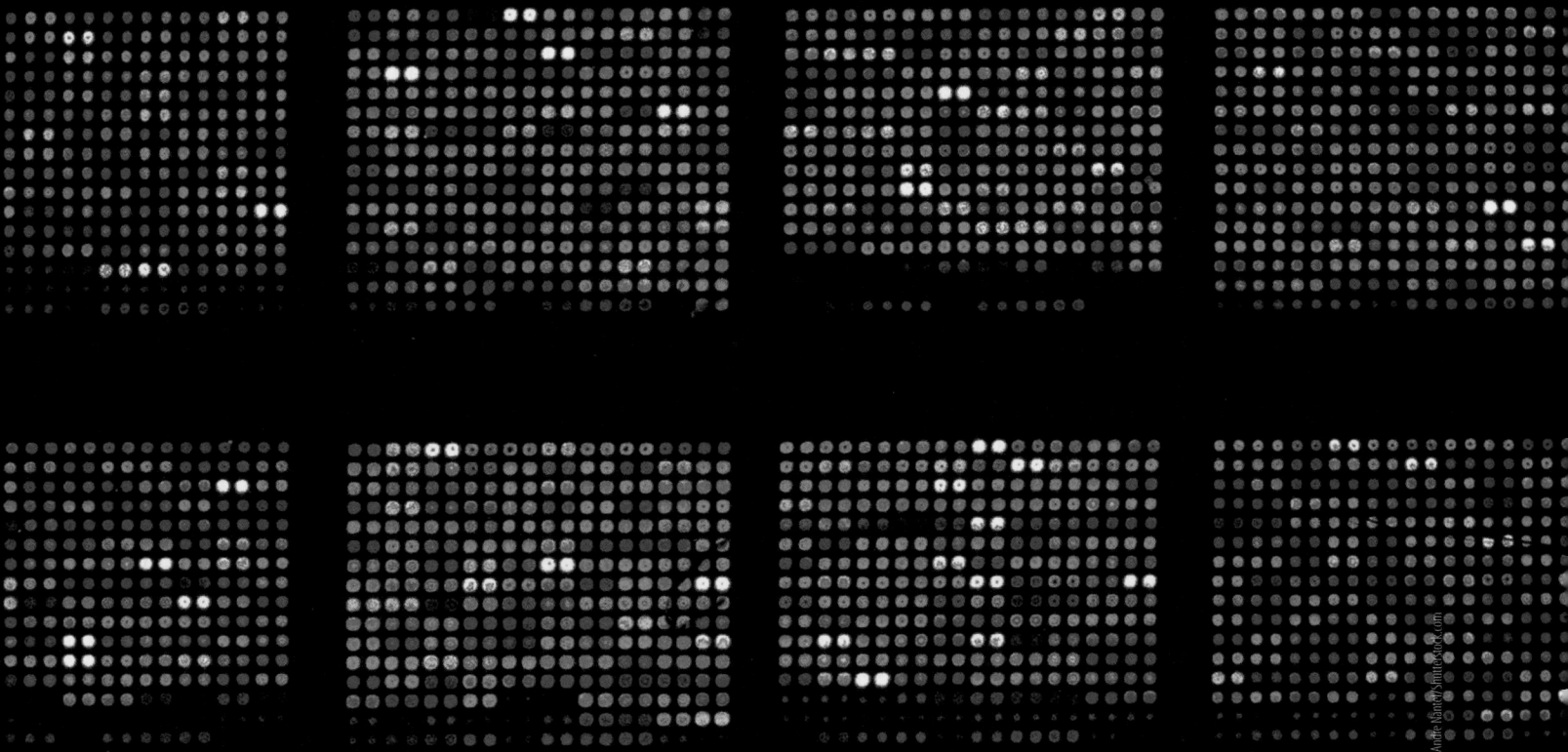

**Results of DNA microarray analysis.** An entire genome can be screened with DNA microarrays to study which protein-coding genes are being expressed. Data are presented as coloured dots that show the relative expression levels of those genes.

# Genomes

# 15

**Why it matters . . .** You just ended a chat session with your brother. He's interested in a "personal genome" from *Seq4You,* a (fictitious) company that says it can do this for just over $100. He's excited because the Facebook sites he regularly reads have been tracking low-cost personal genome companies. He wants you to go along with this and, he says, maybe the two of you can convince your parents to evaluate their own sequences as well. "It'll be fun!"

You were excited at first; this would be a great time to see how Mendel's laws that you read about in Chapter 9 play out in your family. But then you remembered your Ethics class. A group discussion pointed out some sequencing companies make you agree they can use your information "for scientific purposes." Would that include selling your information to insurance companies? Will it be posted online with "anonymized" information, presenting your genetic data but without identifying information? You read a *Nature* paper that outlined different ways that privacy can be breached despite the data being "anonymized."

In fact, one of your study partners last week was talking about a *Vox* article written by a geneticist who had his own genome sequenced and then, as a gift to his parents, bought them kits for sequencing. He wanted to see from whom he got his traits. They all checked an online box to find "close relatives" who also submitted their data. Matches are based on percent identity of nucleotide sequences. The geneticist found someone who would be a "grandfather, uncle, or sibling," and his father found a match who was most likely a child, but none of the geneticist's siblings had ever submitted a sample to the database. This revealed a child his father had sired when he was quite young (and in fact was not aware of) and led to his parent's divorce. Would this test put your family at risk for similar controversy?

There are some tantalizing things you could find out about your ancestry. *Seq4You* uses DNA sequences to trace your ancestry to Europe, Asia, or Africa, or even back to tribes or ancient communities. The report also contains a list of phenotypes you might display, such as going bald or even developing certain diseases, along with probabilities that these might happen. *Seq4You* provides advice about lifestyle changes you could adopt to reduce your risk, but they are not licensed to practice medicine. What about diseases that have no cure, like Huntington disease (HD), which Chapter 17 describes as a dominant, lethal neurodegenerative disease? How would knowing this information help you? You had a grandparent who died after exhibiting Huntington-like symptoms, but no actual diagnosis was made. This might be frightening to know and would change your outlook on life long before the disease struck.

A quick search on the Internet revealed that this company doesn't report HD. You wonder why not, and realize that not only is there an ethics issue—the company doesn't want to be responsible for being the source of that knowledge—but many interesting loci are also not reported. Patents on those genetic areas mean *Seq4You* would have to pay each patent holder to be licensed to report on "their gene." As you dig, you also find out that *Seq4You* reports are not based on your entire sequenced genome. *Seq4You* uses the PCR reaction you read about in Chapter 14 to clone specific areas in the genome, and then sequences only those clones. It's not so much a "genome report" as a list of small sequenced regions within your genome, but ones that aren't restricted for legal or ethical reasons.

Personal genome reports are just one, definitely personal, example of research in the field of genomics: the characterization of whole genomes, including their sequences, structures, functions, and evolution. In this chapter, you will learn about the approaches to genomic analysis and some of the evolutionary insights that have come from them. You will also learn a little about other "-omes": the transcriptome and the proteome. These terms, respectively, refer to the complete set of genes that are transcribed and the total array of proteins that arise from them. This chapter provides context for how scientists use "-omics" approaches to trace the evolutionary history of genes and make hypotheses about the function of gene-like sequences as they are identified through sequencing.

## 15.1 Genomics: An Overview

Genomics is the characterization of whole genomes, including their structures, sequences, functions, and evolution. Genomics provides information about the genes that encode proteins and functional RNA produced by cells and also about pseudogenes (see Section 15.3), which can be transcribed but have no function, "junk DNA," parts of which may have structural benefits for a genome and hidden stories about ancestry and evolution. Having the complete sequence of a genome makes it possible to study the complete set of genes in an organism or a virus, as well as other important sequences of their genomes. The complete sequence of a genome is a tool researchers use to study the organization of genes as a whole and to determine how they function together in networks.

What makes this chapter particularly interesting is that the techniques used to analyze whole genomes are based on principles you studied in Chapter 14, which itself is based on natural processes you studied in Chapters 11 and 12. For example, DNA elongation occurs when the 5′ phosphate of a nucleotide is attached to the 3′ end of a DNA molecule (Section 11.3b). That is how DNA is replicated, and that reaction is also the foundation for modern DNA sequence analysis; that is, modern DNA sequencing is built on the natural chemistry of DNA synthesis.

Sequencing the entire 3-billion-base-pair human genome—the Human Genome Project (HGP)—began in 1990. The task was completed in 2003 by an international consortium of researchers and by a private company, Celera Genomics.

**CONCEPT FIX** Note that the estimate of 3 billion base pairs is for one haploid genome and includes the Y chromosome. Any two humans are unlikely to have exactly the same number of bases in their respective versions of the human genome. ⬡

To develop techniques for the HGP, the genomes of other model organisms were sequenced and used for comparison: *E. coli* (representing prokaryotic cells), the yeast *Saccharomyces cerevisiae* (representing single-celled eukaryotes), *Drosophila melanogaster* and *Caenorhabditis elegans* (the fruit fly and a nematode worm, representing multicellular invertebrate animals), and *Mus musculus* (the mouse, representing nonhuman mammals). Plants were represented by *Arabidopsis thaliana* (called the "fruit fly of the plant kingdom" because of its rapid life cycle, abundant mutant lines, and small chromosome number: five instead of the four found in the fly). Sequencing these model organisms was faster and more economical than working only on the human genome. Experimentation on model organisms developed better sequencing techniques and identified the functions of genes, which could then be used to identify similar genes in the human genome.

Advances in many areas of scientific study have resulted from genomic approaches. For example, Genome Canada oversees diverse projects addressing topics such as Atlantic cod aquaculture, forestry breeding, agricultural crops, microorganisms active in mining and oil sands extraction, industrial production of fungal enzymes, and human health issues, including autism and infectious disease. Because of automation—robots being used to manually handle cloned cultures and reagents, and machines that perform sequencing reactions with little to no human oversight—there has been an exponential growth of organisms' genomic representations in databases. Scientists are currently adding at least one entirely new genome to databases each hour.

For these sequences to be most useful, they need to be available to all researchers. DNA sequences are deposited into public databases that are accessible online. For example, GenBank is an "annotated collection of all publicly available DNA sequences" at the National Institutes of Health (NIH). The address is **http://www.ncbi.nlm.nih.gov/genbank/**. The total number of bases in DNA sequence records at GenBank is increasing exponentially. Computational tools at GenBank enable researchers and others, such as students like yourself, to perform various analyses with the sequence data. Go to **http://www.ncbi.nlm.nih.gov/**, choose "Genome" from the Popular Resources list at the right, and then "Browse by Organism." Add up the numbers in the "Size (Mb)" column and you can find out how much more information has been added since the time this chapter was written (1150 billion as of 6 July 2017). Consider downloading the entire list—provided in a link at the upper right of the page—and use a spreadsheet to add up the bases.

Other genomics databases are also accessible using the Internet, with sequence data organized in different ways. Some are organism-specific databases and others provide summaries of particular genomics studies or information on specific chromosomes or regions within a chromosome. Additional online sites provide search tools, such as BLAST, that search through many databases at once.

Overall, the field of genomics consists of four main areas:

1. **Sequencing:** Obtaining the base-by-base sequence of an entire genome. Usually this process begins with an extensive collection of short, unordered fragment sequences that are then used to reconstruct the original genome sequence using computer algorithms.
2. **Annotation:** Genomes are scanned for sequences that are potential RNA-producing sequences (including mRNAs that contain protein assembly instructions), as well as other identifiable sequences of the genome such as pseudogenes and structural elements such as centromeres and telomeres.
3. **Functional analysis:** Using genome sequence data as a basis to study and understand the functions of genes and other parts of the genome. For protein-coding genes, it also includes determining what proteins they encode and how those proteins function in the organism's metabolic processes.
4. **Evolutionary analysis:** Comparative genomic studies find relationships among sequence data from different organisms to provide clues about how genes and genomes have changed over evolutionary time.

Advances in each of these areas of study are accelerating. New strategies for exploiting the chemistry involved in DNA replication (Chapter 11) are being designed, and technological advances in hardware and information storage allow faster and cheaper data collection. Automation of laboratory tasks has sped up the process, including robots that can grow thousands of individual colonies of bacteria, extract their DNA, and send it to automated sequencers. These sequencers spool data into computers for immediate access by the scientific community at a rate of thousands of nucleotides per second. Sophisticated algorithms in these computers also identify potential gene sequences prior to human eyes even seeing them.

The following sections of this chapter discuss each of the four areas of genomics.

STUDY BREAK QUESTION

1. What additional biological questions can we answer if provided with an organism's genomic sequence, particularly if we have access to sequences of genes whose functions we already know?

## 15.2 Genome Sequencing

Genome sequence determination involves obtaining the sequence of bases in a genome using molecular techniques, and then analyzing these data to reconstruct the original genome. These data can be searched by computers to find non-random sequences that are typical of important genetic elements, such as centromeres, promoters, and protein-binding sites.

### 15.2a Genome Analysis Begins with DNA Sequencing

DNA sequencing was developed in the late 1970s by Allan M. Maxam and Walter Gilbert of Harvard University. They used chemical reactions to cut between specific nucleotides, and the results of many reactions could be combined to reveal the sequence—like solving a puzzle. A few years later, Frederick Sanger, of Cambridge University, designed an even simpler method that terminated newly synthesized pieces of DNA at specific bases so the nucleotides could be read using a separation gel (see Research Method Figure 14.6). Gilbert and Sanger (along with Paul Berg) were awarded the Nobel Prize for Chemistry in 1980 for their work on DNA sequencing. These technologies have evolved since then, particularly in the past few years.

**DNA SEQUENCING METHODS** All DNA sequencing methods have the following steps in common:

1. DNA purification;
2. DNA fragmentation;
3. Amplification of fragments;
4. Sequencing each fragment; and
5. Assembling fragment sequences into longer sequences.

The methods differ in how the amplification is done, the lengths of the fragments, how many fragments are sequenced simultaneously, and how the sequencing reactions themselves are done.

Sanger sequencing was by far the most common DNA sequencing technique used in the past. This method exploits the natural chemistry of DNA synthesis. Elongating chains of DNA are extended one nucleotide at a time by the replication enzymes (see Section 11.3b). Each new nucleotide is added to the 3′ hydroxyl of the elongating chain. By terminating synthesis by adding a nucleotide that lacks a 3′ hydroxyl, and some way to know which specific nucleotide ended elongation, the series of nucleotides can be determined. **Figure 15.1** shows both Sanger sequencing (also called **dideoxynucleotide** sequencing) in its original form using four lanes on a gel, as well as a more recent adaptation of this technique that uses fluorescent markers in single gel lane.

FIGURE 15.1 **Research Method**

## Sanger Sequencing

**Purpose:** To obtain the sequence of a template piece of DNA by manufacturing a new DNA strand on it, but terminating this with dideoxynucleotides to generate fragments that differ in length by one nucleotide each

### Protocol:

a.

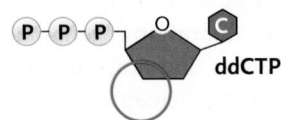

ddCTP

(a) The Sanger (dideoxy) method for DNA sequencing makes use of the DNA polymerizing reaction from Chapter 11. The older four-lane method (c) used radioactive primers, and so the reactants needed to be separated in lanes based on the terminating nucleotide. Newer methods (b) involve fluorescent tags in a single tube and a single separation column.

1. A dideoxyribonucleotide (in this case, dideoxycytosine, or ddCTP) lacks the critical 3′ hydroxyl required for subsequent nucleotides to bind during polymerization (green circle) (a).
2. Figure (a) shows how nucleotides are added to a growing DNA molecule by binding the 3′ hydroxyl. When a ddNTP is added, elongation ends on that nucleotide. Pyrophosphate release (orange circle) can be used in pyrosequencing (described later in this chapter).

b.

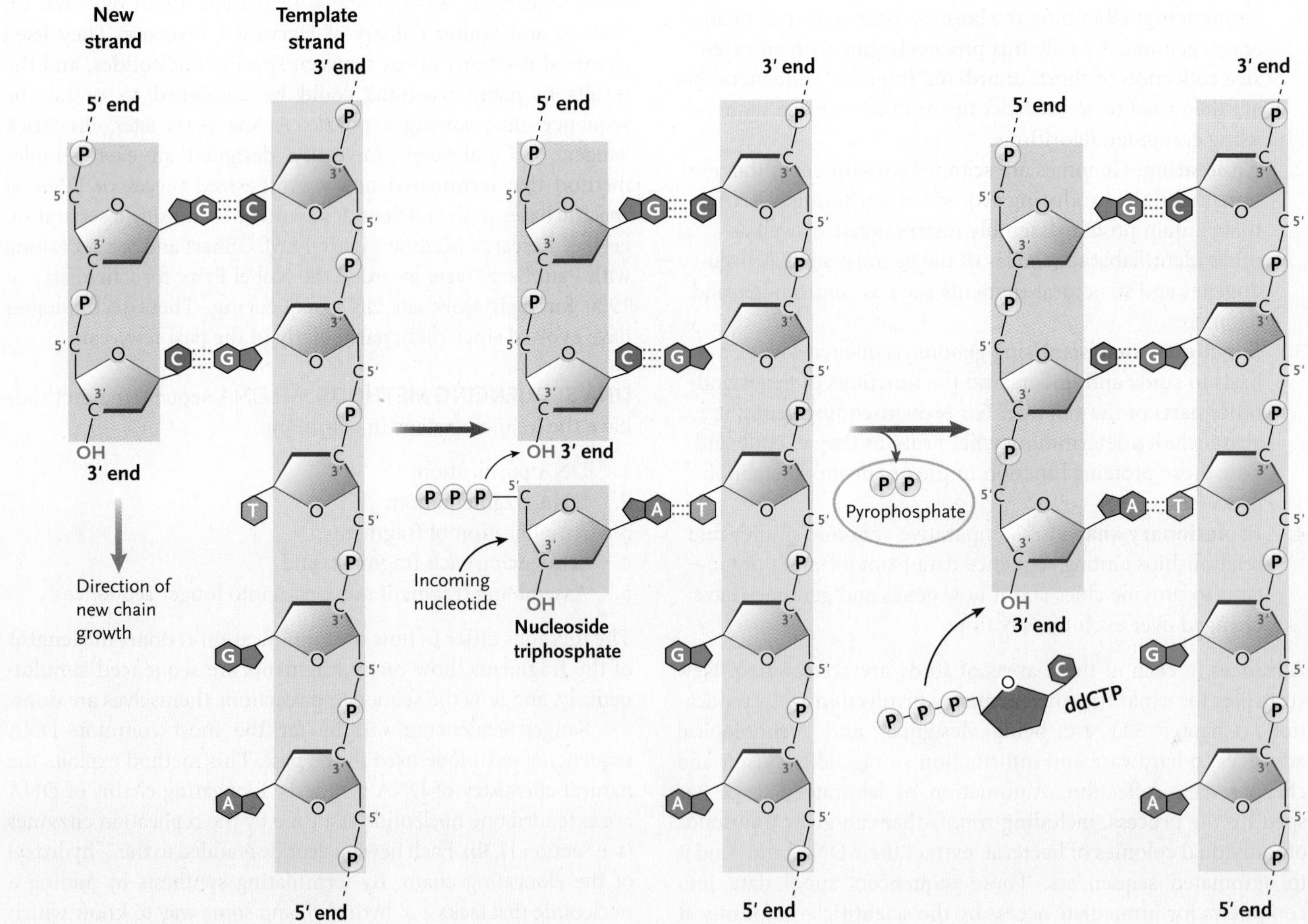

New strand — Template strand

Direction of new chain growth

Incoming nucleotide — Nucleoside triphosphate

Pyrophosphate

ddCTP

3. Four separate tubes are prepared with identical reagents: all four contain DNA polymerase, the template DNA to be sequenced, a primer to stick to the template and provide a 3′ –OH for elongation, and all four deoxyribonucleotides **(b)**. Each tube has a different ddNTP added at a very low concentration (<1% of the dNTPs). The primer is typically labelled with radioactive ³²P so that the locations of fragments can be identified on X-ray film (not shown). Under the tubes in this diagram are examples of short sequences prepared on the template. Note that each tube terminates on the same type of nitrogenous base, the one represented by the ddNTP in that tube.

Four lanes on a polyacrylamide sequencing gel (b) separate molecules by size. Bands represent molecules that differ by a single nucleotide in length. The bottom band is in the "T" lane, signifying primer with a ddTTP at the end. This is the smallest piece. Slightly above are two molecules in the "C" lane. Each ends in ddCTP. The smaller piece contains only primer-TC, and the larger is primer-TCC. The low concentration of ddCTP means that only a few replicating molecules terminate on the first C, others progress to the next, and still others continue until all "C" positions are represented in the tube.

**c.**

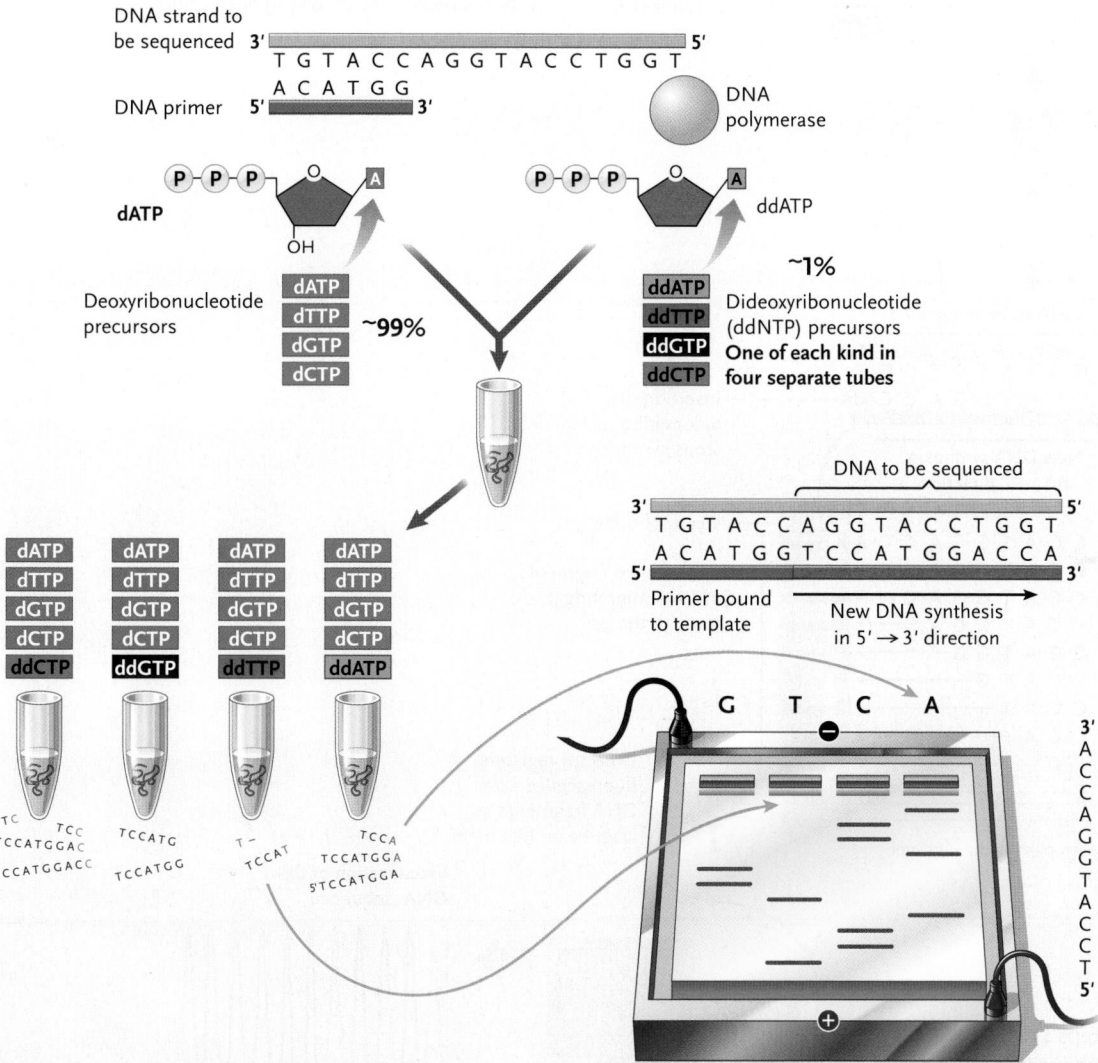

*(Continued)*

FIGURE 15.1 Research Method (*Continued*)

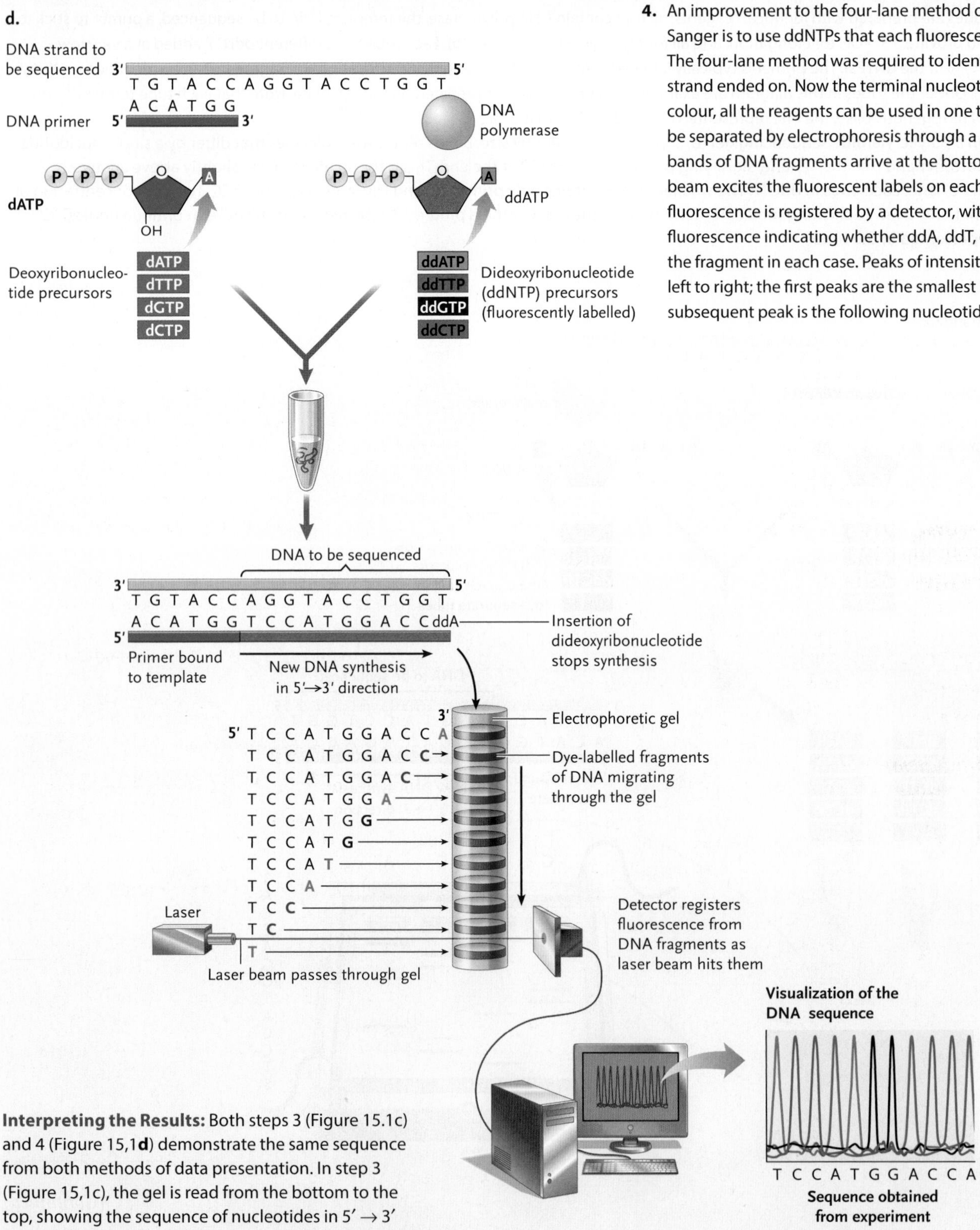

**d.**

DNA strand to be sequenced 3'

T G T A C C A G G T A C C T G G T
A C A T G G

DNA primer 5' ━━━━━ 3'

DNA polymerase

P–P–P O A

**dATP**

OH

ddATP

Deoxyribonucleotide precursors

| dATP |
| dTTP |
| dGTP |
| dCTP |

| ddATP |
| ddTTP |
| ddGTP |
| ddCTP |

Dideoxyribonucleotide (ddNTP) precursors (fluorescently labelled)

**4.** An improvement to the four-lane method originally proposed by Sanger is to use ddNTPs that each fluoresce with a different colour **(d)**. The four-lane method was required to identify which nucleotide the strand ended on. Now the terminal nucleotide can be identified by colour, all the reagents can be used in one tube, and the products can be separated by electrophoresis through a single capillary tube. As the bands of DNA fragments arrive at the bottom of the capillary, a laser beam excites the fluorescent labels on each DNA fragment. The fluorescence is registered by a detector, with the wavelength of the fluorescence indicating whether ddA, ddT, ddG, or ddC is at the end of the fragment in each case. Peaks of intensity can be read 5' to 3' from left to right; the first peaks are the smallest bits of DNA and each subsequent peak is the following nucleotide.

DNA to be sequenced

3' T G T A C C A G G T A C C T G G T 5'
A C A T G G T C C A T G G A C C ddA — Insertion of dideoxyribonucleotide stops synthesis
5'

Primer bound to template

New DNA synthesis in 5'→3' direction

5' T C C A T G G A C C A 3' — Electrophoretic gel
T C C A T G G A C C→ — Dye-labelled fragments of DNA migrating through the gel
T C C A T G G A C →
T C C A T G G A →
T C C A T G G →
T C C A T G →
T C C A T →
T C C A →
T C C →
Laser T C →
T →

Laser beam passes through gel

Detector registers fluorescence from DNA fragments as laser beam hits them

**Visualization of the DNA sequence**

T C C A T G G A C C A

Sequence obtained from experiment

**Interpreting the Results:** Both steps 3 (Figure 15.1c) and 4 (Figure 15,1**d**) demonstrate the same sequence from both methods of data presentation. In step 3 (Figure 15,1c), the gel is read from the bottom to the top, showing the sequence of nucleotides in 5' → 3' order. The template would be the reverse complement of the sequence shown in the gel.

The data from the laser system shown in step 4 (Figure 15.1d) are sent to a computer that displays which of the four possible fluorescent labels is at the end of each DNA strand. The results show colour traces as the DNA bands passed the detector. Each colour indicates a different base. The sequence of the newly synthesized DNA, which is complementary to the template strand, is read from left (5') to right (3').

Note that the primer cannot be sequenced in any method; only the nucleotides added to a primer can be detected.

In recent years, the dideoxy sequencing method has been replaced by faster, cheaper, more automated techniques. In general, these newer high-throughput techniques have decreased sequencing costs by reducing the preparatory steps, automating more of the process, and sequencing over a billion different DNA fragments during the same machine run.

Randomly sheared fragments of DNA are purified from the genome to be sequenced, then adapter nucleotides are added to each end. These allow the pieces to stick to specific spots on a surface (a "chip") or a bead (**Figure 15.2a**) after they are denatured. They stick because the adapter sequences are complementary to oligonucleotides (short DNA pieces) covalently linked to the medium. PCR is performed *in situ,* that is, in place on the bead or chip. Replicated pieces attach near the original template so that each spot on the slide contains millions of identical DNA molecules. This process of amplifying single strands in place is common to many new sequencing techniques. The DNA is manipulated by using heat and complimentary bases to hold onto the adapter segments. These adapters not only hold DNA to a surface, they are also perfect for PCR: their sequence is known, so primers are designed that bind to them.

Figure 15.2b-f demonstrates **pyrosequencing**, which measures the pyrophosphate (recall the orange circle in Figure 15.1b) released by nucleotide addition as A, G, C, and T dNTPs are cycled across the template DNAs. Illumnia/Solexa sequencing, a different technology, uses dNTPs with coloured fluorescent tags that are released by each nucleotide as it is incorporated. In both of these systems, a camera records the timing of a flash (pyrosequencing) or a colour change (Illumina/Solexa) to record each addition.

Pyrosequencing is particularly fast because consecutive nucleotides (C then G in the Figure 15.2g graph) occur as a single flash twice as bright as that of a single nucleotide addition. Having even more of the same nucleotide of the same kind gives even more intense flashes. In pyrosequencing, bases are added in a known order in a repeating cycle. The camera knows when each nucleotide has been added so it can determine which nucleotide elicited a flash.

Flat surfaces covered with DNA attachment sites that are used for other "next generation" or "high-throughput" methods are now most common. The array of template DNA is called a "DNA chip," and methods that detect dye release as nucleotides are added to make the process even faster and more economical.

In all these rapid sequencing methods, thousands of spots on the surface provide simultaneous reads of different samples. The computer stores the images generated during the sequencing reaction and outputs data for each spot as a separate file.

## 15.2b   Hierarchical Genome Sequencing

The original strategy to sequence the entire human genome was intended to take approximately 15 years. This was due to a high level of quality control, rough characterization of clones of genome fragments, and strategizing which clones combine to form an efficient, continuous path spanning the entire chromosome. These chosen clones would create a "golden tiling path," and would be the smallest number of pieces of DNA required to achieve the most efficient and accurate sequence. These would be sequenced multiple times and the sequences compared to eliminate the inevitable misread nucleotides. The accuracy of the final project would have an error rate of less than 1 base per 10 000 nucleotides.

Because of the effort required to choose the best clones, this method is called **hierarchical genome sequencing**—some clones are assessed to be "better" than others. A small group of individuals contributed blood to be used for genome sequencing. They were all volunteers, and only a few people's samples were used. Nobody knows which genomes were actually used. The genetic material was randomly sheared to create many overlapping sequences, which were then cloned into vectors called *bacterial artificial chromosomes* (BACs), which contain up to 350 000 base pairs of DNA. These vectors are too long to sequence directly, but their ends were characterized in such a way that they could be lined up to determine those that create the optimal golden tiling path for each chromosome (**Figure 15.3a**). Each BAC was broken up into subclones of smaller size for sequencing. The sequences were then put together in the order corresponding to the BAC, and the BAC sequences were then reassembled to reveal the genome of each chromosome.

Data were made available to the public through the Internet as they were collected.

## 15.2c   Whole-Genome Shotgun Sequencing

The hierarchical method of sequencing was slow due to the large amount of planning and organization before actual sequencing could take place. J. Craig Venter is a biotechnologist who was frustrated with a sequencing project estimated to take 15 years. He developed **whole-genome shotgun sequencing** (Figure 15.3) to speed things up, and created the company Celera (*celer* is Latin for fast) to use this approach. Instead of cloning large pieces into BACs and characterizing them, genomic DNA was broken into millions of random overlapping fragments. Each fragment was prepared and sequenced. The entire genome was then assembled using computer algorithms that join overlaps between sequences, then stitched together as longer contiguous sequences.

Because the data from government-funded labs were made available online, Celera (a tax-paying, private corporation) used the public data to improve their own work. As a private company, Celera then patented many of the genes they identified to make a profit—something they owed their shareholders—and they kept their own data private.

The tension between the government scientists and those at Celera is an interesting case of law and ethics. Can someone own the genome? What benefits should the owner of a genetic patent realize?

FIGURE 15.2 **Research Method**

## Pyrosequencing

The pyrosequencing method simultaneously produces sequences from multiple samples. A computer controls the release of dNTPs (deoxynucleotide triphosphates), and a camera records flashes when nucleotides are added to the growing DNA strand.

**Purpose:** To obtain sequences from multiple fragments simultaneously

**Protocol:**

1. Adapter DNA sequences are added to each end of fragmented DNA **(a)**. These are then denatured and the adapters are used to hold the DNA to beads containing a sequence complimentary to one of the adapters. Samples are dilute, so each bead has, at most, one piece of DNA attached. Beads are separated from each other in an oil emulsion and PCR is performed within each chamber so that cloned DNA remains on the bead containing the original template. After amplification, complementary strands are denatured so that single-stranded pieces containing exactly the same sequence are attached. These are put into wells on a grid containing enzymes that release photons when pyrophosphate is released. The motto is "one bead is one read," but, because around 200 000 beads are being read simultaneously, a great deal of sequence data are generated as follows:

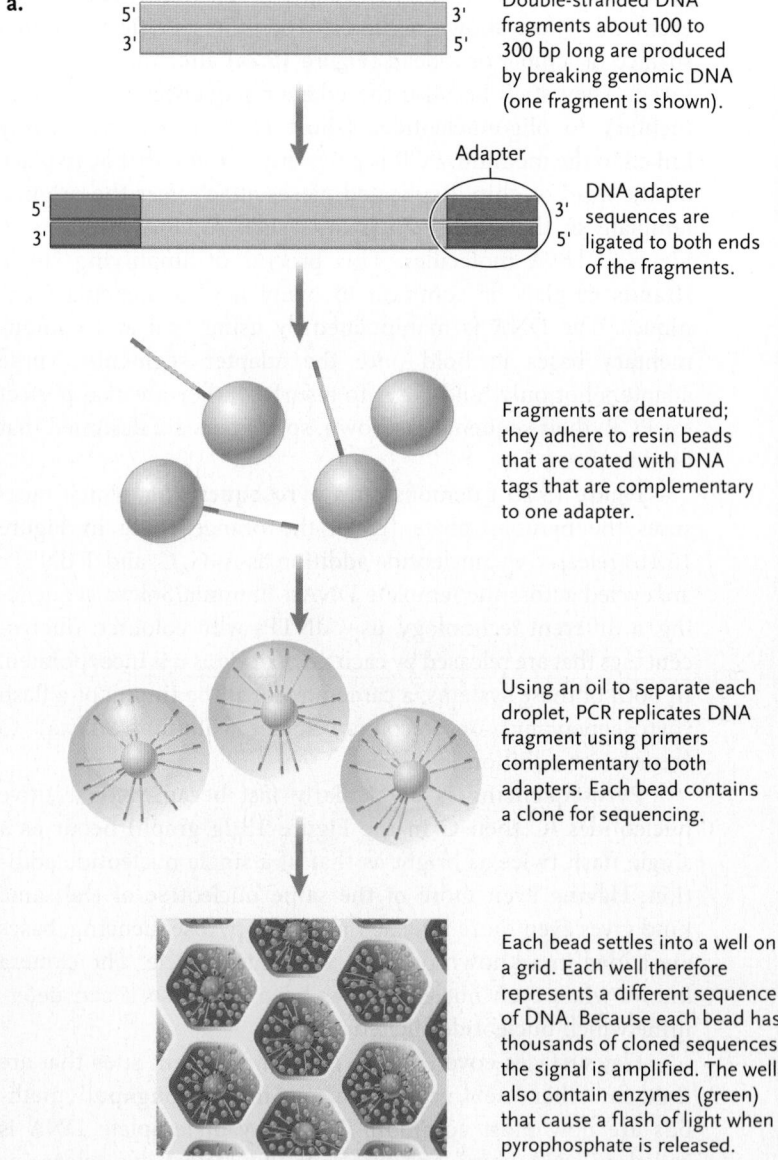

Double-stranded DNA fragments about 100 to 300 bp long are produced by breaking genomic DNA (one fragment is shown).

DNA adapter sequences are ligated to both ends of the fragments.

Fragments are denatured; they adhere to resin beads that are coated with DNA tags that are complementary to one adapter.

Using an oil to separate each droplet, PCR replicates DNA fragment using primers complementary to both adapters. Each bead contains a clone for sequencing.

Each bead settles into a well on a grid. Each well therefore represents a different sequence of DNA. Because each bead has thousands of cloned sequences, the signal is amplified. The wells also contain enzymes (green) that cause a flash of light when pyrophosphate is released.

**b. Template exposed to "A" (dATP)—no incorporation, no PP$_i$**

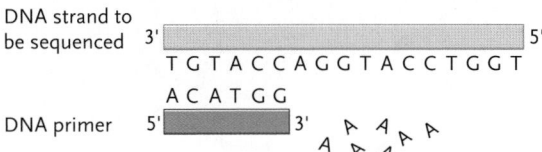

DNA strand to be sequenced 3' ▭ 5'
T G T A C C A G G T A C C T G G T
A C A T G G
DNA primer 5' ▭ 3'
A A A A A
A A A

**c. Template exposed to "G"—no incorporation, no PP$_i$**

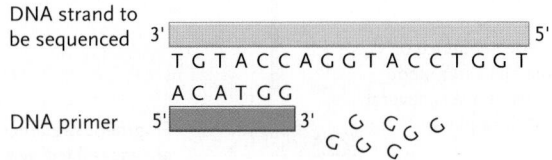

DNA strand to be sequenced 3' ▭ 5'
T G T A C C A G G T A C C T G G T
A C A T G G
DNA primer 5' ▭ 3'
G G G G G
G G G

**d. Template exposed to "C"—no incorporation, no PP$_i$**

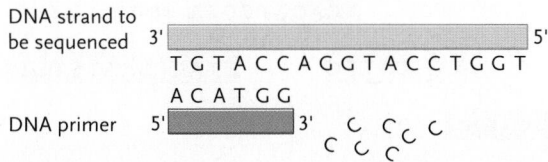

DNA strand to be sequenced 3' ▭ 5'
T G T A C C A G G T A C C T G G T
A C A T G G
DNA primer 5' ▭ 3'
C C C C C
C C C

**e. Template exposed to "T"—incorporation, PP$_i$ released; flash**

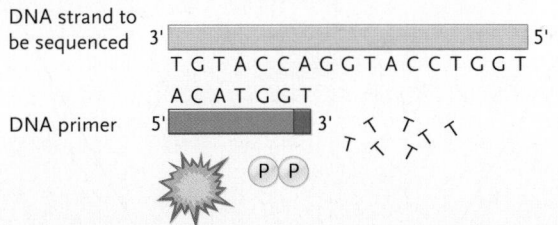

DNA strand to be sequenced 3' ▭ 5'
T G T A C C A G G T A C C T G G T
A C A T G G T
DNA primer 5' ▭ 3'
T T T T T
T T T
✸ P P

**f. Repeat (b) through (e) until template is covered by new DNA**

**g. Pyrosequencing output**

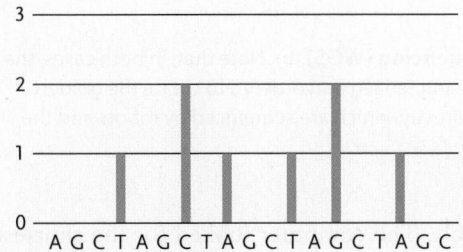

3
2
1
0
A G C T A G C T A G C T A G C T A G C

2. First, a primer complimentary to the exposed adapter is added to every anchored DNA fragment. Every spot on the plate contains a different template to be sequenced, but since the tags are identical, sequencing begins simultaneously for all samples. A pump rapidly cycles through each of the nucleotides A, G, C, and T in order **(b–f)**. Only one will be complementary at the 3' end of the primer, so only during one part of each cycle will pyrophosphate be released. In this case, pyrophosphate is released in (e), allowing enzymes that harness the energy from the pyrophosphate to emit a flash of light. This is recorded by a camera and it is noted that the flash occurred during the addition of "T." The cycle is repeated; the next flash is twice as bright and occurs when "C" is released. This tells the computer that two nucleotides were incorporated, and so on.

**Interpreting the Results:** The computer records every spot on the surface **(g)** and produces individual sequencing reports for the entire set of samples. Each single nucleotide addition provides a flash of a certain magnitude (graph), and sequential additions of a particular nucleotide produce more light.

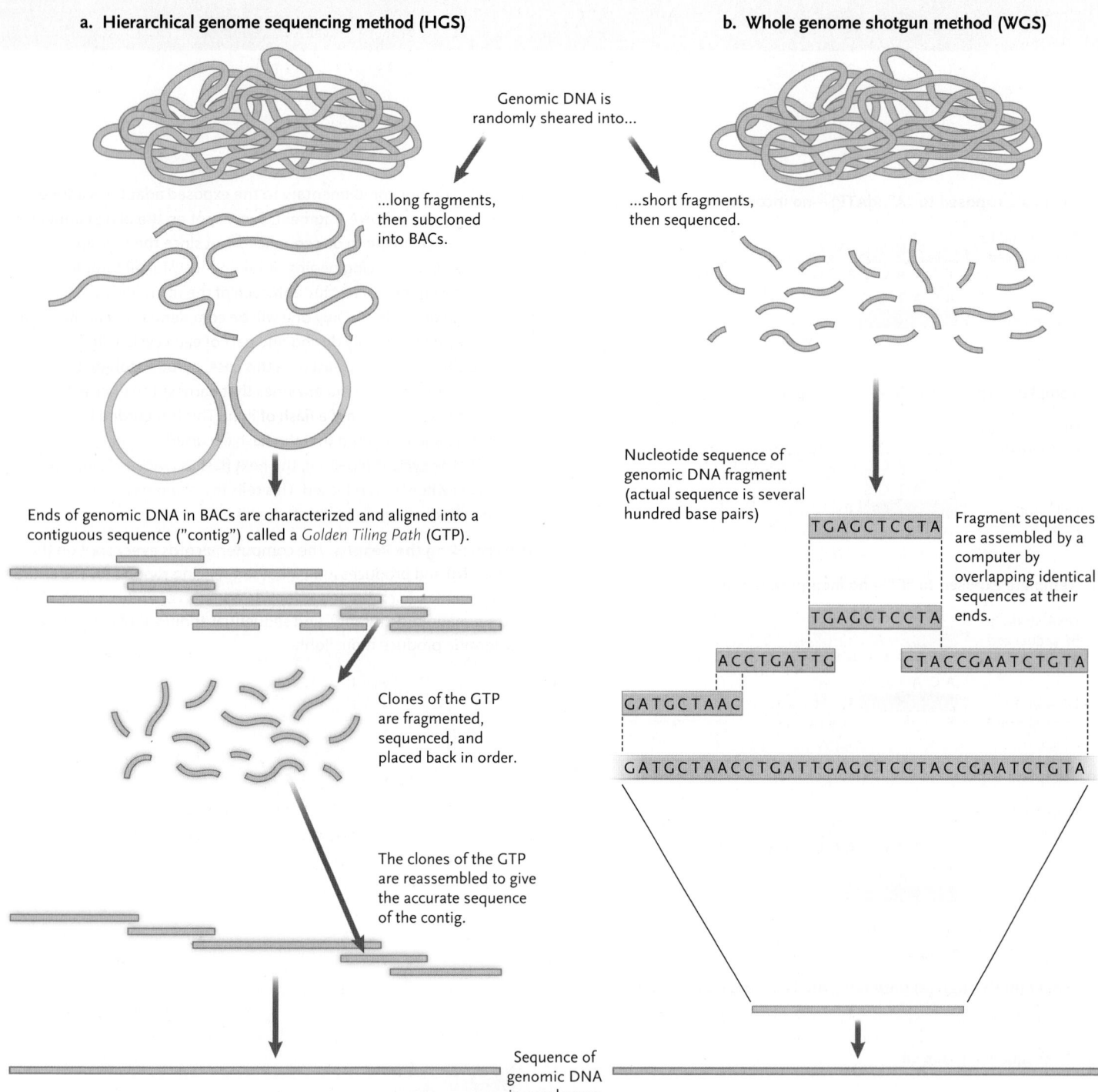

**a. Hierarchical genome sequencing method (HGS)**

Genomic DNA is randomly sheared into...

...long fragments, then subcloned into BACs.

Ends of genomic DNA in BACs are characterized and aligned into a contiguous sequence ("contig") called a *Golden Tiling Path* (GTP).

Clones of the GTP are fragmented, sequenced, and placed back in order.

The clones of the GTP are reassembled to give the accurate sequence of the contig.

Sequence of genomic DNA is now known

**b. Whole genome shotgun method (WGS)**

...short fragments, then sequenced.

Nucleotide sequence of genomic DNA fragment (actual sequence is several hundred base pairs)

TGAGCTCCTA

Fragment sequences are assembled by a computer by overlapping identical sequences at their ends.

TGAGCTCCTA

ACCTGATTG        CTACCGAATCTGTA

GATGCTAAC

GATGCTAACCTGATTGAGCTCCTACCGAATCTGTA

**FIGURE 15.3 Hierarchical genome sequencing (HGS) (a) versus whole-genome shotgun sequencing (WGS) (b).** Note that, in both cases, the genome is sheared but the HGS creates a library using large genome fragments. These fragments are characterized and ordered to create the golden tiling path; only these clones are chosen for further sequencing. WGS creates many smaller fragments directly, which are sequenced by robots and the data automatically assembled based on overlapping edges.

Another interesting question is, Which method worked better? At first, it would seem WGS would allow sequencing to be done more cheaply and rapidly. However, the HGS sequence was higher quality. Forty percent of the human genome is made up of repetitive transposable elements (see Section 15.4b), which were shortened in computer assembly and lost during WGS assembly. The computer looked for the shortest, most efficient sequence during assembly; this was achieved by dropping (what looked like!) overlapping sequences. However, the HGS kept these in the alignments. The result was that genomes determined by the HGS genome were often tens of millions of base pairs larger per chromosome than those determined by WGS, and it better represented the *actual* sequence.

## STUDY BREAK QUESTIONS

1. Imagine you are a scientist in charge of a lab that sequenced a novel gene. Patent protection would prevent other, better equipped labs from doing research that would make your own work irrelevant. Would you patent your gene?
2. Why did the WGS shorten genome sequences when compared to HGS? Which sequences in particular were lost?

## 15.3 Annotation Identifies Genes

A genome sequence is simply a string of A, T, G, and C letters; it tells us practically nothing about the organism from which it derives other than the size of its genome. Once the complete sequence of a genome is determined, the next step is annotation. This identifies functionally important features in the genome. These features include

- Protein-coding genes
- Noncoding RNA genes. "Noncoding" means the transcript is not translated. The transcript is the functional product of the gene, and this group include genes for tRNAs, rRNAs, and snRNAs (Chapter 12), as well as micro-RNAs (miRNAs; Chapter 13).
- Regulatory sequences associated with genes (see Chapter 13).
- Origins of replication (see Chapter 11).
- Transposable elements, viruses, and sequences related to them.
- Pseudogenes: DNA sequences similar to genes, but mutations have changed the genes so that they no longer produce functional products (e.g., deletion of the promoter). Pseudogenes are derived from actual genes.
- Short tandem repeats (STRs). These sequences repeat frequently one-after-the-other (in tandem) in the genome.

Annotation is performed by researchers in the field of **bioinformatics**. This field applies mathematics and computer science to extract information from biological data, including those related to genome structure, function, and evolution.

### 15.3a Identifying Genes Using Automated Predictions

Chapter 12 linked mRNA molecules to protein products. The span in an mRNA starting with the "start codon" and ending with the "stop codon" is called an **open reading frame (ORF)**. Since ORFs begin with the codon AUG and end with one of three termination codons (UAG, UAA, or UGA), they are easy for a computer to spot. ORFs that are longer than 100 codons almost always indicate the presence of a protein-coding gene. Computer algorithms are used to identify possible protein-coding genes in a genome sequence by searching for potential

ORFs. This means searching for an AUG that is separated from a stop codon (UAG, UAA, or UGA) by a stretch of three nucleotide multiples of an adequate length. The search is complicated because

- Either of the two DNA strands could be the template for a given gene, and
- Prokaryotes may use an alternative start codon, such as GUG (valine) or UUG (leucine). Other rare exceptions are also possible in prokaryotes and eukaryotes.
- Eukaryote ORFs are interrupted by introns. These are found in pre-mRNAs encoded by the DNA template.

Each DNA sequence has six reading frames for the three-letter genetic code: three on one strand and three on the other. An ORF can be in any of these frames. This is illustrated in **Figure 15.4** for a theoretical 30-nucleotide segment of DNA.

**CONCEPT** **FIX** Figure 15.4 shows an ORF on the top strand, reading 5′ → 3′ from ATG. Although it is tempting to assume that the top strand containing the ORF is used as the template for transcription, this is not possible: RNA polymerases read template DNA only in the 3′ → 5′ direction. Therefore, template DNA for this ORF is the bottom strand, not the top. It is for this reason the non-template strand is often referred to as the "coding strand." The name makes it sound important, but it isn't directly involved in transcription. It resembles the mRNA for easy interpretation. For this reason, you see the start codon as "ATG," as it is in Figure 15.4. ◼

Searching for protein-coding ORFs is straightforward in prokaryotic genomes: few genes typo have introns (and almost only in Archaeans). Eukaryotic protein-coding genes usually have introns, so more sophisticated algorithms must be used to identify them. For example, some algorithms are good at identifying exons and introns and eukaryotic promoter sequences.

Computer identification of genes is the first step. Experiments using organisms that have specific genes knocked out— *in vitro* studies that can examine protein activity, protein electrophoresis, protein crystallography, and other techniques—identify what each gene does in the first place. Model organisms are easier to study and manipulate. By figuring out gene functions in simpler systems and connecting them to gene and protein sequences, we compile databases that can be searched to identify genes in other organisms.

An ancestral globin gene created a protein with a slight affinity to bind oxygen, promoting oxygenation. A possible

```
        GTC →
      TGT →
    ATG →
5′...ATGTCTGTTGACTGGGTTGGAAGGCAATAG...3′
3′...TACGACAATCTGACCCAACCTTCCGTTATC...5′
                        ← ATC
                      ← TAT
                    ← TTA
```

© Cengage Learning 2017

**FIGURE 15.4 The six reading frames of double-stranded DNA.** In this particular sequence, several of them are short ORFs. The easiest to spot is a tetrapeptide (four amino acids) with an ATG start.

recombination error (**Figure 15.5**) resulted in a duplication of DNA, creating paralogs that, through mutation, had different oxygen affinities. One version is expressed in muscle, the other in blood (**Figure 15.6**). Further duplications and differentiation through mutation created a variety of hemoglobins. These hemoglobins have different binding affinities for oxygen and are expressed at different times during gestation. (Embryonic and fetal hemoglobins have higher oxygen affinities, allowing the developing baby to better collect oxygen from the mother.)

From Chapters 8 and 9 you know about *homologous genes,* which refer to genetic instructions on homologous chromosomes. These may be different alleles, but essentially there is the same (from Greek, *homo*) information. Genes that are passed from parents to offspring that eventually diverge into different species are called **orthologs** (also Greek; *ortho* = ordered, in this case, by descent). Genes that arise through duplication within a genome are considered

to be **paralogs** (*para* = adjacent). Figure 15.6 shows that paralogs form by duplication, and these blocks of genetic information are passed on to descendants. There are orthologous clusters of β-hemoglobin comparable between humans and chimpanzees.

You will recall from Chapter 8 that homologous chromosomes can cross over between each other so that new allele combinations are formed. Crossing over is very precisely determined: DNA sequences must be almost identical for crossover to occur. On occasion, crossover *within* a chromosome arm can occur, or even between *non*homologous chromosomes, especially if similar DNA sequences stabilize the chiasma. Transposable elements (described later in this chapter) increase the frequency of these aberrant crossovers because they are identical sequences of DNA throughout the genome and can "trick" an incorrect crossover event. This, however, has the potential for good: by creating a "backup copy" of a gene, the duplicate and the original can undergo nature's experiments. Genes with

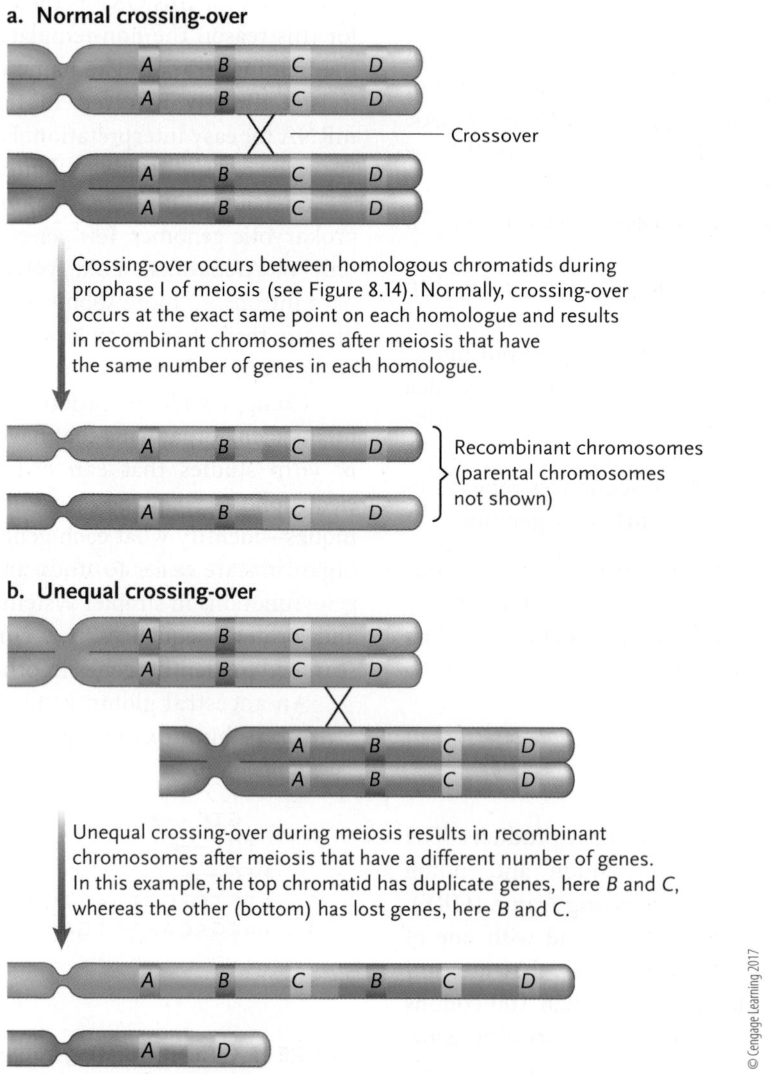

**a. Normal crossing-over**

Crossover

Crossing-over occurs between homologous chromatids during prophase I of meiosis (see Figure 8.14). Normally, crossing-over occurs at the exact same point on each homologue and results in recombinant chromosomes after meiosis that have the same number of genes in each homologue.

Recombinant chromosomes (parental chromosomes not shown)

**b. Unequal crossing-over**

Unequal crossing-over during meiosis results in recombinant chromosomes after meiosis that have a different number of genes. In this example, the top chromatid has duplicate genes, here B and C, whereas the other (bottom) has lost genes, here B and C.

© Cengage Learning 2017

**FIGURE 15.5 Duplication of genes by unequal crossing-over**

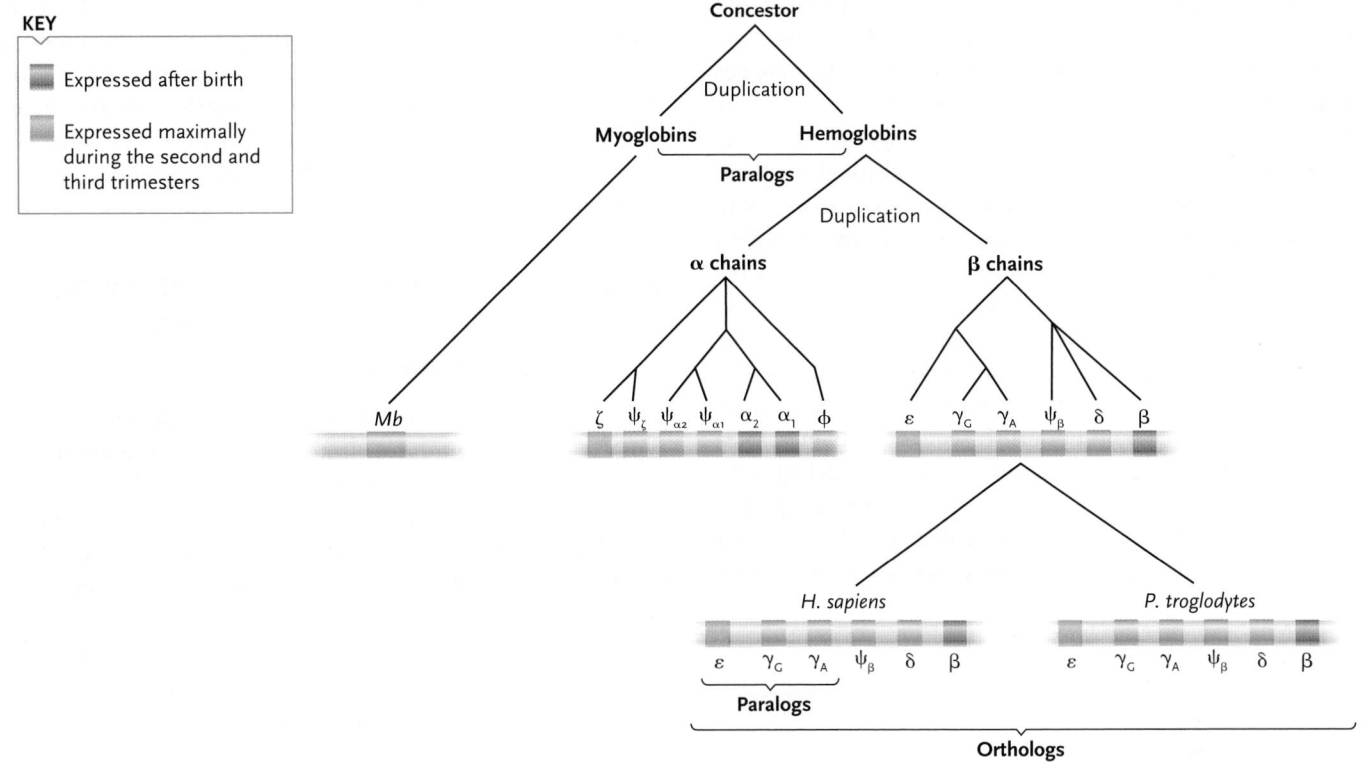

**KEY**

■ Expressed after birth

■ Expressed maximally during the second and third trimesters

**FIGURE 15.6 Gene duplications are shown over evolutionary and chronological time, with more ancestral situations nearest the bottom of the page.** Genes that duplicate within a genome are paralogs; those that are passed from ancestors to descendants are orthologs.

diverging positive effects on the organism can be retained through natural selection.

At first, the duplicate copies of a gene have the same protein-coding sequences and encode identical proteins. The two genes are functionally redundant, meaning that one could be eliminated from the genome with no loss of biological functionality. Often, one of the redundant copies is mutated into a pseudogene or lost by deletion. But if both genes remain functional, they will evolve slowly in different ways as different mutations occur in each gene. Mutations in regulatory sequences may change how each duplicate gene is regulated, or mutations in protein-coding sequences may change the functional properties of the proteins produced by each gene. Over many generations, this evolutionary process can produce two paralogous genes with similar but distinct functions.

## 15.3b  Identifying Genes by Sequence Similarity Searches (BLAST)

One way of identifying DNA or a protein you have sequenced is by comparing it with sequences in databases. These are done by going online to access data. For example, *BLAST* (*Basic Local Alignment Search Tool*), a program at the National Center for Biotechnology Information (**http://blast.ncbi.nlm.nih .gov**), compares the sequence that a researcher submits (the query sequence, which may be either nucleotides or amino

acids) to multiple databases containing well-characterized sequences. BLAST returns the best matches, if any. The matches are listed in order, with the best match at the top. Scrolling down to the bottom can reveal ancestral relationships with other organisms.

Genes of related organisms tend to be similar to each other because they have evolved from genes in common ancestors (**concestors**). Orthologous genes have highly conserved sequences because of their common ancestry. For example, if a gene in the mouse has been characterized experimentally and its sequence is known, and that gene is evolutionarily conserved in mammals, there should be a match for that gene in the human genome sequence.

Sequences can be sorted into ones with known and unknown functions. For the latter, experiments are required to show whether they are real protein-coding genes and, if so, what their functions are. For example, analysis of the human genome sequence initially identified more than a thousand putative ORFs with no sequence similarities to known genes. Most of these function-unknown genes have now been shown to be **pseudogenes**. Such uncertainty makes it difficult to determine the exact number of protein-coding genes in a genome just from its sequence.

**QUANTIFYING MATCHES** How does BLAST select DNA sequences from databases and present them as a list in decreasing order of similarity? If genes were identical, then a "Find" function, like you use in a word processor, could just pluck out the matches. Because of evolution and divergence, which we noted above, an exact match is rare. How, then, are matches found and the quality of the match determined?

BLAST uses a variety of programs, called *algorithms*, to create a **sequence alignment**. The algorithms find rough matches in the database, and then through a series of strict rules try to maximize the raw score that indicates similarity by rewarding matches and penalizing mismatches. Sometimes a gap is introduced between the sequences to allow better matches on either side. Gaps introduce a large penalty to the raw score, but the newly matched flanking nucleotides can make up for this.

**Figure 15.7** shows alignments for β-hemoglobin from human, chimp, chicken, and pufferfish sequences. Figure 15.7a shows a very short alignment between human and chicken, with vertical lines identifying perfect matches. The highlighted "15" in parentheses is the raw score calculated as 24 points for matches (+1 each) minus penalties for each mismatch

**a. BLAST raw score for a small section of human and chicken β-hemoglobin**

Sequence ID: lcl|Query_166273
Range 1: 1 to 27

| Score | Identities |
|-------|-----------|
| 30.2 bits | 24/27 |
| (15) | (89%) |

```
Query 1  TGCCCTGGCCCACAAGTATCACTAAGC  27
         | | | | | | | | |  | | | | | |  | | | | | | | |
Sbjct 1  TGCCCTGGCTCGCAAGTACCACTAAGC  27
```

**b. Nucleotide alignment for a section of β-hemoglobin in four organisms**

```
HumanB-hemo      AATGCCCTGGCCCACAAGTATCACTAAGCTCGCTTTCTTGC
ChimpB-hemo      AATGCCCTGGCCCACAAGTATCACTAAGCTCGCTTTCTTGC
ChickenB-hemo    CATGCCCTGGCTCGCAAGTACCACTAAGCACCAG-----C
PufferfishB-hemo TCTGCTCTGGGAAGACAGTACCACTAAGATGTCCCCCAAGA
                   ***  ****    ****  *******
```

**c. Amino acid alignment for a section of β-hemoglobin in four organisms**

```
HumanB-hemo      KEFTPPVQAAYQKVVAGVANALAHKYH
ChimpB-hemo      KEFTPPVQAAYQKVVAGVANALAHKYH
ChickenB-hemo    KDFTPECQAAWQKLVRVVAHALARKYH
PufferfishB-hemo SKFTPEIQATFQKFLAVVVSALGRQYH
                 ..*** **::**.: *. **.::**
```

**FIGURE 15.7 β-hemoglobin alignments between sequences from human and several model organisms. (a)** Matches and mismatches in an alignment can demonstrate how a bitscore is calculated (+1 for each match and −3 for each mismatch over a 27-nucleotide length = 15). This is for illustrative purposes only; an actual bitscore is modified by other factors, and matched sequences would be considerably longer for proper interpretation. **(b)** Nucleotide alignments are shown for very short stretches within β-hemoglobin genes of four organisms. The arrow shows a gap that was introduced in the chicken sequence to maximize alignments "downstream" (not shown). An asterisk at the bottom indicates identical nucleotides for all sequences queried, and colours are used to illustrate the amino acid of each codon (yellow is a stop codon). **(c)** Another alignment similar to (b), but using amino acids in the alignment. Asterisks at the bottom identify identical amino acids at that position, colons are for amino acids with very similar properties, and periods indicate amino acids with some similarity. The bolded letters show where amino acids represent a significant motif that suggests a critical sequence.

(3 mismatches at −3 points each). Figures 15.7b and 15.7c show alignments of a small segment of mRNA (15.7b) and amino acid (15.7c) from all organisms queried. Note that Figure 15.7c shows the C-termini of the proteins, and colours indicate chemical similarities between the amino acids. Symbols beneath alignments are a shorthand to identify identical residues or similar chemical properties.

### 15.3c Gene Function May Be Determined Using Experiments That Alter the Expression of a Gene

The study of gene function by identifying changes in phenotypes is called **phenomics**. If a researcher can determine how the phenotype of a cell or organism is affected when the expression of a gene is turned off, or reduced significantly, functional properties of the encoded protein may be inferred. As a simple example, if cells grow larger, the gene may be involved in regulating cell size.

Two main kinds of manipulations are used to turn off or significantly reduce the expression of a gene in genome-scale experiments, gene knockout and gene knockdown:

1. *Gene knockout.* In this approach, researchers replace a normal gene on its chromosome with a defective gene that cannot express a functional protein. Usually, the replacement lacks the ORF that encodes the gene's protein product. In effect, this is a deletion mutation that has been engineered genetically. A deletion mutation is a *null mutation* because there is zero expression of the gene's protein product. For a haploid organism, there is only one copy of each gene to knock out, whereas in diploid organisms both copies of each gene must be knocked out. On a genomic scale, experimental manipulations can be done to knockout each gene systematically one by one. The phenotypic consequences of zero expression of each gene can then be ascertained. Major projects have been done, and are being done, to systematically knock out the function of each gene in the genomes of several organisms, including yeast, the fruit fly, the nematode worm, and the mouse. Techniques for making gene knockouts are described in Section 14.2c.

2. *Gene knockdown.* Knocking down a gene's expression can be done using RNA interference (RNAi). As discussed in Section 13.3, RNAi reduces the expression of a gene at the translation level. RNAi has been used to knock down gene expression of each of the approximately 20 000 genes of the nematode worm one by one. The advantage of RNAi in comparison to gene knockouts is that the decrease in function of a gene can be temporary.

### 15.3d Transcriptomics Determines When and Where Genes Are Transcribed

Some genes are transcribed in all cell types, whereas others are transcribed only when and where they are needed (Chapter 13).

Determining when and where genes are active can shed light on their function. For instance, a researcher might be interested in determining at a genomic scale the gene expression patterns in different cell types, at different stages of embryonic development, at different points of the cell division cycle, or in response to mutation or changes in the environment. A medical example is identifying gene expression differences between normal cells and cells that have become cancerous. The experimental analysis itself may be qualitative (analyzing whether or not genes are expressed) or quantitative (analyzing how the level of expression of genes varies).

The complete set of transcripts in a cell is called the **transcriptome**, and the study of the transcriptome is called **transcriptomics**. Note that a transcriptome refers only to those genes in a genome that are transcribed: it consists of a subset of information provided by a genome. You can think of the northern blot technique (Chapter 14, Section 14.2a) as providing one datum for the entire transcriptome.

Analysis of transcriptomes is done using high-throughput hybridization or, increasingly, by sequence-based approaches. A hybridization-based approach uses **DNA microarrays**, also called **DNA chips** (see the initial figure for this chapter). The surface of a DNA microarray is divided into a microscopic grid of about 60 000 spaces. On each space of the grid, a computerized system deposits a microscopic spot containing about 10 000 000 copies of a DNA anchor molecule that is about 20 nucleotides long.

DNA microarrays allow us to compare gene expression under a defined experimental condition compared with expression under the reference condition. The reference condition could be a control, such as cells in the absence of a drug treatment, or a cell line that you're comparing your experimental cells to. **Figure 15.8** shows how a DNA microarray could be used to compare gene expression patterns in normal cells and cancer cells in humans. mRNAs are isolated from each cell type, and cDNAs are made from them that incorporate fluorescent labels: green for one cDNA and red for the other. The two cDNAs are mixed and added to the DNA microarray, where they hybridize on microarray spots composed of complementary DNA probes. A laser excites the fluorescent labels and the resulting green and red fluorescence is detected and quantified. Researchers can identify which genes are expressed in the cells: green shows the first cDNA is most abundant, red the second, and yellow occurs when they are equal. This technique is semi-quantitative because the intensity of colours approximates the amount of gene expression between the two cell types (see Interpreting the Results in the figure).

Other methods of measuring gene transcription are possible, but you should get an idea of the power this provides researchers: the ability to measure the amount of expression from individual genes in the genome.

## 15.3e Proteomics Is the Characterization of All Expressed Proteins

Genome research also includes analysis of the proteins encoded by a genome because proteins are largely responsible for cell function and therefore for most of the functions of an organism. The term **proteome** has been coined to refer to the complete set of proteins that can be expressed by a particular cell. The proteome of a cell is a subset of the transcriptome: not every transcript created from the genome results in a protein. tRNA, rRNA, and a host of other RNA species do not encode proteins. And in fact, many mRNA transcripts are ignored by the cell or otherwise do not allow the complete production of their protein. This is normal.

The study of the proteins created by a cell type is the field of **proteomics**. The number of possible proteins encoded by the genome is larger than the number of protein-coding genes in the genome, particularly in eukaryotes. In eukaryotes, alternative splicing of gene transcripts and variation in protein processing mean that expression of a gene may yield more than one type of protein. Typically, the number of different proteins that an organism produces far exceeds the number of protein-coding genes.

**DETERMINING THE LOCATIONS OF PROTEINS IN CELLS** The location of a protein in a cell is important because it is key to its function. The cellular location of a protein can be studied by tagging the protein in some way and then visualizing the location of the tag microscopically. Different tags are used for visualization using light microscopy or electron microscopy. **Figure 15.9** shows the location of two proteins in a cell.

**IDENTIFYING INTERACTIONS AMONG PROTEINS** Many proteins function by interacting with other proteins. In some cases, proteins (actually polypeptides) interact to form the quaternary structure, and therefore the functional form, of a protein (see *The Purple Pages*). Many multipolypeptide proteins exist, and you have encountered several in this book. Consider the following:

- Hemoglobin is a four-polypeptide protein consisting of two α-globin polypeptides, two β-globin polypeptides, and four associated heme groups.
- RuBP carboxylase/oxygenase (Rubisco), the first enzyme of the light-independent reactions of photosynthesis (see Section 6.3), consists of eight copies of a large polypeptide and eight copies of a small polypeptide.
- The Lac repressor protein that controls the expression of the *lac* operon in *E. coli* (see Section 13.1) consists of four copies of the same polypeptide.

In other interactions among proteins, the interaction is not permanent but instead serves to modulate the function of one or more partners. For example, in Chapter 4 you were introduced to protein kinases, enzymes that transfer a phosphate group from ATP to one or more sites on particular target proteins as part of a signal transduction pathway. The phosphorylation of target proteins occurs as a result of the interaction between an enzymatic protein and each target protein. Once the target protein is phosphorylated, the two

FIGURE 15.8   **Research Method**

## DNA Microarray Analysis of Gene Expression Levels

**Purpose:** DNA microarrays can be used in various experiments, including comparing the levels of gene expression in two different tissues, as illustrated here. The power of the technique is that the entire set of genes in a genome can be analyzed simultaneously.

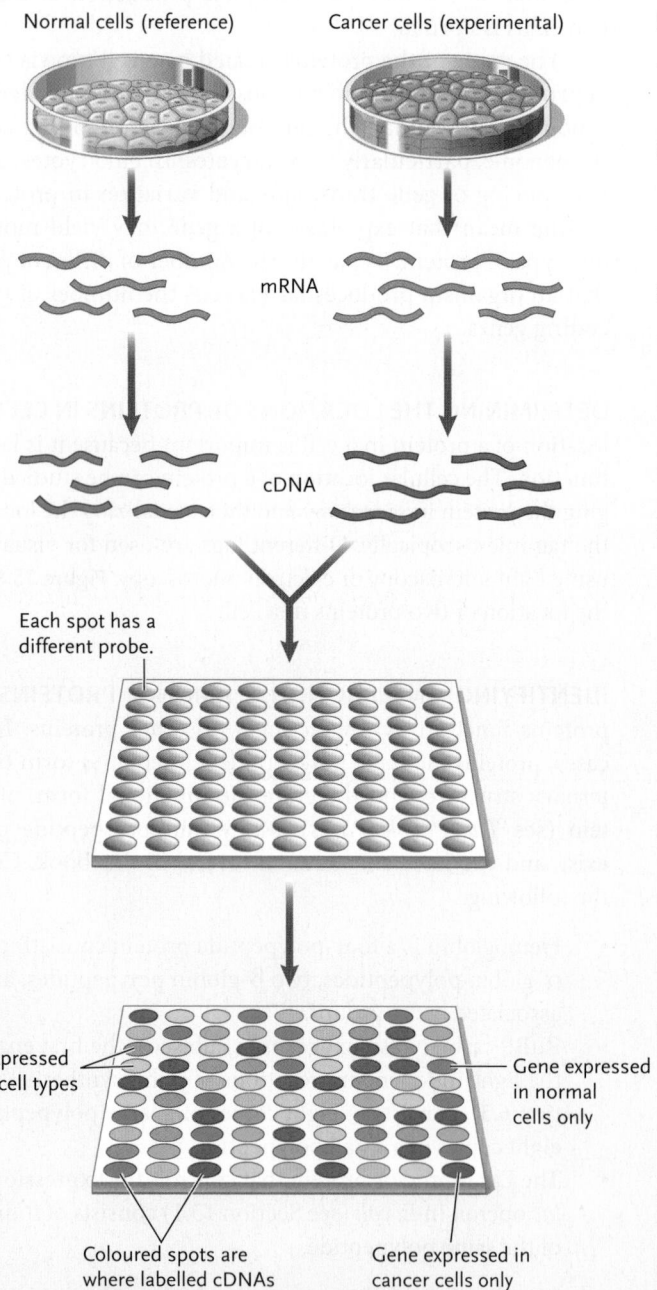

Normal cells (reference)     Cancer cells (experimental)

mRNA

cDNA

Each spot has a different probe.

Gene expressed in both cell types

Gene expressed in normal cells only

Gene expressed in cancer cells only

Coloured spots are where labelled cDNAs have hybridized.

© Cengage Learning 2017

**Protocol:**

1. Isolate mRNAs from a reference cell type (left, normal human cells) and an experimental cell type (right, human cancer cells).

2. Prepare cDNA libraries from each mRNA sample. For the normal cell (reference), the library uses nucleotides with a green fluorescent label, and for the cancer cell (experimental), library nucleotides with a red fluorescent label are used.

3. Denature the cDNAs to single strands, mix them, and pump them across the surface of a DNA microarray containing a set of single-stranded probes representing every protein-coding gene in the human genome. The DNA anchors are spotted on the surface, with each spot containing an anchor sequence for a different known gene. Allow the labelled cDNAs to hybridize with the anchors on the surface of the chip, and then wash off excess cDNAs.

4. Locate and quantify the fluorescence of the labels on the hybridized cDNAs with a laser detection system.

Actual DNA microarray result

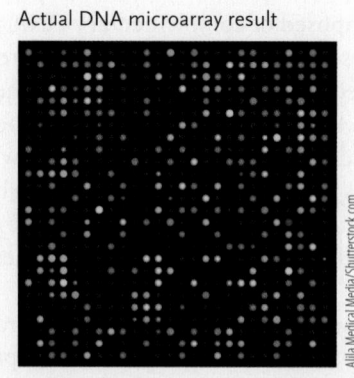

Alila Medical Media/Shutterstock.com

**Interpreting the Results:** The coloured spots on the microarray indicate where the labelled cDNAs have bound to the DNA anchors attached to the chip and therefore which genes were active in normal and/or cancer cells. Moreover, we can quantify the gene expression in the two cell types by the colour detected. A purely green spot indicates that the gene was active in the normal cell but not in the cancer cell. A purely red spot indicates that the gene was active in the cancer cell but not in the normal cell. A yellow spot indicates that the gene was equally active in the two cell types. Fluorescent intensities tell us the relative levels of gene expression in the two cell types. For this particular experiment, we would be able to see how many genes have altered expression in the cancer cells, and exactly how their expression was changed.

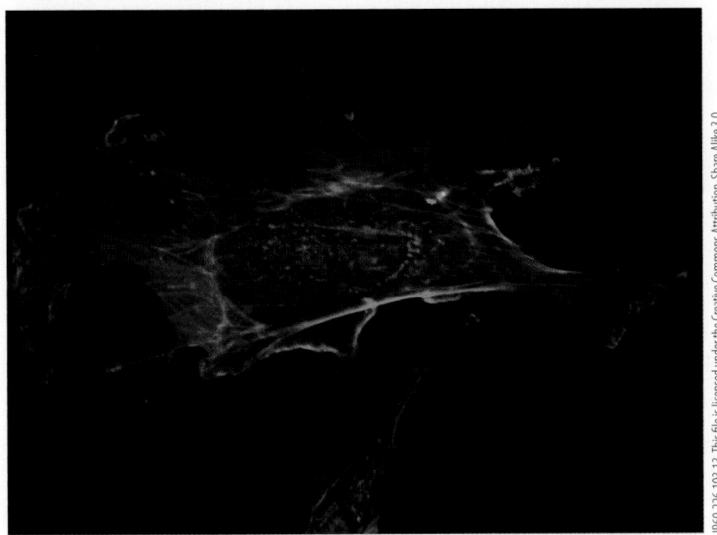

**FIGURE 15.9 Fluorescent tags can show the cellular locations of specific proteins.** Red fluorophores attach to mitochondria and green are attached to antibodies that bind actin. A blue dye shows the position of the nucleus, but it is not a protein-binding stain.

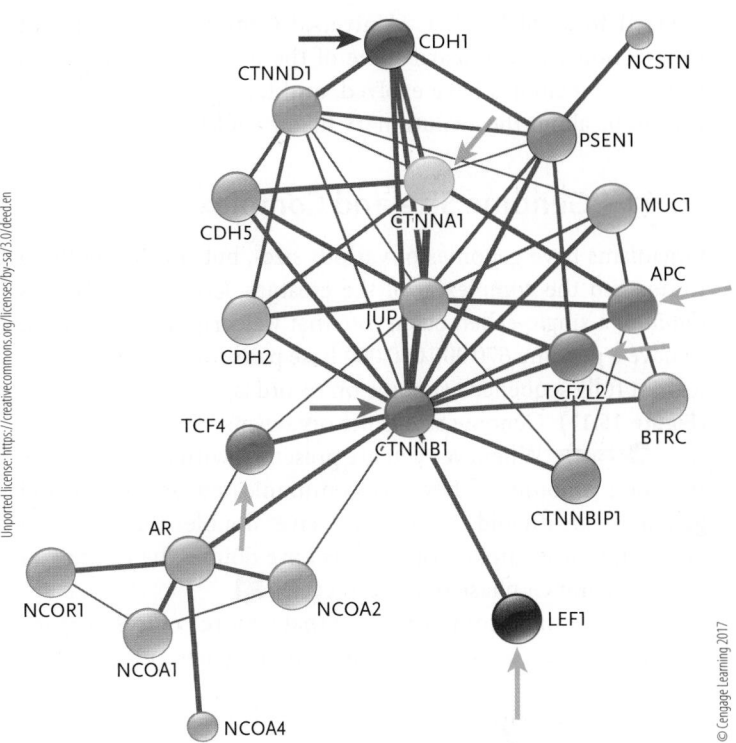

**FIGURE 15.10 The protein-interaction network for human β-catenin (CTNNB1; red arrow), which coordinates many other proteins such as α-catenin (orange arrow) and E-cadherin (green arrow), along with cell-signalling entities (pink arrows).** Thicker lines show stronger associations between proteins.

proteins no longer interact. Proteins never work in isolation: they are members of complex networks that allow them to function properly.

Thousands of interactions have been identified experimentally for a variety of organisms. Protein-interaction networks are constructed using arrays of interactions identified experimentally. These interactions inform us about the details and complexities of the functions of proteins in cells. **Figure 15.10** shows part of a protein-interaction network centred on the human protein β-catenin (cadherin-associated protein; the central CTNNB1 sphere in the figure). α-catenin (CTNNA1) links to E-cadherin (CDH1) in epithelial adherens junctions (a type of cell junction; see Section 2.5). β-catenin also plays a key role in a signalling pathway that is important, for example, in regulating how cell fate is decided during development. Interactions with, for example, APC, LEF1, TCF4, and TCF7L2 (pink arrows) occur as part of that signalling pathway's operation.

**STUDY BREAK QUESTIONS**

1. What kinds of sequences are identified by annotation?
2. How does a gene family evolve?
3. What are the basic principles for creating an alignment score?
4. What are the ways by which the function of a gene identified in a genome sequence may be assigned?
5. What molecules might differ between a reference cell line and an experimental cell line?
6. What is the proteome, and what are the major goals of proteomics?

## 15.4 Comparative Genomics Can Reveal How Genes and Genomes Evolved

Genes in present-day genomes originated from ancestral genomes of organisms that lived millions to billions of years ago. We can trace their evolutionary history by comparing genomes of different groups of present-day organisms. From these comparisons, we can estimate when new genes first appeared in ancient organisms, describe how they changed over time, and gain insights into what molecular processes caused new genes to evolve in the first place.

Comparative genomics has shown that some genes are found in the genomes of almost all present-day organisms. Examples are genes involved in core biological processes like transcription and protein synthesis, including genes for some subunits of RNA polymerase, genes for many of the proteins that make up part of the structure of a ribosome, and most of the aminoacyl–tRNA synthetase enzymes that attach amino acids to tRNA molecules. The proteins coded for by these genes not only perform similar functions in every organism, they are also related evolutionarily. This is strong evidence that all the genes in the genomes of all contemporary organisms can be traced back to a single-celled type of organism sometimes referred to as *LUCA* (Last Universal Common Ancestor). In this section you will learn some of the mechanisms by which genes and genomes have evolved, and how genome sequences inform us about the evolutionary history of life.

## 15.4a Genome Size and Complexity

Organisms have genomes of various sizes, but this has nothing to do with the complexity of the creature. Consider *Polychaos dubium*, a single-celled eukaryote that was originally estimated to have a genome 670 000 000 000 base pairs long (670 Gb). The longest fully sequenced genome on record is for the loblolly pine **(Figure 15.11)**. Genome size is the organism's "**C-value**."

**CONCEPT FIX** Whenever you are presented with a genome size, the total amount of DNA is communicated as the haploid genome, so diploid organisms have double the reported amount; that is, diploid organisms have double the C-value of DNA (during $G_1$ phase of the cell cycle).

It seems to be common sense that a more complex organism such as, say, a fish, should have more genes and therefore a larger genome than a plant; however, Figure 15.11 clearly shows that C-values can vary by several orders of magnitude within a given taxonomic group. **Table 15.1** shows that genome sizes for relatively less complex organisms overlap or exceed those of relatively complex organisms. This observation has been called the "C-value enigma": How do we explain wildly different genome sizes for related organisms of similar complexity? Why would one species of frog have 100 times more DNA in its genome than another species of frog? Why do many unicellular organisms have genomes of greater size than that of whales? It should be apparent now that we cannot just count the bases or the genes in an organism to determine how complex it is.

## 15.4b Bacterial Versus Human Genome Structure

Typical prokaryotic cells have the simplest genome structure: only a few thousand genes, with codes in relatively little DNA, arrayed around a single circular chromosome. This arrangement

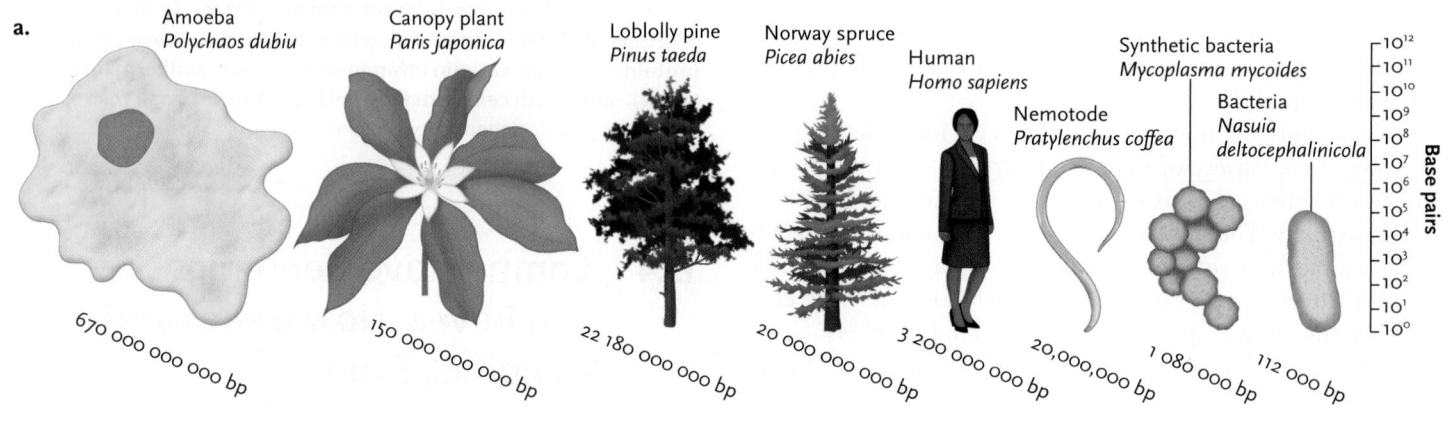

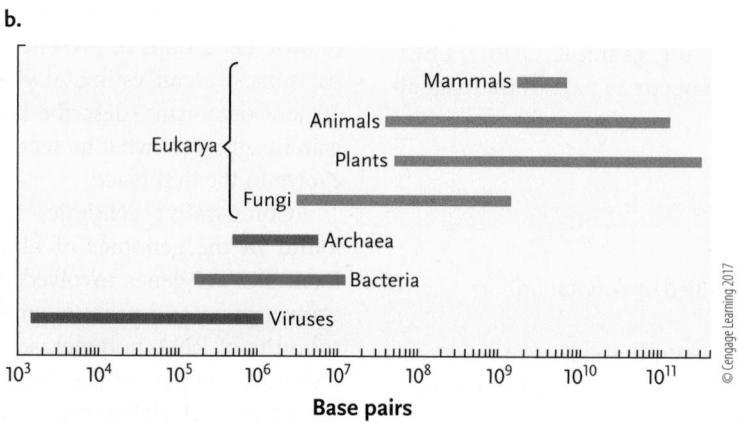

**FIGURE 15.11 Genome sizes chosen from a variety of organisms. (a)** A ranking of large-to-small genomes in selected organisms (note the logarithmic scale). Although humans are found near the middle at ~3.2 billion bases (Gb) in the haploid genome, that genome is approximately 200 times smaller than the estimated size of *Polychaos dubium* (290 Gb). **(b)** Ranges of genome sizes for viruses, bacteria, archaea, and eukaryotes. (Note that the Domain Archaea has not been studied as extensively as the Domain Bacteria, so there may be representatives with substantially larger or smaller genomes than the range given.)

Source: (a) Based on Anna Perman, "The world's largest sequenced genome is just the start," BioMed Central, http://blogs.biomedcentral.com/on-biology/2014/03/20/worlds-largest-sequenced-genome-unlocking-the-loblolly-pine/

## TABLE 15.1 — Genome Sizes and Estimated Number of Protein-Coding Genes for Selected Members of Domains Bacteria, Archaea, and Eukarya

| Domain and Organism | Genome Size (millions of base pairs, Mb) | Protein-Coding Genes |
|---|---|---|
| **Bacteria** | | |
| *Mycoplasma genitalium* | 0.58 | 475 |
| *Escherichia coli* | 4.6 | 4146 |
| **Archaea** | | |
| *Thermoplasma acidophilum* | 1.56 | 1484 |
| *Methanosarcina acetivorans* | 5.75 | 4540 |
| **Eukarya** | | |
| Protists | | |
| *Tetrahymena thermophila* (a ciliated protist) | 146 | > 20000 |
| Fungi | | |
| *Saccharomyces cerevisiae* (a budding yeast) | 12.1 | ~ 6000 |
| *Neurospora crassa* (orange bread mould) | 40 | ~ 10100 |
| Plants | | |
| *Arabidopsis thaliana* (thale cress) | 120 | ~ 26000 |
| *Oryza sativa* (rice) | 411 | ~ 56000 |
| *Capsicum annum* (hot pepper) | ~ 3480 | ~ 34500 |
| *Pinus taeda* (loblolly pine) | ~ 23200 | ~ 50000 |
| Invertebrates | | |
| *Caenorhabditis elegans* (a nematode worm) | 100 | ~ 20000 |
| *Drosophila melanogaster* (fruit fly) | 165 | ~ 13700 |
| *Locusta migratoria* (swarming locust) | 6500 | ~ 17300 |
| Vertebrates | | |
| *Takifugu rubripes* (pufferfish) | 393 | ~ 27000 |
| *Mus musculus* (mouse) | 2600 | ~ 22000 |
| *Homo sapiens* (human) | 3200 | ~ 20500 |

is in contrast to typical eukaryotic organisms that have tens of thousands of genes amid billions of "extra" base pairs organized on several separate linear chromosomes.

**PROFILE OF THE *E. COLI* GENOME** *E. coli* is the most intensively studied model organism. The K12 strain in particular is considered a typical bacterial genome, with the vast majority of its genes on a single circular molecule with one origin of replication (**Figure 15.12a**) and the remainder of its genes on one or more plasmids, each of which is much smaller than the circular chromosome. With about 4.6 Mb and about 4146 protein-coding genes, the *E. coli* K12 genome is in the middle range, size-wise, of bacterial genomes. The noncoding genes are those for rRNAs and tRNAs. There are a small number of transposable elements and repetitive sequences.

Figure 15.12b shows a close-up of a 10 kb segment of the *E. coli* genome containing a number of protein-coding genes to illustrate the following characteristics:

- The genes are close together, with little space between them. Promoters for the genes are located immediately upstream of each transcription unit (not shown in the figure).
- Some of the genes are transcribed using the bottom strand as the template, whereas the others are transcribed using the top strand as the template.
- The genes vary in length, reflecting the lengths of their encoded proteins.

**CONCEPT FIX** Look carefully at Figure 15.12, noticing that some genes are shown in blue and some in orange. Although you may have assumed that one particular strand of the double helix is used as the template (i.e., read by RNA polymerase) for all genes on a chromosome, the figure shows this assumption to be false. One strand of the helix is used as a template for some genes (such as the blue genes in Figure 15.12), and the other strand is used as a template for other genes (the orange genes in Figure 15.12). Recall that templates have to be read $3' \rightarrow 5'$, so, in Figure 15.12, the blue genes are using the bottom strand as their template. ⬡

**Table 15.2** summarizes some of what has been learned about the *E. coli* K12 genome to date with respect to its physical aspects, genes, and gene products.

Other bacterial genomes may be larger or smaller than the *E. coli* K12 genome, but their genome landscapes are similar to that of *E. coli* in several ways. For example, typically, there is one origin of replication, 85%–92% of the DNA codes for proteins, there is a mixture of operons and single-gene transcription units, genes that are transcribed using one DNA strand as the template do not usually overlap others transcribed using the other strand, and there are relatively few transposable elements or repetitive sequences.

**PROFILE OF THE HUMAN GENOME** At about 3.2 billion base pairs, the human genome is about 700 times as long as the *E. coli* genome. Each human individual has 23 pairs of chromosomes. Men have 24 different chromosomes, the 22 autosomes and the

**a. Map of the circular *E. coli* K12 genome showing the genes transcribed clockwise (blue) and the genes transcribed counter-clockwise (orange) and the location of the origin of replication**

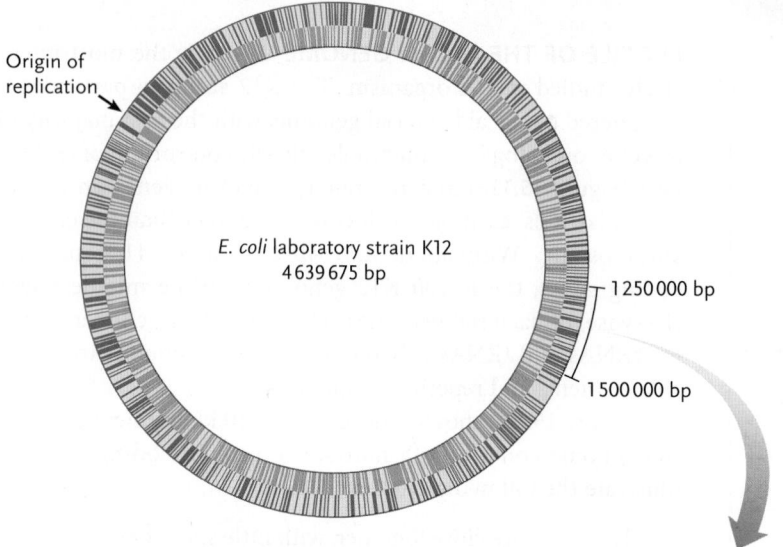

**b. Detail of a 10 kb region of the *E. coli* K12 genome, from about 3:30 on the genome "clock"**

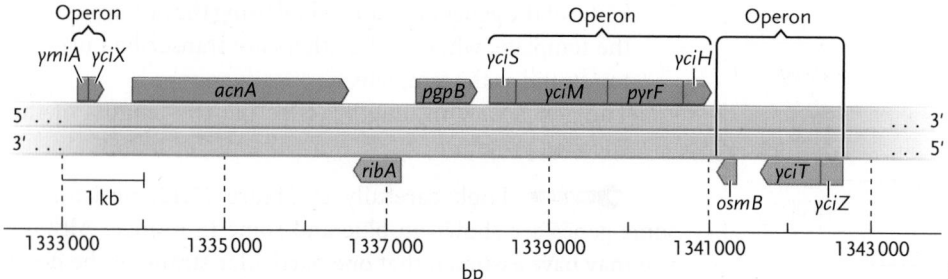

**FIGURE 15.12 The genome of *E. coli*, laboratory strain K12.** Some genes are single transcription units, whereas others are organized into operons (Chapter 13). In the genome as a whole, about one-half of protein-coding genes are organized into operons.

© Cengage Learning 2017

its complement. For the segment shown in Figure 15.13b, both genes happen to be transcribed from the same strand.

- Eukaryotic genes are single transcription units; very rarely are they organized in operons.

Table 15.2 summarizes details of *E. coli* and human genes and genomes. Some of the key features of the human genome are as follows:

- There are about 20 500 protein-coding genes with, on average, 8 exons per gene. This ranges from zero to 100 exons. Exons are only 5% of the ORF, so introns represent about 20%–25% of the entire human genome.

- Each gene averages 20 regulatory sequences for expression. These are distributed over 1000–10 000 base pairs upstream and downstream of each gene, as well as within introns. The sequences encompass 15%–25% of the human genome.

- There are about 12 000 genes that do not encode proteins. They include genes for rRNA, tRNA, snRNA, miRNA, and lncRNA (see Chapters 12 and 13).

- There are thousands of pseudogenes.

- Viral sequences that have inserted into the human genome total nearly 10% of it.

- Forty-five percent of the genome consists of transposable element sequences. Only a tiny fraction of the genome is functionally active.

- Scattered throughout the rest of the chromosome are a variety of short repeated sequences, including centromeres and telomeres.

- Hundreds to thousands of origins of replication per chromosome are in the long, linear eukaryotic chromosomes. There are no consistent, sequence-specific replication origins as in bacteria and yeast.

**CONCEPT FIX** Stop for a moment to total up the previous information about the composition of your genome. Notice that over half of your DNA sequence is transposable elements and viruses that are, or once were, mobile. Although these sequences may well contain genes, they are not coding for human proteins and are often referred to as "**junk DNA.**" Add in the thousands of pseudogenes, introns, and nonessential repetitive sequences and you may be surprised to realize that junk DNA exceeds 90% of your entire genome. ⬡

X and Y chromosomes, whereas women have 23 different chromosomes, the 22 autosomes and the X chromosome. **Figure 15.13a** displays a complete set of human chromosomes, depicting the banding patterns that help researchers identify regions of chromosomes. (Figure 7.12 shows the banding patterns of stained human chromosomes.) Figure 15.13b shows chromosome 6 in more detail and a close-up of a 100 kb segment of the long arm of that chromosome to show the protein-coding genes it contains. Compare this figure with Figure 15.12b, which shows a 10 kb segment of the *E. coli* chromosome, and note the following:

- Eukaryotic genes are farther apart: even though the human genome segment in Figure 15.13b is 10 times as long as the *E. coli* segment shown in Figure 15.12b, it contains only 2 genes. Eukaryotic genes are also longer than those in *E. coli* because they consist of about 95% introns and 5% exons. The right-hand gene in Figure 15.13b illustrates at the DNA level the alternative splicing variants (Section 13.3) for that gene. The different exons for the three gene drawings are shown in pink.

- As in all genomes, some genes are transcribed from one strand of the double helix, and the others are transcribed from

| TABLE 15.2 | Comparison of the *E. coli* K12 and Human Genomes | |
|---|---|---|
| Property | *E. coli* K12 genome | *H. sapiens* genome |
| Chromosomes | 1 circular (plus plasmids) | 23 linear (pairs in diploid cells)* |
| Nucleotides | 4.64 Mb | 3 200 Mb |
| Protein-coding genes | 4 146 | ~ 20 500 |
| Non–protein-coding genes | 176 | ~ 12 000 |
| % coding DNA | 88% | 1.2% |
| Protein-coding genes/Mb | 894 | 7 |
| Average introns/gene | 0 | 8 |
| Average polypeptide length | 330 amino acids | 430 amino acids |

\* There are 24 different human chromosomes: 22 autosomes and the X and Y chromosomes. Each individual has 23 pairs of chromosomes.

## 15.4c Introns and Transposable Genetic Elements Are Agents of Genome Evolution

**INTRONS** You will recall from Chapter 12 that eukaryotic gene sequences often contain introns, sequences that, although transcribed, are "spliced out" before translation. Chapter 12 explained how nucleoprotein machines called *spliceosomes* perform the precise cutting and rejoining of mRNA needed to remove introns while preserving the intended coding sequence of the gene. Table 15.2 shows that one of the most significant differences between the genomes of a typical bacterium, such as *E. coli,* and a typical eukaryote, such as humans, is the absence of these spliceosomal introns in bacteria.

Although bacterial genomes do occasionally contain types of introns called *Group I* and *Group II*, bacteria do not have spliceosomes; these introns splice themselves. Most researchers now agree that Group II introns were likely present in the genome of the proteobacteria that participated in endosymbiosis early in evolution to give rise to the mitochondria of modern eukaryotes (Chapter 2). Once inside eukaryotic cells, the Group II introns transferred to the host genome, where they eventually came under the control of spliceosomes. One of the characteristics that help to explain differences in genome size among modern

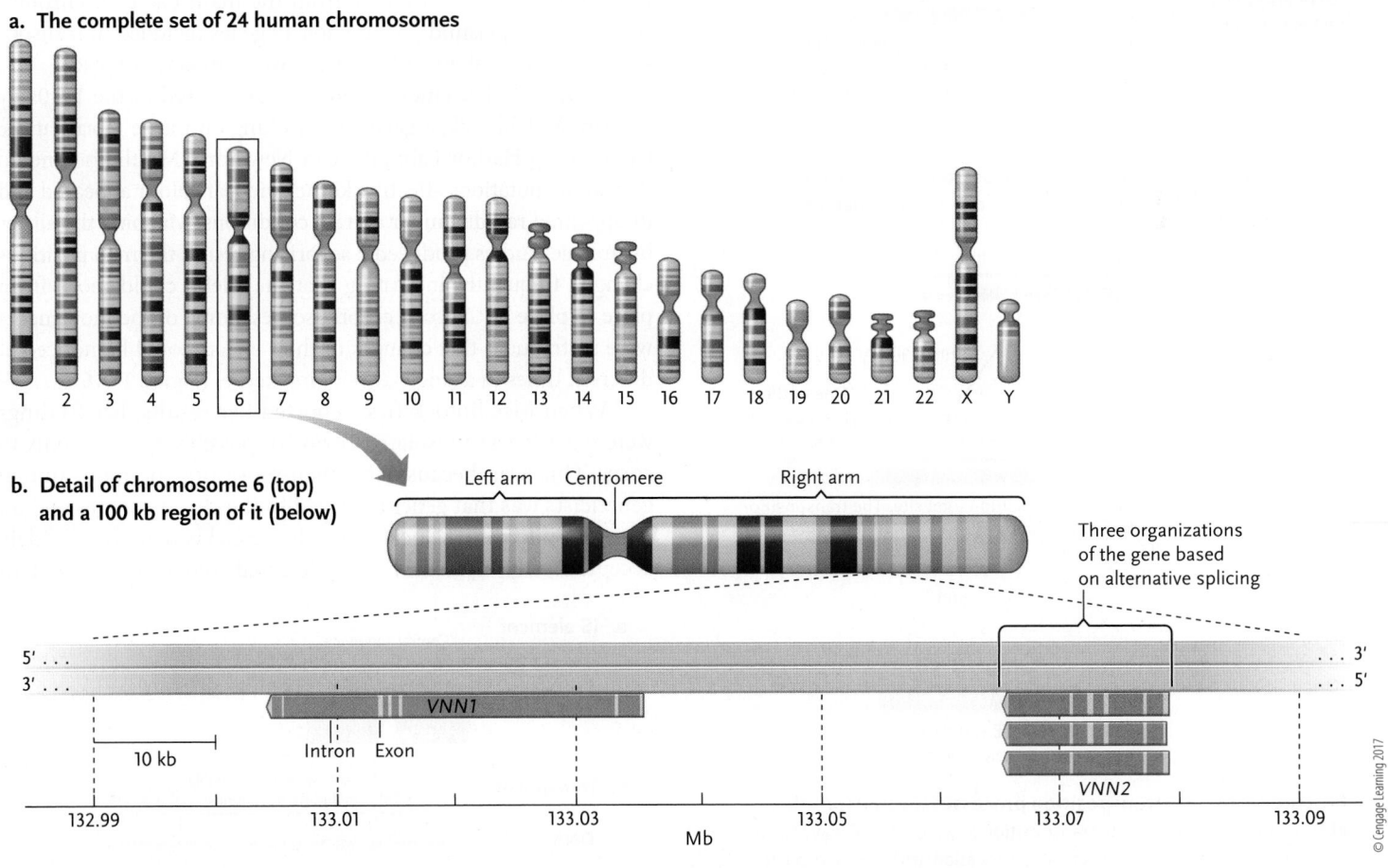

**a. The complete set of 24 human chromosomes**

1 2 3 4 5 6 7 8 9 10 11 12 13 14 15 16 17 18 19 20 21 22 X Y

**b. Detail of chromosome 6 (top) and a 100 kb region of it (below)**

Left arm   Centromere   Right arm

Three organizations of the gene based on alternative splicing

5′ . . .   . . . 3′
3′ . . .   . . . 5′

*VNN1*

10 kb   Intron   Exon   *VNN2*

132.99   133.01   133.03   133.05   133.07   133.09

Mb

© Cengage Learning 2017

**FIGURE 15.13  The human genome. (a)** Chromosomes are sorted in order from smallest to largest in the karyotype. A small region of chromosome 6 is shown in **(b)** and demonstrates two genes, the second of which has alternate splicing arrangements.

eukaryotes is differences in the amount of intron sequences in different lineages.

**TRANSPOSABLE GENETIC ELEMENTS** All organisms contain particular segments of DNA that can move from one place to another within a genome. These elements are known by the term **transposable elements (TEs)**, and their movement is called **transposition**. Transposition usually occurs at a low frequency in either of two ways, depending on the type of element: (1) a cut-and-paste process in which the TE leaves its original location and transposes to a new target location (**Figure 15.14a**), and (2) a copy-and-paste process in which a copy of a TE transposes to a new location, leaving the original TE behind (Figure 15.14b). Transposable elements

**a. Non replicative, cut-and-paste transposition.** The transposable element (TE) leaves one location in the DNA and moves to a new location.

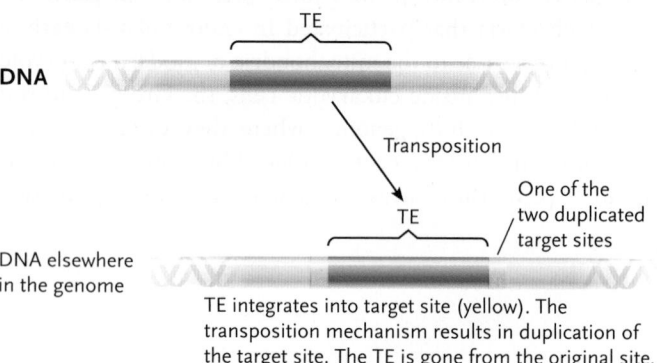

**b. Replicative, copy-and-paste transposition.** A copy of the TE moves to a new location, leaving the original TE behind.

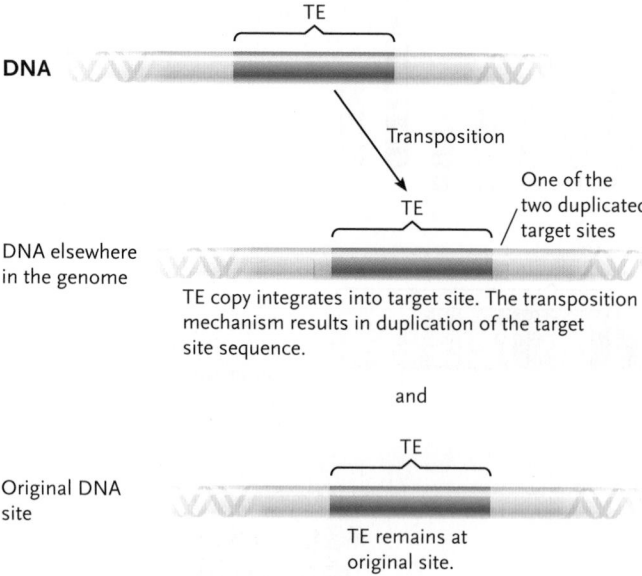

**FIGURE 15.14 Two transposition processes for transposable elements.** (a) Cut-and-paste transposition in which the TE leaves one location in the DNA and moves to a new location. (b) Copy-and-paste transposition in which a copy of the TE moves to a new location, leaving the original TE behind.

are important because of the genetic changes they cause. For example, they produce mutations by transposing into genes and knocking out their functions, and they increase or decrease gene expression by transposing into regulatory sequences of genes. As such, TEs are biological mutagens that increase genetic variability. Over millions of years of copy-and-paste transposition, TEs can accumulate to significant proportions of the genome.

Although transposable elements were first discovered in eukaryotes, we begin our description with **insertion sequences (ISs)** and **transposons**, the two types of elements found in bacteria. Insertion sequences are the simplest TEs. They are relatively small and contain only genes for their transposition, notably the gene for **transposase**, an enzyme that catalyzes some of the recombination reactions for inserting or removing the TE from the DNA (**Figure 15.15**). At each of the two ends of an IS is a short **inverted repeat** sequence, the same DNA sequence running in opposite directions (shown by directional arrows in the figure). The inverted repeat sequences enable the transposase enzyme to identify the ends of the TE when it catalyzes transposition.

The second type of bacterial TE, called a *transposon*, has an inverted repeat sequence at each end enclosing a central region with one or more genes. In a number of bacterial transposons, the inverted repeat sequences are insertion sequences, which provide the transposase for movement of the element (see Figure 15.15). Additional genes in the central region typically code for antibiotic resistance; they can originate from the main bacterial chromosome or from plasmids. These non-IS genes included in transposons are carried along as the TEs move from place to place.

Transposable elements were first discovered in the 1940s by Barbara McClintock, a geneticist working on maize (corn) at the Cold Spring Harbor Laboratory in New York. McClintock noted that some mutations affecting kernel and leaf colour appeared and disappeared rapidly under certain conditions. Mapping the alleles by linkage studies produced a surprising result: the map positions changed frequently, indicating that the alleles could move from place to place in the corn chromosomes. Some of the movements were so frequent that changes in their effects could be noticed at different times in a single developing kernel (**Figure 15.16**).

When McClintock first reported her results, her findings were regarded as an isolated curiosity, possibly applying only to corn. This was because the then-prevailing opinion among geneticists was that genes are fixed in the chromosomes and do not move to other locations. Her conclusions were widely accepted only after TEs were detected and characterized in

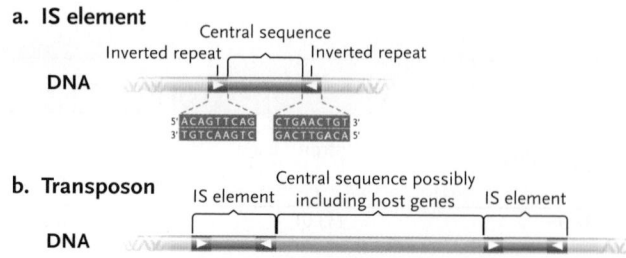

**FIGURE 15.15 Types of bacterial TEs.** (a) IS element. (b) Transposon in which the central sequence is transposed by flanking IS elements

**FIGURE 15.16 Barbara McClintock and corn kernels showing different colour patterns due to the movement of transposable elements.** As TEs move into or out of genes controlling pigment production in developing kernels, the ability of cells and their descendants to produce the dark pigment is destroyed or restored. The result is patterns of pigmented and colourless (yellow) segments in individual kernels.

bacteria in the 1960s. By the 1970s, further examples of TEs were discovered in other eukaryotes, including yeast and mammals. McClintock was awarded a Nobel Prize in 1983.

Eukaryotic TEs fall into two major classes, *DNA transposons* and *retrotransposons,* distinguished by the way the TE sequence moves in the genome:

- **DNA transposons** are TEs that transpose using a DNA intermediate. In most cases, movement of a DNA transposon is by a nonreplicative, cut-and-paste mechanism. A gene for transposase, an enzyme that catalyzes the reactions inserting or removing the TE from DNA, is in the central region of the transposon. Most DNA transposons have *inverted repeat sequences*—the same DNA sequence oriented in opposite directions—at their ends that enable the transposase to recognize the boundaries of the TE for transposition.

- **Retrotransposons** are TEs that transpose using a replicative, copy-and-paste mechanism but, unlike DNA transposons, their transposition occurs via an intermediate RNA copy of the TE (**Figure 15.17**).

Genomic analysis has shown that eukaryotic genomes vary considerably in the TEs they contain. For example, some research studies have revealed the extraordinary fact that about 42% of the human genome consists of retrotransposons, some of which are still active in transposition today. DNA transposons constitute about 3% of the human genome but, as is the case in other primates, none of them is capable of transposition. In corn (*Zea mays*), almost 85% of the genome consists of transposon sequences, the majority of which are retrotransposons. In less-complex eukaryotes, the percentage of transposons comprising the genome is much lower, for example about 5% in chicken, about 26% in zebrafish, about 10% in *Drosophila,* and about 9% in the worm *C. elegans.* The compact genome of pufferfish contains very few transposons. Interestingly, there is an approximate positive correlation between genome size and the percentage of the genome consisting of transposable element

sequences. The inescapable conclusion is that the presence and activity of transposable elements in genomes have played important roles in generating the structures of genomes during genome evolution.

Comparative genomics has also been applied to understanding human evolution. (Human evolution is discussed in Chapter 20.) The human genome was the first mammalian genome sequenced, and researchers now have hundreds of human genomes to compare to discover what makes us human and what is responsible for human variation. We also have well over 100 other mammalian genomes to compare with the human genome. These include genomes of primate species that are closely related to humans, such as the common chimpanzee and the mountain gorilla, as well as less closely related mammals, such as cows and the duck-billed platypus. Comparing the human genome with those of other organisms reveals common features. Human and chimpanzee genomes are strikingly similar, with 96% identical base pairs across the entire genome. In fact, there is more genetic diversity between individual chimpanzees in a single forest than there is between any two humans on Earth.

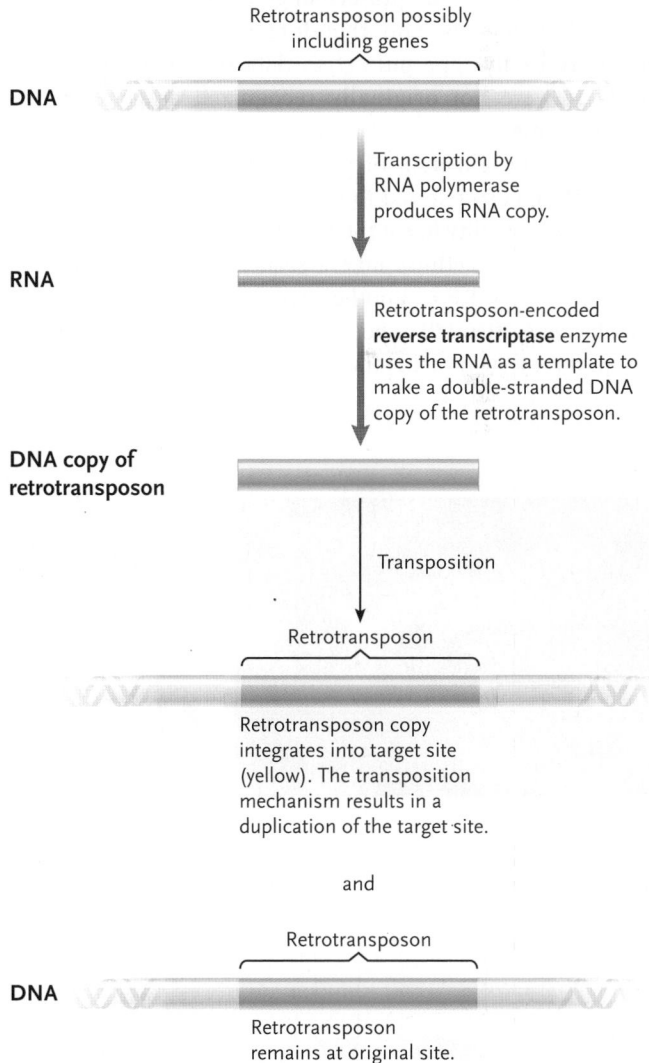

**FIGURE 15.17 Transposition of a eukaryotic retrotransposon to a new location by means of an intermediate RNA copy**

Comparative genomics also provides information about how the arrangement of genes on chromosomes has evolved. Nondisjunction in meiosis can cause entire chromosomes to be duplicated (Figure 10.12), and there is evidence that eukaryotic diversity was dramatically increased through a whole-genome duplication. The pufferfish (*Tetraodon nigroviridis*) was chosen for complete sequencing in 2004 because it is a vertebrate with a relatively small genome (342 Mb). The *Tetraodon* genome project revealed evidence of a complete genome duplication and rearrangement in its evolutionary history. This duplication created **paralogous chromosomes (Figure 15.18)**. Rearrangements can be detected by looking for repeated patterns in the genome. Nucleotide patterns can show paralogous genes, and even the sequence and types of genes are preserved during the rearrangement. Think of a poorly shuffled deck of cards. Although the sequence of cards is different after the shuffle, many card sequences are largely preserved, although they are in different places in the deck. These patterns of genes are called **syntenies**. Syntenies reveal ancestral evolutionary connections. Compared to other eukaryotic genomes, the pufferfish genome contains very few junk DNA sequences and therefore shows the location of genes more easily. The pufferfish data revealed around 900 genes that were not originally recognized as genes in the human genome.

Another phenomenon of genetic rearrangement is that of exon shuffling (also referred to in Section 12.3c). Because transposons have the ability to cut themselves out of DNA and reinsert elsewhere, they sometimes take a sequence from an ORF and place it into the ORF of another gene. The junctions between exons of a gene often fall at points between motifs in a protein—those parts of a protein that carry out specific biological processes. This creates opportunities to mix-and-match functions—new areas for membrane binding, ATP synthesis, or even connecting to other proteins create possibilities for natural selection. Genomic analysis can help identify these events. If a newly sequenced gene of unknown function has a domain characteristic of a similar domain in another gene, it's possible to imagine a hypothetical gene function, even in the absence of directly analyzing the protein!

**PULLING IT TOGETHER** This chapter has looked at how DNA sequences are determined and how they are assembled to represent the genome of an organism. We have examined how gene identities can be inferred based on the sequences of already studied genes in other organisms, and we have noted that the structure of a genome can give clues regarding the origin of genes and genomes. To finish up, consider again the globin gene family, but also with a gene for leghemoglobin (**Figure 15.19**). The prefix "*leg*" is short for *legume*, a plant capable of fixing nitrogen through a symbiotic relationship with bacteria. Fixing nitrogen is an energy-intensive process (Chapter 37, Section 37.3e), and oxygen can disrupt unstable intermediates during fixation. Leghemoglobin, like other globins, reversibly binds oxygen. In an action opposite to that of hemoglobin or myoglobin, it is used to *remove* oxygen from a specific place, rather than oxygenate it.

In Figure 15.19a, a new branch is added to the tree shown in Figure 15.6 to represent divergence of leghemoglobin. Because of the ancient origin of leghemoglobins, they appear rather different from the myoglobins and β-hemoglobins shown in the list (note how they appear between hemoglobin and myoglobin in Figure 15.19b). Despite these differences, leucine, histidine, and lysine residues match up in very similar locations. A gap (indicated by a dash) shows that amino acids

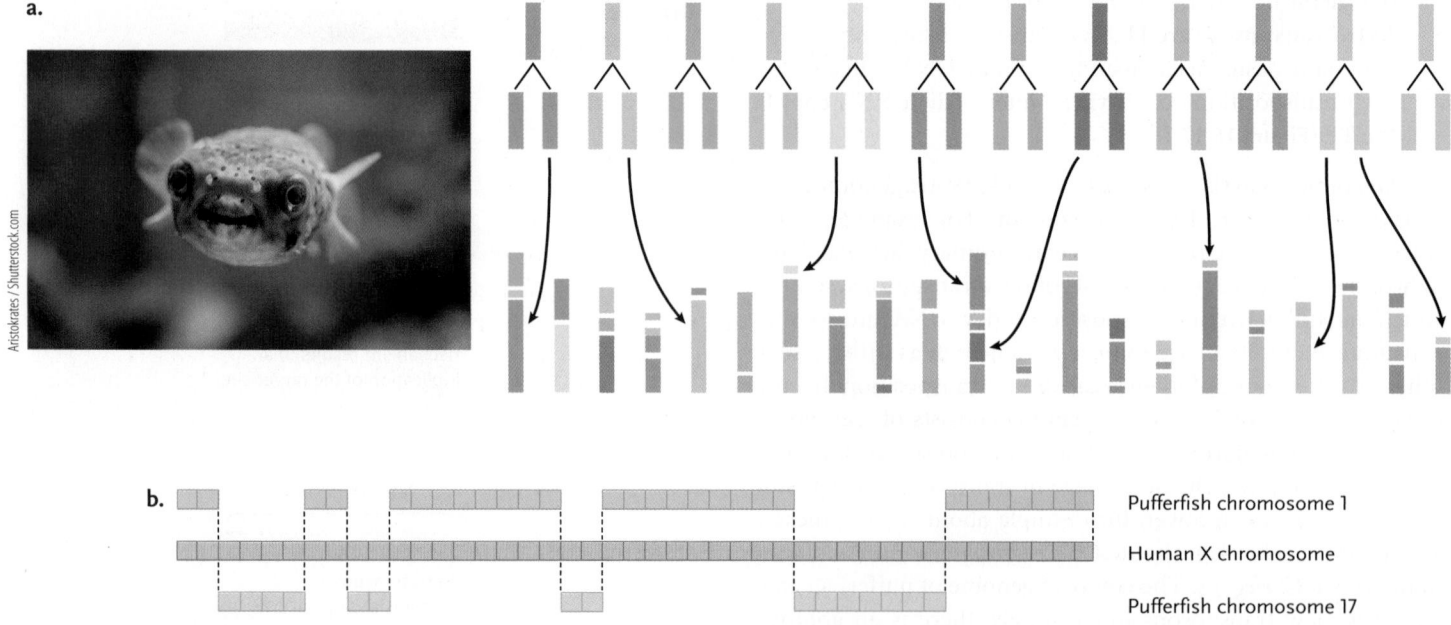

**FIGURE 15.18** **(a)** The genome of *Tetraodon* (pufferfish) is the result of ancestral duplication and rearrangement of an ancestral fish genome. **(b)** Orthologous genes line up in syntenic blocks, showing that the human X chromosome consists of similar gene patterns identified on pufferfish chromosomes 1 and 17.

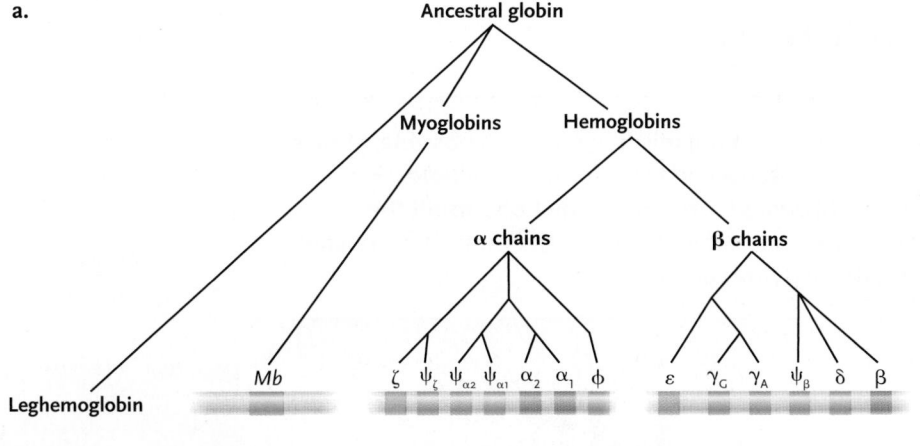

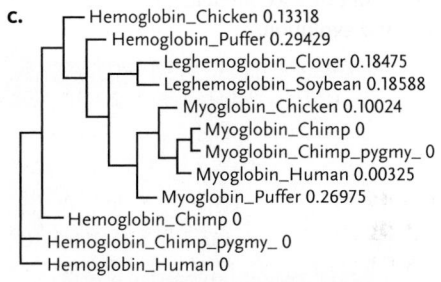

**a.**

Ancestral globin

Myoglobins    Hemoglobins

α chains      β chains

Leghemoglobin     *Mb*    ζ ψ$_ζ$ ψ$_{α2}$ ψ$_{α1}$ α$_2$ α$_1$ φ    ε γ$_G$ γ$_A$ ψ$_β$ δ β

**b.**

| | |
|---|---|
| Hemoglobin_Chimp | TLSELHCDKLHVDPENFRLLGNVLVCVLAH |
| Hemoglobin_Chimp_pygmy_ | TLSELHCDKLHVDPENFRLLGNVLVCVLAH |
| Hemoglobin_Human | TLSELHCDKLHVDPENFRLLGNVLVCVLAH |
| Hemoglobin_Puffer | ELSELHSEKLHVDPDNFKLLSDCLTIVVAT |
| Leghemoglobin_Clover | TLGIVHTQKGVVGP-HFTVVKEALLKTIKE |
| Leghemoglobin_Soybean | ALGSVHAQKAVTDP-QFVVVKEALLKTIKA |
| Myoglobin_Chicken | PLAQTHATKHKIPVKYLEFISEVIIKVIAE |
| Myoglobin_Chimp | PLAQSHATKHKIPVKYLEFISECIIQVLHS |
| Myoglobin_Chimp_pygmy_ | PLAQSHATKHKIPVKYLEFISECIIQVLHS |
| Myoglobin_Human | PLAQSHATKHKIPVKYLEFISECIIQVLQS |
| Myoglobin_Puffer | PLANTHATKHKIPINNFKLIAEVIGKVMEE |
| | *. * *    : .: : : .: |

**c.**

Hemoglobin_Chicken 0.13318
Hemoglobin_Puffer 0.29429
Leghemoglobin_Clover 0.18475
Leghemoglobin_Soybean 0.18588
Myoglobin_Chicken 0.10024
Myoglobin_Chimp 0
Myoglobin_Chimp_pygmy_ 0
Myoglobin_Human 0.00325
Myoglobin_Puffer 0.26975
Hemoglobin_Chimp 0
Hemoglobin_Chimp_pygmy_ 0
Hemoglobin_Human 0

**FIGURE 15.19 Evolutionary paths taken from an ancestral globin in a hypothetical concestor to plants and animals. (a)** Leghemoglobin, a plant protein, separated earliest. Myoglobin and hemoglobin took the other path, and the hemoglobins diverged further. An alignment of representative β-hemoglobin, myoglobin, and leghemoglobin are shown in **(b)**. Note how β-hemoglobin, leghemoglobins, and myoglobins cluster naturally. In **(c)** is a cladogram showing one possibility of genetic relatedness. The leghemoglobins are most similar to each other, as are the myoglobins of the animals, particularly primate myoglobins. This cladistic tree is based on only a single protein, so it is important not to over-interpret evolutionary connections.

of similar properties are found in key positions closer to the C-terminus of the polypeptides.

While Figure 15.19a shows the evolutionary radiation of globins, Figure 15.19c is a "quick and dirty" cladogram representing divergence of the polypeptide sequences. The computer program groups proteins based on the fewest evolutionary changes that separate each polypeptide. Proteins connected by short lines are most similar: note that primates cluster closely for both hemoglobin and myoglobin, and that fish, chicken, and plants have more divergence due to more ancestral connections, as shown in Figure 15.19a. A proper assessment of evolutionary connections should be done with genes that are selected based on uniform change over time, so Figure 15.19c shows only similarity based on sequences and is not a proper measure of evolutionary paths. Although the figure suggests that humans are more closely related to pygmy chimpanzees (bonobo; *Pan paniscus*) than chimpanzees (*Pan troglodytes*), one protein alone cannot definitively demonstrate this ancestral connection.

Aside from tracking the evolutionary descent of globins, note also the powerful predictive role of genomics. The evolutionary history of myoglobin shows how properties of a protein can be assessed based on amino acid sequences. By tracing back lineage and making assumptions about ancestry (which themselves are supported by experiments such as that in Figure 15.19), behaviours of extinct organisms can be hypothesized.

Gene sequencing is the foundation of genomics, and the simple array of genetic or amino acid letters is a powerful tool. Evolution and natural selection are key tools to allow us to make sense of the complex world of biology. A quick experiment on globin genes shows the unity of life through the genetic code. Genes are formed *de novo* at a vanishingly small rate. Diversification of genes, whether through duplication, exon shuffling, or modification through natural selection, is the most common way for meaningful genetic sequences to proliferate. We owe our genetic complexity to billions of years of duplication and refinement.

So, reflect back on the stories that you can form from your mail order *Seq4You* report that your brother suggested in *Why It Matters*. Do you feel you're more interested in a personalized list of four little letters and what they represent in your metabolism, health, and evolutionary history?

### STUDY BREAK QUESTIONS

1. What molecular mechanisms cause tandem duplication of genes and dispersed duplication of genes?
2. Why do new genes produced by exon shuffling have more novel functions than new genes produced by gene duplication?

# Summary Illustration

Now that determining the sequence of an organism's genome is possible, efforts are focused on studying what it represents and the information it holds. From tracing the evolutionary history of genes to making predictions about the functions and significances of genes and other elements, genomics also touches upon the fields of bioinformatics and proteomics.

Genomics is the characterization of whole genomes, including their structures (sequences), functions, and evolution.

**Determining the Functions of the Genes in a Genome**

**Genome Evolution**

**Genome Sequence Determination and Annotation**

Comparative genomics traces the evolution of genomes.

DNA sequencing methods involve DNA purification; DNA fragmentation; amplification of fragments; sequencing each fragment; and assembly of fragment sequences into longer sequences.

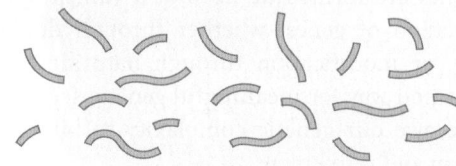

Nucleotide sequence of genomic DNA fragment (actual sequence is several hundred base pairs)

TGAGCTCCTA

Fragment sequences are assembled by a computer by overlapping identical sequences at their ends.

TGAGCTCCTA

ACCTGATTG          CTACCGAATCTGTA

GATGCTAAC

GATGCTAACCTGATTGAGCTCCTACCGAATCTGTA

Sequences are annotated to identify protein-coding genes, noncoding RNA genes, and structural and regulatory elements.

Exons encode amino acid sequences for proteins and may each make up domains of particular protein function, such as binding DNA. When exons in different species are identified in a gene with different domains, a putative function for that gene may be made.

| HumanB-hemo | KEFTPPVQAAYQKVVAGVA**NA**LAHKYH |
|---|---|
| ChimpB-hemo | KEFTPPVQAAYQKVVAGVA**NA**LAHKYH |
| ChickenB-hemo | KDFTPECQAAWQKLVRVVA**HA**LARKYH |
| PufferfishB-hemo | SKFTPEIQATFQKFLAVVV**SA**LGRQYH |
| | ..*** **::**.: *. **.::** |

A BLAST search using the predicted protein sequence can identify proteins of similar sequence with known function.

Phenomics involves identifying how the phenotype of an organism is affected when expression of a gene is turned off or reduced. The function of the protein can be inferred by the effect(s).

a.

b.

Pufferfish chromosome 1

Human X chromosome

Pufferfish chromosome 17

Similarities and differences in DNA sequences in the genomes of present-day organisms are analyzed. Identifying the relationships among sequence data from different organisms helps to identify how genomes have changed over evolutionary time.

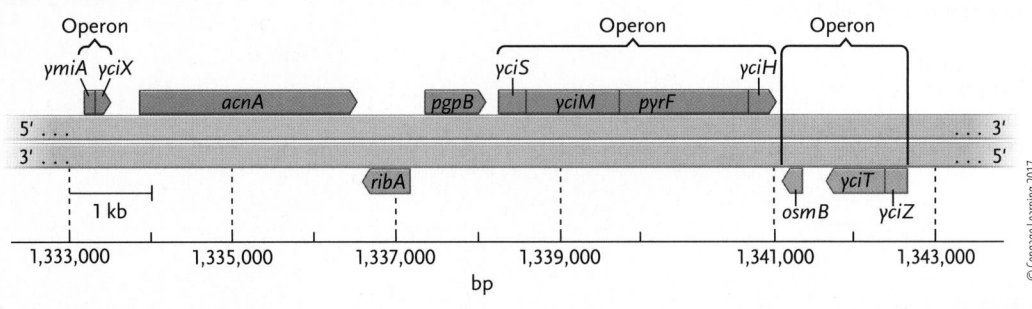

Sequence annotation is done using computer algorithms to identify possible ORFs and to compare the DNA sequence with sequence databases of known functions.

© Cengage Learning 2017

# SELF-TEST QUESTIONS

## Recall/Understand

1. Which of these characteristics applies to pseudogenes and NOT to genes?
   a. They are not transcribed.
   b. They contain longer ORFs.
   c. They do not have introns.
   d. They use a different genetic code.

2. Which of the following is the main reason that searching for ORFs is more useful for annotating bacterial protein-coding genes than it is for annotating eukaryote protein-coding genes?
   a. Eukaryote protein-coding genes contain introns.
   b. The density of protein-coding genes is much higher in eukaryote genomes.
   c. In most bacteria, all the protein-coding genes are located on a single circular chromosome.
   d. Bacterial protein-coding genes are much longer than eukaryotic protein-coding genes.

3. Which of these statements best describes genome size?
   a. Bacteria have genomes that vary widely in size.
   b. The human genome is the largest among eukaryotes.
   c. Organisms with large genomes tend to be more complex than organisms with small genomes.
   d. As genome size increases in a lineage, the number of genes also always increases.

4. Which of the following statements best describes the *E. coli* genome?
   a. It has a much lower gene density than the human genome.
   b. It contains longer genes than the human genome.
   c. All the genes are transcribed from the same template strand of the DNA double helix.
   d. About half the genes in its genome are grouped with other genes in operons.

5. Which of these statements best describes the human genome?
   a. The protein-coding sequences occupy about 75% of the genome.
   b. About 45% of the genome consists of transposable element sequences.
   c. The genome sequence comprises approximately 30 million base pairs.
   d. Human cells have about 10 500 different protein-coding genes.

6. Which of the following makes up about 95% of the average human transcription unit?
   a. short repeat sequences
   b. protein-coding sequences
   c. regulatory sequences
   d. removed nucleotide sequences

7. Draw a dideoxynucleotide and label its carbons. For the base, simply use the letter "N" to mark it.

## Apply/Analyze

8. What would be the result of complete removal of junk DNA from your genome?
   a. Your genome would be more functional.
   b. Your genome would be shorter by 90%.
   c. Your genome would not be affected.
   d. Your genome would be shorter by 10%.

## Create/Evaluate

9. For which of these reasons is the Solexa/Illumina DNA sequencing method faster and less expensive than the Sanger method?
   a. It sequences longer fragments of DNA.
   b. It sequences more DNA fragments at the same time.
   c. It does not require amplification of DNA fragments before sequencing.
   d. It does not require the use of computer algorithms to find places where sequence fragments overlap.

10. Imagine that the DNA sequences of two protein-coding genes are similar, but only for part of the protein-coding sequence. Which one of the following statements does this suggest?
    a. The two proteins have one or more domains in common.
    b. The two proteins were produced by duplication of an ancestral gene.
    c. The two proteins perform the same function.
    d. One of the two genes is a pseudogene.

11. Imagine that two protein-coding genes have very similar nucleotide sequences, and are located right next to each other on a chromosome. Which of these statements does this suggest?
    a. One of them is a duplicate of the other, copied by a retrotransposon.
    b. One of them is a pseudogene.
    c. They were produced by unequal crossing-over.
    d. They are transcribed in the same cell types.

12. At which one of these points of time do the proteins coded for by genes in a multigene family begin to evolve distinct functions?
    a. when gene duplication occurs
    b. when exon shuffling occurs
    c. when the genes are expressed by transcription and translation
    d. when different mutations occur in each protein-coding sequence

13. Compare gene knockout with gene knockdown.

14. Imagine you are working for an absent-minded researcher who is looking in his files for an old-fashioned sequencing autoradiogram, one that has four lanes such as you saw in Figure 15.1c. All he knows is that he was sequencing a very short oligonucleotide of the DNA sequence 5′-CGTAGGTTTACACGTATC-3′ using a primer of the sequence 5′-GTAAAC-3′. Sketch what the gel would look like on the radiogram using the wells containing ddATP, ddTTP, ddCTP, and ddGTP from left to right. This will help you identify the gel he's looking for.

15. How does sequencing the genomes of a greater number of animal species help in annotating and determining the functions of human protein-coding genes?

# EVOLUTION, ECOLOGY, AND THE DIVERSITY OF LIFE

aerogondo/Shutterstock.com

**The Lepidoptera (butterflies and moths) are an order of insects that consists of about 150 000 known species, of which about 20 000 are butterflies.** Some estimates put the total number of Lepidoptera species at 300 000 to 400 000, with most remaining to be discovered in the tropics.

Divided into three units, Evolution and Classification, The Diversity of Life, and Ecology and Behaviour, the chapters of Volume 2 focus on topics that naturalists have been contemplating for well over 100 years but, unlike today, had very few answers. We start this volume with Unit 4 by providing a thorough introduction to the central unifying theme of biology: evolution. We move from early ideas put forward by Aristotle about the organization of the natural world through to a chapter that focuses on what we currently know about the evolution of our own species. Along the way, we acknowledge the insights that led Charles Darwin and Alfred Wallace to the development of the theory of evolution by natural selection. We discuss how their ideas were profoundly shaped by their travels as well as the work of others. Students often struggle to understand evolution because they carry with them a range of misconceptions about how it actually works. We directly address many of these misconceptions at the end of Chapter 16. You will come to recognize the population as the unit of evolutionary change, and with that we introduce in Chapter 17 microevolution: how single populations change because of changes in how common specific gene variants (alleles) are within the population. This leads then into a critical and important discussion of how evolution links with genetics (covered in Unit 3). It is surprising to realize that Mendel and Darwin were contemporaries of each other and that, while natural selection is based on passing on beneficial traits to offspring, Darwin had no idea of the mechanism of heredity. After this two-chapter introduction to evolution, in Chapter 18 we delve into the concept of a species and the processes that result in the formation of new species. You will quickly find out when reading this chapter that, even in the twenty-first century, an all-encompassing and agreed-upon definition of what a species is remains elusive. Why is that? One of the most basic of all questions in science is addressed in Chapter 19: What is life and how did it originate? The focus here starts with a review of the likely conditions on primordial Earth and the major theories that have been put forward regarding the transition from the non-biological world to one teaming with life, a transition that started about 4 billion years ago. The chapter also includes a detailed section describing the rise of the eukaryotic cell through the process of endosymbiosis, and the critical role played by the fossil record in shaping our understanding of biological history. We close Unit 4 by providing a brief overview of the evolution of humans from early hominids and the unique adaptations that humans possess, such as bipedalism.

Armed with a foundational understanding of evolution and speciation, we delve into Unit 5, where we do something that is not easy: we organize into discrete groups and discuss the huge diversity of life that exists on Earth today. Moving from simple bacteria through to the complexity seen in animals and flowering plants, we survey the product of 4 million years of evolution. Recent analysis suggests that the total number of species on Earth ranges from a low of maybe 4 million to some estimates as high as perhaps 1 trillion different species. While estimates for the number of species inhabiting Earth today vary, researchers agree that perhaps as much as 90% of the total biodiversity that has ever existed on the planet has been lost. Extinction is a major topic of the last chapter of the unit, exploring the need and ways to conserve the current biodiversity. The chapter illustrates the fundamental and deleterious impact that our species has had on global diversity.

As Darwin and Wallace both came to understand, many traits of a particular species are the result of adaptations to the specific environmental conditions in which the species is found. The major themes of Unit 4 (evolution) and Unit 5 (species diversity) are brought together in Unit 6, where the overarching theme is ecology: the distribution and abundance of species and how they interact not only with each other but also with the physical environment. One explanation for the huge diversity of species is that Earth offers a huge range of physical environments for specific populations to become adapted.

As presented in Chapters 30 and 31, organisms interact in a wide range of ways with each other and the physical environment. These interactions put limits on the rate of population growth and its steady-state size (carrying capacity). Competition for resources, a major factor in community dynamics, is discussed as are well-studied predator–prey interactions. This discussion ends with the daunting problem of human population growth and its impact on other species as well as being the cause of rapid dwindling of key natural resources. The human population was 6 billion about the time you were born, but is expected to reach 9 billion by the time you are about 50 years old!

We devote an entire chapter to discussing the ecosystem, a group of organisms interacting with the physical environment. The chapter illustrates the strong interconnectivity among species of the ecosystem and their reliance on one another. As well, we discuss how energy and nutrients (carbon, water, nitrogen) flow through and support ecosystem structures. An understanding of the food chain and its dynamics, including the process of biomagnification of toxins, is also presented.

You will see common themes in the chapters in this volume, including evolution, adaptation, diversification, competition, and resources. The central role of the environment in evolutionary history and ongoing evolution are also made apparent. The vital importance of interactions among organisms is another recurring theme. On more than one occasion we discuss the clear and present danger posed to Earth's biodiversity by unrelenting human population growth.

# Chapter Roadmap

## Evolution: The Development of the Theory

The theory of Evolution by Natural Selection is the single central concept that permeates all of biology. It took a 20-something Charles Darwin on an expedition to arrive at its basic tenets, which have not changed.

Steve Bower / Shutterstock.com

**16.1 The Recognition of Change**

To Chapter 5

To Chapter 6

### 16.2 Natural Selection

Individuals with certain inherited traits are better able to survive and reproduce than individuals without those traits.

### 16.3 Evolutionary Biology since Darwin

In the 20th century, the molecular basis of evolutionary change became apparent as important connections developed between evolutionary biology and genetics.

### 16.4 Evolution Is the Core Theory of Modern Biology but Is Plagued by Misconceptions

Evolution by natural selection is one of the unifying themes of biology, yet commonly held misunderstandings have proven hard to fix.

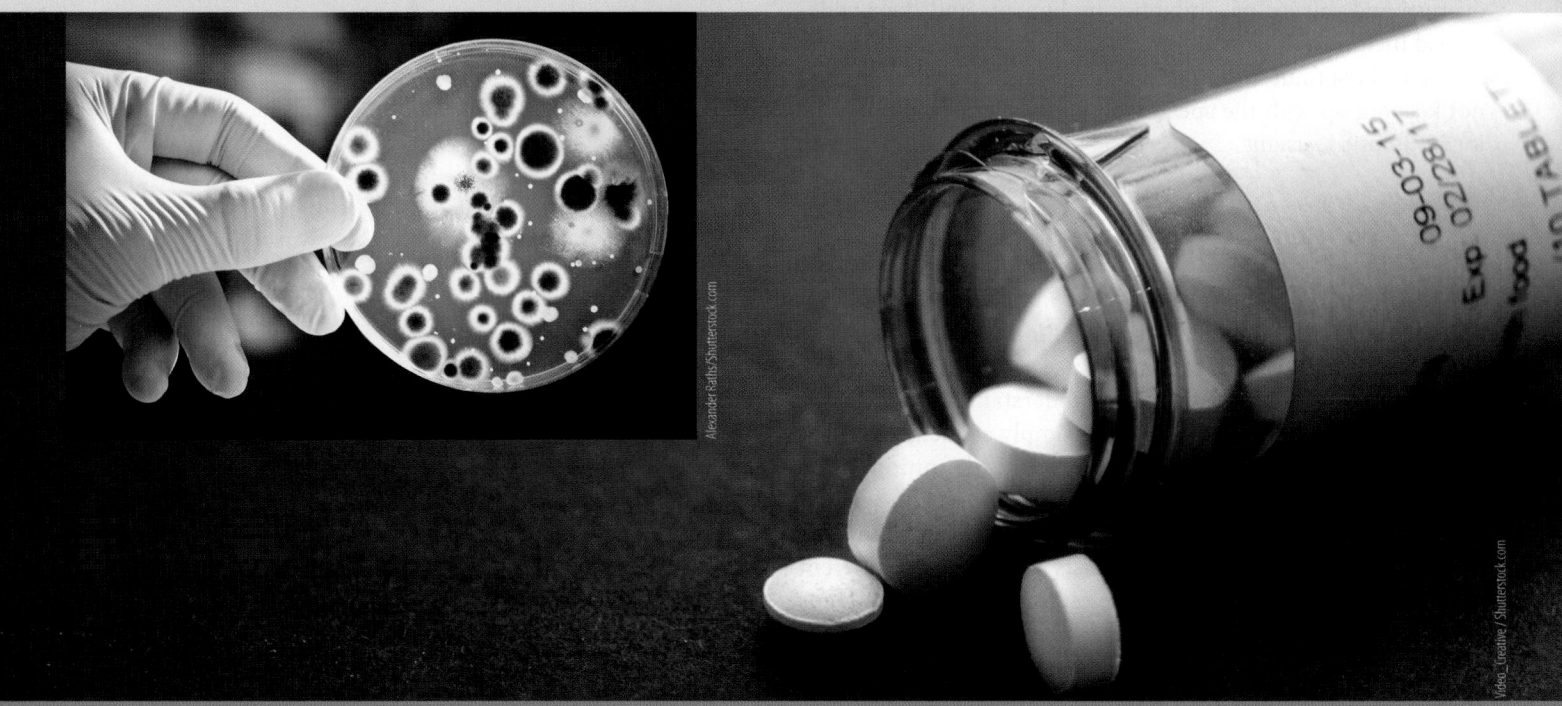

The rate at which new antibiotics are being developed is not keeping up with the speed at which bacteria are becoming antibiotic resistant.

# Evolution: The Development of the Theory

# 16

**Why it matters . . .**  Discovered by Alexander Fleming in 1928, the antibiotic penicillin kills bacteria by inhibiting the function of a crucial enzyme required for cell wall biosynthesis. Penicillin and other antibiotics that became widely available in the 1950s were known as "wonder drugs" for their remarkable ability to stop infections that only a few decades earlier were sometimes fatal.

Today, penicillin is rarely prescribed because it often doesn't work. In fact, whole classes of antibiotics that took years to develop have become essentially useless because many strains of bacteria have become resistant to their action. Over the past decade, Health Canada has seen the incidence of bacterial antibiotic resistance grow to become one of the top health issues in the country. Each year thousands of Canadians become infected with bacteria that are resistant to antibiotics, and many people die from infections that a decade or two ago were easily treated.

What you may not realize is that antibiotic resistance in bacteria is a consequence of evolution by natural selection, which is the focus of this chapter. Antibiotics present bacterial populations with an agent of selection. Within a large population of bacteria, there are a small number of individual cells that are resistant to a particular antibiotic simply because they happen to possess a random mutation that has altered their biochemistry. As a consequence, upon exposure to antibiotic in the environment, while the vast majority of bacterial cells die, the small number of resistant bacteria can continue to grow and divide. As a result, the proportion of drug-resistant bacteria in the population increases over time from one generation to the next.

In October 2014, the Government of Canada released Antimicrobial Resistance and Use in Canada: A Federal Framework for Action. The Framework maps out a coordinated, collaborative federal approach to responding to the threat of antibiotic resistance. The incidence of antibiotic resistance has increased over the past few decades as a result of overuse and misuse of antibiotics by humans and their widespread inclusion in animal feed. While the development of new antibiotics continues, the rate of developing new antibiotics is not keeping up with the speed with which bacteria are becoming antibiotic resistant.

## 16.1 The Recognition of Change

*"Nothing in biology makes sense except in the light of evolution"* is a quote from the Russian-born evolutionary biologist Theodosius Dobzhansky. This famous phrase succinctly reflects the central role evolution plays in our understanding of life. For this chapter we will define evolution simply as the notion that species change over time. We will refine this definition in the next chapter. Not only does evolution explain the underlying common features that organisms possess, it explains the huge diversity of life on Earth—life exists in so many different forms. An understanding of how evolution operates also helps in our understanding of how species continue to change over time in response to environmental challenges, such as climate change.

### 16.1a The Early View Is That Life Is Unchanging

The Greek philosopher Aristotle was a keen observer of nature and he examined the form and variety of organisms in their natural habitats. Careful study of the differences and similarities among organisms led Aristotle to create a ladder-like classification of life. In this system, which would later be called the *Scala Naturae* (Scale of Nature), each organism on Earth occupies a specific step on the ladder that leads from the non-living world at the bottom up ever-increasing levels of complexity. Humans are at the very top of the ladder, just below perfection, God (**Figure 16.1**).

By the fourteenth century, Europeans had merged Aristotle's classification system with the biblical account of creation to arrive at a view of the natural world in which (1) organisms had been specially created by God, (2) species could never change or become extinct, and (3) new species could never arise. At the time, biological research was dominated by natural theology, which provided arguments for the existence of God through the detailed study of nature (God's creation). In the eighteenth century there was no stronger proponent of natural theology than the Swedish botanist Carolus Linnaeus (1707–1778), who undertook the exhaustive goal to classify all organisms. It is Linnaeus that introduced the binomial (two-part) species classification system that is still in place today. In this system, similar-looking organisms are grouped together and organized into broader, more inclusive categories. Interestingly, while Linnaeus noticed similarity among different organisms, he did not ascribe that relationship to anything other than God's design. This discipline of taxonomy that Linnaeus developed is a major topic of Chapter 19.

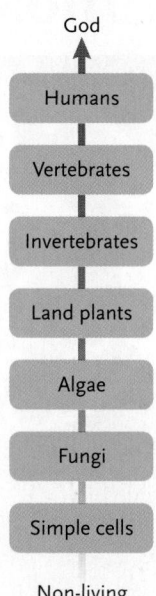

**FIGURE 16.1 Scale of nature.** This hierarchy was proposed by Aristotle, who believed that every organism had a defined position along a scale that moved from the simplest organisms to the most complex.

### 16.1b Lamarck Proposed That Acquired Traits Were Inherited

The idea that organisms can never change was challenged in the eighteenth century by the French naturalist Jean Baptiste de Lamarck (1744–1829), who put forward the first comprehensive theory of evolution: species change over time. In it he proposed a so-called "perfecting principle" whereby simple organisms evolved into more complex ones, moving up the Scale of Nature. Microscopic organisms were replaced at the bottom of the ladder by spontaneous generation—an idea, popular at the time, whereby simple forms of life arose from non-living material. Today, Lamarck is most well-known for, *the inheritance of acquired characteristics.* This is the idea that changes that an organism gains during its lifetime are passed on to its offspring. A contemporary example of Lamarckian inheritance would be that the children of the body builder Arnold Schwarzenegger (**Figure 16.2**) would be stronger and more muscular than the children of someone who didn't weight train. Today of course we know that Lamarck was wrong. Although muscles do grow larger through continued use, structural changes acquired during an organism's lifetime are not inherited by the next generation. Within a few years of Lamarck's death, ideas about how organisms could change over time would be forever changed by the research and theories of the young British naturalist Charles Darwin.

### 16.1c Darwin Proposed the Theory of Evolution by Natural Selection

In 1831, Charles Darwin, who was 22 at the time, was invited to take part in a five-year, around-the-world voyage aboard the naval surveying ship HMS *Beagle*. At the time, Darwin had just dropped out of medical school, determined instead to follow his passion in natural history. The primary purpose of the expedition was to

**FIGURE 16.2** **Acquired characteristics are not inherited.** Arnold Schwarzenegger was an accomplished body builder; however, his acquired physique was not inherited by his children.

Because he was young and did not have a prestigious university position to uphold, Darwin felt no pressure to conform to the ideas popular at the time. During the voyage he objectively took notes about what he saw, collecting a vast assortment of specimens as he went and having them shipped back to England. His observations and notes, together with his extensive readings, provided valuable information that shaped his thinking about evolution. Darwin's major insights came from three major areas of study: (1) geology and the fossil record, (2) the geographic distribution of species, and (3) the comparative morphology of species.

**EARTH'S GEOLOGY AND THE FOSSIL RECORD** During his time on the Beagle, Darwin read Charles Lyell's Principles of Geology, which was published in 1795 and would prove to be a foundational textbook of the science. Lyell championed the idea of the Scottish geologist James Hutton who maintained that the surface of Earth was constantly changing by natural events such as earthquakes, volcanoes, and the erosive action of wind and water operating over very long periods of time. This view went against the dominant idea of the day: the major features of Earth were the result of ancient and supernatural events (e.g., Noah's flood) orchestrated by the hand of God.

In a remarkable coincidence, a changing Earth is something Darwin experienced first-hand when he witnessed one of the most powerful earthquakes in history, the 1835 Concepción earthquake in Chile. Not only did he actually feel the ground shake, he saw the aftermath, including the destruction caused by the earthquake, tsunami waves, and landforms that were uplifted by as much as 10 m.

During his time in Chile, Darwin took the opportunity to climb the Andes Mountains. At a height of about 4000 m, he discovered the fossil shells of marine organisms. Along with experiencing the Concepción earthquake, these fossil findings convinced Darwin that Lyell was right: the geology of Earth is not static, but does change over time. This realization was profound because it set Darwin to thinking that perhaps, like geology, life may also change slowly over time.

Darwin was aware that scientists had begun to uncover fossil animals and plants that, to the surprise of many people, were unlike living species. That the fossil record indicated that some species had become extinct was yet one more piece of evidence that was hard to reconcile with the belief that each organism was specially created by God and that the number of species on Earth is fixed. Darwin collected a huge assortment of fossils during his travels, and while many were unlike any living creature he came across, others did clearly resemble living species. For example, despite an enormous size difference, he observed that living armadillos and fossilized glyptodonts had very similar body armour (**Figure 16.4**). If both species had been created at the same time, and both were found in South America, why didn't glyptodonts still live alongside armadillos? Darwin later wondered whether armadillos might be living descendants of the now-extinct glyptodonts.

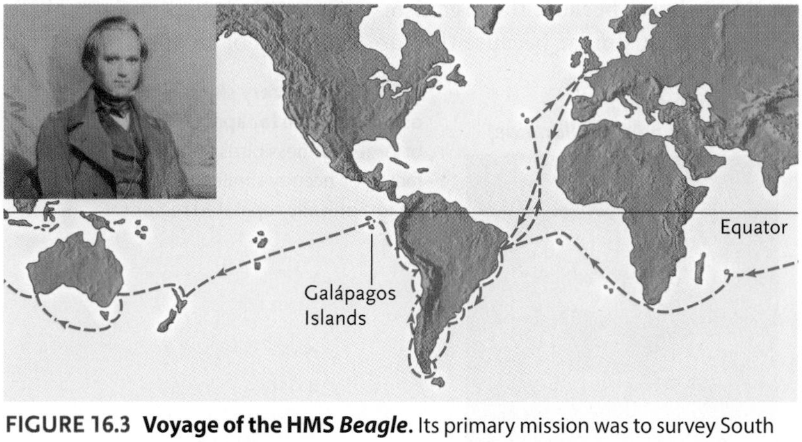

map the coast of South America (**Figure 16.3**). With no specific role on the ship, Darwin was free during the voyage to spend time ashore collecting specimens of plants, animals, and fossils. He also was a keen observer of the various habitats that plants and animals occupied, and took note of the surrounding geology.

Although Darwin was well educated and very well read, he certainly was not a learned university professor with years of experience in a particular field. Interestingly, many Darwin scholars think this lack of experience may have been to his advantage.

**FIGURE 16.3** **Voyage of the HMS Beagle.** Its primary mission was to survey South America. Inset: Darwin in 1840

CHAPTER 16 EVOLUTION: THE DEVELOPMENT OF THE THEORY | **395**

Charles R. Knight painting (negative CK21T), Field Museum of Natural History, Chicago

Steve Bower / Shutterstock.com

**FIGURE 16.4 Ancestors and descendants.** Darwin hypothesized that, even though an extinct glyptodont (top) probably weighed 300–400 times as much as a living nine-banded armadillo (*Dasypus novemcinctus*), their obvious resemblance suggests that they are related.

Darwin realized that the geology of Earth changes slowly over time, and that fossils provided evidence that life did as well.

**GEOGRAPHIC DISTRIBUTION OF SPECIES** As long as naturalists encountered organisms only from Europe and surrounding lands, Aristotle's Scale of Nature was easily followed. But global explorations starting in the fifteenth century provided naturalists with thousands of previously unknown plants and animals. Although some were similar to European species, others were new and very strange.

Studies of the worldwide distribution of plants and animals, now called **biogeography**, raised puzzling questions to many, including Darwin. Was there no limit to the number of species created by God? Where did all these species fit in the Scale of Nature? Why did some species have limited geographical distributions, whereas others were widespread? Why were some species found in Africa or Asia so different from those found in Europe, while others had a similar appearance (**Figure 16.5**)?

One particularly astute observation that Darwin made about oceanic islands is that none that he studied had

terrestrial mammals on them. Later work that he completed after the voyage would confirm that this was a general rule. In contrast, flying mammals (e.g., bats) were found on islands. As well, he noticed that species that were on oceanic islands were clearly most similar to species inhabiting the nearest continent.

Nine hundred kilometres west of South America, on the Galápagos Islands, Darwin found "strange and wonderful creatures," including giant tortoises, lizards, and many species of birds. Darwin noticed that the animals and plants on different islands varied slightly in form. Moreover, many species resembled those on the distant South American mainland. Why did so many different species occupy one small island cluster? Why did these species resemble others from the nearest continent? Darwin hypothesized that the plants and animals of the Galápagos were related to plants and animals on South America but had changed over time.

**COMPARATIVE MORPHOLOGY** At least from the time of Aristotle, anatomists have noted some remarkable similarities among very diverse creatures. For example, the human arm, the flippers of seals, and the wings of bats differ markedly in size, shape, and function (**Figure 16.6**), yet they share very similar underlying structure. If these limbs were specially created for different means of locomotion, naturalists wondered, why didn't God use entirely different materials and structures for walking, swimming, and flying? Natural theologians countered this argument by stating that the body plans were perfect, and there was no need to invent something new for every species. But an eighteenth century French scientist, George-Louis Leclerc (le Comte de Buffon), was still puzzled by the existence of body parts with no apparent function. For example, he noted that the feet of pigs and some other mammals have two toes that never touch the ground. If each species was anatomically perfect for its particular way of life, Buffon asked, why did useless structures exist? Buffon proposed that some animals must have *changed* since their creation. He suggested that **vestigial structures**, these useless parts he observed, must have functioned in ancestral organisms, although he offered no explanation of how functional structures became vestigial.

To Darwin, the striking similarity seen in the features among different organisms had a far simpler explanation. It was because the organisms are related. A group of organisms look similar because they are decedents of an ancestor they all

**African ostrich (*Struthio camelus*)**

Johan Swanepoel / Shutterstock.com

**South American rhea (*Rhea americana*)**

Kenneth W. Fink / Science Source

**Australian emu (*Dromaius novaehollandiae*)**

scooperdigital / Shutterstock.com

**FIGURE 16.5 Very similar-looking organisms live far apart.** These three species of large flightless birds appear very similar. In fact, they occupy similar habitats in geographically separated regions.

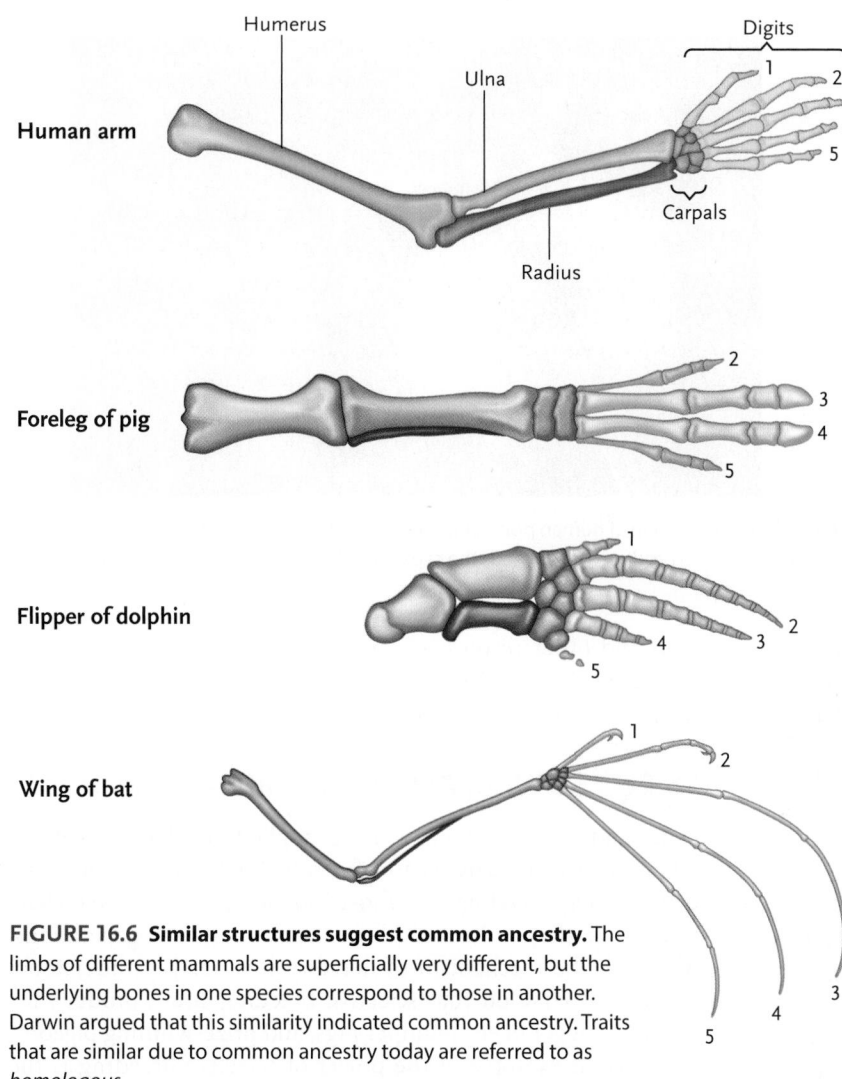

FIGURE 16.6 **Similar structures suggest common ancestry.** The limbs of different mammals are superficially very different, but the underlying bones in one species correspond to those in another. Darwin argued that this similarity indicated common ancestry. Traits that are similar due to common ancestry today are referred to as *homologous*.

shared—a *common ancestor*—and that ancestor possessed those features. The similarity present in a group of organisms because of shared ancestry is called **homology**. We will see in Chapter 19 that one can examine homology at various levels, including through comparing DNA and protein sequences among organisms. To Darwin, the morphological similarity seen among species suggested common ancestry.

## STUDY BREAK QUESTIONS

1. How did Aristotle and Lamarck view evolution?
2. How did Darwin's travels to Chile influence his thinking about evolution?
3. Give an example of a homologous trait (that's not in this chapter!).

## 16.2  Natural Selection

The *Beagle* returned to England in 1836, and Darwin set out reviewing his notes and the vast assortment of specimens he had collected. As well, he presented numerous public lectures and discussed his findings with scholars in various fields. His observations

concerning the fossil record, biogeography, and structural homology indicated to him that all organisms are related by a common ancestor but had changed or evolved over time. Darwin was not the first to propose that organisms changed over time, what set him apart from his predecessors is that he arrived at how evolution occurs, its mechanism. Yet, it would be a remarkable 23 years after returning to England that his theory concerning the mechanism of evolution would become widely known. In 1859, *On the Origin of Species by Means of Natural Selection* was finally published. The first edition sold out in a single day.

### 16.2a  Darwin Was Not Alone in Thinking about Natural Selection

Darwin was not the only one thinking about how species may change over time. The naturalist Alfred Russel Wallace (**Figure 16.7**) had arrived at very similar conclusions to Darwin through eight years of extensive research on the islands of present day Singapore, Malaysia, and Indonesia. Like Darwin, Wallace was a keen observer of nature who kept careful notes and drawings of his observations while collecting a huge number of specimens. Wallace conveyed his ideas on evolution to Darwin in a letter in 1858. Fearing that Wallace may publish his ideas first, Darwin quickly put together *The Origin*, which was published the following year.

FIGURE 16.7 **Alfred Russel Wallace (1823–1913).** Independently of Darwin, Wallace developed a theory of evolution based on natural selection.

CHAPTER 16  EVOLUTION: THE DEVELOPMENT OF THE THEORY  |

**a.**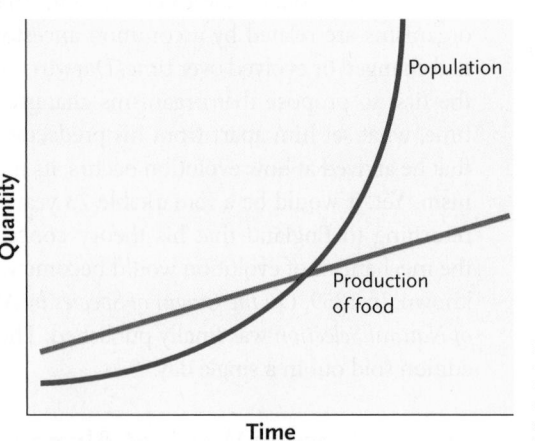

**b.**

Brian A Jackson / Shutterstock.com

Malthus' basic principle

**FIGURE 16.8 Populations have a huge potential to increase over time. (a)** The rate of human population growth increases exponentially, which often exceeds the ability to increase food production. **(b)** In nature, the number of offspring produced far exceeds the capacity of the environment to support all of them. Both situations set up a "struggle for existence."

Many historians suggest that Wallace was, in fact, not upset that Darwin was the first to publish the theory of evolution by natural selection. In fact, Wallace frequently admitted that Darwin's ideas were more thoroughly developed and supported by more examples than his own. Over the years, Darwin and Wallace developed strong respect and admiration for each other and both were bestowed with prestigious honours for their roles in the discovery of natural selection. The fact that, today, Wallace is scarcely remembered is perhaps best explained by the fact that most people connect natural selection, and thus evolution, with the publication of a single book, the one written by Charles Darwin.

## 16.2b The Writings of Thomas Malthus Influenced Darwin and Wallace

The ideas of both Darwin and Wallace about the mechanism by which species could change over time were profoundly influenced by Thomas Malthus, a late eighteenth century political economist. Both men had read *An Essay on the Principle of Population* (1798) in which Malthus laid out how humanity was destined for disaster. This dire prediction was based on Malthus's own calculations: the human population increases exponentially over time while, at best, gains in agricultural technology lead to only modest (arithmetic) increases in the food supply **(Figure 16.8a)**. Malthus was addressing the decline in living conditions in nineteenth century England and suggested that, unless the government somehow controls the birth rate, increased poverty and starvation were inevitable.

Reading Malthus helped clarify in Darwin's mind how the imbalance between population growth and available food could be applied to plants and animals in nature. For example, Darwin and others had observed that the potential of most species to reproduce is far greater than the actual number of offspring that reach adulthood (Figure 16.8b). That no species seems able to reproduce to their full potential indicates that offspring are under a constant "struggle for existence," according to Darwin. Organisms are in competition with one another for limited

food and other resources. They have to escape predation and they have to survive often unfavourable environments (e.g., temperature extremes, drought).

## 16.2c So What Actually Is Natural Selection?

Plant and animal breeders have applied the basic facets of inheritance from parents to offspring for thousands of years. By selectively breeding only those individuals with desired characteristics, they enhanced those traits in future generations. Although the mechanism of heredity was not yet understood, Darwin understood that selective breeding could produce for example, bigger beets, plumper pigs, and prize-winning pigeons.

A good example of the power of selective breeding is the development of corn (*maize*). Corn is actually derived from an ancient Mexican grain called *teosinte*. Over thousands of years, farmers selected the teosinte kernels for replanting that were the largest, easiest to eat and most exposed on the cob. The result of this selective breeding is that, today, a typical cob of corn looks nothing like teosinte **(Figure 16.9)**.

Matt Lavin. This file is licensed under Attribution-ShareAlike 2.0 Generic (CC BY-SA 2.0) license, https://creativecommons.org/licenses/by-sa/2.0/

Sakkara / Shutterstock.com

**FIGURE 16.9 Which would you prefer to eat?** Through selective breeding, or what Darwin called "artificial selection," farmers in what is now Mexico developed corn (right) from teosinte (left) over thousands of years.

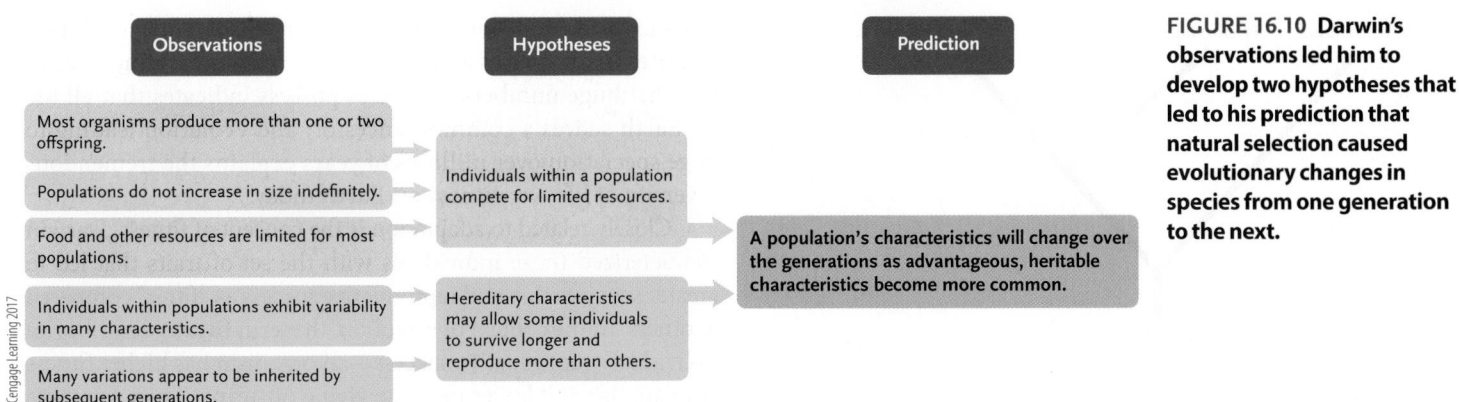

**FIGURE 16.10** Darwin's observations led him to develop two hypotheses that led to his prediction that natural selection caused evolutionary changes in species from one generation to the next.

Darwin referred to selective breeding as **artificial selection**, since humans were selecting the characteristics they wanted in the offspring by choosing parents with those traits. Darwin didn't see why a similar process of selection couldn't also work in nature, but the issue was the mechanism: how would it work?

Darwin started to understand that a major aspect of evolutionary change must reside within a **population**—a group of individuals of a species that live together in a specific place. By understanding this, Darwin could see how Lamarck was wrong. Individual organisms don't evolve over their lifetime. But a population could. It is the population that has the capacity to change from one generation to the next.

Darwin thought about two specific attributes of a population: its size and the amount of variation within it. First, Darwin observed that, while organisms have a huge capacity to reproduce, limiting resources constrain the size of a population. From this, Darwin hypothesized that individuals within the population compete for limited resources **(Figure 16.10)**. Second, Darwin observed that individuals within a population are not identical but differ in certain traits (e.g., size, colour, behaviour), and that these traits tend to be inherited. This in turn led to Darwin hypothesizing that organisms with traits that allow them to outcompete others for limiting resources would leave more offspring. For Darwin, this thinking came together into a single idea, **natural selection**: individuals with certain inherited traits are better able to survive and reproduce than individuals without those traits (Figure 16.10). Individuals in the population that lacked such traits would die leaving fewer, if any, offspring. Thus, advantageous traits would become more common in the next generation.

In other words, from generation to generation, the mechanism that is causing a population to change, or evolve, is *nature selecting* for a set of traits that gives an individual an advantage over others in the particular environment that the population inhabits **(Figure 16.11)**. What is remarkable about natural selection is that Darwin had discovered a mechanism for evolutionary change that no one had ever envisioned, much less documented.

## 16.2d Natural Selection Leads to Adaptation and Increased Fitness

Darwin's insights came from many places, but none seem more significant than his work on the Galápagos Islands. Both Darwin and Wallace were spurred in their thinking through observations on island groups because evolutionary change can often be more easily noticed on islands. Each island in a group is isolated from the others, and conditions on each island can be quite distinct, which leads to differences in the species that inhabit each island. The most famous example of this is what are referred to today as *Darwin's mockingbirds*.

The Galápagos Islands are home to four distinct species of mockingbird (genus *Nesomimus*), which are found on specific islands of the group **(Figure 16.12)**. During his visit to the Galápagos, Darwin collected mockingbirds from different islands, but it wasn't until he got back to England that someone pointed out that the birds from different islands were distinct species. Based on this work, Darwin developed the concept of *descent with modification*. It was clear to Darwin that the underlying similarity of the mockingbirds indicated that birds from all the islands shared a common ancestor (Figure 16.12a) but that, over time, each species had developed distinctly different traits (beak size and shape, coloration). The simplest scenario to explain this is that a population of one species of mockingbird came from mainland South America and colonized most of the

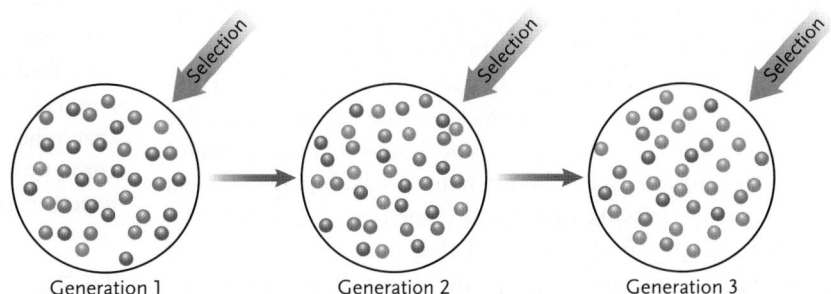

**FIGURE 16.11 Populations change over time.** In this simplistic example, a single population consists of individuals with three different sets of traits (blue, green, orange). Selection pressures (limiting food, resources, predators) favour the growth and reproduction of individuals with a specific set of traits (orange) over the other two. From one generation to the next, the proportion of "orange" individuals in the population increases.

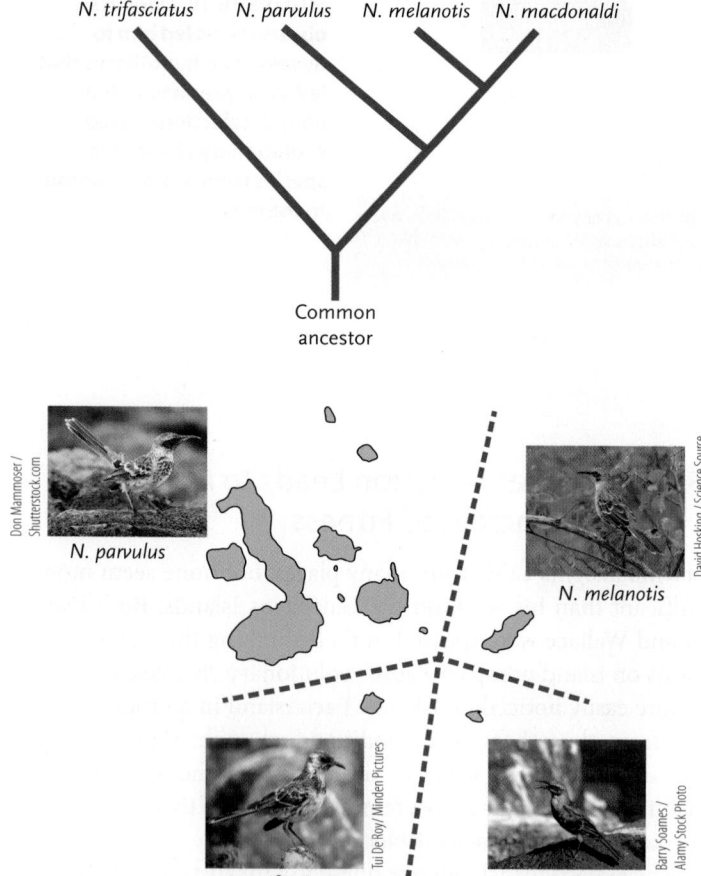

FIGURE 16.12 **The Galápagos mockingbirds are explained by "descent with modification." (a)** The four major mockingbird species (genus *Nesomimus*) are descended from a common ancestor that came from mainland South America thousands of years ago. **(b)** Each of the four species is adapted to the particular environment found on specific islands of the group.

islands at around the same time. Over thousands of years, the populations that developed on different island became less and less alike—their traits diverged. On each island, specific traits would become uniquely modified compared to the traits of birds inhabiting other islands. And all the species become distinct compared to the ancestral mockingbird species from the South American mainland. Darwin's work on mockingbirds would be complemented by even more detailed study of the many species of finches that inhabit the Galápagos Islands.

The evolution of different species of birds on the Galápagos Islands is tied closely to the fact that the islands within the group have different habitats (food sources, microclimate) (Figure 16.12b), which resulted in natural selection favouring a different set of traits on one island compared to another. The inherited aspects of an individual that make it better suited to a particular environment than other individuals are referred to as **adaptation**. From generation to generation, a species becomes better adapted to a specific environment as a consequence of natural selection.

The impact of Darwin's observations on the Galápagos Islands was that he extended his ideas about speciation in

mockingbirds and finches to a broader sense of how evolution operates in all species across the globe. The underlying homology that huge numbers of species possess indicates that all life on Earth shares a common ancestor; and evolution leading to huge speciation over millions of years explains the tremendous diversity of life we witness on Earth today.

Closely related to adaptation is the concept of fitness. Darwin characterized those individuals with the set of traits that led to greater survivorship and reproductive success as "fitter" compared to others. In the context of evolution, the term **fitness** describes an individual's reproductive success—an organism has higher fitness than another if it leaves more surviving offspring. There are three aspects of fitness that are important to understanding how evolution works: (1) *Fitness is a relative concept.* It doesn't matter in absolute terms how many offspring an individual leaves, only that it leaves more than others in the population. (2) *A trait is only valuable if it increases fitness.* We tend to think of traits such as being faster, stronger, bigger as valuable; however, they are only valuable, and thus selected for, if they increase reproductive success. (3) *The traits that increase fitness may change.* If the environment changes (e.g., climate change), those traits that previously increased fitness may not be advantageous any longer.

## STUDY BREAK QUESTIONS

1. How did the work of Thomas Malthus influence Darwin's thinking?
2. Explain how corn was developed from teosinte using artificial selection.
3. Define *natural selection*.

# 16.3 Evolutionary Biology since Darwin

Both Darwin and Wallace laid down the fundamental basis for natural selection and yet, what might surprise you is that neither of them had an understanding of genetics. When *The Origins of Species* came out, Gregor Mendel had just published his work on inheritance in pea plants, and it wasn't until 50 years later, in the early twentieth century, that Thomas Hunt Morgan discerned that genes are carried on chromosomes. His experiments, which are described in Chapter 10, enabled geneticists to forge an important connection between Darwinian evolution and Mendelian genetics that today is referred to as the *modern synthesis* of evolution. At its core, this unification recognized the critical importance that genetic variation within a population plays in evolutionary change.

## 16.3a The Source of Variation in a Population Is Random Mutation

Many of the traits possessed by an organism are inherited because they have a genetic basis: they are coded by DNA. It is the variation in DNA sequence that ultimately gives rise to individuals within a population having different inherited traits. While some traits (e.g., wrinkled versus smooth peas) result from variation in the sequence of a single gene, others (e.g., the shape of a finch's beak) are influenced by the variation in sequence of many genes.

Although all organisms within a population have the same set of genes, the DNA sequence of any particular gene in any particular organism may be different due to past **mutation**—a random and heritable change in the DNA sequence. Mutations arise as an inevitable consequence of the imperfect nature of DNA replication as well as from the effects of certain physical, chemical, and biological agents.

First generation      Several generations later

**FIGURE 16.13 A change in selection causes moth evolution.**

You can think of mutation as supplying the raw material for natural selection to work with—the differences in traits among organisms. It is critical to understand, however, that while mutations are the source of variation, they do not determine the path of evolution. Because mutations are undirected, they can occur anywhere in the genome: in essential genes required for life, or in a DNA sequence that has no function. Thus, some mutations are beneficial to an organism because they increase fitness. Other mutations may be harmful and lower fitness, while many others are "neutral," having no effect on fitness. We will discuss the role of mutation in evolution in considerable detail in the next chapter.

## 16.3b Examples of Natural Selection

Natural selection is referred to as a *theory* of evolution because its basic tenet, *that heritable variation leads to differential survival and reproduction*, has been repeatedly tested and supported using the methodologies of both experimental and observational science (see *The Purple Pages* for a discussion of the scientific method).

Here we present just a few of the hundreds of studies related to natural selection that have been conducted. When reading through each of them, try to identify the key factors driving evolutionary change: What is the genotypic make-up of the starting population? What was the impact of selection on the starting populations? Did the selection change over time and what caused it to change?

**MOTH POPULATIONS EVOLVE IN POLLUTED CITIES** The peppered moth (*Biston betularia*) shows considerable variation in colour due to differences in genes related to pigmentation: some individuals are lightly coloured (*typica*) and others are very dark, almost black in colour (*carbonaria*). The *carbonaria* variety is darker because of increased production of the pigment

melanin. Interestingly, before the mid-1800s, the lightly coloured *typica* moths were very common, with the sighting of a *carbonaria* individual being rare. However, this scenario rapidly changed with the industrial revolution and increased pollution in the north of England related to the use of coal.

The increased burning of coal resulted in soot being deposited on the bark of usually light coloured trees, turning them dark. As the moths rested on the darkly coloured bark, the lightly coloured *typica* moths became much easier for predatory birds to see compared to the darker *carbonaria* moths. The difference in predation resulted in a huge shift in population structure. In Liverpool, a heavily polluted city at the time, from about 1850 to 1900, the proportion of *carbonaria* moths increased from representing 1% of the population to as high as 95% of the population (**Figure 16.13**).

The change in composition of *Biston* populations is a powerful example of how a change in the environment causes a change in natural selection. The darkened trees and increased predation of the light moths shifted selection to favouring the *carbonaria* variety. After the introduction of stricter pollution policies in the twentieth century, the proportions have since rebounded, with the *typica* variety dominating again.

A recent study has uncovered the genetic basis of the colouring in *Biston* moths. Using DNA sequencing to compare the genomes of the two varieties, researchers have discovered that the pigmentation seen in the *carbonaria* variety is triggered by a transposable element—a piece of DNA that can move from one position to another in the genome (see Chapter 15). In *carbonaria* individuals, the transposable element is inserted into the first intron of a gene called *cortex*, which unexpectedly results in increased expression of the gene. It is not yet fully understood how increased *cortex* expression results in increased melanin production. Additionally, in a remarkable piece of detective work, using sophisticated molecular tools and simulations, the same researchers were also able to estimate that the

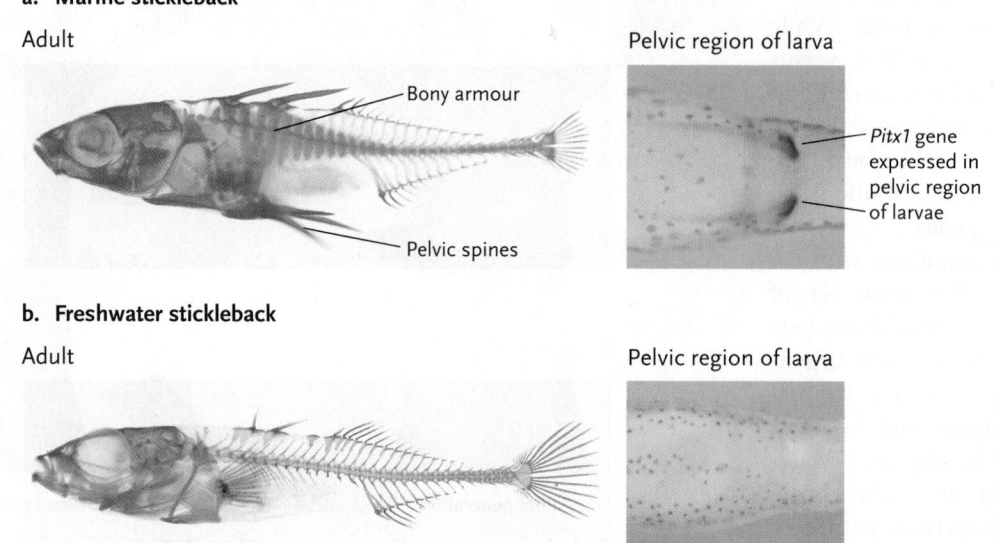

**a. Marine stickleback**

Adult

Pelvic region of larva

Bony armour

Pelvic spines

Pitx1 gene expressed in pelvic region of larvae

**b. Freshwater stickleback**

Adult

Pelvic region of larva

© Michael D. Shapiro and David Kingsley

**FIGURE 16.14 Sticklebacks with and without pelvic spines. (a)** Marine populations of three-spined sticklebacks (*Gasterosteus aculeatus*) have prominent bony plates along their sides and large spines on their dorsal and pelvic fins. The growth of pelvic spines is induced by the expression of the *Pitx1* gene (the purple crescents in the photo on the right) in the pelvic region during embryonic development. **(b)** Many freshwater populations of the same species lack the bony plates and spines. Pelvic spines do not develop in the freshwater sticklebacks because the *Pitx1* gene is not expressed in the pelvic region. Natural selection has apparently fostered these morphological differences in response to the dominant predators in each environment. The skeletons of these specimens, each about 8 cm long, were dyed bright red.

actual mutational event (insertion of the transposable element into *cortex*) producing the *carbonaria* variety probably occurred between 1810 and 1820. This is consistent with the earliest recorded sighting of the *carbonaria* variety being documented in 1848.

**A FISH LOSING ITS ARMOUR INCREASES ITS FITNESS** The three-spined stickleback (*Gasterosteus aculeatus*) is a species of small fish found along the coasts of North America, Europe, and Asia. Ancestors of modern sticklebacks lived in the ocean, moving to freshwater streams and lakes only to reproduce. Since the last ice age (11 000 years ago), when retreating glaciers cut off connections between oceans and lakes, two distinct populations of sticklebacks have arisen: sticklebacks that live exclusively in the ocean and those found only in freshwater habitats (lakes and streams).

To defend against a range of saltwater predatory fish, ancestral and present-day oceanic sticklebacks have bony armour along their sides and display prominent spines. In comparison, lake-dwelling sticklebacks have greatly reduced armour and, in many populations, lack spines on their pelvic fins **(Figure 16.14)**.

Recent research indicates that, over the thousands of years since the two populations became isolated, the loss of the spines and bony plates from freshwater inhabitants reflects adaptation to the new environment. Not only are there far fewer predator fish in freshwater habitats, but the presence of large spines has been shown to be disadvantageous as they are used by dragonfly larvae to attack juvenile sticklebacks. A way to think about these changes in stickleback armour is that the "force" that is driving selection, the *selection pressure*, changed. In a freshwater habitat, having less armour and smaller spines actually

increases fitness. Not only is predation by dragonfly larvae reduced, but the fish no longer have the added metabolic costs associated with building armour and spines. As a result, fish with diminished armour have been shown to grow larger as juveniles, begin breeding sooner, and have higher overwinter survivorship than heavily armoured individuals.

Research has shown that differences in the amount of armour possessed by sticklebacks are an inherited trait. The presence or absence of spines on the pelvic fins of these fishes is governed by the expression of the gene *Pitx1*. In long-spined marine sticklebacks, *Pitx1* is expressed in the embryonic buds from which pelvic fins develop, promoting the development of spines. But *Pitx1* is not expressed in the fin buds of freshwater sticklebacks; hence, pelvic spines do not develop. This loss of *Pitx1* expression has been shown to be due to a mutation to a nearby gene that regulates *Pitx1*.

### 16.3C EXPERIMENTAL EVOLUTION SUPPORTS NATURAL SELECTION

One of the difficulties with evolutionary biology is that what you are studying (evolution) can occur very slowly. A major factor that determines the actual rate of change within a population is **generation time**, which is the average difference in age between a parent and its offspring **(Figure 16.15)**. It is difficult to directly study evolution in humans, for example, because most women don't have children until they are in their 20s. Compare that to the generation time of the fruit fly *Drosophila* (about one week) or a bacterium (less than one hour).

Given that the fundamental processes driving evolutionary change are similar in all organisms, some scientists are using

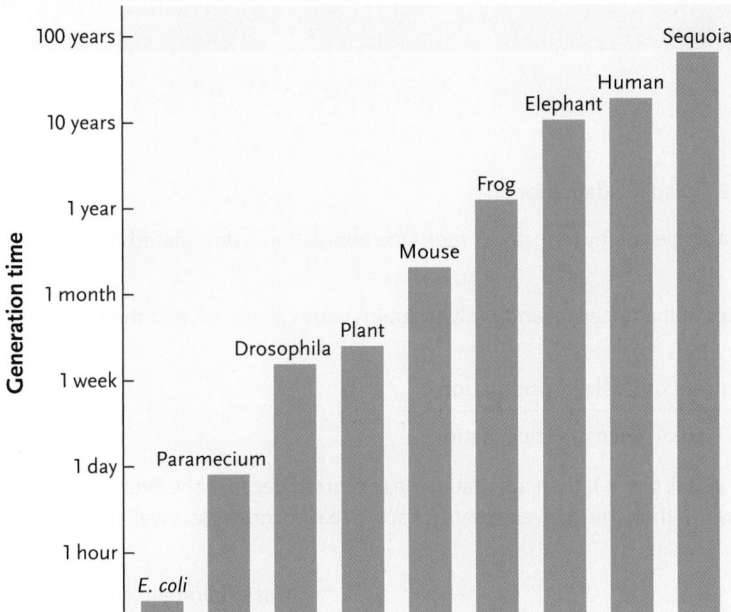

FIGURE 16.15 **Generation time of various organisms.** The age when an organism produces the next generation varies tremendously among different groups. Organisms with short generation times evolve more rapidly than those with longer generation times.

organisms with short generation times to study evolution as it occurs in real time, an approach that is impossible in most animals and plants. In these studies of *experimental evolution*, one can allow populations to evolve under controlled laboratory conditions and include both adequate controls and replicates, hallmarks of good experimental design (see *The Purple Pages*). The power of this approach is that an evolution experiment can be completed in a matter of months, allowing researchers to directly compare an evolved population with the ancestral population from which is was derived. Even Darwin understood the power of such an approach when he remarked in 1859, "we ought to look exclusively to its lineal ancestors; but this is scarcely ever possible." Using organisms that reproduce rapidly, comparing a population directly with its ancestor is straightforward.

An excellent example that illustrates the power of experimental evolution is a set of experiments that were carried out to look at the ability of the bacterium *Escherichia coli* (*E. coli*) to adapt to different growth temperatures (**Figure 16.16**). The typical laboratory strain of *E. coli* grows fastest at 37°C. This is referred to as its *optimal growth temperature*. But if you grow *E. coli* at a lower temperature, say 32°C for many generations, will the population adapt to that temperature - will 32°C become its optimum growth temperature?

This experiment was performed by taking a single liquid culture of *E.coli* and dividing it into two: one was designated the Ancestral population and the second the Evolved population. The Ancestral population was left to grow under normal laboratory conditions of 37°C, while researchers exposed the Evolved population to a growth temperature of 32°C for 2000 generations.

If the Evolved population had become adapted by being grown at 32°C, it should have a greater fitness than the

Ancestral strain at 32°C. But how do you measure reproductive success (fitness) in bacteria? Bacteria reproduce asexually through binary fission: they divide in two. Given this, a population would have higher fitness if it has a higher growth rate. By combining the Ancestral and Evolved populations into a single flask and exposing the flask to a specific temperature for 24 h, you can measure the growth rate of each. How many more cells of one population are there than the other? As shown in Figure 16.16, from the growth rates you can then measure fitness.

**STUDY BREAK QUESTIONS**

1. How do mutations arise in a population?
2. In the example of the peppered moth, what is the agent of selection?
3. Why can bacteria adapt to a changing environment faster than humans can?

## 16.4 Evolution Is the Core Theory of Modern Biology but Is Plagued by Misconceptions

That the theory of evolution by natural selection is so well supported experimentally makes it hard to appreciate the insight and intuition required in the 1800s to formulate a theory that has survived essentially unchanged for 150 years. One of Darwin's contemporaries, the biologist Thomas Huxley, summed up the reaction of many when he quipped that the theory was so obvious, once articulated, that he was surprised he had not thought of it himself.

Disciplines including genetics, molecular biology, developmental biology, systematics, and paleontology have all been profoundly influenced by the findings of evolutionary biology and, in a reciprocal way, these disciplines have provided powerful support for evolutionary biology. As we have seen in this chapter and as will be reinforced in the next four chapters, evolutionary processes explain the natural world without invoking essential life forces, the great chain of being, or a divine guiding hand.

**CONCEPT FIX** Even though evolution is foundational to the understanding of biology, there is no subject in biology that is more poorly understood by the average person, and plagued by misconception by the average student, as evolution. **Figure 16.17** addresses a number of the most common misconceptions about evolution and natural selection.

**STUDY BREAK QUESTIONS**

1. What does it mean when we say mutations are *random*?
2. What role does phenotype play in natural selection?
3. Explain why natural selection will never lead to perfection.

FIGURE 16.16 **Experimental Research**

## Adaptation of *E. coli* to a Change in Temperature

**Question:** Would growing a culture of bacteria for 2000 generations at 32°C lead to adaptation?

**Experiment:** Two populations of the bacterium *E. coli* were started from a single colony (one genotype). One population is designated the Ancestral strain, the other the Evolved strain.

To determine if the Evolved cells actually adapted to 32°C, the growth rates of the Ancestral and Evolved strains were calculated, and the relative fitness (w) determined as

$$\text{Relative fitness (w)} = \frac{\text{Growth rate of Evolved population}}{\text{Growth rate of Ancestral population}}$$

If w = 1, then no adaptation has occurred, as their growth rates would be equal. If w > 1, then adaptation has occurred because the Evolved population grows faster at that temperature than the Ancestral strain. If w < 1, then the Evolved strain, for some reason, grows less well than the Ancestral strain.

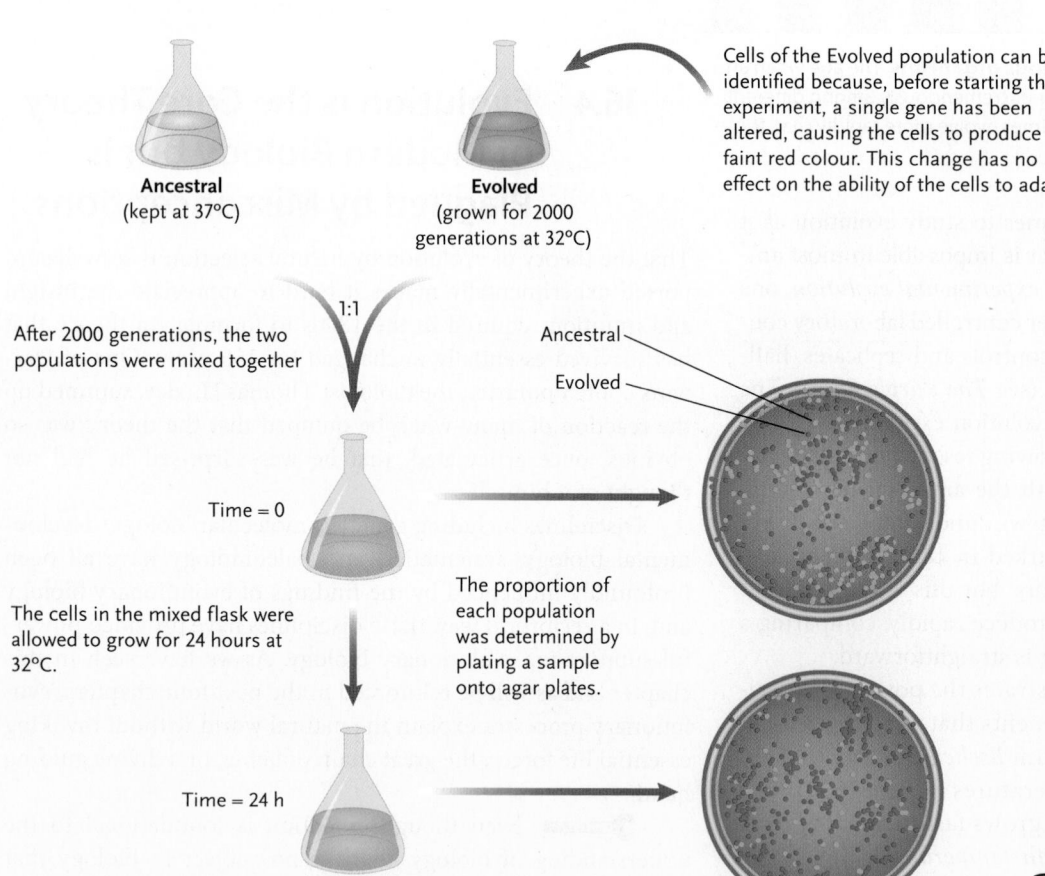

Cells of the Evolved population can be identified because, before starting the experiment, a single gene has been altered, causing the cells to produce a faint red colour. This change has no effect on the ability of the cells to adapt.

**Ancestral** (kept at 37°C)

**Evolved** (grown for 2000 generations at 32°C)

1:1

After 2000 generations, the two populations were mixed together

Ancestral
Evolved

Time = 0

The cells in the mixed flask were allowed to grow for 24 hours at 32°C.

The proportion of each population was determined by plating a sample onto agar plates.

Time = 24 h

This experiment comparing the growth of the Evolved population (32°C for 2000 generations) with the Ancestral population (maintained at 37°C) was conducted at a range of temperatures, from 20°C to 42°C, with the relative fitness calculated at each temperature.

**Results:** The data presented below show the Evolved strain did grow better than the Ancestral strain when growth was measured at temperatures between 20°C and 35°C. This results in a relative fitness (w) of greater than 1. However, at temperatures closer to 40°C, the Ancestral strain, which is adapted to 37°C, grew better than the Evolved strain, resulting in the relative fitness (w) being less than 1.

**Conclusion:** The results indicate that adaptation of the Evolved strain occurred. The data indicate that the relative fitness was greater than 1 at lower growth temperatures, compared to the Ancestral strain. This is what you would predict if evolution had occurred.

Source: Based on data from Albert F. Bennett and Richard E. Lenski, "Evolutionary Adaptation to Temperature II. Thermal Niches of Experimental Lines of Escherichia coli," *Evolution*, Vol. 47, No. 1 (Feb., 1993), pp. 1-12

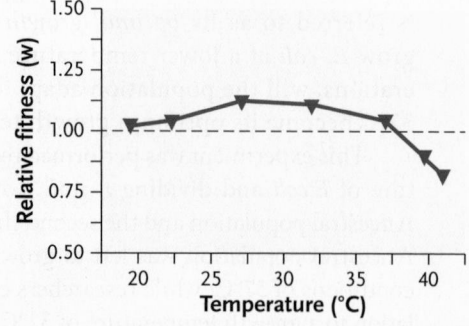

FIGURE 16.17 **Common misconceptions about evolution**

**Evolution and natural selection are the same thing.**

Natural selection is a major mechanism that causes change (evolution) in a population and one that results in adaptation. But natural selection is not the only process that causes evolution. We will discuss the other mechanisms in Chapter 18.

**Evolution occurs slowly.**

The rate of evolution is controlled by a number of factors, one of which is generation time. Bacteria and viruses can evolve very quickly.

**Selection acts on individuals; therefore, individuals evolve.**

Selection does act on individuals that have particular beneficial traits. But the individual cannot change. What changes over time is the makeup of the population.

**Natural selection is not directed.**

Because natural selection can result in some remarkable adaptations, it is tempting to think of it as a force or guiding hand that will lead to perfection. Natural selection is mindless and mechanistic. It just selects among whatever variations exist within the population.

**Because it is driven by mutation, evolution by natural selection is a random process.**

It is true that mutations occur randomly in a genome, and thus changes to traits are random. But natural selection is not random. It selects individuals in a population with certain traits. This results in adaption and increased fitness over time.

**Favourable traits arise in response to a change in the environment.**

Traits that increase the fitness of particular individuals in response to a change in the environment already exist within the population. These came about by random mutation at some time in the past. The change in the environment increases the proportion of individuals with specific traits because they are advantageous.

**Selection acts on the genotype because that is what is inherited.**

Selection that takes place in the environment is based on the specific phenotype of an organism—its traits, not the underlying genotype.

**Humans have stopped evolving.**

It is true that because modern humans can modify their environments, we do not face the same threats to reproduction and survival as our ancestors. Humans still evolve; just differently. Recent evolution of human traits that protect against malaria and the development of lactose tolerance are two examples of recent human evolution.

# Summary Illustration

First proposed by Charles Darwin, natural selection is a mechanism for how species change over time, or evolve. Within a population, there are individuals with certain inherited traits who are better able to survive and reproduce in a particular environment than those without the traits. These advantageous traits become more common in the next generation. From generation to generation, natural selection causes a population to change, or adapt, which can eventually result in the development of a different species.

A population of finches in South America all have small beaks and they feed on plants that produce small seeds.

The island has limited food resources, and is dominated by plants that produce larger seeds.

The birds with larger beaks are more likely to survive and reproduce because they happen to be better adapted to this new environment.

Birds of the next generation (shown here) will tend to have larger beaks.

- - -GTCATGAA- - -   - - -GTCACGAA- - -

A **random mutation** occurs to a gene involved in beak development. Offspring with this mutation have beaks that are larger than offspring that don't have the mutation.

The population migrates to one of the Galapagos Islands.

The offspring vary in beak size.

After many generations, the birds that migrated to the island in the Galapagos will not only have large beaks but also develop other traits that make them distinct from the original population in South America. They will become a distinctly different species.

## Recall/Understand

1. Which of the following did Aristotle propose?
   a. that acquired traits were inherited
   b. that humans are just one of the branches of the evolutionary tree, along with other organisms
   c. that humans are at the top of the evolutionary ladder just below perfection
   d. the existence of God, who created each organism

2. Natural selection acts on _____, with the consequences occurring in _____.
   a. populations; individuals
   b. individuals; the same individuals
   c. individuals; populations
   d. populations; the same populations

3. Which of these statements did Lamarck propose?
   a. There are perfect organisms.
   b. God created organisms.
   c. Species do not change over time.
   d. Acquired characteristics are inheritable.

4. The wings of bats, the forelegs of pigs, and the flippers of dolphins are examples of which of the following?
   a. vestigial structures
   b. homologous structures
   c. acquired characteristics
   d. artificial selection

5. Which of these statements did Darwin mean by "descent with modification"?
   a. that species modifications depend on their ancestors
   b. that species with modifications all have a common ancestor
   c. that species descended from a common ancestor are each adapted, and therefore modified to the particular environment they live in
   d. that species descended from different ancestors have modified characteristics

## Apply/Analyze

6. Which of these people was the first strong proponent of natural theology?
   a. Jean Baptiste de Lamarck
   b. Charles Darwin
   c. Carolus Linnaeus
   d. Aristotle

7. Bioinformatics is a field of science that utilizes genetic sequence comparisons. Which of the following is most likely one of its most basic assumptions?
   a. perfection of organisms
   b. artificial selection
   c. Lamarckian hypothesis
   d. descent with modification

8. Which of these factors should you use if you want to hypothesize that an extinct glyptodont is related to a living nine-banded armadillo?
   a. They lived at different times.
   b. They lived at a same time.
   c. Their body size is the same.
   d. They obviously resemble each other.

9. Darwin's theory *excluded* one of the following Lamarckian ideas. Which one?
   a. Organisms change in response to their environments.
   b. Changes that an organism acquires during its lifetime are passed to its offspring.
   c. All species change with time.
   d. Changes are passed from one generation to the next.

## Create/Evaluate

10. Many of the characteristics we see in living organisms are adaptations to environments in which their ancestors lived, rather than to the environments in which they live today. Which of these statements best explains the reasoning behind this statement?
    a. Natural selection cannot predict characteristics of future environments.
    b. The ancestors' environments were already perfect and their adaptations were adequate.
    c. Natural selection acts on organisms that live in environments that do not change much.
    d. The environmental conditions of the ancestors are the same as those of the descendants.

11. Compare evolution with natural selection.

12. Explain why evolution by natural selection is a non-random process.

13. Which three observations influenced Darwin to infer that individuals within a population compete for limited resources?

14. Which two observations influenced Darwin to infer that hereditary characteristics may allow some individuals to survive longer and reproduce more than others?

15. Consider the monarch butterfly, which feeds on toxic dandelions. Explain why this is an excellent example of protection conferred by ingested cardenolides.

# Chapter Roadmap

## Microevolution: Changes within Populations

In this chapter we look at evolution at the scale of the population. We examine the factors that cause a population to change its genetic make-up from one generation to the next; natural selection is just one of the factors.

### 17.1 Variation in Natural Populations

The phenotypic variation within a population can be influenced by genotype and the environment.

### 17.2 Population Genetics

How does one actually determine if genetic variation exists within a population and if it changes over time?

**From Chapter 9**

### 17.3 The Agents of Microevolution

Four processes can result in a change in allele frequencies from one generation to the next: gene flow, genetic drift, mutation, and natural selection.

### 17.4 Non-random Mating

One requirement of Hardy–Weinberg equilibrium is that mating with respect to genotype is random, but non-random mating is quite common.

### 17.5 Maintaining Genetic and Phenotypic Variation

There exist a number of mechanisms that maintain genetic and therefore phenotypic diversity within populations.

# Microevolution: Changes within Populations

# 17

**Why it matters...** Humpback whales (*Megaptera novaeangliae*) essentially have a global distribution consisting of a number of migrating populations, including the Southern Hemisphere and North Pacific populations. As a result of an international agreement made in 1966 that limited whaling, humpback numbers have rebounded to about 80 000 individuals today. One particularly interesting population of humpbacks that is comprised of about 100 individuals is found localized to the Arabian Sea. While most humpbacks are known to undertake long migrations moving from feeding grounds at northern latitudes to breeding grounds near the equator, the Arabian Sea humpback whales (ASHW) are peculiar in that they do not migrate.

To investigate the population structure of the ASHW compared to the Southern Hemisphere and North Pacific populations, researchers isolated DNA from 67 ASHW and compared it to a similar number of whales from the Southern Hemisphere and North Pacific Populations. Based on DNA sequence differences, researchers were able to conclude that the ASHW was most similar to the population in the Southern Hemisphere, yet different enough that they estimated that the two populations separated about 70 000 years ago. The timing of the divergence seems to coincide with glaciation events that took place at the time.

Using sophisticated molecular analyses based on the DNA sequence data, the researchers were also able to determine that the population of ASHW used to be much larger, but had shrunk due to periodic decreases in food supply and illegal Soviet whaling that was prevalent in the 1960s. These events that cause a sudden drop in population size are called *bottlenecks* and are of concern because, along with decreased numbers, there is also a decrease in the genetic diversity of the population. As we will discuss, small populations that are the result of bottlenecks with low genetic diversity are much more susceptible to disease and have limited ability to survive unfavourable environmental changes.

Because of their large numbers worldwide, humpbacks are classified as "Least Concern" by the International Union for Conservation of Nature (IUCN). But, based on the recent finds on the small population localized to the Arabian Sea, the authors recommend that the status of this particular population should be changed from "Endangered" to "Critically Endangered."

The distinct nature of the ASHW is a result of **microevolution**—change in the genetic makeup of a population from one generation to the next. In this chapter, we will discuss the processes that can drive microevolutionary change. We first examine the extensive variation that exists within natural populations. We then take a detailed look at the most important processes that alter genetic variation within populations, causing microevolutionary change. Finally, we consider how microevolution can fine-tune the functioning of populations within their environments.

## 17.1 Variation in Natural Populations

In most species, the members of a population look pretty much alike. However, even those that look alike, such as the *Cerion* snails in **Figure 17.1**, are not identical. With a scale and ruler, you could detect differences in their weight, as well as in the length and diameter of their shells. With suitable techniques, you could also document variations in their individual biochemistry, physiology, internal anatomy, and behaviour. All these features are examples of **phenotypic variation**—differences in appearance or function.

### 17.1a Evolutionary Biologists Describe and Quantify Phenotypic Variation

Both Darwin and Wallace recognized the importance of heritable phenotypic variation within a population as a driver of natural selection. Some forms of a trait lead to greater reproductive success than other forms. Today, microevolutionary studies often begin by assessing the extent of phenotypic variation within populations. Most characters exhibit **quantitative variation**—individuals differ in small, incremental ways. For example, if you weighed everyone in your biology class, you would see that weight varies almost continuously from your lightest to your heaviest classmate. Humans also exhibit quantitative variation in the length of their toes, the number of hairs on their heads, and their height.

We usually display data on quantitative variation in a bar graph or, if the sample is large enough, as a curve (**Figure 17.2**).

**a. European garden snails** *(Cepaea nemoralis)*

**b. Bahaman land snails** *(Cerion christophei)*

**FIGURE 17.1 Phenotypic variation. (a)** Shells of European garden snails from a population in Scotland vary considerably in appearance. **(b)** By contrast, shells of land snails from a population in the Bahamas look very similar.

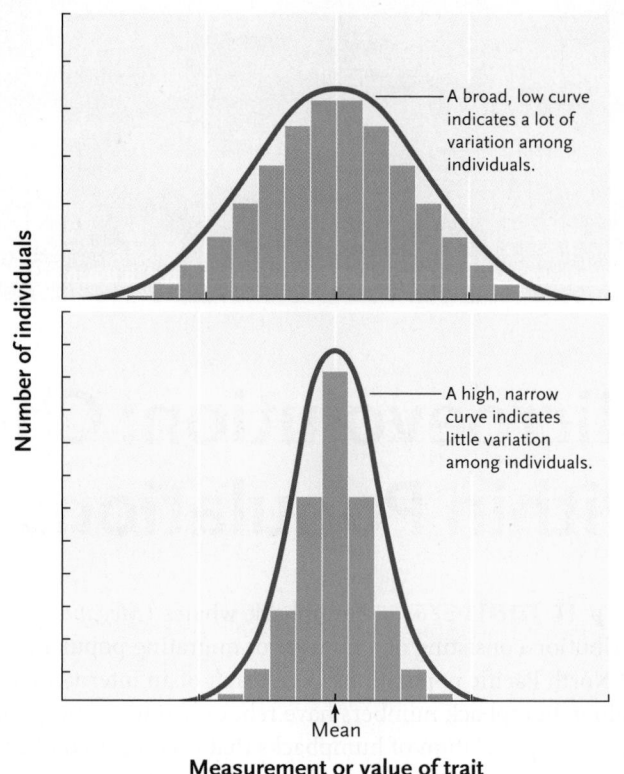

FIGURE 17.2 **Quantitative variation.** Many traits vary continuously among members of a population, and a bar graph of the data often approximates a bell-shaped curve. The mean defines the average value of the trait in the population, and the width of the curve is proportional to the variability among individuals.

The width of the curve is proportional to the amount of variation among individuals, and the *mean* describes the average value of the character. As you will see shortly, natural selection often changes the mean value of a character or its variability within populations.

Other characters, such as those Mendel studied (see Chapter 9), exhibit **qualitative variation**—they exist in two or more discrete states, and intermediate forms are absent. Snow geese, for example, have *either* blue *or* white feathers (**Figure 17.3**). The existence of discrete variants of a character is called a

FIGURE 17.3 **Qualitative variation.** Individual snow geese (*Chen caerulescens*) are either blue or white. Although both colours are present in many populations, geese tend to associate with others of the same colour.

FIGURE 17.4 **Environmental effects on phenotype.** Soil acidity affects the expression of the gene controlling flower colour in the common garden plant *Hydrangea macrophylla*. When grown in acidic soil, it produces deep blue flowers. In neutral or alkaline soil, its flowers are bright pink.

**polymorphism** (*poly* = many; *morphos* = form); we describe such traits as *polymorphic*. The *Cepaea nemoralis* snail shells in Figure 17.1a are polymorphic in background colour, number of stripes, and colour of stripes. Biochemical polymorphisms, such as the human A, B, AB, and O blood types, are also common.

We describe phenotypic polymorphisms quantitatively by calculating the *frequency* of each trait. For example, if you counted 123 blue snow geese and 369 white ones in a population of 492 geese, the frequency of the blue phenotype would be 123/492 or 0.25, and the frequency of the white phenotype would be 369/492 or 0.75.

## 17.1b Phenotypic Variation Can Have Genetic and Environmental Causes

Phenotypic variation within populations may be caused by genetic differences between individuals. But it can also be caused solely by environmental factors that individuals experience, or by an interaction between genetics and the environment. As a result, genetic and phenotypic variations may not be perfectly correlated. Under some circumstances, organisms with different genotypes exhibit the same phenotype. Conversely, organisms with the same genotype sometimes exhibit different phenotypes. For example, the acidity of soil influences flower colour in hydrangeas (**Figure 17.4**).

Knowing whether phenotypic variation is caused by genetic differences, environmental factors, or an interaction of the two is important because only genetically based variation is inherited and thus subject to evolutionary change. Moreover, knowing the causes of phenotypic variation has important practical applications. Suppose, for example, that one field of wheat produced more grain than another. If a difference in the availability of nutrients or water caused the difference in yield, a farmer might choose to fertilize or irrigate

the less productive field. But if the difference in productivity resulted from genetic differences between plants in the two fields, a farmer might plant only the more productive genotype. Because environmental factors can influence the expression of genes, an organism's phenotype is frequently the product of an interaction between its genotype and its environment. In our hypothetical example, the farmer may maximize yield by fertilizing and irrigating the more productive genotype of wheat.

How can we determine whether phenotypic variation is caused by environmental factors or genetic differences? We can test for an environmental cause experimentally by changing one environmental variable and measuring the effects on genetically similar subjects. For example, plants of the same genotype that are grown in full sunlight tend to have smaller leaves and shorter stems than plants grown in the shade. Breeding experiments can demonstrate the genetic basis of phenotypic variation. For example, Mendel inferred the genetic basis of qualitative traits, such as flower colour in peas, by crossing plants with different phenotypes. Breeding experiments are not always practical, however, particularly for organisms with long generation times. Ethical concerns also render these techniques unthinkable for humans. Instead, researchers often study the inheritance of particular traits by analyzing genealogical pedigrees, as discussed in Chapter 10.

### STUDY BREAK QUESTIONS

1. If a population of skunks includes some individuals with stripes and others with spots, would you describe the variation as quantitative or qualitative?
2. What factors contribute to phenotypic variation in a population?

## 17.2 Population Genetics

Most genetics research is focused on the structure of genes, their function, and how they are regulated. As a subdiscipline, **population genetics** is distinct in that it focuses on the genetic variation that exists within a population and how this changes over time as a result of evolution. To predict how certain factors may influence genetic variation, population geneticists first describe the genetic structure of a population. They then create and test hypotheses, formalized in mathematical models, to describe how evolutionary processes may change the genetic structure under specified conditions.

### 17.2a Evolution Is a Change in Allele Frequencies

One of the misconceptions discussed in the previous chapter is that evolution is driven solely by natural selection. Evolution can in fact be caused by four distinct processes: mutation, genetic drift, gene flow, and natural selection. We will strictly define and discuss each of these processes later in this chapter but, for now, just hold on to the understanding that each of these processes acting alone or in combination has the ability to change the traits in a population over time—each one can drive evolutionary change.

Recall from Chapter 16 that a trait is an inherited characteristic of an individual related to their appearance, abilities, and behaviours. Some traits are simple and are coded by a single gene; others are complex and are the result of many genes. **CONCEPT FIX** You may think that the genetic variation that exists in a population is because individuals of the same species have different genes. But that is not exactly right. Rather, the genetic variation is because individuals possess different versions of the same genes. That is, different individuals may carry different **alleles** for one or more genes (**Figure 17.5**). A gene can have several different alleles. In a haploid organism, only one of the possible alleles of a gene exists in a particular individual, but a diploid organism possesses two alleles for each gene. The location of a gene on a chromosome is termed the **locus**. 

In Chapter 16 we defined evolution simply as "species change over time". We can now refine that definition: **evolution** is a change in allele frequencies from one generation to the next. Changing how common a particular allele is within a population (its frequency) changes the genetic makeup of the population. As we will see later in this chapter, mutation, genetic drift, gene flow, and natural selection can each cause evolution because they can each change the frequency of alleles.

The total genetic variability of a population is represented by all the alleles at all the gene loci in all individuals within the population and is referred to as the **gene pool**. As shown in Figure 17.5, the term "gene pool" can also refer only to the frequency of the alleles of one locus within the population.

### 17.2b Populations Often Contain Substantial Genetic Variation

How much genetic variation actually exists within populations? In the 1960s, evolutionary biologists began to use the molecular technique of gel electrophoresis (see Chapter 14) to to detect the presence and size of various proteins. Scientists were able to detect protein differences between individuals, different populations, and different species. For example, the enzyme hexokinase catalyzes the same reaction in different species, but the primary sequence of the enzyme is not identical in those species. The amino acid sequences among different species are similar, but they aren't identical.

Differences in the amino acid sequence of a protein reflect changes in the gene sequence; and even within individuals of the same species, gene sequences are often different. A difference in the nucleotide sequence of a given gene in different individuals of a species is referred to as a **polymorphism**. This means that the gene occurs in different "forms" in the population. This is the same as saying that the gene has different alleles in the population.

Today, advances in technology have lowered the cost of DNA sequencing, which has allowed scientists to survey genetic

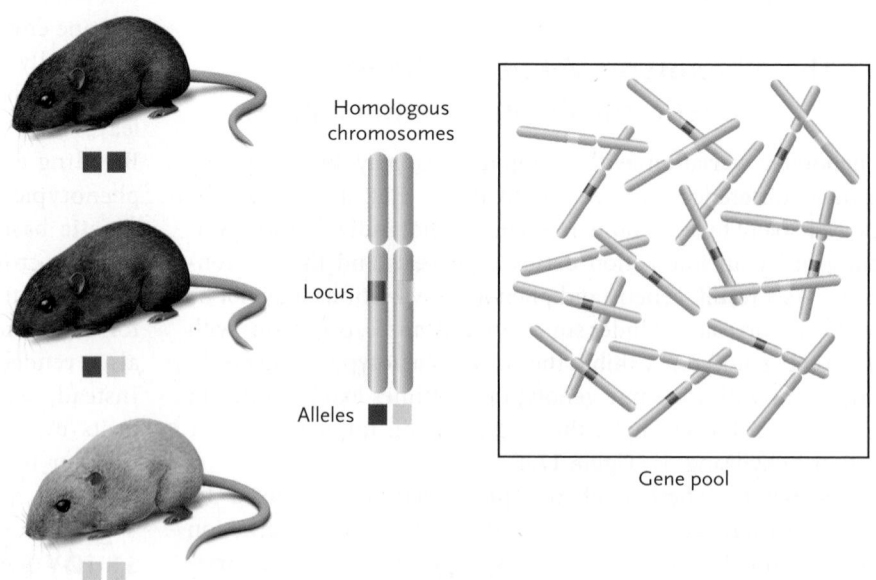

**FIGURE 17.5 Alleles, a locus, and a gene pool.** Fur colour in this mouse is controlled by a single gene, which is located at its locus on homologous chromosomes. The gene for fur colour has two forms, or alleles (brown and yellow). The brown allele is dominant to yellow since, in the heterozygous form, the mouse is brown. The total of all alleles for fur colour in the population is the gene pool for this particular locus.

variation directly and, as a result, researchers have accumulated an astounding knowledge of the sequences of entire genomes. Research has shown that both protein-coding and non-coding regions of DNA harbour extensive genetic variation. This genetic variation may exist within the two copies of a given gene found in heterozygous individuals, as well as between individuals found within a given population, as well as within different populations and different species. A major facet of research in DNA polymorphisms is the study of single-nucleotide polymorphisms (SNPs, also called "snips"; **Figure 17.6**). These single-nucleotide differences can exist between individuals and have been shown to account for about 90% of the genetic variation found in humans.

Genetic variation, the raw material of evolutionary change, has two potential sources: the production of new alleles and the rearrangement of existing alleles into new combinations. As we will discuss later in this chapter, most new alleles arise from a wide range of processes that result in mutation to DNA. Chapter 8 showed how meiosis is a powerful engine for creating novel arrangements of existing alleles through crossing-over between homologous chromosomes, independent assortment of non-homologous chromosomes, and random fertilizations between genetically different sperm and eggs. For example, an organism might carry the alleles *tS* (read as "small *t*, big *s*") on one chromosome, while on the homologous chromosome there are *Ts*. Recombinant offspring from this cross could have the novel arrangement of *TS* alleles on one of its chromosomes. This shuffling of alleles into new combinations can produce an extraordinary number of novel genotypes in the next generation. By one estimate, more than $10^{600}$ combinations of alleles are possible in human gametes, yet there are fewer than $10^{10}$ humans alive today. So, unless you have an identical twin, it is extremely unlikely that another person with your genotype has ever lived or ever will.

## 17.2c Genetic Structure of Populations

Until the development of the tools of molecular biology, determining the genotype that is responsible for a specific phenotype was often very difficult and thus was a major hindrance to population genetics. As well, not only are some traits the products of many genes, but many traits are strongly influenced by the environment. Because of these compounding factors, early population geneticists chose systems to study where a clearly identifiable heritable trait was controlled by a single gene.

A simple system that has been used to study microevolutionary processes is the diploid plant snapdragon (*Antirrhinum* spp.). Flower colour in snapdragons is controlled by a single gene, referred to as the *flower colour locus, C*. Individuals that are homozygous for the $C^R$ allele ($C^R C^R$) have red flowers; individuals that are homozygous for the $C^W$ allele ($C^W C^W$) have white flowers; heterozygotes ($C^R C^W$) have pink flowers. Because of the three distinct phenotypes, it is straightforward to determine the frequency of each genotype in a population and then calculate the frequency of the two alleles.

**Table 17.1** presents data from a population of snapdragons that consists of 1000 individual plants. By examination of the various plant colours within the population, one can determine the frequency of the three genotypes as $C^R C^R = 0.45$, $C^R C^W = 0.5$, and $C^W C^W = 0.05$. Note that the sum of the three genotype frequencies must equal 1.

Now let's calculate the allele frequencies. When a single locus has two alleles, population geneticists denote the frequency of one allele with the letter $p$ and the frequency of the second allele with the letter $q$. Looking at Table 17.1, you can see that the allele frequency of the $C^R$ allele ($p$) equals 0.7, while the allele frequency of the $C^W$ ($q$) allele is 0.3. Like genotype frequencies, the sum of the two allele frequencies must equal 1.

Once we have described the population by determining how common each genotype and allele is (their frequencies), the next question a population geneticist may ask might be, "Is the population evolving?" or "Is there evidence for evolution in the gene controlling flower colour?"

## 17.2d The Hardy–Weinberg Principle Is a Null Hypothesis That Defines a Population That Is Not Evolving

As discussed in *The Purple Pages*, an important aspect of experimental design is the use of a *control*. While some individuals are subjected to an experimental

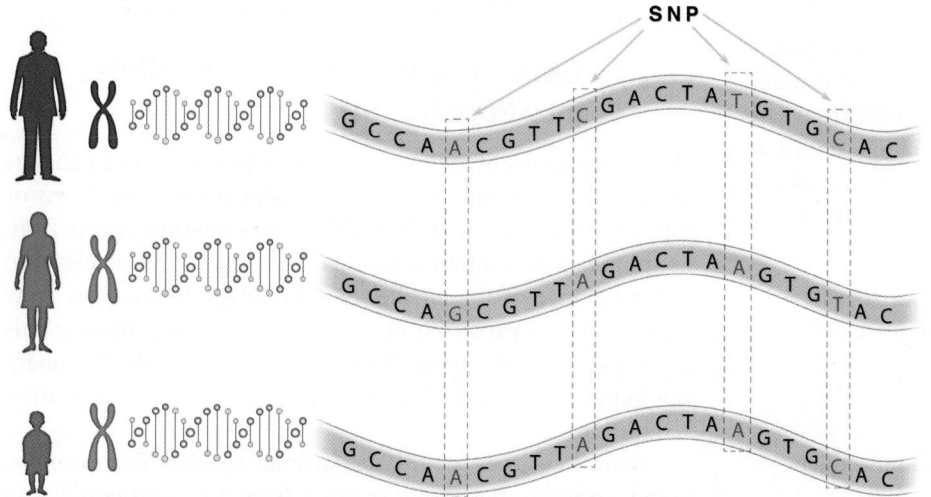

**FIGURE 17.6 The genetic variation that exists within a population includes single-nucleotide differences, called *SNPs*, within the same gene**

Monica Schneider/Science Source

## TABLE 17.1 | Calculation of Genotype Frequencies and Allele Frequencies for the Snapdragon Flower Colour Locus (C)

Because each diploid individual has two alleles at each gene locus, a sample of 1000 individuals has a total of 2000 alleles at the C locus.

| Flower Colour Phenotype | Genotype | Number of Individuals | Genotype Frequency[1] | Total Number of $C^R$ Alleles[2] | Total Number of $C^W$ Alleles[2] |
|---|---|---|---|---|---|
| Red | $C^R C^R$ | 450 | 450/1000 = 0.45 | 2 × 450 = 900 | 0 × 450 = 0 |
| Pink | $C^R C^W$ | 500 | 500/1000 = 0.50 | 1 × 500 = 500 | 1 × 500 = 500 |
| White | $C^W C^W$ | 50 | 50/1000 = 0.05 | 0 × 50 = 0 | 2 × 50 = 100 |
| | Total | 1000 | 0.45 + 0.50 + 0.05 = 1.0 | 1400 | 600 |

To calculate allele frequencies, use the total of 1400 + 600 = 2000 alleles in the sample:

$p$ = frequency of $C^R$ allele = 1400/2000 = 0.7.

$q$ = frequency of $C^W$ allele = 600/2000 = 0.3.

$p + q$ = 0.7 + 0.3 = 1.0.

[1] Genotype frequency = the number of individuals possessing a particular genotype divided by the total number of individuals in the sample.

[2] Total number of $C^R$ or $C^W$ alleles = the number of $C^R$ or $C^W$ alleles present in one individual with a particular genotype multiplied by the number of individuals with that genotype.

treatment, the control individuals are left alone. The importance of the control is that it tells researchers what they would see if the experimental treatment had no effect. However, in field studies using observational rather than experimental data, there is often no suitable control. In such cases, investigators develop conceptual models, from which they can state a **null hypothesis**. The null hypothesis is a prediction of what researchers would see if that particular factor had no effect.

A null hypothesis related to population genetics that was asked in the early twentieth century was: *What would the genetic makeup of a population be at a particular locus if the population was not evolving?* The mathematical method used to answer this is known as the **Hardy–Weinberg principle**, named after an English mathematician, G. H. Hardy, and a German physician, Wilhelm Weinberg.

The Hardy–Weinberg principle is a mathematical model that specifies the conditions that are necessary so that allele frequencies and genotype frequencies do not change from one generation to the next (**Figure 17.7**). This state is referred to as **genetic equilibrium**. According to the Hardy–Weinberg model, genetic equilibrium is possible only if *all* the following conditions are met:

1. The population is closed to migration from other populations.
2. The population is infinite in size.
3. No mutation is occurring in the population.
4. All genotypes in the population survive and reproduce equally well.
5. Individuals in the population mate randomly with respect to genotype.

**STUDY BREAK QUESTIONS**

1. Define *allele*, *locus*, and *gene pool*.
2. Why is the Hardy–Weinberg principle considered a null model of evolution?
3. If the conditions of the Hardy–Weinberg principle are met, when will genotype frequencies stop changing?

## 17.3 The Agents of Microevolution

A population's allele frequencies will change over time if one or more of the five conditions of the Hardy–Weinberg model are violated. In this section, we discuss the processes that can disrupt Hardy–Weinberg equilibrium and thus cause evolution: gene flow, genetic drift, mutation, and natural selection.

### 17.3a Gene Flow Introduces New Alleles into Populations

The allele and genotype frequencies of a population can change due to migration into or out of the population. Organisms or their gametes (e.g., the pollen of flowers) sometimes move from one population to another and may introduce novel alleles into a population, shifting its allele and genotype frequencies away from the values predicted by the Hardy–Weinberg model. This phenomenon, called **gene flow**, violates the Hardy–Weinberg requirement that populations must be closed to migration (Condition 1).

Gene flow is seen in some animal species. For example, young male baboons typically move from one local population to another after experiencing aggressive behaviour by older males. Many marine invertebrates disperse long distances as

FIGURE 17.7     **Research Method**

## Using the Hardy–Weinberg Principle

To see how the Hardy–Weinberg principle can be applied, we will analyze the snapdragon flower colour locus, using the hypothetical population of 1000 plants described in Table 17.1. This locus includes two alleles: $C^R$ (with its frequency designated as $p$) and $C^W$ (with its frequency designated as $q$), and three genotypes: homozygous $C^R C^R$, heterozygous $C^R C^W$, and homozygous $C^W C^W$. Table 17.1 lists the number of plants with each genotype: 450 have red flowers ($C^R C^R$), 500 have pink flowers ($C^R C^W$), and 50 have white flowers ($C^W C^W$). It also shows the calculation of both the genotype frequencies ($C^R C^R = 0.45$, $C^R C^W = 0.50$, and $C^W C^W = 0.05$) and the allele frequencies ($p = 0.7$ and $q = 0.3$) for the population.

### 1. Allele frequencies in parents and gametes

Let's assume for simplicity that each individual produces only two gametes, and that both gametes contribute to the production of offspring. This assumption is unrealistic, of course, but it meets the Hardy–Weinberg requirement that all individuals in the population contribute equally to the next generation. In each parent, the two alleles segregate and end up in different gametes:

450 $C^R C^R$ individuals produce → 900 $C^R$ gametes

500 $C^R C^W$ individuals produce → 500 $C^R$ gametes + 500 $C^W$ gametes

50 $C^W C^W$ individuals produce → 100 $C^W$ gametes

You can readily see that 1400 of the 2000 total gametes carry the $C^R$ allele and 600 carry the $C^W$ allele. The frequency of $C^R$ gametes is 1400/2000, or 0.7, which is equal to $p$; the frequency of $C^W$ gametes is 600/2000 or 0.3, which is equal to $q$. Thus, the allele frequencies in the gametes are exactly the same as the allele frequencies in the parent generation. It could not be otherwise because each gamete carries one allele at each locus.

### 2. Genotype frequencies in offspring

Now assume that these gametes, both sperm and eggs, encounter each other at random. In other words, individuals reproduce without regard to the genotype of a potential mate. We can visualize the process of random mating in the mating table, shown here.

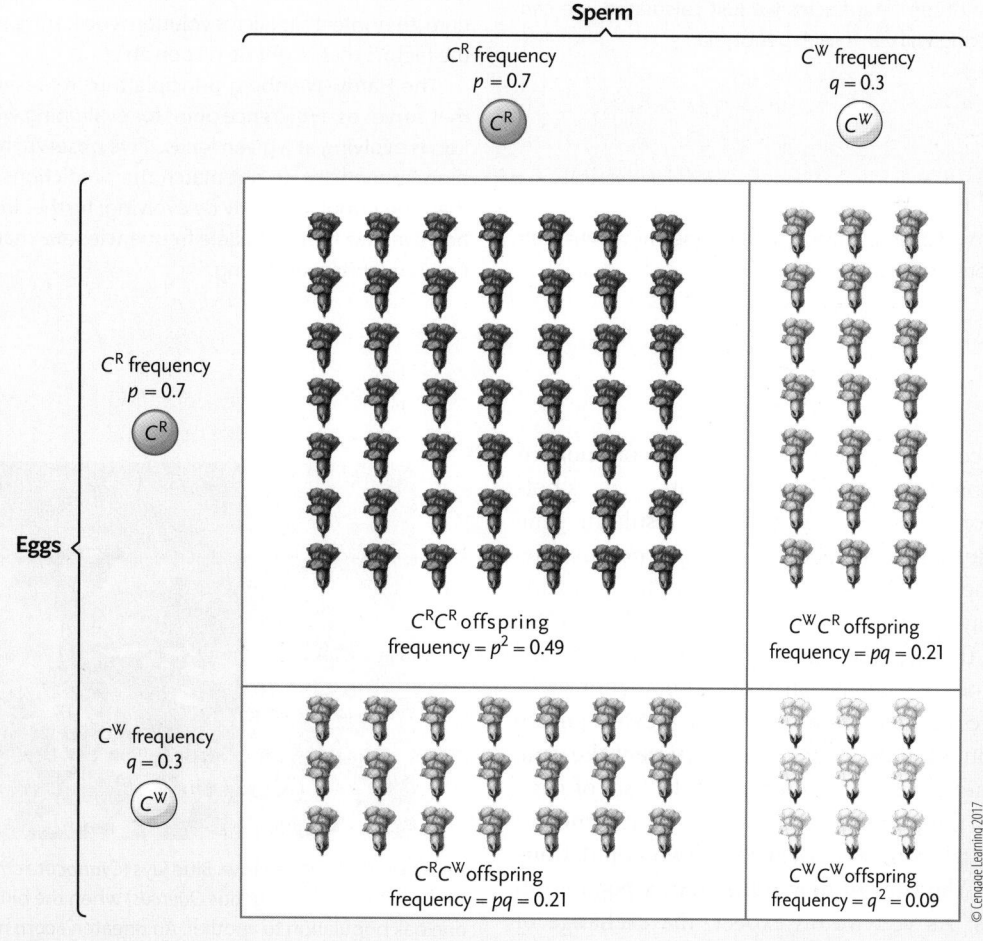

**Sperm**

$C^R$ frequency
$p = 0.7$
$C^R$

$C^W$ frequency
$q = 0.3$
$C^W$

**Eggs**

$C^R$ frequency
$p = 0.7$
$C^R$

$C^W$ frequency
$q = 0.3$
$C^W$

$C^R C^R$ offspring
frequency = $p^2 = 0.49$

$C^W C^R$ offspring
frequency = $pq = 0.21$

$C^R C^W$ offspring
frequency = $pq = 0.21$

$C^W C^W$ offspring
frequency = $q^2 = 0.09$

© Cengage Learning 2017

**Mating table**

*(Continued)*

FIGURE 17.7    **Research Method (*Continued*)**

We can also describe the consequences of random mating—$(p + q)$ sperm fertilizing $(p + q)$ eggs—with an equation that predicts the genotype frequencies in the offspring generation:

$$(p + q) \times (p + q) = p^2 + 2pq + q^2$$

If the population is at genetic equilibrium for this locus, $p^2$ is the predicted frequency of the $C^R C^R$ genotype, $2pq$ is the predicted frequency of the $C^R C^W$ genotype, and $q^2$ is the predicted frequency of the $C^W C^W$ genotype. Using the gamete frequencies determined above, we can calculate the predicted genotype frequencies in the next generation:

$$\text{frequency of } C^R C^R = p^2 = (0.7 \times 0.7) = 0.49$$

$$\text{frequency of } C^R C^W = 2pq = 2(0.7 \times 0.3) = 0.42$$

$$\text{frequency of } C^W C^W = q^2 = (0.3 \times 0.3) = 0.09$$

Notice that the predicted genotype frequencies in the offspring generation have changed from the genotype frequencies in the parent generation: the frequency of heterozygous individuals has decreased, and the frequencies of both types of homozygous individuals have increased. This result occurred because the starting population was *not in equilibrium* at this gene locus. In other words, the distribution of parent genotypes did not conform to the predicted $p^2 + 2pq + q^2$ distribution.

The 2000 gametes in our hypothetical population produced 1000 offspring. Using the genotype frequencies we just calculated, we can predict how many offspring will carry each genotype:

490 red ($C^R C^R$)

420 pink ($C^R C^W$)

90 white ($C^W C^W$)

In a real study, we would examine the offspring to see how well their numbers match these predictions.

### 3. Allele frequencies in offspring

What about the allele frequencies in the offspring? The Hardy–Weinberg principle predicts that they did not change. Let's calculate them and see. Using the method shown in Table 17. 1 and the prime symbol (′) to indicate offspring allele frequencies

$$p' = ([2 \times 490] + 420)/2000 = 1400/2000 = 0.7$$

$$q' = ([2 \times 90] + 420)/2000 = 600/2000 = 0.3$$

You can see from this calculation that the allele frequencies did not change from one generation to the next, even though the alleles were rearranged to produce different proportions of the three genotypes.

### 4. Genetic equilibrium in future generations

The population is now at genetic equilibrium for the flower colour locus; neither the genotype frequencies nor the allele frequencies will change in succeeding generations as long as the population meets the conditions specified in the Hardy–Weinberg model. To verify this, you can calculate the allele frequencies of the gametes for this offspring generation and predict the genotype frequencies and allele frequencies for a third generation. You could continue calculating until you ran out of either paper or patience, but these frequencies will not change.

Researchers use calculations like these to determine whether an actual population is near its predicted genetic equilibrium for one or more gene loci. When they discover that a population is not at equilibrium, they infer that microevolution is occurring, and they can investigate the factors that might be responsible.

The Hardy–Weinberg principle thus represents the null hypothesis that serves as a reference point for evaluating whether or not a population is evolving at a given locus. If we observe that a population's genotype frequencies do not match the predictions of the null hypothesis, then the population *may be* evolving; further information is needed. If, however, we find that allele frequencies are changing over time, evolution is definitely occurring.

---

larvae carried by ocean currents. Gene flow is common in many plant populations in which dispersal agents, such as pollen-carrying wind or seed-carrying animals, result in gene flow. For example, blue jays foster gene flow among populations of oaks by carrying acorns from nut-bearing trees to their winter caches, which may be as much as a mile away **(Figure 17.8)**. Transported acorns that go uneaten may germinate and contribute to the gene pool of a neighbouring oak population.

The importance of gene flow in driving evolutionary change within a population depends on how different the gene pool is between it and other populations and the rate of gene flow into and out of the population. Since the environmental conditions and thus selection experienced by two populations will not be identical, the flow of new alleles into a population may alter its fitness. As you would expect, the exchange of alleles between two populations will decrease the genetic differences between the populations, making them more similar.

**FIGURE 17.8  Gene flow.** Blue jays (*Cyanocitta cristata*) serve as agents of gene flow for oaks (genus *Quercus*) when the birds carry acorns from one oak population to another. An uneaten acorn may germinate and contribute to the gene pool of the population into which it was carried.

## 17.3b Genetic Drift Reduces Genetic Variability within Populations

Sometimes allele frequencies in a population change from one generation to the next simply by chance. This phenomenon, known as **genetic drift**, causes allele frequencies to move up and down in unpredictable ways. Genetic drift can have a major impact on allele frequencies, especially in small populations. This then clearly violates the Hardy–Weinberg assumption of infinitely large population size (Condition 2). Drift generally leads to reduced genetic diversity in small populations because rare alleles are often lost. Genetic drift is driven by two circumstances: founder effects and population bottlenecks.

**FOUNDER EFFECT** When a few individuals colonize a distant locality and start a new population, they carry only a small sample of the parent population's genetic variation. By chance, some alleles may be totally missing from the new population, whereas other alleles that were rare in the original population might be common. This change in the gene pool is called the **founder effect**.

The human medical literature provides some of the best-documented examples of the founder effect. The Old Order Amish, an essentially closed religious community in Lancaster County, Pennsylvania, have an exceptionally high incidence of Ellis–van Creveld syndrome, a genetic disorder caused by a recessive allele. In the homozygous state, the allele produces dwarfism, shortened limbs, and polydactyly (extra fingers). Genetic analysis indicates that, while the incidence of the disease in the general population is about 1 in 60 000, it occurs at a rate of 1 in 200 within the Amish of Lancaster County, with as many as 13% of individuals in the community being heterozygous carriers of the allele.

The high incidence of Ellis–van Creveld syndrome is explained by the founder effect. The Amish community was originally founded by a small group of people from Germany. In fact, the parents of all children with Ellis–van Creveld syndrome can be traced back to a single couple who immigrated to Eastern Pennsylvania in the mid-1700s. The custom of marrying only within the Amish community has led to a much higher incidence of a range of recessive disorders (see "Inbreeding Reduces Heterozygosity," later in this chapter).

**POPULATION BOTTLENECKS** Factors such as disease, starvation, and hunting may kill a large proportion of the individuals in a population, resulting in what is referred to as a *population bottleneck*. The large reduction in population size is associated with a decrease in the size of the gene pool and therefore the genetic diversity of the population. Alleles that were rare in the original population can be totally lost from the population in the event of a bottleneck (**Figure 17.9**).

In the late nineteenth century, for example, hunters nearly wiped out northern elephant seals (*Mirounga angustirostris*) along the Pacific coast of North America. Since the 1880s, when the species received protected status, the population has rebounded from about 20 individuals to more than 160 000

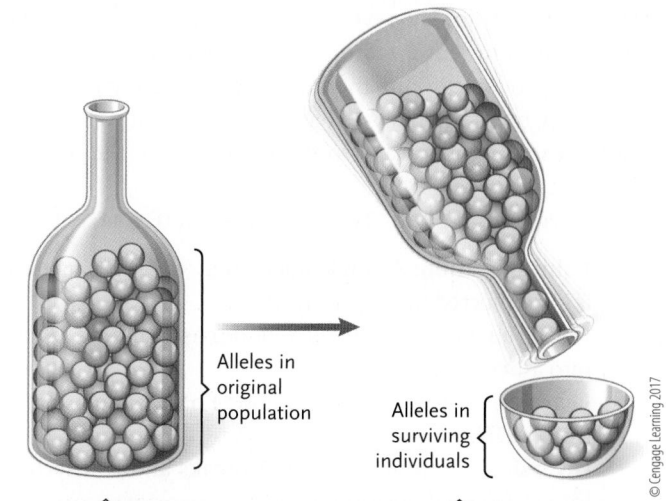

Alleles in original population

Alleles in surviving individuals

© Cengage Learning 2017

The gene pool of the original population, represented by a bottle filled with colored marbles, includes a locus with three alleles. Two of the alleles, represented by blue and green marbles, occur at high frequency; the third allele, represented by red marbles, occurs at low frequency.

If an environmental event randomly kills a large number of individuals in the population, the drastic reduction in population size is described as a population bottleneck. The process is analogous to shaking only a few of the marbles—the survivors—through the neck of the bottle. As a consequence of chance events associated with population bottlenecks, surviving individuals may not have the same allele frequencies as the original population. Rare alleles are inevitably lost.

**FIGURE 17.9 A population bottleneck results in decreased genetic diversity and often the loss of rare alleles**

today. Many would view this as a huge success story of conservation. However, things are not as great as they may seem.

Since this large population is derived from a group of perhaps only 20 individuals, what was lost that can never be regained is the genetic diversity in the original large population. That is, there are far fewer alleles at any one locus in the gene pool today than in the original population.

Both the founder effect and population bottlenecks have important implications for conservation biology. Because, in both cases, they result in populations with very few individuals, there is very little genetic variability. The small size of the total gene pool will remain small regardless of how large the population will become. Endangered species can be protected from extinction, but the lack of genetic variability would suggest that the population will always be more susceptible to disease and less able to cope with environmental perturbations such as climate change.

## 17.3c Mutations Are Random and Create Genetic Novelty

A population can deviate from Hardy–Weinberg equilibrium by the introduction of mutation that can introduce new alleles and therefore change allele frequencies (Condition 3). A **mutation** is a change to the double-strand sequence of DNA. Common factors that cause mutation include radiation (e.g., UV light), which can actually damage individual nucleotides, and some hazardous chemicals that can interfere with

DNA replication. However, most mutations are not caused by some environmental factor, but occur as a result of normal cellular processes. This includes errors in copying DNA during DNA replication as well as the movement of transposable elements (Chapter 15) from one place in the genome to another.

There are five basic types of mutation (**Figure 17.10**):

**Point mutation:** A single nucleotide (base) is changed. This is also referred to as a *substitution*.

**Insertion:** One or more nucleotide base pairs are introduced into a DNA sequence.

**Deletion:** One or more nucleotide base pairs are removed from a DNA sequence.

**Inversion:** A segment of DNA breaks and is inserted back into its original position in the reverse orientation.

**Duplication:** DNA is copied twice. The duplication can be part of a gene, a whole gene, or an entire genome.

As mentioned earlier, genetic recombination between homologous chromosomes during meiosis (see Chapter 8) is a source of genetic variation in a population. But recombination is very precise and generally does not result in mutation.

Mutations can occur in the genomes of any cell (e.g., human skin cells). But it is important to realize that, for mutations to alter allele frequencies within a population, the mutation must occur in the DNA of germ-line cells, those that go on to produce gametes (e.g., sperm and egg). As well, mutations can be considered random and spontaneous events. This means that the precise location within a genome that they occur and when they occur cannot be predicted. Mutations are not directed by the selective pressures on a population to occur in specific genes. For example, mutations within a bacterial population exposed to higher than normal temperatures will not be localized to the genes of heat-sensitive enzymes resulting in the enzymes being better able to function at high temperatures.

Mutation does not tend to result in increased fitness. In fact, most mutations either have no effect on fitness (neutral) or they will be harmful (deleterious) to an organism. This can be explained by thinking of the gene that codes for a protein; let's use the example of the enzyme hexokinase again. What are the chances that a single base change (point mutation) to the hexokinase gene will actually improve the function of the enzyme it codes for? The chance is very small compared to the probability that such a change will have either no effect or actually alter the structure of the enzyme in a negative way (e.g., causing the protein to misfold).

Whether they are beneficial, neutral, or deleterious, how common are mutations? Findings by the research group of Daniel Hartl, who is now at Harvard University, have shed light on the actual rate of mutation through work studying a range of organisms, including yeast, a single cell eukaryote. Their findings indicate that there is about a 0.000 000 03% chance of any one base undergoing a point mutation. However, given a population of millions of yeast cells, each with a genome of about 12 million bases, mutations will arise in thousands of individual cells each generation. Research also indicates that duplications and deletions occur at a rate that is about a thousand times more common than point mutations. In humans, measuring the actual rate of mutation has become much easier in recent years as the cost of sequencing whole genomes has become far more reasonable. By sequencing the entire genomes of two siblings and their parents, it has been shown that each child had 70 mutations that were not found in either parent. This may sound like a lot, but it really isn't. The human genome consists of about three billion base pairs.

The importance of mutation to evolution is not that it allows for rapid change to a population; it doesn't. In fact, genetic drift, gene flow, and natural selection can all change allele frequencies faster. Rather, the value of mutation is that it is the only microevolutionary process that gives rise to genetic novelty. Natural selection is usually the most powerful mechanism driving evolutionary change, but selection is only choosing among alleles that already exist in the population. Natural selection does not create, for example, new proteins that have new advantageous functions. These come about when mutation causes DNA sequences

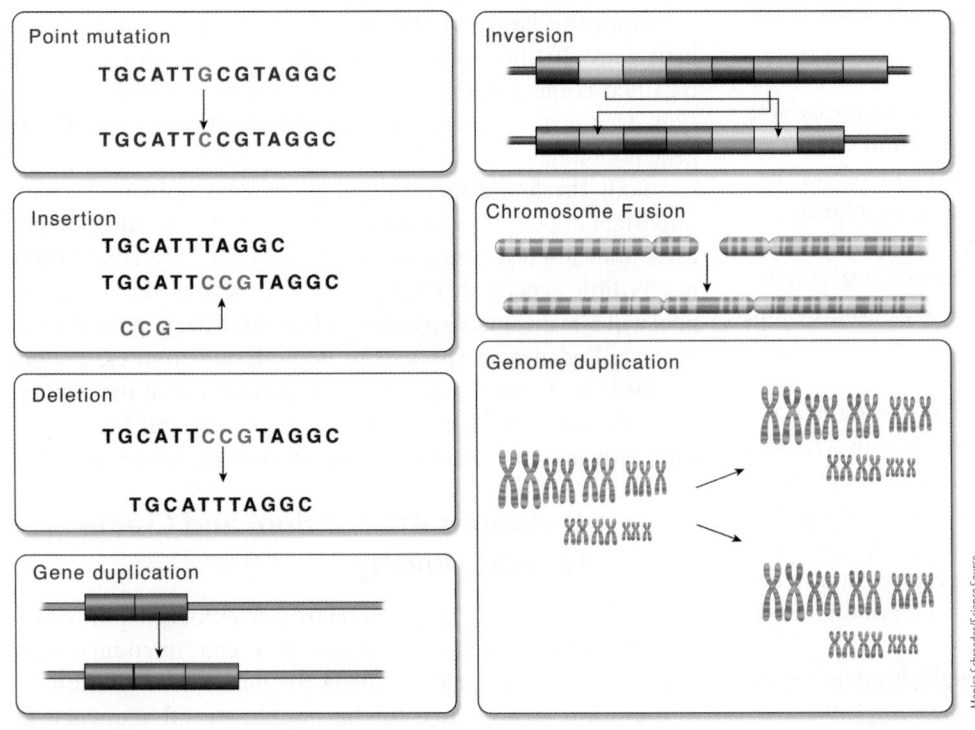

**FIGURE 17.10 There are several different types of mutations.** Each one changes the allele frequency by introducing novel alleles into a population.

Source: Zimmer, Emlen, *Evolution: Making Sense of Life*, Roberts and Company Publishers, 978-1936221363, Figure 5.13

Monika Schroeder/Science Source

to become rearranged into new combinations that give rise to new functions never seen before. If such a novelty is beneficial, the allele will become more common within the population through natural selection.

## 17.3d Natural Selection Shapes Genetic Variability by Favouring Some Traits over Others

As we discussed in Chapter 16, the process of natural selection favours some combination of traits over others, resulting in differential survivorship and reproduction. Since all genotypes in the population do not survive and reproduce equally well, natural selection violates Hardy–Weinberg equilibrium and causes allele and genotype frequencies to differ from those predicted by the model (Condition 4).

Biologists measure the effects of natural selection on phenotypic variation by recording changes in the mean and variability of characters over time. Three modes of natural selection have been identified: directional selection, stabilizing selection, and disruptive selection (**Figure 17.11**).

**DIRECTIONAL SELECTION** Traits undergo **directional selection** when individuals near one end of the phenotypic spectrum have the highest relative fitness. Directional selection shifts a trait away from the existing mean and toward the favoured extreme (see Figure 17.11a). After selection, the trait's mean value is higher or lower than before, and variability in the trait may be reduced.

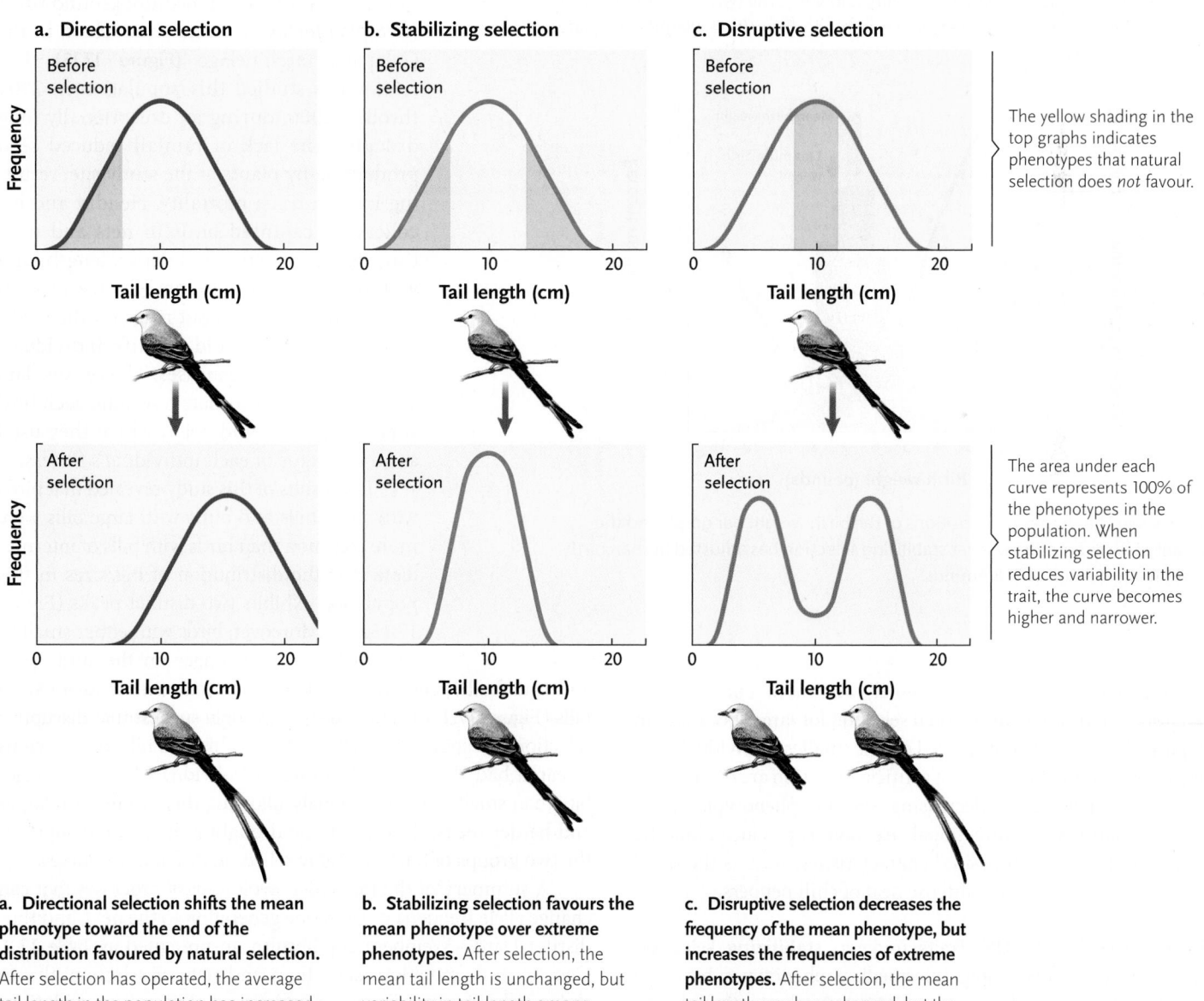

The yellow shading in the top graphs indicates phenotypes that natural selection does *not* favour.

The area under each curve represents 100% of the phenotypes in the population. When stabilizing selection reduces variability in the trait, the curve becomes higher and narrower.

**a. Directional selection shifts the mean phenotype toward the end of the distribution favoured by natural selection.** After selection has operated, the average tail length in the population has increased.

**b. Stabilizing selection favours the mean phenotype over extreme phenotypes.** After selection, the mean tail length is unchanged, but variability in tail length among individuals in the population has decreased.

**c. Disruptive selection decreases the frequency of the mean phenotype, but increases the frequencies of extreme phenotypes.** After selection, the mean tail length may be unchanged, but the variability in tail length among individuals has increased.

**FIGURE 17.11 Three modes of natural selection.** A hypothetic example using tail length of birds as the quantitative trait subject to selection

© Cengage Learning 2017

FIGURE 17.12   **Experimental Research**

## Do Humans Experience Stabilizing Selection?

**Hypothesis:** Human birth weight has been adjusted by natural selection.

**Null Hypothesis:** Natural selection has not affected human birth weight.

**Method:** Geneticists Luigi Cavalli-Sforza and Sir Walter Bodmer of Stanford University collected data on the variability in human birth weight—a character exhibiting quantitative variation—and on the mortality rates of babies born at different weights. They then searched for a relationship between birth weight and mortality rate by plotting both data sets on the same graph. A lack of correlation between birth weight and mortality rate would support the null hypothesis.

**Results:** When birth weight (the bar graph) and mortality rate (the curve) are plotted together, the mean birth weight is seen to be very close to the optimum birth weight (the weight at which mortality is lowest). The two data sets also show that few babies are born at the very low weights and very high weights associated with high mortality.

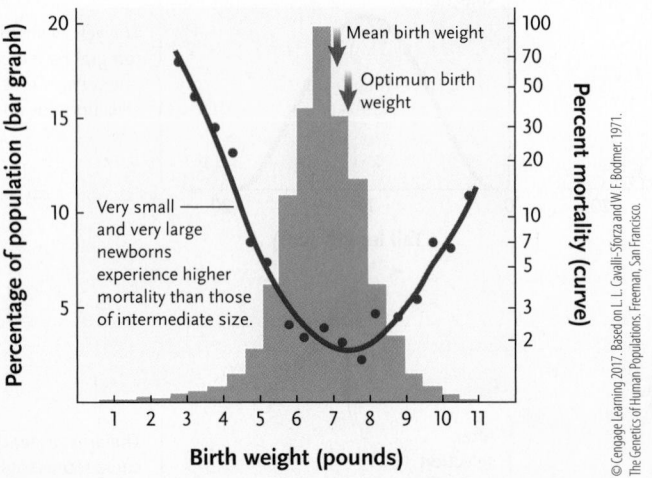

**Conclusion:** The shapes and positions of the birth weight bar graph and the mortality rate curve suggest that stabilizing selection has adjusted human birth weight to an average of 7–8 pounds.

Directional selection is extremely common. For example, predatory fish promote directional selection for larger body size in guppies when they selectively feed on the smallest individuals in a guppy population. Most cases of artificial selection are directional, aimed at increasing or decreasing specific phenotypic traits. Humans routinely use directional selection to produce domestic animals and crops with desired characteristics, such as the small size of Chihuahuas and the intense heat of chili peppers.

**STABILIZING SELECTION** Traits undergo **stabilizing selection** when individuals expressing intermediate phenotypes have the highest relative fitness (see Figure 17.11b). By eliminating phenotypic extremes, stabilizing selection reduces genetic and phenotypic variation, and increases the frequency of intermediate phenotypes. Stabilizing selection is probably the most common mode of natural

selection, affecting many familiar traits. For example, very small and very large human newborns are less likely to survive than those born at an intermediate weight (**Figure 17.12**).

**DISRUPTIVE SELECTION** Traits undergo **disruptive selection** when extreme phenotypes have higher relative fitness than intermediate phenotypes (see Figure 17.11c). Thus, alleles producing extreme phenotypes become more common. Under natural conditions, disruptive selection is much less common than directional selection and stabilizing selection.

Andrew P. Hendry, of McGill University, and his colleagues analyzed a likely case of disruptive selection on bill size in a population of the seed-eating medium ground finch (*Geospiza fortis*) on Santa Cruz Island in the Galápagos archipelago (**Figure 17.13**). The researchers studied this population in 2004 through 2006, during an exceptionally long drought. The lack of rainfall reduced seed production by plants at the study site, resulting in high finch mortality. Hendry and his colleagues captured birds in nets and used three measurements (bill depth, length, and width) to characterize the bill size of each individual. They also put rings on the birds' legs so that they could identify individuals during subsequent censuses. The census data allowed them to estimate how long each bird survived on the study plot, which they used as an indicator of each individual's fitness.

The results of this study revealed that birds with small bills and birds with large bills were more common than birds with bills of intermediate size: the distribution of bill sizes in this population exhibits two distinct peaks (Figure 17.13a, b). Moreover, birds with either small or large bills survived longer on the study plot, and thus had higher fitness, than birds with intermediate sized bills (Figure 17.13c). These results strongly suggest that disruptive selection is responsible for the polymorphism in bill size. Previous research had shown that large-billed individuals have a stronger bite than small-billed individuals, allowing them to feed on larger and harder seeds; thus, when the drought reduced food supplies, the two groups of birds probably relied on different resources.

A summary of the four microevolutionary processes that can change allele frequencies from one generation to the next, and thus disrupt Hardy–Weinberg equilibrium, in presented as **Table 17.2**. Genetic drift, mutation, gene flow, and natural selection all can change allele frequencies of a population and thus drive evolutionary change. However, as you see in Table 17.2, it is only natural selection that consistently improves the ability of a population to grow and reproduce in a particular environment, that is, to adapt.

**a. Small-billed and large-billed medium ground finches**
**(*Geospiza fortis*) from Santa Cruz island**

Dr. Andrew Hendry

**b. Distribution of bill sizes for birds marked in 2004**

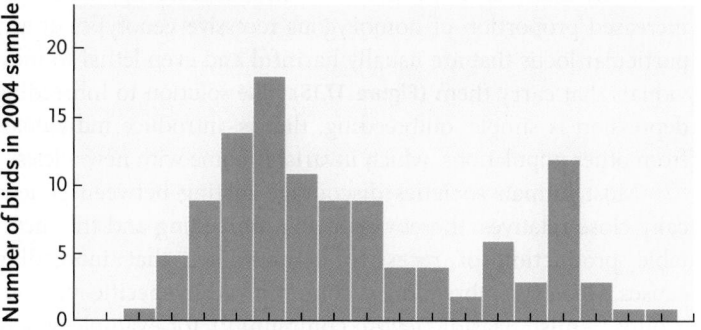

**c. Fitness (survival on the study plot, 2004–2006)**

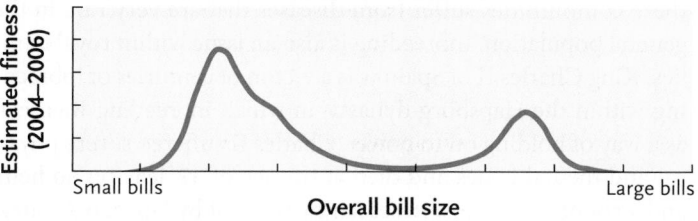

FIGURE 17.13 **Disruptive selection. (a)** Medium ground finches (*Geospiza fortis*) on Santa Cruz Island have bills of varying sizes. In this bill size polymorphism, birds with small bills or large bills are more common **(b)** and have higher fitness **(c)** than birds with bills of intermediate size. Thus, natural selection reduced the frequency of birds with bills of intermediate size and increased the frequencies of birds with either large bills or small bills.

Republished with permission of Royal Society, from *USA Proc. R. Soc. B*, Andrew P. Hendry, Sarah K. Huber, Luis F De León, Anthony Herrel and Jeffrey Podos, vol. 276(1657), 2009; permission conveyed through Copyright Clearance Center, Inc.

The other evolutionary processes do not always result in a population developing increased fitness in a particular environment over time. As well, it is important to remember that microevolutionary processes do not work in isolation of one another. For example, by itself, a rare beneficial mutation to one individual in a population will do little to change allele frequencies, but they can change appreciably after the population is acted upon by natural selection.

**STUDY BREAK QUESTIONS**

1. How is the high incidence of rare diseases within small populations explained by the founder effect?
2. Why is it that mutation does not tend to result in increased fitness?
3. Differentiate between directional, stabilizing, and disruptive selection.

### TABLE 17.2 | Agents of Microevolutionary Change

| Agent | Definition | Effect on Genetic Variation | Effect on Average Fitness |
|---|---|---|---|
| Gene flow | Change in allele frequencies as individuals join a population and reproduce | May introduce genetic variation from another population | Unpredictable effect on fitness; may introduce beneficial or harmful alleles |
| Genetic drift | Random changes in allele frequencies caused by chance events | Reduces genetic variation, especially in small populations; can eliminate rare alleles | Unpredictable effect on fitness; often harmful because of lost genetic diversity |
| Natural selection | Differential survivorship or reproduction of individuals with different genotypes | One allele can replace another or allelic variation can be preserved. | Positive effect on fitness through evolution of adaptations |
| Mutation | Heritable change in DNA | Introduces new genetic variation into population; does not change allele frequencies quickly | Unpredictable effect on fitness; most mutations in protein-coding genes lower fitness |

## 17.4 Non-random Mating

The last requirement of Hardy–Weinberg equilibrium is that individuals select mates at random from the population with respect to their genotypes (Condition 5). However, in many organisms, including some plants and most animals, mating is non-random. Mates are selected because they have a particular phenotype and thus often a particular underlying genotype. Snow geese, for example, usually select mates of their own colour, and a tall woman is more likely to marry a tall man than a short man. As well, in many human societies, cultural and religious traditions influence mate choice.

Non-random mating is a particular case in which Hardy–Weinberg equilibrium is not maintained but, by itself, non-random mating does not result in a change in allele frequencies and thus is not considered a microevolutionary process. (We will revisit this important point.) The two major types of non-random mating are inbreeding and sexual selection.

### 17.4a Inbreeding Reduces Heterozygosity

A common form of non-random mating is **inbreeding**, which is mating between individuals that are genetically related. Because of this, both parents will share many of the same alleles. Inbreeding is a particular issue in small populations, but is a reproductive strategy that is found in many plant species and invertebrate animals.

To look at what happens to the genotypes in a population as a result of inbreeding, let's consider the most extreme scenario, which also is the simplest to understand: a population in which only individuals of identical genotype mate (**Figure 17.14**). Let's start this example with a population (Generation 0) in which the frequency of allele $A$ is 0.5 (the frequency of $a$ then is also 0.5). The population is in Hardy–Weinberg equilibrium and conforms to the ratio $p^2 + 2pq + q^2$. However, the mating that occurs that gives rise to Generation 1 is not random: $AA$ individuals only mate with $AA$ individuals, $Aa$ individuals only mate with $Aa$, and $aa$ individuals only mate with other $aa$ individuals. Now, while both $AA$ and $aa$ individuals give rise only to the same genotypes in their offspring, this is not the case for heterozygotes ($Aa$). $Aa \times Aa$ gives rise to 50% heterozygote offspring and 25% each of $AA$ and $aa$. In fact, in each successive generation, the proportion of heterozygotes in the population decreases by one half (1/4 going to each of $AA$ and $aa$ genotypes), while the proportion of each homozygous genotype increases by 1/4 (Figure 17.14).

This then is one of the major results of inbreeding: an increase in the proportion of both homozygous genotypes in the population over successive generations, and a decrease in the proportion of individuals that are heterozygous. This results in a deviation from Hardy–Weinberg equilibrium. However, a deviation from equilibrium does not mean that evolution occurred. Inbreeding does not cause evolution because the allele frequencies do not change over time. To appreciate this point, note that the allele frequencies of a population at the zygotic stage are equal to the allele frequencies in the pool of successful gametes from which the zygotes are formed. The pattern of mating simply determines the way in which haploid gametes are "packaged" into diploid zygotes. Inbreeding doesn't change the proportion of alleles in a population, it simply moves them from heterozygous into both homozygous genotypes.

In the majority of species, including humans, inbreeding has negative effects on fitness, a phenomenon known as **inbreeding depression**, which is a decline in the average fitness of inbred individuals in a population. The explanation for this is that deleterious alleles (e.g., they may code for a non-functioning protein) tend to be recessive, and yet they perpetuate in a typical population because they are carried in heterozygotes where they are effectively masked. However, as a result of inbreeding, there is an increased proportion of homozygous recessive genotypes at any particular locus that are usually harmful and even lethal to individuals that carry them (**Figure 17.15**). The solution to inbreeding depression is simple: outbreeding, that is, introduce individuals from other populations, which invariably come with new alleles.

Most human societies discourage mating between genetically close relatives, thereby reducing inbreeding and the inevitable production of recessive homozygotes that inbreeding causes. However, inbreeding is common within specific religious groups (Amish, Hasidic Jewish community), for example, where it is customary to marry within the community. As expected, these communities suffer from diseases that are very rare in the general population. Inbreeding is also an issue within royal families. King Charles II of Spain was a victim of centuries of inbreeding within the Hapsburg dynasty, in which inbreeding was seen as a way of holding on to power. Charles II suffered severe physical and mental issues and died at the age of 39, leaving no heirs and a country in chaos. Research carried out by Gonzao Alvarez, of the University of Santiago in Spain, concluded that Charles II was more inbred than the child of a brother and sister.

## 17.4b Sexual Selection Often Exaggerates Showy Structures in Males

One type of non-random mating occurs because individuals consider specific aspects of the other sex before deciding to

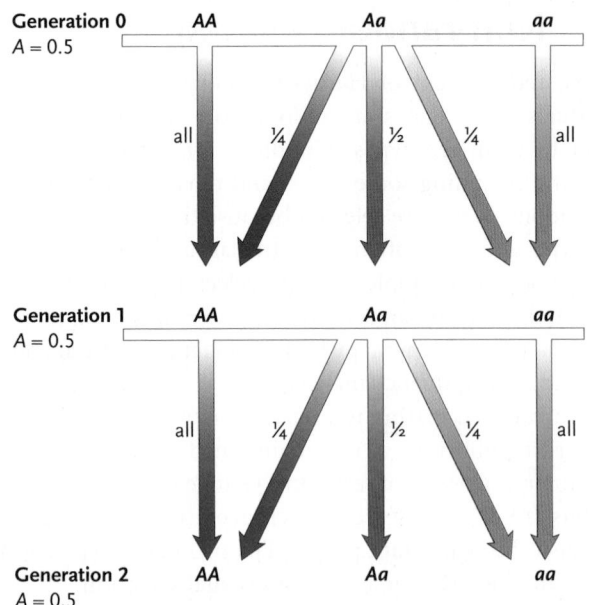

**FIGURE 17.14 Effect of inbreeding on genotypes.** In the extreme case of inbreeding where the same genotypes mate to give rise to the next generation, the proportion of heterozygotes (*Aa*) will decline by 50% each generation while the proportion of homozygotes will increase by 25% each. However, from one generation to the next, the allele frequencies do not change.

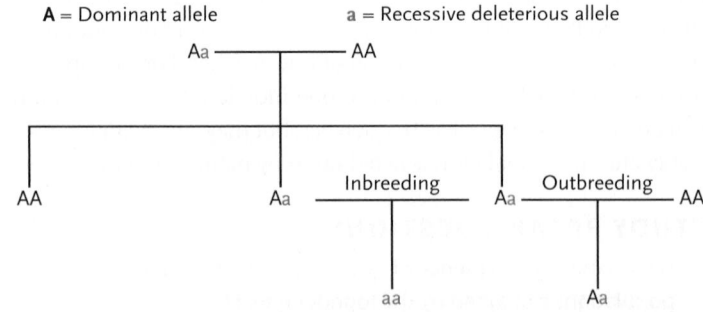

**FIGURE 17.15 Inbreeding increases the likelihood of homozygous recessive individuals (*aa*), resulting in the lowering of the overall fitness of the population (inbreeding depression).** Outbreeding can counter inbreeding depression by introducing new alleles from other populations.

mate with them. This special case of selection called **sexual selection** favours those individuals with specific traits that enhance their ability to mate with individuals of the other sex. Sexual selection usually acts on the males of a species who often possess a range of ornaments, such as brightly coloured feathers, long tails, or impressive antlers and horns, that often form part of elaborate courtship behaviour.

Sexual selection encompasses two related processes. As the result of *intersexual selection* (i.e., selection based on the interactions between males and females), males produce these otherwise useless ornaments simply because females associate them with health and vigour. In many species, intersexual selection is the likely cause of sexual dimorphism—differences in the size or appearance of males and females. Under *intrasexual selection* (i.e., selection based on the interactions between members of the same sex), males use their large body size, antlers, or tusks to intimidate, injure, or kill rival males.

Like directional selection, sexual selection pushes phenotypes toward one extreme. But the products of sexual selection are sometimes bizarre, such as the ridiculously long tail feathers of male, African widowbirds. How could evolutionary processes favour such elaborate structures, which are costly to produce? Research by Malte Andersson, of the University of Gothenburg, Sweden, suggests that the males' long tail feathers are a product of intersexual selection because females are more strongly attracted to males with long tails than to males with short tails; tail length had no effect on a male's ability to compete with other males for space in the habitat **(Figure 17.16)**.

Underlying sexual selection is the reality that females and males do not incur the same costs during reproduction. That is, in almost all sexual species, there is clear sexual asymmetry. Because eggs are more energetically expensive to make than sperm and are limited in number, females are much more heavily invested in successful reproduction than males. Female fitness is closely linked to producing eggs and rearing healthy offspring (e.g., pregnancy, lactation). In contrast, because sperm are energetically very cheap to produce, males can father a huge number of offspring. Male fitness then is limited simply by the number of females an individual male can mate with. This sexual asymmetry means that females need to be far more discriminating than males about who they mate with. They have a limited number of energetically expensive eggs, and identifying a mate that is particularly healthy is important.

## STUDY BREAK QUESTIONS

1. Which agents of microevolution tend to increase genetic variation within populations, and which ones tend to decrease it?
2. Which mode of natural selection increases the representation of the average phenotype in a population?
3. In what way is sexual selection like directional selection?

## 17.5 Maintaining Genetic and Phenotypic Variation

Evolutionary biologists continue to discover extraordinary amounts of genetic and phenotypic variation in most natural populations. How can so much variation persist when, for example, natural selection favours certain alleles over others?

### 17.5a Diploidy Can Hide Recessive Alleles from the Action of Natural Selection

Recall that most eukaryotes have two copies of each chromosome and thus two copies of each gene—they are diploid. It turns out that diploidy is a valuable mechanism that maintains genetic variability in a population. Although recessive alleles may be harmful, this is only the case when both alleles for a particular gene are recessive. Most often, the recessive allele is present in the heterozygous genotype and thus its potentially harmful effect is masked by the presence of the dominant allele. Since natural selection acts on the phenotype of individuals, heterozygous individuals protect the presence of recessive alleles from being selected out of a population.

In most cases, the masking of recessive alleles in heterozygotes makes it almost impossible to eliminate them completely from a population. Even when very rare, the allele will perpetuate among the heterozygotes in the population **(Table 17.3)**. Thus, the diploid state preserves recessive alleles at low frequencies, at least in large populations. In small populations, a combination of natural selection and genetic drift can eliminate harmful recessive alleles.

An important aspect of diploidy is that the maintenance of recessive alleles may have important ecological considerations. Recessive alleles represent genetic diversity and, while under present conditions they may be harmful and lower fitness in the homozygous recessive state, they may prove beneficial to a population if the environmental conditions change.

### 17.5b Balancing Selection Maintains More Than One Allele

**Balancing selection** is a type of natural selection in which more than one allele is actively maintained in a population. Natural selection preserves balanced selection when (1) heterozygotes have higher relative fitness, (2) when different alleles are favoured in different environments, and (3) when the rarity of a phenotype provides a selective advantage.

**HETEROZYGOTE ADVANTAGE** Balanced selection can be maintained by **heterozygote advantage**—when heterozygotes have higher relative fitness than either homozygote. As Darwin first discovered in his experiments on corn, the offspring of crosses between a homozygous dominant individual and a homozygous recessive individual of the same species often exhibit a robustness described as "hybrid vigour." Apparently, being heterozygous at many gene loci provides some advantage,

FIGURE 17.16 **Experimental Research**

## Sexual Selection in Action

**Question:** Is the long tail of the male long-tailed widowbird (*Euplectes progne*) the product of intrasexual selection, intersexual selection, or both?

**Experiment:** Researchers counted the number of females that associated with individual male widowbirds in the grasslands of Kenya. Researchers shortened the tails of some males by cutting the feathers, lengthened the tails of others by gluing feather extensions to their tails, and left a third group essentially unaltered as a control. One month later, the researchers again counted the number of females associating with each male and compared the results from the three groups.

**Results:** Males with experimentally lengthened tails attracted more than twice as many mates as males in the control group, and males with experimentally shortened tails attracted fewer. The researchers observed no differences in the ability of altered males and control group males to maintain their display areas.

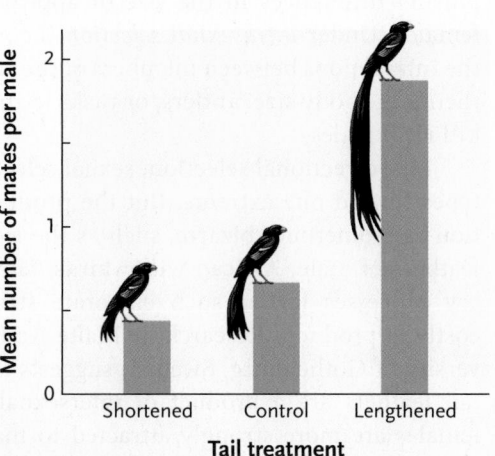

Mean number of mates per male (y-axis)

Tail treatment (x-axis): Shortened, Control, Lengthened

Francois Loubser/Shutterstock

**Conclusion:** Female widowbirds clearly prefer males with experimentally lengthened tails to those with normal tails or experimentally shortened tails. Tail length had no obvious effect on the interactions between males. Thus, the long tail of male widowbirds is the product of intersexual selection.

perhaps by allowing organisms to respond effectively to environmental variation.

The best-documented example of heterozygote advantage with reference to a specific gene locus is the maintenance of the *HbS* (sickle) allele, which codes for a defective form of hemoglobin in humans. As you learned in Chapter 9, hemoglobin is an oxygen-transporting molecule in red blood cells. The hemoglobin produced by the *HbS* allele differs from normal hemoglobin (coded by the *HbA* allele) by just one amino acid. In *HbS/HbS* homozygotes, the faulty hemoglobin forms long, fibrous chains under low oxygen conditions, causing red blood cells to assume a sickle shape (as shown in Figure 9.17). Often, homozygous *HbS/HbS* individuals die of sickle cell anemia before reproducing; yet in tropical and subtropical Africa, *HbS/HbA* heterozygotes make up nearly 25% of many populations.

Why is the harmful allele maintained at such high frequency in some populations? It turns out that sickle cell anemia is common in regions where malarial parasites infect red blood cells in humans (**Figure 17.17**). When heterozygous *HbA/HbS* individuals contract malaria, their infected red blood cells assume the same sickle shape as those of homozygous *HbS/HbS* individuals. The sickled cells lose potassium, killing the parasites, which limits their spread within the infected individual. Heterozygous individuals often survive malaria because the parasites do not multiply quickly inside them, their immune systems can effectively fight the infection, and they retain a large population of uninfected red blood cells. Homozygous *HbA/HbA* individuals are also subject to malarial infection, but because their infected cells do not sickle, the parasites multiply rapidly, causing a severe infection with a high mortality rate.

Therefore, *HbA/HbS* heterozygotes have greater resistance to malaria and are more likely to survive severe malarial infections in areas where the parasite is prevalent. Natural selection preserves the *HbS* allele in these populations because heterozygotes in malaria-prone areas have higher relative fitness than homozygotes for the normal *HbA* allele.

**SELECTION IN DIFFERENT ENVIRONMENTS** Genetic variability can also be maintained within a population when different alleles are favoured in different places or at different times. For example, the shells of European garden snails range in

| TABLE 17.3 | Masking of Recessive Alleles in Diploid Organisms |
| --- | --- |

When a recessive allele is common in a population (top of table), most copies of the allele are present in homozygotes. But when the allele is rare (bottom of table), most copies of it exist in heterozygotes. Thus, rare alleles that are completely recessive are protected from the action of natural selection because they are masked by dominant alleles in heterozygous individuals.

| Frequency of Allele *a* | Genotype Frequencies* | | | % of Allele *a* Copies in | |
| --- | --- | --- | --- | --- | --- |
| | *AA* | *Aa* | *aa* | *Aa* | *aa* |
| 0.99 | 0.0001 | 0.0198 | 0.9801 | 1 | 99 |
| 0.90 | 0.0100 | 0.1800 | 0.8100 | 10 | 90 |
| 0.75 | 0.0625 | 0.3750 | 0.5625 | 25 | 75 |
| 0.50 | 0.2500 | 0.5000 | 0.2500 | 50 | 50 |
| 0.25 | 0.5625 | 0.3750 | 0.0625 | 75 | 25 |
| 0.10 | 0.8100 | 0.1800 | 0.0100 | 90 | 10 |
| 0.01 | 0.9801 | 0.0198 | 0.0001 | 99 | 1 |

\* Population is assumed to be in genetic equilibrium.

colour from nearly white to pink, yellow, or brown, and may be patterned by one to five stripes of varying colour (look back at Figure 17.1a). This polymorphism, which is relatively stable through time, is controlled by several gene loci. The variability in colour and striping pattern can be partially explained by selection for camouflage in different habitats. Predation by song thrushes (Turdus ericetorum) is a major agent of selection for the colour and pattern of these snails in England. Thrushes are visual predators, usually capturing snails that are easy to find. Thus, well-camouflaged snails survive, and the alleles that specify their phenotypes increase in frequency.

**FREQUENCY-DEPENDENT SELECTION** Sometimes, genetic variability is maintained in a population simply because rare phenotypes—whatever they happen to be—have higher relative fitness than more common phenotypes. The rare phenotype will increase in frequency until it becomes so common that it loses its advantage. Such phenomena are examples of *frequency-dependent* selection because the selective advantage enjoyed by a particular phenotype depends on its frequency in the population.

The agents of evolution cause microevolutionary changes in the gene pools of populations. In the next chapter, we examine how microevolution in different populations can cause their gene pools to diverge. The extent of genetic divergence is sometimes sufficient to cause the populations to evolve into different species.

## STUDY BREAK QUESTIONS

1. How does the diploid condition protect harmful recessive alleles from natural selection?
2. What is a balanced polymorphism?
3. Why is the allele that causes sickle cell anemia very rare in human populations that are native to Northern Europe?

**a. Distribution of *HbS* allele**

**b. Distribution of malarial parasite**

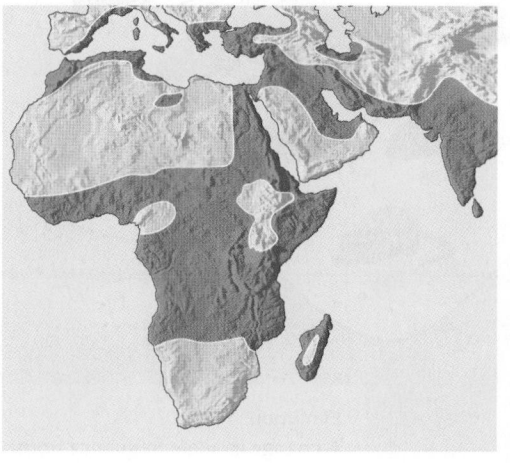

© Cengage Learning 2017. Based on L. L. Cavalli-Sforza and W. F. Bodmer. 1971. The Genetics of Human Populations. Freeman, San Francisco.

**KEY**

Allele frequencies of *HbS* allele
- ▪ >0.14
- ▫ 0.12–0.14
- ▪ 0.10–0.12
- ▪ 0.08–0.10
- ▪ 0.06–0.08
- ▪ 0.04–0.06
- ▫ 0.02–0.04
- ▫ 0.00–0.02

Regions with malaria
- ▪

**FIGURE 17.17 Heterozygote advantage. (a)** The distribution of the *HbS* allele, which causes sickle cell anemia in homozygotes, roughly matches the distribution **(b)** of the malarial parasite *Plasmodium falciparum* in southern Europe, Africa, the Middle East, and India. Gene flow among human populations has carried the *HbS* allele to some malaria-free regions.

# Summary Illustration

Genetic differences among the individuals of a population is due to the existence of different alleles for one or more genes. This genetic variation can change from generation to generation as the frequency of any particular allele within the population changes. Changes in allele frequency from generation to generation is evolution and it often results in changes in the occurrence of particular phenotypes (traits). The study of changing allele frequencies over generations is referred to as *microevolution*, and these changes are driven by four distinct processes: mutation, genetic drift, gene flow, and natural selection.

The Hardy-Weinberg equation can be used to determine whether a population is evolving.

Frequency of heterozygous genotype

$$p^2 + 2pq + q^2 = 1$$

Frequency of homozygous dominant genotype

Frequency of homozygous recessive genotype

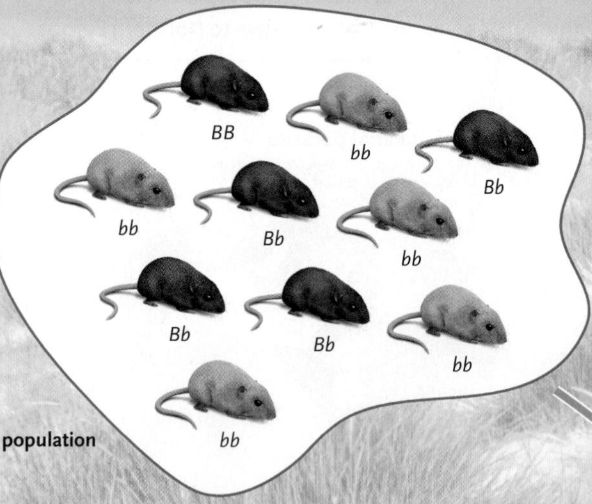

Current population

Frequency of $B = 0.3$
Frequency of $b = 0.7$

For many traits (e.g., fur colour in mice) the proportion of $q^2$ individuals can be visually determined, and from that you can calculate $q$. Given that $p + q = 1$, you can calculate the frequency of $p$. With both $p$ and $q$ you can then use the Hardy–Weinberg formula to determine the frequencies of all three genotypes!

**Evolution**
A change in allele frequency from one generation to the next

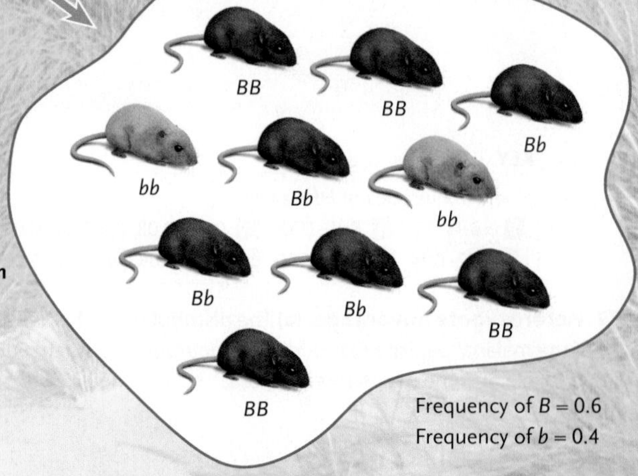

Next generation

Frequency of $B = 0.6$
Frequency of $b = 0.4$

There are four mechanisms that cause a population to evolve.

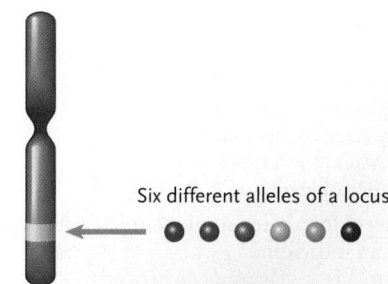

Six different alleles of a locus

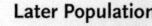

| | Ancestral Population | | Later Population | Result |
|---|---|---|---|---|
| **Hardy-Weinberg equilibrium** | 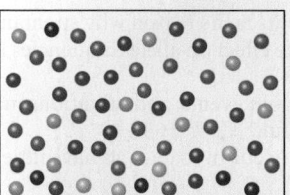 | Random mating and no gene flow, genetic drift, mutation, or natural selection | 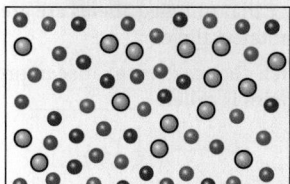 | Allele frequencies do not change |
| **Gene flow** | 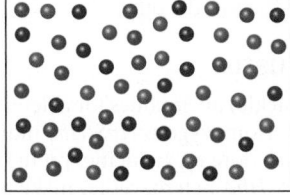 | Individuals with the orange allele enter the population |  | Orange allele becomes more common |
| **Genetic drift** | 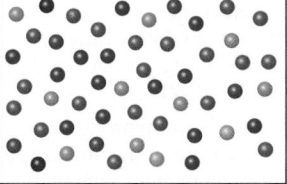 | Chance events cause frequency of certain alleles to change |  | Purple allele is lost |
| **Mutation** | 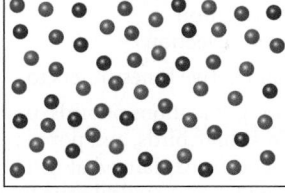 | A red allele becomes an orange allele | 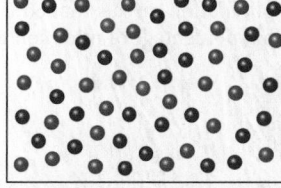 | New allele appears in the population |
| **Natural selection** | 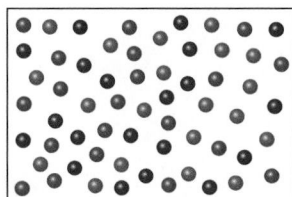 | Environmental factors are unfavourable for red alleles | | Red allele becomes less common |

# SELF-TEST QUESTIONS

## Recall/Understand

1. Which of these characteristics is an example of qualitative phenotypic variation?
   a. the lengths of people's toes
   b. the body sizes of pigeons
   c. human ABO blood types
   d. the number of leaves on oak trees

2. What is the term for a phenotypic characteristic that increases the fitness of an individual?
   a. mutation
   b. founder effect
   c. heterozygote advantage
   d. adaptation

3. Which of these statements is the reason why spontaneous mutations have no immediate effect on allele frequencies in a large population?
   a. Mutations are random events, and mutations may be either beneficial or harmful.
   b. Mutations usually occur in males and have little effect on eggs.
   c. Many mutations exert their effects after an organism has stopped reproducing.
   d. Mutations are so rare that mutated alleles are greatly outnumbered by nonmutated alleles.

4. The phenomenon in which chance events cause unpredictable changes in allele frequencies is called _____.
   a. gene flow
   b. genetic drift
   c. inbreeding
   d. stabilizing selection

5. If a storm kills many small sparrows in a population, but only a few medium-sized and large ones, which type of selection is probably operating?
   a. directional
   b. stabilizing
   c. disruptive
   d. artificial

6. Which of these statements is proposed by the neutral mutation hypothesis?
   a. Complex structures in most organisms have not been fostered by natural selection.
   b. Some mutations have a strongly harmful effect.
   c. Most mutations do not alter organism fitness.
   d. Natural selection cannot counteract the action of gene flow.

## Apply/Analyze

7. A population of mice is at Hardy–Weinberg equilibrium at a gene locus that controls fur colour. The locus has two alleles, $M$ and $m$. A genetic analysis of one population reveals that 60% of its gametes carry the $M$ allele. What percentage of mice contains both the $M$ and the $m$ alleles?
   a. 60%
   b. 48%
   c. 36%
   d. 16%

8. The genotype frequencies in a population are 0.60 $AA$, 0.20 $Aa$, and 0.20 $aa$, and the requirements of the Hardy–Weinberg principle apply. Which of the following genotype frequencies will occur in the offspring generation?
   a. 0.70 $AA$, 0.00 $Aa$, 0.30 $aa$
   b. 0.60 $AA$, 0.20 $Aa$, 0.20 $aa$
   c. 0.49 $AA$, 0.42 $Aa$, 0.09 $aa$
   d. 0.36 $AA$, 0.60 $Aa$, 0.04 $aa$

9. Which of these statements describes how directional selection and sexual selection are similar?
   a. They favour the mean genotypes over extreme genotypes.
   b. They favour the mean phenotypes over extreme phenotypes.
   c. They push phenotypes toward one extreme.
   d. They push genotypes toward one extreme.

10. The Old Order Amish, an essentially closed religious community in Lancaster County, Pennsylvania, have an exceptionally high incidence of Ellis–van Creveld syndrome, a genetic disorder caused by a recessive allele. What is this a result of?
    a. Alleles moving into or out of the Amish population.
    b. The affected individuals have the highest relative fitness.
    c. A few Amish individuals initially colonized Lancaster County.
    d. Affected individuals enhanced their ability to mate with individuals of the other sex.

## Create/Evaluate

11. The $HbS$ (sickle) allele codes for a defective form of hemoglobin in humans. Homozygous $HbS/HbS$ individuals often die of sickle cell anemia before reproducing, yet in tropical and subtropical Africa, $HbS/HbA$ heterozygotes make up nearly 25% of many populations. The high frequency of the harmful allele in some populations is probably an example of which of the following?
    a. natural selection
    b. the concept of relative fitness
    c. Hardy–Weinberg genetic equilibrium
    d. the founder effect

12. Which of these phenomena explains why the allele for sickle cell hemoglobin is common in some tropical and subtropical areas where the malaria parasite is prevalent?
    a. balanced polymorphism
    b. heterozygote advantage
    c. neutral selection
    d. stabilizing selection

13. Explain what relative fitness refers to.

14. Compare two populations of birds: population A consists of predominantly blue birds, and population B consists of predominantly green birds. Explain what will be the consequences of reciprocal and non-reciprocal gene flow between the two populations.

# Chapter Roadmap

## Species and Macroevolution

The species is the most studied taxonomic group. But what defines a species, and how do they develop as a result of evolutionary processes?

### 18.1 What Is a Species?

You would think of all the words in biology that species would be easy to define—it isn't

### 18.2 Maintaining Reproductive Isolation

Reproductive isolation, key to the biological specie concept, is maintained by a number of distinct mechanisms.

### 18.3 The Geography of Speciation

Geography has a major impact on the rate of speciation.

### 18.4 Genetic Mechanisms of Speciation

In many cases, reproductive isolation of species has a simple genetic basis.

**Birds of paradise.** A male Count Raggi's bird of paradise (*Paradisaea raggiana*)

# Speciation and Macroevolution

# 18

**Why it matters . . .** In 1927, nearly 100 years after Darwin boarded the *Beagle*, a young German naturalist named Ernst Mayr embarked on his own journey to the highlands of New Guinea. He was searching for rare "birds of paradise." These birds were known in Europe only through their ornate and colourful feathers, which were used to decorate ladies' hats. On his trek through the remote Arfak Mountains, Mayr identified 137 bird species (including many birds of paradise) based on differences in their size, plumage, colour, and other external characteristics.

To Mayr's surprise, the native Papuans, who were untrained in the ways of Western science, but who hunted these birds for food and feathers, had their own names for 136 of the 137 species he had identified. The close match between the two lists confirmed Mayr's belief that the *species* is a fundamental level of organization in nature.

Mayr also discovered some remarkable patterns in the geographical distributions of bird species in New Guinea. For example, each mountain range he explored was home to some species that lived nowhere else. Closely related species often lived on different mountaintops, separated by deep valleys of unsuitable habitat. In 1942, Mayr published the book *Systematics and the Origin of Species*, in which he described the role of geography in the evolution of new species; the book quickly became a cornerstone of evolutionary biology.

What mechanisms produce distinct species? As you discovered in the previous chapter, microevolutionary processes alter the pattern and extent of genetic and phenotypic variation within populations. When these processes differ between populations, the populations will diverge genetically, and they may eventually become so different that we recognize them as distinct species. Although Darwin's famous book was titled *On the Origin of Species,* he did not dwell on the question of *how* new species arise, although he clearly saw similar species as having shared inherited characteristics and a common ancestry.

Today, evolutionary biologists view **speciation** (the process of species formation) as a series of events that occur through time. However, using a range of approaches, they study the products of speciation, species that are alive today. Because they can rarely witness the process of speciation from start to finish, scientists make inferences about it by studying organisms in various stages of species formation. In this chapter, we consider four major topics: how biologists define and recognize species; how species maintain their genetic identity; how the geographical distributions of organisms influence speciation; and how different genetic mechanisms produce new species.

# 18.1 What Is a Species?

Like the hunters of the Arfak Mountains, most of us recognize the different species that we encounter every day. We can distinguish a cat from a dog and sunflowers from roses. The concept of species is based on our perception that Earth's biological diversity is packaged in discrete, recognizable units, and not as a continuum of forms grading into one another. As biologists have learned more about evolutionary processes—and the dazzling biodiversity those processes have produced—they have developed a variety of complementary species concepts.

## 18.1a The Morphological Species Concept Is a Practical Way to Identify Species

Biologists often describe new species on the basis of visible anatomical characteristics, a process that dates back to Linnaeus' classification of organisms in the eighteenth century (described in Chapter 19). This approach is based on the **morphological species concept**, the idea that all individuals of a species share measurable traits that distinguish them from individuals of other species.

The morphological species concept has many practical applications. For example, researchers use morphological criteria to identify the species of fossilized organisms. And because we can observe the external traits of organisms in nature, field guides to plants and animals list diagnostic (i.e., distinguishing) physical characters that allow us to recognize them (**Figure 18.1**).

Nevertheless, relying exclusively on morphology to identify species can present problems. Some individuals of a single species look very different in size and coloration, for example. Conversely, morphology does not help us distinguish some closely related species that are nearly identical in appearance. Finally, morphological species definitions tell us little about the evolutionary processes that produce new species.

## 18.1b The Biological Species Concept Is Based on Reproductive Isolation

The **biological species concept** emphasizes the dynamic nature of species. Ernst Mayr defined *biological species* as "groups of … interbreeding natural populations that are reproductively isolated from [do not produce fertile offspring with] other such groups." The concept is based on reproductive criteria and is easy to apply, at least in principle. If the members of two populations interbreed and produce fertile offspring *under natural conditions*, they belong to the same species. Their fertile offspring will go on to produce the next generation of that species. If two populations do not interbreed in nature, or fail to produce fertile offspring when they do, they belong to different species.

The biological species concept defines species in terms of population genetics and evolutionary theory. The first half of Mayr's definition notes the genetic *cohesiveness* of species: populations of the same species experience gene flow, which mixes their genetic material. Thus, we can think of a species as one large gene pool, which may be subdivided into local populations.

The second part of the biological species concept emphasizes the genetic *distinctness* of each species. Because populations of different species are reproductively isolated, they cannot exchange genetic information. In fact, the process of speciation is frequently defined as the evolution of reproductive isolation between populations.

The biological species concept also explains why individuals of a species generally look alike: members of the same gene pool share genetic traits that determine their appearance. Individuals of different species generally do not resemble one another as closely because they share fewer genetic characteristics. In practice, biologists often still use similarities or differences in morphological traits as convenient markers of genetic similarity or reproductive isolation.

However, the biological species concept does not apply to the many forms of life that reproduce asexually, including most bacteria and archaeans; some protists, fungi, and plants; and a few animals. In these species, individuals do not breed, so it is pointless to ask whether members of different populations do. Similarly, we cannot use the biological species concept to study extinct organisms, because we have little or no data on their specific reproductive habits. These species must all be defined using morphological or biochemical criteria. Yet, despite its limitations, the biological species concept currently provides the best evolutionary definition of a sexually reproducing species.

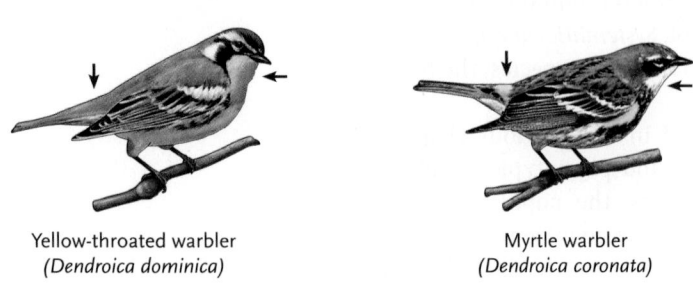

Yellow-throated warbler
(*Dendroica dominica*)

Myrtle warbler
(*Dendroica coronata*)

© Cengage Learning 2017.

**FIGURE 18.1 Diagnostic characters.** Yellow-throated warblers and myrtle warblers can be distinguished by the colour of feathers on the throat and rump.

## 18.1c The Phylogenetic Species Concept Focuses on Evolutionary History

Recognizing the limitations of the biological species concept, biologists have developed dozens of other ways to define a species. A widely accepted alternative is the **phylogenetic species concept**. Using both morphological and genetic sequence data, scientists first reconstruct the evolutionary tree for the organisms of interest. They then define a phylogenetic species as a cluster of populations (the tiniest twigs on this part of the Tree of Life) that emerge from the same small branch. Thus, a phylogenetic species comprises populations that share a recent evolutionary history.

One advantage of the phylogenetic species concept is that biologists can apply it to any group of organisms, including species that have long been extinct, as well as living organisms that reproduce asexually. Proponents of this approach also argue that the morphological and genetic distinctions between organisms on different branches of the Tree of Life reflect the absence of gene flow between them, one of the key requirements of the biological species definition. Nevertheless, because detailed evolutionary histories have been described for relatively few groups of organisms, biologists are not yet able to apply the phylogenetic species concept to all forms of life.

## 18.1d Many Species Exhibit Substantial Geographical Variation

Just as individuals within populations exhibit genotypic and phenotypic variation (see Section 17.1), populations within species also differ both genetically and phenotypically. Neighbouring populations often have shared characteristics because they live in similar environments, exchange individuals, and experience comparable patterns of natural selection. Widely separated populations, by contrast, may live under different conditions and experience different patterns of selection; because gene flow is less likely to occur between distant populations, their gene pools and phenotypes are often somewhat different.

When geographically separated populations of a species exhibit dramatic, easily recognized phenotypic variation, biologists may identify them as different **subspecies (Figure 18.2)**, which are local variants of a species. Individuals from different subspecies usually interbreed where their geographical distributions meet, and their offspring often exhibit intermediate

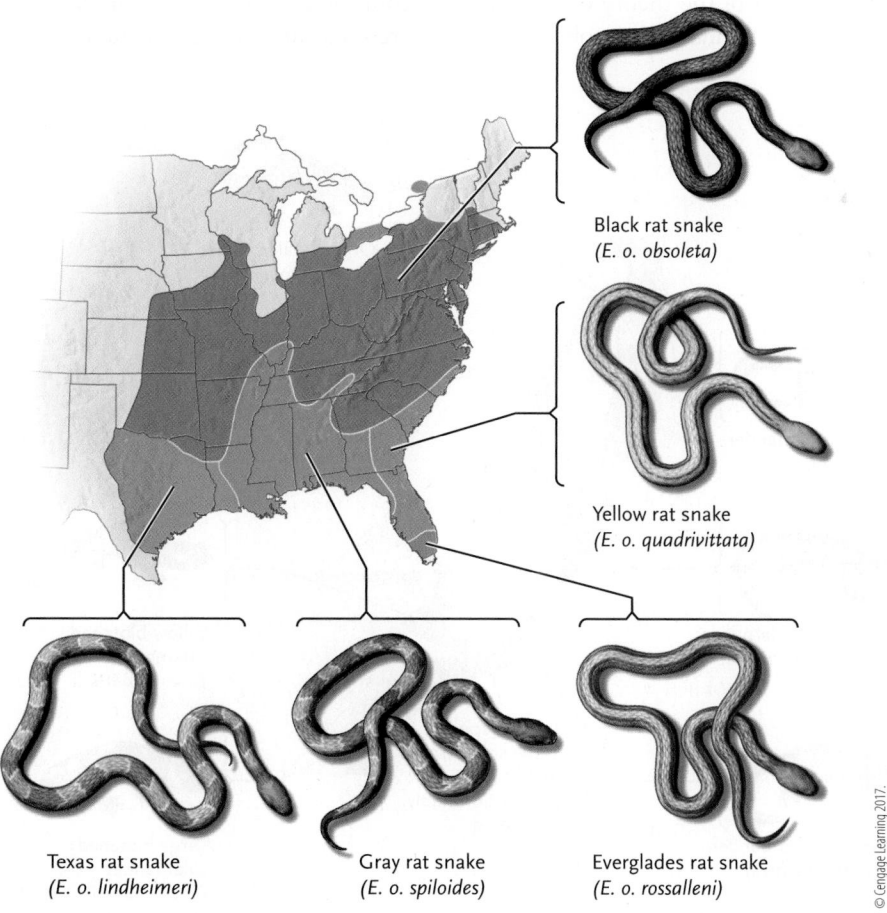

Black rat snake
(*E. o. obsoleta*)

Yellow rat snake
(*E. o. quadrivittata*)

Texas rat snake
(*E. o. lindheimeri*)

Gray rat snake
(*E. o. spiloides*)

Everglades rat snake
(*E. o. rossalleni*)

© Cengage Learning 2017.

**FIGURE 18.2 Subspecies.** Five subspecies of rat snake (*Elaphe obsoleta*) in eastern North America differ in colour and in the presence or absence of stripes or blotches.

phenotypes. Biologists sometimes use the word "race" as short-hand for the term *subspecies*.

Various patterns of geographical variation, as well as analyses of how the variation may relate to climatic or habitat variation, have provided great insight into the speciation process. Two of the best-studied patterns are *ring species* and *clinal variation*.

**RING SPECIES** Some plant and animal species have a ring-shaped geographical distribution that surrounds uninhabitable terrain. Adjacent populations of these **ring species** can exchange genetic material directly, but gene flow between distant populations occurs only through the intermediary populations.

The lungless salamander *Ensatina eschscholtzii* an example of a ring species: it is widely distributed in the coastal mountains and the Sierra Nevada of California, but it cannot survive in the hot, dry Central Valley (**Figure 18.3**). Seven subspecies differ in biochemical traits, colour, size, and ecology. Individuals from adjacent subspecies often interbreed where their geographical distributions overlap, and intermediate phenotypes are fairly common. But at the southern end of the Central Valley, adjacent subspecies rarely interbreed. Apparently, they have differentiated to such an extent that they can no longer exchange genetic material directly.

**CONCEPT FIX** One misconception about speciation is that, although it is a foundational aspect of the theory of evolution by natural selection, it has never actually been observed in nature or in the laboratory. But there are countless examples, including the salamander example above, where populations become so divergent that they can no longer exchange genetic material and thus become distinct species. ⬡

Are the southernmost populations of this salamander subspecies or different species? A biologist who saw *only* the southern populations, which coexist without interbreeding, might define them as separate species; however, they still have the potential to exchange genetic material through the intervening populations that form the ring. Therefore, biologists recognize these populations as belonging to the same species. Most likely, the southern subspecies are in an intermediate stage of species formation.

**CLINAL VARIATION** When a species is distributed over a large, environmentally diverse area, some traits may exhibit a **cline**, a smooth pattern of variation across a geographical gradient. For example, many birds and mammals in the northern hemisphere show clinal variation in body size (**Figure 18.4**) and the relative length of their appendages. In general, populations living in colder environments have larger bodies and shorter appendages, a pattern that is usually interpreted as a mechanism to conserve body heat (see Chapter 38).

Clinal variation usually results from gene flow between adjacent populations that are each adapting to slightly different conditions. However, if populations at opposite ends of a cline are separated by great distances, they may exchange very little

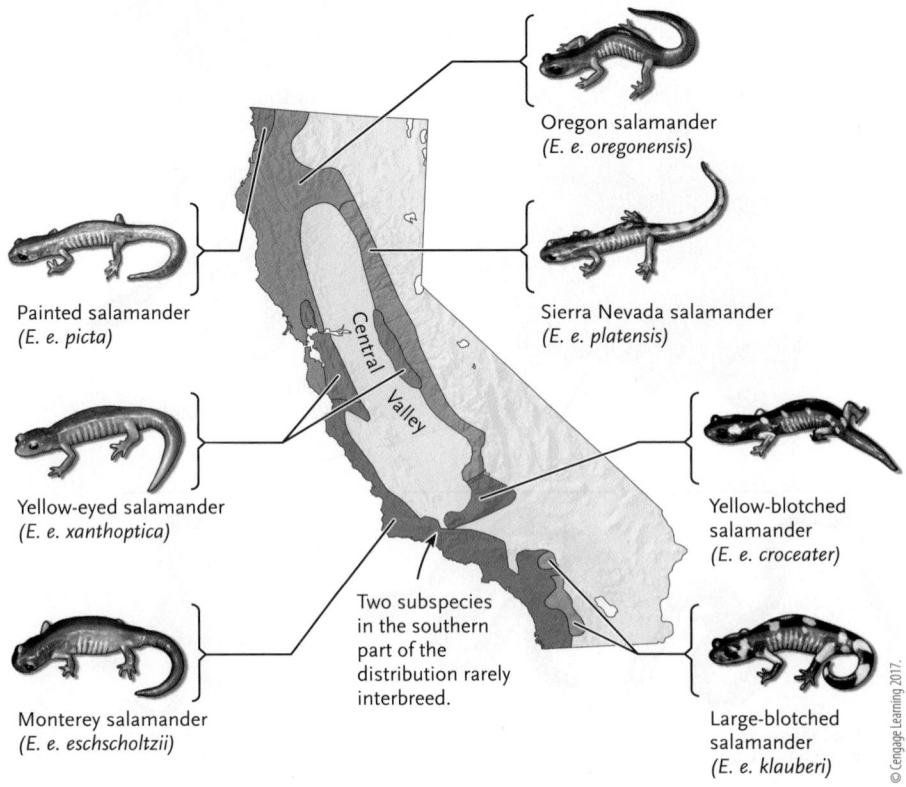

**FIGURE 18.3  Ring species.** Six of the seven subspecies of the salamander *Ensatina eschscholtzii* are distributed in a ring around California's Central Valley. Subspecies often interbreed where their geographical distributions overlap. However, the two subspecies that nearly close the ring in the south (marked with an arrow), the Monterey salamander and the yellow-blotched salamander, rarely interbreed.

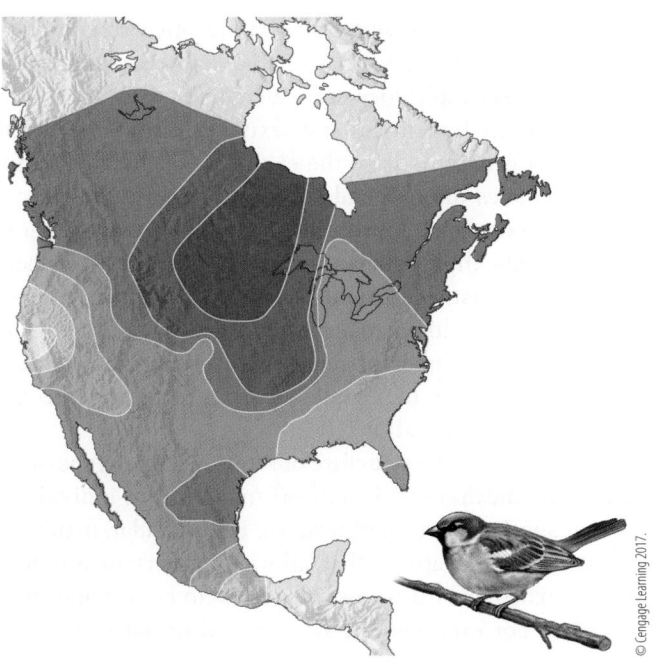

**FIGURE 18.4 Clinal variation.** House sparrows (*Passer domesticus*) exhibit clinal variation in overall body size, which was summarized from measurements of 16 skeletal features. Darker shading in the map indicates larger size.

genetic material through reproduction. Thus, when a cline extends over a large geographical gradient, distant populations may be genetically and morphologically distinct.

Despite the geographical variation that many species exhibit, even closely related species are genetically and morphologically different from each other. In the next section, we consider the mechanisms that maintain the genetic distinctness of closely related species by preventing their gene pools from mixing.

**STUDY BREAK QUESTIONS**

1. How do the morphological, biological, and phylogenetic species concepts differ?
2. What is clinal variation?

## 18.2 Maintaining Reproductive Isolation

The biological species concept uses the criterion of reproductive isolation to define species of sexually reproducing organisms: most individuals produce offspring by mating with another individual of their own species. Indeed, a variety of biological characteristics, collectively described as **reproductive isolating mechanisms**, prevent individuals of different species from mating and producing successful progeny. Thus, by reducing the chance of interspecific (between-species) mating and the production of **hybrid** offspring (i.e., offspring with parents of different species), these isolating mechanisms prevent the gene pools of distinct species from mixing.

Reproductive isolating mechanisms operate at different times during the reproductive process, and biologists categorize them as occurring either before or after an egg is fertilized (summarized in **Table 18.1**): **prezygotic isolating mechanisms** exert their effects before fertilization and the production of a zygote (a fertilized egg); **postzygotic isolating mechanisms** operate after fertilization and zygote formation. These isolating mechanisms are not mutually exclusive, and two or more of them may affect the outcome of a between-species interaction.

### 18.2a Prezygotic Isolating Mechanisms Prevent the Production of Hybrid Offspring

Biologists have identified five mechanisms that can prevent the production of hybrid offspring. Four of these mechanisms limit the frequency of interspecific matings, whereas one blocks interspecific fertilizations. These five prezygotic mechanisms are *ecological*, *temporal*, *behavioural*, *mechanical*, and *gametic isolation*.

Species living in the same geographical region may experience **ecological isolation** if they live in different habitats. For example, lions and tigers were both common in India until the mid-nineteenth century, when hunters virtually exterminated the Asian lions. However, because lions live in open grasslands and tigers in dense forests, the two species did not encounter one another and did not interbreed. Lion–tiger hybrids are sometimes born in captivity, but they do not occur under natural conditions.

| TABLE 18.1 | Reproductive Isolating Mechanisms | |
|---|---|---|
| **Timing Relative to Fertilization** | **Mechanism** | **Mode of Action** |
| Prezygotic ("premating") mechanisms | Ecological isolation | Species live in different habitats. |
| | Temporal isolation | Species breed at different times. |
| | Behavioural isolation | Species cannot communicate. |
| | Mechanical isolation | Species cannot physically mate. |
| | Gametic isolation | Species have nonmatching receptors on gametes. |
| Postzygotic ("postmating") mechanisms | Hybrid inviability | Hybrid offspring do not complete development. |
| | Hybrid sterility | Hybrid offspring cannot produce gametes. |
| | Hybrid breakdown | Hybrid offspring have reduced survival or fertility. |

© Cengage Learning 2017.

Species living in the same habitat can experience **temporal isolation** if they mate at different times of day or different times of year. For example, the fruit flies *Drosophila persimilis* and *Drosophila pseudoobscura* overlap extensively in their geographical distributions, but they do not interbreed, in part because *D. persimilis* mates in the morning and *D. pseudoobscura* in the afternoon. Similarly, two species of pine in California are reproductively isolated where their geographical distributions overlap: even though both rely on the wind to carry male gametes (pollen grains) to female gametes (ova) in other cones, *Pinus radiata* releases pollen in February and *Pinus muricata* releases pollen in April.

Many animals rely on specific signals, which may differ dramatically between species, to identify the species of a potential mate. **Behavioural isolation** results when the signals used by one species are not recognized by another. For example, female birds rely on the song, colour, and displays of males to identify members of their own species. Similarly, female fireflies identify males by their flashing patterns (**Figure 18.5**). These behaviours

(collectively called *courtship displays*) are often so complicated that signals sent by one species are like a foreign language that another species simply does not understand.

Mate choice by females and sexual selection (discussed in Chapter 17) generally drive the evolution of mate recognition signals. Females often spend substantial energy in reproduction, and choosing an appropriate mate (i.e., a male of her own species) is critically important for the production of successful young. By contrast, a female that mates with a male from a different species is unlikely to leave any surviving offspring at all. Over time, the number of males with recognizable traits, as well as the number of females able to recognize the traits, increases in the population.

Differences in the structure of reproductive organs or other body parts (**mechanical isolation**) may prevent individuals of different species from interbreeding. In particular, many plants have anatomical features that allow only certain pollinators, usually particular bird or insect species, to collect and distribute pollen. For example, the flowers and nectar of two native

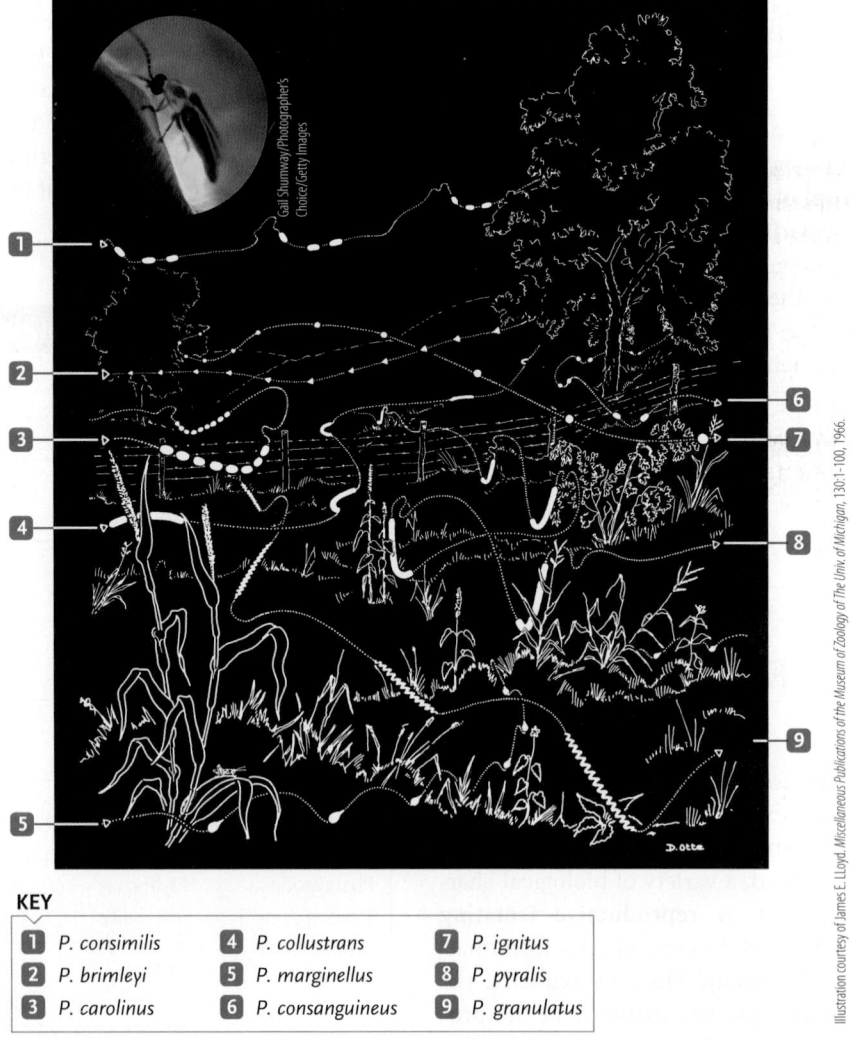

**KEY**

| | | |
|---|---|---|
| 1 *P. consimilis* | 4 *P. collustrans* | 7 *P. ignitus* |
| 2 *P. brimleyi* | 5 *P. marginellus* | 8 *P. pyralis* |
| 3 *P. carolinus* | 6 *P. consanguineus* | 9 *P. granulatus* |

**FIGURE 18.5 Behavioural reproductive isolation.** Male fireflies use bioluminescent signals to attract potential mates. The different flight paths and flashing patterns of males in nine North American *Photinus* species are represented here. Females respond only to the display given by males of their own species. The inset photo shows *P. pyralis*.

California plants, the purple monkey-flower (*Mimulus lewisii*) and the scarlet monkey-flower (*Mimulus cardinalis*), attract different animal pollinators (**Figure 18.6**). *M. lewisii* is pollinated by bumblebees. It has shallow purple flowers with broad petals that provide a landing platform for the bees. Bright yellow streaks on the petals serve as "nectar guides," directing bumblebees to the short nectar tube and reproductive parts, which are located among the petals. Bees enter the flowers to drink their concentrated nectar, and they pick up and deliver pollen as their legs and bodies brush against the reproductive parts of the flowers. *M. cardinalis*, by contrast, is pollinated by hummingbirds. It has long red flowers with no yellow streaks, and the reproductive parts extend above the petals. The red colour attracts hummingbirds but lies outside the colour range detected by bumblebees. The nectar of *M. cardinalis* is more dilute than that of *M. lewisii* but is produced in much greater quantity, making it easier for hummingbirds to ingest. When a hummingbird visits *M. cardinalis* flowers, it pushes its long bill down the nectar tube and its forehead touches the reproductive parts, picking up and delivering pollen. Recent research has demonstrated that, where the two monkey-flower species grow side by side, animal pollinators restrict their visits to either one species or the other 98% of the time, providing nearly complete reproductive isolation.

Even when individuals of different species mate, **gametic isolation**, an incompatibility between the sperm of one species and the eggs of another may prevent fertilization. Many marine invertebrates release gametes into the environment for external fertilization. The sperm and eggs of each species recognize one another's complementary surface proteins (see Chapter 44), but the surface proteins on the gametes of different species do not match. In animals with internal fertilization, sperm of one species may not survive and function within the reproductive tract of another. Interspecific matings between some *Drosophila* species, for example, induce a reaction in the female's reproductive tract that blocks "foreign" sperm from reaching eggs. Parallel physiological incompatibilities between a pollen tube and a stigma prevent interspecific fertilization in some plants.

## 18.2b Postzygotic Isolating Mechanisms Reduce the Success of Hybrid Individuals

If prezygotic isolating mechanisms between two closely related species are incomplete or ineffective, sperm from one species sometimes fertilizes an egg of the other species. In such cases, the two species will be reproductively isolated if their offspring (interspecific hybrids) have lower fitness than the offspring of intraspecific (within-species) matings. Three postzygotic isolating mechanisms, *hybrid inviability*, *hybrid sterility*, and *hybrid breakdown*, can reduce the fitness of hybrid individuals.

Many genes govern the complex processes that transform a zygote into a mature organism. Hybrid individuals have two sets of developmental instructions, one from each parent species, which may not interact properly for the successful completion of embryonic development. As a result, hybrid organisms frequently die as embryos or at an early age, a phenomenon called **hybrid inviability**. For example, domestic sheep and goats can mate and fertilize one another's ova, but the hybrid embryos always die before coming to term, presumably because the developmental programs of the two parent species are incompatible.

Although some hybrids between closely related species develop into healthy and vigorous adults, they may not produce functional gametes. This **hybrid sterility** often results when the parent species differ in the number or structure of their chromosomes, which cannot pair properly during meiosis. Such hybrids have zero fitness because they leave no descendants. The most familiar example is a mule, the product of mating between a female horse ($2n = 64$) and a male donkey ($2n = 62$). Zebroids, the offspring of matings between horses and zebras, are also usually sterile hybrids (**Figure 18.7**).

Some first-generation hybrids (F1; see Section 9.1b) are healthy and fully fertile. They can breed with other hybrids and with both parental species. However, the second generation (F2), produced by matings between F1 hybrids, or between F1 hybrids and either

**Purple monkey-flower**
**(*Mimulus lewisii*)**

**Scarlet monkey-flower**
**(*Mimulus cardinalis*)**

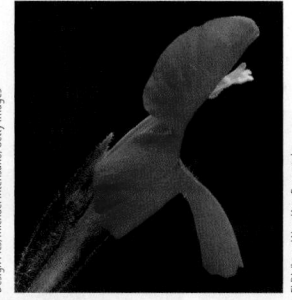

**FIGURE 18.6 Mechanical reproductive isolation.** Because of differences in floral structure, two species of monkey-flower attract different animal pollinators. *Mimulus lewisii* attracts bumblebees, and *Mimulus cardinalis* attracts hummingbirds.

**FIGURE 18.7 Interspecific hybrids.** Horses and zebroids (hybrid offspring of horses and zebras) running in a mixed herd. Zebroids are usually sterile.

parental species, may exhibit reduced survival or fertility, a phenomenon known as **hybrid breakdown**. For example, experimental crosses between *Drosophila* species may produce functional hybrids, but the offspring of hybrids experience high rates of chromosomal abnormalities and harmful types of genetic recombination. Thus, reproductive isolation is maintained between the species because there is little long-term mixing of their gene pools.

## STUDY BREAK QUESTIONS

1. What is the difference between prezygotic and postzygotic isolating mechanisms?
2. When a male duck of one species performed a courtship display to a female of another species, she interpreted his behaviour as aggressive rather than amorous. What type of reproductive isolating mechanism does this scenario illustrate?

## 18.3 The Geography of Speciation

As Ernst Mayr recognized, geography has a huge impact on whether gene pools have the opportunity to mix. Biologists define two modes of speciation, based on the geographical relationship of populations as they become reproductively isolated: *allopatric speciation* (*allo* = different; *patria* = homeland) and *sympatric speciation* (*sym* = together).

### 18.3a Allopatric Speciation Occurs between Geographically Separated Populations

**Allopatric speciation** may take place when a physical barrier subdivides a large population or when a small population becomes separated from a species' main geographical distribution. Allopatric speciation occurs in two stages. First, two populations become *geographically* separated, preventing gene flow between them. Then, as the populations experience distinct mutations as well as different patterns of natural selection and genetic drift, they may accumulate genetic differences that isolate them *reproductively*. Allopatric speciation is probably the most common mode of speciation in large animals.

Geographical separation sometimes occurs when a barrier divides a large population into two or more units (**Figure 18.8**). For example, hurricanes may create new channels that divide low coastal islands and the populations inhabiting them. Uplifting mountains or landmasses as well as rivers or advancing glaciers can also produce barriers that subdivide populations. The uplift of the Isthmus of Panama, caused by movements of Earth's crust about 5 million years ago, separated a once-continuous shallow sea into the eastern tropical Pacific Ocean and the western tropical Atlantic Ocean. Populations of marine organisms were subdivided by this event. In the tropical Atlantic Ocean, populations experienced patterns of mutation, natural selection, and genetic drift that were different from those experienced by populations in the tropical Pacific Ocean. As a result, the populations diverged genetically, and pairs of closely related species now live on either side of this divide (**Figure 18.9**).

In other cases, small populations may become isolated at the edge of a species' geographical distribution. Such peripheral populations often differ genetically from the central population because they are adapted to somewhat different environments. Once a small population is isolated, founder effects and small population size may promote genetic drift (see Section 17.3), and natural selection may favour the evolution of distinctive

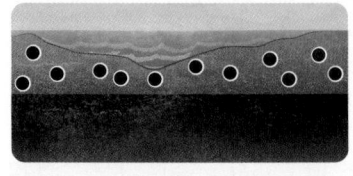 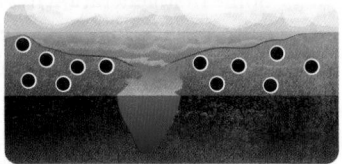  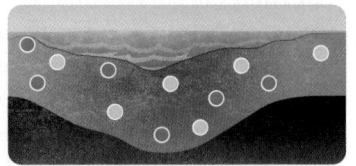

**1** At first, a population is distributed over a large geographical area.

**2** A geographical change separates the original population, creating a barrier to gene flow.

**3** In the absence of gene flow, the separated populations evolve independently and diverge into different species.

**4** When another geographical change allows individuals of the two species to come into secondary contact, they do not interbreed.

**FIGURE 18.8 Model of allopatric speciation and secondary contact**

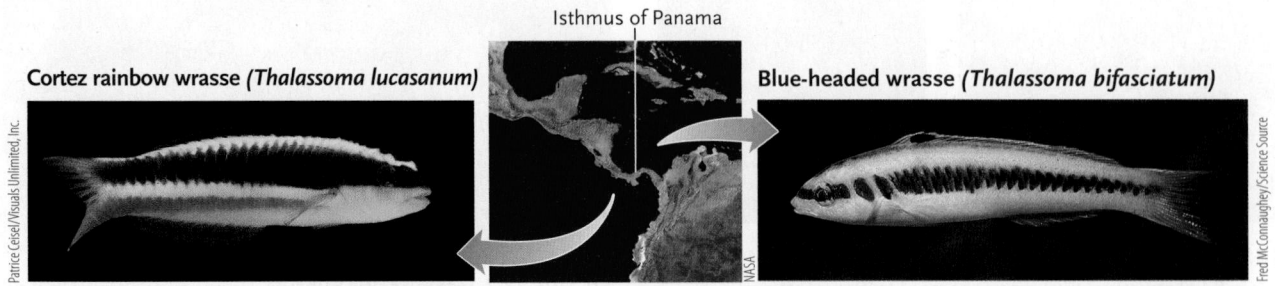

**FIGURE 18.9 Geographical separation.** The uplift of the Isthmus of Panama divided an ancestral wrasse population. The Cortez rainbow wrasse now occupies the eastern Pacific Ocean, and the blue-headed wrasse now occupies the western Atlantic Ocean.

traits. If the isolated population experiences limited gene flow from the parent population, these agents of evolution will foster genetic differentiation between them. In time, the accumulated genetic differences may lead to reproductive isolation.

Populations established by colonization of oceanic islands represent extreme examples of this phenomenon. The founder effect makes the populations genetically distinct. And on oceanic archipelagos, such as the Galápagos and Hawaiian Islands, individuals from one island may colonize nearby islands, founding populations that differentiate into distinct species. Each island may experience multiple invasions, and the process may be repeated many times within the archipelago, leading to the evolution of a **species cluster**, a group of closely related species recently descended from a common ancestor (**Figure 18.10**). Sometimes a species cluster can evolve relatively quickly; for example, the nearly 800 species of fruit flies now living on the Hawaiian Islands evolved in less than 5 million years, an average of just over 6000 years per species.

## 18.3b Secondary Contact Provides a Test of Whether Allopatric Speciation Has Occurred

Allopatric populations may reestablish contact when a geographical barrier is eliminated or breached (see Figure 18.8, step 4). Such **secondary contact** (contact after a period of geographical isolation) provides a test of whether the genes in the populations have diverged enough to make them reproductively isolated. If their gene pools did not differentiate much during geographical separation, the populations will interbreed and merge into one, a phenomenon described as **species fusion**. But if, during their separation, the populations accumulated enough genetic differences to be reproductively isolated on secondary contact, they will be separate species. (The ecological consequences of secondary contact are described in Chapter 30.)

During the early stages of secondary contact, prezygotic reproductive isolation may be weak or incomplete. Some members of each population may mate with individuals from the other, producing viable, fertile offspring in areas called **hybrid zones**. Although some hybrid zones may persist for hundreds or thousands of years, they are generally narrow, and ecological or geographical factors maintain the separation of the gene pools for the majority of individuals in both species.

For example, the breeding ranges of Bullock's oriole (*Icterus bullocki*) and the Baltimore oriole (*Icterus galbula*) overlap in the Midwest of North America (**Figure 18.11**). In 2011, Matthew D. Carling, Lindsay G. Serene, and Irby J. Lovette of Cornell University published a genetic analysis of orioles where the geographical ranges overlap. Their research confirmed that the hybrid zone is narrow (only 325 km wide) and that it encompasses an area where two distinctive environments mix. Bullock's orioles live in the hotter and drier habitats to the west of the hybrid zone; Baltimore orioles occupy the cooler and moister habitats to the east. Researchers hypothesize that, although hybrid individuals may survive and reproduce in the

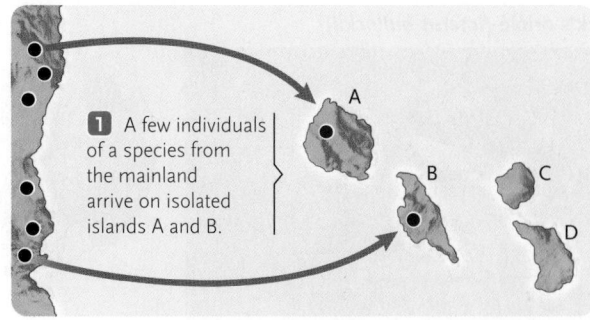

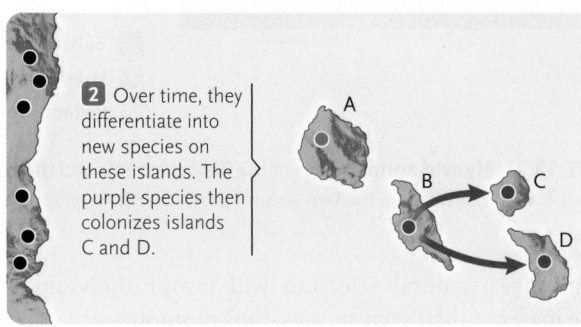

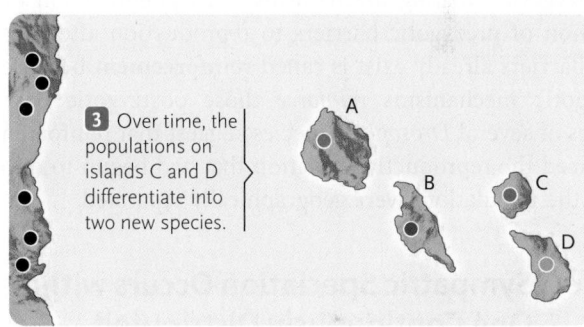

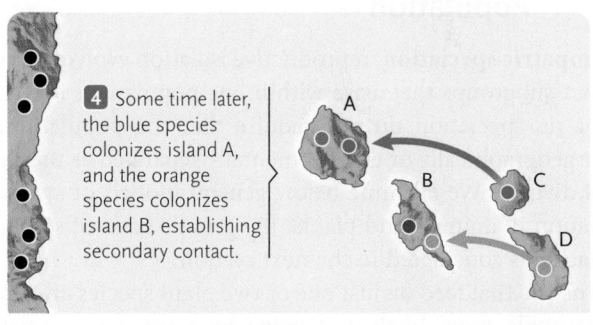

**FIGURE 18.10 Hypothetical evolution of a species cluster on an archipelago.** Letters identify four islands in an archipelago; coloured dots represent different species. The ancestor of all the species is represented by black dots on the mainland. At the end of the process, islands A and B are each occupied by two species, and islands C and D are each occupied by one species, all of which evolved on the islands.

mixed habitat where the species' ranges overlap, hybrids may not be well adapted to either the dry habitats to the west or the moist habitats to the east. Thus, if natural selection eliminates hybrids outside the narrow hybrid zone, the two species will remain reproductively isolated.

Postzygotic isolating mechanisms often cause hybrids to have lower fitness than either parent species. Under these

**Bullock's oriole (*Icterus bullockii*)**

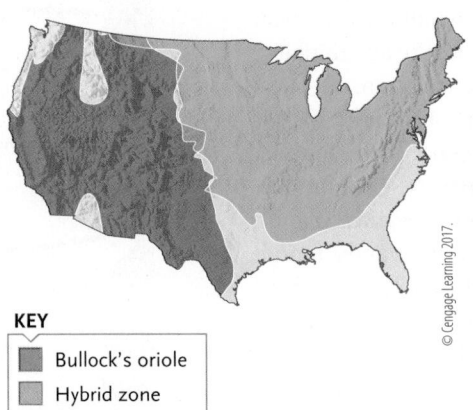

**Baltimore oriole (*Icterus galbula*)**

KEY

- Bullock's oriole
- Hybrid zone
- Baltimore oriole

**FIGURE 18.11 Hybrid zones.** Males of the Bullock's oriole and the Baltimore oriole differ in colour and courtship song, but in mixed habitats where their geographical ranges overlap, the two species produce hybrid offspring.

circumstances, natural selection will favour individuals that choose mates of their own species, thus promoting the evolution of prezygotic isolating mechanisms. This phenomenon of the evolution of prezygotic barriers to reproduction after postzygotic barriers already exist is called **reinforcement** because the prezygotic mechanisms *reinforce* those postzygotic barriers. Studies of several *Drosophila* species suggest that reinforcement enhanced the reproductive isolation that had begun to develop while the populations were geographically separated.

## 18.3c Sympatric Speciation Occurs within One Continuously Distributed Population

In **sympatric speciation**, reproductive isolation evolves between distinct subgroups that arise within one population. Models of sympatric speciation do not require that the populations be either geographically or environmentally separated as their gene pools diverge. We examine below general models of sympatric speciation in animals and plants; the genetic basis of sympatric speciation is considered in the next section.

Insects that feed on just one or two plant species are among the animals most likely to evolve by sympatric speciation. These insects generally carry out most important life cycle activities on or near their "host" plants. Adults mate on the host plant; females lay their eggs on it; and larvae feed on the host plant's tissues, eventually developing into adults, which initiate another round of the life cycle. Host plant choice is genetically determined in many insect species; in others, individuals associate with the host plant species they ate as larvae.

Theoretically, a genetic mutation could suddenly change some insects' choice of host plant. Mutant individuals would shift their life cycle activities to the new host, and then interact primarily with others preferring the same new host, an example of ecological isolation. These individuals would collectively form a separate subpopulation, called a **host race**. Reproductive isolation could evolve between different host races if the individuals of each host race are more likely to mate with members of their own host race than with members of another. Some biologists criticize this model, however, because it assumes that the genes controlling two traits, the insects' host plant choice and their mating preferences, change simultaneously. Moreover, host plant choice is controlled by multiple gene loci in some insect species, and it is clearly influenced by prior experience in others.

The apple maggot (*Rhagoletis pomonella*) is the most thoroughly studied example of possible sympatric speciation in animals (**Figure 18.12**). This fly's natural host plant in eastern North America is the hawthorn (*Crataegus* species), but at least two host races have appeared in the past 150 years. The larvae of a new host race were first discovered feeding on apples in New York State in the 1860s. In the 1960s, a cherry-feeding host race appeared in Wisconsin.

Genetic analyses have shown that variations at just a few gene loci underlie differences in the feeding preferences of *Rhagoletis* host races. Other genetic differences cause the host races to develop at different rates, and adults of the three races

**FIGURE 18.12 Sympatric speciation in animals.** Male and female apple maggots (*Rhagoletis pomonella*) court on a hawthorn leaf. The female will later lay her eggs on the fruit, and the offspring will feed, mate, and lay their eggs on hawthorns as well.

mate during different summer months. Nevertheless, individuals show no particular preference for mates of their own host race, at least under simplified laboratory conditions. Thus, although behavioural isolation has not developed between races, ecological and temporal isolation may separate adults in nature. Researchers are still not certain that the different host races are reproductively isolated under natural conditions.

In 2010, Andrew P. Michel, of the University of Notre Dame, and colleagues elsewhere in the United States and Germany published a genomic analysis of the apple- and hawthorn-feeding races of *Rhagoletis*. Their results suggest that, over the past 150 years, the two races have diverged at many loci in their genomes—not just at the loci that influence food choice and developmental rate—and that the divergence has largely been driven by disruptive selection, a diversifying form of natural selection (described in Chapter 17).

Sympatric speciation often occurs in plants through a genetic phenomenon, **polyploidy**, in which an individual has one or more *extra* copies of the entire haploid complement of chromosomes. Polyploidy can lead to speciation because these large-scale genetic changes may prevent polyploid individuals from breeding with individuals of the parent species. Nearly half of all flowering plant species are polyploid, including many important crops and ornamental species. The genetic mechanisms that produce polyploid individuals in plant populations are well understood; we describe them in the next section as part of a broader discussion of the genetics of speciation.

## STUDY BREAK QUESTIONS

1. What are the two stages required for allopatric speciation?
2. Why might insects from different host races be unlikely to mate with each other?

# 18.4 Genetic Mechanisms of Speciation

What genetic changes lead to reproductive isolation between populations? In this section we examine three genetic mechanisms that can lead to reproductive isolation: *genetic divergence* between allopatric populations, *polyploidy* in sympatric populations, and *chromosome alterations* that occur independently of the geographical distributions of populations.

## 18.4a Genetic Divergence in Allopatric Populations Can Lead to Speciation

In the absence of gene flow, geographically separated populations inevitably accumulate genetic differences through the action of mutation, genetic drift, and natural selection.

How much genetic divergence is necessary for speciation to occur? To understand the genetic basis of speciation in closely related species, researchers first identify the specific causes of reproductive isolation. They then use standard techniques of genetic analysis along with new molecular, genomic, and bioinformatic approaches to analyze the genetic mechanisms that establish reproductive isolation. In cases of postzygotic reproductive isolation, mutations in just a few gene loci can establish reproductive isolation. For example, if two common aquarium fishes, swordtails (*Xiphophorus helleri*) and platys (*Xiphophorus maculatus*), mate, two genes induce the development of lethal tumours in their hybrid offspring. When hybrid sterility is the primary cause of reproductive isolation between *Drosophila* species, at least five gene loci are responsible. About 55 gene loci contribute to postzygotic reproductive isolation between the European fire-bellied toad (*Bombina bombina*) and the yellow-bellied toad (*Bombina variegata*).

In cases of prezygotic reproductive isolation, some mechanisms have a surprisingly simple genetic basis. For example, a single mutation reverses the direction of coiling in the shells of some snails (*Bradybaena* species): some individuals coil in a clockwise spiral and others in a counterclockwise spiral. Snails with shells that coil in opposite directions cannot approach each other closely enough to mate, making reproduction between them mechanically impossible.

Many traits that now function as prezygotic isolating mechanisms may have evolved in response to sexual selection (described in Chapter 17). In sexually dimorphic species, this evolutionary process exaggerates showy structures and courtship behaviours in males, the traits that females use to identify appropriate mates. When two populations encounter one another on secondary contact, these traits may also prevent interspecific mating. For example, many closely related duck species exhibit dramatic variation in the appearance of males, but not females (**Figure 18.13**), an almost certain sign of sexual selection. Yet these species hybridize readily in captivity, producing offspring that are both viable and fertile.

Reproductive isolation and speciation in ducks and other sexually dimorphic birds probably results from geographical isolation and sexual selection on just a few morphological and behavioural characteristics that influence their mating behaviour. Thus, sometimes the evolution of reproductive isolation

**Mallard ducks (Anas platyrhynchos)**  **Pintail ducks (Anas acuta)**

**FIGURE 18.13 Sexual selection and prezygotic isolation.** In closely related species, such as mallard and pintail ducks, males have much more distinctive coloration than females, a sure sign of sexual selection at work.

may not require much genetic change at all. Indeed, sexual selection appears to increase the rate at which new species arise: bird lineages that are sexually dimorphic generally include more species than do related lineages in which males and females have a similar appearance.

## 18.4b Polyploidy Is a Common Mechanism of Sympatric Speciation in Plants

Polyploidy is common among plants, and it may be an important factor in the evolution of some fish, amphibian, and reptile species. Polyploid individuals can arise from chromosome duplications within a single species (autopolyploidy) or through hybridization of different species (allopolyploidy).

**AUTOPOLYPLOIDY** In **autopolyploidy (Figure 18.14a)**, a diploid (2n) individual may produce, for example, tetraploid (4n) offspring, each of which has four complete chromosome sets. Autopolyploidy often results when gametes, through an error in either mitosis or meiosis, spontaneously receive the same number of chromosomes as a somatic cell. Such gametes are called **unreduced gametes** because their chromosome number has not been reduced compared with that of somatic cells.

Diploid pollen can fertilize the diploid ovules of a self-fertilizing individual, or it may fertilize diploid ovules on another plant with unreduced gametes. The resulting tetraploid offspring can reproduce either by self-pollination or by breeding with other tetraploid individuals. However, a tetraploid plant cannot produce fertile offspring by hybridizing with its diploid

**a. Speciation by autopolyploidy in plants**
A spontaneous doubling of chromosomes during meiosis produces diploid gametes. If the plant fertilizes itself, a tetraploid zygote will be produced.

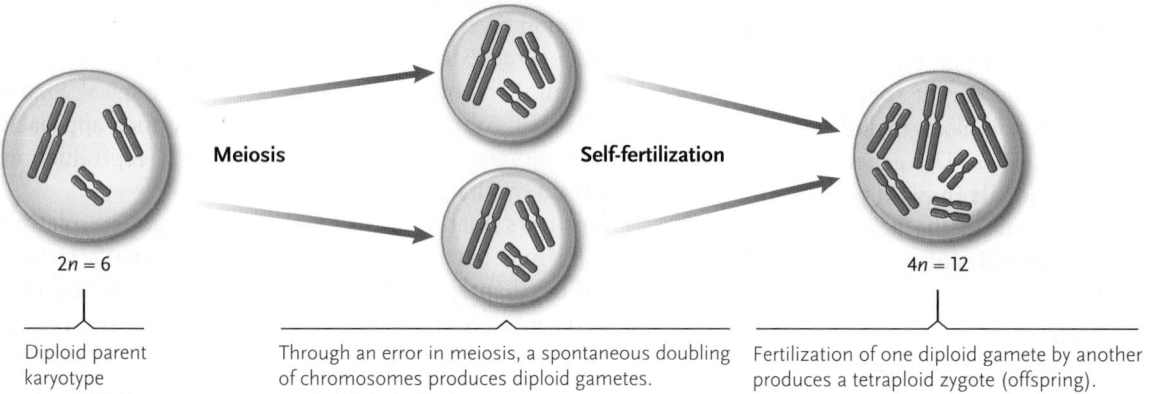

Diploid parent karyotype

Through an error in meiosis, a spontaneous doubling of chromosomes produces diploid gametes.

Fertilization of one diploid gamete by another produces a tetraploid zygote (offspring).

**b. Speciation by hybridization and allopolyploidy in plants**
A hybrid mating between two species followed by a doubling of chromosomes during mitosis in gametes of the hybrid can instantly create sets of homologous chromosomes. Self-fertilization can then generate polyploid individuals that are reproductively isolated from both parent species.

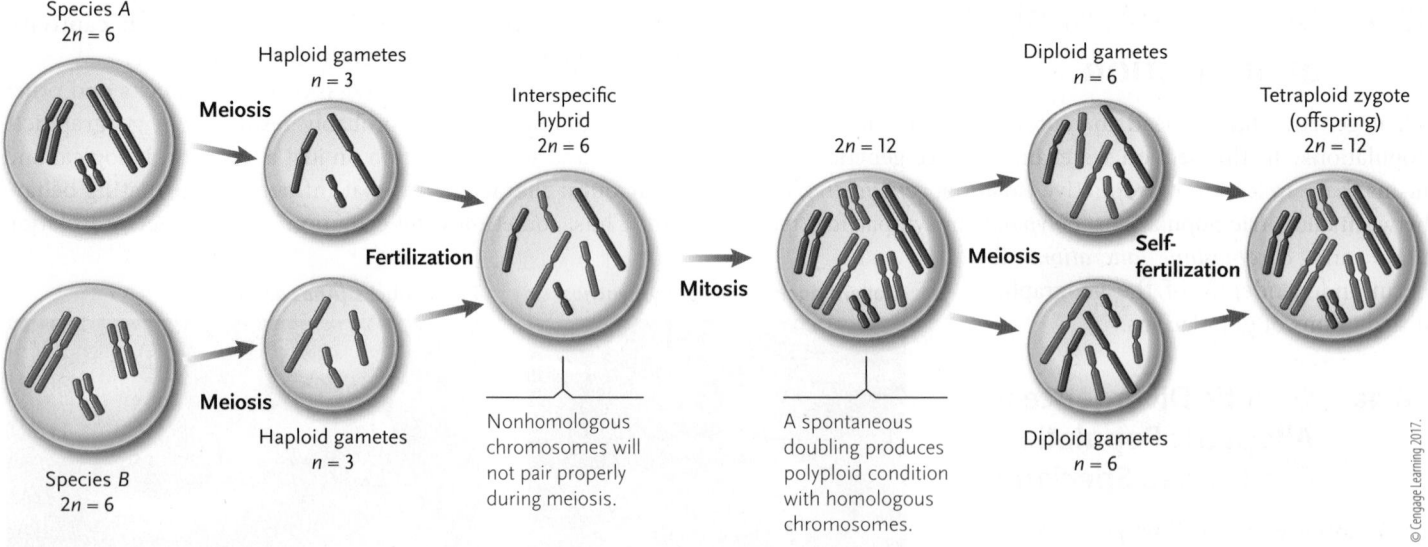

Nonhomologous chromosomes will not pair properly during meiosis.

A spontaneous doubling produces polyploid condition with homologous chromosomes.

© Cengage Learning 2017.

**FIGURE 18.14 Polyploidy in plants. (a)** Speciation by autopolyploidy in plants can occur by a spontaneous doubling of chromosomes during meiosis, producing diploid gametes. If the plant fertilizes itself, a tetraploid zygote will result. **(b)** Speciation by hybridization and allopolyploidy in plants can occur when two species mate, producing a hybrid. If chromosomes are doubled during mitosis in gametes of the hybrid, sets of homologous chromosomes are created instantly. Self-fertilization can then generate polyploid individuals that are reproductively isolated from both parent species.

parents. The fusion of a diploid gamete with a normal haploid gamete produces a triploid (3*n*) offspring, which is usually sterile because its odd number of chromosomes cannot segregate properly during meiosis. Thus, the tetraploid is reproductively isolated from the original diploid population. Many species of grasses, shrubs, and ornamental plants, including violets, chrysanthemums, and nasturtiums, are autopolyploids, having anywhere from 4 to 20 complete chromosome sets.

**ALLOPOLYPLOIDY** In **allopolyploidy** (Figure 18.14b), two closely related species hybridize and subsequently form polyploid offspring. Hybrid offspring are sterile if the two parent species have diverged enough that their chromosomes do not pair properly during meiosis. However, if the hybrid's chromosome number is doubled, the chromosome complement of the gametes is also doubled, producing homologous chromosomes that *can* pair during meiosis. The hybrid can then produce polyploid gametes and, through self-fertilization or fertilization with other doubled hybrids, establish a population of a new polyploid species. Compared with speciation by genetic divergence, speciation by allopolyploidy can be extremely rapid, causing a new species to arise in one generation without geographical isolation.

Even when sterile, polyploids are often robust, growing larger than either parent species. For that reason, both autopolyploids and allopolyploids—including plantains (cooking bananas), coffee, cotton, potatoes, sugarcane, and tobacco—have been important to agriculture. For example, bread wheat (*Triticum aestivum*), a staple food for at least 30% of the worldwide human population, arose through a series of hybridization events. Recent research by members of the International Wheat Genome Sequencing Consortium that was published in the journal *Science* in July 2014 has begun to reveal details of its genetics and ancestry **(Figure 18.15)**. The bread wheat genome includes three diploid subgenomes (identified as AA, BB, and DD) that originated in different

ancestors. About 6.5 million years ago, divergence from a wheat-like ancestor produced lineages with subgenomes AA and BB. One million years later, hybridization between descendants of those lineages produced the lineage with subgenome DD. All three subgenomes are diploid, with two sets of seven chromosomes (2*n* = 14). Then, about 800 000 years ago, a hybridization between two species in lineage AA (*T. monococcum* and *T. urartu*) with one species from lineage BB (a close relative of

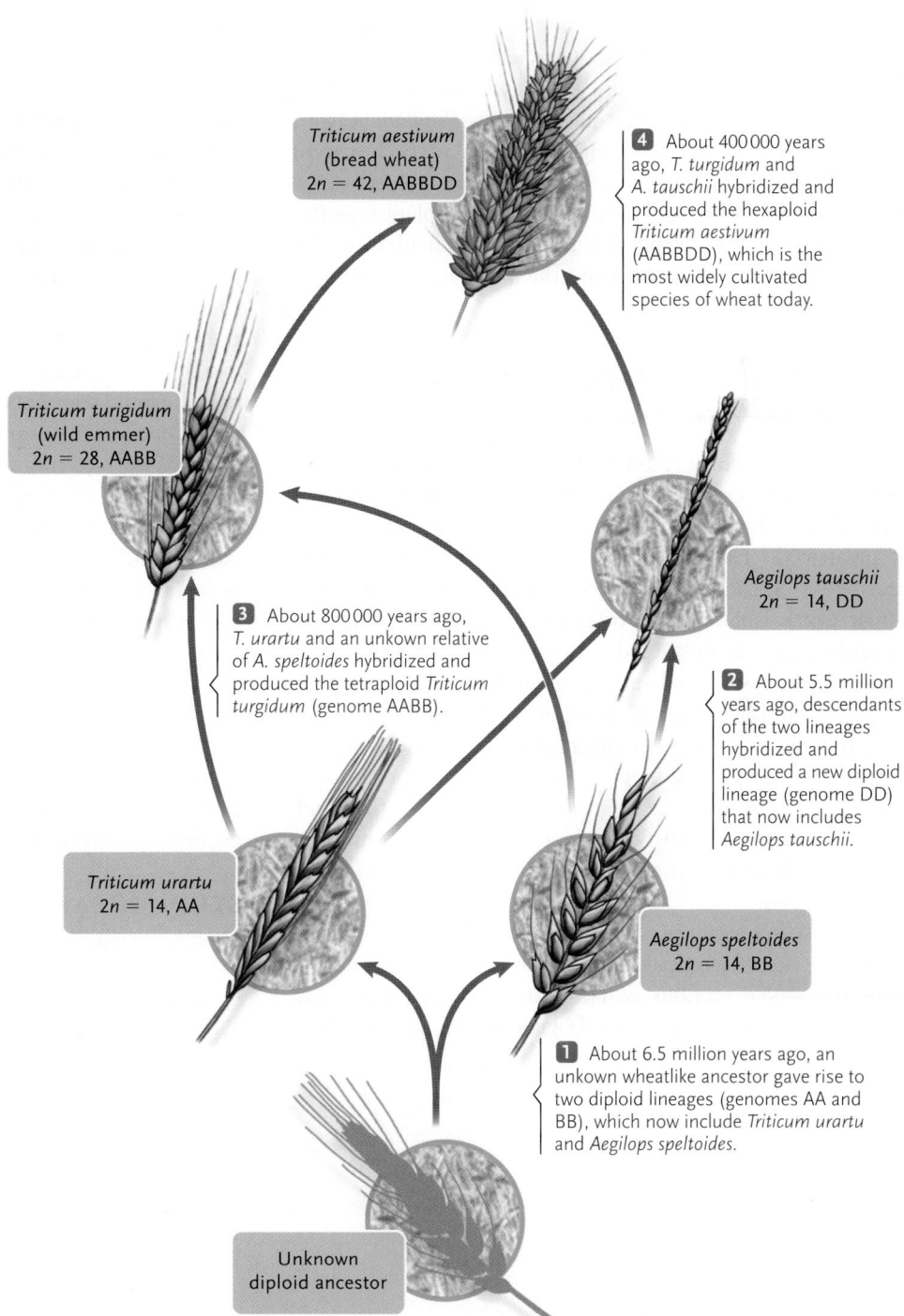

**4** About 400 000 years ago, *T. turgidum* and *A. tauschii* hybridized and produced the hexaploid *Triticum aestivum* (AABBDD), which is the most widely cultivated species of wheat today.

*Triticum aestivum* (bread wheat) 2*n* = 42, AABBDD

*Triticum turigidum* (wild emmer) 2*n* = 28, AABB

*Aegilops tauschii* 2*n* = 14, DD

**3** About 800 000 years ago, *T. urartu* and an unkown relative of *A. speltoides* hybridized and produced the tetraploid *Triticum turgidum* (genome AABB).

**2** About 5.5 million years ago, descendants of the two lineages hybridized and produced a new diploid lineage (genome DD) that now includes *Aegilops tauschii*.

*Triticum urartu* 2*n* = 14, AA

*Aegilops speltoides* 2*n* = 14, BB

**1** About 6.5 million years ago, an unkown wheatlike ancestor gave rise to two diploid lineages (genomes AA and BB), which now include *Triticum urartu* and *Aegilops speltoides*.

Unknown diploid ancestor

© Cengage Learning 2017.

**FIGURE 18.15 The evolution of wheat.** Researchers believe the evolution of common bread wheat (*Triticum aestivum*) resulted from a series of hybridizations, some of which produced allopolyploid species.

*Aegilops speltoides*) produced a tetraploid (2*n* = 28, AABB) wheat, emmer (*Triticum turgidum*), which is still cultivated in the Middle East. About 400 000 years ago, *T. turgidum* hybridized with a diploid species in lineage DD (*A. tauschii*), producing the hexaploid (2*n* = 42, AABBDD) bread wheat (*T. aestivum*) that is widely grown today. Each of the three ancestors contributed two sets of seven chromosomes to bread wheat, making it a hexaploid with a total of 42 chromosomes.

Plant breeders often try to increase the probability of forming an allopolyploid by using chemicals that foster nondisjunction of chromosomes during mitosis. In the first such experiment, undertaken in the 1920s, scientists crossed a radish and a cabbage, hoping to develop a plant with both edible roots and edible leaves. Instead, the new species, *Raphanobrassica*, combined the least desirable characteristics of each parent, growing a cabbagelike root and radish like leaves. Recent experiments have been more successful. For example, plant scientists have produced an allopolyploid grain, triticale, that has the disease resistance of its rye parent and the high productivity of its wheat parent.

## 18.4c Chromosome Alterations Can Foster Speciation

Other changes in chromosome structure or number may also foster speciation. Closely related species often have a substantial number of chromosome differences between them, including inversions, translocations, deletions, and duplications (described in Section 10.3). These differences, which may foster postzygotic isolation, can often be identified by comparing the *banding patterns* in stained chromosome preparations from the different species. In all species, banding patterns vary from one chromosome segment to another. When researchers find identical banding patterns in chromosome segments from two or more related species, they know that they are examining comparable portions of the species' genomes. Thus, the banding patterns allow scientists to identify specific chromosome segments and compare their positions in the chromosomes of different species.

The banding patterns of humans and their closest relatives among the apes—chimpanzees, gorillas, and orangutans—reveal that whole sections of chromosomes have been rearranged over evolutionary time (**Figure 18.16**). For example,

humans have a diploid complement of 46 chromosomes, whereas chimpanzees, gorillas, and orangutans have 48 chromosomes. The difference can be traced to the fusion (i.e., the joining together) of two ancestral chromosomes into chromosome 2 of humans; the ancestral chromosomes are separate in the other three species.

Moreover, banding patterns suggest that the position of the centromere in human chromosome 2 closely matches that of a centromere in one of the chimpanzee chromosomes, reflecting their close evolutionary relationship. But this centromere falls within an inverted region of the chromosome in gorillas and orangutans, reflecting their evolutionary divergence from chimpanzees and humans. (Recall from Section 10.3 that an inverted chromosome segment has a reversed orientation, so the order of genes on it is reversed relative to the order in a segment that is not inverted.) Nevertheless, humans and chimps differ from each other in centromeric inversions in six other chromosomes.

How might such chromosome rearrangements promote speciation? In a paper published in 2003, Arcadi Navarro, of the Universitat Pompeu Fabra in Spain, and Nick H. Barton, of the University of Edinburgh in Scotland, compared the rates of evolution in protein-coding genes that lie within rearranged chromosome segments of humans and chimpanzees to those in genes outside the rearranged segments. They discovered that proteins evolved more than twice as quickly in the rearranged chromosome segments. Navarro and Barton reasoned that, because chromosome rearrangements inhibit chromosome pairing and recombination during meiosis, new genetic variations favoured by natural selection would be conserved within the rearranged segments. These variations accumulate over time, contributing to genetic divergence between populations with the rearrangement and those without it. Thus, chromosome rearrangements can be a trigger for speciation: once a chromosome rearrangement becomes established within a population, that population will diverge more rapidly from populations lacking the rearrangement. The genetic divergence eventually causes reproductive isolation.

### STUDY BREAK QUESTIONS

1. How can natural selection promote reproductive isolation in allopatric populations?
2. How does polyploidy promote speciation in plants?

FIGURE 18.16 **Observational Research**

## Chromosomal Similarities and Differences among Humans and the Great Apes

**Question:** Does chromosome structure differ between humans and their closest relatives among the apes?

**Hypothesis:** Large-scale chromosome rearrangements contributed to the development of reproductive isolation between species within the evolutionary lineage that includes humans and apes.

**Prediction:** Chromosome structure differs markedly between humans and their close relatives among the great apes: chimpanzees, gorillas, and orangutans.

**Method:** Jorge J. Yunis and Om Prakash, of the University of Minnesota Medical School, used Giemsa stain to visualize the banding patterns on metaphase chromosome preparations from humans, chimpanzees, gorillas, and orangutans. They identified about 1000 bands that are present in humans and in the three ape species. By matching the banding patterns on the chromosomes, the researchers verified that they were comparing the same segments of the genomes in the four species. They then searched for similarities and differences in the structure of the chromosomes.

**Results:** Analysis of human chromosome 2 reveals that it was produced by the fusion of two smaller chromosomes that are still present in the other three species. Although the position of the centromere in human chromosome 2 matches that of the centromere in one of the chimpanzee chromosomes, in gorillas and orangutans it falls within an inverted segment of the chromosome.

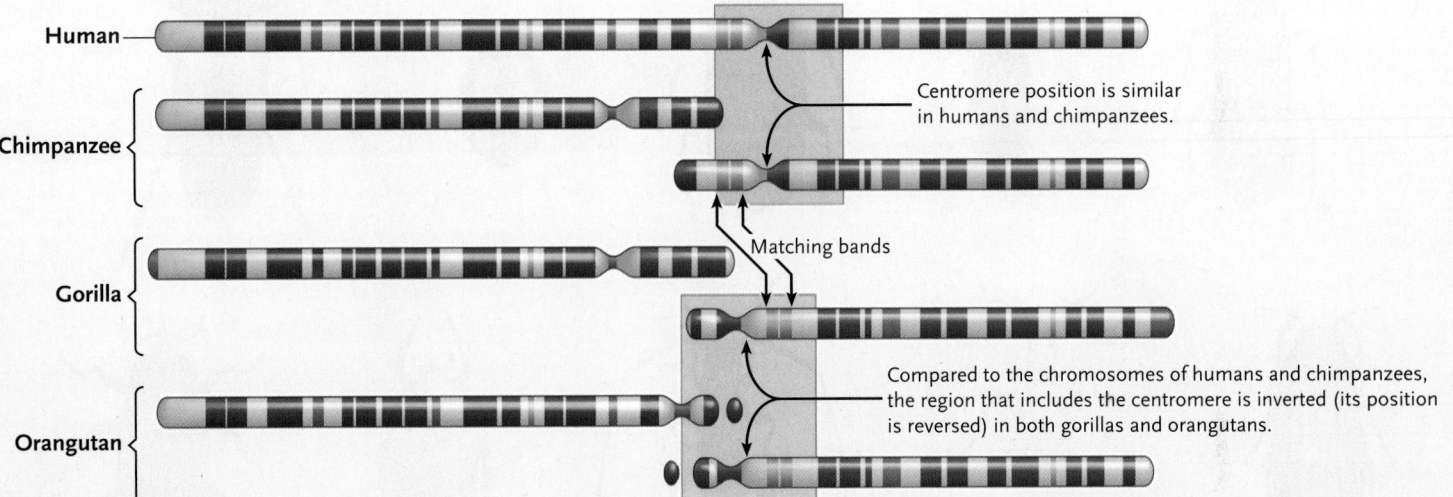

**Conclusion:** Differences in chromosome structure between humans and both gorillas and orangutans are more pronounced than they are between humans and chimpanzees. Structural differences in the chromosomes of these four species may contribute to their reproductive isolation.

Source: © Cengage Learning 2017. Based on J. J. Yunis and O. Prakash. 1982. The origin of man: A chromosomal pictorial legacy. *Science* 215:1525–1530.

# Summary Illustration

When microevolutionary processes differ between populations of a species, the populations will diverge genetically and may eventually be recognized as distinct species. Macroevolution refers to the broader pattern of events that occur, which result in species formation. Studying speciation involves understanding how individual species are defined and recognized, as well as events that influence the process.

There are an estimated 350 000 different species of beetles. But what is a species?

**Morphological Species**
If two organisms look the same, they are the same species.

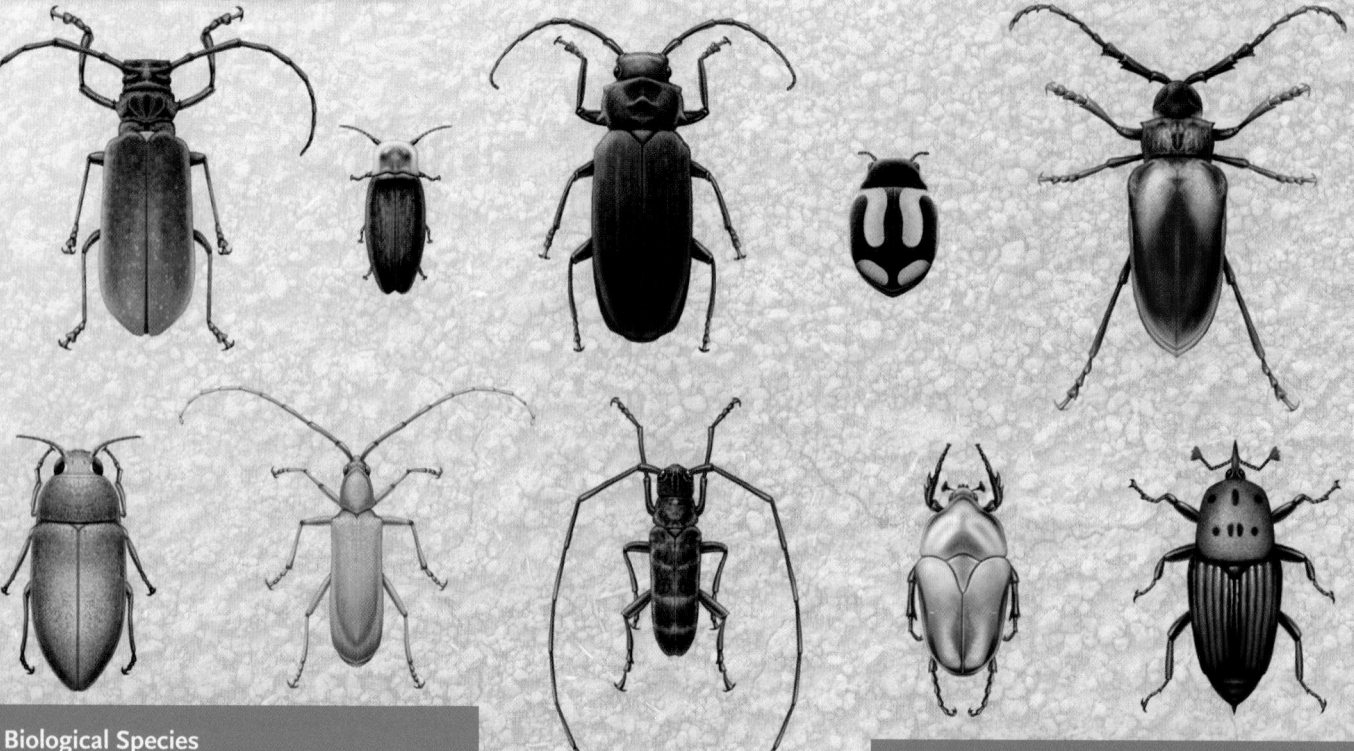

**Biological Species**
If the members of two populations interbreed and produce fertile offspring, then they belong to the same species.

**Phylogenetic Species**
Populations that share a recent evolutionary history belong to the same species.

Species can exhibit geographical variation. Populations can differ genetically and phenotypically due to geographical separation.

| A | B | C | D | E |

Clinal variation across five populations of a species

Individual populations may form a ring around a geographic barrier. Populations at the two extremes of the cline, however, are unable to reproduce.

Reproductive isolation prevents individuals of different species from mating and producing viable progeny. This maintains the genetic identity of a species.

| Prezygotic isolating mechanisms | | Postzygotic isolating mechanisms |
|---|---|---|
| Premating | Mating | Fertilization |

**Species 1**

**Ecological isolation**
Species at the same locale occupy different habitats.

**Temporal isolation**
Species reproduce at different seasons or different times of day.

**Species 2**

**Behavioural isolation**
In animal species, courtship behaviour differs, or individuals respond to different songs, calls, pheromones, or other signals.

**Mechanical isolation**
Genitalia between species are unsuitable for one another.

**Gametic isolation**
Sperm cannot reach or fertilize the egg.

**Hybrid inviability**
Fertilization occurs, but the zygote does not survive.

**Hybrid sterility**
The hybrid survives, but is sterile.

**Hybrid breakdown**
The hybrid is fertile, but the $F_2$ hybrid has reduced fitness.

**Hybrid offspring**

The two modes of speciation are defined based on the geographical relationships of the populations.

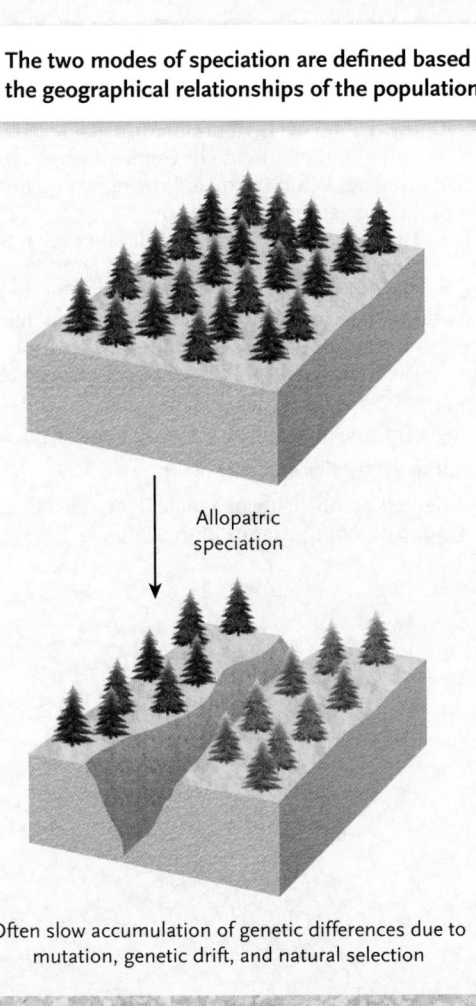

Allopatric speciation

Often slow accumulation of genetic differences due to mutation, genetic drift, and natural selection

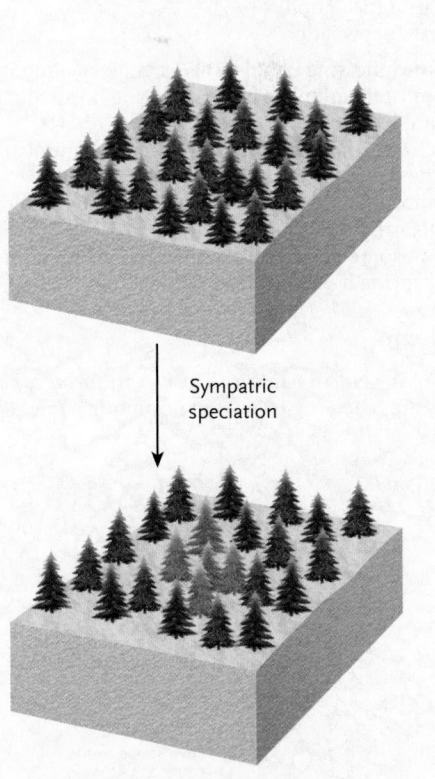

Sympatric speciation

Sometimes very rapid genetic isolation, often due to formation of polyploids (e.g., autopolyploidy, allopollyploidy)

# SELF-TEST QUESTIONS

## Recall/Understand

1. Who is the "father" of the science that identifies, names, and classifies new species?
   a. Charles Darwin
   b. Alfred Wallace
   c. Carolus Linnaeus
   d. Jean Baptiste de Lamarck

2. On what basis does the biological species concept define species?
   a. reproductive characteristics
   b. biochemical characteristics
   c. morphological characteristics
   d. behavioural characteristics

3. Which of the following is a characteristic of prezygotic isolating mechanisms?
   a. They generally prevent zygotes from surviving and reproducing.
   b. They generally prevent individuals of different species from producing zygotes.
   c. They are found only in plants.
   d. They are observed only in organisms that reproduce asexually.

4. In the model of allopatric speciation, which of the following is characteristic of the geographical separation of two populations?
   a. It occurs only after speciation is complete.
   b. It allows gene flow between them.
   c. It reduces the relative fitness of hybrid offspring.
   d. It inhibits gene flow between them.

5. Adjacent populations that produce hybrid offspring with low relative fitness may be undergoing which of the following?
   a. clinal isolation
   b. parapatric speciation
   c. allopatric speciation
   d. sympatric speciation

6. Which of the following could be an example of allopolyploidy?
   a. Chromosome number in the offspring is exactly half that of the parents.
   b. Gametes and somatic cells have the same number of chromosomes.
   c. Chromosome number increases by one in a gamete and in the offspring it produces.
   d. Chromosome number decreases by one in a gamete and in the offspring it produces.

## Apply/Analyze

7. The name of the North American beaver is *Castor canadensis*. What does the "*canadensis*" part of its unique name represent?
   a. genus
   b. epithet
   c. domain
   d. family

8. If two species of holly (genus *Ilex*) flower during different months, how might their gene pools be kept separate?
   a. mechanical isolation
   b. ecological isolation
   c. gametic isolation
   d. temporal isolation

9. While attempting to cross a llama with an alpaca for finer wool, an animal breeder found that the hybrid offspring rarely lived more than a few weeks. Which of the following terms best explains this outcome?
   a. prezygotic reproductive isolation
   b. postzygotic reproductive isolation
   c. sympatric speciation
   d. polyploidy

10. Which of the following would apply to evaluating hybrid zones?
    a. the behaviour of the individuals
    b. the morphology of the individuals
    c. the prezygotic isolation mechanisms
    d. the postzygotic isolating mechanisms

## Create/Evaluate

11. Suppose that you observe two neighbouring populations of squirrels coexisting in the wild. You consult the literature and you find that these two populations are genetically connected, but that they still do not interbreed. Based on the information that you collected, which of the following are these populations most likely?
    a. hybrid species
    b. same species
    c. ring species
    d. different species

12. Suppose that an original population gets separated by a river flow, and that the individuals came into contact after the river had dried up. Which of the following would most likely indicate that the speciation has occurred?
    a. The individuals in one population look morphologically different from the individuals in another population.
    b. The individuals of the two populations do not interbreed.
    c. The individuals in one population look morphologically the same as individuals in another population.
    d. The individuals of the two populations interbreed successfully.

13. Suggest three limitations of the biological species concept.

14. Compare species and subspecies.

15. A tigon is an offspring of a male tiger and a female lion. Explain why we do not see tigons in the wild.

# Chapter Roadmap

## Systematics and Phylogenetics: Revealing the Tree of Life

The diversity of life on Earth is astonishing. In this chapter we discuss the approaches scientists use to organize this diversity: from how organisms are named and classified to the tools and techniques employed to understand evolutionary relationship among species.

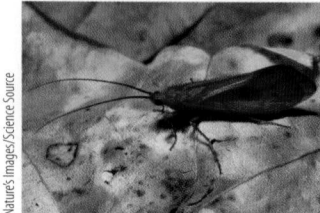

### 19.1 Nomenclature and Classification

Using a system of binomial nomenclature, species are grouped into a taxonomic hierarchy.

### 19.2 Phylogenetic Trees

Phylogenetic trees attempt to depict the evolutionary history of a group of organisms.

### 19.3 Sources of Data for Phylogenetic Analyses

Phylogenetic trees are built using a range of data, from morphological characters to molecular sequences.

### 19.4 Traditional Classification and Paraphyletic Groups

Traditional systematics assesses the amount of phenotypic divergence between lineages as well as the patterns of branching evolution that produced them.

### 19.5 The Cladistic Revolution

Compared to transitional methods, with cladistics, classifications are based solely on evolutionary relationships.

### 19.6 Phylogenetic Trees as Research Tools

Phylogenetic trees are very useful tools that facilitate research in many areas of biology.

### 19.7 Molecular Phylogenetic Analyses

The building of phylogenetic relationships based on sequence data has resolved some evolutionary puzzles that were not easily addressed using other techniques.

Barbie pagoda fungus (*Podoserpula miranda*), discovered in 2011 in New Caledonia

# Systematics and Phylogenetics: Revealing the Tree of Life

# 19

**Why it matters ...** Mention the word "malaria" and people envision old movies about the tropics: explorers wander through the jungle in pith helmets and sleep under mosquito netting; clouds of insects hover nearby, ready to infect them with *Plasmodium*, the protistan parasite that causes this disease. You may be surprised to learn, however, that less than 100 years ago, malaria was also a serious threat in the southeastern United States and much of Western Europe.

Scientists puzzled over the cause of malaria for thousands of years. Hippocrates, a Greek physician who worked in the fifth century BCE, knew that people who lived near malodorous marshes often suffered from fevers and swollen spleens. Indeed, the name *malaria* is derived from the Latin for "bad air." By 1900, scientists had established that mosquitoes, *Plasmodium*'s intermediate hosts, transmit the parasite to humans. Mosquitoes breed in standing water, and anyone living nearby is likely to suffer their bites.

Until the 1920s, scientists thought that the mosquito species *Anopheles maculipennis* carried malaria in Europe. But some areas with huge populations of these insects had little human malaria, whereas other areas had relatively few mosquitoes and a high incidence of the disease.

Then, a French researcher reported variation in the mosquitoes, and Dutch scientists identified two forms of the "species," only one of which seemed to carry malaria. The breakthrough came in 1924, when a retired public health inspector in Italy discovered that individual mosquitoes—all thought to be the same species—produced eggs with one of six distinctive surface patterns (**Figure 19.1**).

**a.** *Anopheles* mosquito feeding on human blood

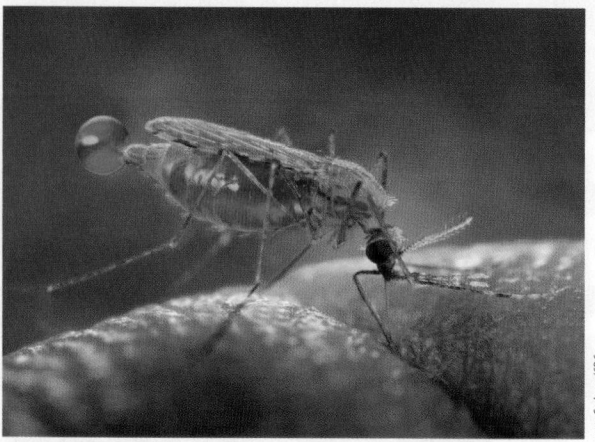

James Gathany/CDC

**b.** Eggs of six European *Anopheles* mosquito species

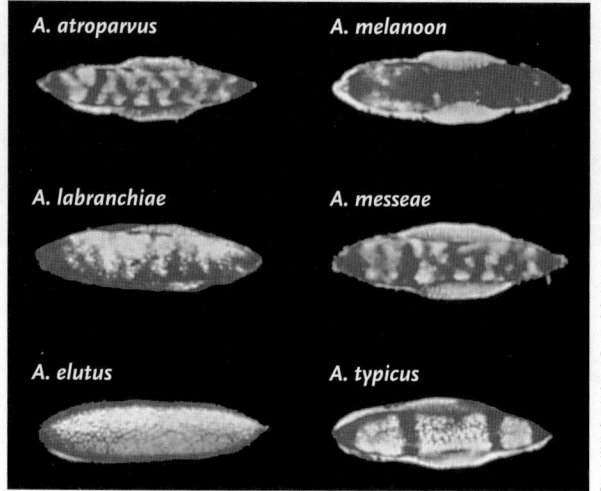

*A. atroparvus*

*A. melanoon*

*A. labranchiae*

*A. messeae*

*A. elutus*

*A. typicus*

From L. W. Hackett, Malaria in Europe. Oxford University Press, 1937.

**FIGURE 19.1 Carriers of malaria. (a)** Like other *Anopheles* mosquitoes, *A. gambiae* frequently take a blood meal from a human host. **(b)** Differences in surface patterns on the eggs of *Anopheles* mosquitoes in Europe helped researchers identify six separate species. The adults of all six species look remarkably alike.

Further research revealed that the name *Anopheles maculipennis* had been applied to six separate mosquito species. Although the adults of these species are almost indistinguishable, their eggs are clearly different. The species are reproductively isolated from each other, and they differ ecologically: some breed in brackish coastal marshes, others in inland freshwater marshes, and still others in slow-moving streams. Only some of these species have a preference for human blood, and researchers eventually determined that only three of them routinely transmit malaria to humans.

These discoveries explained why the geographical distributions of mosquitoes and malaria did not always match. And government agencies could finally fight malaria by eradicating the disease-carrying species. Health workers drained marshes to prevent mosquitoes from breeding. They used insecticides to kill mosquito larvae or introduced fish of the genus *Gambusia*, the mosquitofish, which eats them. These targeted control

programs were very successful in the early and middle decades of the twentieth century.

Today, with the increased mobility of humans, agricultural products, and other goods, some mosquito species—as well as many other organisms—are invading habitats made more hospitable by global climate change (discussed further in Unit 6). Some mosquito species have expanded their geographical ranges substantially: introduced mosquito species have been discovered on all continents except Antarctica. Mosquitoes carry numerous agents of disease, and biologists are now devising new ways to recognize, and eradicate, the species that pose the greatest threats to human welfare.

The historic eradication of malaria in Europe owes a debt to **systematics**, the branch of biology that studies the diversity of life and its evolutionary relationships. Systematic biologists (*systematists* for short) identify, describe, name, and classify organisms, organizing their observations within a framework that reflects the organisms' evolutionary relationships. In this chapter, we briefly describe the traditional approach to classification. We then focus attention on how systematists working today develop hypotheses about the evolutionary relationships of all the branches, twigs, and leaves on the Tree of Life.

## 19.1 Nomenclature and Classification

The Swedish naturalist Carl von Linné (1707–1778), better known by his Latinized name, Carolus Linnaeus, was the first modern practitioner of **taxonomy**, the science that identifies, names, and classifies new species. A professor at the University of Uppsala, Linnaeus sent ill-prepared students around the world to gather specimens, losing perhaps a third of his followers to the rigors of their expeditions. Although he may not have been a commendable student adviser, Linnaeus developed the basic system of naming and classifying organisms that biologists embraced for two centuries.

### 19.1a Linnaeus Developed the System of Binomial Nomenclature

Linnaeus invented the system of **binomial nomenclature** in which species are assigned a Latinized two-part name, or **binomial**. The first part of the name identifies a **genus** (plural, *genera*), a group of species with similar characteristics. The second part is the **specific epithet**, or species name. When identifying and naming a new species, Linnaeus used the morphological species concept (described in Section 18.1), assigning the same scientific name to individuals that shared anatomical characteristics.

A combination of the generic name and the specific epithet provides a unique name for every species. For example, *Ursus maritimus* is the polar bear and *Ursus arctos* is the brown bear. By convention, the first letter of a generic name is always capitalized; the specific epithet is never capitalized; and the entire binomial is italicized. In addition, the specific epithet is never used without the full or abbreviated generic name preceding it because the same specific epithet is often given to species in different genera. For instance, *Ursus americanus* is the American black bear, *Homarus americanus* is the Atlantic lobster, and *Bufo americanus* is the American toad. If you were to order just *"americanus"* for dinner, you might be dismayed when your plate arrived—unless you have an adventurous palate!

Nonscientists often use different common names to identify a species. For example, *Bothrops asper*, a poisonous snake native to Central and South America, is called *barba amarilla* (meaning "yellow beard") in some places and *cola blanca* (meaning "white tail") in others; biologists have recorded about 50 local names for this species. Adding to the confusion, the same common name is sometimes used for several different species. Binomials, however, allow people everywhere to discuss organisms unambiguously.

Many binomials are descriptive of the organism or its habitat. *Asparagus horridus*, for example, is a spiny plant. Other species, such as the South American bird *Rhea darwinii*, are named for notable biologists. The naming of newly discovered species follows a formal process of publishing a description of the species in a scientific journal. International commissions meet periodically to settle disputes about scientific names.

## 19.1b Linnaeus Devised the Taxonomic Hierarchy to Organize Information about Species

Linnaeus described and named thousands of species on the basis of their morphological similarities and differences. Keeping track of so many species was no easy task, so he devised a **classification**, a conceptual filing system that arranges organisms into ever more inclusive categories. Linnaeus' classification, called the **taxonomic hierarchy**, includes a nested series of formal categories (from most inclusive to least): domain, kingdom, phylum, class, order, family, genus, species, and subspecies (**Figure 19.2**). The organisms included within any category of the taxonomic hierarchy compose a **taxon** (plural, *taxa*). Woodpeckers, for example, are a taxon (Picidae) at the family level, and pine trees are a taxon (*Pinus*) at the genus level.

Species that are included in the same taxon at the bottom of the hierarchy (i.e., in the same genus or family) generally share many characteristics. By contrast, species that are included in the same taxon only near the top of the hierarchy (i.e., the same kingdom or phylum) generally share much fewer traits (see Figure 19.2). The hierarchy has been a great convenience for biologists because every taxon is defined by a set of shared characteristics. Thus, when a biologist refers to a

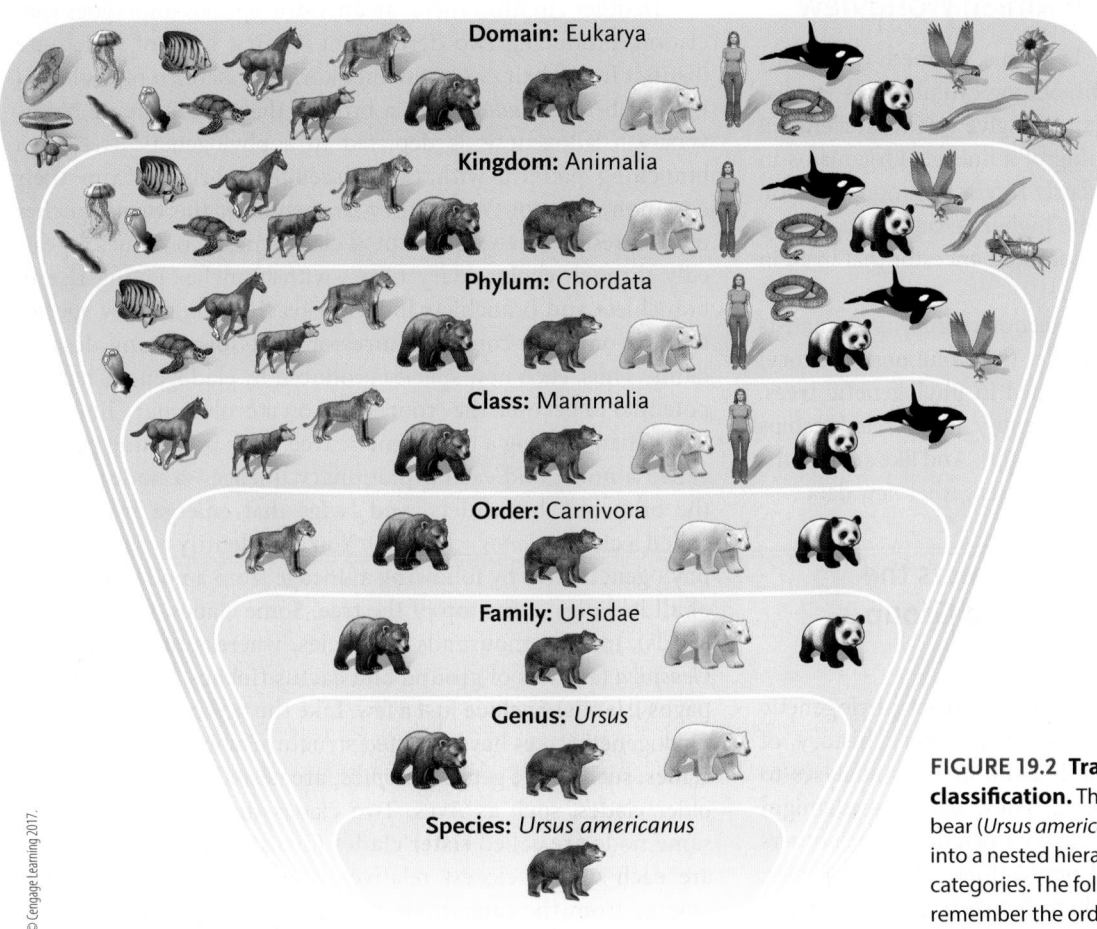

**Domain:** Eukarya

**Kingdom:** Animalia

**Phylum:** Chordata

**Class:** Mammalia

**Order:** Carnivora

**Family:** Ursidae

**Genus:** *Ursus*

**Species:** *Ursus americanus*

© Cengage Learning 2017

**FIGURE 19.2 Traditional hierarchical classification.** The classification of the American black bear (*Ursus americanus*) illustrates how each species fits into a nested hierarchy of even more inclusive categories. The following sentence can help you remember the order of categories in a classification, from Domain to Species: Diligent Kindly Professors Cannot Often Fail Good Students.

member of the family Picidae, all of his or her colleagues understand that the biologist is talking about a medium-sized bird that uses its stout bill to drill holes in tree trunks.

**STUDY BREAK QUESTIONS**

1. How does the system of binomial nomenclature minimize ambiguity in the naming and identification of species?
2. How does the taxonomic hierarchy help biologists organize information about different species?

## 19.2 Phylogenetic Trees

As we discussed briefly in Chapter 16, Linnaeus devised the taxonomic hierarchy long before Darwin published his theory of evolution. His goals were to illuminate the details of God's creation and to devise a practical way for naturalists to keep track of their discoveries. But the science of systematics changed in response to Darwin's idea that all organisms in the Tree of Life are descended from a distant common ancestor: systematists began to focus on discovering the evolutionary relationships between groups of organisms.

### 19.2a Systematists Adapted Linnaeus' Approach to a Darwinian Worldview

The taxonomic hierarchy that Linnaeus defined was easily adapted to Darwin's concept of branching evolution; as we discussed in Chapter 18, ancestral species give rise to descendant species through repeated branching of a lineage. Organisms in the same genus generally share a fairly recent common ancestor, whereas those assigned to the same higher taxonomic category, such as a class or phylum, share a common ancestor that lived in the more distant past.

In the second half of the nineteenth century, systematists began to reconstruct the **phylogeny** (i.e., the evolutionary history) of organisms. Phylogenies are illustrated in **phylogenetic trees**, which are formal hypotheses that identify likely relationships among species and higher taxonomic groups. And like all hypotheses, they are constantly revised as scientists gather new data.

### 19.2b A Phylogenetic Tree Depicts the Evolutionary History of a Group of Organisms

Contemporary evolutionary biologists construct phylogenetic trees to illustrate the hypothesized evolutionary history of organisms. Researchers tailor the breadth of their analyses to match specific research questions. Thus, some trees might include the evolutionary history of all known organisms; others a small cluster of closely related populations within a species; and still others a group somewhere between those extremes. Regardless of how wide a range of organisms is included, all

phylogenetic trees share a specific structure and depict key relationships in similar ways (**Figure 19.3**).

For example, phylogenetic trees are usually drawn along an implicit or explicit timeline. In this book, phylogenetic trees are generally depicted vertically; the most ancient organisms and evolutionary events are at the bottom of the tree (often labelled "long ago"), and the most recent are at the top (often labelled "present"). The common ancestor of all species included in the tree is described as the **root** of the tree. In a few cases in this book, trees are presented with the root on the left, with time passing from left to right.

The tempo of evolution varies within and among lineages. In some cases, evolutionary changes may accumulate slowly in a lineage as the environment shifts over time. This pattern of gradual phyletic change is often described as *anagenesis*. If the changes through time are substantial and the fossil record is incomplete, paleontologists who discover morphologically distinct fossils in different strata may assign them different species names and say that "the ancestral species A evolved into the descendant species B." But the production of such "new" species by anagenesis does not increase biodiversity; rather, it is simply the gradual transformation of one "species" into another as its characteristics shifted over time. Anagenesis is often illustrated by a straight line in a phylogenetic tree.

In other circumstances, an ancestral species undergoes speciation, producing two descendant species, both of which are distinct from their common ancestor. This pattern of evolution is described as *cladogenesis*, a process that *does* increase biodiversity. Cladogenesis is depicted in a phylogenetic tree by a branching pattern, with two descendants arising from their common ancestor. When they first emerge, the two branches may represent new species. But as cladogenesis continues repeatedly through evolutionary time—with branches giving rise to branchlets and branchlets to twigs—each of those new species may become the common ancestor of its own many descendants. Thus, each new species produced by cladogenesis has the potential to become the "root" of its own evolutionary lineage.

When reading a phylogenetic tree, each branching point is called a **node**, and each evolutionary lineage—a node with all the branches, branchlets, and twigs that emerge from it—is called a **clade** (*klados* = branch). You can identify a clade on any phylogenetic tree by following a lineage from a node to the tips of all its twigs at the top of the tree. Some clades, such as Aves (birds), include thousands of species, whereas others, such as *Geospiza* (a genus of ground and cactus finches from the Galápagos Islands), include just a few. Like the taxonomic hierarchy, phylogenetic trees have a nested structure: younger and smaller clades, such as the genus *Geospiza*, are nested within larger and older clades, such as Aves. Two clades that emerge from the same node are called **sister clades** (or *sister taxa*) because they are each other's closest relatives; similarly, two species that emerge from the same node near the very top of the tree are described as **sister species**.

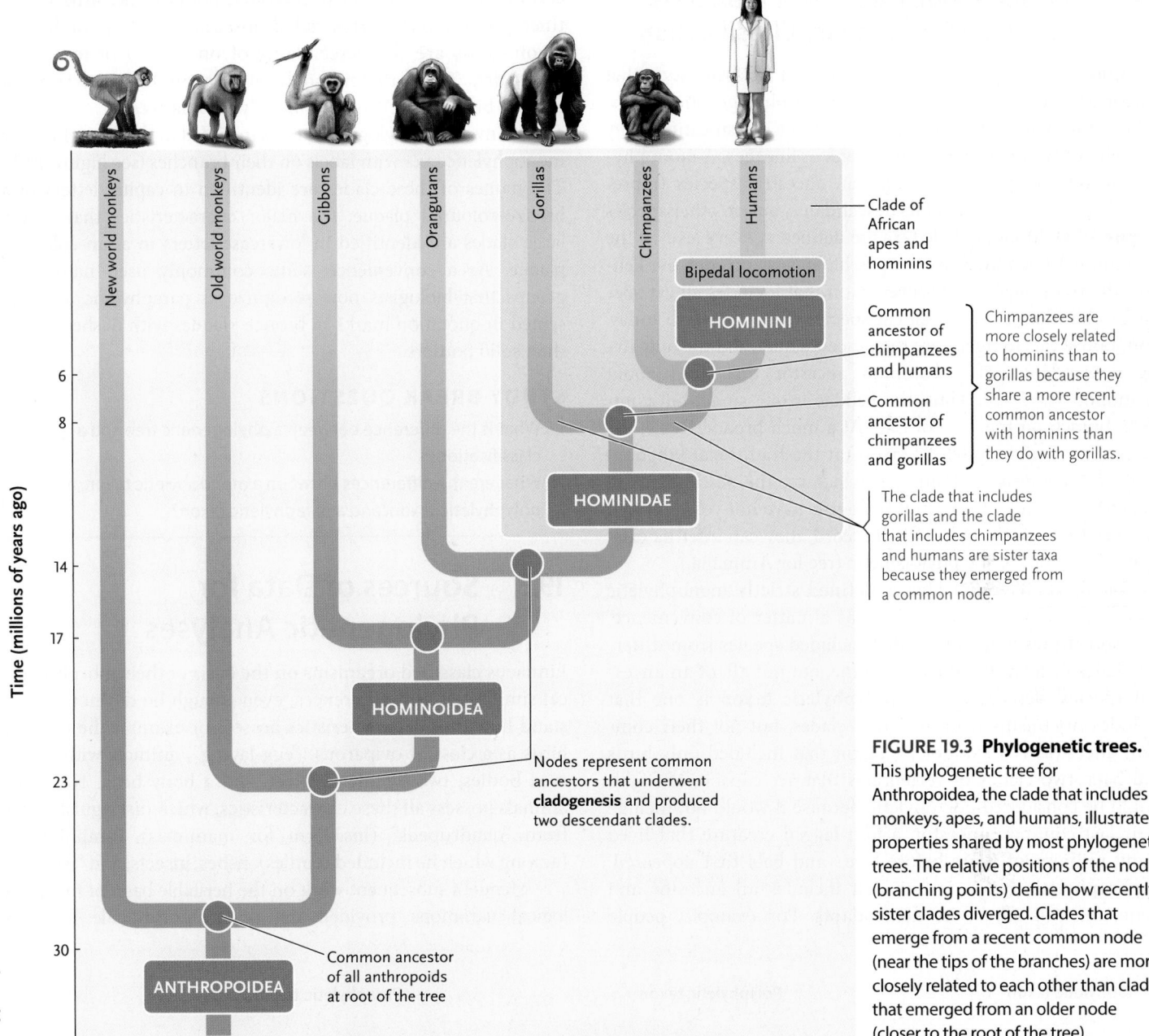

**FIGURE 19.3 Phylogenetic trees.**
This phylogenetic tree for Anthropoidea, the clade that includes monkeys, apes, and humans, illustrates properties shared by most phylogenetic trees. The relative positions of the nodes (branching points) define how recently sister clades diverged. Clades that emerge from a recent common node (near the tips of the branches) are more closely related to each other than clades that emerged from an older node (closer to the root of the tree).

Labels within figure:
- Clade of African apes and hominins
- Bipedal locomotion
- HOMININI
- Common ancestor of chimpanzees and humans
- Chimpanzees are more closely related to hominins than to gorillas because they share a more recent common ancestor with hominins than they do with gorillas.
- Common ancestor of chimpanzees and gorillas
- The clade that includes gorillas and the clade that includes chimpanzees and humans are sister taxa because they emerged from a common node.
- HOMINIDAE
- Nodes represent common ancestors that underwent **cladogenesis** and produced two descendant clades.
- HOMINOIDEA
- Common ancestor of all anthropoids at root of the tree
- ANTHROPOIDEA

Axis: Time (millions of years ago) — 6, 8, 14, 17, 23, 30

Top labels: New world monkeys, Old world monkeys, Gibbons, Orangutans, Gorillas, Chimpanzees, Humans

© Cengage Learning 2017.

**Depiction of time:** If a phylogenetic tree includes an explicit time axis, the positions of the nodes reveal when on the geological time scale a clade originated; the length of the vertical branch between nodes indexes how long an ancestral group persisted before it diversified. In most phylogenetic trees in this book, the time scale is not precise; often it is not even specified. The sequence of nodes indicates the order in which clades appeared; the lengths of the branches contain no specific information about the time since two clades diverged.

**Depiction of relatedness:** Horizontal spacing between clades in most of this book's phylogenetic trees does not indicate their degree of difference or their degree of relatedness. However, when the horizontal distance between species or clades is meaningful, how the distances should be interpreted is explained in the horizontal axis label, the figure legend, or the text.

**Number of descendants:** Most nodes in phylogenetic trees have two branches emerging from them, reflecting the evolution of two descendants from one ancestor. When biologists have not yet discovered the detailed pattern of branching that produced the diversity of clades in the tree, you may see three or more branches emerging from a node or from a horizontal branch. These nodes are currently "unresolved"; future research will allow the portrayal of these evolutionary relationships more precisely.

**Relative ages of clades:** In most phylogenetic trees in this book, the clades have been arranged from oldest on the left to youngest on the right. But any clade can be rotated around a node without changing the meaning of the phylogenetic tree. When reading a phylogenetic tree, focus on which clades share more recent common ancestors, indicated by the relative positions of the nodes from which they emerge.

**Summary:** Phylogenetic trees provide hypotheses about the evolutionary histories of the organisms included in the analysis. The common ancestor of sister clades is depicted on the node from which the two clades emerge. An implied or explicit timeline identifies the sequence in which new clades arose from their ancestors. Clades with a common ancestor closer to the top of the tree are more closely related than those with a common ancestor closer to the root of the tree.

## 19.2c Phylogenetic Trees Allow Biologists to Define Evolutionary Classifications

Evolutionary biologists working today want a classification that mirrors the branching patterns of a group's phylogenetic history. When converting a phylogenetic tree into a classification, they try to identify only **monophyletic taxa** or lineages. A monophyletic taxon comprises one clade, an ancestral species (represented by a node) and *all* of its descendants, but no other species (**Figure 19.4**). Monophyletic taxa are defined at every level of the taxonomic hierarchy. For example, biologists consider the Felidae (the traditional family-level taxon that includes all cat species) to be monophyletic: all cat species living on Earth today, from house cats to tigers, are the descendants—and the only living descendants—of a common ancestor that lived about 25 million years ago. Thus, the Felidae is one small, but complete, branch on the Tree of Life. At a much broader scale, the Animalia is a monophyletic taxon (at the traditional kingdom level) that comprises all animals, which are the descendants of one common ancestor. Even if biologists have not yet identified the very first animal in the fossil record, they can infer its existence at the root of the phylogenetic tree for Animalia.

Biologists have not always defined strictly monophyletic taxa. Because of missing data, or as a matter of convenience, they sometimes named taxa that included species from different clades or taxa that included some, but not all, of an ancestral species' descendants. A **polyphyletic taxon** is one that includes organisms from different clades, but not their common ancestor. For example, a taxon that included only birds and bats, two clades of vertebrates that are capable of flight, would be considered polyphyletic because it would not include their last common ancestor, a four-legged creature that lived many millions of years before birds and bats first appeared. A **paraphyletic taxon** is one that includes an ancestor and some, *but not all*, of its descendants. For example, people

commonly used to define terrestrial dinosaurs and birds as distinct groups. But "terrestrial dinosaurs" was a paraphyletic taxon: birds are the descendants of one group of terrestrial dinosaurs. Thus, the monophyletic taxon Dinosauria must include birds, as well as their nonflying relatives.

Many of the phylogenetic trees included in this book identify monophyletic taxa with labels on their branches (see Figure 19.3). The names of these clades are identified in capital letters in a bronze-coloured plaque; the major characteristics that define large clades are identified in lowercase letters in a tan-coloured plaque. As a convenience, some commonly used names for groups that biologists now recognize as paraphyletic are presented in quotation marks in bronze plaques with dashed rather than solid borders.

### STUDY BREAK QUESTIONS

1. What is the difference between a phylogenetic tree and a classification?
2. What are the differences between a monophyletic taxon, a polyphyletic taxon, and a paraphyletic taxon?

## 19.3 Sources of Data for Phylogenetic Analyses

Linnaeus classified organisms on the basis of their morphological similarities and differences, even though he did not understand how those characteristics arose. For example, he defined birds as a class of oviparous ("egg-laying") animals with feathered bodies, two wings, two feet, and a bony beak. No other animals possess all these characteristics, which distinguish birds from "quadrupeds" (his term for mammals), "amphibians" (among which he included reptiles), fishes, insects, and "worms."

Mendel's subsequent work on the heritable basis of morphological variations provided the scientific rationale for this

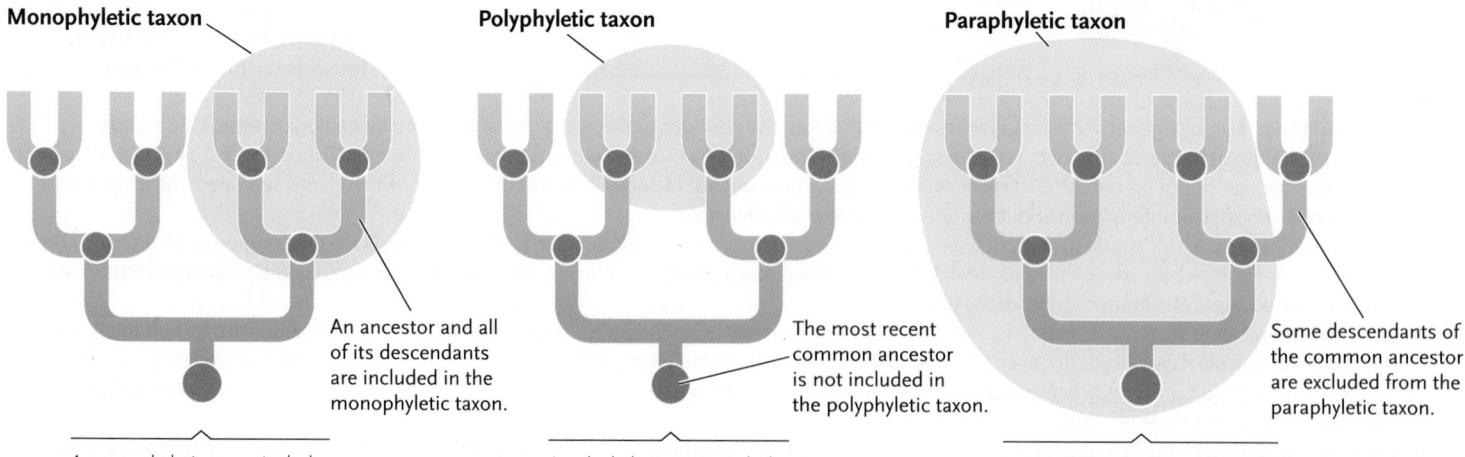

**Monophyletic taxon**

An ancestor and all of its descendants are included in the monophyletic taxon.

A monophyletic taxon includes an ancestral species and all of its descendants.

**Polyphyletic taxon**

The most recent common ancestor is not included in the polyphyletic taxon.

A polyphyletic taxon includes species from different evolutionary lineages.

**Paraphyletic taxon**

Some descendants of the common ancestor are excluded from the paraphyletic taxon.

A paraphyletic taxon includes an ancestral species and only some of its descendants.

**FIGURE 19.4 Defining taxa in a classification.** Although systematists can identify different groups of species in a phylogenetic tree as a taxon, a major goal of contemporary systematics is to identify taxa that are monophyletic groups.

endeavour: modern systematists infer that morphological differences serve as indicators of underlying genetic differences between species and lineages. Today, with our much deeper understanding of the genetic basis of variation, systematists undertake phylogenetic analyses using a variety of organismal and molecular characters. Indeed, any heritable trait (i.e., any trait with a genetic basis) that is intrinsic to the organism can be used in a phylogenetic analysis; phenotypic differences caused by environmental variation are excluded. In this section we first consider a general criterion for evaluating characters, and then examine examples of how a few specific types of characters are useful in this effort.

## 19.3a The Analysis of Homologous Characters Sheds Light on Evolutionary Relationships

A basic premise of phylogenetic analyses is that phenotypic similarities between organisms reflect their underlying genetic similarities. As you may recall from Chapter 16, species that are morphologically similar have often inherited the genetic basis of their resemblance from a common ancestor. Similarity that results from shared ancestry, such as the four limbs of all tetrapod vertebrates, is called **homology**, and biologists frequently describe such traits in two or more species as *homologies* or *homologous characters*. Any trait, from genetic sequences to anatomical structures to mating behaviours, can be described as homologous in two or more species as long as they inherited the trait from their common ancestor.

Even though characters are homologous, they may differ greatly among species, especially if their function has changed over time. For example, the stapes, a bone in the middle ear of tetrapod vertebrates, evolved from, and is therefore homologous to, the hyomandibula, a bone that supported the jaw joint of early fishes. The ancestral function of the bone is retained in some modern fishes, but its structure, position, and function are different in tetrapods (**Figure 19.5**).

Distantly related species living in different biogeographical realms are sometimes very similar in appearance. For example, the overall form of cactuses in the Americas is extraordinarily similar to that of spurges in Africa (**Figure 19.6**). But these lineages arose independently long after those continents had separated; **thus**, cactuses and spurges did not **inherit their** similarities from a shared ancestor. Their overall resemblance is the product of **convergent evolution**, the evolution of similar adaptations in distantly related organisms that occupy similar environments. Phenotypic similarity that evolved independently in different lineages is called **homoplasy**, which is often the product of convergent evolution; biologists describe such similarities as *homoplasies* or *homoplastic characters*. Some biologists use the terms *analogies* or *analogous characters* for homoplastic characters that serve a similar function in different species.

When scientists encounter similar morphological traits, how can they determine whether they are homologous or homoplastic? First, homologous structures are similar in anatomical detail and in their relationship to surrounding structures. For

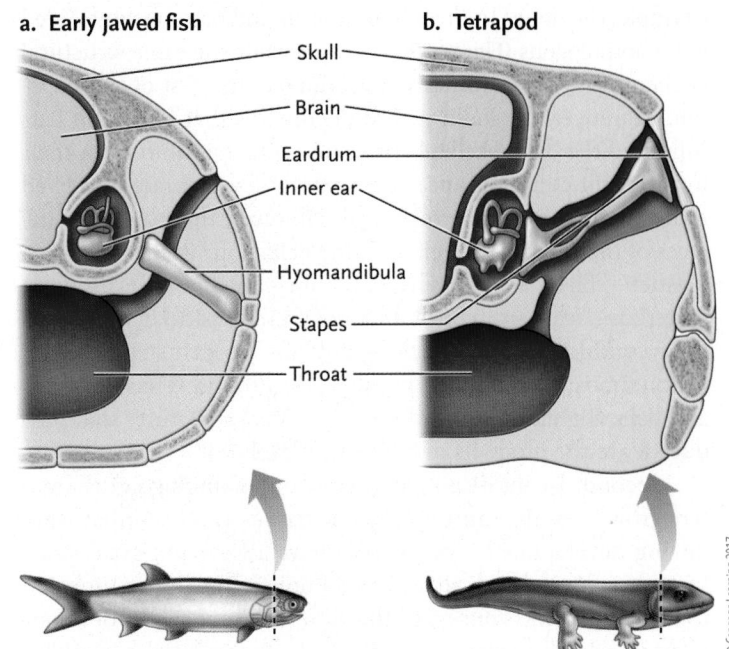

**FIGURE 19.5 Homologous bones, different structure, and function.** The hyomandibula, which braced the jaw joint against the skull in early jawed fishes **(a),** is homologous to the stapes, which transmits sound from the eardrum to the inner ear in four-legged vertebrates, exemplified here by an early tetrapod **(b).** Both large illustrations show a cross-section through the head just behind the jaw joint, as depicted in the small illustrations.

**FIGURE 19.6 Convergent evolution in plants. (a)** North American cactuses (family Cactaceae) are strikingly similar to **(b)** African spurges (family Euphorbiaceae). Convergent evolution adapted both groups to desert environments with thick, water-storing stems, spiny structures that discourage animals from feeding on them, CAM photosynthesis (see Chapter 6), and stomata that open only at night.

example, the bones in the wings of birds and bats are considered to be homologous (**Figure 19.7**). They include the same structural elements and have similar connections to the rest of the skeleton. Moreover, the fossil record documents that birds and bats inherited the basic skeletal structure of the forelimb from their most recent common ancestor, a tetrapod vertebrate that lived more than 300 million years ago. However, the large flat surfaces of their wings, as well as flying behaviour itself, are homoplastic. The wing surfaces are made of different materials—feathers in birds and membranous skin in bats—and their common ancestor, lacking any hint of such structures on its forelimbs, was confined to life on the ground. Thus, for birds and bats, flight and some of the anatomical structures that produce it are the products of convergent evolution.

Second, in multicellular organisms, homologous characters grow from the same embryonic tissues and in similar ways during development. Systematists have always put great stock in embryological indications of homology on the assumption that evolution has conserved the pattern of embryonic development in related organisms. Indeed, recent discoveries in evolutionary developmental biology have revealed that the genetic controls of developmental pathways are very similar across a wide variety of organisms. Genomic techniques are revealing remarkable shared similarities in the underlying genetic and cellular mechanisms that have contributed to the evolution of convergent characters in species that are not closely related.

## 19.3b Morphological Characters Provide Abundant Clues to Evolutionary Relationships

Morphological structures often provide useful information for phylogenetic analyses. Structural differences between organisms, which often reflect underlying genetic differences, are easy to measure in preserved or living specimens. Moreover, morphological characteristics are often clearly preserved in the fossil record, allowing the comparison of living species with their extinct relatives.

The morphological traits that are useful in phylogenetic analyses vary from group to group. In flowering plants, the details of flower anatomy may reveal common ancestry. Among vertebrates, the presence or absence of scales, feathers, and fur, as well as the structure of the skull and jaws, help scientists to reconstruct the evolutionary history of major groups. Sometimes researchers use obscure characters of unknown function. But differences in the number of scales on the backs of lizards or in the curvature of a vein in the wings of bees may be good indicators of the genetic differentiation that accompanied or followed speciation—even if we do not know *why* these differences evolved.

Sometimes characteristics found only in the earliest stages of an organism's life cycle can provide evidence of evolutionary relationships. For example, analyses of the embryos of vertebrates revealed that they are rather closely related to sea cucumbers, sea stars, and sea urchins and even more closely related to a group of nearly shapeless marine invertebrates called sea squirts or tunicates.

Despite their usefulness, morphological characters alone cannot reveal the details of all evolutionary relationships. For example, some salamander species in North America differ in relatively few morphological features, even when they are genetically, physiologically, and behaviourally distinct. Moreover, researchers cannot easily compare the structures of organisms—such as flatworms and dogs—that share very few morphological traits.

## 19.3c Behavioral Characters Are Useful When Animal Species Are Not Morphologically Distinct

When external morphology cannot be used to differentiate animal species, systematists often examine their behaviours for clues about their relationships. For example, two species of tree frog (*Hyla versicolor* and *Hyla chrysoscelis*) commonly occur together in forests of the central and eastern United States. Both species have bumpy skin and adhesive pads on their toes that enable them to climb vegetation. They also have grey backs, white bellies, yellowish-orange coloration on their thighs, and large white spots below their eyes. The frogs are so similar that even experts cannot easily tell them apart.

How do we know that these frogs represent two species? During the breeding season, males of each species use a distinctive mating call to attract females (**Figure 19.8**). The difference in calls is a prezygotic, reproductive isolating mechanism that prevents females from mating with males of a different species (see Chapter 18). Prezygotic isolating mechanisms

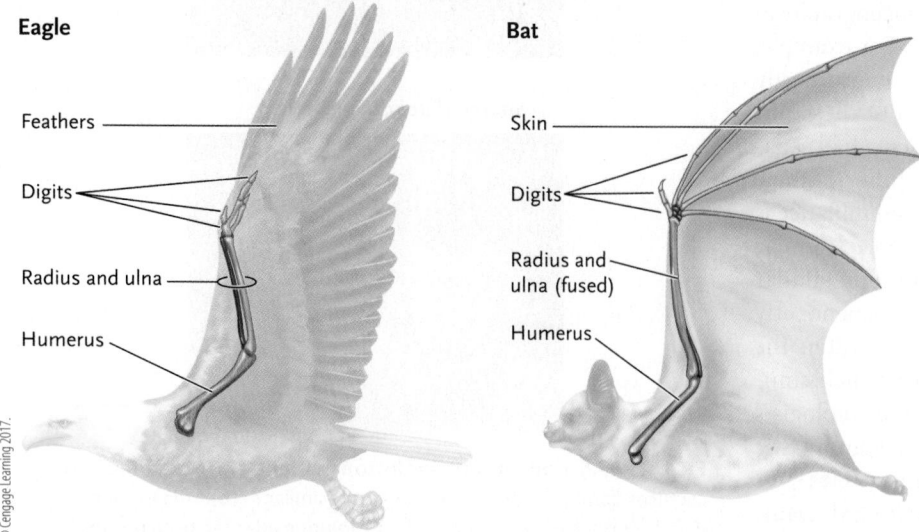

**Eagle**

Feathers

Digits

Radius and ulna

Humerus

**Bat**

Skin

Digits

Radius and ulna (fused)

Humerus

© Cengage Learning 2017.

**FIGURE 19.7 Assessing homology.** The wing skeletons of birds and bats are homologous structures with the same basic elements. However, similarities in the flat wing surfaces are homoplastic because the surfaces are composed of different tissues.

Hyla versicolor      Hyla chrysoscelis

Frequency

Time      Time

© Cengage Learning 2017.

Psychotic Nature/Shutterstock.com

**FIGURE 19.8 Morphologically similar frog species.** The frogs *Hyla versicolor* and *Hyla chrysoscelis* are so similar in appearance that one photo can depict both species. Male mating calls, visualized in sound spectrograms for the two species, are very different. The spectrograms, which depict call frequency on the vertical axis and time on the horizontal axis, show that *H. chrysoscelis* has a faster trill rate.

are excellent systematic characters because they are often the traits that animals themselves use to recognize members of their own species. The two frog species also differ in chromosome number—*H. chrysoscelis* is diploid and *H. versicolor* is tetraploid—which is a postzygotic isolating mechanism.

## 19.3d Molecular Sequences Are Now a Commonly Used Source of Phylogenetic Data

For roughly 200 years, systematists building on Linnaeus' work relied on a variety of organismal traits to analyze evolutionary relationships and classify organisms. Today, most systematists conduct phylogenetic analyses using molecular characters, such as the nucleotide base sequences of DNA and RNA. Because DNA is inherited, shared changes in molecular sequences—insertions, deletions, or substitutions—provide clues to the evolutionary relationships of organisms.

Use of polymerase chain reaction (PCR) technology makes it easy for researchers to produce numerous copies of specific segments of DNA for analysis (see Chapter 14); the technique is so effective that it allows scientists to sequence minute quantities of DNA taken from dried or preserved specimens in museums and even from some fossils. Technological advances have automated the sequencing process, and researchers use analytical software to compare new data to known sequences filed in online data banks. Nuclear DNA is frequently used in phylogenetic

analyses, and the publication of complete genome sequences for an ever-expanding list of organisms allows researchers to undertake broad comparative studies.

Molecular sequences have certain practical advantages over organismal characters. First, they provide abundant data: every base in a nucleic acid can serve as a separate, independent character for analysis. Moreover, because many genes have been conserved by evolution, molecular sequences can be compared between distantly related organisms that share no organismal characteristics. They can also be used to study closely related species with only minor morphological differences.

Molecular characters have certain drawbacks, however. For example, only 4 alternative character states (the 4 nucleotide bases) exist at each position in a DNA or RNA sequence, and only 20 alternative character states (the 20 amino acids) at each position in a protein. (You may want to review *The Purple Pages* on the structures of these molecules.)

Because of the limited number of character states, researchers may find it difficult to assess the homology of a nucleotide base substitution that appears at the same position in the DNA of two or more species. For organismal characters, biologists can determine homology by analyzing the characters' embryonic development, details of their function, or their presence in the fossil record. But molecular characters have no embryonic development; biologists still do not understand the functional significance of many molecular differences they discover; and researchers have only recently improved techniques that allow them to sequence DNA found in fossils. Nevertheless, systematists have devised complex statistical tools that allow them to discern whether molecular similarities are likely to be homologous or homoplastic.

Despite these potential disadvantages, molecular sequences allow researchers to sample the genome directly, and systematists have successfully used sequence data to analyze phylogenetic relationships that organismal characters were unable to resolve. For example, the phylogenetic tree for animals is based on data from several different nucleic acid molecules.

### STUDY BREAK QUESTIONS

1. Why do systematists use homologous characters in their phylogenetic analyses?
2. Why are morphological traits often helpful in tracing the long-term evolutionary relationships within a group of organisms?
3. What are three advantages of using molecular characters in phylogenetic analyses?

## 19.4 Traditional Classification and Paraphyletic Groups

For a century after Darwin published his theory of evolution, systematists followed an approach called **traditional systematics**. Researchers constructed phylogenetic trees and classified organisms by assessing the amount of phenotypic divergence between lineages, as well as the patterns of branching evolution that had produced them. In other words, they focused on the products of anagenesis (i.e., evolutionary change through the accumulation of new or modified characteristics), as well as the products of cladogenesis (i.e., the new species and lineages produced through branching evolution). Thus, their classifications did not always strictly reflect the patterns of branching evolution (**Figure 19.9**).

For example, the fossil record for tetrapod (four-legged) vertebrates reveals that the amphibian and mammalian lineages each diverged early. The remaining lineages, collectively called Reptilia, diverged into the Lepidosauromorpha (including living lizards and snakes) and the Archelosauromorpha (including living turtles, crocodilians, and birds). Thus, although crocodilians, with their scaly skin and sprawling posture, outwardly resemble lizards, evolutionary biologists have long recognized that crocodilians share a more recent common ancestor with birds.

Even though the phylogenetic tree shows six living clades, the traditional classification recognizes only four classes of tetrapod vertebrates: Amphibia, Mammalia, Reptilia, and Aves. These groups are given equal ranking because each represents a distinctive body plan and way of life. However, the traditionally defined taxon Reptilia is clearly paraphyletic because, even though crocodilians share a common ancestor with birds, Reptilia includes the former taxon but not the latter. Traditional systematists justified this definition of Reptilia because it included morphologically similar animals with close evolutionary relationships. Crocodilians were classified with lizards, snakes, and turtles because they share a distant common ancestry and are covered with dry, scaly skin. Traditional systematists also argued that the key innovations initiating the adaptive radiation of birds—a high metabolic rate, wings, and flight—represent such extreme divergence from the ancestral morphology that birds merited recognition as a separate class. As you will learn in Section 19.5, a different approach produces classifications that do not suffer from such inconsistencies.

### STUDY BREAK QUESTION

1. Why does a classification produced by traditional systematics sometimes include paraphyletic groups?

## 19.5 The Cladistic Revolution

In the 1950s and 1960s, some researchers criticized the traditional classifications based on two distinct phenomena, branching evolution and morphological divergence, as inherently unclear. How can we tell *why* two groups are classified in the same higher taxon? They might have shared a recent common ancestor, as did lizards and snakes. Alternatively, they may have retained some ancestral characteristics after being separated on different branches of a phylogenetic tree, as is the case for lizards and crocodilians.

To avoid such confusion, many systematists followed the philosophical and analytical lead of Willi Hennig, a German entomologist (i.e., a scientist who studies insects), who published the influential book *Phylogenetic Systematics* in 1950; its

**a. Traditional classification**

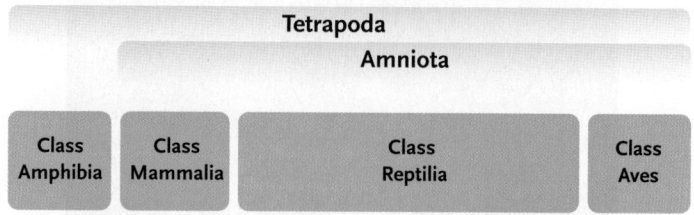

**b. Cladistic classification**

**c. Phylogenetic tree**

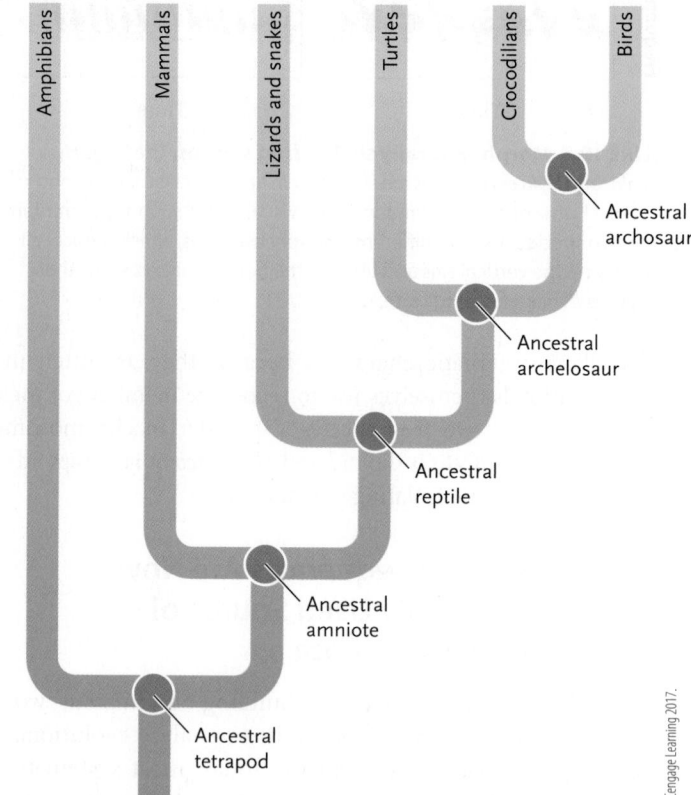

**FIGURE 19.9 Phylogenetic trees and classifications for tetrapod vertebrates.** **(a)** The traditional classification and **(b)** the cladistic classifications for tetrapod vertebrates are very different. **(c)** The phylogenetic tree for these animals illustrates why the cladistic classification reflects their evolutionary history better than the traditional classification does.

English translation appeared in 1966. Hennig and his followers argued that classifications should be based solely on evolutionary relationships. This approach, which is called **cladistics**, produces phylogenetic hypotheses and classifications that reflect only the branching pattern of evolution; it ignores morphological divergence altogether.

## 19.5a Cladistic Analyses Focus on Recently Evolved Character States

Like traditional systematics, cladistics analyzes the evolutionary relationships among organisms by comparing their organismal and, more recently, genetic characteristics. Each **character** can exist in two forms, described as **character states**. Evolutionary processes change characters over time from an original, **ancestral character state** to a newer, **derived character state**. Character states that were present in the ancestors of a clade are considered ancestral; those that are new in descendants are considered derived. For example, ancient fishes, which represent the ancestral vertebrates, had fins, but some of their descendants, the tetrapods, which appeared much later in the fossil record, have limbs. In this example, fins are the ancestral character state, and limbs are the derived character state.

In the jargon of cladistics, a derived character state is called an **apomorphy** (*apo* = away from; *morphe* = form), and a derived character state found in two or more species is called a **synapomorphy** (*syn* = together). The presence of a synapomorphy (i.e., a *shared derived character state*) among species provides a clue that they may be members of the same clade. Once a derived character state becomes established in a species, it is likely to be present in that species' descendants. Thus, unless they are lost or replaced by newer characters over evolutionary time, *synapomorphies can serve as markers for monophyletic lineages.*

Systematists define synapomorphies only when comparing character states among species. Thus, any particular character state is derived *only in relation to* an ancestral character state observed in other organisms, either an older version of the character or its absence. For example, most species of animals lack a vertebral column. However, one animal clade, the vertebrates—including fishes, amphibians, reptiles, birds, and mammals—has that structure. Thus, when systematists compare vertebrates to all other animals, the absence of a vertebral column is the ancestral character state, and the presence of a vertebral column is derived.

How can systematists distinguish between ancestral and derived character states? In other words, how can they determine the direction in which a character has evolved? The fossil record, if it is detailed enough, can provide unambiguous information. For example, biologists are confident that the presence of a vertebral column is a derived character state because fossils of animals that lived before vertebrates lack that structure.

In the absence of evidence from fossils, systematists frequently use a technique called **outgroup comparison** to identify ancestral and derived character states. Using this approach, systematists compare characters in the *ingroup*, the clade under study, to those in an *outgroup*, one or a few species that are related to the clade but are not included within it. Character states observed in the outgroup are considered ancestral, and those observed *only* in the ingroup are considered derived. And because the outgroup and the ingroup are phylogenetically related, outgroup comparison allows researchers to hypothesize the root (i.e., the common ancestor shared by the outgroup and the ingroup) of the phylogenetic tree. Most modern butterflies, for example, have six walking legs, but species in two families have four walking legs and two small, non-walking legs. Which is the ancestral character state, and which is derived? Outgroup comparison with other insects, which are not included in the butterfly clade, demonstrates that most insects have six walking legs as adults; this result suggests that six walking legs is ancestral and four is derived (**Figure 19.10**).

## 19.5b Cladistics Uses Synapomorphies to Reconstruct Evolutionary History and Classify Organisms

Following the cladistic method, biologists construct phylogenetic trees and classifications by grouping together only those species that *share derived character states*. Ancestral character states, because they are shared by the ingroup and the outgroup, do not help to define the ingroup. For example, mammals are a clade, a monophyletic lineage, because they possess a unique set of synapomorphies: hair, mammary glands, and a reduced number of bones in the lower jaw. The ancestral character states found in mammals, such as a vertebral column and four legs, do not distinguish them from other tetrapod vertebrates. Thus, these shared ancestral character states are not useful in defining the mammal clade.

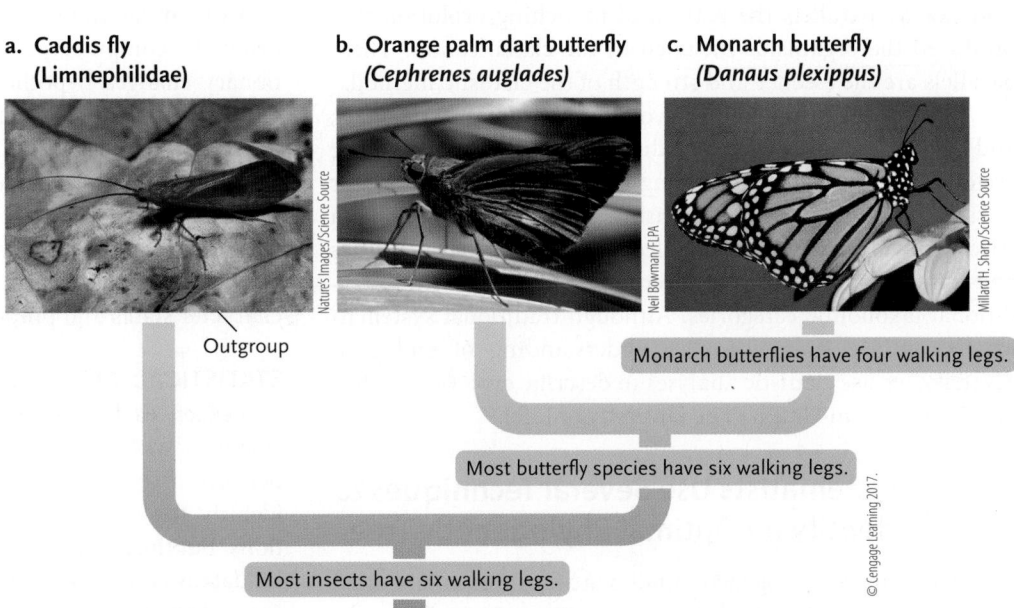

**a. Caddis fly (Limnephilidae)**

**b. Orange palm dart butterfly (*Cephrenes augiades*)**

**c. Monarch butterfly (*Danaus plexippus*)**

Outgroup

Monarch butterflies have four walking legs.

Most butterfly species have six walking legs.

Most insects have six walking legs.

**FIGURE 19.10 Outgroup comparison.** Most adult insects, such as **(a)** the caddis fly and **(b)** the orange palm dart butterfly, have six walking legs. This comparison of butterflies with other insects suggests that the four walking legs of **(c)** the monarch butterfly represents the derived character state.

The results of a cladistic analysis are presented in a phylogenetic tree that illustrates the hypothesized sequence of evolutionary branchings that produced the organisms under study (see Figure 19.9c): a common ancestor is hypothesized at each node, and every branch portrays a strictly monophyletic group. Once a researcher identifies a suitable outgroup and the ancestral and derived character states, a cladistic analysis is straightforward (**Figure 19.11**). The synapomorphies that define each clade are sometimes listed on the branches.

The use of molecular sequence data in phylogenetic analyses relies on the same logic that underlies analyses based on organismal characters, like those considered above: species included within a clade are expected to exhibit more molecular synapomorphies than do species from different clades. The comparison of sequences in the ingroup to those in the outgroup may allow a researcher to define ancestral and derived character states.

The classifications produced by cladistic analysis often differ radically from those of traditional systematics (compare Figure 19.9b with Figure 19.9a). In a cladistics classification, pairs of nested taxa are defined directly from the two-way branching pattern of the phylogenetic tree. Thus, the clade Tetrapoda (the traditional amphibians, reptiles, birds, and mammals) is divided into two taxa: the Amphibia (tetrapods that do not have an amnion, as discussed in Chapter 27) and the Amniota (tetrapods that have an amnion). The Amniota is subdivided into two taxa on the basis of skull morphology and other characteristics: Synapsida (mammals) and Reptilia (turtles, lizards, snakes, crocodilians, and birds). The Reptilia is further divided into the Lepidosauromorpha (lizards and snakes) and the Archelosauromorpha. The latter taxon is divided into Testudomorpha (turtles) and the Archosauromorpha (crocodilians and birds). Thus, a strictly cladistic classification exactly parallels the pattern of branching evolution that produced the organisms included in the classification. These parallels are the essence and strength of the cladistic method.

Most biologists value the evolutionary focus, clear goals, and precise methods of the cladistic approach. In fact, some systematists advocate abandoning the Linnaean hierarchy for classifying and naming organisms. They propose using a strictly phylogenetic system, called **PhyloCode**, that identifies and names clades instead of pigeonholing organisms into traditional taxonomic categories. Although traditional systematics has guided many people's understanding of biological diversity, we use cladistic analyses to describe evolutionary lineages and taxa in Unit 5 (The Diversity of Life).

## 19.5c  Systematists Use Several Techniques to Identify an Optimal Phylogenetic Tree

In practice, most phylogenetic studies are far more complicated than the examples discussed above and in **Figure 19.12**. Researchers may collect data on hundreds of characters in dozens of species. After scoring each character state as ancestral or derived in every species, a systematist uses one or more computer programs to generate a set of alternative phylogenetic trees. The output of these analyses is often substantial: an analysis of 5 species can produce 15 possible phylogenetic trees; an analysis of 50 species can produce $3 \times 10^{76}$.

Faced with such an unimaginably large number of alternative hypotheses, how does a systematist decide which phylogenetic tree is the "best" representation of a clade's evolutionary history? This problem is complex, because, when evaluating large data sets, we expect to see some similarities that arise when convergent evolution causes distantly related organisms to evolve similar traits independently; because such traits are not synapomorphies, they are false indicators of relatedness that confound the analysis. We also expect to find some differences between closely related organisms if natural selection or some other microevolutionary process caused a derived character state to be reversed or lost. How can we tell which of the many possible phylogenetic hypotheses is the most likely to represent the evolutionary history of the group? Researchers use several approaches to sort through the alternatives, two of which we describe below.

**PARSIMONY APPROACH** Many systematists adopt a philosophical concept, the **principle of parsimony**, to identify the optimal phylogenetic tree. This principle states that the simplest plausible explanation of any phenomenon is the best. If we assume that any complex evolutionary change is an unlikely event, then it is extremely unlikely that the same complex change evolved twice in one lineage. Thus, when the principle is applied to phylogenetic analyses, it suggests that the "best" phylogenetic tree is the one that hypothesizes the smallest number of evolutionary changes needed to account for the distribution of character states within a clade; in effect, this approach minimizes the number of homoplasies (i.e., the independent evolution of similar traits) in the tree (Figure 19.12). To apply the principle, computer programs evaluate the number of evolutionary changes hypothesized by each phylogenetic tree they generate, and the researcher identifies the one with the fewest hypothesized changes as the most plausible.

The principle of parsimony also allows researchers to identify homologous characters and infer their ancestral and derived states. Once the most parsimonious phylogenetic tree is identified, a researcher can visualize the distribution of derived character states and pinpoint when each evolved.

**STATISTICAL APPROACHES** When comparing two genome sequences, each base in a strand of DNA can be treated as a character with four possible states (A, G, T, or C). One could perform a parsimony analysis on molecular sequence data to identify the phylogenetic tree that assumes the fewest mutations. But the application of the parsimony approach to molecular data is complicated by several factors. First, given that there are only four possible character states at each position in a nucleic acid, identical changes in nucleotides often arise independently. Second, segments of DNA that do not code for proteins are less likely than coding regions to be affected by natural

FIGURE 19.11   **Research Method**

## Using Cladistics to Construct a Phylogenetic Tree

**Purpose:** Systematists construct phylogenetic trees to visualize hypothesized evolutionary relationships among organisms. The cladistic method requires a researcher to group together organisms that share derived characters states. The derived character states identified in the tan plaques are the synapomorphies that define each clade.

**Protocol:**

1. *Select the organisms to study.* To demonstrate the method, we develop a phylogenetic tree for the nine groups of living vertebrates: lampreys, sharks (and their close relatives), bony fishes, amphibians (frogs and salamanders), turtles, lizards (including snakes), crocodilians (including alligators), birds, and mammals. We also include marine animals called lancelets (Chordata, Cephalochordata) as the outgroup. Lancelets are closely related to, but not included within, the vertebrates. The inclusion of an outgroup allows biologists to identify ancestral versus derived character states and root the tree.

2. *Choose the characters on which the phylogenetic tree will be based.* Our simplified example is based on the presence or absence of nine characters: (1) vertebral column, (2) jaws, (3) swim bladder or lungs, (4) paired limbs (with one bone connecting each limb to the body),

(5) extraembryonic membranes (such as the amnion), (6) mammary glands, (7) dry, scaly skin somewhere on the body, (8) one opening on each side of the skull in front of the eye, and (9) feathers.

3. *Score the character states in each group.* Because lancelets serve as the outgroup in this analysis, we consider character states observed in lancelets as ancestral; any deviation from the lancelet pattern is considered derived. Because lancelets lack all the characters in our analysis, the presence of each character is the derived condition. We tabulate data on the distribution of ancestral (–) and derived (+) characters in all species included in the analysis.

4. *Construct the phylogenetic tree from information in the table, grouping organisms that share derived character states.* All groups except lancelets have vertebrae. Thus, we group organisms that share this derived character state on the right-hand branch, identifying them as a monophyletic lineage. Lancelets are on their own branch to the left, indicating that they lack vertebrae.

   All the remaining organisms except lampreys have jaws. (Lancelets also lack jaws, but we have already separated them out and do not consider them further.) Place all groups with jaws, a derived character state, on the right-hand branch. Lampreys are separated out to the left, because they lack jaws. Again, the branch on the right represents a monophyletic lineage.

**c.**

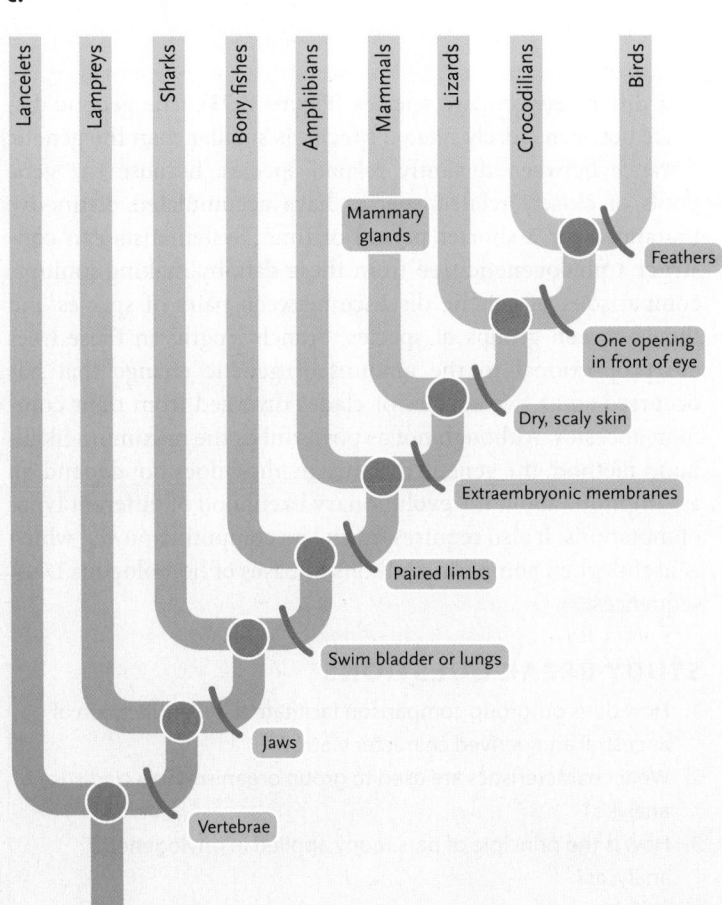

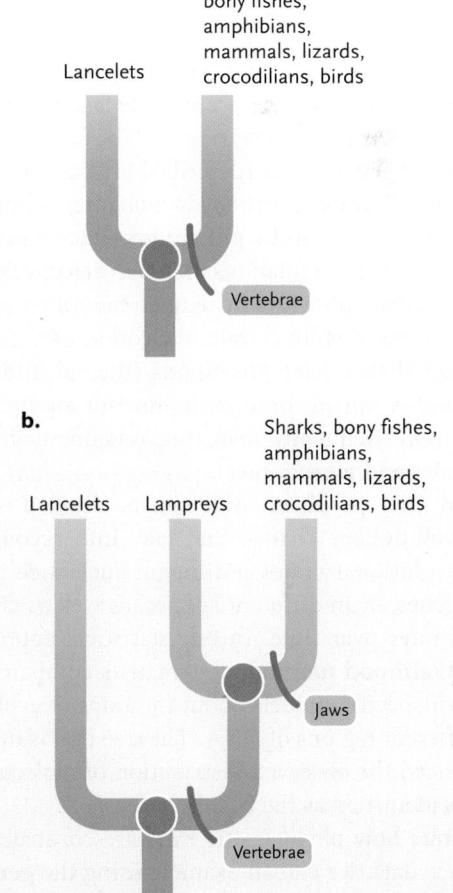

*(Continued)*

© Cengage Learning 2017.

FIGURE 19.11    **Research Method** (*Continued*)

**5.** *Construct the rest of the phylogenetic tree using the same step-by-step procedure to separate the remaining groups.* In our completed tree, six groups share a swim bladder or lungs; five share paired limbs; and four have extraembryonic membranes during development. Some groups are distinguished by the unique presence of a derived character state, such as feathers in birds.

**Interpreting the Results:** Although phylogenetic trees provide information about evolutionary relationships, the common ancestors represented by the branch points are often hypothetical. You can tell from the tree, however, that birds are more closely related to lizards than they are to mammals. Follow the branches of the tree from birds and lizards back to their node. Next, trace the branches of birds and mammals to their node. You can see that the bird–mammal node is closer to the root of the tree than the bird–lizard node is. Nodes that are closer to the bottom of the tree indicate a more distant common ancestry than those closer to the top. Note also that this simplified example produces a phylogenetic tree that is easy to interpret because the data set includes no homoplastic similarities and no conflicting evidence. Most phylogenetic analyses include many such complications.

| | Vertebrae | Jaws | Swim bladder or lungs | Paired limbs | Extraembryonic membranes | Mammary glands | Dry, scaly skin | One opening in front of eye | Feathers |
|---|---|---|---|---|---|---|---|---|---|
| **Lancelets** | – | – | – | – | – | – | – | – | – |
| **Lampreys** | + | – | – | – | – | – | – | – | – |
| **Sharks** | + | + | – | – | – | – | – | – | – |
| **Bony fishes** | + | + | + | – | – | – | – | – | – |
| **Amphibians** | + | + | + | + | – | – | – | – | – |
| **Mammals** | + | + | + | + | + | + | – | – | – |
| **Lizards** | + | + | + | + | + | – | + | – | – |
| **Crocodilians** | + | + | + | + | + | – | + | + | – |
| **Birds** | + | + | + | + | + | – | + | + | + |

selection. As a result, mutations accumulate faster in noncoding regions, causing them to evolve rapidly. Third, because of the degeneracy of the genetic code (described in Chapter 12), mutations in the third codon position do not often influence the amino acid composition of the protein for which a gene codes. As a result, third codon mutations are often selectively neutral, and they accumulate more rapidly than do mutations in the first or second positions. Finally, certain nucleotide substitutions are more common than others: transitions (the substitution of a purine for another purine, or a pyrimidine for another pyrimidine) occur more frequently than transversions (substitutions between purines and pyrimidines).

To avoid this problem, systematists develop statistical models of evolutionary change that take into account variations in the evolutionary rates at different nucleotide positions, in different genes, or in different species, as well as changes in evolutionary rates over time. In one statistical approach, the **maximum likelihood method**, systematists compare alternative trees with specific models about the rates of evolutionary change in different regions of DNA. The tree that is most likely to have produced the observed distribution of molecular character states is identified as the best hypothesis.

To illustrate how phylogenetic trees are constructed from DNA sequence data, we cite an example using the **genetic distance method**, which calculates the overall proportion of bases that differ between two species (**Figure 19.13**). The genetic distance between closely related species is smaller than the genetic distance between distantly related species, because the gene pools of closely related species have accumulated distinctive mutations for a shorter period of time. Systematists can construct a phylogenetic tree from these data by making multiple comparisons of genetic distance between pairs of species and then between groups of species; branch lengths in these trees are proportional to the amount of genetic change that has occurred since two species or clades diverged from their common ancestor. Although not as powerful as the maximum likelihood method, the genetic distance method does not depend on assumptions about the evolutionary likelihood of different types of mutations. It also requires much less computing power, which is useful when comparing billions of bases of homologous DNA sequences.

## STUDY BREAK QUESTIONS

1. How does outgroup comparison facilitate the identification of ancestral and derived character states?
2. What characteristics are used to group organisms in a cladistic analysis?
3. How is the principle of parsimony applied in phylogenetic analyses?

## a. Distribution of character states in six clades of vascular plants

Ferns represent the outgroup: all of its character states are considered ancestral.

| Characters (possible states) | Ferns (outgroup) | Gnetophytes | Cycads | Ginkgophytes | Conifers | Angiosperms |
|---|---|---|---|---|---|---|
| Archegonium (present or lost) | Present | Lost | Present | Present | Present | Lost |
| Double fertilization (absent or present) | Absent | Present | Absent | Absent | Absent | Present |
| Pollen tube growth (haustorium or tube) | Absent | Tube | Haustorium | Haustorium | Tube | Tube |
| Sperm flagella (present or lost) | Present | Lost | Present | Present | Lost | Lost |
| Vessels (absent or present) | Absent | Present | Absent | Absent | Absent | Present |

Two alternative phylogenetic trees for the six clades illustrate different hypotheses about their evolutionary relationships. Bars across the branches mark the hypothesized evolution of derived character states in both trees.

**b. Phylogenetic tree hypothesizing five evolutionary changes**

**c. Phylogenetic tree hypothesizing 10 evolutionary changes**

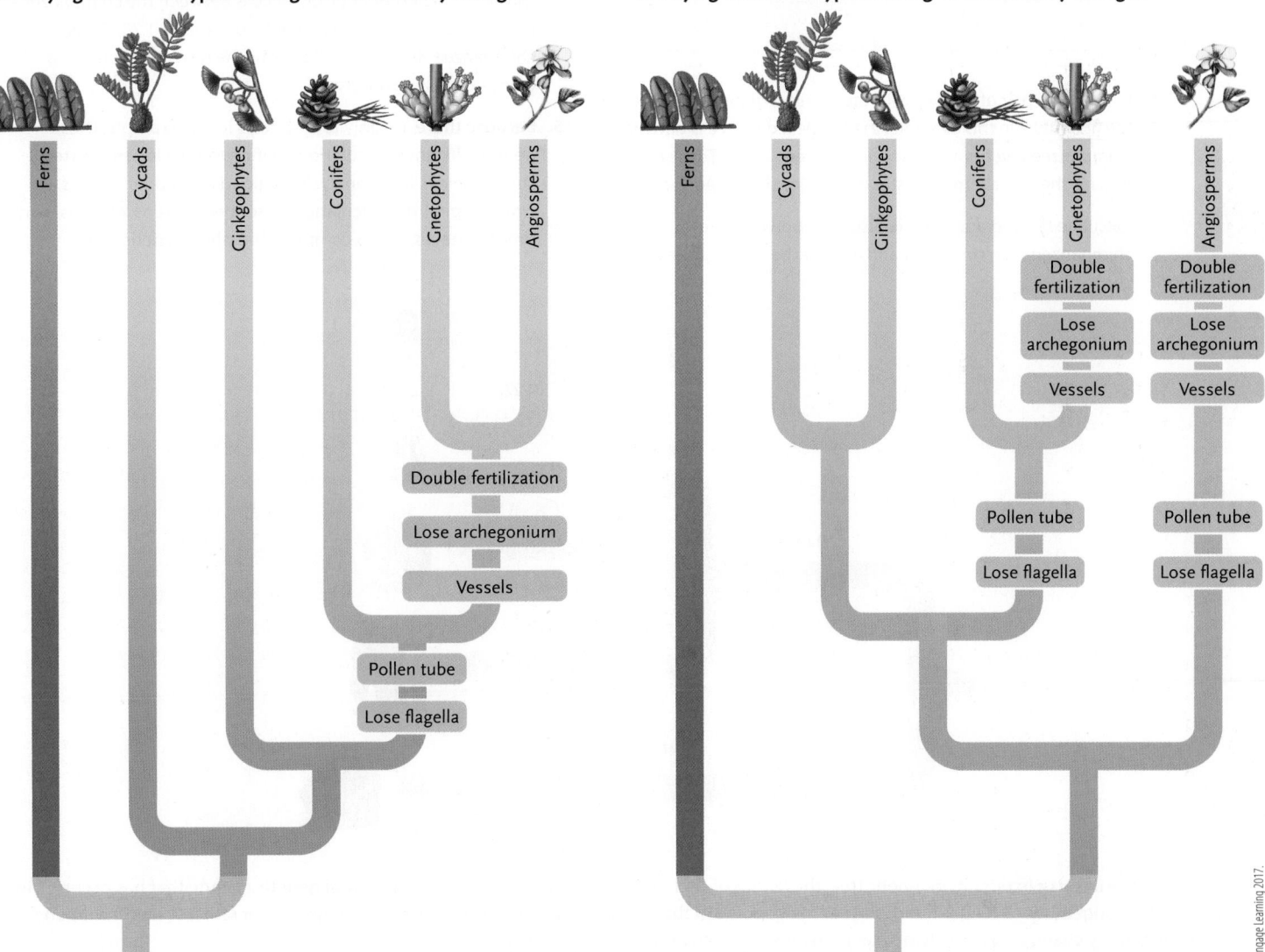

**FIGURE 19.12 The principle of parsimony. (a)** Based on this set of 5 characters, **(b)** the phylogenetic tree with 5 hypothesized evolutionary changes is more parsimonious than **(c)** the tree that hypothesizes 10 evolutionary changes. In the absence of additional data, a systematist would accept the more parsimonious tree as the best working hypothesis. (The characters and clades of vascular plants are discussed in detail in Chapter 26.)

FIGURE 19.13   **Research Method**

## Using Genetic Distances to Construct a Phylogenetic Tree

**Purpose:** Systematists use data on genetic distances (the overall differences in DNA sequences) among species to reconstruct their phylogenetic tree.

**Protocol:**

1. Calculate the genetic distance between each pair of species. The genetic distances between humans and three species of great apes are shown in the first table.

|  | Chimpanzee | Gorilla | Orangutan |
|---|---|---|---|
| **Human** | 1.37 | 1.75 | 3.40 |
| **Chimpanzee** |  | 1.81 | 3.44 |
| **Gorilla** |  |  | 3.50 |

2. Identify the pair of species with the smallest genetic distance in the first table; in this example, the smallest distance is between chimpanzee and human (genetic distance = 1.37). These two species therefore form a cluster of two closely related species.

3. Calculate the average genetic distances between the chimpanzee–human cluster and each of the other species in the analysis, gorilla and orangutan. For example, the genetic distance between the chimpanzee–human cluster and gorilla is the average of the human–gorilla genetic distance and the chimpanzee–gorilla genetic distance [(1.75 + 1.81)/2 = 1.78]. The newly calculated genetic distances are shown in the second table.

|  | Gorilla | Orangutan |
|---|---|---|
| **Chimpanzee–human cluster** | 1.78 | 3.42 |
| **Gorilla** |  | 3.50 |

4. Identify the two groups (individual species or clusters) with the smallest genetic distance in the second table. In this example, the next smallest genetic distance is between the chimpanzee–human cluster and gorilla (genetic distance = 1.78). Thus, chimpanzee–human–gorilla forms the next cluster, leaving orangutan as the outgroup.

5. Because there are only four species in our example, these genetic distance calculations define the phylogenetic tree shown below. If the analysis included additional species, we would repeat the calculation described in steps 2 to 4 as many times as necessary to complete the phylogenetic tree.

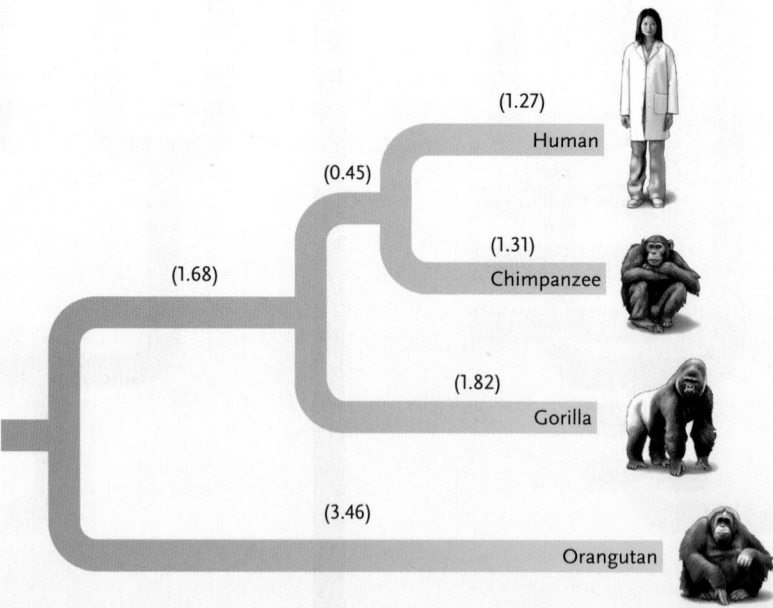

**Interpreting the Results:** In our phylogenetic tree, the length of each branch is proportional to the amount of genetic change that has occurred in that branch. A longer branch length indicates that the genome of that species has evolved at a correspondingly higher rate (i.e., has undergone more evolutionary change since the two sister branches emerged from their common ancestor).

Source: © Cengage Learning 2017. Based on A. Scally et al. 2012. Insights into hominid evolution from the gorilla genome sequence. *Nature* 483:169–175.

## 19.6 Phylogenetic Trees as Research Tools

In addition to providing a wealth of information about the patterns of branching evolution across the entire spectrum of living organisms, phylogenetic trees are useful tools that facilitate research in all areas of biology.

### 19.6a Molecular Clocks Estimate the Time of Evolutionary Divergences

Although many biological molecules have been conserved by evolution, different adaptive changes and neutral mutations accumulate in separate lineages from the moment they first diverge. Because mutations that arise in noncoding regions of DNA do not affect protein structure, they are probably not often eliminated by natural selection. If mutations accumulate in these segments at a reasonably constant rate, differences in their DNA sequences can serve as a **molecular clock**, indexing the time at which two species diverged. Large differences imply divergence in the distant past, whereas small differences suggest a more recent common ancestor.

Because different molecules exhibit individual rates of evolutionary change, every molecule is an independent clock, ticking at its own rate. Researchers study different molecules to track evolutionary divergences that occurred at different times in the past. For example, mitochondrial DNA (mtDNA) evolves relatively quickly; it is useful for dating evolutionary divergences that occurred within the past few million years. Studies of mtDNA have illuminated aspects of the evolutionary history of humans. By contrast, chloroplast DNA (cpDNA) and genes that encode ribosomal RNA evolve much more slowly, providing information about divergences that date back hundreds of millions of years.

To calibrate molecular clocks, researchers examine the degree of genetic difference between species in relation to their time of divergence estimated from the fossil record. Alternatively, the clock can be calibrated biogeographically with independent data on when volcanic islands first emerged from the sea or when landmasses separated.

The reliability of molecular clocks depends on the constancy of evolutionary change in the DNA segment analyzed. Some researchers have noted that even DNA segments that are thought to be selectively neutral may show variable rates of evolution. Many factors can influence the rates at which mutations accumulate, and researchers must be cautious when evaluating divergence times estimated with this technique, especially if there are no independent data to corroborate the estimates.

### 19.6b Phylogenetic Trees Allow Biologists to Propose and Test Hypotheses

Accurate phylogenetic trees are essential tools for analyses that biologists describe as the "comparative method." With this approach, researchers compare the characteristics of different species to assess the homology of their similarities and infer where on the phylogenetic tree a particular trait appeared. The comparative method is used to study almost any sort of organismal trait, but in this section we will focus on parental care behaviour.

As noted in Figure 19.9b, birds and crocodilians are included within the Archosauria, a clade that also includes nonavian dinosaurs (i.e., extinct terrestrial dinosaurs that are not included within the bird clade), pterosaurs (an extinct group of flying vertebrates, not closely related to bats but with wing surfaces formed by skin), and a number of other groups that became extinct in the early Mesozoic era. Crocodilians and birds share certain anatomical characteristics, such as a four-chambered heart and the one-way flow of air through their lungs. They also share behavioural characteristics, including the production of mating calls (songs in birds and roars in crocodilians), nest-building behaviour, and parental care of their young. Female crocodilians guard their nests and keep them moist with urine. They also excavate the nest as the young hatch, and then carry them to standing water. Young stay with their mother for about a year, feeding on scraps of food that fall from her mouth.

Did similar parental care behaviour evolve independently in birds and crocodilians, or is it truly a synapomorphy? Did most Mesozoic archosaurs care for their young as birds and crocodilians do today? The comparative method seeks answers to these questions by examining the phylogenetic tree for archosaurs (**Figure 19.14**). As you can readily see, crocodilians and birds lie on widely separated branches of the archosaur tree, with pterosaurs and nonavian dinosaurs positioned between them. The most parsimonious inference about the evolution of parental care behaviour is that it evolved once in the common ancestor of crocodilians and birds. If that inference is correct, then nonavian dinosaurs and pterosaurs probably also cared for their young in the nest. Indeed, that prediction was confirmed in 1995, when Mark A. Norell, of George Washington University, and his colleagues discovered a fossil of a nonavian dinosaur (*Oviraptor*) sitting on a nest full of eggs.

### STUDY BREAK QUESTIONS

1. What assumption underlies the use of genetic sequence differences between species as a molecular clock?
2. Are birds more closely related to nonavian dinosaurs or to crocodilians?

## 19.7 Molecular Phylogenetic Analyses

The application of molecular techniques to phylogenetic analyses has allowed systematic biologists to resolve some evolutionary puzzles that could not be addressed with older techniques.

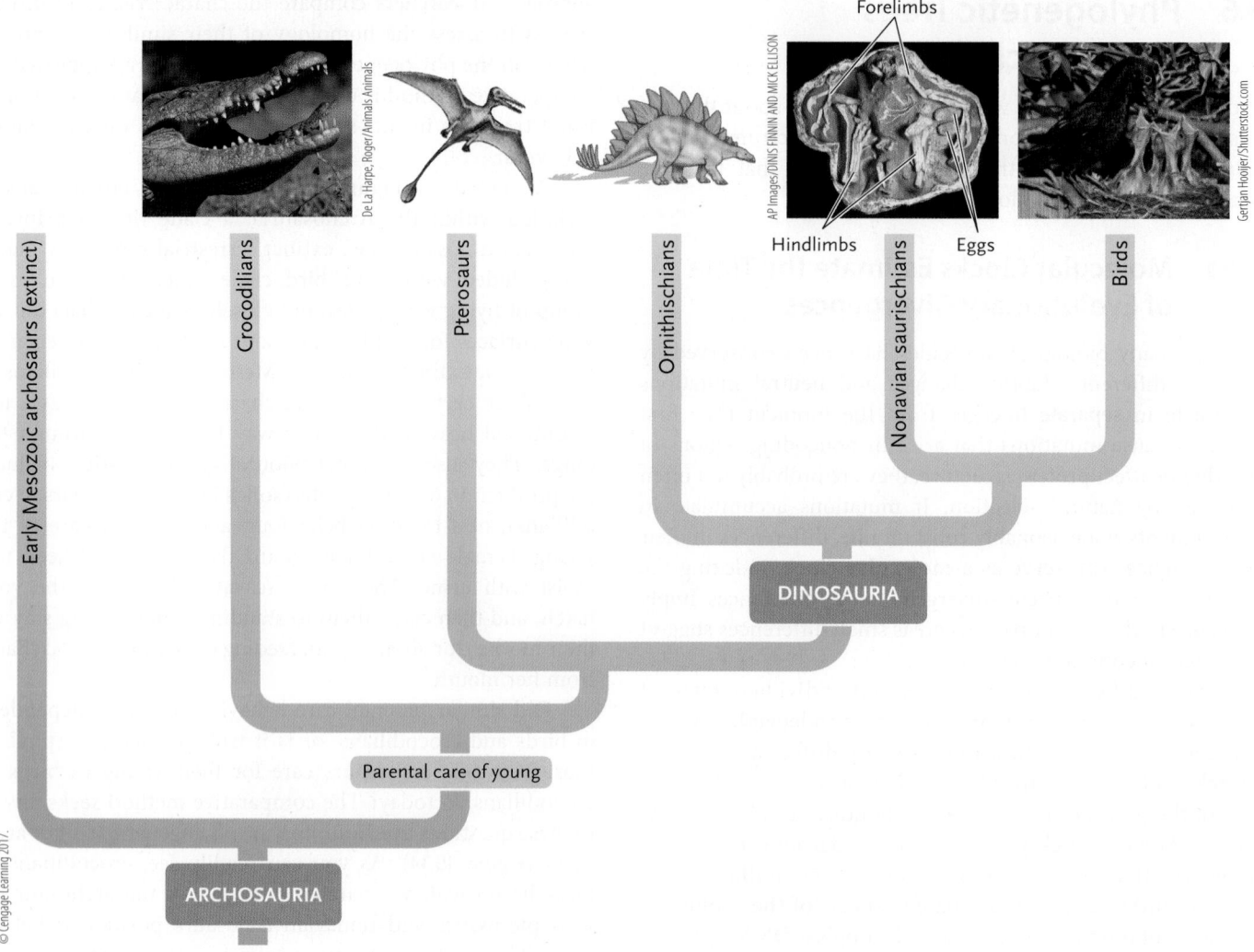

**FIGURE 19.14 Phylogenetic trees and the comparative method.** By examining the distribution of parental care behaviour on a cladogram of archosaurs, biologists predicted that nonavian dinosaurs probably incubated their eggs and cared for their young. A fossil described in 1995 confirmed that prediction.

In this section we describe how molecular analyses have enabled public health researchers to identify sources of HIV infection in humans and elucidate the relationships among the three domains of the Tree of Life.

### 19.7a Molecular Phylogenetic Analyses Pinpoint the Origins of Infectious Diseases

Phylogenetic analyses also allow physicians and public health workers to identify the origin of infectious agents and follow their spread through a population. Many pathogenic organisms and viruses mutate as they proliferate, establishing derived character states that are ripe for phylogenetic analysis.

The human immunodeficiency virus (HIV), the agent that causes acquired immunodeficiency syndrome (AIDS) in humans, began to infect large numbers of people in the 1980s. As its devastating effects on humans became apparent, scientists scrambled to discover its origin. Genetic analyses linked it to the lentiviruses, specifically simian immunodeficiency virus (SIV), which infects dozens of monkey species as well as chimpanzees in Africa. Surprisingly, SIV does not cause illness in those animals, perhaps because their populations developed immunity to it after a long period of exposure.

Two distinct strains of HIV infect humans: HIV-1 is common in central Africa, and HIV-2 is common in West Africa. Did these strains evolve within human hosts, or did they exist before the virus was first transmitted to humans? An analysis by Beatrice H. Hahn of the University of Alabama at Birmingham and the Howard Hughes Medical Institute and colleagues at other institutions identified three major clades of SIV. The clade that infects chimpanzees includes HIV-1, and one of the clades that infect monkeys includes HIV-2 (**Figure 19.15**). Thus, the two strains of HIV apparently originated in nonhuman hosts. Scientists suspect that the transmission to humans occurred multiple times when hunters who were butchering bush meat—chimpanzees in central Africa and sooty mangabey monkeys in West Africa—acquired the virus through cuts on their hands.

In Chapter 21 we will see how DNA sequence data have been used to construct a tree of the entire tree of life. In addition to showing some surprising branching patterns, this tree clearly indicates that all life on Earth today share a common ancestor.

## STUDY BREAK QUESTION

1. Did HIV originate in humans, or was the infection acquired from other animals?

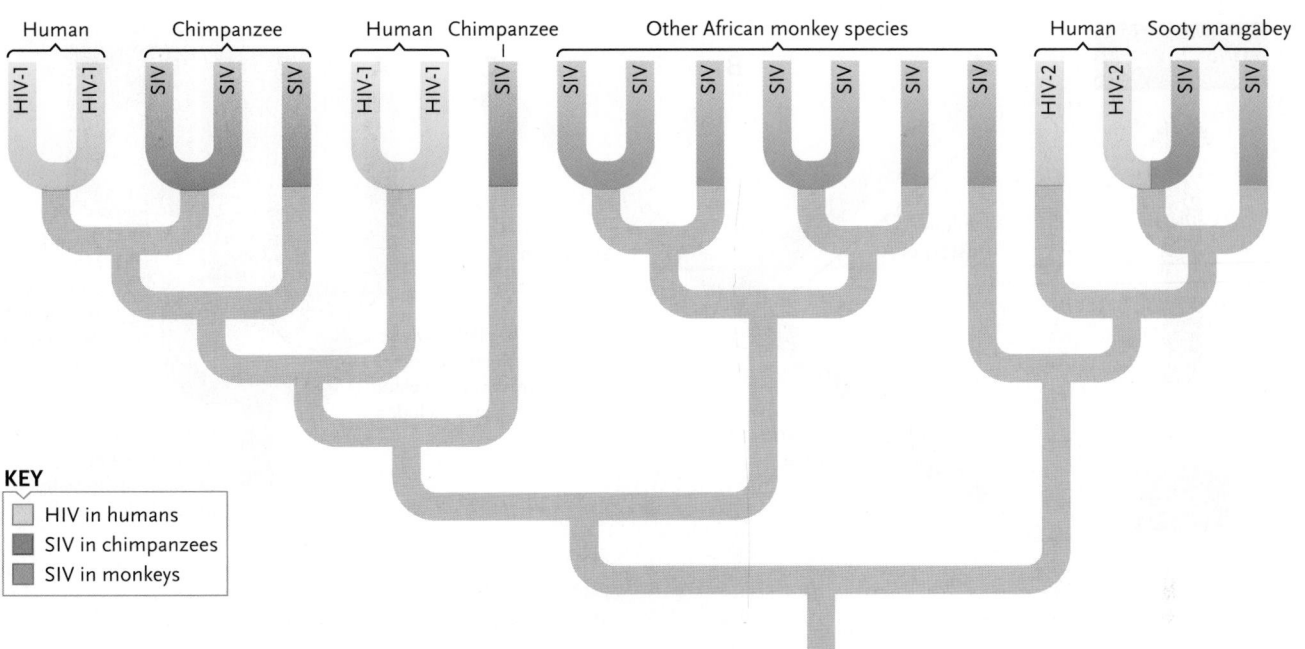

**KEY**
- ☐ HIV in humans
- ■ SIV in chimpanzees
- ■ SIV in monkeys

© Cengage Learning 2017.

**FIGURE 19.15 Phylogenetic trees and public health.** A phylogenetic tree for strains of simian immunodeficiency virus (SIV) and human immunodeficiency virus (HIV) suggests that the virus was transmitted to humans independently from chimpanzees and sooty mangabey monkeys.

# Summary Illustration

Systematics is the branch of biology that studies the diversity of life and its evolutionary relationships (i.e., phylogenies). Phylogenetic trees illustrate hypotheses about the likely relationships among species and higher taxonomic groups. These trees can be tailored to include varying breadths of analyses, but all share a common basic structure and depict key relationships in similar ways.

A phylogenetic tree attempts to depict the evolutionary history of a group of organisms.

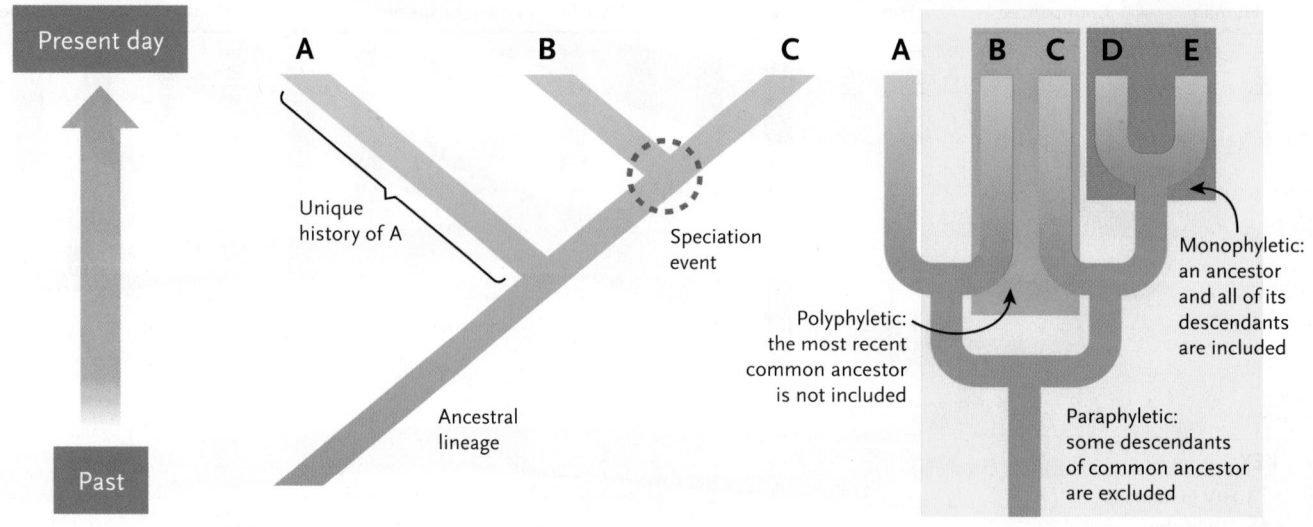

Present day

A    B    C

Unique history of A

Speciation event

Ancestral lineage

Past

A    B    C    D    E

Polyphyletic: the most recent common ancestor is not included

Monophyletic: an ancestor and all of its descendants are included

Paraphyletic: some descendants of common ancestor are excluded

An underlying assumption is that taxa that are closely related should look more similar to each other than taxa that are more distantly related.

### Homology

Cat    Hawk    Dove

Wings

Wings are homologous characters in hawks and doves because both inherited wings from their common winged ancestor.

### Homoplasy

Hawk    Bat    Cat

Wings

Wings are homoplasious (or analagous) characters in hawks and bats because they evolved independently (e.g., convergent evolution).

Traditional systematics classification considers both morphological divergence and patterns of branching evolution. Cladistics classification reflects only the branching pattern of evolution.

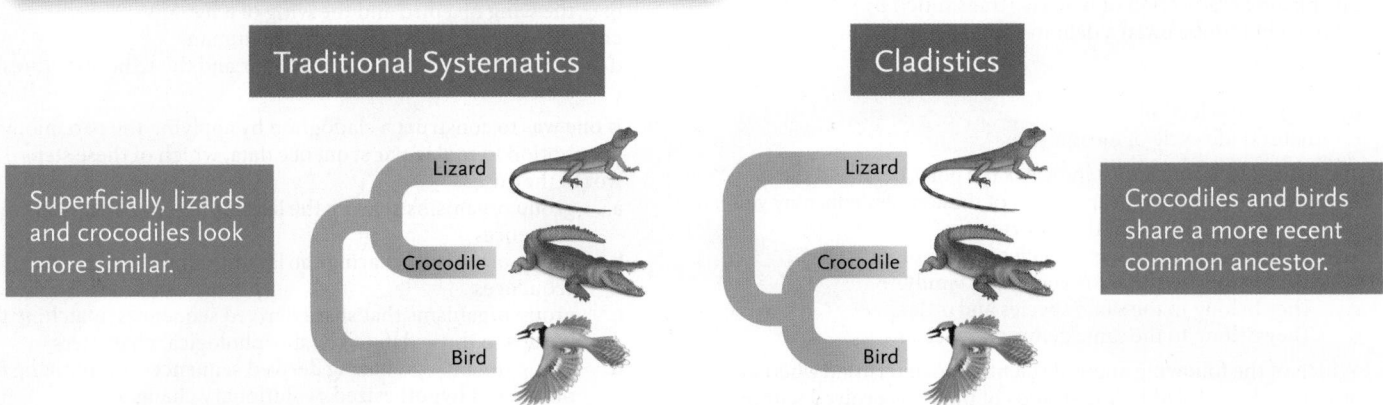

## Traditional Systematics

Superficially, lizards and crocodiles look more similar.

Lizard

Crocodile

Bird

## Cladistics

Crocodiles and birds share a more recent common ancestor.

Lizard

Crocodile

Bird

**Cladistics** uses synapomorphies to reconstruct evolutionary histories.

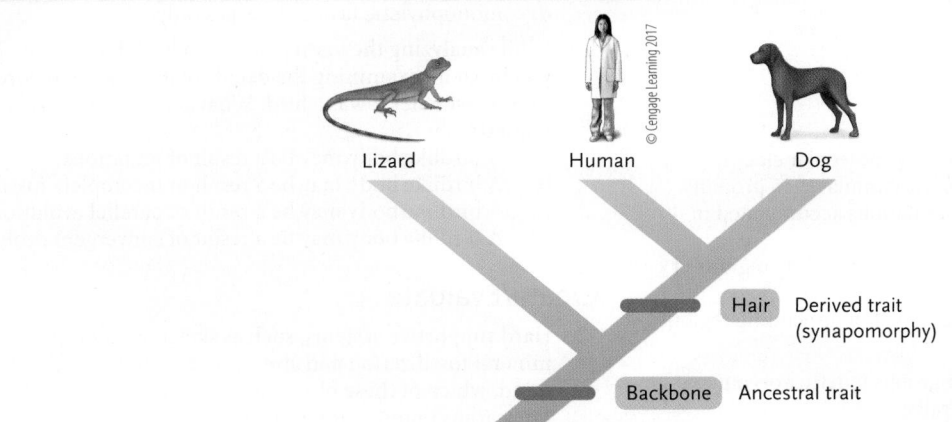

Lizard

Human

Dog

© Cengage Learning 2017

Hair — Derived trait (synapomorphy)

Backbone — Ancestral trait

A synapomorphy is a derived trait that is found in two or more species; one or more synapomorphies are used to define a specific clade. Being derived, synapomorphic traits appear for the first time in the last common ancestor of the clade.

## Principle of Parsimony

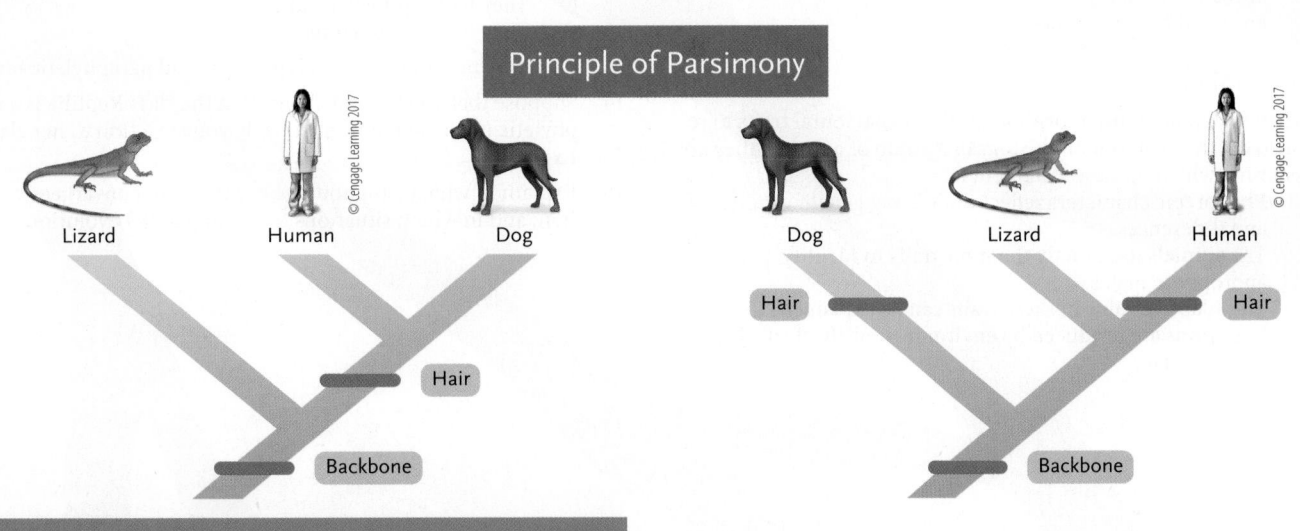

Lizard

Human

Dog

© Cengage Learning 2017

Hair

Backbone

Dog

Lizard

Human

© Cengage Learning 2017

Hair

Hair

Backbone

Compared to the tree at the right, this one is more likely to be correct, as it requires fewer evolutionary changes (principle of parsimony).

# SELF-TEST QUESTIONS

## Recall/Understand

1. The historic eradication of malaria (transmitted by some mosquitoes) in Europe owed a debt to which of the following?
   b. systematics
   c. ecology
   d. artificial selection
   e. natural life cycle of mosquitoes

2. The name *Ursus maritimus* indicates the polar bear, and the name *Ursus arctos* the brown bear. Which of these statements may you *most* likely conclude from this information?
   a. They belong to the same species and family.
   b. They belong to the same genus and family.
   c. They belong to the same species and order.
   d. They belong to the same genus and species.

3. Which of the following allowed scientists to determine whether or not the HIV-1 and HIV-2 strands of the virus evolved within human hosts?
   a. genetic analysis
   b. phylogenetic tree analyses
   c. molecular phylogenetic analyses
   d. molecular genetic analyses

4. Which of the following portrays a phylogenetic tree of a group of organisms?
   a. its classification
   b. its evolutionary history
   c. its domain
   d. its distribution

5. Which of these conditions can serve as a molecular clock?
   a. sudden differences in mutations accumulated in proteins
   b. constant rate of differences in mutations accumulated in proteins
   c. differences in mutations accumulated in coding regions of DNA at a reasonably constant rate
   d. differences in mutations accumulated in noncoding regions of DNA at a reasonably constant rate

6. In a cladistic analysis, a systematist groups together organisms that share which of these types of traits?
   a. derived homologous
   b. derived homoplasious
   c. ancestral homologous
   d. ancestral homoplasious

## Apply/Analyze

7. When systematists use morphological or behavioural traits to reconstruct the evolutionary history of a group of animals, they are assuming which of these statements?
   a. Phenotypic characters reflect underlying genetic similarities and differences.
   b. The animals use exactly the same traits to identify appropriate mates.
   c. The adaptive value of these traits can be explained.
   d. Variations are produced by environmental effects during development.

8. Which of these pairs of structures is a homoplasious pair?
   a. the wing skeleton of a bird and the wing skeleton of a bat
   b. the wing of a bird and the wing of a fly
   c. the eye of a fish and the eye of a human
   d. the wing structures of a pterosaur and the wing structures of a bird

9. If one was to construct a cladogram by applying the parsimony assumption to molecular sequence data, which of these steps would they use?
   a. group organisms sharing the least number of ancestral sequences
   b. group organisms sharing the largest number of ancestral sequences
   c. group organisms that share derived sequences, matching the groups to those defined by morphological characters
   d. group organisms sharing derived sequences, minimizing the number of hypothesized evolutionary changes

10. Suppose you want to convert a phylogenetic tree into a classification. What would you need to identify in order to achieve this?
    a. both monophyletic and paraphyletic taxa or lineages
    b. paraphyletic taxa or lineages only
    c. polyphyletic taxa or lineages only
    d. monophyletic taxa or lineages only

11. While analyzing the fossil record of a birdlike-bodied organism, you insist on examining the details of its skeleton before determining whether it was a bird. What is the significance of your request?
    a. A birdlike body may be a result of mutations.
    b. A birdlike body may be a result of incomplete fossilization.
    c. A birdlike body may be a result of parallel evolution.
    d. A birdlike body may be a result of convergent evolution.

## Create/Evaluate

12. Hard supportive systems, such as skeletons, lend themselves to mineral fossilization and appearance of more fossils. With this in mind, which of these observations is suggestive of soft-bodied Ediacarans found in fossils records?
    a. They had cell walls.
    b. They had hidden bones.
    c. They had supportive cuticle.
    d. They had exoskeletons.

13. Compare monophyletic, polyphyletic, and paraphyletic taxa.

14. Suppose that your friend claims that the class Reptilia is a monophyletic taxon. What is most likely your reaction to her claim? Explain.

15. Explain in which situations we use the term convergent evolution, and in which situations the term parallel evolution.

# Chapter Roadmap

## Humans and Evolution

This chapter provides an account of what is known about the evolution of Homo sapiens. Much of our understanding comes from the fossil record but has more recently been supplemented by molecular tools that have shed new light on the evolutionary history of humans.

### 20.1 The Fossil Record of Hominins

Fossil specimens have allowed researchers to develop a map of the evolution of the hominin lineage, starting in Africa between 5 and 10 million years ago.

### 20.2 Morphology and Bipedalism

An upright posture and bipedal locomotion distinguish hominins from apes.

### 20.3 Human Features That Do Not Fossilize

We have little knowledge of how early humans behaved, their social networks, or how language developed.

### 20.4 Dispersal of Early Humans

There exist competing hypotheses about whether modern humans spread out from Africa, or if they were descendants of ancestors that had spread through Europe and Asia.

### 20.5 Hominins and the Species Concepts

We have evidence that modern humans interbred with Neandertals, so perhaps they were not a distinct species.

©AAAC/Topham/The Image Works

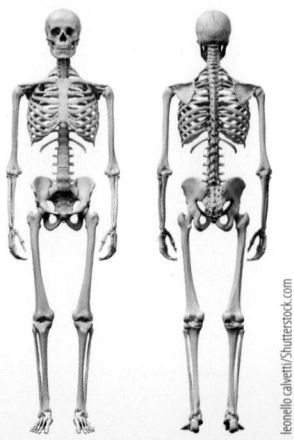

leonello calvetti/Shutterstock.com

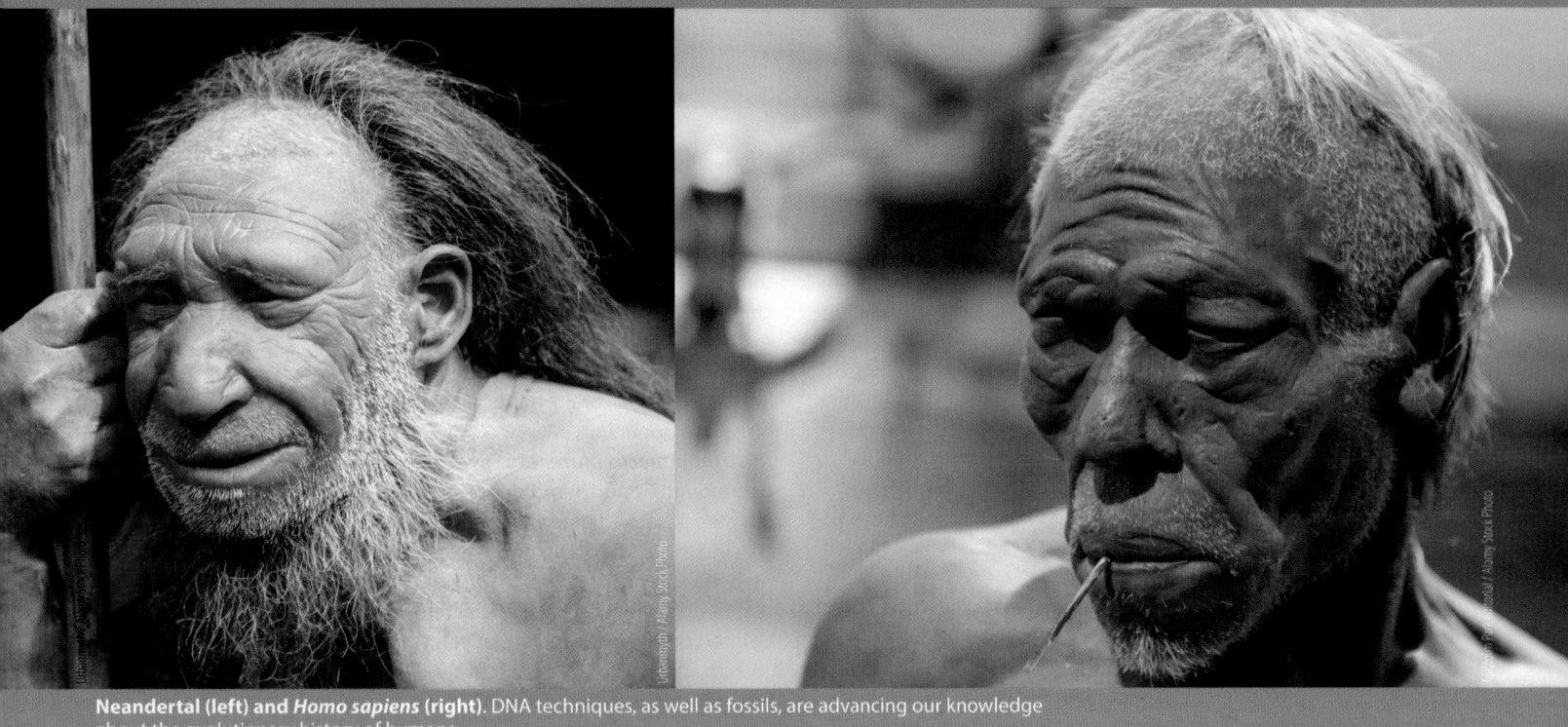

**Neandertal (left) and *Homo sapiens* (right).** DNA techniques, as well as fossils, are advancing our knowledge about the evolutionary history of humans.

# Humans and Evolution

# 20

**Why it matters …** From about 500 000 to 30 000 years ago, Neandertals (*Homo neanderthalensis*) roamed much of Europe and eastern and central Asia. Humans (*Homo sapiens*) arrived in the area about 40 000 years ago. Neandertals were shorter, more heavily built, and stronger than humans, and their brains were larger as well. But the Neandertals disappeared about 30 000 years ago, and paleontologists have often wondered why humans won out. Hypotheses include interbreeding between the two species (or subspecies), larger eyes in the Neandertal, and climate change. Only about 2% of the DNA of modern Europeans is Neandertal, so why didn't the two species simply interbreed and blend together? Also, surprisingly, no Neandertal mitochondrial DNA (mtDNA) has shown up in human mtDNA. Since mtDNA is passed only from mother to child, this suggests that, while Neandertal fathers and human mothers might have produced viable offspring, Neandertal mothers and human fathers could not. Was this the only thing that separated *H. sapiens* from *H. neanderthalensis*?

Recently, researchers in Seattle have developed the "Brainscan Atlas," a genetic reference about how the human brain is constructed and how it develops embryonically. Drs. Mohammed Uddin and Stephen Scherer, at Toronto's Hospital for Sick Children, used the Atlas and the Exome Variant Server (a database of all of a human's exomes) to determine which genes were responsible for autism. Uddin and Scherer determined that about 1700 genes were related only to brain development, not to any other function in the body. They then discovered that at least one-third of these 1700 genes had been implicated by other researchers in other brain and cognitive disorders.

Now, back to the Neandertal conundrum: Uddin and Scherer suddenly thought that the 1700 genes could somehow be related to what makes humans uniquely human. People with autism have difficulties with communication and socialization; could these abilities also be what set us apart from Neandertals?

# The Cast of Characters: Fossil Hominins

Most of our ancestors' fossils have been found in Africa **(Figure 1)**. Brain size varies with overall body size, so that large individuals (typically males) have more brain size than smaller ones (typically females). Across the species presented here, brain size ranges from the size of chimpanzee brain size (275–500 cm³, *Orrorin tugenensis*) to that of *Homo sapiens* (1000–1900 cm³). Species of *Australopithecus* have brain sizes of about 400–500 cm³; *Homo habilis* about 640 cm³. *Homo erectus* brain size ranges from 930 to 1030 cm³; *Homo neanderthalensis* from 1300 to 1600 cm³.

**Orrorin tugenensis:** In 2000, researchers found 13 fossils of *O. tugenensis* ("first man" in a local African language), a species that lived in the forests of eastern Africa about 6 mya. The thigh bones and pelvis indicate that it was bipedal.

**Ardipithecus ramidus:** In 1994, *Ardipithecus ramidus* was described from bone fragments (teeth and jaw fragments) collected in South Africa. These hominids stood 120 cm tall and had apelike teeth. The October 2, 2009, issue of *Science* included 11 papers about *A. ramidus* by an international team of researchers who reported data from 110 specimens. This species lived from about 6 to 4 mya, and many of its features overturned ideas about the evolution of our own species. The structure of its pelvis and feet suggested that it was bipedal. Both males and females had small canine teeth (compared to those of other primates), which imply reduced competition between males, presumably for females in estrus, in turn suggesting concealed ovulation (see Chapter 44). Bipedal locomotion could have enabled the hominins to exploit both land surface and trees in the search for food and shelter. Bipedal animals can carry food and be more effective provisioners. Many features of *A. ramidus* demonstrate that our ancestors showed an earlier than expected departure from a chimpanzee-like existence.

**Australopithecus africanus:** The first australopith to be described, *Australopithecus africanus*, was discovered by Raymond Dart in 1924. With its relatively small brain, this bipedal species was not immediately recognized as a hominin.

**Australopithecus afarensis:** Specimens of more than 60 individuals have been found in northern Ethiopia. The sample includes about 40% of a female's skeleton, named "Lucy" (Figure 20.5; apparently the Beatles' song "Lucy in the Sky with Diamonds" was playing on the radio when the skeleton was first uncovered). *A. afarensis* lived 3.5 to 3 mya. This species retained several ancestral characters, including moderately large and pointed canine teeth and a relatively small brain. Males and females were 150 cm and 120 cm tall respectively. Skeletal analyses suggest that Lucy was fully bipedal, a conclusion supported by fossilized footprints preserved in a layer of volcanic ash (Figure 20.1). In 2010, the description of a male specimen of *Australopithecus afarensis* ("big man") provided further evidence of bipedalism, specifically, details of the pelvic girdle and sacrum not preserved in Lucy. Furthermore, a well-preserved scapula (shoulder blade) provided no evidence of suspensory climbing evident in the scapulae of great apes.

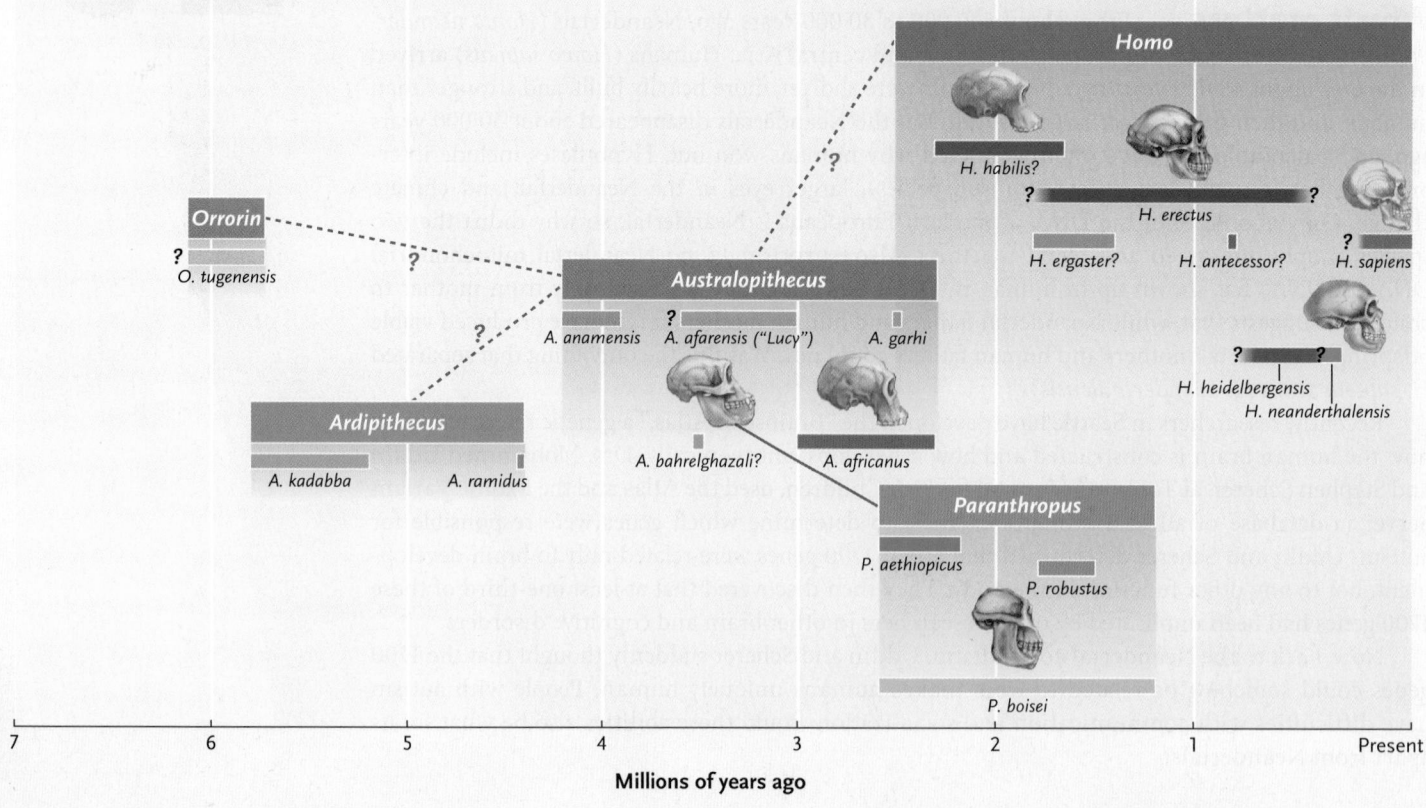

© Cengage Learning 2017.

**Figure 1   Hominin timeline showing several of the species described in the text.** These species lived at the same place and time in eastern and southern Africa. The timeline is shown for each species, and question marks indicate uncertainty about classification and/or ages of fossils. Some skulls are reconstructions from fragments.

**Australopithecus anamensis:** One of the oldest known species in the genus, *Australopithecus anamensis* lived in eastern Africa around 4 mya. Its teeth had thick enamel, which is typically a derived hominin character. A fossilized thigh bone suggests that it was bipedal.

**Australopithecus sediba:** In September 2011, the journal *Science* published a series of papers describing the newly discovered *Australopithecus sediba*, an "early" (2 mya) version of Lucy (*A. afarensis*). The fossils, from the Malapa site in South Africa, provided a new perspective on the evolution of humans. The ankles and feet suggest a combination of climbing ability (arboreal life style) and bipedalism that differed from that of Lucy. The pelvis of *A. sediba* shared features, such as the sacral and pubic areas, with those of Lucy and other australopithecines. But in the shape of its ilium, *A. sediba* resembled species of *Homo*. These features in *A. sediba* suggest that giving birth to offspring with large brains had not yet appeared at this stage of australopithecine evolution.

Some of the fossil *A. sediba* had nearly complete wrists and hands, indicating the capacity for strong flexion typically associated with tree climbing. But the long thumb and short fingers of *A. sediba* imply a capacity for precision gripping (see Figure 20.8), suggesting the potential for the use of tools. Construction of a virtual endocast of the skull of *A. sediba* indicates that the frontal lobes of the brain were generally like those of other australopithecines. But the features of the brain suggest its gradual reorganization toward the appearance in species of *Homo*.

This new fossil demonstrates, once again, how such a find can influence our view of evolutionary history. This is not a "missing link" but rather a species whose features reflect the general state of evolutionary development of species in the genus *Australopithecus*. It also presages the transitions that later occur with the emergence of species in the genus *Homo*.

**Homo habilis:** Pliocene fossils of the earliest *Homo* are fragmentary and widely distributed in space and time. They are thought to have belonged to *Homo habilis* (meaning "handy man"). From 2.3 to 1.7 mya, *H. habilis* occupied the woodlands and savannas of eastern and southern Africa, sharing these habitats with various species of *Paranthropus*. The two genera are easy to distinguish because the brains of *H. habilis* were at least 20% larger, and their **incisors** were larger and **molars** smaller than those of *Paranthropus* spp. They ate hard-shelled nuts and seeds, as well as soft fruits, tubers, leaves, and insects. They may also have hunted small prey or scavenged carcasses left by larger predators.

Researchers have found numerous tools dating to the time of *H. habilis* but are not sure which species made them. Many hominid species of that time probably cracked marrowbones with rocks or scraped flesh from bones with sharp stones. Paleoanthropologist Louis Leakey was the first to discover evidence of tool-*making* at eastern Africa's Olduvai Gorge, which cuts through a great sequence of sedimentary rock layers. The oldest tools at this site are crudely chipped pebbles, probably manufactured by *H. habilis*. However, humans are not the only animals to *use* tools (see Chapter 32).

**Homo erectus:** Early in the Pleistocene, about 1.8 mya, a new species of humans, *Homo erectus* ("upright man"), appeared in eastern Africa **(Figure 2)**. One nearly complete skeleton suggests that *H. erectus* was taller than its ancestors and had a much larger brain, a thicker skull, and protruding brow ridges. *H. erectus* made fairly sophisticated tools, such as hand axes **(Figure 3)** used to cut food and other materials, to scrape meat from bones, and to dig for roots. *H. erectus* probably ate both plants and animals and may have hunted and scavenged animal prey. Archaeological data point to their use of fire to cook food and to keep warm. Near Lake Turkana in Kenya, fossils identified as *Homo* and dating from 1.55 to 1.45 mya were described in 2007. These suggested that *H. erectus* and *H. habilis* lived together in the same habitats for a considerable time, much as chimps and gorillas do today. Adult male *H. erectus* were much larger than adult females, suggesting a polygynous lifestyle, one male with several females (see Chapter 32).

About 1.5 mya, the pressure of growing populations apparently forced groups of *H. erectus* out of Africa. They dispersed northward from eastern Africa into both northwestern Africa and Eurasia. Some moved eastward through Asia as far as the island of Java. Judging from its geographic distribution, *H. erectus* was successful in many environments. It produced several descendant

**Homo erectus**

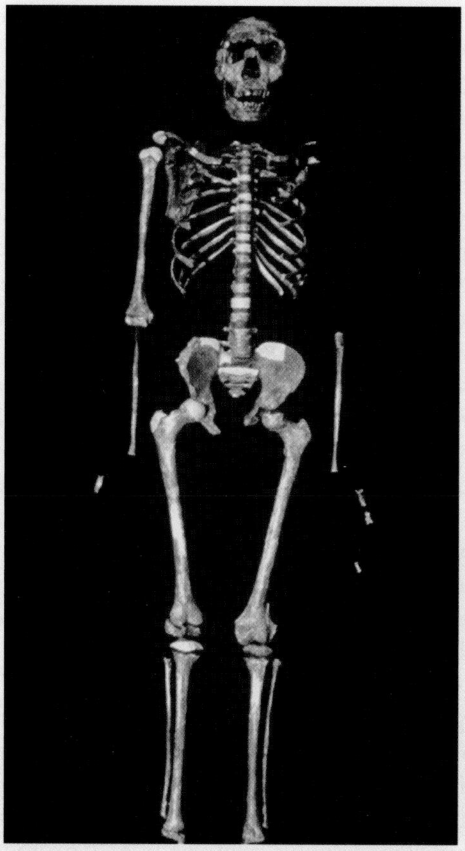

**Hand axe**

*Science VU/NM/Visuals Unlimited, Inc.*

*©AAAC/Topham/The Image Works*

**Figure 2  *Homo erectus*, a nearly complete skeleton from Kenya**

**Figure 3  A hand axe found at a site used by *Homo erectus***

CHAPTER 20   HUMANS AND EVOLUTION   |   **479**

species, of which modern humans (*H. sapiens*, meaning "wise man") are the only survivors. Now-extinct descendants of *H. erectus*, archaic humans, first appeared at least 400 000 years ago. They generally had larger brains, rounder skulls, and smaller molars than *H. erectus*.

***Homo floresiensis:*** *H. floresiensis* was described in 2004 from Flores Island in Indonesia. Although first proposed as a distinct species, its small size was used to support the view that it was just a small individual. In 2013, analyses of various aspects of the morphology of *H. floresiensis* indicated that it was not a dwarf or microcephalic, rather a distinct species most closely related to *H. erectus*.

***Homo neanderthalensis:*** Neandertals lived in Europe and western Asia from 150 000 to 28 000 years ago. They are the best known of the archaic humans and sometimes have been treated as a subspecies of *Homo sapiens*. Compared with modern humans, they had a heavier build, more pronounced brow ridges, and slightly larger brains. Neandertals were culturally and technologically sophisticated. They made complex tools, including wooden spears, stone axes, flint scrapers, and knives. At some sites, they built shelters of stones, branches, and animal hides, and they routinely used fire. They were successful hunters and probably ate nuts, berries, fishes, and bird eggs. Some groups buried their dead, and they may have had rudimentary speech. There is evidence that some were cannibals.

In 1997, two teams of researchers independently analyzed short segments of mtDNA extracted from the fossilized arm bone of a Neandertal. Unlike nuclear DNA, which individuals inherit from both parents, only mothers pass mtDNA to offspring. mtDNA does not undergo genetic recombination (see Chapter 8) and has a high mutation rate, making it useful for phylogenetic analyses. If mutation rates in mtDNA are fairly constant, this molecule can serve as a **molecular clock**. Comparing the Neandertal sequence with mtDNA from 986 living humans revealed three times as many differences between the Neandertals and modern humans as between pairs of modern humans in their sample. These data suggest that Neandertals and modern humans are different species that diverged from a common ancestor 690 000 to 550 000 years ago.

***Homo sapiens:*** Modern humans differ from Neandertals and other archaic humans in having a slighter build, less-protruding brow ridges, and a more prominent chin. The earliest fossils of modern humans found in Africa and Asia are 150 000 years old; those from the Middle East are 100 000 years old. Fossils from about 20 000 years ago are known from Western Europe, the most famous being those of the Cro-Magnon deposits in southern France. The widespread appearance of modern humans roughly coincided with the demise of Neandertals in Western Europe and the Middle East, 40 000 to 28 000 years ago.

Dr. Ajit Varki at the University of California, San Diego, thinks that, despite the physical similarities between humans and Neandertals, they could have been very different in **social behaviour** and in their abilities to communicate. Consequently, children with one *H. sapiens* parent and one *H. neanderthalensis* parent could have been "cognitively sterile," and therefore unable to really communicate with each other. This research was published in 2014.

DNA techniques as well as fossils are advancing our knowledge about the evolutionary history of humans. In this chapter we focus on some of the most important changes in our ancestry. We consider the implications of **bipedalism**, showing that it is much more than walking erect on two legs. We also present some recently discovered fossils and consider how the biological species concept applies to our own species.

## 20.1 The Fossil Record of Hominins

A combination of genetic and morphological analyses of living and fossil species indicates that, between 10 and 5 mya in Africa, **hominoids** (superfamily Hominoidea, including apes and humans) diverged into several lineages. One lineage, the **hominins** (family Hominidae, subfamily Homininae), includes modern humans and our bipedal ancestors (see Figure 19.3 and "The Cast of Characters: Fossil Hominins"). Where only one species of hominin (*Homo sapiens*) exists today, several species lived in the past.

Most of the hominins that lived in eastern and southern Africa from 6 to 1 mya are currently classified in the genera

*Australopithecus* (*australo* = southern; *pithecus* = ape) and *Paranthropus* (*para* = beside; *anthropus* = man). With large faces, protruding jaws, and small skulls and brains, these hominins resembled apes. Between 3.7 and 1 mya, several other species of hominins occurred in eastern and southern Africa. These adult males ranged from 40 to 50 kg in mass and from 130 to 150 cm in height; females were smaller. Most of these species had deep jaws and large molars, suggesting a diet of hard food, such as nuts, seeds, and other vegetable products. *Australopithecus africanus*, known only from southern Africa, had small jaws and teeth, suggesting a diet of softer food. The phylogenetic relationships among species in the genera *Australopithecus* and *Paranthropus*, and their exact relationships to later hominids, are not yet fully understood (see Figure 19.3 and "The Cast of Characters: Fossil Hominins"). *Australopithecus* was likely ancestral to humans (various species in the genus *Homo*).

**CONCEPT FIX** Many people believe that evolutionary biologists say that our species evolved *from* apes. But while the fossil record clearly demonstrates that the evolutionary lineage to which *H. sapiens* belongs includes chimps and gorillas (Figure 19.3), the lineage leading to humans has been distinct from the one leading to gorillas and chimps for over 6 million years. Belonging to an evolutionary lineage does not mean one species in the lineage gives rise to another. Evolutionary biologists are not proposing that humans evolved from apes, but that apes are our closest living relatives (see "Chromosomal Similarities and Differences among the Great Apes" in Chapter 18).

## 20.2 Morphology and Bipedalism

Upright posture and bipedal locomotion distinguish hominins from apes. Bipedal locomotion meant, largely, that the hands were not used in locomotion, allowing them to become specialized for other activities such as carrying things and using and making tools. Sometimes paleontologists find fossilized hominin footprints, indicating bipedalism (Figure 20.1), but usually the fossil record of mammals such as *Homo sapiens* consists mainly of bones and teeth, the body parts most often fossilized. Bipedalism is obvious from the feet, thighs, pelvis, shoulders, and arms of these fossil and human skeletons (Figure 20.2). When appropriate fossils are available, it may be possible to learn when the skeletal features associated with bipedalism appeared over time.

Bipedalism in hominins involves a suite of anatomical features, not just the pattern of footfall and walking and running behaviour.

FIGURE 20.1 **Mary Leakey discovered these fossilized footprints of an australopithecine made in soft, damp volcanic ash about 3.7 mya.** The footprints appear to have been made by an adult and a youngster.

### 20.2a Feet, Legs, and Pelvis

Paleontologists have long inferred bipedalism from the structure of the thigh bones (femora) and pelvis (Figure 20.3). Both ends of the femur, at the hip and knee joints, are larger in the human than in the chimpanzee because more weight is directed through the human joints. Humans have a smaller angle at the hip end of the femur (the ball and socket joint) because of their upright stance. Also, human leg bones (both the upper leg and lower leg) are longer than in chimpanzees; however, chimps have longer foreleg bones than humans have.

More recently, the metatarsals (the long foot bones) provided additional features for recognizing bipedalism in hominins. For example, the fourth metatarsals of *Australopithecus afarensis* were more like those of humans than those of either

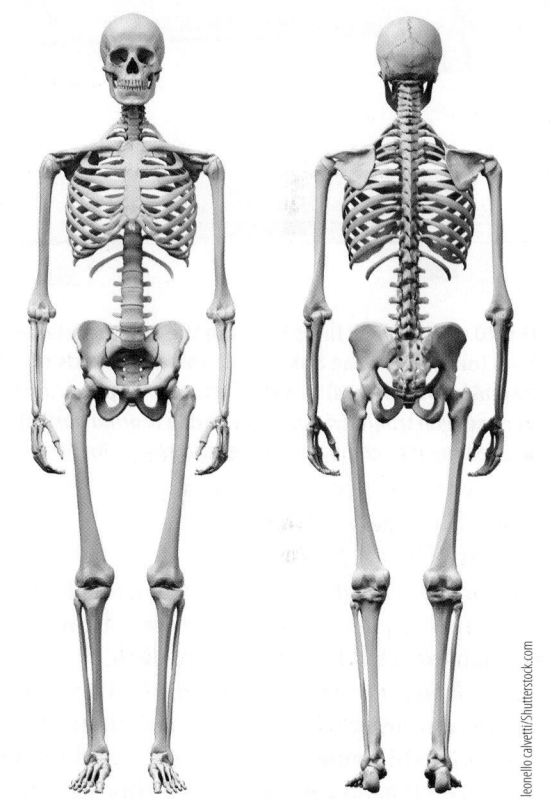

FIGURE 20.2 **Human skeleton, front and back views**

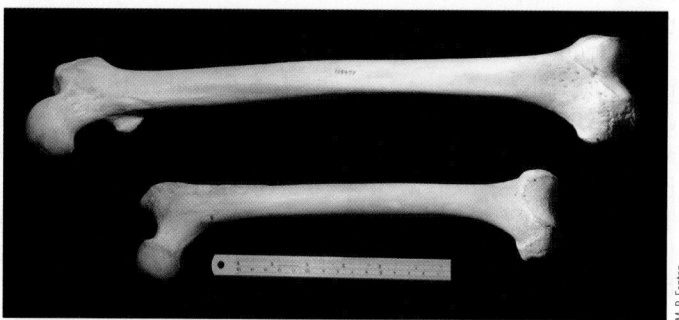

FIGURE 20.3 **A comparison of the thigh bones (femora) of a chimpanzee (bottom) and a human (top)**

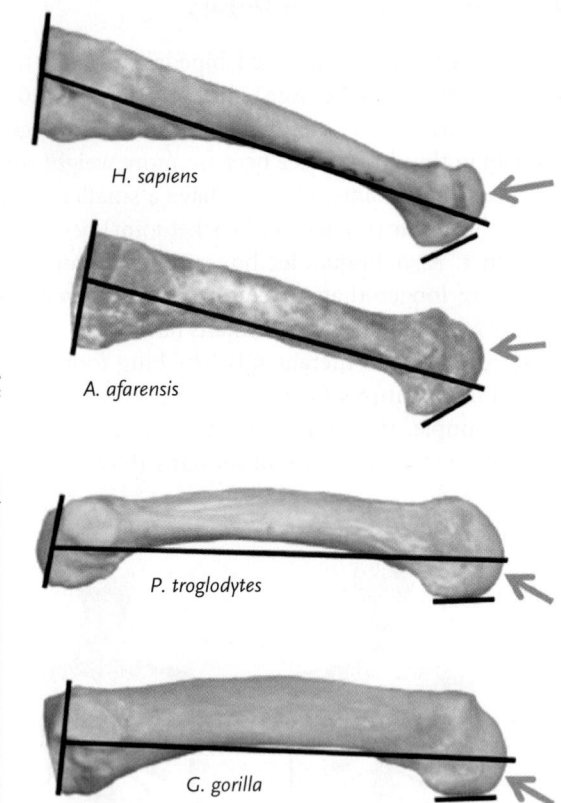

**FIGURE 20.4** **The black lines indicate the angles between the proximal (on the left, the ankle end) and distal ends of the fourth metatarsal bone (arrows) of a human,** *Australopithecus afarensis*, **a chimpanzee (***Pan troglodytes***), and a gorilla (***Gorilla gorilla***).** Note the angle in the hominins compared to the parallel lines in the ape species.

chimps or gorillas **(Figure 20.4)**. Comparable features also appeared in *Ardipithecus ramidus* from 3.4 mya, indicating a longer than expected history of bipedalism.

*Australopithecus sediba* from the Malapa site in South Africa was an earlier (about 2 mya) version of Lucy (*Australopithecus afarensis*; **Figure 20.5**). The ankles and feet of *A. sediba* suggest a combination of climbing ability (arboreal lifestyle) and bipedalism that differed from that of Lucy. The sacral and pubic areas of the pelvis of *A. sediba* resemble those of Lucy and other australopithecines, but the shape of the ilium of *A. sediba* resembled that of species of *Homo*.

In 2007, S. K. S. Thorpe, R. L. Holder, and R. H. Crompton proposed that bipedalism arose in an arboreal setting. Specifically, they asserted that hand-assisted bipedalism allowed the ancestors of humans and great apes to move on flexible supports (branches) that would otherwise have been too small. Thorpe et al. compared human and orangutan (*Pongo abelii*) locomotion and found that orangutans walking on flexible branches increase knee and hip extension, just as humans do when running on a springy track. In a bipedal gait, humans and orangutans flex the hind limbs in a manner that differs from the gait of gorillas and chimps.

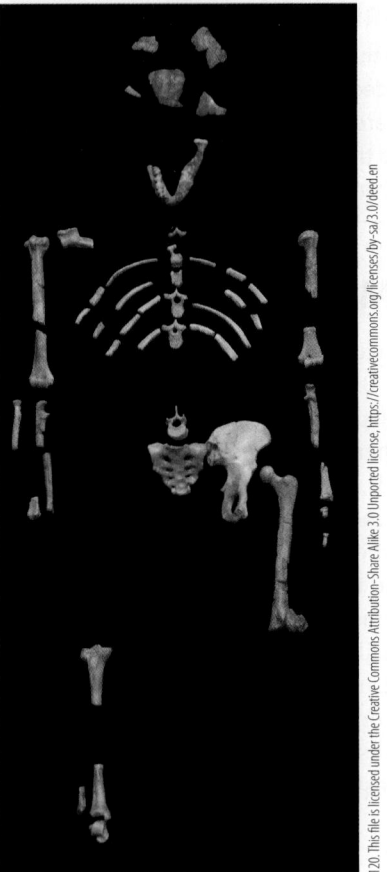

**FIGURE 20.5** **The fossil skeleton of** *Australopithecus afarensis*, **popularly known as "Lucy"**

## 20.2b Shoulders and Arms

The importance of climbing for australopiths is supported by the appearance of their shoulder blades (scapulae). The angle of the socket (glenoid fossa; **Figure 20.6**) that receives the head of the upper arm bone (humerus) faces cranially (toward the head), as it does in apes that hang from their arms. In humans, the glenoid fossa faces laterally but changes with age. A lateral-facing glenoid fossa also contributes to humans' ability to throw projectiles such as spears or stones at high speeds.

Species in the genus *Homo* have three specializations associated with throwing ability:

1. They have a "long waist" because of an increase in the number of lumbar vertebrae combined with longer

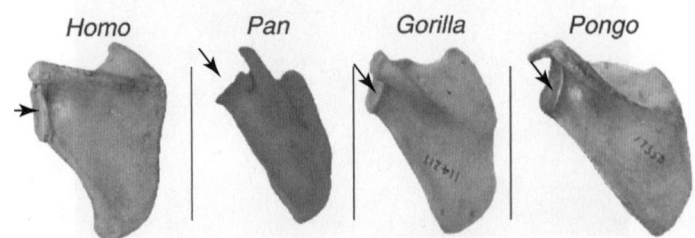

*Homo*     *Pan*     *Gorilla*     *Pongo*

**FIGURE 20.6** **A comparison of the shoulder blades (scapulae) of a human, a chimp (***Pan***), a gorilla, and an orangutan (***Pongo***) showing the orientation of the glenoid fossa (arrows)**

individual vertebrae. The long waist allows the movement of hips and thorax (the portion of the body between head and abdomen) to be decoupled, resulting in a large range of motion of the shoulders and the development of torque.

2. Torsion of the humerus (upper arm bone) between the orientation of its head and the axis of the elbow extends the range of motion during rotation.

3. The laterally directed glenoid fossa aligns the moment generated by flexing of a muscle, the pectoral muscles, with the rotation of the torso.

This set of specializations appeared more than 2 mya in *Homo erectus*. It permits elastic storage of energy, which contributes to accurate spear throwing. Effective throwing increased the hunting potential of species in the genus *Homo*.

## 20.2c   Hands

Species in the genus *Homo* have hands that are quite distinct from those of apes. The palms and fingers are short, while the thumbs are long, strong, and mobile **(Figure 20.7)**. This results in our ability to use two different grips **(Figure 20.8)**, a power grip and a precision grip, allowing manipulative skills and a capacity to make precise tools. The proportions of hominin hands also deliver a performance advantage when striking with

**FIGURE 20.8  Power grip versus precision grip.** Hominins grasp objects in two distinct ways. The power grip **(a)** allows us to grasp an object firmly, whereas the precision grip **(b)** allows us to manipulate objects by fine movements.

a fist. Buttressing of the elements in the hand increases the stiffness of the joint between the second metacarpal (a hand bone) and phalanges (finger bones), enabling hominins to punch with more force. The ability to present our hands palms up (supination) or palms down (pronation) also increases their versatility.

Increasing the force that can be delivered can also be achieved by the leverage associated with attaching a handle or strap (haft) to a projectile point, such as a spear or an arrow. At Kathu Pan in South Africa, hafted tools date from 500 000 years ago. Hafted tools such as spears further enhance the impact of high-velocity throwing, while shorter stabbing blows reflect the importance of the power grip. Other tools found among hominin fossils include stone cutting tools used to take meat off bones and stone axes used for chopping trees. Through time, the tools found show improvement in the technique and the fine motor skills required to make them.

## 20.2d   Pelvis and Birth

Female hominins suffer at least one consequence of being bipedal, namely the shift in the body's centre of mass during pregnancy. A marked posterior concavity of individual lower back (lumbar) vertebrae stabilizes the centre of mass of the upper body over the hips. Bipedal females have a derived curvature of

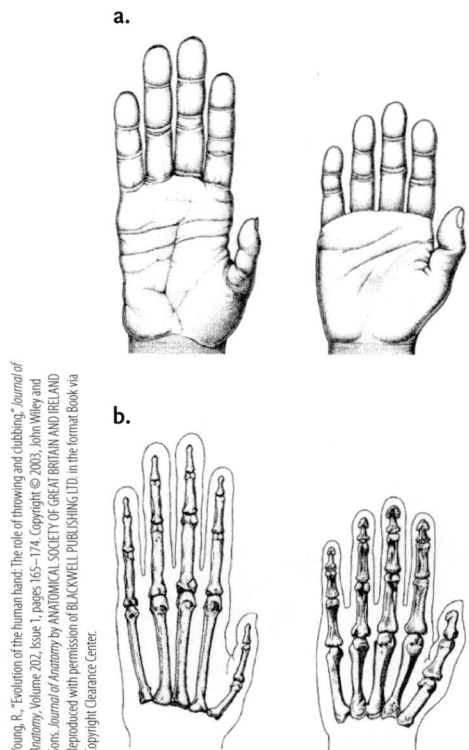

Young, R., "Evolution of the human hand: The role of throwing and clubbing." *Journal of Anatomy*, Volume 202, Issue 1, pages 165–174. Copyright © 2003, John Wiley and Sons. *Journal of Anatomy* by ANATOMICAL SOCIETY OF GREAT BRITAIN AND IRELAND Reproduced with permission of BLACKWELL PUBLISHING LTD. in the format Book via Copyright Clearance Center.

**FIGURE 20.7  The chimp's hands (left) are adapted for grasping branches, while human hands (right) are adapted for precision and power grips.** The relatively longer thumbs of humans also contribute to our precision grip.

the lumbar area and reinforcement of those vertebrae to compensate for the additional load associated with pregnancy. The anatomy of the pelvis and lower back of *Australopithecus* indicates that these adaptations to bipedalism preceded the evolution of species in the genus *Homo*. Compared to modern humans, the birth canals of Neandertals were not as specialized. The birth process in our species is specialized and may be a relatively recent development.

### STUDY BREAK QUESTIONS

1. Name three morphological specializations associated with bipedalism.
2. What effect do these specializations have on hominins, and how do they distinguish hominins from chimps?

## 20.3  Human Features That Do Not Fossilize

Some features characteristic of humans are unlikely to fossilize, such as behavioural and soft tissue features associated with social organization and language. The structure of jaws and teeth as well as fossilized dung (coprolites) can be used to infer (jaws and teeth) or reveal (coprolites) what fossil animals ate.

Although jaw and tooth structure can suggest the ability to eat hard food, our ancestors may have used tools to break up hard foodstuffs and fire to soften and cook them. Meanwhile, early hominins exploited a range of habitats and thrived on a diversity of food.

Humans show a great capacity for making friends—not genetically related individuals—with whom they have long-term, non-reproductive relationships that involve cooperation and mutual influence. These relationships underlie social networks, a feature of many social species. In humans, social networks may include individuals of other species, such as dogs and cats. Social networks and associated cooperative behaviour are well known from human hunter–gatherer societies, such as the Hadza of Tanzania. One apparently unique feature of human social networks is the common use of some land areas by different groups. This leads to a pattern of movement among groups (dispersal) that enhances social learning and a cumulative culture.

Effective communication among individuals is an essential part of social networks. One aspect is an individual's ability to read and interpret the body language (see Chapter 32) of another. Humans use both body cues and facial expressions to distinguish between intense positive and negative emotions **(Figure 20.9)**.

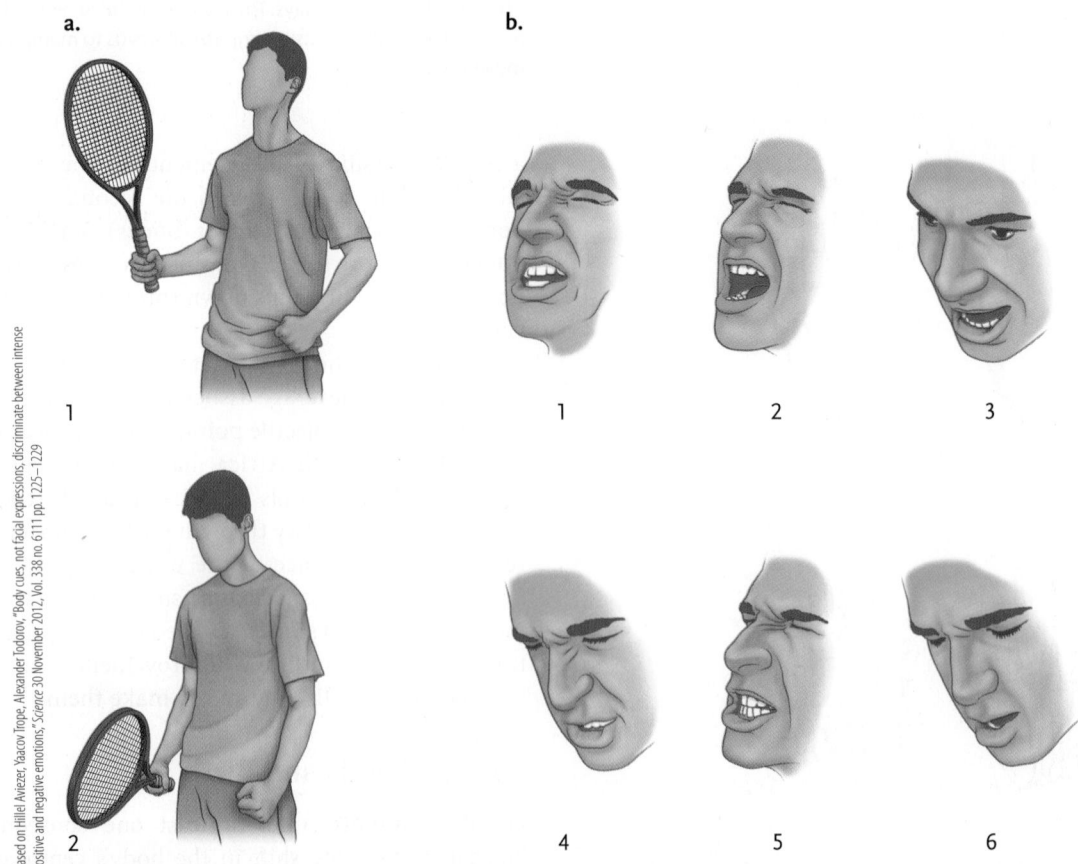

a.

1

2

b.

1 2 3

4 5 6

Based on Hillel Aviezer, Yaacov Trope, Alexander Todorov, "Body cues, not facial expressions, discriminate between intense positive and negative emotions," *Science* 30 November 2012, Vol. 338 no. 6111 pp. 1225–1229

**FIGURE 20.9** **(a)** Body language in response to winning (1) and losing (2) a point. **(b)** Facial expressions presented as isolated views in response to winning (2, 3, 5) and losing (1, 4, 6) a point

Source: Based on Hillel Aviezer, Yaacov Trope, Alexander Todorov, "Body cues, not facial expressions, discriminate between intense positive and negative emotions," *Science* 30 November 2012, Vol. 338 no. 6111 pp. 1225–1229

Language is a means of communication that involves symbolism and syntax. Although language is sometimes considered a hallmark of *Homo sapiens*, other animals also use a combination of symbolism and syntax in communication. For example, when a vervet monkey (*Chlorocebus pygerythrus*) gives the "eagle" alarm call, its fellows look skyward and move closer to the trunks of trees. When the same monkey gives a "leopard" alarm call, other monkeys in trees look down and those on the ground climb trees.

Language is not unique to *H. sapiens*, and it is not clear when language appeared in human evolution. The *FOXP2* gene is associated with speech and language in *H. sapiens*, and genomic analysis reveals that *H. sapiens* and *Homo neanderthalensis* have similar *FOXP2* genes, implying that Neandertals had language. A trait of many (all?) present-day human languages is a combination of simple categories (to minimize details) and a high level of informativeness to maximize communication efficiency.

### STUDY BREAK QUESTIONS

1. How does communication figure in the evolution of humans?
2. What are friends? How do they distinguish humans from other animals?

## 20.4 Dispersal of Early Humans

There are two main theories about the dispersal of our ancestors from Africa. The **African emergence hypothesis** proposes that early hominin descendants (archaic humans) left Africa and established populations in the Middle East, Asia, and Europe. Some time later, 200 000 to 100 000 years ago, *H. sapiens* arose in Africa and also migrated into Europe and Asia. Perhaps through competition, *H. sapiens* eventually drove archaic humans to extinction. This hypothesis suggests that all modern humans are descended from a fairly recent African ancestor.

The **multiregional hypothesis** suggests that populations of *H. erectus* and archaic humans had spread through much of Europe and Asia by 500 000 years ago, and modern humans (*H. sapiens*) evolved from descendants of these earlier dispersals. Although these geographically separated populations may have experienced some evolutionary differentiation, gene flow between them prevented reproductive isolation and maintained them as a single but variable species, *H. sapiens*.

Paleontological data do not clearly support either hypothesis but, as of 2011, genetic data **(Figure 20.10)** generally supported the African emergence hypothesis. Further work on the Y chromosomes of thousands of men from Africa, Europe, Asia, Australia, and the Americas has confirmed that all modern humans are the descendants of a single migration out of Africa.

A rapid exodus of anatomically modern humans out of Africa may have occurred along the coast of the Indian Ocean. Archaeological material from the United Arab Emirates suggests that early emigrants may have taken advantage of lower sea levels to move along the Arabian coast around 60 000 years ago.

Earlier dispersal is clear from material found at Attirampakkam in India. These fossils indicate that Acheulian humans (probably *Homo erectus*) had occupied this site by about 1.5 mya. Acheulian cultures are typified by large cutting tools with bifaces. Other records indicate that hominins (*Homo floresiensis*) were on Flores Island (Indonesia) by 1 mya. Humans occupied sites on the highlands in New Guinea by about 49 000 years ago. These humans exploited endemic nuts (*Pandanus* spp.) and appeared to have cleared forests to promote growth of their preferred plants. The timing of the arrival of humans in the New World is less well known. Dating of sites at caves in Oregon indicates human occupancy by about 12 000 years ago.

### 20.4a The Denisovans

Genetic information in the form of DNA recovered from a finger bone of a girl who lived over 50 000 years ago indicates that she had dark skin, brown hair, and brown eyes. The girl's fossilized bone fragments were found in Denisova Cave in Siberia. The name of the cave has been applied to the people, Denisovans, who apparently were a sister group to the Neandertals. Subsequent genomic analysis revealed that the Denisovans lived in Southeast Asia and interbred with the ancestors of today's Melanesians.

Vital components of our immune system (HLA class I) were acquired through the *HLA-B*73* allele inherited from Denisovans in west Asia. Genome analysis also indicates that some *HLA* haplotypes entered modern European and Oceanian human populations from both Neandertals and Denisovans.

### STUDY BREAK QUESTIONS

1. What evidence supports the African emergence hypothesis?
2. By when had humans arrived in India? How do we know?

## 20.5 Hominins and the Species Concepts

The history of hominins clearly demonstrates the challenges inherent in recognizing species and the boundaries between them. This example is particularly illuminating because it involves paleontological, archaeological, and genomic evidence. The genomic analysis shows that the ancestors of modern humans interbred with both Neandertals and Denisovans. If we apply the biological species concept (see Chapter 18), these three groups are not separate species. If we apply the phylogenetic species concept, the distinction is less clear. The morphological evidence from fossils is incomplete and does not necessarily settle the matter.

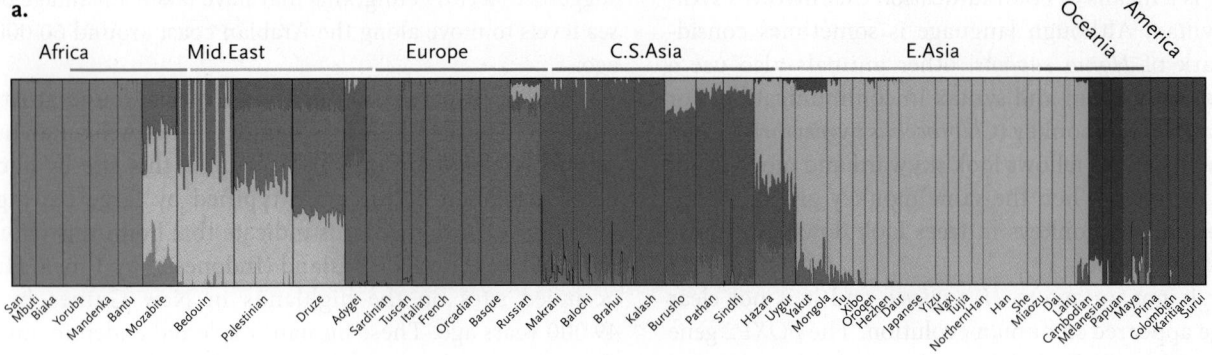

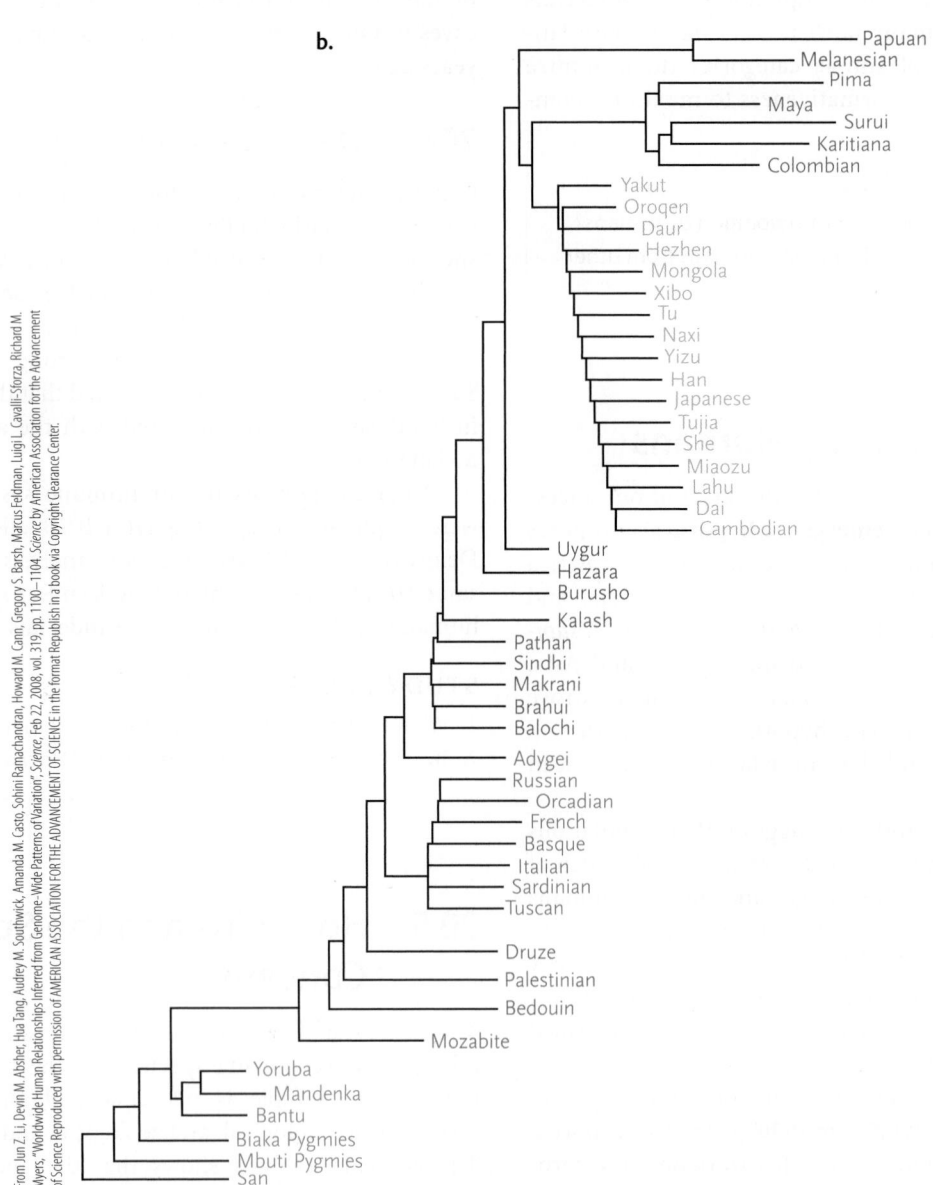

**FIGURE 20.10 Out of Africa. (a)** Genetic data from 650 000 common single-nucleotide polymorphism loci from 928 humans were used to construct an individual ancestry and population dendrogram. **(b)** Maximum likelihood tree of 51 populations shows a single origin in sub-Saharan Africa and a subsequent radiation across Asia to the New World and Polynesia.

In 2013, the description of fossil hominins from Georgia (Dmanisi) changed our view of our ancestors. In 2000, these fossils from 1.7 mya were identified as *Homo georgicus*, but the 2013 presentation of data from five skulls shows the same amount of variation in morphology that we know from living populations of humans and chimpanzees. This discovery suggests a highly variable lineage and obliges us to reconsider which of the named species of *Homo* are valid.

With recent advances in molecular technology, we are learning a great deal more about our evolutionary history. The story continues about what sets humans apart from other animals, whether it is communication abilities, social cooperation, or even an understanding of the future. As we will see later in the book, our animal ancestry is still clear, whether the topic is population ecology (Chapter 29) or animal behaviour (Chapter 32).

## STUDY BREAK QUESTIONS

1. What is the impact of the fossils from Dmanisi on our view of species diversity in the genus *Homo*?

2. How do the "species" of hominins fit the biological species concept?

# Summary Illustration

The study of human evolution focuses on the time since human and chimpanzee lineages diverged from their common ancestor, approximately 6 million years ago. DNA techniques and fossils of hominins, species most closely related to humans, have provided our current understanding of human evolution. At times, several hominin species coexisted. Eventually, all became extinct except one, *Homo sapiens*.

Bipedal locomotion allowed hands to be free to perform more activities, such as carrying things and making and using tools.

**Bipedalism**
- Upright posture and bipedalism distinguish hominins from apes.
- The oldest evidence showing upright walking is about 6 to 7 million years old. However, these species still climbed trees and had ape-like features (e.g., *Orrorin tugenensis* and *Sahelanthropus tchadensis*).

**Quadrupedalism**
*Pan troglodytes*
(modern chimpanzee)

**Bipedalism**
*Homo sapiens*
(modern human)

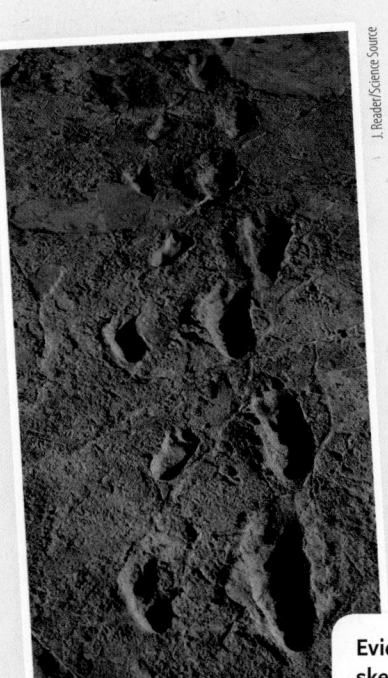

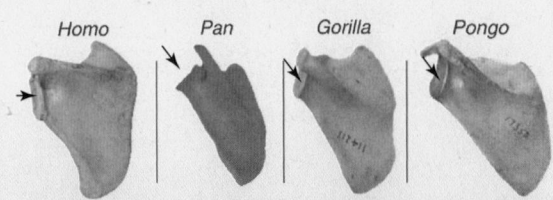

*Homo*   *Pan*   *Gorilla*   *Pongo*

Shoulder blades show whether the species hangs from its arms (apes) or has the ability to throw projectiles (humans).

From Green and Alemseged, "Australopithecus afarensis Scapular Ontogeny, Function, and the Role of Climbing in Human Evolution," *Science* 26 October 2012: Vol. 338 no. 6106 pp. 514–517. *Science* by American Association for the Advancement of Science Reproduced with permission of AMERICAN ASSOCIATION FOR THE ADVANCEMENT OF SCIENCE in the format Republish in a book via Copyright Clearance Center.

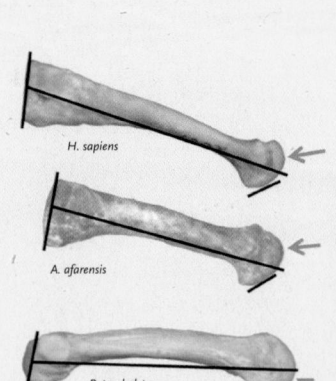

*H. sapiens*

*A. afarensis*

*P. troglodytes*

*G. gorilla*

Metatarsals can distinguish bipedalism.

From Carol V. Ward, William H. Kimbel, and Donald C. Johanson, "Complete fourth metatarsal and arches in the foot of *Australopithecus afarensis*," *Science* 11 February 2011: Vol. 331 no. 6018 pp. 750–753. *Science* by American Association for the Advancement of Science Reproduced with permission of AMERICAN ASSOCIATION FOR THE ADVANCEMENT OF SCIENCE in the format Republish in a book via Copyright Clearance Center.

Evidence of bipedalism includes fossilized hominin footprints and, more commonly, skeletal features (e.g., bones of feet, hands, thighs, pelvis, shoulders, and arms).

488

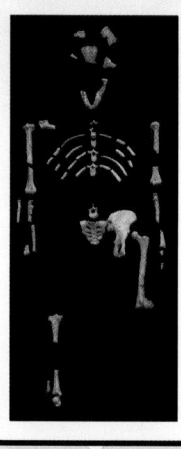

Fossils of more than 60 *Australopithecus afarensis* individuals have been found in northern Ethiopia (including "Lucy," shown here). Males and females were between 120 and 150 cm tall and are thought to have been fully bipedal.

Compared to its ancestors, *Homo erectus* was taller and had a larger brain and a thicker skull. They made sophisticated tools, such as hand axes, and used fire.

Between 150 000 and 30 000 years ago, Neandertals, with shorter, heavier builds than humans, lived in Europe and Asia.

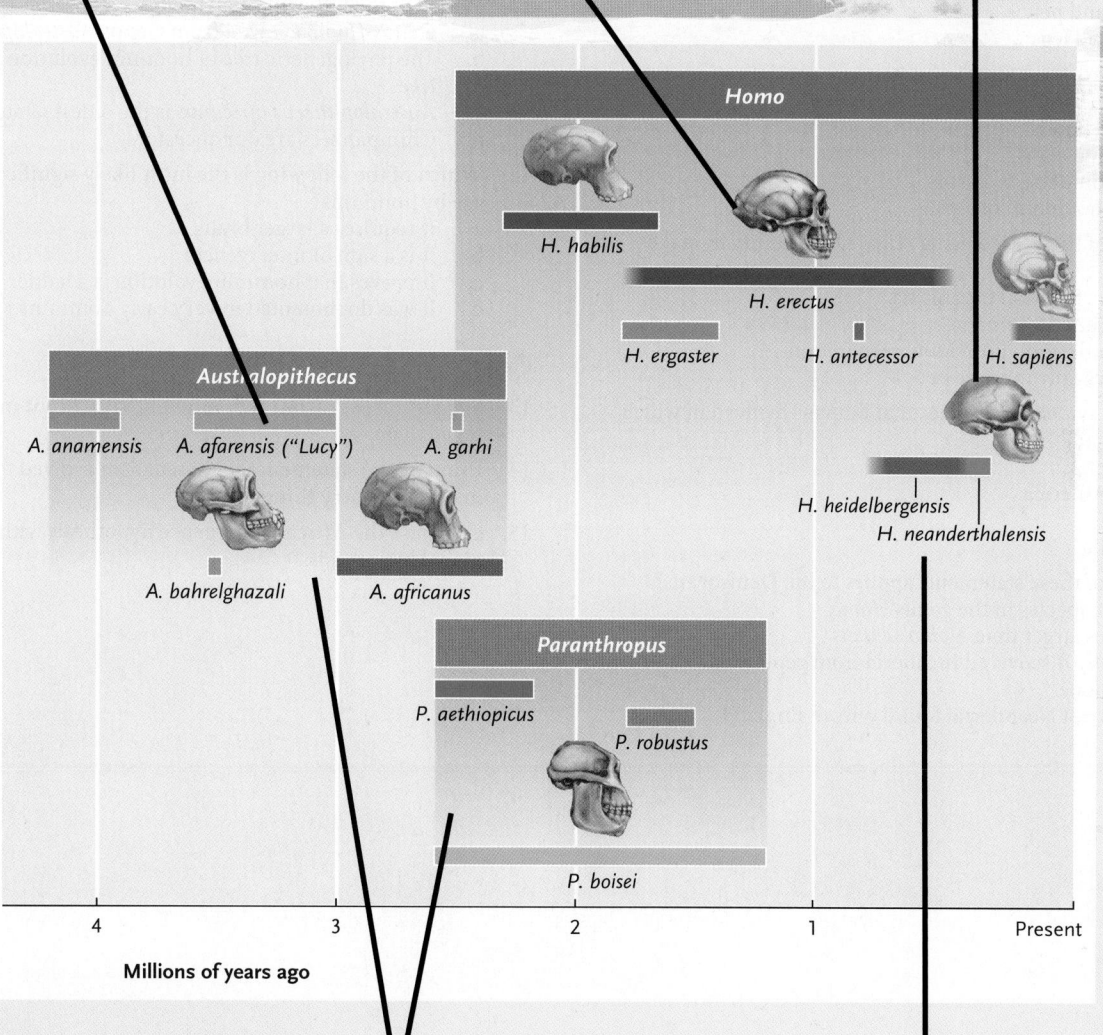

Most of the hominins that lived in eastern and southern Africa from 1 to 6 mya are classified in the genera *Australopithecus* and *Paranthropus*. They resembled apes, with large faces, protruding jaws, and small skulls and brains.

Species in the genus Homo have hands quite distinct from apes, giving them the ability to use grips that allow manipulative skills and the crafting of precise tools.

# SELF-TEST QUESTIONS

## Recall/Understand

1. Which of these statements can be applied to Neandertals (*Homo neanderthalensis*)?
   a. They did not occur in the same places and times as *Homo sapiens*.
   b. They did not interbreed with *Homo sapiens*.
   c. They were not behaviourally distinct from *Homo sapiens*.
   d. They were extinct by 20 000 years ago.

2. Which of these factors applies to the family Hominidae?
   a. excludes gorillas and chimps
   b. first appear in the fossil record about 1 mya
   c. includes species in the genera *Homo, Australopithecus,* and *Paranthropus*
   d. includes only species in the genus *Homo*

3. In hominids, bipedalism involves specializations of which of these structures?
   a. feet and legs
   b. knees and ankles
   c. ankles and pelvis
   d. pelvis and legs

4. Which of these structures in humans are specializations for throwing?
   a. feet and hands
   b. hands and arms
   c. feet, shoulders, and arms
   d. waist, shoulders, and arms

5. Which one of these statements refers to the ability to make friends?
   a. It occurs in social organisms.
   b. It is unique to humans.
   c. It depends upon individual recognition.
   d. It occurs only in some people.

6. A variety of evidence indicates that humans evolved in which place?
   a. Africa
   b. South America
   c. Europe
   d. Australia

7. Which one of these statements applies to the Denisovans?
   a. another species in the genus *Homo*
   b. a species larger than *Homo sapiens*
   c. originally discovered in Siberia from genetic analysis of one finger bone
   d. a variety of Neandertal found only in England

8. Which of the following species of fossil hominin is the oldest?
   a. *Homo neanderthalensis*
   b. *Homo sapiens*
   c. *Ardipithecus ramidus*
   d. *Australopithecus sediba*

9. When did hominins move out of Africa?
   a. 3 million years ago
   b. 2 million years ago
   c. 1.5 million years ago
   d. 100 thousand years ago

## Apply/Analyze

10. Which of these statements describes genetic similarity among humans, chimps, gorillas, and orangutans?
    a. They all belong to the same species.
    b. They share a relatively recent common ancestor.
    c. They are evidence of creation.
    d. They can interbreed and produce fertile offspring.

11. Which of the following statements is a misconception?
    a. Genus *Homo* evolved from Genus *Australopithecus*.
    b. The phylogenetic tree of hominin evolution is a very bushy tree.
    c. *Australopithecus africanus* is the oldest of australopiths.
    d. Chimpanzees are our ancestors.

12. Which of the following is the most likely significance of tool usage by hominins?
    a. It requires a larger brain.
    b. It is a sign of intelligence.
    c. It proves that hominin evolution is a ladder in progress.
    d. It was documented in very early hominins.

## Create/Evaluate

13. Suggest three reasons that might be significant in evolving of bipedalism.

14. Evaluate the statement that bipedalism evolved to free the hands in order to carry things.

15. Compare the African emergence hypothesis with the multiregional hypothesis.

# Chapter Roadmap

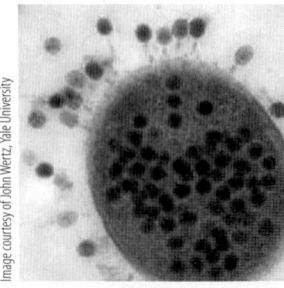

## Defining Life and Its Origins

Earth is 4.6 billion years old and there is evidence that life may have developed within the first 600 million years. In this chapter we discuss what the conditions were like on early Earth that led to the development of life as well as the major events that occurred after. You will realize that there are two fundamental questions of biology that remain hard to answer: what is life actually, and how did life evolve?

### 21.1 What Is Life?

All forms of life possess seven key characteristics.

### 21.2 The Chemical Origins of Life

Experiments have shown that the major biological molecules can be synthesized in the laboratory.

### 21.3 From Macromolecules to Life

Having the molecules required for life is one thing, but how life actually got started remains largely a mystery.

### 21.4 Evidence of the Earliest Life

The earliest forms of life were almost certainly heterotrophic prokaryotic cells; we just don't know for sure.

Many molecules move across membranes by diffusion: from high to low concentration.

**From Chapter 6**

### 21.5 Eukaryotes and the Rise of Multicellularity

The development of oxygenic photosynthesis followed by aerobic respiration was critical to the development of the eukaryotic cell.

**From Chapter 2**

### 21.6 The Fossil Record

The study of fossils has provided a wealth of information about the evolution of life, but the fossil record is incomplete.

### 21.7 The Tree of Life

The three domains of life have the same evolutionary origin and have shared genetic information.

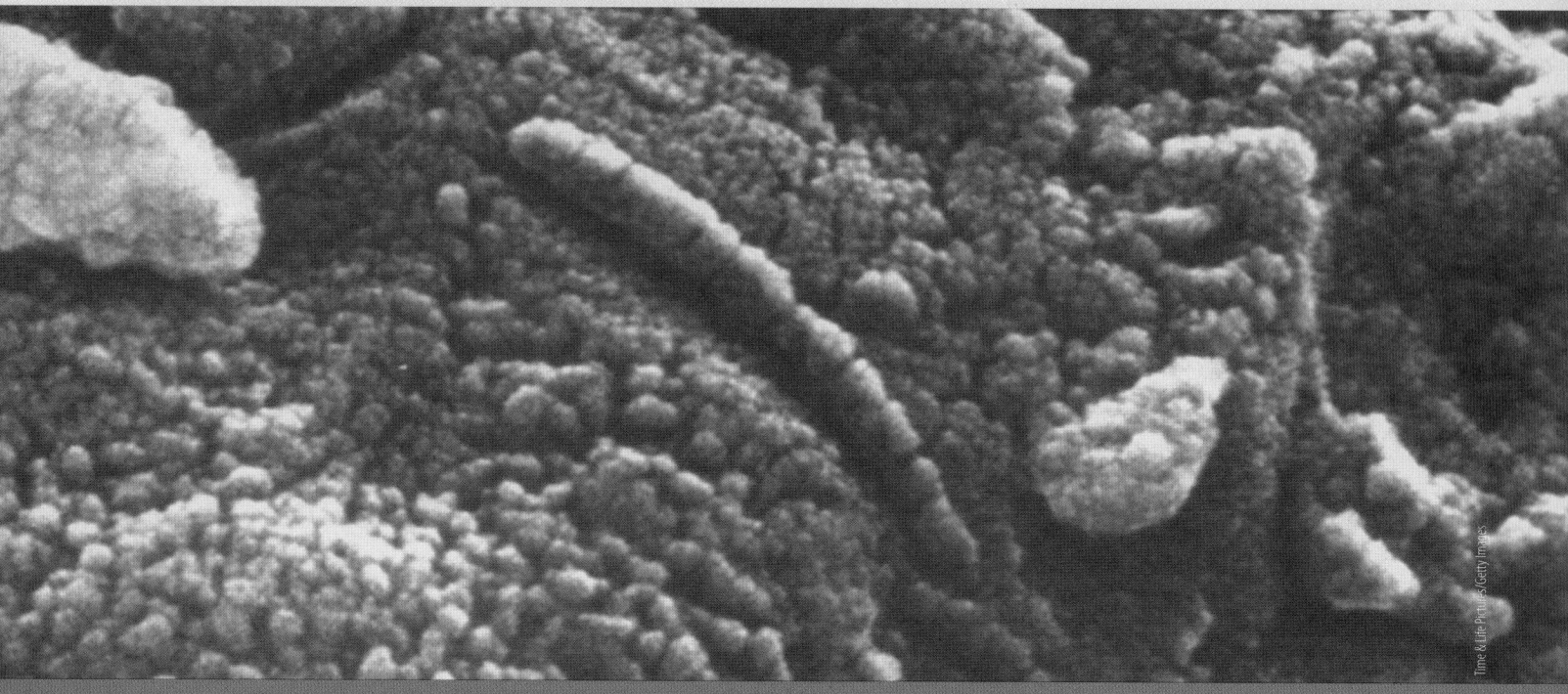

**Scanning electron microscope image of a portion of the meteorite ALH84001.** The elongate structure in the centre may be a fossilized microorganism.

# Defining Life and Its Origins

# 21

**Why it matters . . .**   In 1984, a group of scientists in the Antarctic discovered a 1.9 kg meteorite that they catalogued as ALH84001. Initial studies of the meteorite showed that it was about 4.5 billion years old, which is about the same age as the solar system. Its chemical composition indicated that it had originated from Mars and had impacted Earth approximately 13 000 years ago. The meteorite garnered headlines around the world in 1996 when an article was published in the prestigious journal *Science* with evidence that ALH84001 contained distinct evidence that life had at one time existed on Mars.

Chemical analysis showed that, when on Mars, ALH84001 had at one time been fractured and subsequently infiltrated by liquid water. Using scanning electron microscopy, the coauthors of the article observed very small, elliptical, ropelike, and tubular structures in the fractured surfaces of ALH84001 that look very similar to fossilized prokaryotic cells. Furthermore, the scientists found microscopic mineral "globules" that bear strong resemblance to mineral alterations caused by primitive cells on Earth.

The analysis of meteorites for microfossils continues and remains controversial. In 2011, an article published in the *Journal of Cosmology* provided additional evidence of bacteria-like fossils within meteorites. Using sophisticated electron microscopy techniques and chemical analysis on three freshly fractured carbonaceous meteorites, data are presented in the article that show the presence of filaments that are strikingly similar in shape to cyanobacteria, a dominant form of photosynthetic bacteria on Earth. The difficulty of unequivocally assigning these structures as remnants of ancient life will continue to make the conclusions of such analyses controversial.

In this chapter, we explore some of the most basic of biological questions: What is life and how did life evolve? After introducing the fundamental characteristics that all organisms share, we work through a discussion of the origins of life. Starting with how biologically important molecules could have been synthesized in the absence of life, we move through hypotheses regarding how the very first cells may have developed, and consider how the molecules that are central to information transfer (DNA, RNA, protein) may have evolved. A central question to evolution of life that we discuss is about what gave rise to eukaryotic organisms. The importance and limitations of the fossil record in addressing questions about the evolution of life are considered. The chapter closes with a discussion of how the molecular tool of DNA sequencing has been used to compare organisms and has allowed scientists to develop a comprehensive tree of life.

## 21.1  What Is Life?

All life is composed of cells—the fundamental unit of all life. But what is life? How can we define it? Picture a frog sitting on a rock, slowly shifting its head to follow the movements of insects flying nearby **(Figure 21.1)**. You know instinctively that the frog is alive and the rock is not. But if you examine both at the atomic level, you will find that the difference between them is lost. The types of elements and atoms found in living things are also found in non-living forms of matter. As well, living cells obey the same fundamental laws of physics and chemistry as the **abiotic** (non-living) world. For example, the biochemical reactions that take place within living cells, although remarkable, are only modifications of chemical reactions that occur outside cells.

### 21.1a  Seven Characteristics Shared by All Life Forms

Although life seems relatively easy to recognize, it is not easy to define using a single sentence, or even two. Life is defined most effectively by a list of attributes that all forms of life possess. As detailed in **Figure 21.2**, all life displays order, harnesses and utilizes energy, reproduces, responds to stimuli, exhibits homeostasis, grows and develops, and evolves.

There are a small number of biological systems that straddle the line between the **biotic** and the abiotic worlds. The best

example of this is a virus **(Figure 21.3)**. Viruses are very small infectious agents that you will learn more about in Chapter 22. They display many of the properties of life, including the ability to reproduce and evolve over time. However, the characteristics of life that a virus has are based on its ability to infect cells. For example, although viruses contain nucleic acids (DNA and RNA), they lack the cellular machinery and metabolism to use that genetic information to synthesize their own proteins. To make proteins, they have to infect living cells and essentially hijack their translational machinery and metabolism to reproduce. You can find other entities that display some, but not all of life's properties that are not alive. Computer programs, for example, have as many characteristics of life as do viruses. For this reason, most scientists do not consider viruses to be alive.

### 21.1b  The Characteristics of Life Are Emergent

Each of the characteristics of life depicted in Figure 21.2 reflects a remarkable complexity resulting from a hierarchy of interactions that begins with atoms and progresses through molecules to macromolecules and cells. Depending upon the organism, this hierarchy may continue upward in complexity and include organelles, tissues, and organs. The seven properties of life shown in Figure 21.2 are a result of emergent properties because they come about, or emerge, from many simpler interactions that, in themselves, do not have the properties found at the higher levels. For example, the ability to harness and utilize energy is not a property of molecules or proteins or biological membranes in isolation; rather, the ability emerges from the interactions of all three of these as part of a metabolic process. In this way, not only is the structural or functional complexity of living systems more than the sum of the parts, but it is fundamentally different.

A classic example that illustrates the concept of emergence is a type of termite nest called a *cathedral* **(Figure 21.4)**. These elegantly complex structures, most common in Australia, can grow to over 3 m tall and are the product of the activities of thousands of termites. Remarkably, there is no master plan that is followed or "queen" that gives instructions. Termites build up the mound cell by cell, based on local conditions, totally unaware of the overall structure that emerges.

#### STUDY BREAK QUESTIONS

1. List the seven fundamental characteristics common to all life.
2. What does it mean that life displays emergent properties?

## 21.2  The Chemical Origins of Life

You may recall, as discussed in Chapter 2, that one of the tenets of the cell theory states that cells arise only from the growth and division of preexisting cells. This tenet has probably been true

**FIGURE 21.1  Red-eyed tree frog on a rock**

Sacha Burkard/Shutterstock.com

**a. Display order:** All forms of life, including this flower, are arranged in a highly ordered manner, with the cell being the fundamental unit that exhibits all properties of life.

harmeet/StockXchng

**e. Exhibit homeostasis:** Organisms are able to regulate their internal environment such that conditions remain relatively constant. Sweating is one way in which the human body attempts to remove heat and thereby maintain a constant temperature.

© Tim Pannell/CORBIS

**b. Harness and utilize energy:** Like this hummingbird, all forms of life acquire energy from the environment and use it to maintain their highly ordered state.

Steve Byland/Shutterstock.com

**f. Grow and develop:** All organisms increase their size by increasing the size and/or number of cells. Many organisms also change over time.

Karin Duthie/Alamy

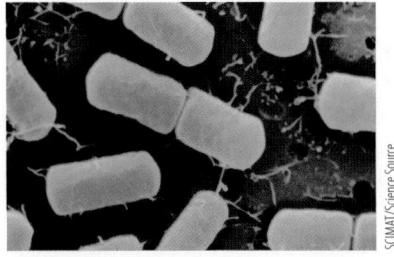

**c. Reproduce:** All organisms have the ability to make more of their own kind. Here, some of the bacteria have just divided into two daughter cells.

SCIMAT/Science Source

**g. Evolve:** Populations of living organisms change over the course of generations to become better adapted to their environment. The snowy owl illustrates this perfectly.

Stanislav Duben/Shutterstock.com

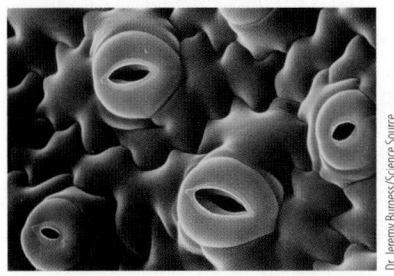

**d. Respond to stimuli:** Organisms can make adjustments to their structure, function, and behaviour in response to changes to the external environment. A plant can adjust the size of the pores (stomata) on the surface of its leaves to regulate gas exchange.

Dr. Jeremy Burgess/Science Source

**FIGURE 21.2 The seven characteristics of life**

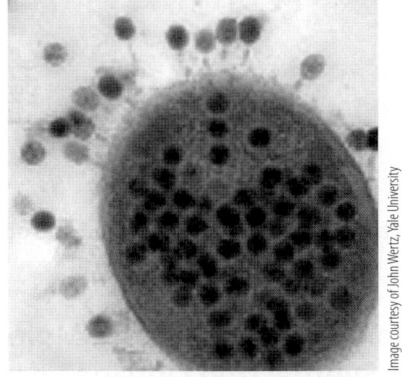

Image courtesy of John Wertz, Yale University

**FIGURE 21.3 Bacteriophage infecting a bacterium.** Notice the bacteriophages on the cell surface as well as inside the bacterium. A bacteriophage is a type of virus, and most scientists do not consider viruses to be alive.

for hundreds of millions of years, yet there must have been a time when this was not the case. There must have been a time when no cells existed, when there was no life. It is thought that, over the course of hundreds of millions of years, cells with the characteristics of life arose out of a mixture of molecules that existed on primordial Earth. In this section we discuss the formation of the solar system and present hypotheses for how biologically important molecules could have been synthesized on early Earth in the absence of life.

## 21.2a Earth Is 4.6 Billion Years Old

Earth was formed approximately 4.6 billion years ago. To give us some sense of just how long 4.6 billion years is, as well as the relative timing of some major events in the history of life on Earth, **Figure 21.5** condenses the entire history of Earth into a unit of time that we are more familiar with: one year. With 4.6 billion years condensed into a single year, each day represents an interval of 12.6 million years!

CHAPTER 21 DEFINING LIFE AND ITS ORIGINS | **495**

**FIGURE 21.4  A termite cathedral.** The sophisticated structure of a termite nest emerges from the simple work of thousands of individual termites. In a similar way, the complex properties of life emerge from much simpler molecular interactions.

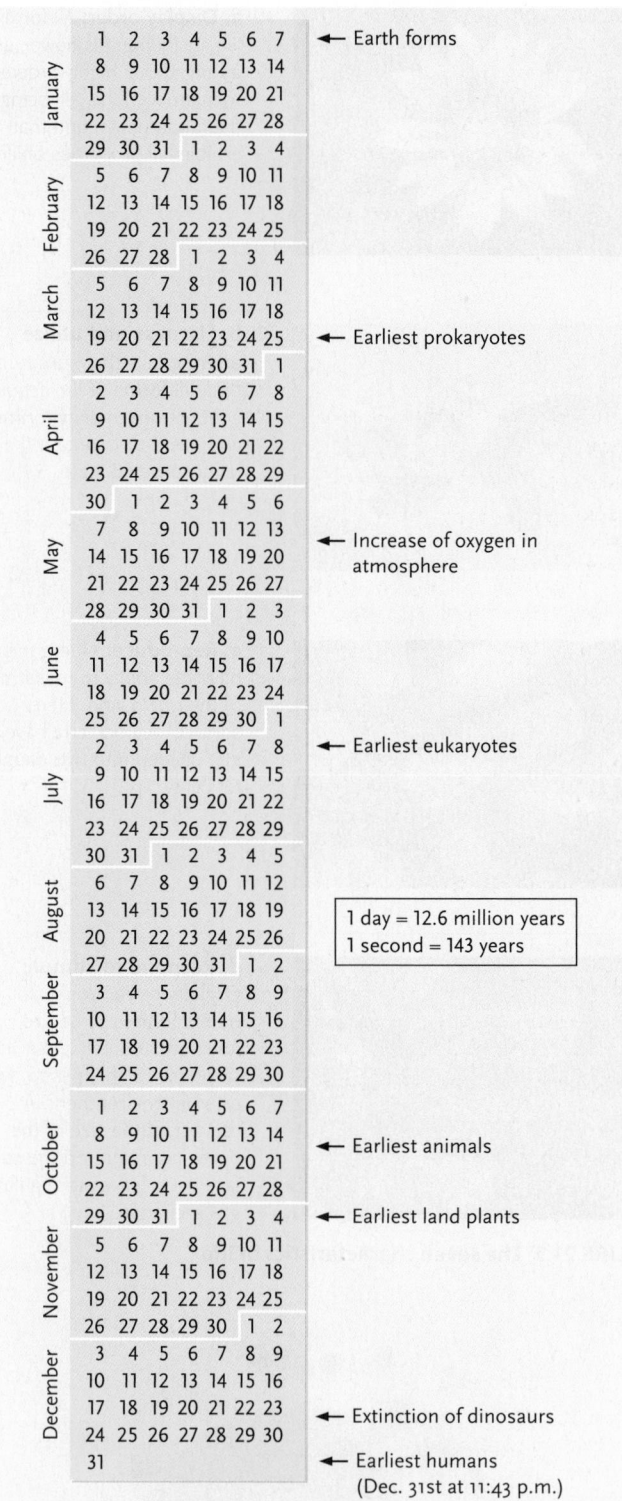

| | | | | | | | |
|---|---|---|---|---|---|---|---|
| | 1 | 2 | 3 | 4 | 5 | 6 | 7 | ← Earth forms |

**FIGURE 21.5  The history of Earth condensed into one year**

Using our condensed version of the history of Earth, we set the date of the formation of Earth as January 1 at 12:00 a.m. We will discuss this in detail later, but based on chemical evidence, life may have started as early as 4.0 billion years ago. This translates to mid-March in our one-year calendar. The first clear fossil evidence of prokaryotic cells occurs in late March, or about 3.5 billion years ago. Fossil evidence of eukaryotes has been dated to about 2 billion years ago, which is not until early July using our one-year analogy. Perhaps surprisingly, animals do not make an appearance until mid-October (about 525 million years ago), and land plants until the following month. The extinction of dinosaurs, which was completed by about 65 million years ago, does not occur until late December. What about humans? We may think humans, *Homo sapiens,* have been around a long time, but relative to other forms of life, the roughly 150 thousand years that modern humans have existed is a very short period of time—a blip on our time scale. Using our year analogy, modern humans have existed only since December 31, more precisely, since December 31 at 11:43 p.m.!

## 21.2b  Biologically Important Molecules Can Be Synthesized Outside Living Cells

All forms of life are composed of four classes of essential macromolecules: nucleic acids, proteins, lipids, and polysaccharides (see *The Purple Pages* for an overview of these molecules).

These molecules are constantly being synthesized within cells by various biochemical pathways and metabolic processes. But if these molecules are an absolute requirement for life, then simple forms of these molecules must have been produced early on in the absence of life, in what is referred to as *abiotic synthesis*. There are three major hypotheses proposed to explain how these macromolecules were produced by abiotic processes: reducing atmosphere, deep-sea vents, and extraterrestrial origins.

## HYPOTHESIS 1: REDUCING ATMOSPHERE

The early atmosphere of about 4 billion years ago was vastly different from the one today. The primordial atmosphere probably contained an abundance of water vapour from the evaporation of water at the surface, as well as large quantities of hydrogen ($H_2$), carbon dioxide ($CO_2$), ammonia ($NH_3$), and methane ($CH_4$). There was an almost complete absence of oxygen ($O_2$). In the 1920s, two scientists, Aleksandr Oparin and John Haldane, independently proposed that organic molecules, essential to the formation of life, could have formed in the atmosphere of primordial Earth. A critical aspect of what is known as the *Oparin–Haldane hypothesis* is that the early atmosphere was a *reducing atmosphere* because of the presence of large concentrations of molecules such as hydrogen, methane, and ammonia. These molecules contain an abundance of electrons and hydrogen, and they would have entered into reactions with one another that would have yielded larger and more complex organic molecules.

In comparison to the proposed reducing atmosphere of primordial Earth, today's atmosphere is classified as an *oxidizing atmosphere*. The presence of high levels of oxygen prevents complex, electron-rich molecules from being formed because oxygen is a particularly strong oxidizing molecule and would itself accept the electrons from organic molecules and be reduced to water. Apart from allowing for the buildup of electron-rich molecules, the lack of oxygen in the primordial atmosphere also meant that there was no ozone ($O_3$) layer, which only developed after oxygen levels in the atmosphere began to increase. Both Oparin and Haldane hypothesized that, without the ozone layer, energetic ultraviolet light was able to reach the lower atmosphere and, along with abundant lightning, provided the energy needed to drive the formation of biologically important molecules.

Experimental evidence in support of the Oparin–Haldane hypothesis came in 1953 when Stanley Miller, a graduate student of Harold Urey's at the University of Chicago, created a laboratory simulation of the reducing atmosphere believed to have existed on early Earth. Miller placed components of a reducing atmosphere—hydrogen, methane, ammonia, and water vapour—in a closed apparatus and exposed the gases to an energy source in the form of continuously sparking electrodes (**Figure 21.6**). Water vapour was added to the "atmosphere" in one part of the apparatus and subsequently condensed back into water by cooling in another part. After running the experiment for one week, Miller found a large assortment of organic compounds, including urea; amino acids; and lactic, formic, and acetic acids after condensing the atmosphere into a liquid. In fact, as much as 15% of the carbon that was originally in the methane at the start of the experiment ended up in molecules that are common in living organisms.

Other chemicals have been tested in the Miller–Urey apparatus, including hydrogen cyanide (HCN) and formaldehyde ($CH_2O$), which are considered to have been among the substances formed in the primitive atmosphere. When cyanide and formaldehyde were added to the simulated primitive atmosphere in Miller's apparatus, all the building blocks of complex biological molecules were produced: amino acids; fatty acids; the **purine** and **pyrimidine** components of nucleic acids; sugars such as glyceraldehyde, ribose, glucose, and fructose; and phospholipids, which form the lipid bilayers of biological membranes.

Over the years since the Miller–Urey experiment was first conducted, considerable debate has developed in the scientific community over whether the atmosphere of primitive Earth contained enough methane and ammonia to be considered reducing. Some geologists have suggested that, based on the analysis of volcanic activity, primitive Earth was probably somewhat less reactive—neither reducing nor oxidizing—with molecules including nitrogen gases ($N_2$), carbon monoxide (CO), and carbon dioxide ($CO_2$) the most dominant. Even with this composition, scientists have been able to successfully synthesize the same crucial building blocks of life in the laboratory. Regardless of the actual composition of the atmosphere on

**~4.5 billion years ago**

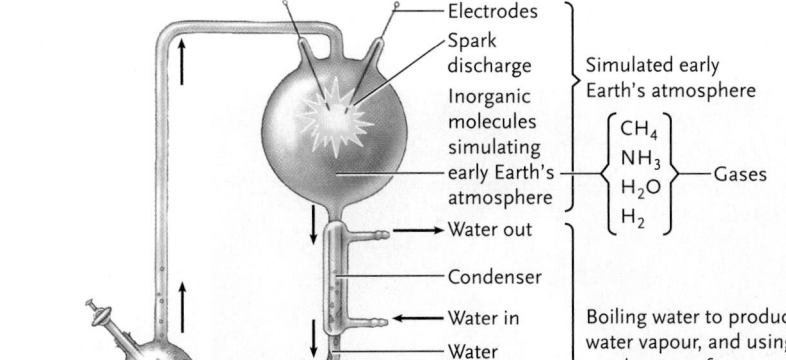

FIGURE 21.6 **The Miller–Urey experiment.** Using this apparatus, Stanley Miller, a graduate student, demonstrated that organic molecules can be synthesized under conditions simulating primordial Earth.

primordial Earth, the significance of the Miller–Urey experiment cannot be overstated. It was the first experiment to demonstrate the abiotic formation of molecules critical to life, such as amino acids, nucleotides, and simple sugars, and it showed that they could be produced relatively easily. At the time, this remarkable finding laid the groundwork for further research into the origins of life.

**HYPOTHESIS 2: DEEP-SEA VENTS** Apart from originating in the atmosphere, an alternative hypothesis maintains that the complex organic molecules necessary for life could have originated on the ocean floor at the site of deep-sea (hydrothermal) vents. These cracks are found around the globe near sites of volcanic or tectonic activity and release superheated, nutrient-rich water at temperatures in excess of 300°C, as well as reduced molecules, including methane, ammonia, and hydrogen sulfide ($H_2S$; **Figure 21.7**). Today, the areas around these vents support a remarkable diversity of life. Many of these life forms are of tremendous scientific interest because of their ability to thrive in an environment that is characterized by extreme pressure and the total absence of light.

**HYPOTHESIS 3: EXTRATERRESTRIAL ORIGINS** It is entirely possible that the key organic molecules required for life to begin came from space. Each year more than 500 meteorites impact Earth, many of which belong to the class called *carbonaceous chondrites*, which are particularly rich in organic molecules. One of the most famous is the Murchison meteorite that landed in Murchison, Victoria, Australia, in 1969 **(Figure 21.8)**. Analysis of the Murchison meteorite showed that it contains an assortment of biologically important molecules, including a range of amino acids such as glycine, glutamic acid, and alanine, as well as purines and pyrimidines. Even if our life did not arise from extraterrestrial sources, the presence of these molecules is evidence that abiotic production of life's chemicals is possible.

**FIGURE 21.7 Deep-sea vent.** Researchers from the Woods Hole Oceanographic Institute watch from inside the submersible Alvin as a "black smoker" chimney erupts from a seafloor vent. The regions surrounding these vents have been found to be teeming with a diversity of life.

**FIGURE 21.8 The Murchison meteorite.** Many meteorites have been shown to contain a range of biologically important molecules, including a number of amino acids.

## 21.2c Life Requires the Synthesis of Polymers

Primordial Earth contained very little oxygen and, because of this, complex organic molecules could have existed for much longer than would be possible in today's oxygen-rich world. Even if they did accumulate on early Earth, molecules such as amino acids and nucleotides are **monomers**, which are simpler and easier to synthesize than the key chemical components of life, such as nucleic acids and proteins, which are polymers (macromolecules formed from the bonding together of individual monomers). Nucleic acids are polymers of nucleotides, proteins are polymers of amino acids, and polysaccharides (starch, cellulose) are polymers of simple sugars. Polymers are synthesized by dehydration synthesis, which is discussed in *The Purple Pages*.

Today, the synthesis of proteins and nucleic acids requires protein-based catalysts called *enzymes*, and results in macromolecules that often consist of hundreds to many thousands of monomers linked together. So how do you make the polymers that are required for life without sophisticated enzymes? The basis of a working hypothesis to address this question must be built from the supposition that the very earliest forms of life must have been very simple, far simpler than a modern bacterium, for example. Scientists hypothesize that a polymer that consists of even 10–50 monomers may have been of sufficient length to impart a specific function (like a protein) or store sufficient information (like a nucleic acid) to make their formation advantageous to an organism. It is, however, doubtful that polymerization could have occurred in the aqueous environment of early Earth, as it would be very rare for monomers to interact precisely enough with one another to polymerize. It is more likely that solid surfaces, especially clays, could have provided the type of environment necessary for polymerization to occur **(Figure 21.9)**. Clays consist of very

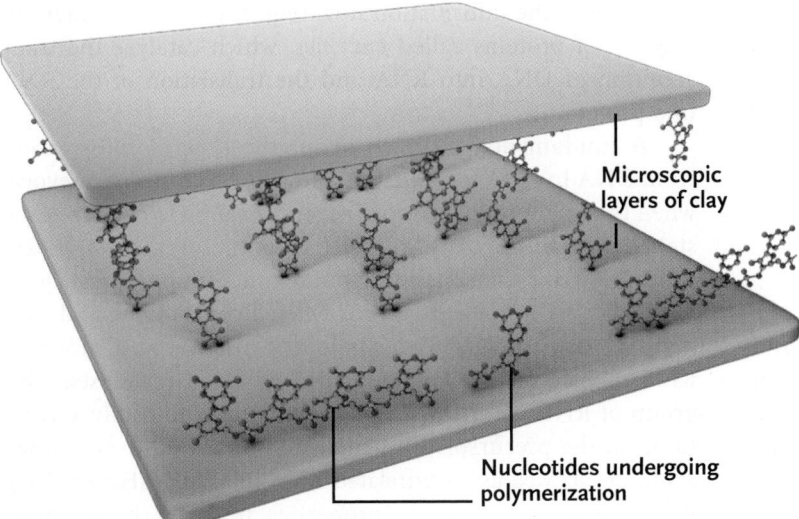

**FIGURE 21.9 Clay surfaces catalyze polymerization.** The charged, microscopic, layered structure of clay allows for the formation of relatively short polymers of proteins and nucleic acids.

Labels: Microscopic layers of clay; Nucleotides undergoing polymerization

Andrew Swift

thin layers of minerals separated by layers of water only a few nanometres thick. The layered structure of clay is also charged, allowing for molecular adhesion forces to bring monomers together in precise orientations that could more readily lead to polymer formation. Clays can also store the potential energy that may have been used for energy-requiring polymerization reactions. This *clay hypothesis* is supported by laboratory experiments that demonstrate that the formation of short nucleic acid chains and polypeptides can be synthesized on a clay surface.

**STUDY BREAK QUESTIONS**

1. For understanding the origins of life, what was the significance of the Miller–Urey experiment?
2. What is the difference between a reducing atmosphere and an oxidizing atmosphere?

## 21.3 From Macromolecules to Life

In the previous section, we discussed how processes present on early Earth could have generated macromolecules crucial to the development of life. However, if we are to develop a comprehensive model for the origin of life, we need to explain the evolution of three key attributes of a modern cell: (1) a membrane-defined compartment, the cell; (2) a system to store genetic information and use it to guide the synthesis of specific proteins; and (3) energy-transforming pathways to bring in energy from the surroundings and harness it to sustain life. In this section, we discuss possible scenarios for the

evolution of these key attributes and consider a number of hypotheses, some of which are supported by laboratory experiments.

### 21.3a Lipid Spheres May Have Led to the Development of Cells

A critical step along the path to life is the formation of a membrane-defined compartment. Such a compartment would allow for primitive metabolic reactions to take place in an environment that is distinctly different than the external surroundings; the concentration of key molecules could be higher, and greater complexity could be maintained in a closed space. **Protobiont** is the term given to a group of abiotically produced organic molecules that are surrounded by a membrane or membranelike structure. Laboratory experiments have shown that protobionts could have formed spontaneously (i.e., without any input of energy), given the conditions on primordial Earth. An early type of protobiont could have been similar to a liposome, which is a lipid vesicle in which the lipid molecules form a bilayer very similar to a cell membrane **(Figure 21.10)**. Liposomes can easily be made in the laboratory and are **selectively permeable**, allowing only some molecules to move in and out. As well, liposomes can swell and contract depending on the osmotic conditions of their environment.

Recent research from the laboratory of Jack Szostak at Harvard University has shown that the presence of clay not only catalyzes the polymerization of nucleic acids but also accelerates the formation of lipid vesicles. As well, clay particles often become encapsulated in these vesicles, which would provide catalytically active surfaces within membrane vesicles upon which key reactions could take place. Researchers continue to

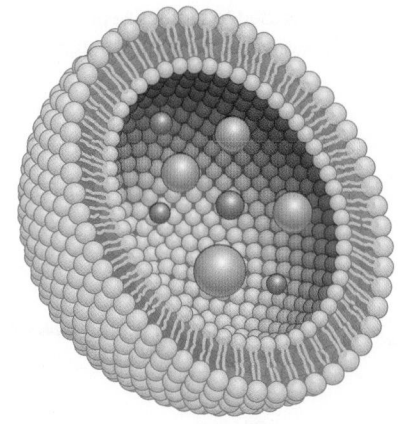

a.

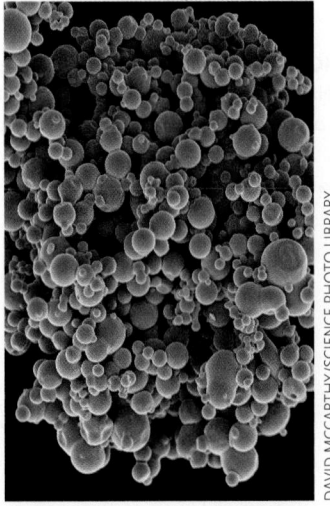

b.

DAVID MCCARTHY/SCIENCE PHOTO LIBRARY

**FIGURE 21.10 Liposome. (a)** An artist's rendition of a liposome, which is composed of a lipid bilayer. Liposomes can assemble spontaneously under simulated primordial conditions. **(b)** SEM image of lipid vesicles assembled from phospholipids in the laboratory

experiment with producing different types of protobionts in the laboratory as a step toward understanding the origins of the first living cell. Present-day thinking is that a lipid membrane system must have evolved simultaneously with a genetic information system (see below).

## 21.3b RNA Can Carry Information and Catalyze Reactions

As discussed in earlier chapters, DNA is the molecule that provides every cell with the genetic instructions necessary to function. Recall as well that the information in DNA is copied into RNA, which directs protein synthesis on ribosomes. Even the simplest prokaryotic cell contains thousands of proteins, each coded by a unique DNA sequence, a gene. The flow of information from DNA to RNA to protein is common to all forms of life and is referred to as the *central dogma* **(Figure 21.11)**.

Each step of the information flow requires the involvement of a group of proteins called *enzymes*, which catalyze the transcription of DNA into RNA and the translation of the RNA into protein.

A fundamental question about the flow of information from DNA to RNA to protein is: How did such a system evolve when the final products, proteins, are required to catalyze each step (e.g., transcription, translation) of the process? A breakthrough in our understanding of how such a system may have evolved came in the early 1980s when Thomas Cech and Sydney Altman, working independently, discovered a group of RNA molecules that could themselves act as catalysts. This group of RNA catalysts, called **ribozymes**, can catalyze reactions on the precursor RNA molecules that lead to their own synthesis, as well as on unrelated RNA molecules **(Figure 21.12)**. Ribozymes have catalytic properties because these single-stranded molecules can fold into very specific shapes based on intramolecular hydrogen bonding or base pairing. The fact that specificity in folding imparts specificity in function is very common to proteins, especially enzymes, where precise three-dimensional shape is critical for reacting with substrate molecules. Protein folding is discussed in more detail in *The Purple Pages*.

The discovery of ribozymes revolutionized thinking about the origin of life. Instead of the contemporary system that requires all three molecules—DNA, RNA, and protein—early life may have existed in an "RNA world," where a single type of molecule, RNA, could serve as a carrier of information (due to its nucleotide sequence) and a structural/functional molecule similar to a protein (due to its ability to form unique three-dimensional shapes). Before the discovery of ribozymes, enzymes were the only known biological catalysts. For their remarkable discovery, Sydney Altman and Thomas Cech shared the Nobel Prize in Chemistry in 1989.

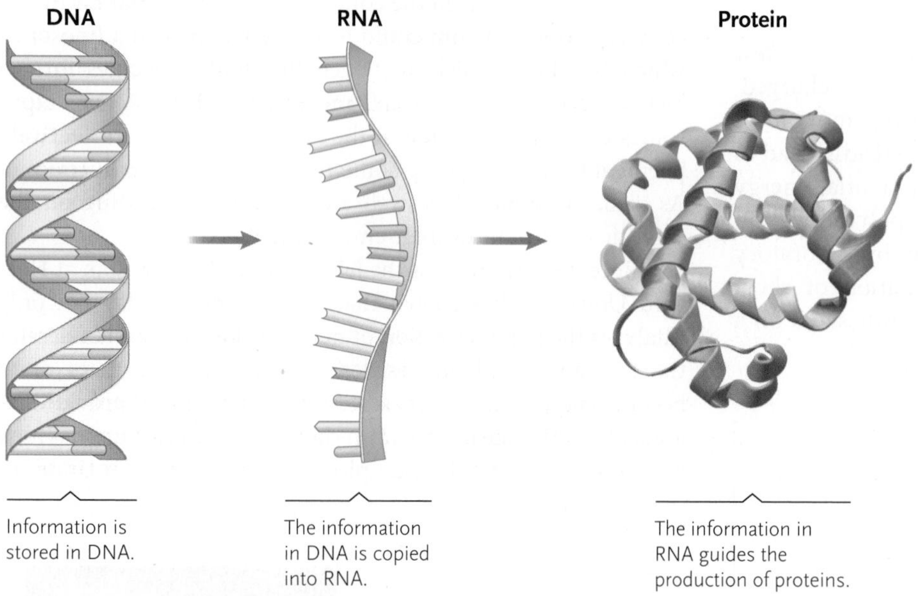

**DNA**  **RNA**  **Protein**

Information is stored in DNA.

The information in DNA is copied into RNA.

The information in RNA guides the production of proteins.

**FIGURE 21.11 The central dogma.** Information in DNA is used to synthesize proteins through an RNA intermediate. How did such a system evolve when the product, proteins, is required in modern-day cells to catalyze each step?

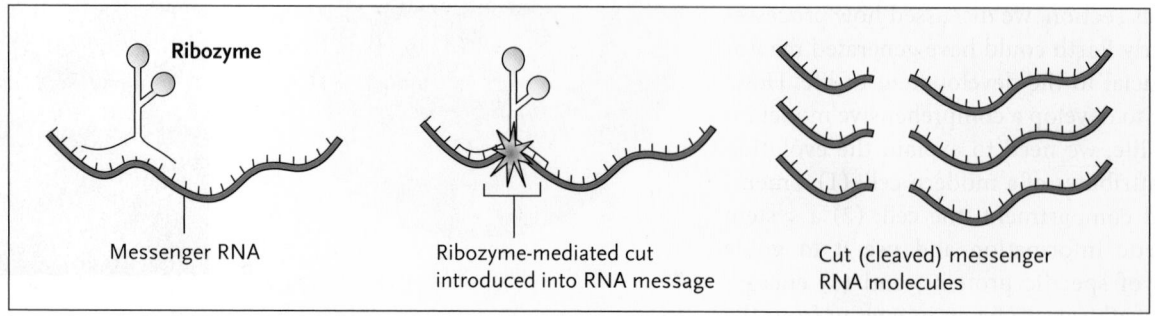

Messenger RNA

Ribozyme-mediated cut introduced into RNA message

Cut (cleaved) messenger RNA molecules

**FIGURE 21.12 Ribozyme.** An example of a ribozyme binding to an RNA molecule and catalyzing its breakage. Within a modern-day cell, such reactions may help control gene expression by altering the abundance of functional messenger RNA (mRNA) molecules.

## 21.3c RNA Is Replaced by DNA for Information Storage and Proteins for Catalysis

If life developed in an RNA world, where RNA served as both an information carrier and a catalyst, why is it that, in all contemporary organisms, genetic information is stored in DNA, and why do enzymes (proteins) catalyze the vast majority of biological reactions? The simple answer is that they do the respective jobs of information storage (DNA) and catalysis (protein) far better than RNA does by itself; thus, the evolution of these molecules would have given organisms that had them a distinct advantage over others that relied solely on RNA.

A possible scenario for the development of today's system of information transfer is shown in **Figure 21.13**. The first cells may have contained only RNA, which was self-replicating and could catalyze a small number of reactions critical for survival. It is hypothesized that a small population of RNA molecules then evolved that could catalyze the formation of very short proteins before the development of ribosomes. Recall that, in contemporary organisms, the ribosome is required for protein synthesis. It is interesting to note that the ribosome, which plays a key role as an intermediate between RNA and protein, is composed of about two-thirds RNA and one-third protein. In fact, it is the RNA component of the ribosome, and not the protein, that actually catalyzes the incorporation of amino acids onto a growing peptide chain. So the ribosome can be considered a type of ribozyme.

Cells that evolved the ability to use the information present in RNA to direct the synthesis of even small proteins would be at a tremendous advantage because proteins are far more versatile than RNA molecules for three reasons. First, the catalytic power of most enzymes is much greater than that of a ribozyme. A typical enzyme can catalyze the same reaction using a pool of substrate molecules many thousands of times a second. By comparison, the rate of catalysis of most ribozymes is one-tenth to one-hundredth that of enzymes. Second, while the number of ribozymes is very small, a typical cell synthesizes a huge array of different proteins. Twenty different kinds of amino acids, in different arrangements, can be incorporated into a protein, whereas an RNA molecule is composed of different combinations of only four nucleotides. Third, amino acids can interact chemically with each other in bonding arrangements not possible between nucleotides. For these reasons, proteins are the dominant structural and functional molecule of a modern cell.

Continuing with the possible scenario shown in Figure 21.13, the evolution of DNA would have followed that of proteins. Compared with RNA, molecules of DNA are more structurally complex. Not only is DNA double stranded, but it also contains the sugar deoxyribose, which is more difficult to synthesize than the ribose found in molecules of RNA. A possible sequence begins with DNA nucleotides being produced by random removal of an oxygen atom from the ribose subunits of RNA nucleotides. At some point, the DNA nucleotides paired with the RNA informational molecules and were assembled into complementary copies of the RNA sequences. Some modern-day viruses carry out this RNA-to-DNA reaction using the enzyme reverse transcriptase (see Chapter 22). Once the DNA copies were made, selection may have favoured DNA, as it is a much better way to store information than RNA, for three main reasons:

- Each strand of DNA is chemically more stable, and less likely to degrade, than a strand of RNA.
- The base uracil found in RNA is not found in DNA; it has been replaced by thymine. This may be because the conversion of cytosine to uracil is a common mutation in DNA. By utilizing thymine in DNA, any uracil is easily recognized as a damaged cytosine that needs to be repaired.
- DNA is double stranded, so in the case of a mutation to one of the strands, the information contained on the complementary strand can be used to correctly repair the damaged strand.

The stability of DNA is illustrated by the fact that intact DNA can be successfully extracted from tissues that are many thousands of years old. The well-known novel and the movie *Jurassic Park* are based on this demonstrated ability. By comparison, RNA needs to be isolated quickly, even from freshly isolated cells, using a strict protocol to prevent its degradation.

## 21.3d The Evolution of Biological Energy Sources

Life has an absolute requirement for energy. As open systems, all forms of life are constantly bringing in energy and using it to maintain their organized structure and to drive biosynthetic reactions (see Section 3.1). Thus, harnessing energy in the environment was an absolute requirement for the earliest of life

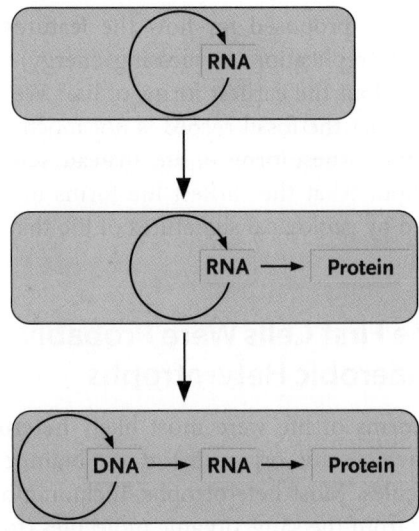

**FIGURE 21.13 Possible scenario for the evolution of the flow of information from DNA to RNA to protein**

forms. Today, life on Earth derives almost all its energy from photons coming from the Sun, but photosynthesis is not thought to have evolved until hundreds of millions of years after the first forms of life. Instead, the earliest living things are most likely to have evolved in places where energy was released through geochemical activity.

Some geochemical activity persists on Earth today, giving us the opportunity to study environmental conditions that may be similar to those in which life first evolved, but geochemical activity was even more abundant at the time life originated. One very promising candidate for the site of life's origin are alkaline hydrothermal vents. These are sources of free energy because the chemical reactions that take place within them cause the water they release to be chemically distinct from the surrounding ocean water. The vent water is rich in $H_2$ and $CH_4$ and has very low concentrations of free $H^+$, whereas ocean water has higher concentrations of $H^+$, $CO_2$, and bicarbonate ($HCO_3^-$). At the time life originated on Earth, the oceans were much richer in $CO_2$ than they are today. By reacting with water, $CO_2$ produces $H^+$ and $HCO_3^-$, so that all three of these molecules would have been even more concentrated in ancient ocean water than they are in oceans today.

Chemical reactions that take place where the vent water encounters ocean water cause calcium carbonate to precipitate out of the water, forming chimneys made of calcium carbonate that are honeycombed with microscopic pores that the water percolates through (see chapter-opening photo). Within these porous chimneys, the two different chemical environments of the vent water and the ocean water encounter each other. Because a fresh supply of alkaline water is constantly released from the vent, the interface between vent water and ocean water is constantly out of equilibrium. We discussed in Chapter 3 that free energy is at a minimum when any system reaches equilibrium, so the non-equilibrium conditions produced by the alkaline vents represent a continually renewing source of energy.

One very intriguing source of energy in the vent environment is the $H^+$ concentration gradient between the ocean water and vent water, because this is still a prime energy source for living things today. Although some ATP is made in living things today directly by substrate-level phosphorylation (see Section 5.3), during glycolysis, for example, most ATP molecules are produced by ATP synthase enzymes using energy released from the diffusion of $H^+$ down a concentration gradient (see Section 5.5). Scientists studying the alkaline vent environment have hypothesized that the importance of $H^+$ gradients as sources of energy for all living things may be a relic of the release of energy stored in $H^+$ gradients in calcium carbonate chimneys.

A second source of energy in the vent environment is the difference in electron affinity between the reduced $H_2$ and $CH_4$ in the vent water and the more oxidized $CO_2$ in the ocean water. In Chapter 5, you learned how energy is released as electrons are transferred between reduced molecules such as NADH and the oxidized carrier complexes of the mitochondrial electron transfer system. This is just one example of the many electron transfer systems that release energy in a wide variety of living things today. The interface between the reduced $H_2$ and $CH_4$ in vent water and oxidized $CO_2$ in ocean water would have provided a perfect opportunity for the evolution of energy-releasing electron transfer reactions in the earliest cells (protobionts). The fact that electron transfer systems are such common and indispensable mechanisms for releasing energy in living things today may be a relic of the evolution of life in an alkaline vent chemical environment. Some of the microscopic compartments in alkaline vent chimneys are only micrometres in diameter, in other words, about the size of a cell. These structures provide a promising model of how protocells could have evolved to make use of the non-equilibrium chemical conditions of alkaline vents. According to one hypothesis, molecular replicators may have taken up residence in microscopic compartments in the porous chimneys, and lipid membranes may have formed on the inner surfaces of the chamber walls of these compartments and across the porous openings (Figure 21.14). By growing within chimneys, protocells would have been ideally placed to take advantage of the enduring $H^+$ concentration gradients and oxidation–reduction differences between the vent water and surrounding ocean water. The energy provided by these gradients could have supported the synthesis of organic molecules and the maintenance of molecular organization in protocells.

### STUDY BREAK QUESTIONS

1. What are ribozymes, and what is their significance in our understanding of the origins of life?
2. In what ways is DNA better than RNA for storing genetic information?
3. Describe how H+ gradients could be generated in alkaline hydrothermal vents.

## 21.4 Evidence of the Earliest Life

Given hypotheses proposed for how the features of life may have developed (replication, harnessing energy), what do we actually know about the earliest forms of life? We will see later in this chapter that the fossil record is not much help in shedding light on the earliest forms of life. Instead, scientists rely on hypotheses about what the earliest life forms must have been like, supported by geological signatures of life that early organisms left behind.

### 21.4a The First Cells Were Probably Anaerobic Heterotrophs

The earliest forms of life were most likely **heterotrophs** (see Chapter 6), which are organisms that obtain carbon from organic molecules. Most heterotrophs, including humans, also obtain energy from the same organic molecules (food). Central to most forms of heterotrophy are the respiratory pathways of glycolysis and fermentation. These pathways are found in

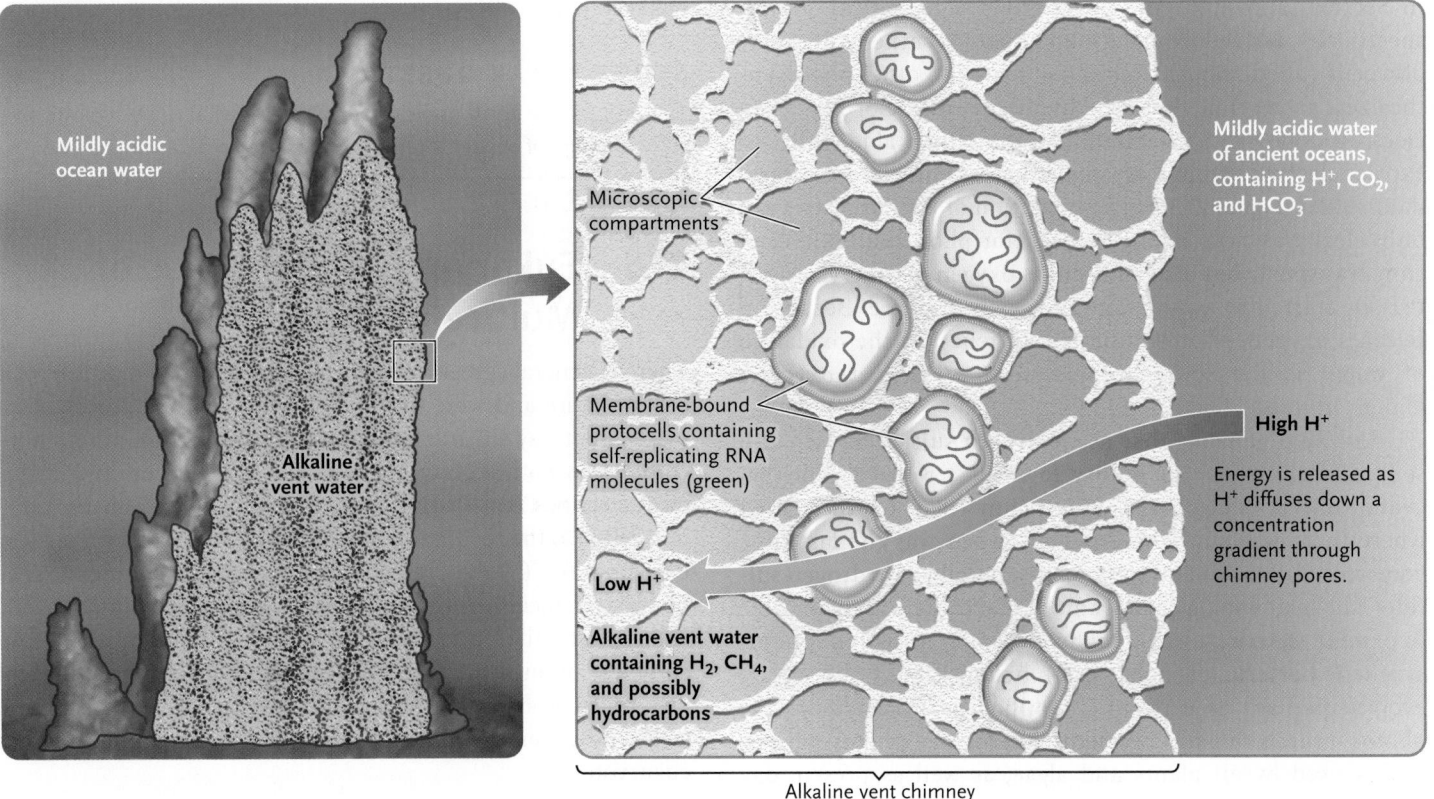

**a. Cross-sectional view through an alkaline vent chimney**

Mildly acidic ocean water

Alkaline vent water

**b. Magnified cross section through part of an alkaline vent chimney**

Microscopic compartments

Membrane-bound protocells containing self-replicating RNA molecules (green)

Low H⁺

Alkaline vent water containing $H_2$, $CH_4$, and possibly hydrocarbons

Mildly acidic water of ancient oceans, containing H⁺, $CO_2$, and $HCO_3^-$

High H⁺

Energy is released as H⁺ diffuses down a concentration gradient through chimney pores.

Alkaline vent chimney

**FIGURE 21.14 A hypothesis for the origin of cells in alkaline vent chimneys. (a)** A cross-sectional view through an alkaline vent chimney. Within the porous material of the chimney, warm (30°C–90°C) alkaline water issuing from the vent mixes with cooler and mildly acidic ocean water. **(b)** A magnified cross-sectional view through a part of the chimney. Membrane-bound protocells containing populations of self-replicating RNA molecules are shown, which are hypothesized to have formed within the microcompartments of the porous chimneys.

virtually all forms of life and are relatively simple, the energy present in organic molecules being used directly to synthesize ATP. There is no requirement for membrane bound complexes, which is necessary for electron transport chains, and there is no requirement for $O_2$, which was found in only trace amounts in the early atmosphere. Thus, the earliest forms of life were most certainly anaerobic.

Compared to heterotrophs, **autotrophs** obtain carbon from the environment in an inorganic form, most often carbon dioxide. Plants and other photosynthetic organisms are the dominant autotrophs today and are classified as photoautotrophs because they use light as an energy source. As discussed in Chapter 6, the products of the light reactions, ATP and NADPH, are used to synthesize organic molecules from $CO_2$.

## 21.4b Oxygenic Photosynthesis Led to a Rise in Oxygen in the Atmosphere

Starting about 2.5 billion years ago, oxygen ($O_2$) levels in the atmosphere began increasing. Evidence for this comes from dating a type of sedimentary rock called *banded iron* **(Figure 21.15)**.

Geologists believe that these distinctive striped rocks were formed in the sediments of lakes and oceans when dissolved oxygen reacted with the iron in the water, forming a red-coloured precipitate, iron oxide (rust), which ended up being incorporated into the resulting sedimentary rock formations (see Figure 21.15).

**FIGURE 21.15 Banded iron.** The rust layers in banded iron formations provide evidence for the rise of atmospheric oxygen.

An obvious question to ask is: where did the oxygen come from? There is clear evidence—which we will discuss in Section 21.6—that the oxygen had a biological source, specifically derived from a group of photosynthetic prokaryotic cells called *cyanobacteria*. Compared to other photosynthesizers at the time that used hydrogen sulfide or $Fe_2^+$ as an electron donor, cyanobacteria had the remarkable ability to extract electrons from a molecule that was much more abundant: water **(Figure 21.16)**. The oxidation of water releases not only electrons, which can be used for photosynthetic electron transport, but also molecular oxygen ($O_2$). Over time, this $O_2$ started to accumulate in the atmosphere. Because it releases oxygen, photosynthesis that relies on the oxidation of water as the source of electrons is termed *oxygenic photosynthesis*.

Unlike organisms that use hydrogen sulfide or $Fe_2^+$ as a source of electrons, the ability to oxidize water meant that cyanobacteria could thrive almost anywhere on the planet where there was sunlight. After all, when was the last time you crossed campus and stepped in a puddle of hydrogen sulfide? The huge ecological advantage that came with being able to oxidize water resulted in an explosion of growth of photosynthetic bacteria (cyanobacteria). Astonishingly, although it evolved perhaps as early as 2.5 billion years ago, oxygenic photosynthesis remains the dominant form of photosynthesis and is used by all plants and algae, as well as present-day cyanobacteria.

The oxygen that accumulated in the atmosphere was simply a by-product of oxygenic photosynthesis. But it led to the next remarkable development in the evolution of early life: aerobic respiration. As discussed in Chapter 5, compared to anaerobic respiration, the pathway of oxidative phosphorylation that required $O_2$ for electron transport results in a huge increase in the amount of ATP that can be generated from the breakdown of food molecules (e.g., glucose). The huge advantage to be gained in energy production led to the evolution of prokaryotic cells that could undergo aerobic respiration. This in turn set the stage for the next huge step: the evolution of the eukaryotic cell.

**STUDY BREAK QUESTION**

1. Compared to anoxygenic photosynthesis, what is the ecological advantage of oxygenic photosynthesis to an organism?

## 21.5 Eukaryotes and the Rise of Multicellularity

There is general agreement that the first cells had a prokaryotic cell structure and were morphologically and functionally simple. Present-day eukaryotic cells are, in comparison, vastly more complex in both structure and function. There are two major characteristics that distinguish eukaryotic cells from prokaryotic cells: (1) the separation of DNA and cytoplasm by a nuclear envelope, and (2) the presence in the cytoplasm of membrane-bound organelles with specialized functions: mitochondria, chloroplasts, the endoplasmic reticulum (ER), and the Golgi complex, among others. In this section, we discuss how eukaryotes most probably evolved from associations of prokaryotic cells, and we end with a discussion of the rise of multicellular eukaryotes.

### 21.5a The Theory of Endosymbiosis Suggests That Mitochondria and Chloroplasts Evolved from Ingested Prokaryotic Cells

One feature that is found in virtually all eukaryotic cells is energy-transforming organelles: mitochondria and chloroplasts. A wealth of evidence indicates that mitochondria and chloroplasts are actually descended from free-living prokaryotic cells **(Figure 21.17)**: mitochondria are descended from aerobic bacteria, and chloroplasts are descended from cyanobacteria. The established model of **endosymbiosis** states that the prokaryotic ancestors of modern mitochondria and chloroplasts were engulfed by larger prokaryotic cells, forming a mutually advantageous relationship called a **symbiosis**. Slowly, over time, the **host** cell and the endosymbionts became inseparable parts of the same single-celled organism.

If the theory of endosymbiosis is correct and both mitochondria and chloroplasts are indeed descendants of bacteria, then these organelles should share some clear structural and biochemical features with the forms of life that they evolved from. Six lines of evidence suggest that both chloroplasts and mitochondria have distinctly prokaryotic characteristics that are not found in other eukaryotic organelles:

1. **Morphology.** The shape and size of both mitochondria and chloroplasts are similar to those of prokaryotic cells.
2. **Reproduction.** A cell cannot synthesize a mitochondrion or a chloroplast. Just like free-living prokaryotic cells,

**a.**

**b.**

$$2H_2O + \text{light energy} \longrightarrow 4H^+ + 4e^- + O_2$$

Biophoto Associates/Science Source

**FIGURE 21.16 Cyanobacteria. (a)** Micrograph of a filamentous cyanobacterium of the genus *Nostoc*. **(b)** Ancient cyanobacteria, like modern photosynthetic organisms, were able to use water as an electron donor for photosynthesis. A consequence was the formation of oxygen ($O_2$), which accumulated in the atmosphere.

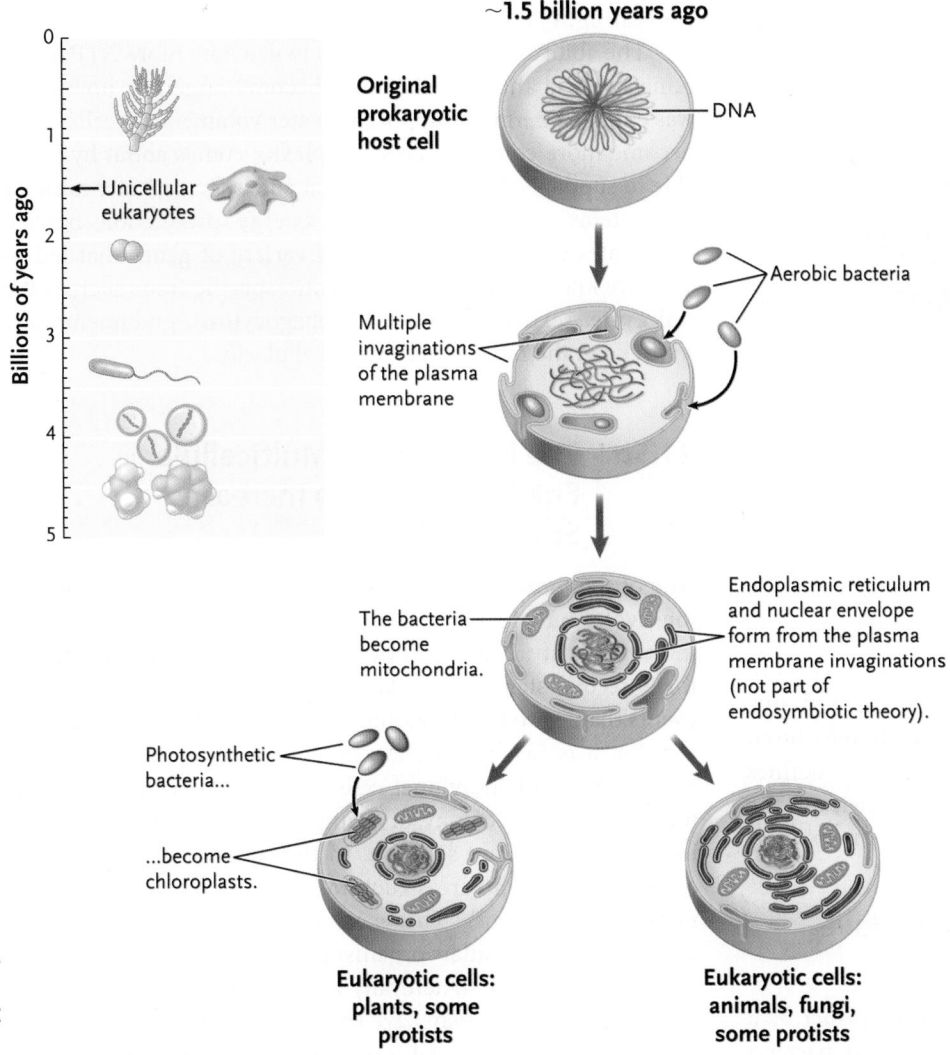

**~1.5 billion years ago**

Original prokaryotic host cell

DNA

Unicellular eukaryotes

Billions of years ago

Aerobic bacteria

Multiple invaginations of the plasma membrane

The bacteria become mitochondria.

Endoplasmic reticulum and nuclear envelope form from the plasma membrane invaginations (not part of endosymbiotic theory).

Photosynthetic bacteria...

...become chloroplasts.

Eukaryotic cells: plants, some protists

Eukaryotic cells: animals, fungi, some protists

**FIGURE 21.17 The theory of endosymbiosis.** The mitochondrion is thought to have originated from an aerobic prokaryote that lived as an endosymbiont within an anaerobic prokaryote. The chloroplast is thought to have originated from a photosynthetic prokaryote that became an endosymbiont within an aerobic cell that had mitochondria.

© Cengage Learning 2017.

where daughter cells arise by cell division, new mitochondria and chloroplasts are derived from the division of preexisting organelles. Both chloroplasts and mitochondria divide by binary fission, which is how prokaryotic cells divide (see Chapter 23).

3. **Genetic information.** If the ancestors of mitochondria and chloroplasts were free-living cells, then these organelles should contain their own DNA. Both mitochondria and chloroplasts contain their own DNA, which contain both protein-coding and non-coding genes (see Chapter 12) that are essential for organelle function. As with prokaryotic cells, the DNA molecule in most mitochondria and chloroplasts is circular, while the DNA molecules in the nucleus are linear.

4. **Transcription and translation.** Both chloroplasts and mitochondria contain a complete transcription and transla-

tional machinery. They contain ribosomes and tRNAs that are necessary to translate organelle mRNAs into proteins.

5. **Electron transport.** Similar to free-living prokaryotic cells, both mitochondria and chloroplasts have electron transport chains and the enzyme ATP synthase, which together are used to generate chemical energy. The electron transport chains of bacteria and archaea are found associated with the plasma membrane.

6. **Sequence analysis.** Sequencing of the genes that encode the RNA component of the ribosome (ribosomal RNA or rRNA) firmly establishes that these organelles belong on the bacterial branch of the tree of life (we will discuss this later in the chapter). The sequence of chloroplast rRNA most closely matches that of cyanobacteria, and the sequence of mitochondrial rRNA is most similar to that of heterotrophic bacteria.

Whereas virtually all eukaryotic cells contain mitochondria, only plants and algae contain both mitochondria and chloroplasts. This fact suggests that endosymbiosis occurred in stages (see Figure 21.17), with the event leading to the evolution of mitochondria occurring first. Once eukaryotic cells with the ability for aerobic respiration developed, some became photosynthetic after taking up cyanobacteria, evolving into the plants and algae of today.

## 21.5b The Endomembrane System May Be Derived from the Plasma Membrane

As detailed in Chapter 2, in addition to energy-transforming organelles (mitochondria and chloroplasts), eukaryotic cells are characterized by an endomembrane system: a collection of internal membranes that divide the cell into structural and functional regions. These include the nuclear envelope, the ER, and the Golgi complex. As we have just seen, there is very strong evidence in support of the endosymbiotic origin of chloroplasts and mitochondria; however, the origin of the endomembrane system remains less clear. The most widely held hypothesis is that it is derived from the infolding of the plasma

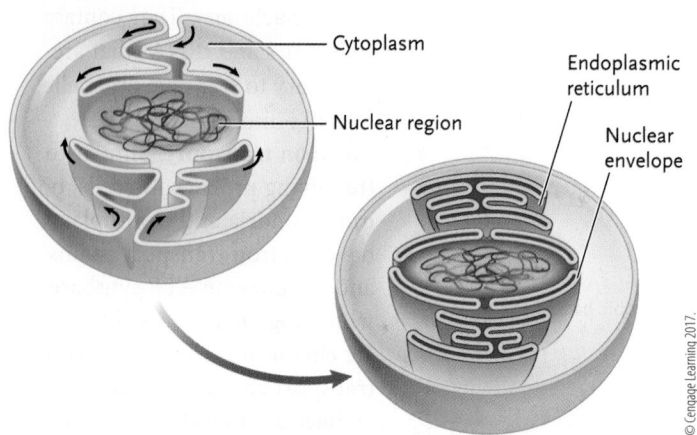

**FIGURE 21.18** A hypothetical route for the formation of the nuclear envelope and ER through segments of the plasma membrane that were brought into the cytoplasm by endocytosis

membrane **(Figure 21.18)**. Researchers hypothesize that, in cell lines leading from prokaryotic cells to eukaryotes, pockets of the plasma membrane may have extended inward and surrounded the nuclear region. Some of these membranes fused around the DNA, forming the nuclear envelope, which defines the nucleus. The remaining membranes formed vesicles in the cytoplasm that gave rise to the ER and the Golgi complex.

## 21.5c Solving an Energy Crisis May Have Led to Eukaryotes

Bacteria and archaea outnumber eukaryotes on the planet by a huge margin. Compared to eukaryotes, archaea and bacteria show remarkable biochemical flexibility, being able to use an assortment of molecules as sources of energy and carbon and thrive in harsh environments uninhabitable to eukaryotes. That said, prokaryotic cells are simple: they lack the complexity of eukaryotes, which evolved into a tremendous diversity of forms, including plants, fungi, and animals. Within each of these groups are cells with remarkable specialization in form and function (e.g., cells of the flower of a plant, muscle and brain cells of animals). Contrast this to archaea and bacteria, which have remained remarkably simple even though they evolved as early as 4 billion years ago.

The reason that bacteria and archaea have remained very simple is that increased complexity requires increased energy, and while eukaryotic cells can generate huge amounts of it, prokaryotic cells cannot. Mitochondria, like their aerobic progenitor bacteria, undergo aerobic respiration, which generates much greater amounts of ATP from the breakdown of organic molecules than pathways of anaerobic metabolism (see Chapter 5). As well, while a typical aerobic bacterium relies on its plasma membrane for many functions, including nutrient and waste transport and energy production, a typical eukaryotic cell contains hundreds of mitochondria, each

having a huge internal membrane surface area dedicated to generating ATP.

The ability of early eukaryotes to generate more ATP led to remarkable changes. Cells could become larger, as now there was enough energy to support a greater volume. And cells could become more complex. This complexity comes about by being able to support a larger genome that codes for a greater number of proteins. By overcoming an energy production barrier, eukaryotes could support a wider variety of genes that led to what we know today to be eukaryotic-specific traits such as the **cell cycle,** sexual reproduction, phagocytosis, endomembrane trafficking, the nucleus, and multicellularity.

## 21.5d The Evolution of Multicellular Eukaryotes Led to Increased Specialization

One of the most profound transitions in the history of life was the evolution of multicellular eukaryotes. Clear evidence of multicellularity, in the form of species of algae, appears in the fossil record starting about 1.2 billion years ago. The actual events that led to the development of multicellularity are a mystery but it is easy to envision how it may have occurred. Perhaps a group of individual cells of a particular species came together to form a colony, or a single cell divided and the resulting two cells did not separate. In the simplest of multicellular organisms, all cells are structurally and functionally autonomous (independent). This gave way to a key trait of more advanced multicellular organisms: division of labour. Over time, cells became structurally and functionally distinct. For example, some cells may have specialized in harvesting energy, whereas others developed a role related to the motility of the organism. In a multicellular system, the cells cooperate with one another for the benefit of the entire organism. Over evolutionary time, this specialization of cell function led to the development of the specialized tissues and organs that are so clearly evident in larger eukaryotes.

Like the earliest forms of life, there is little, if any, evidence in the fossil record of the earliest multicellular organisms. How they arose and developed is still an area of intense research. It is thought, however, that multicellularity arose more than once, most probably independently along each of the lineages leading to fungi, plants, and animals. A very useful model for the study of multicellularity is found in a group of green algae called the *volvocine*. All the members of this group are evolutionarily closely related and span the full range of size and complexity, from the unicellular *Chlamydomonas* through various colonial genera to the multicellular *Volvox* **(Figure 21.19)**. Unlike a true multicellular organism, a cell colony is a group of cells that are all of one type; there is no specialization in cell structure or function. *Volvox* consists of a sphere of two to three thousand small, flagellated *Chlamydomonas*-like cells that provide the individual *Volvox* with the ability to move. In addition, within the sphere lie

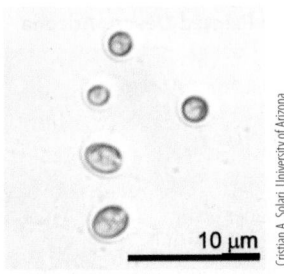
*Chlamydomonas reinhardtii,* a unicellular alga

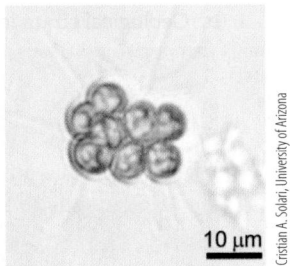
*Gonium pectorale,* a group of eight undifferentiated cells

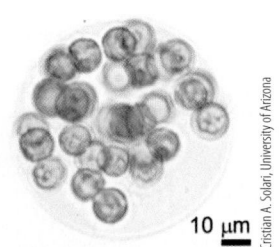
*Eudorina elegans,* a spherical colony of undifferentiated cells

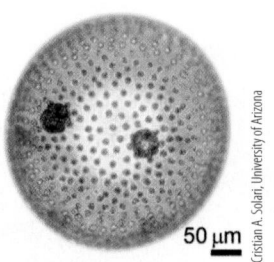
*Volvox aureu,* smaller somatic cells and a few reproductive cells

**FIGURE 21.19 Differences in degree of multicellularity among volvocine algae**

about 16 large nonmotile cells that serve a specialized role in reproduction.

## 21.6 The Fossil Record

Testing hypotheses related to how the first forms of life could have developed on early Earth is a robust area of research involving scientists with expertise in Chemistry, Earth Science, and Biology. However, we can only speculate at what the first forms of life really were like because we have no direct evidence of their existence. This section provides an overview of what we actually do know about the history of life on Earth as reflected by the remains of organisms that have been preserved in the fossil record.

### 21.6a The Fossil Record Is Invaluable but Incomplete

The fossil record provides the only direct evidence about what life was like millions of years ago. Fossilized skeletons, shells, stems, leaves, and flowers tell us about the size and appearance of ancient animals and plants. The fossil record also has allowed scientists to see how species have changed over time as it chronicles the proliferation and extinction of evolutionary lineages, and it provides data on the geographical distribution of extinct species. As discussed in Chapter 16, Darwin's ability to compare fossil specimens with living relatives was very influential in his development of the notion of natural selection.

Obviously the fossil record is an invaluable resource to understand the past, but it is important to note that it represents only a small fraction of the organisms that once lived on Earth, and thus it vastly underrepresents the diversity of life. The fossil record only really represents a record of the most successful of organisms; those that were very abundant, had wide distributions, and possessed hard parts that could be fossilized (see below). Soft-bodied organisms with small geographic distributions that lived in environments where erosion was a dominant process are underrepresented in the fossil record, if they are in it at all.

### 21.6b Fossils Form When Organisms Are Buried by Sediments or Preserved in Oxygen-Poor Environments

Most fossils form in sedimentary rocks. Rain and runoff constantly erode the land, carrying fine particles of rock and soil downstream to a swamp, a lake, or the sea. Particles settle to the bottom as sediments, forming successive layers, called *strata*, over millions of years (**Figure 21.20**). The weight of newer sediments compresses the older layers beneath them into a solid matrix: sand into sandstone and silt, or mud into shale. Fossils form within the layers when the remains of organisms are buried in the accumulating sediments. Because sedimentation superimposes new layers over old ones, the lowest strata in a sedimentary rock formation are usually the oldest, and the highest layers are the newest.

The process of fossilization is a race against time because the soft remains of organisms are quickly consumed by scavengers or decomposed by microorganisms. Thus, fossils usually preserve the details of hard structures, such as the bones, teeth, and shells of animals and the wood, leaves, and pollen of plants. During fossilization, dissolved minerals replace some parts molecule by molecule, leaving a fossil made of stone (**Figure 21.21a**); other fossils form as moulds, casts, or impressions in material that is later transformed into solid rock (Figure 21.21b).

In some environments, the near absence of oxygen prevents decomposition, and even soft-bodied organisms are preserved. Some plants, insects, and tiny lizards and frogs are embedded in amber, the fossilized resin of coniferous trees (Figure 21.21c). Other organisms are preserved in glacial ice, deeply frozen soil, coal, tar pits, or the highly acidic water of peat bogs (Figure 21.21d). Sometimes organisms are so well preserved that researchers can examine their internal anatomy, cell structure, food in their digestive tracts, and even their DNA sequences.

#### a. Sedimentation

Highest strata contain the most recent fossils.

Lowest strata contain the oldest fossils.

#### b. Geological strata in the Painted Desert, Arizona

**FIGURE 21.20 Sedimentation and geological strata. (a)** Sedimentation deposits successive layers at the bottom of a lake or sea. **(b)** Over millions of years, the upper layers compress those below them into rock. When the rocks are later exposed by uplifting or erosion, the different layers are evident as geological strata.

#### a. Petrified wood (Araucariaceae)

#### b. *Sphenopteris*

#### c. Mosquitoes in amber

#### d. Mammoth *(Mammonteus)* in permafrost

**FIGURE 21.21 Fossils. (a)** Petrified wood in Arizona formed when minerals replaced the wood of dead trees, molecule by molecule. These forests lived during the late Triassic period, about 225 million years ago. **(b)** The remains of a fern (*Sphenopteris*) from the Carboniferous period, 300 million years ago, were preserved in coal. **(c)** These 10-million-year-old mosquitoes were trapped in the oozing resin of a coniferous tree and are now encased in amber. **(d)** A frozen baby mammoth that lived about 40 000 years ago was discovered embedded in Siberian permafrost in 1977.

## 21.6c The Earliest Fossils

The earliest indirect evidence of life, which predates any actual fossil evidence, comes from research looking at the carbon composition of ancient rocks. Early photosynthetic organisms would have had the ability to take $CO_2$ from the atmosphere and use it to synthesize various organic molecules (see Chapter 6 for details). During this process, organisms would have preferentially incorporated the carbon-12 isotope ($^{12}C$) over other isotopes such as carbon-13 ($^{13}C$) (see *The Purple Pages* for a discussion of isotopes). Researchers have discovered sedimentary rocks originating from the ocean floor that contain deposits that have lower levels of the $^{13}C$ isotope than expected. The most likely explanation is that the deposits are actually the remains of carbon molecules of ancient microbes. These sediments have been dated to approximately 3.9 billion years ago. If correct, this would push the origins of life to perhaps as early as 4 billion years ago, approximately 600 million years after Earth was formed.

The earliest conclusive evidence of life is found in the fossilized remains of structures called *stromatolites*, the oldest being formed about 3.5 billion years ago. A **stromatolite** is a type of layered rock that is formed when microorganisms bind particles of sediment together, forming thin sheets **(Figure 21.22)**. Modern stromatolites are found in habitats characterized by warm shallow water and are most common in Australia. Modern-day stromatolites are formed by the action of a specific group of photosynthetic bacteria called *cyanobacteria*. Because they were able to undertake oxygenic photosynthesis, cyanobacteria (see Figure 21.16) were not the earliest forms of life but rather must have been preceded by much simpler organisms.

**a.**

Bill Bachmann/Science Source

**b.**

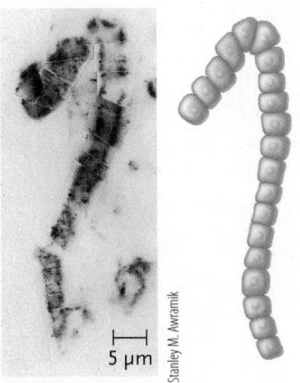

Stanley M. Awramik

**FIGURE 21.22 Early fossil evidence of life. (a)** Stromatolites exposed at low tide in Western Australia's Shark Bay. These mounds, which consist of mineral deposits made by photosynthetic cyanobacteria, are about 2000 years old; they are highly similar in structure to fossil stromatolites that formed more than 3 billion years ago. **(b)** Structures that are believed to be a strand of fossil prokaryote cells in a rock sample that is 3.5 billion years old.

### 21.6d Scientists Assign Relative and Absolute Dates to Geological Strata and the Fossils They Contain

The sediments found in any one place form recognizable strata (layers) that differ in colour, mineral composition, particle size, and thickness (see Figure 21.20b). If they have not been disturbed, the strata are arranged in the order in which they formed, with the youngest layers on top.

Geologists of the early nineteenth century deduced that the fossils discovered in a particular sedimentary stratum, no matter where on Earth it is found, represent organisms that lived and died at roughly the same time in the past. Because each stratum formed at a specific time, the sequence of fossils in the lowest (oldest) to the highest (newest) strata reveals their *relative ages*. Geologists originally used the sequence of strata and their distinctive fossil assemblages to establish the geological time scale **(Table 21.1)**.

Although the geological time scale provides a relative dating system for sedimentary strata, it does not tell us how old the rocks and fossils actually are. But many rocks contain unstable radioisotopes, which, from the moment they form, begin to break down into other, more stable elements. The breakdown proceeds at a steady rate that is unaffected by chemical reactions or environmental conditions such as temperature or pressure. Using a technique called **radiometric dating**, scientists can estimate the age of a rock by noting how much of an unstable "parent" isotope has decayed to another form. By measuring the relative amounts of the parent radioisotope and its breakdown products and comparing this ratio with the isotope's **half-life** (the time it takes for half a given amount of radioisotope to decay), researchers can estimate the *absolute age* of the rock **(Figure 21.23)**. Table 21.1 presents these age estimates along with the major geological and evolutionary events of each period.

#### STUDY BREAK QUESTIONS

1. What biological materials are the most likely to fossilize?
2. Why does the fossil record provide an incomplete portrait of life in the past?
3. What sorts of information can paleobiologists discern from the fossil record?

## 21.7 The Tree of Life

At the time of Darwin, scientists had a hard time explaining the huge diversity of life that biologists were discovering; it was varied and many organisms did not seem to have obvious connections with others. With the use of modern DNA sequencing technology, it is now remarkably easy to build a single tree of life. The most surprising feature of this tree is that it has a single starting point. DNA can be shown to

**TABLE 21.1**  **The Geological Time Scale and Major Evolutionary Events**

| Eon | Era | Period | Epoch | Millions of Years Ago | Major Evolutionary Events | Mass Extinctions |
|---|---|---|---|---|---|---|
| Phanerozoic | Cenozoic | Quaternary | Holocene | 0.01 | Origin of modern humans; major glaciations | RIP |
| | | | Pleistocene | 2.6 | | |
| | | | Pliocene | 5.3 | Origin of bipedal human ancestors | |
| | | Neogene | Miocene | 23.0 | Angiosperms and mammals further diversify and dominate terrestrial habitats | |
| | | | Oligocene | 33.9 | Primates diversify; origin of apes | |
| | | Paleogene | Eocene | 55.8 | Angiosperms and insects diversify; modern orders of mammals differentiate | |
| | | | Paleocene | 65.5 | Grasslands and deciduous woodlands spread; modern birds, mammals, snakes, pollinating insects diversify; continents approach current positions | RIP Cretaceous |
| | Mesozoic | Cretaceous | | 145.5 | First angiosperms; insects, marine invertebrates, fishes, dinosaurs diversify; asteroid impact causes mass extinction at end of period, eliminating most dinosaurs and many other groups | |
| | | Jurassic | | 201.6 | Gymnosperms abundant in terrestrial habitats; modern fishes diversify; dinosaurs diversify and dominate terrestrial habitats; frogs, salamanders, lizards, birds, and placental mammals appear; continents continue to separate | RIP Triassic |
| | | Triassic | | 251.0 | Predatory fishes and reptiles dominate oceans; gymnosperms dominate terrestrial habitats; diversification of dinosaurs; early mammals; Pangaea starts to break up; mass extinction at end of period | RIP Permian |
| | Paleozoic | Permian | | 299.0 | Insects and amniotes abundant and diverse in swamp forests; some amniotes colonize oceans; fishes colonize freshwater habitats; continents coalesce into Pangaea, causing glaciation and decline in sea level; huge volcanic eruptions cause mass extinction at end of period, eliminating 85% of species worldwide | |
| | | Carboniferous | | 359.0 | Vascular plants form large swamp forests; first flying insects; amphibians diversify; first amniotes appear | RIP Devonian |
| | | Devonian | | 416.0 | Terrestrial vascular plants diversify; fungi, invertebrates, tetrapod vertebrates colonize land; first insects and seed plants; major glaciation at end of period; mass extinction, mostly of marine life | |
| | | Silurian | | 444.0 | Jawless fishes diversify; first jawed fishes, first terrestrial arthropods and vascular plants | RIP Ordovician |
| | | Ordovician | | 488.0 | Major radiations of marine invertebrates and jawless fishes; first terrestrial plants, fungi, and animals; major glaciation at end of period causes mass extinction of marine life | RIP Cambrian |
| | | Cambrian | | 542.0 | Appearance of modern animal phyla, including vertebrates (Cambrian explosion); simple marine communities; mass extinctions eliminate many groups at end of period | |
| Proterozoic | | | | 2500 | High concentration of oxygen in atmosphere; origin of eukaryotic cells; evolution and diversification of protists, fungi, soft-bodied animals | |
| Archean | | | | 3850 | Origin of life; evolution of prokaryotes, including anaerobic and photosynthetic bacteria; oxygen starts to accumulate in atmosphere; origin of aerobic respiration | |
| Hadean | | | | 4600 | Formation of Earth, including crust, atmosphere, and oceans | |

FIGURE 21.23   **Research Method**

## Radiometric Dating

Knowing the number of half-lives that have passed allows you to estimate the age of the sample.

**Purpose:** Radiometric dating allows researchers to estimate the absolute age of a rock sample or fossil.

**Protocol:**

1. Knowing the approximate age of a rock or fossil, select a radioisotope that has an appropriate half-life. Because different radioisotopes have half-lives ranging from seconds to billions of years, it is usually possible to choose one that brackets the estimated age of the sample under study. For example, if you think that your fossil is more than 10 million years old, you might use uranium-235. The half-life of $^{235}U$, which decays into the lead isotope $^{207}Pb$, is about 700 million years. Or if you think that your fossil is less than 70 000 years old, you might select carbon-14. The half-life of 14C, which decays into the nitrogen isotope $^{14}N$, is 5730 years.

| Radioisotopes Commonly Used in Radiometric Dating | | | |
|---|---|---|---|
| Radioisotope (Unstable) | More Stable Breakdown Product | Half-Life (Years) | Useful Range (Years) |
| Samarium-147 $\longrightarrow$ | Neodymium-143 | 106 billion | >100 million |
| Rubidium-87 $\longrightarrow$ | Strontium-87 | 48 billion | >10 million |
| Thorium-232 $\longrightarrow$ | Lead-208 | 14 billion | >10 million |
| Uranium-238 $\longrightarrow$ | Lead-206 | 4.5 billion | >10 million |
| Uranium-235 $\longrightarrow$ | Lead-207 | 700 million | >10 million |
| Potassium-40 $\longrightarrow$ | Argon-40 | 1.25 billion | >100000 |
| Carbon-14 $\longrightarrow$ | Nitrogen-14 | 5730 | <70000 |

© Cengage Learning 2017

2. Prepare a sample of the material and measure the quantities of the parent radioisotope and its more stable breakdown product.

**Interpreting the Results:** Compare the relative quantities of the parent radioisotope and its breakdown product (or some other stable isotope) to determine what percentage of the original parent radioisotope remains in the sample. Then use a graph of radioactive decay for that isotope to determine how many half-lives have passed since the sample formed.

**Theory of radiometric dating**

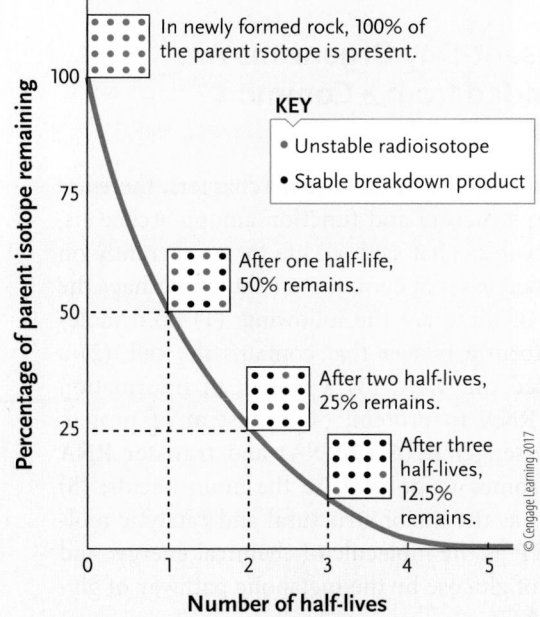

In newly formed rock, 100% of the parent isotope is present.

**KEY**
- Unstable radioisotope
- Stable breakdown product

After one half-life, 50% remains.

After two half-lives, 25% remains.

After three half-lives, 12.5% remains.

© Cengage Learning 2017

*Percentage of parent isotope remaining* (y-axis: 0, 25, 50, 75, 100)
*Number of half-lives* (x-axis: 0, 1, 2, 3, 4, 5)

**Radiometric dating of a fossilized mollusk**

Photodisc/Getty Images

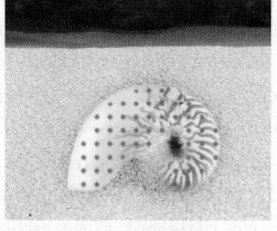
Photodisc/Getty Images

Photodisc/Getty Images

A living mollusk absorbed trace amounts of $^{14}C$, a rare radioisotope of carbon, and large amounts of $^{12}C$, which is the more stable and common isotope of carbon.

When the mollusk died, it was buried in silt and fossilized. From the moment of its death, the ratio of $^{14}C$ to $^{12}C$ began to decline through radioactive decay. Because the half-life of $^{14}C$ is 5,730 years, half of the original $^{14}C$ was eliminated from the fossil in 5,730 years and half of what remained was eliminated in another 5,730 years.

After the fossil was discovered, a scientist determined that its $^{14}C$ to $^{12}C$ ratio was one-eighth (12.5%) of the $^{14}C$ to $^{12}C$ ratio in living organisms. Thus, radioactive decay had proceeded for three half-lives—about 17,000 years—since the mollusk's death.

connect lineages as diverse as prokaryotes and peacocks, or hummingbirds and humans.

## 21.7a Analyses of Gene Sequences Have Revealed the Branching Pattern of the Entire Tree of Life

The ultimate in phylogenetic analysis is to produce a tree that shows the evolutionary relationship among all living organisms. The first efforts to create the "tree of life" were based on morphological analyses: differences in what organisms look like. In the 1960s and early 1970s, biologists organized living systems into five kingdoms based largely on morphological differences. All organisms with prokaryotic morphology were grouped into the kingdom Monera. Eukaryotic organisms were divided into four kingdoms: Fungi, Plantae, Animalia, and "Protista." The kingdom Protista was always recognized as a polyphyletic "grab bag" of unicellular organisms (discussed further in Chapter 24).

As we discussed in Chapter 19, relying on morphological characteristics to build phylogenetic trees can lead to problems, since two organisms may look superficially similar but have very different evolutionary histories. For example, trying to resolve the branches of the tree that contains organisms with prokaryotic cell structure proved very difficult. This was simply because there was a lack of significant structural variability for analysis. As well, it wasn't clear how closely or distantly some of these prokaryotic groups were related to eukaryotes.

By the 1970s, evolutionary biologists realized that using differences in the sequence of particular genes or proteins would provide a far more powerful approach to building the Tree of Life than relying on what organisms looked like. Given our understanding of evolution and how differences in sequence arise, if you compare the sequence of a specific gene among different organisms, those with fewer differences can be assumed to be more closely related than species where the sequence of the gene is more different. The problem then became what sequence to compare. Ideally you want to choose a single gene, but which one? Here are the important criteria:

1. Because you want to build a tree that contains representatives from all major groups of life, the gene must be universal: it must be present in all forms of life.

2. You want the gene sequence to be strongly conserved. Although it is essential that there is variation in the sequence, too much variation will make it hard to compare the sequences between two distantly related organisms. Genes critical for the survival of the cell are ideal for this purpose.

3. You want the gene to be fairly long, because the longer the gene sequence, in essence, the more information it contains. In fact, longer genes are statistically harder to match, and therefore consistencies in their sequence are more convincing than shorter sequences that may have similarities for reasons other than a common history.

Using these criteria, Carl R. Woese, a microbiologist at the University of Illinois at Urbana-Champaign, realized that the gene that codes for the RNA molecule that makes up the small subunit of the ribosome (rRNA) was an ideal candidate. Ribosomes, the organelles that that translate messenger RNA molecules into proteins (see Section 12.4), are found in all forms of life and are remarkably similar in their structure. Recall as well that ribosomes contain both protein and RNA as components of their structure.

Starting in 1977, the phylogenetic tree that Carl Woese and his colleagues built based on rRNA sequences completely changed how scientists saw the tree of life (**Figure 21.24**). Instead of the old five kingdoms, the rRNA data clearly delineated only three primary lineages of organisms, which we refer to as domains: Bacteria, Archaea, and Eukarya. **Table 21.2** lists the major molecular and cellular distinctions of these three domains. According to this hypothesis, the domains Bacteria and Archaea consist of prokaryotic organisms, and only Eukarya consists of eukaryotes. The domain Bacteria includes well-known microorganisms. Archaea includes microorganisms that live in physiologically harsh environments, such as hot springs and very salty habitats, as well as less extreme environments. The domain Eukarya includes the familiar animals, plants, and fungi as well as the many lineages formerly included among the "Protista," which is not a monophyletic group. As the tree in Figure 21.24 suggests, Archaea and Eukarya are more closely related to each other than either is to Bacteria. The next unit of this book is devoted to detailed analyses of the biology and evolutionary relationships between and within these three domains.

## 21.7b All Present-Day Organisms Are Descended from a Common Ancestor, LUCA

As will be discussed in detail in subsequent chapters, there are clear distinctions in structure and function among archaeans, bacteria, and eukaryotes. That said, all life forms currently on Earth share a remarkable set of common attributes. Perhaps the most fundamental of these are the following: (1) lipid molecules assemble to form a bilayer that contains the cell; (2) a genetic system based on DNA; (3) a system of information transfer: DNA to RNA to protein; (4) a system of protein assembly using messenger RNA (mRNA) and **transfer RNA** (tRNA) using ribosomes to polymerize the amino acids; (5) reliance on proteins as the major structural and catalytic molecule; (6) use of ATP as the molecule of chemical energy; and (7) the breakdown of glucose by the metabolic pathway of glycolysis to generate ATP.

The fact that these seven attributes are shared by all life on Earth suggests that all present-day organisms are descended from a common ancestor (Figure 21.24) that had all these attributes. We call the original life form from which all archaea, bacteria, and eukaryotes are descended LUCA, which stands for "Last Universal Common Ancestor" (see Figure 21.24).

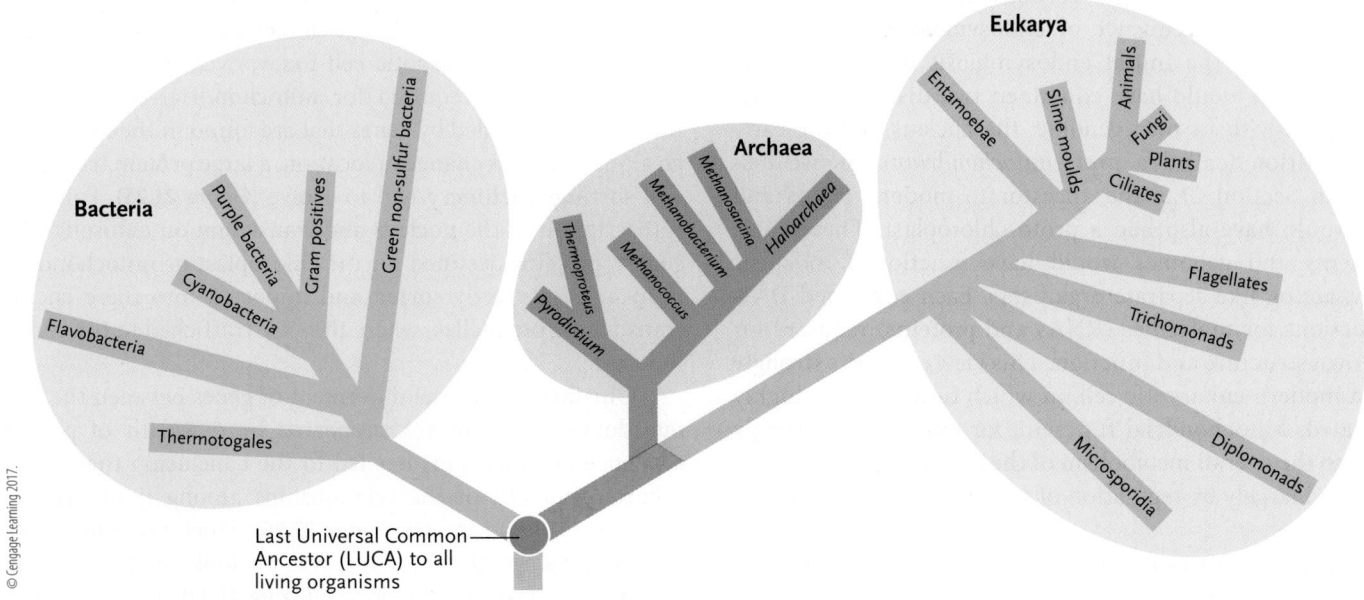

**FIGURE 21.24 The three domains in the Tree of Life.** Carl R. Woese's analysis of rRNA sequences suggests that all living organisms can be classified into one of three domains: Bacteria, Archaea, or Eukarya.

| TABLE 21.2 | Some Differences among the Three Domains | | |
|---|---|---|---|
| Character | Bacteria | Archaea | Eukarya |
| Chromosome structure | Circular | Circular | Linear |
| DNA location | Nucleoid | Nucleoid | Nucleus |
| Chromosome segregation | Binary fission | Binary fission | Meiosis/mitosis |
| Introns in genes | Rare | Common | Common |
| Operons | Present | Present | Absent |
| Initiator tRNA | Formylmethionine | Methionine | Methionine |
| Ribosomes | 70S | 70S | 80S |
| Membrane-enclosed organelles | Absent | Absent | Present |
| Membrane lipids | Ester-linked | Ether-linked | Ester-linked |
| Peptidoglycan in cell wall | Present | Absent | Absent |
| Methanogenesis | Absent | Present | Absent |
| Temperature tolerance | Up to 90°C | Up to 120°C | Up to 70°C |

Recent sequence analysis of certain proteins that have representatives in all three domains of life has given strong quantitative support to the common-ancestry hypothesis.

**CONCEPT FIX** You may think that LUCA was the earliest and only form of life to exist on early Earth, but that is probably not the case. LUCA was the ancestor to all life that currently exists but that is not to say that life evolved only once. It is quite possible that life arose many times on early Earth, each form perhaps having some of the seven attributes listed above. The similarities across all domains of life present today indicate, however, that only one of these primitive life forms has descendants that survive today.

## 21.7c Horizontal Gene Transfer

Our discussion of phylogenetic analysis has emphasized the importance of direct descent: the transmission of traits from ancestors to descendants through the inheritance of DNA. But as scientists analyze the complete genome sequences of an ever-growing list of organisms, they are discovering that the three domains in the Tree of Life have not had entirely independent evolutionary histories. Although inheritance from one generation to the next, what we can refer to as **vertical gene transfer**, has produced the clades of organisms we recognize today, the movement of genetic material between unrelated organisms, what is referred to as **horizontal gene transfer**, has also been important. Horizontal gene transfer, which is common in bacteria, can occur between different species, introducing genes from one species into another. As well, gene transfer can occur through viral infection.

Horizontal gene transfer between the major divisions of life was also a consequence of endosymbiosis (see Section 21.5). Following the initial endosymbiosis event, the early eukaryotic cell would have contained two distinct compartments, each with its own genome: the nucleus and the early mitochondrion (called a *proto-mitochondrion*). As we discussed in Section 21.5, the ancestor to modern plants and algae would have also had a proto-chloroplast. These compartments and genomes would have functioned independently, acting like separate organisms. Each contained DNA instructions for molecules (RNAs and proteins) required for their own structure and function. This view contrasts strongly with a modern eukaryotic cell, in which functions are highly integrated. Mitochondrial function, for example, is strongly linked to the overall metabolism of the cell. This integration is controlled largely by regulation of gene expression within the nucleus.

Two major processes led to this integration of function between the various compartments: First, some of the genes that were within the proto-mitochondrion or proto-chloroplast were lost. Most of these genes would have been redundant as the nucleus would already have genes that encode proteins with the same function. Second, many of the genes within the proto-mitochondrion and proto-chloroplast were relocated to the nucleus through horizontal gene transfer. It is understood that gene transfer to the nucleus was evolutionarily advantageous as it would have centralized genetic information and its control in one place, the nucleus. It's important to realize that the outcome of this horizontal gene transfer was not a change in gene function, only a change in its location.

In a typical eukaryotic cell today, over 90% of the thousands of proteins required for mitochondrial or chloroplast function are encoded by genes that are found in the nucleus. To go along with this change of location, a large protein trafficking and sorting machinery had to evolve **(Figure 21.25)**. Following transcription in the nucleus and translation on cytosolic ribosomes, proteins destined for the chloroplast or mitochondrion need to be correctly sorted and imported into these energy-transducing organelles, where they are trafficked to the correct location.

Our ideas about the movement of genes between the various domains of life are supported by a wealth of genome sequence analysis. This has led to the conclusion that a more accurate portrait of the relationships among living systems looks more like a network **(Figure 21.26)**. Thus, a true portrait of the relationships among living systems looks more like a web than the tree Darwin envisioned **(Figure 21.27)**. The next unit of this book is devoted to detailed analyses of the biology and evolutionary relationships between and within the three domains: Bacteria, Archaea, and Eukarya.

## STUDY BREAK QUESTIONS

1. What is the evidence in support of endosymbiosis?
2. What are the key traits of a multicellular organism?

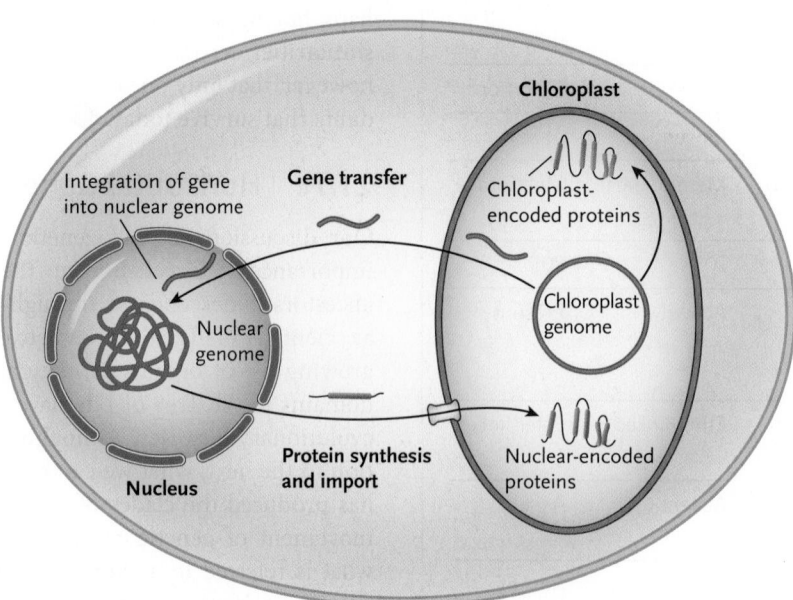

**FIGURE 21.25 Horizontal gene transfer.** Over evolutionary time, some protein-coding genes that were once part of the chloroplast or mitochondrial genome have been relocated to the nuclear genome. Following transcription of these genes, translation occurs in the cytosol before protein import into the organelle (mitochondrion or chloroplast).

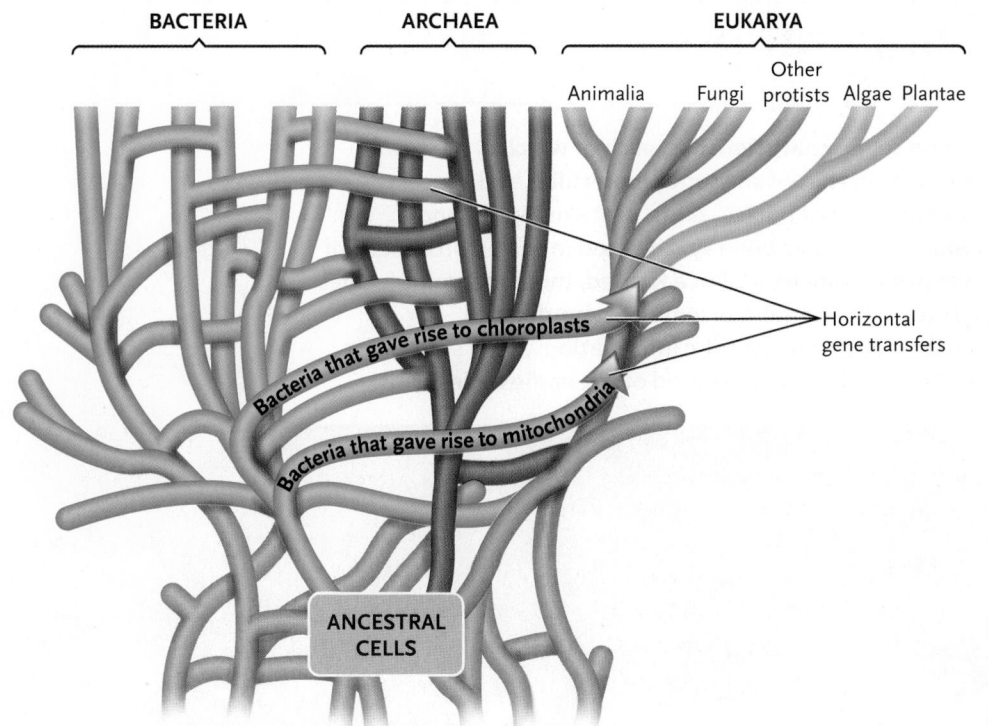

**FIGURE 21.26 Horizontal gene transfer between the three major trunks of the Tree of Life.** Horizontal gene transfer was an important process in producing present-day clades. As shown in this stylized phylogenetic tree, molecular analyses suggest that mitochondria evolved from an aerobic bacterium that was engulfed by an anaerobic archaean, transforming it into a eukaryotic cell. Over time, many genes on the mitochondrial chromosome were transferred to nuclear chromosomes, an example of horizontal gene transfer. Later in the history of life, photosynthetic bacteria were engulfed by eukaryotic cells; the engulfed bacteria evolved into chloroplasts, which are responsible for photosynthesis in algae and plants.

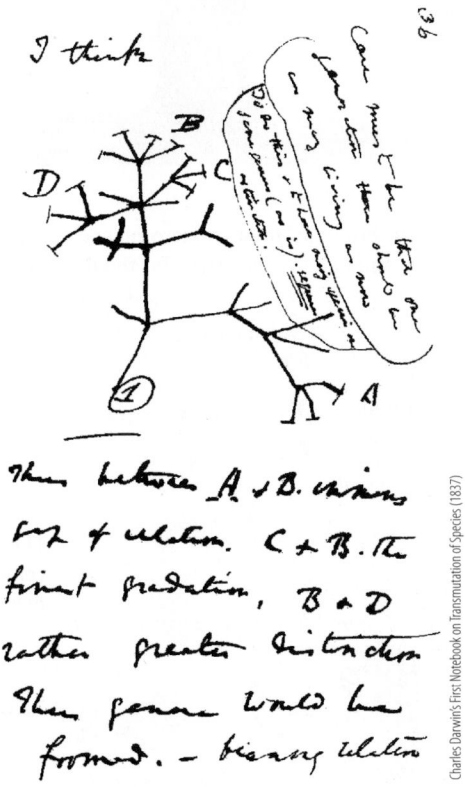

**FIGURE 21.27 Darwin's Evolutionary Tree.** This entry from his notebook on the "transmutation of species" demonstrates that Charles Darwin first thought about the branching pattern of evolution in 1837, more than 20 years before he published *On the Origin of Species*.

CHAPTER 21 DEFINING LIFE AND ITS ORIGINS |

# Summary Illustration

Life is often defined by seven characteristics, each of which is the result of a hierarchy of interactions between atoms, molecules, and processes. All forms of life are composed of nucleic acids, proteins, lipids, and polysaccharides, which must have been synthesized in the environment of the primordial Earth prior to life itself. Once formed, these macromolecules would then support the development of a membrane-defined compartment, a system for storing genetic information, and a system for harnessing energy—critical features required of the earliest life forms.

## What Is Life?

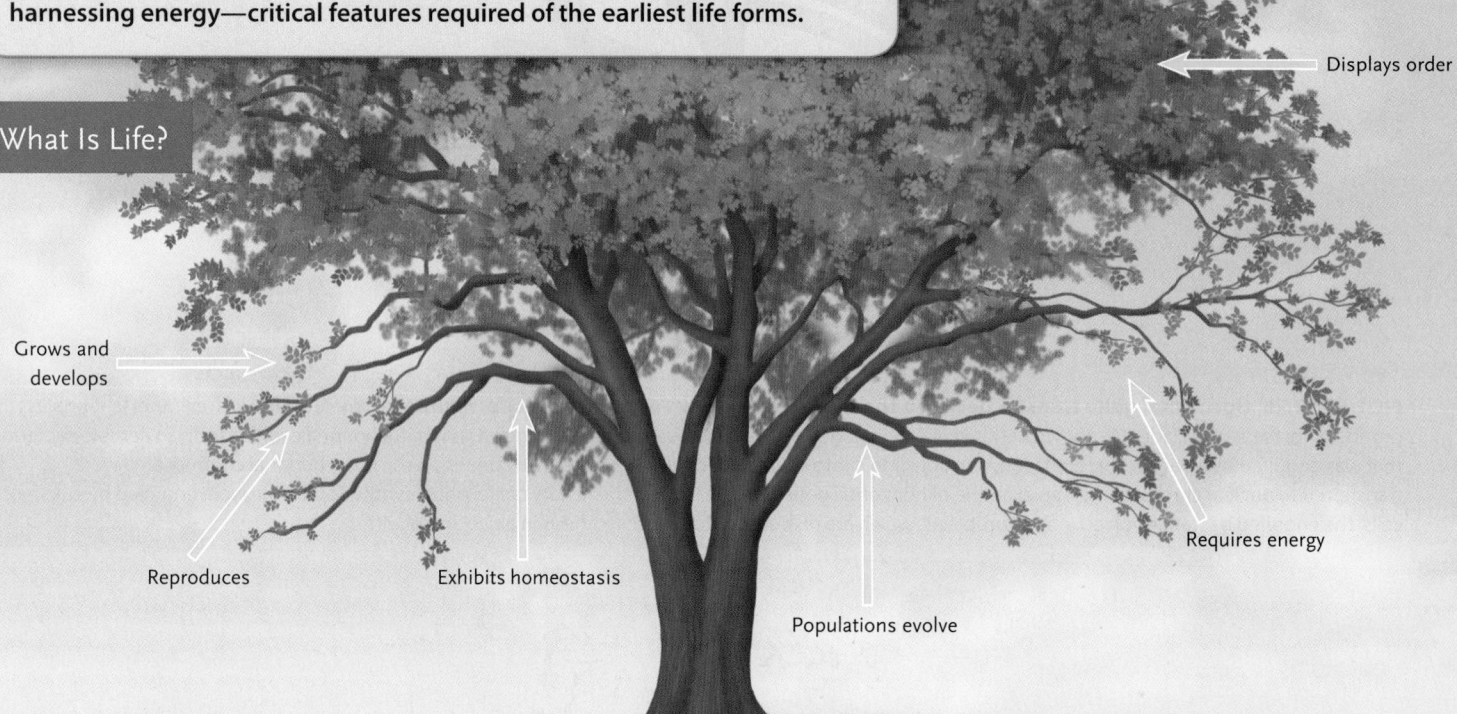

Responds to stimuli

Displays order

Grows and develops

Reproduces

Exhibits homeostasis

Populations evolve

Requires energy

## Scenario Leading to Modern Cells

The presence of certain polymeric macromolecules (e.g., nucleic acids, proteins, and lipids) was crucial for the development of life.

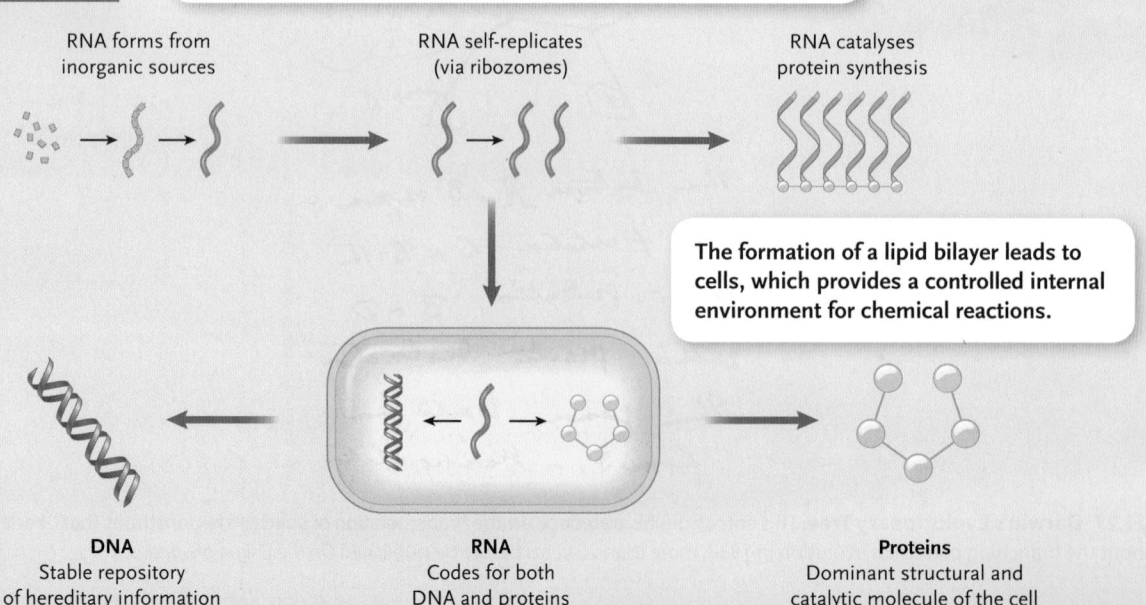

RNA forms from inorganic sources

RNA self-replicates (via ribozomes)

RNA catalyses protein synthesis

The formation of a lipid bilayer leads to cells, which provides a controlled internal environment for chemical reactions.

**DNA**
Stable repository of hereditary information

**RNA**
Codes for both DNA and proteins

**Proteins**
Dominant structural and catalytic molecule of the cell

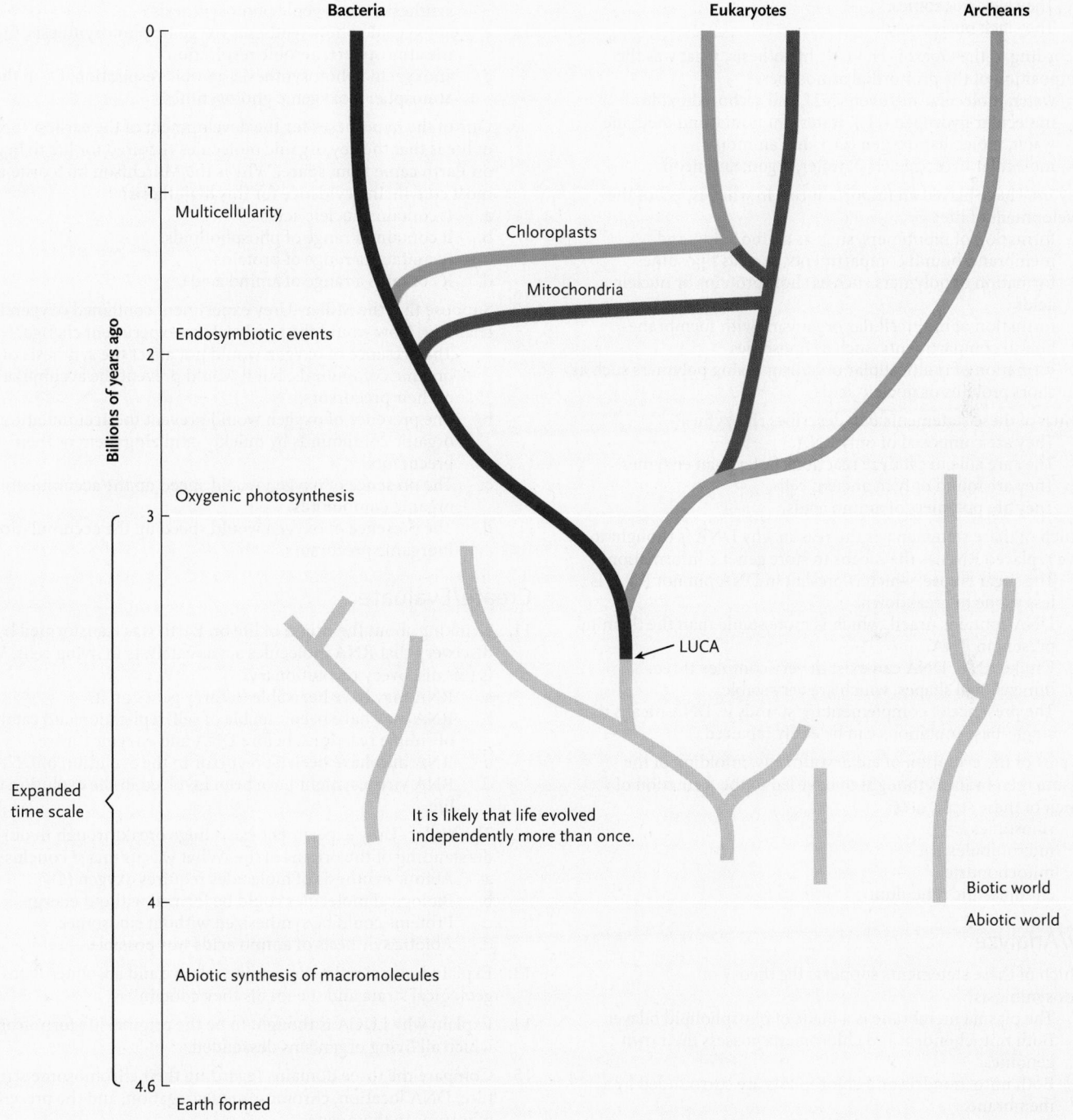

## The Tree of Life

Bacteria   Eukaryotes   Archeans

**Billions of years ago**

0

1 — Multicellularity

Chloroplasts

Mitochondria

— Endosymbiotic events

2

— Oxygenic photosynthesis

3

← LUCA

Expanded time scale

It is likely that life evolved
independently more than once.

4

Biotic world
Abiotic world

Abiotic synthesis of macromolecules

4.6 — Earth formed

The origin and evolution of life required certain key events to occur over Earth's history.
The earliest forms of life were most likely anaerobic heterotrophs. The development of
oxygenic photosynthesis in certain groups of prokaryotic cells led to oxygen accumulating
in the atmosphere. In turn, this led to the evolution of aerobic respiration, which allowed
for increased production of ATP. Increased energy production is a prerequisite for the
evolution of the eukaryotic cell, greater cell complexity, and multicellularity.

## Recall/Understand

1. Why are viruses NOT considered a form of life?
   a. They do not have a nucleus.
   b. They are not made of protein.
   c. They lack ribosomes.
   d. They lack nucleic acid.

2. According to the Oparin–Haldane hypothesis, what was the composition of the primordial atmosphere?
   a. water, molecular nitrogen (N2), and carbon dioxide
   b. molecular hydrogen ($H_2$), water, ammonia, and methane
   c. water, molecular oxygen ($O_2$), and ammonia
   d. molecular hydrogen ($H_2$), water, argon, and neon

3. Clay may have played an important role in what aspect of the development of life?
   a. formation of monomers, such as amino acids, and membrane-bound compartments, such as liposomes
   b. formation of polymers such as short proteins or nucleic acids
   c. formation of multicellular organisms with membrane-bound compartments, such as liposomes
   d. formation of multicellular organisms using polymers such as short proteins or nucleic acids

4. Which of these statements *best* describes ribozymes?
   a. They are composed of only RNA.
   b. They are able to catalyze reactions faster than enzymes.
   c. They are found only in ancient cells.
   d. They are polymers of amino acids.

5. Which of these statements is the reason why DNA is thought to have replaced RNA as the means to store genetic information?
   a. The sugar ribose, which is present in DNA but not RNA, is less prone to breakdown.
   b. DNA contains uracil, which is more stable than the thymine present in RNA.
   c. Unlike RNA, DNA can exist in very complex three-dimensional shapes, which are very stable.
   d. The presence of complementary strands in DNA means that single-base mutations can be easily repaired.

6. As part of the evolution of eukaryotic cells, infolding of the plasma membrane is thought to have led to the formation of which of these structures?
   a. ribosomes
   b. microtubules
   c. mitochondria
   d. endoplasmic reticulum

## Apply/Analyze

7. Which of these statements supports the theory of endosymbiosis?
   a. The plasma membrane is a made of phospholipid bilayer.
   b. Both mitochondria and chloroplasts possess their own genomes.
   c. Both mitochondria and chloroplasts are surrounded by a membrane.
   d. The nuclear envelope is derived from infolding of the plasma membrane.

8. Which of these lists of events is in the correct order by first appearance?
   a. $O_2$ in the atmosphere, anoxygenic photosynthesis, aerobic respiration, oxygenic photosynthesis
   b. $O_2$ in the atmosphere, aerobic respiration, oxygenic photosynthesis, anoxygenic photosynthesis
   c. anoxygenic photosynthesis, oxygenic photosynthesis, $O_2$ in the atmosphere, aerobic respiration
   d. anoxygenic photosynthesis, aerobic respiration, $O_2$ in the atmosphere, oxygenic photosynthesis

9. One of the hypotheses for the development of the earliest forms of life is that the key organic molecules required for life to begin on Earth came from space. Why is the Murchison meteorite the most convincing evidence for this hypothesis?
   a. It contains nucleic acids.
   b. It contains a range of phospholipids.
   c. It contains a range of proteins.
   d. It contains a range of amino acids.

10. Suppose that the Miller–Urey experiment contained oxygen in its chamber. How would the results of the experiment change?
    a. The presence of oxygen would not affect the synthesis of organic compounds, but it would prevent the accumulation of their precursors.
    b. The presence of oxygen would prevent the accumulation of organic compounds by quickly oxidizing them or their precursors.
    c. The presence of oxygen would speed up the accumulation of organic compounds.
    d. The presence of oxygen would speed up the accumulation of inorganic precursors.

## Create/Evaluate

11. Thinking about the origin of life on Earth was transformed by the discovery that RNA molecules act as catalysts in living cells. Why is this discovery revolutionary?
    a. RNA may have been able to carry genes on it.
    b. RNA may have been capable of self-replication and catalysis of simple reactions, before DNA and enzymes arose.
    c. RNA may have been a precursor in the evolution of DNA.
    d. RNA viruses might have been involved in the evolution of life.

12. The Miller–Urey experiment was a huge breakthrough in our understanding of the origins of life. What was its major conclusion?
    a. Abiotic synthesis of molecules requires oxygen ($O_2$).
    b. Biological molecules could be formed without energy.
    c. Proteins could be synthesized without ribosomes.
    d. Abiotic synthesis of amino acids was possible.

13. Explain how scientists determine relative and absolutes dates of geological strata and the fossils they contain.

14. Explain why LUCA is thought to be the original life form from which all living organisms descended.

15. Compare the three domains regarding their chromosome structure, DNA location, chromosome segregation, and the presence of introns in their genes.

# Chapter Roadmap

**Viruses, Viroids, and Prions: Infectious Biological Particles**

Viruses, viroids, and prions, non-cellular, elegant in their simplicity, highjack the machinery of cells of both prokaryotes and eukaryotes.

### 22.1 What Is a Virus? Characteristics of Viruses

Viruses are non-living infective agents consisting of a nucleic acid genome enclosed in a protein coat. Recognition proteins that enable the virus to attach to host cells extend from the surface of infectious viruses.

**From Chapter 5**

**From Chapter 7**

**From Chapter 10**

**From Chapter 12**

**From Chapter 21**

### 22.2 Viruses Infect Bacterial, Animal, and Plant Cells by Similar Pathways

Viruses reproduce by entering a host cell and directing the cellular machinery to make new particles of the same kind.

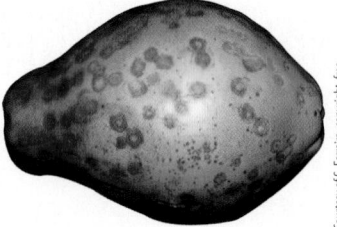

Courtesy of S. Ferreira, copyright-free

### 22.3 Treating and Preventing Viral Infections

These agents do not respond to antibiotics and other treatment methods. Research efforts have focused on development of vaccines and on preventing infection by viruses that cause serious or fatal diseases.

### 22.4 Viruses May Have Evolved from Fragments of Cellular DNA or RNA

Viruses may have evolved after cells and descended from nucleic acid fragments that "escaped" from a cell.

### 22.5 Viroids and Prions Are Infective Agents Even Simpler in Structure than Viruses

Viroids, which infect crop plants, consist of only a very small, single-stranded, RNA molecule. Prions, which cause brain diseases in some animals, are infectious proteins with no associated nucleic acid.

**To Chapter 26**

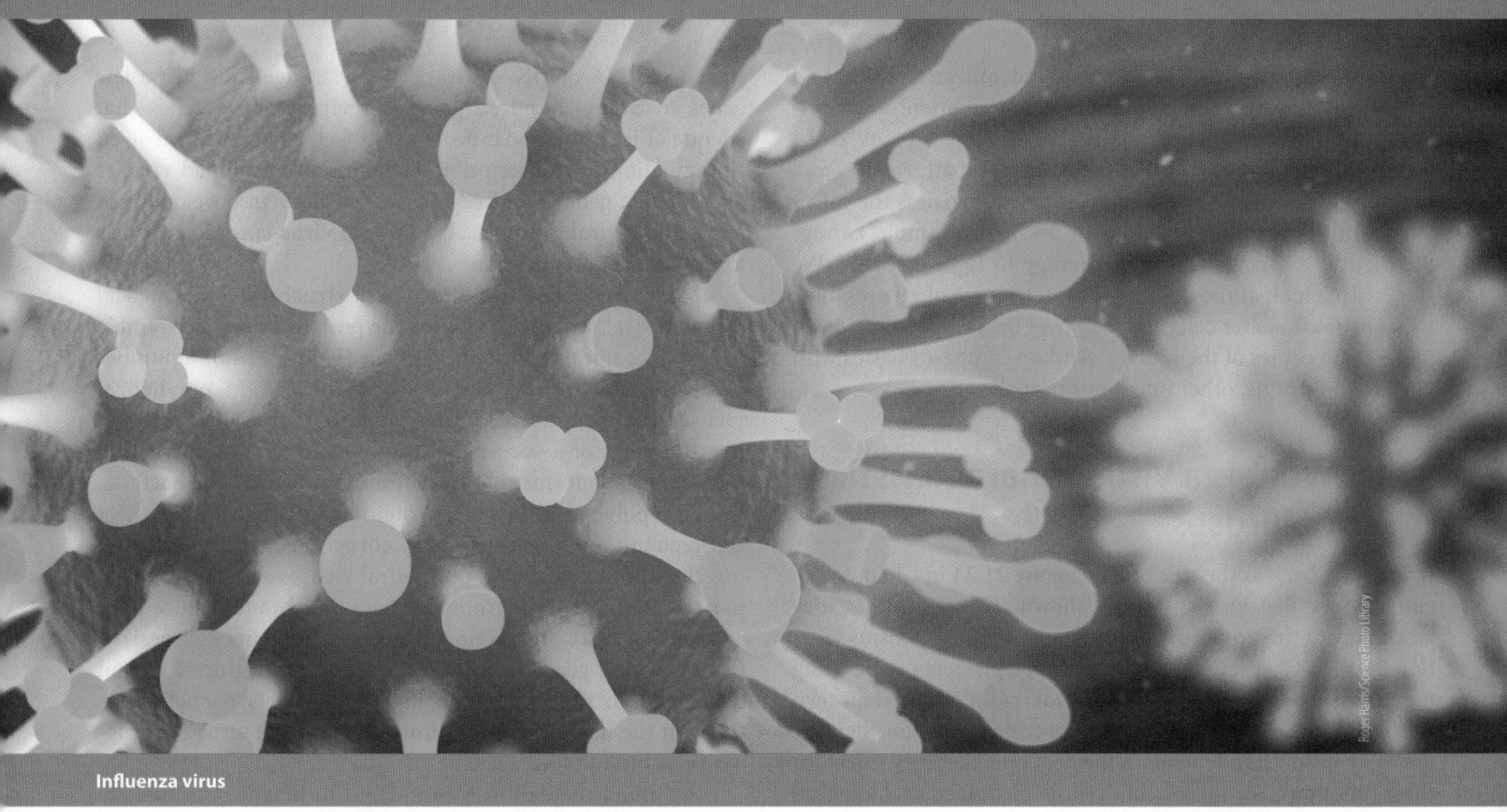

Influenza virus

# Viruses, Viroids, and Prions: Infectious Biological Particles

# 22

**Why it matters . . .** Imagine yourself sitting in a crowded airplane bound from London, United Kingdom, to Vancouver. The person sitting beside you has a runny nose; is sneezing, coughing, and sucking on lozenges; and appears to have a fever. Recognizing that your seatmate is exhibiting many of the symptoms of influenza, a respiratory illness caused by the influenza virus shown in the micrograph above, you worry that the virus will spread to you through your seatmate's coughing and sneezing.

At any given time, 5%–15% of the global population of people exhibit the symptoms of influenza, and each year about 500 000 people die from influenza A. Recent research has shown that new strains of influenza A arise each year from just a few initial sources in East and Southeast Asia and then spread around the world. As influenza viruses travel through populations around the world, they evolve, changing so much that the vaccines we developed in previous years are no longer effective, and new vaccines must be developed.

Understanding the global pattern of influenza migration will help the World Health Organization to develop effective vaccines. Knowing which strains cause the initial outbreak in Asia allows scientists to formulate vaccines to target these strains, offering people in other regions some protection from the illness.

Why was the 1918 Spanish flu pandemic so deadly? And why do we need to develop new flu vaccines so often? We investigate these questions later in this chapter. We also look at the beneficial roles played by viruses—not all are pathogenic—and investigate ways in which we may be able to harness the infective abilities of viruses for our own uses. For example, can we use viruses as vectors for gene therapy to fight diseases? We start with a look at the defining characteristics of viruses: how they are able to enter cells and take over the cell's machinery to make more copies of themselves. And we compare viruses with viroids and prions, other infectious particles.

## 22.1 What Is a Virus? Characteristics of Viruses

If you look back at the tree of life (Figure 21.24 in Chapter 21), you'll notice that viruses are not shown. That is because they lack many of the properties of life shared by all organisms (Section 21.1a in Chapter 21), and so are not considered to be living organisms. For example, viruses cannot reproduce on their own and they lack a metabolic system to provide energy for their life cycles; instead, they depend on the host cells that they infect for these functions. For this reason, viruses are infectious biological particles rather than organisms. The structure of a virus is reduced to the minimum necessary to transmit its genome from one host cell to another. A virus is simply one or more nucleic acid molecules surrounded by a protein coat, or **capsid** (Figure 22.1a, b). Some capsids might be enclosed within a membrane, or **envelope**, derived from their host cell's membrane (Figure 22.1c). So a virus, while able to evolve, is not a cell: it does not have cytoplasm enclosed by a plasma membrane, as do all known living organisms.

The nucleic acid genome of a virus may be either DNA or RNA and can be composed of either a single strand or a double strand of RNA or DNA. Viral genomes range from just a few genes to over a hundred genes; all viruses have genes that encode at least their coat proteins, as well as proteins involved in regulation of transcription. Genomes of **enveloped viruses** also include genes required for the synthesis of envelope proteins. Some viral genomes also include virus-specific enzymes for nucleic acid replication.

Most viruses take one of two basic structural forms, helical or polyhedral. In **helical viruses** the protein subunits assemble in a rodlike spiral around the genome (Figure 22.1a). A number of viruses that infect plant cells are helical. In **polyhedral viruses**, the coat proteins form triangular units that fit together like the parts of a soccer ball (Figure 22.1b). The polyhedral viruses include forms that infect animals, plants, and bacteria. In some polyhedral viruses, protein spikes that provide host cell recognition extend from the corners, where the facets fit together. Both helical and polyhedral viruses can be enveloped in a membrane derived from the host's membrane (Figure 22.1c and **Figure 22.2**). In enveloped viruses, proteins synthesized from the viral genome in the host cell are transported to and embedded in the membrane before the virus particle buds through the host cell. These proteins allow the virus to recognize and bind to host cells.

Although they are not considered to be alive, viruses are classified into orders, families, genera, and species using several criteria, including virus size and structure, genome structure (RNA or DNA, single stranded or double stranded), and how their nucleic acid is replicated. More than 4000 species of viruses have been classified into more than 80 families. The family names end in -*viridae* (**Table 22.1**) and may refer either to the geographic region where the virus was first discovered or to the structure of the virus. For example, Coronaviridae, the family to which the influenza virus and SARS (Severe Acute Respiratory Disorder) belong, is named for the "crown" of protein spikes on the capsid, as shown in the photomicrograph at

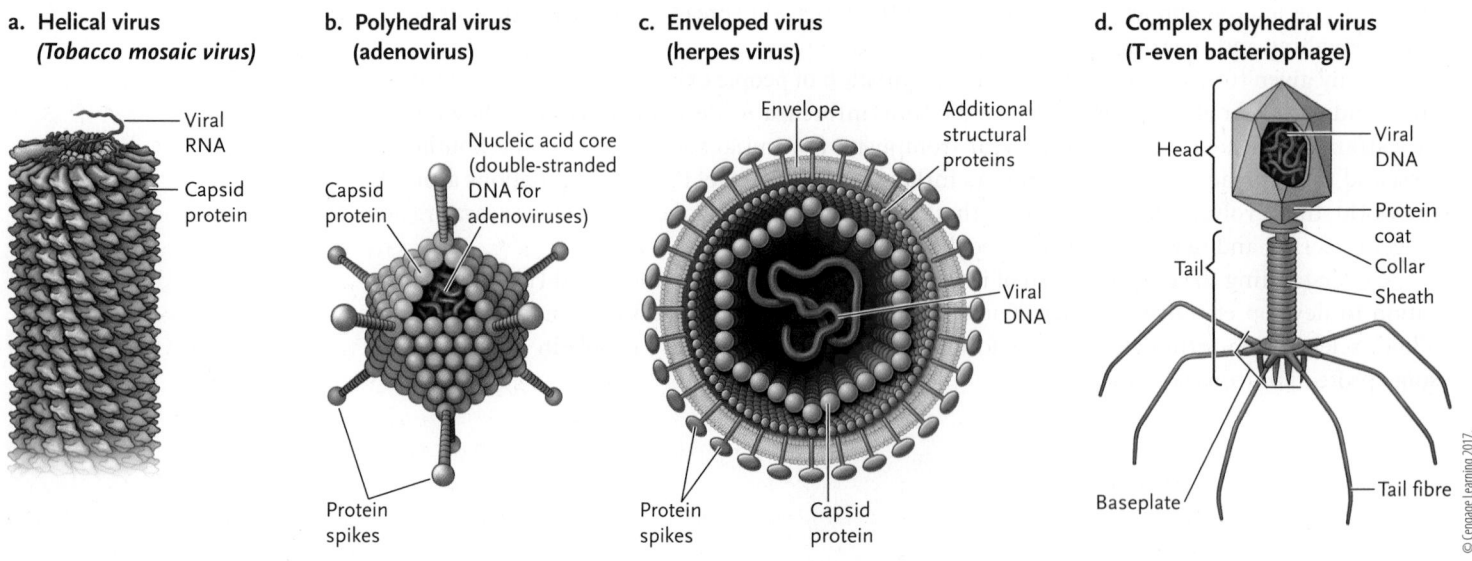

**a. Helical virus** *(Tobacco mosaic virus)* — Viral RNA, Capsid protein

**b. Polyhedral virus** (adenovirus) — Capsid protein, Nucleic acid core (double-stranded DNA for adenoviruses), Protein spikes

**c. Enveloped virus** (herpes virus) — Envelope, Additional structural proteins, Protein spikes, Viral DNA, Capsid protein

**d. Complex polyhedral virus** (T-even bacteriophage) — Head, Tail, Viral DNA, Protein coat, Collar, Sheath, Baseplate, Tail fibre

© Cengage Learning 2017.

**FIGURE 22.1 Viral structure.** All viruses consist of nucleic acid surrounded by a protein coat, but they can have a very wide range of sizes and shapes.

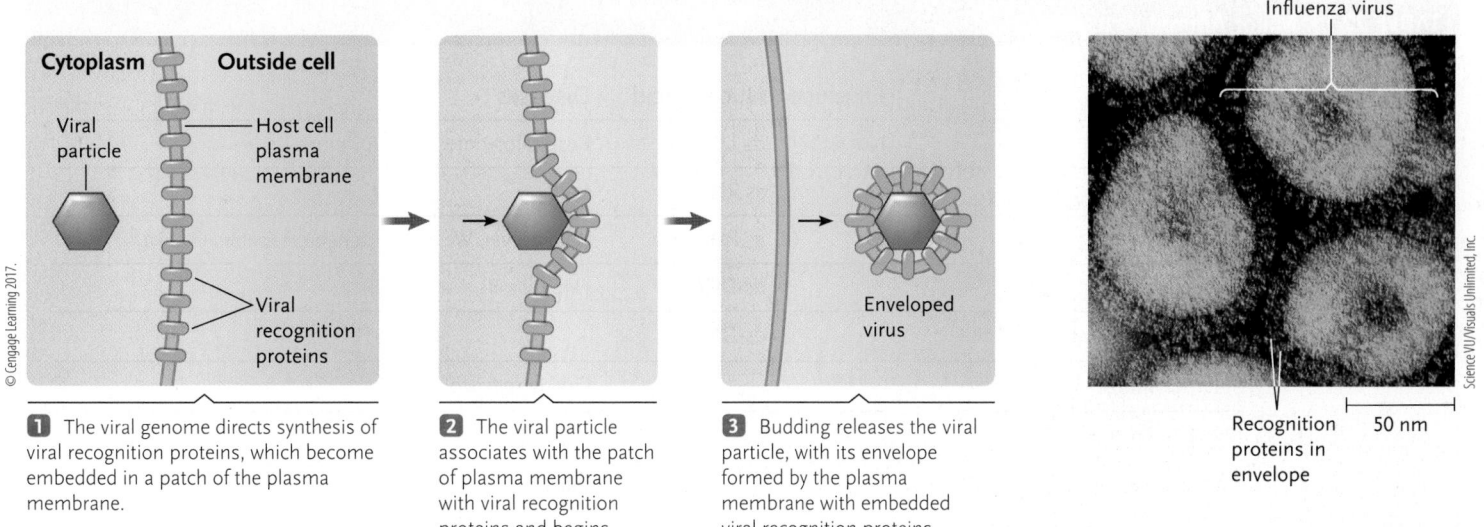

Cytoplasm    Outside cell

Viral particle

Host cell plasma membrane

Viral recognition proteins

**1** The viral genome directs synthesis of viral recognition proteins, which become embedded in a patch of the plasma membrane.

**2** The viral particle associates with the patch of plasma membrane with viral recognition proteins and begins budding out of the cell.

**3** Budding releases the viral particle, with its envelope formed by the plasma membrane with embedded viral recognition proteins.

Enveloped virus

Influenza virus

Recognition proteins in envelope

50 nm

© Cengage Learning 2017.

Science VU/Visuals Unlimited, Inc.

**FIGURE 22.2  How enveloped viruses acquire their envelope**

the start of this chapter (*corona* = crown). Like some bacteria, some viruses are named for the disease they cause; these names can be one or two words, for example, herpesvirus or Ebola virus. Each type of virus is made up of many strains, which are differentiated by their virulence.

As is the case for our look at prokaryotic organisms in the next chapter, we will just scratch the surface of viral diversity in this chapter. For example, there are millions of viruses in every millilitre of ocean water, most of which have not been identified. As we learn more about viruses, the classification system will change.

Every living organism is likely permanently infected by one or more kinds of viruses. Usually, a virus infects only a single species or a few closely related species. A virus may even infect only one organ system or a single tissue or cell type in its host. However, some viruses are able to infect unrelated species, either naturally or after mutating.

Of the roughly 80 viral families described to date, 21 include viruses that cause human diseases. Viruses also cause diseases of wild and domestic animals. Plant viruses cause annual losses of millions of tonnes of crops, especially cereals, potatoes, sugar beets, and sugar cane. (**Table 22.1** lists some important families of viruses that infect animals.) The effects of viruses on the organisms they infect range from undetectable to merely bothersome to seriously debilitating or lethal. For instance, some viral infections of humans, such as those causing cold sores or the common cold, are usually little more than a nuisance to healthy adults. Others cause some of the most severe and deadly human diseases, including AIDS, encephalitis, and Ebola hemorrhagic fever.

However, not all viruses are pathogens. Many viruses actually benefit their hosts; for example, infection by certain non-pathogenic viruses protects human hosts against pathogenic viruses. The "protective" viruses interfere with replication or

other functions of the pathogenic viruses. Some viruses also act to defend their host cells. For example, one of the primary reasons that bacteria do not completely overrun this planet is that they are destroyed in incredibly huge numbers by viruses known as **bacteriophages**, or **phages** for short (*phagein* = to eat) (Figure 22.1d). Viruses also provide a natural means to control some insect pests, such as spruce budworm.

Viruses are vital components of ecosystems and may be the dominant entity in some ecosystems, such as the oceans. We don't yet fully understand their roles in these ecosystems, but it is clear that they affect nutrient cycling through their effects on prokaryotic organisms. For example, in certain regions of the ocean, a few genera of cyanobacteria dominate the marine phytoplankton, making major contributions to global photosynthesis. Bacteriophages infect these cyanobacteria, causing high levels of mortality, thus influencing cyanobacterial population dynamics as well as the release of nutrients from bacterial cells. But these viruses also help keep photosynthesis going in their cyanobacterial hosts, as recently discovered by Nicholas Mann and colleagues at the University of Warwick. As you read in Chapter 6, one of the proteins that make up photosystem II is very susceptible to light-induced damage and so is constantly being replaced by newly synthesized molecules. As long as the cell can make new protein quickly enough to keep up with damage, photosynthesis can continue, but if the rate of damage to photosystem II exceeds the repair rate, the rate of photosynthesis will drop. When these bacteriophages infect cyanobacteria, they shut down their host's protein synthesis. Without continued synthesis of the photosystem protein, photosynthesis should slow down following infection; but it doesn't. How is the photosynthetic rate maintained? Mann and his colleagues found that the virus's genome includes genes for this protein; expression of these viral proteins enables the repair rate to keep up with

TABLE 22.1 | Major Animal Viruses

| Viral Families | Viral Genera | Envelope | Nucleic Acid | Diseases |
|---|---|---|---|---|
| Adenoviridae | Adenovirus | No | ds DNA | Respiratory infections, tumours |
| Coronaviridae | *Betacoronavirus* | Yes | ss RNA | SARS |
| Flaviviridae | *Flavivirus* | Yes | ss RNA | Yellow fever, West Nile, dengue, hepatitis C, Zika |
| Hepadnaviridae | Hepadnavirus | Yes | ds DNA | Hepatitis B |
| | Human herpesvirus | Yes | ds DNA | |
| | Herpes simplex I | | | Oral herpes, cold sores |
| | Herpes simplex II | | | Genital herpes |
| | Varicella-zoster virus | | | Chickenpox, shingles |
| | Herpesvirus 4 (Epstein–Barr virus) | | | Infectious mononucleosis |
| Orthomyxoviridae | Orthomyxovirus | Yes | ss RNA | Influenza |
| Papillomaviridae | Papillomavirus | No | ds DNA | Human papillomavirus (genital warts) |
| Papovaviridae | Papovavirus | No | ds DNA | Benign and malignant warts |
| Paramyxoviridae | Paramyxovirus | Yes | ss RNA | Measles, mumps, pneumonia |
| Picornaviridae | Picornavirus | No | ss RNA | |
| | Enterovirus | | | Polio, hemorrhagic eye disease, gastroenteritis |
| | Rhinovirus | | | Common cold |
| | Hepatitis A virus | | | Hepatitis A |
| | Aphthovirus | | | Foot-and-mouth disease in livestock |
| Poxviridae | Poxvirus | Yes | ds DNA | Smallpox, cowpox |
| Retroviridae | Retrovirus | Yes | ss RNA | |
| | HTLV I, II | | | T-cell leukemia |
| | HIV | | | AIDS |
| Rhabdoviridae | Rhabdovirus | Yes | ss RNA | Rabies, other animal diseases |

ds = double-stranded; HTLV = human T-lymphotropic virus; ss = single-stranded

light-induced damage, allowing the cell to photosynthesize. Although the virus is doing this for "selfish" reasons (i.e., to ensure that its host has sufficient resources for the virus to complete its life cycle), the outcome of this association is that much of the carbon fixed on Earth may be facilitated by virus-controlled photosynthesis.

## STUDY BREAK QUESTIONS

1. What is a virus?
2. List three features of viruses that distinguish them from living organisms.

## 22.2 Viruses Infect Bacterial, Animal, and Plant Cells by Similar Pathways

Viral particles move by random molecular motions until they contact the surface of a host cell. For infection to occur, the virus or the viral genome must then enter the cell. Inside the cell, the viral genes are expressed, leading to replication of the viral genome and assembly of progeny viruses. The new viral particles, or **virions** as the extracellular form of a virus is known, are then released from the host cell, a process that often ruptures the host cell, killing it.

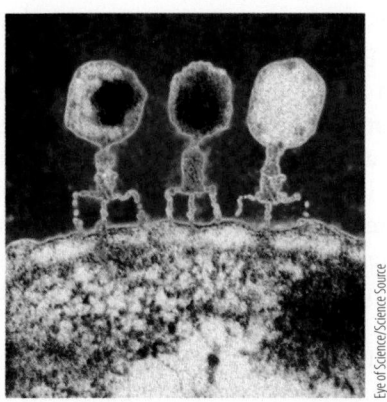

**FIGURE 22.3 Bacteriophages injecting their DNA into *E. coli***

## 22.2a Bacteriophages: Viruses That Infect Bacteria

We have learned a great deal about the infective cycles of viruses, as well as the genetics of both viruses and bacteria, from studies of the bacteriophages infecting *Escherichia coli* (*E. coli*). Some of these are **virulent bacteriophages**, which kill their host cells during each cycle of infection, whereas others are **temperate bacteriophages**. Temperate bacteriophages enter an inactive phase while inside the host cell and can be passed on to several generations of daughter cells before becoming active and killing their host.

**VIRULENT BACTERIOPHAGES** Among the virulent bacteriophages infecting *E. coli*, the **T-even bacteriophages** T2, T4, and T6 have been the most valuable in genetic studies. The coats of these phages are divided into a *head* and a *tail* (Figure 22.1d). A double-stranded linear molecule of DNA is packed into the head. The tail, assembled from several different proteins, has **recognition proteins** at its tip that can bind to the surface of the host cell. Once the tail is attached, it functions as a sort of syringe that injects the DNA genome into the cell **(Figure 22.3)**.

Infection begins when a T-even phage collides randomly with the surface of an *E. coli* cell and the tail attaches to the host cell wall (**Figure 22.4**, step 1). An enzyme present in the viral coat, *lysozyme*, then digests a hole in the cell wall, through which the tail injects the DNA of the phage (step 2). The proteins of the viral coat remain outside. Throughout its life cycle within the bacterial cell, the phage uses host cell machinery to express its genes. One of the proteins produced early in the infection is an enzyme that breaks down the bacterial chromosome. The phage gene for a DNA polymerase that replicates the phage's DNA is also expressed early on. Eventually, 100–200 new viral DNA molecules are synthesized (step 3). Later in the infection, the host cell machinery transcribes the phage genes for the viral coat proteins (step 4). As the head and tail proteins assemble, the replicated viral DNA is packed into the heads (step 5).

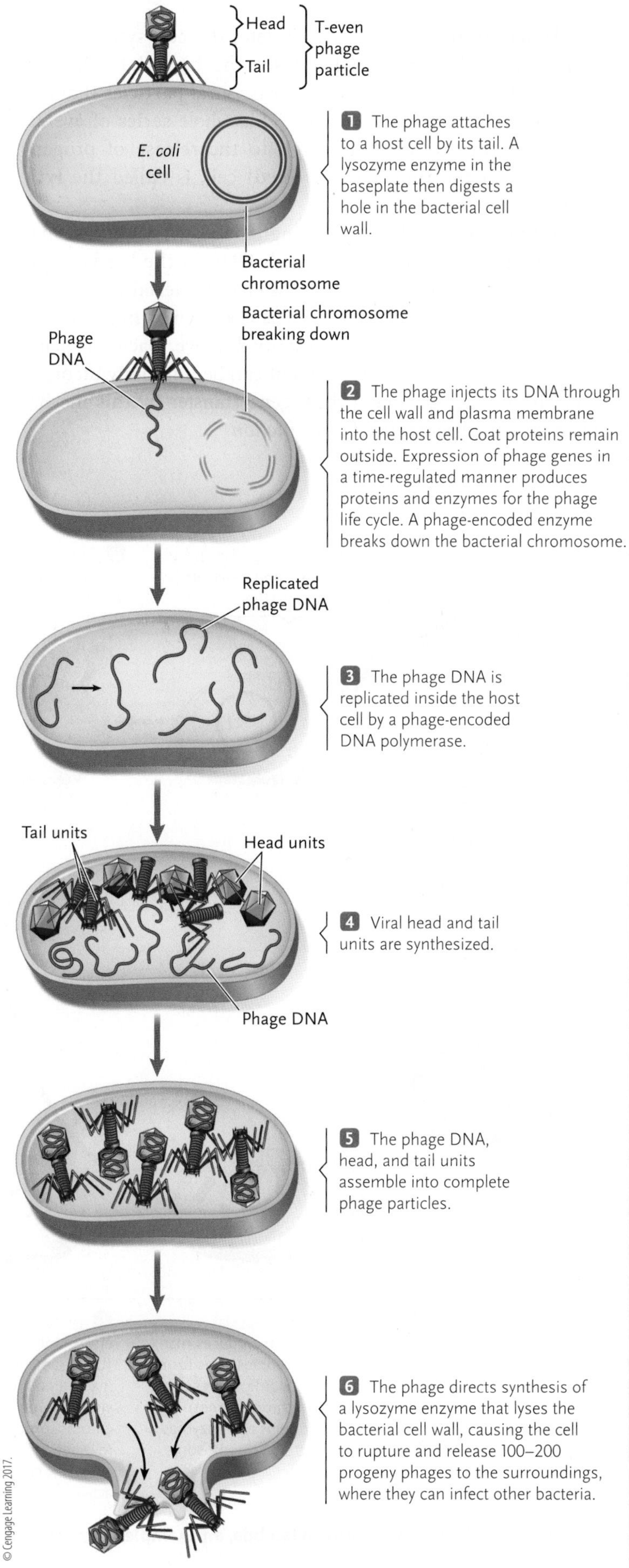

**FIGURE 22.4 The infective cycle of a T-even bacteriophage, an example of a virulent phage**

Head
Tail
T-even phage particle

*E. coli* cell

**1** The phage attaches to a host cell by its tail. A lysozyme enzyme in the baseplate then digests a hole in the bacterial cell wall.

Bacterial chromosome

Phage DNA

Bacterial chromosome breaking down

**2** The phage injects its DNA through the cell wall and plasma membrane into the host cell. Coat proteins remain outside. Expression of phage genes in a time-regulated manner produces proteins and enzymes for the phage life cycle. A phage-encoded enzyme breaks down the bacterial chromosome.

Replicated phage DNA

**3** The phage DNA is replicated inside the host cell by a phage-encoded DNA polymerase.

Tail units

Head units

**4** Viral head and tail units are synthesized.

Phage DNA

**5** The phage DNA, head, and tail units assemble into complete phage particles.

**6** The phage directs synthesis of a lysozyme enzyme that lyses the bacterial cell wall, causing the cell to rupture and release 100–200 progeny phages to the surroundings, where they can infect other bacteria.

When viral assembly is complete, the cell synthesizes a phage-encoded lysozyme that lyses the bacterial cell wall, causing the cell to rupture and release viral particles that can infect other *E. coli* cells (step 6). This whole series of events, from infection of a cell through to the release of progeny phages from the ruptured (or **lysed**) cell, is called the **lytic cycle**.

Some virulent phages (although not T-even phages) may package fragments of the host cell's DNA in the heads as the viral particles assemble. This transfer of bacterial genes from one bacterium to another via a virus is known as *transduction*. In the type of transduction described above, bacterial genes from essentially any DNA fragment can be randomly incorporated into phage particles; thus, gene transfer by this mechanism is termed *generalized transduction*.

**A SCIENTIST'S FAVOURITE TEMPERATE *E. COLI* BACTERIOPHAGE, LAMBDA** The infective cycle of the bacteriophage lambda (λ), an *E. coli* phage used extensively in research, is typical of temperate phages. Phage lambda infects *E. coli* in much the same way as the T-even phages. The phage injects its double-stranded, linear DNA chromosome into the bacterium (**Figure 22.5**, step 1). Once inside, the linear chromosome forms a circle and then follows one of two paths. Sophisticated molecular switches govern which path is followed at the time of infection.

One path is the lytic cycle, which is like the lytic cycles of virulent phages. The lytic cycle (Figure 22.5, left side) starts with steps 1 and 2 (infection) and then goes directly to steps 7 through 9 (production and release of progeny virus) and back to step 1. A second and more common path is the **lysogenic**

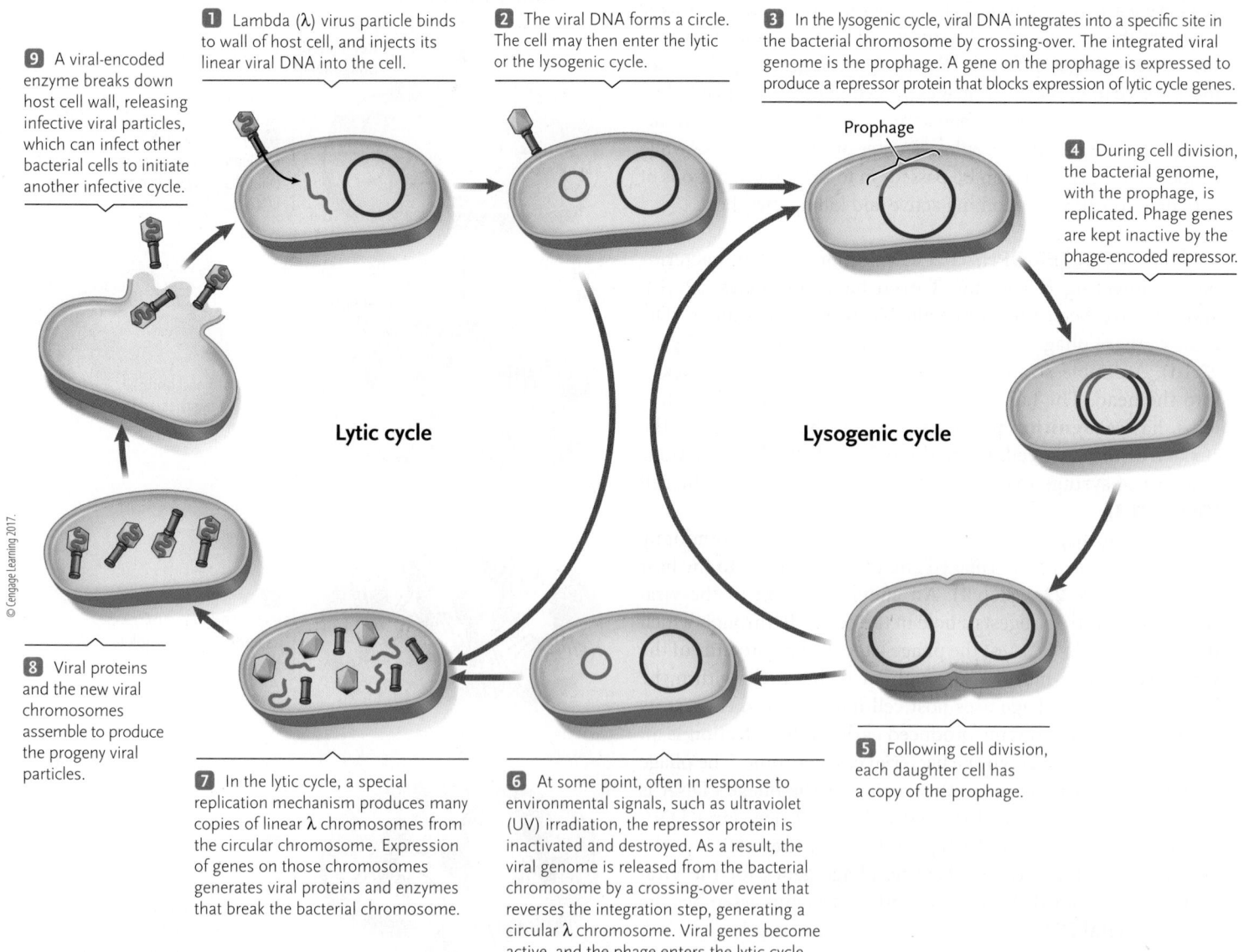

**FIGURE 22.5 The infective cycle of lambda, an example of a temperate phage, which can go through the lytic cycle or the lysogenic cycle**

cycle (Figure 22.5, right side). This cycle begins when the viral chromosome integrates into the host cell's DNA by recombination (Figure 22.5, steps 1 through 3). The DNA of a temperate phage typically inserts at one or possibly a few specific sites in the bacterial chromosome through the action of a phage-encoded enzyme that recognizes certain sequences in the host DNA. Once integrated, the lambda genes are mostly inactive, so no structural components of the phage are made. While inserted in the host cell DNA, the virus is known as a **prophage** (*pro* = before). When the host cell DNA replicates, so does the integrated viral DNA, which is passed on to daughter cells along with the host cell DNA (Figure 22.5, steps 4 and 5).

What triggers the integrated prophage to become active (step 6)? Certain environmental signals, such as nutrient availability and ultraviolet irradiation, stimulate this change, causing the prophage to enter the lytic cycle (Figure 22.5, steps 6 through 9). Genes that were inactive in the prophage are now transcribed. Among the first viral proteins synthesized are enzymes that excise the lambda chromosome from the host chromosome. The result is a circular lambda chromosome that replicates itself and directs the production of linear viral DNA and coat proteins. This active stage culminates in the lysis of the host cell and the release of infective viral particles.

The excision of the prophage from its host's DNA is not always precise, resulting in the inclusion of one or more host cell genes with the viral DNA. These genes are replicated with the viral DNA and packed into the coats, and may be carried to a new host cell in the next cycle of infection. Clearly, only genes that are adjacent to the integration site(s) of a temperate phage can be cut out with the viral DNA, can be included in phage particles during the lytic stage, and can undergo transduction. Accordingly, this mechanism of gene transfer is termed **specialized transduction**.

## 22.2b Animal Viruses

Viruses infecting animal cells follow a pattern similar to that for bacterial cells, except that both the viral coat and the genome enter a host cell. Depending on the virus, removal of the coat to release the genome occurs during or after cell entry; the envelope does not enter the cell.

Viruses without an envelope, such as poliovirus, bind by their recognition proteins to the plasma membrane and are then taken into the host cell by endocytosis. The virus coat and genome of some enveloped viruses, such as herpesvirus, HIV, and the virus causing rabies, enter the host cell by fusion of their envelope with the host cell plasma membrane. Other enveloped viruses, such as influenza virus, enter host cells by endocytosis.

Once inside the host cell, the genome directs the synthesis of additional viral particles by basically the same pathways as bacterial viruses. Some animal viruses replicate themselves in very complex ways; one example is HIV, the virus that causes AIDS **(Figure 22.6)**. HIV, a retrovirus, contains two copies of

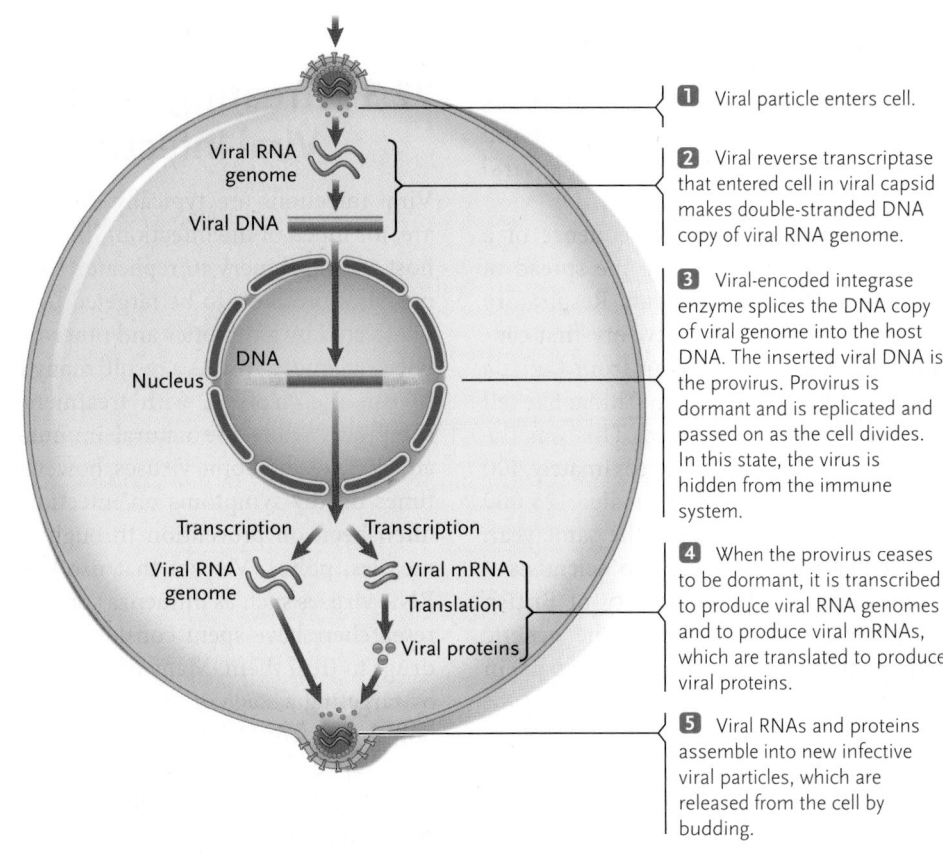

**FIGURE 22.6 The steps in HIV infection of a host cell**

1 Viral particle enters cell.

2 Viral reverse transcriptase that entered cell in viral capsid makes double-stranded DNA copy of viral RNA genome.

3 Viral-encoded integrase enzyme splices the DNA copy of viral genome into the host DNA. The inserted viral DNA is the provirus. Provirus is dormant and is replicated and passed on as the cell divides. In this state, the virus is hidden from the immune system.

4 When the provirus ceases to be dormant, it is transcribed to produce viral RNA genomes and to produce viral mRNAs, which are translated to produce viral proteins.

5 Viral RNAs and proteins assemble into new infective viral particles, which are released from the cell by budding.

© Cengage Learning 2017.

single-stranded RNA. It also carries several molecules of an enzyme, reverse transcriptase, in its capsid. Replication of retroviruses is unusual: the virus's genome enters the host cell along with reverse transcriptase, which generates a complementary strand of DNA from viral RNA. A second strand of DNA is then synthesized using the first strand as a template. The resulting double-stranded DNA integrates into the host cell's DNA as a provirus (comparable to the prophage previously described). This DNA is transcribed by the host cell into mRNA, which is translated to produce viral proteins, including capsid proteins and reverse transcriptase molecules. New virus particles are released from the cell to infect other cells or to be passed to new hosts. In some cases, newly completed viruses rupture the host cell's plasma membrane, typically killing the cell.

The vast majority of animal virus infections are asymptomatic because causing disease is of no benefit to the virus. However, a number of pathogenic viruses cause diseases in a variety of ways. Some viruses (e.g., herpesvirus) cause cell death when progeny viruses are released from the cell. This can lead to massive cell death, destroying vital tissues such as nervous tissue or white or red blood cells, or causing lesions in skin and mucous membranes. Other viruses release cellular molecules when infected cells break down, which can induce fever and inflammation (e.g., influenza virus). Yet other viruses alter gene function when they insert into the host cell DNA, leading to cancer and other abnormalities.

Some animal viruses enter a **latent phase**, similar to the lysogenic cycle for bacteriophages, in which the virus remains in the cell in an inactive form. The herpesviruses that cause oral and genital ulcers in humans remain in a latent phase in the cytoplasm of some body cells for the life of the individual. At times, particularly during periods of stress, the virus becomes active in some cells, directing viral replication and causing ulcers to form as cells break down during viral release.

Understanding the life cycle and genetic sequence of a virus is important in combatting and tracking the spread of viral diseases. For example, SARS (Severe Acute Respiratory Syndrome) became the first pandemic in the twenty-first century of a previously unknown cause. A woman from Canada contracted the virus in 2003 while travelling in China. She fell ill upon her arrival to Toronto, where she died. This was the first of two outbreaks in the Toronto area. Approximately 400 people subsequently became ill and 44 people died; 25 000 Torontonians were placed in quarantine. Later the same year, using samples from infected patients from Toronto, scientists at the Michael Smith Laboratories at the University of British Columbia mapped its genetic sequence. Using the genetic sequence data, the origin of the virus was shown to be bats, in which infection is asymptomatic.

## 22.2c Plant Viruses

Plant viruses may be rodlike or polyhedral. Although most include RNA as their nucleic acid, some contain DNA. None of the known plant viruses have envelopes. They enter cells through mechanical injuries to leaves and stems; they can also be transmitted from one plant to another during pollination or via herbivorous animals such as leafhoppers, aphids, and nematodes. Plant viruses can also be transmitted from one generation to the next in seeds. Once inside a cell, plant viruses replicate via the same processes as animal viruses. However, within plants, virus particles can pass from infected to healthy cells through plasmodesmata, the openings in cell walls that interconnect the cytoplasm of plant cells, and through the vascular system.

Plant viruses are generally named and classified by the type of plant they infect and their most visible effects. *Tomato bushy stunt virus*, for example, causes dwarfing and overgrowth of leaves and stems of tomato plants; and *tobacco mosaic virus* causes a mosaic-like pattern of spots on the leaves of tobacco plants. Most species of crop plants can be infected by at least one destructive virus.

The tobacco mosaic virus was the first virus to be isolated, disassembled, and reassembled in a test tube (Figure 22.1a).

### STUDY BREAK QUESTIONS

1. What is the difference between a virulent phage and a temperate phage?
2. What are the two types of transduction? How do they differ from each other?
3. How do plant viruses differ from animal viruses?

## 22.3 Treating and Preventing Viral Infections

Viral infections are typically difficult to treat because viruses are, for much of the infection, "hidden" inside host cells and use host cell machinery to replicate. Thus, there often are no obvious viral products to be targeted by drugs. Viral infections are unaffected by antibiotics and other treatment methods used for bacterial infections. As a result, many viral infections are allowed to run their course, with treatment limited to relieving the symptoms while the natural immune defences of the patient attack the virus. Some viruses, however, cause serious and sometimes deadly symptoms on infection; for these, the focus has often been on prevention through vaccine development (e.g., measles, polio). Viruses that use their own polymerases (e.g., RNA viruses such as influenza) provide more obvious targets, so researchers have spent considerable effort developing antiviral drugs to treat them. Many of these drugs fight the virus directly by targeting a stage of the viral life cycle; for example, the drug Sofosbuvir targets RNA polymerase, which is essential for viral RNA replication (**Figure 22.7**).

The influenza virus illustrates the difficulties inherent in controlling or preventing viral diseases. As mentioned at the start of the chapter, the influenza type A virus causes flu

FIGURE 22.7   **Experimental Research**

## A New Discovery for Hepatitis C Therapy

**Question:** Which form of β-D-20-deoxy-20-R-fluoro-20-β-C-methyl nucleoside (group of compounds shown to be effective inhibitors of the hepatitis C nonstructural protein 5B (NS5B)) should be developed into a therapy for hepatitis C virus (HCV)?

**Experiment:** β-D-20-deoxy-20-R-fluoro-20-β-C-methyl nucleoside compounds were identified and purified by NMR (nuclear magnetic resonance), MS (mass spectrometry), high performance liquid chromatography (HPLC), crystallization, and X-ray. Assays for anti-viral activity as well as cell and mitochondrial toxicity were performed on a subset of original compounds. Testing for chemical stability was done with simulated intestinal and gastric fluids as well as human liver and plasma. Animal testing was performed on rats, dogs, and monkeys.

**50** (PSI-7976)          **51** (PSI-7977)

## Structures of diastereomers 50 and 51

**Results:** A phosphate derivative of the β-D-20-deoxy-20-R-fluoro-20-β-C-methyluridine nucleoside (51) showed significant antiviral activity in the livers of rats, dogs, and monkeys when administered *in vivo* and was stable in a human environment. An X-ray structure determined the stereochemistry of diastereomer 51, which was selected as a clinical development candidate.

**Conclusions:** The identification of a new drug therapy was a major breakthrough in the treatment of hepatitis C. It is estimated that 170 million people worldwide are infected with the virus, with approximately 80% having chronic hepatitis C, which in many cases leads to cirrhosis (scarification of the liver) and/or carcinoma (cancer in epithelial cells). Standard treatments until this time were regular injections with interferon (protease inhibitor) and oral ribavirin. The severe side effects and long treatment duration made this therapy unsatisfactory. Current therapies target NS5B, which is an RNA polymerase and essential for viral RNA replication. This research led to the development of the first anti-hepatitis C medication (Sofosbuvir; named after the principle investigator Michael J. Sofia) that targeted binding proteins and has very few side effects, high efficacy, and shorter drug administration time.

Source: Michael J. Sofia, et al. 2010. Discovery of a β-D-20-Deoxy-20-r-fluoro-20-β-C-methyluridine Nucleotide Prodrug (PSI-7977) for the Treatment of Hepatitis C Virus. J. Med. Chem. 53, 7202–7218

epidemics that sweep over the world each year. Why does a new vaccine have to be developed each year? One reason for the success of this virus is that its genome consists of eight separate pieces of RNA. When two different influenza viruses infect the same individual, these RNA pieces can assemble in random combinations derived from either parent virus. The new combinations can change the protein coat of the virus, making it unrecognizable to antibodies developed against either parent virus. Being "invisible" to these antibodies means that new virus strains can infect people who have already had the flu caused by a different strain, or who had flu shots effective against only the parent strains of the virus. Random mutations in the RNA genome of the virus add to the variations in the coat proteins that make previously formed antibodies ineffective.

In the 1918 Spanish flu pandemic, the influenza virus killed many of its hosts. Why was this strain so virulent? Researchers have learned that the 1918 influenza virus had mutations in the polymerase genes that replicated the viral genome in host cells, likely making this strain capable of replicating more efficiently.

Other viruses that infect humans are also considered to have evolved from a virus that previously infected other animals. HIV is one of these. Until the second half of the twentieth century, infections of this virus were apparently restricted almost entirely to chimpanzees and gorillas in Africa. Now the virus infects nearly 36 million people worldwide, with the greatest concentration of infected individuals in sub-Saharan Africa.

As illustrated by this example, our efforts to control or eliminate human diseases caused by viral pathogens are complicated when dealing with viruses that have broad host specificity and can infect other animals besides humans. Because other animals can harbour these viruses, we can never successfully eradicate the diseases they cause. For example, the influenza virus can infect birds, swine, and other animals in addition to humans.

Also, as human encroachment on wildlife habitats increases, we create the potential for the evolution of new human viruses, as strains that infect other animals mutate to infect humans. These factors, together with increasing global travel and trade, create the potential for a new human pathogenic virus to readily become a global problem, as we have experienced with HIV. A better understanding of the evolution and life cycles of viruses is crucial if we are to prevent or treat emerging viral diseases.

**STUDY BREAK QUESTION**

1. Why can a viral infection be more difficult to treat than a bacterial infection?

## 22.4 Viruses May Have Evolved from Fragments of Cellular DNA or RNA

Where did viruses come from? Several different hypotheses have been proposed to explain the origin of viruses. Some biologists have suggested that, because viruses can duplicate only by infecting a host cell, they probably evolved after cells appeared. They may represent "escaped" fragments of DNA molecules that once formed part of the genetic material of living cells or an RNA copy of such a fragment. The fragments first became surrounded by a protective layer of protein with recognition functions, and then these fragments escaped from their parent cells. As viruses evolved, the information encoded in the core of the virus became reduced to a set of directions for producing more viral particles of the same kind.

More recent hypotheses suggest that viruses are very ancient, with virus-like particles predating the first cells. The first viruses originated from the "primordial gene pool," the pool of RNA that is thought to have been the first genetic material.

Regardless of when viruses originated, they do not share a common evolutionary origin. Thus, unlike cellular life, there is no common ancestor for all viruses and we cannot draw a phylogenetic tree for all viruses. However, viruses have played an important role in the evolution of cellular life because of their ability to integrate their genes into their hosts and to acquire genes from their hosts, as described above. In this way, viruses can be a source of new cellular genetic material, providing new enzymes and other proteins to a cell. Viruses may also have

played a more direct role in the evolution of eukaryotic cells: some biologists have suggested that the nucleus originated from a large, double-stranded DNA virus that infected prokaryotic cells, resulting in the first eukaryotic cell.

**STUDY BREAK QUESTION**

1. Why do some biologists think viruses must have originated after cells evolved, rather than predating cells?

## 22.5 Viroids and Prions Are Infective Agents Even Simpler in Structure than Viruses

**Viroids**, first discovered in 1971, are small infectious pieces of RNA. Although the RNA is single stranded, bonding within the molecule causes it to become circular. Viroids are smaller than any virus and lack a protein coat. They also differ from viruses in that their RNA genome does not code for any proteins. Viroids are plant pathogens that can rapidly destroy entire fields of citrus, potatoes, tomatoes, coconut palms, and other crop plants. How do viroids cause such devastating diseases without synthesizing any proteins?

The manner in which viroids cause disease remains unknown. In fact, researchers believe that there is more than one mechanism. Recent research indicates that the viroid may cause disease when its RNA interacts with molecules in the cell. For example, it may disrupt normal RNA processing of the host cell: if the viroid's RNA sequence is complementary to the mRNA of the host cell, it can bind to the host's mRNA, thus preventing normal protein synthesis and causing disease.

Like viruses and viroids, **prions** are small infectious particles, but they are not based on nucleic acids; instead, they are infectious protein molecules (the term "prion" is a loose acronym for *pro*teinaceous *in*fectious particle). Prions cause spongiform encephalopathies (SEs), degenerative diseases of the nervous system in mammals characterized by loss of motor control and erratic behaviour. The brains of affected animals are full of spongy holes (**Figure 22.8**; hence the "spongiform" designation) and deposits of proteinaceous material. Under the microscope, aggregates of misfolded proteins, called *amyloid fibres*, are seen in brain tissues; the accumulation of these proteins is the likely cause of the brain damage. SEs progress slowly, meaning animals may be sick for a long time before their symptoms become obvious, but death is inevitable.

One SE disease is *scrapie*, a brain disease that causes sheep to rub against fences, rocks, or trees until they scrape off most of their wool. In cattle, a similar disease is bovine spongiform encephalopathy (BSE), also known as "mad cow disease." Humans also have SE diseases, such as *kuru*, found among cannibals in New Guinea who became infected by eating raw human brain during ritual feasts following the death of an individual. *Creutzfeldt–Jakob disease (CJD)* is a very rare SE

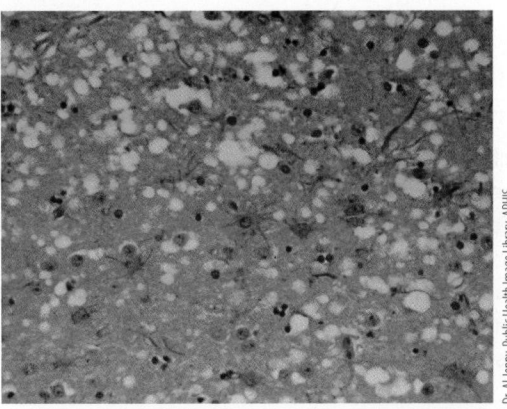

**FIGURE 22.8 Bovine spongiform encephalopathy (BSE).** The light-coloured patches in this thin section from a brain damaged by BSE are areas where tissue has been destroyed.

disease that affects about one person in a million per year, globally. The symptoms of CJD include rapid mental deterioration, loss of vision and speech, and paralysis; autopsies show spongy holes and deposits in brain tissue similar to those of cattle with BSE. We don't know how CJD is transmitted naturally, but we know it can be transmitted inadvertently, for example, with corneal transplants.

Spongiform encephalopathy diseases hit the headlines worldwide in the late 1980s when farmers in the United Kingdom reported a new disease, later determined to be BSE, spreading among their cattle. It is estimated that over 900 000 cattle in the United Kingdom were affected, many of which entered the human food chain before they developed symptoms. Where did BSE come from? The source was determined to be meat and bone meal fed to the cows; this meal came from the carcasses of sheep and cattle. The practice of feeding animal meal to cattle had been followed for years, but a money-saving change in processing in the early 1980s (a reduction in how long rendered material was held at high temperature) allowed the infectious agent—maybe from scrapie-infected sheep—to survive in the meat and bone meal. Worse was to come when it became evident that BSE had spread to humans who had eaten contaminated beef. This new human disease, known as *variant CJD*, is linked to eating meat products from cattle with BSE. Between 1996, when variant CJD was first described, and 2007, there were 208 cases from 11 countries, with the vast majority of these in the United Kingdom. A 12-year study of human tissue samples removed during appendix operations in the United Kingdom suggests that about 1 in

every 2000 people in the United Kingdom is a carrier for variant CJD. Will these people actually develop the disease? Evidence from studies of kuru suggests that it may take more than 50 years for prion diseases to develop, so there is some concern that a spike in variant CJD cases is still to come.

Concern about variant CJD explains why the discovery of even one steer with BSE can wreak havoc on a country's beef exports, as happened in Canada when an infected cow was found in Alberta in 2003. The United States closed its border to all beef from Canada within a day, followed shortly by border closings of 40 other countries. Loss of these markets caused serious economic hardship for Canadian ranchers and farmers.

What is the cause of BSE and other SE diseases, and how does this causative agent spread? Stanley Prusiner was awarded a Nobel Prize for demonstrating that infectious proteins cause these diseases. Prions are the only known infectious agents that do not include a nucleic acid molecule, and their discovery changed some fundamental views of biology.

**CONCEPT FIX** Did you know that our brains have prions? These are called *normal prions* and there is an indication that they are important for maintaining myelin around nerve cells. Mice lacking normal prion proteins have subtle impairments in memory and cognition. Perhaps the inability of the misfolded prion proteins to carry out their normal functions results in dementia and the other symptoms of BSE.

Our current understanding of prion infection is that prion proteins are able to survive passage through the stomach of an animal consuming them; they then enter that animal's bloodstream and proceed to the brain, where they somehow interact with normal prion proteins, causing these proteins to change shape to become abnormal and infectious. Prion proteins and the normal precursor proteins share the same amino acid sequences but differ in how they are folded. Prions are somehow able to impose their folding on normal proteins, thus "infecting" the normal proteins. As the infection spreads, neural functioning is impaired and protein fibrils accumulate, producing aggregations of fibrils that trigger apoptosis of infected cells, leading to the SE characteristic of these diseases.

In this chapter, we focused on the simplest biological entities: viruses, viroids, and prions, which possess only some of the properties of life.

## STUDY BREAK QUESTION

1. How do viroids and prions differ from viruses? How do they differ from each other?

# Summary Illustration

Viruses, viroids, and prions are non-cellular, infectious biological particles. Although viruses have a wide range of shapes and sizes, all consist of one or more nucleic acid molecules surrounded by a protein coat. Some are also surrounded by a membranous envelope. Viruses can infect bacterial, animal, and plant cells, and rely on these hosts for reproduction and essential metabolic processes. Viroids are plant pathogens that consist solely of small pieces of circular RNA. Prions are protein molecules that cause degenerative diseases of mammalian nervous systems.

**Tobacco mosaic virus (ssRNA)**

**Enterobacteria phage T4 (dsDNA)**

**Hepatitis B (dsDNA)**

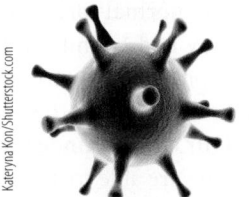

**Influenza (flu) (ssRNA)**

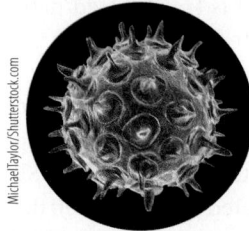

**Chickenpox shingles (dsDNA)**

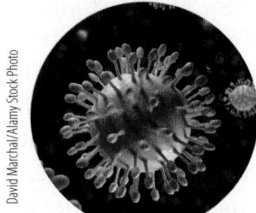

**Hepatitis C (ssRNA)**

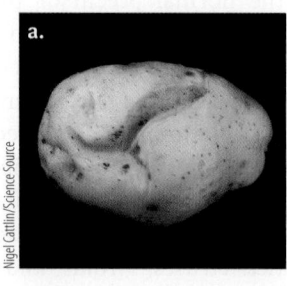

a.  b.

Potato spindle tuber disease. (a) Infected potato. (b) Illustration of viroid

Viroids are plant pathogens.

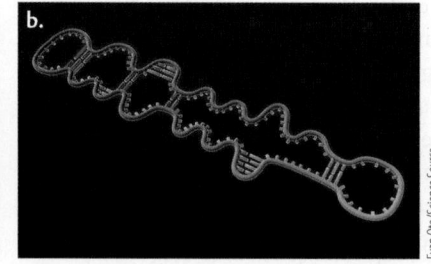

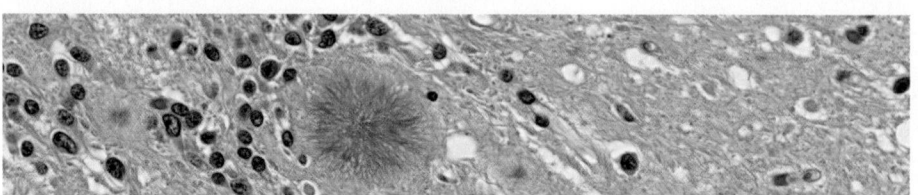

Human brain tissue showing an amyloid plaque from a person with a case of variant Creutzfeldt-Jakob disease (vCJD), a fatal human neurodegenerative condition caused by protein particles called *prions*. It is contracted by eating beef from cows that have bovine spongiform encephalopathy (BSE), also known as "mad cow disease."

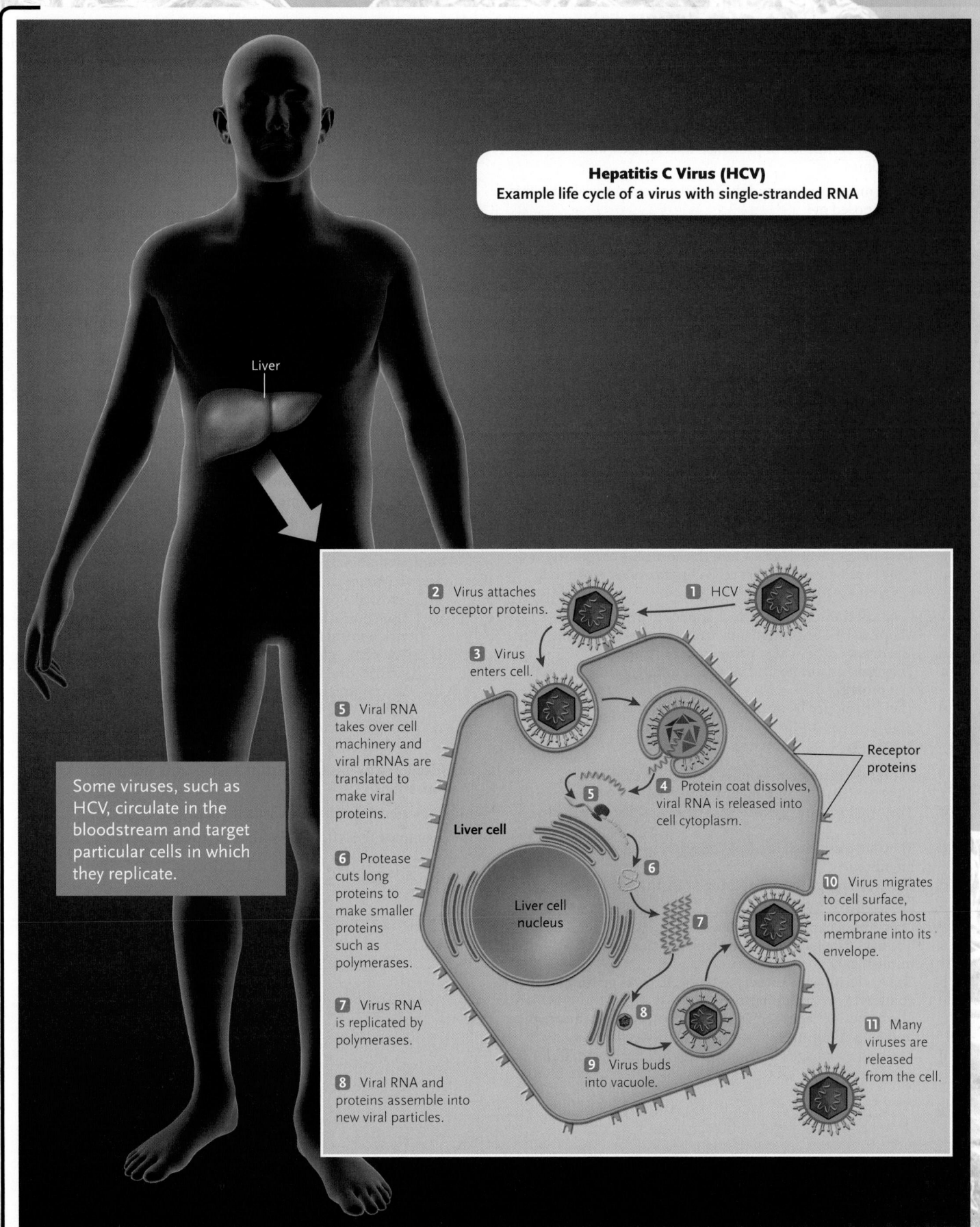

**Hepatitis C Virus (HCV)**
**Example life cycle of a virus with single-stranded RNA**

Liver

Some viruses, such as HCV, circulate in the bloodstream and target particular cells in which they replicate.

**2** Virus attaches to receptor proteins.

**1** HCV

**3** Virus enters cell.

**5** Viral RNA takes over cell machinery and viral mRNAs are translated to make viral proteins.

**4** Protein coat dissolves, viral RNA is released into cell cytoplasm.

Receptor proteins

**Liver cell**

**6** Protease cuts long proteins to make smaller proteins such as polymerases.

Liver cell nucleus

**10** Virus migrates to cell surface, incorporates host membrane into its envelope.

**7** Virus RNA is replicated by polymerases.

**9** Virus buds into vacuole.

**11** Many viruses are released from the cell.

**8** Viral RNA and proteins assemble into new viral particles.

# SELF-TEST QUESTIONS

## Recall/Understand

1.  Which of these statements best defines a virus?
    a.  a naked fragment of nucleic acid
    b.  a disease-causing group of proteins
    c.  an entity composed of proteins and nucleic acids
    d.  an entity composed of proteins, nucleic acids, and ribosomes

2.  Viruses form a capsid around their nucleic acid core. What is this capsid composed of?
    a.  protein
    b.  lipoprotein
    c.  glycoprotein
    d.  polysaccharides

3.  Which of the following is synthesized by reverse transcriptase?
    a.  RNA from DNA
    b.  DNA from RNA
    c.  proteins from DNA
    d.  proteins from RNA

4.  Which of these statements best describes viroids?
    a.  the smallest type of virus
    b.  small infectious pieces of DNA
    c.  small infectious pieces of RNA
    d.  infectious pieces of DNA wrapped in a protein coat

5.  Which of these statements best describes temperate phages?
    a.  They cannot lyse host cells.
    b.  They turn their host cell into a prophage.
    c.  They integrate their DNA into the host cell's chromosomes.
    d.  They break down the host cell's chromosomes when their DNA enters the cell.

6.  Which one of these characteristics applies to prions?
    a.  They can be transmitted only from animals to humans.
    b.  The diseases they cause progress very rapidly.
    c.  They have an amino acid sequence different from the normal protein.
    d.  They reproduce by misfolding normal proteins.

## Apply/Analyze

7.  Which of these statements applies to viral envelopes?
    a.  They contain glycoproteins of viral origin.
    b.  They are located between the virus's capsid and its nucleic acid.
    c.  They are composed of a lipid bilayer derived from the viral membrane.
    d.  They are composed of peptidoglycan, the same material as bacterial cell walls.

8.  What happens when a bacteriophage enters the lysogenic stage?
    a.  The bacteriophage enters the host cell and kills it immediately.
    b.  The bacteriophage enters the host cell, picks up host DNA, and leaves the cell unharmed.
    c.  The bacteriophage merges with the host cell's plasma membrane, forming an envelope, and then exits the cell.
    d.  The bacteriophage's DNA integrates into the host cell's genome.

9.  Which of these characteristics applies to both animal viruses and bacterial viruses?
    a.  They commonly have envelopes.
    b.  Only their nucleic acid enters the host cell.
    c.  They have a capsid divided into a head and a tail.
    d.  They bind to specific receptors on the host cell.

10. Which of the following characteristics distinguishes plant viruses from animal viruses?
    a.  Plant viruses are easily curable.
    b.  Plant viruses are covered by a membrane envelope.
    c.  Plant viruses lack the ability to actively infect a host cell.
    d.  Plant viruses lack the ability to replicate their RNA genome.

## Create/Evaluate

11. Suppose that your friend has chickenpox. Which of the following you might conclude?
    a.  She was infected with *Flavivirus* during her recent trip to Africa.
    b.  She was infected with *Flavivirus*, which she contacted after being in contact with livestock.
    c.  She was infected with varicella-zoster virus, and her immune system will prevent the onset of shingles later in her life.
    d.  She was infected with varicella-zoster virus, which might later in her lifetime also give her shingles.

12. You recently travelled to a tropical island and, upon your return, you start feeling fatigued, nauseated, and have a loss of appetite. You feel some abdominal pain on your right side beneath your lower ribs and you notice your stool is clay-coloured. Which of the following is the most likely reason for your condition?
    a.  You contracted hepatitis B, caused by a virus from Papovaviridae viral family.
    b.  You contracted hepatitis B, caused by a virus from Picornaviridae viral family.
    c.  You contracted hepatitis A, caused by a virus from Picornaviridae viral family.
    d.  You contracted hepatitis A, caused by a virus from Papovaviridae viral family.

13. Explain why it is typically difficult to treat and prevent viral infections.

14. Describe the cycle of a virulent phage.

15. Compare the lytic cycle with the lysogenic cycle.

# Chapter Roadmap

## Bacteria and Archaea

Prokaryotes look simple; they are unicellular and lack nuclei, mitochondria, and any other membrane-bound organelle. Yet, they can be found in almost every habitat, including those so inhospitable that no eukaryote could survive.

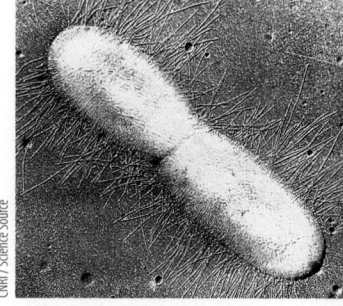

CNRI / Science Source

**From Chapter 2**

**From Chapter 4**

**From Chapter 5**

**From Chapter 12**

### 23.1 The Full Extent of the Diversity of Bacteria and Archaea Is Unknown
Prokaryotes cannot be cultured easily, and habitats are difficult to access.

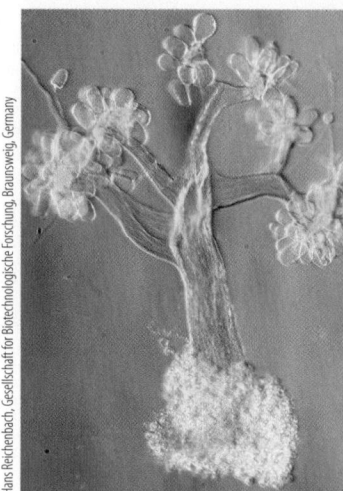

Hans Reichenbach, Gesellschaft für Biotechnologische Forschung, Braunschweig, Germany

### 23.2 Prokaryotic Structure and Function
Archaea and bacteria show great diversity in their modes of obtaining energy and carbon. They share two modes with eukaryotic organisms (chemoheterotrophy and photoautotrophy), but two other modes are unique to prokaryotic organisms: chemoautotrophs obtain energy by oxidizing inorganic substrates and use carbon dioxide as their carbon source, and photoheterotrophs use light as a source of energy and obtain their carbon from organic molecules.

### 23.3 The Domain Bacteria
Bacteria are divided into more than a dozen evolutionary branches, including Gram-negative proteobacteria, Gram-negative green bacteria, cyanobacteria, Gram-positive bacteria, spirochetes, and chlamydias.

**To Chapter 25**

**To Chapter 26**

### 23.4 The Domain Archaea
Archaea include the Euryarchaeota (methanogens, extreme halophiles, and some extreme thermophiles); the Crenarchaeota (most of the extreme thermophiles, but also some psychrophiles and mesophiles); and the Korarchaeota (known only from DNA samples).

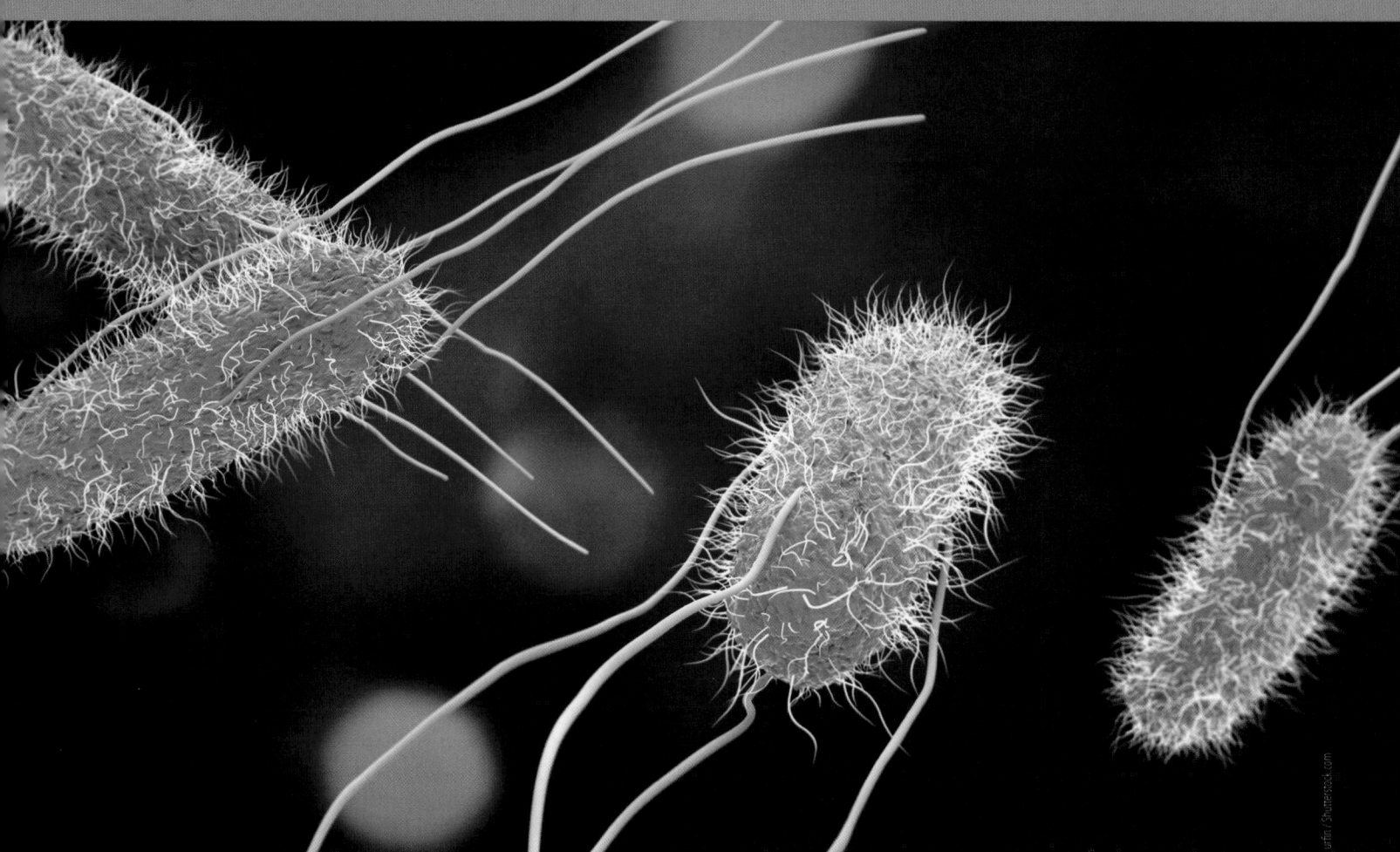

The bacterium *Salmonella* serotype *Typhi*

# Bacteria and Archaea

# 23

**Why it matters . . .** Who are you? What makes you "you"? Would you feel less like "you" if you knew that most of the cells in your body weren't human cells at all? The bacterial cells on and in our bodies outnumber our cells by 10 to 1. And given that, as Princeton University scientist Bonnie Bassler points out, the average person has about 30 000 human genes but more than 3 million bacterial genes, we are, at most, 1% human! But these bacteria aren't alien invaders; many of them are crucial for making us unique individuals. There are about a hundred trillion bacteria of hundreds (or thousands) of different species lining your large intestine. When you were born, your gut was sterile, but immediately after birth, your intestines started to be colonized; the exact composition of these "pioneers" depends on where you were born and whether you were breastfed, among other factors. The early colonists were essential for the normal development of your gut as an infant. And throughout your life, your gut bacteria have continued to help you in many ways: they help digest your food, synthesize vitamin K, and produce antimicrobial factors to protect you from pathogens. Recent research has revealed that the diversity of your gut bacteria plays a role in your odds of developing metabolic diseases and becoming obese, and may even be involved in your mental health.

**CONCEPT FIX** The idea that all bacteria cause disease is a major misconception; nothing could be farther from the truth. In addition to the benefits discussed above, most known bacteria and members of the other group of prokaryotic organisms, archaea, play a crucial role in ecosystems, recycling nutrients and breaking down compounds that no other organisms can. Others carry out reactions important in food production, in industry (e.g., production of pharmaceutical products), and in **bioremediation** of polluted sites. ⬡

In this chapter, we first look at the structure and function of prokaryotic organisms, emphasizing the features that differentiate them from other organisms, and conclude with a look at the diversity of these fascinating organisms.

# 23.1 The Full Extent of the Diversity of Bacteria and Archaea Is Unknown

While reading this chapter, keep in mind that everything we know so far about bacteria and archaea is based on a tiny fraction of the total number of species. We have isolated and identified only about 6000 species, which may be as low as 1% of the total number. We know almost nothing about the prokaryotic organisms of entire habitats, such as the oceans, which make up 70% of Earth's surface. Why have we identified so few, and why are we not even sure how many prokaryotic organisms there might be? In the past, we identified and classified bacteria and archaea based on external features (e.g., cell wall structure) and physiological differences, which meant that we had to be able to grow the organisms in culture. We have learned a great deal about the biology of some bacteria and archaea, but have been unable to learn much about the majority of prokaryotic organisms, since they cannot be grown in culture (e.g., those that require extreme physicochemical conditions). Recently, molecular techniques have been developed that allow us to isolate and clone DNA from an environment and then analyze gene sequences; this means that we can now identify and characterize bacteria and archaea without having to culture them. This approach, known as **metagenomics**, enables us to investigate the diversity of prokaryotic organisms in a wide range of environments. However, our understanding of the full extent of microbial diversity faces other challenges, such as the fact that many environments (e.g., the deep ocean and Earth's crust) are remote and thus very difficult and/or costly to sample.

## 23.1a Prokaryotic Organisms Make Up Two of the Three Domains of Life

Two of the three domains of living organisms, **Archaea** and **Bacteria**, consist of prokaryotic organisms (the third domain, **Eukarya**, includes all eukaryotes). Bacteria are the prokaryotic organisms most familiar to us, including those responsible for diseases of humans and other animals, as well as those that we rely on for production of cheese, yogurt, chocolate, and other foods. Archaea are not as well known, as they were discovered only about 40 years ago. As you will see in this chapter, archaea share some cellular features with eukaryotes and some with bacteria but have still other features that are unique. Many of the archaea live under very extreme conditions that no other organisms, including bacteria, can survive.

# 23.2 Prokaryotic Structure and Function

We begin our survey by examining prokaryotic cellular structures, modes of reproduction, and how prokaryotes obtain energy and nutrients.

In general, prokaryotic organisms are the smallest cells in the world that lack a distinct nucleus and other organelles **(Figure 23.1)**. Few species are more than 1 to 2 μm long (although the longest is 600 μm long, which is larger than some eukaryotes!); 500–1000 such cells would fit side by side across the dot on this letter "i." Despite the small size of bacteria and archaea, they dominate life on Earth; current estimates of total prokaryotic diversity are in the billions of species, and their total collective mass, their **biomass**, on Earth exceeds that of animals and may be greater than that of all plant life. Prokaryotic organisms colonize every niche on Earth that supports life, and even occur deep in Earth's crust. They also colonize other organisms; for example, huge numbers of bacteria inhabit the surfaces and cavities of a healthy human body, including the skin, mouth and nasal passages, and large intestine. As mentioned in *Why It Matters*, collectively, the bacteria in and on your body outnumber all the other cells in your body. It is not surprising that the diversity of bacteria and archaea should be so much greater than that of eukaryotes because, for about 3 billion years, they were the only forms of life on Earth and so had time to diversify and expand into every habitat on Earth before the first eukaryotes appeared on the scene (see Chapter 2).

## 23.2a Prokaryotic Cells Appear Simple in Structure Compared with Eukaryotic Cells

Three cell shapes are common among prokaryotes: spiral, spherical (or **coccoid**; *coccus* = berry), and cylindrical (known as **rods**). However, some archaea have square cells **(Figure 23.2)**.

At first glance, a typical prokaryotic cell seems much simpler than a eukaryotic cell **(Figure 23.3)**: images taken with standard electron microscopy typically reveal little more than a cell wall and plasma membrane surrounding cytoplasm that has DNA concentrated in one region and ribosomes scattered throughout. The chromosome is not contained in a membrane-

a.
b.
c.
100 μm
20 μm
0.5 μm
Dr. Tony Brain & David Parker / Science Source
Dr. Tony Brain & David Parker / Science Source
Dr. Tony Brain & David Parker / Science Source

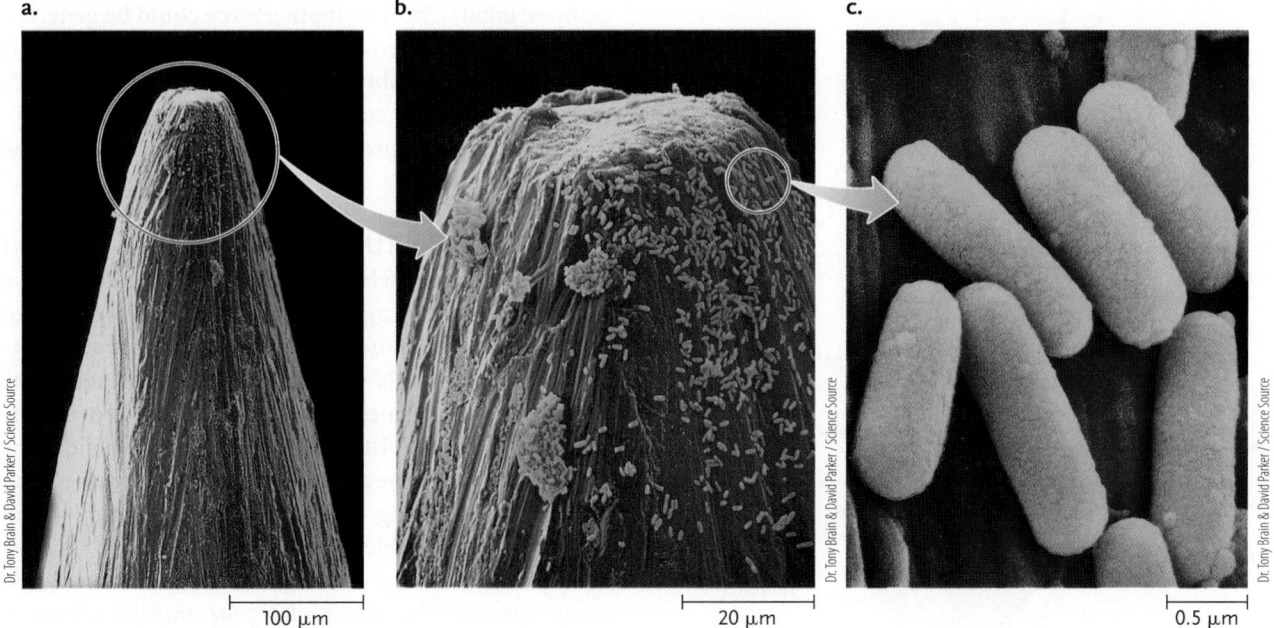

**FIGURE 23.1** ***Bacillus* bacteria on the point of a pin.** Cells magnified **(a)** 70 times, **(b)** 350 times, and **(c)** 14 000 times.

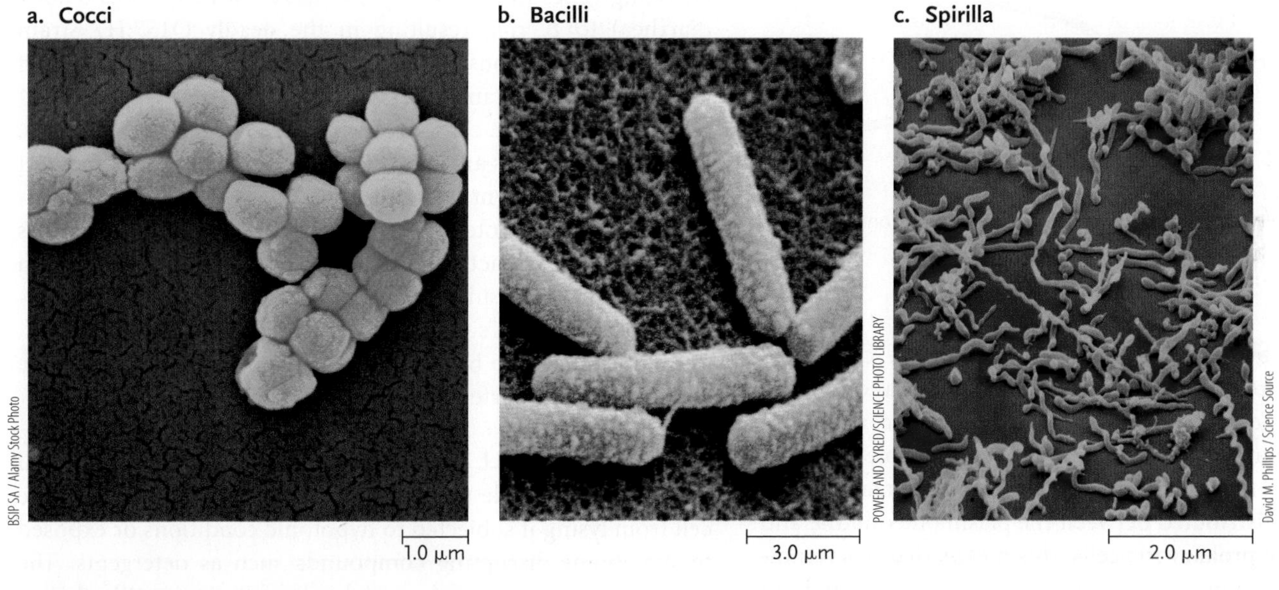

a. Cocci
b. Bacilli
c. Spirilla
1.0 μm
3.0 μm
2.0 μm
BSIP SA / Alamy Stock Photo
POWER AND SYRED/SCIENCE PHOTO LIBRARY
David M. Phillips / Science Source

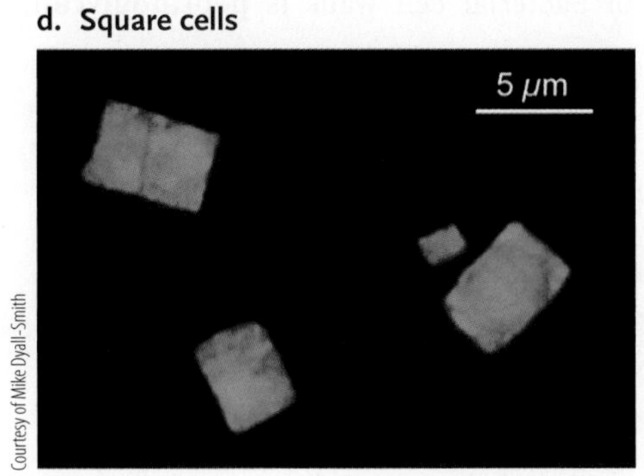

d. Square cells
5 μm
Courtesy of Mike Dyall-Smith

**FIGURE 23.2 Common shapes of prokaryotic cells. (a)** Scanning electron microscope (SEM) image of *Micrococcus*, a coccoid bacterium. **(b)** SEM image of *Salmonella*, a rod-shaped bacterium. **(c)** SEM image of *Spiroplasma*, a spiral bacterium. **(d)** Acridine orange–stained cells of *Haloquadratum walsbyi*, a square archaeon

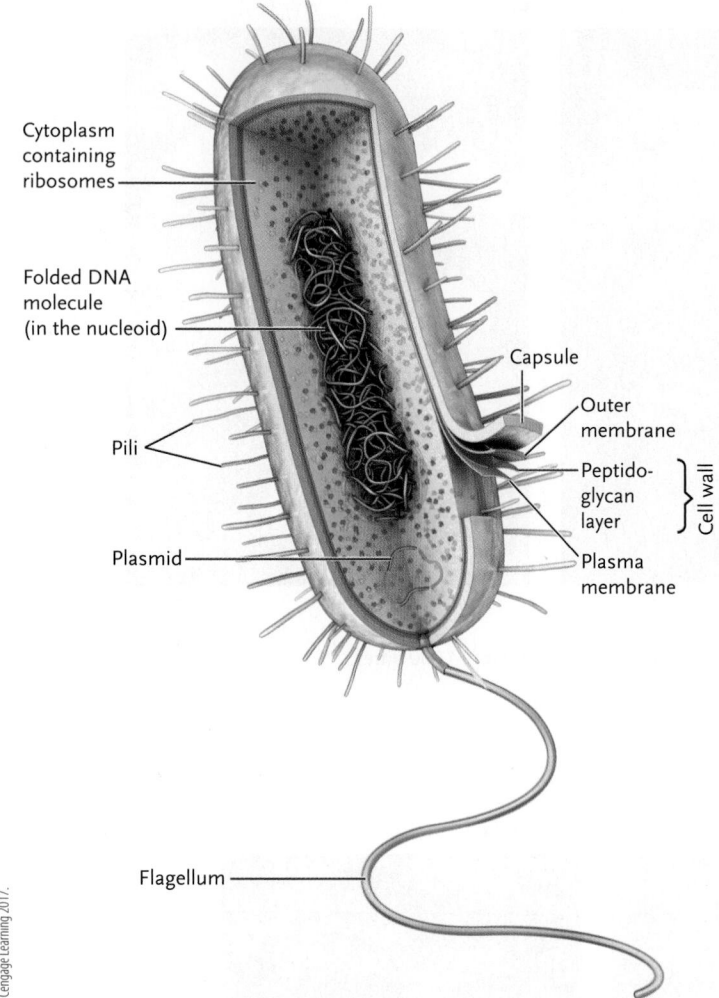

Cytoplasm
containing
ribosomes

Folded DNA
molecule
(in the nucleoid)

Pili

Plasmid

Flagellum

Capsule

Outer
membrane

Peptido-
glycan
layer

Plasma
membrane

Cell wall

© Cengage Learning 2017.

**FIGURE 23.3  The structure of a bacterial cell.** The high concentration of ribosomes gives the cytoplasm a granular appearance.

bound nucleus but is packed into an area of the cell called the **nucleoid**. Prokaryotic cells have no membranous cytoplasmic organelles equivalent to the endoplasmic reticulum (ER) or Golgi complex of eukaryotic cells (see Chapter 2). With few exceptions, the reactions carried out by organelles in eukaryotes are distributed between the plasma membrane and the cytoplasm of prokaryotic cells; this means that macromolecules such as proteins are very concentrated in the cytoplasm of these cells, making the cytoplasm quite viscous. This evident simplicity of prokaryotic cells led people to regard these cells as featureless and disorganized. New microscopic techniques reveal that prokaryotic cells do have a cytoskeleton, not homologous to that of a eukaryote but serving some of the same functions. In fact, recent research carried out by Laura van Niftrik, of the Netherlands, and her colleagues has identified a prokaryotic organelle! Certain bacteria that obtain energy by oxidizing ammonia have an internal, membrane-bound compartment where ammonia oxidation occurs. It was hypothesized that, as ammonia oxidation proceeds inside this

compartment, a proton-motive force could be generated across the membrane, generating ATP. Van Niftrik and her colleagues found that the membrane around this compartment does contain ATP synthase, supporting the above hypothesis. Thus, it appears that some prokaryotic cells have organelles with specialized functions.

**INTERNAL STRUCTURES**  The genome of most prokaryotic cells consists of a single, circular DNA molecule, although some, such as the causative agent of Lyme disease (*Borrelia burgdorferi*), have a linear chromosome. Many prokaryotic cells also contain small circles of DNA called **plasmids (Figure 23.4)**, which generally contain genes for nonessential but beneficial functions such as antibiotic resistance. Plasmids replicate independently of the cell's chromosome and can be transferred from one bacterium to another, resulting in genetic recombination **(Figure 23.5)**. This makes it possible for genes for antibiotic resistance to be readily shared among prokaryotic cells, even among cells of different species. This *horizontal gene transfer* allows antibiotic resistance and other traits to spread very quickly. Horizontal gene transfer also occurs when bacterial cells take up DNA from their environment (e.g., from other cells that have lysed) or when viruses transfer DNA from one bacterium to another (see Chapter 22). Evidence indicates that a virus transferred toxin-encoding genes from *Shigella dysenteriae* (which causes bloody diarrhea) to *E. coli*, resulting in the deadly O157:H7 strain responsible for serious illness or even death in people eating beef and other food contaminated with this bacterium.

Like eukaryotic cells, prokaryotic cells contain ribosomes. Bacterial ribosomes are smaller than eukaryotic ribosomes but carry out protein synthesis by essentially the same mechanisms as those of eukaryotes (see Chapter 12). Archaeal ribosomes resemble those of bacteria in size but differ in structure; protein synthesis in Archaea is a combination of bacterial and eukaryotic processes, with some unique archaeal features. As a result, antibiotics that stop bacterial infections by targeting ribosome activity do not interfere with archaeal protein synthesis.

**PROKARYOTIC CELL WALLS**  Most prokaryotic cells have a cell wall that lies outside their plasma membrane and protects the cell from lysing if subjected to hypotonic conditions or exposed to membrane-disrupting compounds such as detergents. The primary component of bacterial cell walls is **peptidoglycan**,

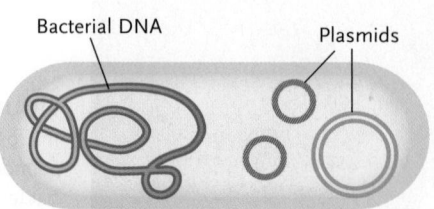

Bacterial DNA

Plasmids

**FIGURE 23.4  Plasmids inside a prokaryotic cell**

**FIGURE 23.5**   **Experimental Research**

## Genetic Recombination in Bacteria

**Question:** Does genetic recombination occur in bacteria?

**Experiment:** To answer the question, Lederberg and Tatum used two mutant strains of *E. coli*: Mutant strain 1's genotype was *bio⁻ met⁻ leu⁺ thr⁺ thi⁺*, where the "1" means a normal allele and the "2" means a mutant allele. This strain required biotin and methionine to grow. Mutant strain 2's genotype was *bio⁺ met⁺ leu⁻ thr⁻ thi⁻*; it required leucine, threonine, and thiamine to grow.

Lederberg and Tatum plated about 100 million cells of a mixture of the two mutant strains on minimal medium, which lacked any of the nutrients the strains needed for growth. As controls, they also plated large numbers of the two mutant strains individually on minimal medium.

**Results:** No colonies grew on the control plates, meaning that the mutant alleles in the strains had not mutated back to normal alleles. However, for the mixture of mutant strain 1 and mutant strain 2, several hundred colonies grew on the minimal medium.

**Conclusion:** To grow on minimal medium, the bacteria must have been able to make biotin, methionine, leucine, threonine, and thiamine; meaning that they had the genotype *bio⁺ met⁺ leu⁺ thr⁺ thi⁺*. Lederberg and Tatum concluded that the colonies on the plate must have resulted from genetic recombination between mutant strains 1 and 2.

© Cengage Learning 2017. Based on J. Lederberg and E. Tatum. 1946. Gene recombination in *Escherichia coli*. *Nature* 158:558.

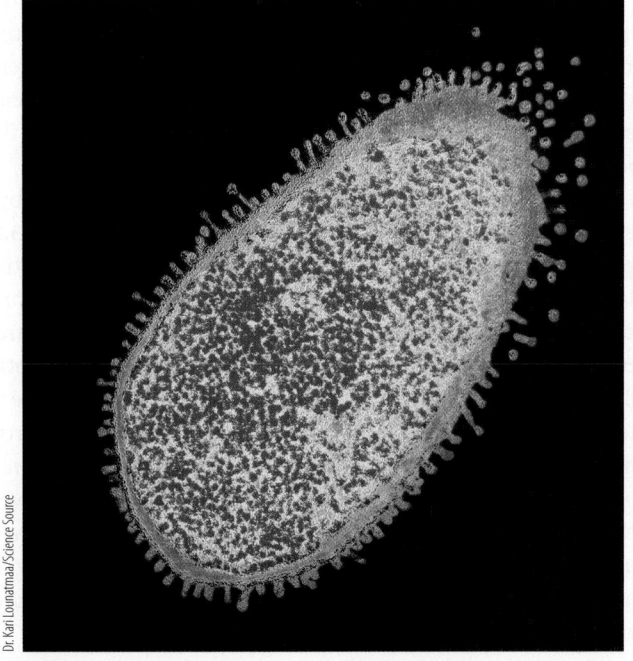

a polymer of sugars and amino acids that forms linear chains. Peptide cross-linkages between the chains give the cell wall great strength and rigidity. The antibiotic penicillin prevents the formation of these cross-linkages, resulting in a weak cell wall that is easily ruptured, killing the cell **(Figure 23.6)**.

Bacteria can be divided into two broad groups, Gram-positive and Gram-negative cells, based on their reaction to the **Gram stain procedure** traditionally used as the first step in identifying an unknown bacterium. Cells are first stained with crystal violet and then treated with iodine, which forms a complex with crystal violet. The cells are then rinsed with ethanol and counterstained with safranin. Some cells retain the crystal violet–iodine complex and thus appear purple when viewed under the microscope; these are termed Gram-positive cells. In other bacteria, ethanol washes the crystal violet–iodine complex out of the cells, which are colourless until counterstained with safranin; these Gram-negative cells appear pink under the microscope. The differential response to staining is related to differences in cell wall structure: **Gram-positive** bacteria have cell walls composed almost entirely of a single, relatively thick layer of peptidoglycan **(Figure 23.7a)**. This thick peptidoglycan layer retains the crystal violet–iodine complex inside the cell.

**FIGURE 23.6  Image showing degradation of the cell wall following antibiotic treatment.** The cell will eventually lyse, killing the bacterium.

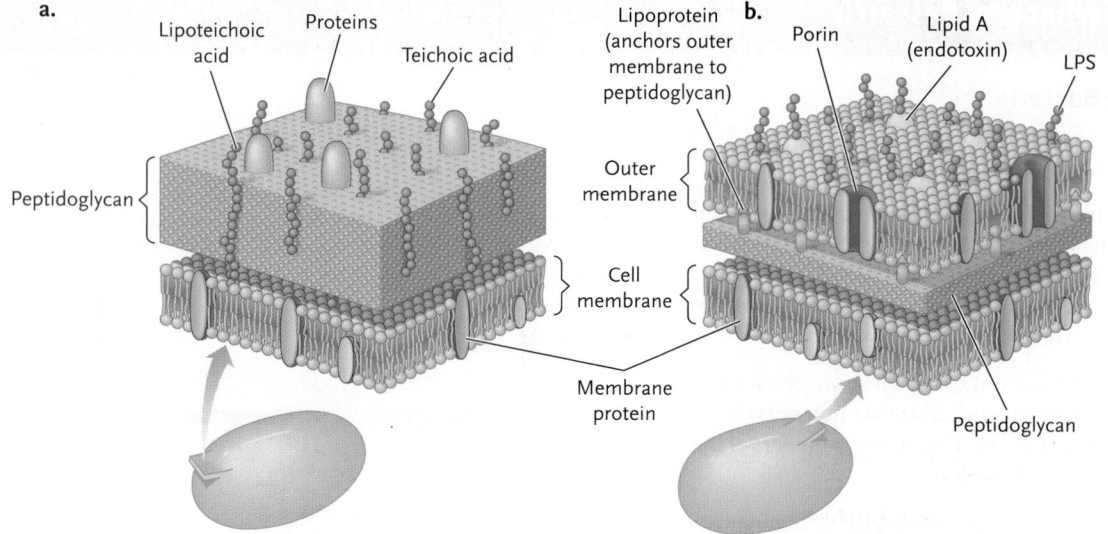

**a.**

Lipoteichoic acid — Proteins — Teichoic acid

Peptidoglycan

Cell membrane

Membrane protein

**b.**

Lipoprotein (anchors outer membrane to peptidoglycan) — Porin — Lipid A (endotoxin) — LPS

Outer membrane

Cell membrane

Membrane protein

Peptidoglycan

**FIGURE 23.7 Cell wall structure in Gram- positive and Gram-negative bacteria.** **(a)** The thick cell wall in Gram-positive bacteria. **(b)** The thin cell wall of Gram-negative bacteria has a thin peptidoglycan layer and outer membrane with lipopolysaccharides (LPSs). The uppermost part of LPS is the O antigen, a carbohydrate chain that elicits an antibody response in vertebrates exposed to Gram-negative bacteria such as *E. coli* O157:H7. More information on the toxic effects of lipid A, which embeds LPSs in the outer membrane, is provided in Section 23.2e.

**Gram-negative** cells have only a thin peptidoglycan layer in their walls, and the crystal violet–iodine complex is washed out. In contrast, the cell wall of Gram-negative bacteria has two distinct layers (Figure 23.7b): a thin peptidoglycan layer just outside the plasma membrane and an **outer membrane** external to the peptidoglycan layer. This outer membrane contains **lipopolysaccharides (LPSs)** and thus is very different from the plasma membrane. The outer membrane protects Gram-negative bacteria from potentially harmful substances in the environment; for example, it inhibits entry of penicillin. Therefore, Gram-negative cells are less sensitive to penicillin than are Gram-positive cells.

The cell walls of some archaea are assembled from a molecule related to peptidoglycan but with different molecular components and bonding structure. Others have walls assembled from proteins or polysaccharides instead of peptidoglycan. Archaea have a variable response to the Gram stain, so this procedure is not useful in identifying archaea.

The cell wall of many prokaryotic cells is surrounded by a layer of polysaccharides known as a **capsule (Figure 23.8)**. Capsules are "sticky" and play important roles in protecting cells in different environments. Cells with capsules are protected to some extent from desiccation, extreme temperatures, bacterial viruses, and harmful molecules such as antibiotics and antibodies. In many pathogenic bacteria, the presence or absence of the protective capsule differentiates infective from non-infective forms. For example, normal *Streptococcus pneumoniae* bacteria are capsulated and virulent, causing severe pneumonia in humans and other mammals. Mutant *S. pneumoniae* without capsules are nonvirulent and can easily be eliminated by the body's immune system when they are injected into mice or other animals.

**FLAGELLA AND PILI** Many prokaryotic cells can move actively through liquids and even through films of liquid on a surface, most commonly via **flagella** (singular, *flagellum* = whip) extending from the cell wall (see Figure 23.3). As outlined in

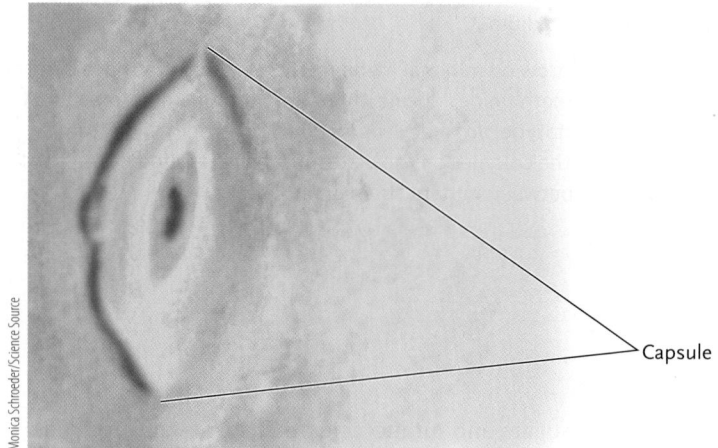

Capsule

**FIGURE 23.8 Capsules surrounding the cell wall of *Rhizobium*, a Gram-negative soil bacterium**

Chapter 2, prokaryotic flagella are very different from eukaryotic flagella in both structure and pattern of movement. Prokaryotic flagella are made of rigid helical proteins, some of which act as a motor rotating the flagellum much like the propeller of a boat. Archaeal flagella are superficially similar to bacterial flagella and carry out the same function, but the two types of flagella contain different components, develop differently, and are coded for by different genes.

Some prokaryotic cells have rigid shafts of protein called **pili** (singular, *pilus* = hair) extending from their cell walls **(Figure 23.9a)**, which enable them to adhere to or move along a surface. One type, called a *sex pilus*, not only allows bacterial cells to adhere to each other but also acts as a conduit for the transfer of plasmids from one cell to another (Figure 23.9b). Other types of pili enable bacteria to bind to animal cells. The bacterium that causes gonorrhea (*Neisseria gonorrhoeae*) uses pili to adhere to cells of the throat, eye, urogenital tract, or rectum in humans. In 2005, it was discovered that the pili of

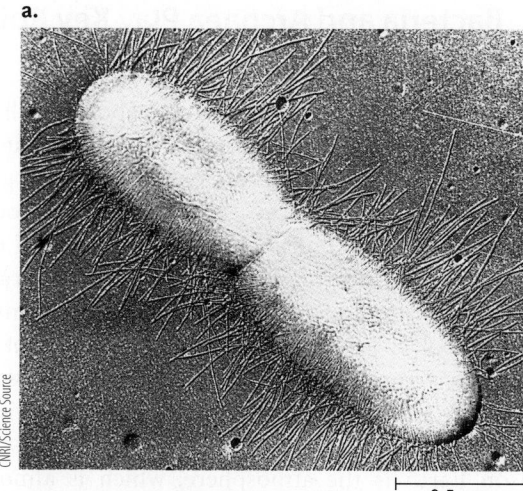

a.

CNRI/Science Source

0.5 μm

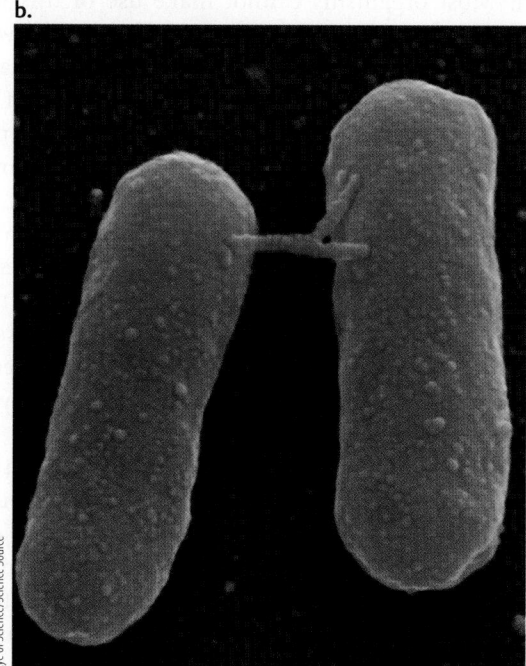

b.

Eye of Science/Science Source

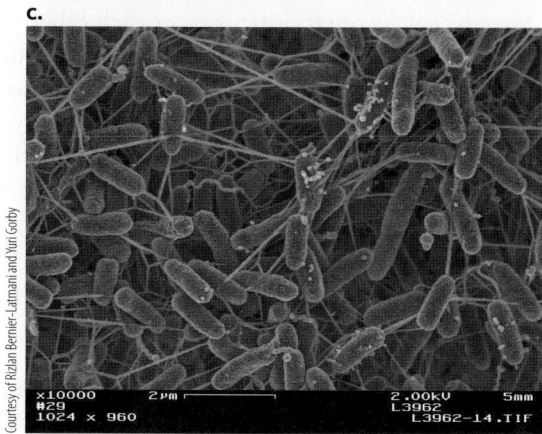

c.

Courtesy of Rizlan Bernier-Latmani and Yuri Gorby

×10000    2 μm    2.00kV    5mm
#29    L3962
1024 × 960    L3962-14.TIF

**FIGURE 23.9** **(a)** Pili extending from the surface of a dividing *E. coli* bacterium. **(b)** Sex pilus connecting two bacterial cells. **(c)** Nanowires (pili that conduct electricity) on *Shewanella oneidensis*. Note that these nanowires are much longer than the cells.

some bacteria (e.g., species of *Geobacter* and *Shewanella*) conduct electricity; these "nanowires" transfer electrons out of the cell onto minerals such as iron oxides in their environment (Figure 23.9c). Such electricity-generating bacteria hold promise for the development of microbial fuel cells as an alternative energy source.

Even though prokaryotes are simpler and less structurally diverse than eukaryotic cells, they are much more diverse metabolically, as we will now explore.

### 23.2b Prokaryotic Organisms Have the Greatest Metabolic Diversity of All Organisms

Organisms can be grouped into four modes of nutrition based on sources of energy and carbon (see **Table 23.1**).

In this approach to classification, we focus on carbon rather than other nutrients because carbon is the backbone of all organic molecules synthesized by an organism. Organisms such as plants that synthesize organic carbon molecules using inorganic carbon ($CO_2$) are **autotrophs** (*auto* = self; *troph* = nourishment). (Note that, although $CO_2$ contains a carbon atom, oxides containing carbon are considered inorganic molecules.) All animals are **heterotrophs**, meaning that they obtain carbon from organic molecules, either from living hosts or from organic molecules in the products, wastes, or remains of dead organisms.

Organisms are also divided according to the source of the energy they use to drive biological activities. **Chemotrophs** (*chemo* = chemical) obtain energy by oxidizing inorganic or organic substances, whereas **phototrophs** obtain energy from light. Combining the carbon and energy sources allows us to group living organisms into four categories (Table 23.1).

Prokaryotic organisms (bacteria and archaea) show the greatest diversity in their modes of securing carbon and energy;

| TABLE 23.1 | | Modes of Nutrition Used by Living Organisms | |
|---|---|---|---|
| Energy Source | | Oxidation of Molecules* | Light |
| **Carbon source** | $CO_2$ | **Chemoautotroph** Some bacteria and archaea; no eukaryotes | **Photoautotroph** Some bacteria, some protists, and most plants |
| | **Organic molecules** | **Chemoheterotroph** Some bacteria, archaea, and protists; also fungi, animals, and even some plants | **Photoheterotroph** Some bacteria |

* Inorganic molecules for chemoautotrophs, and organic molecules for chemoheterotrophs.

CHAPTER 23 BACTERIA AND ARCHAEA

they are the only representatives of two of the categories, chemoautotrophs and photoheterotrophs. **Photoheterotrophs** use light as an energy source and obtain carbon from organic molecules rather than from $CO_2$. **Chemoautotrophs** are commonly referred to as *lithotrophs* (*lithos* = rock; thus, "rock-eaters"). As this name suggests, chemoautotrophs obtain energy by oxidizing inorganic substances such as hydrogen, iron, sulfur, ammonia, and nitrites and use $CO_2$ as their carbon source. Chemolithotrophs thrive in habitats such as deep-sea hydrothermal vents **(Figure 23.10)**, where reduced inorganic compounds are abundant. The ability of these organisms to harness energy from these compounds makes them the foundation upon which the rest of the vent community ultimately depends, just as terrestrial organisms rely on the ability of plants and other photoautotrophs to capture light energy.

We breathe oxygen to provide the final electron acceptor for the electrons we remove from our food and pass down an electron transport chain (ETC) to make ATP via aerobic respiration (Chapter 5). Some prokaryotic organisms also use oxygen as a final electron acceptor; like us, these are aerobic organisms, or **aerobes**. Aerobes may be **obligate aerobes**; that is, they cannot survive without oxygen. But some prokaryotic organisms "breathe" metals, using metals as the final electron acceptor for electrons; these organisms obtain energy via anaerobic respiration. **Anaerobic respiration** can also involve other inorganic molecules, such as nitrate or sulfate, as the final electron acceptors. Only prokaryotic organisms are capable of this type of respiration. **Obligate anaerobes** are poisoned by oxygen and survive either by fermentation, in which organic molecules are the final electron acceptors, or by anaerobic respiration. **Facultative anaerobes** use $O_2$ when it is present, but under anaerobic conditions, they live by fermentation or anaerobic respiration. As you learned in Chapter 5, prokaryotic organisms carry out a wider range of fermentation reactions than do eukaryotes; many of these fermentations are economically important to humans, for example, in the production of foods such as cheese, yogurt, and chocolate.

**FIGURE 23.10 Hydrothermal vents on the ocean floor**

## 23.2c Bacteria and Archaea Play Key Roles in Biogeochemical Cycles

The ability of prokaryotic organisms to metabolize such a wide range of substrates makes them key players in the life-sustaining recycling of elements such as carbon, oxygen, and nitrogen. The pathway by which a chemical element moves through an ecosystem is known as a **biogeochemical cycle**. As an element flows through its cycle, it is transformed from one form to another; prokaryotic organisms are crucial in many of these transformations. We will look at the nitrogen cycle as an example of the key role prokaryotic organisms play in biogeochemical cycles.

Nitrogen is a component of proteins and nucleotides and so is of vital importance for all organisms. The largest source of nitrogen on Earth is the atmosphere, which is almost 80% nitrogen. Why can't we just use this abundant atmospheric nitrogen? Most organisms cannot make use of this nitrogen because they cannot break the strong triple bond between the two nitrogen atoms. Only some bacteria and archaea can break this bond, using the enzyme nitrogenase, and convert $N_2$ into forms that can be used by other organisms. In this conversion process, known as **nitrogen fixation**, $N_2$ is reduced to ammonia ($NH_3$). Ammonia is quickly ionized to ammonium ($NH_4^+$), which prokaryotic cells then use to produce nitrogen-containing molecules such as amino acids and nucleic acids. Nitrogen fixation is the only means of replenishing the nitrogen sources used by most organisms; in other words, all organisms rely on nitrogen fixed by bacteria. Examples of nitrogen-fixing bacteria are cyanobacteria and *Rhizobium* (which is symbiotic with plants; see Chapter 37).

Other prokaryotic organisms carry out **nitrification**, the oxidation of ammonium ($NH_4^+$) to nitrate ($NO_3^-$). This oxidation process is carried out in two steps by two types of nitrifiers, ammonia oxidizers and nitrate oxidizers, present in soil and water. Ammonium oxidizers convert ammonium to nitrite ($NO_2^-$), whereas nitrite oxidizers convert nitrite to nitrate. Nitrate is then taken up by plants and fungi and incorporated into their organic molecules. Animals obtain nitrogen in organic form by eating other organisms or each other.

In sum, nitrification makes nitrogen available to many other organisms, including plants, animals, and bacteria that cannot metabolize ammonia. The metabolic versatility of bacteria and archaea is one factor that accounts for their abundance and persistence on the planet; another factor is their impressive reproductive capacity.

## 23.2d Asexual Reproduction Can Result in Rapid Population Growth

In prokaryotic organisms, asexual reproduction is the normal mode of reproduction. In this process, a parent cell divides by binary fission into two daughter cells that are exact genetic copies of the parent **(Figure 23.11)**. Reproducing by binary fission means that, under favourable conditions, populations of prokaryotic organisms can have very rapid exponential growth as one cell becomes two, two become four, and so on. Some prokaryotic cells can double their population size in only 20 minutes, and will even begin a second round of cell division before the first round is complete. Thus, one cell, given ideal conditions, can produce millions of cells in only a few hours.

These short generation times, combined with the small genomes (roughly one-thousandth the size of the genome of an average eukaryote), mean that prokaryotic organisms have higher mutation rates than do eukaryotic organisms. This translates to roughly 1000 times as many mutations per gene, per unit time, per individual as for eukaryotes. Genetic variability in prokaryotic populations, the basis for their diversity, derives largely from mutation and to a lesser degree from horizontal gene transfer (see Chapter 8). Further, the typically much larger populations of prokaryotic organisms compared with eukaryotes contribute to the much greater genetic variability in bacteria and archaea. In short, prokaryotic organisms have an enormous capacity to adapt, which is one reason for their evolutionary success.

As we have seen, the success of bacteria is beneficial to humans in many ways but can also be detrimental to us when dealing with successful pathogenic bacteria. In the next section, we investigate how some bacteria cause disease and how they are able to resist treatment with antibiotics.

### 23.2e  Pathogenic Bacteria Cause Diseases by Different Mechanisms

Some bacteria produce **exotoxins**, toxic proteins that leak from or are secreted from the bacterium. For example, botulism food poisoning is caused by the exotoxin of the Gram-positive bacterium *Clostridium botulinum*, which grows in poorly preserved foods **(Figure 23.12)**. The botulism exotoxin, botulin, is one of the most poisonous substances known: just a few nanograms can cause severe illness. What makes botulin so toxic? It produces muscle paralysis that can be fatal if the muscles that control breathing are affected. Interestingly, botulin is used under the brand name Botox for the cosmetic removal of wrinkles and in the treatment of migraine headaches and some other medical conditions. Exotoxins produced by certain strains of *Streptococcus pyogenes* have "superantigen properties" (i.e., overactivation of the immune system) that cause necrotizing fasciitis ("flesh-eating disease"). In 1994, Lucien Bouchard, who was then premier of Quebec, lost a leg to this disease.

Other bacteria cause disease through **endotoxins**. Endotoxins are the lipid A portion of the LPS molecule of the

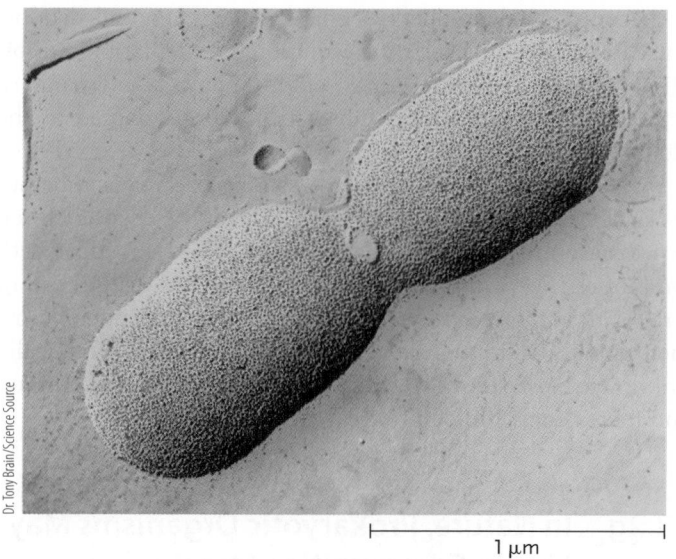

**FIGURE 23.11** *E. coli* **cell dividing by binary fission.** Note that a septum is forming between the two daughter cells.

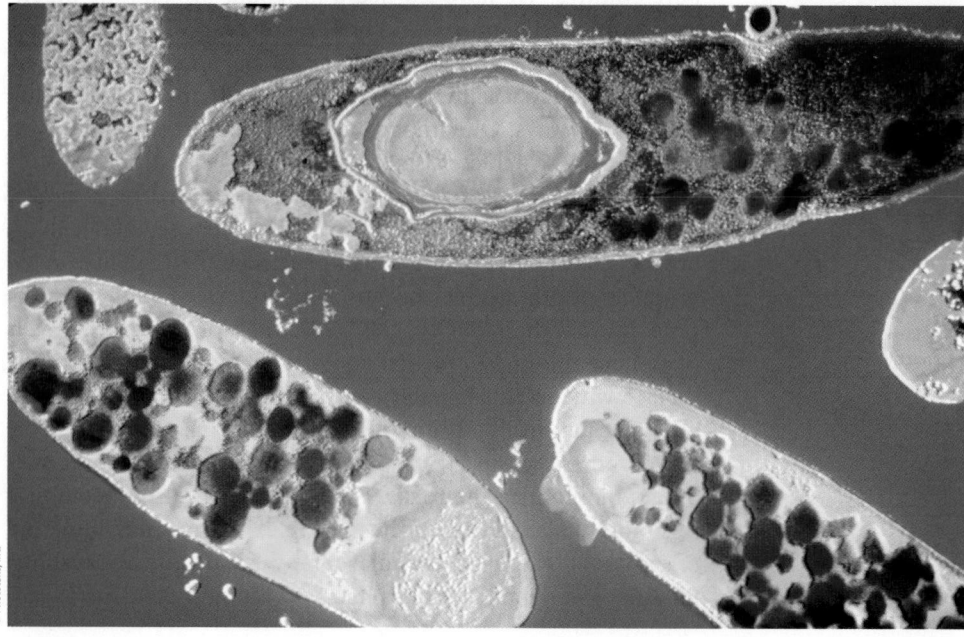

**FIGURE 23.12  The bacterium *Clostridium butyricum*, one of the *Clostridium* species that produces the toxin botulin (colourized TEM).** The large stained structure in the cells is a spore (a survival structure).

outer membrane of all Gram-negative bacteria, such as *E. coli*, *Salmonella*, and *Shigella*. When a Gram-negative cell lyses, the LPSs of the outer membrane are released; exposure to a specific component of this layer, known as *lipid A*, causes endotoxic shock. When Gram-negative bacteria enter the bloodstream, endotoxin overstimulates the host's immune system, triggering inflammation and an often lethal immune response. Endotoxins have different effects, depending on the bacterial species and the site of infection.

## 23.2f Pathogenic Bacteria Commonly Develop Resistance to Antibiotics

An **antibiotic** is a natural or synthetic substance that kills or inhibits the growth of bacteria and other microorganisms. Prokaryotic organisms and fungi produce these substances naturally as defensive molecules, and we have also developed ways to synthesize several types of antibiotics. Different types of antibiotics have different modes of action: for example, streptomycins, produced by soil bacteria, block protein synthesis in their targets, whereas penicillins, produced by fungi, target the peptide cross-linkages in peptidoglycan, as described above.

How are bacteria able to block the actions of antibiotics? There are various mechanisms by which bacteria resist antibiotics **(Figure 23.13)**. For example, some bacteria are able to pump antibiotics out of the cell using membrane-bound pumps. They can also produce molecules that bind to the antibiotic or enzymes that break down the antibiotic, rendering it ineffective against its target. Alternatively, a simple mutation can result in a change in the structure of the antibiotic's target, so that the antibiotic cannot bind to it. Finally, bacteria can develop new enzymes or pathways that are not inhibited by the antibiotic.

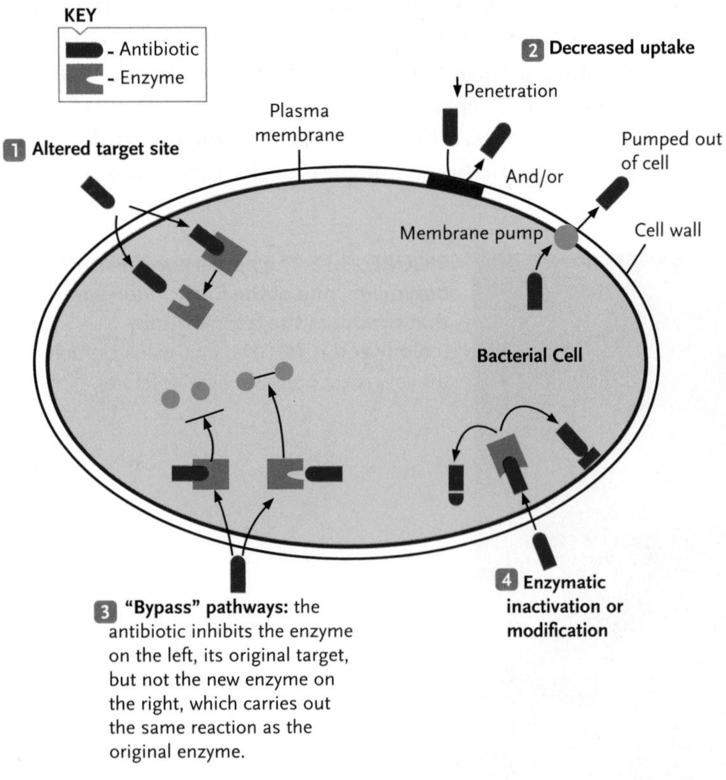

Bacteria can develop resistance through mutations, but they can also acquire resistance via horizontal gene transfer (e.g., plasmid transfer). Taking antibiotics routinely in mild doses or failing to complete a prescribed dosage may contribute to the spread of resistance by selecting strains that can survive in the presence of the drug; there is, however, current research that puts this widely held belief into question. Antibacterial agents that may promote resistance are commonly included in such commercial products as soaps, detergents, and deodorants. Resistance is a form of evolutionary adaptation: antibiotics alter the bacterium's environment, conferring a reproductive advantage on those strains best adapted to the altered conditions.

The development of resistant strains has made tuberculosis, cholera, typhoid (photo at beginning of chapter) fever, gonorrhea, and other bacterial diseases difficult to treat with antibiotics. For example, as recently as 1988, drug-resistant strains of *Streptococcus pneumoniae*, which causes pneumonia, meningitis, and middle-ear infections, were practically unknown. Now, resistant strains of *S. pneumoniae* are common and increasingly difficult to treat.

## 23.2g In Nature, Prokaryotic Organisms May Live in Communities Attached to a Surface

Often, researchers grow bacteria and archaea as individuals in pure cultures. We have learned a lot about prokaryotic organisms from these pure cultures but, in nature, prokaryotic organisms rarely exist as individuals or as pure cultures. Instead, bacteria and archaea live in communities where they interact in a variety of ways. One important type of community is known as a **biofilm**, which consists of a complex aggregation of microorganisms attached to a surface and surrounded by a film of polymers **(Figure 23.14)**. Life in a biofilm offers several benefits: organisms can adhere to hospitable surfaces, they can live on the products of other cells, conditions within the biofilm promote gene transfer between species, and the biofilm protects cells from harmful environmental conditions. Biofilms form on any surface with sufficient water and nutrients. For example, you're probably familiar with how slippery rocks in a stream can be when you try to step from one to the next; the slipperiness is due to biofilms on the rocks. Dental plaque is also a biofilm; if this biofilm spreads below the gum line, it causes inflammation of the gums (gingivitis). Regular removal of plaque by brushing, flossing, and dental checkups helps prevent gingivitis.

**KEY**
- Antibiotic
- Enzyme

[1] Altered target site

Plasma membrane

[2] Decreased uptake

↓ Penetration

And/or

Pumped out of cell

Membrane pump

Cell wall

Bacterial Cell

[3] "Bypass" pathways: the antibiotic inhibits the enzyme on the left, its original target, but not the new enzyme on the right, which carries out the same reaction as the original enzyme.

[4] Enzymatic inactivation or modification

**FIGURE 23.13 Four major mechanisms of antibiotic resistance.** See the text for further explanation of each mechanism.

Biofilms have practical consequences for humans, both beneficial and detrimental. On the beneficial side, for example, are the health effects each of us gains from the bacteria that live in biofilms in our gastrointestinal tracts. We also make use of biofilms in commercial applications: biofilms on solid supports are used in sewage treatment plants to process organic matter before the water is discharged, and they can be effective in bioremediating toxic organic molecules contaminating groundwater. But biofilms can also be harmful to human health. Biofilms adhere to many kinds of surgical equipment and supplies, including catheters, pacemakers, and artificial joints. Even if the bacteria colonizing these devices are not pathogenic, their presence is obviously not desirable given that these devices should be sterile. Given their nature, the presence of any Gram-negative bacteria is a concern. As well, many heterotrophic bacteria will become opportunistic pathogens, given the right conditions. Biofilm infections are difficult to treat because bacteria in a biofilm are up to 1000 times as resistant to antibiotics as are the same bacteria in liquid cultures. For example, outbreaks of the disease caused by *E. coli* O157:H7 have been caused by biofilms that are very difficult to wash off spinach, lettuce, and other produce.

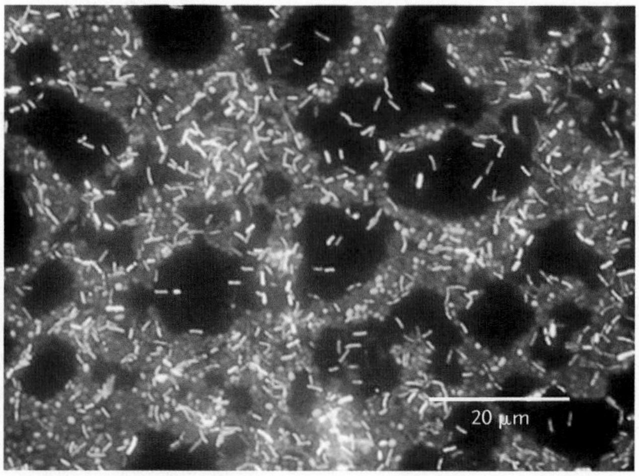

How does a biofilm form? Imagine a surface, such as a rock in a stream, over which water is flowing **(Figure 23.15)**. Due to the nutrients in the water, the surface rapidly becomes coated with polymeric organic molecules, such as polysaccharides or glycoproteins. Once the surface is conditioned with organic molecules, free cells attach in a reversible manner in a matter of seconds (see Figure 23.15, step 1). If the cells remain attached, the association may become irreversible (step 2), at which point the cells grow and divide on the surface (step 3). Next, the physiology of the cells changes and they begin to secrete *extracellular polymeric substances* (EPSs), slimy, gluelike substances similar to the molecules found in bacterial capsules. EPS extends between cells in the mixture, forming a matrix that binds cells to each other and anchors the complex to the surface, thereby establishing the biofilm (step 4). The slime layer entraps a variety of materials such as dead cells and insoluble minerals. The physiological change accompanying the formation of a biofilm results from marked changes in a prokaryotic organism's gene expression pattern—in effect, the prokaryotic cells in a biofilm become very different organisms. Over time, other organisms are attracted to and join the biofilm; depending on the environment, these may include other bacterial species, algae, fungi, or protozoa producing diverse microbial communities. Prokaryotic organisms in a biofilm communicate with each other via **quorum sensing**; in fact, this communication is part of biofilm formation: it allows cells to start secreting EPS when a high enough cell density is reached.

Much remains to be learned about how organisms form and interact within a biofilm, and how changes in gene expression during the transition are regulated.

Emerg Infect Dis © 2002 Centers for Disease Control and Prevention (CDC)

20 μm

**FIGURE 23.14  Biofilm grown on a stainless steel surface**

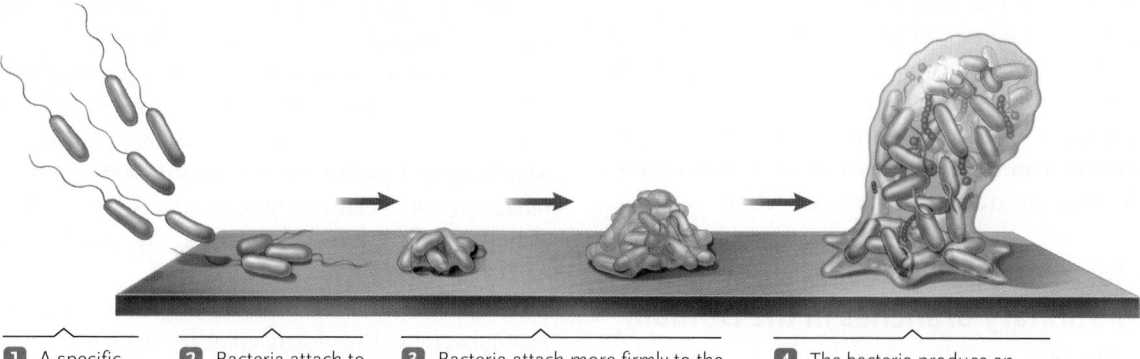

**1** A specific environmental signal changes gene expression in free bacteria.

**2** Bacteria attach to a surface coated with polysaccharides and glycoproteins, which results in more free bacteria attaching. A monolayer forms.

**3** Bacteria attach more firmly to the surface and form small colonies.

**4** The bacteria produce an extracellular matrix that enables the biofilm to mature, producing its three-dimensional shape.

© Cengage Learning 2017.

**FIGURE 23.15  Steps in the formation of a biofilm**

In the next two sections, we describe the major groups of prokaryotic organisms.

## STUDY BREAK QUESTIONS

1. What features differentiate a prokaryotic cell from a eukaryotic cell? What features do both kinds of cells have?
2. How does the presence of a capsule affect the ability of the human body to mount an immune response to those bacteria?
3. How is a pilus similar to a flagellum? How is it different?
4. How does the amount of peptidoglycan in a bacterial cell wall relate to its Gram-stain reaction?
5. What is the difference between a chemoheterotroph and a photoautotroph?
6. What is the difference between an obligate anaerobe and a facultative anaerobe?
7. What is the difference between nitrogen fixation and nitrification? Why are nitrogen-fixing prokaryotic organisms important?
8. What is binary fission?
9. What is the difference between an endotoxin and an exotoxin? Explain how they differ with respect to how they cause disease.
10. Explain four mechanisms by which bacteria protect themselves from antibiotics.
11. What is a biofilm? Give an example of a biofilm that is beneficial to humans and another that is harmful. What advantages do prokaryotic cells in a biofilm gain?
12. What is quorum sensing?

## 23.3 The Domain Bacteria

As for other organisms, classification of bacteria and archaeans has been revolutionized by molecular techniques that allow researchers to compare nucleic acid and protein sequences as tests of evolutionary relatedness. Ribosomal RNA (rRNA) sequences have been most widely used in the evolutionary studies of prokaryotic organisms. Researchers have identified several evolutionary branches within each prokaryotic domain (Figure 23.16), but these classifications will likely change in the future when full genomic sequences can be compared. We discuss the major groups of the domain Bacteria, which is much better characterized than the domain Archaea, in this section, and those of the domain Archaea in the next section.

### 23.3a Molecular Studies Reveal Numerous Evolutionary Branches in the Domain Bacteria

Bacteria as a domain is much better characterized than Archaea; sequencing studies reveal that bacteria have several distinct and separate evolutionary branches. We restrict our discussion to five particularly important groups: proteobacteria, cyanobacteria, Gram-positive bacteria, spirochetes, and chlamydias (see Figure 23.16).

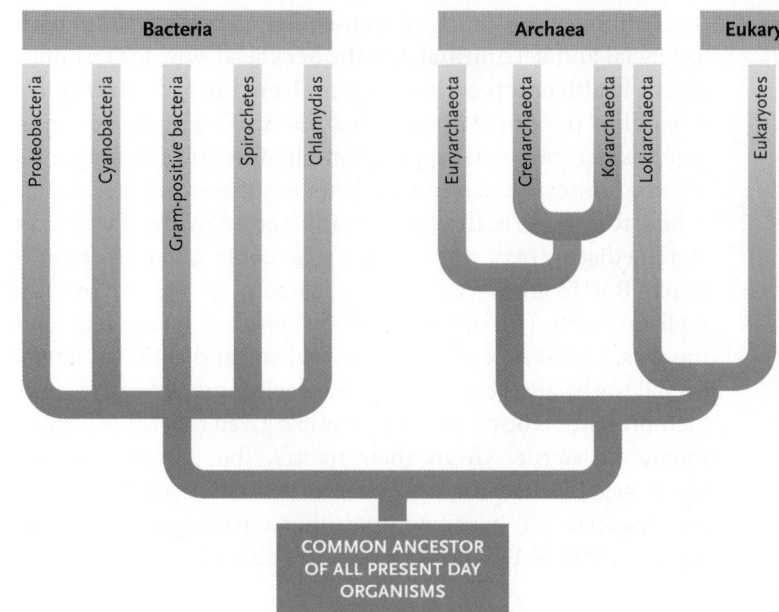

FIGURE 23.16 An abbreviated phylogenetic tree of Bacteria and Archaea

PROTEOBACTERIA: THE PURPLE BACTERIA AND THEIR RELATIVES This highly diverse group of Gram-negative bacteria likely evolved from a purple photosynthetic ancestor. Their purple colour comes from their photosynthetic pigment, a type of chlorophyll distinct from that of plants. Many present-day species are either photoautotrophs (the purple sulfur bacteria) or photoheterotrophs (the purple non-sulfur bacteria); both groups carry out a type of photosynthesis that does not use water as an electron donor and does not release oxygen as a by-product.

Other present-day proteobacteria are **chemoheterotrophs** that are thought to have evolved as an evolutionary branch following the loss of photosynthetic capabilities in an early proteobacterium. The evolutionary ancestors of mitochondria are considered likely to have been ancient non-photosynthetic proteobacteria.

Among the chemoheterotrophs classified with the proteobacteria are *E. coli*; plant pathogenic bacteria; and bacteria that cause human diseases such as bubonic plague, gonorrhea, various forms of gastroenteritis and dysentery, as well as *Helicobacter pylori*, a cause of gastric ulcers. The proteobacteria also include both free-living and symbiotic nitrogen-fixing bacteria.

Myxobacteria are an unusual group of non-photosynthetic proteobacteria that form colonies held together by the slime they produce. Enzymes secreted by the colonies digest "prey"— other bacteria, primarily—that become stuck in the slime. When environmental conditions become unfavourable, as when soil nutrients or water are depleted, myxobacteria form a fruiting body, a differentiated multicellular stage large enough to be visible to the naked eye (Figure 23.17). The fruiting body contains clusters of spores that are dispersed to form new

FIGURE 23.17 **The fruiting body of *Chondromyces crocatus*, a myxobacterium.** Cells of this species collect together to form the fruiting body.

a.

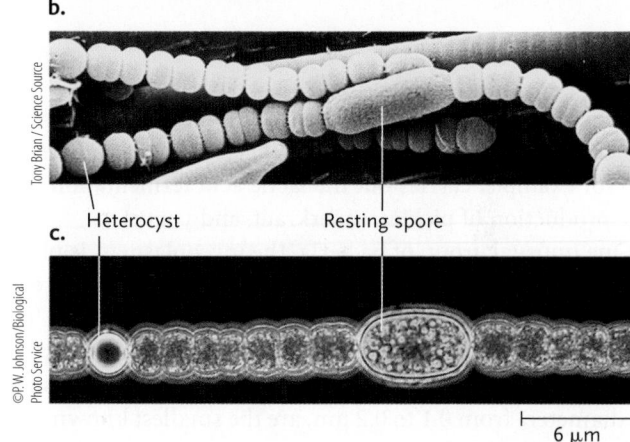

b.

Heterocyst        Resting spore

c.

6 μm

FIGURE 23.18 **Cyanobacteria. (a)** A population of cyanobacteria covering the surface of a pond. **(b)** and **(c)** Chains of cyanobacterial cells. Some cells in the chains form spores. The heterocyst is a specialized cell that fixes nitrogen.

colonies when the fruiting body bursts. Quorum sensing is involved in spore formation.

**CYANOBACTERIA** These Gram-negative photoautotrophs are blue-green in colour **(Figure 23.18)** and carry out photosynthesis by the same pathways and using the same chlorophyll as eukaryotic algae and plants. Like plants and algae, they release oxygen as a by-product of photosynthesis.

The direct ancestors of present-day cyanobacteria were the first organisms to use the water-splitting reactions of photosynthesis. As such, they were critical to the accumulation of oxygen in the atmosphere, which allowed the evolutionary development of aerobic organisms. Chloroplasts probably evolved from early cyanobacteria that were incorporated into the cytoplasm of primitive eukaryotes, which eventually gave rise to the algae and higher plants, as discussed in Chapter 26. In addition to releasing oxygen, present-day cyanobacteria help fix nitrogen into organic compounds in aquatic habitats and act as symbiotic partners with fungi in lichens (see Chapter 25).

**GRAM-POSITIVE BACTERIA** This large group contains many species that live primarily as chemoheterotrophs. Some cause human diseases, including *Bacillus anthracis*, the causal agent of anthrax; *Staphylococcus*, which causes some forms of food poisoning, toxic shock syndrome, pneumonia, and meningitis; and *Streptococcus* **(Figure 23.19)**, which causes strep throat,

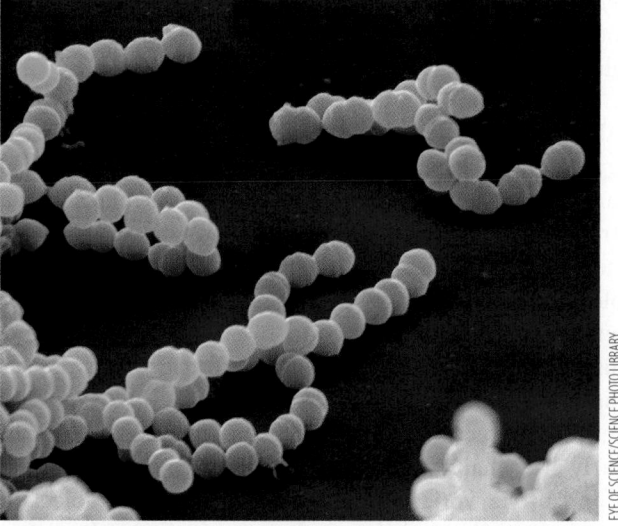

FIGURE 23.19 *Streptococcus* **bacteria forming the long chains of cells typical of many species in this genus**

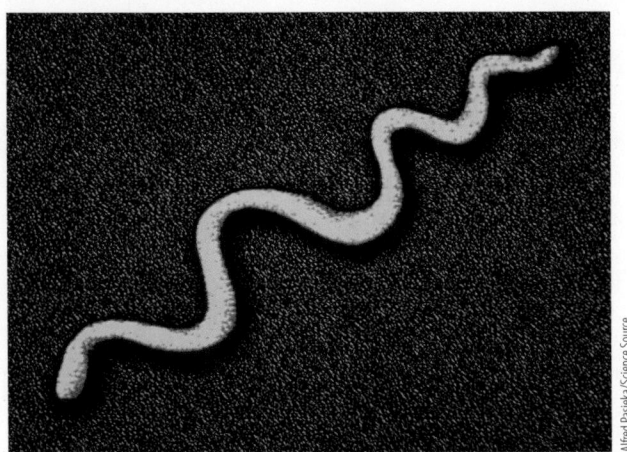

**FIGURE 23.20** *Treponema pallidum*, a spirochete bacterium that causes syphilis (scanning electron microscope image)

necrotizing fasciitis, and some forms of pneumonia. However, some Gram-positive bacteria are beneficial to humans: *Lactobacillus*, for example, carries out the lactic acid fermentation used in the production of pickles, sauerkraut, and yogurt.

One unusual group of bacteria, the mycoplasmas, is placed among the Gram-positive bacteria by molecular studies even though they show a Gram-negative staining reaction. This staining reaction results because they are naked cells that secondarily lost their cell walls in evolution. Some mycoplasmas, with diameters from 0.1 to 0.2 μm, are the smallest known cells.

**SPIROCHETES** These organisms have helically spiralled flagella embedded in their cytoplasm, causing the cells to move in a twisting, corkscrew pattern **(Figure 23.20)**. Their corkscrew movements enable them to move in viscous environments such as mud and sewage, where they are common. Some spirochetes are harmless inhabitants of the human mouth; another species, *Treponema pallidum*, is the cause of syphilis. Termites have symbiotic spirochetes in their intestines that enable them to digest cellulose.

**CHLAMYDIAS** These bacteria are unusual because, although they are Gram-negative and have cell walls with an outer membrane, they lack peptidoglycan. All the known chlamydias are intracellular parasites that cause various diseases in animals. One bacterium of this group, *Chlamydia trachomatis*, is responsible for one of the most common sexually transmitted infections of the urinary and reproductive tracts of humans and also causes trachoma, an infection of the cornea that is the leading cause of blindness in humans.

In this section, you have seen that bacteria thrive in nearly every habitat on Earth. However, some members of the second prokaryotic domain, the Archaea, the subject of the next section, live in habitats that are too forbidding even for bacteria.

**STUDY BREAK QUESTIONS**

1. What methodologies have been used to classify prokaryotic organisms?
2. What were the likely characteristics of the evolutionary ancestor of present-day proteobacteria?
3. How does photosynthesis in photosynthetic proteobacteria differ from photosynthesis in cyanobacteria?

## 23.4 The Domain Archaea

The first Archaea were isolated from extreme environments, such as hot springs, hydrothermal vents on the ocean floor, and salt lakes **(Figure 23.21)**. For that reason, these prokaryotes were called *extremophiles* (organisms that live in extreme environments). Subsequently, archaea have also been found living in less extreme environments.

Archaea share some cellular features with eukaryotes and some with bacteria, and have other features that are unique **(Table 23.2)**.

a.

b.

**FIGURE 23.21 Typically extreme archaeal habitats. (a)** Highly saline water in Great Salt Lake, Utah, coloured red–purple by archaeans. **(b)** Hot, sulfur-rich water in Emerald Pool, Yellowstone National Park, brightly coloured by the oxidative activity of archaea, which convert H2S to elemental sulfur

**TABLE 23.2 | Characteristics of the Bacteria, Archaea, and Eukarya**

| Characteristic | Bacteria | Archaea* | Eukarya |
|---|---|---|---|
| DNA arrangement | Single; circular in most, but some linear and/or multiple | Single, circular | Multiple linear molecules |
| Chromosomal proteins | Prokaryotic histonelike proteins | Five eukaryotic histones | Five eukaryotic histones |
| Genes arranged in operons | Yes | Yes | No |
| Nuclear envelope | No | No | Yes |
| Mitochondria | No | No | Yes |
| Chloroplasts | No | No | Yes |
| Peptidoglycan in cell wall | Present | Absent; some have pseudopeptidoglycan | Absent |
| Membrane lipids | Unbranched; linked by ester linkages | Branched; linked by ether linkage; may have polar heads at both ends | Unbranched; linked by ester linkages |
| RNA polymerase | Limited variations | Multiple types | Multiple types |
| Ribosomal proteins | Prokaryotic | Some prokaryotic, some eukaryotic | Eukaryotic |
| First amino acid placed in proteins | Formylmethionine | Methionine | Methionine |
| Aminoacyl–tRNA synthetases | Prokaryotic | Eukaryotic | Eukaryotic |
| Cell division proteins | Prokaryotic | Prokaryotic | Eukaryotic |
| Proteins of energy metabolism | Prokaryotic | Prokaryotic | Eukaryotic |

* Given that very few Archaea have been identified or cultured, the information in this table is based on an extremely small data set.

## 23.4a  Unique Characteristics of Archaea

Among their unique characteristics are certain features of their plasma membranes and cell walls. The lipid molecules in archaeal plasma membranes are unlike those in the plasma membranes of the majority of bacteria: there is a different linkage between glycerol and the hydrophobic tails, and the tails are isoprenes rather than fatty acids (see Chapter 4). Also, some lipids have polar head groups at both ends. Why would such seemingly minor differences be significant? These unique lipids are more resistant to disruption, making the plasma membranes better suited to extreme environments. Similarly, the unique cell walls of archaea are more resistant to extremes than those of bacteria; some archaea can even survive being boiled in strong detergents!

Many archaea are chemoautotrophs, whereas others are chemoheterotrophs. Interestingly, no known member of the Archaea has been shown to be pathogenic.

## 23.4b  Molecular Studies Reveal Three Evolutionary Branches in the Archaea

The phylogeny of Archaea is poorly developed relative to Bacteria and in quite a state of flux because a tremendous number of archaea have not been cultured, meaning that we have only metagenomic data for most of these organisms. Based on differences in rRNA sequence data, the domain Archaea is divided into three groups (see Figure 23.16). Two major groups, the **Euryarchaeota** and the **Crenarchaeota,** contain archaea that have been cultured in the laboratory. The third and fourth groups, the **Korarchaeota** and **Lokiarchaeota**, have been recognized solely on the basis of DNA taken from environmental samples.

**EURYARCHAEOTA** These organisms are found in various extreme environments. They include methanogens, extreme halophiles, and some extreme thermophiles, as described below.

*Methanogens* (methane generators) live in low-oxygen environments **(Figure 23.22)** and represent about one-half of all known species of Archaea. Methanogens are obligate anaerobes that live in the anoxic (oxygen-lacking) sediments of swamps, lakes, marshes, and sewage works, as well as in more moderate environments, such as the rumen of cattle and sheep, the large intestine of dogs and humans, and the hindgut of insects such as termites and cockroaches. Methanogens generate energy by converting various substrates such as carbon dioxide and hydrogen gas or acetate into methane gas, which is released into the atmosphere.

*Halophiles* are salt-loving organisms. Extreme halophilic Archaea live in highly saline environments such as the Dead Sea and on foods preserved by salting. They require a minimum NaCl concentration of about 1.5 M (about 9% solution) to

**FIGURE 23.22 A colony of the methanogenic archaeon _Methanosarcina_, which lives in the sulfurous, waterlogged soils of marshes and swamps**

survive and can live in a fully saturated solution (5.5 M, or 32%). Most are aerobic chemoheterotrophs, which obtain energy from sugars, alcohols, and amino acids using pathways similar to those of bacteria. Many extreme halophiles use light as a secondary energy source, supplementing the oxidations that are their primary source of energy.

_Extreme thermophiles_ live in extremely hot environments such as hot springs and ocean floor hydrothermal vents. Their optimal temperature range for growth is 70°C to 95°C, close to the boiling point of water. By comparison, no eukaryotic organism is known to live at a temperature higher than 60°C. Thermophilic archaea are important commercially. For example, they are very important in biotechnological applications as sources of enzymes that function under extreme physicochemical conditions (e.g., high temperature, high salinity).

Some extreme thermophiles are members of the Euryarchaeota, but most belong to the **Crenarchaeota**, the next group that we discuss.

**CRENARCHAEOTA** This group includes most of the extreme thermophiles, which have a higher optimal temperature range than those belonging to the Euryarchaeota. For example, the most thermophilic member of this group, _Pyrobolus_, dies below 90°C, grows optimally at 106°C, and can survive an hour of autoclaving at 121°C! (Autoclaving is a process using sustained high-pressured steam to sterilize items.) _Pyrobolus_ lives in ocean floor hydrothermal vents, where the pressure creates water temperatures greater than the boiling point of water on Earth's surface.

Also in this group are **psychrophiles** ("cold loving"), organisms that grow optimally in cold temperatures in the range from –10°C to –20°C. These organisms are found mostly in the Antarctic and Arctic oceans, which are frozen most of the year, and in the intense cold at ocean depths.

Mesophilic members of the Crenarchaeota make up a large part of plankton found in cool marine waters, where they are food sources for other marine organisms.

**KORARCHAEOTA** This group has been recognized solely on the basis of DNA samples obtained from marine and terrestrial hydrothermal environments. To date, no members of this group have been isolated and cultivated in the lab, and nothing is known about their physiology. Molecular data indicate that they are the oldest archaeal lineage.

**LOKIARCHAEOTA** A research team in Sweden has made a very exciting discovery while sampling deep marine sediments near hydrothermal vents along the Arctic Mid-Ocean Ridge. Spang's research group identified archaean DNA that shares a number of genes with eukarya (lineage that includes all nucleated organisms) that had previously been thought to be unique to eukarya. It was called *Lokiarchaeota* based on the name of the vent field from which it was discovered, Loki's Castle. The strong support for Lokiarchaeota and Eukarya being sister groups has phylogenetic and taxonomic implications. Lokiarchaeota is clearly archaean, so in Figure 23.16 the archaea grouping is paraphyletic. To resolve this, the three-domain system will need to be modified into either a two-domain or a four-domain system. There is anticipation that a more immediate ancestor to the eukaryotes will soon be discovered.

In this chapter, we have focused on bacteria and archaea, whose metabolic diversity and environmental range and ecological importance belie their structural simplicity. In the next five chapters, we investigate more structurally complex organisms: the eukaryotic protists, fungi, plants, and animals.

## STUDY BREAK QUESTIONS

1. What distinguishes members of the domain Archaea from members of the domains Bacteria and Eukarya?
2. How does a methanogen obtain energy? In which group or groups of Archaea are methanogens found?
3. Where do extreme halophilic Archaea live? How do they obtain energy? In which group or groups of Archaea are the extreme halophiles found?
4. What are extreme thermophiles and psychrophiles?

# Summary Illustration

Bacteria and Archaea represent two of the three domains of living organisms. These prokaryotic organisms lack a nucleus and membrane-bound organelles. Common structural features include a genome that consists of a single, circular DNA molecule; ribosomes; a cell wall; flagella; and pilli. Although structurally simple, prokaryotes have the greatest metabolic diversity of all organisms.

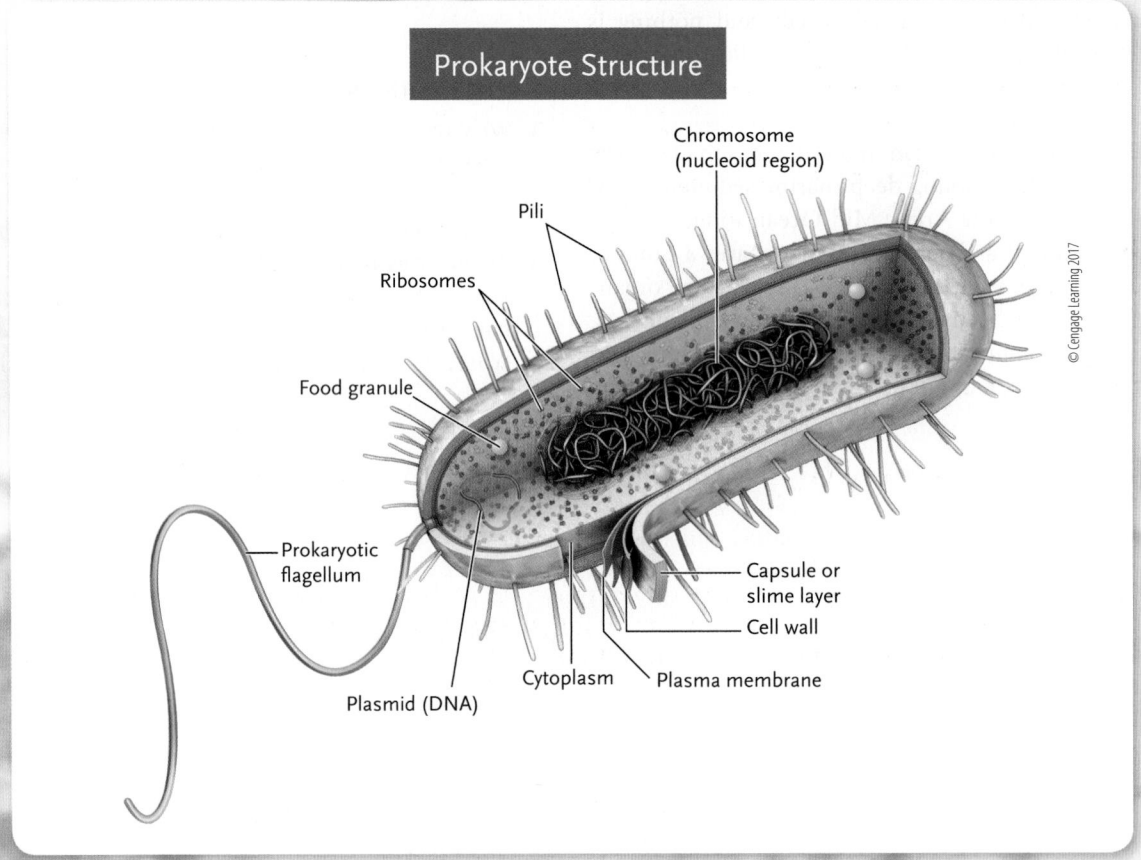

### Prokaryote Structure

Chromosome (nucleoid region)
Pili
Ribosomes
Food granule
Prokaryotic flagellum
Plasmid (DNA)
Cytoplasm
Plasma membrane
Cell wall
Capsule or slime layer

© Cengage Learning 2017

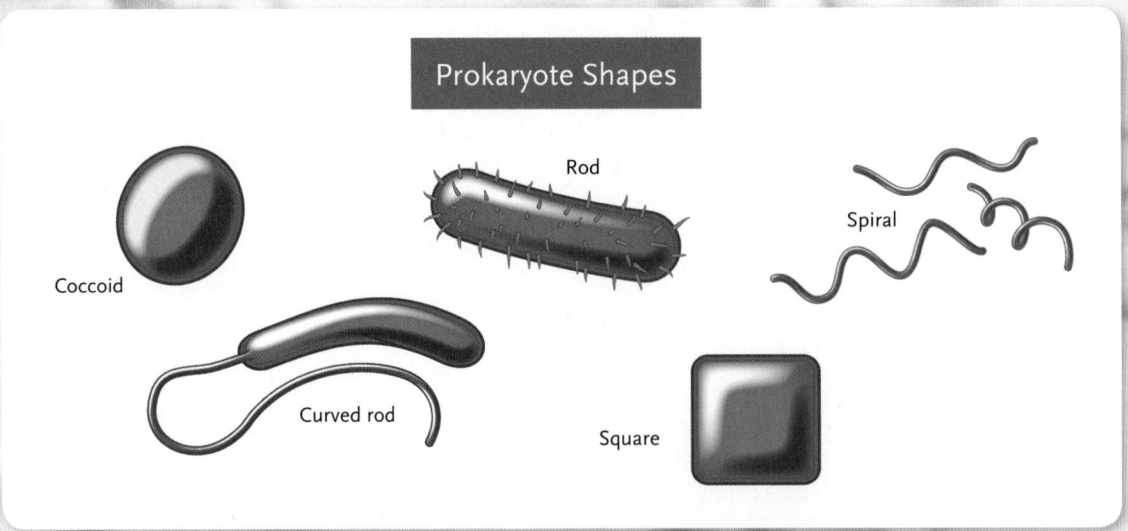

### Prokaryote Shapes

Coccoid
Rod
Spiral
Curved rod
Square

There are four modes of nutrition, based on sources of energy and carbon. Energy transformation can occur aerobically, anaerobically, or by fermentation.

**Chemoheterotrophs** obtain carbon from organic molecules and energy from oxidizing organic molecules.

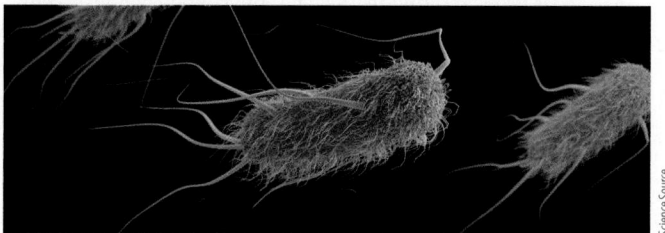

*Escherichia coli* is common in the lower intestine of humans.

**Photoautotrophs** obtain carbon from carbon dioxide and energy from light.

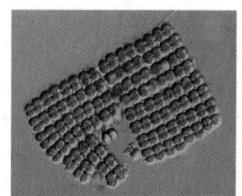

*Merismopedia elegans*, a cyanobacterium, forms rectangular colonies in a mucilaginous matrix.

**Chemoautotrophs** obtain carbon from carbon dioxide and energy from oxidizing inorganic molecules.

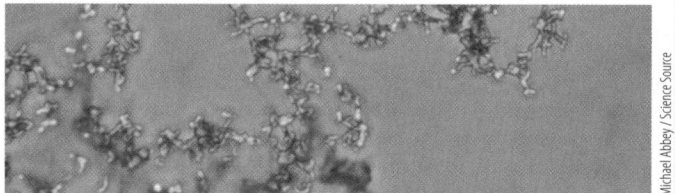

*Thiobacillus thioparus*, a sulphur-oxidizing bacterium, breaks down stone.

**Photoheterotrophs** obtain carbon from organic molecules and energy from light.

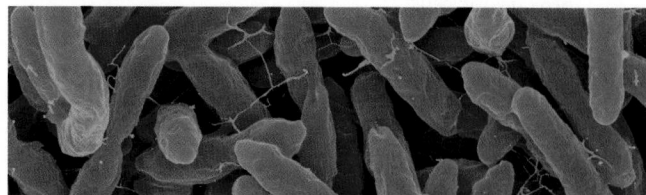

Roseobacters make up about 25% of bacterial biomass in coastal marine waters.

Nitrogen fixation is an important way prokaryotes contribute to the nitrogen cycle. They are the only organisms that convert atmospheric nitrogen into a usable form. Symbioses with plants and other organisms develop around this ability.

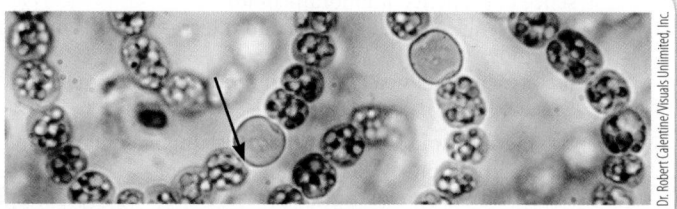

*Nostoc*, a filamentous cyanobacterium, has cells called *heterocysts* (indicated with arrow) in which nitrogen is fixed.

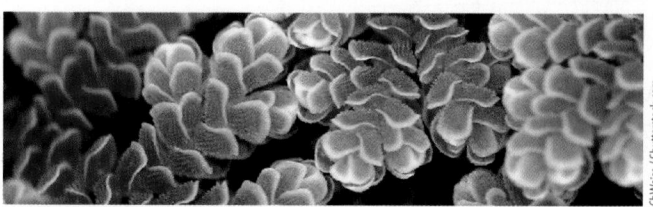

*Azolla* is a fern that houses *Nostoc* in cavities in its leaves and, in turn, receives fixed nitrogen from the cyanobacterium.

## Prokaryotes—Two Groups

### Bacteria

Bacteria sit at the bottom of food webs as they are important decomposers and nitrogen fixers. They also live in the gut of many organisms, including humans, to break down food. Bacteria are the sources of a number of antibiotics as well as flavouring (the sour in sourdough, the tang in yogurt).

### Archaea

Archaea differ from bacteria in cell membrane and cell wall composition. Many archaea are extremophiles, living where other organisms cannot (low oxygen, high salinity, extreme temperatures).

# SELF-TEST QUESTIONS

## Recall/Understand

1. Which of the following structures is found in prokaryotic cells?
   a. cellulosic cell walls
   b. ribosomes
   c. mitochondria
   d. nuclear membrane

2. Which of these statements best describes Archaea?
   a. Their cell walls contain peptidoglycan.
   b. Most are pathogens.
   c. Many are extremophiles.
   d. They have no traits in common with eukaryotic cells.

3. Which of these statements applies to plasmids?
   a. They are pieces of RNA taken up from the environment by prokaryotic cells.
   b. They are small circular pieces of RNA outside a cell's chromosomes.
   c. They are small circular pieces of non-chromosomal DNA.
   d. They are pieces of DNA taken up from the environment by prokaryotic cells.

4. Which of these processes converts ammonium ($NH_4^+$) to nitrate ($NO_3$)?
   a. nitrogen fixation
   b. ammonification
   c. nitrification
   d. denitrification

5. Which of these groups of bacteria are oxygen-producing photoautotrophs?
   a. spirochetes
   b. cyanobacteria
   c. proteobacteria
   d. green bacteria

6. Which statement refers to chlamydias?
   a. They lack peptidoglycan and are Gram-positive.
   b. They lack peptidoglycan and are Gram-negative.
   c. They are not pathogenic and have an outer membrane in the cell wall.
   d. They are pathogenic and lack an outer membrane in the cell wall.

## Apply/Analyze

7. You have isolated an unknown bacterium that produces a toxin. You are trying to determine if it is an endotoxin or an exotoxin. Which of the following features would be associated with the toxin if it were an endotoxin?
   a. It would be secreted from the cell.
   b. It would be a part of the cell wall.
   c. It would be a part of the plasma membrane.
   d. It would be produced by an archaeon.

8. A bacterium that oxidizes nitrite as its only energy source was found deep in a cave. How would you classify this bacterium based on its carbon and energy source?
   a. as a chemolithotroph
   b. as a chemoheterotroph
   c. as a photoautotroph
   d. as a photoheterotroph

9. Which of these lists shows the order of steps by which prokaryotic cells form a biofilm?
   a. cells grow and divide; the cells' physiology changes; cells attach to a surface that is covered in organic polymers; cells secrete extracellular polymers that "glue" the cells to the surface and to each other
   b. the cells' physiology changes; cells grow and divide; cells secrete extracellular polymers that "glue" the cells to the surface and to each other; cells attach to a surface that is covered in organic polymers
   c. cells secrete extracellular polymers that "glue" the cells to the surface and to each other; cells attach to a surface that is covered in organic polymers; cells grow and divide; the cells' physiology changes
   d. cells attach to a surface that is covered in organic polymers; cells grow and divide; the cells' physiology changes; cells secrete extracellular polymers that "glue" the cells to the surface and to each other

## Create/Evaluate

10. You are growing a facultative anaerobic archaeon in culture under two conditions: one culture is in anaerobic conditions, and the other is in aerobic conditions. How would you expect the growth of the cells to compare between the two cultures?
    a. Growth would be greater in the culture in aerobic conditions.
    b. Growth would be greater in the culture in anaerobic conditions.
    c. Growth would be great in both conditions.
    d. Growth would be negligible in both conditions.

11. Suppose that you found an unknown microorganism and you want to determine if it is a bacterium or an archaeon. Which of these features would help you conclude that it is an archaeon?
    a. the absence of peptidoglycan in the cell wall and the presence of branched membrane lipids
    b. the presence of peptidoglycan in the cell wall and the absence of branched membrane lipids
    c. the presence of circular DNA and the presence of a nuclear envelope
    d. the presence of linear DNA and the absence of a nuclear envelope

12. Suppose that you want to have a Botox treatment. What is the link between the Botox treatment and bacteria?
    a. Botox is a mixture of cyanobacteria, which can capture light and produce lots of oxygen, which is good for our skin.
    b. Botox is the brand name for botulin, an exotoxin produced by a bacterium that causes botulism.
    c. Botox is made of endotoxin, which is produced by a Gram-negative bacterium and causes food poisoning.
    d. Botox is made of cultured bacteria that have been dried and turned into a powder that is used for treatment.

13. Distinguish between different prokaryotes based on their relationship with oxygen.

14. Contrast Gram-positive and Gram-negative bacteria.

15. Contrast the habitats of different extremophiles.

# Chapter Roadmap

### Protists

Protists live in a number of different habitats, including aquatic and terrestrial, as well as within other eukaryotes.

**From Chapter 2** →

**24.1 The Vast Majority of Eukaryotes Are Protists**

Most eukaryotes are protists, with the exception of land plants, animals, and fungi.

**From Chapter 5** →

**From Chapter 6** →

**24.2 Characteristics of Protists**

Protists have a diversity of morphologies: they can be single-celled, colonial, or multicellular organisms.

**From Chapter 12** →

**From Chapter 21** →

**24.3 Protists' Diversity Is Reflected in Their Metabolism, Reproduction, Structure, and Habitat**

Protists have a range of life styles: autotrophs, heterotrophs, mixotrophs, saprotrophs, mutualistic symbionts, and parasites. This diversity is reflected in their structure, reproduction, and habitat.

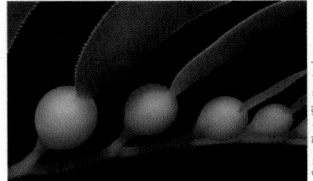

**From Chapter 21** →

**24.4 The Eukaryotic Supergroups and Their Key Protist Lineages**

In this chapter we classify the eukaryotes into five supergroups, most of which are exclusively protists: Excavata, Chromalveolata, Rhizaria, Unikonta (includes fungi and animals), and Plantae (includes land plants).

**To Chapter 25** →

**To Chapter 26** →

**To Chapter 27** →

**24.5 Some Protist Lineages Arose from Primary Endosymbiosis and Others from Secondary Endosymbiosis**

Chloroplasts arose via endosymbiosis events: 1. primary endosymbiosis: a eukaryotic cell engulfed a cyanobacterium; 2. secondary endosymbiosis: a non-photosynthetic eukaryote engulfed a photosynthetic eukaryote.

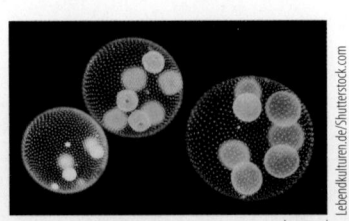

200 μm

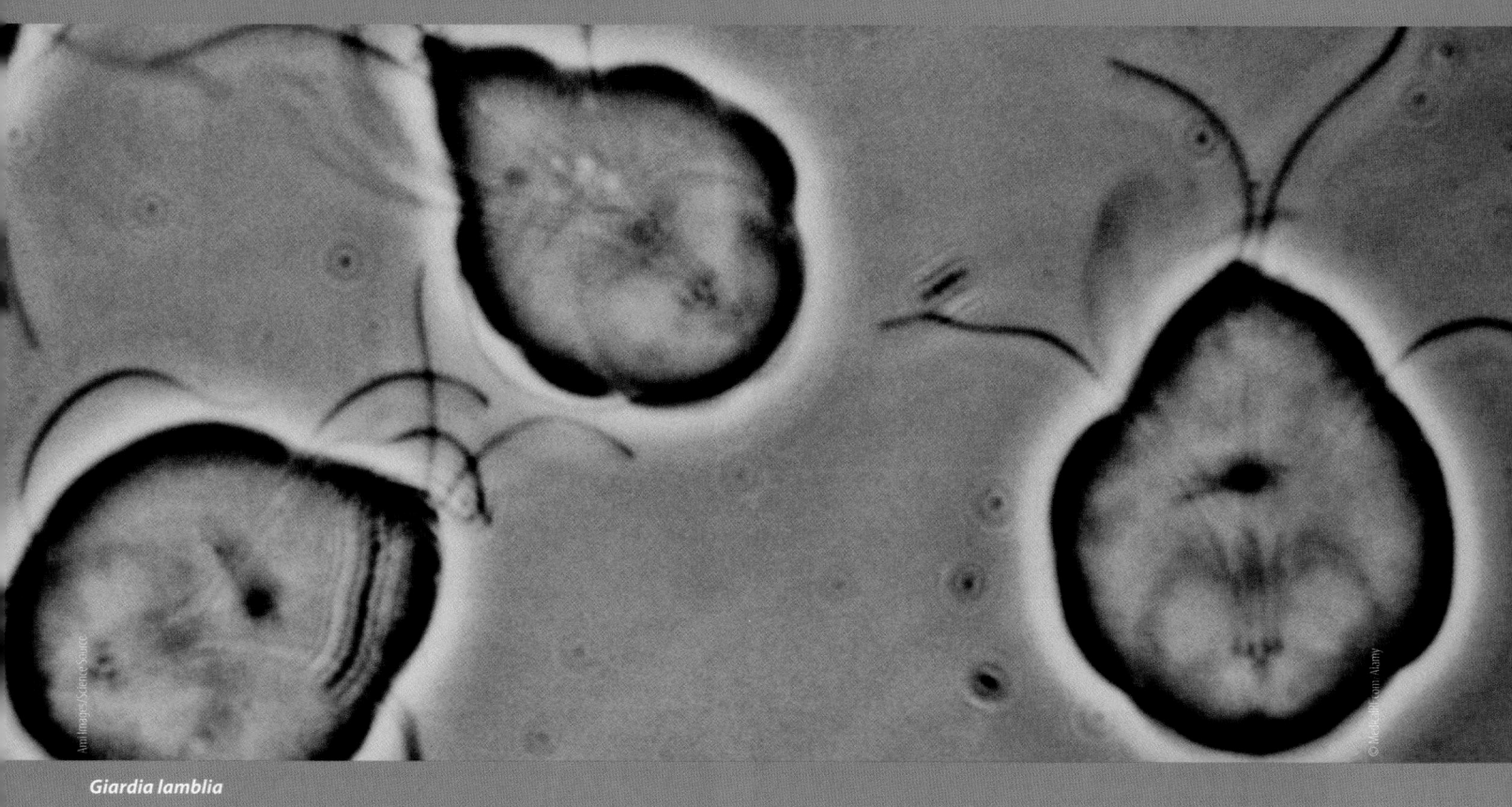

*Giardia lamblia*

# Protists

24

**Why it matters . . .** You are on a backpacking trip in your favourite wilderness area on a hot and sunny day. You pause to take a drink of water from your water bottle but discover it is almost empty. You are very thirsty, so you refill your bottle from a nearby stream. The water is clear and cold and looks clean, and, besides, you're out in the middle of nowhere, so it must be safe to drink, right? You continue on the hike and feel fine. But a few days after you get home, you don't feel so great: you have abdominal pain, cramps, and diarrhea. Your doctor says that you have giardiasis, or "beaver fever," caused by *Giardia lamblia*, the most common intestinal parasite in North America (it is very prevalent in water bodies formed by beaver dams). What is *Giardia*, and how does it make you sick?

   *Giardia* is a single-celled eukaryote that can exist in two forms: a dormant cyst and a motile feeding stage. When you drank from that seemingly clean stream, you ingested some cysts. The cysts can survive for months, so it is important to boil or filter water when you are out hiking or camping. In your small intestine, the cysts released the motile feeding stage, **trophozoites** (*troph* = food; *zoon* = animal), shown in the photographs above. Using their multiple flagella, the trophozoites, with their numerous flagella were able to swim about in your intestinal space and attach themselves to the epithelial cells of your intestine. Infection with *Giardia* can become chronic, causing inflammation and reduction of the absorptive capacity of the gut. Why doesn't your immune system detect the presence of *Giardia* and get rid of the parasite? *Giardia* can alter the proteins on its surface that your immune system relies on to recognize an invader, so it escapes recognition; thus, *Giardia* infections can be persistent or recur.

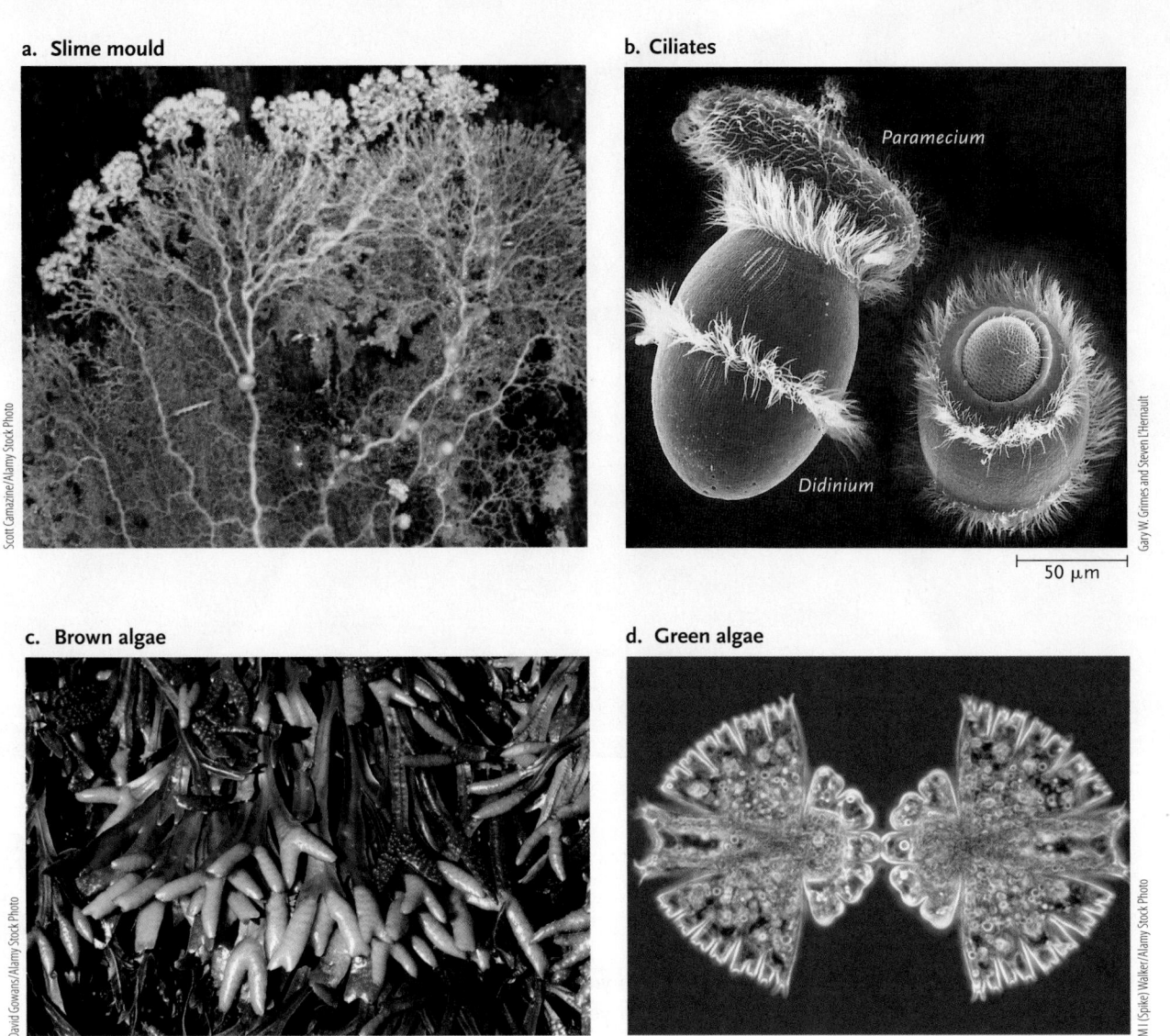

**a. Slime mould**

**b. Ciliates**

*Paramecium*

*Didinium*

50 μm

**c. Brown algae**

**d. Green algae**

25 μm

**FIGURE 24.1 A sampling of protist diversity. (a)** *Physarum*, a plasmodial slime mould. **(b)** *Didinium*, a ciliate, consuming another ciliate, *Paramecium*. **(c)** *Fucus gardneri* (common rockweed), a brown alga growing in rocky intertidal zones. **(d)** *Micrasterias*, a single-celled green alga, here shown dividing in two

*Giardia* is a **protist** (Greek; *protistos* = the very first). Protists are a very heterogeneous collection of about 200 000 eukaryotes. Most are unicellular and microscopic, but some are large, multicellular organisms. Like their most ancient ancestors, almost all these eukaryotic species are aquatic. **Figure 24.1** shows a number of protists, illustrating their great diversity.

## 24.1 The Vast Majority of Eukaryotes Are Protists

The diversity among protists makes it very difficult to define what a protist is. The simplest definition, and the one that we will use in this book, is that a protist is any eukaryotic organism that is not an animal, a land plant, or a fungus. Earlier classifications grouped all these "other" eukaryotes together in one kingdom, Protista. This oversimplified classification reflected our earlier understanding of eukaryote biology, which traditionally has been based almost entirely on the study of animals, land plants, and fungi. But these groups are only three branches of the very large and diverse tree of living eukaryotes **(Figure 24.2)**. This evolutionary tree is based on molecular data, which are considered the most informative data for determining evolutionary relationships. The tree shows that eukaryotic organisms are divided into approximately five "supergroups," a taxonomic level above that of Kingdom. As you can see by looking at Figure 24.2, the vast majority of eukaryotes are not land plants, animals, or fungi but protists. The tree shown here represents our current understanding of the relationships among eukaryotic organisms, which is actively changing as

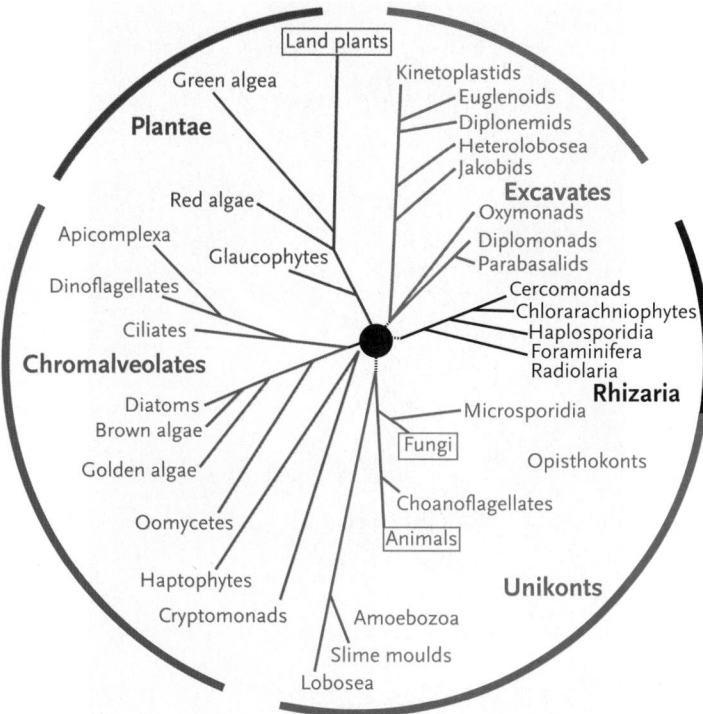

**FIGURE 24.2 Major lineages of protists within the supergroups of eukaryotic organisms.** The current evolutionary tree for eukaryotes divides these organisms among approximately five supergroups: Excavata, Unikonta (including animals and fungi), Plantae (including land plants and their algal relatives), Chromalveolata, and Rhizaria. Selected lineages of protists in each supergroup are discussed in this chapter. Branch lengths are arbitrary.

Source: Eugene V Koonin, 2010 and direct communication with Patrick Keeling (UBC)

researchers continue to investigate the evolutionary history of eukaryotes. The actual number of supergroups is still being debated, with some researchers dividing eukaryotes into additional supergroups to those shown in Figure 24.2. You may notice that the "root" of the tree—the last eukaryote common ancestor (LECA)—is not identified. The identity of this ancestral group is a major mystery that researchers are actively working to unravel.

The first eukaryotes likely evolved about 1.5–2 billion years ago (bya) ago. While we don't fully understand how they evolved, we know that endosymbiosis played an important role in the process. Eukaryotes contain mitochondria (although some have very reduced versions of this organelle) and many also contain chloroplasts. As outlined in Chapter 2, mitochondria and chloroplasts are the descendants of free-living prokaryotes that, over evolutionary time, became organelles. All mitochondria are thought to have arisen from a single endosymbiotic event, but the history of chloroplasts is more complex. We will return to the evolution of chloroplasts at the end of this chapter, once you have had a chance to become familiar with the various groups of protists.

In this chapter, we will start with an overview of features of protists and then focus on key protist lineages in each of the

eukaryotic supergroups. In this way, you will gain an understanding of how diverse protists are morphologically, functionally, and ecologically. As you read about the various groups of protists, think about how they differ from animals and plants, and how learning about these "other" eukaryotes changes your understanding of eukaryote biology. Protists are sometimes called the "rule-breakers" of the eukaryotic world: many of the general rules, or "facts," that we think we know about eukaryotic organisms are revealed as not being generally true at all once protists are considered, forcing us to rethink what is "typical" or "normal" in eukaryote biology.

### STUDY BREAK QUESTION

1. By what process did eukaryotes such as protists acquire mitochondria and chloroplasts?

## 24.2 Characteristics of Protists

Because protists are eukaryotes, the boundary between them and prokaryotic organisms is clear and obvious. Unlike bacteria and archaea, protists have a membrane-bound nucleus with multiple linear chromosomes. In addition to cytoplasmic organelles, including mitochondria and chloroplasts (in some species), protists have microtubules and microfilaments, which provide motility and cytoskeletal support. As well, they share characteristics of transcription and translation with other eukaryotes.

The phylogenetic relationship between protists and other eukaryotes is more complex (Figure 24.2). Over evolutionary time, the eukaryotic family tree branched out in many directions. Almost all eukaryotic lineages are protists with the exception of three groups: animals, land plants, and fungi, which arose from protist ancestors. Although some protists have features that resemble those of the fungi, plants, or animals, several characteristics are distinctive. In contrast to fungi, most protists are motile or have motile stages in their life cycles, and their cell walls are made of cellulose, not chitin.

*How do photosynthesizing protists differ from plants?* Unlike plants, many photoautotrophic protists can also live as heterotrophs, and some regularly combine both modes of nutrition. Protists do not retain developing embryos in parental tissue, as plants do, nor do they have highly differentiated structures equivalent to roots, stems, and leaves. Photosynthetic protists are often referred to as *algae*; these protists are generally aquatic and often unicellular and microscopic (although many are multicellular). However, the different groups of algae are not closely related to each other (Figure 24.2), so the term *algae* does not indicate any sort of relatedness among organisms referred to by that term.

*How do protists differ from animals?* Unlike protists, all animals are multicellular and have features such as an internal digestive tract and complex developmental stages. Protists also lack features that characterize many animals, including nerve cells; highly differentiated structures such as limbs and a heart; and collagen, an extracellular support protein.

**STUDY BREAK QUESTION**

1. What features distinguish protists from prokaryotic organisms? What features distinguish them from fungi, plants, and animals?

## 24.3 Protists' Diversity Is Reflected in Their Metabolism, Reproduction, Structure, and Habitat

As you might expect from looking at Figure 24.2, protists are highly diverse in habitat, structure, metabolism, and reproduction.

### 24.3a Habitat

Protists live in aqueous habitats, including aquatic or moist terrestrial locations, such as oceans, freshwater lakes, ponds, streams, and moist soils, and within host organisms. In bodies of water, small photosynthetic protists collectively make up the **phytoplankton** (*phytos* = plant; *planktos* = drifting), the organisms that capture the energy of sunlight in nearly all aquatic habitats. These phototrophs provide organic substances and oxygen for heterotrophic bacteria, other protists, and the small crustaceans and animal larvae that are the primary constituents of **zooplankton** (*zoe* = life, usually meaning animal life). Although protists are not animals, biologists often include them among the zooplankton. Phytoplankton and larger multicellular protists forming seaweeds collectively account for about half the Earth's total organic matter produced by photosynthesis.

In the moist soils of terrestrial environments, protists play important roles among the detritus feeders that recycle matter from organic back to inorganic form. In their roles in phytoplankton, in zooplankton, and as detritus feeders, protists are enormously important in world ecosystems.

Protists that live in host organisms are **parasites**, obtaining nutrients from the host. Indeed, many of the parasites that have significant effects on human health are protists, causing diseases such as malaria, sleeping sickness, and amoebic dysentery.

### 24.3b Structure

Most protists are single cells, while others live as **colonies** (**Figure 24.3**) in which individual cells show little or no differentiation and are potentially independent. Within colonies, individuals use cell signalling to cooperate on tasks such as feeding and movement. Some protists are large multicellular organisms; for example, the giant kelp of coastal waters can rival forest trees in size.

FIGURE 24.3 **Colonial protist (Dinobryon)**

20 μm

WIM VAN EGMOND/VISUALS UNLIMITED, INC./SCIENCE PHOTO LIBRARY

Many single-celled and colonial protists have complex intracellular structures, some found nowhere else among living organisms (**Figure 24.4**). These unique structures reflect key aspects of the habitats in which protists live. For example, consider a single-celled protist living in a freshwater pond. Its cytoplasm is hypertonic to the water surrounding it, meaning that water flows into the cell by osmosis. How can the protist stop itself from bursting? A specialized cytoplasmic organelle, the **contractile vacuole**, gradually fills with fluid. When this vacuole reaches its maximum size, it moves to the plasma membrane and forcibly contracts, expelling the fluid to the outside through a pore in the membrane.

The cells of some protists are supported by an external cell wall or by an internal or external shell built up from organic or mineral matter; in some, the shell takes on highly elaborate forms. Instead of a cell wall, other protists have a **pellicle**, a layer of supportive protein fibres located inside the cell just under the plasma membrane, providing strength and flexibility (**Figure 24.5**).

At some time during their lives, almost all protists move. Some move by amoeboid motion, in which the cell extends one or more lobes of cytoplasm called **pseudopodia** (*false feet*; see **Figure 24.6**); the rest of the cytoplasm and the nucleus then flow into the pseudopodium, completing the movement. Other protists move by the beating of flagella or cilia. In some protists,

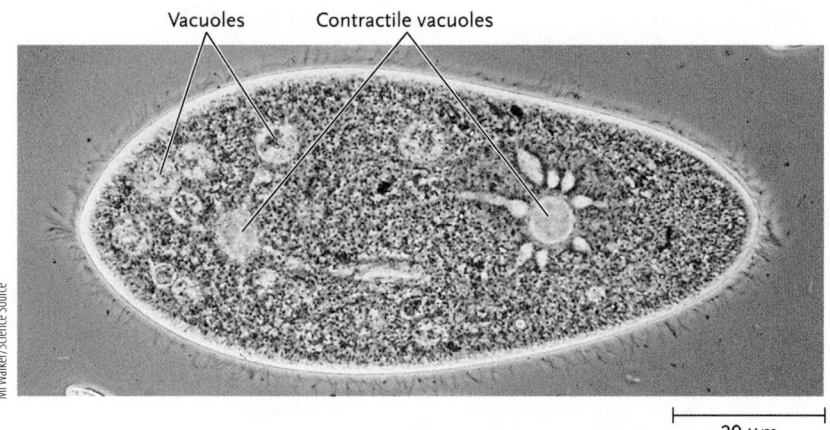

Vacuoles    Contractile vacuoles

20 µm

MI Walker/Science Source

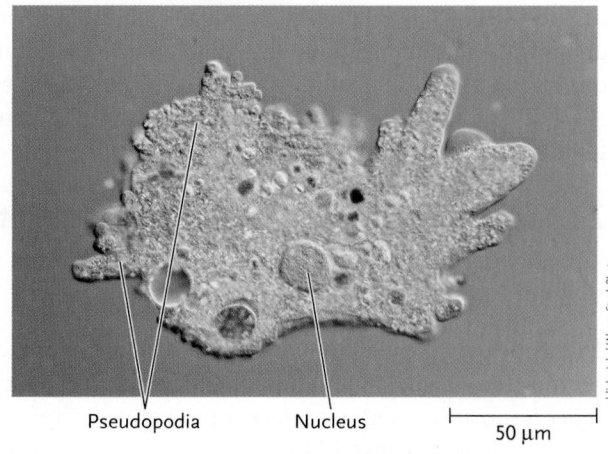

Pseudopodia    Nucleus    50 µm

blickwinkel/Alamy Stock Photo

**FIGURE 24.6** *Amoeba proteus* of the Amoebozoa is perhaps the most familiar protist of all.

Food vacuole    Food residues being ejected    Gullet    Cilia    Trichocysts

Contractile vacuole emptied    Macronucleus    Micronucleus    Contractile vacuole filled

© Cengage Learning 2017. Based on V. & J. Pearse and M. & R. Buchsbaum, Living Invertebrates, The Boxwood Press, 1987.

**FIGURE 24.4 A ciliate, *Paramecium*, showing the cytoplasmic structures typical of many protists**

Source: Redrawn from V. & J. Pearse and M. & R. Buchsbaum, *Living Invertebrates*. The Boxwood Press, 1987.

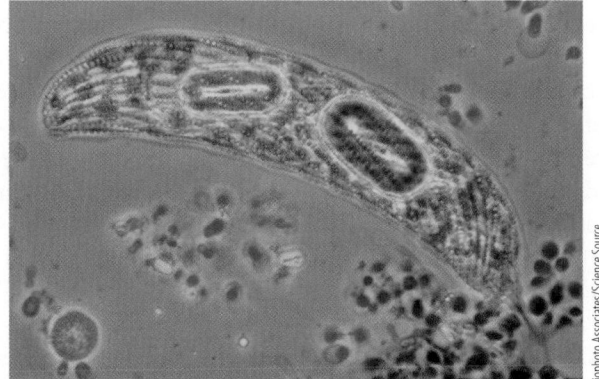

Biophoto Associates/Science Source

**FIGURE 24.5 *Euglena spirogyra*, showing pellicle (strips of protein fibres)**

## 24.3c Metabolism

Almost all protists are aerobic organisms that live either as heterotrophs—obtaining carbon from organic molecules produced by other organisms—or as photoautotrophs—producing organic molecules for themselves by photosynthesis (see Chapter 6). Some heterotrophic protists obtain organic molecules by engulfing part or all of other organisms (*phagocytosis*) and digesting them internally. Others absorb small organic molecules from their environment by diffusion. Some protists can live as either heterotrophs or autotrophs.

## 24.3d Reproduction

Reproduction may be asexual, by mitosis, or sexual through meiotic cell division and formation of gametes. In protists that reproduce by both mitosis and meiosis, the two modes of cell division are often combined into a **life cycle** that is highly distinctive among the different protist groups. We do not yet have a complete understanding of the reproductive biology of many protists.

### STUDY BREAK QUESTION

1. Define each of the following terms in your own words, and indicate the role that each plays in the life of a protist: *pellicle, pseudopodia, contractile vacuole.*

cilia are arranged in complex patterns, with an equally complex network of microtubules and other cytoskeletal fibres supporting the cilia under the plasma membrane.

Many protists can exist in more than one form, for example, as a motile form and as a nonmotile cyst that can survive unfavourable conditions. This morphological variability allows the species to live in different habitats at different stages in its life.

## 24.4 The Eukaryotic Supergroups and Their Key Protist Lineages

In this section, we look at the biological features of the major protist lineages in each eukaryote supergroup shown in Figure 24.2. Our focus is the ecological or economic importance of each lineage, the habitats in which you would find these organisms, and key features that differentiate the group from other protists. As you read through the information on each lineage, think about how the structural features of that group relate to its habitat and lifestyle.

## 24.4a Excavata Are Unicellular, Flagellated Protists, Many of Which Lack Mitochondria

This supergroup takes its name from the hollow (excavated) ventral feeding groove found in most members. Protists of this supergroup are sometimes referred to as *protozoa* (*proto* = first; *zoon* = animal) because, like animals, they ingest their food and move by themselves. We will consider five lineages of Excavates: euglenids, diplonemids, kinetoplastids, diplomonads, and parabasalids.

**EUGLENIDS** You have probably seen an example of one genus of euglenids, *Euglena*, in your earlier biology classes (**Figure 24.7**), as they are often used to illustrate how some protists have plant-like features (photosynthesis) combined with features that we consider animal-like (movement). Euglenids are important primary producers in freshwater ponds, streams, and lakes, and even some marine habitats. Most are autotrophs that carry out photosynthesis using the same photosynthetic pigments and mechanisms as plants. If light is not available, many of the photosynthetic euglenids can also live as heterotrophs by absorbing organic molecules through the plasma membrane or by engulfing small particles. Organisms that can act as autotrophs and heterotrophs are called **mixotrophs**. Other euglenids lack chloroplasts and live entirely as heterotrophs.

The name *Euglena* roughly translates as "eyeball organism," a reference to the large *eyespot* that is an obvious feature of photosynthetic euglenids (Figure 24.7). The eyespot contains pigment granules in association with a light-sensitive structure and is part of a sensory mechanism that stimulates cells to swim toward moderately bright light or away from intensely bright light so that the organism finds optimal conditions for photosynthetic activity. In addition to an eyespot, euglenids contain numerous organelles, including a contractile vacuole.

Rather than an external cell wall, euglenids have a spirally grooved pellicle formed from strips of transparent protein-rich material underneath the membrane (Figure 24.5). In some euglenids, the strips are arranged in a spiral pattern, allowing the cell to change its shape in a wriggling sort of motion (known as *euglenoid movement*) that allows the cell to change direction. Euglenids can also swim by whiplike movements of flagella that extend from one end of the cell. Most have two flagella: one rudimentary and short, the other long.

**DIPLONEMIDS** Diplonemids are flagellated unicells that have recently been touted the "most prolific predator known." University of British Columbia's Patrick Keeling, evolutionary

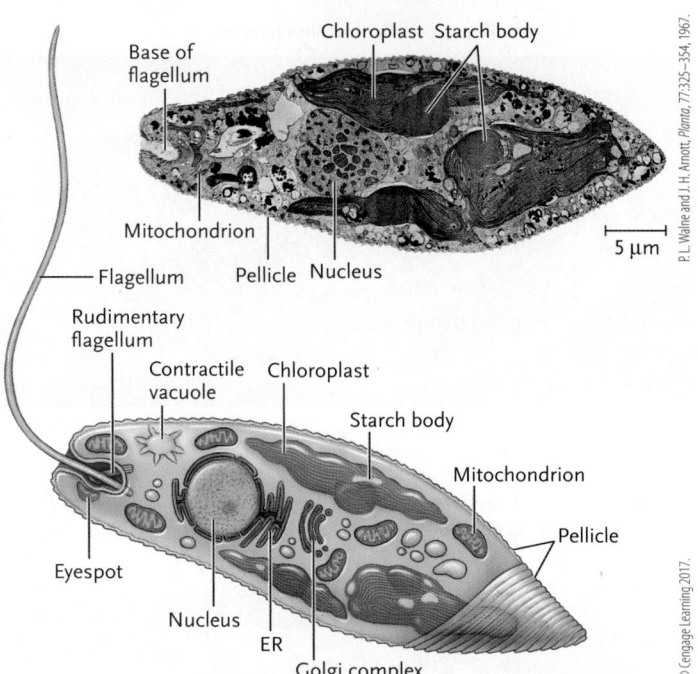

**FIGURE 24.7 Body plan and an electron micrograph of *Euglena gracilis*.** The plane of section in the electron micrograph has cut off all but the base of the flagellum.

microbiologist, gave a recent interview on CBC radio where he told the fascinating story about how this group of organisms, while likely the most abundant and diverse marine planktonic lineage, have not been given much attention. Their existence was known, but they were considered an evolutionary peculiarity. It is only recently that a research team from France, using different tools, discovered DNA sequences of this group in ocean samples. Dr. Keeling's research group wanted to find and characterize the actual organism. Members of the research team collected samples in the north Pacific Ocean. They not only discovered 10 different species of diplonemids, but they also determined that one of the species is the most abundant marine heterotrophic eukaryote. The abundance of this predator has broad ecological implications as it has a central position in the ocean food web (**Figure 24.8**).

**KINETOPLASTIDS** Sleeping sickness is a fatal disease endemic to sub-Saharan Africa. Although the disease was almost eradicated about 40 years ago, it has been making a comeback due to wars, the subsequent refugee movement, and damage to healthcare systems. Sleeping sickness is caused by various subspecies of *Trypanosoma brucei* (**Figure 24.9**) that are transmitted from one host to another by bites of the tsetse fly. Early symptoms include fever, headaches, rashes, and anemia. Untreated, the disease damages the central nervous system, leading to a sleeplike coma and eventual death. The disease has proved difficult to control because the same trypanosomes infect wild mammals, providing an inexhaustible reservoir for the parasite. Other trypanosomes, also transmitted by insects, cause Chagas disease in

FIGURE 24.8 **Observational Research**

## Isolation and Identification of Marine Diplonemids, Potentially the Most Abundant Marine Organism

**Hypothesis:** Diplonemids, previously known from only a single environmental gene from marine planktonic samples, are predacious unicellular flagellates.

**Prediction:** Diplonemids play a significant role in the marine ecosystem due to their abundance and diversity; they have been touted as the most prolific predator known.

**Method:** Samples were taken at different locations in the Pacific Ocean at varying depths. Heterotrophic marine protists were manually isolated, examined microscopically, photographed, and the SSU rRNA (small subunit ribosomal RNA) sequenced.

**Results:** Ninety-two colourless flagellates were isolated. Sequence data helped to identify 40 cells, of which 25% were diplonemids; this supports the claim that they are abundant planktonic eukaryotes. Diplonemids are colourless, oblong to elliptical in shape, approximately 20 µm in length, and have two subapical flagella (below or near the tip).

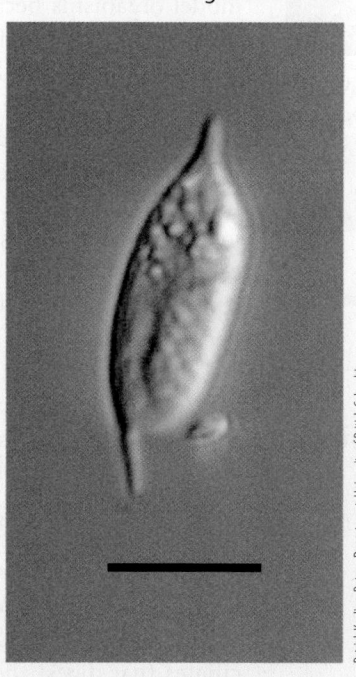

Patrick Keeling, Botany Department, University of British Columbia

**Conclusions:** Prior to this research, marine diplonemids were identified through surveys of only a single gene. During this study, 10 representatives were documented, including one of the single-most common heterotrophic marine eukaryotes, which is potentially the principle consumer of other microscopic protists, including primary producers (i.e., algae). They therefore have a central position in the marine food chain, and as such would have a significant role in the oceans' responses to global climate change.

parasites that lack mitochondria and move by means of flagella. Because they lack mitochondria, these organisms are limited to producing ATP via glycolysis (see Chapter 5). Originally, the lack of mitochondria in many Excavata led biologists to consider this group as the most ancient line of protists; however, it now appears that the ancestor of this group did have mitochondria. The nuclei of Excavata that lack mitochondria contain genes derived from mitochondria, and they also have organelles that likely evolved from mitochondria. These Excavata may have lost their mitochondria as an adaptation to the parasitic way of life, in which oxygen is in short supply.

**Diplomonad** means *double cell*, and these organisms do look like two cells together (see the figure at the beginning of the chapter), with their two apparently identical, functional nuclei and multiple flagella arranged symmetrically around the cell's longitudinal axis. The best-known diplomonad is *Giardia lamblia*, profiled at the beginning of this chapter. Some are free living, but many live in animal intestines; some diplomonads do not cause harm to the host, whereas others, like *Giardia*, live as parasites.

**Parabasalids** include the sexually transmitted disease trichomoniasis is caused by *Trichomonas vaginalis* (**Figure 24.10a**). The infection is usually symptomless in men, but in women, *T. vaginalis* can cause severe inflammation and irritation of the vagina and vulva. If untreated, trichomoniasis can cause infection of the uterus and fallopian tubes that can result in infertility. Luckily, drugs can easily cure the infection.

Central and South America and leishmaniasis in many tropical countries. Humans with Chagas disease have an enlarged liver and spleen and may experience severe brain and heart damage; leishmaniasis causes skin sores and ulcers, as well as liver and spleen damage.

Like trypanosomes, other kinetoplastids are heterotrophs that live as animal parasites. Kinetoplastid cells are characterized by a single mitochondrion that contains a large DNA-protein deposit called a *kinetoplast* (Figure 24.9). Most kinetoplastids also have a leading and a trailing flagellum, which are used for movement. In some cases, the trailing flagellum is attached to the side of the cell, forming an undulating membrane that allows the organism to glide along or attach to surfaces.

**DIPLOMONADS AND PARABASALIDS** Like many Excavata, diplomonads and parabasalids are single-celled animal

Parabasalids take their names from cytoplasmic structures associated with the nucleus, *parabasal bodies*; some biologists consider these structures to be the Golgi apparatus of these cells. Parabasalids are also characterized by a sort of fin called an **undulating membrane**, formed by a flagellum buried in a fold of the cytoplasm, in addition to freely beating flagella. The buried flagellum allows parabasalids to move through thick viscous fluids, such as those lining human reproductive tracts.

Other parabasalids (e.g., *Trichonympha*; Figure 24.10b) are symbionts that live in the guts of termites and other wood-eating insects, digesting the cellulose in the wood for their hosts. As if this endosymbiotic relationship were not complex enough, biologists recently discovered that the protists themselves cannot produce the enzymes necessary to break down cellulose but instead rely on bacterial symbionts to do it.

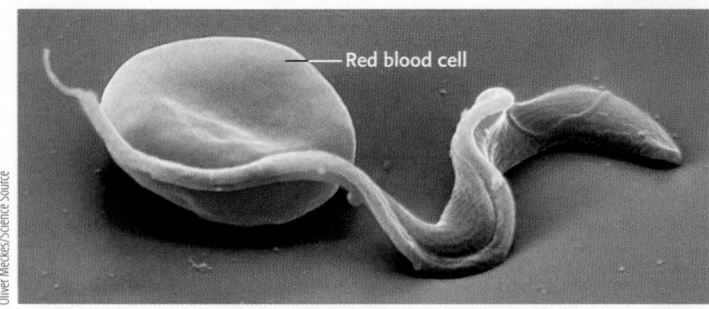

Red blood cell

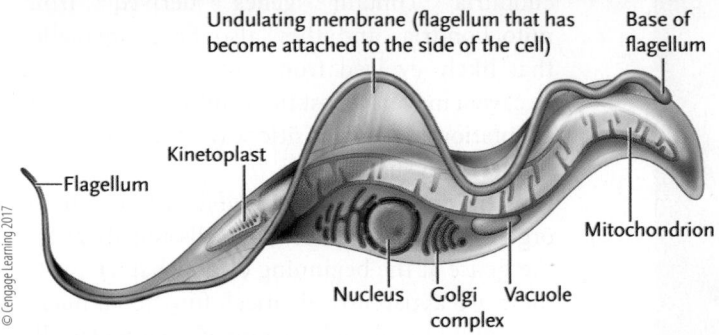

Undulating membrane (flagellum that has become attached to the side of the cell)

Base of flagellum

Flagellum

Kinetoplast

Mitochondrion

Nucleus

Golgi complex

Vacuole

**FIGURE 24.9** *Trypanosoma brucei*, **the parasitic kinetoplastid that causes African sleeping sickness**

## 24.4b Chromalveolates Have Complex Cytoplasmic Structures and Move via Flagella or Cilia

This group is named for the small, membrane-bound vesicles called *alveoli* (*alvus* = belly) in a layer just under the plasma membrane. The chromalveolates supergroup includes two motile, free-living lineages as well as a motile parasitic group. We will take a closer look at some representative lineages over the next few pages.

**CILIATES** This group of protists has helped us understand key aspects of eukaryotic cells, such as the existence of telomeres at the ends of eukaryotic chromosomes and the function of telomerase. These protists are examples of model organisms—organisms that are easily manipulated and easily raised in the lab and for which we have abundant data, for example, genome sequences (see *The Purple Pages*). Several protists are ideal model organisms because, even though they are single celled, the complexity of their structures and functions is comparable to that of humans and other animals. One ciliate, *Tetrahymena* (**Figure 24.11**), was the organism in which telomeres and telomerase were discovered; it was also the cell in which the first motor protein was identified, cell cycle control mechanisms were first described, and ribozymes were discovered. The involvement of ciliates with scientific research dates back several centuries: they were among the first organisms observed in the seventeenth century by the pioneering microscopist Anton van Leeuwenhoek.

The ciliates are a large group, with nearly 10 000 known species of primarily single-celled but highly complex heterotrophic organisms that swim by means of cilia (see Figures 24.4 and 24.11). Any sample of pond water or bottom mud contains a wealth of these creatures. Some ciliates live individually, whereas others are colonial. Certain ciliates are animal parasites; others live and reproduce in their hosts as mutually beneficial symbionts. A compartment of the stomach of cattle and other grazing animals contains large numbers of symbiotic ciliates that digest the cellulose in their hosts' plant diet. The host animals then digest the excess ciliates.

Ciliates have many highly developed organelles, including a mouthlike gullet lined with cilia, structures that exude toxins and other defensive materials from the cell surface, contractile vacuoles, and a complex system of food vacuoles. A pellicle reinforces the cell's shape. A complex cytoskeleton anchors the

**a.** *Trichomonas vaginalis*

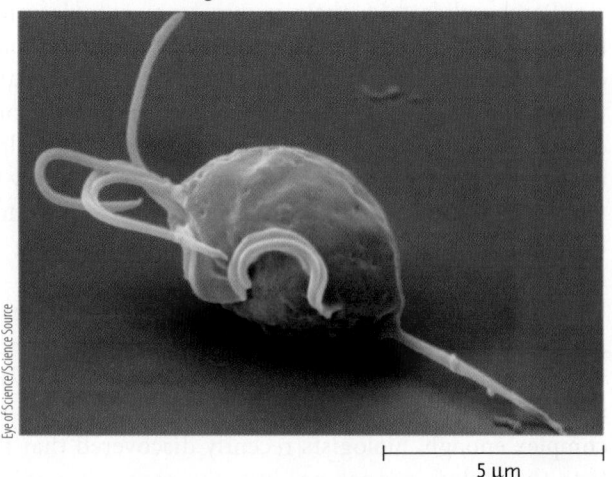

5 μm

**b.** *Trichonympha*

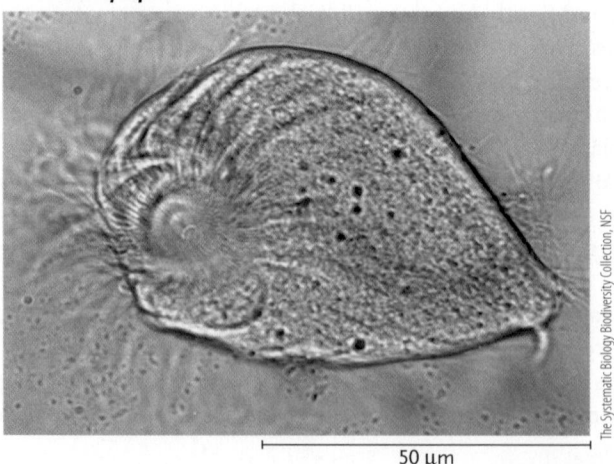

50 μm

**FIGURE 24.10 Examples of parabasalids (Excavata). (a)** A parabasalid, *Trichomonas vaginalis*, that causes a sexually transmitted disease, trichomoniasis. **(b)** *Trichonympha*, a parabasalid that lives in the guts of termites

### a. Ciliate

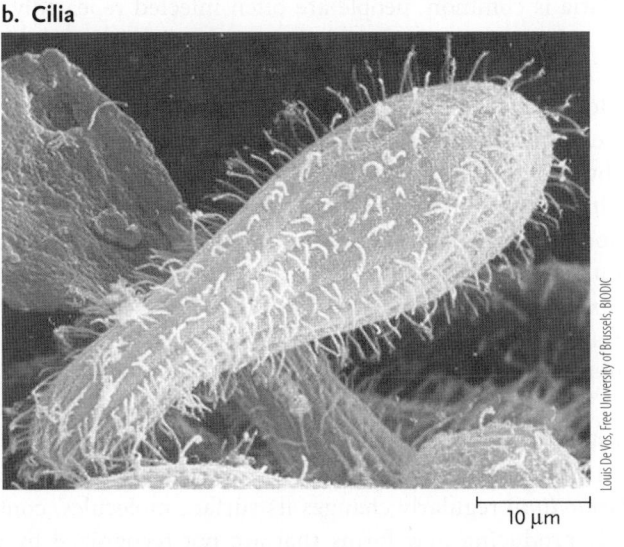

Jacek Gaertig, University of Georgia, Athens

10 µm

### b. Cilia

Louis De Vos, Free University of Brussels, BIODIC

10 µm

**FIGURE 24.11** *Tetrahymena*, **a ciliate. (a)** Stained with fluorescent dye to show cilia and microtubules. **(b)** SEM image showing cilia

cilia just below the pellicle and coordinates the ciliary beating. The cilia can stop and reverse their beating in synchrony, allowing ciliates to stop, back up, and turn if they encounter negative stimuli.

Ciliates are the only eukaryotes that have two types of nuclei in each cell: one or more small nuclei called *micronuclei* and a single larger *macronucleus* (see Figure 24.4). A **micronucleus** is a diploid nucleus that contains a complete complement of genes. It functions primarily in cellular reproduction, which may be asexual or sexual. The number of micronuclei present depends on the species. The **macronucleus** develops from a micronucleus but loses all genes except those required for basic functions (e.g., feeding, metabolism) of the cell and for synthesis of ribosomal RNA. The macronucleus contains numerous copies of these genes, allowing it to synthesize large quantities of proteins and rRNA.

Ciliates abound in freshwater and marine habitats, where they feed voraciously on bacteria, algae, and each other. *Paramecium* and *Tetrahymena* are typical of the group (see Figures 24.4 and 24.11). Their rows of cilia drive them through their watery habitat, rotating the cell on its long axis while it moves forward or back and turns. The cilia also sweep water laden with prey and food particles into the gullet, where food vacuoles form. The ciliate digests food in the vacuoles and eliminates indigestible material through an anal pore. Contractile vacuoles with elaborate, raylike extensions remove excess water from the cytoplasm and expel it to the outside. When under attack or otherwise stressed, *Paramecium* discharges many dartlike protein threads from surface organelles called **trichocysts**.

**DINOFLAGELLATES** In spring and summer, the coastal waters of Canada sometimes turn reddish in colour (**Figure 24.12a**). These **red tides** are caused by a population explosion, or *bloom*, of certain dinoflagellates that make up a large proportion of marine phytoplankton. These protists typically have a shell formed from cellulose plates (Figure 24.12b). The beating of flagella, which fit into grooves in the plates, makes dinoflagellates spin like a top (*dinos* = spinning) as they swim.

Red tides are caused by conditions such as increased nutrient runoff into coastal waters (particularly from farms and industrial areas), warm ocean surface temperatures, and calm water. Red tides occur in the waters of many other

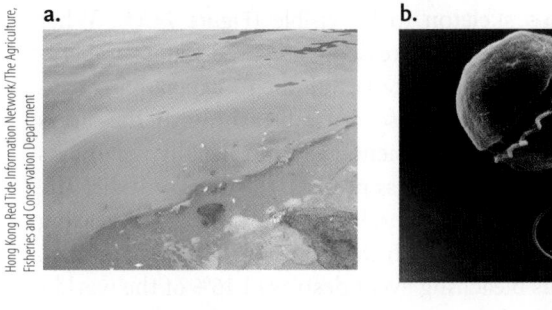

**a.**

Hong Kong Red Tide Information Network/The Agriculture, Fisheries and Conservation Department

**b.**

David M. Phillips/Science Source

50 µm

**FIGURE 24.12 (a)** Red tide caused by dinoflagellate bloom. **(b)** *Karenia brevis*, a toxin-producing dinoflagellate

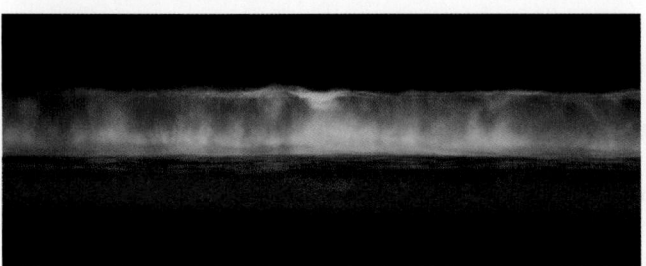

**FIGURE 24.13** Bioluminescent dinoflagellates (*Lingulodinium polyedrum*) lighting a breaking wave at midnight

**FIGURE 24.14** Bleached elkhorn coral *(Acropora palmata)*

countries besides Canada and are more common in warmer waters. Some red tide dinoflagellates produce a toxin that interferes with nerve function in animals that ingest them.

More than 4500 dinoflagellate species are known, and most, like those that cause red tides, are single-celled organisms in marine phytoplankton. Their abundance in phytoplankton makes dinoflagellates a major primary producer of ocean ecosystems. You can sometimes see their abundance because some are **bioluminescent**; that is, they glow or release a flash of light, particularly when disturbed. Dinoflagellate luminescence can make the sea glow in the wake of a boat at night and coat nocturnal surfers and swimmers with a ghostly light (**Figure 24.13**). Why do these organisms emit light? One explanation is that this burst of light would be likely to scare off predators. The production of light is caused by the enzyme *luciferase* and its substrate *luciferin* in forms similar to the system that produces light in fireflies.

Dinoflagellates live as heterotrophs or autotrophs; many can carry out both modes of nutrition. Some dinoflagellates live as symbionts in the tissues of other marine organisms, such as jellyfish, sea anemones, corals, and molluscs, and give these organisms their distinctive colours. Dinoflagellates in coral use the coral's carbon dioxide and nitrogenous waste while supplying 90% of the coral's carbon. The vast numbers of dinoflagellates living as photosynthetic symbionts in tropical coral reefs allow the reefs to reach massive sizes; without dinoflagellates, many coral species would die. When stressed, corals eject their endosymbionts, a phenomenon known as *coral bleaching* because the absence of the pigmented dinoflagellates allows the coral's calcareous skeleton to be visible (**Figure 24.14**). What causes the coral to become stressed? Increased water temperatures appear to be the main cause, although exposure to contaminants such as oil can also cause bleaching. If the stress causing the bleaching is transient, the coral usually regains its endosymbionts, but if the stress persists, the coral will die. The severity and spatial extent of coral bleaching has been increasing over the past few decades such that it is now a global problem. In 1998, a serious bleaching event destroyed 16% of the world's reefs. Localized high ocean temperatures in the Caribbean in 2005 resulted in more than 80% of corals bleaching, with more than 40% of these being killed.

**APICOMPLEXANS** **Apicomplexans** are nonmotile parasites of animals. They take their name from the *apical complex*—a group of organelles at one end of a cell—which helps the cell attach to and invade host cells. Apicomplexans absorb nutrients through their plasma membranes (rather than by engulfing food particles) and lack food vacuoles. One genus, *Plasmodium*, is responsible for malaria, one of the most widespread and debilitating human diseases. About 500 million people are infected with malaria in tropical regions, including Africa, India, Southeast Asia, the Middle East, Oceania, and Central and South America. In 2012, malaria killed an estimated 627 000 people, about half as many as were killed by AIDS that year. It is particularly deadly for children younger than six years. In many countries where malaria is common, people are often infected repeatedly, with new infections occurring alongside preexisting infections.

*Plasmodium* is transmitted by 60 different species of mosquitoes, all members of the genus *Anopheles*. Infective cells develop inside the female mosquito, which transfers the cells to human or bird hosts (**Figure 24.15**). The infecting parasites multiply in their hosts, initially in liver cells and then in red blood cells. Their growth causes red blood cells to rupture in regular cycles every 48 or 72 hours, depending on the *Plasmodium* species. The ruptured red blood cells clog vessels and release the parasite's metabolic wastes, causing cycles of chills and fever.

The victim's immune system is ineffective because, during most of the infective cycle, the parasite is inside body cells and thus "hidden" from antibodies. Furthermore, like *Giardia*, *Plasmodium* regularly changes its surface molecules, continuously producing new forms that are not recognized by antibodies developed against a previous form. In this way, the parasite keeps one step ahead of the immune system, often making malarial infections essentially permanent. For a time, malaria was controlled in many countries by insecticides such as DDT. However, the mosquitoes developed resistance to the insecticides and have returned in even greater numbers than before the spraying began.

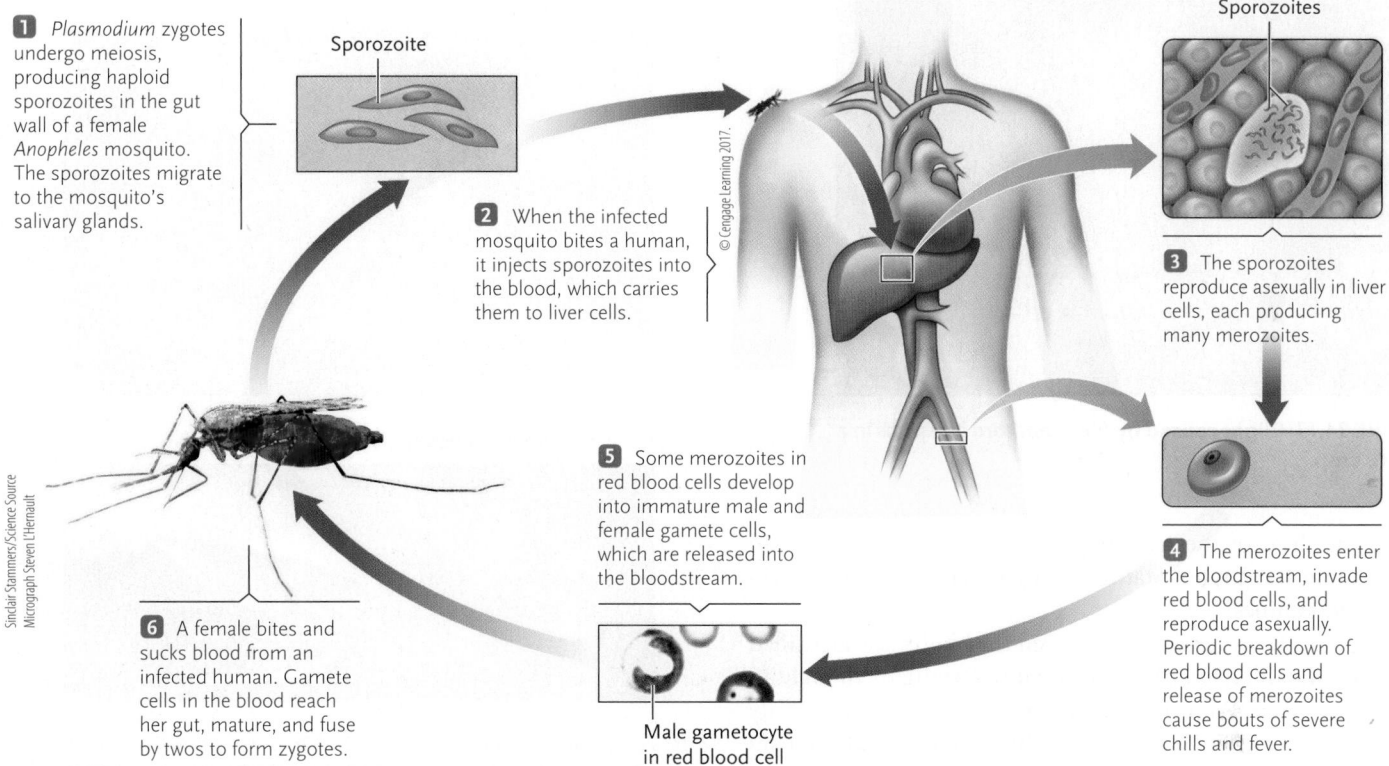

1. *Plasmodium* zygotes undergo meiosis, producing haploid sporozoites in the gut wall of a female *Anopheles* mosquito. The sporozoites migrate to the mosquito's salivary glands.

Sporozoite

2. When the infected mosquito bites a human, it injects sporozoites into the blood, which carries them to liver cells.

Sporozoites

3. The sporozoites reproduce asexually in liver cells, each producing many merozoites.

4. The merozoites enter the bloodstream, invade red blood cells, and reproduce asexually. Periodic breakdown of red blood cells and release of merozoites cause bouts of severe chills and fever.

5. Some merozoites in red blood cells develop into immature male and female gamete cells, which are released into the bloodstream.

6. A female bites and sucks blood from an infected human. Gamete cells in the blood reach her gut, mature, and fuse by twos to form zygotes.

Male gametocyte in red blood cell

FIGURE 24.15  **Life cycle of a *Plasmodium* species that causes malaria**

In addition to the asexual reproduction described above for *Plasmodium*, apicomplexans also reproduce sexually, forming gametes that fuse and then form cysts. As in *Giardia*, when a host organism ingests the cysts, they divide to produce infective cells. Many apicomplexans use more than one host species for different stages of their life cycle. For example, another organism in this group, *Toxoplasma*, has the sexual phase of its life cycle in cats and the asexual phases in humans, cattle, pigs, and other animals. Feces of infected cats contain cysts; humans ingesting or inhaling the cysts develop toxoplasmosis, a disease that is usually mild in adults but can cause severe brain damage or even death to a fetus. Because of the danger of toxoplasmosis, pregnant women should avoid emptying litter boxes or otherwise cleaning up after a cat.

**The groups of chromalveolates discussed below** all share a distinctive arrangement of flagella at some stage of their life cycles. As indicated in Figure 24.16, motile cells in these organisms have two different flagella: one smooth and a second covered with bristles, giving it a "hairy" appearance (**Figure 24.16**). In many of these chromalveolates, the flagella occur only on reproductive cells such as eggs and sperm. This group of chromalveolates includes the oomycetes (water moulds), diatoms, golden algae, and brown algae. Recall that algae is a general term for photosynthetic protists, but the different groups of algae are not closely related to each other, so the term does not imply a phylogenetic grouping.

**OOMYCETES: WATER MOULDS AND DOWNY MILDEWS** In Ireland, the summer of 1846 started off warm and sunny. This was a welcome change, as the previous summer had been cool and damp, causing the potato crop to fail. But then the weather turned wet and cold again, and within one week at the end of July, the entire potato crop was destroyed: the leaves rotted and the tubers turned to black, putrid mush (**Figure 24.17**). Worse was to come: the unseasonably cool and damp growing seasons persisted until 1860, causing the potato crops to fail year after year. These crop failures were catastrophic because potatoes were virtually the only food source for most people. Altogether,

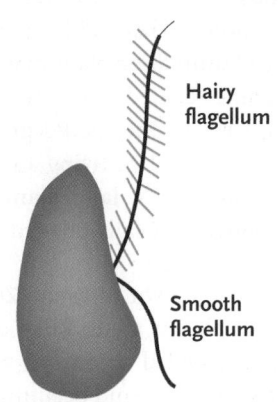

Hairy flagellum

Smooth flagellum

FIGURE 24.16  **Stramenopile protist, with "smooth" and "hairy" flagella**

FIGURE 24.17 **Blight caused by *Phytophthora infestans* in a potato crop**

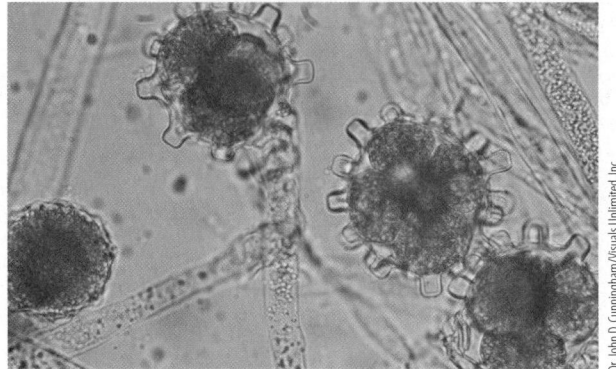

a. **Water mould**

b. **Water mould infecting fish**

c. **Downy mildew**

FIGURE 24.18 **Oomycetes. (a)** The water mould *Saprolegnia parasitica.* **(b)** S. parasitica growing as cottony white fibres on the tail of an aquarium fish. **(c)** Downy mildew, *Plasmopara viticola*, growing on grapes. At times, it has nearly destroyed vineyards in Europe and North America.

about one-third of the Irish population died or emigrated (to Canada and the United States, among other countries) due to the potato famines.

In 1861, the organism that caused the blight was identified as a water mould, *Phytophthora infestans*. Originally thought to be a fungus, *P. infestans* produces infective cells that are easily dispersed by wind and water. The blight caused by this organism has recently re-emerged as a serious disease in potato-growing regions of Canada and the United States due to the migration of new strains from Mexico that are resistant to existing pesticides.

Oomycetes (**Figure 24.18a**) are commonly known as *water moulds*, but they are not fungi at all; however, they do share some features with fungi. Like fungi, oomycetes grow as microscopic, nonmotile filaments called **hyphae** (singular, *hypha*), forming a network called a **mycelium** (Figure 24.18b). Also like fungi, they are heterotrophs, which secrete enzymes that digest the complex molecules of surrounding organic matter or living tissue into simpler molecules that are small enough to be absorbed into their cells. Other features, however, set the Oomycota apart from the fungi; chief among them are differences in nucleotide sequence, which clearly indicate close evolutionary relationships to other heterokonts rather than to the fungi.

The water moulds live almost exclusively in freshwater lakes and streams or moist terrestrial habitats, where they are key decomposers. Dead animal or plant material immersed in water commonly becomes coated with cottony water moulds. Other water moulds, such as the mould growing on the fish shown in Figure 24.18b, parasitize living aquatic animals. The downy mildews are parasites of land plants (Figure 24.18c). Oomycetes may reproduce asexually or sexually.

DIATOMS The organisms shown in **Figure 24.19** may not look like living organisms at all but instead like artwork or jewels. These are **diatoms**, single-celled organisms with a glassy silica shell, which is intricately formed and beautiful in many species. The two halves of the shell fit together like the top and bottom of a Petri dish or box of chocolates. Substances move in and out

of the cell through elaborately patterned perforations in the shell. Diatom shells are common in fossil deposits. In fact, more diatoms are known as fossils than as living species: some 35 000 extinct species have been described compared with 7000 living species. For about 180 million years, diatom shells have been accumulating into thick layers of sediment at the bottom of lakes and seas.

In fact, you probably use diatoms—or their remnants—a couple times a day when you brush your teeth. Many toothpastes contain a mild abrasive to assist in removing plaque, a bacterial biofilm that forms on your teeth. This abrasive is commonly made from grinding the fossilized shells of diatoms into a fine powder, called *diatomaceous earth*. In addition to toothpaste, diatomaceous earth is used in filters, as an insulating material, and as a pesticide. Diatomaceous earth kills crawling insects and insect larvae by abrading their exoskeleton, causing

**FIGURE 24.19 Diatoms.** Depending on the species, the shells are either radially or bilaterally symmetrical, as seen in this sample.

Jan Hinsch/Science Source

them to dehydrate and die. Insects also die when they eat the powder, but larger animals, including humans, are unaffected by it.

Diatoms are photoautotrophs that carry out photosynthesis by pathways similar to those of plants. They are among the primary photosynthetic organisms in marine plankton and are also abundant in freshwater habitats as both phytoplankton and bottom-dwelling species. Although most diatoms are free living, some are symbionts inside other marine protists. One diatom, *Pseudonitzschia*, produces a toxic amino acid that can accumulate in shellfish. The amino acid, which acts as a nerve

poison, causes amnesic shellfish poisoning when ingested by humans; the poisoning can be fatal.

Asexual reproduction in diatoms occurs by mitosis followed by a form of cytoplasmic division in which each daughter cell receives either the top or the bottom half of the parent shell. The daughter cell then secretes the missing half, which becomes the smaller, inside shell of the box. The daughter cell receiving the larger top half grows to the same size as the parent shell, but the cell receiving the smaller bottom half is limited to the size of this shell. As asexual divisions continue, the cells receiving bottom halves become progressively smaller. When a minimum size is reached, sexual reproduction is triggered. The cells produce flagellated gametes, which fuse to form a zygote. The zygote grows to normal size before secreting a completely new shell with full-sized top and bottom halves.

Although flagella are present only in gametes, many diatoms move by an unusual mechanism in which a secretion released through grooves in the shell propels them in a gliding motion.

**GOLDEN ALGAE** Nearly all golden algae are autotrophs and carry out photosynthesis using pathways similar to those of plants. Their colour is due to a brownish carotenoid pigment, fucoxanthin, which masks the green colour of the chlorophylls **(Figure 24.20a)**. However, most of these organisms can also live as heterotrophs if there is insufficient light for photosynthesis. They switch to feeding on dissolved organic molecules or preying on bacteria and diatoms. Golden algae are important in

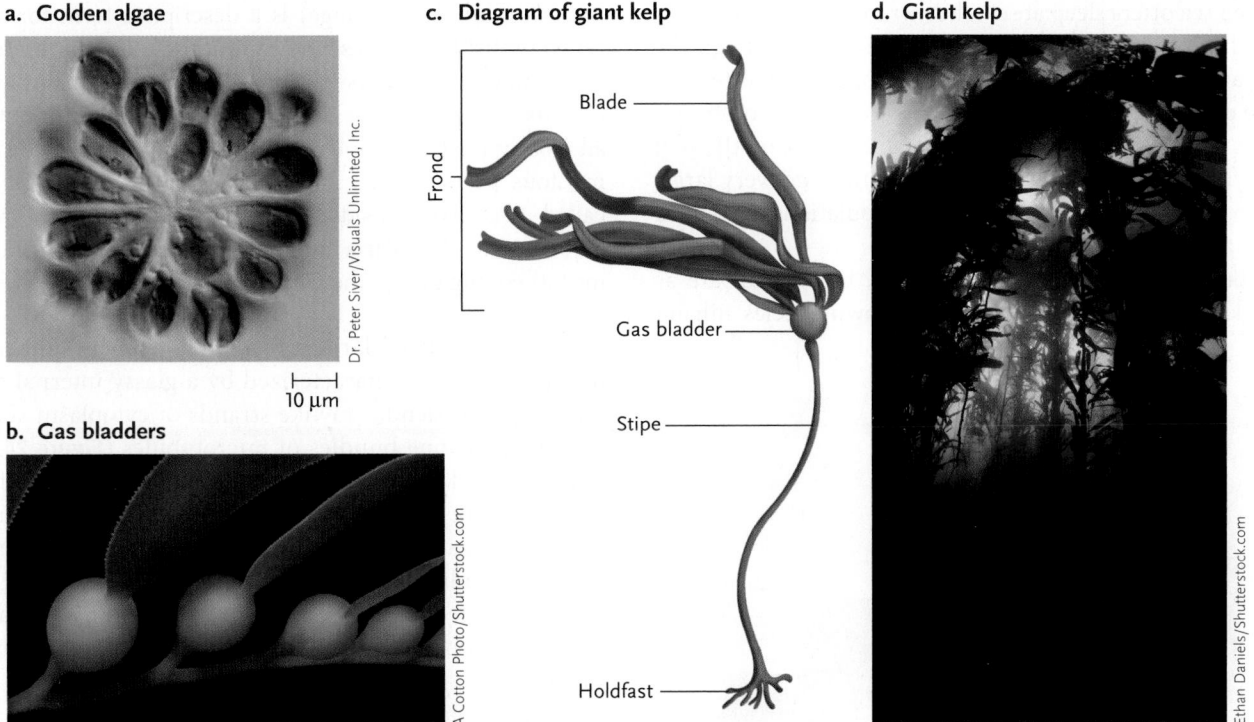

**FIGURE 24.20 Golden and brown algae. (a)** A microscopic swimming colony of *Synura*. Each cell bears two flagella, which are not visible in this light micrograph. **(b)** Gas bladders connect kelp's stipes ("stems") to its blades ("leaves"). **(c)** The fronds of giant kelp are borne on stalks known as *stipes*, which are anchored to the substrate by holdfasts. **(d)** A forest of *Macrocystis pyrifera* (giant kelp)

freshwater habitats and in *nanoplankton*, a community of marine phytoplankton composed of huge numbers of extremely small cells. During the spring and fall, blooms of golden algae are responsible for the fishy taste of many cities' drinking water.

Most golden algae are colonial forms (see Figures 24.3 and 24.20a) in which each cell of the colony bears a pair of flagella. The golden algae have glassy shells, but in the form of plates or scales rather than in the Petri dish form of the diatoms.

**BROWN ALGAE** If you were asked where in Canada you'd find forests of giant trees, you'd likely think of the **temperate rainforests** in British Columbia. But there are also vast underwater forests in the waters off the British Columbia coast, formed not by trees but by a type of brown algae known as *kelp* (*Macrocystis integrifolia*), which can grow to lengths of 30 m. A related species, giant kelp (*M. pyrifera*) (Figure 24.20b–d), can grow up to 60 m long. Kelps are the largest and most complex of all protists. Their tissues are differentiated into leaflike *blades*, stalklike *stipes*, and rootlike *holdfasts* that anchor them to the bottom. Hollow gas-filled bladders give buoyancy to the stipes and blades and help keep them upright and oriented toward the sunlit upper layers of water (Figure 24.20b). The stipes of some kelps contain tubelike vessels, similar to the vascular elements of plants, which rapidly distribute the products of photosynthesis throughout the body of the alga. Kelps have an astonishingly fast growth rate: giant kelp can grow up to 30 cm per day!

Just as for terrestrial forests, kelp forests provide food and habitat for many marine organisms. Herds of sea otters (*Enhydra lutris*), for example, tend to live in and near kelp forests. When sea otters sleep at sea, they wrap kelp around themselves to keep from drifting away (**Figure 24.21**). Although the forest is an important habitat for the sea otters, the otters, in turn, are critical for the survival of these forests. Sea otters are one of the few predators of sea urchins, which graze on the kelp and can cause deforestation if their populations get very large. Predation by sea otters keeps sea urchin populations in control, preventing destruction of kelp forests.

All brown algae are photoautotrophs, but not all are as large as kelps. Nearly all of the 1500 known species inhabit

temperate or cool coastal marine waters. Like golden algae, brown algae contain fucoxanthin, which gives them their characteristic colour. Their cell walls contain cellulose and a mucilaginous polysaccharide, alginic acid. This alginic acid, called **algin** when extracted, is an essentially tasteless substance used to thicken such diverse products as ice cream, salad dressing, jellybeans, cosmetics, and floor polish. Brown algae are also harvested as food crops and fertilizer.

Life cycles among the brown algae are typically complex and in many species consist of alternating haploid and diploid generations (**Figure 24.22**). The large structures that we recognize as kelps and other brown seaweeds are diploid **sporophytes**, so called because they give rise to haploid spores by meiosis. The spores, which are flagellated swimming cells, germinate and divide by mitosis to form an independent, haploid **gametophyte** generation. The gametophytes produce haploid gametes (egg and sperm). Most brown algal gametophytes are multicellular structures only a few centimetres in diameter. Cells in the gametophyte, produced by mitosis, differentiate to form nonmotile eggs or flagellated, swimming sperm cells. The sperm cells have the two different types of flagella characteristic of heterokont protists. Fusion of egg and sperm produces a diploid zygote that grows by mitotic divisions into the sporophyte generation. This complex life cycle is very similar to that of land plants (see Chapter 26).

## 24.4c Rhizaria Are Eukaryotes with Filamentous Pseudopods

*Amoeba* (*amoibe* = change) is a descriptive term for a single-celled protist that moves by means of pseudopodia, as described earlier in this chapter (see Figure 24.6). Several major groups of protists contain amoebas, which are similar in form but are not all closely related. Amoebas in the Rhizaria produce stiff, filamentous pseudopodia, and many produce hard outer shells, called *tests*. We consider here two heterotrophic groups of amoebas, the Radiolaria and the Foraminifera, and a third, photosynthesizing group, the Chlorarachniophyta.

**RADIOLARIA** Radiolarians (*radiolus* = small sunbeam) are marine organisms characterized by a glassy internal skeleton and **axopods**, slender raylike strands of cytoplasm supported internally by long bundles of microtubules (**Figure 24.23a, b**). This glassy skeleton is heavy—when radiolarians die, their skeletons sink to the ocean floor—so how do radiolarians keep afloat? The axopods provide buoyancy, as do the numerous vacuoles and lipid droplets in the cytoplasm. Axopods are also involved in feeding: prey stick to the axopods and are then engulfed, brought into the cell, and digested in food vacuoles.

Radiolarian skeletons that accumulate on the ocean floor become part of the sediment, which, over time, hardens into sedimentary rock. The presence of radiolarians in such rocks is very useful to the oil industry as indicators of oil-bearing strata.

**FIGURE 24.21 A sea otter (*Enhydra lutris*) wrapped in kelp**

worldswildlifewonders/Shutterstock.com

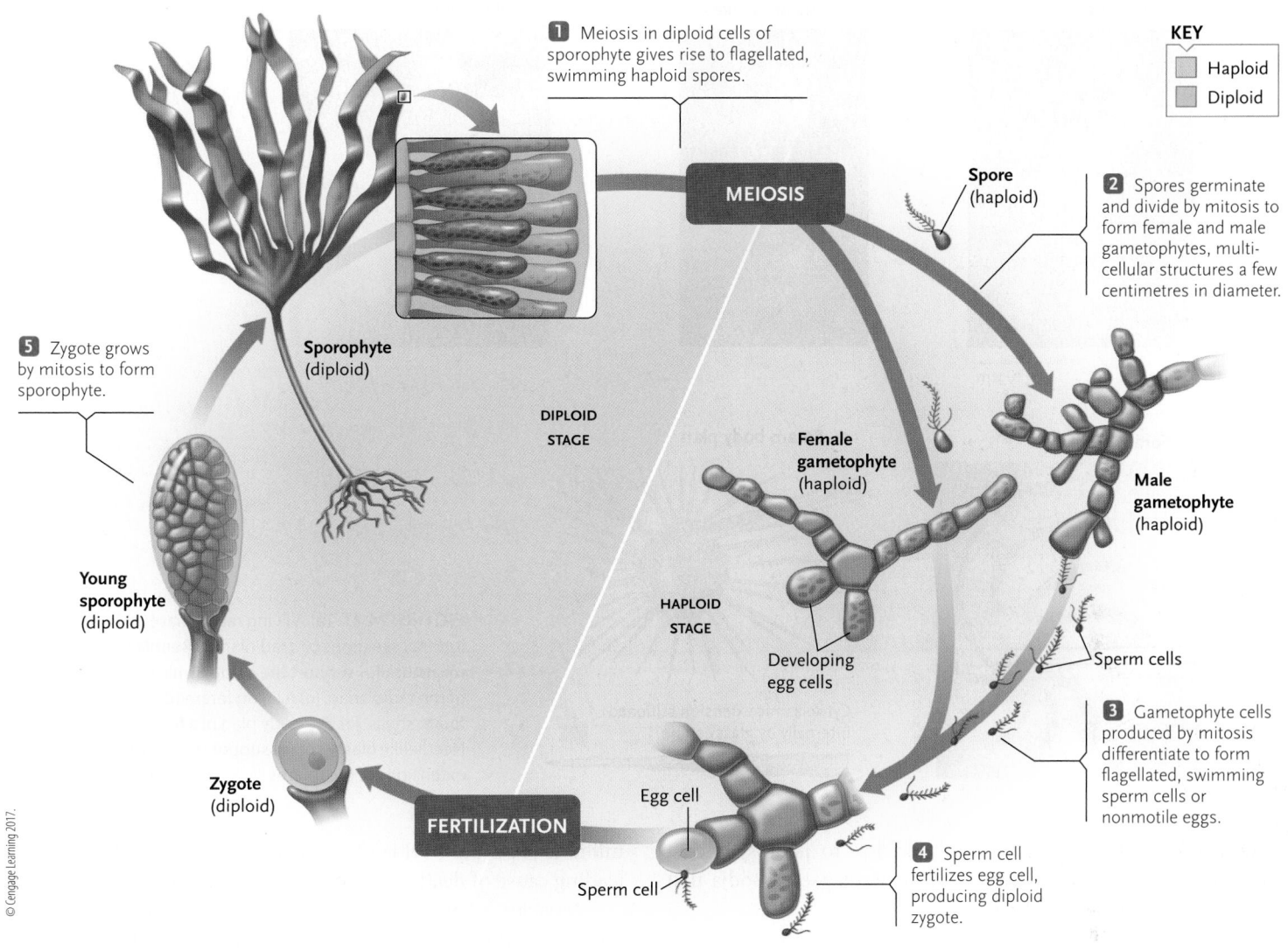

**KEY**
- Haploid
- Diploid

**1** Meiosis in diploid cells of sporophyte gives rise to flagellated, swimming haploid spores.

**MEIOSIS**

**2** Spores germinate and divide by mitosis to form female and male gametophytes, multicellular structures a few centimetres in diameter.

Spore (haploid)

Sporophyte (diploid)

**5** Zygote grows by mitosis to form sporophyte.

DIPLOID STAGE

Female gametophyte (haploid)

Male gametophyte (haploid)

Young sporophyte (diploid)

HAPLOID STAGE

Developing egg cells

Sperm cells

**3** Gametophyte cells produced by mitosis differentiate to form flagellated, swimming sperm cells or nonmotile eggs.

Zygote (diploid)

Egg cell

**FERTILIZATION**

Sperm cell

**4** Sperm cell fertilizes egg cell, producing diploid zygote.

© Cengage Learning 2017.

**FIGURE 24.22 The life cycle of the brown alga *Laminaria*, which alternates between a diploid sporophyte stage and a haploid gametophyte stage**

**FORAMINIFERA: FORAMS** These organisms take their name from the perforations in their shells (*foramen* = little hole), through which extend long slender strands of cytoplasm supported internally by a network of needlelike spines. Their shells consist of organic matter reinforced by calcium carbonate (Figure 24.23c–e). Most foram shells are chambered spiral structures that, although microscopic, resemble those of molluscs.

Like radiolarians, forams live in marine environments. Some species are planktonic, but they are most abundant on sandy bottoms and attached to rocks along the coasts. Forams feed in a manner similar to that of radiolarians: they engulf prey that adhere to the strands and conduct them through the holes in the shell into the central cytoplasm, where they are digested in food vacuoles. Some forams have algal symbionts that carry out photosynthesis, allowing them to live as both heterotrophs and autotrophs.

Marine sediments are typically packed with the shells of dead forams. The sediments may be hundreds of feet thick: the White Cliffs of Dover in England are composed primarily of the shells of ancient forams. Most of the world's deposits of limestone and marble contain foram shells; the great pyramids of ancient Egypt are built from blocks cut from fossil foram deposits. Because distinct species lived during different geologic periods, they are widely used to establish the age of sedimentary rocks containing their shells. As they do with radiolarian species, oil prospectors use forams as indicators of hydrocarbon deposits because layers of forams often overlie oil.

**CHLORARACHNIOPHYTA** Chlorarachniophytes are an obscure group of amoebas that contain chloroplasts. They are studied by biologists investigating the origin and evolution of chloroplasts as they acquired their chloroplasts by secondary endosymbiosis (discussed later in this chapter). Interestingly, they are both

**a. Radiolarian**

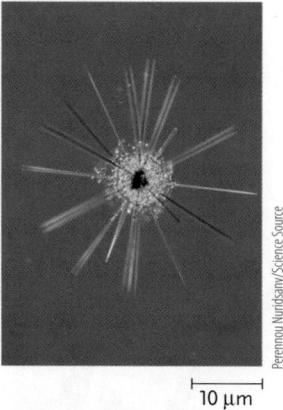

**b. Radiolarian skeleton**

**c. Living foram**

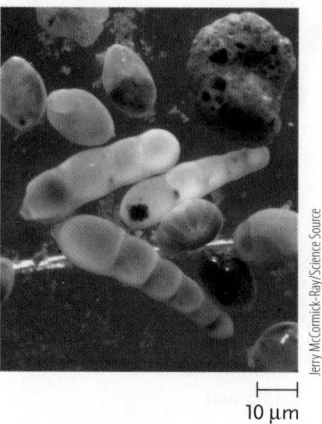

10 µm

10 µm

**d. Foram shells**

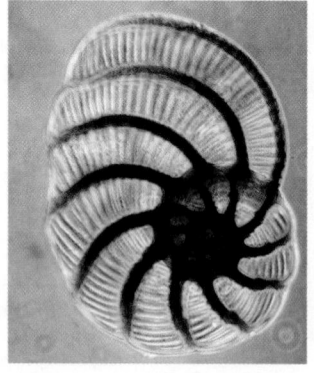

**e. Foram body plan**

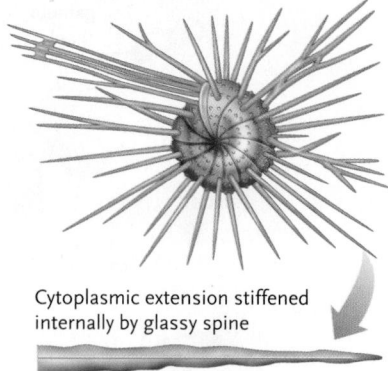

Cytoplasmic extension stiffened
internally by glassy spine

**FIGURE 24.23** **(a)** A living radiolarian. **(b)** The internal skeletons of a radiolarian. Bundles of microtubules support the cytoplasmic extensions of the radiolarian. **(c)** A living foram **(d)** Empty foram shells. **(e)** The body plan of a foram. Needlelike glassy spines support the cytoplasmic extensions of the forams.

autotrophic and heterotrophic; in addition to photosynthesis, they engulf food with the many filamentous pseudopodia that extend from the cell surface.

## 24.4d The Unikont Supergroup Includes Slime Moulds and Most Amoebas

The unikonts include most of the amoebas other than those in Rhizaria, as well as the cellular and plasmodial slime moulds. All members of this group use pseudopods for locomotion and feeding for all or part of their life cycles.

**AMOEBAS** Amoebas of the unikonts are single-celled organisms that are abundant in marine and freshwater environments and soil. All amoebas are microscopic, although some species can grow to 5 mm in size and so are visible with the naked eye. Some amoebas are parasitic, such as the 45 species that infect the human digestive tract. One of these parasites, *Entamoeba histolytica*, causes amoebic dysentery. Cysts of this amoeba contaminate water supplies and soil in regions with inadequate sewage treatment. When ingested, a cyst breaks open to release an amoeba that feeds and divides rapidly in the digestive tract. Enzymes released by the amoebas destroy cells lining the intestine, producing the ulcerations, painful cramps, and debilitating diarrhea characteristic of the disease. Amoebic dysentery afflicts

millions of people worldwide; in less-developed countries, it is a leading cause of death among infants and small children.

Most amoebas, however, are heterotrophs that feed on bacteria, other protists, and bits of organic matter. Unlike the stiff, supported pseudopodia of Rhizaria, pseudopods of amoebas extend and retract at any point on their body surface and are unsupported by any internal cellular organization; amoebas are thus "shape-shifters." How can an amoeba capture a fast-moving organism? As an amoeba moves, its cytoplasm doesn't just move but also changes state, from a more liquid state to a more solid state and back again, allowing the amoeba to send out pseudopodia in different directions very quickly. These fast-moving pseudopods can capture even fast-swimming prey such as ciliates (**Figure 24.24**).

Amoebas reproduce only asexually, via binary fission. In unfavourable environmental conditions, some amoebas can form a cyst, essentially by rolling up and secreting a protective membrane. They survive as cysts until favourable conditions return.

**SLIME MOULDS** After a very wet spring in 1973, residents of Dallas, Texas, were alarmed to see large, yellow blobs that resembled scrambled eggs *crawling* on their lawns. People thought it was an alien invasion. Luckily, a local biologist was able to prevent mass panic by identifying the blobs as slime

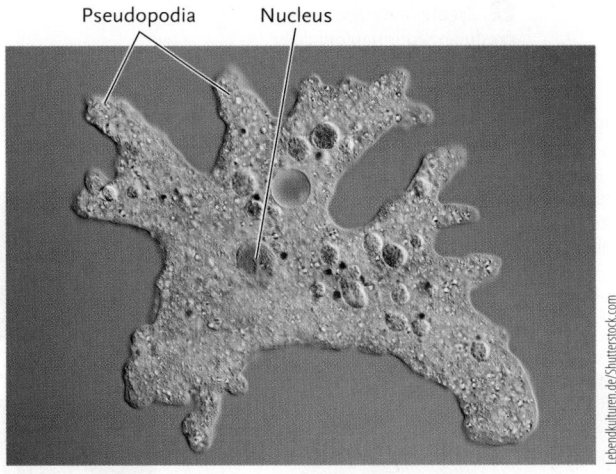

Pseudopodia    Nucleus

**FIGURE 24.24  An amoeba capturing prey with pseudopods**

moulds, unusual heterotrophic protists. Slime moulds exist for part of their lives as individuals that move by amoeboid motion, but then come together in a coordinated mass—essentially, a large amoeba—that ultimately differentiates into stalked structures called **fruiting bodies**, in which spores are formed.

There are two major evolutionary lineages of slime moulds: the **cellular slime moulds** and the **plasmodial slime moulds**, which differ in cellular organization. Both types of slime moulds have been of great interest to scientists because of their ability to differentiate into fruiting bodies with stalks and spore-bearing structures. This differentiation is much simpler than the complex developmental pathways of other eukaryotes, providing a unique opportunity to study cell differentiation at its most fundamental level. Slime moulds also respond to stimuli in their environment, moving away from bright light and toward food. We have learned a great deal about eukaryotic signalling pathways, cell differentiation, and cell movement from studies of slime moulds.

Slime moulds live on moist, rotting plant material such as decaying leaves and bark. The cells engulf particles of dead organic matter, along with bacteria, yeasts, and other microorganisms, and digest them internally. They can be a range of colours: brown, yellow, green, red, and even violet or blue.

These organisms exist primarily as individual cells, either separately or as a coordinated mass. Among the 150 or so species of cellular slime moulds, *Dictyostelium discoideum* is the best known. Its life cycle begins when a haploid spore lands in a suitably moist environment containing decaying organic matter (**Figure 24.25**). The spore germinates into an amoeboid cell that grows and divides mitotically into separate haploid cells as long as the food source lasts. When the food supply dwindles, some of the cells release a **chemical signal** in pulses; in response, the amoebas move together and form a sausage-shaped mass that crawls in coordinated fashion like a slug. Some "slugs," although not much more than a millimetre in length, contain more than 100 thousand individual cells. At some point, the "slug" stops moving and differentiates into a

stalked fruiting body, with some cells becoming spores, whereas others form the stalk. The cells that form the stalk die in the process, essentially sacrificing themselves so that a stalk can form. Why is formation of a stalk crucial? Raising the spore-forming cells higher up in the air increases the likelihood that spores will be carried away by air currents and dispersed farther away from the parent. Because the cells forming the slug and fruiting body are all products of mitosis, this is asexual reproduction.

Cellular slime moulds also reproduce sexually: two haploid cells fuse to form a diploid zygote (also shown in Figure 24.25) that enters a dormant stage. Eventually, the zygote undergoes meiosis, producing four haploid cells that may multiply inside the spore by mitosis. When conditions are favourable, the spore wall breaks down, releasing the cells. These cells grow and divide into separate amoeboid cells.

**Plasmodial slime moulds** exist primarily as a multinucleate **plasmodium**, in which individual nuclei are suspended in a common cytoplasm surrounded by a single plasma membrane. (This is not to be confused with *Plasmodium*, the genus of apicomplexans that causes malaria.) There are 888 known species of plasmodial slime moulds. The plasmodium (**Figure 24.26a**) flows and feeds by phagocytosis like a single huge amoeba—a single cell that contains thousands to millions or even billions of diploid nuclei surrounded by a single plasma membrane. The plasmodium, which may range in size from a few centimetres to more than a metre in diameter, typically moves in thick, branching strands connected by thin sheets. The movements occur by cytoplasmic streaming, driven by actin microfilaments and myosin. These plasmodia are what the people in Dallas thought were aliens invading; after a period of heavy rain, plasmodia will sometimes crawl out of the woods to appear on lawns or the mulch of flowerbeds.

At some point, often in response to unfavourable environmental conditions, fruiting bodies form on the plasmodium. At the tips of the fruiting bodies, nuclei become enclosed in separate cells. These cells undergo meiosis, forming haploid, resistant spores that are released from the fruiting bodies and carried by water or wind. If they reach a favourable environment, the spores germinate to form gametes that fuse to form a diploid zygote. The zygote nucleus then divides repeatedly without an accompanying division of the cytoplasm, forming many diploid nuclei suspended in the common cytoplasm of a new plasmodium.

Plasmodial slime moulds are particularly useful in research because they become large enough to provide ample material for biochemical and molecular analyses. Actin and myosin extracted from *Physarum polycephalum*, for example, have been used in studies of actin-based motility. A further advantage of plasmodial slime moulds is that the many nuclei of a plasmodium usually replicate and pass through synchronous mitosis, making them useful in research that tracks the changes that take place in the cell cycle. More recently, slime moulds have been used in robotics research.

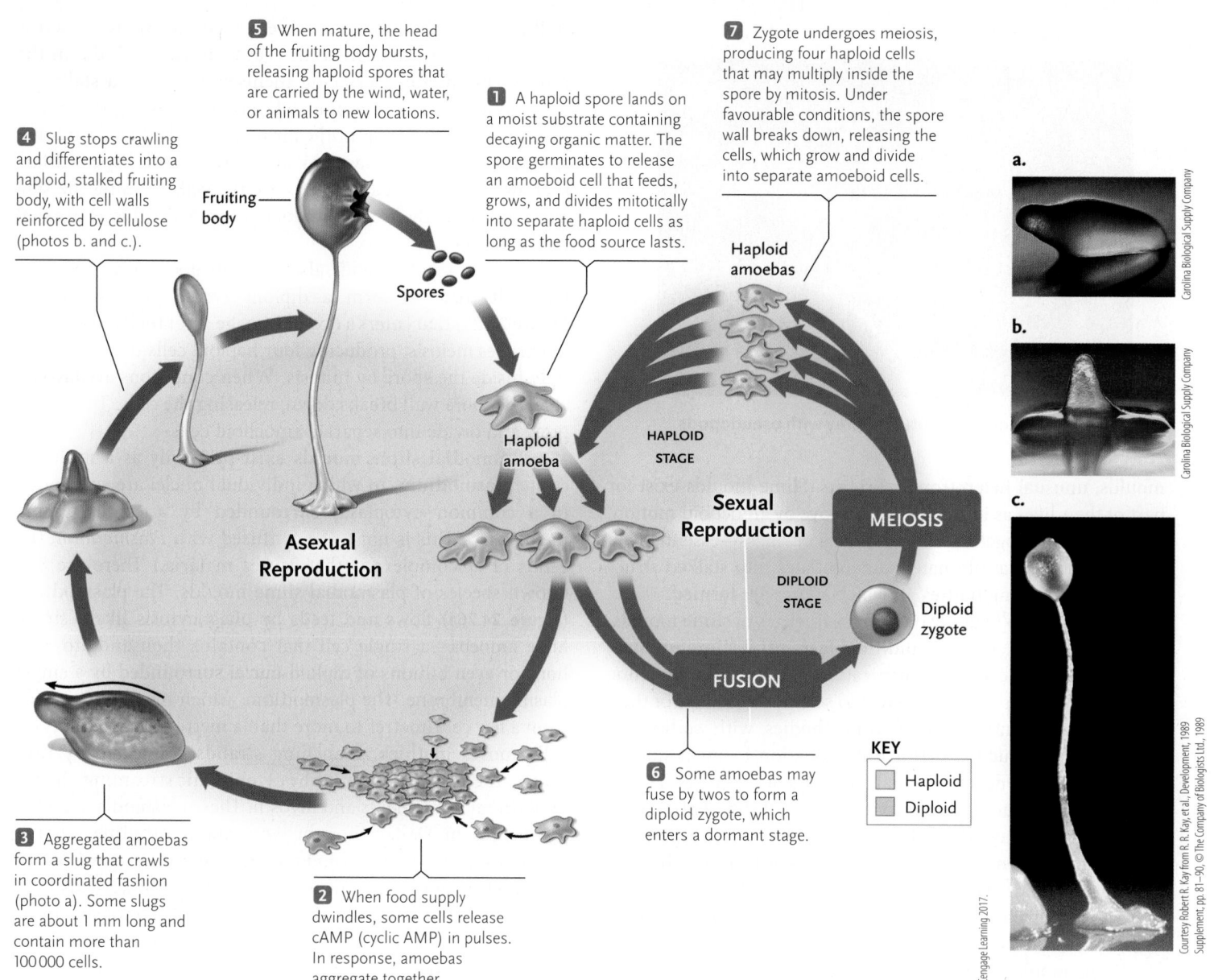

**FIGURE 24.25 Life cycle of the cellular slime mould *Dictyostelium discoideum*.** The light micrographs show **(a)** a migrating slug, **(b)** an early stage in fruiting body formation, and **(c)** a mature fruiting body.

**5** When mature, the head of the fruiting body bursts, releasing haploid spores that are carried by the wind, water, or animals to new locations.

**1** A haploid spore lands on a moist substrate containing decaying organic matter. The spore germinates to release an amoeboid cell that feeds, grows, and divides mitotically into separate haploid cells as long as the food source lasts.

**7** Zygote undergoes meiosis, producing four haploid cells that may multiply inside the spore by mitosis. Under favourable conditions, the spore wall breaks down, releasing the cells, which grow and divide into separate amoeboid cells.

**4** Slug stops crawling and differentiates into a haploid, stalked fruiting body, with cell walls reinforced by cellulose (photos b. and c.).

Fruiting body

Spores

Haploid amoebas

**Asexual Reproduction**

Haploid amoeba

**HAPLOID STAGE**

**Sexual Reproduction**

**MEIOSIS**

**DIPLOID STAGE**

Diploid zygote

**FUSION**

**6** Some amoebas may fuse by twos to form a diploid zygote, which enters a dormant stage.

**3** Aggregated amoebas form a slug that crawls in coordinated fashion (photo a). Some slugs are about 1 mm long and contain more than 100 000 cells.

**2** When food supply dwindles, some cells release cAMP (cyclic AMP) in pulses. In response, amoebas aggregate together.

**KEY**

☐ Haploid
☐ Diploid

a.

b.

c.

**CHOANOFLAGELLATES** Also included in the unikonts are the choanoflagellates. Opisthokonta (*opistho* = posterior; *kontos* = flagellum) are named for the single posterior flagellum found at some stage in the life cycle of these organisms. This diverse group includes the choanoflagellates, protists thought to be the ancestors of fungi and animals.

**Choanoflagellata** (*choanos* = collar) are named for the collar surrounding the flagellum that the protist uses to feed and, in some species, to swim (**Figure 24.27**). The collar resembles an upside-down lampshade and is made up of small finger-like projections (microvilli) of the plasma membrane. As the flagellum moves water through the collar, these projections engulf bacteria and particles of organic matter in the water.

About 150 species of choanoflagellates live in either marine or freshwater habitats. Some species are mobile, with the flagellum pushing the cells along (in the same way that animal sperm are propelled by their flagella), but most choanoflagellates are *sessile* (attached by a stalk to a surface). A number of species are colonial with a cluster of cells on a single stalk; these colonial species are of great interest to biologists studying the evolution of multicellularity in animals.

Why are choanoflagellates thought to be the ancestor of animals? Both molecular and morphological data indicate that a choanoflagellate type of protist gave rise to animals; for example, there are many morphological similarities between choanoflagellates and the collar cells (choanocytes) of sponges

a.

b.

FIGURE 24.26 **Slime moulds.** **(a)** Plasmodia of slime moulds. **(b)** Fruiting bodies of slime moulds

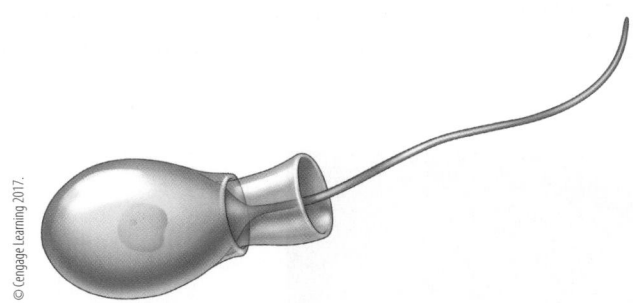

FIGURE 24.27 **A choanoflagellate**

as well as the cells that act as excretory organisms in flatworms and rotifers (see Chapter 27). Comparisons of nucleic acid sequences done to date also support the hypothesis that choanoflagellates are the closest living relatives to animals. Molecular data also indicate that a choanoflagellate-like organism was also likely the ancestor of the fungi (see Chapter 25).

### 24.4e Plantae Include the Red and Green Algae and Land Plants

The Plantae supergroup consists of the red and green algae, which are protists, and the land plants. These three groups of photoautotrophs share a common evolutionary origin. Here we describe the two types of algae; we discuss land plants and how they evolved from green algae in Chapter 26.

**RHODOPHYTA: RED ALGAE** Nearly all the 7000 known species of red algae, which are also known as the *Rhodophyta* (*rhodon* = rose), are small marine seaweeds (**Figure 24.28**). Approximately 5% are found in freshwater lakes and streams or in soils. If you have had sushi, then you have eaten red algae: *Porphyra* is harvested for use as the *nori* wrapped around fish and rice.

Rhodophyte cell walls contain cellulose and mucilaginous pectins that give red algae a slippery texture. These pectins are

Filamentous red alga

FIGURE 24.28 **Red algae.** *Antithamnion plumula*, showing the filamentous and branched body form most common among red algae

widely used in industry and science. Extracted **agar** is used as a culture medium in the laboratory and as a setting agent for jellies and desserts. **Carrageenan** is used to thicken and stabilize paints, dairy products such as ice cream, and many other emulsions.

Some species secrete calcium carbonate into their cell walls; these coralline algae are important in building coral reefs; in some places, they play a bigger role in reef building than do corals.

Red algae are typically multicellular organisms, with diverse morphologies, although many have plantlike bodies composed of stalks bearing leaflike blades. Although most are free-living autotrophs, some are parasites that attach to other algae or plants.

Although most red algae are reddish in colour, some are greenish purple or black. The colour differences are produced by accessory pigments, *phycobilins*, that mask the green colour of their chlorophylls. Phycobilins absorb the shorter wavelengths of light (green and blue-green light) that penetrate to the ocean depths, allowing red algae to grow at deeper levels than any other algae. Some red algae live at depths up to 260 m if the water is clear enough to transmit light to these levels.

Red algae have complex reproductive cycles involving alternation between diploid sporophytes and haploid gametophytes. No flagellated cells occur in the red algae; instead, gametes are released into the water to be brought together by random collisions in currents.

**CHLOROPHYTA: GREEN ALGAE** The green algae, or Chlorophyta (*chloros* = green), carry out photosynthesis using the same pigments as plants, whereas other photosynthetic protists contain pigment combinations that are very different from those of land plants. This shared pigment composition is one line of evidence that one lineage of green algae was the ancestor of land plants. With at least 16 thousand species, green algae show more diversity than any other algal group. They also have very diverse morphologies, including single-celled, colonial, and multicellular species (**Figure 24.29**; see also Figure 24.1d). Multicellular forms have a range of morphologies, including filamentous,

tubular, and leaflike forms. Most green algae are microscopic, but some range upward to the size of small seaweeds.

Most green algae live in freshwater aquatic habitats, but some are marine, others live on rocks, soil surfaces, or tree bark, or even in snow. Other organisms rely on green algae to photosynthesize for them by forming symbiotic relationships. For example, most lichens are symbioses between green algae and fungi (see Chapter 25), and many animals contain green algal chloroplasts, or entire green algae, as symbionts in their cells.

Life cycles among the green algae are as diverse as their body forms. Many can reproduce either sexually or asexually, and some alternate between haploid and diploid generations. Gametes in different species may be undifferentiated flagellated cells or differentiated as a flagellated sperm cell and a nonmotile egg cell. Most common is a life cycle with a multicellular haploid phase and a single-celled diploid phase (**Figure 24.30**).

Among all the algae, the green algae are the most closely related to land plants, based on molecular, biochemical, and morphological data. Evidence of this close relationship includes

**a. Single-celled green alga**

Borut Furlan/WaterFrame/Getty Images

1 cm

**b. Colonial green alga**

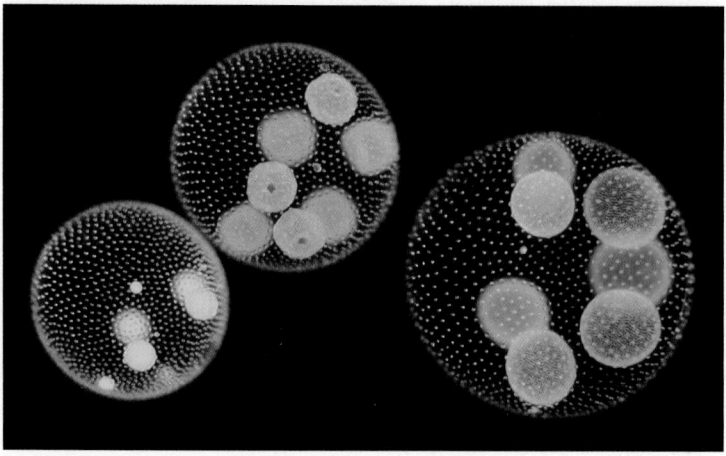

Lebendkulturen.de/Shutterstock.com

200 μm

**c. Multicellular green alga**

Marevision/age fotostock/Getty Images

**FIGURE 24.29 Green algae. (a)** A single-celled green alga, *Acetabularia*, which grows in marine environments. Each individual in the cluster is a large single cell with a rootlike base, a stalk, and a cap. **(b)** A colonial green alga, *Volvox*. Each green dot in the spherical wall of the colony is a potentially independent, flagellated cell. Daughter colonies can be seen within the parent colony.
**(c)** A multicellular green alga, *Ulva*, common to shallow seas around the world

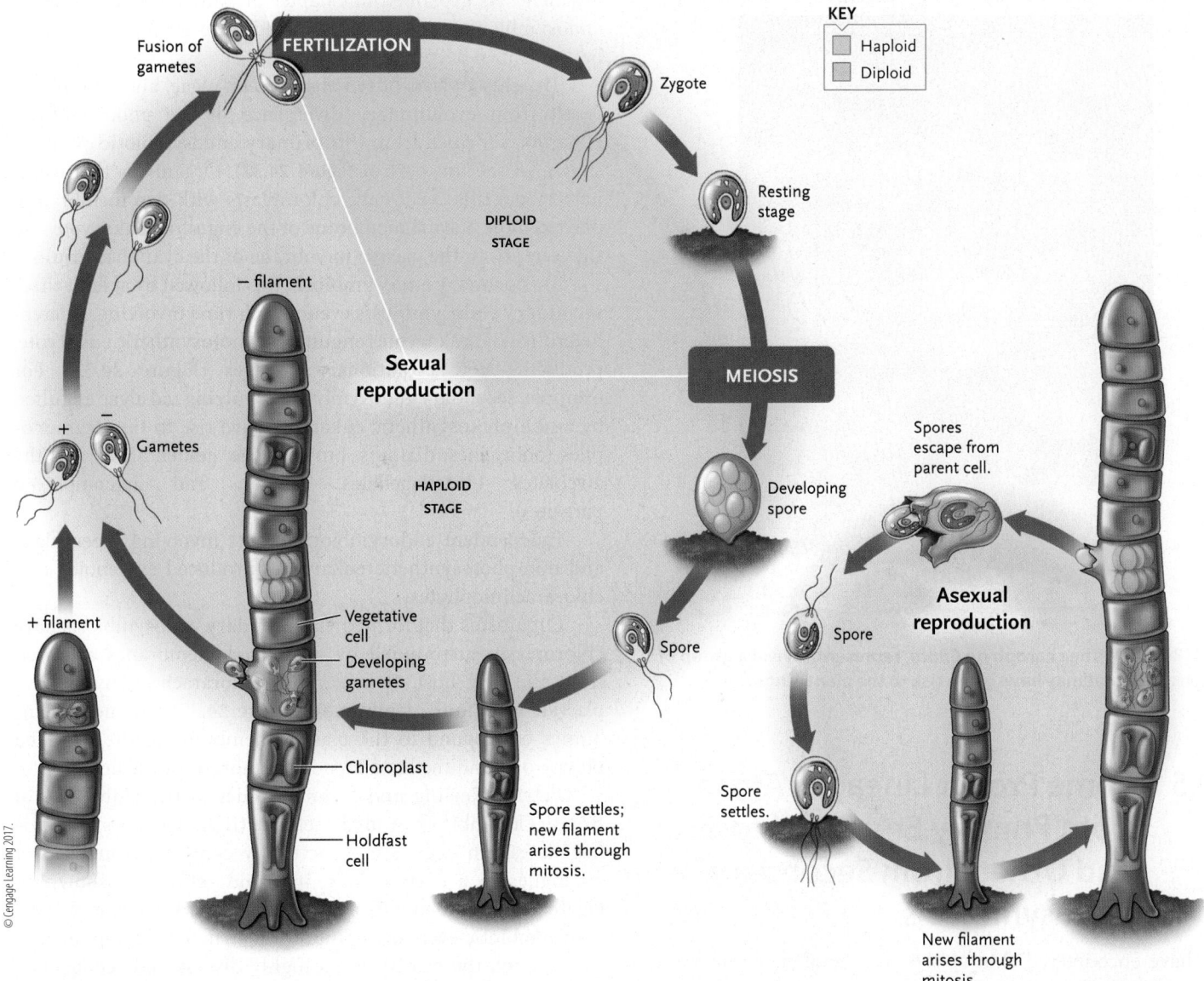

**KEY**
- Haploid
- Diploid

Fusion of gametes

**FERTILIZATION**

Zygote

DIPLOID STAGE

Resting stage

− filament

**Sexual reproduction**

**MEIOSIS**

+ − Gametes

HAPLOID STAGE

Developing spore

Spores escape from parent cell.

+ filament

**Asexual reproduction**

Spore

Spore

Vegetative cell

Developing gametes

Spore

Chloroplast

Spore settles; new filament arises through mitosis.

Spore settles.

Holdfast cell

New filament arises through mitosis.

**FIGURE 24.30** **The life cycle of the green alga *Ulothrix*, in which the haploid stage is multicellular and the diploid stage is a single cell, the zygote.** + and − are morphologically identical mating types ("sexes") of the alga.

not only the shared photosynthetic pigments, but also the use of starch as storage reserve and the same cell wall composition.

Which green alga might have been the ancestor of modern land plants? The evidence points to a group known as the **charophytes** as being most similar to the algal ancestors of land plants. This does not mean that modern-day charophytes are the ancestors of land plants but rather that the two groups have a common ancestor. Charophytes, including *Chara* (**Figure 24.31**), *Spirogyra*, *Nitella*, and *Coleochaete*, live in freshwater ponds and lakes. Their ribosomal RNA and chloroplast DNA sequences are more closely related to plant sequences than those of any other green alga. We discuss the

evolution of land plants from an algal ancestor more thoroughly in Chapter 26.

## STUDY BREAK QUESTIONS

1. For each of these protist groups, indicate the cell structure that characterizes the group: apicomplexans, dinoflagellates, euglenoids, radiolarians.
2. Which eukaryotic supergroups contain amoeboid forms?
3. What is the major difference between cellular slime moulds and plasmodial slime moulds?

Reproductive structures

Dr. John Clayton, National Institute of Water and Atmospheric Research, New Zealand

**FIGURE 24.31** The charophyte *Chara*, representative of a group of green algae that may have given rise to the plant kingdom

## 24.5 Some Protist Lineages Arose from Primary Endosymbiosis and Others from Secondary Endosymbiosis

We have encountered chloroplasts in a number of eukaryotic organisms in this chapter: red and green algae, euglenoids, dinoflagellates, stramenopiles, chlorarachniophytes, and land plants. How did these chloroplasts evolve? Unlike the endosymbiotic event that gave rise to mitochondria, endosymbiosis involving photoautotrophs happened more than once, resulting in the formation of a wide range of photosynthetic eukaryotes.

About 1 bya, the first chloroplasts evolved from free-living photosynthetic prokaryotic organisms (cyanobacteria) ingested by eukaryote cells that had already acquired mitochondria (see Chapter 21). In some cells, the cyanobacterium was not digested but instead formed a symbiotic relationship with the engulfing host cell: it became an endosymbiont, an independent organism living inside another organism. Over evolutionary time, the prokaryotic organism lost genes no longer required for independent existence and transferred most of its genes to the host's

nuclear genome. In this process, the endosymbiont became an organelle. As explained in Chapter 21, moving genes from the endosymbiont to the nucleus would have given the host cell better control of cell functioning.

The chloroplasts of red algae, green algae, and land plants result from evolutionary divergence of the photosynthetic eukaryotes formed from this primary endosymbiotic event (as shown in the top part of **Figure 24.32**). Organisms that originated from this event have chloroplasts with two membranes, one from the plasma membrane of the engulfing eukaryote and the other from the plasma membrane of the cyanobacterium.

This **primary endosymbiosis** was followed by at least three **secondary endosymbiosis** events, each time involving different heterotrophic eukaryotes engulfing a photosynthetic eukaryote, producing new evolutionary lineages (Figure 24.32). For example, secondary endosymbiosis involving red algae engulfed by a non-photosynthetic eukaryote gave rise to the stramenopiles (oomycetes, diatoms, brown algae, golden algae) and the alveolates (dinoflagellates, ciliates, and apicomplexan parasites).

Independent endosymbiotic events involving green algae and non-photosynthetic eukaryotes produced euglenoids and chlorarachniophytes.

Organisms that formed via secondary endosymbiosis have chloroplasts surrounded by additional membranes acquired from the new host. For example, chlorarachniophytes have plastids with four membranes (Figure 24.32). The new membranes correspond to the plasma membrane of the engulfed phototroph and the food vacuole membrane of the host.

Patrick Keeling and Brian Leander at the University of British Columbia examined ocelloids (light detectors) of dinoflagellates. An ocellus is structurally complex, composed of analogues to a cornea, lens, iris, and retina. As shown in **Figure 24.33**, mitochondria and plastids, which resulted from endosymbiotic events, are important structural components.

In sum, the protists are a highly diverse and ecologically important group of organisms. Their complex evolutionary relationships, which have long been a subject of contention, are now being revised as new information is discovered, including more complete genome sequences. A deeper understanding of protists is also contributing to a better understanding of their recent descendants, the fungi, plants, and animals. We turn to these descendants in the next four chapters, beginning with the fungi.

### STUDY BREAK QUESTION

1. In primary endosymbiosis, a non-photosynthetic eukaryotic cell engulfed a photosynthetic cyanobacterium. How many membranes surround the chloroplast that evolved?

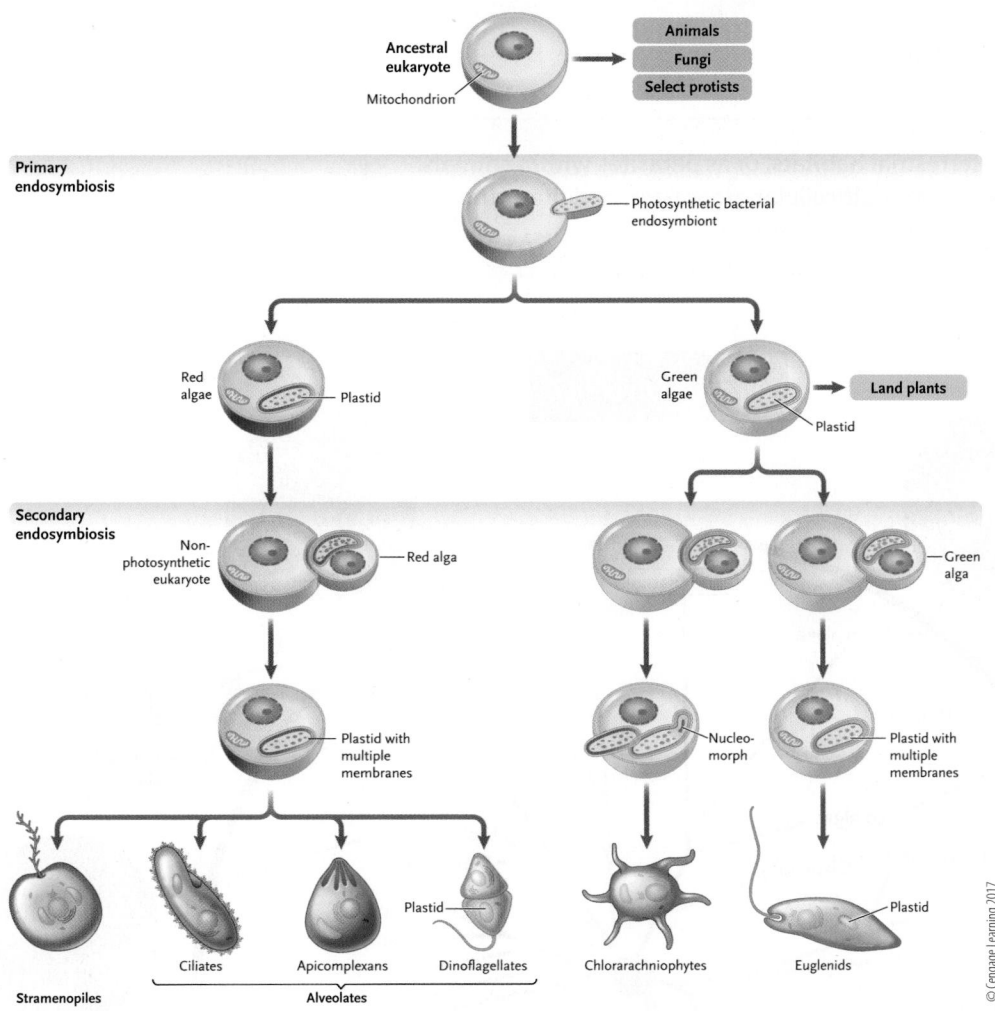

© Cengage Learning 2017

**FIGURE 24.32 The origin and distribution of plastids among the eukaryotes by primary and secondary endosymbiosis**

a.

b.

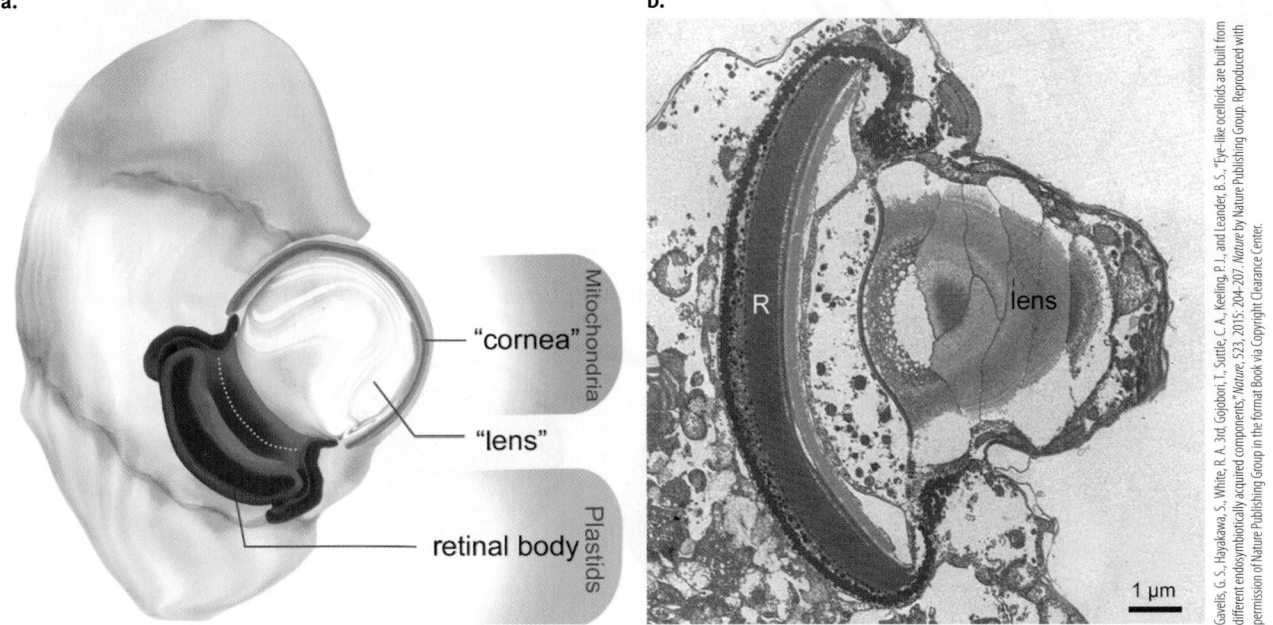

Gavelis, G. S., Hayakawa, S., White, R. A. 3rd, Gojobori, T., Suttle, C. A., Keeling, P. J., and Leander, B. S., "Eye-like ocelloids are built from different endosymbiotically acquired components," *Nature*, 523, 2015: 204-207. *Nature* by Nature Publishing Group. Reproduced with permission of Nature Publishing Group in the format Book via Copyright Clearance Center.

**FIGURE 24.33 Organelles in the ocelloid. (a)** Illustration of *Nematodinium* showing the basic components of the ocelloid with their putative organellar origins. **(b)** Transmission electron micrograph of the ocelloid of *Erythropsidinium*; lens and retinal body (R)

# Summary Illustration

Protists live in aquatic or moist terrestrial habitats, or as parasites within animals. They may be single-celled, colonial, or multicellular organisms, and they range in size from microscopic to some of Earth's largest organisms.

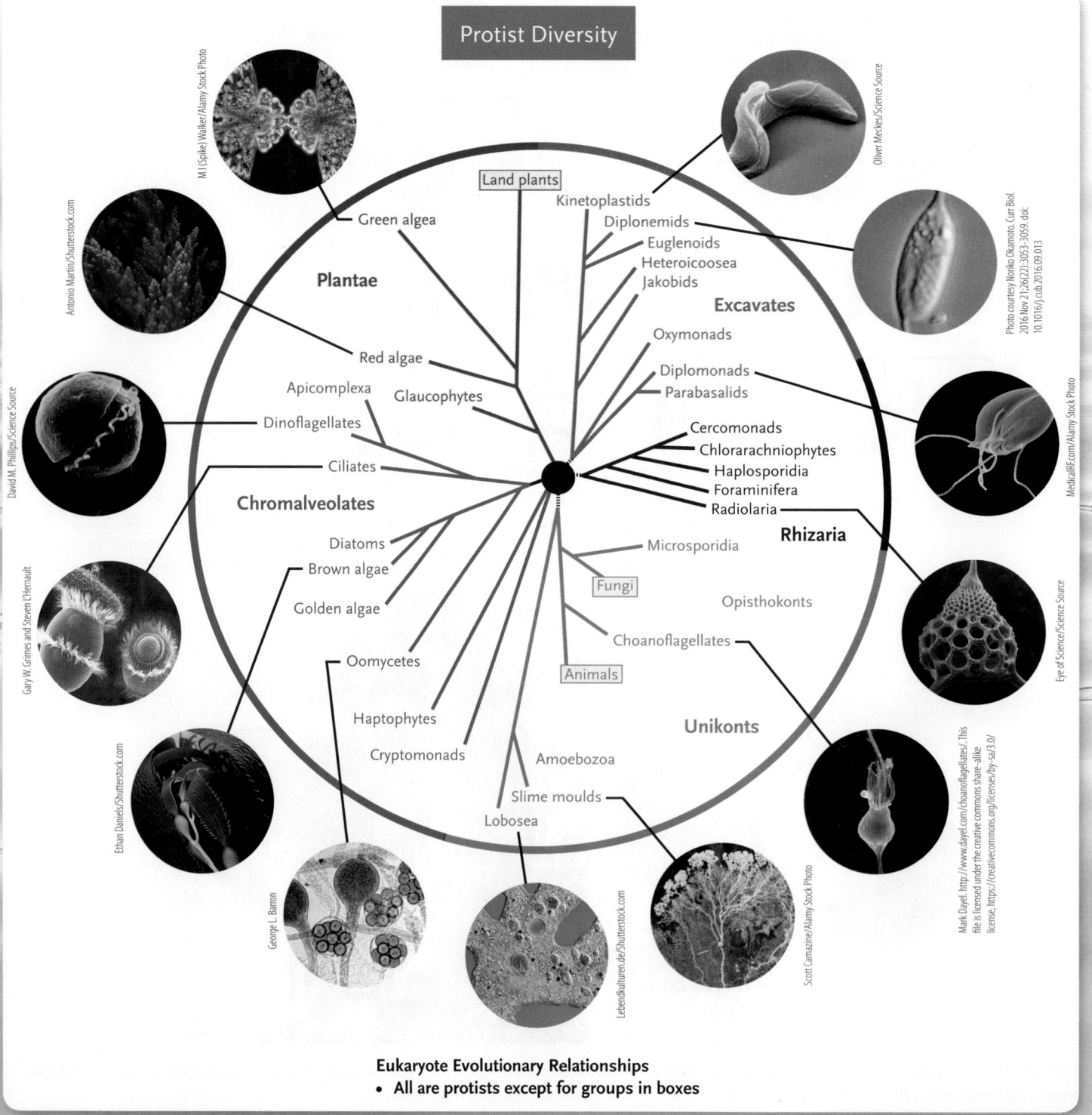

## Protist Diversity

Land plants
Green algea
Kinetoplastids
Diplonemids
Euglenoids
Heteroicoosea
Jakobids

**Plantae**

**Excavates**

Oxymonads

Red algae

Diplomonads
Parabasalids

Apicomplexa — Glaucophytes

Dinoflagellates

Cercomonads
Chlorarachniophytes
Haplosporidia
Foraminifera
Radiolaria

Ciliates

**Chromalveolates**

**Rhizaria**

Microsporidia

Diatoms

Fungi

Brown algae

Opisthokonts

Golden algae

Choanoflagellates

Oomycetes

Animals

**Unikonts**

Haptophytes

Amoebozoa

Cryptomonads

Slime moulds

Lobosea

### Eukaryote Evolutionary Relationships
• All are protists except for groups in boxes

## Modes of obtaining energy and carbon

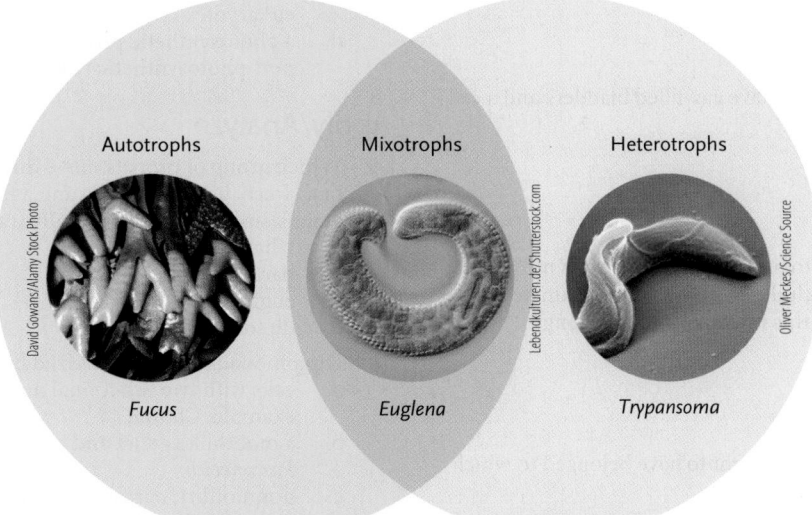

Autotrophs

Mixotrophs

Heterotrophs

*Fucus*

*Euglena*

*Trypansoma*

David Gowans/Alamy Stock Photo

Lebendkulturen.de/Shutterstock.com

Oliver Meckes/Science Source

## SYMBIOSES

### Mutualistic example:

Some organisms rely on green algae (or cyanobacteria) to photosynthesize for them by forming symbiotic relationships. For example, lichens are a symbiosis between green algae and fungi. It is a mutualistic association because both organisms benefit.

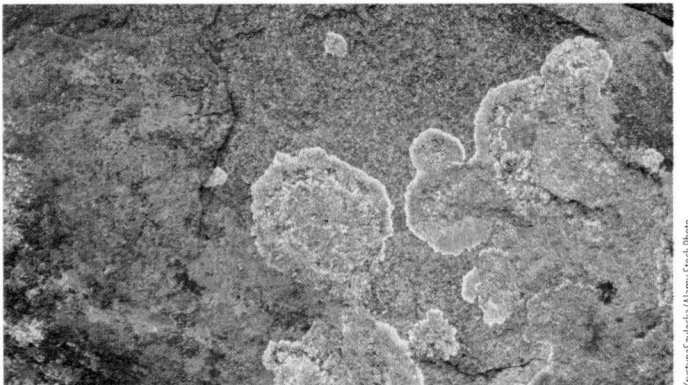

KrystynaSzulecka/Alamy Stock Photo

### Parasitic example:

*Trichonympha vaginalis* infects the genitals of both men and women. The unicellular organism is sexually transmitted and obtains nutrients from its host directly through its cell membrane as well as by phagocytosis. It is a parasitic association because it has a negative impact on its host.

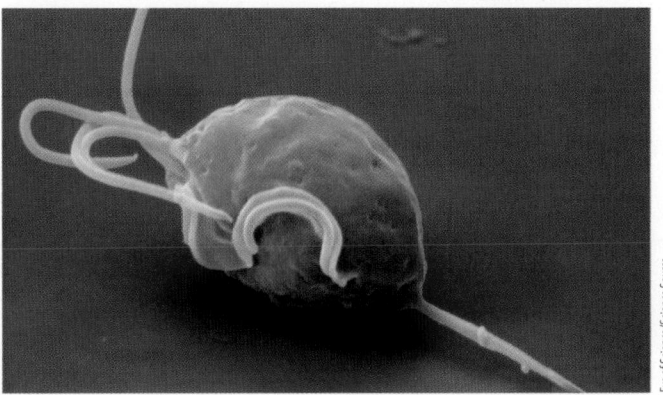

Eye of Science/Science Source

### ENDOSYMBIOSES

An endosymbiotic event gave rise to mitochondria, whereas endosymbiosis involving photoautotrophs occurred more than once, resulting in the formation of a wide range of photosynthetic eukaryotes.

## Recall/Understand

1. Which of the following groups is the greatest contributor to protist fossil deposits?
   a. oomycetes
   b. brown algae
   c. golden algae
   d. diatoms

2. Which of the following groups have gas-filled bladders and a cell wall composed of alginic acid?
   a. oomycetes
   b. brown algae
   c. golden algae
   d. diatoms

3. *Plasmodium* is transmitted to humans by the bite of a mosquito (*Anopheles*). Its life cycle includes infective spores, gametes, and cysts. To which group does this infective protist belong?
   a. oomycetes
   b. euglenoids
   c. dinoflagellates
   d. apicomplexans

4. The ancestor of land plants is thought to have belonged to which group of protists?
   a. red algae
   b. diatoms
   c. green algae
   d. golden algae

5. In oil exploration, the presence of shells is an indicator of oil-rich rock layers. To which group of protists would these shells belong?
   a. diatoms
   b. foraminiferans
   c. golden algae
   d. red algae

6. Which supergroup are animals thought to have evolved from?
   a. Excavata
   b. Rhizaria
   c. Unikonta
   d. Chromalveolata

7. Which of these statements describes cellular slime moulds?
   a. They are autotrophs.
   b. They move using cilia.
   c. They reproduce only asexually.
   d. They form a fruiting body that produces spores.

8. The double membrane observed in algal chloroplasts is thought to involve the combining of which two organisms?
   a. two ancestral, photosynthetic, prokaryotic organisms
   b. two ancestral, non-photosynthetic, prokaryotic organisms
   c. a non-photosynthetic eukaryote with a photosynthetic eukaryote
   d. a photosynthetic prokaryotic organism with a non-photosynthetic eukaryote

## Apply/Analyze

9. Which group of protists move through viscous fluids using both freely beating flagella and a flagellum buried in a fold of cytoplasm, and cause a sexually transmitted disease in humans?
   a. ciliates
   b. parabasalids
   c. euglenoids
   d. diplomonads

10. Diplomonads are characterized by which of these features?
    a. cells with two functional nuclei and multiple flagella; for example, *Giardia*
    b. a mouthlike gullet and a hairlike surface; for example, *Paramecium*
    c. nonmotility, parasitism, and sporelike infective stages; for example, *Toxoplasma*
    d. large protein deposits, movement by two flagella that are part of an undulating membrane; for example, *Trypanosoma*

## Create/Evaluate

11. Contrast protists and animals.

12. Contrast photosynthetic protists and plants.

13. Explain how protist diversity is reflected in their metabolism.

14. Explain why protist diversity is reflected in their habitat.

15. Contrast the different modes of reproduction in protists.

# Chapter Roadmap

### Fungi
From nutrient recyclers to important symbionts to disease vectors to food, fungi have many important roles in our world.

### 25.1 General Characteristics of Fungi
Morphology ranges from single-celled yeasts to multicellular filaments (mycelium). The mycelium grows within its nutrition source. The cell walls are made of chitin.

apiguide/Shutterstock.com

**From Chapter 5**

**From Chapter 6**

**To Chapter 26**

**To Chapter 27**

**To Chapter 31**

**To Chapter 36**

### 25.2 Evolution and Diversity of Fungi
Fungi evolved over 700 million years ago from a protistan ancestor that is more closely related to the ancestors of animals than to plants. Today we recognize five phyla: Chytridiomycota (causes chytridiomycosis in frogs), Zygomycota (fruit moulds), Glomeromycota (mycorrhizae), Ascomycota (cup fungi), Basidiomycota (mushrooms, puffballs).

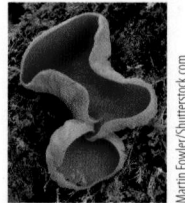

Martin Fowler/Shutterstock.com

**To Chapter 31**

**To Chapter 36**

### 25.3 Fungal Lifestyles
All fungi are heterotrophs, and they obtain carbon by degrading dead organic matter (as saprotrophs) or from living hosts (as symbionts). The plethora of lifestyles makes fungi very important players in all ecosystems.

POWER AND SYRED/SCIENCE PHOTO LIBRARY

The mushroom-forming fungus *Inocybe fastigiata*, a forest-dwelling species that commonly lives in close association with conifers and hardwood trees

# Fungi

25

**Why it matters . . .** What do ringworm, beer, and penicillin have in common? Fungus! Ringworm is not a worm at all, but a dermatophyte (skin fungus) closely related to the fungus that causes athlete's foot. Beer and other alcoholic beverages rely on the fermenting action of fungi for their alcohol content and fizz. They are also ingredients in foods, such as flavourful cheeses and leavened breads. Some moulds, such as *Penicillium*, provide humans with life-saving antibiotics, such as penicillin. While fungi can be beneficial, many species cause disease in humans, other animals, and plants; some even produce carcinogenic toxins. As you know from previous chapters, species such as the yeast used to make beer, *Saccharomyces cerevisiae*, and the mould *Neurospora crassa* have long been pivotal model organisms in studies of DNA structure and function and in the development of genetic engineering methods.

In addition to human uses, fungi play many other roles on Earth. Evidence suggests that fungi were present on land at least 760 mya and possibly much earlier. Their presence on land was likely crucial for the successful colonization of land by plants that relied on symbiotic associations with the fungi to obtain nutrients from the nutrient-poor soils of early land environments. Over the course of the intervening millennia, evolution equipped fungi with a remarkable ability to break down a wide range of compounds from both living and dead organisms. This makes them

**FIGURE 25.1 Example of a wood decay fungus: sulfur shelf fungus (*Polyporus*)**

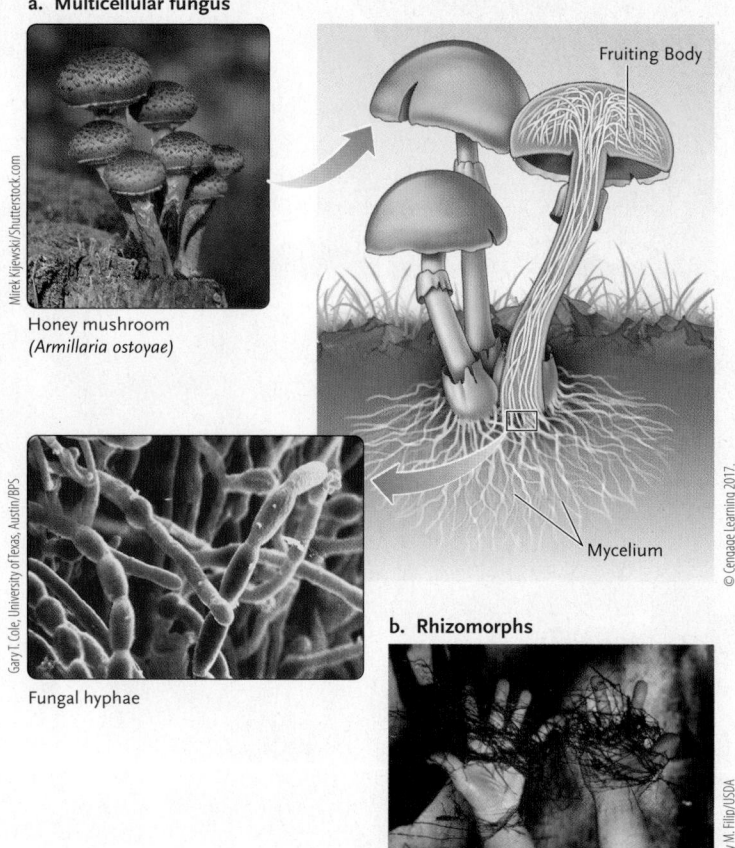

a. Multicellular fungus

Honey mushroom
(*Armillaria ostoyae*)

Fungal hyphae

Fruiting Body

Mycelium

b. Rhizomorphs

**FIGURE 25.2 Fungal structure: mycelia, hyphae. (a)** Illustration of themycelium of a mushroom-forming fungus, which consists of branching septate hyphae. *Inset:* Micrograph of fungal hyphae **(b)** Rhizomorph – a cordlike aggregation of hyphae formed by some basidiomycete fungi.

essential components in all ecosystems and Earth's premier decomposers **(Figure 25.1)**.

Despite their profound impact on ecosystems and other life forms, most of us have only a passing acquaintance with fungi, perhaps limited to the mushrooms on our pizza or the invisible but annoying types that cause skin infections, such as athlete's foot. This chapter provides you with an overview of fungal biology. We begin with the features that set fungi apart from all other organisms, and discuss the diversity of fungi existing today before revisiting associations between fungi and other organisms.

## 25.1 General Characteristics of Fungi

We begin our survey of fungi by examining the features that distinguish fungi from other forms of life, how fungi obtain nutrients, and adaptations for reproduction and growth that enable fungi to spread far and wide through the environment.

Fungi are heterotrophic eukaryotes that obtain carbon by breaking down organic molecules synthesized by other organisms. Although all fungi are heterotrophs, fungi can be divided into two broad groups based on how they obtain carbon. If a fungus obtains carbon from non-living material, it is a **saprotroph**. Fungi that decompose dead plant and animal tissues, for example, are saprotrophs. If a fungus obtains carbon from living organisms, it is a **symbiont**. Symbiosis is the living together of two (or sometimes more) organisms for extended periods; symbiotic relationships range along a continuum from **parasitism**, in which one organism benefits at the expense of the other, to **mutualism**, in which both organisms benefit. Although we often think of fungi as decomposers, fully half of all identified fungi live as symbionts with another organism.

Regardless of their nutrient source, fungi feed by **absorptive nutrition**: they secrete enzymes into their environment, breaking down large molecules into smaller soluble molecules that can then be absorbed into their cells. This mode of nutrition means that fungi cannot be stationary, as they would then deplete all the food in their immediate environment. Instead, fungi have evolved the ability to proliferate quickly through their environment, digesting nutrients as they grow. How can fungi proliferate so quickly? Although some fungi grow as unicellular yeasts, which reproduce asexually by **budding** or binary fission (see Figure 25.13), most are composed of **hyphae** ("web"; singular, *hypha*; **Figure 25.2**), fine filaments that spread through whatever substrate the fungus is growing in—soil, decomposing wood, your skin—forming a network, or **mycelium** (Figure 25.2). Hyphae are essentially tubes of cytoplasm surrounded by cell walls made of chitin, a polysaccharide also found in the exoskeletons of insects and other arthropods.

Hyphae grow only at their tips, but because a single mycelium contains many, many tips, the entire mycelium grows outward very quickly. Together, this **apical growth** and absorptive nutrition account for much of the success of fungi. As the hyphal tips extend, they exert a mechanical force, allowing them to push through their substrate, releasing enzymes and absorbing nutrients as they go. Fungal species differ in the particular digestive enzymes they synthesize, so a substrate that is a suitable food source for one species may be unavailable to another. Although there are exceptions, fungi typically thrive only in moist environments, where they can directly absorb water, dissolved ions, simple sugars, amino acids, and other small molecules. When some of a mycelium's hyphal filaments contact a source of food, growth is channelled in the direction of the food source.

Nutrients are absorbed at the porous tips of hyphae; small atoms and molecules pass readily through these tips, and then transport mechanisms move them through the underlying plasma membrane. Some hyphae have regular cross-walls, or **septa** ("fences" or "walls"; singular, *septum*), that separate a hypha into compartments **(Figure 25.3)**, whereas others lack septa and are effectively one large cell. But even septate hyphae should be thought of as interconnected compartments rather than separate cells, as all septa have pores that allow cytoplasm and, in some fungi, even nuclei and other large organelles to flow through the mycelium. By a mechanism called **cytoplasmic streaming** (flow of cytoplasm and organelles around a cell or, in this case, a mycelium), nutrients obtained by one part of a mycelium can be translocated to other non-absorptive regions, such as reproductive structures.

When a fungus releases enzymes into its substrate, it faces competition from bacteria and other organisms for the nutrients that are now available. How can a fungus prevent these competitors from stealing the nutrients that it has just expended energy and resources to obtain? Many fungi produce antibacterial compounds and toxins that inhibit the growth of competing organisms. Many of these compounds are **secondary metabolites**, which are not required for day-to-day survival but are beneficial to the fungus. As we will see, many of these compounds not only are important in the life of a fungus but also benefit organisms associated with the fungus. Many are also of commercial or medical importance to humans; for example, the antibiotic penicillin is a secondary metabolite produced by a species of *Penicillium*.

Fungi reproduce by spores, and this spore production can be amazingly prolific, with some species of fungi producing billions of spores per day **(Figure 25.4)**. These spores are microscopic, featherlight, and able to survive in the environment for extended periods after they are released. Reproducing via such spores allows fungi to be opportunists, germinating only when favourable conditions exist and quickly exploiting food sources that occur unpredictably in the environment. Releasing vast numbers of spores, as some fungi do, improves the odds that the spores will germinate and produce a new individual.

Spores can be produced asexually or sexually; some fungi produce both asexual and sexual spores at different stages of their lives. Sexual reproduction in fungi is complex. In all organisms, sexual reproduction involves three stages: the fusion of two haploid cells (**plasmogamy**), bringing together their two nuclei in one common cytoplasm. Cytoplasmic fusion in most organisms is quickly followed by nuclear fusion (**karyogamy**), but in fungi the cells can remain bi-nucleate as the organism grows. Nuclear fusion is often followed by meiosis to produce genetically distinct haploid spores. As we will see, fungi are unique in that plasmogamy and karyogamy can be separated in time for durations ranging from seconds to many years.

FIGURE 25.4 **Spore production by fungal fruiting bodies.** Some fruiting bodies can release billions of spores per day.

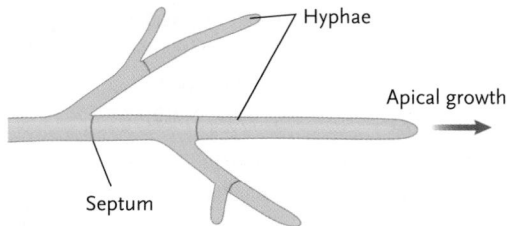

FIGURE 25.3 **Septa.** In some fungi, septa divide each hypha into separate compartments.

Hyphae

Apical growth

Septum

**STUDY BREAK QUESTIONS**

1. What physical features distinguish fungi from other organisms?
2. How do fungi reduce competition for resources?
3. By what means do fungi reproduce? Why is this mode of reproduction advantageous?
4. What is the advantage of mycelial growth?

## 25.2 Evolution and Diversity of Fungi

### 25.2a Fungi Were Present on Earth by at Least 760 Million Years Ago

For many years, fungi were classified as plants because the earliest classification schemes had only two kingdoms, plants and animals. Fungi, like plants, have cell walls and do not move, so they were grouped with plants. As biologists learned more about the distinctive characteristics of fungi, however, it became clear that fungi should be treated as a separate kingdom.

**CONCEPT FIX** The idea that fungi are most closely related to plants has persisted, but this is a misconception! The discovery of chitin in fungal cells and recent comparisons of DNA and RNA sequences all indicate that fungi and animals are more closely related to each other than they are to other eukaryotes. The close biochemical relationship between fungi and animals may explain why fungal infections are typically so resistant to treatment and why it has proved rather difficult to develop drugs that kill fungi without damaging their human or other animal hosts. ⬡

Analysis of the sequences of several genes suggests that the lineages leading to animals and fungi likely diverged between 760 mya and 1 billion years ago (bya). What were the first fungi like? We do not know for certain; phylogenetic studies indicate that fungi first arose from a single-celled, flagellated protist. In Chapter 24 you were introduced to the choanoflagellates. Single-celled choanoflagellates evidently gave rise to the lineage of animals. These are closely related to nucleariids (single-celled amoebas), belonging to a different line of protists. This suggests that multicellular forms of animals and fungi evolved independently.

Although traces of what may be fossil fungi exist in rock formations nearly 1 billion years old, the oldest fossils that we can confidently assign to the modern **kingdom Fungi** appear in rock strata laid down in the late Proterozoic (900–570 mya).

### 25.2b Once They Appeared, Fungi Radiated into Several Major Lineages

Most likely, the first fungi were aquatic. When other kinds of organisms began to colonize land, they may well have brought fungi along with them. For example, researchers have discovered what appear to be mycorrhizae—symbiotic associations of a fungus and a plant—in fossils of some of the earliest-known land plants.

Over time, fungi diverged into the strikingly diverse lineages that we consider in the rest of this section **(Table 25.1)**. Today, there are approximately 100 000 described species of fungi, with at least 1.6 million more that have not yet been described.

As the lineages diversified, different adaptations associated with reproduction arose. For example, structures in which sexual spores are formed and mechanisms by which spores are dispersed became larger and more elaborate over evolutionary time. Traditionally, therefore, biologists have classified fungi primarily by the distinctive structures produced in sexual reproduction. These features are still useful indicators of the phylogenetic standing of a fungus, but the powerful tools of molecular analysis are bringing many revisions to our understanding of the evolutionary journey of fungi.

The evolutionary origins and lineages of fungi have been obscure ever since biologists began puzzling over the

| TABLE 25.1 | Summary of Fungal Phyla | | |
|---|---|---|---|
| Phylum | Body Type | Key Feature | |
| Chytridiomycota (chytrids) | One to several cells | Motile spores propelled by flagella; usually asexual | |
| Zygomycota (zygomycetes) | Hyphal | Sexual stage in which a resistant zygospore forms for later germination | |
| Glomeromycota (glomeromycetes) | Hyphal | Hyphae associated with plant roots, forming arbuscular mycorrhizae | |
| Ascomycota (ascomycetes) | Hyphal | Sexual spores produced in sacs called *asci* | |
| Basidiomycota (basidiomycetes) | Hyphal | Sexual spores (basidiospores) form in basidia of a prominent fruiting body (basidiocarp). | |
| Cryptomycota (proposed) | Single cell | Sporelike parasites | |

© Cengage Learning 2017.

characteristics of this group. With the advent of molecular techniques for research, these topics have become extremely active and exciting areas of biological research that may shed light on fundamental events in the evolution of all eukaryotes. Currently, we recognize five phyla of fungi, known formally as the Chytridiomycota, Zygomycota, Glomeromycota, Ascomycota, and Basidiomycota **(Figure 25.5)**. However, we know now that two of these phyla, the Chytridiomycota and the Zygomycota, are not monophyletic (i.e., they are taxa that do not contain only one ancestor and all of its descendants). The earliest diverging branch of fungi indicated in Figure 25.5 is the Cryptomycota, included here at the phylum level (Figure 25.5). It is a clade encompassing groups of single-celled fungi. The classification scheme presented in Figure 25.5 will soon change to reflect this new information. Why do classifications of organisms change so often? Bear in mind that classification schemes such as those presented here are hypotheses that explain our best understanding of evolutionary relationships among organisms at any one time; like any other hypotheses, classification schemes are open to revision as we find out more about the organisms. Molecular data also suggest that some other eukaryotic organisms currently classified elsewhere may actually be fungi; we haven't included those organisms in this chapter but instead will focus on the groups of fungi that are best understood. Even though fungal classification will change greatly over the next few years, we summarize the major phyla recognized today as a way of illustrating the diversity of this group of organisms.

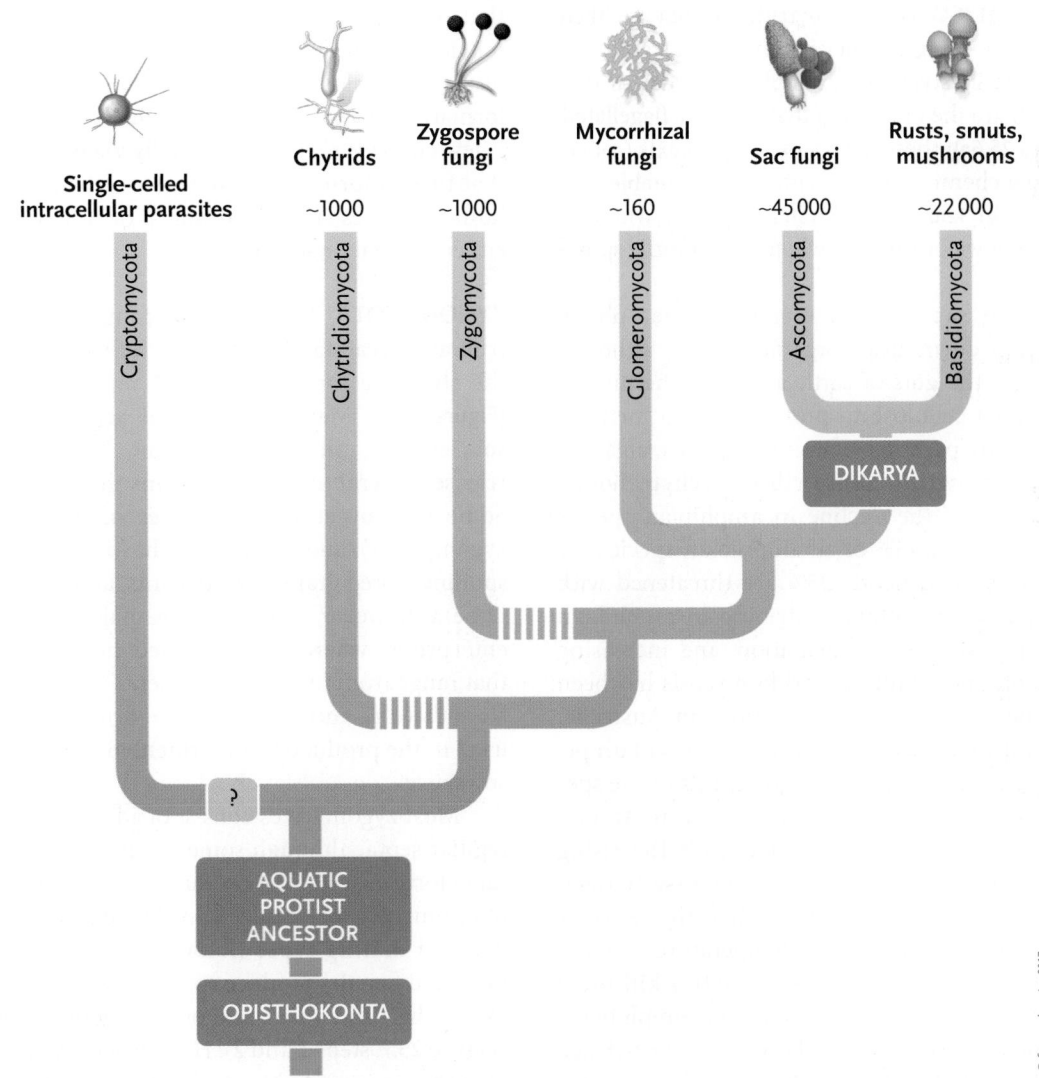

**FIGURE 25.5 A phylogeny of fungi.** This scheme represents a widely accepted view of the general relationships between major groups of fungi, but it may well be revised as new molecular findings provide more information. The dashed lines indicate that two groups, the chytrids and the zygomycetes, are probably paraphyletic—they include subgroups that are not all descended from a single ancestor. Based on genomic studies, some mycologists place microsporidia and certain fungi formerly classified as chytrids in a new, basal phylum, the Cryptomycota. The question mark indicates ongoing debate about whether the clade meets the technical definition of a phylum.

**a. Chytridiomycosis in a frog**

Skin surface

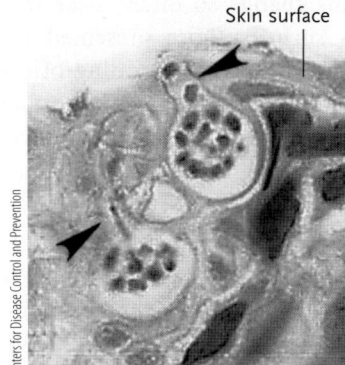

**b. Harlequin frog**

**FIGURE 25.6 Chytrids. (a)** Chytridiomycosis, a fungal infection, shown here in the skin of a frog. The two arrows point to flask-shaped, spore-producing cells of the parasitic chytrid *Batrachochytrium dendrobatidis*, which has devastated populations of harlequin frogs **(b)**.

**PHYLUM CHYTRIDIOMYCOTA** The Chytridiomycota are likely the most ancient group of fungi, as they retain several traits characteristic of an aquatic lifestyle. For example, chytrids (as they are commonly called) are the only fungi that produce flagellated, motile spores **(Figure 25.6a)**; these spores use chemotaxis (movement in response to a chemical gradient) to locate suitable substrates. Chytrids live in soil or freshwater habitats, wherever there is at least a film of water through which their motile spores can swim.

Most chytrids are saprotrophs, organisms that obtain nutrients by breaking down dead organic matter, although some are symbionts in the guts of cattle and other herbivores where they break down cellulose to provide carbon for their hosts, and still others are parasites of animals, plants, algae, or other fungi. These tiny fungi also cause a disease, chytridiomycosis, that is one cause of the decline in amphibian species worldwide. Globally, at least 43% of all amphibian species are declining in population, and nearly 33% are threatened with extinction. Although many factors contribute to amphibian decline, including habitat loss, fragmentation, and increasing levels of environmental pollutants, chytridiomycosis has been linked to the decline of amphibian populations in Australia, New Zealand, Central and South America, and parts of Europe. This disease has wiped out an estimated two-thirds of the species of harlequin frogs (*Atelopus*) in the American tropics (Figure 25.6b). The epidemic has correlated with the rising average temperature in the frogs' habitats, an increase credited to global climate change. Studies show that the warmer environment provides optimal growing temperatures for the chytrid pathogen. How does infection by a chytrid kill these animals? The fungus colonizes the skin of amphibians (Figure 25.6b), which interferes with the electrolyte balance and functioning of organs because amphibians take up water and exchange gases through their skins.

Most chytrids are unicellular, although some live as chains of cells and have rhizoids (branching filamentous extensions)

that anchor the fungus to its substrate and that may also absorb nutrients from the substrate (Figure 25.6a). The vegetative stage of most chytrids is haploid; asexual reproduction involves the formation of a **sporangium**, in which motile spores are formed. A few chytrids reproduce sexually via male and female gametes that fuse to form a diploid zygote. This cell may form a mycelium that gives rise to sporangia, or it may directly give rise to either asexual or sexual spores.

**ZYGOMYCOTA** This group of fungi includes the moulds on fruit and bread familiar to many of us and takes its name from the structure formed in sexual reproduction, the **zygospore (Figure 25.7)**. Many zygomycetes are saprotrophs that live in soil, feeding on organic matter. Their metabolic activities release mineral nutrients in forms that plant roots can take up. Some zygomycetes are parasites of insects (and even other zygomycetes), and some wreak havoc on human food supplies, spoiling stored grains, bread, fruits, and vegetables **(Figure 25.8)**. Others, however, have become major players in commercial enterprises, where they are used in manufacturing products that range from industrial pigments to pharmaceuticals such as steroids (e.g., anti-inflammatory drugs). Zygomycetes are also used in the production of fermented foods such as tempeh and soy sauce.

Most zygomycetes consist of a haploid mycelium that lacks regular septa, although some groups have septa, and in others, septa form to wall off reproductive structures and aging regions of the mycelium. Sexual reproduction occurs when mycelia of different **mating types** (known as + and – types, rather than male and female) produce specialized hyphae that grow toward each other and form sex organs (**gametangia**) at their tips (Figure 25.7, steps 1 and 2). How do gametangia find each other? Pheromones secreted by each mycelium stimulate the development of sexual structures in the complementary strain and cause gametangia to grow toward each other. The gametangia fuse, forming a thick-walled structure, a **zygosporangium**

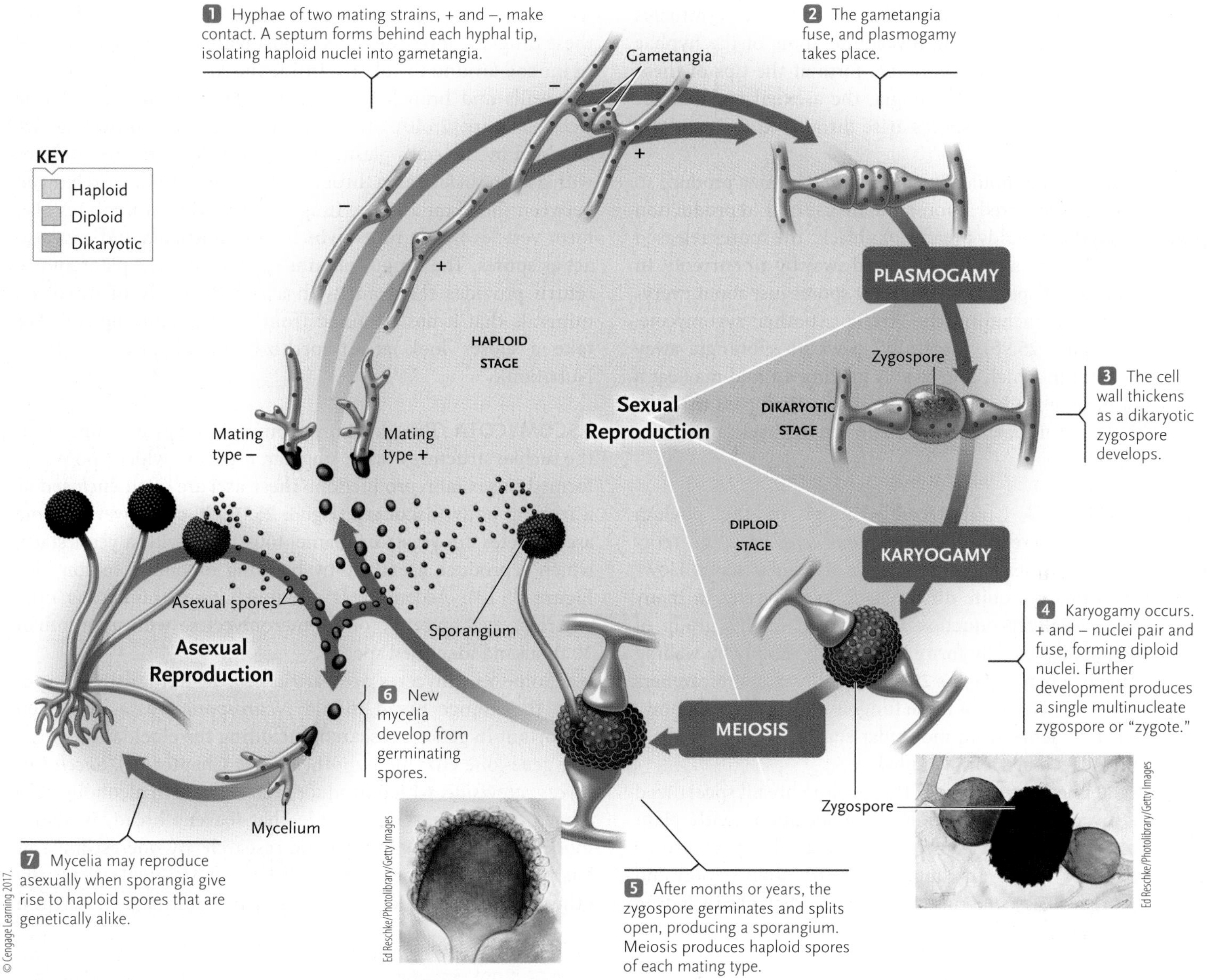

**1** Hyphae of two mating strains, + and −, make contact. A septum forms behind each hyphal tip, isolating haploid nuclei into gametangia.

Gametangia

**2** The gametangia fuse, and plasmogamy takes place.

**KEY**
- Haploid
- Diploid
- Dikaryotic

**PLASMOGAMY**

HAPLOID STAGE

Zygospore

**Sexual Reproduction**

DIKARYOTIC STAGE

**3** The cell wall thickens as a dikaryotic zygospore develops.

Mating type −    Mating type +

DIPLOID STAGE

**KARYOGAMY**

Asexual spores

**Asexual Reproduction**

Sporangium

**4** Karyogamy occurs. + and − nuclei pair and fuse, forming diploid nuclei. Further development produces a single multinucleate zygospore or "zygote."

**6** New mycelia develop from germinating spores.

**MEIOSIS**

Zygospore

Mycelium

Ed Reschke/Photolibrary/Getty Images

**7** Mycelia may reproduce asexually when sporangia give rise to haploid spores that are genetically alike.

© Cengage Learning 2017.

Ed Reschke/Photolibrary/Getty Images

**5** After months or years, the zygospore germinates and splits open, producing a sporangium. Meiosis produces haploid spores of each mating type.

**FIGURE 25.7  Life cycle of the bread mould *Rhizopus stolonifer*, a zygomycete.** Asexual reproduction is common, but different mating types (+ and −) also reproduce sexually. In both cases, haploid spores are formed and give rise to new mycelia.

humbak/Shutterstock.com

**FIGURE 25.8  Zygomycete fungus growing on strawberries**

(Figure 25.7, step 3), which can remain dormant for months or years, allowing the zygomycete to survive unfavourable environmental conditions. Eventually, meiosis occurs in the zygosporangium, forming a meiosporangium that will produce haploid spores by meiosis. (Figure 25.7, step 5). Note that meiosis does not always produce gametes! We often tend to characterize meiosis as the formation of gametes, probably because we are so familiar with how sexual reproduction occurs in humans and other animals. But in many organisms, such as fungi and plants, meiosis results in the formation of haploid spores.

Like other fungi, however, zygomycetes also reproduce asexually, as shown in steps 6 and 7 of Figure 25.7. When a haploid spore lands on a favourable substrate, it germinates and gives rise to a branching mycelium. Some of the hyphae grow upward, and saclike sporangia form at the tips of these aerial hyphae. Inside the sporangia, the asexual cycle comes full circle as new haploid spores arise through mitosis and are released.

The black bread mould *Rhizopus stolonifer* may produce so many charcoal-coloured sporangia in asexual reproduction **(Figure 25.9a)** that mouldy bread looks black. The spores released are lightweight, dry, and readily wafted away by air currents. In fact, winds have dispersed *R. stolonifer* spores just about everywhere on Earth, including the Arctic. Another zygomycete, *Pilobolus* (Figure 25.9b), forcefully spews its sporangia away from the dung in which it grows. A grazing animal may eat a sporangium on a blade of grass; the spores then pass through the animal's gut unharmed and begin the life cycle again in a new dung pile.

**GLOMEROMYCOTA** Until recently, fungi in the phylum Glomeromycota were classified as zygomycetes based on morphological similarities such as the lack of regular septa. However, these fungi are quite dissimilar to zygomycetes in many ways (e.g., sexual reproduction is unknown in this group of fungi, with spores usually forming asexually simply by walling off a section of a hypha **(Figure 25.10b)**, causing many researchers to question the inclusion of these fungi in the phylum Zygomycota. Recent evidence from molecular studies resulted in these fungi being placed in their own phylum.

The 160 known members of this phylum are all specialized to form **mycorrhizae**, or symbiotic associations with plant roots. These fungi have a tremendous ecological importance, as they collectively make up roughly half the fungi in soil and form mycorrhizal associations with many land plants, including most major crop species such as wheat and maize. Mycelia of these fungi colonize the roots of host plants and also proliferate in the soil around the plants. Inside the roots, hyphae penetrate cell walls and branch repeatedly to form **arbuscules** ("little trees"; Figure 25.10). The branches of each arbuscule are enfolded by the cell's plasma membrane, forming an interface with a large surface area through which nutrients are exchanged between the plant and the fungus. Some glomeromycetes also form vesicles inside roots, which store nutrients and can also act as spores. The fungus obtains sugars from the plant and in return provides the plant with a steady supply of dissolved minerals that it has obtained from the surrounding soil. We take a closer look at mycorrhizae in Chapter 36 (Plant Nutrition).

**ASCOMYCOTA** The phylum Ascomycota takes its name from the saclike structures (**asci**; singular, *ascus*) in which spores are formed in sexual reproduction. These asci are often enclosed in a fruiting body (**ascocarp**; **Figure 25.11a, b, c**). However, some ascomycetes are yeasts or filamentous fungi with a yeast stage, which reproduce asexually by budding or binary fission (see Figure 25.13). Ascomycetes are much more numerous than chytrids, zygomycetes, or glomeromycetes, with more than 30 thousand identified species.

Some ascomycetes are very useful to humans. One species, the orange bread mould *Neurospora crassa*, has been important in genetic research, including the elucidation of the one gene–one enzyme hypothesis (see Chapter 12). *Saccharomyces cerevisiae*, which produces the ethanol in alcoholic beverages and the carbon dioxide that leavens bread, is also a model organism used in genetic research. By one estimate, it has been the subject of more genetic experiments than any other eukaryotic microorganism. This multifaceted phylum

**a. Sporangia of Rhizopus nigricans**

**b. Sporangia (dark sacs) of *Pilobolus***

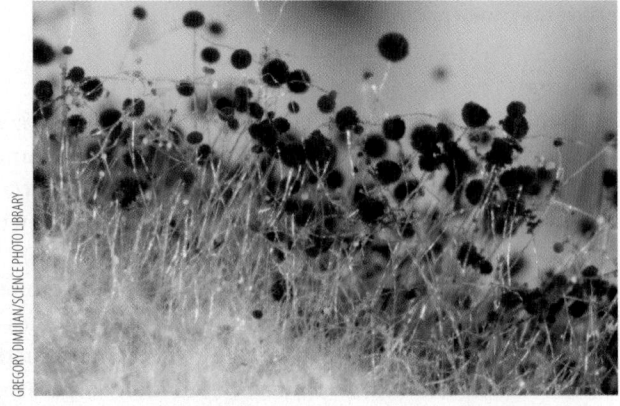

500 μm

**FIGURE 25.9 Two of the numerous strategies for spore dispersal by zygomycetes. (a)** The sporangia of *Rhizopus stolonifer*, shown here on a slice of bread, release powdery spores that are easily dispersed by air currents. **(b)** In *Pilobolus*, the spores are contained in a sporangium (the dark sac) at the end of a stalked structure. When incoming rays of sunlight strike a light-sensitive portion of the stalk, turgor pressure (pressure against a cell wall due to the movement of water into the cell) inside a vacuole in the swollen portion becomes so great that the entire sporangium may be ejected outward as far as 2 m—a remarkable feat given that the stalk is only 5 to 10 mm tall.

## a. Arbuscules and Vesicle in roots colonized by arbuscular mycorrhizal fungus

## b. Arbuscules inside root

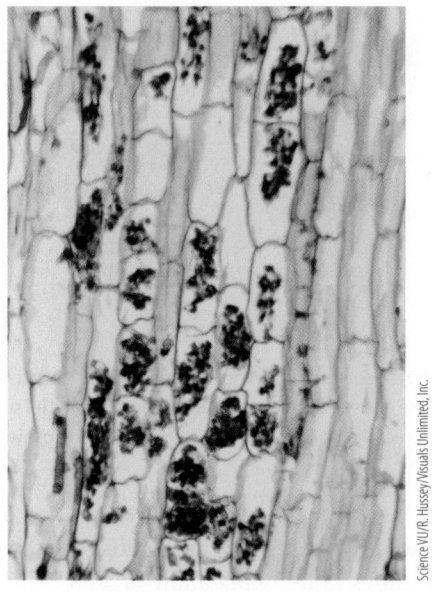

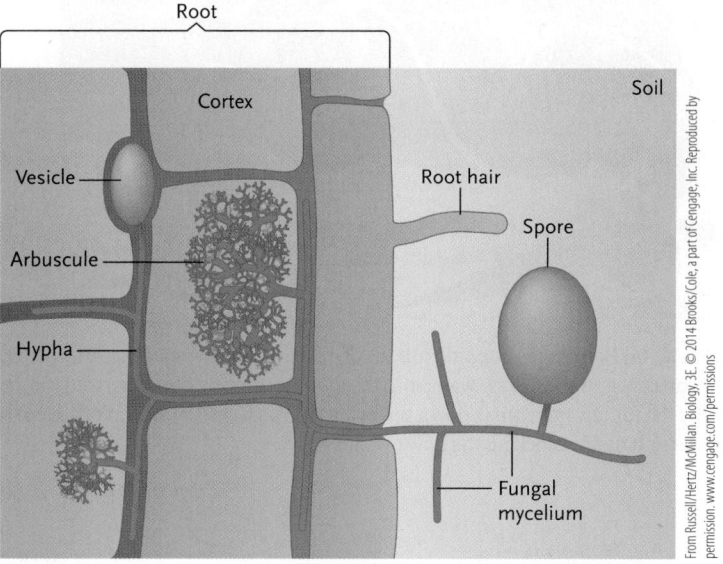

**FIGURE 25.10 Glomeromycete fungus forming a mycorrhiza. (a)** Root cells of leek growing in association with the glomeromycete fungus *Glomus versiforme* (longitudinal section). **(b)** Arbuscules and vesicle that have formed as fungal hyphae branch after entering the root.

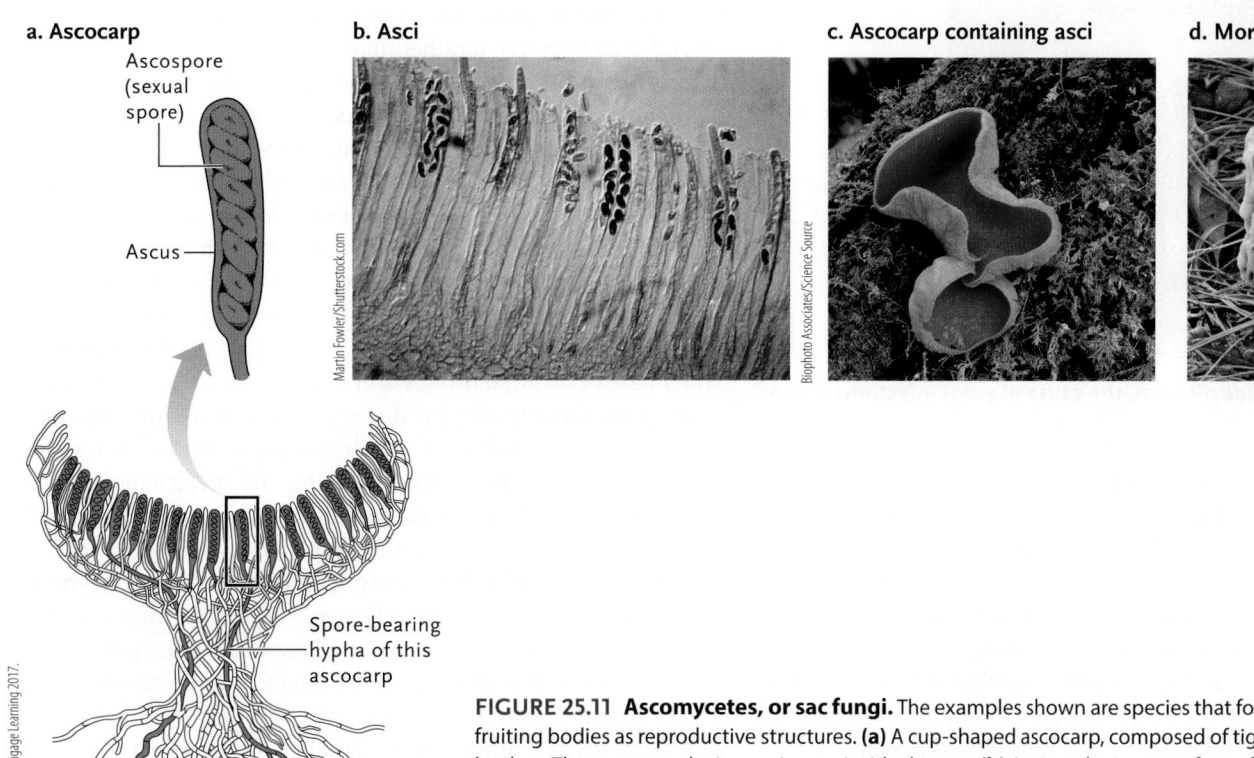

## a. Ascocarp

Ascospore (sexual spore)

Ascus

Spore-bearing hypha of this ascocarp

## b. Asci

## c. Ascocarp containing asci

## d. Morel

**FIGURE 25.11 Ascomycetes, or sac fungi.** The examples shown are species that form multicellular fruiting bodies as reproductive structures. **(a)** A cup-shaped ascocarp, composed of tightly interwoven hyphae. The spore-producing asci occur inside the cup. **(b)** Asci on the inner surface of an ascocarp. **(c)** Scarlet cup fungus (*Sarcoscypha*). **(d)** A true morel (*Morchella esculenta*), a prized edible fungus

also includes gourmet delicacies such as truffles (*Tuber melanosporum*) and the succulent morel *Morchella esculenta* (Figure 25.11d).

Many ascomycetes are saprotrophs, playing a key role in the breakdown of cellulose and other polymers. Ascomycetes are also common in symbiotic associations, forming mycorrhizae and lichens (see Section 25.3). A few ascomycetes prey on various agricultural insect pests—some are even carnivores that trap their prey in nooses **(Figure 25.12a)**—and thus have potential for use as biological pesticides.

**a. A trapping ascomycete**

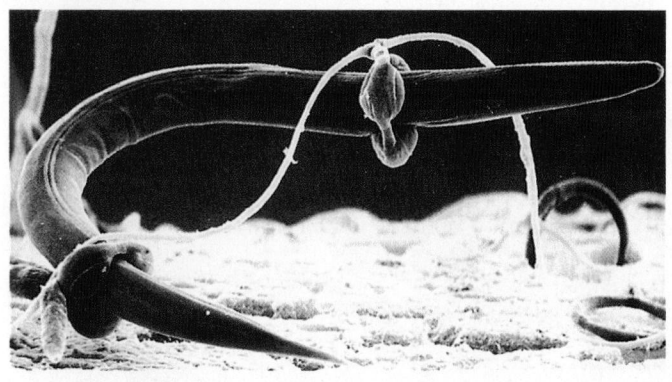

George L. Barron

**b. Stump of pine tree infected with blue-stain fungus**

U.S. Forest Service

**FIGURE 25.12** **(a)** Nematode-trapping fungus. Hyphae of this ascomycete (*Arthrobotrys*) form nooselike rings. When a prey organism enters the loop, rapid changes in ion concentration draw water into the loop by osmosis. The increased turgor pressure causes the noose to tighten, trapping its prey. Enzymes produced by the fungus then break down the nematode's tissues. **(b)** Stump of a pine tree infected with blue-stain fungus. The fungus grows into the tree's water-conducting tissue, blocking the flow of water.

**Yeast cells**

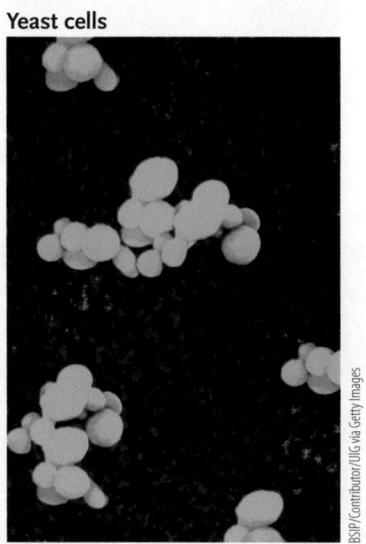

BSIP/Contributor/UIG via Getty Images

**FIGURE 25.13** *Candida albicans,* **the cause of yeast infections of the mouth and vagina**

However, other ascomycetes are devastating plant pathogens, including the blue-stain fungi that are associated with mountain pine beetles and contribute to the death of beetle-infested trees (Figure 25.12b). Several ascomycetes can be serious pathogens of humans. The yeast *Candida albicans* **(Figure 25.13)** infects mucous membranes, especially of the vagina and mouth (causing a condition called *thrush*). Another yeast, *Pneumocystis jirovecii*, causes virulent pneumonia in AIDS patients and other immunocompromised people.

*Claviceps purpurea*, a parasite on rye and other grains, causes ergotism, a disease marked by vomiting, hallucinations, convulsions, and, in severe cases, gangrene and even death. It has even been suggested that this fungus was the cause of the Salem witch hunts of seventeenth century New England. Other ascomycetes cause nuisance infections, such as athlete's foot and ringworm.

Most ascomycetes grow as haploid mycelia with regular septa; large pores in the septa allow organelles, including nuclei, to move with cytoplasm through the mycelium. Sexual reproduction generally involves fusion of hyphae from mycelia of + and − mating types **(Figure 25.14)**. The cytoplasms of the two hyphae fuse, but fusion of the nuclei is delayed, resulting in the formation of **dikaryotic hyphae** that contain two separate nuclei and thus are referred to as $n + n$ rather than $n$ or $2n$. Sacs (asci) form at the tips of these dikaryotic hyphae; inside the asci, the two nuclei fuse, forming a diploid zygote nucleus, which then undergoes meiosis to produce four haploid nuclei. Mitosis usually follows, resulting in the formation of eight haploid spores (**ascospores**).

Unlike zygomycetes, ascomycetes do not produce asexual spores in sporangia. Instead, modified hyphae produce numerous asexual spores called **conidia** ("dust"; singular, *conidium*), such as those seen when powdery mildew attacks grasses, roses, and other common garden plants **(Figure 25.15a)**. The mode of conidial production varies from species to species, with some ascomycetes producing chains of conidia, whereas in others, the conidia are produced on a hypha in a series of "bubbles," rather like a string of detachable beads (Figure 25.15b). Either way, conidia are formed and released much more quickly than zygomycete spores.

Asexual reproductive structures look very different from the sexual stages and are often not formed at the same time or under the same conditions as the sexual stage of the life cycle. These differences resulted in the asexual stages of many ascomycetes being classified as separate organisms from the sexual stages of the same species. Since fungal classification traditionally relied on features produced in sexual reproduction, these asexual stages could not be placed in any of the phyla; instead, researchers grouped them together in an artificial group called the *Deuteromycota* (also known as *Fungi Imperfecti*, or the "imperfect fungi"—imperfect meaning that a sexual stage is absent). Well-known examples of fungi once classified as deuteromycetes are *Penicillium* and *Aspergillus*. Certain species of *Penicillium*

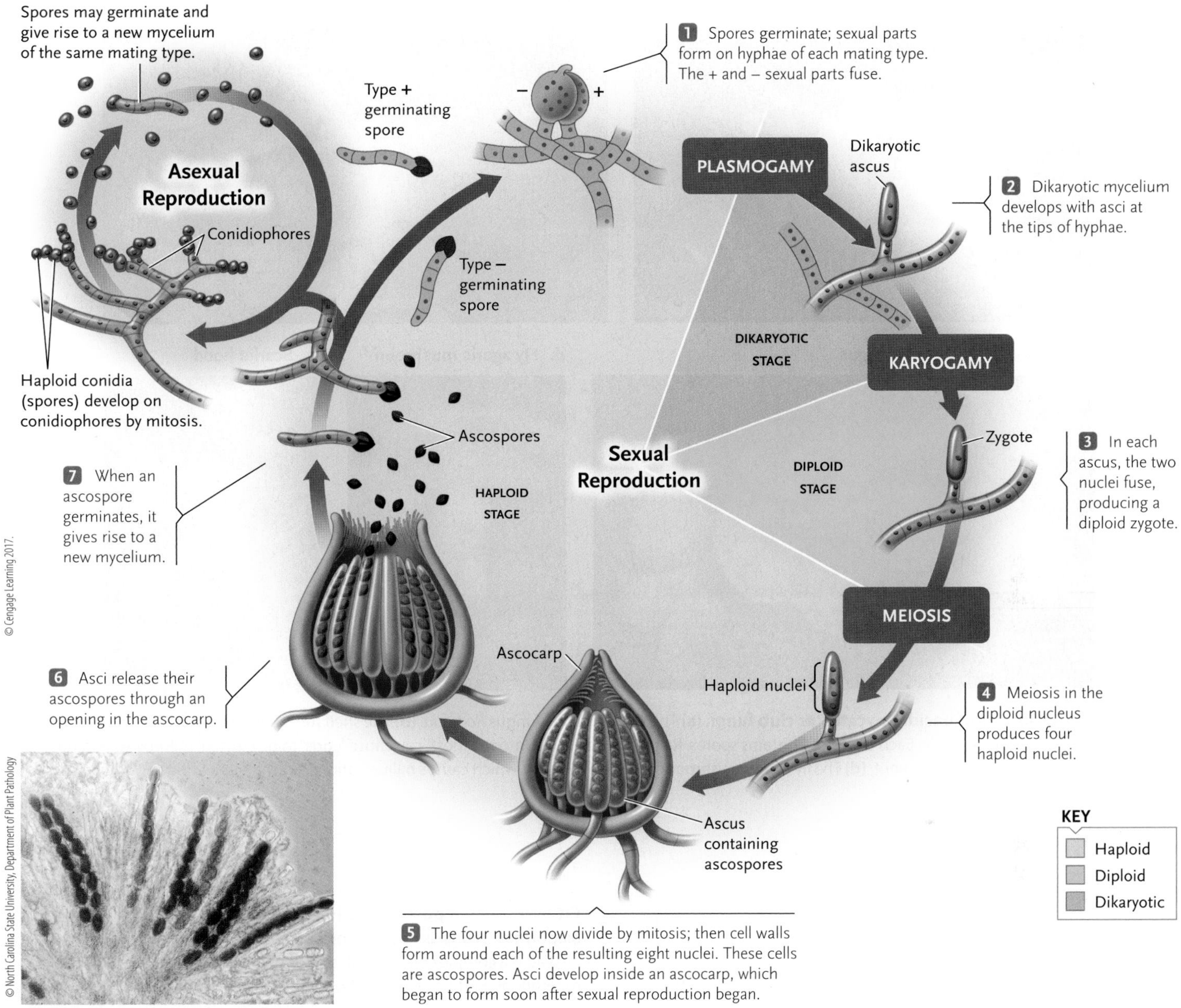

# Life cycle diagram (Figure 25.14)

Spores may germinate and give rise to a new mycelium of the same mating type.

**Asexual Reproduction**

Conidiophores

Haploid conidia (spores) develop on conidiophores by mitosis.

Type + germinating spore

Type − germinating spore

**1** Spores germinate; sexual parts form on hyphae of each mating type. The + and − sexual parts fuse.

**PLASMOGAMY**

Dikaryotic ascus

**2** Dikaryotic mycelium develops with asci at the tips of hyphae.

**DIKARYOTIC STAGE**

**KARYOGAMY**

Zygote

**DIPLOID STAGE**

**3** In each ascus, the two nuclei fuse, producing a diploid zygote.

**Sexual Reproduction**

Ascospores

**HAPLOID STAGE**

**7** When an ascospore germinates, it gives rise to a new mycelium.

**MEIOSIS**

Haploid nuclei

**4** Meiosis in the diploid nucleus produces four haploid nuclei.

**6** Asci release their ascospores through an opening in the ascocarp.

Ascocarp

Ascus containing ascospores

**5** The four nuclei now divide by mitosis; then cell walls form around each of the resulting eight nuclei. These cells are ascospores. Asci develop inside an ascocarp, which began to form soon after sexual reproduction began.

**KEY**
- ☐ Haploid
- ☐ Diploid
- ☐ Dikaryotic

© Cengage Learning 2017.

© North Carolina State University, Department of Plant Pathology

**FIGURE 25.14** Life cycle of the ascomycete *Neurospora crassa*

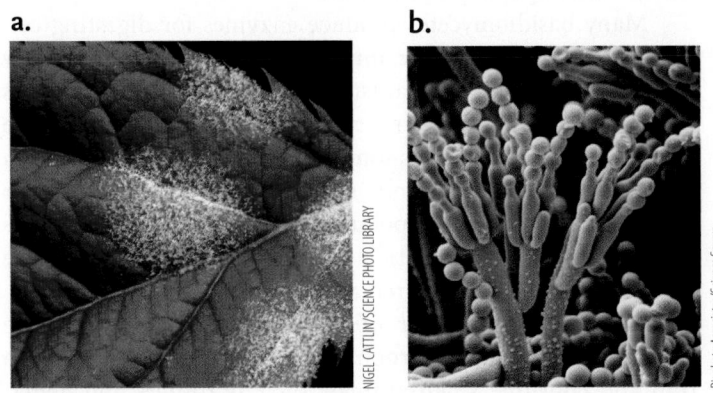

**a.**

**b.**

NIGEL CATTLIN/SCIENCE PHOTO LIBRARY

Biophoto Associates/Science Source

**FIGURE 25.15** **(a)** Powdery mildew on leaves. **(b)** Conidia of *Penicillium*. Note the rows of conidia (asexual spores) atop the elongate cells that produce them.

(Figure 25.15b) are the source of the penicillin family of antibiotics, whereas others produce the aroma and distinctive flavours of Camembert and Roquefort cheeses. Strains of *Aspergillus* grow in damp grain or peanuts. Their metabolic wastes, known as *aflatoxins*, can cause cancer in humans who eat the poisoned food over an extended period. With the development of molecular sequencing techniques, many fungi that were classified as deuteromycetes can now be reassigned to the appropriate phylum; most are ascomycetes, but some are basidiomycetes, which also produce conidia in asexual reproduction.

**BASIDIOMYCOTA** The 24 000 or so species of fungi in the phylum Basidiomycota include the mushroom-forming species, bracket fungi, stinkhorns, smuts, rusts, and puffballs **(Figure 25.16)**. The common name for this group is club fungi

**a. Coral fungus**

Stephen Farhall/Shutterstock.com

**b. Shelf fungus**

apiguide/Shutterstock.com

**c. White-egg bird's nest fungus**

Jeffrey Lepore/Science Source

**d. Fly agaric mushroom**

Arve Bettum/Shutterstock.com

**e. Scarlet hood**

Dave Pressland/FLPA/Science Source

**FIGURE 25.16 Examples of basidiomycetes, or club fungi. (a)** The light red coral fungus *Ramaria*. **(b)** The shelf fungus *Polyporus*. **(c)** The white-egg bird's nest fungus *Crucibulum laeve*. Each tiny "egg" contains spores. Raindrops splashing into the "nest" can cause "eggs" to be ejected, thereby spreading spores into the surrounding environment. **(d)** The fly agaric mushroom *Amanita muscaria*, which causes hallucinations. **(e)** The scarlet hood *Hygrophorus*

**FIGURE 25.17 A portion of a lignin molecule.** Unlike most other biopolymers, lignin is not composed of regularly repeating monomers, but instead is a complex polymer of various phenylpropanoid units joined together by a range of diverse bonds, making it very difficult to degrade.

due to the club-shaped cells (**basidia**; singular, *basidium*) on which sexual spores are produced.

Many basidiomycetes produce enzymes for digesting cellulose and lignin, and are important decomposers of woody plant debris. Very few organisms can degrade lignin due to its very complex, irregular structure (**Figure 25.17**). The ability to degrade lignin also enables some basidiomycetes to break down complex organic compounds such as DDT, PCBs, and other persistent environmental pollutants that are structurally similar to lignin. Bioremediation of contaminated sites by these fungi is a very active research area.

A surprising number of basidiomycetes, including the prized edible oyster mushrooms (*Pleurotus ostreatus*), can also trap and consume small animals such as rotifers and nematodes by secreting paralyzing toxins or gluey substances that immobilize the prey, in a manner similar to that shown earlier for ascomycetes (Figure 25.12). As is the case for insectivorous plants, such as the pitcher plants (*Sarracenia purpurea*) discussed in Chapters 19 and 31, this adaptation gives the fungus access to a rich source of molecular nitrogen, an essential nutrient that is often scarce in terrestrial habitats. For example, the wood that is the substrate for many basidiomycetes is high in carbon but low in nitrogen; many wood-decay fungi have been found to be carnivorous, obtaining supplemental nitrogen from various invertebrates.

Some basidiomycetes form mycorrhizae with the roots of forest trees, as discussed in Chapter 36 (Plant Nutrition). Recent research has shown that these mycorrhizae can be drawn into associations with achlorophyllous plants (plants that lack chlorophyll and so cannot carry out photosynthesis), which thus obtain nutrients from the trees via shared mycorrhizal fungi. Other basidiomycetes, the rusts and smuts, are parasites that cause serious diseases in wheat, rice, and other plants. Still others produce millions of dollars' worth of the common edible button mushroom (*Agaricus bisporus*) sold in grocery stores. *Amanita muscaria* (Figure 25.16d) has been used in the religious rituals of ancient societies in Central America, Russia, and India. Other species of this genus, including the death cap mushroom *Amanita phalloides*, produce deadly toxins. The *A. phalloides* toxin, called α-amanitin, halts gene transcription, and hence protein synthesis, by inhibiting the activity of RNA polymerase. Within 8–24 hours of ingesting as little as 5 mg of the mushroom, vomiting and diarrhea begin. Later, kidney and liver cells start to degenerate; without intensive medical care, death can follow within a few days. You can read more about the effect of amanitin on gene expression in Chapter 12.

Most basidiomycetes are mycelial, although some grow as yeasts. The mycelium of many basidiomycetes contains two different, separate nuclei as a result of fusion between two different haploid mycelia and is thus a dikaryon (**Figure 25.18**). A dikaryotic mycelium is formed following fusion of the two

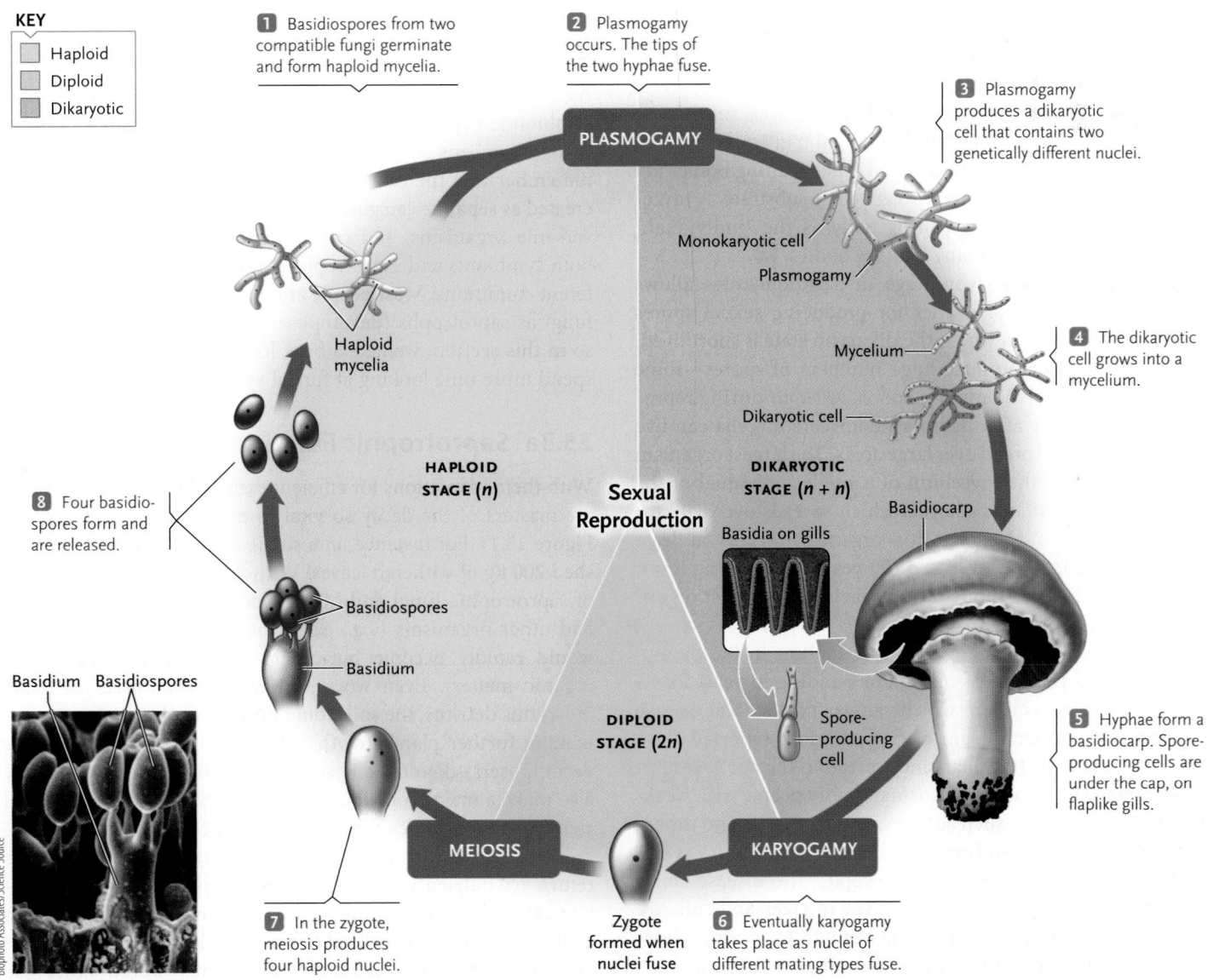

**FIGURE 25.18 Generalized life cycle of the basidiomycete *Agaricus bisporus*, a species known commonly as the *button mushroom*.** During the dikaryotic stage, cells contain two genetically different nuclei, shown here in different colours. Inset: Micrograph showing basidia and basidiospores

haploid mycelia when both types of nuclei divide and migrate through the mycelium such that each hyphal compartment contains two dissimilar nuclei.

Basidiomycete fungi can grow for most of their lives as dikaryon mycelia, a major departure from an ascomycete's short-lived dikaryotic stage. After an extensive mycelium develops, favourable environmental conditions trigger the formation of fruiting bodies (**basidiocarps**) in which basidia develop. A basidiocarp consists of tight clusters of hyphae; the feeding mycelium is buried in the substrate. The shelflike bracket fungi visible on trees are basidiocarps, as are the structures we call mushrooms and toadstools. Each mushroom is a short-lived reproductive body consisting of a stalk and a cap; basidia develop on "gills," the sheets of tissue on the underside of the cap. Inside each basidium, the two nuclei fuse; meiosis follows, resulting in the formation of four haploid **basidiospores** on the outside of the basidium (Figure 25.18). Why does the fungus expend energy and resources on such elaborate spore-dispersal structures? A layer of still air occurs just above the ground (and any other surface); by elevating the basidia above this layer, the fungus increases the likelihood that its spores will be carried away by the wind.

**CONCEPT FIX** People often assume when they see a mushroom sprouting from the ground that this fungal fruiting body is an individual. Not true! Mushrooms and other fruiting bodies are produced by mycelia growing through their substrate. A mycelium, not a mushroom or fruiting body, is the "individual." One mycelium produces many fruiting bodies. ⬡

The prolonged dikaryon stage in basidiomycetes allows them many more opportunities for producing sexual spores than in ascomycetes, in which the dikaryon state is short lived. Fruiting bodies can produce huge numbers of spores—some species can produce 100 million spores *per hour* during reproductive periods, day after day! Basidiomycete mycelia can live for many years and spread over large areas. The largest organism on Earth could be the mycelium of a single individual of the basidiomycete *Armillaria ostoyae*, which spreads over 8.9 km$^2$ of land in eastern Oregon. This organism weighs at least 150 tonnes and is likely at least 2400 years old, making it not only the largest but also one of the heaviest and oldest organisms on Earth.

As for ascomycetes, asexual reproduction in basidiomycetes involves formation of conidia or budding in yeast forms such as *Cryptococcus gattii*, which causes cryptococcal disease in humans. A virulent strain of *C. gattii*, first reported from Vancouver Island in 1999, has since spread to the northwestern United States and California. Normally, only people with weakened immune systems, such as transplant recipients and cancer patients, are at risk from fungal pathogens, but *C. gattii* is different, causing disease in healthy people. The disease starts when spores of the fungus, which lives in trees and soil, are inhaled. In the lungs, the spores germinate to produce yeast cells that proliferate by budding in the warm, moist lung environment; the yeast cells then spread to the central nervous system via the bloodstream. The disease is characterized by a severe cough, fever, and, if the nervous system is affected, seizures and other neurological symptoms.

## STUDY BREAK QUESTIONS

1. What evidence is there that fungi are more closely related to animals than to plants?
2. Name the five phyla of the kingdom Fungi, and describe the reproductive adaptations that distinguish them.
3. What are the two main differences between asexual spores produced by zygomycetes and asexual spores produced by ascomycetes?
4. Fungi reproduce sexually or asexually but, for many species, the life cycle includes an unusual stage not seen in other organisms. What is this genetic condition, and what is its role in the life cycle?

# 25.3 Fungal Lifestyles

As mentioned earlier, fungi can be categorized as saprotrophs or symbionts, depending on whether they obtain nutrients from living organisms or from dead organic matter. It is important to remember that the categories of *saprotroph* and *symbiont* were created as separate categories to classify fungi, but fungi are very versatile organisms, and many fungi are capable of acting as both symbionts and saprotrophs at different times or under different conditions. Most people are more familiar with the role of fungi as saprotrophs (decomposers) rather than as symbionts, so in this section, we take a brief look at saprotrophy and then spend more time looking at fungal symbioses.

## 25.3a Saprotrophic Fungi

With their adaptations for efficient extracellular digestion, fungi are masters of the decay so vital to terrestrial ecosystems (see Figure 25.1). For instance, in a single autumn, one elm tree can shed 200 kg of withered leaves! Without the metabolic activities of saprotrophic fungi and other decomposers such as bacteria and other organisms (e.g., earthworms), natural communities would rapidly become buried in their own **detritus** (dead organic matter). Even worse, without decomposers to break down this detritus, the soil would become depleted of nutrients, making further plant growth impossible. As fungi (and other decomposers) digest the dead tissues of other organisms, they also make a major contribution to the recycling of the chemical elements those tissues contain. For instance, over time, the degradation of organic compounds by saprotrophic fungi helps return key nutrients such as nitrogen and phosphorus to ecosystems. But the prime example of this recycling virtuosity involves carbon. The respiring cells of fungi and other decomposers give off carbon dioxide, liberating carbon that would otherwise remain locked in the tissues of dead organisms. Each year, this activity recycles a vast amount of carbon to plants, the primary producers of nearly all ecosystems on Earth.

However, there is a downside to the impressive enzymatic abilities of saprotrophic fungi; for example, when they decompose materials that are part of our houses, they can cause major economic and health problems. Fungi growing on wood and drywall following flooding or water damage to a building **(Figure 25.19a)** not only weaken the structural integrity of the building but also can be health hazards. The airborne spores of these fungi act as allergens, and some can also cause more serious health problems; for example, some fungi can colonize and grow in sinus cavities. Another example is dry rot, which causes millions of dollars in damage to buildings in Europe, Asia, and Australia (Figure 25.19b). Dry rot is notorious not only because it causes widespread and costly damage but also because the responsible fungus, *Serpula lacrymans*, seems to have the mysterious ability to break down dry wood completely, which should not be possible—as described above, wood decay usually happens once wood becomes wet. Does this fungus really have the amazing ability to break down dry wood? In fact, this fungus is as dependent on water for growth as any other, but it can form specialized mycelial cords, which very efficiently transport water and nutrients over long distances through concrete, bricks, and other unfavourable substrates until the fungus at last finds wood. Then the mycelial cords release water into the substrate, allowing the fungus to spread through the wood and begin the process of decay.

## 25.3b Symbiotic Fungi

Symbiotic associations range from mutualism, in which both partners benefit, to parasitism, in which one partner benefits at the expense of the other. Many fungal parasites are pathogens, parasites that cause disease symptoms in their hosts. We discussed several examples of fungal diseases in humans and other animals earlier in this chapter as well as very important, mutually beneficial symbioses, including mycorrhizae. Mycorrhizae are important for plant growth and will be featured in Chapter 36. In Chapter 30 general features of symbiotic associations are discussed more fully; here, we will explore examples of the symbioses fungi form with other organisms.

**LICHENS ARE ASSOCIATIONS BETWEEN A FUNGUS AND ONE OR MORE PHOTOSYNTHETIC ORGANISMS** Up until recently, it was thought that lichens were composed of two symbionts: a fungus (mycobiont), most commonly an ascomycete; and a unicellular green alga or blue-green bacteria (photobiont). A research group discovered that a third symbiont, a basidiomycete yeast, is also present in many lichens (see **Figure 25.20**).

Lichens grow as crusts on rocks, bark, or soil; as flattened leaflike forms; or as radially symmetrical cups, treelike structures, or hairlike strands **(Figure 25.21)**. This range of morphologies has intrigued scientists for years. Lichens have vital ecological roles and important human uses. They secrete acids that eat away at rock, breaking it down and converting it to soil that can support plants. Animals, such as caribou (*Rangifer tarandus*), rely on lichens for their winter forage. Some environmental chemists monitor air pollution by monitoring lichens, most of which cannot grow in heavily polluted air because they cannot discriminate between pollutants and mineral nutrients present in the atmosphere. Just as they do for mineral nutrients, lichens efficiently absorb airborne pollutants and concentrate them in their tissues. Humans use lichens as sources of dyes and perfumes, as well as medicines. Lichen chemicals are currently being explored as a source of natural pesticides.

How are lichens constructed? The primary fungus (called the **mycobiont**) makes up most of the body (**thallus**) of the lichen, with the photosynthetic partner (**photobiont**) usually confined to a thin layer inside the lichen thallus (Figure 25.21a). When present, the basidiomycete yeast cells are found in the cortex—the thick outer layer. To make matters more complicated, some lichens have two photobionts: a green algal photobiont inside the thallus and a cyanobacterial photobiont contained in "pockets" on or in the thallus. Because lichens are composite organisms, it may seem odd to talk of lichen

**a.**

**b.**

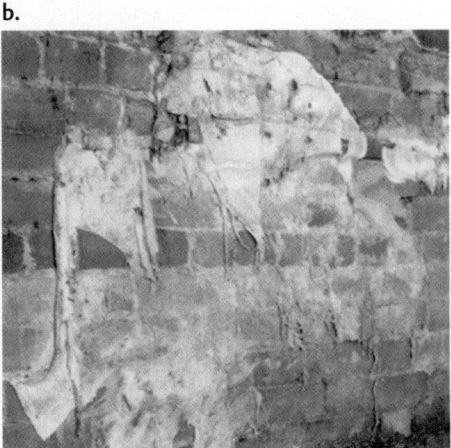

**FIGURE 25.19** **(a)** Mould growth following flooding. **(b)** Mycelium of dry rot (*Serpula lacrymans*) emerging through a wall

FIGURE 25.20 **Experimental Research**

## Hidden Third Partner in Lichen Symbiosis

**Question:** Why were two species of ascomycete lichens, while genetically identical, very different in appearance?

**Experiment:** *Bryoria tortuosa* **(a)** is yellow and produces an abundance of a nasty secondary compound, vulpinic acid, whereas *Bryoria fremontii* **(c)** is brown and produces the toxin in only small amounts. Initially, mRNA transcriptome analysis (Chapter 12) revealed no correlation between genotype and phenotype in the two lichens. Researchers broadened their analysis to include basidiomycete transcriptomes. Having discovered the presence of a basidiomycete yeast, they tested to see if there was a correlation between the presence of the yeast and the production of vulpinic acid.

**Results:** When the analysis included basidiomycete transcriptomes, researchers found a third partner in this symbiosis, a basidiomycete yeast (*Cyphobasidium*). The amount of vulpinic acid was correlated with the presence of the yeast; the yeast was more abundant in thalli with high concentrations of vulpinic acid **(b)** than in those with low concentrations **(d)**.

**Conclusions:** The discovery of an additional basidiomycete yeast symbiont was an unexpected outcome of this research, and has changed what we know about lichen symbiosis. The long-held assumption that the primary fungus (ascomycete) is responsible for the production of vulpinic acid has now been put into question. Is the yeast or the ascomycete responsible for its synthesis? To answer this question, the biosynthetic pathway of the compound will have to be elucidated.

Source: Toby Spribille, et al. 2016. Basidiomycete yeasts in the cortex of ascomycete macrolichens. *Science* (July: published online); DOI: 10.1126/science. aaf8287.

a. *B. tortuosa*   b.

c. *B. fremontii*   d.

**Differential abundance of Cyphobasidiales yeasts in B. *tortuosa* (b) and B. *fremontii* (d)**

From Toby Spribille, et al. "Basidiomycete yeasts in the cortex of ascomycete macrolichens," *Science* 29 Jul 2016: Vol. 353, Issue 6298, pp. 488–492. *Science* by American Association for the Advancement of Science Reproduced with permission of AMERICAN ASSOCIATION FOR THE ADVANCEMENT OF SCIENCE in the format Republish in a book via Copyright Clearance Center.

"species," but biologists do give lichens binomial names, which are based on the mycobiont. More than 13 500 different lichen species are recognized, each a unique combination of a particular species of fungus and one or more species of photobiont. As you might expect for a compound organism, reproduction can be complicated; it is not enough for each organism to reproduce itself, because formation of a new lichen requires that both partners be dispersed and end up together. Many lichens reproduce asexually by specialized fragments such as the **soredia** (singular, *soredium*; Figure 25.21b). Each soredium consists of photobiont cells wrapped in hyphae; the soredia can be dispersed by water, wind, or passing animals.

Inside the thallus, specialized hyphae of the mycobiont wrap around and sometimes penetrate photobiont cells, which become the fungus's sole source of carbon. Often the mycobiont absorbs up to 80% of the carbohydrates produced by the photobiont. Benefits for the photobiont are less clear-cut, in part because the drain on nutrients hampers its growth and because the mycobiont often controls reproduction of the photobiont. In one view, many and possibly most lichens are

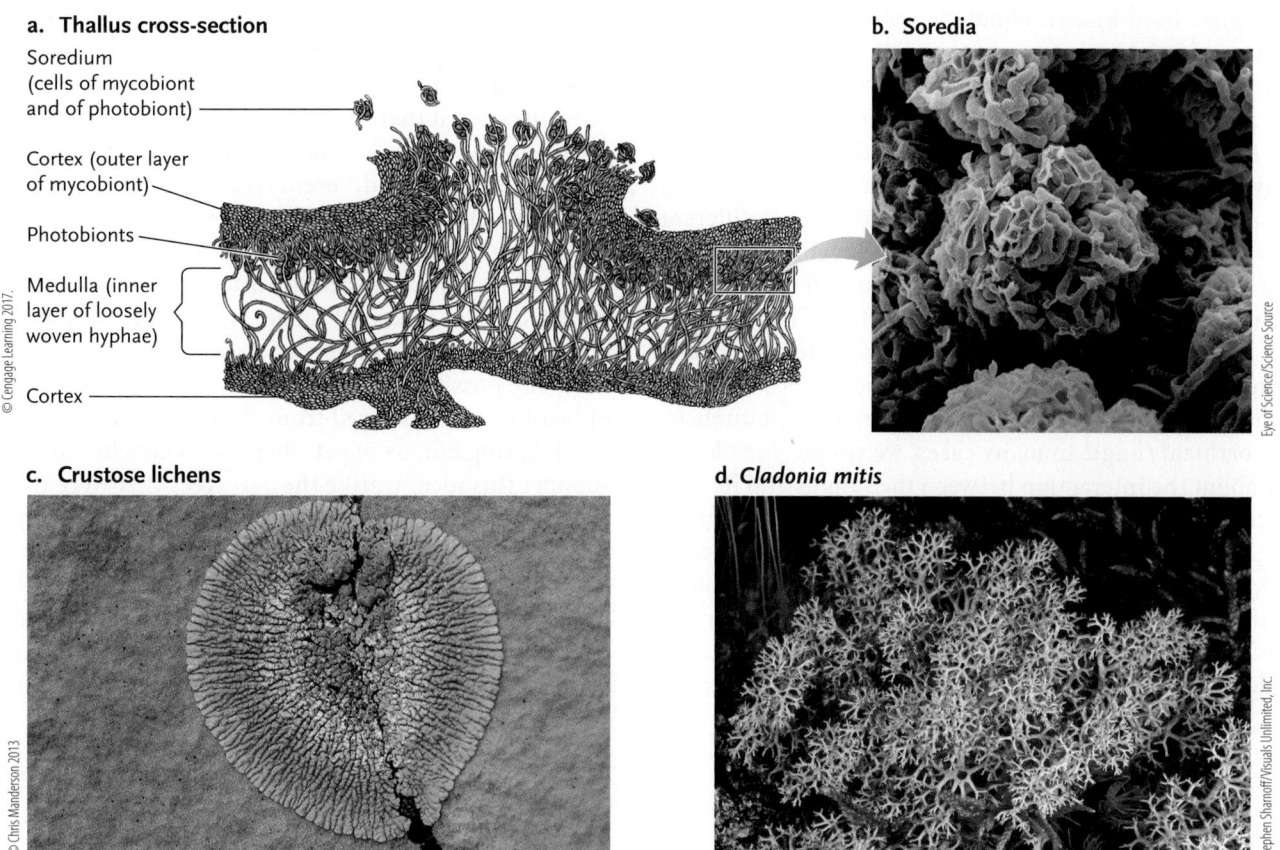

**a. Thallus cross-section**

Soredium (cells of mycobiont and of photobiont)

Cortex (outer layer of mycobiont)

Photobionts

Medulla (inner layer of loosely woven hyphae)

Cortex

**b. Soredia**

**c. Crustose lichens**

**d. *Cladonia mitis***

**FIGURE 25.21 Lichens. (a)** Diagram of a cross-section through the thallus of the foliose lichen *Lobaria verrucosa*. **(b)** Soredia, which contain both hyphae and algal cells, are a type of dispersal fragment by which lichens reproduce asexually. **(c)** Crustose lichens. **(d)** Cladonia mitis, a branching, treelike lichen

parasitic symbioses, with the fungus enslaving the photobiont. On the other hand, although it is relatively rare to find a lichen photobiont species living independently in the same conditions under which the lichen survives, it may eke out an enduring existence as part of a lichen; some lichens have been dated as being more than 4000 years old! Studies have also revealed that at least some green algae clearly benefit from the relationship. Such algae are sensitive to desiccation and intense ultraviolet radiation. Sheltered by the lichen's fungal tissues, a green alga can thrive in locales where alone it would perish.

Lichens often live in harsh, dry microenvironments, including on bare rock and wind-whipped tree trunks. Some lichens actually live *inside* rocks. Unlike plants, lichens do not control water loss from their tissues; instead, their water status reflects that of their environment, and some lichens may dry out and re-wet several times a day. Lichens are very slow growing, even though the photobiont may have photosynthetic rates comparable to those of free-living species. What happens to all the carbohydrates made in photosynthesis if they are not used to fuel growth? The mycobiont takes much of the carbohydrate made by the photobiont and uses it to synthesize sec-

ondary metabolites and other compounds that allow the lichen to survive the repeated wet–dry cycles and extreme temperatures common in their habitats. These compounds give lichens their vibrant colours and may also inhibit grazing on lichens by slugs and other invertebrates. The mycobiont uses other lichen chemicals to control the photobiont; some chemicals regulate photobiont reproduction, whereas others cause photobiont cells to "leak" carbohydrates to the mycobiont. The transfer of nutrients and interactions between the basidiomycete yeast and the other partners in this symbiosis are unclear. In the lichens where they have been identified, it is apparent that they contribute to chemical defences and pigmentation. We still have much to learn about the physiological interactions between lichen partners.

**ENDOPHYTES ARE FUNGI LIVING IN THE ABOVE-GROUND TISSUES OF PLANTS** Just as the roots of many plants are colonized by fungi, so too are leaves and shoots **(Figure 25.22)**. Although some of these fungi are pathogens, many others evidently peacefully coexist with their plant hosts and in some cases are beneficial.

Biologists have known about the presence of these leaf endophytes for some time, but recent discoveries have revealed a startling diversity of these fungi, sometimes within a single plant. Samples of plants from temperate regions have been revealed to have tens of different species of endophytes in a single plant, but tropical plants are truly impressive, with several reports of hundreds of different types of endophytes being isolated from a single plant. Most of these endophytes have not yet been identified to species as researchers have not yet observed sexual stages, so it is difficult to know how many species of endophytes are really living in these tropical plants. A bigger question is, what are these endophytes doing in these leaves? Are they mutualists, like mycorrhizal fungi? In many cases, we simply don't know enough about the interaction between the fungus and its host to answer these questions but, in some cases, the fungi do benefit their plant hosts by producing toxins that deter herbivores. Synthesis of toxins and other secondary metabolites has made these endophytes of great potential importance to humans. For example, the anticancer drug taxol (sold under the tradename Taxol) was originally isolated from the bark of the Pacific yew tree (*Taxus brevifolia*). Production of taxol from this source was limited since the tree is quite rare and makes only a small amount of taxol. However, researchers later discovered that a fungal endophyte living in the needles of the Pacific yew also makes taxol, as do other endophytes living in completely different tree species. Evidence indicates that taxol inhibits the growth of other fungi, so these endophytes may be producing it to protect themselves. Did the genes to produce taxol get transferred from the fungi to the plant? Such horizontal gene transfer is known to have occurred in the evolution of organelles such as mitochondria. The possibility that the genes necessary for biosynthesis of taxol were transferred from the endophyte to its host plant is intriguing but, as of yet, there is no conclusive evidence to support this idea. Unlike the yew trees that were the original source of taxol, these endophytic fungi can be grown very easily in the lab, so we may be able to produce large amounts of this promising anti-cancer drug, also very easily. What other sources of medicines are out there, hiding inside plants? The possibility of finding new antibiotics and medicinal compounds makes saving rainforests even more urgent, as

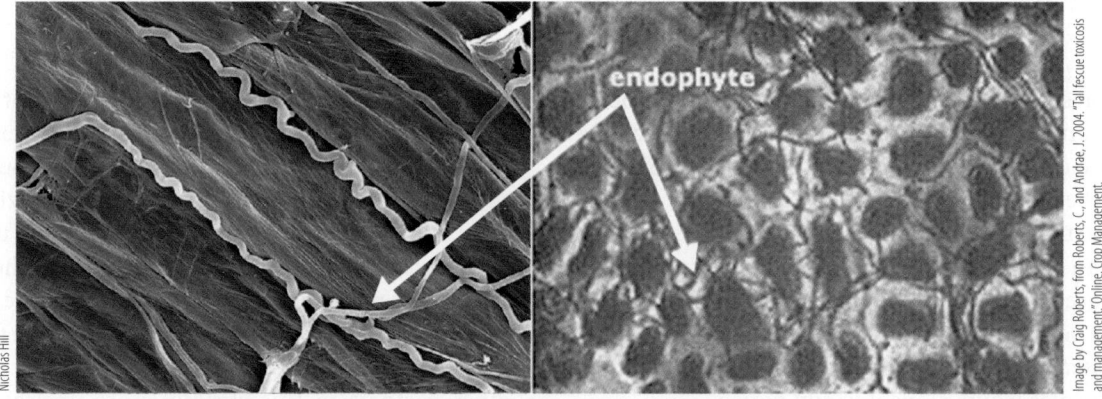

Nicholas Hill

Image by Craig Roberts, from Roberts, C. and Andrae, J. 2004. "Tall fescue toxicosis and management." Online. Crop Management.

**FIGURE 25.22 Endophytes growing inside stem (left) and seed (right)**

FIGURE 25.23 **Rust fungus on a leaf**

not only the trees are disappearing but the endophytes inside them as well.

**RUSTS AND CROPS** Wheat, barley, oats, and rye are main crops on the Canadian prairies and are susceptible to a number of pathogens, including rust fungus. This fungus gets its name from the small spore producing lesions that are often reddish **(Figure 25.23)**. Rusts are basidiomycetes that often require two hosts to complete their life cycle and have five spore stages. For example, wheat rust (*Puccinia graminis*) lives within the shoot tissues of grasses such as wheat. It produces spores (Figure 25.23) to infect more wheat. As summer comes to an end, sexual spores are produced that end up overwintering in the dead shoots. These are the basidiospores and they can infect only the alternate host, barberry. The basidiospores germinate and hyphae grow through the barberry's leaf tissues, absorbing nutrients. Cup-shaped spore-producing structures are produced on the upper surface and are carried in a sticky exudate by insects (or rain water) to other leaves of the same plants or nearby barberry plants. This is the stage at which plasmogamy occurs. The spores act as gametes and are delivered to special receptive hyphae that project from these spore-producing structures. The spores and the receptive hyphae must be of different mating types for plasmogamy to occur. Like other basidiomycetes, the resulting dikaryotic mycelium will grow through the leaf (absorbing nutrients) and produce spore-producing structures on the lower side of the barberry leaf. These spores are wind dispersed and must land on wheat (or other grass) to germinate. Understanding this complicated life cycle was important, as huge crop losses were suffered due to wheat rust. In the early 1900s there was a major barberry eradication program that was very successful. By 1917 the growth of this plant was prohibited. Barberry is still on the Prohibited Plant List of Canada, but you can find rust-resistant varieties of barberry wheat in nurseries. Introduction of barberry is regulated through the Canadian Food Inspection Agency (CFIA). Many rust-resistant varieties of wheat have also been developed, but resistance by the rust is a continuing battle. Plant breeders must keep one step ahead of these constantly evolving fungi. Rust negatively impacts the health of wheat because it lowers yields by absorbing valuable nutrients needed in fruit development, reducing the photosynthetic tissue of the plants due to fungal growth, as well increasing water loss due to impairment of the epidermis.

Even though fungi are not closely related to plants in an evolutionary sense, you can see that relationships between fungi and plants play important roles in the lives of both types of organisms. Many saprotrophic and parasitic fungi depend on plants or their products as a source of carbon. Plants rely on fungi for nutrients, either directly through mycorrhizal relationships or indirectly through the role of fungi as decomposers. The very first land plants likely relied on mycorrhizal associations to survive in the harsh new environments they faced. In the next chapter, we look at how land plants evolved and diversified.

## STUDY BREAK QUESTIONS

1. Describe the difference between a saprotroph and a symbiont. Discuss two examples of each type of life style.
2. What is a lichen? Explain how the partners contribute to the whole organism.
3. What is an endophyte? Why is its relationship with its plant hosts of interest to medical researchers?

# Summary Illustration

Fungi occur as single-celled yeasts or multicellular filamentous organisms. They gain nutrition by extracellular digestion and absorption. Saprotrophic species feed on non-living organic matter, while others are symbionts.

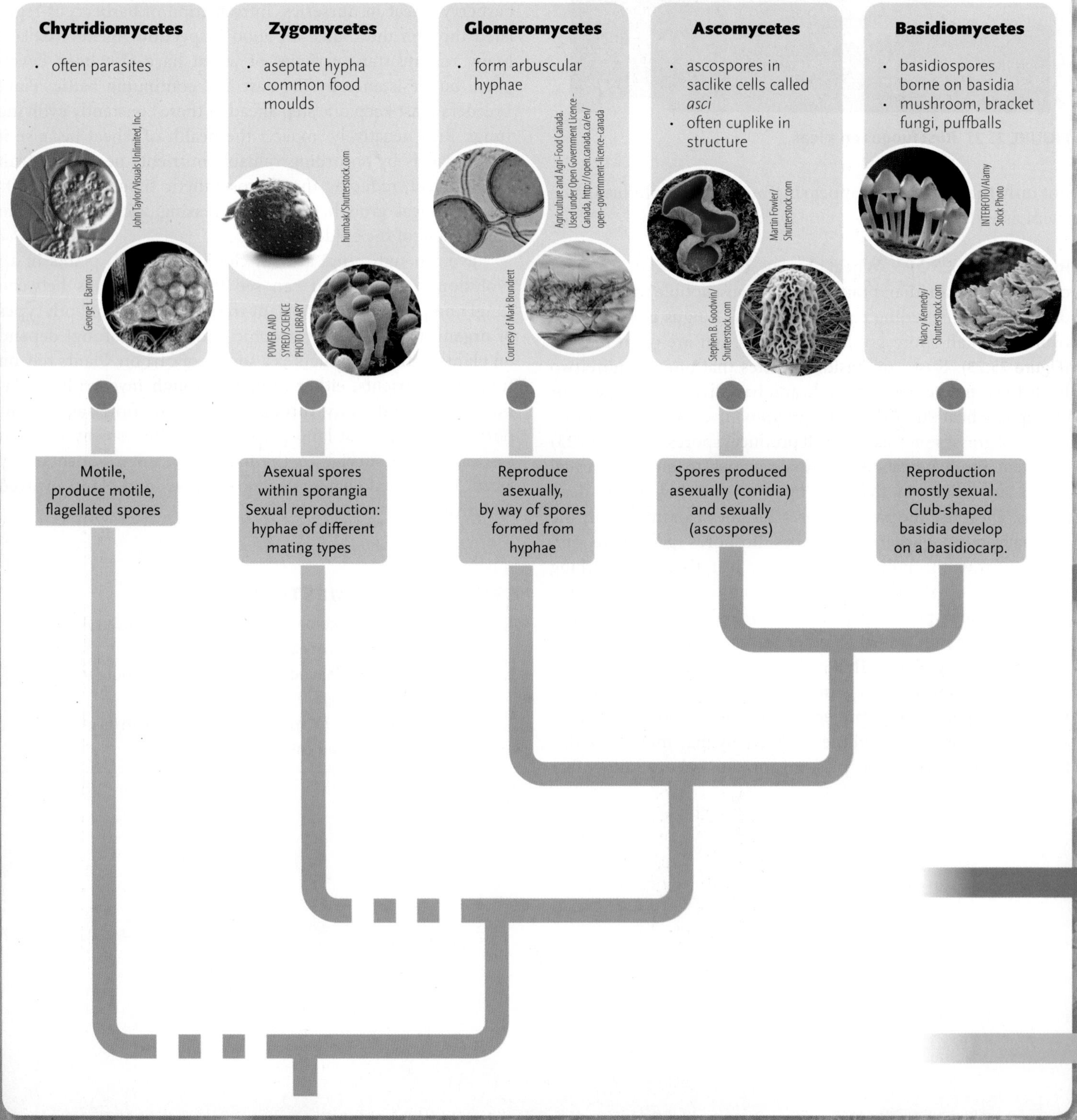

### Chytridiomycetes

- often parasites

### Zygomycetes

- aseptate hypha
- common food moulds

### Glomeromycetes

- form arbuscular hyphae

### Ascomycetes

- ascospores in saclike cells called *asci*
- often cuplike in structure

### Basidiomycetes

- basidiospores borne on basidia
- mushroom, bracket fungi, puffballs

**Chytridiomycetes:** Motile, produce motile, flagellated spores

**Zygomycetes:** Asexual spores within sporangia. Sexual reproduction: hyphae of different mating types

**Glomeromycetes:** Reproduce asexually, by way of spores formed from hyphae

**Ascomycetes:** Spores produced asexually (conidia) and sexually (ascospores)

**Basidiomycetes:** Reproduction mostly sexual. Club-shaped basidia develop on a basidiocarp.

John Taylor/Visuals Unlimited, Inc.

George L. Barron

humbak/Shutterstock.com

POWER AND SYRED/SCIENCE PHOTO LIBRARY

Agriculture and Agri-Food Canada. Used under Open Government Licence–Canada. http://open.canada.ca/en/open-government-licence-canada

Courtesy of Mark Brundrett

Martin Fowler/Shutterstock.com

Stephen B. Goodwin/Shutterstock.com

INTERFOTO/Alamy Stock Photo

Nancy Kennedy/Shutterstock.com

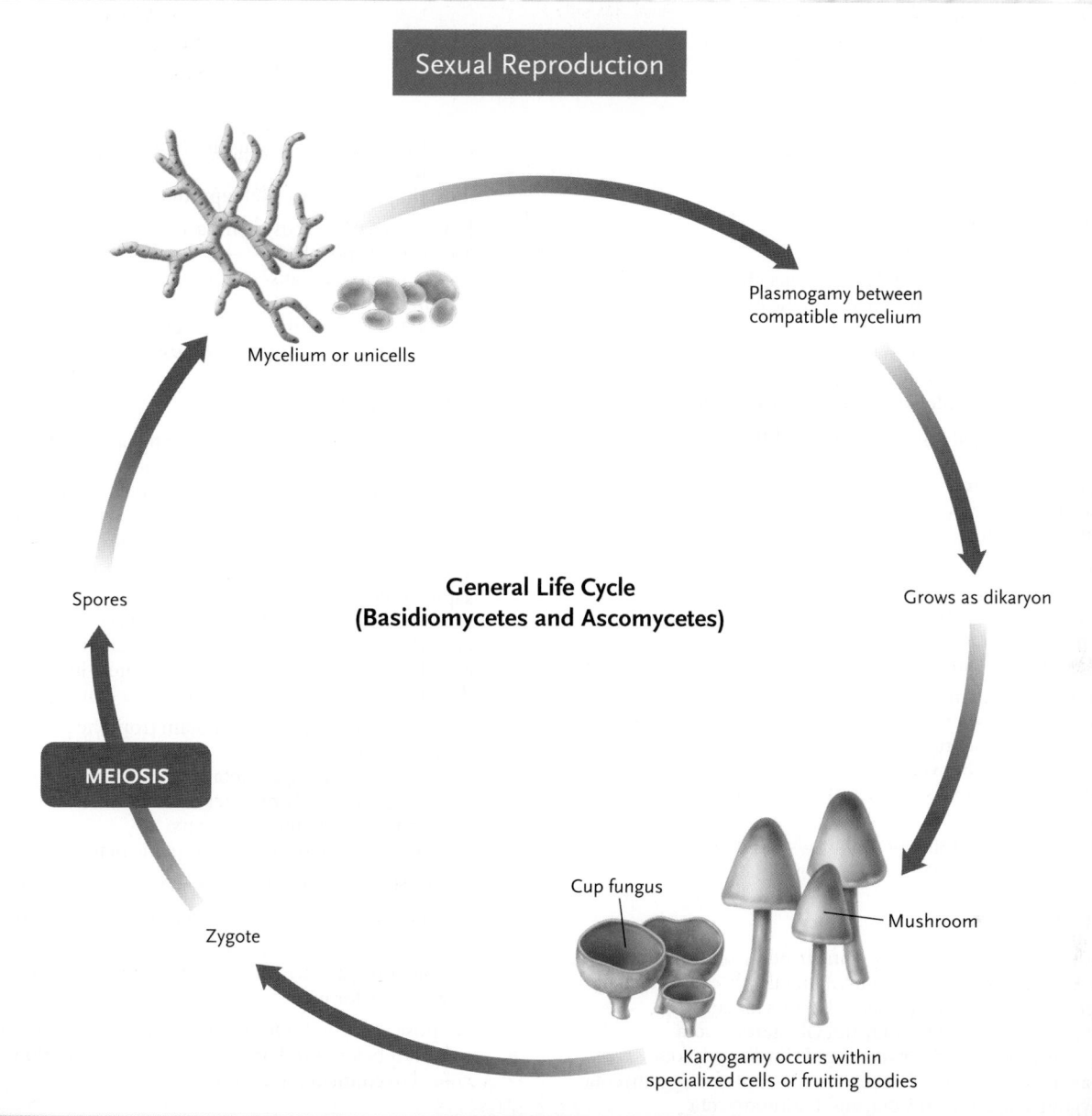

## Sexual Reproduction

### General Life Cycle
### (Basidiomycetes and Ascomycetes)

Mycelium or unicells

Plasmogamy between compatible mycelium

Grows as dikaryon

Mushroom

Cup fungus

Karyogamy occurs within specialized cells or fruiting bodies

Zygote

MEIOSIS

Spores

**Asexual Reproduction** is accomplished through the production of asexual spores, budding, and fragmentation.

**Saprotrophic species** feed on non-living organic matter and are key decomposers contributing to the recycling of carbon and other nutrients in ecosystems.

Many fungi are **symbionts**, obtaining nutrients from organic matter of living hosts. These symbioses range from parasitism, in which the fungus benefits at the expense of its host, to mutualism, in which both the fungus and its host benefit (e.g., mycorrhizae).

## Recall/Understand

1. Which of these traits is common to all fungi?
   a. parasitism
   b. septate hyphae
   c. reproduction via spores
   d. a prolonged dikaryotic phase

2. Which one of the following is/are the chief characteristic(s) traditionally used to classify fungi into the major fungal phyla?
   a. cell wall features
   b. sexual reproductive structures
   c. adaptations for obtaining water
   d. nutritional dependence on non-living organic matter

3. Which of these fungal reproductive structures is diploid?
   a. ascospore
   b. zygosporangium
   c. basidiocarp
   d. gametangium

4. Which of these features characterizes a zygomycete?
   a. septate hyphae
   b. + and − mating strains
   c. mostly sexual reproduction
   d. a life cycle in which karyogamy does not occur

5. Which of these statements *best* describes a lichen?
   a. an association between a green alga or a cyanobacterium, and one or more fungi
   b. an association between a basidiomycete and an ascomycete
   c. a fungus that breaks down rock to provide nutrients for an alga
   d. an organism that spends half its life cycle as a photosymbiont and the other half as a mycobiont

## Apply/Analyze

6. At lunch, you eat a mushroom, some truffles, a little Camembert cheese, and, accidentally also a bit of mouldy bread. Which of these groups of fungi is represented in this meal?
   a. Zygomycota, Ascomycota, and Glomeromycota
   b. Ascomycota, Basidiomycota, and Glomeromycota
   c. Basidiomycota, and Glomeromycota, but not Zygomycota
   d. Zygomycota, Ascomycota, and Basidiomycota

7. Which of these statements is the reason that some fungi were placed in Deuteromycota, or Fungi Imperfecti, rather than in a phylum?
   a. They form flagellated spores.
   b. They grow as single cells, rather than as hyphae.
   c. The reproductive stage in their life cycle is unknown or absent.
   d. They lack an asexual reproductive stage in their life cycle.

8. In which of these ecosystems are mycorrhizal associations crucial for survival and why?
   a. in deserts, because the soils lack sugar
   b. in deserts, because of the drought
   c. in tropical rainforests, because soils are too damp
   d. in tropical rainforests, because soils are poor in mineral ions

## Create/Evaluate

9. Which of these descriptions is the most accurate of a mushroom?
   a. a collection of saclike cells called *asci*
   b. the nutrient-absorbing region of an ascomycete
   c. the nutrient-absorbing region of a basidiomycete
   d. a reproductive structure formed only by basidiomycetes

10. Which form of nutrient acquisition classifies a fungus as a saprotroph?
    a. The fungus has external digestion.
    b. The fungus forms extensive mycelia in the soil.
    c. The fungus obtains carbon from non-living organisms.
    d. The fungus obtains carbon from a living organism.

11. What do mycorrhizal fungi obtain from the plants with which they associate?
    a. increased nitrogen uptake
    b. a regular supply of water
    c. carbon in the form of sugars
    d. the ability to decompose organic material

12. Contrast life cycles of humans with the general life cycle of fungi.

13. Compare and contrast arbuscular mycorrhizae with ectomycorrhizae.

14. Consider ways in which fungi affect humans, and evaluate their importance for us.

15. Suppose that you found a new organism and you want to determine if it belongs to Fungi. What evidence would you need to collect to confirm it is a fungus?

# Chapter Roadmap

## Plants
The advent of land plants made it possible for animals to diversify onto land.

From Chapter 6

### 26.1 Defining Characteristics of Land Plants
Land plants are multicellular eukaryotes with cellulose cell walls. Most, but not all, are photoautotrophs. All have an alternation of generations life cycle.

From Chapter 23

From Chapter 24

### 26.2 The Transition to Life on Land
Plants are thought to have evolved from charophyte green algae between 490 and 425 mya. Adaptations to terrestrial life in the earliest land plants include a poikilohydry, multicellular envelope that protects developing gametes, and an embryo sheltered inside a parent plant.

To Chapter 33

To Chapter 34

To Chapter 36

Ed Reschke

### 26.3 Bryophytes: Nonvascular Land Plants
Bryophytes differ from all other land plants by having no xylem or phloem tissues, as well as having a dominant gametophyte stage.

Dave Powell, USDA Forest Service, Bugwood.org

From Chapter 25

### 26.4 Seedless Vascular Plants
Seedless vascular land plants include the lycophytes (club mosses), whisk ferns, horsetails, and ferns. Like the bryophytes, they rely on water for fertilization.

Michael P. Gadomski/Science Source

### 26.5 Gymnosperms: The First Seed Plants
During the Mesozoic, gymnosperms were the dominant land plants. Today, conifers are the primary vegetation of forests at higher latitudes and elevations, and have important economic uses as sources of lumber and other products.

To Chapter 33

To Chapter 34

To Chapter 35

To Chapter 36

To Chapter 37

### 26.6 Angiosperms: Flowering Plants
Angiosperms (Anthophyta) have dominated the land for more than 100 million years and are currently the most diverse plant group.

*Monotropa uniflora*, a heterotrophic plant that lacks chlorophyll

# Plants

# 26

**Why it matters . . .** You are out for a walk in Cathedral Grove on Vancouver Island, British Columbia; you are busy thinking about other things and so are not paying close attention to the plants that you're walking by—they are just a pleasing green background. Suddenly, a small white plant, like the one shown in the photo above, catches your eye. At least you think it's a plant. But aren't all plants green? How can there be a completely white plant?

What you have found is a plant known as *ghost flower* or *Indian pipe* (*Monotropa uniflora*), which does not produce chlorophyll and so cannot photosynthesize.

**CONCEPT FIX** We often assume that all plants are photoautotrophs, making their own organic carbon molecules from atmospheric $CO_2$ and sunlight. But some plants, such as *Monotropa*, are completely heterotrophic, living on organic carbon obtained from other plants. And other plants that do have chlorophyll supplement their carbon supply by being heterotrophic in low light levels or under other conditions that limit photosynthesis. How do heterotrophic plants get carbon? Some directly parasitize green plants, but others, like *Monotropa*, feed on neighbouring photosynthetic plants through shared root-colonizing fungi (mycorrhizal fungi; see Chapter 25). So, contrary to popular belief, not all plants are photosynthetic and green. ⬡

So, if being green isn't a unifying feature of all plants, what is? What features could you look for to determine whether this *Monotropa* is a plant? What characteristics set plants apart from other organisms? And how did plants evolve? In this chapter, we investigate these questions and look at the adaptations to terrestrial life that have made plants so successful. Their success is attributed in part to their ability to thrive in habitats where animals can't survive for long, and some plants are able to grow much larger and live much longer than any animal. Together with photosynthetic bacteria and protists, plant tissues provide the nutritional foundation for nearly all ecosystems on Earth. Humans also use plants as sources of medicinal drugs, wood for building, fibres for paper and clothing, and a wealth of other products. The partnership between humans and plants has a long evolutionary history: we first domesticated cereal plants 9000 years ago, but this was not the earliest relationship between humans and plants. Our early ancestors, like modern-day primates, would have relied heavily on plants in their diet.

Despite the long history between plants and humans, there is still much about plant biology that we don't understand and many questions that remain to be answered.

We start this chapter by considering the defining characteristics of plants and then look at the evolution of plants and their adaptations to life on land. We conclude by looking at the diversity of land plants.

## 26.1 Defining Characteristics of Land Plants

Land plants are eukaryotes. As we learned from the *Monotropa* example, not all are capable of photosynthesizing, but almost all plants are photoautotrophs (organisms that use light as their energy source and carbon dioxide as their carbon source; see Chapter 6). Like animals, all land plants are multicellular, but if you took a piece of tissue from *Monotropa* and looked at it under the microscope, you'd see that, unlike animal cells, plant cells have walls, which are made of cellulose. All plants are sessile, or stationary (not able to move around); no terrestrial animals are sessile, although some aquatic ones are. Plants also differ from animals in having an **alternation of generations** life cycle.

In most animals, the diploid stage dominates the life cycle and produces gametes (sperm or eggs) by meiosis. Gametes are the only haploid stage, and it is short-lived: fusion of gametes produces a new diploid organism. (Some animals, for example, social insects such as bees and wasps, have a different life cycle.) In other organisms, such as many green algae, the haploid stage dominates the life cycle; the haploid alga spends much of its life producing and releasing gametes into the surrounding water. The single-celled zygote is the only diploid stage, and it divides by meiosis to produce spores that give rise to the haploid stage again.

In contrast, land plants have two multicellular stages (generations) in their life cycles: one diploid and one haploid

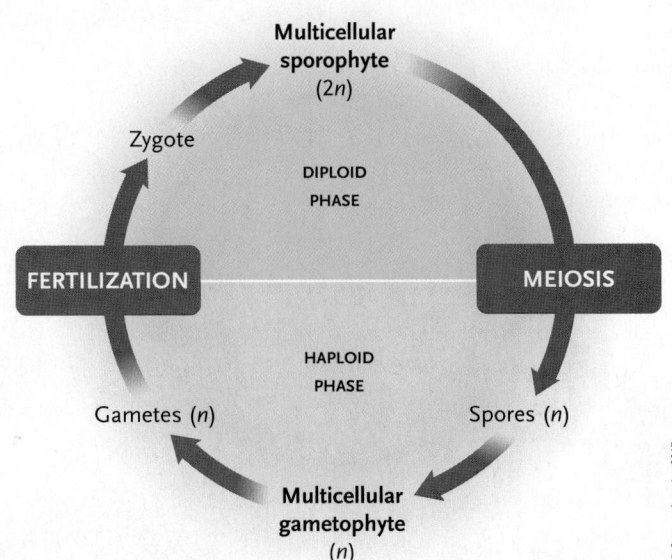

**FIGURE 26.1 Overview of the alternation of generations, the basic pattern of the plant life cycle.** The relative dominance of haploid and diploid phases is different for different plant groups.

**(Figure 26.1).** The diploid generation produces spores and is called a **sporophyte** (*phyte* = plant, hence, "spore-producing plant"). The haploid generation produces gametes by mitosis and is called a **gametophyte** ("gamete-producing plant"). The haploid phase of the plant life cycle begins within specialized structures on the sporophyte called *sporangia* (singular, *sporangium*). Within each sporangium (*angium* = vessel or chamber, hence, "spore-producing chambers"), haploid spores with thick cell walls are produced by meiosis. So, in plants, meiosis produces spores, not gametes. When a spore germinates, it divides by mitosis to produce a multicellular haploid gametophyte. The gametophyte produces structures called *gametangia*, which produce eggs and sperm. It also nourishes and protects the forthcoming sporophyte generation. Each generation gives rise to the other: hence the name *alternation of generations* for this life cycle.

The final defining feature of land plants is that the embryo (new sporophyte generation) is retained inside gametophyte tissue. The reasons for retention of embryos in parental tissue and for the rather complex life cycle will become clearer after we've looked at the evolution of plants and their transition onto land.

### STUDY BREAK QUESTIONS

1. What features of land plants differentiate them from other eukaryotes, for example, from fungi? From animals?
2. What is an alternation of generations life cycle? How does this differ from the life cycle of most animals?
3. What does meiosis produce in plants?
4. Differentiate between a gametophyte and a sporophyte in terms of ploidy and what is produced.

## 26.2 The Transition to Life on Land

Along the shores of the ancient ocean, the only sound was the rhythmic muffled crash of waves breaking in the distance. There were no birds or other animals, no plants with leaves rustling in the breeze. In the preceding eons, cells that produce oxygen as a by-product of photosynthesis had evolved, radically changing Earth's atmosphere. Solar radiation had converted much of the oxygen into a dense ozone layer—a shield against lethal doses of ultraviolet radiation—that had kept early organisms below the water's surface. Now was the time to explore the land.

Cyanobacteria were probably the first to adapt to intertidal zones and then to spread into shallow, coastal streams. Later, green algae and fungi made the same journey. Around 480 million years ago (mya), one group of green algae living near the water's edge, or perhaps in a moist terrestrial environment, became the ancestors of modern plants. Several lines of evidence indicate that these algae were charophytes (a group discussed in Chapter 24): both charophytes and modern land plants have cellulose cell walls, they store energy captured during photosynthesis as starch, and their light-absorbing pigments include both chlorophyll *a* and chlorophyll *b*. Molecular genetic data also support the relationship between charophytes and land plants. Like other green algae, the charophyte lineage that produced the ancestor of land plants arose in water and has aquatic descendants today **(Figure 26.2)**. Yet, because terrestrial environments pose very different challenges than aquatic environments, evolution in land plants produced a range of adaptations crucial to survival on dry land.

The algal ancestors of plants probably invaded land about 450 mya. We say "probably" because the fossil record is inconclusive in pinpointing when the first truly terrestrial plants appeared, and many important stages in evolution are not represented in the fossil record. Even in more recent deposits, the most commonly found plant fossils are just microscopic bits and pieces; easily identifiable parts such as leaves, stems, roots, and reproductive parts seldom occur together. Whole fossilized plants are extremely rare. Adding to the challenge, some chemical and structural adaptations to life on land arose independently in several plant lineages. Despite these problems, botanists have been able to gain insight into several innovations and overall trends in plant evolution.

While the ancestors of land plants were making the transition to a fully terrestrial life, some remarkable adaptive changes unfolded. For example, the earliest land plants were exposed to higher levels of harmful UV radiation than their aquatic ancestors had experienced. Gradual changes in existing metabolic pathways resulted in the ability to synthesize simple phenylpropanoids—molecules that absorb UV radiation—which enhanced the plants' ability to live on land. Where did these new metabolic pathways and associated enzyme functions come from? They did not simply appear because the plants needed them.

**CONCEPT FIX** The idea that evolution involves organisms "trying" to adapt, or that natural selection gives organisms what they need to survive, is one of the major misconceptions about evolution. Natural selection cannot sense what a species "needs," and organisms cannot try to adapt: if some individual organisms in the population have traits that allow them to survive and reproduce more in that environment than other individuals, then they will pass on these traits to more offspring, and the frequency of the traits in the population will increase. But the organism cannot "try" to get the right genes. Research shows that new enzyme functions usually follow duplication of genes, which can occur in various ways (e.g., an error during crossing-over of meiosis). Mutations in the second copy of a gene will not have negative effects on the host because the other copy retains its original function; thus, over time the second copy tends to accumulate mutations. If the changes in this gene provide advantages to the host plant, then that gene is selected for. In this way, new enzyme functions and metabolic pathways evolve. ⬡

Eons of natural selection sorted out solutions to fundamental problems, among them, avoiding desiccation, physically supporting the plant body in air, obtaining certain nutrients from soil, and reproducing sexually in environments where water would not be available for dispersal of eggs and sperm. With time, plants evolved features that not only addressed these problems but also provided access to a wide range of terrestrial environments. Those ecological opportunities opened the way for a dramatic radiation (rapid evolution and divergence; see Chapter 19) of varied plant species, and for the survival of plant-dependent animal life. Today the **kingdom Plantae** encompasses more than 300 000 living species, organized in this textbook into 10 phyla. These modern plants range from mosses, horsetails, and ferns to conifers and flowering plants **(Figure 26.3)**.

**FIGURE 26.2 *Chara*, a stonewort.** This representative of the charophyte lineage is known commonly as a stonewort due to the calcium carbonate that accumulates on its surface.

BOB GIBBONS/SCIENCE PHOTO LIBRARY

**a. Mosses growing on rocks**

**b. A jack pine**

**c. An orchid**

**FIGURE 26.3 Representatives of the kingdom Plantae. (a)** Mosses growing on rocks. Mosses evolved relatively soon after plants made the transition to land. **(b)** A jack pine (*Pinus banksiana*). This species and other conifers belonging to the phylum Coniferophyta represent the gymnosperms. **(c)** An orchid, *Calypso bulbosa*, is a showy example of a flowering plant.

**a. Cuticle on the surface of a leaf**

Cuticle    Epidermal cell

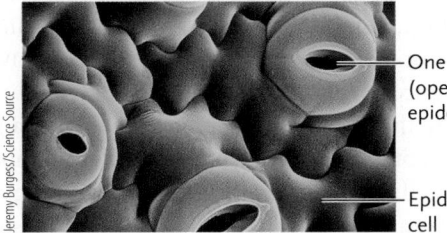

**b. Stomata**

One stoma (opening in epidermis)

Epidermal cell

**FIGURE 26.4 Adaptations for limiting water loss. (a)** A waxy cuticle covers the epidermis of land plants and helps reduce water loss. **(b)** Surface view of stomata in the epidermis (surface layer of cells) of a leaf. Stomata allow carbon dioxide to enter plant tissues and oxygen and water to leave.

## 26.2a Early Biochemical and Structural Adaptations Enhanced Plant Survival on Land

The greatest challenge plants had to overcome to thrive on land was how to survive in the dry terrestrial conditions. Unlike most modern-day plants, the earliest land plants had neither a waterproof **cuticle** (an outer waxy layer that prevents water loss from plant tissues) nor tissues with sufficient mechanical strength to allow for upright growth. These limitations restricted these early plants to moist habitats and made it necessary for them to stay small and grow close to the ground. Like modern-day mosses, these plants were **poikilohydric** (*poikilo* = variable; *hydric* = relating to water). Poikilohydric plants have little control over their internal water content and do not restrict water loss. Instead, their water content fluctuates with moisture levels in their environment: as their habitat dries out, so do their tissues, and their metabolic activities virtually cease. When external moisture levels rise, they quickly rehydrate and become metabolically active. In other words, poikilohydric plants are drought tolerators that can survive drying out; vascular plants, which regulate their internal water content and restrict water loss, are drought avoiders, with numerous adaptations to prevent drying out or with plant parts (e.g., underground stems) that can survive if the rest of the plant dries out.

Later-evolving plants were able to regulate water content and restrict water loss because they had cuticles covering their outer surfaces (**Figure 26.4a**), as well as **stomata** (singular, *stoma*; *stoma* = mouth) pores in the cuticle-covered surfaces (Figure 26.4b) that open and close to regulate water loss (and are the main route for carbon dioxide to enter leaves; see Chapter 34). These plants also had water-transport tissues that also provided support for upright growth, described further in Section 26.2c.

## 26.2b Symbiotic Associations with Fungi Were Likely Required for Evolution of Land Plants

The ancestor of land plants was not the first organism to colonize terrestrial habitats; certain bacteria, protists, and fungi had been present at least since the late Proterozoic (around 540 mya). Almost all modern-day plants form symbiotic associations, known as *mycorrhizae*, with certain soil fungi (see Chapter 25). In these associations, the fungus colonizes the plant's roots and grows prolifically in the soil beyond the root system, producing a very large network that takes up soil nutrients. (See Chapter 37.) Both partners generally benefit by a two-way exchange of nutrients: the plant provides the fungus with carbon, and the fungus increases the plant's supply of soil nutrients, which it is able to obtain much more efficiently than the plant's own roots. Such mutually beneficial relationships may have been essential to the evolution of land plants and to their success in terrestrial habitats, given that the first land plants lacked roots and that the soils of early Earth were nutrient poor.

## 26.2c Lignified Water-Conducting Cells Provided Strength and Support for Plants to Grow Upright

The earliest land plants remained small because they lacked the mechanical support necessary to grow taller. Growing low to the ground helped them stay moist but was not very effective in capturing light: since all early land plants were low growing, there would have been intense competition for light. If any plant had been able to grow taller than its neighbours, it would have had a major advantage. But how could a plant support upright growth against the force of gravity? Plants require strengthening tissue to grow upright. And, since diffusion is not effective over longer distances, growing up and away from the ground surface also requires an internal water circulation system. Some of the early land plants did have specialized water-conducting cells that transported water through the plant body, but these cells did not provide mechanical strength. Later land plants synthesized lignin, a polymer of phenylpropanoids (the molecules mentioned earlier that absorb UV radiation). Lignin was deposited in cell walls, particularly in the water-conducting cells, providing support and rigidity to those tissues and allowing the plants to grow upright. These lignified water-conducting cells make up a tissue called *xylem*.

Xylem is one type of **vascular tissue** (*vas* = duct or vessel). Plants with this tissue (and the other type of vascular tissue, **phloem**, which conducts sugars through the plant body) are known as **vascular plants**. It is important to note that some plants, such as some mosses, that lack vascular tissues do have tissues that conduct water and sugars through their bodies. These tissues are not the same as xylem and phloem (e.g., their water-conducting cells do not have walls reinforced with lignin) and are likely not homologous with xylem and phloem, so they are not called vascular tissues. Thus, these plants are referred to as **nonvascular plants**. Chapter 34 explains how xylem and phloem perform these key internal transport functions.

Clearly, plants with lignified tissues had a benefit over plants lacking lignin and, over time, they evolved to become the dominant plants in most habitats on Earth. Ferns, conifers, and flowering plants—most of the plants you are familiar with—are vascular plants. Supported by lignin and with a well-developed vascular system, the body of a plant can grow very large. Extreme examples are the giant redwood trees of the northern California coast, some of which are more than 90 m tall. By contrast, nonvascular plants lack lignin, although some do have simple internal transport systems and are generally small **(Table 26.1)**.

Vascular plants also have **apical meristems**, regions of constantly dividing cells near the tips of shoots and roots that produce all tissues of the plant body. Meristem tissue is the foundation for a vascular plant's extensively branching stem and root systems and is a central topic of Chapter 33.

## 26.2d Root and Shoot Systems Were Adaptations for Nutrition and Support

The body of a nonvascular plant is not differentiated into true roots and stems, structures that are fundamental adaptations for absorbing nutrients from soil and for support of an erect

| TABLE 26.1 | Trends in Plant Evolution Traits Derived from Algal Ancestor: Cell Walls with Cellulose, Energy Stored in Starch, Chlorophylls *a* and *b* (main photosynthetic pigments). | | | | |
|---|---|---|---|---|---|
| Bryophytes | Ferns and Their Relatives | Gymnosperms | Angiosperms | | Functions of This Trait in Land Plants |
| Cuticle | → | | | → | Protection against water loss and pathogens |
| Stomata | → | | | → | Regulation of water loss and gas exchange ($CO_2$ in; $O_2$ out) |
| Nonvascular (although some have specialized water-conducting cells without lignin) | → Vascular (have xylem and phloem) | → | | → | Internal tubes that transport water and nutrients |
| | Lignin | → | | → | Mechanical support for vertical growth |
| | Apical meristem | → | | → | Branching shoot system |
| | Roots, stems, leaves | → | | → | Enhanced uptake, transport of nutrients, and enhanced photosynthesis |
| Haploid phase dominant | → Diploid phase dominant | → | | → | Genetic diversity |
| One spore type (homospory) | → Homospory in most but heterospory (two spore types) in some | → Heterospory | | → | Promotion of genetic diversity |
| Motile sperm | → | Nonmotile sperm | → | | Protection of gametes within parent body |
| Seedless | → | Seeds | → | | Protection of embryo |

plant body. The evolution of sturdy stems, the basis of an aerial *shoot system,* went hand in hand with the capacity to synthesize lignin. To become large, land plants also require a means of anchoring aerial parts in the soil, as well as effective strategies for obtaining soil nutrients. **Roots**, anchoring structures that also absorb water and nutrients in association with mycorrhizal fungi, were the eventual solution to these problems. The earliest fossils showing clear evidence of roots are from vascular plants, although the exact timing of this change is uncertain. Ultimately, vascular plants developed specialized **root systems**, which generally consist of underground, cylindrical, absorptive structures with a large surface area that favours the rapid uptake of soil, water, and dissolved mineral ions. The root system has been called "the hidden half" of a plant: "half" refers to the fact that there is as much plant biomass below ground as there is above ground. And there are other similarities between above- and below-ground parts of plants: the fine roots of a root system go through regular cycles of growth and death, just as do the leaves of most plants. "Hidden" refers to the fact that the root system is hidden from our sight below ground, meaning that we cannot study it very easily. For this reason, we know less about root systems than about the above-ground parts of plants, although recent technological advances are changing this situation.

Above ground, the simple stems of early land plants also became more specialized, evolving into **shoot systems** in vascular plants. Shoot systems have stems and leaves that arise from apical meristems and that function in the absorption of light energy from the sun and carbon dioxide from the air. Stems grew larger and branched extensively after the evolution of lignin. The mechanical strength of lignified tissues almost certainly provided plants with several adaptive advantages. For instance, a strong internal scaffold could support upright stems

bearing leaves and other photosynthetic structures, and so help increase the surface area for intercepting sunlight. Also, reproductive structures borne on aerial stems might serve as platforms for more efficient launching of spores from the parent plant.

Structures we think of as "leaves" arose several times during plant evolution. In general, leaves represent modifications of stems and can be divided into two types: microphylls are narrow leaves with only one vein or strand of vascular tissue; megaphylls are broader leaves with multiple veins. **Figure 26.5** illustrates the basic steps of possible evolutionary pathways by which these two types of leaves evolved. In some early plants, microphylls may have evolved as flaplike extensions of the main stem. In contrast, megaphylls likely evolved from a modified branch system when photosynthetic tissue filled in the gaps between neighbouring branches.

Other land plant adaptations were related to the demands of reproduction in a dry environment. As described in more detail shortly, these adaptations included multicellular chambers that protect developing gametes, and a multicellular embryo that is sheltered inside the tissues of a parent plant.

## 26.2e In the Plant Life Cycle, the Diploid Phase Became Dominant

As early plants moved into drier habitats, their life cycles also modified considerably. The haploid gametophyte phase became physically smaller and less complex and had a shorter life span, whereas the opposite occurred with the diploid sporophyte phase. In mosses and other nonvascular plants, the sporophyte is a little larger and longer lived than in green algae, and in vascular plants, the sporophyte is clearly larger and more complex and lives much longer than the gametophyte **(Figure 26.6)**. When

**a. Development of microphylls as an offshoot of the main vertical axis**

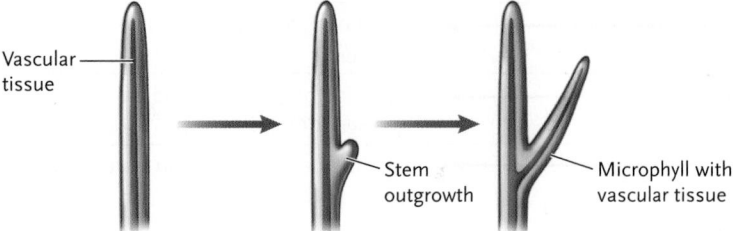

Vascular tissue

Stem outgrowth

Microphyll with vascular tissue

**b. Development of megaphylls in a branching pattern**

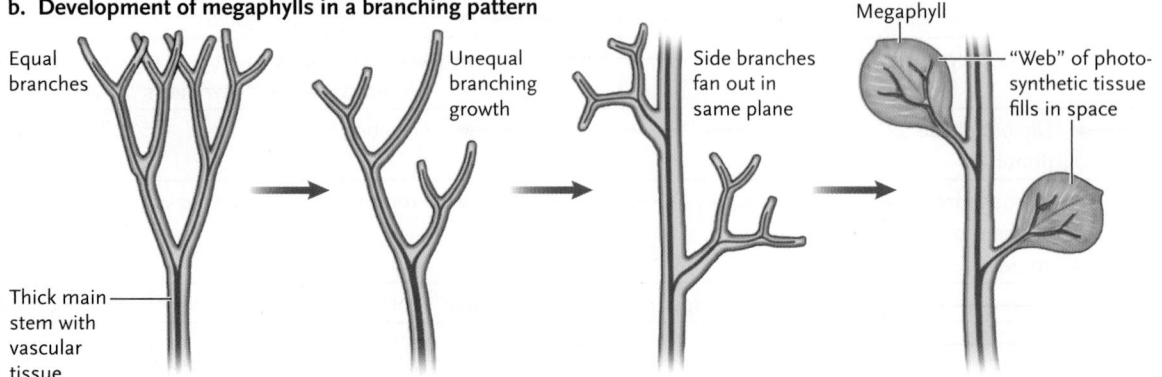

Equal branches

Thick main stem with vascular tissue

Unequal branching growth

Side branches fan out in same plane

Megaphyll

"Web" of photosynthetic tissue fills in space

© Cengage Learning 2017.

**FIGURE 26.5 Evolution of leaves. (a)** One type of early leaflike structure may have evolved as offshoots of the plant's main vertical axis; there was only one vein (transport vessel) in each leaf. Today, the seedless vascular plants known as *lycophytes* (*club mosses*) have this type of leaf. **(b)** In other groups of seedless vascular plants, leaves arose in a series of steps that began when the main stem evolved a branching growth pattern. Small side branches then fanned out and photosynthetic tissue filled the space between them, becoming the leaf blade. With time, the small branches modified into veins.

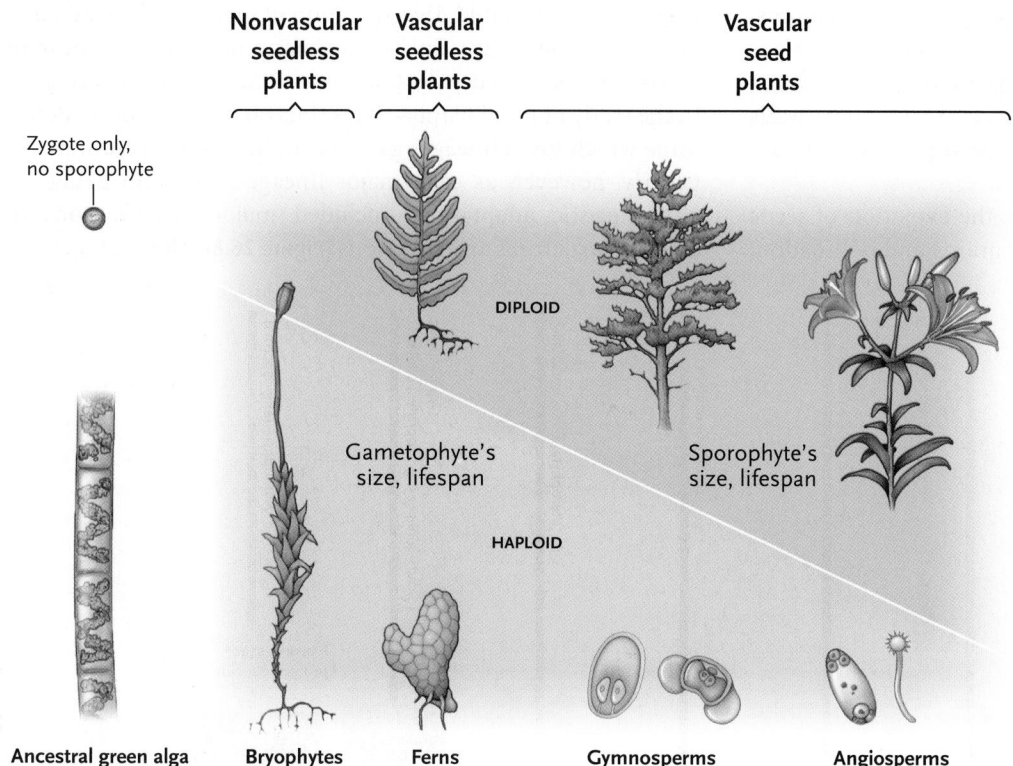

Nonvascular seedless plants — Vascular seedless plants — Vascular seed plants

Zygote only, no sporophyte

DIPLOID

Gametophyte's size, lifespan

Sporophyte's size, lifespan

HAPLOID

Ancestral green alga — Bryophytes — Ferns — Gymnosperms — Angiosperms

© Cengage Learning 2017.

**FIGURE 26.6 Evolutionary trend from dominance of the gametophyte (haploid) generation to dominance of the sporophyte (diploid) generation, represented here by existing species ranging from a green alga (*Ulothrix*) to a flowering plant.** This trend developed as early plants colonized habitats on land. In general, the sporophytes of vascular plants are larger and more complex than those of bryophytes, and their gametophytes are smaller and less complex. In this diagram, the fern represents seedless vascular plants.

you look at a pine tree, for example, you see a large, long-lived sporophyte. The sporophyte generation begins after fertilization, when the zygote divides by mitosis to produce a multicellular diploid organism. Its body will eventually develop sporangia, which produce spores by meiosis.

Why did the diploid phase become dominant over evolutionary time? Many botanists hypothesize that the trend toward "diploid dominance" reflects the advantage of being diploid in land environments; if there is only one copy of DNA, as in a haploid plant, and if a deleterious mutation occurs or if the DNA is damaged (e.g., by UV radiation, which is a greater problem on land than in aquatic habitats), the consequences could be fatal. In contrast, the sporophyte phase of that plant is diploid and so has a "backup" copy of the DNA that can continue to function normally even if one strand is damaged. However, it is important to remember that the land plants that do have a dominant haploid stage, such as mosses, are very successful plants in certain habitats. The lack of a dominant diploid stage has certainly not caused them to become extinct.

## 26.2f Some Vascular Plants Evolved Separate Male and Female Gametophytes

When a plant makes only one type of spore, it is said to be **homosporous** ("same spore"; **Figure 26.7a**). Usually, a gametophyte that develops from such a spore is bisexual—it can produce both sperm and eggs. However, some homosporous plants have ways to produce male and female sex organs on different gametophytes or to otherwise prevent self-fertilization, as described below in ferns. The sperm have flagella and are

**a. *Lycopodium***

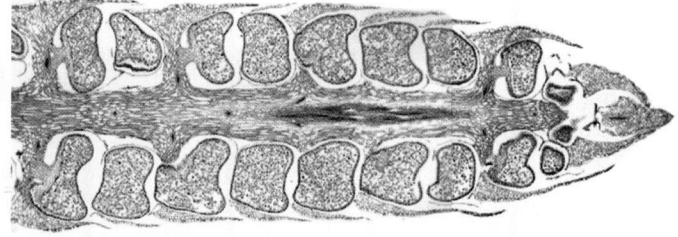

**b. *Selaginella***

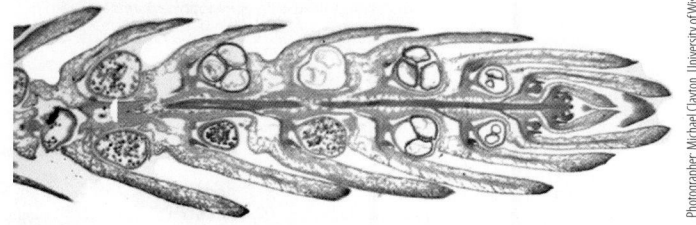

Photographer: Michael Clayton, University of Wisconsin Plant Teaching Collection, http://botit.botany.wisc.edu

**FIGURE 26.7 Longitudinal sections through strobili of two lycophytes,** (a) ***Lycopodium*** and (b) ***Selaginella*.** Lycopodium is a homosporous plant that produces spores of only one type, as can be seen in (a). Note that the sporangia of *Lycopodium* are all the same. The *Selaginella* strobilus shown here is from a heterosporous plant, which produces megasporangia (containing a few large megaspores) and microsporangia (containing numerous small microspores) in the same strobilus.

motile because they must swim through liquid water to encounter eggs.

Other vascular plants, including gymnosperms and angiosperms, are **heterosporous** (Figure 26.7b). They produce two types of spores—one type is smaller than the other—in two different types of sporangia. The smaller spores are **microspores**, which develop into male gametophytes, and the larger **megaspores** will develop into female gametophytes. Heterospory and the development of gametophytes inside spore walls are important steps in the evolution of the seed, as we will see further on.

As you will read in a later section, the evolution of seeds and related innovations, such as pollen grains and pollination,

helped spark the rapid diversification of plants in the Devonian period, 360–408 mya. In fact, so many new fossils appear in Devonian rocks that paleobotanists—scientists who specialize in the study of fossil plants—have thus far been unable to determine which fossil lineages gave rise to the modern plant phyla. Clearly, however, as each major lineage came into being, its characteristic adaptations included major modifications of existing structures and functions **(Figure 26.8)**. The next sections

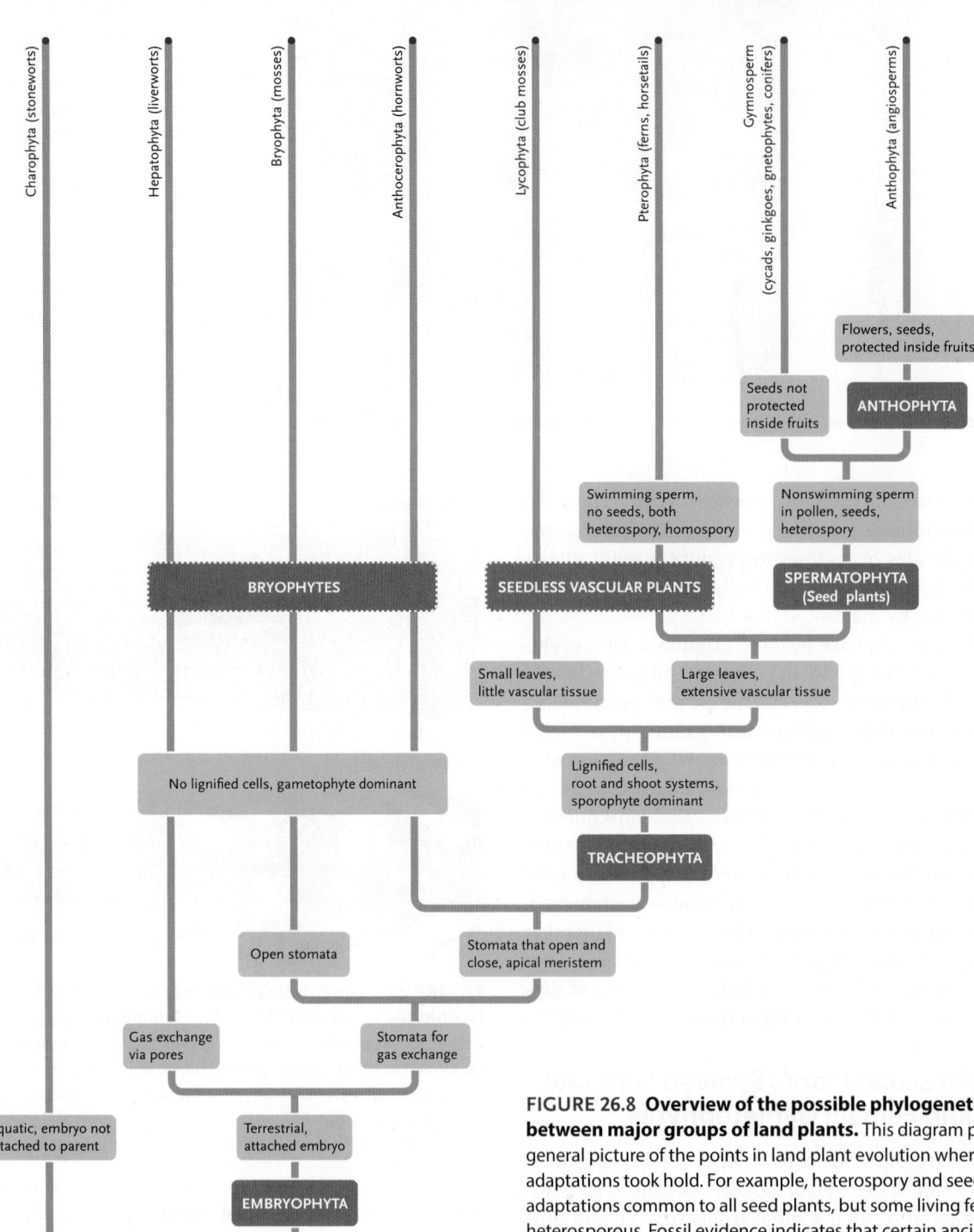

**FIGURE 26.8 Overview of the possible phylogenetic relationships between major groups of land plants.** This diagram provides only a general picture of the points in land plant evolution where major adaptations took hold. For example, heterospory and seeds are shown as adaptations common to all seed plants, but some living fern species are also heterosporous. Fossil evidence indicates that certain ancient lycophytes and horsetails also produced two types of spores, and some had seeds as well. Cycads and ginkgoes are unlike other gymnosperms in that they have swimming sperm. Roots may have evolved independently in several lineages.

© Cengage Learning 2017.

fill out this general picture, beginning with the plants that are the living representatives of the earliest land plants.

## STUDY BREAK QUESTIONS

1. What features do land plants share with their closest living relatives, the charophyte algae? What features differentiate the two groups?
2. How did mycorrhizal fungi fulfill the role we associate with roots in early land plants?
3. What is the main difference between the specialized water-conducting cells present in some nonvascular plants and those of vascular plants? How did this difference influence the evolution of vascular plants?
4. How did plant adaptations such as a root system, a shoot system, and a vascular system collectively influence the evolution of land plants?
5. Describe the difference between homospory and heterospory, and explain how heterospory paved the way for other reproductive adaptations in land plants.

**Figure 26.9 Bryophytes of arid habitats. (a)** Moss growing on exposed rock. **(b)** Mosses and other plants in alpine tundra

## 26.3 Bryophytes: Nonvascular Land Plants

The **bryophytes** (*bryon* = moss)—liverworts, hornworts, and mosses—are important both ecologically and economically. As colonizers of bare land, their small bodies trap particles of organic and inorganic matter, helping to build soil on bare rock and stabilizing soil surfaces with a biological crust in harsh places such as coastal dunes, inland deserts, and embankments created by road construction. In boreal forests and Arctic tundras, bryophytes constitute as much as half the biomass, and they are crucial components of the **food web** that supports animals in these ecosystems. People have long used *Sphagnum* and other absorbent "peat" mosses (which typically grow in bogs and fens) for everything from primitive diapers and filtering whiskey to increasing the water-holding capacity of garden soil. Peat moss has also found use as a fuel; each day, the Rhode generating station in Ireland, one of several that use peat in that nation, burns 2000 tonnes of peat to produce electricity.

Bryophytes have a combination of traits that allow them to bridge aquatic and land environments. Because bryophytes lack cells strengthened by lignin and are poikilohydric, it is not surprising that they are small and commonly grow on wet sites along creek banks (see Figure 26.3a); in bogs, swamps, or the dense shade of damp forests; and on moist tree trunks or rooftops. However, some mosses live in very dry environments, such as **alpine tundra** and **arctic tundra (Figure 26.9)**. Being poikilohydric enables them to live in such seemingly inhospitable habitats.

Bryophytes retain many of the features of their algal ancestors: they produce flagellated sperm that must swim through water to reach eggs, which is another reason they are small: the sperm must be able to swim between plants in a film of water (e.g., from rain or dew), which is only possible if the plants are relatively close to the ground. They also lack xylem and phloem (although some do have specialized conductive tissues). Bryophytes have parts that are rootlike, stemlike, and leaflike. However, the "roots" are **rhizoids** that serve only to anchor the plant to its substrate and do not take up any water or nutrients from the substrate. Bryophyte "stems" and "leaves" are not considered to be true stems and leaves like those of vascular plants because they lack vascular tissue and because they did not evolve from the same structures as vascular plant stems and leaves did. (Said another way, stems and leaves are not homologous in bryophytes and vascular plants.)

In other ways, bryophytes are clearly adapted to land. The sporophytes (but not the longer-lived gametophytes) of some species have a water-conserving cuticle and stomata. And, as is true of all plants, the bryophyte life cycle has both multicellular gametophyte and sporophyte phases, but the sporophyte is permanently associated with the gametophyte (it never becomes independent of the gametophyte) and lives for a shorter time than the gametophyte. **Figure 26.10** shows the green, leafy gametophyte of a moss plant, with diploid sporophytes attached to it by slender stalks. Bryophyte gametophytes produce gametes inside a protective organ called a **gametangium** (plural, *gametangia*). The gametangia in which bryophyte eggs form are flask-shaped structures called **archegonia** (*archi* = first;

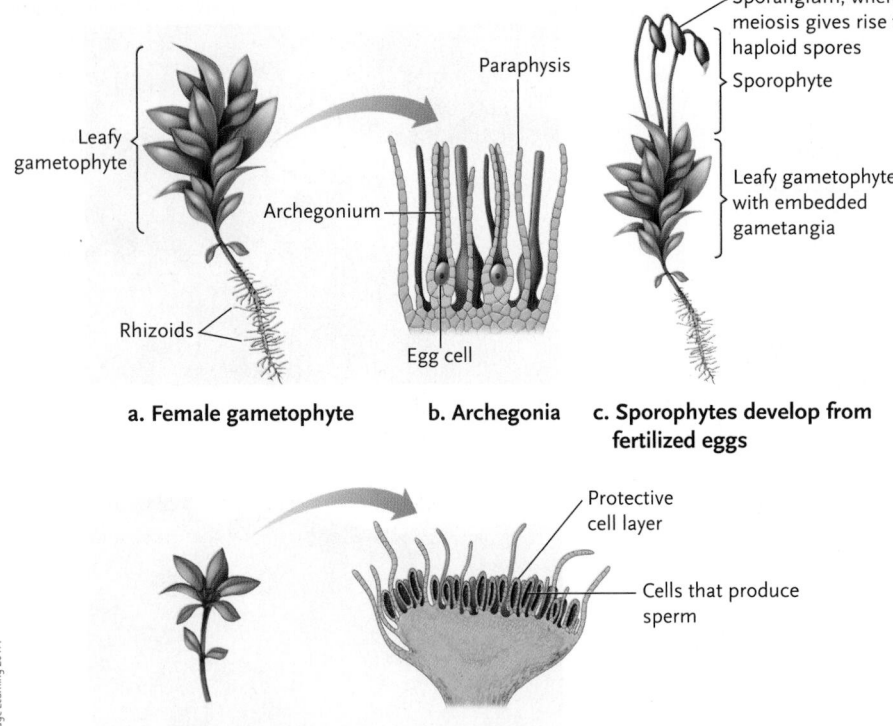

a. Female gametophyte

Leafy gametophyte

Rhizoids

b. Archegonia

Paraphysis

Archegonium

Egg cell

c. Sporophytes develop from fertilized eggs

Sporangium, where meiosis gives rise to haploid spores

Sporophyte

Leafy gametophyte, with embedded gametangia

d. Male gametophyte

e. Antheridia

Protective cell layer

Cells that produce sperm

© Cengage Learning 2017.

**FIGURE 26.10 Gametangia are multicellular structures that enclose and protect gametes—a bryophyte innovation.** *Rhizomnium* bears gametangia (archegonia and antheridia) on separate gametophyte plants. **(a, b)** The archegonia are clustered in the tip of the female gametophyte interspersed with paraphyses (filaments that protect the archegonia). **(c)** A sporophyte develops from a fertilized egg. It has a sporangium in which meiosis occurs to produce haploid spores. **(d)** The antheridia are club-shaped gametangia that contain cells from which sperm arise. **(e)** The antheridia are clustered at the very tip of the male gametophyte plant and are interspersed with paraphyses.

a. **Thallus of *Calypogeia muelleriana***

b. **Thallus of *Marchantia***

c. **Male gametophyte**

d. **Female gametophyte**

e. **Asexual reproductive structures**

Gemmae

**FIGURE 26.11 Examples of liverworts. (a)** Thallus of a leafy liverwort, *Calypogeia muelleriana*. **(b)** Thallus of the thalloid liverwort *Marchantia*, **(c)** male thallus with antheridia-bearing structures **(d)** female thallus with archegonia-bearing structures. *Marchantia* and some other liverworts also reproduce asexually by way of **(e)** gemmae, multicellular vegetative bodies that develop in tiny cups on the plant body. Gemmae can grow into new plants when splashing raindrops transport them to suitable sites.

*gonos* = seed). Flagellated sperm form in rounded gametangia called **antheridia** (*antheros* = flowerlike; singular, *antheridium*). The sperm swim through a film of water to the archegonia to fertilize eggs. Each fertilized egg gives rise to a diploid embryo sporophyte, which stays attached to the gametophyte and produces spores—and the cycle repeats.

Despite these similarities to more complex plants, bryophytes are unique in several ways. Unlike vascular plants, the gametophyte is much longer lived than the sporophyte and is photosynthetic, whereas the sporophyte remains attached to the gametophyte and depends on the gametophyte for much of its nutrition.

Bryophytes are not a monophyletic group (i.e., they did not all evolve from a common ancestor); instead, the various bryophytes evolved as separate lineages, in parallel with vascular plants.

## 26.3a Liverworts Resemble the First Land Plants

Liverworts make up the phylum **Hepatophyta**, so called because early herbalists thought that these small plants were shaped like the lobes of the human liver (*hepat* = liver; *wort* = herb). The resemblance might be a little vague to modern eyes. While some of the 6000 species of liverworts consist of a flat, branching, ribbonlike plate of tissue closely pressed against damp soil, other liverworts are leafy and superficially resemble mosses, although the arrangement of leaves is different **(Figure 26.11)**. This simple body, called a **thallus** (plural, *thalli*), is the gametophyte generation. Threadlike rhizoids anchor the gametophytes to their substrate. None have true stomata, the openings that regulate gas exchange in most other land plants, although some species do have pores. They lack some features present in the other two groups of bryophytes; this evidence, together with molecular data, suggests that the first land plants likely resembled modern-day liverworts.

We will look at one genus, *Marchantia* (Figure 26.11), as an example of liverwort reproduction. Separate male and female gametophytes produce sexual organs (antheridia and archegonia) on tall stalks (Figure 26.11c, d). The motile sperm released from antheridia are splashed and then swim through surface water to reach the eggs inside archegonia. After fertilization, a small diploid sporophyte develops inside the archegonium, matures there, and produces haploid spores by meiosis. During meiosis, sex chromosomes segregate, so some spores have the male genotype and others the female genotype. As in other liverworts, the spores develop inside jacketed sporangia that split open to release the spores. A spore that is carried by air currents to a suitable location germinates and gives rise to a haploid gametophyte, which is either male or female. *Marchantia* and some other liverworts can also reproduce asexually by way of **gemmae** (*gem* = bud; singular, *gemma*), small cell masses that form in cuplike growths on a thallus (Figure 26.11e). Gemmae can grow into new thalli when rainwater splashes them out of the cups and onto an appropriately moist substrate.

## 26.3b Many Mosses Have Specialized Cells for Water and Nutrient Transport

Chances are that you have seen, touched, or sat on at least some of the approximately 10 000 species of mosses. The use of the name **Bryophyta** for this phylum underscores the fact that mosses are the best-known bryophytes, forming tufts or carpets of vegetation on the surface of rocks, soil, or bark.

The moss life cycle, diagrammed in **Figure 26.12**, begins when a haploid (*n*) spore lands on a wet soil surface. After the

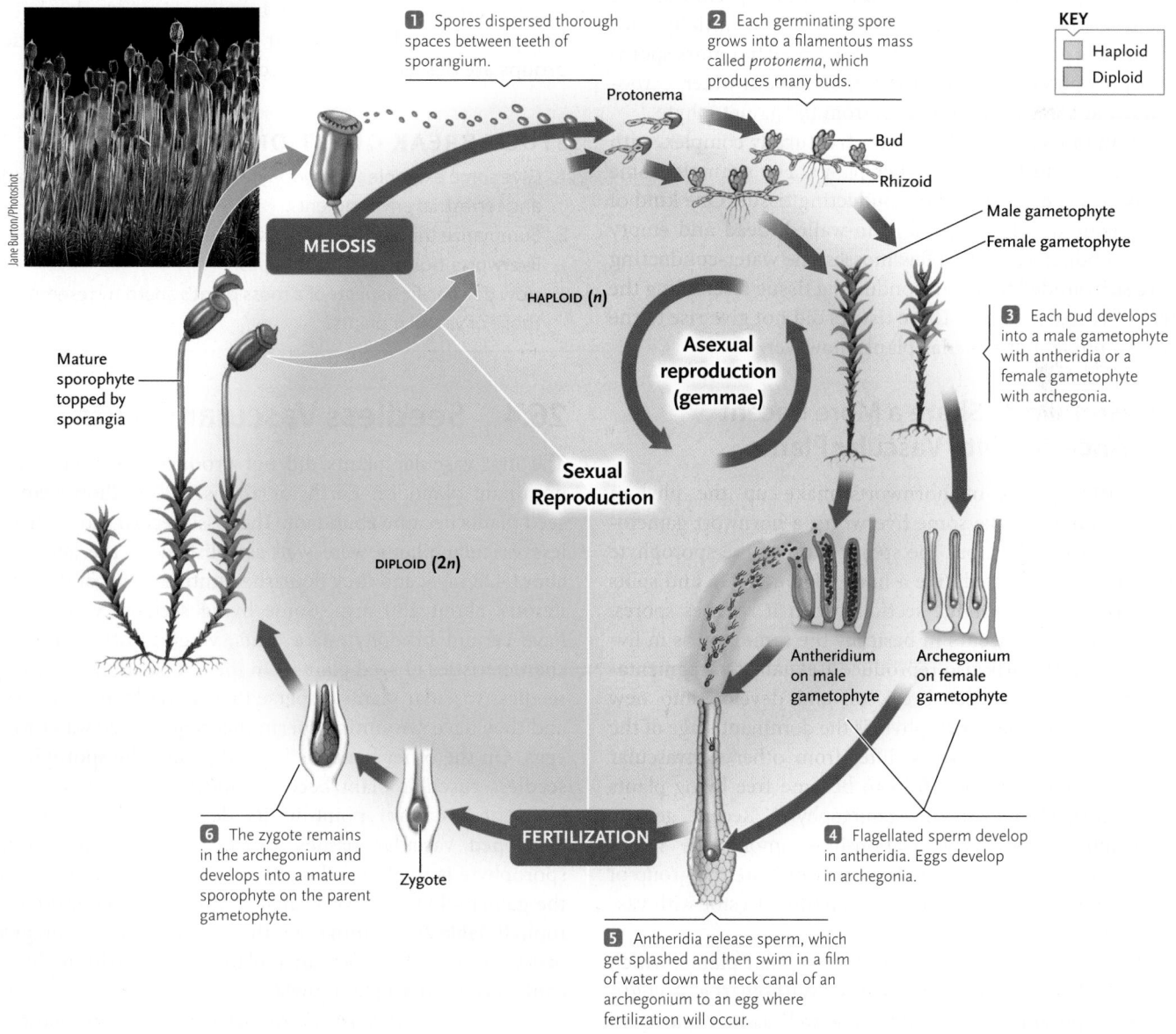

**FIGURE 26.12 Life cycle of the moss *Polytrichum***

spore germinates, it elongates and branches into a filamentous web of tissue called a **protonema** ("first thread"), which can become dense enough to colour the surface of soil, rocks, or bark visibly green. After several weeks of growth, the budlike cell masses on a protonema develop into leafy, green gametophytes anchored by rhizoids. A single protonema can be extremely prolific, producing bud after bud, thus giving rise to a dense clone of genetically identical gametophytes. Leafy mosses may also reproduce asexually by gemmae produced at the surface of rhizoids and on above-ground parts.

Antheridia and archegonia are produced at the tips of male and female gametophytes respectively. Propelled by flagella, sperm released from antheridia swim through a film of dew or rainwater and down a channel in the neck of the archegonium, attracted by a chemical gradient secreted by each egg. Fertilization produces the new sporophyte generation inside the archegonium in the form of diploid zygotes that develop into small mature sporophytes, each consisting of a sporangium on a stalk. Moss sporophytes may eventually develop chloroplasts and nourish themselves photosynthetically but, initially, they depend on the gametophytes for food. Even after a moss sporophyte begins photosynthesis, it still must obtain water, carbohydrates, and some other nutrients from the gametophyte.

Certain moss gametophytes are structurally complex, with features similar to those of higher plants. For example, some species have a central strand of conducting tissue. One kind of tissue is made up of elongated, thin-walled, dead and empty cells that conduct water. In a few mosses, the water-conducting cells are surrounded by sugar-conducting tissue resembling the phloem of vascular plants. These tissues did not give rise to the xylem and phloem of vascular plants, however.

### 26.3c Hornworts Share a More Recent Ancestor with Vascular Plants

Roughly 100 species of hornworts make up the phylum **Anthocerotophyta**. Like some liverworts, a hornwort gametophyte has a flat thallus, but the sporangium of the sporophyte phase is long and pointed, like a horn **(Figure 26.13)**, and splits into two or three ribbonlike sections when it releases spores. Sexual reproduction occurs in basically the same way as in liverworts, and hornworts also reproduce asexually by fragmentation as pieces of a thallus break off and develop into new individuals. While the gametophyte is the dominant stage of the hornwort life cycle, hornworts differ from other nonvascular plants in that their sporophytes can become free-living plants that are independent of the gametophyte! Recent genetic research into evolutionary relationships among the major groups of land plants indicates that hornworts are the group of bryophytes that have a more recent common ancestor with vascular plants.

In the next section, we turn to the vascular plants, which have lignified water-conducting tissue. Without the strength and support provided by this tissue, as well as its capacity to move water and minerals efficiently throughout the plant body,

**FIGURE 26.13 The hornwort *Anthoceros*.** The base of each long slender sporophyte is embedded in the flattened leafy gametophyte.

large sporophytes could not have survived on land. Unlike bryophytes, modern vascular plants are monophyletic—all groups are descended from a common ancestor.

### STUDY BREAK QUESTIONS

1. Give some examples of bryophyte features that bridge aquatic and terrestrial environments.
2. Summarize the main similarities and differences among liverworts, hornworts, and mosses.
3. How do specific aspects of a moss plant's anatomy resemble those of vascular plants?

## 26.4 Seedless Vascular Plants

The first vascular plants did not produce seeds and were the dominant plants on Earth for almost 200 million years, until seed plants became abundant. The fossil record shows that seedless vascular plants were well established by the late Silurian, about 428 mya, and they flourished until the end of the Carboniferous, about 250 mya. Some living seedless vascular plants have certain bryophyte-like traits, whereas others have some characteristics of seed plants. On the one hand, like bryophytes, seedless vascular plants disperse themselves by releasing spores, and they have swimming sperm that require free water to reach eggs. On the other hand, as in seed plants, the sporophyte of a seedless vascular plant becomes independent of the gametophyte at a certain point in its development and has well-developed vascular tissues (xylem and phloem). Also, the sporophyte is the larger, longer-lived stage of the life cycle, and the gametophytes are very small, with some even lacking chlorophyll. **Table 26.2** summarizes these characteristics and gives an overview of seedless vascular plant features within the larger context of modern plant phyla.

In the late Paleozoic era, seedless vascular plants were Earth's dominant vegetation. Some lineages have endured to

TABLE 26.2 | Plant Phyla and Major Characteristics

| Phylum | Common Name | Number of Species | Common General Characteristics |
|---|---|---|---|
| **Bryophytes: nonvascular plants; gametophyte dominant, free water required for fertilization, cuticle and stomata present in some** | | | |
| Hepatophyta | Liverworts | 6 000 | Leafy or simple flattened thallus, rhizoids; spores in capsules; moist, humid habitats |
| Bryophyta | Mosses | 10 000 | Simple flattened thallus, rhizoids; hornlike sporangia; moist, humid habitats |
| Anthocerotophyta | Hornworts | 100 | Flattened or frilly thallus; some have hydroids; spores in capsules; moist, humid habitats; colonizes bare rock, soil, or bark |
| **Seedless vascular plants: sporophyte dominant, free water required for fertilization, cuticle and stomata present** | | | |
| Lycophyta | Club mosses | 1 000 | Microphylls, true roots; most species have sporangia on sporophylls; mostly wet or shady habitats |
| Pterophyta | Ferns, whisk ferns, horsetails | 13 000 | *Ferns:* Finely divided, large megaphyllous leaves; sporangia often in sori; habitats from wet to arid. *Whisk ferns:* Branching stem from rhizomes; sporangia on stem scales; tropical to subtropical habitats. *Horsetails:* Hollow photosynthetic stem, scalelike leaves, sporangia in strobili; swamps, disturbed habitats |
| **Gymnosperms: vascular plants with "naked" seeds; sporophyte dominant, fertilization by pollination, cuticle and stomata present, megaphylls present** | | | |
| Cycadophyta | Cycads | 185 | Shrubby or treelike with palmlike leaves, pithy stems; male and female strobili on separate plants; widespread distribution |
| Ginkgophyta | Ginkgo | 1 | Woody-stemmed tree, deciduous fan-shaped leaves; male, female structures on separate plants; temperate areas of China |
| Gnetophyta | Gnetophytes | 70 | Shrubs or woody vines; one has strappy leaves; male and female strobili on separate plants; limited to deserts, tropics |
| Coniferophyta | Conifers | 550 | Mostly evergreen, woody trees and shrubs with needlelike or scalelike leaves; male and female cones usually on same plant |
| **Angiosperms: plants with flowers and seeds protected inside fruits; sporophyte dominant, fertilization by pollination, cuticle and stomata present, megaphylls present; major groups: monocots and eudicots** | | | |
| Angiosperms = Anthophytes | Flowering plants | 268 500+ (including monocots and dicots, as well as magnoliids, other basal angiosperms) | Wood and herbaceous plants; nearly all land habitats, some aquatic |
| Monocots | Grasses, palms, lilies, orchids, and others | (60 000) | One cotyledon; parallel-veined leaves common; bundles of vascular tissue scattered in stem; flower parts in multiples of three |
| Eudicots | Most fruit trees, roses, beans, potatoes, and others | (200 000) | Most species have two cotyledons; net-veined leaves common; central core of vascular tissue in stem; flower parts in multiples of four or five |

© Cengage Learning 2017.

the present but, collectively, these survivors total fewer than 14 000 species. The taxonomic relationships between various lines are still under active investigation, and comparisons of gene sequences from the genomes in chloroplasts, nuclei, and mitochondria are revealing previously unsuspected links between some of them. In this book, we assign seedless vascular plants to two phyla, the Lycophyta (club mosses and their close relatives; the common name "club moss" for lycophytes is misleading, as they are vascular plants, not mosses) and the Pterophyta (ferns, whisk ferns, and horsetails).

## 26.4a Early Seedless Vascular Plants Flourished in Moist Environments

What did the first vascular plant look like? There are no living relatives of the earliest vascular plants, so we rely on fossil data to answer this question. The extinct genus *Rhynia* was one of the earliest ancestors of modern seedless vascular plants. Based on fossil evidence, the sporophytes of the first vascular plants, such as *Rhynia* and related genera **(Figure 26.14)**, lacked leaves and roots. Above-ground photosynthetic stems produced sporangia

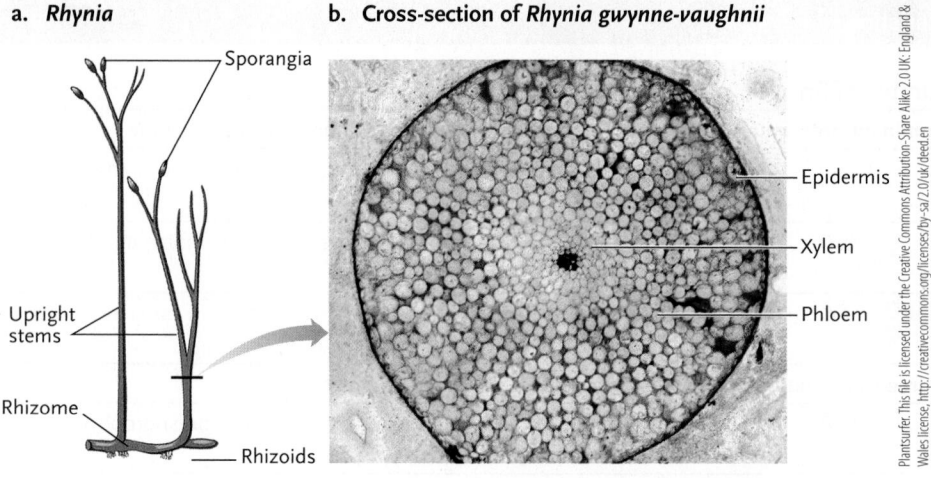

a. *Rhynia*

b. Cross-section of *Rhynia gwynne-vaughnii*

Sporangia

Upright stems

Rhizome

Rhizoids

Epidermis

Xylem

Phloem

Plantsurfer. This file is licensed under the Creative Commons Attribution–Share Alike 2.0 UK: England & Wales license, http://creativecommons.org/licenses/by-sa/2.0/uk/deed.en

**FIGURE 26.14** *Rhynia*, **an early seedless vascular plant. (a)** Fossil-based reconstruction of the entire plant, about 30 cm tall. **(b)** Cross-section of the stem, approximately 3 mm in diameter. This fossil was embedded in chert approximately 400 mya. Still visible in it are traces of the transport tissues xylem and phloem, along with other specialized tissues.

© Cengage Learning 2017.

a. Lycophyte tree
(*Lepidodendron*)

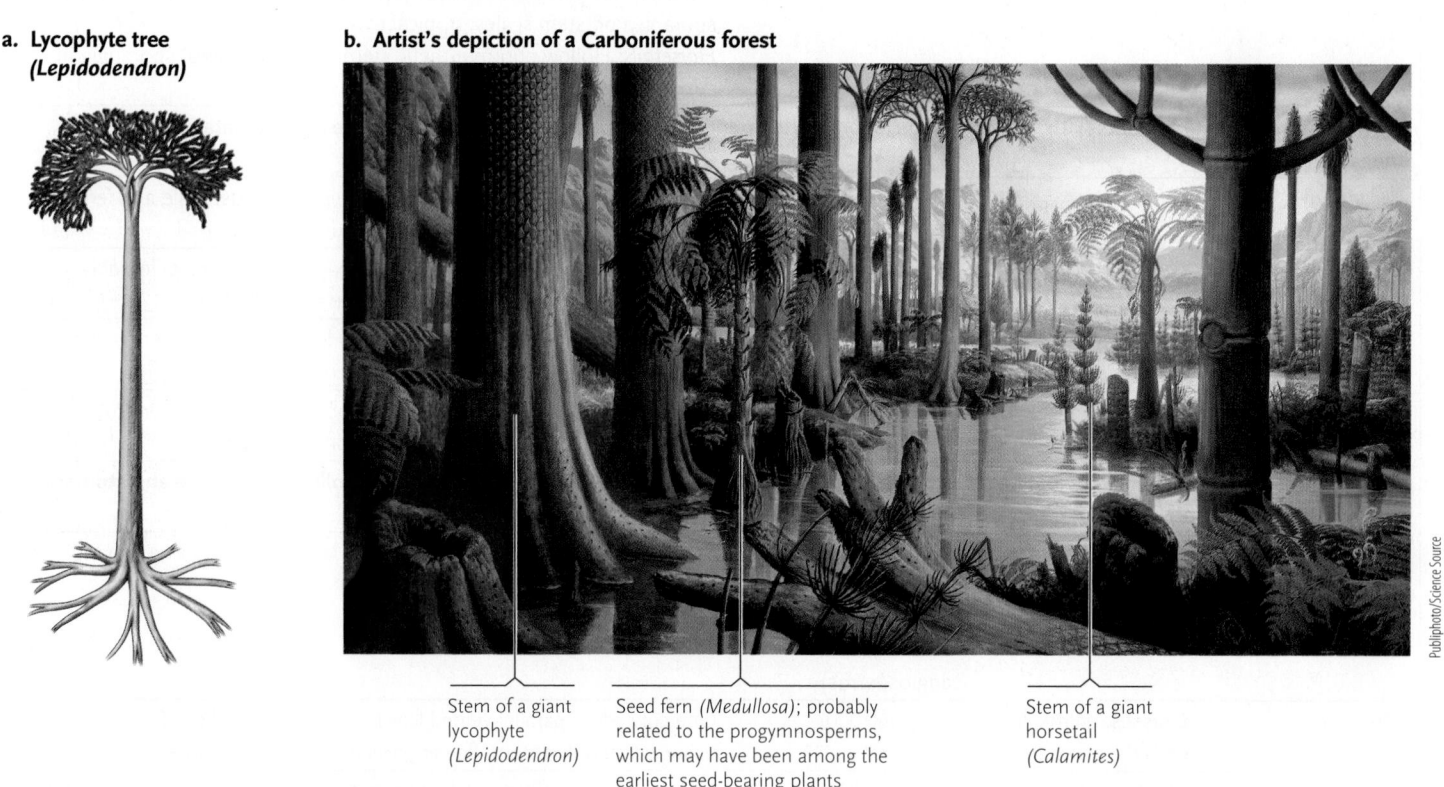

b. Artist's depiction of a Carboniferous forest

Stem of a giant lycophyte (*Lepidodendron*)

Seed fern (*Medullosa*); probably related to the progymnosperms, which may have been among the earliest seed-bearing plants

Stem of a giant horsetail (*Calamites*)

Publiphoto/Science Source

**FIGURE 26.15 Reconstruction of the lycophyte tree *Lepidodendron* and its environment. (a)** Fossil evidence suggests that *Lepidodendron* grew to be about 35 m tall with a trunk 1 m in diameter. **(b)** Lush forests of the Carboniferous period were dominated by early seedless vascular plants.

at the tips of branches. Below ground, the plant body was supported by **rhizomes**, horizontal modified stems that can penetrate a substrate and anchor the plant. *Rhynia*'s simple stems had a central core of xylem, an arrangement seen in many existing vascular plants. Mudflats and swamps of the damp Devonian period were dominated by *Rhynia* and related plants (Figure 26.14). Although these and other now-extinct phyla came and went, ancestral forms of both modern phyla of seedless vascular plants appeared.

Carboniferous forests were swampy places dominated by members of the phylum **Lycophyta**, and fascinating fossil specimens of this group have been unearthed in North America and Europe. One example is *Lepidodendron*, which had broad, straplike leaves and sporangia near the ends of the branches **(Figure 26.15a)**. It also had xylem and other tissues typical of all modern vascular plants. Also abundant at the time were representatives of the phylum **Pterophyta**, including ferns and giants such as *Calamites*—huge horsetails that could have a trunk diameter of 30 cm. Some early seed plants were also present, including now-extinct fernlike plants, called *seed ferns*, that bore seeds at the tips of their leaves (Figure 26.15b).

Characterized by a moist climate over much of the planet and by the dominance of seedless vascular plants, the Carboniferous period continued for 150 million years, ending when climate patterns changed during the Paleozoic era. Most modern seedless vascular plants are confined largely to wet or humid environments because they require external water for reproduction. However, some are poikilohydric and can survive in a dehydrated state for long periods of time.

## 26.4b Modern Lycophytes Are Small and Have Simple Vascular Tissues

Lycophytes were highly diverse 350 mya, when some tree-sized forms inhabited lush swamp forests. Today, however, such giants are no more. The most familiar of the 1000 or so living species of lycophytes are club mosses (e.g., species of *Lycopodium* and *Selaginella*), which grow on forest floors, in alpine meadows, and in some prairie habitats **(Figure 26.16)**. For example, *Selaginella densa* (Figure 26.16b) is a dominant plant in shortgrass prairies of western North America. Club moss sporophytes have upright or horizontal stems that contain xylem and bear small green leaves and roots. Sporangia are clustered at the bases of specialized leaves, called **sporophylls** (*phyll* = leaf; thus, sporophyll = "spore-bearing leaf"). Sporophylls are clustered into a **cone** or **strobilus** (plural, *strobili*) at the tips of stems. Most lycophytes are homosporous, but some are heterosporous, producing two types of spores that will in turn produce separate male and female gametophytes.

## 26.4c Ferns, Whisk Ferns, Horsetails, and Their Relatives Make Up the Diverse Phylum Pterophyta

Second in size only to the flowering plants, the phylum Pterophyta (*pteron* = wing) contains a large and diverse group of vascular plants: the 13 000 or so species of ferns, whisk ferns, and horsetails. Most ferns, including some that are popular houseplants, are native to tropical and temperate regions. Some floating species are less than 1 cm across, whereas some tropical tree ferns grow to 25 m tall. Other species are adapted to life in Arctic and Alpine tundras, salty mangrove swamps, and semi-arid deserts.

**FEATURES OF FERNS.** The familiar plant body of a fern is the sporophyte phase **(Figure 26.17)**, which produces an above-ground clump of leaves. Young leaves are tightly coiled, and as they emerge above the soil, these fiddleheads (so named because they resemble the scrolled pegheads of violins) unroll and expand. The fiddleheads of some species are edible when cooked, tasting similar to fresh asparagus, but be sure you have collected the right type of fiddlehead—some species contain a carcinogen.

Sporangia are produced on the lower surface or margins of leaves. Often, several sporangia are clustered into a rust-coloured **sorus** ("heap"; plural, *sori*; see Figure 26.17). Spores released from sporangia develop into gametophytes, which are typically small, heart-shaped, and anchored to the soil by rhizoids. Antheridia and archegonia develop on the underside of gametophytes, where moisture is trapped. Inside an antheridium is a globular packet of haploid cells, each of which develops into a helical sperm with many flagella. When water is present, the antheridium bursts, releasing the sperm. If mature archegonia are nearby, the sperm swim toward them, drawn by a chemical attractant that diffuses from the neck of the archegonium, which is open when free water is present.

In some ferns, antheridia and archegonia are produced on a single bisexual gametophyte. In other ferns, the first spores to germinate develop into bisexual gametophytes, which produce a chemical (antheridiogen) that diffuses through the substrate and causes all later-germinating spores to develop into male gametophytes. What is the advantage of producing a few bisexual gametophytes followed by many male gametophytes? If a bisexual gametophyte is surrounded by several male gametophytes that developed from other spores, it is more likely that eggs will be fertilized by sperm from one of the male

**a.** *Lycopodium* **sporophyte**

Strobilus

Ed Reschke

**b.** *Selaginella densa* **sporophytes**

Dave Powell, USDA Forest Service, Bugwood.org

**FIGURE 26.16**
**Lycophytes. (a)** *Lycopodium* sporophyte, showing the conelike strobili in which spores are produced. **(b)** *Selaginella* densa sporophytes

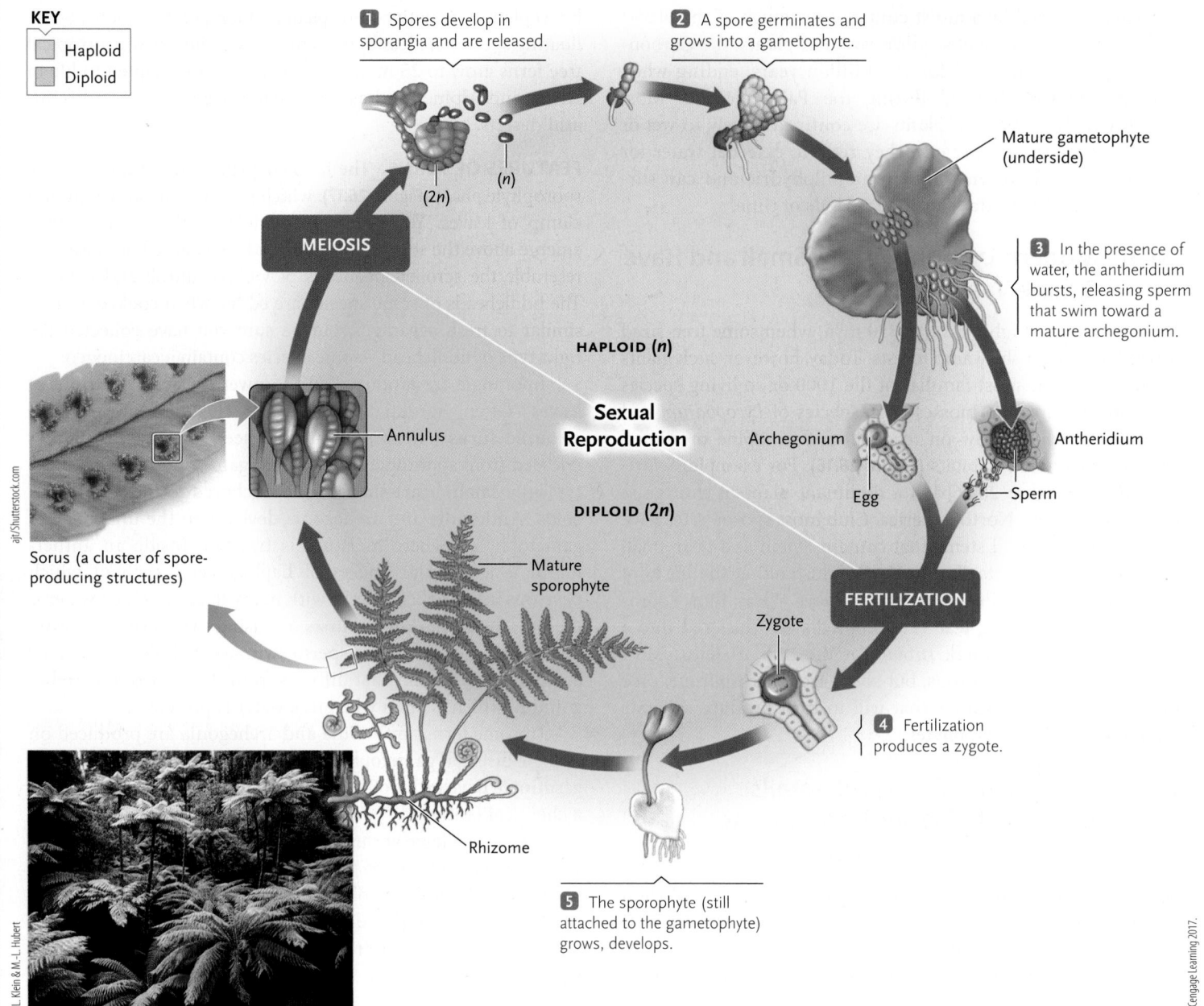

**KEY**

- Haploid
- Diploid

**1** Spores develop in sporangia and are released.

**2** A spore germinates and grows into a gametophyte.

(2*n*)    (*n*)

**MEIOSIS**

Mature gametophyte (underside)

**3** In the presence of water, the antheridium bursts, releasing sperm that swim toward a mature archegonium.

**HAPLOID (*n*)**

**Sexual Reproduction**

Archegonium    Antheridium

Egg    Sperm

**DIPLOID (2*n*)**

Annulus

Sorus (a cluster of spore-producing structures)

Mature sporophyte

**FERTILIZATION**

Zygote

**4** Fertilization produces a zygote.

Rhizome

**5** The sporophyte (still attached to the gametophyte) grows, develops.

**Figure 26.17  Life cycle of a chain fern (*Woodwardia*).** The photograph shows part of a forest of tree ferns (*Cyathea*) in Australia's Tarra-Bulga National Park.

gametophytes rather than by its own sperm, thus increasing the genetic diversity of the resulting zygote.

An embryo is retained on and nourished by the gametophyte for the first part of its life but soon develops into a young sporophyte larger than the gametophyte, with its own green leaf and root system. Once the sporophyte is nutritionally independent, the parent gametophyte degenerates and dies.

**FEATURES OF WHISK FERNS** The whisk ferns and their relatives are represented by only 2 genera, with about 10 species in total. They grow in tropical and subtropical regions, often as epiphytes. We will discuss one genus, *Psilotum* (**Figure 26.18**).

The sporophytes of *Psilotum* resemble the extinct vascular plants in that they lack true roots and leaves. Instead, small,

leaflike scales adorn an upright, green, branching stem, which arises from a horizontal rhizome system anchored by rhizoids. Symbiotic fungi colonize the rhizoids, increasing the plant's uptake of soil nutrients (read more about these mycorrhizal fungi in Chapter 25). The stem is photosynthetic and bears sporangia above the small scales. Gametophytes of *Psilotum* are non-photosynthetic and live underground (**Figure 26.19**); like the sporophyte, they obtain nutrients via symbioses with mycorrhizal fungi.

**FEATURES OF HORSETAILS** The ancient relatives of modern-day horsetails included treelike forms taller than a two-storey building. Only 15 species in a single genus, *Equisetum*, have survived to the present (**Figure 26.20**). Horsetails grow in moist soil

**FIGURE 26.18 Sporophyte of a whisk fern (*Psilotum*), a seedless vascular plant.** Three-lobed sporangia occur at the ends of stubby branchlets; inside the sporangia, meiosis gives rise to haploid spores.

**a. Sporophyte stem**     **b. Sporangia**

Strobilus, an aggregation of sporangia and sporophylls at the tip of the horsetail sporophyte

**c.** This longitudinal section through a horsetail's strobilus shows sporangia containing spores formed by meiosis.

**FIGURE 26.20 A species of *Equisetum*, the horsetails. (a)** Vegetative stem. **(b)** Strobili, which bear sporangia. **(c)** Close-up of sporangium and associated structures on a strobilus

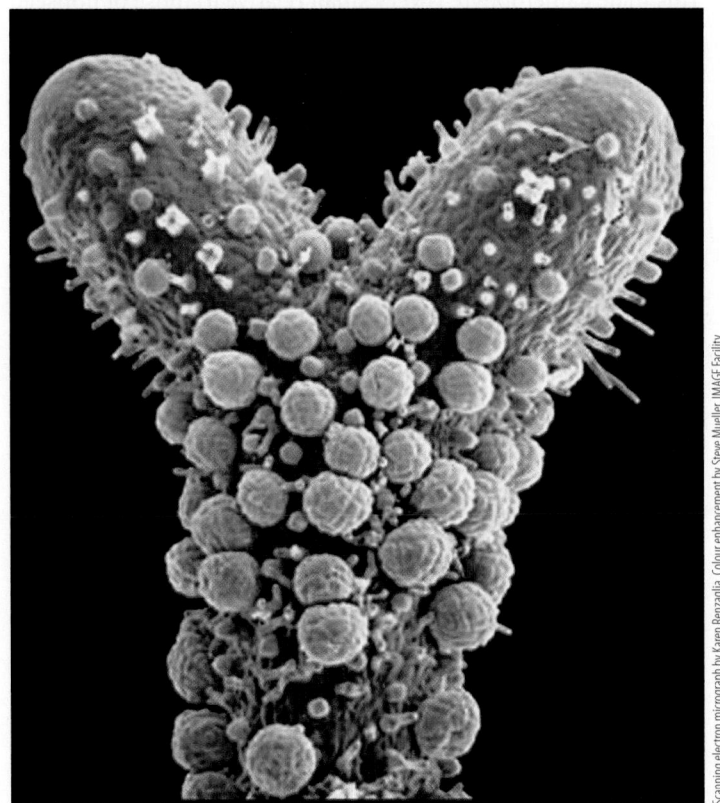

0.5 mm

**FIGURE 26.19 Scanning electron micrograph image of the subterranean gametophyte of *Psilotum*.** Antheridia have been coloured blue, and the smaller archegonia have been coloured pink.

along streams and in disturbed habitats, such as roadsides and beds of railway tracks. Their sporophytes typically have underground rhizomes and roots that anchor the rhizome to the soil. Small, scalelike leaves are arranged in whorls about a photosynthetic stem that is stiff and gritty because horsetails accumulate silica in their tissues. Pioneers used them to scrub out pots and pans—hence their other common name, "scouring rushes."

As in lycophytes, *Equisetum* sporangia are borne in strobili. Haploid spores germinate within a few days to produce gametophytes, which are free-living plants about the size of a small pea.

## 26.4d Some Seedless Vascular Plants Are Heterosporous

Most seedless vascular plants are homosporous, but some (e.g., some lycophytes and some ferns) are heterosporous, producing microspores and megaspores in separate sporangia (see Figure 26.7). Both types of spores are usually shed from sporangia and germinate on the ground some distance from the parent plant. In many heterosporous plants, the gametophytes produced by the spores develop inside the spore wall; this **endosporous** development provides increased protection for the gametes and, later, for the developing embryo. The microspore gives rise to a male gametophyte, which produces motile sperm. At maturity, the microspore wall will rupture, releasing the sperm, which swim to the female gametophyte; water is thus still required for fertilization in these plants. The megaspore produces a female gametophyte inside the spore wall; archegonia of this gametophyte produce eggs, as in other seedless plants.

# 26.5 Gymnosperms: The First Seed Plants

**Gymnosperms** include conifers and their relatives. The earliest fossils identified as gymnosperms are found in Devonian rocks. By the Carboniferous, when nonvascular plants were dominant, many lines of gymnosperms, including conifers, had also evolved. These radiated during the Permian period; the Mesozoic era that followed, 65–248 mya, was the age not only of the dinosaurs but of the gymnosperms as well.

The evolution of gymnosperms marked sweeping changes in plant structures related to reproduction. The evolution of gymnosperms included important reproductive adaptations: pollen and pollination, the ovule, and the seed. The fossil record has not revealed the sequence in which these changes arose, but all of them contributed to the radiation of gymnosperms into land environments.

As a prelude to our survey of modern gymnosperms, we begin by considering some of these innovations.

## 26.5a Major Reproductive Adaptations Occurred as Gymnosperms Evolved

The word *gymnosperm* is derived from the Greek *gymnos*, meaning "naked," and *sperma*, meaning "seed." As this name indicates, gymnosperms produce seeds that are exposed, not enclosed in fruit, as are the seeds of other seed plants.

**OVULES: INCREASED PROTECTION FOR FEMALE GAMETO-PHYTE AND EGG** How did seeds first arise? Think about the heterosporous plants described in the previous section and picture two steps that would lead us toward the development of a seed. In the first step, spores are not shed from the plant but instead are retained inside sporangia on the sporophyte. In the second step, the number of megaspores is reduced to just one per sporangium (i.e., four megaspores are produced by meiosis, but only one survives). These two steps result in retention of a single megaspore inside a megasporangium on a plant (**Figure 26.21**). As in all land plants, the megaspore will give rise to a female gametophyte; because this is a heterosporous plant, the gametophyte will develop inside the megaspore wall and inside the megasporangium. Physically connected to the sporophyte and surrounded by protective layers, a female gametophyte

no longer faces the same risks of predation or environmental assault that can threaten a free-living gametophyte.

This new structure, an egg developing inside a gametophyte that is retained not only inside the spore wall but also inside integument and megasporangial tissues, is an **ovule**. When fertilized, an ovule becomes a **seed**; the fertilized egg will produce an embryo surrounded by nutritive tissue, encased in integument that becomes the seed coat.

Look at Figure 26.21 and note the megasporangium surrounded by integument. These layers provide protection for gametes and embryos, but they create a problem: How can sperm get to the egg now that the gametophyte is enclosed inside these layers of tissue? The solution is two-fold. First, there is a hole in the integument called the *micropyle* through which the pollen enters the ovule. Second, similar to internal fertilization in animals, there is penetration of the sporangial tissue and release of sperm inside the female gametophyte. In the next section, we look at the male gametophyte in seed plants.

**POLLEN: ELIMINATING THE NEED FOR WATER IN REPRODUCTION** As for megaspores, the microspores of seed plants are not dispersed. Instead, they are retained inside microsporangia and enveloped in additional layers of sporophyte tissue. As in other heterosporous plants, each microspore produces a male gametophyte, which develops inside the microspore wall. This male gametophyte is very small relative to those of nonseed plants—it is made of only a few cells—and is called a **pollen grain**. Pollen grains are transferred to female reproductive parts via air currents or on the bodies of animal pollinators; this transfer is known as **pollination**. When the pollen grain lands on female tissue, the pollen grain germinates to produce a **pollen tube (Figure 26.22)**, a cell that grows through female gametophyte tissue by invasive growth and carries the nonmotile sperm to the egg.

Pollen and pollination were enormously important adaptations for gymnosperms because the shift to non-swimming sperm, along with a means for delivering them to female gametes, meant that reproduction no longer required liquid water. The only gymnosperms that have retained swimming sperm are the cycads and ginkgoes described below, which have relatively few living species and are restricted to just a few native habitats.

**SEEDS: PROTECTING AND NOURISHING PLANT EMBRYOS** As described above, a seed is the structure that forms when an ovule matures, after a pollen grain reaches it and a sperm fertilizes the egg. Seeds consist of three basic parts: (1) the embryo sporophyte; (2) the tissues surrounding the embryo containing nutrients that nourish it until it becomes established as a seedling with leaves and roots; and (3) a tough, protective outer seed coat (**Figure 26.23**). This complex structure makes seeds ideal packages for protecting an embryo from drought, cold, or other adverse conditions. As a result, seed plants enjoy a tremendous

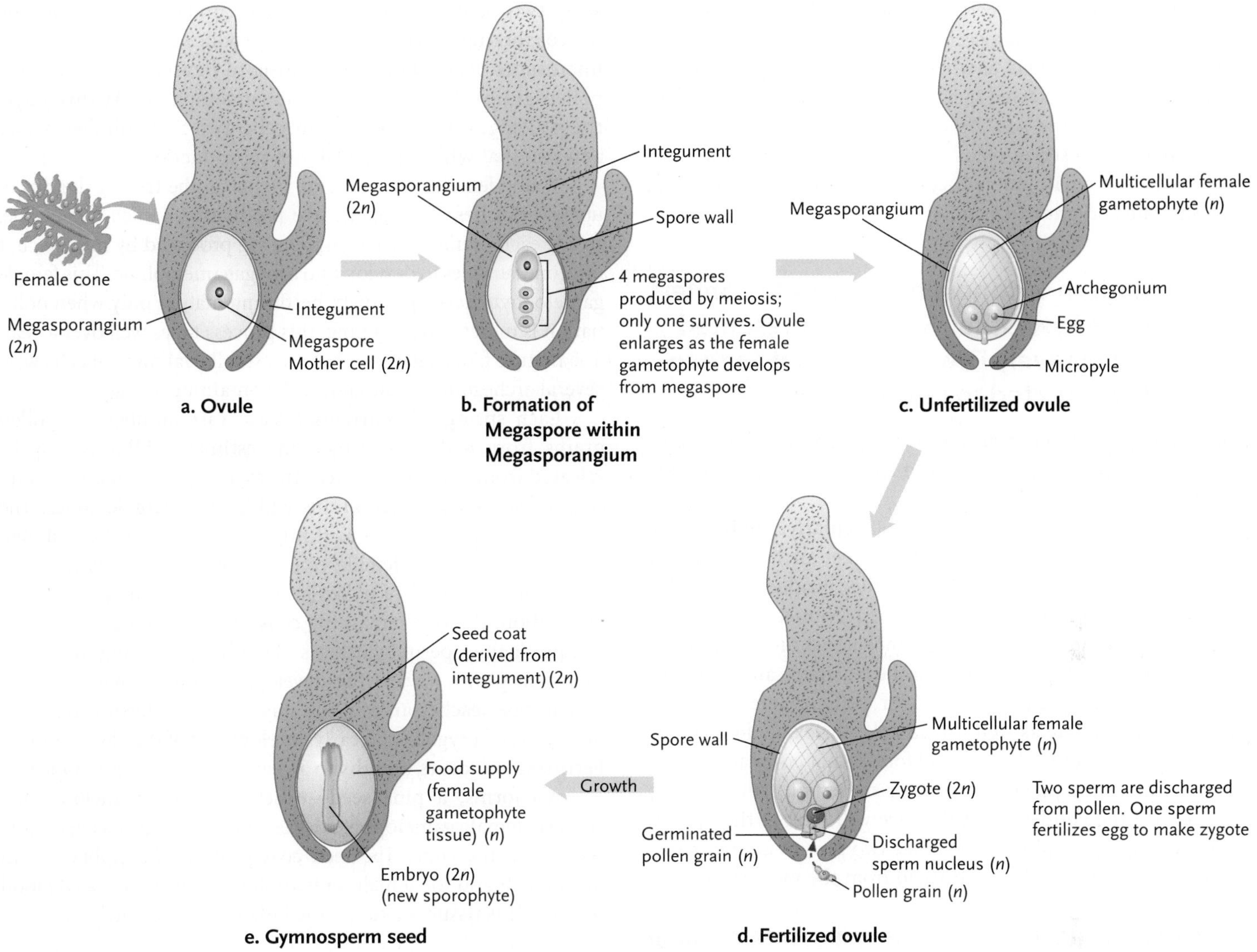

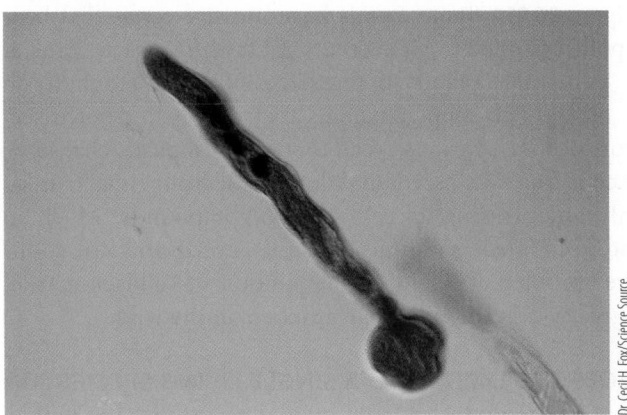

**a. Ovule**

Female cone

Megasporangium (2n)

Integument

Megaspore Mother cell (2n)

**b. Formation of Megaspore within Megasporangium**

Megasporangium (2n)

Integument

Spore wall

4 megaspores produced by meiosis; only one survives. Ovule enlarges as the female gametophyte develops from megaspore

**c. Unfertilized ovule**

Megasporangium

Multicellular female gametophyte (n)

Archegonium

Egg

Micropyle

**e. Gymnosperm seed**

Seed coat (derived from integument) (2n)

Food supply (female gametophyte tissue) (n)

Embryo (2n) (new sporophyte)

Growth

**d. Fertilized ovule**

Spore wall

Multicellular female gametophyte (n)

Zygote (2n)

Germinated pollen grain (n)

Discharged sperm nucleus (n)

Pollen grain (n)

Two sperm are discharged from pollen. One sperm fertilizes egg to make zygote

**FIGURE 26.21 Structure of a gymnosperm ovule**

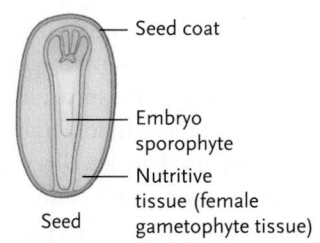

**FIGURE 26.22 Pollen tube extending from germinating pollen grain at bottom right**

Dr. Cecil H. Fox/Science Source

Seed coat

Embryo sporophyte

Nutritive tissue (female gametophyte tissue)

Seed

**FIGURE 26.23 Generalized view of the seed of a pine, a gymnosperm**

survival advantage over species that simply release spores to the environment. Encased in a seed, the embryo can also be transported far from its parent, as when ocean currents carry coconut seeds ("coconuts" protected in large, buoyant fruits) hundreds of kilometres across the sea. As discussed in Chapter 35, some plant embryos housed in seeds can remain dormant for months or years before environmental conditions finally prompt them to germinate and grow.

## 26.5b Modern Gymnosperms Include Conifers and a Few Other Groups Represented by Relatively Few Species That Tend to Be Restricted to Certain Climates

Today there are about 800 gymnosperm species. The sporophytes of nearly all are large trees or shrubs, although a few are woody vines.

Economically, gymnosperms, particularly conifers, are vital to human societies. They are sources of lumber, paper pulp, turpentine, and resins, among other products. They also have huge ecological importance. Their habitats range from **tropical forests** to deserts, but gymnosperms are most dominant in the cool-temperate zones of the Northern and Southern Hemispheres. They flourish in poor soils, where flowering plants don't compete as well. In Canada, for example, gymnosperms make up most of the boreal forests that cover about one-third of the country's landmass. Our survey of gymnosperms begins with the conifers, and then we will look at the cycads, ginkgoes, and gnetophytes; the latter two groups are remnants of lineages that have all but vanished from the modern scene.

**CONIFERS ARE THE MOST COMMON GYMNOSPERMS** About 80% of all living gymnosperm species are members of one phylum, the **Coniferophyta**, or conifers ("cone bearers"). Examples are pines, spruces, and firs. Coniferous trees and shrubs are longer lived and anatomically and morphologically more complex than any sporophyte phase we have discussed so far. Characteristically, they form woody cones, and most have needlelike leaves that are adapted to dry environments. For instance, needles have a thick cuticle, sunken stomata, and a fibrous epidermis, all traits that reduce the loss of water vapour.

Pines and many other gymnosperms produce resins, a mix of organic compounds that are by-products of metabolism. Resin accumulates and flows in long resin ducts through the wood, inhibiting the activity of wood-boring insects and certain microbes. Pine resin extracts are the raw material of turpentine, and (minus the volatile terpenes) the sticky rosin applied to violin bows enhances tone. Fossil resin is known as *amber* and is commonly used in jewellery; amber often contains fossilized insects or even small animals.

We know a great deal about the pine life cycle (**Figure 26.24**), so it is a convenient model for gymnosperms. Male cones are relatively small and delicate (about 1 cm long) and are borne on the lower branches. Each cone consists of many sporophylls with two microsporangia on their undersides. Inside the microsporangia, **microspores** are produced by meiosis. Each microspore then undergoes mitosis to develop into a winged pollen grain—an immature male gametophyte. At this stage, the pollen grain consists of four cells, two that will degenerate and two that will function later in reproduction.

Young female cones develop higher in the tree, at the tips of upper branches. Two ovules are produced on each cone scale. Inside each ovule, four megaspores are produced by meiosis, but only one survives to develop into a megagametophyte. This female gametophyte develops slowly, becoming mature only when pollination is under way; in a pine, this process takes well over a year. The mature female gametophyte is a small oval mass of cells with several archegonia at one end, each containing an egg.

Each spring, air currents release vast numbers of pollen grains from male cones: by some estimates, billions may be released from a single pine tree. The extravagant numbers ensure that at least some pollen grains will land on female cones. The process is not as random as it might seem: studies have shown that the contours of female cones create air currents that can favour the "delivery" of pollen grains near the cone scales. After pollination, the two remaining cells of the pollen grain divide, one producing sperm by mitosis, the other producing the pollen tube that grows toward the developing gametophyte. When a pollen tube reaches an egg, the stage is set for fertilization, the formation of a zygote, and early development of the plant embryo. Fertilization occurs months to a year after pollination. Once an embryo forms, a pine seed—which, remember, includes the embryo, female gametophyte tissue, and seed coat—is eventually shed from the cone. The seed coat protects the embryo from drying out, and the female gametophyte tissue serves as its food reserve. This tissue makes up the bulk of a "pine nut."

**CYCADS ARE RESTRICTED TO WARMER CLIMATES** During the Mesozoic era, the **Cycadophyta** (*kykas* = palm), or cycads, flourished along with the dinosaurs. About 185 species have survived to the present, but they are confined to the tropics and subtropics.

At first glance, you might mistake a cycad for a small palm tree (**Figure 26.25**). Some cycads have massive cones that bear either pollen or ovules. Air currents or crawling insects transfer pollen from male plants to the developing gametophyte on female plants. Poisonous alkaloids that may help deter insect predators occur in various cycad tissues. In tropical Asia, some people consume cycad seeds and flour made from cycad trunks, but only after rinsing away the toxic compounds. Much in demand from fanciers of unusual plants, cycads in some countries are uprooted and sold in what amounts to a black-market trade, greatly diminishing their numbers in the wild.

**GINKGOES ARE LIMITED TO A SINGLE LIVING SPECIES** The phylum **Ginkgophyta** has only one living species, the ginkgo (or maidenhair) tree (*Ginkgo biloba*), which grows wild today only in warm-temperate forests of central China. Ginkgo trees are large, diffusely branching trees with characteristic fan-shaped

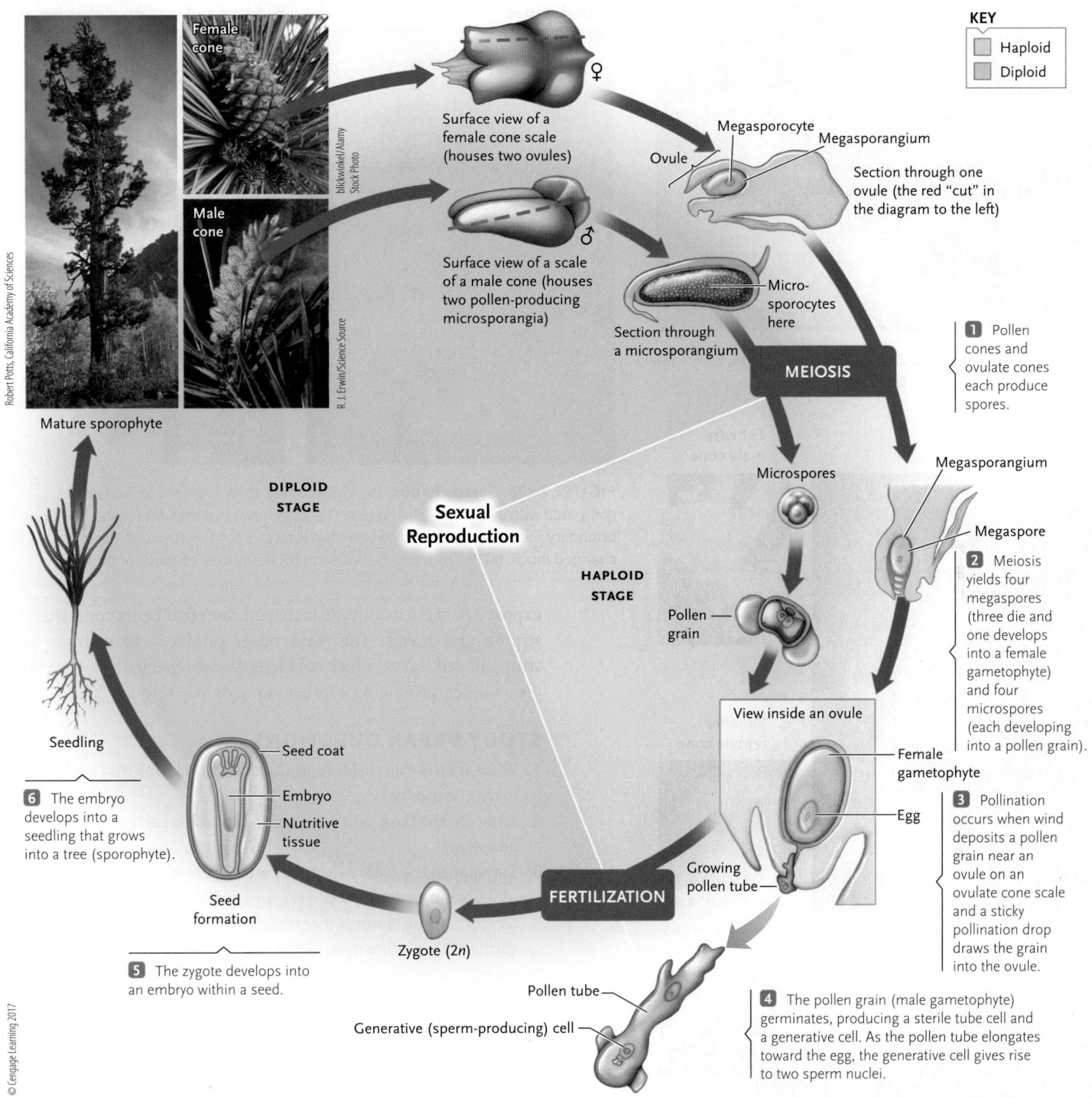

**FIGURE 26.24 Life cycle of a representative ponderosa pine.** Pines are the dominant conifers in the Northern Hemisphere, and their large sporophytes provide a heavily exploited source of wood.

Labels within figure:

Female cone

blickwinkel/Alamy Stock Photo

Male cone

R. J. Erwin/Science Source

Robert Potts, California Academy of Sciences

Mature sporophyte

Surface view of a female cone scale (houses two ovules)

Surface view of a scale of a male cone (houses two pollen-producing microsporangia)

Ovule

Megasporocyte

Megasporangium

Section through one ovule (the red "cut" in the diagram to the left)

Microsporocytes here

Section through a microsporangium

**MEIOSIS**

**KEY**
Haploid
Diploid

**1** Pollen cones and ovulate cones each produce spores.

**DIPLOID STAGE**

**Sexual Reproduction**

**HAPLOID STAGE**

Microspores

Megasporangium

Megaspore

**2** Meiosis yields four megaspores (three die and one develops into a female gametophyte) and four microspores (each developing into a pollen grain).

Pollen grain

View inside an ovule

Female gametophyte

Egg

Growing pollen tube

**3** Pollination occurs when wind deposits a pollen grain near an ovule on an ovulate cone scale and a sticky pollination drop draws the grain into the ovule.

Seed coat

Embryo

Nutritive tissue

**6** The embryo develops into a seedling that grows into a tree (sporophyte).

Seedling

Seed formation

**FERTILIZATION**

Zygote (2n)

**5** The zygote develops into an embryo within a seed.

Pollen tube

Generative (sperm-producing) cell

**4** The pollen grain (male gametophyte) germinates, producing a sterile tube cell and a generative cell. As the pollen tube elongates toward the egg, the generative cell gives rise to two sperm nuclei.

© Cengage Learning 2017

leaves (**Figure 26.26**) that turn a brilliant yellow in autumn. Nursery-propagated male trees are often planted in cities because they are resistant to insects, disease, and air pollutants. The female trees are equally pollution resistant, but gardeners avoid them because their seeds produce a foul odour that only a ginkgo could love. The leaves and seeds have been used in traditional Chinese medicine for centuries. The extract of the leaves is one of the most intensely investigated herbal medicines; there is some evidence that it assists in blood flow and so may be effective in the treatment of circulatory disorders.

**GNETOPHYTES INCLUDE SIMPLE SEED PLANTS WITH INTRIGUING FEATURES** The phylum Gnetophyta contains three genera—*Gnetum*, *Ephedra*, and *Welwitschia*—that together include about 70 species. Moist, tropical regions are home to about 30 species of *Gnetum*, which includes both trees and

FIGURE 26.25 The cycad *Zamia* showing a large, terminal female cone and fernlike leaves

**a. *Ephedra* plant**

**b. *Ephedra* male cone**

**c. *Ephedra* female cone**

Yang Y, Wang Q (2013) The Earliest Fleshy Cone of Ephedra from the Early Cretaceous Yixian Formation of Northeast China. PLoS ONE 8(1): e53652. https://doi.org/10.1371/journal.pone.0053652

**d. *Welwitschia* plant with female cones**

FIGURE 26.27 **Gnetophytes. (a)** Sporophyte of *Ephedra*, with close-ups of its **(b)** pollen-bearing cones and **(c)** seed-bearing cone, which develop on separate plants. **(d)** Sporophyte of *Welwitschia mirabilis*, with seed-bearing cones

leathery-leafed vines (lianas). About 35 species of *Ephedra* grow in desert regions of the world (**Figure 26.27a–c**).

Of all the gymnosperms, *Welwitschia* is the most bizarre. This seed-producing plant grows in the hot deserts of southwest Africa. The bulk of the plant is a deep-reaching taproot. The only

**a. Ginkgo tree**

**b. Fossil and modern ginkgo leaves**

**c. Male cone**

**d. Ginkgo seeds**

FIGURE 26.26 ***Ginkgo biloba.* (a)** A ginkgo tree. **(b)** A fossilized ginkgo leaf compared with a leaf from a living tree. The fossil formed at the Cretaceous–Tertiary boundary. Even though 65 million years have passed, the leaf structure has not changed much. **(c)** Pollen-bearing cones and **(d)** fleshy-coated seeds of the *Ginkgo*

exposed part is a woody, disk-shaped stem that bears cone-shaped strobili and leaves. The plant never produces more than two strap-shaped leaves, which split lengthwise repeatedly as the plant grows older, producing a rather scraggly pile (Figure 26.27d).

## STUDY BREAK QUESTIONS

1. What are the four major reproductive adaptations that evolved in gymnosperms?
2. What are the basic parts of a seed, and how is each one adaptive?
3. Summarize the main similarities and differences among ginkgoes, cycads, gnetophytes, and conifers.
4. Describe some features that make conifers structurally more complex than other gymnosperms.

## 26.6 Angiosperms: Flowering Plants

Of all plant phyla, the flowering plants, or **angiosperms**, are the most successful today. At least 260 000 species are known (**Figure 26.28** shows a few examples), and botanists regularly discover new ones in previously unexplored regions of the tropics. The word *angiosperm* is derived from the Greek *angeion* ("vessel") and *sperma* ("seed"). The "vessel" refers to the modified sporophyll, called a *carpel*, that surrounds and protects the ovules. Carpels are located in the centre of **flowers**—reproductive structures that are a defining feature of angiosperms. Another defining feature is the **fruit**—botanically speaking, a structure that helps protect and disperse seeds.

In addition to having flowers and fruits, angiosperms are the most ecologically diverse plants on Earth, growing on dry land and in **wetlands**, fresh water, and the seas. Angiosperms

a. Flowering plants in a desert

b. Alpine angiosperms

c. Triticale, a grass

d. The carnivorous plant Venus flytrap

**FIGURE 26.28 Flowering plants.** Diverse photosynthetic species are adapted to nearly all environments, ranging from **(a)** deserts to **(b)** snowlines of high mountains. **(c)** Triticale, a hybrid grain derived from parental stocks of wheat (*Triticum*) and rye (*Secale*), is one example of the various grasses used by humans. **(d)** The carnivorous plant Venus flytrap (*Dionaea muscipula*) grows in nitrogen-poor soils and traps insects as an additional source of nitrogen.

range in size from tiny duckweeds that are about 1 mm long to towering *Eucalyptus* trees more than 60 m tall.

## 26.6a The Fossil Record Provides Little Information about the Origin of Flowering Plants

The evolutionary origin of angiosperms has confounded plant biologists for well over a hundred years. Charles Darwin called it the "abominable mystery" because flowering plants appear suddenly in the fossil record, without a fossil sequence that links them to any other plant groups. As with gymnosperms, attempts to reconstruct the earliest flowering plant lineages have produced several conflicting classifications and family trees. Some paleobotanists hypothesize that flowering plants arose during the Jurassic period; others propose that they evolved in the Triassic from now-extinct gymnosperms or from seed ferns. However, progress in this area does not rely solely on fossil evidence; molecular data can be used to test hypotheses, and the

combination of molecular, morphological, and fossil evidence offers great promise in solving this mystery.

The fossil record has yet to reveal obvious transitional organisms between flowering plants and either gymnosperms or seedless vascular plants. As the Mesozoic era ended and the modern Cenozoic era began, great extinctions occurred among both plant and animal kingdoms. Gymnosperms declined and dinosaurs disappeared. Flowering plants, mammals, and social insects flourished, radiating into new environments. Today we live in what has been called "the age of flowering plants."

## 26.6b Angiosperms Are Subdivided into Several Groups, Including Monocots and Eudicots

Angiosperms are assigned to the phylum **Anthophyta**, a name that derives from the Greek *anthos*, meaning "flower." The great majority of angiosperms are classified as either monocots or eudicots, which are differentiated on the basis of morphological features such as the number of flower parts and the pattern of vascular tissue in stems and leaves. The two groups also differ in terms of the morphology of their embryos: **monocot** embryos have a single leaflike structure called a *cotyledon*, whereas **eudicot** ("true dicots") embryos generally have two cotyledons (see Table 26.2).

Botanists currently recognize several other groups of plants in addition to eudicots and monocots, but figuring out the appropriate classification for and relationships among these other groups is an ongoing challenge and an extremely active area of plant research. In this chapter, we focus only on monocots and eudicots.

There are at least 60 000 species of monocots, including 10 000 grasses and 20 000 orchids. **Figure 26.29a** gives some idea of the variety of living monocots, which include grasses, palms, lilies, and orchids. The world's major crop plants (wheat, corn, rice, rye, sugar cane, and barley) are all monocots and are all domesticated grasses. Eudicots are even more diverse, with nearly 200 000 species (Figure 26.29b). They include flowering shrubs and trees, most nonwoody (herbaceous) plants, and cacti. We will take a closer look at angiosperms in Chapter 35, which focuses on the structure and function of flowering plants.

## 26.6c Many Factors Contributed to the Adaptive Success of Angiosperms

Flowering plants likely originated about 140 mya. It took only about 40 million years—a short span in geologic time—for angiosperms to eclipse gymnosperms as the prevailing form of plant life on land. Several factors fuelled this adaptive success **(Figure 26.30)**. As with other seed plants, the large, diploid sporophyte phase dominates a flowering plant's life cycle, and the sporophyte retains and nourishes the much smaller gametophytes. But flowering plants also show some evolutionary innovations not seen in gymnosperms.

**MORE EFFICIENT TRANSPORT OF WATER AND NUTRIENTS**
Where gymnosperms have only one type of water-conducting cell in their xylem, angiosperms have an additional, more specialized type of cell that is larger and open ended and thus moves water more rapidly from roots to shoots (see Chapter 34). Also, modifications in angiosperm phloem tissue allow it to more efficiently transport sugars produced in photosynthesis through the plant body.

### a. Representative monocots

Wheat (*Triticum*)

Trillium (*Trillium*)

Western wood lily
(*Lilium philadelphicum*)

### b. Representative eudicots

Wild rose (*Rosa acicularis*)

Twinflower (*Linnaea borealis*)

Claret cup cactus
(*Echinocereus triglochidiatus*)

**FIGURE 26.29 Examples of monocots and eudicots. (a)** Representative monocots: wheat (*Triticum*), trillium (*Trillium*), and Western wood lily (*Lilium philadelphicum*). **(b)** Representative eudicots: wild rose (*Rosa acicularis*), twinflower (*Linnaea borealis*), and cactus (*Echinocereus triglochidiatus*)

FIGURE 26.30    **Experimental Research**

## Exploring a Possible Early Angiosperm Adaptation for Efficient Photosynthesis in Dim Environments

**Question:** Did modifications in light-sensitive pigments shape the early evolution of flowering plants?

**Experiment:** Sarah J. Mathews and J. Gordon Burleigh, of the University of Missouri, and Michael J. Donoghue, of Yale University, hypothesized that the first angiosperms may have evolved in the dim understory of moist land habitats dominated by large Mesozoic gymnosperms and ferns.

1. The researchers began by looking at genes, designated *PHYA* and *PHYC*, that encode phytochromes (pigments) that allow seed plants to detect light of red and far-red wavelengths—wavelengths that predominate in dim light. The nucleotide sequences of *PHYA* and *PHYC* are about 50% identical and evidently are the descendants of a duplicated ancestral *PHY* gene. *PHYC* is sensitive to relatively bright light but apparently does not respond to dim light, and *PHYA* is highly sensitive to dim light and is inactivated by bright light.

2. The researchers obtained amino acid sequence data for key functional domains of the phytochrome proteins encoded by *PHYA* and *PHYC* in 45 plant species. Most of the species were angiosperms; several conifers represented the presumed ancestral gene. Analysis of the data focused on both the number of substitutions in the targeted phytochrome amino acid sequences and the biochemical effects of the substitutions.

**Results:** In the tree branch leading from the presumed ancestral *PHY* gene to *PHYA*, 32 amino acid substitutions occurred. Of these, 11 were best interpreted as shifts associated with selection pressure. In the branch leading to *PHYC*, only 7 substitutions occurred; 4 were best interpreted as associated with selection pressure. A phylogenetic tree based on these results displayed genetic divergences as branch points.

**Conclusion:** Diverging molecular characteristics of *PHYA* and *PHYC* correlated with diverging functions of the phytochromes the genes encode. PHYA evidently evolved under strong selection pressure. The availability of phytochrome A (phyA) possibly allowed early angiosperm seedlings to grow in mostly dim light conditions, as in the shade of Mesozoic forests.

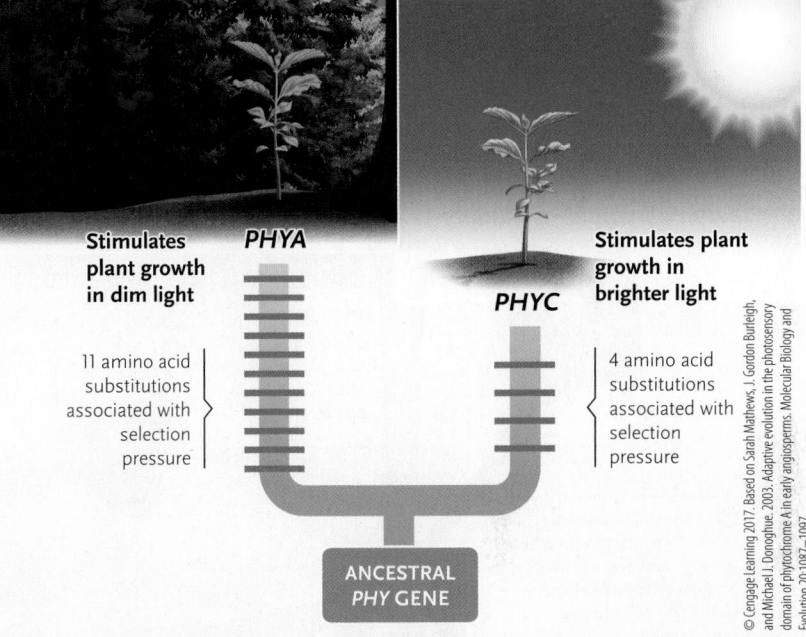

Amino acid sequences of key functional domains of phyA and phyC proteins from conifer, multiple angiosperms

Computer analysis

Stimulates plant growth in dim light

**PHYA**

11 amino acid substitutions associated with selection pressure

**PHYC**

Stimulates plant growth in brighter light

4 amino acid substitutions associated with selection pressure

ANCESTRAL PHY GENE

© Cengage Learning 2017. Based on Sarah Mathews, J. Gordon Burleigh, and Michael J. Donoghue. 2003. Adaptive evolution in the photosensory domain of phytochrome A in early angiosperms. Molecular Biology and Evolution 20:1087–1097.

**ENHANCED NUTRITION AND PHYSICAL PROTECTION FOR EMBRYOS** Other changes in angiosperms increased the likelihood of successful reproduction and dispersal of offspring. For example, a two-step, double-fertilization process in the ovules of flowering plants produces both an embryo and a unique nutritive tissue (called *endosperm*) that nourishes the embryonic sporophyte **(Figure 26.31)**. The ovule containing a female gametophyte is enclosed within an ovary, made up of one or more carpels, depending on the plant, that shelters the ovule against desiccation and attack by herbivores or pathogens. After fertilization, an ovary develops into a fruit that not only protects seeds but also helps disperse them; for instance, when an animal eats a fruit, seeds may pass through the animal's gut none the worse for the journey and be released in a new location in the animal's feces. Above all, angiosperms have flowers, the unique reproductive organs that you will read much more about in Chapter 35.

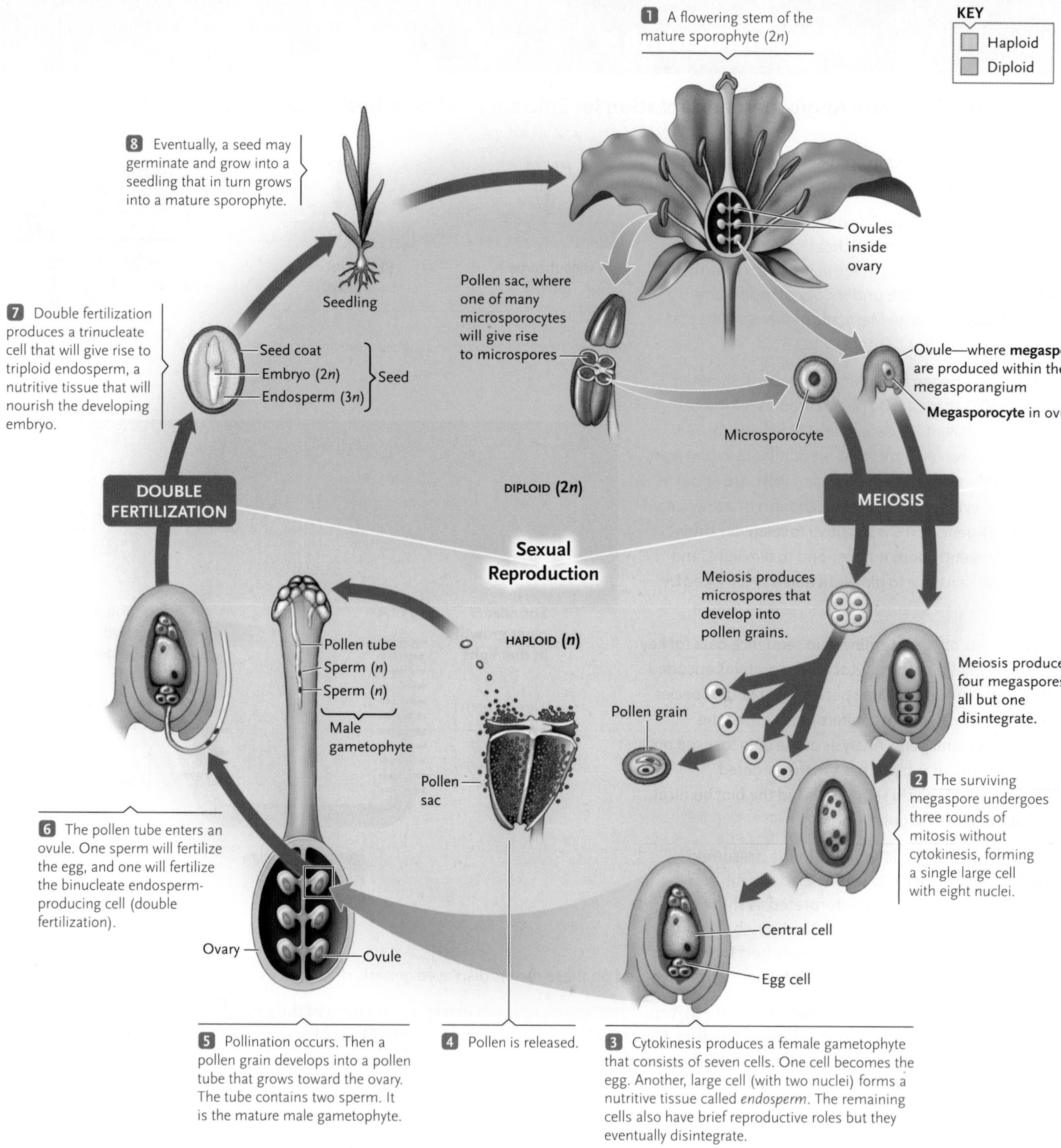

**FIGURE 26.31 Life cycle of a typical flowering plant.** Double fertilization is a notable feature of the cycle. The male gametophyte delivers two sperm to an ovule. One sperm fertilizes the egg, forming the embryo, and the other fertilizes the endosperm-producing cell, which nourishes the embryo.

## 26.6d Angiosperms Co-evolved with Animal Pollinators

The evolutionary success of angiosperms is due not only to the adaptations just described, but also to the efficient mechanisms of transferring pollen to female reproductive parts. Whereas a conifer depends on air currents to disperse its pollen, as do such

angiosperms as grasses, many angiosperms co-evolved with pollinators: insects, bats, birds, and other animals that transfer pollen from male floral structures to female reproductive parts, often while obtaining nectar. Nectar is a sugar-rich liquid secreted by flowers to attract pollinators. Pollen itself is a reward for some pollinators, such as bees, that use it as a food resource. So, while plants benefit from their animal pollinators, there is also a cost to the plant in providing a reward to the pollinator. Co-evolution occurs when two or more species interact closely in the same ecological setting. A heritable change in one species affects selection pressure operating between them, so that the other species evolves as well. Over time, plants have co-evolved with their pollinating animals.

In general, a flower's reproductive parts are positioned so that visiting pollinators will brush against them. In addition, many floral features correlate with the morphology and behaviour of specific pollinators. For example, reproductive parts may be located above nectar-filled floral tubes that are the same length as the feeding structure of a preferred pollinator. Nectar-sipping bats **(Figure 26.32a)** and moths forage by night. They pollinate intensely sweet-smelling flowers with white or pale petals that are more visible than coloured petals in the dark. The long thin mouthparts of moths and butterflies reach nectar in narrow floral tubes or floral spurs. The Madagascar hawkmoth uncoils a mouthpart the same length—an astonishing 22 cm—as the narrow flower of the orchid it pollinates, *Angraecum sesquipedale* (Figure 26.32b). Red and yellow flowers attract birds (Figure 26.32c), which have good daytime vision but a poor sense of smell. Hence, bird-pollinated plants do not squander metabolic resources to make fragrances. By contrast, flowers of species that are pollinated by beetles or flies may smell like rotten meat, dung, or decaying matter. This trickery by the plants is known as *signal mimicry*: the plant uses visual and olfactory signals to trick a pollinator into visiting it; some of these plants provide no nutritional reward for

their pollinators at all. Daisies and other fragrant flowers with distinctive patterns, shapes, and red or orange components attract butterflies, which forage by day.

Bees see ultraviolet light and visit flowers with sweet odours and parts that appear to humans as yellow, blue, or purple (Figure 26.32d). Produced by pigments that absorb ultraviolet light, the colours form patterns called "nectar guides" that attract bees, which may pick up or drop off pollen during the visit. Here, as in our other examples, flowers contribute to the reproductive success of plants that bear them.

In this chapter, we have introduced some of the strategies that plants use to meet the challenges of life on Earth; they face the same challenges as animals and other terrestrial organisms (attract a mate, reproduce, disperse offspring, and survive unfavourable conditions) but have had to find ways to do all of these without being able to move around (they are sessile). Many of these topics are followed up in more detail in the chapters dealing with plant biology (Chapters 33 to 37).

The next two chapters introduce animals. As you read these chapters, look for similarities and differences in how they have addressed the challenges of life compared to plants.

## STUDY BREAK QUESTIONS

1. What are the advantages and costs to plants of using animals to disperse their pollen?
2. List at least three adaptations that have contributed to the evolutionary success of angiosperms as a group.

**Figure 26.32 Co-evolution of flowering plants and animal pollinators.** The colours and configurations of some flowers, and the production of nectar or odours, have co-evolved with specific animal pollinators. **(a)** At night, nectar-feeding bats sip nectar from flowers of the giant saguaro cactus (*Carnegiea gigantea*), transferring pollen from flower to flower in the process. **(b)** The hawkmoth (*Xanthopan morganii praedicta*) has a proboscis long enough to reach nectar at the base of the equally long floral spur of the orchid *Angraecum sesquipedale*. **(c)** A ruby-throated hummingbird (*Archilochus colubris*) sipping nectar from a hibiscus blossom (*Hibiscus*). The long narrow bill of hummingbirds co-evolved with long narrow floral tubes. **(d)** Under ultraviolet light, the bee-attracting pattern of a gold-petalled marsh marigold becomes visible to human eyes.

a. **Bat pollinating a giant saguaro**

b. **Hawkmoth pollinating an orchid**   c. **Hummingbird visiting a hibiscus flower**   d. **Bee-attracting pattern of a marsh marigold**

Visible light    UV light

# Summary Illustration

Land plants are multicellular eukaryotes with cellulose cell walls and a number of adaptations to terrestrial life, including protecting gametes in multicellular chambers and sheltering embryos inside parent plants.

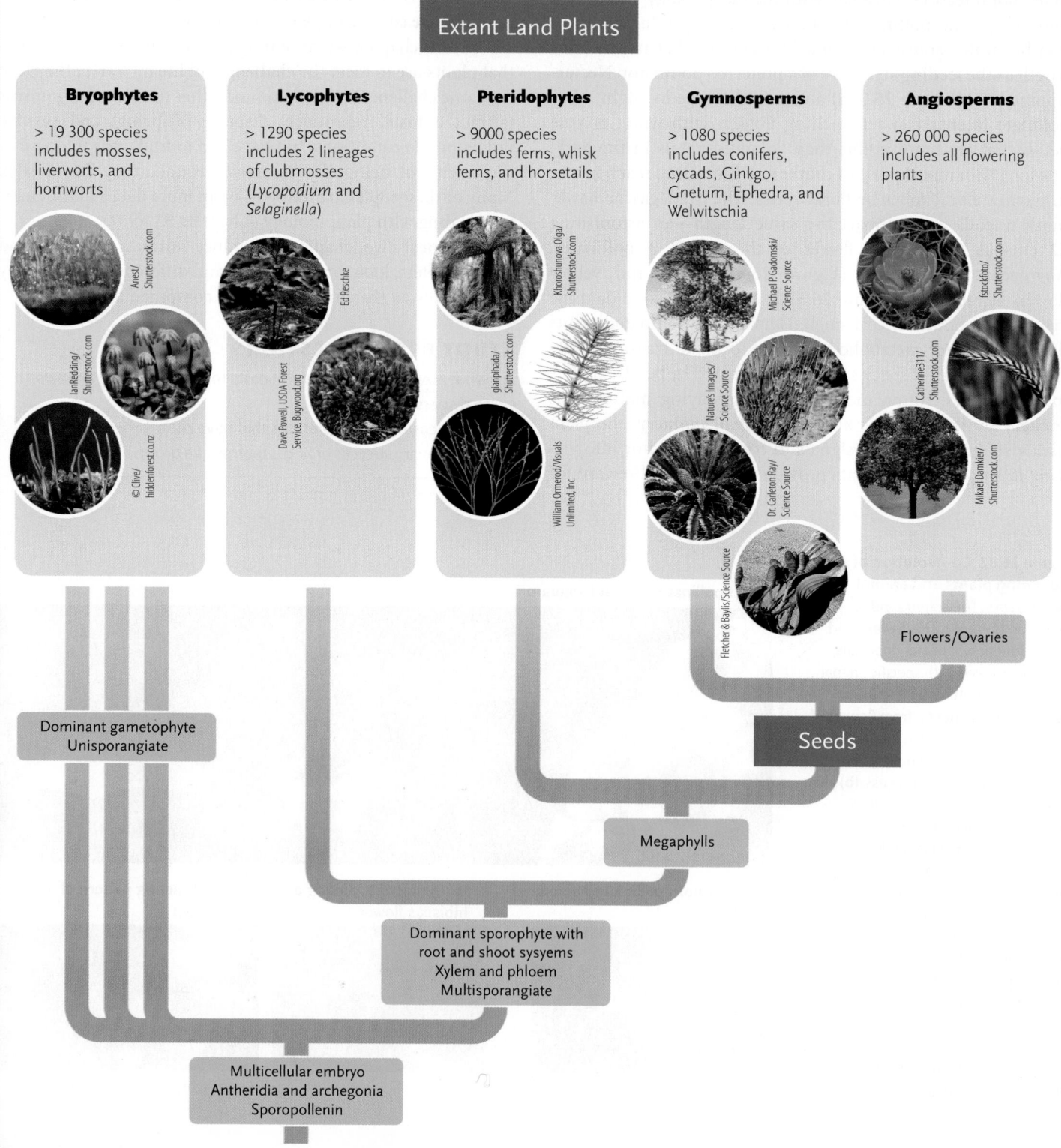

## Extant Land Plants

### Bryophytes
> 19 300 species includes mosses, liverworts, and hornworts

Anest/Shutterstock.com

IanRedding/Shutterstock.com

© Clive/hiddenforest.co.nz

### Lycophytes
> 1290 species includes 2 lineages of clubmosses (*Lycopodium* and *Selaginella*)

Ed Reschke

Dave Powell, USDA Forest Service, Bugwood.org

### Pteridophytes
> 9000 species includes ferns, whisk ferns, and horsetails

Khoroshunova Olga/Shutterstock.com

gianpihada/Shutterstock.com

William Ormerod/Visuals Unlimited, Inc.

### Gymnosperms
> 1080 species includes conifers, cycads, Ginkgo, Gnetum, Ephedra, and Welwitschia

Michael P. Gadomski/Science Source

Nature's Images/Science Source

Dr. Carleton Ray/Science Source

Fletcher & Baylis/Science Source

### Angiosperms
> 260 000 species includes all flowering plants

fstockfoto/Shutterstock.com

Catherine311/Shutterstock.com

Mikael Damkier/Shutterstock.com

---

Flowers/Ovaries

Seeds

Dominant gametophyte
Unisporangiate

Megaphylls

Dominant sporophyte with root and shoot sysyems
Xylem and phloem
Multisporangiate

Multicellular embryo
Antheridia and archegonia
Sporopollenin

(Background) Sacey.K Photography/Shutterstock.com

# Comparing the Gametophytes of the Main Lineages of Land Plants

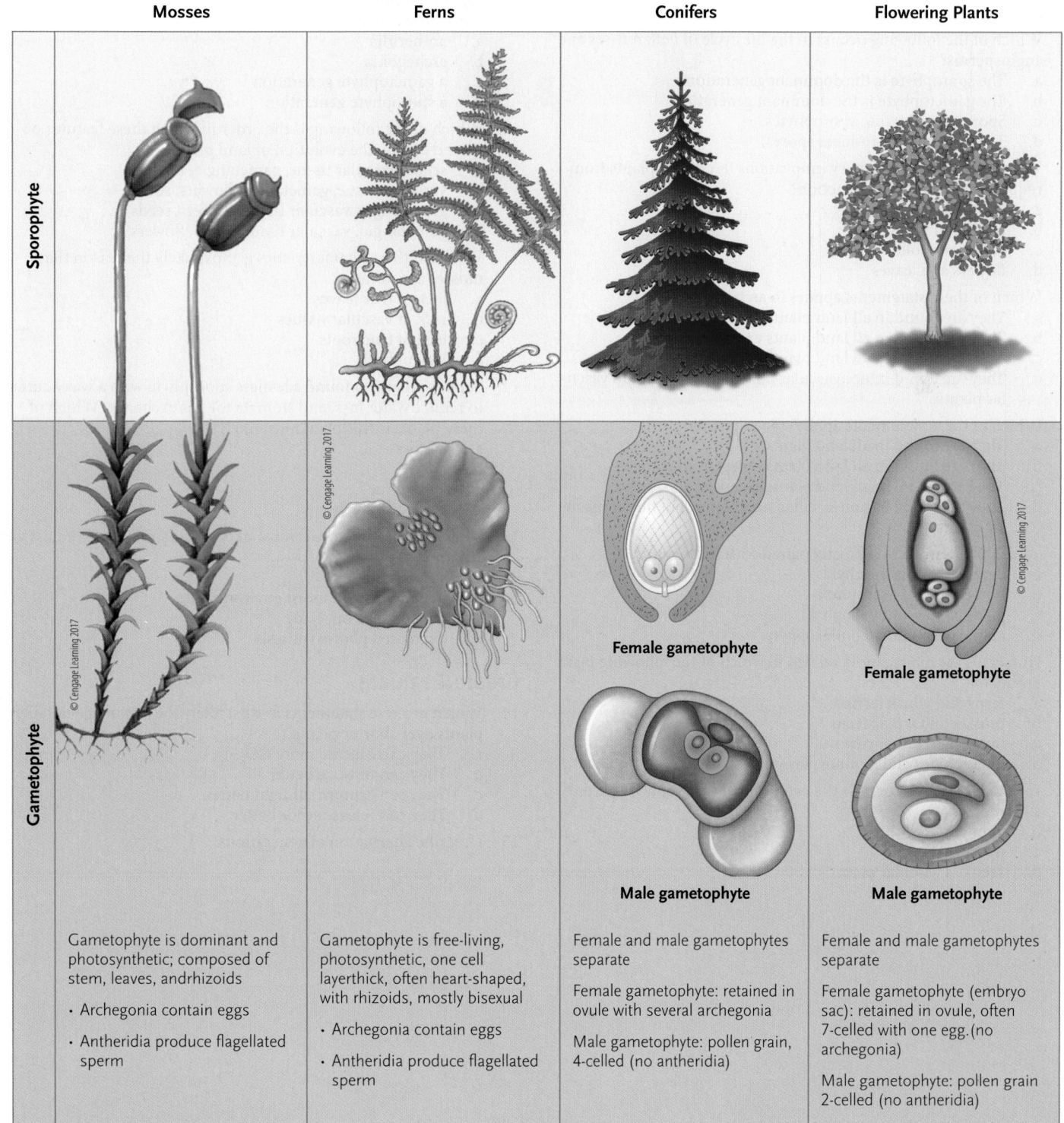

|  | Mosses | Ferns | Conifers | Flowering Plants |
|---|---|---|---|---|
| **Sporophyte** | | | | |
| **Gametophyte** | | | Female gametophyte / Male gametophyte | Female gametophyte / Male gametophyte |

**Mosses**

Gametophyte is dominant and photosynthetic; composed of stem, leaves, andrhizoids

- Archegonia contain eggs
- Antheridia produce flagellated sperm

**Ferns**

Gametophyte is free-living, photosynthetic, one cell layerthick, often heart-shaped, with rhizoids, mostly bisexual

- Archegonia contain eggs
- Antheridia produce flagellated sperm

**Conifers**

Female and male gametophytes separate

Female gametophyte: retained in ovule with several archegonia

Male gametophyte: pollen grain, 4-celled (no antheridia)

**Flowering Plants**

Female and male gametophytes separate

Female gametophyte (embryo sac): retained in ovule, often 7-celled with one egg.(no archegonia)

Male gametophyte: pollen grain 2-celled (no antheridia)

## Recall/Understand

1. Which of the following occurred during land plant evolution?
   a. becoming seedless
   b. producing only one type of spore
   c. producing nonmotile gametes
   d. haploid generation becoming dominant

2. Which of the following occurs in the life cycle of *both* mosses and angiosperms?
   a. The sporophyte is the dominant generation.
   b. The gametophyte is the dominant generation.
   c. Spores develop into sporophytes.
   d. The sporophyte produces spores.

3. Which of these evolutionary innovations freed land plants from requiring water for reproduction?
   a. lignified stems
   b. fruits and roots
   c. seeds and pollen
   d. flowers and leaves

4. Which of these statements applies to archegonia?
   a. They are found in all land plants.
   b. They are found in all land plants except seed plants.
   c. They are found in all land plants except angiosperms.
   d. They are found in nonvascular land plants, but not in vascular plants.

5. Which of these statements applies to antheridia?
   a. They are found in all land plants.
   b. They are found in all land plants except seed plants.
   c. They are found in all land plants except angiosperms.
   d. They are found in nonvascular land plants, but not in vascular plants.

6. Which plant group is correctly paired with its phylum?
   a. cycads and Hepatophyta
   b. horsetails and Pterophyta
   c. gnetophytes and Bryophyta
   d. angiosperms and Coniferophyta

7. Horsetails are most closely related to which of the following plant groups?
   a. ferns and whisk ferns
   b. mosses and whisk ferns
   c. liverworts and hornworts
   d. gnetophytes and gymnosperms

8. In which of these groups is the evolution of true roots first seen?
   a. mosses
   b. conifers
   c. liverworts
   d. seedless vascular plants

## Apply/Analyze

9. Your neighbour notices moss growing between bricks on her patio. Closer examination reveals tiny brown stalks with round tops emerging from leafy shoots. Which of the following are these brown structures most likely?
   a. antheridia
   b. archegonia
   c. a gametophyte generation
   d. a sporophyte generation

10. Which of the following is the order in which these features occurred during the evolution of land plants?
    a. seeds, vascular tissue, gametangia, flowers
    b. vascular tissue, gametangia, flowers, seeds
    c. gametangia, vascular tissue, flowers, seeds
    d. gametangia, vascular tissue, seeds, flowers

11. Which of these characteristics is most likely the reason that mosses are so short?
    a. lack of true leaves
    b. lack of vascular tissues
    c. lack of true roots
    d. lack of bark

12. Suppose that you found a leafless sporophyte with a waxy cuticle to reduce water loss, and stomata for gas exchange. Which of these plants is this plant most likely?
    a. a moss
    b. a fern
    c. a pine tree
    d. an angiosperm

13. Which of these factors is most likely a constraint for seedless vascular plants?
    a. short height
    b. dependence on moist environments
    c. dependence on shade
    d. decreased photosynthesis

## Create/Evaluate

14. Which of these statements is most likely the advantage of taller plants over shorter plants?
    a. They can capture more $CO_2$.
    b. They can fertilize better.
    c. They can capture sunlight better.
    d. They can release seeds better.

15. Describe alternation of generations.

# Chapter Roadmap

## Animals

The kingdom Animalia is monophyletic, meaning that all animals share a common ancestry. Animals are eukaryotic, multicellular organisms. Animal cells may be organized into different morphological types, reflecting their role in the functioning of the animal as a single unit.

**27.1 What Is an Animal?**

**27.2 Key Innovations in Animal Evolution**

**27.3 Molecular Phylogenetics and Classification**

**27.4 The Basal Phyla**

**27.5 The Protostomes**

**27.6 Lophotrochozoa Protostomes**

**27.7 Ecdysozoa Protostomes**

**27.8 The Deuterostomes**

**27.9 The Origin and Diversification of Vertebrates**

**27.10 Agnathans: The Jawless Fishes**

**27.11 Jawed Fishes: Jaws Meant New Feeding Opportunities**

**27.12 Early Tetrapods and Modern Amphibians**

**27.13 The Origin and Mesozoic Radiations of Amniotes**

**27.14 Turtles and Tortoises (Subclass Testudinata)**

**27.15 Living Diapsids: Sphenodontids, Squamates, and Crocodylians**

**27.16 Birds**

**27.17 Mammalia: Monotremes, Marsupials, and Placentals**

Octopus, a highly evolved mollusc of the animal kingdom, capable of complex learning and behaviour

# Animals

# 27

**Why it matters . . .** In 1977, the research submersible Alvin investigated a temperature anomaly in the Galapagos Rift, an area on the sea floor of the Pacific Ocean off the west coast of South America. This rift is where two of Earth's massive tectonic plates slowly moved apart, resulting in hydrothermal vents that spew out mineral-rich fluids that can be as hot as 400°C. In this unique environment, Alvin found a previously unimagined ecosystem, similar to that shown in **Figure 27.1**. A dominant member of this ecosystem is *Riftia pachyptila*, which is over 2 m long and has a plume of bright red tentacles extending from a chitinous tube.

Adult *Riftia* lack a gut, mouth, and anus. Is this an animal or a plant? You may be surprised to learn that it is an animal, a giant tubeworm. Like other animals, *Riftia* are multicellular and lack cell walls. Adult *Riftia* acquire food through a richly vascularized organ, the trophosome, which is home to millions of chemoautotrophic bacteria that oxidize sulfide, which is commonly found at hydrothermal vents. *Riftia* take up sulfide and the bacteria oxidize it to sulfate **(Figure 27.2)**. The energy released is used to fix carbon and synthesize organic molecules, a process analogous to photosynthesis (see Chapter 6). *Riftia* has a uniquely adapted hemoglobin that is not poisoned by sulfides and has separate binding sites for oxygen and for sulfides.

*Riftia* is one of many species fuelled by sulfide oxidation at deep-sea vent sites. Other species with symbiotic relationships with chemoautotrophic bacteria include giant clams (*Bathymodiolus*), which have bacteria in their gills. In addition, tube worms such as *Alvinella* (named after the submersible) have bacteria in their tubes. Yeti crabs (*Kiwa hirsuta*) culture bacteria on the fine

**FIGURE 27.1  A large colony of *Riftia pachyptila* at a vent site on the Galapagos Rift**

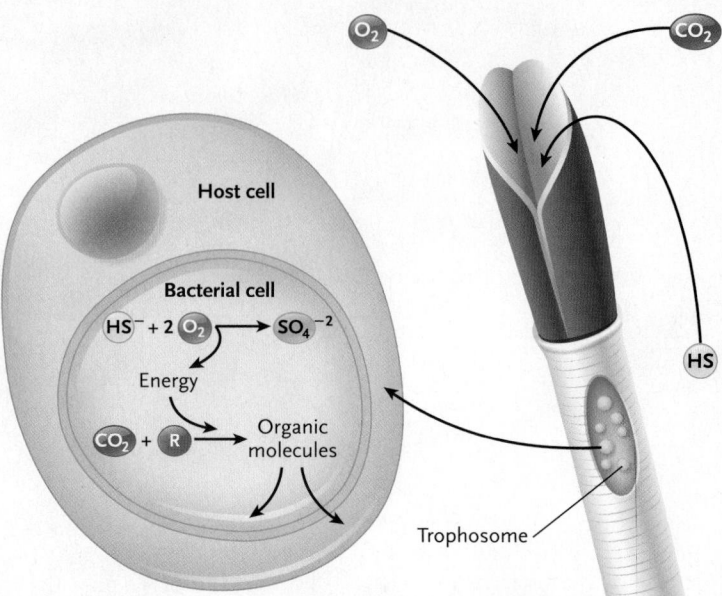

**FIGURE 27.2  Pathways involved in chemoautosynthesis in *Riftia***

Source: Tunnicliffe, V. (1992). "Hydrothermal vent communities of the deep sea," *American Scientist*, 80: 336–349.

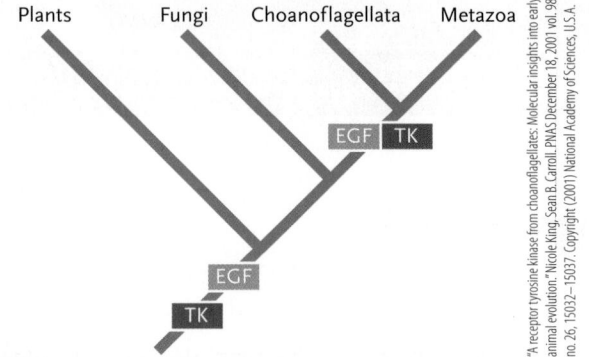

"A receptor tyrosine kinase from choanoflagellates: Molecular insights into early animal evolution." Nicole King, Sean B. Carroll. PNAS December 18, 2001 vol. 98 no. 26, 15032–15037. Copyright (2001) National Academy of Sciences, U.S.A.

**FIGURE 27.3  Tyrosine kinase (TK) and epidermal growth factor (EGF) are found in most eukaryotic organisms.** Only in Choanoflagellata and Metazoa are TK and EGF found as linked domains associated with a TK receptor. This, and other molecular evidence, supports placing the Choanoflagellata as a sister group to Metazoa.

setae covering their bodies. These species are the base of a food network that includes predators and scavengers in a complex community.

*Riftia* obviously belong to the kingdom Animalia because they lack cell walls and chloroplasts; however, they have undergone an almost unprecedented number of taxonomic reclassifications. Now molecular phylogenetic techniques—which involve studying DNA and RNA sequences—seem to have solved this taxonomic puzzle, classifying *Riftia pachyptila* as a sedentary annelid. Classifying animals to taxonomic groups is generally done based on body plans, a recurring theme in this chapter.

## 27.1  What Is an Animal?

The **kingdom Animalia** is monophyletic, meaning that all animals share a common ancestry. Animals are eukaryotic, multicellular organisms. Their cell membranes are in direct contact with one another, unlike plants and fungi, where walls surround individual cells. Animal cells may be organized into different morphological types (see Chapter 38), reflecting their role in the functioning of the animal as a single unit.

All animals are **heterotrophs**, which means they depend on other life forms for food, either by direct consumption or through a parasitic association. Most animals use oxygen to metabolize their food through aerobic respiration, and most store excess energy as glycogen, oil, or fat.

All animals are **motile**—able to move from place to place— at some time in their lives. Motile adults are most familiar but, in some species (e.g., mussels (Section 27.6e) and barnacles (Section 27.7h), only the young (larvae) are motile. These larvae eventually settle and turn into **sessile** (stationary) adults. Animals typically perceive and respond to information about the environment in which they live.

Animals reproduce either asexually or sexually, and many switch from one mode to the other. Sexually reproducing species produce haploid **gametes** (eggs and sperm) that fuse to form diploid **zygotes** (fertilized eggs). Many invertebrates are polymorphic and can exist as two or more distinct forms. Polymorphic development is important for the success of many of the inverte-

brate groups because it allows a species to use the resources of different habitats during different life stages (e.g., barnacles; Figure 27.62). This is particularly important for those living as parasites, since polymorphic larvae are part of a life cycle needs to reach a final host (e.g., tapeworms; Figure 27.34).

## 27.1a  Animals Probably Arose from a Colonial Flagellate

Biologists agree that the common ancestor of all animals was probably a colonial, flagellated protist that lived in the Precambrian, at least 700 mya. Molecular evidence suggests that, from this unknown ancestor, there evolved the Choanoflagellata (see Chapter 24)—a group of flagellated protists found in aquatic environments—and a sister group, the Metazoa (multicellular animals; **Figure 27.3**).

**Hypothesized evolution of a two-layered animal body plan**

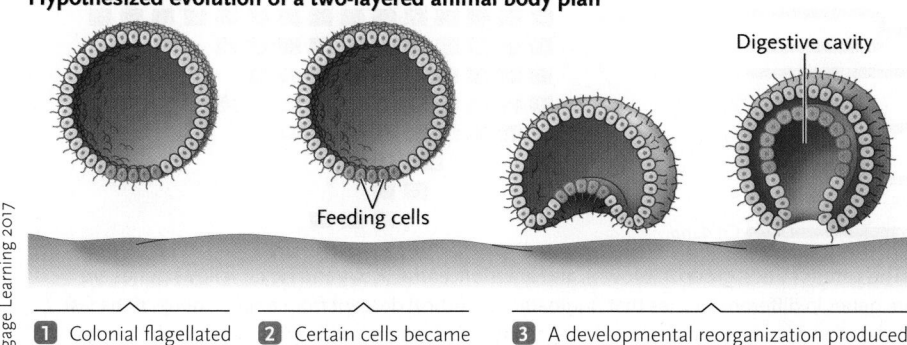

Digestive cavity

Feeding cells

**1** Colonial flagellated ancestor with unspecialized cells

**2** Certain cells became specialized for feeding and other functions.

**3** A developmental reorganization produced a two-layered animal with a sac-within-a-sac body plan.

© Cengage Learning 2017

**FIGURE 27.4 Animal origins.** Animals may have arisen from a colonial, flagellated protist in which cells became specialized for specific functions. This putative ancestor would have had a developmental reorganization that resulted in two cell layers. The cell movements illustrated here are similar to those that occur during the development of many animals, as described in Chapter 44 and elsewhere in this chapter. Associated with this, cells became specialized for different functions, such as the feeding cells giving rise to the digestive cavity (shown here).

In 1874, the German embryologist Ernst Haeckel first proposed such a colonial, flagellated animal ancestor. He suggested that the ancestor was a hollow, ball-shaped organism with unspecialized cells. Over evolutionary time, its cells became specialized for particular functions, and a developmental reorganization produced a double-layered, sac-within-a-sac body plan **(Figure 27.4)**. The embryology of many living animals roughly parallels this hypothetical evolutionary transformation. Haeckel included this hypothetical organism among what he called the "Metazoa" (*meta* = more developed; *zoon* = animal) to distinguish them from the Protozoa, and this name is still used today.

**STUDY BREAK QUESTIONS**

1. What characteristics distinguish animals from plants?
2. What early steps may have led to the first metazoans?

# 27.2 Key Innovations in Animal Evolution

Once established, the animal lineage diversified quickly into many different **body plans**. Body plans describe the way that animals are built. They are the "blueprint" of cellular organization that encompasses such things as symmetry, segmentation, and formation and position of limbs. Several key morphological innovations help to unravel the evolutionary relationships among the major groups of animals. These innovations include the following:

- development of different tissues
- type of body symmetry
- presence or absence of a body cavity
- patterns of embryonic development
- body segmentation

## 27.2a Tissue Development

In most Metazoa, the process of development gives rise to two or three layers of cells. **Tissues**, which are groups of similarly differentiated cells that are specialized for particular functions,

eventually arise from these layers of cells. In most metazoans, embryonic tissues form as either two or three concentric **germ layers** (see Chapter 44). The innermost layer, the **endoderm**, develops into the lining of the gut (digestive system) and, in some animals, respiratory organs. The outermost layer, the **ectoderm**, forms the external covering and the nervous system. Between the two, the **mesoderm** forms the muscles of the body wall and most other organs.

Some animals appear to have only a **diploblastic** body plan, a plan based on two embryonic layers: endoderm and ectoderm. However, most animals are **triploblastic**, having all three clearly identifiable germ layers.

## 27.2b Body Symmetry

The most obvious feature of an animal's body plan is its shape. Most animals are bilaterally symmetrical in that they can be divided vertically into two mirror image halves, with anterior, posterior, dorsal, and ventral regions **(Figure 27.5)**. Most animals also are **cephalized**—their sense organs are concentrated at the anterior end (i.e., the head).

Animal body plans are differentiated by a relatively small toolbox of genes. *Hox* genes are one group responsible for differentiating body parts along the anterior–posterior axis.

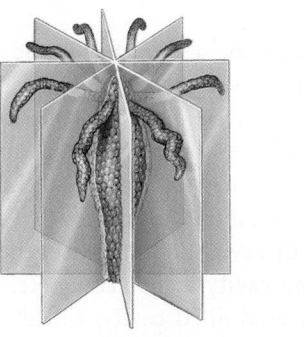

Radial symmetry

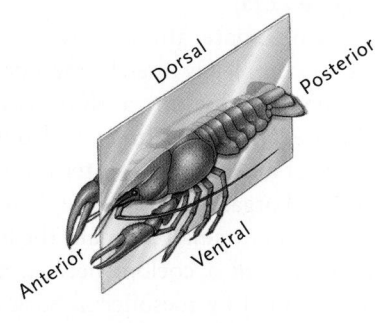

Dorsal

Posterior

Anterior

Ventral

Bilateral symmetry

© Cengage Learning 2017

**FIGURE 27.5 Patterns of body symmetry.** Most animals are bilaterally symmetrical.

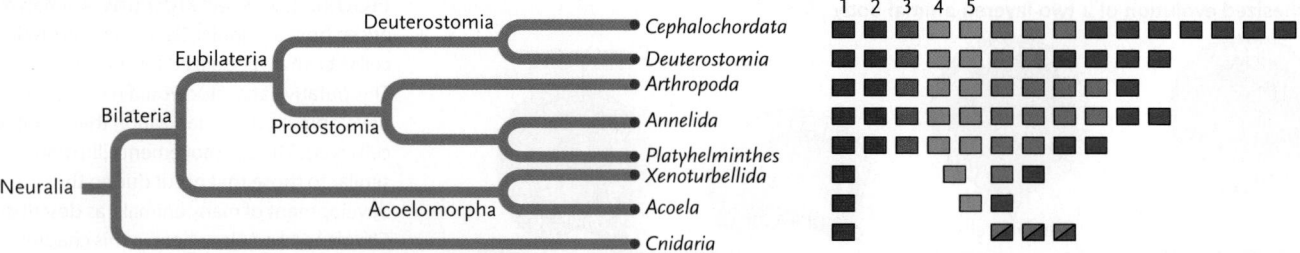

**FIGURE 27.6** *Hox* **genes of major eumetazoan groups.** The anterior (red), group 3 (brown), and anterior central (*Hox*4 and *Hox*5; yellow) genes are arranged according to presumed orthologous genes. These are genes in different species that originated by vertical descent from a single gene of the last common ancestor. Only the numbers of the posterior central (green) and posterior (blue) genes are indicted. There is uncertainty about the orthology of genes shown in blue–green. More complex animals on the phylogenetic tree have a greater number of *Hox* genes.

Source: Nielsen, C., (2010), "After all" Xenoturbella is an acoelomoph!" *Evolution & Development.* 12(3): 241-243. ©2010 Wiley Periodicals, Inc. *Evolution & Development* by Society for Integrative and Comparative Biology Reproduced with permission of BLACKWELL PUBLISHING, INC. in the format Book via Copyright Clearance Center.

More complex animals have a greater number of *Hox* genes than simpler animals **(Figure 27.6).**

**Radial symmetry** means that body parts are regularly arranged around a central axis, like spokes on a wheel. Animals in the phylum Cnidaria (hydras, jellyfishes, and sea anemones) have traditionally been viewed as having radial symmetry. Challenging this view is the recognition that the primitive body plan of the Cnidaria, as seen in sea anemones (see Figure 27.19), is not fully radially symmetrical. Further, the homeobox (*Hox*) genes that determine body axes in bilaterally symmetrical animals are also part of the sea anemone genome. For example, the dorsal–ventral axis of both invertebrates and vertebrates is determined by the interaction of a pair of genes from the *Wnt* family of homeobox genes. In a sea anemone, genes orthologous to these genes are active but only in a small region that will become the lip of the mouth. It appears that the symmetry of Cnidaria (part bilateral, part radial), like that in other groups displaying a superficial radial symmetry, is an adaptation to life where environmental inputs may come from any direction.

## 27.2c Body Cavities

In most bilaterally symmetrical animals, a body cavity separates the gut from the muscles of the body wall. **Acoelomate** animals (*a* = without; *koiloma* = cavity), such as flatworms (phylum Platyhelminthes), lack such a cavity. A mass of cells derived largely from mesoderm pack the region between gut and body wall **(Figure 27.7a).**

**Coelomate** animals have a **coelom**, a fluid-filled body cavity completely lined by mesoderm. In vertebrates, this lining is the **peritoneum**, a thin tissue derived from mesoderm (Figure 27.7c). The inner and outer layers of the peritoneum connect and form **mesenteries**, membranes that surround the internal organs and suspend them within the coelom.

In many small animals, the body cavity does not meet the definition of a coelom because the cavity is not completely surrounded by mesoderm. Such a fluid-filled cavity, called a **pseudocoelom** (*pseudo* = false), commonly lies between the endoderm of the gut and the mesodermal musculature (Figure 27.7b). Pseudocoelomate groups appear in different parts of the evolutionary tree, reflecting various levels of convergence. In Rotifers, the pseudocoelom is a remnant of part of the embryonic blastocoel. In Arthropoda and Mollusca, remnants of a true coelom remain in the reproductive system and around the heart. The rest of the body cavity is a hemocoel that supplies circulatory fluid and resembles a pseudocoel because it contacts all tissues and organs.

The body plan of coelomate and pseudocoelomate animals forms a "tube within a tube." The digestive system is the inner tube, and the body wall forms the outer tube. The body cavity, coelom or pseudocoelom, may serve at least four functions:

1. It can be used for transport of nutrients and products of metabolism.
2. It provides an environment in which eggs and sperm can develop.
3. It can serve as a **hydrostatic skeleton**, providing a basis for locomotion.
4. It provides space for the functioning of internal organs. The different parts of the digestive tract are muscular and use such movements as churning and peristalsis to process food. This can only occur if these structures are suspended and free to move.

## 27.2d Patterns of Embryological Development

Embryological evidence suggests that bilaterally symmetrical animals are divided into two lineages, **protostomes** (meaning "first opening," a reference to the initial development of the mouth) and **deuterostomes** (meaning "second opening," where the mouth develops later) **(Figure 27.8).**

After fertilization, the zygote undergoes a series of cell divisions, called **cleavage**. The first two cell divisions divide a zygote into four wedges from top to bottom. In animals with **spiral cleavage**, subsequent cell divisions occur at oblique angles to the vertical axis of the embryo, producing a mass in which each cell lies in the groove between the pair of cells below it (see Figure 27.8a, left side). Spiral cleavage is characteristic of most protostomes. **Radial cleavage** occurs in

**a.** In acoelomate animals, no body cavity separates the gut and body wall.

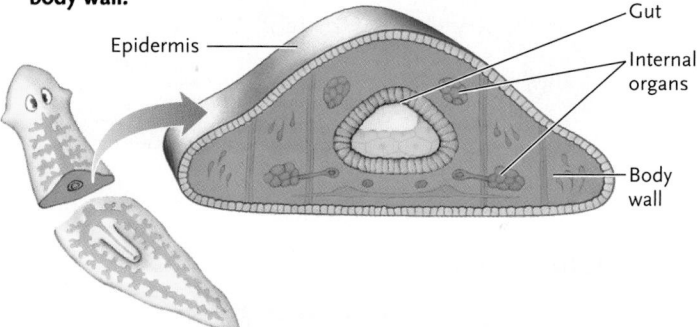

Epidermis — Gut — Internal organs — Body wall

**b.** In pseudocoelomate animals, the pseudocoelom forms between the gut (a derivative of endoderm) and the body wall (a derivative of mesoderm).

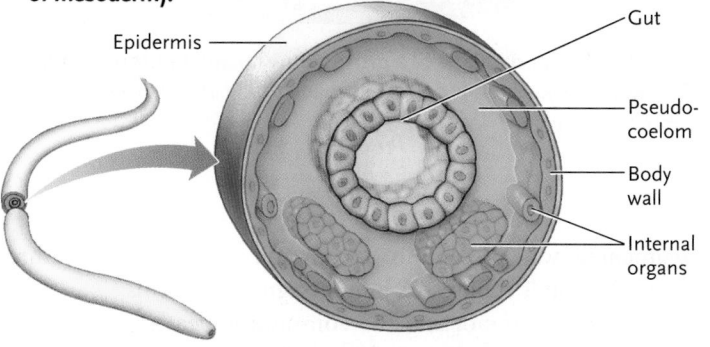

Epidermis — Gut — Pseudo-coelom — Body wall — Internal organs

**c.** In coelomate animals, the coelom is completely lined by peritoneum (a derivative of mesoderm).

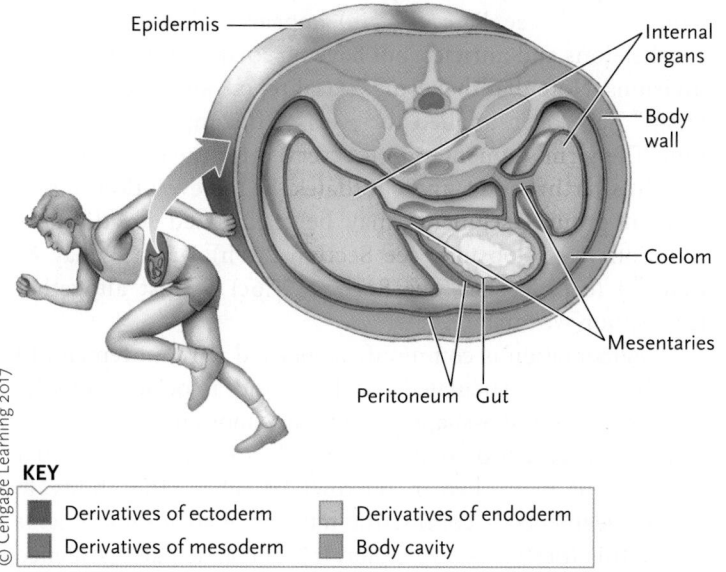

Epidermis — Internal organs — Body wall — Coelom — Mesenteries — Peritoneum — Gut

**KEY**

| | |
|---|---|
| ■ Derivatives of ectoderm | ■ Derivatives of endoderm |
| ■ Derivatives of mesoderm | ■ Body cavity |

© Cengage Learning 2017

**FIGURE 27.7 Body plans for bilaterally symmetrical animals**

| Protostomes | Deuterostomes |
|---|---|

**a. Cleavage**

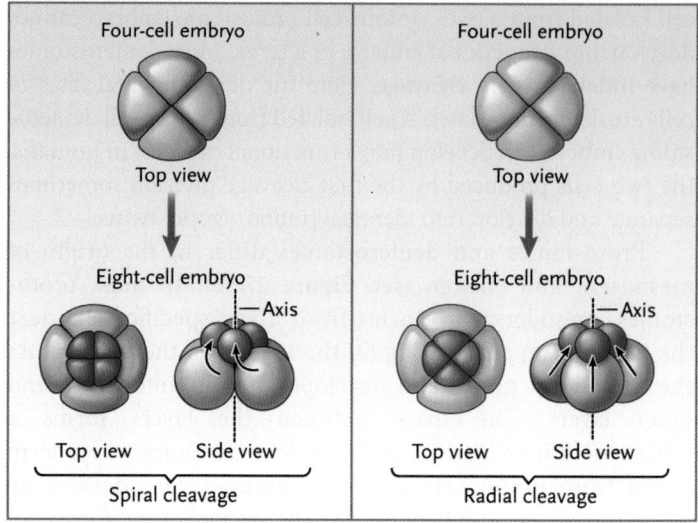

Four-cell embryo — Top view — Eight-cell embryo — Axis — Top view — Side view — Spiral cleavage

Four-cell embryo — Top view — Eight-cell embryo — Axis — Top view — Side view — Radial cleavage

**b. Mesoderm and coelom formation**

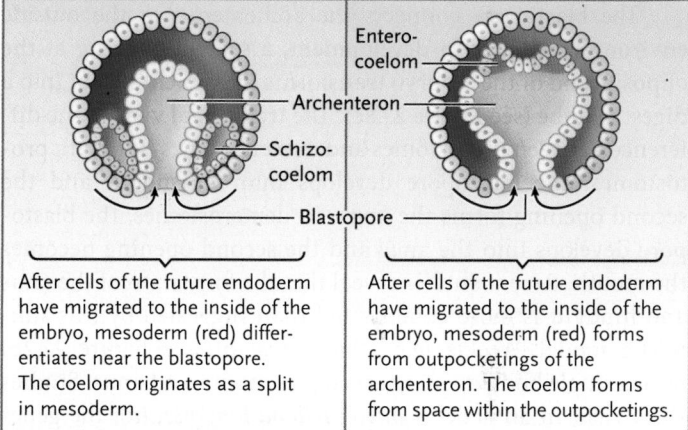

Entero-coelom — Archenteron — Schizo-coelom — Blastopore

After cells of the future endoderm have migrated to the inside of the embryo, mesoderm (red) differentiates near the blastopore. The coelom originates as a split in mesoderm.

After cells of the future endoderm have migrated to the inside of the embryo, mesoderm (red) forms from outpocketings of the archenteron. The coelom forms from space within the outpocketings.

**c. Origin of mouth and anus**

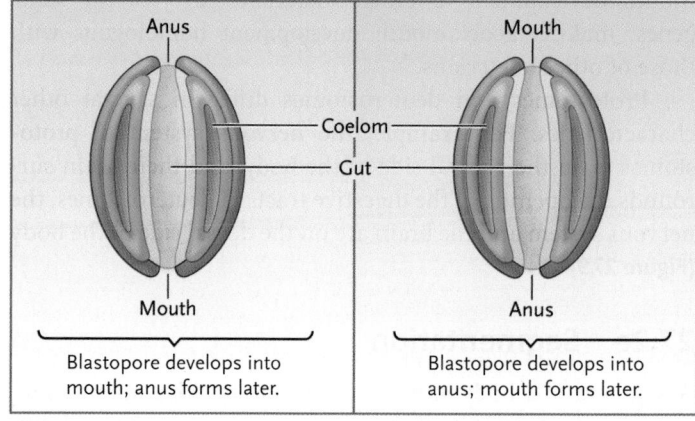

Anus — Coelom — Gut — Mouth

Mouth — Coelom — Gut — Anus

Blastopore develops into mouth; anus forms later.

Blastopore develops into anus; mouth forms later.

**KEY**

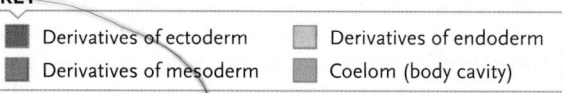

| | |
|---|---|
| ■ Derivatives of ectoderm | ■ Derivatives of endoderm |
| ■ Derivatives of mesoderm | ■ Coelom (body cavity) |

© Cengage Learning 2017

**FIGURE 27.8 Protostomes and deuterostomes.** The two lineages of coelomate animals differ in **(a)** cleavage patterns, **(b)** the origin of mesoderm and the coelom, and **(c)** the polarity of the digestive system.

deuterostomes. Here the third cell division is perpendicular to the vertical axis of the embryo. The fourth cell division is vertical, producing a mass of cells stacked directly above and below one another (see Figure 27.8a, right side).

Protostomes and deuterostomes differ in the timing of important developmental events. During cleavage, genes are activated at specific times, determining a cell's developmental path and ultimate fate. Many protostomes undergo **determinate cleavage**. Each cell's developmental path (what tissue it will become) is determined as the cell is being produced. Thus, one cell isolated from a two- or four-cell protostome embryo cannot develop into a functional embryo or a larva. Most deuterostomes have **indeterminate cleavage**. Here the developmental fates of cells are determined later. A cell isolated from a four-cell deuterostome embryo can develop into a functional embryo. In humans, the two cells produced by the first cleavage division sometimes separate and develop into identical (monozygotic) twins.

Protostomes and deuterostomes differ in the origin of mesoderm and coelom (see Figure 27.8b). In most protostomes, mesoderm originates from a few specific cells near the **blastopore**, an opening on the surface of the embryo. As the mesoderm grows and develops, it splits into inner and outer layers. The space between the layers forms a **schizocoelom** (*schizo* = split). In deuterostomes, mesoderm forms from outpocketings of the **archenteron** (developing gut). The space pinched off by an outpocketing forms an **enterocoelom** (*entero* = intestine).

The blastopore connects the archenteron to the outside environment. Later in development, a second opening at the opposite end of the embryo transforms the pouchlike gut into a digestive tube (see Figure 27.8c). The traditional view of the difference between protostomes and deuterostomes is that, in protostomes, the blastopore develops into the mouth and the second opening forms the anus. In deuterostomes, the blastopore develops into the anus and the second opening becomes the mouth. Recent studies reveal that the formation of the anus and hindgut is more complicated than suggested by this simplistic model. Acoela (e.g., *Praeconvoluta*, see Figure 27.26) have a single body opening serving as mouth and anus. Studies show that, in an acoel (*Convolutriloba longifissura*), the genes *Brachyury* and *Goosecoid* are expressed in part of the mouth. Mouth development in other bilaterians involves the same genes, making acoel mouth development homologous with those of other bilaterians.

Protostomes and deuterostomes differ in several other characteristics. For example, the nervous system of protostomes is on the ventral side of the body, and their brain surrounds the opening of the digestive tract. In deuterostomes, the nervous system and the brain are on the dorsal side of the body **(Figure 27.9)**.

## 27.2e  Segmentation

A **segment** is a body structure that repeats along an anterior–posterior axis and itself has an anterior–posterior polarity. Annelid worms (see Section 27.6c), lobsters (see Section 27.7h), and chordates (see Section 27.8c) are animals with segmented body plans. These three animals are classified in different and separate lineages (Lophotrochozoa, Ecdysozoa, and Deuterostomia, respectively). In each lineage, there are closely related species that are not segmented. This means that either segmentation has evolved separately three times, or that the potential to be

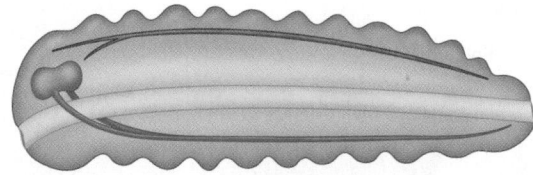

**a. Protostome**

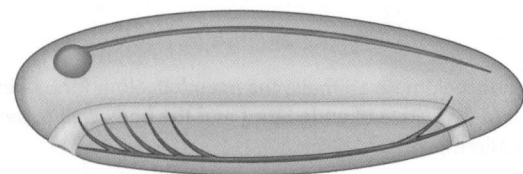

**b. Deuterostome**

**FIGURE 27.9  Body plans of a protostome** (a) **and deuterostome** (b). The nerve cord is blue, the gut is yellow, and the heart and major blood vessels are red.

segmented was present in a common ancestor of the three examples and is suppressed in non-segmented forms.

Evidence supporting the common appearance of potential segmentation comes from other phyla. For example, Nemertea (see Section 27.6d) have a repeating pattern in their ventral nervous system. Superficially, mud dragons (Phylum Kinorhyncha; see Figure 27.49) appear to have segmented exoskeletons and muscles, but have no corresponding internal divisions. Note that the terms "serial repetition" and "metamerism" have been applied to levels of incomplete segmentation. The term segmentation is reserved for the body plans of annelids, arthropods, and chordates. In the evolution of segmented groups, segments may be specialized for different functions (e.g., lobsters; see Section 27.7h), or they may be reduced (e.g., leeches, see Section 27.6c) or lost altogether (e.g., spoon worms).

Segmentation is commonly associated with movement. In vertebrates, the articulated backbone and associated muscles combine to permit S-shaped side-to-side motion, as seen in the locomotion of fish or snakes. Annelids are capable of similar motion, but many live in burrows or tubes. The ability to expand segments by contracting muscles of adjacent segments assists this lifestyle (see Chapter 46). The articulated stiffened cuticle of arthropods serves as a point of attachment for muscles, providing significant leverage and strength. Arthropods have taken advantage of segmental appendages to assign special functions, such as feeding, locomotion, reproduction, or gas exchange, to particular appendages.

**CONCEPT**  Many people believe that all invertebrate animals are protostomes. The truth is that the deuterostomes include many species (some whole phyla) that lack backbones, some of which are invertebrates and some are protochordates, or members of the phylum Chordata. ⬡

1. What is a tissue, and what three primary tissue layers are present in the embryos of most animals? Explain the fate of each layer.
2. What kind of symmetry does an earthworm have?
3. What is the function of the coelom, and what is the importance of the fluid?

## 27.3 Molecular Phylogenetics and Classification

Traditionally, biologists have traced phylogenetic history using morphological innovations just described, along with embryological patterns and the fossil record (see Chapter 19). This evidence has been used to construct phylogenetic trees, which represent hypotheses about relatedness among phyla. Phyla with similar developmental and morphological patterns are presumed to share common ancestries. For example, annelids and arthropods are **schizocoelous** (they have a coelom formed by a split in the mesoderm) segmented coelomates, which are presumed to share a common ancestor. This interpretation is supported by the fossil record as well as by velvet worms (Phylum Onychophora) that appear to have characteristics of both phyla.

Increasingly, molecular sequence data are being used to determine relationships among groups of animals. Such analyses are commonly based on similarities in the nucleotide sequences in small subunit ribosomal RNA and mitochondrial DNA, as well as sequences of specific genes. These analyses are used to construct molecular cladograms. **Figure 27.10** is a

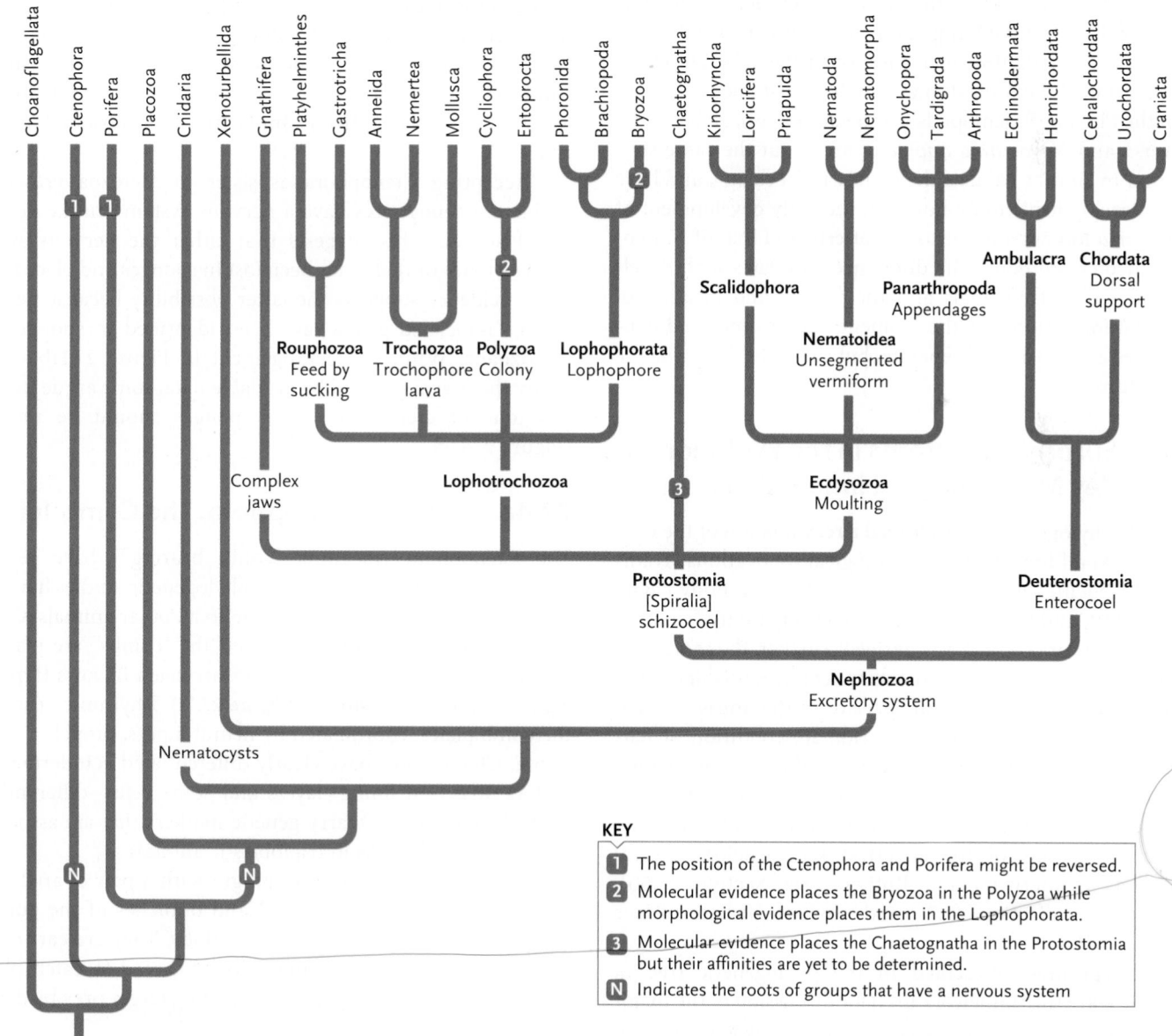

**FIGURE 27.10 A molecular phylogeny for metazoans based on sequence data for several molecules.** As new data are collected, continued revisions of phylogeny and taxonomic relationships will most likely continue.

phylogenetic tree developed from cladograms based on molecular sequences. This tree is a working hypothesis based on information currently available.

This phylogeny, based on molecular characters, includes major lineages originally defined by morphological innovations and embryological characters. In 2017, both molecular and traditional approaches confirmed the separation of phyla of deuterostomes from all other groups within Bilateria.

Currently, Protostomia and Deuterostomia are viewed as separate lineages within Metazoa. Protostomia is, in turn, subdivided into two major lineages: Lophotrochozoa and Ecdysozoa. The name Lophotrochozoa (*lophos* = crest; *troch* = wheel; *zoa* = animals, plural of zoon) refers to both the "lophophore," a feeding structure found in three phyla (see Figure 27.47), and the "trochophore," a type of larva found in annelids and molluscs (see Figure 27.29). The name Ecdysozoa (*ekdero* = strip off the skin) refers to the cuticle that these species secrete and periodically replace; the shedding of the cuticle is called **ecdysis**.

Interestingly, a 2016 paper questioned the apparent clearcut separation of the protostomes and deuterostomes. Two species in the Phylum Brachiopoda (see Section 27.6i), *Terebratalia transversa* and *Novocrania anomala*, are about the same size, are found in similar habitats, have the same ecology, and have similar development times; however, the early development of *T. transversa* follows a protostome pattern, and that of *N. anomala* is deuterostomous. The difference correlates with developmental molecular signals and the timing and location of mesoderm formation. For the moment, protostomes and deuterostomes are considered separate, but this is likely to change in the future.

## 27.3a Surprising Patterns in the Evolution of Key Morphological Innovations

Molecular phylogeny has also forced a reevaluation of the evolution of several important morphological innovations. Traditional phylogenies implied that the absence of a body cavity was ancestral, and that the presence of a body cavity (whether pseudocoelom or coelom) was derived. Further, the molecular tree suggests that the schizocoelomate condition is ancestral, having evolved in the common ancestor of the lineage. If that hypothesis is correct, then the acoelomate condition of flatworms results from the evolutionary loss of the schizocoelom, rather than being an ancestral condition. Similarly, the molecular tree shows that a pseudocoelom evolved independently from modifications of the ancestral schizocoelom several times (e.g., Syndermata and Rotifera (see Section 27.5b); Ecdysozoa (see Section 27.7); and phylum Nematoda (see Section 27.7d).

The hypotheses presented in the phylogenetic tree in Figure 27.10 are the framework used for discussion of the major phyla in the remainder of this chapter. A key thing to remember, however, is that this phylogeny is provisional and new data may lead to revisions.

**STUDY BREAK QUESTIONS**
1. How is molecular analysis used in creating phylogenetic trees?
2. Describe the way molecular phylogeny has changed how biologists view the absence of the coelom.

## 27.4 The Basal Phyla

A major challenge in animal phylogeny lies in understanding the relationships among animal groups at the base of the phylogenetic tree. Included in this basal group are Porifera (sponges), Cnidaria (hydroids, jellies, anemones, and corals), Ctenophora (comb jellies), and Placozoa (*Trichoplax*).

Traditionally, the Porifera have been viewed as sister to the rest of Metazoa, and Cnidaria and Ctenophora seen as sister groups **(Figure 27.11a)**. However, analysis of a large number of transcriptosomes (complexes of RNA processing proteins within the nucleus) places Ctenophora as the sister group to the rest of Metazoa, and does not support a close relationship to Cnidaria. Data supporting a Ctenophora–Cnidaria relationship are artifacts arising from similarities in ribosomal protein genes.

Accepting Ctenophora as sister to Metazoa presents a problem. Ctenophores have a nervous system, unlike Porifera and Placozoa. This suggests that either the nervous system evolved twice or that it has been lost in sponges and placozoans. Some evidence supports the latter possibility because nervous system-associated genes have been identified in sponges and placozoans. While the arrangement in Figure 27.11b is currently the best supported by available data, some argue that the positions of ctenophores and sponges should be reversed (Figure 27.11c).

## 27.4a Phylum Ctenophora: The Comb Jellies

The Ctenophora (meaning "comb bearing") have recently become of major interest because phylogenetic studies have suggested that they are the sister group to all other animals. Ctenophores have a gelatinous body, and the "combs" are plates of fused cilia that project like a comb, arranged in rows (typically eight) on their outer surface **(Figure 27.12)**. Rhythmic beating of the comb plates, coordinated by neural inputs, propels a ctenophore. Ctenophores have clearly differentiated ectodermal and endodermal (gut lining) layers and some cells—differentiated from the endoderm—carry genetic markers that are associated with mesodermal cells in triploblastic animals.

Ctenophores have a through gut with a pair of anal pores (suggesting bilateral symmetry) and branches of the gut that carry nutrients to all regions of the body. They are carnivores, either using cells discharging a sticky thread to catch planktonic prey, or in some species swallowing larger prey by distension of the mouth.

Evidence that Ctenophora are the sister group to all other animals surprised biologists because ctenophores are

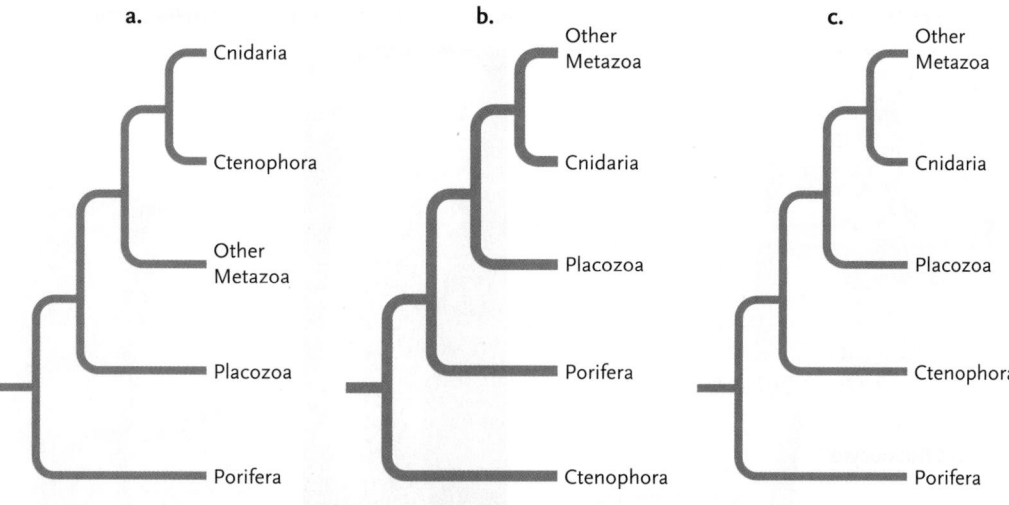

**FIGURE 27.11** **(a)** A traditional arrangement of the basal phyla. **(b)** The arrangement best supported by current data. **(c)** An alternative arrangement supported by some data

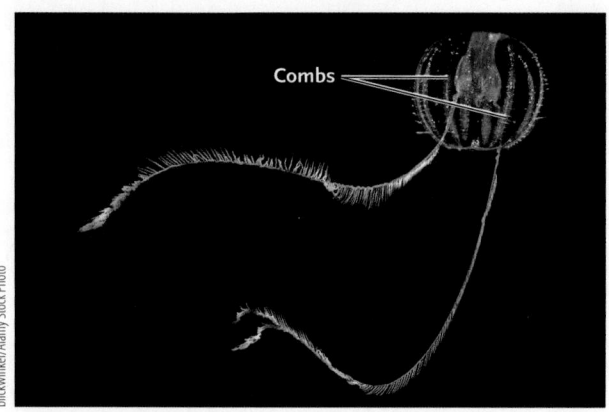

**FIGURE 27.12** **Comb jellies, such as *Pleurobrachia pileus*, collect prey on their tentacles.**

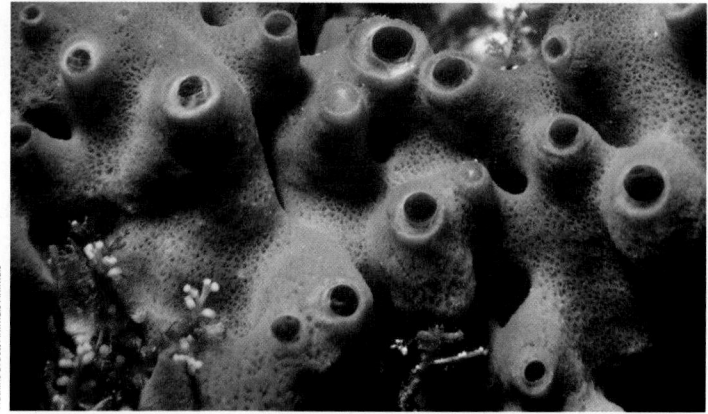

**FIGURE 27.13** **Sponges are asymmetrical and sessile as adults.**

significantly more complex than Porifera (sponges), which were previously placed in this position (see Figure 27.11). *Hox* genes play a role in the organization of the body plan of all animal groups; however, no *Hox* type genes have been identified in ctenophores.

### 27.4b Phylum Porifera: The Sponges

Of the 8000 species of living sponges **(Figure 27.13)**, only a few species live in fresh water. Sponges are asymmetric and adults are sessile. They have been abundant since the Cambrian. The shapes of sponges vary with their habitats: they may be encrusting, barrel shaped, tubular, or stalked.

The development of more than one non-reproductive cell type is a metazoan characteristic. In sponges, an outer layer of epithelial cells (the **pinacoderm**) includes **porocytes**, cylindrical cells that allow water to pass **(Figure 27.14)**. This layer has a basement membrane in some sponges and must be regarded as a tissue layer, along with the organized inner cell lining. **Choanocytes**, food trapping cells with a collar of microtubules around a flagellum that drives water through the body cavity

(the **spongocoel**), are arranged in different ways in different groups. A gelatinous matrix, the **mesohyl** includes **amoeboid** cells called **archaeocytes** that transport nutrients and wastes. Most sponges depend on spicules for their rigidity. Spicules may be made of calcium or silica in different sponge groups and are secreted by specialized cells known as **sclerocytes**.

Sponges are typically **suspension feeders**. Choanocytes draw a current of water into the spongocoel through the porocytes that then leaves via the osculum. Cells inside the osculum have two cilia and have genetic characteristics common to sensory cells. Information from the osculum travels to the porocytes, which are contractile and regulate water flow rates through the sponge. Particles of food captured by choanocytes are passed to amoebocytes, which distribute food to all the cells throughout the sponge and may also store food reserves.

Sponges are typically **monoecious**, meaning individuals produce both sperm and eggs. Sperm are released into the environment, and eggs (**oocytes**) are retained in the mesohyl. Sperm are drawn in with water captured by choanocytes that carry sperm to oocytes. Sponges have various types of larvae. Some are free swimming, and others crawl over the substrate.

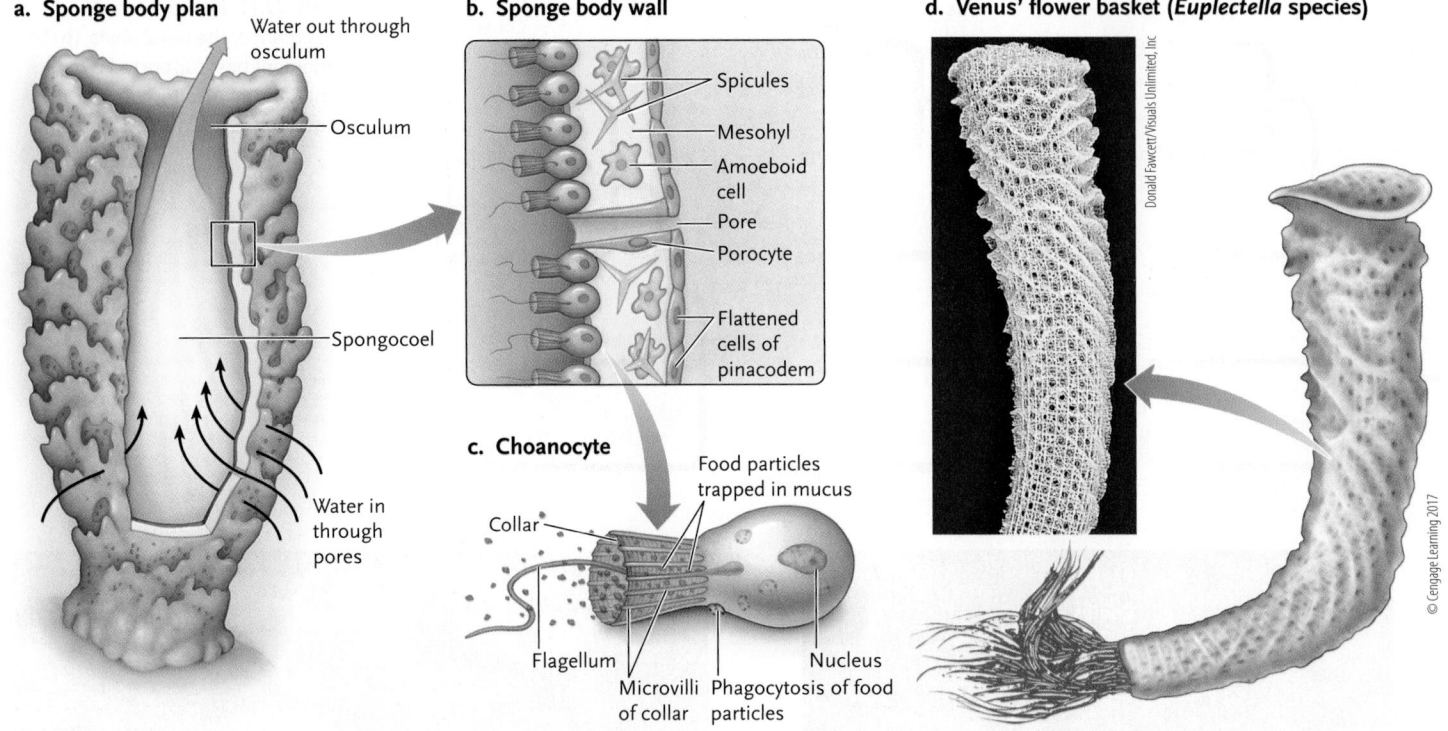

**a. Sponge body plan**

Water out through osculum

Osculum

Spongocoel

Water in through pores

**b. Sponge body wall**

Spicules

Mesohyl

Amoeboid cell

Pore

Porocyte

Flattened cells of pinacodem

**c. Choanocyte**

Collar

Flagellum

Microvilli of collar

Food particles trapped in mucus

Nucleus

Phagocytosis of food particles

**d. Venus' flower basket (*Euplectella* species)**

Donald Fawcett/Visuals Unlimited, Inc

© Cengage Learning 2017

**FIGURE 27.14  The body plan of sponges.** Most sponges have **(a)** simple body plans and **(b)** relatively few cell types. **(c)** Beating flagella on the choanocytes create a flow of water through incurrent pores, into the spongocoel, and out through the osculum. **(d)** Venus's flower basket (*Euplectella* sp.), a marine sponge, has spicules of silica fused into a rigid framework.

Settled larvae develop into sessile adults. Sponges also reproduce asexually: small fragments break off an adult and grow into new sponges. Under difficult conditions, sponges may produce reduction bodies, which are clusters of food-filled archaeocytes enclosed by a membrane and a layer of pinacoderm. When favourable conditions return, archaeocytes are dispersed from the reduction body to develop directly into new sponges. In some freshwater sponges, reduction bodies have developed further into **gemmules**—thick-walled capsules that have spicules reinforcing the wall. Gemmules can withstand extreme conditions, such as a pond drying up in midsummer or freezing in winter.

Even with a very simple, basic body plan, sponges have achieved remarkable diversity. Sponges formed very large reefs during the Mesozoic, and a modern reef of glass sponges has been found off the west coast of Canada.

Sponges may serve as refuges for other species. Bacteria and cyanobacteria can be found in the mesohyl. Other species gain protection in the spongocoel. Male and female shrimp (*Spongicola* species) may enter the spongocoel of the Venus's flower basket when small, feed on material brought in by the sponge, and grow large enough that they are unable to leave. The pair of shrimp spend their entire lives in the prison formed by the elaborate basket of spicules. Some sponges are carnivorous and catch small arthropods by entangling them in hook-shaped spicules on the surface. Prey are then tangled in filamentous structures and digested.

Recent molecular evidence places sponges with other Metazoa in one monophyletic lineage. Sponges do not form distinct nervous tissue, but they have genes that are associated with nervous systems in other groups. Although sponges are asymmetric, each species has a particular body form. This demands intercellular communication of developmental information. A *Hox*-related gene identified in a sponge could play a role in regulating body form. Current interpretation of this and other molecular data confirms that sponges and other Metazoa share a common ancestry.

### 27.4c  Phylum Placozoa: Plate Animals

For many years, *Trichoplax adherens* (**Figure 27.15**) was the only known species of placozoan. Found on hard substrata in shallow marine environments, *Trichoplax* has a worldwide distribution. Molecular studies of specimens collected from around the world show that, while there are only small differences in morphology, there are seven clades within the species and a number of genotypes within each clade.

*Trichoplax* has five cell types arranged in upper and lower epithelial layers, with three layers of fibre cells running across the central space. Shiny spheres, secreted in either the cavity of the animal or in association with a fibre layer, are on the upper surface and may release defensive chemicals that deter potential predators such as flatworms, polychaete worms, and small snails.

*Trichoplax* reproduces asexually by simple division of the body. While sperm have not been isolated from *Trichoplax*, a number of genetic markers for developing sperm have been identified, and oocyte development (accompanied by degeneration of the parent) can be induced in the laboratory. This provides strong evidence that sexual reproduction is also a part of *Trichoplax* biology.

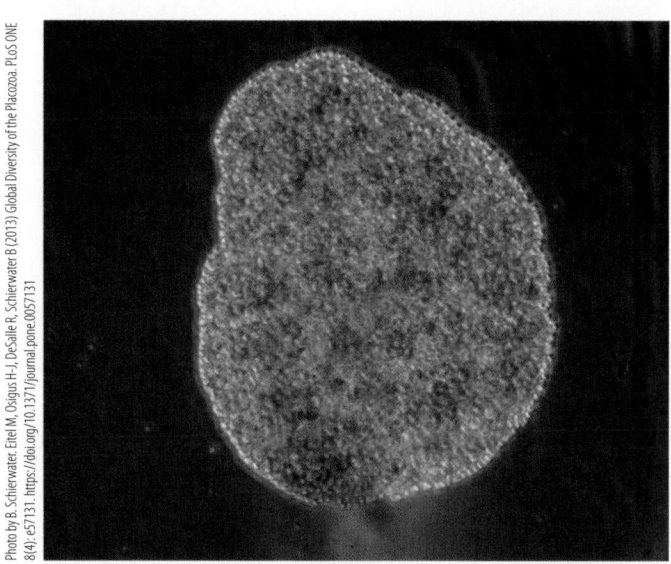

FIGURE 27.15 *Trichoplax* **resembles a multicellular amoeba with two layers of cells.** Placozoans have no nervous system but cells are specialized for different functions. The refractile bodies on the upper surface of the animal are the shiny spheres.

*Photo by B. Schierwater, Eitel M, Osigus H-J, DeSalle R, Schierwater B (2013) Global Diversity of the Placozoa. PLoS ONE 8(4): e57131. https://doi.org/10.1371/journal.pone.0057131*

## 27.4d Phylum Cnidaria: Hydroids, Jellies, Anemones, and Corals

Most of the over 10 000 species in the phylum Cnidaria (from the Greek word *knide* = nettle; the stem of *knizein* = to scratch or scrape) are marine. Cnidarians have a saclike body enclosing a gastrovascular cavity with one opening, the mouth, which is surrounded by food-collecting tentacles. Cnidarians may be vase-shaped with upward-pointing **polyps** or bell-shaped, with downward-pointing **medusae (Figure 27.16)**. Most polyps attach to a substrate at the *aboral* (opposite the mouth) end, while medusae are typically free-swimming.

Cnidarians are the simplest animals that have specialized tissues and nerve cells (see Figure 27.16c). The epidermis includes nerve cells, contractile cells, and **cnidocytes**, which are cells specialized for the capture of crustaceans, fish, and other prey. Each cnidocyte contains a **nematocyst (Figure 27.17)**. When a nematocyst is discharged, the capsule opens and three stylets spring together to form a beak that punctures the surface of the prey. This takes place within 1.5 microseconds and involves huge forces. Discharge of nematocysts may be triggered by touch, vibrations, or chemical stimuli. Nematocysts are not innervated but their sensitivity is regulated by the condition of the whole animal. Nematocyst toxins can paralyze small prey by disrupting nerve cell membranes, and some nematocysts are sufficiently potent to cause extreme pain to humans. Other types of nematocyst may be sticky or coil around objects.

The gastrodermis includes sensory receptor cells, gland cells, and phagocytic nutritive cells. Gland cells secrete enzymes

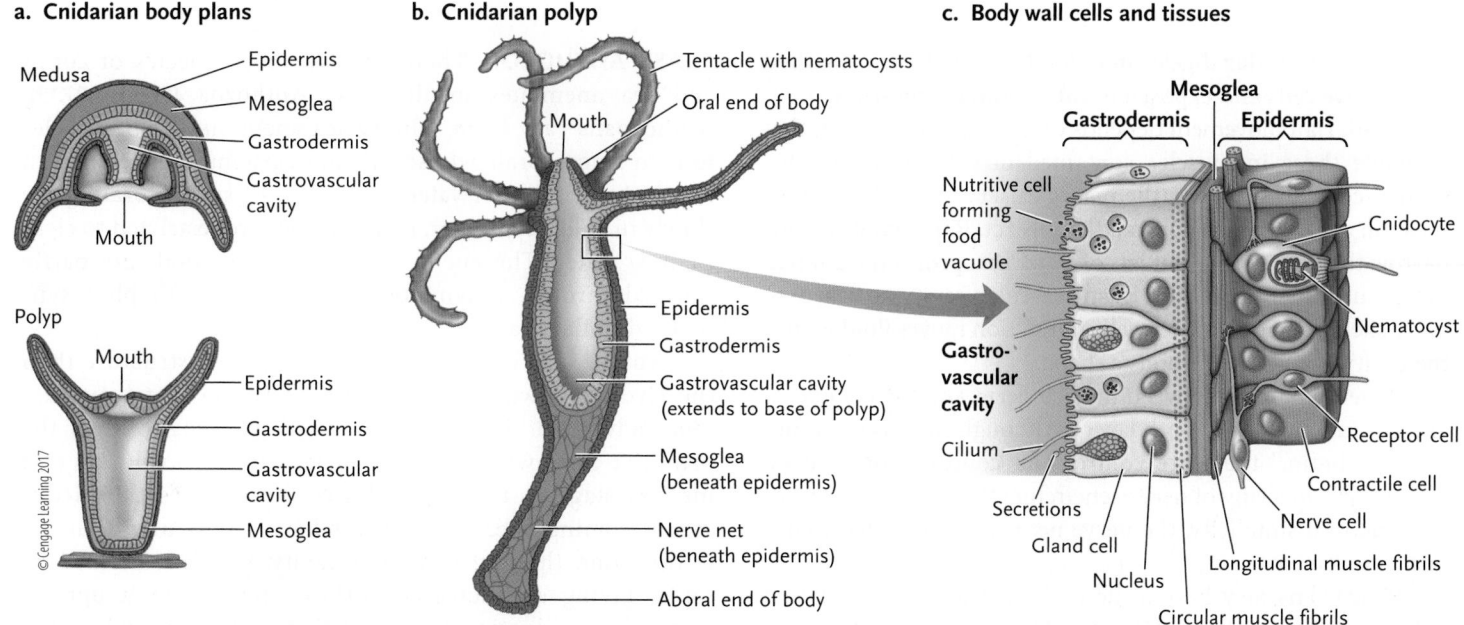

FIGURE 27.16 **The cnidarian body plan. (a)** Cnidarians exist in either polyp or medusa forms. **(b)** The body is organized around a gastrovascular cavity. **(c)** The two tissue layers in the body wall, the gastrodermis and the epidermis, include a variety of cell types.

## a. *Hydra* consuming a crustacean

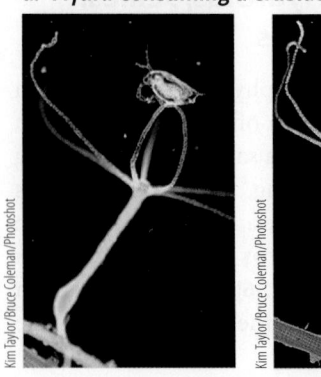

Kim Taylor/Bruce Coleman/Photoshot

Kim Taylor/Bruce Coleman/Photoshot

**FIGURE 27.17 Predation by cnidarians.**
**(a)** A polyp of a freshwater *Hydra* captures a small crustacean with its tentacles and swallows it whole. **(b)** Stages in nematocyst discharge: (i) undischarged nematocyst; (ii, iii) capsule opens and stylets are fired into prey; (iv) lamellae lock the nematocyst into the prey; (v) the stylets fold back and the hollow thread extends. The complete process is completed in about 700 nanoseconds and involves acceleration forces of over 5 million *g*.

## b. Cnidocytes

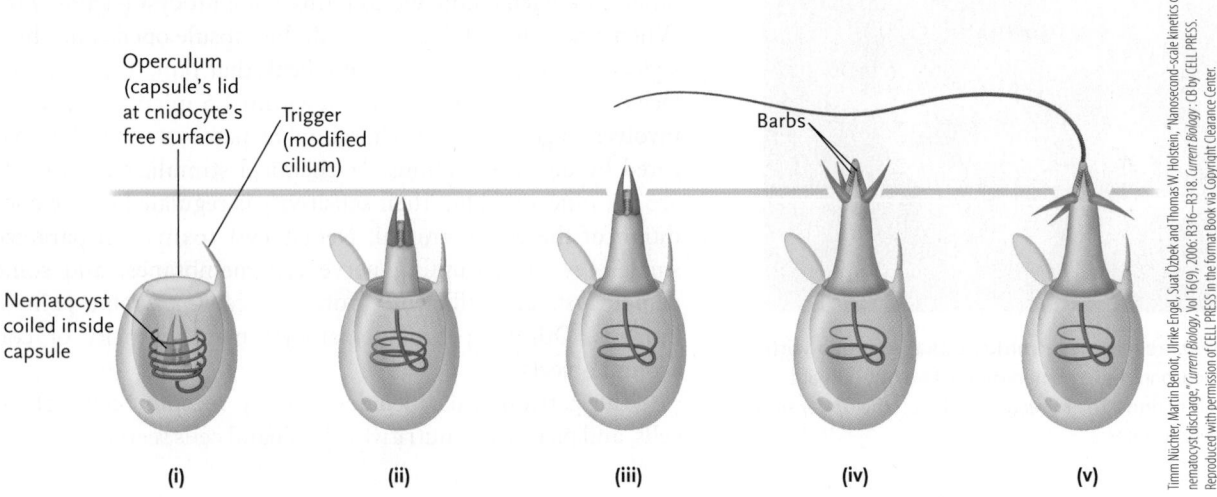

Operculum (capsule's lid at cnidocyte's free surface)

Trigger (modified cilium)

Barbs

Nematocyst coiled inside capsule

(i)  (ii)  (iii)  (iv)  (v)

Timm Nüchter, Martin Benoit, Ulrike Engel, Suat Özbek and Thomas W. Holstein, "Nanosecond-scale kinetics of nematocyst discharge," *Current Biology*, Vol 16(9), 2006; R316–R318. *Current Biology* - CB by CELL PRESS. Reproduced with permission of CELL PRESS in the format Book via Copyright Clearance Center.

for the **extracellular digestion** of food, which is then engulfed by nutritive cells and exposed to **intracellular digestion**.

Cnidarian movement depends on contraction of fibres that resemble those in muscles contained in extensions of ectodermal cells. In medusae, the mesoglea serves as a deformable skeleton against which contractile cells act. Rapid contractions narrow the bell, forcing out jets of water that propel the animal. Polyps use their fluid-filled gastrovascular cavity as a hydrostatic skeleton. Coordinated cell contraction moves fluid within the cavity, changing the body's shape.

A **nerve net** lies between the ectoderm and the endoderm and has junctions with both layers. Although there is no recognizable "brain," there are control and coordination centres, particularly in a ring of nerves encircling the mouth. In spite of its structural simplicity, the nerve net permits directed swimming movements.

Cnidarians may have a life cycle that alternates between polyp and medusa forms **(Figure 27.18)** and some exist in only one form. Sexual reproduction typically produces a ciliated larval stage, the **planula**, that settles and undergoes metamorphosis into the polyp form.

**CLASS ANTHOZOA** There are over 6000 species of corals and sea anemones in the class Anthozoa **(Figure 27.19)**. Anthozoans vary from solitary sea anemones lacking skeletons to stony corals whose calcium carbonate skeletons can form gigantic underwater reefs. While some corals grow slowly in cold deep water, many species are restricted to clear shallow water. The energy needs of these corals are partly fulfilled through a symbiotic relationship with photosynthetic dinoflagellates.

Anthozoans have a more complex polyp structure than the Hydrozoa, which led to the assumption that they were more advanced. The Anthozoa are now recognized as the primitive form within the Cnidaria, with the evolution of a medusa stage in the other classes (grouped as the Medusozoa) coming later. Anthozoans have a muscular pharynx leading into the gastrovascular cavity, which is divided by septa, giving an increased surface area for food uptake. Asexual reproduction is by budding or fission, and sexual reproduction produces eggs that develop into ciliated larvae that settle and metamorphose into polyps that may produce colonies by budding.

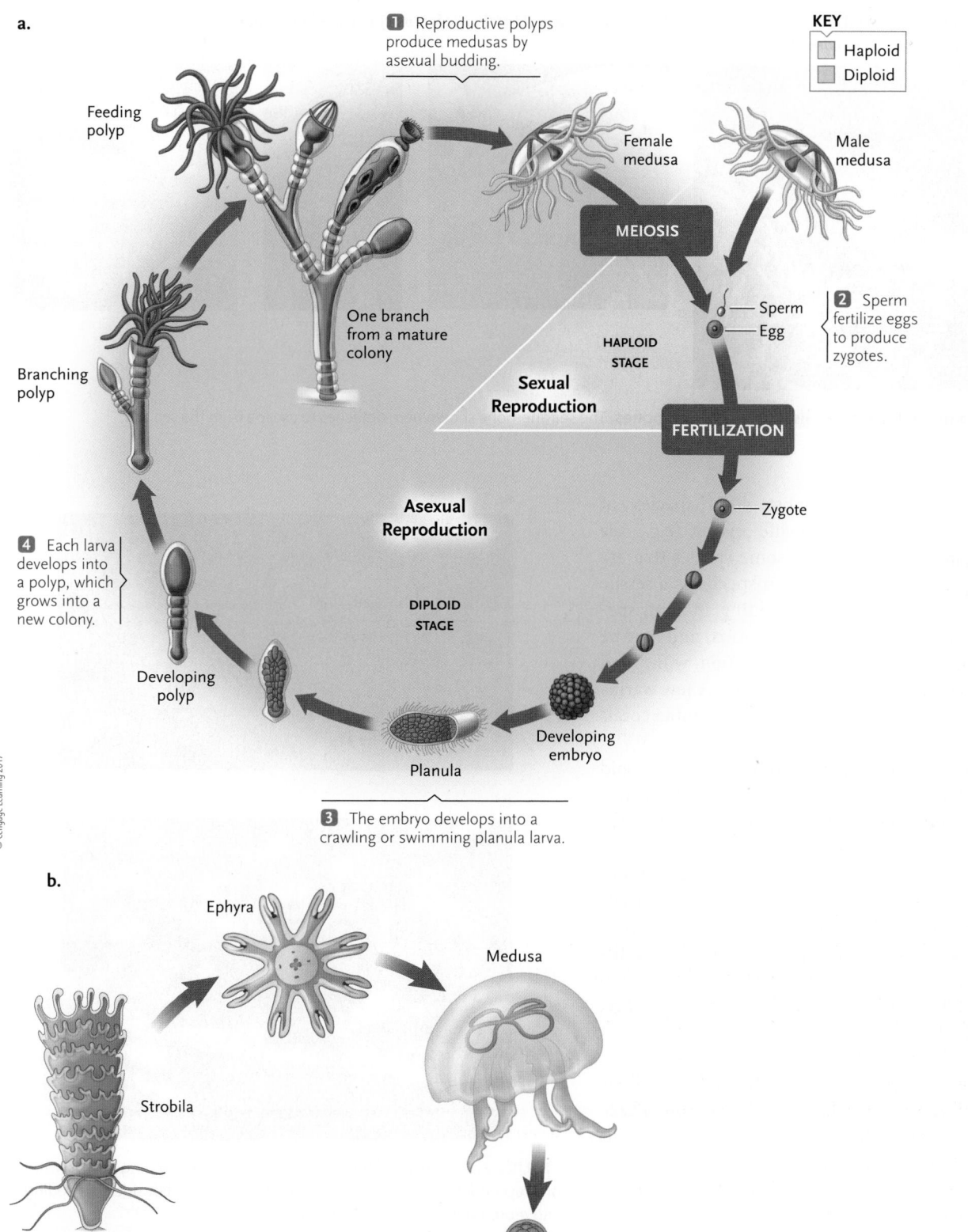

a.

**1** Reproductive polyps produce medusas by asexual budding.

KEY
Haploid
Diploid

Feeding polyp

Female medusa

Male medusa

MEIOSIS

One branch from a mature colony

Sperm
Egg

**2** Sperm fertilize eggs to produce zygotes.

HAPLOID STAGE

Sexual Reproduction

FERTILIZATION

Branching polyp

Zygote

Asexual Reproduction

**4** Each larva develops into a polyp, which grows into a new colony.

DIPLOID STAGE

Developing polyp

Developing embryo

Planula

**3** The embryo develops into a crawling or swimming planula larva.

© Cengage Learning 2017

b.

Ephyra

Medusa

Strobila

Embryo

Planula larva

Scyphistoma

**FIGURE 27.18 (a)** The life cycle of *Obelia* includes a dominant polyp and short-lived medusa stages. **(b)** The *Aurelia* (Scyphozoa) life cycle has a short-lived polyp phase and a dominant medusa phase.

**a. Staghorn coral**
**(*Acropora cervicornis*)**

Tentacle of one polyp

Interconnected skeletons of polyps of a colonial coral

Mark_Doh/iStock/Getty Images Plus

**b. Sea anemone (*Urticina lofotensis*) escape behaviour**

F.S. Westmorland

**FIGURE 27.19 Anthozoans include (a) corals and (b) sea anemones.** The sea anemone shown here detaches to escape from the sea star.

**CLASS HYDROZOA** Among the almost 4000 species of Hydrozoa, there is a wide range of life cycles (e.g., see Figure 27.18 and **Figure 27.20**), including some species that are free-swimming polyps. A typical hydrozoan species is a sessile marine colony that develops asexually by budding. In many species, polyps are polymorphic (have different forms) and may be specialized for feeding, defence, or reproduction with food shared through connected gastrovascular cavities. A few warm-water species secrete a calcareous skeleton and resemble corals (Anthozoa).

Some pelagic hydrozoans have both polyp and medusoid forms in the same colony; for example, Portuguese man-of-war has a medusoid bell modified to form a carbon monoxide-filled sail surrounded by feeding and reproductive polyps.

*Hydra* (**Figure 27.21**) lives in fresh water and has solitary polyps that attach to rocks, twigs, and leaves. Under favourable conditions, *Hydra* reproduces by budding. Under adverse conditions, it produces eggs and sperm. Zygotes, formed by fertilization, are encapsulated in a protective coating but develop and grow when conditions improve. There is no larval stage; eggs hatch into small *Hydra*.

**CLASS SCYPHOZOA** The medusa stage predominates in the 200 species of the class Scyphozoa, or jellyfish (**Figure 27.22**). They range from 2 cm to more than 2 m in diameter. Nerve cells near the margin of the bell control their tentacles and coordinate the rhythmic activity of contractile cells, which move the animal. Specialized sensory cells are clustered at the edge of the bell: statocysts sense gravity, and ocelli are sensitive to light. Scyphozoan medusae are either male or female, releasing gametes into the water, where fertilization takes place.

**CLASS CUBOZOA** Most of the 20 known species of box jellyfish, the Cubozoa (**Figure 27.23**), are cube-shaped medusae only a few centimetres tall, but the largest species grows to 25 cm in height. Nematocyst-rich tentacles grow in clusters from the four

**a.**

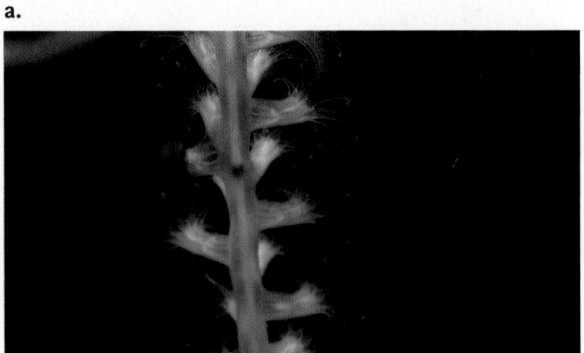

NOAA

**b.**

Lovell and Libby Langstroth © California Academy of Sciences

**FIGURE 27.20 Colonial hydroids. (a)** *Aegina citrea* feeding polyps, with one reproductive medusa being budded away on the left side. **(b)** Feeding and reproductive polyps of *Obelia* sp.

corners of the boxlike medusa, and groups of light receptors and image-forming eyes occur on the four sides of the bell. The eyes have lenses and retinas that can detect features around the animal and coordinate swimming so that the jelly can patrol back and forth along a length of shore. Unlike scyphozoan jellyfish, cubozoans are active swimmers. They eat small fish and invertebrates, immobilizing their prey with one of the deadliest

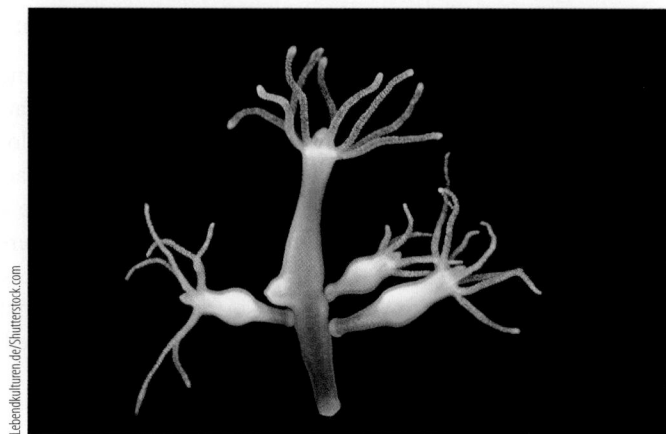

**FIGURE 27.21** *Hydra* exists as a solitary polyp with no medusa stage in its life cycle.

**FIGURE 27.22** Most species of Scyphozoa, such as *Chrysaora quinquecirrha*, live as free medusae.

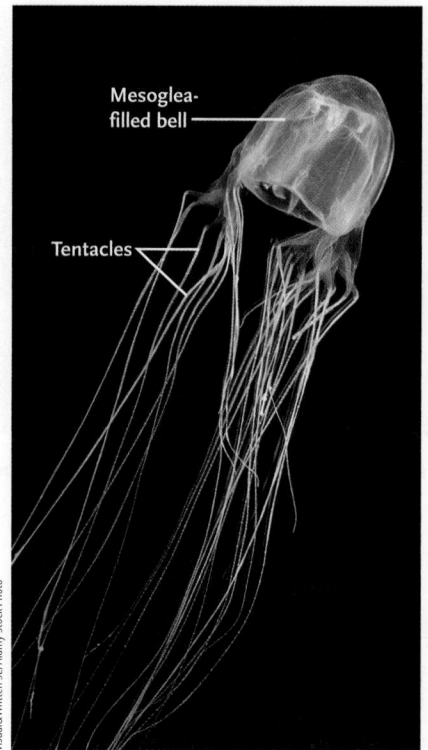

**Figure 27.23** Cubozoans, such as *Chironex fleckeri*, are strong swimmers that actively pursue prey.

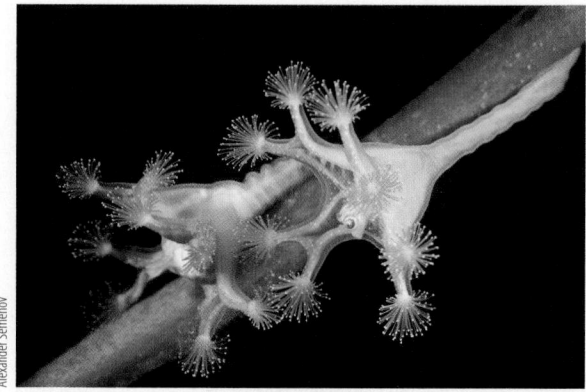

**FIGURE 27.24** *Lucernaria quadricornis* is a staurozoan.

toxins produced by animals. Cubozoans live in tropical and subtropical coastal waters, where they sometimes pose a serious threat to swimmers. The nematocysts of some species (e.g., a group of species known as *Irukandji jellies*, which have a box less than a centimetre across but tentacles a metre long) can inflict considerable pain to, and may kill, humans.

**CLASS STAUROZOA** Recently separated from Scyphozoa, Staurozoa are viewed as the sister group to the Cubozoa. In these classes, unlike the Scyphozoa, the medusa forms as a single bud from the tip of a reduced polyp (**Figure 27.24**).

Staurozoans are attached medusa with a stalk, originating at the apex of the medusa and attaching the animal to the substratum. The bell of the medusa divides to form eight arms, each tipped by a cluster of nematocytes that attack and hold prey.

**CLASS MYXOZOA** The Myxozoa, a group of parasites previously classified among Protista, are simplified medusozoans and truly cnidarians. What had been called "polar capsules" in protists are now recognized as nematocysts. These dark-stained inclusions are obvious in **Figure 27.25**, a typical parasitic myxozoan (*Myxobolus cerebralis*) found in salmon. These inclusions cause "whirling disease."

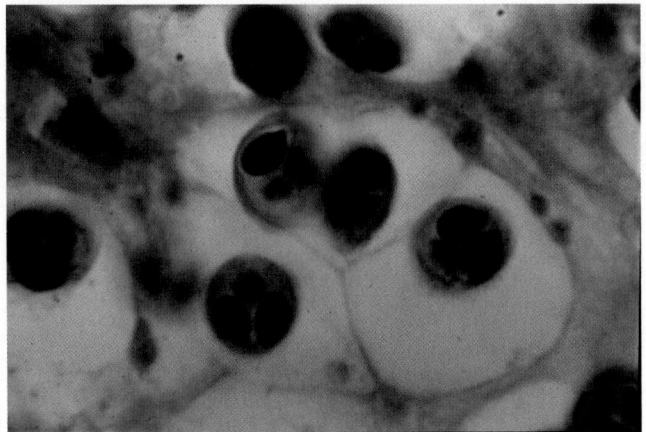

NOAA

**FIGURE 27.25** *Myxobolus cerebralis* **isolated from a salmon**

**a.**

Michael Owen

**b.**

Barve, A. and A. Hejnol. (2014). Development and juvenile anatomy of the nemertodermatid *Meara stichopi* (Bock) Westblad 1949 (Acoelomorpha). Frontiers in Zoology 11 50.

0.5 mm

**c.**

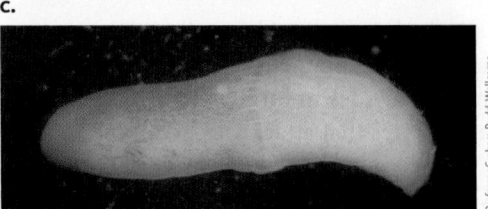

Professor Graham Budd, Wellcome Images. Licensed under Creative Commons Attribution (CC BY 4.0) terms and conditions https://creativecommons. org/licenses/by/4.0

**FIGURE 27.26 (a)** *Praeconvoluta castinea* (Acoela): notice the single statocyst toward the left (anterior) end. Food is taken in through a mouth and held between the central parenchymal cells, where digestion is extracellular. **(b)** *Meara stichopi* (Nemertodermatidae). Paired statocysts are characteristic of this group; the mouth and pharynx are more developed than in the Acoela. **(c)** *Xenoturbella*. The groove around the middle of the animal appears to be sensory.

### 27.4e Phylum Xenacoelomorpha: Flatworms

The Xenacoelomorpha, a group of flatworms, is a sister grouping to the Bilateria. They are sometimes grouped with all other bilaterians, which have a specialized excretory system. Xenacoelomorpha includes three groups: the Acoela, the Nemertodermatidae, and the Xenoturbellida **(Figure 27.26)**. All three groups have a single opening to the gut and lack an anus. Xenoturbellids were initially classified as molluscs, because of mollusc DNA that the animals had obtained from their food. After suggestions that xenoturbellids were degenerate deuterostomes were disproved, the group found its proper position alongside Acoela.

**STUDY BREAK QUESTIONS**

1. Do sponges exhibit symmetry?
2. How does a sponge gather food from its environment?
3. How do cnidarians capture, consume, and digest their prey?
4. Describe the difference between a polyp and a medusa.

## 27.5 The Protostomes

Phyla viewed as more advanced than the basal phyla can be labelled as Nephrozoa on the basis that an excretory system is present. Nephrozoa are divided into two major groups: Protostomia and Deuterostomia **(Figure 27.27)**. The protostomes include the Gnathifera and phyla that are members of the Lophotrochozoa (Rouphozoa, Trochozoa, Polyzoa, Lophophorata) and Ecdysozoa (Scalidophora, Nematoidea, Panarthropoda) groups. At this time, Phylum Chaetognatha is classified as Protostomia.

### 27.5a Phylum Chaetognatha: Arrow Worms

Chaetognatha means "bristle jaws." In fact, the bristles are for capturing and holding prey; the true jaws are hidden below the hood of the head. Chaetognaths are marine predators, most in the plankton, a few species are benthic. Chaetognaths have a dartlike body, typically with two pairs of lateral fins and a tail fin; they swim rapidly but in short bursts. Chaetognaths have a muscular pharynx, a through gut, cerebral ganglia, nerve cords that have both dorsal and ventral elements, and a hermaphroditic reproductive system. There are only a small number of species of arrow worm (about 150), but they are ubiquitous and abundant in all oceans and are a major part of marine food chains.

The phylogeny of the chaetognaths remains uncertain. They have some deuterostome features (a post-anal tail and elements of a dorsal nervous system), but molecular evidence places them in the Protostomia.

### 27.5b Gnathifera

Gnathifera means "jaw bearing," and the clade includes the Gnathostomulida, Syndermata, and the recently described Micrognathozoa. In these groups, the jaws are complex and

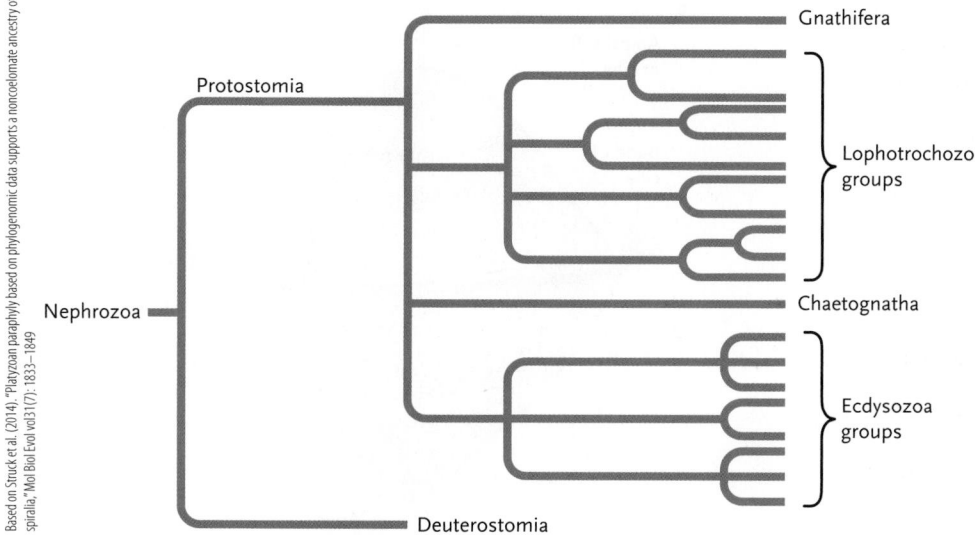

Based on Struck et al. (2014), "Platyzoan paraphyly based on phylogenomic data supports a noncoelomate ancestry of spiralia," Mol Biol Evol vol3 1(7): 1833–1849

**FIGURE 27.27** **Relationships of the higher animal phyla**

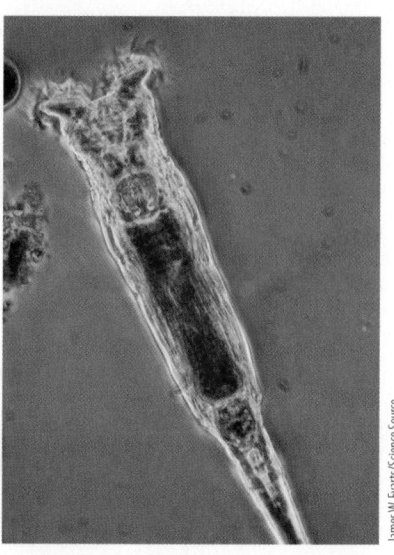

James W. Evarts/Science Source

**FIGURE 27.28** **A rotifer showing the corona (upper left)**

located in the pharynx. In all three groups, the jaws are composed of similar microtubular elements.

Gnathostomulids are minute animals with a ferocious set of jaws. They have a mouth and gut but no anus. They expel undigested food material through their mouths. Micrognathozoa is known by a single genus, *Limnognathia*, which at 100 μm long may be the smallest known animal. These animals have the most complex jaws of any animal.

Syndermata combines two groups previously viewed as separate phyla: Rotifera and parasitic Acanthocephala. The Rotifera (meaning "wheel bearing") are named for the appearance of circular motion in the cilia, known as the *corona*, which set up feeding currents around the mouth **(Figure 27.28)**. There are over 2000 species of rotifers, mostly in freshwater (a few are marine) and usually less than 1 mm long. The pharynx includes a muscular bulb (the mastax) in which the jaws (trophi) break algal and bacterial cell walls in food collected by the corona. Rotifers are pseudocoelomate and have a protonephridial excretory system. Many rotifers are parthenogenetic, an asexual reproductive mode that allows rapid population increase under favourable conditions. Some species are polymorphic, with different morphs appearing under different environmental conditions. Acanthocephala (meaning "thorny headed") are endoparasitic worms. Their lack of jaws makes them a surprising inclusion in Gnathifera. Their position is based on molecular phylogeny data, combined with their morphological features being close to that of Rotifera.

## STUDY BREAK QUESTIONS

1. What feature separates the basal phyla from the Nephrozoa?
2. What two major groups are the Nephrozoa divided into?

## 27.6   Lophotrochozoa Protostomes

This large grouping includes phyla with a **lophophore** feeding structure, which is a ring of ciliated feeding tentacles, and phyla that develop from a **trochophore** or modified trochophore larva **(Figure 27.29)**.

### 27.6a   Phylum Platyhelminthes: The Flatworms

"Flatworms" is a direct translation of "platy" and "helminthes." There are over 20 000 species of platyhelminth described; of these, 80% are parasitic. Platyhelminthes are triploblastic, bilaterally symmetrical acoelomates **(Figure 27.30)**. They have a gut (lost in most parasitic species), an opening that acts as both a mouth and an anus, and a simple excretory system (called a **flame cell** system). The nervous system consists of two or more ventral nerve cords connected by nerve fibres. A concentration of nervous cell tissue, called the **ganglion**, acts as a primitive brain. Most free-living species have **ocelli**, or "eye spots." There is no circulatory system. Oxygen and carbon dioxide exchange occurs by diffusion over the body surface.

In traditional classifications, free-living species were grouped in the Turbellaria. **Figure 27.31** shows a simplified view of a current phylogeny.

Catenulida are a small group of aquatic flatworms that have a simple pharynx and a ciliated gut cavity. One genus, *Paracatenula*, has no gut but is packed with chemoautotrophic bacteria that derive energy from the oxidation of sulfide. Rhabditophora includes over a dozen orders of flatworms. They take their name from the rhabdites, which are rods formed in the epidermis and that are discharged when a predator threatens, dissolving to produce a chemical repellant. Order Tricladida (meaning "three branches") refers to the form of the gut with

CHAPTER 27   ANIMALS   |   **659**

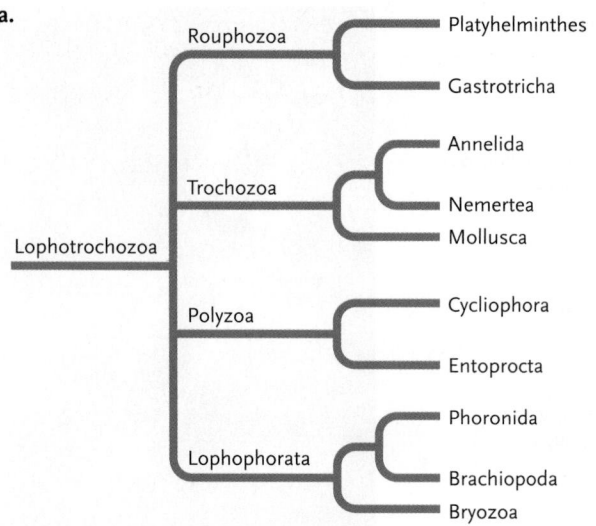

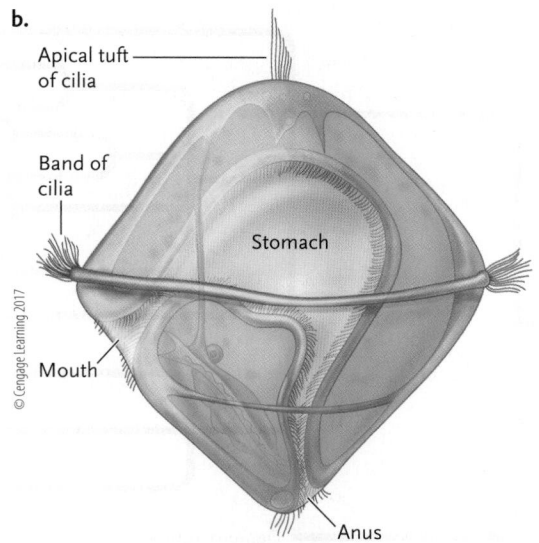

**FIGURE 27.29** **(a)** The lophotrochozoan protostomes. **(b)** Animals such as molluscs and annelids pass through a trochophore larval stage at the conclusion of embryological development.

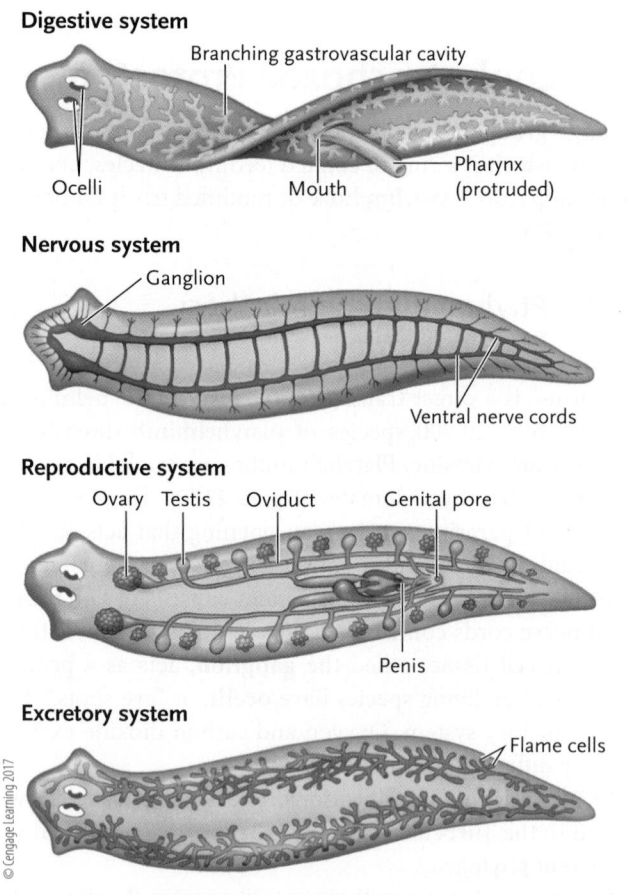

**FIGURE 27.30** **Platyhelminthes, represented by this freshwater planarian, have digestive, nervous, reproductive, and excretory systems.**

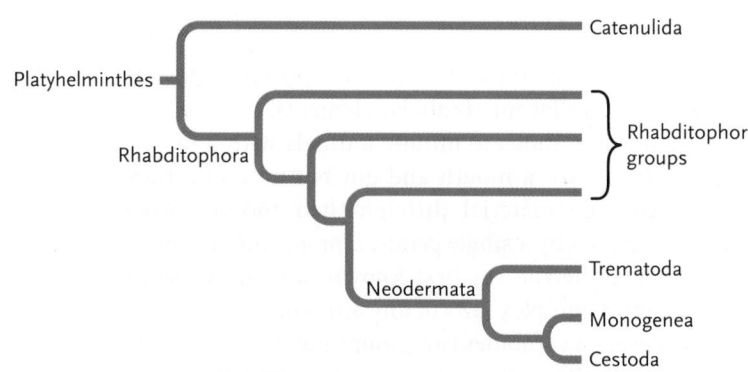

**FIGURE 27.31** **A simplified phylogeny of the Platyhelminthes**

**a.** *Microplana termitophaga*

**b.** *Pseudoceros dimidiatus*

**FIGURE 27.32** **(a)** *Microplana termitophaga* attacking a termite nest. **(b)** *Pseudoceros dimidiatus*

one branch anterior to the pharynx and two branches posterior. Tricladida includes some flatworms living in damp terrestrial environments; an example is *Microplana termitophaga* **(Figure 27.32a)**, a predator of termites in southern Africa.

Polycladida (referring to a many-branched gut) are another large order of Rhabditophora. Many polyclads are brightly coloured (Figure 27.32b). There are many species in this group that have yet to be described.

Neodermata is a grouping within Rhabditophora that includes the three parasitic orders, Trematoda, Monogenea, and Cestoda. Trematodes are vertebrate parasites and many cause serious health problems. The Chinese liver fluke (Figure 27.33) is estimated to be found in the liver, bile ducts, and gall bladder of about 30 million people in Southeast Asia. Oral and ventral attachment suckers are characteristics of the trematodes.

### a. Clonorchis sinensis

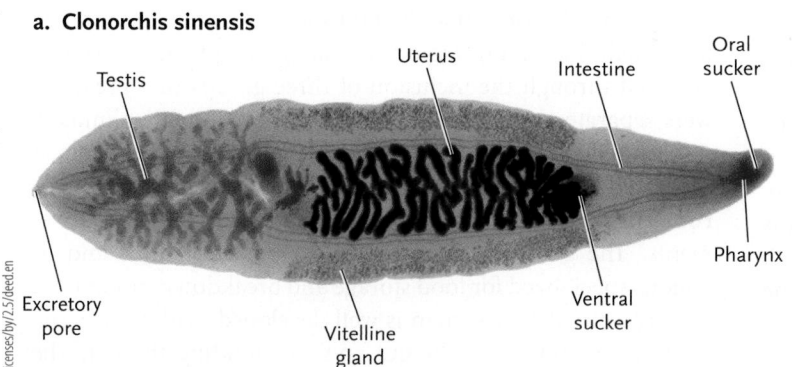

Testis
Uterus
Intestine
Oral sucker
Excretory pore
Vitelline gland
Ventral sucker
Pharynx

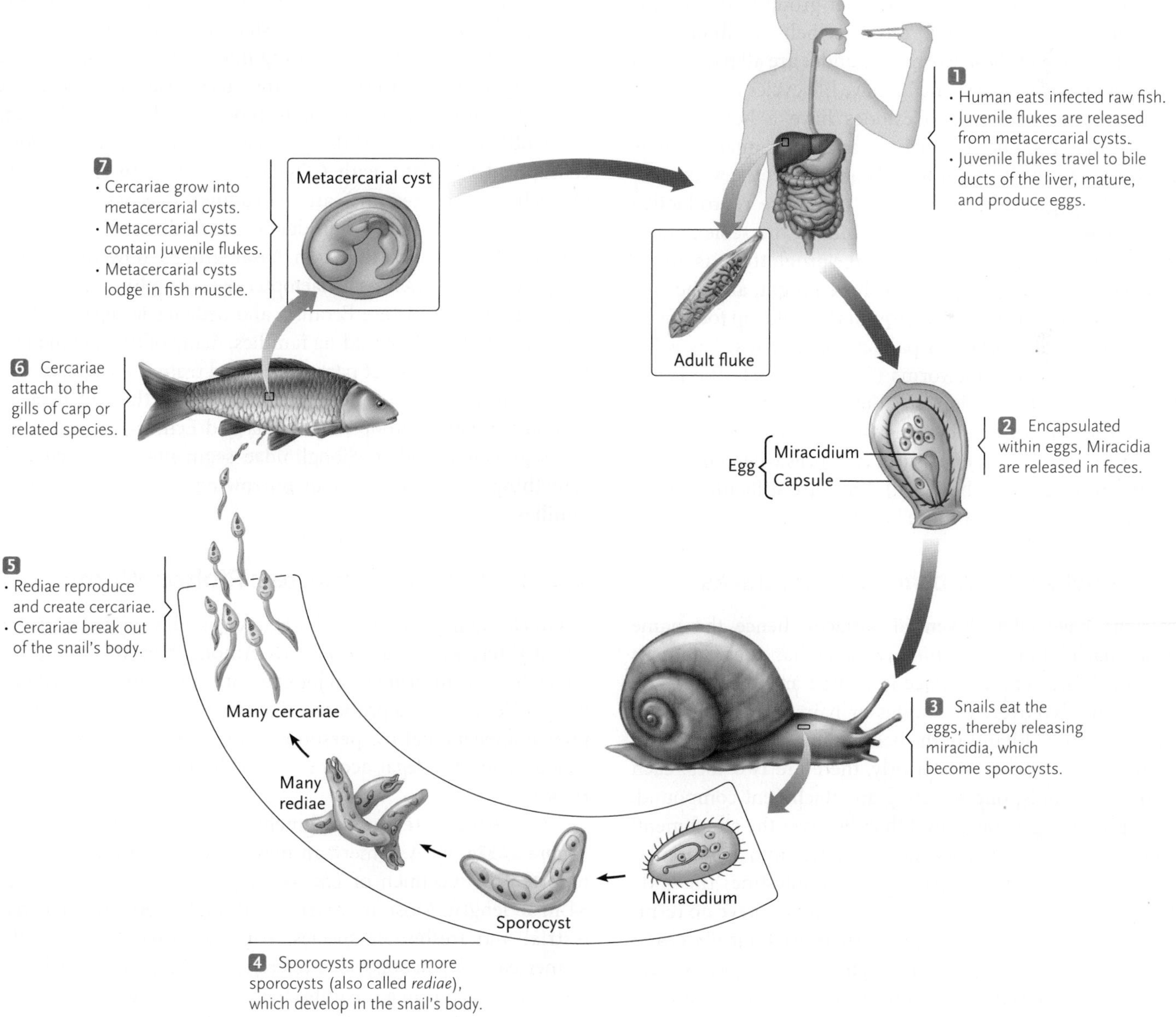

**FIGURE 27.33** **(a)** A stained specimen of *Clonorchis sinensis* (Chinese liver fluke). **(b)** Life cycle of *Clonorchis*

### b.

**1**
- Human eats infected raw fish.
- Juvenile flukes are released from metacercarial cysts.
- Juvenile flukes travel to bile ducts of the liver, mature, and produce eggs.

Adult fluke

**7**
- Cercariae grow into metacercarial cysts.
- Metacercarial cysts contain juvenile flukes.
- Metacercarial cysts lodge in fish muscle.

Metacercarial cyst

**6** Cercariae attach to the gills of carp or related species.

Egg { Miracidium / Capsule

**2** Encapsulated within eggs, Miracidia are released in feces.

**5**
- Rediae reproduce and create cercariae.
- Cercariae break out of the snail's body.

Many cercariae

Many rediae

**3** Snails eat the eggs, thereby releasing miracidia, which become sporocysts.

Miracidium

Sporocyst

**4** Sporocysts produce more sporocysts (also called *rediae*), which develop in the snail's body.

The life cycle of trematodes is complex and involves at least one intermediate host (usually a snail). Figure 27.33b shows the life cycle of *Clonorchis* and the stages that develop in the first intermediate host, a snail, and the second host, a freshwater fish, before the final human host is infected. It is typical of parasite life cycles that each passage from one host to another has a low probability of success. While many eggs are produced, few will be eaten by a snail. The stages in a snail involve asexual divisions to achieve a reproductive amplification that increases the probabilities of reaching the human host.

Monogenea have no intermediate host in their life cycle. Using hooks or suckers on attachment structures, monogeneans attach to the scales or gills of marine and freshwater fish. Fish gills are thin walled and richly vascularized; monogeneans break the epidermis and feed on blood leaking from the wound. Monogenean eggs hatch as ciliated larvae and may attach to the same host as the parent or develop from eggs stuck to the sea bed. Such eggs have the remarkable ability to hatch within seconds if a suitable host is nearby.

Cestoda, or tapeworms, are the sister group to the Monogenea **(Figure 27.34)**. "Cestoda" means a belt or ribbon and describes the shape of these worms. Cestodes are all parasitic in the intestines of vertebrates, and all have life cycles involving at least one intermediate host. Cestodes have a holdfast, the **scolex**, that may have hooks, suckers, and other modifications for attachment to the host gut wall. From the scolex, a series of units, called **proglottids**, each have a complete reproductive system. Tapeworms have cerebral ganglia in the scolex and a pair of lateral nerves runs through all the proglottids, as does a pair of excretory canals. Tapeworms have no gut, and the surface of the body is covered by microvilli that take up food from the host gut. *Taenia solium*, a parasite of humans, has a life cycle that is typical of tapeworms (Figure 27.34c). The larval stage, the cysticercus, develops in humans and may reach sites other than the gut. It can encyst in other organs and such cysts may have serious harmful effects (e.g., seizures when tapeworm cysts start to develop in the brain). They are difficult to treat without causing the patient more harm.

## 27.6b Phylum Gastrotricha: Hairy Backs

Gastrotricha have ciliated ventral surfaces, hence the name "hairy stomach," but the common name has these animals upside down! The ventral surface is ciliated and the body surface is commonly covered by scales or hairs. Gastrotrichs are small (< 3 mm) inhabitants of the benthic surface in marine and freshwater environments. Posteriorly, there are two toes, each with a pair of glands, one secreting an attachment compound, the other producing a compound that dissolves the attachment. Gastrotrichs are detritivores—food is taken into a muscular pharynx and crushed before passing to the intestine. The body cavity of gastrotrichs is a pseudocoelom, and they have no respiratory or circulatory systems. Gastrotrichs are typically cross-fertilizing hermaphrodites, although some species are parthenogenetic. Development is determinate and gastrotrichs

are eutelic (i.e., they have a fixed number of non-reproductive cells in their body).

## 27.6c Phylum Annelida: Segmented Worms

The phylum name comes from *anellus*, meaning "a small ring." This is a reference to the grooves between segments present in many annelids. More than 21 000 species of annelid have been described. Based on molecular data, the phylum has been enlarged through the inclusion of three groups that previously were separate phyla (Echiura, Sipunculidea, and Siboglinidae).

Annelids are highly segmented **(Figure 27.35)**. Segments are separated by intersegmental **septa**. A double ventral nerve cord runs from cerebral ganglia in the head and connects all segments. The gut runs from mouth to posterior anus and has regions specialized for food storage and breakdown in some species. The circulatory system is well developed, with vessels running above and below the gut and surrounding the gut. They lack a discrete respiratory system. Oxygen and carbon dioxide can be exchanged with the surrounding sea water by diffusion through the skin. The excretory system has open funnels (nephrostomes) in each segment, leading into nephridial tubes in the next segment. In freshwater and terrestrial annelids, the nephridial tubes may be elaborate and reabsorb salts and water.

Until recently, annelids were viewed as two classes, Polychaeta and Clitellata, with Clitellata including two subclasses, Oligochaeta (earthworms) and Hirudinea (leeches; see **Figure 27.36**). Molecular analysis produces a very different cladogram **(Figure 27.37)**. Notice that two basal groups (Oweniidae and Magelonidae) as well as Chaetopteridae, Amphinomidae, and Sipuncula branch before Errantia and Sedentaria separate. Sedentaria includes tube-building families, many of them with anterior tentacles that collect particles of food from the water, as well as scavengers and the ectoparasitic leeches in the Clitellata. In two quite separate groups, Sipuncula and Echiuridae, adults are not segmented, and in Siboglinidae segmentation is reduced, something seen also in small burrowing worms in the basal families.

## 27.6d Phylum Nemertea: Ribbon Worms

In Greek mythology, the sea god Nereus and his wife Doris had 50 daughters, known as the *nereids*. Among them was Nemertes, famed for her unerring legal judgements. A feature of the ribbon worms Nemertea is a proboscis that is rapidly extended to strike prey. It appears that the person who described the group transposed Nemertes' legal accuracy into the proboscis aim of the ribbon worms!

Nemertea are non-segmented, flat bodied worms **(Figure 27.38a, b)**. A nemertean may be the longest animal ever reported. A specimen of *Lineus longissimus* was measured at 54 m in length. Most are marine, although there are a few terrestrial and freshwater species. An alternative name for the Nemertea is Rhynchocoela, a reference to the proboscis (*rhynch* = snout), which is in a separate cavity from the gut. Some have a

a. Tapeworm
Scolex
Photo Researchers/Science Source/Getty Images
b. Scolex
Scolex
Proglottids
Andrew Syred/Science Source

**FIGURE 27.34** **(a)** Cestodas, or tapeworms, have long bodies that contain **(b)** a scolex that is used to attach to the host's intestinal wall. **(c)** The life cycle of *Taenia solium* is typical of tapeworms.

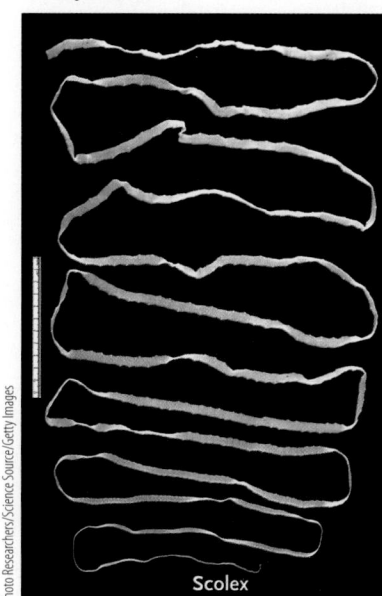

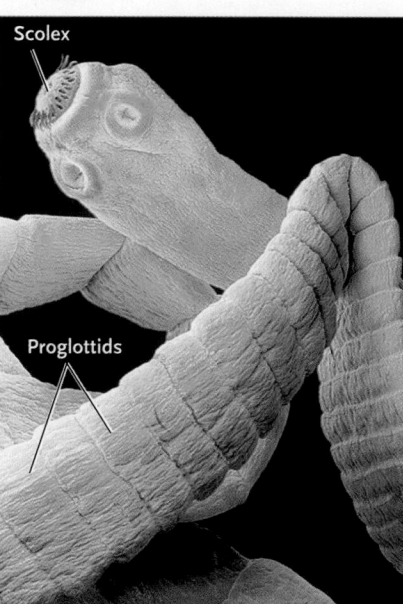

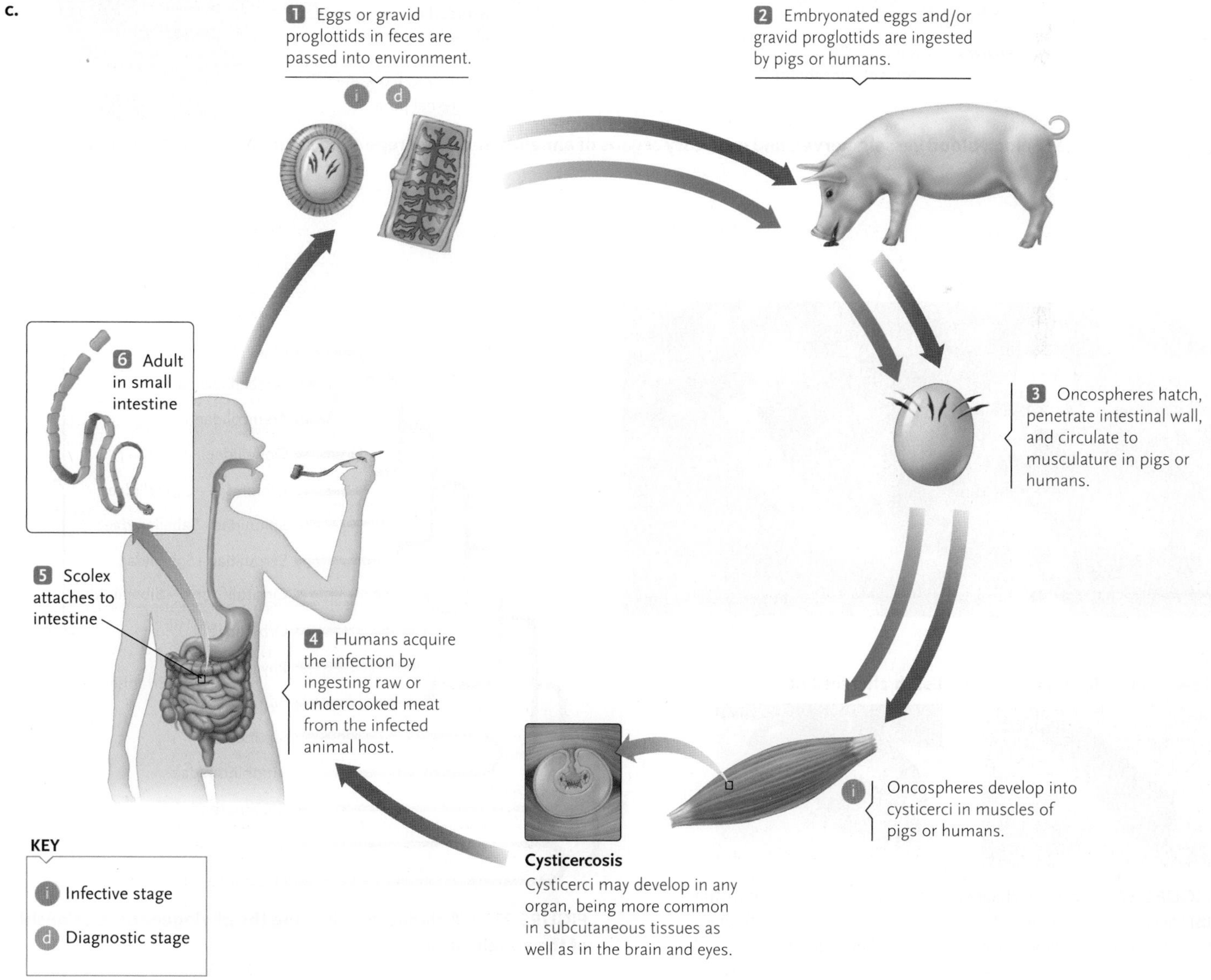

c.
1 Eggs or gravid proglottids in feces are passed into environment.
i d
2 Embryonated eggs and/or gravid proglottids are ingested by pigs or humans.
3 Oncospheres hatch, penetrate intestinal wall, and circulate to musculature in pigs or humans.
i Oncospheres develop into cysticerci in muscles of pigs or humans.
Cysticercosis
Cysticerci may develop in any organ, being more common in subcutaneous tissues as well as in the brain and eyes.
4 Humans acquire the infection by ingesting raw or undercooked meat from the infected animal host.
5 Scolex attaches to intestine
6 Adult in small intestine
KEY
i Infective stage
d Diagnostic stage

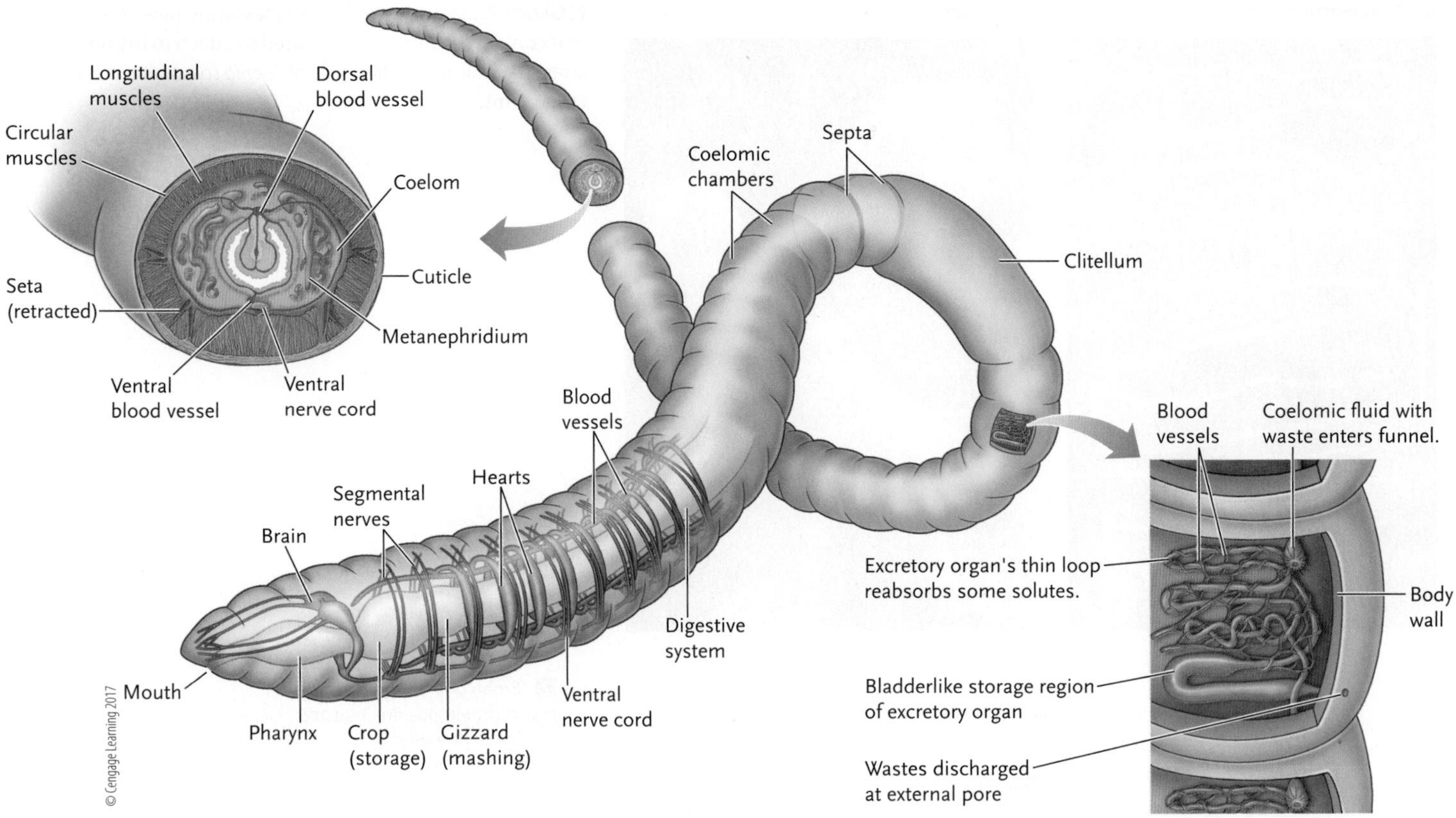

FIGURE 27.35 **The coelom, blood vessels, nerves, and excretory organs of annelids appear as repeating structures in most segments.**

a.

b.

**Leech before feeding**          **Leech after feeding**

FIGURE 27.36 **(a)** Oligochaetes, such as earthworms, are terrestrial. **(b)** Leeches live in water and are blood feeders. They have a highly branched gut that allows them to consume large blood meals.

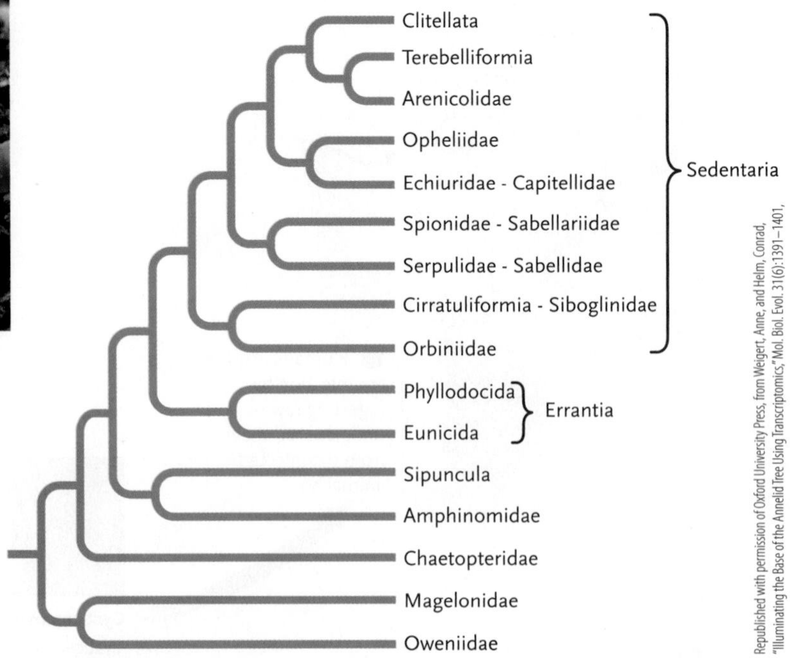

FIGURE 27.37 **A cladogram showing the phylogenetic relationships of the annelid groups**

Republished with permission of Oxford University Press, from Weigert, Anne, and Helm, Conrad, "Illuminating the Base of the Annelid Tree Using Transcriptomics," Mol. Biol. Evol. 31(6):1391–1401, 2014; permission conveyed through Copyright Clearance Center, Inc.

**a. Ribbon worm (*Lineus* species)**

**b. Ribbon worm anatomy**

Proboscis pore · Proboscis · Rhynchocoel

Mouth · Intestine · Proboscis retractor muscle · Anus

Everted proboscis

© Cengage Learning 2017

**Figure 27.38** **(a)** Ribbon worms can be brightly coloured. **(b)** The rhynchocoel contains a proboscis.

barb that impales the prey, while in others the proboscis wraps around the prey. Nemertea are traditionally described as acoelomate, although the **rhynchocoel** is surrounded by mesoderm and hence a true coelom. The mouth of nemerteans is ventral and a little behind the front. In primitive nemertean groups, the proboscis extends from the rhynchocoel at the tip; in more evolved groups the proboscis and the mouth share a single ventral opening.

Nemerteans lack a cuticle, but ciliated epidermal cells, mucus-secreting cells, and rhabdites cover the body surface. They have a circulatory system whereby fluid flows through circulatory vessels that carry nutrients to tissues and remove waste. The fluid is moved through the vessels when the vessels are compressed by body movements.

Nemerteans reproduce asexually by fragmentation; even small pieces of a ribbon worm can regenerate to a complete individual. Sperm and ova are shed from males and females, and fertilization is external. A free-swimming larva develops, and a new adult differentiates within the body of the larva.

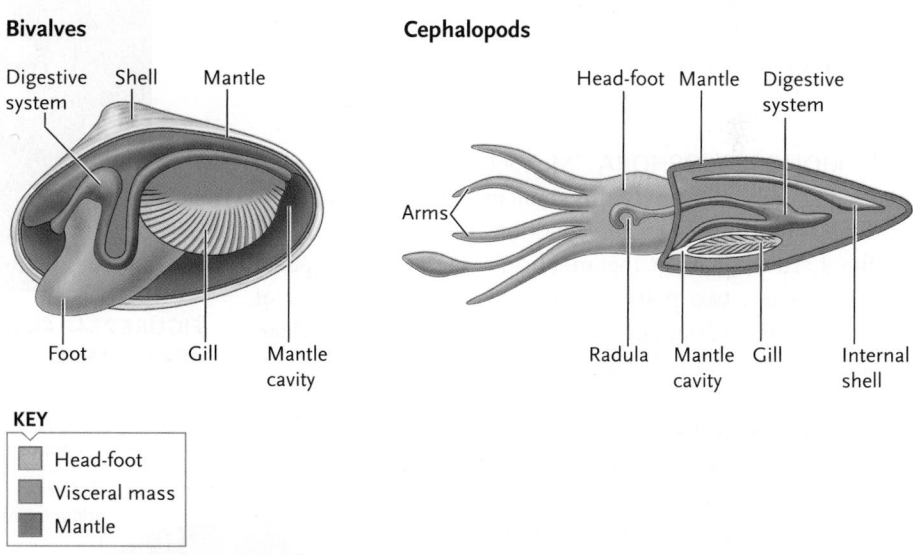

**Chitons**

Shell · Digestive system · Mantle

Head · Radula · Foot · Gill · Mantle cavity

**Gastropods**

Sensory tentacles · Shell · Mantle

Head · Radula · Gill · Foot · Digestive system

**Bivalves**

Digestive system · Shell · Mantle

Foot · Gill · Mantle cavity

**Cephalopods**

Head-foot · Mantle · Digestive system

Arms

Radula · Mantle cavity · Gill · Internal shell

**KEY**
- Head-foot
- Visceral mass
- Mantle

**FIGURE 27.39 Common features in the mollusc body plan include the head–foot, visceral mass, and mantle.**

## 27.6e Phylum Mollusca: Slugs, Snails, and Squid

The name Mollusca comes from the Latin *molluscus*, meaning "soft." Beneath or without their shell, molluscs are soft-bodied animals. Molluscs evolved as benthic animals at a time when the number, and variety, of predatory species was increasing.

Molluscs evolved a dorsal spicule covering, that later became a shell, as a defensive adaptation. Estimates suggest that there are 200 000 species of living mollusc living in all environments and about 70 000 in the fossil record.

The molluscan body plan has several common features **(Figure 27.39)**. Three regions are the visceral mass, head–foot, and mantle. The **visceral mass** contains the digestive, excretory, and reproductive systems, and the heart. The muscular **head–foot** often provides the major means of locomotion, except in cephalopods (e.g., octopuses, squid). In the more active groups, the head area of the head–foot region is well defined and carries sensory organs and a brain. The mouth often includes a toothed **radula**, which scrapes food into small particles or drills through the shells of prey. A well-known feature of this phylum is a shell. This protective shell of calcium carbonate is secreted by the **mantle**, a folding of the body wall that may enclose the visceral mass. The mantle also defines a space, the **mantle cavity**, that houses the gills (delicate respiratory structures). In most molluscs, cilia on the mantle and gills generate a steady flow of water into the mantle cavity. Most molluscs have an **open circulatory system** in which **hemolymph**, a bloodlike fluid, leaves the circulatory vessels and bathes tissues directly. Hemolymph pools in spaces called *sinuses* and then drains into vessels that carry it back to the heart.

The sexes are usually separate, although many snails are hermaphroditic. Fertilization may be internal or external. In some snails, eggs and sperm are produced simultaneously in the same organ, an ovotestis. In others, the hermaphroditism is serial, with younger snails producing sperm and older individuals switching to egg production. Fertilization is often internal in these organisms, and in simultaneous hermaphrodites, there is a mutual exchange of sperm during copulation.

There are eight classes of living molluscs **(Figure 27.40)**. Although members of the phylum have common characteristics, they have evolved an extraordinary diversity in form and lifestyle, ranging from sessile clams to the agile octopus capable of learned behaviour.

**CLASS MONOPLACOPHORA** "Monoplacophora" describes the "single plate" shell form of this small group of deep-sea molluscs. Internally there is serial repetition of several organ systems: there are six pairs of metanephridia, eight pairs of pedal retractor muscles, two pairs of heart atria, and two pairs of gonads. While the advantages of serial repetition are not clear, this does not represent reduced segmentation.

**CLASS POLYPLACOPHORA (THE CHITONS)** *Polyplacophora* means "many plates" **(Figure 27.41)**. In reality, the shell typically is divided into eight plates. The division of the shell is not reflected internally and is an adaptation to allow the animal to fit closely to rough rock surfaces where chitons browse on the algal and bacterial film. The mantle edge extends beyond the shell as a girdle that, in some species, may grow up and around the shell.

**CLASS BIVALVIA (CLAMS, SCALLOPS, OYSTERS, AND MUSSELS)** As their name implies, bivalves are enclosed within two

shells that are hinged together by an elastic ligament **(Figure 27.42)**. In the development of the shell, it first forms as a figure 8; the crossover in the eight is not calcified and forms the dorsal hinge when the two loops of the eight fold down and calcify. When **abductor muscles** contract the shell closes, and relaxation of the muscles allows the shell to open.

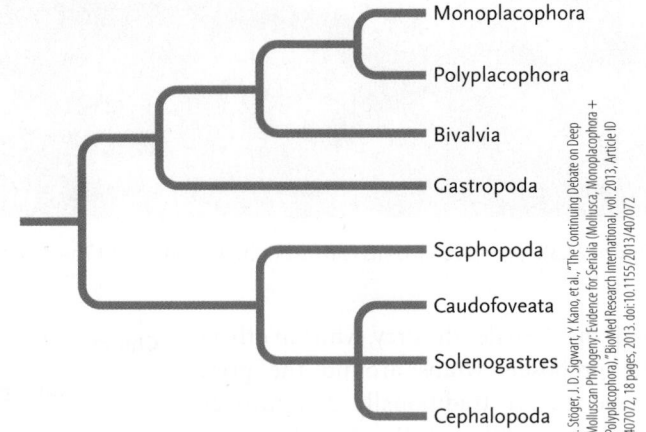

I. Stöger, J. D. Sigwart, Y. Kano, et al., "The Continuing Debate on Deep Molluscan Phylogeny: Evidence for Serialia (Mollusca, Monoplacophora + Polyplacophora)," BioMed Research International, vol. 2013, Article ID 407072, 18 pages, 2013. doi:10.1155/2013/407072

**FIGURE 27.40 Molluscan phylogeny**

**FIGURE 27.41 Chitons use their foot and mantle to grip rocks and other surfaces.**

**a. Bivalve body plan**

Ligament (connects to opposite shell)
Mouth
Anterior adductor muscle
Left mantle
Posterior adductor muscle
Water flows out through excurrent siphon.
Water flows in through incurrent siphon.
Foot   Palps   Left gill   Right shell

© Cengage Learning 2017

**b. Giant clam (Tridachna gigas)**

treetstreet/iStock/Getty Images

**FIGURE 27.42 (a)** Bivalves are enclosed within two shells. **(b)** Although some bivalves are tiny, giant clams of the South Pacific can be more than 1 m across and weigh 225 kg.

### a. Gastropod body plan

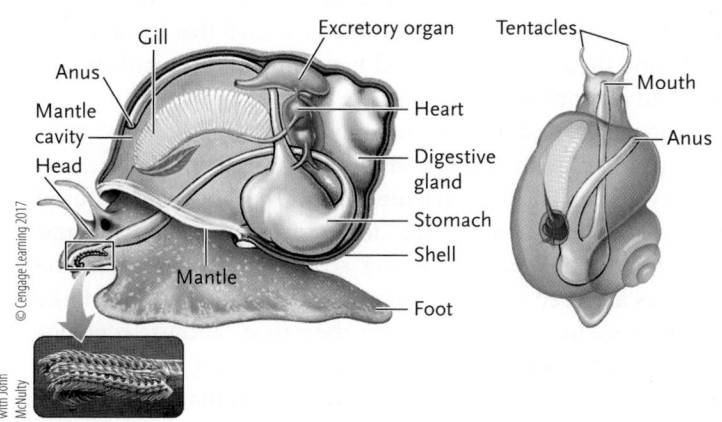

Gill
Anus
Mantle cavity
Head

Excretory organ
Heart
Digestive gland
Stomach
Shell
Foot
Mantle

Tentacles
Mouth
Anus

Radula

© Cengage Learning 2017

Danielle Zacherl with John McNulty

### b. Terrestrial snail (*Helix pomatia*)

KOO/Shutterstock.com

### c. Marine nudibranch (*Flabellina iodinea*)

iStock.com/Thornberry

**FIGURE 27.43** **(a)** Most gastropods have a coiled shell that contains the visceral mass. **(b)** The terrestrial snail (*Helix pomatia*) is a typical gastropod. **(c)** This marine nudibranch (*Flabellina iodine*) is an example of a shell-less marine snail.

Bivalves have evolved a highly modified molluscan form, specialized for burrowing and filter feeding. The foot is spade-like and can be expanded and contracted as blood is pumped in or as muscles contract, an alternating motion that penetrates the substratum and then anchors as the shell is pulled down. The hinge of the shell allows the valves to gape and form an anchor as the foot is extended.

Bivalves lack a distinct head and radula. Two tubes, called *siphons*, are formed from part of the mantle. Beating cilia on the gills draw water into the mantle cavity through the incurrent siphon. This water carries oxygen and nutrients. Water exits through the excurrent siphon, carrying away wastes. Primitive bivalves have palps on either side of the mouth that are extended into the substratum to collect food; in these species, the gills are small. In most bivalves, the gills are enormously expanded: an estimate has the gill area about 300 times that needed for gas exchange. The palps are reduced and sort food from the gills into the mouth.

Bivalves are a commercially important, including both harvested and cultured species of clams, oysters, scallops, and mussels.

**CLASS GASTROPODA (SNAILS AND SLUGS)** Gastropoda (*gastro* = stomach; *poda* = foot) are the largest molluscan group, containing around 75% of the described species. Gastropods, while mostly marine, have freshwater and terrestrial species and include predators, herbivores, filter feeders, and detritivores (consume dead or composing plant and animal matter). They exhibit a wide range of morphologies. Aquatic and marine gastropods use gills to obtain oxygen. Terrestrial gastropods have replaced gills by heavy vascularization of the mantle cavity, allowing the surface to operate like a lung **(Figure 27.43)**. The nervous and sensory systems of gastropods are well developed. Tentacles on the head include chemical and touch receptors; the eyes detect changes in light intensity but don't they form images. Many gastropods have lost or reduced shells, such as the terrestrial and sea slugs, which leaves them vulnerable to predators.

Understanding the appearance of the gastropods demands understanding two different processes of twisting. The most obvious is the coiling of the gastric hump from the conical form of a limpet **(Figure 27.44a)** to that of a snail (Figure 27.44b). The coiled shell allows expansion of the intestine, digestive

### a. Common limpet

M. B. Fenton

### b. Terrestrial snail

M. B. Fenton

**FIGURE 27.44** **(a)** This common limpet is a gastropod that has a conical shell and lives on rocks in the intertidal zone. **(b)** Terrestrial snails, such as this *Helix pomatia,* have a coiled shell.

gland, and gonad in a way that allows them to be balanced above the foot. The second twist is less obvious and is a change that occurs during development. It involves rotation of the mantle cavity, gills, and anus from their posterior position to an anterior arrangement, a process known as *torsion*.

**CLASS SCAPHOPODA (THE TOOTH SHELLS)** The name Scaphopoda translates as "boat foot" and refers to the shape of the burrowing foot. The common name describes the tusklike shape of the shell. A scaphopod shell is a tapering tube, and the animal lives with the small end protruding above the substratum and the wide end buried. Seawater currents enter, and leave, the open end, and respiratory gas exchange occurs over the surface of the mantle. The foot is extended from the wide opening, as are a number of tentacles, known as **captacula**, that surround the mouth. The captacula extend into the seabed and collect small food items (particularly protists) and transfer them to the mouth. The anus opens into the mantle cavity, and wastes are washed out in the exhalant water stream.

**CLASS CAUDOFOVEATA** The name means a tail (*cauda*) pit (*fove*) and refers to the posterior chamber that encloses a pair of **ctenidia**, comb-like respiratory structures. The body has anterior, trunk, and posterior regions and is covered by spicules—perhaps a predecessor to the evolution of a rigid shell. Caudofoveates use the muscle of the anterior and trunk regions to burrow, leaving the gills above the substratum surface. They feed on foraminiferans, diatoms, and detritus. While only 120 species of Caudofoveata have been described, the majority of which are from the deep sea, it is probable that there are many species yet to be collected.

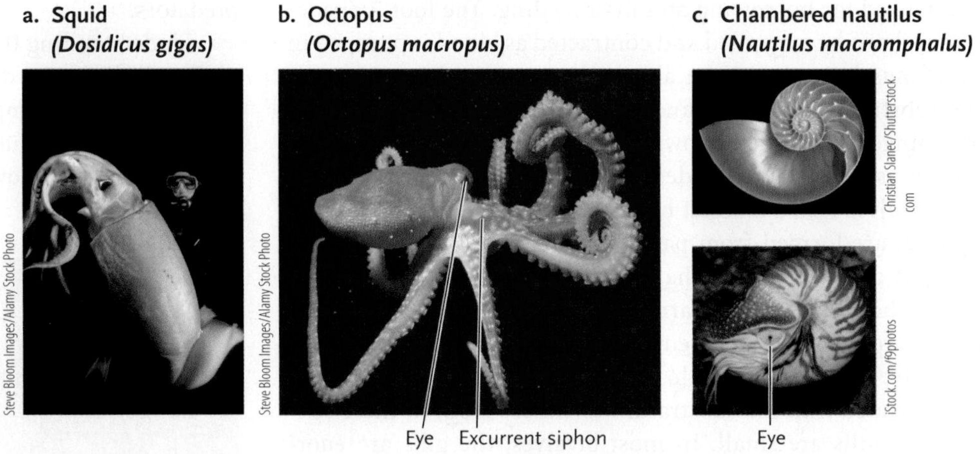

**CLASS SOLENOGASTRES** The Solenogastres are like the caudofoveates in having a wormlike shape and a body covered by spicules rather than a shell. The name comes from *solen* (= grooved) and *gaster* (= stomach), and it describes the way in which the foot is sunken into a groove on the ventral surface. Solenogastres are predators, feeding mostly on cnidarians either by direct predation or by sucking body fluid after penetrating the body wall of their prey.

**CLASS CEPHALOPODA (SQUID AND OCTOPUS)** Cephalopoda translates as "head footed" and describes the way in which the molluscan foot has evolved into the tentacles and head of the cephalopods. The group includes nautilus, squid, and octopus **(Figure 27.45)**, and there are about 1000 living species and more than 10 times as many fossil species. The evolutionary history of the cephalopods includes shell reduction.

Fossil belemnites (straight) and ammonites (coiled) had heavy shells. In modern groups, the nautiloids retain a light external shell, the cuttlefish have a porous internal shell that has a role in regulating their buoyancy, squid have only a thin cartilaginous pen, and octopuses have no shell.

Internally, cephalopod anatomy follows the standard molluscan model, with specializations that relate to the size and activity of cephalopods **(Figure 27.46)**. The body has a fused head and foot. The ancestral "foot" forms a set of arms and tentacles. Suction pads, adhesive structures, or hooks on the tentacles are used to capture prey. Cephalopods have beaklike jaws that are used to bite or crush their food. Because cephalopods are highly active, they need lots of oxygen. Unique to molluscan groups, they have a **closed circulatory system**: hemolymph is confined within the walls of hearts and vessels. The closed system allows cephalopods to have much smaller blood volumes and provides increased pressure to vascular fluid. The systemic heart is supplemented by two branchial

**a. Squid**
*(Dosidicus gigas)*

**b. Octopus**
*(Octopus macropus)*

Eye  Excurrent siphon

**c. Chambered nautilus**
*(Nautilus macromphalus)*

Eye

*Steve Bloom Images/Alamy Stock Photo*
*Steve Bloom Images/Alamy Stock Photo*
*Christian Slanec/Shutterstock.com*
*iStock.com/R9photos*

**FIGURE 27.45 (a, b)** Squids and octopuses are the most familiar cephalopods. **(c)** The chambered nautilus retains a shell.

**Internal anatomy of squid**

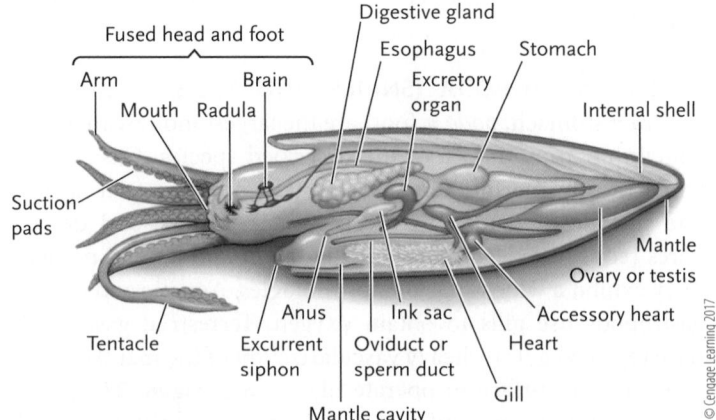

**FIGURE 27.46 The squid anatomy is like that of other cephalopods.** It has a fused head and foot, and most organs are enclosed by the mantle.

© Cengage Learning 2017

hearts that pump hemolymph through the ctenidia. They speed the flow of hemolymph through blood vessels and gills, enhancing the uptake of oxygen and release of carbon dioxide. They have a discrete kidney that is closely associated with the circulatory system. Oxygen is carried by hemocyanin, a pigment that carries only 25% as much oxygen as hemoglobin.

Compared with other molluscs, cephalopods have large and complex brains, which connect to muscles of the mantle. This allows for quick response to food and danger. They are also highly intelligent: octopuses can learn to recognize shapes and can be trained to approach or avoid certain objects.

Cephalopods swim by jet propulsion. When muscles in the mantle relax, water is drawn into the mantle cavity and then expelled under pressure through the muscular siphon. Manipulating the position of the mantle and siphon allows a cephalopod to control the rate and direction of movement. Octopuses also walk on their arms, and squid and cuttlefish fins are involved in slow swimming.

The ink sac is a special feature of cephalopods. In shallow-water species, the ink sac contains a melanin suspension that can be released as a cloud, confusing a predator and allowing the cephalopod to escape. Deep-sea species have commonly replaced the ink with a colony of phosphorescent bacteria that produce a cloud of light when released, allowing escape into the darkness.

Cephalopods also have a remarkable ability to change colour. This is achieved through the expansion (by muscle strands) and contraction (by elasticity) of pigment containing chromatophores. Colour change is under neural control and, while mostly controlled through the highly developed eyes, can also be modulated by a general light sensitivity of the epidermis.

## 27.6f   Phylum Entoprocta

The name Entoprocta means "inside anus" and describes the position of the anus inside the ring of tentacles. Entoprocts are colonial and almost all species are marine. Entoprocts lack a coelom; the space between gut and body wall is filled by connective-tissue strands. The tentacles are solid and are withdrawn by curling. Superficially, they resemble tube-dwelling annelid worms.

## 27.6g   Phylum Cycliophora

The first described species of cycliophoran, *Symbion pandora*, lives commensally on the mouthparts of the Norway lobster (*Nephrops norvegicus*). *Symbion* has a complex life cycle that includes an asexual stage that multiplies on its lobster host. When the host is about to moult, the cycliophoran is triggered to move into a sexually reproductive phase. A male is produced that attaches to a bud that develops as a female; the fertilized female swims freely, its gut degenerates, and a larva develops in its place. The larva then swims free to seek another host. Adults resemble small hydralike cnidarians.

## 27.6h   Phylum Phoronida: Horseshoe Worms

Phoronids are benthic worms that secrete a chitinous tube that is either attached to or buried in the substratum. Their common name comes from the shape of the lophophore that is coiled around the mouth in a horseshoe-like shape (**Figure 27.47**). Phoronids have a U-shaped gut, with the anus outside the lophophore. A pair of metanephridial funnels discharge metabolic wastes near the anus. Phoronids live in low oxygen environments and, an adaptation unique among invertebrates, have hemoglobin in their blood system that is contained in corpuscles; weight for weight, a phoronid carries twice as much oxygen as a human.

## 27.6i   Phylum Brachiopoda: Lamp Shells

Brachiopods resemble clams in having a bivalve shell. Unlike clams, where the shell valves are lateral, brachiopods have dorsal and ventral shell valves. The common name "lamp shells" comes from the shape of one valve resembling that of an oil lamp. The phylum name translates as "arm" (*brach*) "footed" (*pod*) and comes from the two arms of the lophophore that can be seen when the shell is open. There are about 400 living species of brachiopod, but the group was a dominant part of the Paleozoic

**a. Phoronida**
**(*Plumatella repens*)**

**b. Brachiopoda**
**(*Terebratulina septentrionalis*)**

**c. Bryozoa (*Phoronis hippocrepia*)**

FIGURE 27.47 **The lophophore is a feathery structure that lophophorate animals use to obtain food.**

fauna, with over 30 000 species described. Theories suggest competition between brachiopods and bivalve molluscs, combined with the great Permian extinction, led to the decline in brachiopod diversity.

## 27.6j Phylum Bryozoa: Moss Animals

*Bryo-* means "moss," which is how colonies of bryozoans appear. Bryozoans are colonial lophophorates found in marine and fresh waters. Individual zooids in the colony are protected by a body wall that may be of chitin or, in many cases, may be mineralized. Each zooid has a U-shaped gut and resembles a miniature phoronid. Bryozoans are polymorphic (composed of different individuals), with feeding zooids supplying food to reproductive zooids, defensive zooids, and zooids specialized for cleaning the surface of the colony. Zooids are able to coordinate their activities. While individual zooids collect food, they will cooperate with neighbours to use the tentacles to flick non-food items away from the colony.

**STUDY BREAK QUESTIONS**

1. What characteristic reveals the close evolutionary relationship of bryozoans, brachiopods, and phoronids?
2. Describe the three regions of the mollusc body.
3. Which organ systems exhibit segmentation in most annelid worms?

## 27.7 Ecdysozoa Protostomes

Twenty-five years ago, it was heretical to think that segmented arthropods and annelids might not be closely related. It followed that Onychophora, with features of both groups, were not associated with the evolutionary line between annelids and arthropods. An early contribution of using molecular analysis to understand phylogeny came from studies of 18S ribosomal DNA of protostome groups. The results showed that the protostomes must be divided into a clade of animals that moult a non-living cuticle (Ecdysozoa) and Lophotrochozoa. The analysis showed no support for a group that would link Arthropoda and Annelida.

Recent molecular studies support splitting Ecdysozoa into three groups: Scalidophora Nematozoa, and Panarthropoda **(Figure 27.48)**.

- Scalidophora includes the phyla Kinorhyncha, Loricifera, and Priapulida. Like other ecdysozoans they have a chitinous cuticle that is moulted. All three phyla have an anterior region (introvert) that can be retracted or extended and scalids—spines, hooks, or finger-like projects on the introvert that are continuous with the chitinous cuticle.
- Nematozoa includes the phyla Nematoda and Nematomorpha. Both lack circular muscle and have longitudinal muscle divided into four cords. Both have a cuticle supported

by a fibre lattice. While chitin is characteristic of all ecdysozoans, its presence is limited to the pharyngeal lining of nematodes and the larval cuticle of nematomorphs.

- Panarthropoda includes the phyla Onychophora, Tardigrada, and Arthropoda. Members of all three phyla have legs, claws, a double ventral nerve cord, and a segmented body plan. There is dispute over the relationship of the three phyla. Current evidence supports the tardigrades as being the sister group to the Arthropoda.

## 27.7a Phylum Kinorhyncha: Mud Dragons

The name of this phylum is based on the words *kines* (move) and *rhynch* (snout) and refers to the way in which the head is extended and retracted. There are about 250 described species of kinorhynch, living from the marine intertidal down to the deep sea. Kinorhynch adults have a head and neck and an 11-segmented body **(Figure 27.49)**. The head bears a group of anterior stylets and, behind them, numerous scalids (finger-like projections). Extension and withdrawal of the head moves the scalids to pull the animal through soft substrata.

Kinorhynchs feed on decaying organic material, algae, and bacteria as they burrow. They have a muscular pharynx and a simple through gut. Intersegmental muscles control movement of the body, the body cavity is a pseudocoel, and excretion is via a pair of protonephridial organs. Kinorhynchs are dioecious and hatch as small adult forms, although with fewer segments.

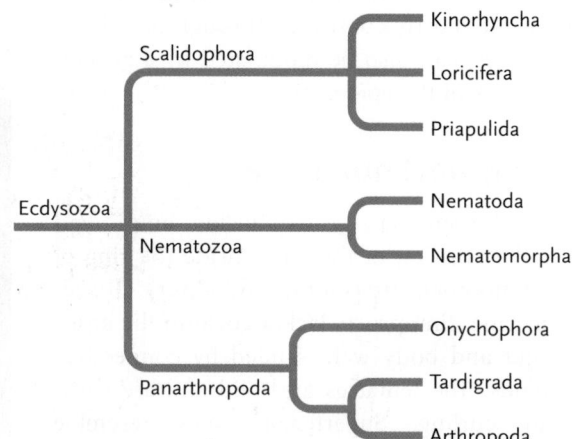

**FIGURE 27.48** A current view of the phylogeny of the Ecdysozoa

**FIGURE 27.49** A kinorhynch from the Bay of Fundy

## 27.7b Phylum Loricifera: The Brush Heads

A *lorica* is a corselet (part of a suit of armour), and in the case of loriciferans the outer sheath into which the animal can withdraw. Loriciferans have a frontal cone with two rings of scalids that, in some species, move the animal across the sea bed, and in others have been seen to be used in swimming. Loriciferans have a simple through gut, and some species are pseudocoelomate; others are acoelomate. Most species are dioecious and produce an egg that hatches to a form resembling a small adult. A few species are parthenogenetic.

The surprise finding from these animals is that they do not have mitochondria, normally present in all living eukaryotes. Instead, they have hydrogenosomes, organelles known only from some protists that supply energy through anaerobic pathways.

## 27.7c Phylum Priapulida: Penis Worms

The common name for Priapulida comes from the Greek god of fertility (*Priapus*), a figure depicted with a large penis. The rounded anterior part of a priapulid worm is suggested to resemble the head of a penis. Priapulids are a small group of marine, burrowing, predatory worms. There are about 25 living species. The body is divided into an anterior introvert, where the mouth is located. There are rings of scalids on the introvert, which grip the substrate as the introvert is moved in and out of the trunk. There is a simple through gut. The body cavity is undivided and is now thought to be a hemocoel. Cells carrying hemerythrin, a respiratory pigment, move through the fluid in the body cavity. Priapulans burrow by eversion and contraction of the introvert combined with peristaltic movements of the body. The body cavity fluid acts as a hydrostatic skeleton for movement.

## 27.7d Phylum Nematoda: Round Worms

Nematoda (*nemata* = thread) include about 30 000 described species, although estimates suggest that the phylum includes well over a million species, making it the second largest animal phylum. The phylum is distributed in all possible habitats, and over 50% of its members are parasitic (**Figure 27.50**).

The upper 10 cm of a soil layer has been estimated to contain over a million nematodes per square metre. Nematodes constitute over 90% of the fauna of the sea bed and the group are well known as extremophiles, living in habitats where other organisms cannot survive. A frequently mentioned nematode is a species found in German beer coasters (now known to occur in other habitats, as it is also found living in the paste binding of library books). Cultures of the nematode *Caenorhabditis elegans* were on the ill-fated space shuttle Columbia. Nematodes in three of five containers found in the debris field in Texas were found to have survived the temperature conditions of Earth reentry as well as estimated forces of 2500*g*.

Nematodes are typically elongated, circular in cross-section, and tapered at both ends. Their body wall is protected by a cuticle that is moulted as they grow and reinforced by three layers of fibres arranged at alternating angles to each other. This arrangement gives strength while maintaining flexibility. The gut runs from an anterior mouth that opens into a muscular pharynx, leading to a thin-walled intestine and a posterior anus. Inside the body wall run four cords of longitudinal muscles, separated by dorsal and ventral nerve cords and lateral excretory canals (**Figure 27.51**).

Nematode musculature is unusual in two ways. First, rather than nerves running to the muscle, the muscle itself has connectives that run to the nerve cords. Secondly, there is no circular muscle; differential contraction of the longitudinal muscle bends the worm, while hydrostatic pressure in the pseudocoelom opposes this change in shape and straightens the worm when the muscles relax. This hydrostatic mechanism is similar to that used in penis worms. High pressure in the pseudocoelom collapses the gut and the pharynx operates as a

**FIGURE 27.50 Some roundworms, such as these *Anguillicola crassus*, are parasites of plants or animals.**

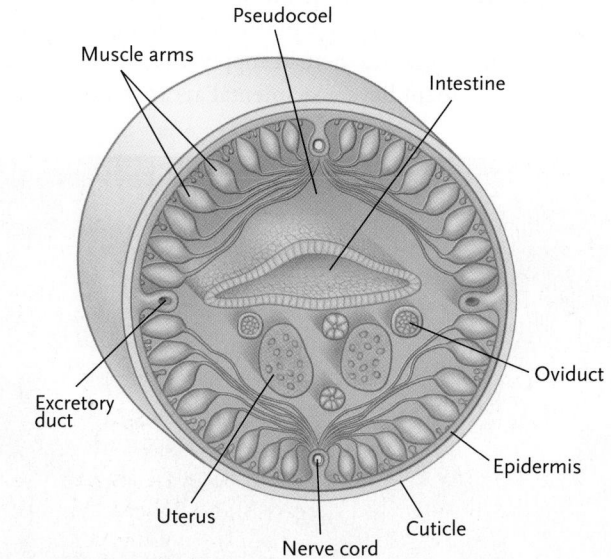

**FIGURE 27.51 A cross-section of a typical nematode**

pump, forcing food back into the intestine against the pressure. Free-living nematodes feed on decaying matter, fungi, bacteria, and other organic materials. A soil nematode has been shown to eat about 5000 bacterial cells a minute, a measure that shows the importance of nematodes in an ecosystem.

## 27.7e Phylum Nematomorpha: Horsehair Worms

As their name suggests, Nematomorpha are long (typically 50–100 cm), thin (usually only 2–3 mm diameter) worms. Adult nematomorphs are short-lived and have no excretory or circulatory system. There is a non-functional gut, and the worms do not eat. Females produce strings of eggs from which larvae hatch and then enter an intermediate host, frequently a beetle. Larvae grow in the host, absorbing food over their body wall, and will then moult to the adult form. At this time, they affect the behaviour of their host, stimulating movement and causing the host to seek water, where the newly emerged adult leaves through the host anus.

## 27.7f Phylum Onychophora: Velvet Worms

Onychophora means "claw bearing" and refers to the claws at the tip of each pair of the animal's lobe-like appendages (Figure 27.52). Their common name, "velvet worm," comes from the soft appearance of their cuticle.

Onychophorans are segmented animals, although the only external evidence of segmentation lies in the pair of legs on each segment. The head has three pairs of modified appendages: a pair of sensory antennae, a pair of hardened mandibles within the mouth, and a pair of papillae through which a sticky slime can be discharged. Onychophorans are the champion spitters of the animal kingdom. A 5 cm animal can fire strands of slime at prey 50 cm away to immobilize the prey, which is then killed by an injection of toxic saliva.

Internally, the separation of the 13–43 segments (varying with species) is clear. There is a pair of glands opening at the base of each pair of legs, the neural supply and muscles associated with leg movement have a segmental arrangement, and on each segment there is an opening, the spiracle, into a tracheal system that resembles that of the insects. An important difference is that insect spiracles can be sealed shut, and onychophoran spiracles have no closing mechanism. This makes them a site for water loss, which restricts the habitats in which the onychophorans can live. Fertilization is internal, and in many onychophorans sperm is stored in a reservoir where it remains functional for several months. Some species are oviparous (egg laying), others ovoviviparous (eggs hatch in the uterus), and some viviparous (eggs hatch and young develop in the uterus). Some viviparous species actually have a placenta to provide food to the developing young.

## 27.7g Phylum Tardigrada: Water Bears

The name Tardigrada means "slow walker," an apt description of the locomotion of these small (0.05–1.5 mm long) animals. There are about 1000 described tardigrade species (and an estimated 10 000 species in total) living in marine, freshwater, and semi-terrestrial environments. Tardigrades (Figure 27.53) are segmented, with a head, three trunk segments, and a caudal segment; each segment behind the head bears a pair of lobe-like legs equipped with terminal claws, hooks, or suckers.

Tardigrades have a muscular pharynx that sucks food through the mouth from punctures, made by extending stylets through the mouth, in plant cells. There is a through gut, with tubular glands branching from the hindgut. Most tardigrade species are dioecious and oviparous (a few are parthenogenetic), and eggs are commonly thick walled. Like several other groups of small animals, tardigrades are eutelic (each species has a fixed number of non-reproductive cells).

Tardigrades are famous for their cryptobiotic adaptations. Difficult environmental conditions trigger a controlled dehydration, followed by loss of cuticular permeability and enormously reduced metabolism. Tardigrades in this state can withstand extreme challenges of heat, cold, noxious chemicals, radiation, and pressure. In this state, tardigrades can survive for up to 10 years and can still be revived when placed in water. Despite this adaptation, tardigrades are not viewed as extremophiles since they do not normally live in extreme environments.

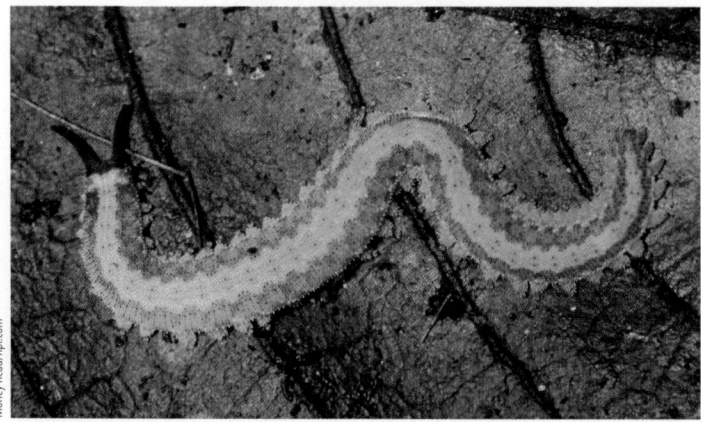

**FIGURE 27.52 An onychophoran from Ecuador**

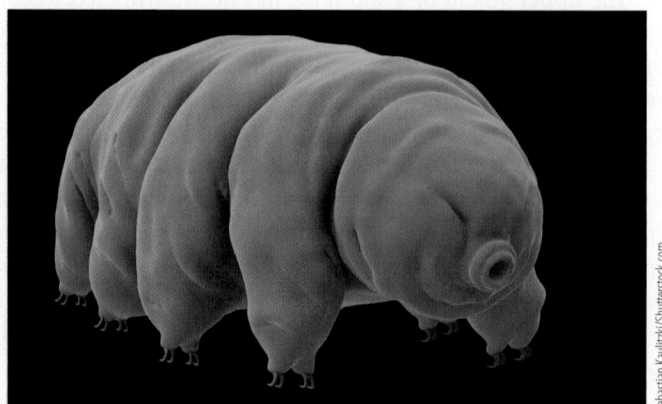

**FIGURE 27.53 A tardigrade**

## 27.7h Phylum Arthropoda: Joint-Legged Animals

The phylum Arthropoda (*arthro* = joint; *pod* = foot) includes four living groups (Chelicerata, Myriapoda, Crustacea, and Insecta) and has a species count vastly greater than any other phylum. Compare the species numbers in **Figure 27.54** to the roughly 5500 known species of mammals! This diagram shows only the living arthropod groups. The hard exoskeleton of arthropods results in their being common as fossils. Huge numbers of species (e.g., 17 000 species of trilobites) have been described from the early Cambrian onward in groups that became extinct, including some that played a dominant role in the ecosystem of the time.

Arthropods are segmented animals, frequently with some segments or groups of segments specialized for different functions; fusion of segments is common. Arthropod bodies are covered by an **exoskeleton**, a continuous layer of cuticle made of a mixture of chitin and proteins. Cuticle is commonly hardened by a process of tanning (sclerotization), which involves two dopamine derivatives, N-acetyldopamine and N-P-alanyldopamine, which are oxidized to quinones that cross-link with amino acids in the cuticular proteins. In crustaceans, the cuticle may be additionally thickened and hardened by the incorporation of calcium carbonate. Many factors affect cuticle hardness, particularly the relative amounts of chitin and protein, with more chitin (up to 4:1 ratio) making flexible cuticle and 1:1 chitin:protein making for rigid cuticle. If there were no flexible cuticle, arthropod bodies would be rigid and immobile. The demands of movement are met by the cuticle at joints (e.g., between segments and limb joints) being unsclerotized and flexible.

While an exoskeleton provides excellent protection, and muscles running between skeletal elements offer efficient locomotion, the exoskeleton makes growth impossible. Arthropods can grow only by a series of moults in which the old exoskeleton is shed. The body enlarges while its covering is soft, and the new cuticle hardens over the enlarged body. Moulting is regulated by a complex interaction between internal conditions and environmental conditions, and is controlled by neural and neurosecretory messages.

In soft-bodied animals, support comes from a hydrostatic skeleton formed by fluid in a gastric compartment (e.g., sea anemones), pseudocoel (e.g., nematodes), or coelom (e.g., annelid worms). In the arthropods, support comes from the exoskeleton. The coelom is greatly reduced and the body cavity is a hemocoel. Development of a circulatory system in arthropods may be minimal or may have a heart and a highly complex series of branching vessels that open into the hemocoel and transport materials throughout the body.

The exoskeleton is a barrier to the exchange of gasses and fluids over the body surface. These exchanges are performed by different excretory and respiratory structures in each arthropod group, and are discussed in the following sections.

Arthropods have a complex nervous system with a central nervous system developed by fusion of ganglia in the head segments, a double ventral nerve cord that includes giant neurons for fast conduction, segmental ganglia, and extensive neural development.

**SUBPHYLUM CHELICERATA** The name of this group comes from the first appendages, known as **chelicerae** (*chela* = claw; *cera* = horn). These are a small pair of pincerlike appendages used to bite or grasp prey. Chelicerates have a body that is divided into two main regions: a cephalothorax, also called a **prosoma** (formed from fusion of the head and thorax), and the abdomen, also called the **opisthosoma**. Chelicerata includes three classes: Pycnogonida, Xiphosura, and Arachnida.

Pycnogonids are known as *sea spiders*, although they are distantly related to true spiders. A typical pycnogonid **(Figure 27.55)** has four pairs of long thin legs. The head is small and bears a proboscis that is inserted into food (pycnogonids are predators or scavengers). The abdomen is vestigial. Liquid food is sucked into a gut that runs to a terminal anus, which has branches that extend into the basal parts of each leg.

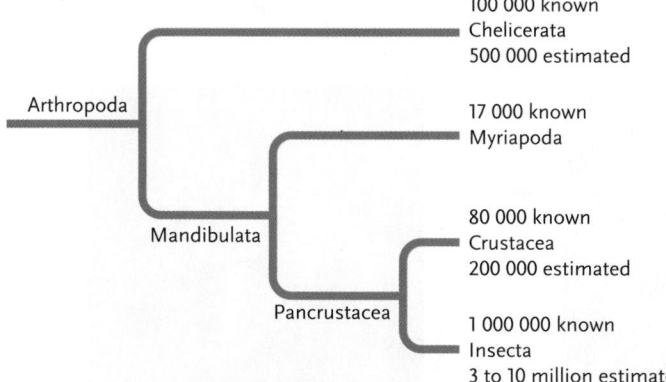

**FIGURE 27.54 A current view of arthropod phylogeny showing the numbers of identified species, as well as estimates of the number of species still to be described**

Figure 27.55 **A pycnogonid (*Nymphon leptocheles*) feeding on a hydroid (*Tubularia* sp.)**

Pycnogonids are gonochoristic—eggs are released and fertilized externally and are then carried to hatching by the male.

Xiphosurans, the horseshoe crabs **(Figure 27.56)**, are distantly related to true crabs (crustaceans). The name Xiphosura is based on the terms *xiphos* (= sword) and *uros* (= tail) and refers to the spinelike telson used to help right the animal if water movement turns it over. The body of a xiphosuran is divided into an anterior prosoma and a posterior opisthosoma (of which the spikelike telson is the last segment). There are five pairs of walking legs, and a pair of chelicerae on the ventral side of the prosoma. The leg bases are jawlike and grind food between them before passing it forward to the mouth. The ventral side of the opisthosoma has a series of flaplike gills. Although the cuticle is thick and hard, it is not strengthened by incorporation of calcium carbonate.

The arachnids represent almost all the chelicerates, which includes over 100 000 species in about 10 recognized orders. Arachnids have four pairs of legs on the prosoma, and most digest food to a liquid form before taking it into the gut. Included in this class are the mites, ticks, scorpions, and spiders **(Figure 27.57)**.

Spiders are unusual among animals in having only flexor muscles in their legs. They extend their legs by hydraulic action that depends upon on blood being pumped from the hemocoel. There is only one herbivorous species of spider, the rest are predatory, eating mostly other arthropods. A characteristic of the spiders is the modification of the chelicerae as fangs through which venom is injected into prey. Spider webs are a familiar mechanism of prey capture, although there are interesting variations in the use of silk. The jumping spiders (Salticidae) do not spin webs but actively pursue their prey and have exceptional vision for prey detection. The large eyes are telescopic and use differential focus of different colours to measure the distance to a prey.

**FIGURE 27.56** *Limulus polyphemus* **is the only living xiphosuran.**

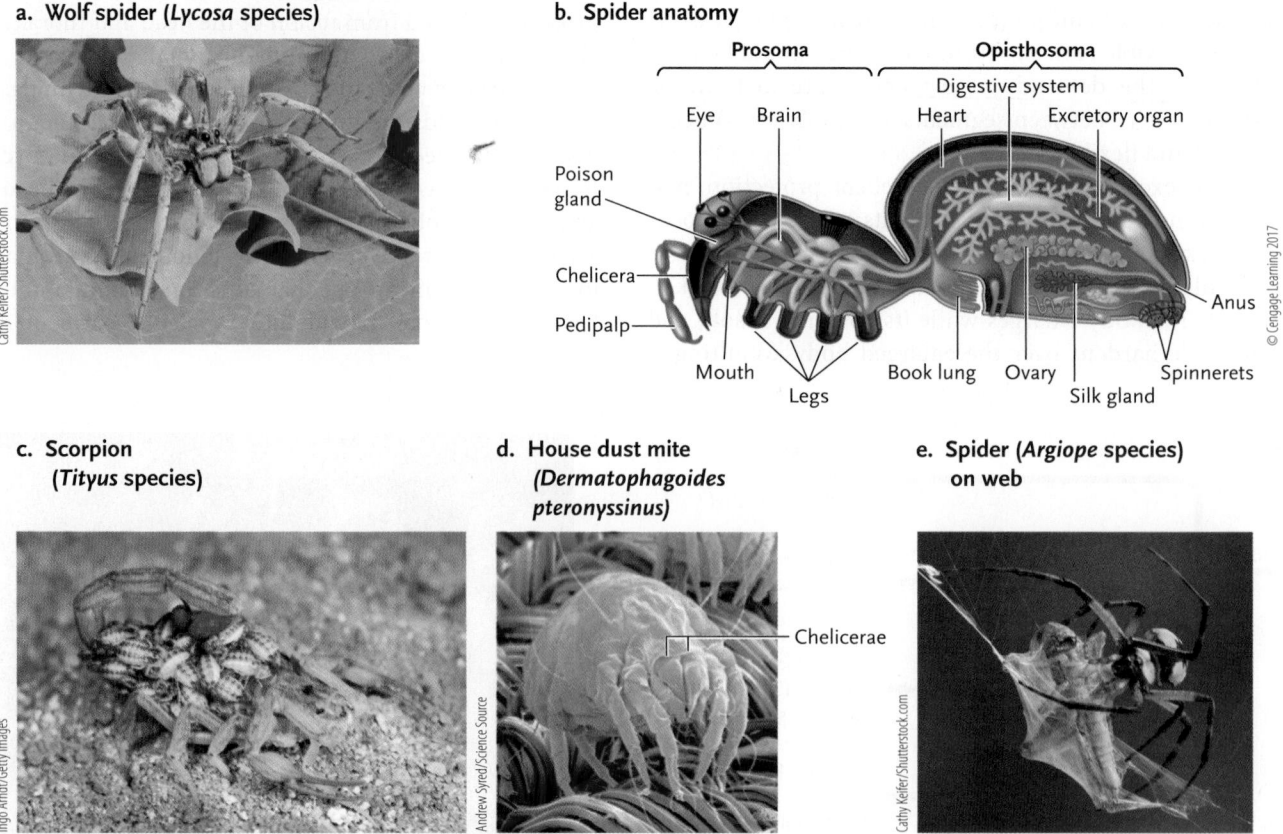

**FIGURE 27.57 Examples of arachnids. (a)** Wolf spiders are harmless to humans. **(b)** The spider anatomy exemplifies the arachnid body plan. **(c)** Scorpions are nocturnal predators characterized by the grasping pedipalps and segmented tail tipped with a stinger. **(d)** This dust mite is viewed using a scanning electron microscope. **(e)** Spider webs are used to capture prey.

**SUBPHYLUM MYRIAPODA** The Myriapoda include the Chilopoda (centipedes), Diplopoda (millipedes), Pauropoda, and Symphyla **(Figure 27.58)**. Myriapods have two body regions: a head and a segmented trunk. The head bears a single pair of antennae and a pair of eyes. Each segment bears a pair of legs, despite the appearance of the millipedes, whose name, Diplopoda, comes from the appearance of two pairs per segment (a result of segmental fusion). Millipedes, pauropods, and symphylans are herbivores and detritivores in leaf litter and in loose soil. Centipedes are predatory and have developed poison fangs through modification of the first pair of legs **(Figure 27.59)**.

**SUBPHYLUM CRUSTACEA** This group name refers to the hardened exoskeleton of many crustaceans. The group is characterized by having two pairs of antennae and appendages that divide into two branches. The evolution of the Crustacea is one of specialization of body regions, segments, and appendages for different functions. Crustaceans have so many different body plans that they are divided into many groups and subgroups. The crabs, lobsters, and shrimps (examples of decapods; meaning "10 feet") number more than 10 000 species alone. The great majority of crustaceans are marine. There are freshwater species, such as crayfish, and some groups have invaded the terrestrial environment.

In Decapoda **(Figure 27.60)**, the head bears the sensory antennae; the mandibles and food handling depends on the maxillae and the first three thoracic appendages (maxillipeds). Food is captured by the **chelipeds**, and there are four pairs of walking legs. The abdominal **swimmerets** circulate water (and in females ventilate eggs), and the telson and uropods allow for backward escape swimming. The exoskeleton forms a **carapace**, which is a protective covering that extends backward from the head. Most crustaceans exhibit complex movements and behaviours, and have elaborate sensory and nervous systems.

The extent, and nature, of segmental fusion and specialization is the basis of the separation of the groups within the Crustacea.

Many crustaceans, such as copepods **(Figure 27.61)**, are present in the billions in freshwater and marine plankton. Most are only a few millimetres long. Plankton crustaceans are among the most abundant animals on Earth. They feed on microscopic algae and detritus and are themselves food for other animals.

Adult barnacles are sessile marine crustaceans that live within a shell **(Figure 27.62)**. Their larvae are free swimming and attach permanently to substrates such as rocks and hulls of ships. They then secrete a shell, which is a modified exoskeleton. A barnacle feeds by opening the shell and using six pairs of feathery legs to capture plankton and transfer it to its mouth.

Two large orders of crustaceans are Isopoda and Amphipoda (*iso* = equal; *amphi* = around). Isopods are typically dorsoventrally flattened and have legs evenly spread to either side. Amphipods are typically laterally compressed and commonly lie on their sides in a curve around their legs. *Bathynomus* is a giant (~25 cm long) isopod from the deep ocean. The phenomenon of

**a. Millipede (*Spirobolus* species)**

**b. Centipede (*Scolopendra* species)**

**FIGURE 27.58 (a)** Millipedes and **(b)** centipedes have a head and a segmented body.

**FIGURE 27.59 The forcipules (poison claws) of a centipede (*Scolopendra*)**

deep-sea gigantism is not understood, but it is suggested that the size of this detritivore allows it to forage over a large area in search of scarce food. *Phronima* **(Figure 27.63)** is not a typical amphipod and is adapted for a predatory life, where it enters the body of a urochordate (see Section 27.8) and devours its prey from the inside. While only a few millimetres long, *Phronima* served as the model for the monster in the film *Aliens*.

**SUBPHYLUM HEXAPODA** The name of this group refers to arthropods that have three pairs of legs. It includes the Insecta **(Figure 27.64)** as well as some other smaller classes. Three groups

**a. Crab (*Ocypode* species)**

**b. Lobster (*Homarus americanus*)**

**c. Lobster external anatomy**

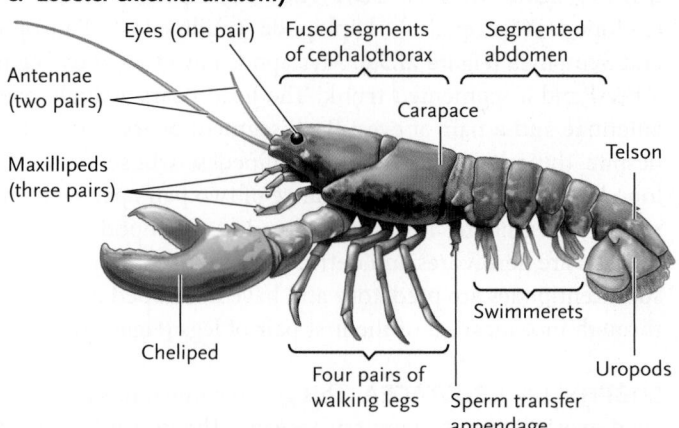

Eyes (one pair)
Fused segments of cephalothorax
Segmented abdomen
Antennae (two pairs)
Carapace
Maxillipeds (three pairs)
Telson
Cheliped
Four pairs of walking legs
Sperm transfer appendage
Swimmerets
Uropods

FIGURE 27.60 **(a)** Crabs and **(b)** lobsters are examples of decapods. **(c)** Lobster anatomy shows the main features of decapod crustaceans.

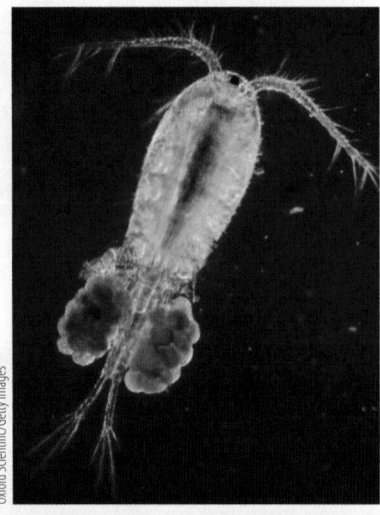

FIGURE 27.61 **Copepods are tiny crustaceans that can be found by the billions in plankton.**

FIGURE 27.62 **These gooseneck barnacles attach themselves to the hulls of ships.**

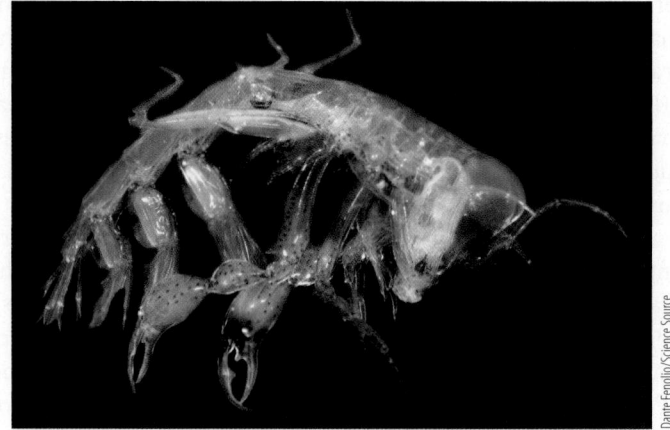

FIGURE 27.63 ***Phronima* sp., an Amphipoda**

have **entognathous** mouth parts, meaning the mouth parts can be withdrawn into a capsule in the head. There are also a large number of groups that are **ectognathous**, which have exposed mouth parts. These two divisions are almost synonymous with Apterygota (wingless) and Pterygota (winged).

The insect body plan includes a head, a thorax, and an abdomen **(Figure 27.65)**. Insects possess a pair of **compound eyes** and one pair of sensory antennae. The thorax contains three pairs of walking legs and often one or two pairs of wings. Segmentation has been reduced. Only some muscles, ventral nerve cord, and dorsal blood vessel are segmented. The insect respiratory system is a **tracheal system**. A branching network of tubes carry oxygen from openings in the exoskeleton to cells throughout the body. **Malpighian tubules** transport nitrogenous waste to the digestive system for excretion. Particularly fascinating about the insects is the specialized mouthparts, which reflect the nature of the food source. For example, insects that bite have piercing structures with a narrow channel to suck up blood, while butterflies have a long proboscis to drink nectar **(Figure 27.66)**.

**a.** Silverfish (Thysanura, *Lepisma saccharina*) are wingless, an ancestral trait within insects.

**b.** Dragonflies (Odonata, *Epitheca cynosura*) have aquatic larvae that are active predators; adults capture other insects in mid-air.

**c.** Male praying mantids (Mantodea, *Mantis religiosa*) are often eaten by the larger females during or immediately after mating.

**d.** This stag beetle (Coleoptera, *Lucanus cervus*) is one of more than 250,000 beetle species that have been described.

**e.** Fleas (Siphonaptera, *Ctenocephalides canis*) have strong legs with an elastic ligament that allows these parasites to jump on and off their animal hosts.

**f.** Crane flies (Diptera, *Tipula* species) look like giant mosquitoes, but their mouthparts are not useful for biting other animals; the adults of most species live only a few days and do not feed at all.

**g.** The luna moth (Lepidoptera, *Actias luna*), like other butterflies and moths, has wings that are covered with colourful microscopic scales.

**h.** Like many other ant species, fire ants (Hymenoptera, *Solenopsis invicta*) live in large cooperative colonies. Fire ants—named for their painful sting—were introduced into southeastern North America, where they are now serious pests.

**FIGURE 27.64  There are about 30 subgroups of insects, eight of which are represented here.**

**External anatomy of a grasshopper**

Antenna  Head  Thorax  Abdomen

Tympanum (hearing organ)

Wing

Compound eye

Mouth parts

Legs

**Internal anatomy of a female grasshopper**

Brain  Dorsal blood vessel  Heart

Ovary

Mouth  Ventral nerve cord with ganglia  Digestive system  Malpighian tubules

**FIGURE 27.65  The body plan of an insect includes a head, a thorax, and an abdomen.**

A factor in the success of insects is the evolution of life cycles that allow developing stages to utilize resources from different environments than those of adults. Arthropod development depends on moulting (ecdysis) and is regulated through the pro-hormone ecdysone, a steroid, that is converted to the active moult hormone 20-hydroxyecdysone. After hatching from an egg, an insect passes through development stages called **instars**. There are three types of metamorphosis in the development of insects **(Figure 27.67)**. In each of these sequences, the moult from one stage to the next is regulated by physiological and environmental conditions that trigger a neurosecretory pathway from the brain that activates the prothoracic gland to secrete ecdysone.

CHAPTER 27  ANIMALS

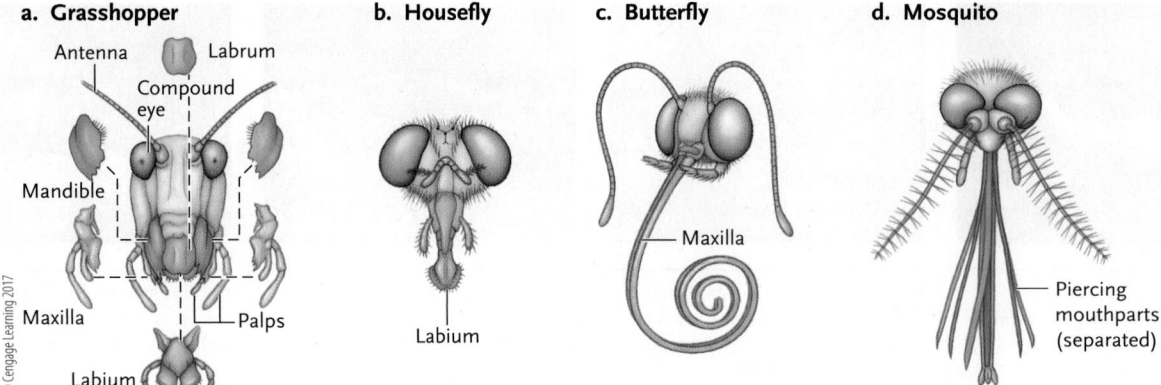

**a. Grasshopper**

Antenna    Labrum
    Compound
    eye
Mandible

Maxilla

Palps

Labium

**b. Housefly**

Labium

**c. Butterfly**

Maxilla

**d. Mosquito**

Piercing
mouthparts
(separated)

© Cengage Learning 2017

**FIGURE 27.66 Insects have specialized mouth parts that have evolved over time to allow for different methods of feeding. (a)** In plant feeders, the labrum covers the mouthparts and has sensory functions. The mandibles are for chewing, and paired maxillae, with palps, scoop the food. The labium is most posterior, represents a fused pair of appendages, and contains many sensory structures and palps. This basic plan has evolved and allowed insects to **(b)** sponge up food, **(c)** drink nectar, and **(d)** pierce skin to consume blood.

**a. No metamorphosis**

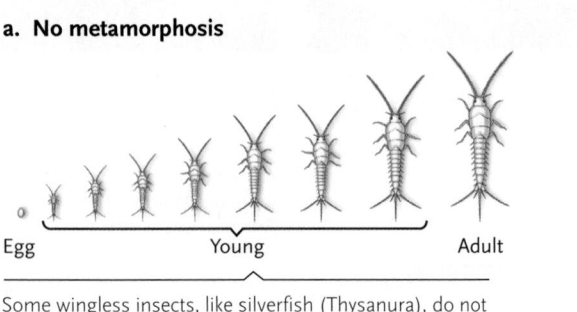

Egg           Young           Adult

Some wingless insects, like silverfish (Thysanura), do not undergo a dramatic change in form as they grow.

**b. Metamorphosis without a pupa (hemimetaboly)**

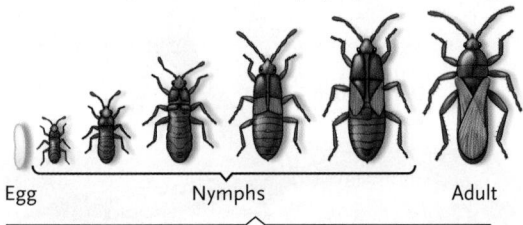

Egg         Nymphs          Adult

Other insects, such as true bugs (Hemiptera), have incomplete metamorphosis; they develop from nymphs into adults with relatively minor changes in form.

**c. Metamorphosis with a pupa (holometaboly)**

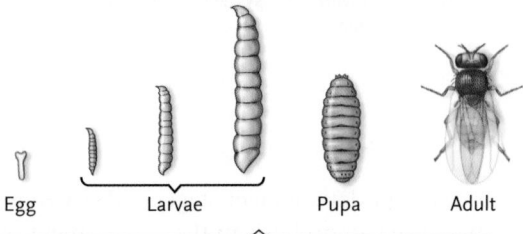

Egg      Larvae      Pupa     Adult

© Cengage Learning 2017

Fruit flies (Diptera) and many other insects have complete metamorphosis; they undergo a total reorganization of their internal and external anatomy when they pass through the pupal stage of the life cycle.

**FIGURE 27.67 Patterns of postembryonic development in insects**

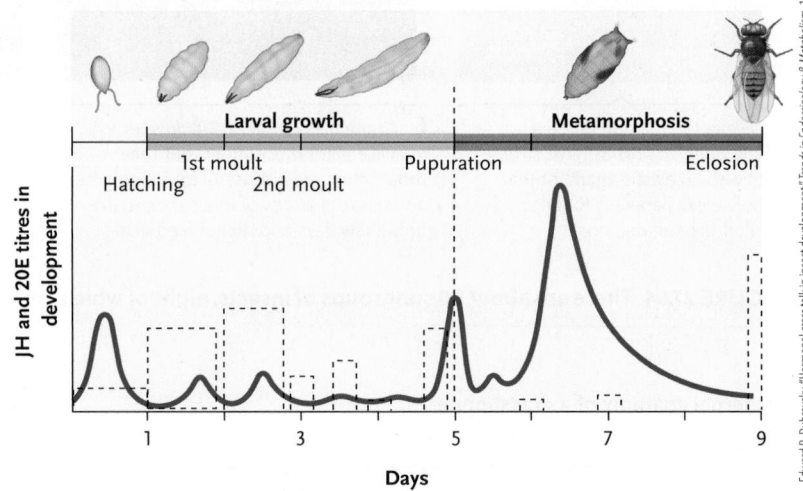

Larval growth          Metamorphosis

1st moult          Pupuration          Eclosion
Hatching   2nd moult

JH and 20E titres in development

Days

Edward B. Dubrovsky, "Hormonal cross talk in insect development," *Trends in Endocrinology & Metabolism*, 16(1): 6–11. Copyright © 2004 Elsevier Ltd. *Trends in Endocrinology and Metabolism*: TEM by ELSEVIER SCIENCE PUBLISHERS Reproduced with permission of ELSEVIER LTD. in the format Book via Copyright Clearance Center.

**FIGURE 27.68 Juvenile hormone (dotted lines) and 20-hydroxyecdysone (solid line) levels in the development of *Drosophila* (holometabolous development).** 20E = 20-hydroxyecdysone

These three developmental modes divide the insects into three groups. Apterygotes (i.e., wingless) undergo **incomplete metamorphosis** whereby there are minimal changes in morphology. They simply grow and shed their exoskeleton. Most insects undergo **complete metamorphosis**. In this case, the larvae that hatch are very different from the adults; they live in different habitats and eat different food. The Exopterygota (meaning that the wings develop externally) metamorphose without a pupa; and in the Endopterygota, the wings develop internally in the **pupa** stage, which is a sessile stage before larva transform into sexually mature adults.

Juvenile hormone (JH) is a sesquiterpenoid hormone secreted into the blood from the corpora allata (behind the brain). Levels of JH determine the outcome of each moult. In a hemimetabolous life cycle, metamorphosis is gradual from one instar to the next; JH levels decline a little at each instar. In a holometabolous life cycle (**Figure 27.68**), there is a major decline in JH when the final larva moults to produce a pupal stage.

Flight is a major factor in the success of insects in the terrestrial environment. Flight provides a way of escaping danger, as well as searching for food, mates, or suitable environments. Fossil evidence does not provide a clear picture of how insect wings evolved. The probability is that flat lateral cuticular extensions first provided stability in jumps and falls, and that these evolved into static surfaces for gliding and then into moving wings. Muscles power the wings directly in dragonflies (Odonata; see **Figure 27.69a**) but, in most advanced insect orders, the muscles are arranged indirectly (Figure 27.69b) and wing movement is a response to deformation of the thorax. Vertical muscles compress the thorax dorsoventrally and raise the wings, and horizontal muscles restore the thorax shape and power the downstroke. The extremes of insect flight include sphynx moths reaching speeds of 50 km/hour (house flies are slow at 6–8 km/hour), painted lady butterflies migrating 6400 km from Iceland to North Africa, small fly wing beats of 600 Hz (compared to the slowest butterfly rates of 5 Hz), and fossil dragon flies that had a 60 cm wingspan.

Insects demonstrate remarkable communication abilities in various modes, including chemical messages (pheromones), sound, and light signals. Pheromones may convey many types of information, including mate attraction, alarm, and food locations. Many male moths have featherlike antennae that have evolved to detect minute amounts of pheromone from a female. Gypsy moths may sense just a few molecules of pheromone from a female a kilometre away. In flying toward the source of the scent, they zigzag to maintain an average path along the line of greatest concentration. The gypsy moth pheromone has been identified and produced synthetically as gyplure for use in traps for pest control. Pheromones can provide directional information on the ground as well as in the air. Leafcutter ants mark a trail from a food source to the nest. The trail pheromone is secreted from the venom gland and includes volatile and non-volatile components. Pheromones may also carry an alarm message. When a honeybee stings a vertebrate **(Figure 27.70)**, the barbs of the sting catch in the flesh and the sting is torn from the body. As the sting attachment breaks, a pheromone sac at its base is ruptured to release an alarm pheromone; this triggers a response from other bees to attack the threat to the hive.

The sounds of summer include a background of grasshopper chirps and the metallic buzz of cicadas. Grasshopper sounds are produced by stridulation—a mechanism in which a file (rough surface) on the hind legs is rubbed against a scraper at the base of the forewings. Male grasshoppers stridulate to attract females and, in some species, females also stridulate in response. Grasshoppers hear sounds through a tympanal organ at the base of the abdomen. Cicadas use a different mechanism to produce sounds that may be as loud as 120 dB, about the sound level of a jet plane taking off. Male cicadas have a membrane, supported by ribs, known as the *tymbal*, in the anterior region of the abdomen. This membrane is vibrated by a tymbal muscle at frequencies between 2 and 10 kHz, and sound production is amplified by a large air cavity in the abdomen. Female cicadas do not produce calls and hear the male call through a tympanal organ similar to that of grasshoppers.

In fireflies, which are actually beetles, flashing light signals are the basis of communication between females and males **(Figure 27.71)**. Light is produced by a light organ in the abdomen and depends on the action of an enzyme, luciferase, on a luciferin substrate, a reaction that requires ATP, $Mg^{2+}$, and oxygen. Different species have different patterns of flash duration and frequency. Some female fireflies in the genus *Photuris* imitate the flash patterns of other species to attract them as prey—leading to these insects being called *femmes fatales*!

a.

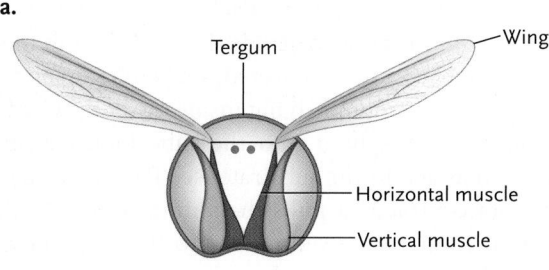

b.

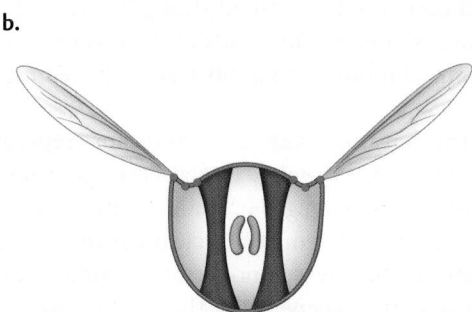

**FIGURE 27.69** **(a)** Direct flight muscles connect directly to the wings at either side of their pivot point. **(b)** Indirect flight muscles move the wings through changes in the shape of the thorax.

**FIGURE 27.70** **A honeybee (*Apis mellifera*) with its sting embedded in a human**

**FIGURE 27.71** Ventral view of a female *Photinus* sp. flashing light

The examples insect biology described in this section have been drawn from the larger and more familiar orders of insects. There are over a million described species of insects classified in about 29 orders, some including only a few species while the largest group, the Coleoptera (beetles), includes well over 300 000 species. Insect biology fills libraries and many careers—a world worthy of exploration.

## STUDY BREAK QUESTIONS

1. If an arthropod's rigid skeleton cannot be expanded, how does the animal grow?
2. Compare the body plans of the four groups of living arthropods.
3. How do the life stages differ between insects that have incomplete metamorphosis and those that have complete metamorphosis?

# 27.8 The Deuterostomes

Membership in the Deuterostomia **(Figure 27.72)** is restricted to animals in which the anus develops from the blastopore, and the mouth from a second opening. The body plans of these animals vary from star shaped and radially symmetrical, through asymmetrical to bilaterally symmetrical. At first glance, deuterostome animals, such as echinoderms, chordates, and hemichordates, are not obviously similar. This reflects modifications of their bodies that mask underlying developmental and genetic features **(Figure 27.73)**.

## 27.8a Phylum Echinodermata

The phylum Echinodermata (*echino* = spiny; *derm* = skin) includes 6500 species of sea stars, sea urchins, sea cucumbers, brittle stars, and sea lilies. These slow-moving or sessile bottom-dwelling animals are important herbivores and predators living in oceans, from the shallow coastal waters to the depths. The phylum was diverse in the Paleozoic, but only a remnant of that fauna remains. Echinoderms vary in size from less than 1 cm in diameter to more than 50 cm long. Adult echinoderms develop from bilaterally symmetrical, free-swimming larvae. As the larvae develop, they assume a secondary radial symmetry, often organized around five rays, or "arms" **(Figure 27.74)**. Many echinoderms have an oral surface, with the mouth facing the substrate, and an aboral surface facing in the opposite direction. Virtually all echinoderms have an internal skeleton made of calcium-stiffened ossicles that develop from mesoderm. In some groups, fused ossicles form a rigid container called a *test*. In most species with these features, spines or bumps project from the ossicles.

The internal anatomy of echinoderms is unique among animals. They have a well-defined coelom and a complete digestive system, but they lack both excretory and respiratory systems. Most species have a minimal circulatory system. In many species, gases are exchanged and metabolic wastes are eliminated through projections of the epidermis and peritoneum near the base of the spines. These radially symmetrical animals have no obvious head or central brain. The nervous system is organized around nerve cords that encircle the mouth and branch into the radii. Sensory cells are abundant in the skin.

Echinoderms move using tube feet operated by a system of fluid-filled canals, the **water vascular system** (see Figure 27.74e). In a sea star, for example, water enters the system through the madreporite, a sievelike plate on the aboral surface. A short tube connects it to the ring canal, which surrounds the **esophagus**. The ring canal branches into five radial canals that extend into the arms. Each radial canal is connected to numerous tube feet that protrude through holes in the plates. Each tube foot has a mucus-covered, suckerlike tip and a small muscular bulb, the ampulla, lying inside the body. Contraction of an ampulla forces fluid into the tube foot, causing it to lengthen and attach to the substrate (see Figure 27.74f). When the tube foot contracts, it pulls the animal along. As the tube foot shortens, water is forced back into the ampulla, and the tube foot releases its grip on the substrate. The tube foot can then take another step forward, reattaching to the substrate. Although each tube foot has limited strength, the coordinated action of hundreds or even thousands of them is so strong that they can hold an echinoderm to a substrate even against strong wave action.

Echinoderms have separate sexes, and most reproduce by releasing gametes into the water. Radial cleavage is so clearly apparent in the transparent eggs of some sea urchins that they are commonly used to demonstrate cleavage in introductory biology laboratories. A few echinoderms reproduce asexually by splitting in half and regenerating the missing parts. Other echinoderms regenerate body parts lost to predators. Four-day-old sand dollars (*Dendraster excentricus*) asexually clone themselves in response to the odour of fish (in mucus), apparently a defensive response.

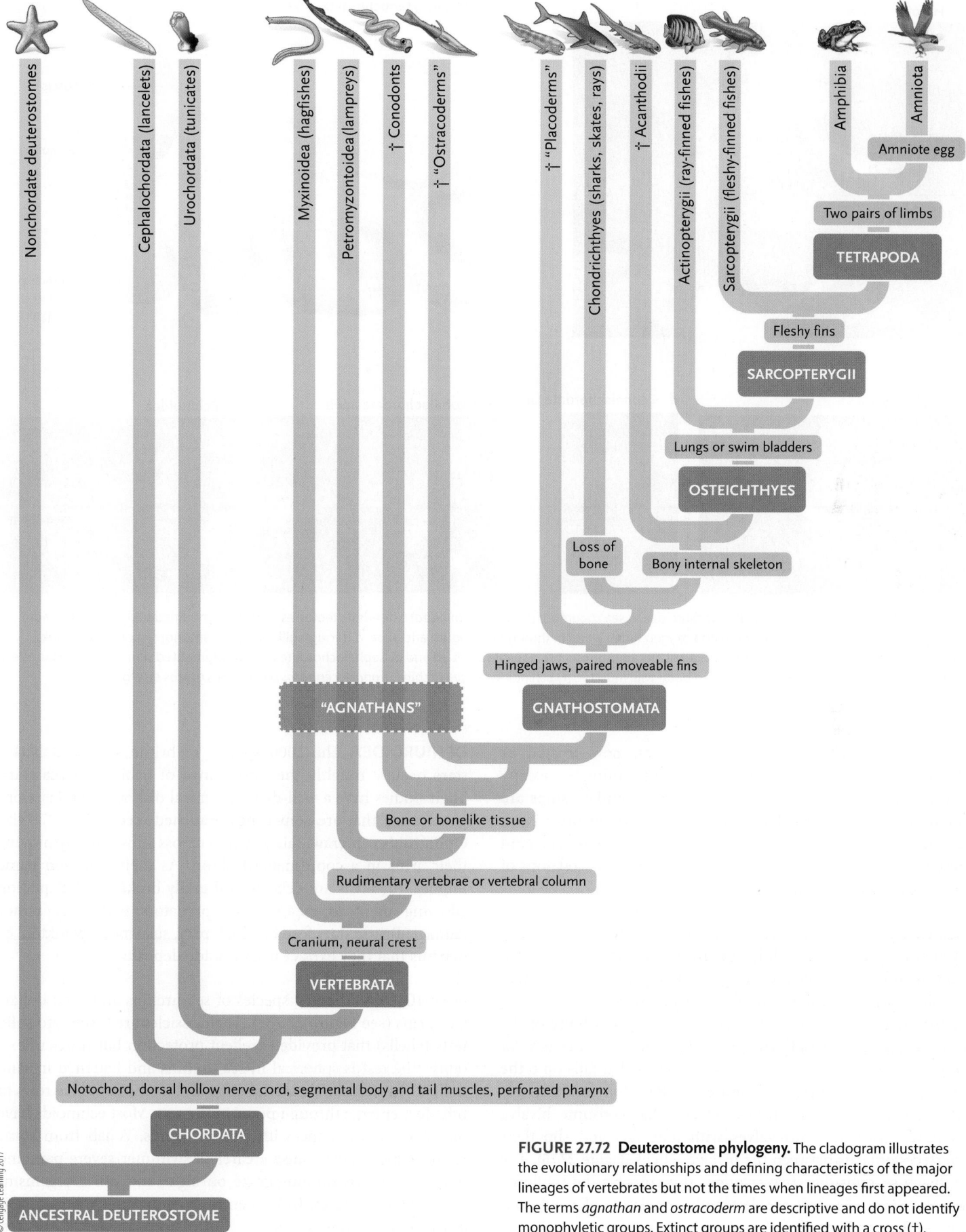

**FIGURE 27.72 Deuterostome phylogeny.** The cladogram illustrates the evolutionary relationships and defining characteristics of the major lineages of vertebrates but not the times when lineages first appeared. The terms *agnathan* and *ostracoderm* are descriptive and do not identify monophyletic groups. Extinct groups are identified with a cross (†).

© Cengage Learning 2017

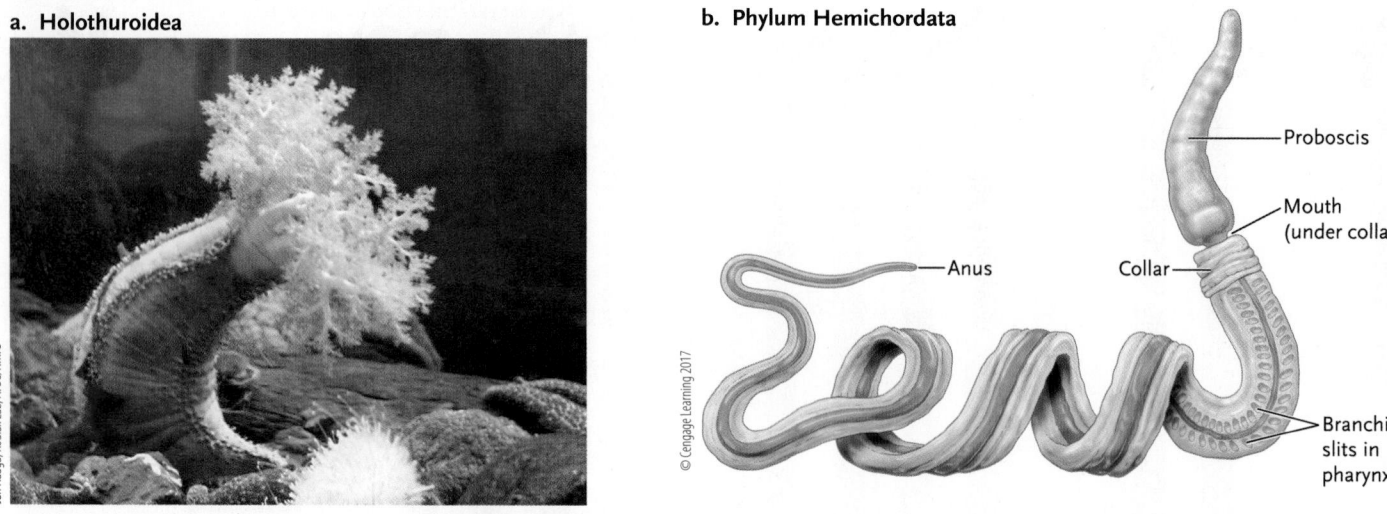

**a. Holothuroidea**

**b. Phylum Hemichordata**

Proboscis

Mouth (under collar)

Anus   Collar

Branchial slits in pharynx

**c. Urochordates**   **d. Cephalochordate larva**   **e. Cephalochordate adult**   **f. Echinoidea**

**FIGURE 27.73 Deuterostomes. (a)** Holothuroidea. A sea cucumber (*Cucumaria miniata*) extends its tentacles, which are modified tube feet. **(b)** Phylum Hemichordata. Acorn worms draw food- and oxygen-laden water in through the mouth and expel it through gill slits in the anterior region of the trunk. **(c)** Urochordates. A tadpolelike tunicate larva will metamorphose into a sessile adult. **(d** and **e)** Cephalochordates. The unpigmented skin of an adult lancelet (*Brachiostoma species*) reveals its segmented body-wall muscles. **(f)** Echinoidea. A sea urchin (*Strongylocentrotus purpuratus*) grazes on algae.

Echinoderms include the sea daisies, now treated as Asteroidea. These small, medusa-shaped animals occupy sunken, waterlogged wood in the deep sea. Sunken ships are often important habitats for these and other marine organisms. The five other groups, described below, are more diverse and better known. Some students will be familiar with skeletons of echinoderms often found on beaches **(Figure 27.75)**.

**ASTEROIDEA** Sea stars live on rocky shorelines to depths of 10 000 m. Many are brightly coloured. The body consists of a central disk surrounded by 5–20 radiating "arms" (see Figure 27.74a), with the mouth centred on the oral surface. The ossicles of the endoskeleton are not fused, permitting flexibility of the arms and disk. **Pedicellariae** are small pincers at the base of short spines. They are used to remove debris that falls onto the animal's aboral surface (see Figure 27.74f). Many sea stars eat invertebrates and small fishes. Species that consume bivalve molluscs grasp the two valves with tube feet and slip their everted stomachs between the bivalve's shells **(Figure 27.76)**. The stomach secretes digestive enzymes that dissolve the mollusc's tissues. Some sea stars are destructive predators of corals and may endanger many reefs.

**OPHIUROIDEA** The 2000 species of brittle stars and basket stars occupy roughly the same range of habitats as sea stars. Their bodies have a well-defined central disk and slender, elongated arms that are sometimes branched (see Figure 27.74b). Ophiuroids can crawl fairly swiftly across substrates by moving their arms in a coordinated fashion. As their common name implies, the arms are delicate and easily broken, an adaptation allowing them to escape from predators with only minor damage. Brittle stars feed on small prey, suspended plankton, or detritus that they extract from muddy deposits.

**ECHINOIDEA** The 950 species of sea urchins and sand dollars lack arms (see Figure 27.73f). Their ossicles are fused into solid tests (shells) that provide excellent protection but restrict flexibility. The test is spherical in sea urchins and flattened in sand dollars. These animals use tube feet in locomotion. Five rows of tube feet emerge through pores in the test. Most echinoids have movable spines, some with poison glands. A jab from some tropical species can cause a careless swimmer severe pain and inflammation. Echinoids graze on algae and other organisms that cling to surfaces. In the centre of an urchin's oral surface is a five-part nipping jaw that is controlled by powerful muscles.

**a. Asteroidea:** This sea star (*Fromia milleporella*) lives in the intertidal zone.

**b. Ophiuroidea:** A brittle star (*Ophiothrix suensonii*) perches on a coral branch.

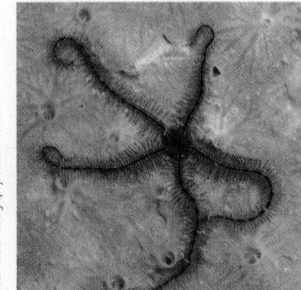

**c. Crinoidea:** A feather star (*Himerometra robustipinna*) feeds by catching small particles with its numerous tentacles.

**d. Internal anatomy**

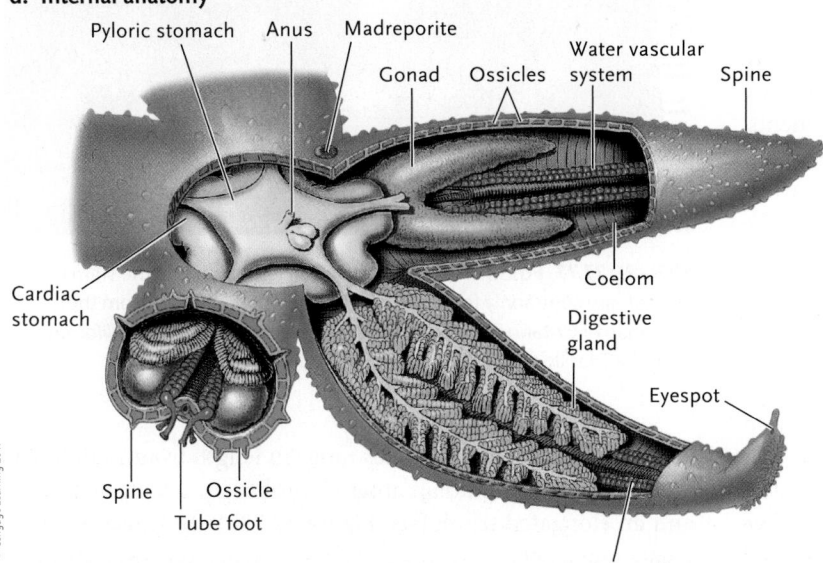

Pyloric stomach · Anus · Madreporite · Gonad · Ossicles · Water vascular system · Spine · Coelom · Digestive gland · Eyespot · Cardiac stomach · Spine · Ossicle · Tube foot · Row of ampullae

**e. Water vascular system**

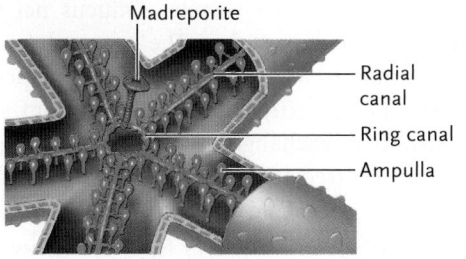

Madreporite · Radial canal · Ring canal · Ampulla

**f. Tube feet**

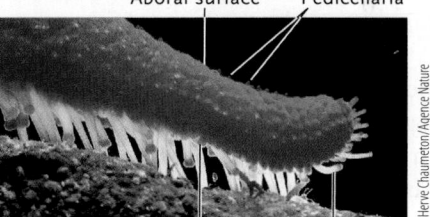

Aboral surface · Pedicellaria · Oral surface · Tube foot

**FIGURE 27.74 Echinoderm diversity. (a–c)** Echinoderms exhibit secondary radial symmetry, usually organized as five rays around an oral–aboral axis. The coelom **(d)** is well developed in echinoderms, as illustrated by this cutaway diagram of a sea star. The water vascular system **(e)**, unique in the animal kingdom, operates the tube feet. Tube feet **(f)** are responsible for locomotion. Note the pedicellariae on the upper surface of the star's arm.

**FIGURE 27.75 Shown here are skeletons of echinoderms that are often found on beaches, including a sea urchin, two sand dollars, and three starfish.**

**FIGURE 27.76 Sea star feeding on a mussel.** Even when the tide is out in Haida Gwaii, sea stars hunt mussels.

Some species damage kelp beds, disrupting the habitat of young lobsters and other crustaceans. Echinoid ovaries are a gourmet delicacy in many countries, making these animals a prized natural resource.

**HOLOTHUROIDEA** Sea cucumbers are elongated animals that lie on their sides on the ocean bottom; they number about 1500 species. Although they have five rows of tube feet, their endoskeleton is reduced to widely separated microscopic plates. The body, which is elongated along the oral–aboral axis, is soft and fleshy, with a tough, leathery covering. Modified tube feet form a ring of tentacles around the mouth. The central disk and mouth point upward rather than toward the substrate (see Figure 27.73a). Some species secrete a mucus net that traps plankton or other food particles. The net and tentacles are inserted into the mouth, where the net and the trapped food are ingested. Other species extract food from bottom sediments. Many sea cucumbers exchange gases through an extensively branched respiratory tree arising from the rectum, the part of the digestive system just inside the anus at the aboral end of the animal. A well-developed circulatory system distributes oxygen and nutrients to tissues throughout the body.

Sea cucumbers are actually home for a specialized symbiotic fish. *Carapus bermudensis*, the pearl fish, enters sea cucumber's cloacal opening tail-first, allowing them to emerge head-first. The cloaca is the chamber receiving urine, feces, and reproductive products. Pearl fish are members of a group that usually live in the tubes of other animals, including the cavities of bivalves. These fishes have thin, elongated bodies. They have lost the pelvic fins and scales, and the anal opening has moved forward to a position under the head. This adaptation ensures that the fish defecates outside the body of the sea cucumber. These fishes use olfactory cues to find the "correct" host.

**CRINOIDEA** The 600 living species of sea lilies and feather stars are the surviving remnants of a diverse and abundant fauna that lived 500 million years ago (mya; see Figure 27.74c). Most species occupy marine waters of medium depth. Between five and several hundred branched arms surround the disk that contains the mouth. New arms are added as a crinoid grows larger. The branches of the arms are covered with tiny, mucus-coated tube feet that trap suspended microscopic organisms. Sessile sea lilies have the central disk attached to a flexible stalk that can reach 1 m in length. By contrast, adult feather stars can swim or crawl weakly, attaching temporarily to substrates. The disks making up sea lily stalks, called *ossicles*, are common fossils in many deposits **(Figure 27.77)**.

## 27.8b Phylum Hemichordata

The 80 species of **acorn worms** comprising this phylum have a dorsally situated stiffening rod, or chord. Compared to the chordates, this short rod, called the *stomochord*, is reflected in the name "hemichord" (*hemi* = half). Acorn worms are sedentary marine animals living in U-shaped tubes or burrows in coastal

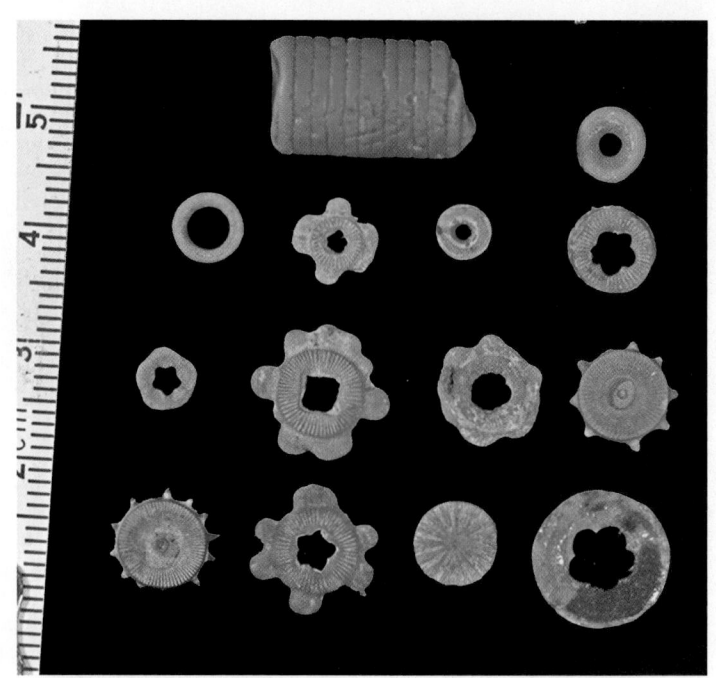

**FIGURE 27.77 Fossil crinoid stems.** Ossicles making up the stems of crinoids are commonly fossilized. The individual ossicles are from the Devonian of Ontario. The section of complete stem is *Encrinus liliiformis*, from the Triassic of Germany. Scale is in millimetres.

sand or mud. Their soft bodies range in length from 2 cm to 2 m and are organized into an anterior proboscis, a tentacled collar, and an elongated trunk (see Figure 27.73b). They use the muscular, mucus-coated proboscis to construct burrows and trap food particles. Acorn worms also have pairs of gill slits in the pharynx, the part of the digestive system just posterior to the mouth. Beating cilia create a flow of water, which enters the pharynx through the mouth and exits through the gill slits. As water passes through, suspended food particles are trapped and shunted into the digestive system, and gases are exchanged across the partitions between gill slits. The dorsal nerve cord, coupled with feeding and respiration, reflects a close evolutionary relationship between hemichordates and chordates. Pterobranchia are the other class of animals in this phylum. These uncommon marine animals are colonial and live in tubes. They superficially resemble some cnidarians.

## 27.8c Phylum Chordata

This phylum includes the evolutionary lines of invertebrates, the Urochordata and the Cephalochordata, as well as the more diverse line, the Vertebrata (animals with backbones). A notochord, a dorsal hollow nerve cord, and pharyngeal slits (a perforated pharynx) are three key morphological features distinguishing chordates from all other deuterostomes. These features occur during at least some time in a chordate's life cycle. Chordates also have segmental muscles in the body wall and tail **(Figure 27.78)**. Collectively, these structures enable higher levels of activity and unique modes of aquatic locomotion, as well as

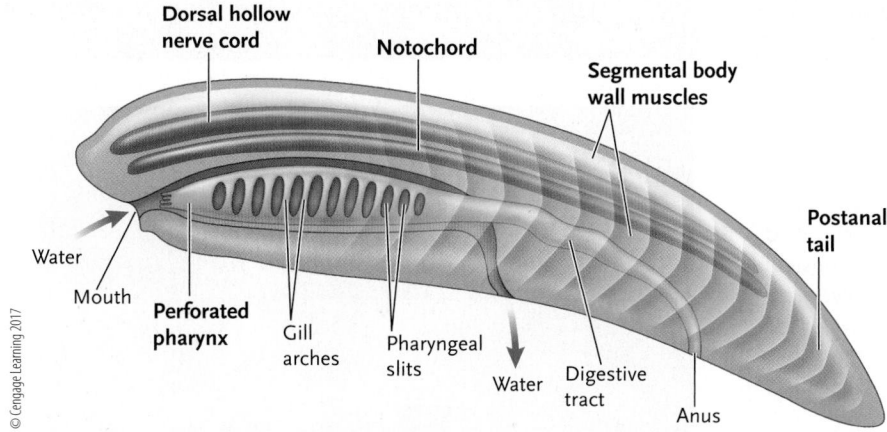

**FIGURE 27.78 Diagnostic chordate characteristics.** Chordates have a notochord, a dorsal hollow nerve cord, pharyngeal (gill) slits (a perforated pharynx), and a muscular post-anal tail with segmental body wall and tail muscles. Other basic features also are shown but they are not unique to chordates.

more efficient feeding and acquisition of oxygen. In the past, cephalochordates were considered to be the sister group to the chordates. Recent analyses suggest that the Urochordata are sister to the Chordata.

Early in chordate embryonic development, the **notochord** (*noto* = back; *chord* = string), a flexible rod, develops from mesoderm dorsal to the developing digestive system (see Research in Biology). The notochord is constructed of fluid-filled cells surrounded by tough connective tissue. It supports the embryo from head to tail. The notochord is the skeleton of invertebrate chordates, serving as an anchor for body-wall muscles. When these muscles contract, the notochord bends but does not shorten. Waves of contractions pass down one side of the animal and then up the other, sweeping the body and tail back and forth in a smooth and continuous movement. Thus, the chordate body swings left and right during locomotion, propelling the animal forward. The chordate tail, which is posterior to the anus, provides most of the propulsion in some aquatic species. Segmentation allows each muscle block to contract independently. Unlike the bodies of annelids and other nonchordate invertebrates, the chordate body does not shorten when the animal is moving. Remnants of the notochord persist as gelatinous disks between the vertebrae of some adult vertebrates.

The central nervous system of chordates is a hollow nerve cord on the dorsal side of the embryo (Chapter 45). Most nonchordate invertebrates have ventral, solid nerve cords. In vertebrates, an anterior enlargement of the nerve cord forms the brain. In invertebrates, an anterior concentration of nervous system tissue is a ganglion and may be referred to as a "brain."

Gill (pharyngeal) slits perforate the chordate pharynx. The pharynx is part of the digestive system and is located just behind the mouth. **Gill slits** are paired openings originating as exit holes for water that carried particulate food into the mouth, allowing chordates to gather food by filtration. Invertebrate chordates also collect oxygen and release carbon dioxide across the walls of the pharynx. In fishes, gill arches have evolved as supporting structures between the slits in the pharynx.

Invertebrate chordates and fishes retain a perforated pharynx throughout their lives. In most air-breathing vertebrates, the slits are present only during embryonic development and in some larvae.

**SUBPHYLUM UROCHORDATA** The 2500 species of urochordates (*uro* = tail) float in surface waters or attach to substrates in shallow marine habitats. Sessile adults of many species secrete a gelatinous or leathery "tunic" around their bodies and squirt water through a siphon when disturbed. Adults can attain lengths of several centimetres. In the most common group of sea squirts (Ascidiacea), swimming larvae have notochords, dorsal hollow nerve cords, and gill slits, features lacking in the sessile adults. Larvae eventually attach to substrates and transform into sessile adults. During metamorphosis, larvae lose most traces of the notochord and tail as their basketlike pharynx enlarges. The nerve chord remains but is no longer dorsal. In adults, beating cilia pull water into the pharynx through an incurrent siphon. A mucus net traps particulate food, which is carried with the mucus to the gut. Water passes through the gill slits, enters a chamber called the **atrium**, and is expelled through the **atrial siphon** along with digestive wastes and carbon dioxide **(Figure 27.79)**. Oxygen is absorbed across the walls of the pharynx. In some urochordates, the larvae are neotenous, acquiring the ability to reproduce and remaining active throughout their life cycles.

**SUBPHYLUM CEPHALOCHORDATA** All 28 species of cephalochordates (*cephalo* = head) live in warm, shallow, marine habitats, where they lie mostly buried in sand (see Figure 27.73e). Although generally sedentary, they have well-developed body-wall muscles and a prominent notochord. Most species are included in the genus *Branchiostoma* (formerly *Amphioxus*). Lancelet bodies, which are 5–10 cm long, are pointed at both ends, like the double-edged surgical tools for which they are named **(Figure 27.80)**. Adults have light receptors on the head as well as chemical sense organs on tentacles that grow from the **oral hood**. Lancelets use cilia to draw food-laden water through hundreds of pharyngeal slits; water flows into the atrium and is expelled through the **atriopore**. Most gas exchange occurs across the skin.

**SUBPHYLUM VERTEBRATA (CRANIATA)** Species in this subphylum have a distinct head, making them craniate, and most have a **backbone (spine)** made up of individual bony vertebrae (Chapters 19 and 45). This internal skeletal feature provides structural support for muscles and protects the nervous system and other organs. In addition, the internal skeleton and attached muscles allow most vertebrates to move rapidly. Vertebrates are the only animals with bone, a connective tissue in which cells secrete the mineralized matrix that surrounds them

## The Tully Monster

The Tully monster, *Tullimonstrum gregarium* **(Figure 1)**, is from the Late Carboniferous of Illinois in the United States. Since its fossil discovery and description, this mainly soft-bodied animal has been tentatively classified with species in five different groups of animals (phyla). Tully Monsters have been considered to be nemerteans (see Section 27.6d), polychaete annelids, gastropod molluscs (see Section 27.6e), conodonts (see Section 27.10), and some early arthropods (Section 27.7h). Other interpretations suggested that the Tully Monster was the only evidence of a now extinct phylum of animals.

The correct phylogenetic placement of an organism should reflect and convey information about its evolutionary relationship(s) to other organisms. Considerable energy and technological prowess is expended in the development of accurate phylogenies. When the organism, such as a Tully Monster, is known only as a fossil, some evidence is not available.

In 2016, the results of further close examination of the fossil Tully Monster revealed characteristics that clearly place these animals in the phylum Chordata (see Section 27.8c), the phylum that includes vertebrates such as humans. The fine-grained fossil Tully Monster reveals that the structure of the eyes, especially the retinae, unambiguously indicate that this animal was a vertebrate. There is no evidence of a notochord in Tully Monsters, probably reflecting lack of fossilization, the same situation that occurs in fossil lamprey and hagfish. The Tully Monster specimens also lack details of the branchial area, again suggesting lack of pigmentation and fossilization. Some biologists argue that lampreys are the closest living relatives of Tully Monsters.

Tully Monsters' lack of notochord and gill slits complicated correct assignment of the creature to a phylum. But the evidence from the eyes,

**Figure 1 A reconstruction of the Tully Monster, front and rear views.** Note the gill openings along the side of the body and the extraordinary stalked eyes.

in particular the retinae, were pivotal in assigning Tully Monsters to Vertebrata in the phylum Chordata. The movement of Tully Monsters among animal phyla is but one recent example of ongoing changes to the classification of animals. A more profound change is the current recognition that the historical (and traditional) grouping of animals into protostomes (see Section 27.2d) and deuterostomes (see Section 27.2d) is more artificial than real.

**a. Larval tunicate (*Oikopleura* species)**

Mouth    Atriopore    **Dorsal hollow nerve cord**    **Segmental body wall and tail muscles**

**Pharynx with slits**    Gut    **Notochord**    **Postanal tail**

**b. Adult tunicate (*Rhopalaea crassa*)**

Water enters.

Atrial siphon    Incurrent siphon

Water exits.    **Pharynx with slits**

Atrium    Tunic

Gut    Heart

**FIGURE 27.79 (a)** The tadpolelike tunicate larva metamorphoses into an adult, a sessile filter feeder. **(b)** In the adult, the atriopore becomes the atrial siphon.

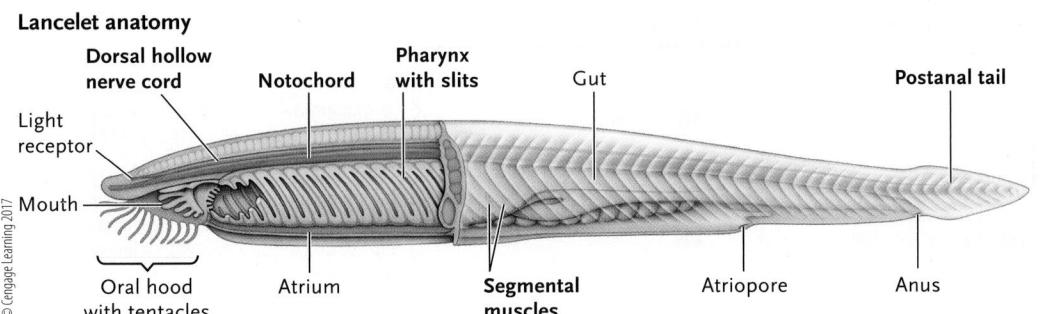

**Lancelet anatomy**

Dorsal hollow nerve cord · Notochord · Pharynx with slits · Gut · Postanal tail · Light receptor · Mouth · Oral hood with tentacles · Atrium · Segmental muscles · Atriopore · Anus

© Cengage Learning 2017

**FIGURE 27.80** A drawing showing the internal anatomy of an adult lancelet (*Branchiostoma*)

(Chapter 46). One vertebrate lineage, the cartilaginous fishes (class Chondrichthyes), may have lost its bone over evolutionary time. These animals, mostly sharks and rays, have skeletons of cartilage, a dense, flexible connective tissue that can be a developmental precursor of bone (Chapters 45 and 46).

At the anterior end of the vertebral column, the head is usually protected by a bony **cranium**, or skull. The backbone surrounds and protects the dorsal nerve cord, and the bony cranium surrounds the brain. The cranium, vertebral column, ribs, and sternum (breastbone) make up the **axial skeleton**. Most vertebrates also have a **pectoral girdle** anteriorly and a **pelvic girdle** posteriorly that attach bones in the fins or limbs to the axial skeleton. The bones of the two girdles and the appendages constitute the appendicular skeleton.

Vertebrates have neural crest cells (Chapter 45), a unique cell type distinct from endoderm, mesoderm, and ectoderm. Neural crest cells arise next to the developing nervous system but migrate throughout the body. Neural crest cells ultimately contribute to uniquely vertebrate structures, such as parts of the cranium, teeth, sensory organs, **cranial nerves**, and the medulla (the interior part) of the adrenal glands.

The brains of vertebrates are larger and more complex than those of invertebrate chordates. Moreover, the vertebrate brain is divided into three regions, the forebrain, midbrain, and hindbrain, each governing distinct nervous system functions (Chapter 45).

### STUDY BREAK QUESTIONS

1. What are echinoderms? How do adult echinoderms develop?
2. Use a table to compare an echinoderm and a human by system: (a) digestive, (b) excretory, (c) respiratory, (d) circulatory, and (e) nervous.
3. Using a sea star as an example, describe how echinoderms move.
4. How do hemichordates feed?
5. List four morphological features distinguishing chordates from other deuterostomes.
6. Explain the purpose and structure of gill slits.
7. What is the function of a backbone?

## 27.9 The Origin and Diversification of Vertebrates

Biologists have used embryological, molecular, and fossil evidences to trace the origin of vertebrates and to chronicle the evolutionary diversification of the group that includes humans. We suspect that vertebrates arose from a cephalochordate-like ancestor through duplication of genes that regulate development. The change to vertebrates was marked by the emergence of neural crest cells, bone, and other vertebrate traits. Biologists hypothesize that an increase in the number of genes that control the expression of other genes (homeotic) may have facilitated the development of more complex anatomy. In terms of organization, remember that there is no compelling reason to believe that "more complex" is superior to "simple."

*Hox* genes are homeotic genes that influence the three-dimensional shape of the animal and the locations of important structures such as eyes, wings, and legs, particularly along the head-to-tail axis of the body. *Hox* genes are arranged on chromosomes in a particular order, forming the *Hox* gene complex. Each gene in the complex governs the development of particular structures. Animal groups with the simplest structure, such as cnidarians, have 2 *Hox* genes; those with more complex anatomy, such as insects, have 10; chordates typically have up to 13 or 14. Lineages with many *Hox* genes generally have more complex anatomy than those with fewer *Hox* genes.

Molecular analyses reveal that the entire *Hox* gene complex was duplicated several times in the evolution of vertebrates, producing multiple copies of all the genes in the *Hox* complex **(Figure 27.81)**. The cephalochordate *Branchiostoma* has one *Hox* gene complex, whereas hagfish, the most ancestral living vertebrate, has two. All vertebrates with jaws have at least four sets of *Hox* genes, and some fishes have seven. Evolutionary biologists who study development hypothesize that the duplication of *Hox* genes and other tool-kit genes allowed the evolution of new structures. Although original copies of these genes maintained their ancestral functions, duplicate copies were available to assume *new* functions, leading to the development of novel structures such as the vertebral column and jaws. These changes coincided with the adaptive radiation of vertebrates.

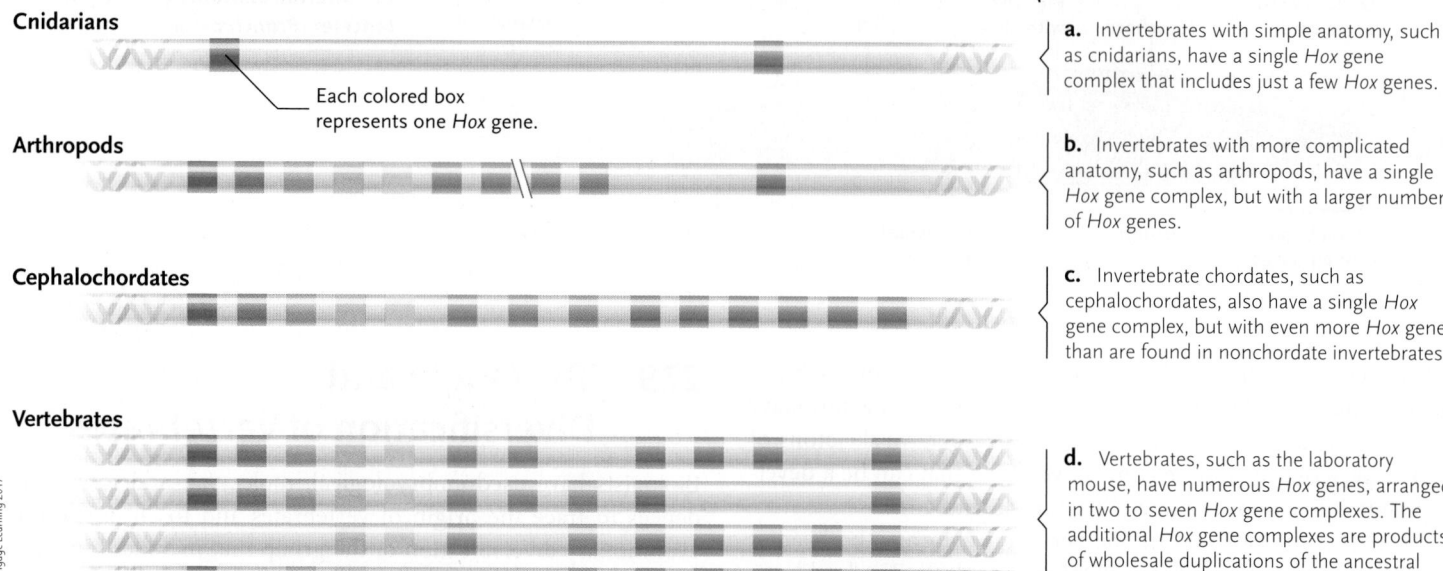

Each row of colored boxes represents one *Hox* gene complex.

**Cnidarians**

Each colored box represents one *Hox* gene.

**a.** Invertebrates with simple anatomy, such as cnidarians, have a single *Hox* gene complex that includes just a few *Hox* genes.

**Arthropods**

**b.** Invertebrates with more complicated anatomy, such as arthropods, have a single *Hox* gene complex, but with a larger number of *Hox* genes.

**Cephalochordates**

**c.** Invertebrate chordates, such as cephalochordates, also have a single *Hox* gene complex, but with even more *Hox* genes than are found in nonchordate invertebrates.

**Vertebrates**

**d.** Vertebrates, such as the laboratory mouse, have numerous *Hox* genes, arranged in two to seven *Hox* gene complexes. The additional *Hox* gene complexes are products of wholesale duplications of the ancestral *Hox* gene complex.

© Cengage Learning 2017

**FIGURE 27.81** *Hox* genes and the evolution of vertebrates. The *Hox* genes in different animals appear to be homologous, indicated here by their colour and position in the complex. Vertebrates have many more individual *Hox* genes than invertebrates, and the entire *Hox* gene complex was duplicated in the vertebrate lineage.

The oldest known vertebrate fossils are from the early Cambrian (about 550 mya) in China. Both *Myllokunmingia* and *Haikouichthys* were fish-shaped animals about 3 cm long (**Figure 27.82**). In both species, the brain was surrounded by a cranium of fibrous connective tissue or cartilage. They also had segmental body-wall muscles and fairly well-developed fins, but neither shows any evidence of bone. In 2014 Morris and Caron redescribed *Metaspriggina* based on new fossil material, much of it from the Burgess Shales. This animal resembled the slightly older *Myllokunmingia* and *Haikouichthys* but had more prominent eyes and may have been more basal to the origin of vertebrates than the older forms. Again, the discovery of new fossil material often changes our view of the relationships among animals.

The early vertebrates gave rise to numerous descendants that varied greatly in anatomy, physiology, and ecology. New feeding mechanisms and locomotor structures were correlated with their success. Today, vertebrates occupy nearly every habitat on Earth and eat virtually all other organisms. Biologists tend to identify vertebrates with four key morphological innovations: cranium, vertebrae, bone, and neural crest cells. Important biological changes during the evolution of vertebrates included improved access to energy (food), which involved mobility and jaws, combined with effective aerobic metabolism (access to oxygen).

The earliest vertebrates lacked jaws (Agnatha, *a* = not; *gnath* = jawed), but Agnatha is not a monophyletic group. Although most became extinct by the end of the Paleozoic, two ancestral lineages, Myxinoidea (hagfishes) and Petromyzontidae (lampreys), survive today. All other vertebrates have

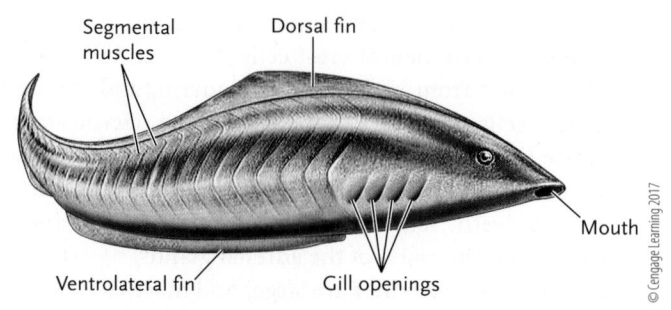

Segmental muscles · Dorsal fin · Mouth · Ventrolateral fin · Gill openings

© Cengage Learning 2017

**FIGURE 27.82** Cambrian agnathan, *Haikouichthys*, was more like a hagfish than a lamprey, but generally similar to an ammocoetes larva of lampreys, living agnathans.

movable jaws and form the monophyletic lineage **Gnathostomata** (*gnath* = jawed; *stoma* = mouth). The first jawed fishes, the Acanthodii and the Placodermi, are now extinct, but several other lineages of jawed fishes are still abundant. Included are Chondrichthyes, fishes with cartilaginous skeletons (sharks, skates, chimaeras), and Teleostei (actinopterygians and sarcopterygians), with bony endoskeletons. Although all jawless vertebrates and most jawed fishes live mainly in water, mudskippers (*Periophthalmus* species), climbing perch (*Anabas* species), and some eels regularly venture onto land. Many fish have developed lunglike structures for breathing atmospheric oxygen, but most use gills to extract dissolved oxygen from water. Lungs may be an ancestral trait in vertebrates.

Gnathostomata also includes the monophyletic lineage **Tetrapoda** (*tetra* = four; *pod* = foot), most of which use four limbs for locomotion. Many tetrapods are amphibious, semi-terrestrial, or terrestrial, although some, such as sea turtles and porpoises, are secondarily aquatic. Adult tetrapods generally use lungs to breathe atmospheric oxygen. Within the Tetrapoda, one lineage, the Amphibia (such as frogs and salamanders), typically needs standing water to complete its life cycle. Another lineage, the Amniota, comprises animals with specialized eggs that can develop on land. Shortly after their appearance, amniotes diversified into three lineages: one ancestral to living mammals; another to living turtles; and a third to lizards, snakes, alligators, and birds.

## STUDY BREAK QUESTIONS

1. What are the four key morphological innovations that are used to identify vertebrates?

2. What is a *Hox* gene, and how does it influence the diversity of vertebrates?

## 27.10 Agnathans: The Jawless Fishes

Lacking jaws, the earliest vertebrates used a muscular pharynx to suck water containing food particles into the mouth, and used gills both to acquire dissolved oxygen and to filter food from the water. The agnathans that flourished in the Paleozoic varied greatly in size and shape and possessed different combinations of vertebrate characters.

Lampreys and hagfishes, the two living groups of agnathans, have skeletons composed entirely of cartilage. Although fossil lampreys or hagfishes older than the Devonian have been found, the absence of bone in their living descendants suggests that they arose early in vertebrate history, before the evolution of bone. The first fossil lamprey from the Devonian of South Africa is unmistakably a lamprey. Hagfishes and lampreys have a well-developed notochord but no true vertebrae or paired fins. Their skin lacks scales. Individuals grow to a maximum length of about 1 m **(Figure 27.83)**. Two possible phylogenies for hagfishes and other vertebrates are presented, but at this time, there are too few data to decide which is most likely to be correct.

The axial skeletons of the 60 living species of hagfishes include only a cranium and a notochord. No specialized structures surround the dorsal nerve cord. Hagfishes are marine scavengers that burrow in sediments on continental shelves. They eat invertebrate prey and dead or dying fishes. In response to predators, they secrete immense quantities of sticky, noxious slime. When no longer threatened, a hagfish ties itself into a knot and wipes the slime from its body. The life cycle of a hagfish lacks a larval stage.

The 38 living species of lamprey have a more specialized axial skeleton than hagfishes. Their notochord is surrounded by dorsally pointing cartilage that partially covers the nerve cord, perhaps representing an early stage in the evolution of the vertebral column. About half the living lamprey species are parasitic as adults and use the sucking disk around their mouths to attach to the bodies of fish (or other prey), rasp a hole in the host's body, and ingest body fluids. In most species, sexually mature adults migrate from the ocean or a lake to the headwaters of a stream, where they reproduce and then die. The filter-feeding **ammocoetes** larvae of lampreys resemble adult cephalochordates. They burrow into mud and develop for as long as seven years before metamorphosing and migrating to the sea or lake to live as adults.

Conodonts and ostracoderms were early jawless vertebrates with bony structures. Conodonts are mysterious bone-like fossils, mostly less than 1 mm long, occurring in oceanic rocks from the early Paleozoic through the early Mesozoic. Called **conodont** elements, these abundant fossils were originally described as supporting structures of marine algae or feeding structures of ancient invertebrates. Recent analyses of their mineral composition reveal that they were made of dentine, a bonelike component of vertebrate teeth. In the 1980s and 1990s, many questions about conodonts were answered by the discovery of fossils of intact conodont animals with these elements.

We now know that conodonts were elongate, soft-bodied animals 3–10 cm long. They had a notochord, a cranium, segmental body-wall muscles, and large, movable eyes **(Figure 27.84a)**. The conodont elements at the front of the mouth were forward-pointing, hook-shaped structures (the original fossils) apparently used in the collection of food. Conodont elements in the pharynx were stouter, making them suitable for crushing food. Paleontologists now classify conodonts as vertebrates, the earliest ones with bonelike structures.

**Ostracoderms** (*ostrac* = shell; *derm* = skin) include an assortment of jawless fishes representing several evolutionary lines that lived from the Ordovician through the Devonian (Figure 27.84b). Like their invertebrate chordate ancestors, ostracoderms probably used the pharynx to draw water with food particles into the mouth, and used gills to filter food from water. The muscular pharynx was more efficient than that of agnathans, using currents generated by cilia. Greater flow rates allowed ostracoderms to collect food more rapidly and achieve larger body sizes. Although most ostracoderms were much smaller, some were 2 m long.

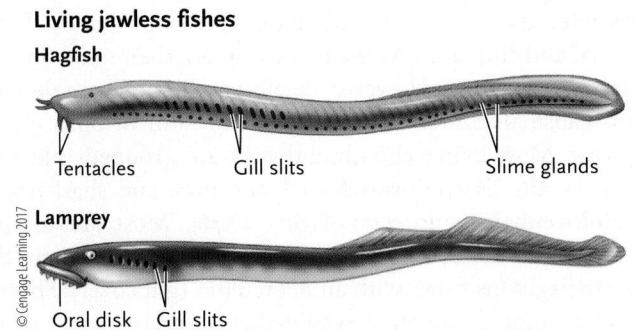

**Living jawless fishes**

**Hagfish**

Tentacles    Gill slits    Slime glands

**Lamprey**

Oral disk    Gill slits

© Cengage Learning 2017

**FIGURE 27.83 Two groups of jawless fishes are the hagfish and lamprey**

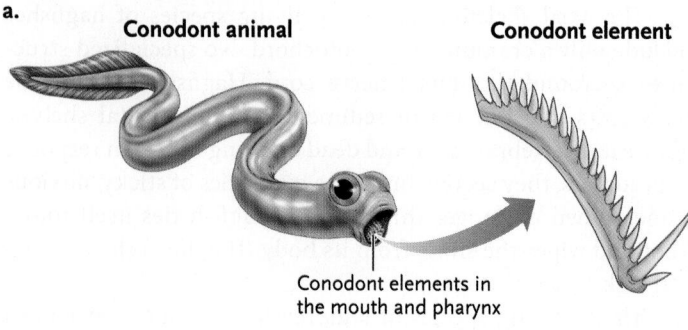

**a.**

Conodont animal          Conodont element

Conodont elements in
the mouth and pharynx

**b. Ostracoderm**

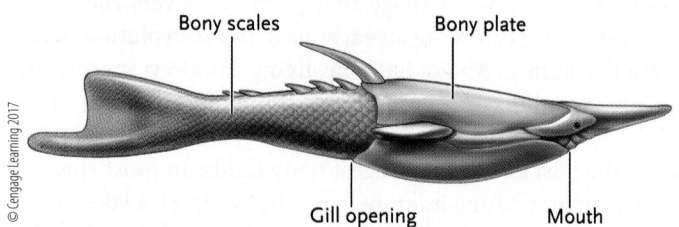

Bony scales          Bony plate

Gill opening          Mouth

© Cengage Learning 2017

**FIGURE 27.84 Extinct agnathans. (a)** Conodonts were elaborate, soft-bodied animals with bonelike feeding structures in the mouth and pharynx. **(b)** *Pteropsis*, an ostracoderm, had large bony plates on its head and small body scales on the rest of its body. It was about 6 cm long.

The skin of ostracoderms was heavily armoured with bony plates and scales. Although some had paired lateral extensions of their bony armour, they could not move them in the way living fishes move paired fins. Ostracoderms lacked a true vertebral column, but they had rudimentary support structures surrounding the nerve cord. Ostracoderms had other distinctly vertebrate-like characteristics. Their head shields indicate that their brains had the three regions (forebrain, midbrain, and hindbrain) typical of all later vertebrates (see Chapter 45).

**STUDY BREAK QUESTIONS**

1. How did the earliest vertebrates feed without jaws?
2. Compare the hagfish and the lamprey based on body structure, feeding habits, and life cycles.

# 27.11 Jawed Fishes: Jaws Meant New Feeding Opportunities

The first gnathostomes were jawed fishes. Jaws meant that they could eat more than just filtered food particles and take larger food items with higher energy content. The renowned anatomist and paleontologist Alfred Sherwood Romer described the evolution of jaws as "perhaps the greatest of all advances in vertebrate history." Hinged jaws allow vertebrates to grasp, kill, shred, and crush large food items. Some species also use their jaws for defence, for grooming, to construct nests, and to transport young. Jaws may serve more than one purpose. Another important development is tooth-on-tooth contact, which increases the

effectiveness of chewing, particularly cutting and grinding. This is a recurrent theme among gnathostome vertebrates from fish to reptiles and mammals.

Embryological evidence suggests that jaws evolved from paired gill arches in the pharynx of a jawless ancestor **(Figure 27.85)**. One pair of ancestral **gill arches** formed bones in the upper and lower jaws, whereas a second pair was transformed into the **hyomandibular bones** that braced the jaws against the cranium. Nerves and muscles of the ancestral suspension-feeding pharynx control the movement and actions of jaws. Jawed fishes also had fins, first appearing as folds of skin and movable spines that stabilized locomotion and deterred predators. Movable fins appeared independently in several lineages, and by the Devonian, most jawed fishes had unpaired (dorsal, anal, and caudal) and paired (pectoral and pelvic) fins **(Figure 27.86)**.

## 27.11a Classes Acanthodii and Placodermi Were Early Lineages

The spiny "sharks" (*acanth* = spine) persisted from the late Ordovician through the Permian. Most of these sharklike fishes were less than 20 cm long, with small, light scales, streamlined bodies, well-developed eyes, large jaws, and numerous teeth. Although acanthodians were not true sharks, they were probably fast swimmers and efficient predators. Many of them lived in fresh water. Most had a row of ventral spines and fins with internal skeletal support on each side of the body. The anatomy of acanthodians suggests a close relationship to bony fishes of today.

The placoderms (*plac* = plate; *derm* = skin) appeared in the Silurian and diversified in the Devonian and Carboniferous, but left no direct descendants. Some species of *Dunkleosteus* **(Figure 27.87)** were huge. The bodies of placoderms were covered with large, heavy plates of bone anteriorly, and smaller scales posteriorly. Their jaws had sharp cutting edges but no separate teeth, and their paired fins had internal skeletons and powerful muscles.

## 27.11b Class Chondrichthyes Includes Sharks and Rays

The cartilaginous fishes (*chondr* = cartilage; *ichthy* = fish) are represented today by about 850 living species of sharks, skates and rays, and chimeras. As the name implies, their skeletons are entirely cartilaginous. However, the absence of bone is a derived trait because all earlier fishes had bony armour or bony endoskeletons. Most living chondrichthyans are grouped into two subclasses, the **Elasmobranchii** (skates, rays, and sharks) and the **Holocephali** (chimeras) **(Figure 27.88)**. Most are marine predators. With about 40 living species, holocephalians are the only cartilaginous fishes with an operculum (gill cover). Sharks, rays, and chimeras are often exhibited at aquaria.

Skates and rays are dorsoventrally flattened (see Figure 27.88b) and swim by undulating their enlarged pectoral fins.

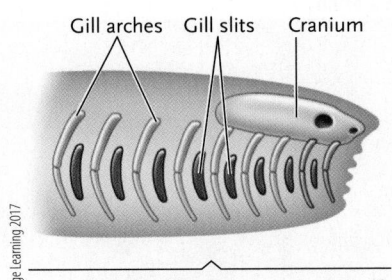

Gill arches  Gill slits  Cranium

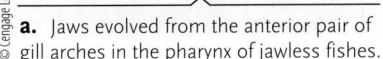

**a.** Jaws evolved from the anterior pair of gill arches in the pharynx of jawless fishes.

© Cengage Learning 2017

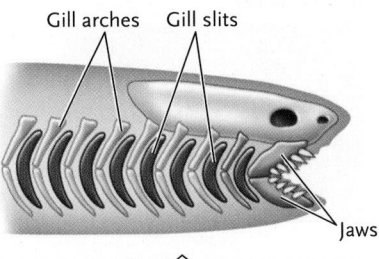

Gill arches  Gill slits

Jaws

**b.** In early jawed fishes, the upper jaw was firmly attached to the cranium.

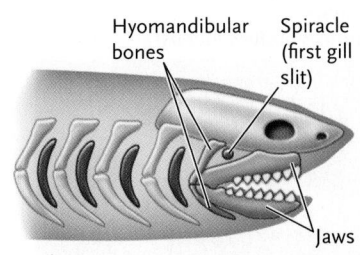

Hyomandibular bones  Spiracle (first gill slit)

Jaws

**c.** In later jawed fishes, the jaws were supported by the hyomandibular bones, which were derived from a second pair of gill arches.

**FIGURE 27.85  The evolution of jaws.** In two early lineages of jawed fishes (Acanthodii and Placodermi), the upper jaw (**maxillae, premaxillae**) was firmly attached to the cranium, and the lower jaw moved up and down. This meant an inflexible mouth that simply snapped open and shut. Acanthodians and placoderms had bony internal skeletons.

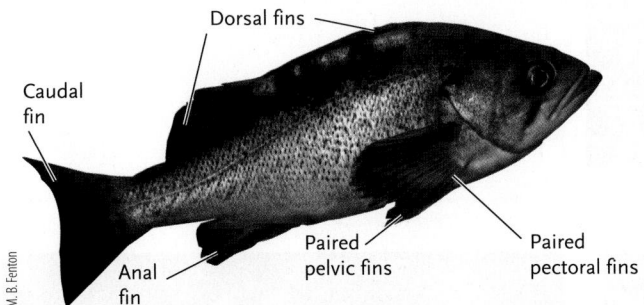

Dorsal fins

Caudal fin

Anal fin

Paired pelvic fins

Paired pectoral fins

M. B. Fenton

**FIGURE 27.86  Fish fins.** Most fishes have both paired and unpaired fins.

**Skull of *Dunkleosteus***

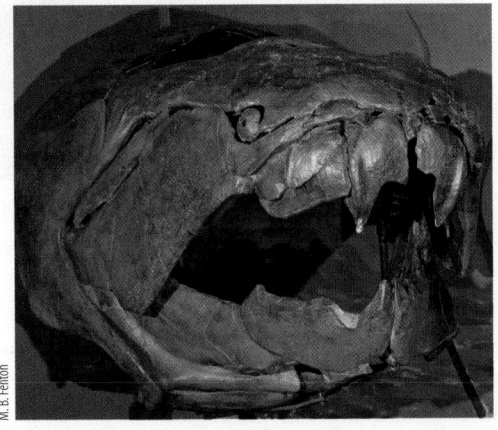

M. B. Fenton

**FIGURE 27.87  The placoderm *Dunkleosteus* was gigantic, growing to 10 m long.** Although some acanthodians had teeth, placoderms had only sharp cutting edges. The 3 m long skull of a *Dunkleosteus* demonstrates how impressive placoderms could be.

Most are bottom dwellers that often lie partly buried in sand. They eat hard-shelled invertebrates (such as molluscs), which they crush with rows of flattened teeth **(Figure 27.89a)**. The largest species, the manta ray (*Manta birostris*), measures 6 m across and eats plankton in the open ocean. Some rays have electric organs that stun prey with shocks of as much as 200 volts. There are species of freshwater skates and rays in some rivers in the tropics. For example, in the Mekong River basin, some *Himantura chaophraya* are 2 m across.

Sharks (see Figure 27.88a) are among the ocean's dominant predators. Flexible fins, lightweight skeletons, streamlined bodies, and the absence of heavy body armour allow most sharks to rapidly pursue prey. Their livers often contain **squalene**, an oil that is lighter than water, which increases their buoyancy. The great white shark (*Carcharodon carcharias*), the largest living predatory species of shark, can be 10 m long. At 18 m, the whale shark (*Rhincodon typus*) is the world's largest fish, and it eats only plankton. Sharks' teeth are designed for cutting. *Isistius plutodus,* the cookie-cutter shark, uses piercing teeth in its upper jaw to attach to its prey, biting with the lower jaw and its cutting teeth while rotating its body (see Figure 27.89b). The feeding process removes a disk of flesh from the prey. The combination of serrated teeth and flexible, extensible jaws makes the effects of shark bites astonishing and frightening. The insatiable human market for shark fin soup has drastically reduced populations of sharks worldwide. This has changed marine ecosystems (see Chapter 31).

Elasmobranchs have remarkable adaptations for acquiring and processing food. Their teeth develop in whorls under the fleshy parts of the mouth. New teeth migrate forward as old worn teeth break free (see Figure 27.89). In many sharks, the upper jaw is loosely attached to the cranium, and it swings down during feeding. As the jaws open, the mouth spreads wide, sucking in large, hard-to-digest chunks of prey, which are swallowed intact, allowing for hurried eating. Although the elasmobranch digestive system is short, it includes a corkscrew-shaped **spiral valve** that slows the passage of material and increases the surface area available for digestion and absorption (see Chapter 39).

Elasmobranchs also have well-developed sensory systems. In addition to vision and olfaction, they use **electroreceptors** to detect weak electric currents produced by other animals. Their **lateral line system**, a row of tiny sensors in canals along both sides of the body, detects vibrations in water (see Figure 45.19).

**a. Grey reef shark**
**(*Carcharhinus amblyrhynchos*)**

iStock.com/Josh Friedman

**b. Manta ray**

Roy V. Rea

**c. Sawfish**

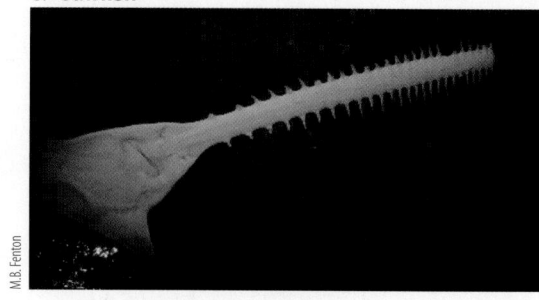

M.B. Fenton

**d. Chimaera**

M.B. Fenton

**e. Shark egg**

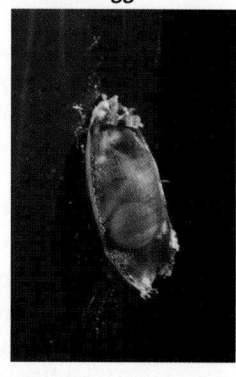

M.B. Fenton

**FIGURE 27.88 Chondrichthyes include** (a) **sharks,** (b) **skates and rays,** (c) **sawfish, and** (d) **chimeras, or ratfish.** The eggs of many sharks **(e)** include a large visible yolk that nourishes the developing embryo.

**a.**

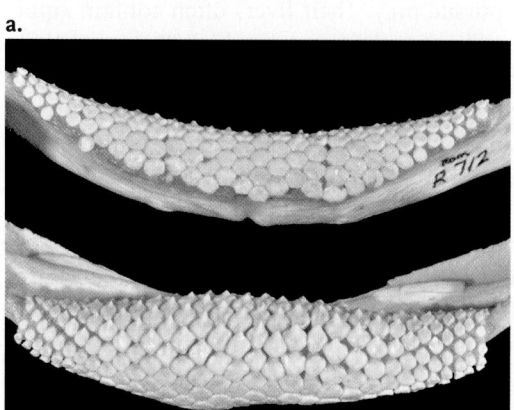

M. B. Fenton

**b.**

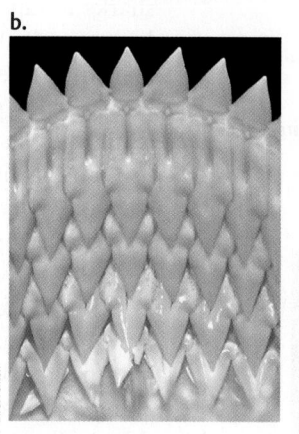

M. B. Fenton

**c.**

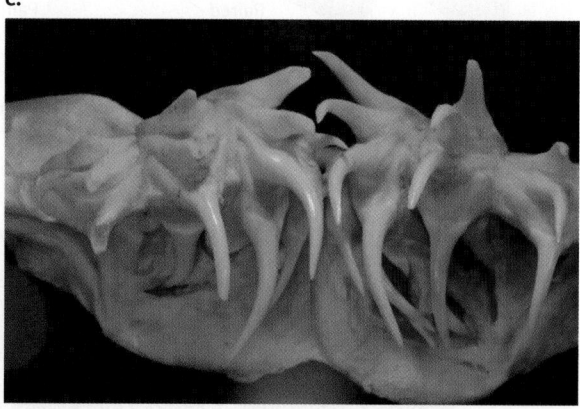

M. B. Fenton

**FIGURE 27.89 Elasmobranch teeth. (a)** The teeth of barndoor skates (*Dipturus laevis*; see also Chapter 28) are specialized for crushing hard prey, such as bivalve molluscs. **(b)** Cookie-cutter sharks (*Isistius plutodus*) use cutting teeth to remove disks of flesh. **(c)** The goblin shark, *Mitsukurina owstoni*, eats soft-bodied prey. In **(a)** and **(b)**, the replacement pattern of the teeth (from back to front of the jaws) is obvious.

They use urea as an osmolyte that makes their body fluids more concentrated than sea water. Freshwater skates have much lower concentrations of urea in their blood than their saltwater relatives do. (For more about osmoregulation, see Chapter 42.)

People of the Gilbert Islands in the South Pacific made fearsome weapons by attaching shark teeth to clubs made of palm wood **(Figure. 27.90)**. These weapons provide modern biologists with a window on the shark community of the waters around the islands over 100 years ago. The weapons, known as *terbutjes*, were festooned with shark teeth set in grooves and held in place with braided palm fibres. Terbutjes made in the last half of the nineteenth century included teeth of spot-tail (*Carcharinus sorrah*) and dusky sharks (*Carcharinus obscurus*),

two species not currently known to occur in those waters. Thus, these terbutjes provide an unexpected glimpse into changes in the predator assemblages of the region.

Anyone who has seen sharks in action will appreciate that many of them are enthusiastic biters. The all-too-often gory sight of the results of shark bites furthers this impression. Small wonder that some people have made weapons whose cutting edges are made of shark teeth. The effectiveness of the cutting edges of the weapons appears clear, but terbutjes were probably designed to draw blood rather than deliver killing blows.

Chondrichthyans have evolved numerous reproductive specializations. Males have a pair of organs, **claspers**, the pelvic fins, which help transfer sperm into the female. Fertilization occurs internally. In many species, females produce yolky eggs with tough leathery shells. Others retain the eggs within the oviduct until the young hatch. A few species nourish young in utero (see Chapter 44).

### 27.11c The Bony Fishes Represent Over 95% of Fish Today

Fishes with bony endoskeletons (cranium, vertebral column with ribs, and bones supporting their movable fins) are the most successful of all vertebrates, whether the count is of numbers of species or of individuals. The endoskeleton provides lightweight support compared with the bony armour of ostracoderms and placoderms, enhancing their locomotor efficiency.

Bony fishes have numerous adaptations that increase swimming efficiency. The scales of most bony fishes are small, smooth, and lightweight, and their bodies are covered with a protective coat of mucus that retards bacterial growth and minimizes drag as water flows past the body.

Bony fishes first appeared in the Silurian and rapidly diversified into two lineages, Actinopterygii and Sarcopterygii. The ray-finned fishes (Actinopterygii; *acti* = ray; *ptery* = wing) have fins supported by thin and flexible bony rays, whereas the fleshy-finned fishes (Sarcopterygii; *sarco* = flesh) have fins supported by muscles and an internal bony skeleton. Ray-finned fishes are more diverse as measured by numbers of species, and today vastly outnumber fleshy-finned fishes. The approximately 30 000 living species of bony fishes occupy nearly every aquatic habitat and represent more than 95% of living fish species. Adults range from 1 cm to more than 6 m in length. In the Yangtze River basin, *Psephurus gladius,* the Chinese paddlefish, can weigh up to 500 kg. The fleshy-finned fishes were on the evolutionary lineage that led to amphibians. In some Devonian fossil species, the lobe fins have bones that are precursors to limbs and digits.

**CLASS ACTINOPTERYGII** Sturgeons **(Figure 27.91a)** and paddlefishes, the most ancestral members of this group, are characterized by mostly cartilaginous skeletons. These large fishes live in rivers and lakes of the Northern Hemisphere. Sturgeons eat detritus and invertebrates, whereas paddlefish eat plankton. Gars (Figure 27.91b) and bowfins are remnants of a more recent radiation. They occur in the eastern half of North America, where they eat fish and other prey. Gars are protected from predators by a heavy coat of bony scales.

The subclass Teleostei represents the latest radiation of Actinopterygii, one that produced a wide range of body forms

**FIGURE 27.90 (a)** April Hawkins of the Royal Ontario Museum in Toronto provides an indication of the size of a terbutje. **(b)** Braided palm fibres hold three shark teeth in grooves in a palm wood terbutje.

a. **Sevruga sturgeon (*Accipenser stellatus*)**

b. **Long-nosed gar (*Lepisosteus osseus*)**

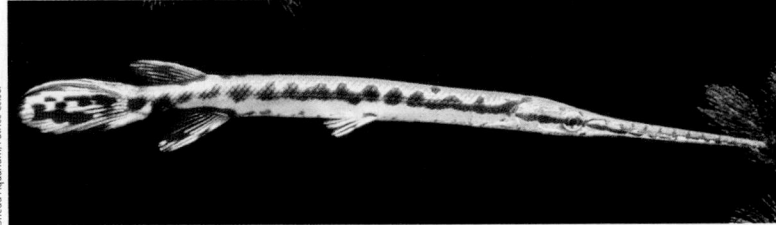

**FIGURE 27.91** Ancestral actinopterygians (ray-finned bony fishes) are represented today by sturgeons (a) and gars (b).

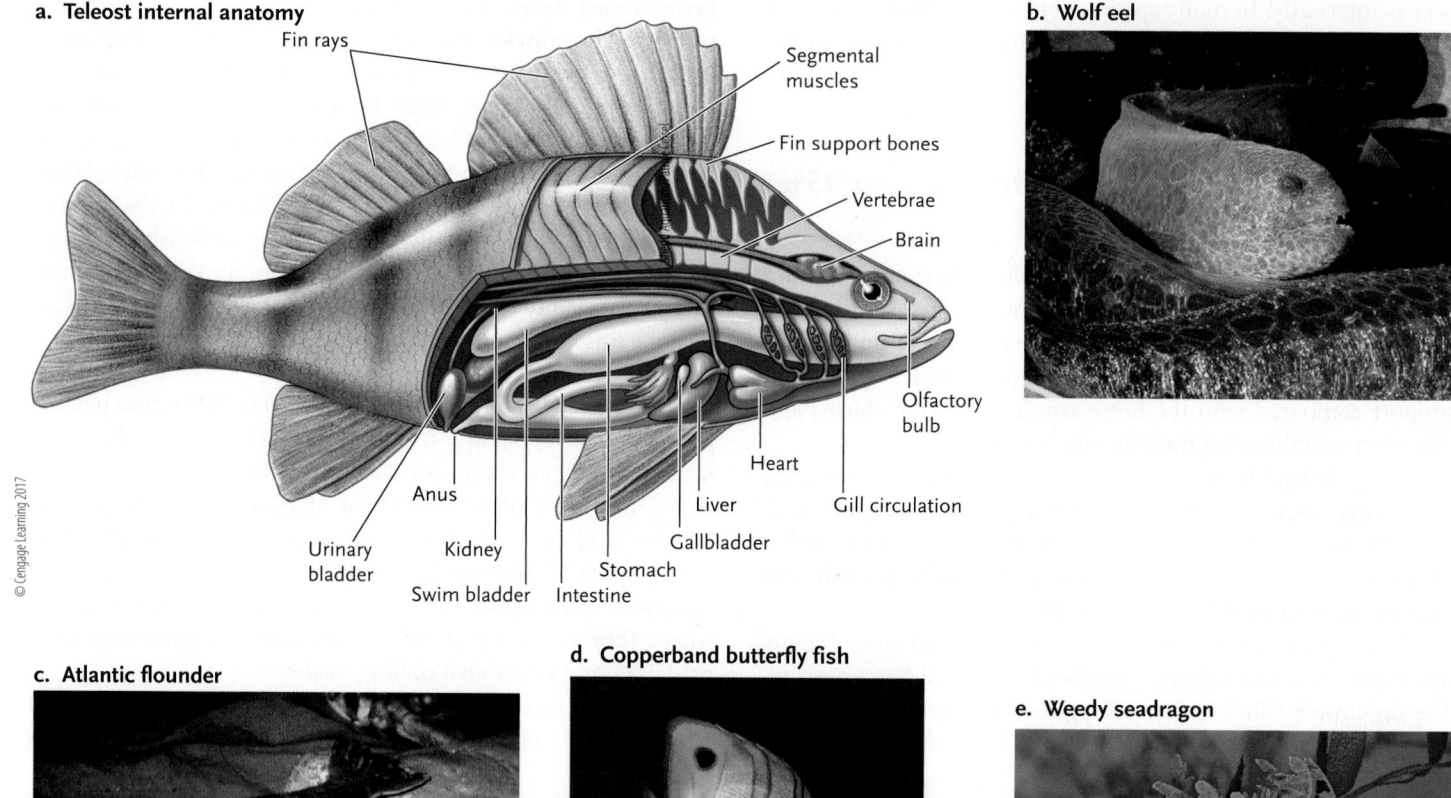

**a. Teleost internal anatomy**

Fin rays

Segmental muscles

Fin support bones

Vertebrae

Brain

Olfactory bulb

Gill circulation

Heart

Liver

Gallbladder

Stomach

Intestine

Swim bladder

Kidney

Anus

Urinary bladder

© Cengage Learning 2017

**b. Wolf eel**

M. B. Fenton

**c. Atlantic flounder**

M. B. Fenton

**d. Copperband butterfly fish**

M. B. Fenton

**e. Weedy seadragon**

M. B. Fenton

**FIGURE 27.92** **This range of bony fishes provides an indication of the range of body forms in the groups. (a)** The basic anatomy provides a map to "typical" fish. **(b)** The wolf eel (*Anarrhichthys ocellatus*) is predatory, **(c)** as is the Atlantic flounder (*Paralichthys* spp.). **(d)** The copperband butterfly fish (*Chelmon rostratus*) is a denizen of coral reefs. **(e)** The weedy seadragon (*Phyllopteryx taeniolatus*) is closely related to sea horses.

**(Figure 27.92)**. Teleosts have an internal skeleton made almost entirely of bone. On either side of the head, the **operculum**, a flap of the body wall, covers a chamber that houses the gills. Sensory systems (see Chapter 45) generally include large eyes, a lateral line system, sound receptors, chemoreceptive nostrils, and taste buds.

Variations in jaw structure and teeth give different species of teleosts access to a wide range of food from plankton, macroalgae, invertebrates, or other vertebrates. Teleosts exhibit remarkable adaptations for feeding and locomotion. When some teleosts open their mouths, bones at the front of the jaws swing forward to create a circular opening. Folds of skin extend backward, forming a tube through which they suck food. Like Chondrichthyes, Actinopterygii exhibit great variation in tooth structure **(Figure 27.93)**. Species such as piranhas (*Serrasalmus*) are notorious for their bites. Other species have teeth specialized for crushing hard prey, such as bivalve molluscs. Whereas the piranha's teeth are on the premaxilla, maxilla, and mandible (as they are in mammals and many other vertebrates), the crushing teeth of ray-finned fishes often occur on the bones of the pharynx.

In many modern ray-finned fishes, a gas-filled **swim bladder** serves as a hydrostatic organ that increases buoyancy (see Figure 27.92a). The swim bladder is derived from an ancestral air-breathing lung that allowed early actinopterygians to gulp air, supplementing gill respiration in aquatic habitats where dissolved oxygen concentration is low.

Many have symmetrical tail fins posterior to the vertebral column that provide power for locomotion. Their pectoral fins often lie high on the sides of the body, providing fine control over swimming. Some species use pectoral fins for acquiring food, for courtship, and for care of eggs and young. Some teleosts use pectoral fins for crawling on land (e.g., mudskippers, *Periophthalmus* species; and climbing perch, *Anabas* species) or gliding in the air (flying fish, family Exocoetidae).

Most marine species produce small eggs that hatch into larvae that live among the plankton. Eggs of freshwater teleosts are generally larger and hatch into tiny versions of the adults.

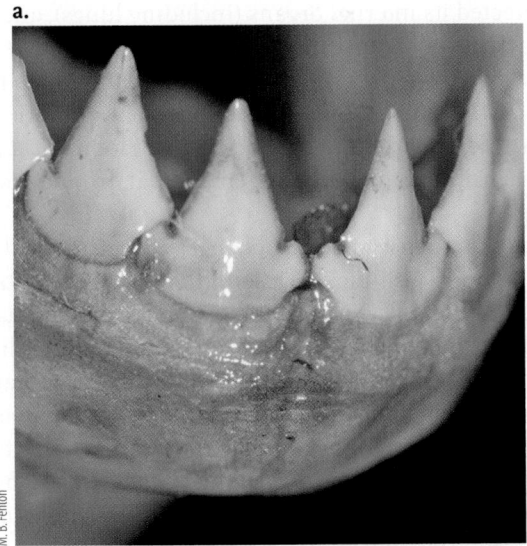

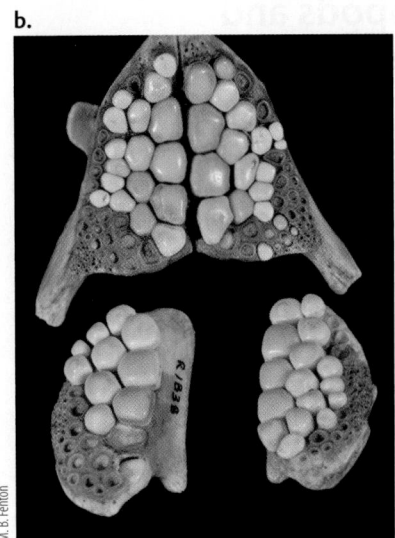

**FIGURE 27.93 Teleost teeth.** Like Chondrichthyes, bony fishes have also developed cutting **(a)** and crushing **(b)** teeth. The cutting teeth are those of a piranha (*Serrasalmus* species). The crushing teeth are from a black drum (*Pogonias cromis*).

**a. Coelacanth**

**b. Australian lungfish**

**FIGURE 27.94 Sarcopterygians. (a)** The coelacanth (*Latimeria chalumnae*) is now one of eight living species of lobe-finned fishes. **(b)** The Australian lungfish (*Neoceratodus forsteri*) is one of six living lungfish species.

Parents often care for their eggs and young, fanning oxygen-rich water over them, removing fungal growths, and protecting them from predators. Some freshwater species, such as guppies, give birth to live young.

**CLASS SARCOPTERYGII** The two groups of fleshy-finned fishes, lobe-finned fishes and lungfishes, are represented by eight living species **(Figure 27.94)**. Although lobe-finned fishes were once thought to have been extinct for 65 million years, a living coelacanth (*Latimeria chalumnae*) was discovered in 1938 near the Comoros Islands, off the southeastern coast of Africa. A population of these metre-long fishes live at depths of 70–600 m, feeding on other fishes and squid. Remarkably, a second population of coelacanths was discovered in 1998, 10 000 km east of the Comoros, when a specimen was found in an Indonesian fish market. Analyses of the DNA of the Indonesian specimen indicated that it is a distinct species (*Latimeria menadoensis*).

Lungfishes have changed relatively little over the past 200 million years. Six living species are distributed on southern continents. Australian lungfishes live in rivers and pools, using their lungs to supplement gill respiration when dissolved oxygen concentration is low. South American and African species live in swamps and use their lungs for breathing during the annual dry season, which they spend encased in a mucus-lined burrow in the dry mud. When the rains begin, water fills the burrow and the fishes awaken from dormancy. During their periods of dormancy, these fishes excrete urea.

**STUDY BREAK QUESTIONS**

1. What did the evolution of jaws mean for fish?
2. What anatomical and physiological characteristics make sharks dominant ocean predators?
3. What is the lateral line system? What does it do?

## 27.12 Early Tetrapods and Modern Amphibians

The fossil record suggests that tetrapods evolved in the late Devonian from a group of lobe-finned fishes (also known as *fleshy-finned*), called the "Osteolepiformes." Osteolepiformes and early tetrapods shared several derived characteristics, including dental and cranial features. In both groups, infoldings of tooth surfaces probably increased the functional area of the tooth. They also shared shapes and positions of bones on the dorsal side of their crania and in their appendages.

Some problems of moving onto land were identified earlier. During dry periods in swampy, late Devonian habitats, drying pools may have forced osteolepiform ancestors to move over-land to adjacent pools that still had water. During these excursions, the fish may have found that land plants, worms, and arthropods provided abundant food, and oxygen was more readily available in air than in water. Furthermore, there may well have been fewer terrestrial predators at that time, but this interpretation is open to question.

Osteolepiformes usually had strong, stout fins that allowed them to crawl on mud. Of particular importance were crescent-shaped bones in their vertebral columns that provided strong intervertebral connections. Their nostrils led to sensory pits housing olfactory (odour) receptors (see Chapter 45). They almost certainly had lungs, allowing them to breathe atmospheric oxygen. Like living lungfishes, they could also have excreted urea or uric acid rather than ammonium, which is toxic.

The earliest tetrapod with nearly complete skeletal data is the semi-terrestrial, metre-long *Ichthyostega*. Compared with its fleshy-finned ancestors, *Ichthyostega* had a more robust vertebral column, sturdier limb girdles and appendages, a ribcage that protected its internal organs (including lungs), and a neck. Fishes lack necks because the pectoral girdle is fused to the cranium. In *Ichthyostega*, several vertebrae separated the pectoral girdle and the cranium, allowing the animal to move its head to scan the environment and capture food. *Ichthyostega* retained a fishlike lateral line system, caudal fin, and scaly body covering.

Life on land also required changes in sensory systems. In fishes, the body wall picks up sound vibrations and transfers them directly to sensory receptors. Sound waves are harder to detect in air. The appearance of a **tympanum** (ear drum) in early tetrapods apparently allowed them to detect vibrations in air associated with airborne sounds. The tympana are specialized membranes on either side of the head. The tympanum connects to the **stapes**, a bone homologous to the hyomandibula, which had supported the jaws of fishes (see Figure 19.5, Chapter 19). The stapes, in turn, transfers vibrations to the sensory cells of an inner ear. In mammals, as we will see (Chapter 45), there are three auditory ossicles.

### 27.12a Class Amphibia Includes Frogs, Toads, Salamanders, and Caecilians

Most of the over 6000 living species of amphibians (*amphi* = both; *bios* = life) are small, and their skeletons contain fewer bones than those of Paleozoic tetrapods, such as *Ichthyostega*. All living amphibians are carnivorous as adults, but the aquatic larvae of some are herbivores. Fossil amphibians, such as *Eryops* **(Figure 27.95)**, were large and predatory.

The thin, scaleless skin of most living amphibians is well supplied with blood vessels and can be a major site of gas exchange. To operate in oxygen uptake, the skin must be moist and thin enough to bring blood into close contact with air.

**FIGURE 27.95 A fossil amphibian.** This amphibian, *Eryops*, from the Texas Permian, was about 1.8 m long and was strikingly different from living amphibians.

M. B. Fenton

Having moist skin limits amphibians to moist habitats. Many species of living amphibians keep their skin surfaces moist, and some are lungless, but most use lungs in gaseous exchange. The evolution of lungs was accompanied by modifications of the heart and circulatory system that increased the efficiency with which oxygen is delivered to body tissues (see Chapter 44). Some adult frogs have a waxy coating on their skin, making them as waterproof as lizards **(Figure 27.96)**.

The life cycles of many amphibians include larval and adult stages. In frogs, larvae (tadpoles) hatch from fertilized eggs and eventually metamorphose into adults (see Chapter 44). The larvae of most frog species are aquatic, but adults may live their lives in water (be aquatic), move between land and water (be amphibious), or live entirely on land (be terrestrial). Some salamanders are paedomorphic (see Chapter 16), which means that the larvae attain sexual maturity without changing to the adult form or moving to land. On the other hand, some frogs and salamanders reproduce on land, omitting the larval stage altogether. In these species, tiny adults emerge directly from fully developed eggs. However, the eggs of terrestrial breeders dry out quickly unless they are laid in moist places.

Modern amphibians are represented by three lineages **(Figure 27.97)**, but the evolutionary origin of frogs, salamanders, and caecilians has remained unresolved. The 2008 description of a small fossil from the Lower Permian of Texas suggests that frogs and salamanders have a relatively close common ancestor, and that caecilians are distantly related to them.

Populations of practically all amphibians have declined rapidly in recent years. These declines are probably due to exposure to acid rain, high levels of ultraviolet B radiation, and fungal and parasitic infections. Another major factor in the decline of amphibians may be habitat splitting, the human-induced disconnection of habitats essential to the survival of amphibians can cause adult amphibians to move across inhospitable habitats (roads, power line rights-of-way) to reach breeding habitats.

**ANURA** The 3700 species of frogs and toads (*an* = without; *uro* = tail) have short, compact bodies, and the adults lack tails.

**FIGURE 27.96 Waterproof frogs. (a)** *Chiromantis xerampelina* from southern Africa and **(b)** *Phyllomedusa sauvagii* from South America make their skin waterproof with a waxy secretion. These frogs are as waterproof as chameleons. They also excrete uric acid to further conserve water.

**a. A frog**

**b. A salamander**

**c. A caecilian**

**FIGURE 27.97 Living amphibians.** Anurans, such as **(a)** a red-eyed frog (*Agalychnis callidryas*) and **(b)** a tiger salamander from Riding Mountain National Park in Manitoba (*Amblystoma tigrinum*), and caecilians, such as **(c)** *Caecilia nigricans* from Colombia

Their elongated hind legs and webbed feet allow them to hop on land or to swim. A few species are adapted to dry habitats, encasing themselves in mucus cocoons to withstand periods of drought. The Pacific tailed frog, *Ascaphus truei*, occurs in coastal British Columbia.

**URODELA** The 400 species of newts and salamanders (*uro* = tail; *del* = visible) have an elongated, tailed body and four legs. They walk by alternately contracting muscles on either side of the body, much the way fishes swim. Species in the most diverse group, the lungless salamanders, are fully terrestrial throughout their lives, using their skin and the lining of the throat for gas exchange.

**GYMNOPHIONA** The 200 species of caecilians (*gymn* = naked; *ophioneos* = snakelike) are legless, burrowing animals with wormlike bodies. They occupy tropical habitats throughout the world. Unlike other extant amphibians, caecilians have small bony scales embedded in their skin. Fertilization is internal, and females give birth to live young. In some species, the mother's skin produces a milk-like substance for the young, which use specialized teeth to collect it from the mother's body.

---

**STUDY BREAK QUESTIONS**

1. Present four lines of evidence suggesting that tetrapods arose from Osteolepiformes.
2. Why was the development of the tympanum important to life on land?
3. What characteristics allow amphibians to use their skin as a major site of gas exchange?

---

## 27.13 The Origin and Mesozoic Radiations of Amniotes

The amniote lineage that today includes reptiles, birds, and mammals arose during the Carboniferous. Then seed plants and insects began to invade terrestrial habitats, providing additional food and cover for early terrestrial vertebrates. Amniotes take their name from the amnion, a fluid-filled sac that surrounds the embryo during development (see Chapter 44). Although the fossil record includes many skeletal remains of early amniotes, it provides little direct information about soft body parts and physiology. Four key features of living amniotes allow life on dry land and liberate them from reliance on standing water:

1. Skin is waterproof: keratin and lipids in the cells make skin relatively impermeable to water.
2. **Amniote (amniotic) eggs** can survive and develop on dry land because they have four specialized membranes and a hard or leathery shell perforated by microscopic pores **(Figure 27.98)**. Amniote eggs are resistant to desiccation. The membranes protect the developing embryo and

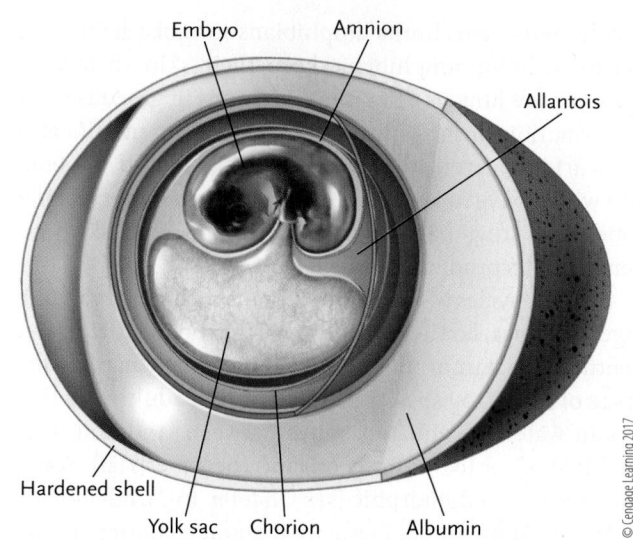

**FIGURE 27.98 The amniote egg.** A water-retaining egg with four specialized membranes surrounded by a hard or leathery shell allowed amniotes and their descendants to reproduce in dry environments. The chorion surrounds the amnion, which in turn surrounds the amniotic fluid.

facilitate gas exchange and excretion. The shell mediates the exchange of air and water between the egg and its environment. Developing amniote embryos can excrete uric acid, which is stored in the allantois of the embryo, which will later become the bladder. Generous supplies of **yolk** in the egg are the developing embryo's main energy source, whereas **albumin** supplies water and other materials. There is no larval stage, and hatchling amniotes are miniature versions of the adult. Amniote eggs are the ancestral condition, but in some reptiles and most mammals, development takes place within the body of the mother (see Chapter 44).

3. Some amniotes produce urea and/or uric acid as a waste product of nitrogen metabolism (see Chapter 42). Although ammonia ($NH_3^+$) is less expensive (metabolically) to produce, it is toxic and must be flushed away with water. Urea is much less toxic than ammonia and therefore easier to store and to void. Uric acid is even less toxic and, because it is insoluble, it can be stored or voided without risk while conserving water.

4. A skeleton provides support and points of attachment for muscles, allowing locomotion and survival on land.

The abundance and diversity of fossils of amniotes indicate that they were extremely successful, quickly replacing many nonamniote species in terrestrial habitats. During the Carboniferous and Permian, amniotes produced three major radiations: synapsids, anapsids, and diapsids **(Figure 27.99)**, distinguishable by the numbers of bony arches in the temporal region of the skull (in addition to the openings for the eyes; **Figure 27.100**). The bony arches demarcate fenestrae, openings in the skull that allow space for contraction (and expansion) of large and powerful jaw muscles.

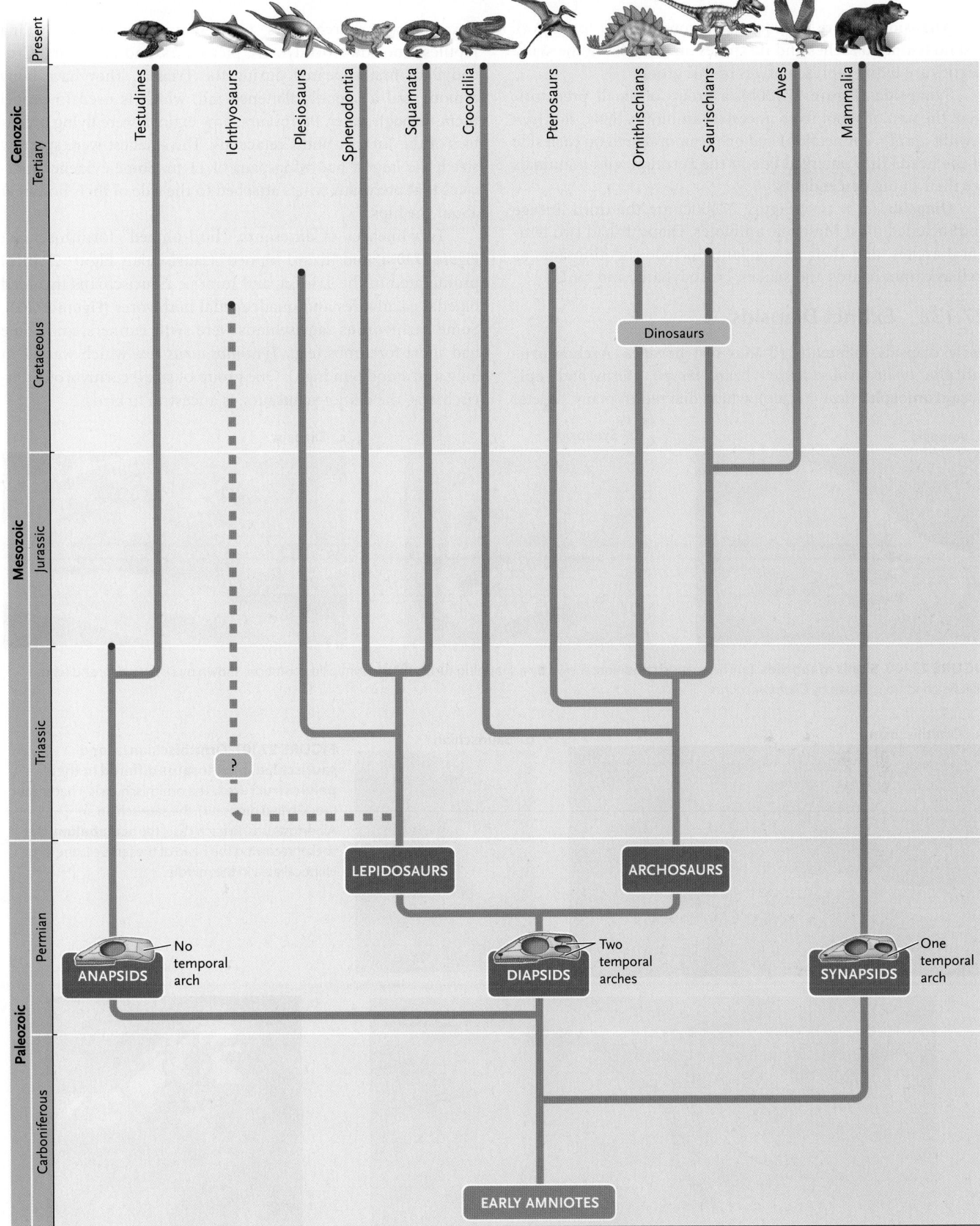

**FIGURE 27.99 Amniote ancestry.** The early amniotes gave rise to three lineages (anapsids, synapsids, and diapsids) and numerous descendants. The lineages are distinguished by the number of bony arches in the temporal region of the skull (indicated on the small icons).

**Anapsida** (Figure 27.100a), the second lineage (*an* = not), had no temporal arches and no spaces on the sides of the skull. Turtles are living representatives of this group.

**Synapsida** (Figure 27.100b), a group of small predators, were the first offshoot from ancestral amniotes. Synapsids (*syn* = with; *apsid* = connection) had one temporal arch on each side of the head. They emerged late in the Permian, and mammals are their living descendants.

**Diapsida** (*di* = two; Figure 27.100c) are the third lineage and included most Mesozoic amniotes. Diapsids had two temporal arches, and their descendants include the dinosaurs as well as extant lizards and snakes, crocodylians, and birds.

## 27.13a    Extinct Diapsids

Early diapsids differentiated into two lineages, **Archosauromorpha** (*archo* = ruler; *sauro* = lizard; *morph* = form) and **Lepidosauromorpha** (*lepi* = scale), which differed in many skeletal characteristics. Archosaurs (archosauromorphs), or "ruling reptiles," include crocodylians, pterosaurs, and dinosaurs. Crocodylians first appeared during the Triassic. They have bony armour and a laterally flattened tail, which is used to propel them through water. Pterosaurs, now extinct, were flying predators of the Jurassic and Cretaceous. The smallest were sparrow sized; the largest had wingspans of 11 m. Some evidence indicates that pterosaur wings attached to the side of their bodies at about the hips.

Two lineages of dinosaurs, "bird-hipped" (ornithischian; **Figure 27.101a**) and "lizard-hipped" (saurischian; Figure 27.101b) proliferated in the Triassic and Jurassic. Saurischians included bipedal carnivores and quadrupedal herbivores **(Figure 27.102)**. Some carnivorous saurischians were swift runners, and some had short forelimbs (e.g., *Tyrannosaurus rex*, which was 12 m long and stood 6 m high). One group of small carnivorous saurischians, the deinonychusaurs, is ancestral to birds.

**a. Anapsid**

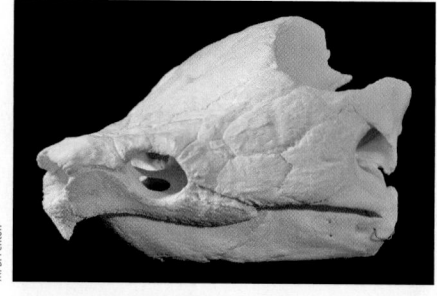

**b. Synapsid**

**c. Diapsid**

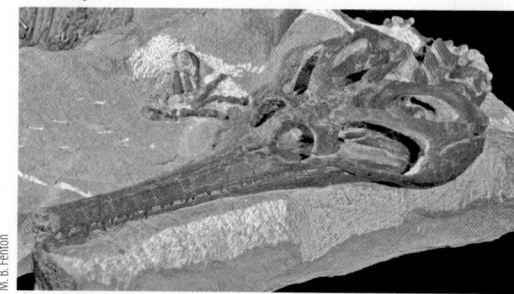

**FIGURE 27.100  Skulls of reptiles. (a)** The anapsid condition, shown by a snapping turtle; **(b)** the synapsid condition, shown by *Dimetrodon;* and **(c)** the diapsid condition, shown by *Champsosaurus*

**a. Ornithischian**

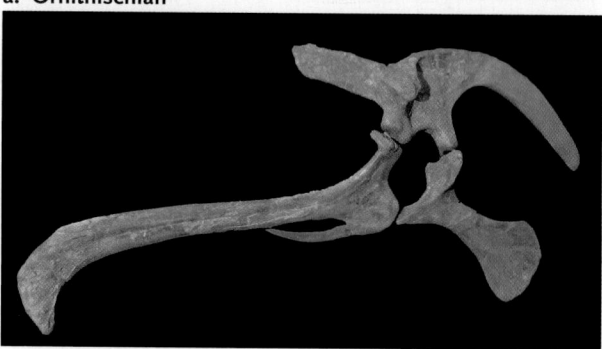

**b. Saurischian**

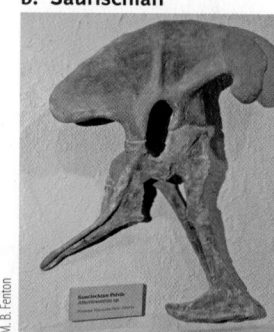

**FIGURE 27.101  Ornithischian** (a) **and saurischian** (b) **dinosaurs differed in their pelvic structures.** The ornithischian is a hadrosaur (duck-billed dinosaur), the saurischian an Albertosaurus. In each case, the **acetabulum**, the socket receiving the head of the femur, is the large elliptical area in the middle.

**a.**

**b.**

**FIGURE 27.102  Saurischian dinosaurs.** While *Ornitholestes hermanni* **(a)** stood less than 1 m at the shoulder, the fearsome *Tyrannosaurus rex* **(b)** was about 12 m long. Both were carnivores.

a. *Lambeosaurus*

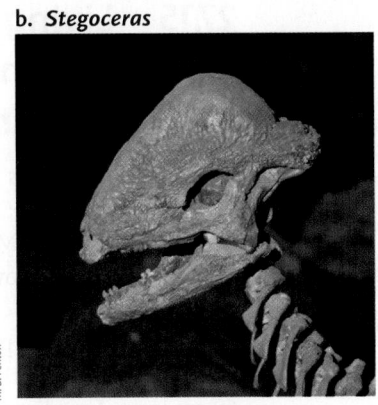
b. *Stegoceras*

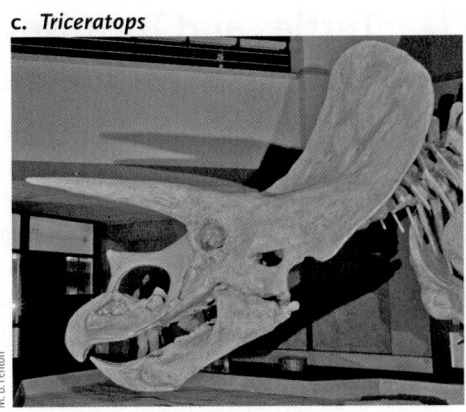
c. *Triceratops*

**FIGURE 27.103 Ornithischian dinosaurs.** These herbivores varied in size: **(a)** the 15 m long *Lambeosaurus lambei*; **(b)** the smaller, thick-skulled *Stegoceras*; and **(c)** the 10 m long *Triceratops horridus*.

a.

b.
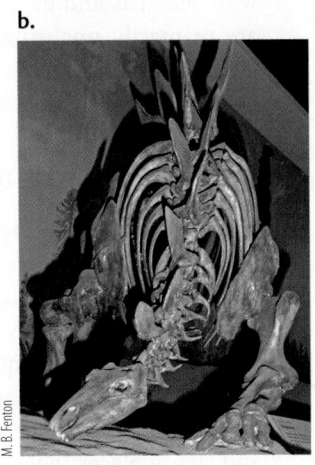

**FIGURE 27.104 Large, lumbering herbivores.** Other ornithischian dinosaurs included the 18 m long *Camarasaurus supremus* **(a)** and the 9 m long *Stegosaurus armatus* **(b)**. The latter had distinctive plates along its back.

a.

b.

c.
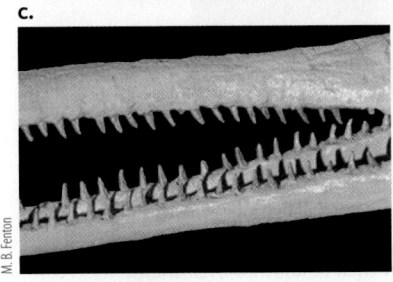

d.
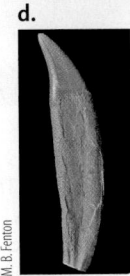

**FIGURE 27.105 Reptile teeth.** As usual, teeth reflect the dietary habits of dinosaurs. Herbivorous dinosaurs, *Diplodocus longus* **(a)** and hadrosaur **(b)**, had teeth adapted for gathering plant material (a) and grinding it (b). These teeth differed from those of a fish-eating reptile such as a champsosaur **(c)**. A tooth of a *Tyrannosaurus rex* changed distinctly over its length. The biting part of the tooth **(d)** had enamel and serrated edges. There was no enamel on the part of the tooth located within the socket of the skull.

By the Cretaceous, some herbivorous saurischians were gigantic, and many had long, flexible necks **(Figure 27.103)**. *Apatosaurus* (previously known as *Brontosaurus*) was 25 m long and may have weighed 50 000 kg. The largely herbivorous ornithischian dinosaurs had large, chunky bodies **(Figure 27.104)**. This lineage included armoured, or plated, dinosaurs (*Ankylosaurus* and *Stegosaurus*), duck-billed dinosaurs (*Hadrosaurus*), horned dinosaurs (*Styracosaurus*), and some with remarkably thick skulls (*Pachycephalosaurus*). Ornithischians were most abundant in the Jurassic and Cretaceous.

Lepidosaurs (Lepidosauromorpha) are the second major lineage of diapsids. This diverse group included both marine and terrestrial animals. Fossil lepidosaurs include champsosaurs, which were freshwater fish eaters, and the marine fish-eating plesiosaurs, with long, paddle-like limbs that they used like oars. Fossil lepidosaurs also included ichthyosaurs, porpoise-like animals with laterally flattened tails. Like today's whales, ichthyosaurs were highly specialized for marine life and did not return to land to lay eggs. Indeed, it appears that ichthyosaurs, like today's whales, gave birth to live young. Squamates, the living lizards and snakes, are the third important group within this lineage. *Sphenodon*, the tuatara, is the last living genus of a once diverse group of lizard-like squamates.

The teeth of reptiles provide important clues about their diets **(Figure 27.105)** and show interesting parallels with the teeth of other vertebrates.

## STUDY BREAK QUESTIONS

1. Where do amniotes get their name? Why are amniote eggs resistant to desiccation?
2. What four key features liberate living amniotes from reliance on standing water?
3. Name and describe three major radiations of amniotes during the Carboniferous and Permian.

## 27.14 Turtles and Tortoises (Subclass Testudinata)

The turtle body plan, defined largely by a bony, boxlike shell, has changed little since the group first appeared during the Triassic (**Figure 27.106**). A turtle's ribs are fused to the inside of the shell and, in contrast to other tetrapods, the pectoral and pelvic girdles lie within the ribcage. The shell is formed from large, keratinized scales covering the bony plates. It includes a dorsal carapace and a ventral **plastron**. Like living birds, turtles have keratinized beaks and lack teeth.

The 250 living species occupy terrestrial, fresh-water, and marine habitats. They range from 8 cm to 2 m in length. Turtles use a keratinized beak in feeding, whether they eat animal or plant material. When threatened, most species retract into their shells. Many species are now endangered because adults are hunted for meat and their eggs are eaten by humans and other predators. Young are often collected for the pet trade, and the beaches favoured as nesting sites by marine species are too often used as tourist attractions.

**STUDY BREAK QUESTION**

1. Describe the body plan of a turtle.

## 27.15 Living Diapsids: Sphenodontids, Squamates, and Crocodylians

*Sphenodon punctatus* is one of two living species of sphenodontids (*sphen* = wedge; *dont* = tooth), or tuataras, a lineage that was diverse in the Mesozoic (**Figure 27.107a**). These lizardlike animals are best known as tetrapods with a "third," or pineal, eye, a reflection of earlier vertebrates such as lampreys with pineal eyes (see also photoreceptors in Chapter 1). They survive on a few islands off the coast of New Zealand. Adults are about 60 cm long. They live in dense colonies, where males and females defend small territories. They often share underground burrows with seabirds and eat invertebrates and small vertebrates. They are primarily nocturnal and maintain low body temperatures during periods of activity. Their survival is threatened by two introduced predators, cats and rats.

### 27.15a Lizards and Snakes

Lizards and snakes (Figure 27.107b, c) are covered by overlapping, keratinized scales (*squam* = scale) that protect against dehydration. Squamates periodically shed their skin while growing, much the way arthropods shed their exoskeletons (see Section 27.7h). Most squamates regulate their body temperature behaviourally (see Chapter 42), so they are active only when weather conditions are favourable. They shuttle between sunny and shady places to warm up or cool down as needed.

**a. The turtle skeleton**

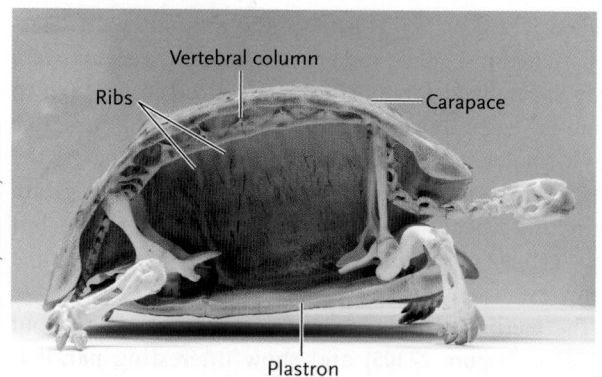

**b. Spiny softshell turtle (*Apalone spinifera*)**

**c. Green sea turtle (*Chelonia mydas*)**

**FIGURE 27.106 Testudines. (a)** The turtle skeleton. **(b)** Most turtles can withdraw their heads and legs into a bony shell, for example this spiny softshell *Apalone spinifera*. **(c)** But marine (sea) turtles, like green turtles (*Chelonia mydas*), cannot withdraw their heads into their shells.

**a. Tuartara (*Sphenodon punctatus*)**

**b. Zebra-tailed lizard (*Callisaurus draconoides*)**

**c. Western diamondback rattlesnake**

**FIGURE 27.107** **(a)** Sphenodontia includes the tuartara (*Sphenodon punctatus*) and one other species. **(b)** Zebra-tailed lizard (*Callisaurus draconoides*). **(c)** Western diamondback rattlesnakes have fangs that are used to inject toxin into prey.

**a.**

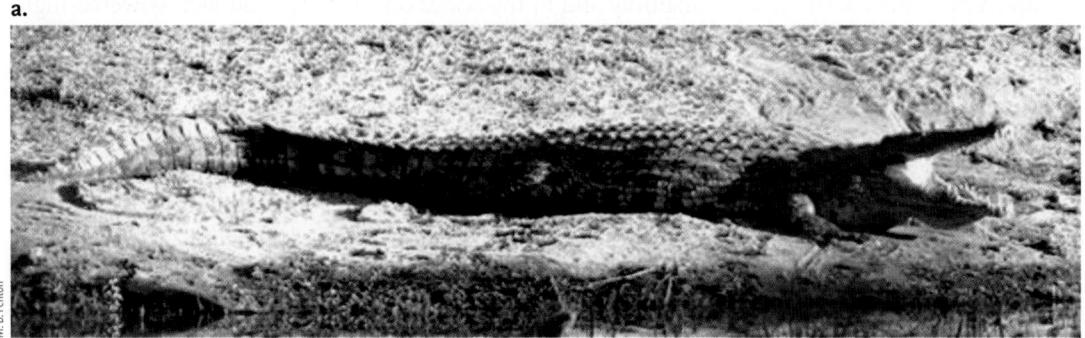

**b.**

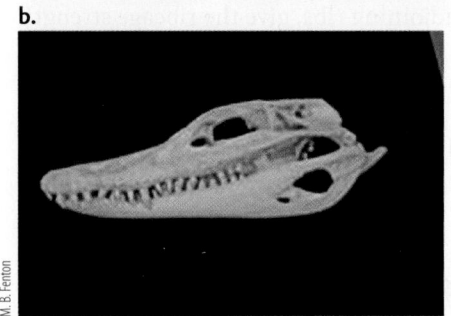

**c.**

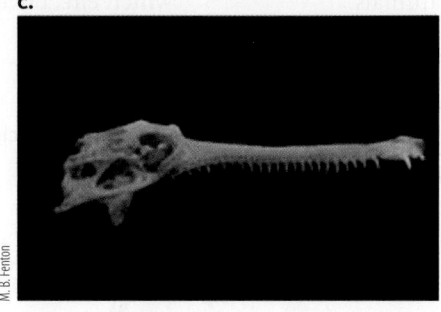

**FIGURE 27.108** **Crocodylians. (a)** A 3 m long Nile crocodile (*Crocodylus niloticus*) basks in Kruger National Park, South Africa. **(b)** The skull of an alligator (*Alligator mississippiensis*) and **(c)** a gavial (*Gavialis gangeticus*) illustrate the range of variation among living crocodylians. In the Cretaceous, the group was much more diverse, exhibiting a greater variety of morphology and locomotion.

Most of the 3700 lizard species are less than 15 cm long, but Komodo dragons (*Varanus komodoensis*) grow to nearly 3 m in length (see Figure 45.24, Chapter 45). Lizards occupy a wide range of habitats and are especially common in deserts and the tropics. One species (*Lacerta vivipara*) occurs within the Arctic Circle. Most lizards eat insects, although some consume leaves or meat.

The 2300 species of snakes evolved from a lineage of lizards that lost their legs over evolutionary time. Streamlined bodies make snakes efficient burrowers or climbers. Many subterranean species are 10 or 15 cm long, whereas giant constrictors may grow to 10 m. Unlike lizards, all snakes are predators that swallow prey whole. Compared with their lizard ancestors, snake skull bones are reduced in size and connected to each other by elastic ligaments. This gives snakes a remarkable capacity to stretch their mouths. Some snakes can swallow food items that are larger than their heads (see Chapter 39). Snakes also have well-developed sensory systems for detecting prey. The flicking tongue carries airborne molecules to sensory receptors in the roof of the mouth. Most snakes can detect vibrations on the ground and some, such as rattlesnakes, have heat-sensing organs (see Figure 45.39, Chapter 45). Many snakes kill by constriction, which suffocates prey. Other species produce venoms, toxins that immobilize, kill, and partially digest prey. Snakes that take larger prey tend to be ambush hunters.

### 27.15b Crocodiles and Alligators

The 21 species of alligators and crocodiles, along with birds, are the living remnants of the archosaurs **(Figure 27.108)**. Crocodylians are aquatic predators that eat other vertebrates. Striking anatomical adaptations distinguish them from living lepidosaurs, including a four-chambered heart (see Chapters 19 and 41) that is homologous to the heart in birds, analogous to this structure in mammals. In some crocodylians, muscles that originate on the pubis insert on the liver and pericardium. When these muscles contract, the liver moves toward the tail, creating negative pressure in the chest cavity and drawing air in. This situation is analogous to the role of the diaphragm in mammals.

The snouts of alligators are broad compared to those of crocodiles. But the gavial has the longest and narrowest snout of living crocodylians. Saltwater crocodiles (*Crocodylus porosus*) and Nile crocodiles are the largest living reptiles, reaching up to 8 m in length.

American alligators (*Alligator mississippiensis*) exhibit strong maternal behaviour, perhaps reflecting their relationship to birds. Females guard their nests ferociously and, after the young hatch, free their offspring from the nest. The young stay close to the mother for about a year, feeding on scraps that fall from her mouth and living under her watchful protection.

Many species of alligators and crocodiles are endangered because their habitats have been disrupted by human activities. They have been hunted for their meat and leather and because larger individuals are predators of humans. There is hope, however, as some populations of American alligators have recovered in the wake of efforts to protect them. In Africa and Australia, crocodiles are farmed for their meat and skin.

In the past, crocodylians were more diverse in body form than modern species. During the Mesozoic, there were running (cursorial) species as well as others showing specializations of teeth strikingly similar to those of mammals. These included teeth with narrow cutting edges, like the carnassial teeth (see Section 27.17b) of carnivorous mammals.

**STUDY BREAK QUESTIONS**

1. How do snakes kill their prey?
2. What features of crocodylians are homologous to those of birds? Which ones are analogous to those of mammals?

## 27.16 Birds

Birds (or aves) appeared in the Jurassic as descendants of carnivorous, bipedal, theropod dinosaurs (see Figure 19.9, Chapter 19). Birds belong to the archosaur lineage, and their evolutionary relationship to dinosaurs is evident in their skeletal anatomy and in the scales on their legs and feet. Powered flight gave birds access to new **adaptive zones**, likely contributing to their astounding evolutionary success. Some species of birds are flightless, and some of these are bipedal runners. Other birds are weak fliers.

Three skeletal features associated with flight in birds are the **keeled sternum** (breastbone), the **furculum** (wishbone), and the **uncinate processes** on the ribs **(Figure 27.109)**. The keel on the sternum anchors the flight muscles, and the furculum acts like a spring, storing and releasing energy and making muscle contraction more efficient. The uncinate processes, which effect overlap of adjoining ribs, give the ribcage strength

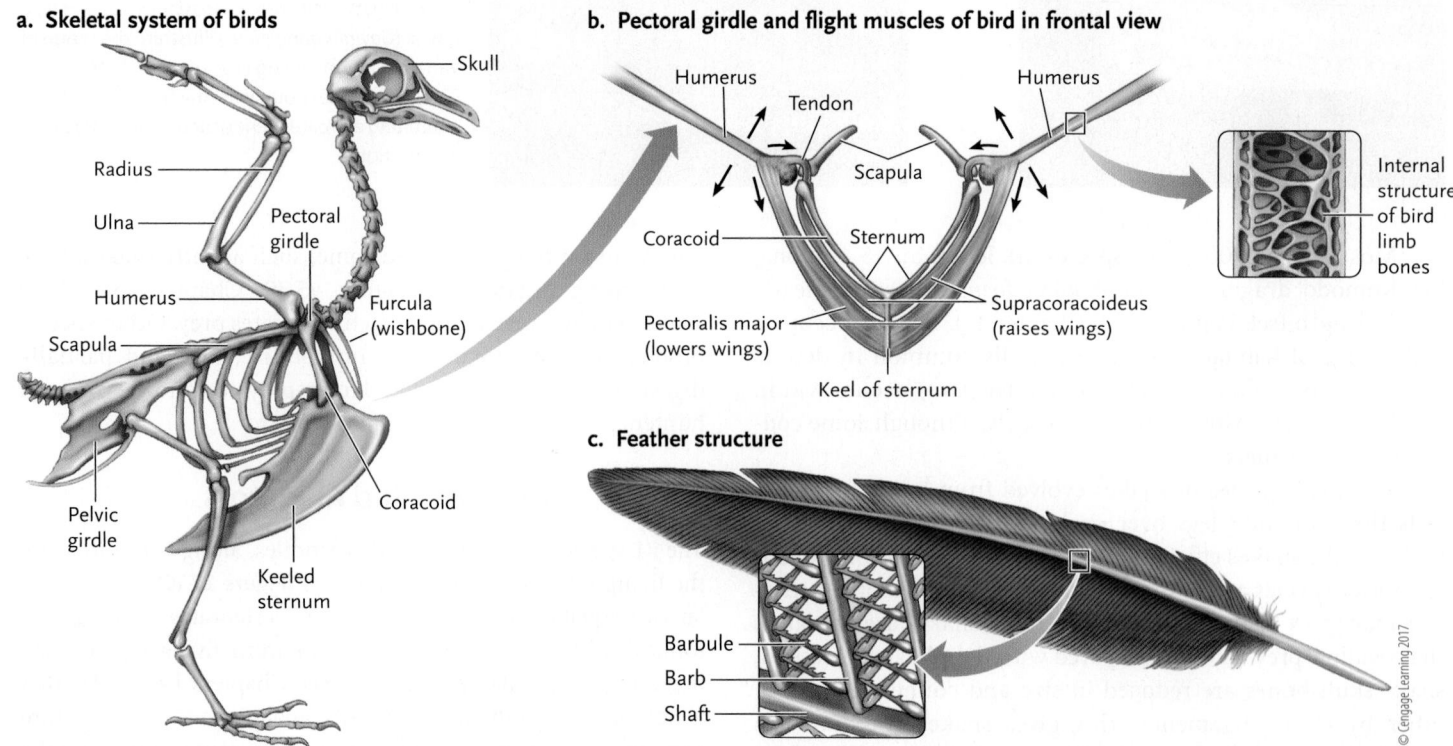

**a. Skeletal system of birds**

Skull
Radius
Ulna
Pectoral girdle
Humerus
Scapula
Furcula (wishbone)
Pelvic girdle
Coracoid
Keeled sternum

**b. Pectoral girdle and flight muscles of bird in frontal view**

Humerus
Tendon
Humerus
Scapula
Coracoid
Sternum
Pectoralis major (lowers wings)
Supracoracoideus (raises wings)
Keel of sternum
Internal structure of bird limb bones

**c. Feather structure**

Barbule
Barb
Shaft

© Cengage Learning 2017

**FIGURE 27.109 Flying birds generate lift and propulsion by flapping their wings. (a)** The bird skeleton includes a boxlike trunk, short tail, long neck, lightweight skull and beak, and well-developed limbs. In large birds, limb bones are hollow. **(b)** Two sets of flight muscles originate on the keeled sternum: one set raises the wings; the other lowers them. **(c)** Flexible feathers form an airfoil on the wing surface.

and they anchor intercostal muscles. In flightless species, the sternum often lacks a keel **(Figure 27.110)**, penguins that "fly" through the water retain the keel, making them an exception. However, flightless species often have uncinate processes.

Birds' skeletons are light and strong. The skeleton of a 1.5 kg frigate bird (*Fregata magnificens*) weighs just 100 g, far less than the mass of its feathers. The bones of birds tend to be lighter and less dense than those of mammals. Most birds have hollow limb bones with small supporting struts that crisscross the internal cavities. Birds have reduced numbers of separate bony elements in the wings, skull, and vertebral column (especially the tail), so the skeleton is rigid. The bones associated with flight are generally large, and the wing bones are long. In general, the skeleton reflects the bird's way of life. Note that many birds have sclerotic rings, which are bones in the eye.

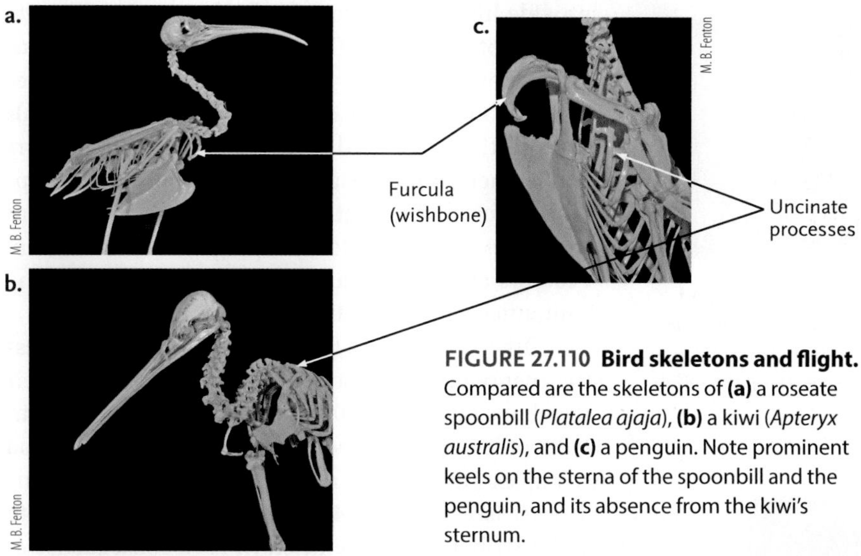

The approximately 9000 living bird species show extraordinary ecological specializations built on the same body plan. Living birds are traditionally classified into nearly 30 orders **(Figure 27.111)**. Rather than teeth, all extant birds use a dense, heavy, keratinized bill for feeding. Bird bills show considerable diversity, reflecting different feeding behaviours. Birds offer many examples of convergence, such as species that feed at flowers: the hummingbirds of the New World and the sunbirds of the Old World. Many species have a long, flexible neck that allows them to use their bills for feeding, grooming, nest building, and social interactions. Keratinized bills can also be very light, even the spectacular bills of hornbills and toucans **(Figure 27.112)**. A bird's bill usually reflects its diet. Seed and nut eaters, such as finches and

**FIGURE 27.110 Bird skeletons and flight.** Compared are the skeletons of **(a)** a roseate spoonbill (*Platalea ajaja*), **(b)** a kiwi (*Apteryx australis*), and **(c)** a penguin. Note prominent keels on the sterna of the spoonbill and the penguin, and its absence from the kiwi's sternum.

Furcula (wishbone)

Uncinate processes

a. **European starling**

b. **Downy woodpecker**

c. **Brown-headed parrot**

d. **Turkey vulture**

e. **White-bellied sunbird**

f. **Ruby-throated hummingbird**

**FIGURE 27.111 The six species shown here illustrate some of the diversity of bills of extant birds.** Included are **(a)** the generalist European starling (*Sturnus vulgaris*), **(b)** a downy woodpecker (*Picoides pubescens*), **(c)** a brown-headed parrot (*Poicephalus cryptoxanthus*), **(d)** a turkey vulture (*Cathartes aura*), **(e)** a white-bellied sunbird (*Cinnyris talatala*), and **(f)** a ruby-throated hummingbird (*Archilochus colubris*).

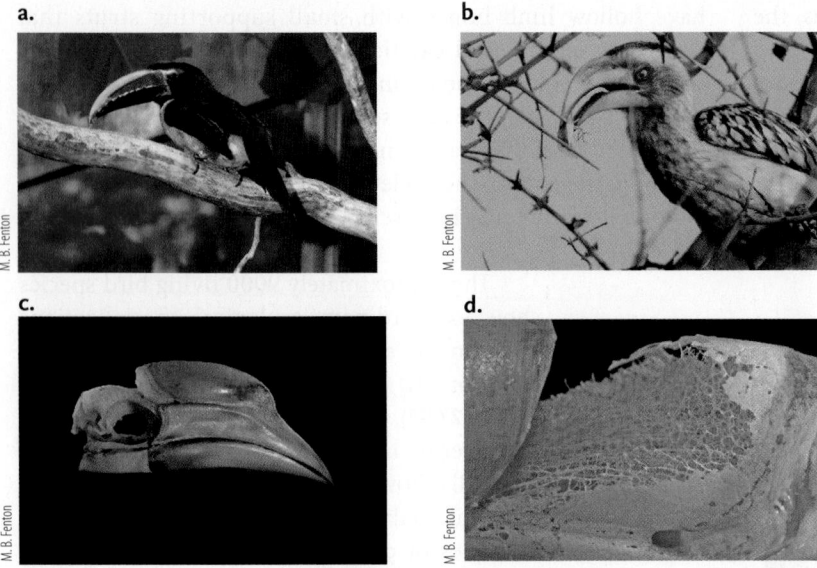

**FIGURE 27.112** Both green aracari, such as **(a)** the toucan (*Pteroglossus viridis*), and hornbills, such as **(b)** the yellow-billed hornbill (*Tockus leucomelas*), have enlarged bills. **(c)** A Malabar pied hornbill, *Anthracoceros coronatus*. The details of the bill of a Malabar pied hornbill **(d)** show how the keratinized bill overlies porous bone, making the whole structure strong but lightweight.

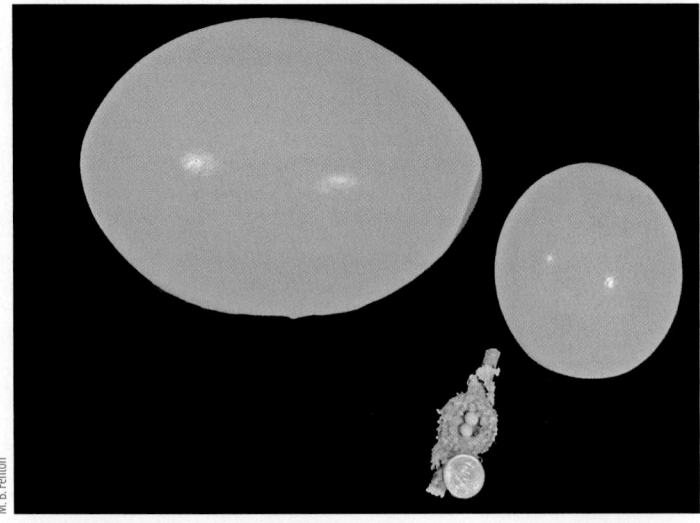

**FIGURE 27.113** **Bird eggs range in size from those of elephant birds (*Aepyornis* of Madagascar, left) to ostriches (*Struthio camelus*, right) to hummingbirds (bottom).** The scale: a Canadian $2 coin is 2.8 cm in diameter.

parrots, have deep, stout bills that crack hard shells. Carnivorous hawks and carrion-eating vultures have sharp beaks to rip flesh. Nectar-feeding hummingbirds and sunbirds have long slender bills to reach into flowers, although many perching birds also have slender bills to feed on insects. The bills of ducks are modified to extract particulate matter from water.

Birds' soft internal organs are modified to reduce mass. Most birds lack a urinary bladder, so uric acid paste is eliminated with digestive wastes. Females have only one ovary and never carry more than one mature egg at a time. Eggs are laid as soon as they are shelled. Egg sizes give an indication of the range of size in birds **(Figure 27.113)**. Birds range in size from a bee hummingbird (*Mellisuga helenae*) at 2 g, to ostriches (*Struthio camelus*) at about 150 kg.

All living birds have **feathers (Figure 27.114)**, sturdy, lightweight structures derived from scales in the skin of their reptilian ancestors. Each feather has numerous barbs and barbules with tiny hooks and grooves that maintain the feathers' structures, even during vigorous activity. Flight feathers on the wings provide lift, whereas contour feathers streamline the surface of the body. Down feathers form an insulating cover close to the skin. Moulting replaces feathers once or twice each year. But not all animals with feathers are birds. Several extinct archosaurs had feathers, but these animals had none of the adaptations for flight. Feathers may have originated as insulators, whether for keeping heat out or in. Feathers also serve many other functions, including camouflage and signalling.

Other adaptations for flight allow birds to harness the energy needed to power their flight muscles. Their metabolic rates are 8–10 times as high as those of comparably sized reptiles, allowing them to process energy-rich food rapidly. A complex and efficient respiratory system and a four-chambered heart (see Chapters 40, 19, and 41) enable them to consume and distribute oxygen efficiently. As a consequence of high rates of metabolic heat production, most birds maintain a high and constant body temperature (see Chapter 42).

Flying birds were abundant by the Cretaceous. Even in the Jurassic, *Archaeopteryx* had a furculum and was capable of at least limited flight. Until 2008, two main theories purported to explain the evolution of flight in birds. Proponents of the *top-down* theory argued that ancestral birds lived in trees and glided down from them in pursuit of insect prey. Gliding and access to prey are key elements of this theory. Proponents of the *bottom-up* theory proposed that a protobird was a runner (cursorial) and ran in pursuit of prey and jumped up to catch it.

In 2008, Kenneth P. Dial and two colleagues proposed the *ontogenetic-transitional wing* (OTW) hypothesis to explain the evolution of flight in birds. They asserted that the transitional stages leading to the development of flight in modern birds corresponded to its evolutionary development. Key to the OTW theory is the observation that, in developing from flightless hatchlings to flight-capable juveniles, individual birds move their protowings in the same ways as adults move fully developed wings. Dial and his colleagues noted that flap-running allows as yet flightless birds to move over obstacles. The OTW theory provides another look at the evolution of flight, and its predictions can be tested with fledglings of extant species. The combination of wings and bipedalism is central to the OTW hypothesis. Birds are bipedal, and pterosaurs may have been. Bats, however, are not bipedal, so the OTW hypothesis does not explain the evolution of flight in that group.

The first known radiation of birds produced the enantiornithines ("opposite" birds), the dominant birds of the

**FIGURE 27.114 Feathers can serve a thermoregulatory and/or a signalling function. (a)** A roadrunner (*Geococcyx californianus*) lifts feathers on its back to warm up by exposing underlying dark areas to the morning sun. Contrasting colour patterns enhance communication in **(b)** a male northern cardinal (*Cardinalis cardinalis*) and **(c)** a female royal flycatcher (*Onychorhynchus coronatus*).

Jurassic and Cretaceous. Ornithurines are modern birds **(Figure 27.115)**. Like dinosaurs, many mammals, and other organisms, the enantiornithines did not survive the extinctions that marked the end of the Cretaceous (see Chapter 28). Many enantiornithines flew, reflected by keeled sterna, furcula, and other "modern" skeletal features. Others, such as *Hesperornis*, were swimmers that used their feet for propulsion and, unlike penguins, had unkeeled sterna. Ornithurines include modern groups of wading birds and seabirds, first known from late Cretaceous rocks. Woodpeckers, perching birds, birds of prey, pigeons, swifts, the flightless ratites, penguins, and some other groups were all present by the end of the Oligocene. Birds continued to diversify through the Miocene.

All birds have well-developed sensory and nervous systems, and their brains are proportionately larger than those of comparably sized diapsids. Large eyes provide sharp vision, and most species also have good hearing, which nocturnal hunters such as owls use to locate prey. Vultures and some other species have a good sense of smell, which they use to find food. Migrating birds use polarized light, changes in air pressure, and Earth's magnetic field for orientation.

Many birds exhibit complex social behaviour, including courtship, territoriality, and parental care. Many species use vocalizations and visual displays to challenge other individuals

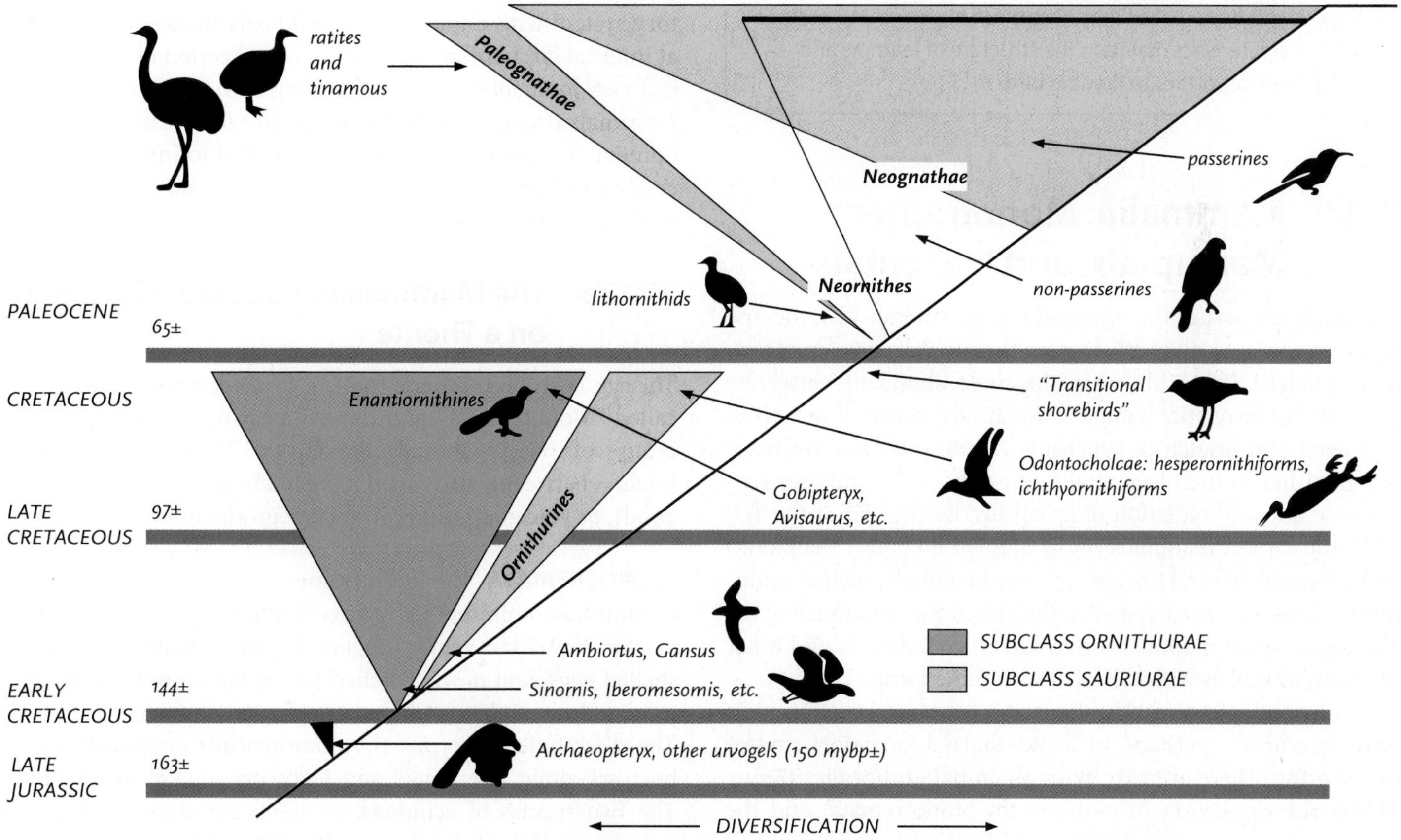

ratites and tinamous

Paleognathae

Neognathae

passerines

Neornithes

non-passerines

PALEOCENE 65±

lithornithids

"Transitional shorebirds"

CRETACEOUS

Enantiornithines

Odontocholcae: hesperornithiforms, ichthyornithiforms

LATE CRETACEOUS 97±

Ornithurines

Gobipteryx, Avisaurus, etc.

SUBCLASS ORNITHURAE

SUBCLASS SAURIURAE

EARLY CRETACEOUS 144±

Ambiortus, Gansus

Sinornis, Iberomesomis, etc.

LATE JURASSIC 163±

Archaeopteryx, other urvogels (150 mybp±)

◄—— DIVERSIFICATION ——►

**FIGURE 27.115 Evolution of birds.** Enantiornithines, or opposite birds, were dominant in the Mesozoic but coexisted with ornithurine (more modern) birds in the early Cretaceous. The enantiornithines did not survive the extinctions at the end of the Cretaceous. By the Miocene, passerine birds had become the dominant land birds. Names of genera for some fossil birds make it easier to find more information about these animals.

Source: From Alan Feduccia, "Explosive Evolution in Tertiary Birds and Mammals," *Science* 3 February 1995: Vol. 267 no. 5198 pp. 637-638. *Science* by American Association for the Advancement of Science Reproduced with permission of AMERICAN ASSOCIATION FOR THE ADVANCEMENT OF SCIENCE in the format Republish in a book via Copyright Clearance Center.

or attract mates. Most raise their young in nests, using body heat to incubate eggs. The nest may be a simple depression on a gravel beach, a cup woven from twigs and grasses, or a feather-lined hole in a tree.

Many bird species make semi-annual, long-distance migrations (see Chapter 32). Golden plovers (*Pluvialis dominica*) and the godwit (*Limosa lapponica*) migrate over 20 000 km a year going to and from their summer and winter ranges. Migrations are a response to seasonal changes in climate. Birds travel toward the tropics as winter approaches; in spring, they return to high latitudes to breed and to use seasonally abundant food sources.

Some people think that birds can fly because of air spaces within their bones. In reality, many of the bones of birds are laminated structures with hollows that reduce the density of their skeletons, but this is true even of flightless birds such as ostriches. Birds, bats, pterosaurs, and insects fly because they have wings and muscles to flap them, in addition to other morphological and physiological specializations. ⬡

### STUDY BREAK QUESTIONS

1. What three skeletal features are associated with bird flight? Which ones are missing in flightless birds?
2. What adaptations make flight possible in birds and pterosaurs?
3. What characteristics maintain the structure of feathers and make them important to flight in birds?

## 27.17 Mammalia: Monotremes, Marsupials, and Placentals

Mammals are part of the synapsid lineage (therapsids), the first of the amniotes to diversify. During the late Paleozoic, medium- to large-sized synapsids were the most abundant vertebrate predators in terrestrial habitats. Therapsids were one successful and persistent branch of synapsids. Therapsids were relatively mammal-like in their legs, skulls, jaws, and teeth, and they represented an early radiation of synapsids. By the end of the Triassic, the earliest mammals (most of them no bigger than a rat) had appeared. Several lineages of early mammals, such as multituberculates, persisted and even flourished through much of the Mesozoic. These mammals coexisted with dinosaurs and other diapsids, as well as with the enantiornithine birds.

Paleontologists hypothesize that most Mesozoic mammals were nocturnal, perhaps to avoid diurnal predators and/or overheating. There are two living mammalian lineages (**Figure 27.116**): the egg-laying Prototheria (or Monotremata) and the live-bearing Theria (marsupials and placentals).

Several features distinguish mammals from other vertebrates, but mammalian diversity makes it difficult to generalize absolutely about definitive characteristics. Living mammals are relatively easy to recognize. They are usually furry and have a diaphragm (a sheet of muscle separating the chest cavity from the viscera); most are **endothermic** (warm blooded) and bear live young. In mammals, most blood leaves the heart through the **left aortic arch** (the main blood vessel leaving the heart; see Chapter 41). Mammals have two occipital condyles where the skull attaches to the neck, as well as a secondary palate (the plate of bones forming the roof of the mouth). They are **heterodont** and **diphyodont (Figure 27.117)**. Heterodont means that different teeth are specialized for different jobs. Diphyodont means that there are two generations of teeth (milk or deciduous teeth, and adult teeth). But some mammals have no teeth and others lay eggs. The secondary palate allows mammals to breathe and chew, or breathe while sucking without releasing hold on the nipple, an essential part of nursing.

Endothermy means that mammals typically maintain an elevated and stable body temperature so that they can be active under different environmental conditions. They can do this because of their metabolic rates and insulation. Heterodont teeth make mammals more efficient at mechanically dealing with their food (chewing), reducing the lag between the time food is consumed and when the energy in it is available to the consumer. Heterodont teeth are correlated with improved jaw articulation, in mammals between the dentary (lower jaw) and squamosal (bone on the skull). The diaphragm means that mammals are reasonably efficient at breathing, and the circulatory system with a four-chambered heart makes them efficient at internal circulation of resources or collection of wastes. Milk is a rich food source, and by feeding it to their young, female mammals provide the best opportunity for growth and development. The **cortex** of the brain is central to information processing and learning. Mammals' brains are another key to their evolutionary success.

### 27.17a The Mammalian Radiation: Variations on a Theme

The egg-laying Prototheria (*proto* = first; *theri* = wild beast), also called "Monotremata," and the live-bearing Theria are the two groups of living mammals. Among the Theria, the Metatheria (*meta* = between), also called *marsupials*, and the Eutheria (*eu* = good), or placentals, differ in their reproductive adaptations.

**MONOTREMATA** The **monotremes** (*mono* = one; *trema* = perforation) are represented by three living species that occur only in the Australian region (**Figure 27.118**). Females lay leathery shelled eggs, and newly hatched young lap up milk secreted by modified sweat glands (mammary glands) on the mother's belly. The duck-billed platypus (*Ornithorhynchus anatinus*) lives in burrows along riverbanks and feeds on aquatic invertebrates. The two species of echidnas, or spiny anteaters (*Tachyglossus aculeatus* and *Zaglossus bruijni*), feed on ants or termites.

**MARSUPIALIA** Represented by 240 species, marsupials (*marsupion* = purse; Metatheria) are characterized by short **gestation** periods. The young are briefly (as few as 8–10 days in some

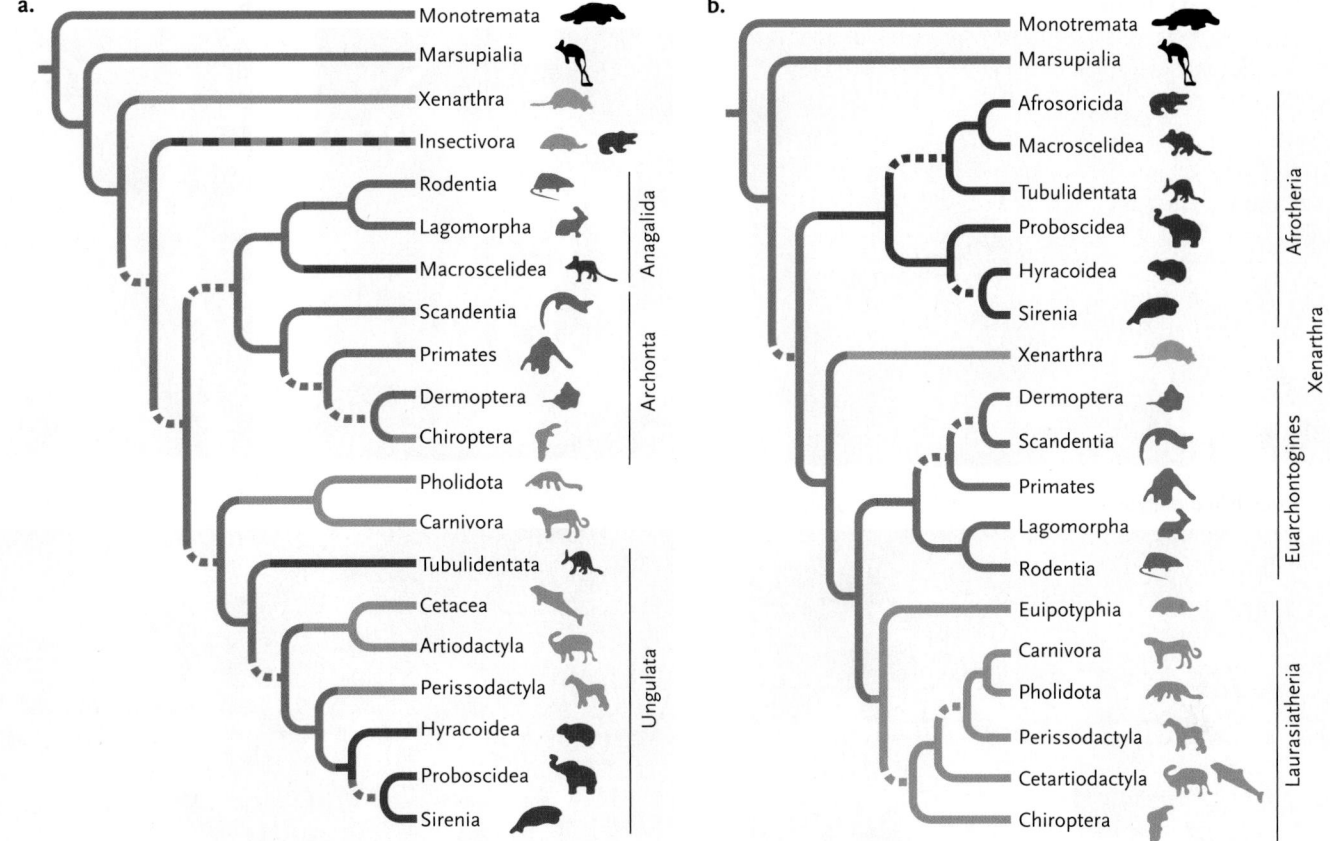

**FIGURE 27.116 Modern mammals.** Prevailing phylogenies of mammals derived from **(a)** morphological and **(b)** molecular data

Source: Mark S. Springer, Michael J. Stanhope, Ole Madsen and Wilfried W. de Jong, "Molecules consolidate the placental mammal tree," 19(8), 2004: 430-438, *Trends in Ecology & Evolution* by TRENDS JOURNALS. Reproduced with permission of TRENDS JOURNALS in the format Book via Copyright Clearance Center.

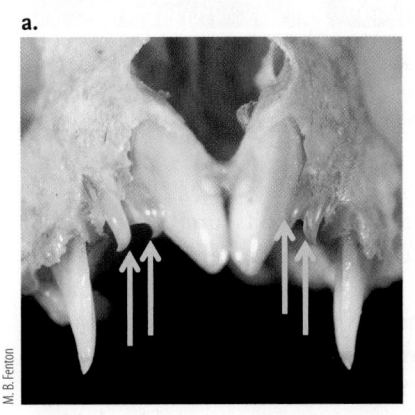

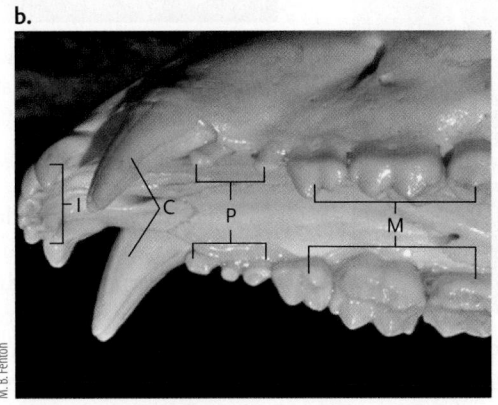

**FIGURE 27.117 Mammal teeth.** In most mammals, the teeth are diphyodont, meaning that milk (deciduous) teeth are replaced by permanent teeth. **(a)** The skull of a vampire bat (*Desmodus rotundus*) clearly shows four deciduous teeth (arrows), as well as permanent teeth. The teeth of mammals are also heterodont, meaning that different teeth are specialized to do different jobs. **(b)** In this bear (*Ursus americanus*), incisors (I), a canine (C), **premolars** (P), and molars (M) are obvious.

species and up to 30 days in others) nourished in the uterus via a placenta and are then born at an early stage of development. Newborns use their forelimbs to drag themselves from the vagina and across the mother's belly fur to her abdominal pouch, the marsupium, where they complete their development attached to a teat. Marsupials are prevalent among the native mammals of Australia and are also diverse in South America **(Figure 27.119)**. One species, the opossum (*Didelphis virginiana*), occurs as far north as Canada. South America once had a diverse marsupial fauna, which declined after the Isthmus of Panama bridged the seaway between North America and South America (see Chapter 18), allowing placental mammals to move southward.

**EUTHERIA** Placental mammals are represented by 4000 living species. They complete embryonic development in the mother's uterus, nourished through a **placenta**, until they reach an advanced stage of development (**viviparous**). Some species, such as humans, are helpless at birth (**altricial**), but others, such as horses, are born with fur and are quickly mobile (**precocial**). Biologists divide the eutherians into about 18 orders, of which only 8 have more than 50 living species **(Figure 27.120)**. Rodents (Rodentia) make up about 45% of eutherian species, and bats (Chiroptera) make up another 22%. We belong to the primates, along with 169 other species, representing about 5% of the current mammalian diversity.

**a. Short-nosed echidna**

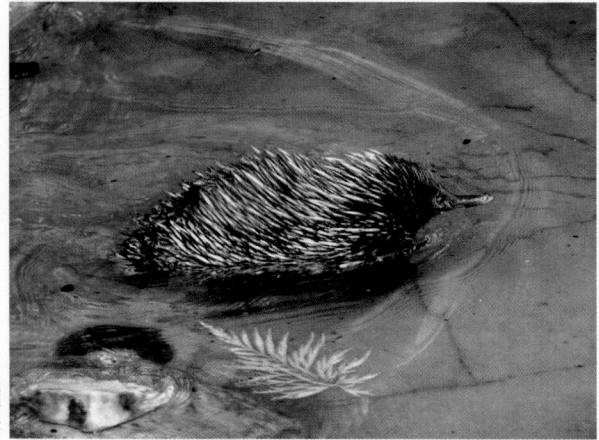

**b. Duck-billed platypus**

**FIGURE 27.119 Marsupials. (a)** A kangaroo (*Macropus giganteus*) carries her joey in her pouch; **(b)** a male koala (*Phascolarctos cinereus*) naps; and **(c)** an opossum from Guyana (*Didelphis* species) emerges from its den after dark to feed.

**FIGURE 27.118 Monotremes. (a)** The short-nosed echidna (*Tachyglossus aculeatus*) is terrestrial. **(b)** The duck-billed platypus (*Ornithorhynchus anatinus*) raises its young in a streamside burrow.

The diversity of eutherian mammals is reflected partly in modes of locomotion. Whales and dolphins (order Cetacea) and manatees and dugongs (order Sirenia) are descended from terrestrial ancestors, but live their entire lives in water. They can no longer function on land, unlike seals and walruses (order Carnivora), which feed under water but rest and breed on land. Bats (order Chiroptera) use wings for powered flight, and mammals from several lineages can glide.

Although early mammals appear to have been insectivorous, the diets of modern eutherians are diverse. Odd-toed ungulates (*ungula* = hoof) such as horses and rhinoceroses (order Perissodactyla), even-toed ungulates such as cows and camels (order Artiodactyla), and rabbits and hares (order Lagomorpha) are mainly vegetarian. Some of the vegetarians use fermentation to digest cellulose (see Chapter 39). **Carnivores** (order Carnivora) usually consume other animals, but some, such as the giant panda (*Ailuropoda melanoleuca*), are vegetarians. Most bats eat insects, but some feed on flowers, fruit, or nectar, and some, the vampires, consume blood. Many whales and dolphins prey on fishes and other animals, but some eat plankton. Some groups, including rodents and primates, feed opportunistically on both plant and animal matter. Ants and termites are the preferred food of a variety of mammals, both prototherian and therian.

## 27.17b Evolutionary Convergence and Mammalian Diversity

Eating mainly ants and termites is a common mammalian approach across the tropics and subtropics. This is true in the New World (South and Central America) and in Africa, Southeast Asia, and Australia **(Figure 27.121)**. Ant-eating mammals

FIGURE 27.120 **This figure illustrates some of the diversity of eutherian mammals.** Included are **(a)** a big brown bat (*Eptesicus fuscus*), **(b)** two dwarf mongooses (*Helogale parvula*), **(c)** a steenbok (*Raphicerus campestris*), and **(d)** a white rhino and her calf (*Ceratotherium simum*).

FIGURE 27.121 Included here are ventral (palatal) views of the skulls and dentitions of **(a)** a giant anteater (*Myrmecophaga tridactyla*), **(b)** an aardvark (*Orycteropus afer*), **(c)** a pangolin (*Manis* spp), and **(d)** a spiny anteater (*Tachyglossus aculeatus*). **(e)** Also shown is a front view of a lesser anteater (*Tamandua tetradactyla*), showing forelimbs specialized for digging.

typically have no teeth or small peglike teeth, combined with long, extensible tongues. These animals often are excellent diggers, a reality reflected by specialized forelimbs (Figure 27.121e). Among the ant and termite eaters, aardwolves are the most strikingly different **(Figure 27.122)**. Aardwolves are most closely related to hyenas, species that eat larger prey and are equipped with very large teeth. Ants and termites are large, predictable, energy-rich foods, so it is little wonder that mammalian lineages

such as monotremes, marsupials, and eutherians have specialized on them as food. Specializations for eating ants and termites appear in four eutherian orders.

Mammals with teeth typically have two generations, milk teeth and permanent teeth **(Figure 27.123)**. This occurs because, in young mammals, the jaw bones are too small to accommodate permanent teeth. Whereas reptiles, amphibians, fish, and sharks can replace teeth many times, mammals replace them

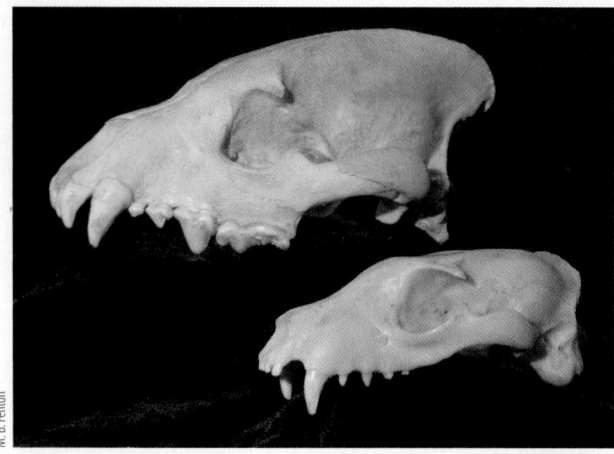

FIGURE 27.122  **Divergence.** The spotted hyena (*Crocuta crocuta;* top) and the aardwolf (*Proteles cristatus;* bottom) are in the same family (Hyaenidae). The spotted hyena is a carnivorous scavenger with massive teeth capable of cutting tendons and crushing bones. The aardwolf eats mainly ants and termites and has reduced teeth (and a differently shaped skull). The *Crocuta* skull is about 30 cm long. Both belong to the order Carnivora.

only once. Teeth wear with age. When the teeth are worn out, the animal can no longer feed itself properly and dies. Elephants deal with this problem by having only four active molars in the jaw at any one time. The new molar grows in from the back **(Figure 27.124)**, replacing the worn one. In rodents and some other mammals (and also in hadrosaur dinosaurs), molar (and for rodents and lagomorphs, incisor) teeth grow continuously. Here the teeth are curved so that pressure during biting is not directed at the points of growth (see also Chapter 39).

Diet also affects tooth wear **(Figure 27.125)**. Off the Pacific coast of Canada, different groups of killer whales have different diets, which are reflected by tooth wear. Killer whales from the open ocean eat mainly sharks whose abrasive skin causes wear on teeth (Figure 27.125a). The patterns of wear are different on resident killer whales that eat mainly fish (salmon), or transient killer whales that eat mainly marine mammals (Figure 27.125b, c).

a.          b.

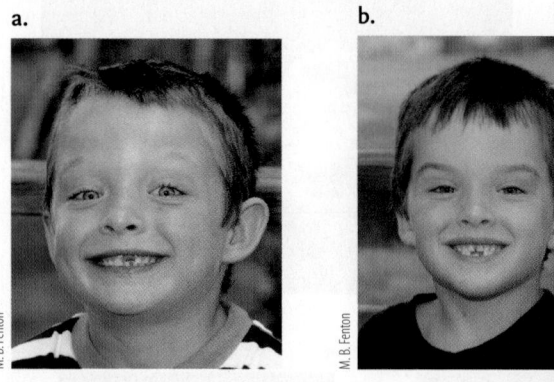

FIGURE 27.123  **In mammals, such as Callum** (a) **and Iain** (b) **Downie, gap-toothed grins show replacement of deciduous (or milk) teeth by permanent teeth.** These pictures, taken on 16 July 2011, show dizygotic twins and illustrate that the timing of tooth replacement differs between them.

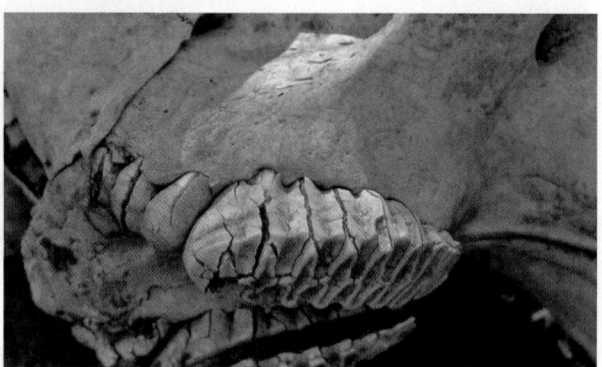

FIGURE 27.124  **Tooth wear and replacement.** Elephants (*Loxodonta africana*) have four functional molars in the mouth at any one time (one in each jaw quadrant). New molars push into the tooth row from the back.

Tory Kallman/Shutterstock.com

**FIGURE 27.125 Tooth wear on killer whales varies widely, depending on diet.** For more information, see Ford et al., (2011) "Shark predation and tooth wear in a population of northeastern Pacific killer whales." *Aquatic Biology*. Vol. 11: 213–224 (dos: 10.3354/ab00307).

## STUDY BREAK QUESTIONS

1. What features are found in most mammals and distinguish them from other vertebrates?
2. How is heterodont different from diphyodont?
3. Distinguish among monotremes, marsupials, and placentals.

# Summary Illustration

Animals are heterotrophic, multicellular organisms that usually produce gametes and are grouped in about 40 phyla. Groupings by phylum reflect key characters and shared features. Arrangement by phylum typically has reflected body plans and symmetry as well as patterns of development, including number of germ layers. The types of body cavities also influence classification, as does genetic and molecular relatedness. Variability in life style and life history reflect the diversity of animals.

## Key Innovations of Animals

| Protostomes | Deuterostomes |
|---|---|

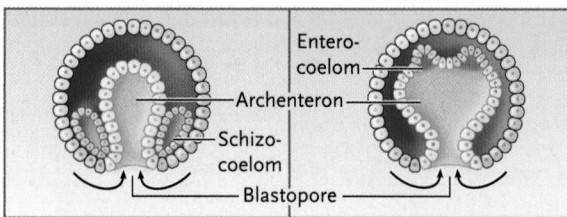

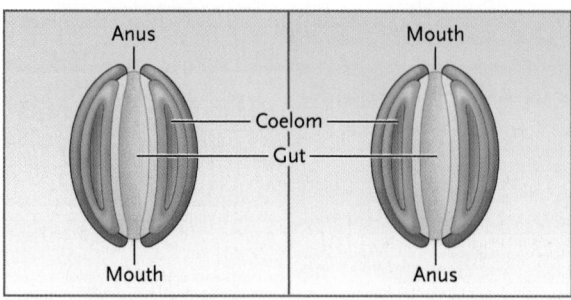

### Protostomes vs. deuterostomes

What makes an animal a protostome or a deuterostome depends on how cleavage proceeds and how the archenteron, coelom, and the gut form in early development.

### Symmetry

Animals can be asymmetric, radially symmetric, or bilaterally symmetric.

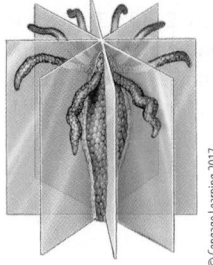

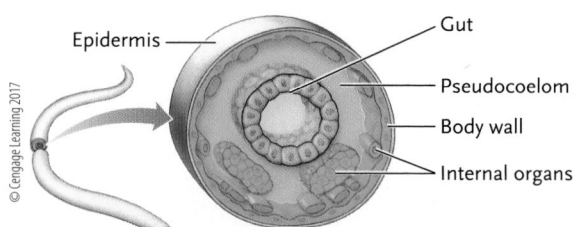

### Body plans

Animals can have two or three germ layers. If an animal has three layers, it can be a pseudocoelomate, such as this worm, or a coelomate, such as a human. If only two germ layers are present, such as in flatworms, then these organisms are acoelomates.

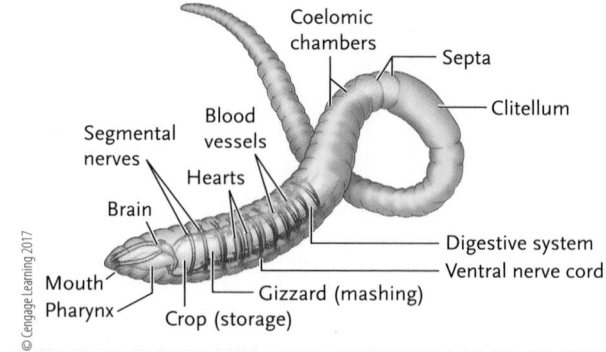

### Segmentation

Some animals are segmented, and this separates some groups from others that are not. Segmentation divides the body into a series of repeating units, such as the worm shown here. Other annelids, the arthropods, and chordates (think vertebral column) are also segmented.

# Relatedness

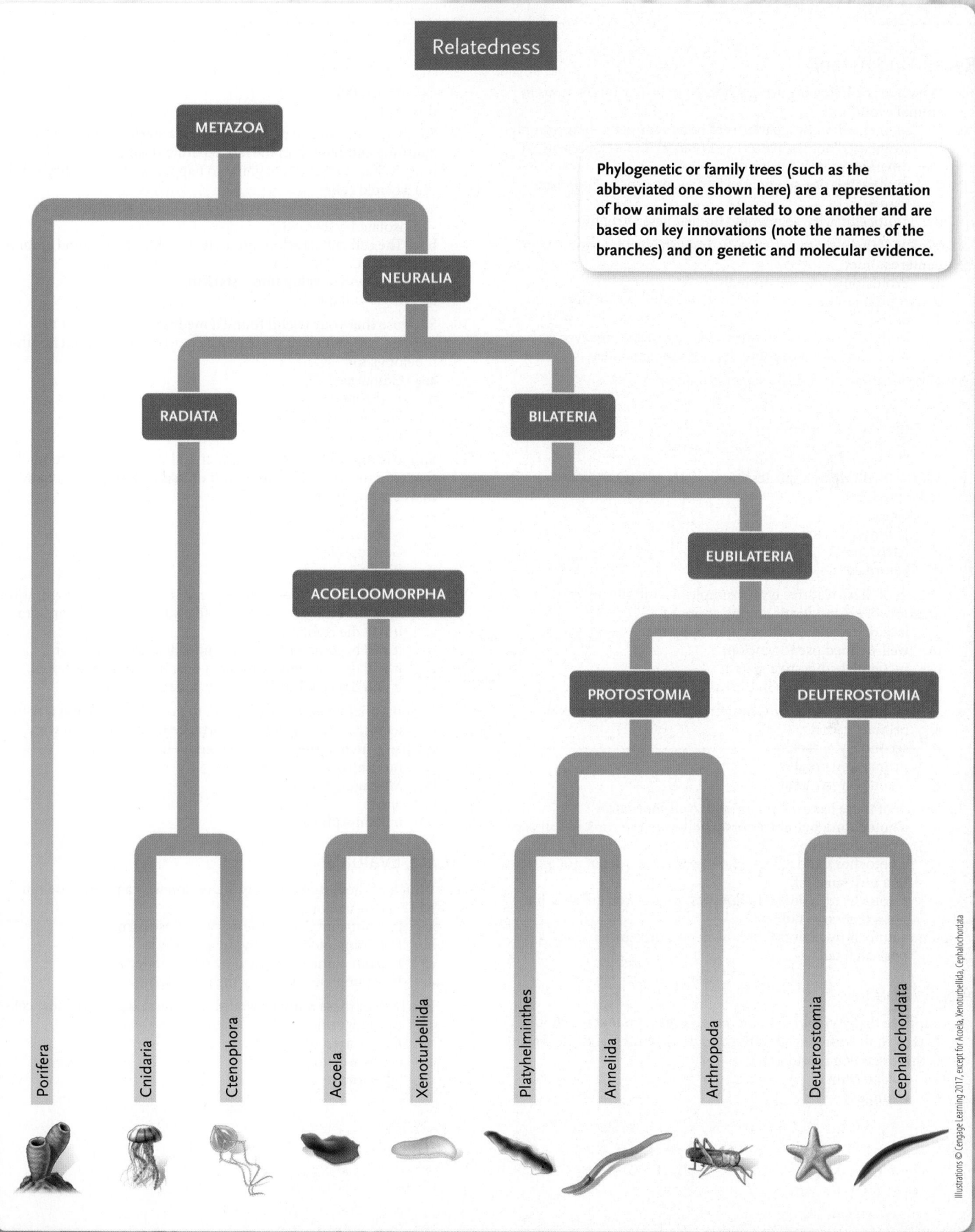

Phylogenetic or family trees (such as the abbreviated one shown here) are a representation of how animals are related to one another and are based on key innovations (note the names of the branches) and on genetic and molecular evidence.

Illustrations © Cengage Learning 2017, except for Acoela, Xenoturbellida, Cephalochordata

# SELF-TEST QUESTIONS

## Recall/Understand

1. Which of the following are considered to be key innovations in animal evolution?
   a. segmented bodies, patterns of body symmetry, heterotrophy
   b. segmented bodies, patterns of body symmetry, presence of different tissues
   c. multicellularity, segmented bodies, presence of different tissues
   d. multicellularity, segmented bodies, heterotrophy

2. Which of these characteristics distinguishes a protostome from a deuterostome?
   a. Protostomes are not animals.
   b. A protostome coelom forms from space within the outpocketing.
   c. Protostomes undergo spiral cleavage of the embryo.
   d. A protostome blastopore develops into an anus.

3. How many basal phyla do scientists identify?
   a. 1
   b. 2
   c. 3
   d. 4

4. Which phylum has a species count vastly greater than any other phylum?
   a. Cnidaria
   b. Echinodermata
   c. Arthropoda
   d. Chordata

5. Which of these features is an example of a unique internal anatomy of echinoderms among animals?
   a. lack of excretory and respiratory systems
   b. well-defined pseudocoelom
   c. incomplete digestive system
   d. lack of sensory cells in the skin

6. Which one of these body symmetries do echinoderms exhibit?
   a. primary radial
   b. secondary radial
   c. primary bilateral
   d. secondary bilateral

7. Which of these features are unique to all chordates?
   a. a notochord, but not a dorsal hollow nerve cord, gill slits, or a post-anal tail
   b. a notochord and a dorsal hollow nerve cord, but not gill slits or a post-anal tail
   c. a notochord, a dorsal hollow nerve cord, and gill slits, but not a post-anal tail
   d. a notochord, a dorsal hollow nerve cord, gill slits, and a post-anal tail

## Apply/Analyze

8. Suppose that you found an unknown organism that is a motile heterotroph without cell walls in its body. Which of the following is this organism most likely?
   a. a bacterium
   b. a fungus
   c. an animal
   d. a plant

9. Suppose that you isolate one cell from a starfish embryo, and you continue culturing it in the lab, separate from the original embryo. What is most likely going to happen with the embryo and the isolated cell?
   a. The original embryo will develop into a starfish, but the isolated cell will die.
   b. The cell will develop into a starfish, but the original embryo will die.
   c. Each will develop into a starfish.
   d. Both will die.

10. Suppose that your friend found a medusa and you want to impress her. Which of these phyla can you correctly tell her that it belongs to?
    a. Cnidaria
    b. Arthropoda
    c. Echinodermata
    d. Porifera

11. Suppose that you go out for dinner and you order a seafood dish that contains clams, scallops, and mussels. Which class of animals are you about to eat?
    a. Cephalopoda
    b. Scaphopoda
    c. Gastropoda
    d. Bivalvia

12. Suppose that you expose a tardigrade to an extreme dehydration. Which of the following will most likely happen to the tardigrade?
    a. It will die right away.
    b. It will become more active and will search for water.
    c. It will dry out and turn into a dust in about a few hours.
    d. It will dry out, but will revive if placed in water.

13. Suppose that your friend asks you to provide one characteristic of insects that has a special importance for coevolution with plants. Which of the following could it be?
    a. mouthparts
    b. Malpighian tubules
    c. wings
    d. metamorphosis

## Create/Evaluate

14. Which of these statements is the reason why a pseudocoelom is NOT a true coelom?
    a. It is not completely lined by the mesoderm.
    b. It is completely lined by the endoderm.
    c. It is not completely lined by the endoderm.
    d. It is completely lined by the mesoderm.

15. In which of these animals would you most likely find flame cells?
    a. round worms
    b. flatworms
    c. arrow worms
    d. tapeworms

16. In which of these animals would you most likely find a toothed radula?
    a. lobsters
    b. slugs
    c. worms
    d. corals

17. Animals may have arisen from a colonial, flagellated protist in which cells became specialized for specific functions. Explain why we think this might be true.

18. Provide an analogy for radial symmetry. Justify your selection.

19. What are *Hox* genes? Use examples to describe their importance.

20. Four key features of living amniotes allow life on dry land and liberate them from reliance on standing water. Describe these four features.

# Chapter Roadmap

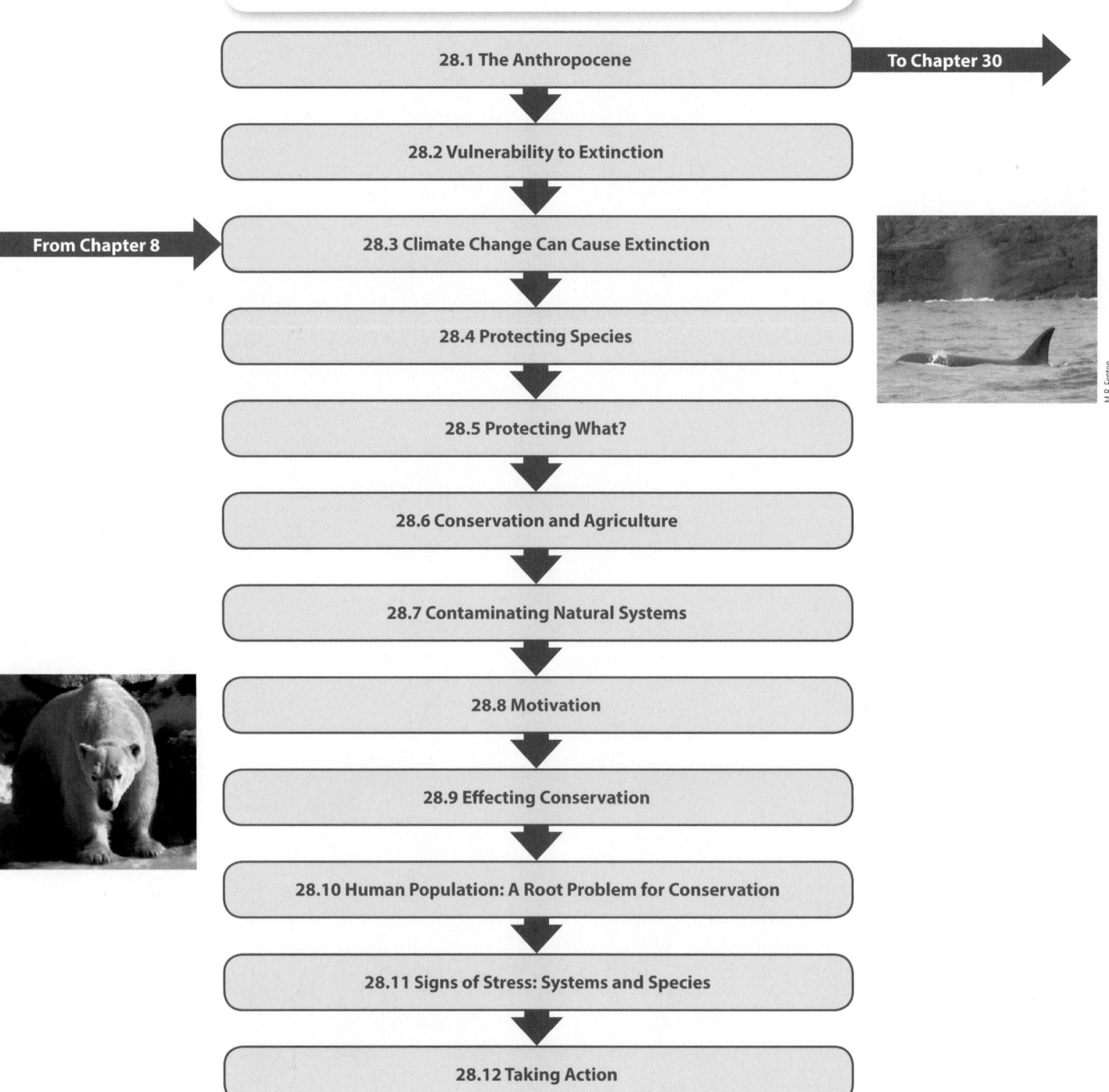

## Conservation of Biodiversity

At almost every turn, there are examples of human activities driving other species to extinction. A range of examples associated with extinction and the threat of extinction are introduced in this chapter. Steps that can be taken to protect biodiversity, including some successes and some failures, are also considered.

**28.1 The Anthropocene** → To Chapter 30

**28.2 Vulnerability to Extinction**

From Chapter 8 → **28.3 Climate Change Can Cause Extinction**

**28.4 Protecting Species**

**28.5 Protecting What?**

**28.6 Conservation and Agriculture**

**28.7 Contaminating Natural Systems**

**28.8 Motivation**

**28.9 Effecting Conservation**

**28.10 Human Population: A Root Problem for Conservation**

**28.11 Signs of Stress: Systems and Species**

**28.12 Taking Action**

M.B. Fenton

M.B. Fenton

**Two mounted specimens of passenger pigeons.** These specimens are in the Zoological Collections of the Department of Biology at The University of Western Ontario. Unfortunately, specimens like these are all that remains of a once abundant species. The importance of such collections is obvious to those who try to understand evolution and extinction.

# Conservation of Biodiversity

# 28

**Why it matters . . .** Martha, the last passenger pigeon (*Ectopistes migratorius*), died in the Cincinnati Zoo on 1 September 1914. This marked the death of a species, which is also known as an *extinction*. In the early 1800s, there may have been as many as 3.5 billion passenger pigeons in the wild in North America. These abundant and widespread birds seemed unlikely candidates for extinction. Human overharvesting of these tasty animals has been invoked to explain their disappearance. Huge flocks and breeding colonies made these birds easy targets for hunters. This pressure, combined with land clearing for agriculture, appeared to account for the birds' rapid extinction. Female passenger pigeons laid one egg a year (= clutch size of 1), making the species even more vulnerable to rapid declines in population.

In 2014, analysis of ancient DNA obtained from specimens of passenger pigeons allowed biologists and computer scientists to examine the details of populations of these birds. The results provide a different view of this extinction event. Various analyses using ecological niche models supported the view that populations of passenger pigeons showed dramatic oscillations in size. Genetic analyses indicated that the population of passenger pigeons showed no evidence of structures into sub-populations or subspecies. Further genetic analysis indicated a relatively small number of individuals contributing offspring to the population. Known as the *effective population size*, for passenger pigeons this was about $3.3 \times 10^5$. These analyses indicated a long-term, effective population size varying from 0.5 to $1.7 \times 10^5$ over the last million years, with a minimum of $2.1 \times 10^4$ at the end of the last glacial maximum. These estimates of effective population size are consistently about 1/10 000 of the census population presumed in the 1800s. By comparison, the effective population size for humans is $1.7 \times 10^4$, while the census population exceeds $7 \times 10^9$.

The extinction of the passenger pigeon should alert us to the reality that being abundant and widespread does not necessarily make a species secure in a conservation sense. Indeed, declines in populations can identify vulnerable species and alert us to the importance of taking steps to protect them. In the absence of information about population declines, population sizes can be misleading. For example, in 2005 in Ontario, Canada, the population estimate of an open field songbird, the bobolink (*Dolichonyx oryzivorus*; **Figure 28.1**), was 400 000 breeding pairs. By 2010 this had declined to 285 000 breeding pairs. Our experience with the passenger pigeon should alert us to the importance of using a steep decline in population to identify species that appear to be numerous yet are vulnerable to declining to extinction. And yet, listing the bobolink as a threatened species was not uniformly regarded as a prudent, timely step.

The onus is on us as citizens of the planet to conserve biodiversity, whether the focus is species or habitats. One of the main problems we must overcome is the attitude of many humans. Today a common reflection of this attitude is that being able to do something (afford to, have the means to) is justification enough for doing it—whether the project involves making space for a shopping mall by draining a wetland or cutting down the trees in a woodlot.

If we as a species can recognize the importance of biodiversity and accept that the world is not ours to do with as we please, what would we do next? What is the best route to protecting and conserving biodiversity? Should we focus on species? On genetic diversity? On ecosystems? How should we blend these approaches to achieve the best support for the endeavour? How can we engage people in this important activity and perhaps move them away from a human-centric view of the world?

As we shall see, at almost every turn there are examples of human activities driving other species to extinction. The motivations for human actions range from little more than greed to people's daily efforts to survive. The purpose of this chapter is to introduce you to a range of situations and examples associated with the reduction of biodiversity by extinction and the threat of extinction. We also consider steps that can be taken to protect biodiversity, including some successes and some failures.

## 28.1 The Anthropocene

In the past 500 years there has been a large increase in the size of the human population (see Figure 29.21). This increase coincides with greater habitat destruction and disruption as well as other by-products of human civilization. The trend continues, and further increases in the human population coincide with further destruction and modification of habitats. The period of the past 500 years is known as the *Anthropocene*. During this time, at least 322 species of terrestrial vertebrates have gone extinct, and the populations of an additional 25% of living species have declined considerably. The same general patterns emerge from data about invertebrate animals as those from plants. To many biologists, the Anthropocene is the "sixth major extinction," caused directly and indirectly by one species, *Homo sapiens*. But extinctions are an ongoing part of Earth's history, reflected in background rates of extinction. David Raup of the University of Chicago has estimated background rates at about 10% of species every one million years, 50% every 100 million years.

A mass extinction occurs when the rate of extinction rises well above the background rate. Before the Anthropocene, the fossil record indicates that there were at least five mass extinctions in Earth's history:

- First at the end of the Ordovician and beginning of the Devonian
- Second at the end of the Devonian
- Third at the end of the Permian
- Fourth at the end of the Triassic
- Fifth at the end of the Cretaceous.

The Permian extinction was the most severe, and more than 85% of the species alive then disappeared forever. This extinction was the end of the trilobites, many amphibians, and the trees of the coal swamp forests. At the end of the Cretaceous, the last mass extinction, half the species on Earth disappeared, including most dinosaurs.

Mass extinctions have a huge impact on the species that survive them. The losses of biodiversity (the numbers of species) affect the productivity and stability of ecosystems. At this stage in the Anthropocene, at least 50% of ice-free ecosystems have been converted to cropland and pasture. The remaining ecosystems are in varying stages of disturbance, which means changes in nutrient eutrophication, fire suppression, frequency of fire, decimation of predators, climate warming, and drought. Changes in plant diversity influence the levels of nitrogen, carbon dioxide, fire, levels of herbivory, and the availability of water.

An analysis of the situation documented by 12 multiyear studies revealed that changes in the diversity of plants (primary producers) profoundly affect the global environment. Work on

**FIGURE 28.1 Bobolink**

FotoRequest/Shutterstock.com

islands in the West Indies revealed that human factors more than geographic area and isolation determine species compositions of island communities of anole lizards. Today, foremost among the human-related factors are those relating to economic isolation and the introduction of exotic species.

Many researchers believe that an asteroid impact caused the Cretaceous mass extinction. The resulting dust cloud could have blocked the sunlight necessary for photosynthesis. This would have started a chain reaction of extinctions that began with microscopic marine organisms. Geologic evidence supports this hypothesis. Rocks dating to the end of the Cretaceous period (65 mya) contain a highly concentrated layer of iridium, a metal that is rare on Earth but common in asteroids. The impact from an iridium-laden asteroid only 10 km in diameter could have caused an explosion equivalent to a billion tonnes of TNT, scattering iridium dust around the world. Geologists have identified the likely site of the impact: the 180 km diameter submarine Chicxulub crater off Mexico's Yucatán peninsula.

Although scientists agree that an asteroid struck Earth then, many question its precise relationship to the mass extinction. Dinosaurs had begun their decline at least 8 million years earlier, and many persisted for at least 40 000 years after the impact. Moreover, other groups of organisms did not suddenly disappear, as one would expect after a global calamity. The Cretaceous extinction took place over tens of thousands of years. Furthermore, some organisms survived periods of extinction, such as ginkgo trees (*Ginkgo biloba*), horseshoe crabs (*Limulus polyphemus*), and coelacanths (*Latimeria chalumnae*).

Even today we cannot blame the extinctions of most species on the activities of humans. But our increasing technological capability and prowess coincide with a burgeoning population of people. This situation is exacerbated by the philosophical view that humans are disconnected from nature. Thus, we are becoming better and better at destroying the biota of the planet. Taking action requires identifying root causes and then trying to make changes that will alleviate the problems.

**STUDY BREAK QUESTIONS**

1. What is extinction?
2. What is the Anthropocene?
3. When did three major extinctions occur?
4. Why is iridium important in identifying the cause for the extinction of dinosaurs?

## 28.2  Vulnerability to Extinction

The passenger pigeon, a widespread and abundant species, was vulnerable because of a combination of human impact, small clutch size, and dramatic oscillations in sizes of populations. Here are five examples of pending, imminent, or recent extinctions. They illustrate the diversity of threats and the vulnerabilities of species.

### 28.2a  Pacific Water Shrew

We expect that species occurring in small populations with a limited geographic distribution (range) are more vulnerable to extinction than species such as the passenger pigeon. Limited geographic distribution and specific habitat requirements typify the Pacific water shrew (*Sorex bendirii*; **Figure 28.2**), but other factors pose immediate threats to the species in Canada.

Pacific water shrews occur in a small area along the Pacific coast of North America (**Figure 28.3a**); there are few actual records of specimens of the animal in Canada (Figure 28.3b), suggesting a small population. To make matters worse, the prime habitat for Pacific water shrews in Canada is directly threatened by the urban sprawl of the city of Vancouver (Figure 28.3c). How long will they last?

### 28.2b  Black Rhino

Black rhinos (*Diceros bicornis*) were widespread in Africa. Like the four other species of living rhinos, black rhinos teeter on the brink of extinction. In 1960 there may have been 60 000 black rhinos living in the wild (**Figure 28.4a**). This large (1.5 m at the shoulder, 1400 kg) browsing mammal was widespread in sub-Saharan Africa (Figure 28.4b). Adult males and females have two distinctive "horns" (**Figure 28.5a**; see also Figure 28.4a), actually formed from hair. Rhinos use the horns to protect themselves and their young from predators and other rhinos. By 1981, the populations in the wild had been reduced to between 10 000 and 15 000, and reduced further to about 3500 by 1987. In less than 30 years, the species was almost exterminated in the wild. Although black rhinos had been hunted as trophies, this source of mortality did not drive them to the brink of extinction.

People use rhino horn (Figure 28.5a) in different ways and it commands a high price in a competitive market. In China, bowls made from rhino horn (Figure 28.5b) were believed to have had magical properties, removing or neutralizing poisons. Therefore, travelling nobles were served wine in their own rhino horn bowls to minimize the chances of their being poisoned. In India and other areas, from India to the Koreas,

**FIGURE 28.2  Pacific water shrew, a 10 g mammal with a small geographic range**

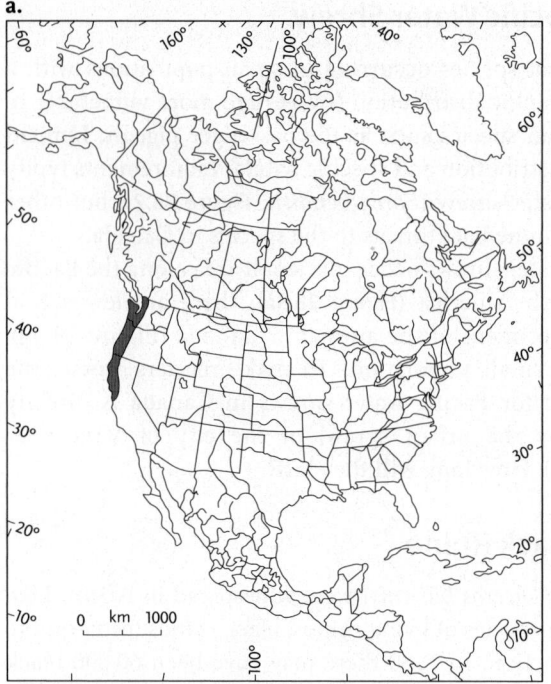

a.

Baseline Thematic Mapping Present Land Use Mapping
at 1:220 000

*COSEWIC Assessment and Update Status Report on the Pacific Water Shrew Sorex bendirii in Canada.* 2006. Figure 2, p. 6.
© Her Majesty The Queen in Right of Canada, Environment Canada, 2014. Reproduced with the permission of the Minister
of Public Works and Government Services Canada.

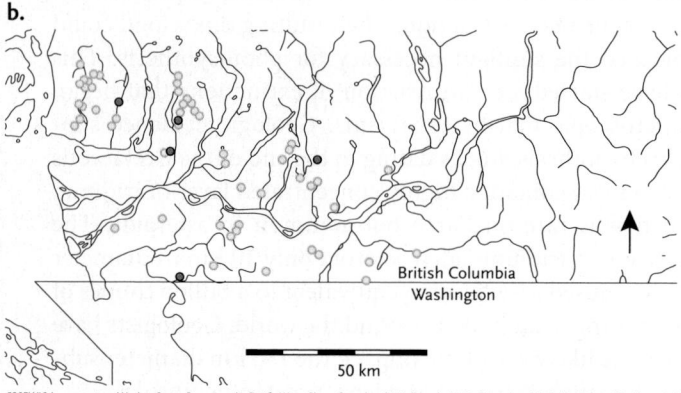

b.

*COSEWIC Assessment and Update Status Report on the Pacific Water Shrew Sorex bendirii in Canada.* 2006. Figure 5, p. 15. © Her Majesty The Queen in Right of
Canada, Environment Canada, 2014. Reproduced with the permission of the Minister of Public Works and Government Services Canada.

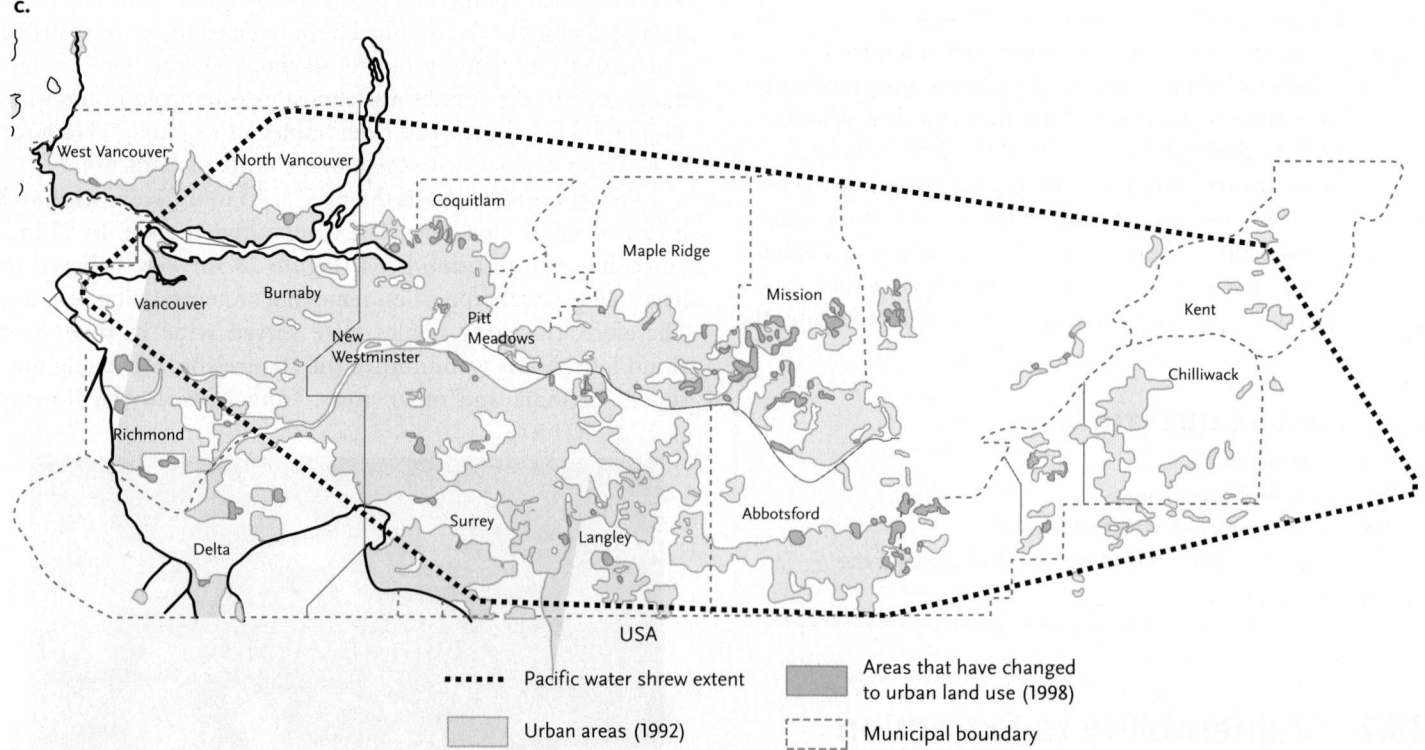

c.

*COSEWIC Assessment and Update Status Report on the Pacific Water Shrew Sorex bendirii in Canada.* 2006. Figure 6, p. 18. Map prepared by Susan Jesson, BC Conservation Foundation 13-Oct. -04, while under contract with Environment Canada. © Her Majesty The Queen in Right of Canada, Environment Canada, 2014.
Reproduced with the permission of the Minister of Public Works and Government Services Canada.

**FIGURE 28.3 (a)** The distribution of *Sorex bendirii,* the Pacific water shrew. **(b)** Lower Fraser Valley locations where it was found (solid circles) or not found (open circles). **(c)** For comparison, the same area is shown with changes in the availability of urban lands in 1992 and 1998. Data on the map are from 2004.

**FIGURE 28.4** **(a)** Black rhinos (*Diceros bicornis*) were widespread and common in Africa in 1960 (orange area on the map in (b)). **(b)** Today their range (dark spots in orange areas) is much reduced, reflecting diminished populations. Note the oxpecker (*Buphagus africanus*; see Chapter 30) sitting on the rhino.

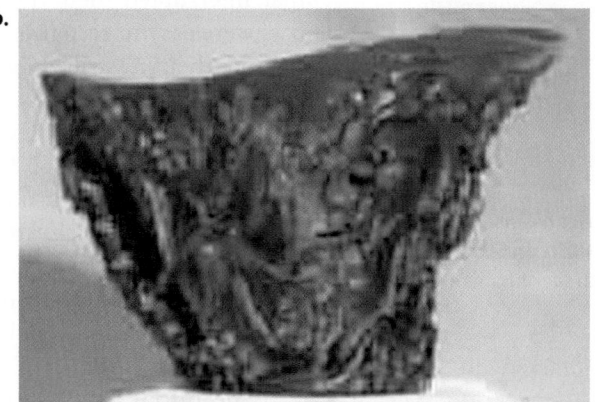

**FIGURE 28.5** **(a)** A horn from a black rhino in Zimbabwe is shown with **(b)** a rhino horn bowl from China and **(c)** a jambiya with a rhino horn handle.

powdered rhino horn is used as a fever suppressant. Contrary to popular belief, rhino horn does not appear to have been used as an aphrodisiac, an early version of Viagra.

To some people of the Arabian Peninsula, a ceremonial dagger, a jambiya, is a symbol of status. Jambiyas with rhino horn handles (Figure 28.5c) are particularly highly prized. In 1973, when the price of oil jumped from US$4 to US$12 a barrel, the ensuing "energy crisis" meant a larger market for jambiyas because more people could afford them. Increased cash flow and easy access to military weapons such as Kalashnikov assault rifles (**Figure 28.6**) provided an incentive and a means to kill rhinos. The epidemic of poaching started in northern Kenya and spread southward throughout the continent. Poaching for their horns catastrophically reduced populations of black rhinos. Although black rhinos had long survived in the presence of predators, including *Homo sapiens*, they could not survive the poachers. In 1984, going for a walk at night around the headquarters of Mana Pools National Park in Zimbabwe almost always meant meeting a black rhino. By 1987, the rhinos were very scarce, and by 1990 they were gone from there.

**FIGURE 28.6** **A Kalashnikov assault rifle (an AK), a weapon widely used in the poaching of animals in many parts of the world**

## 28.2c American Ginseng

The case of the black rhino demonstrated how targeted harvesting can drive a species to the brink of extinction even when it is protected and lives mainly in national parks or game reserves. American ginseng (**Figure 28.7**) is another target species, now Endangered in Canada because of harvesting. The species used to grow wild from southwestern Quebec and southern Ontario south to Louisiana and Georgia. This 20- to 70 cm-tall perennial

CHAPTER 28 CONSERVATION OF BIODIVERSITY |

**FIGURE 28.7** A herbarium specimen of American ginseng (*Panax quinquefolius*) collected in southwestern Ontario on 5 July 1890. Herbarium collections too often are the only way to see specimens of plants that used to be common and abundant.

is long lived in rich, moist, mature, sugar maple–dominated woods. In Canada, the species has been protected since 1973, but populations continued to decline. In 2000, there were 22 viable populations in Ontario and Quebec, but none was secure. Black rhinos and ginseng had been common about 50 years ago, but by 2008, both demonstrated the risks of being rare and valuable. They are also examples of the need for immediate on-the-ground enforcement of regulations and laws protecting species and habitats.

## 28.2d   Mauritian Calvaria Tree

If you visit the island of Mauritius, you might notice that the few remaining Mauritian Calvaria trees (*Sideroxylon majus*) are slowly dying of old age. Their passing will mark the extinction of this species. This will occur even though the trees have continued to bloom and produce seeds. The key to the pending extinction of the Mauritian Calvaria tree is the earlier extinction of dodos. To germinate, seeds of these trees had to pass through the dodo's digestive tract. The dodo (**Figure 28.8**) was a medium-sized flightless bird that lived on the island of Mauritius. When European sailors first visited the island, they used dodos as fresh meat.

Then, as the island was settled, the birds were exposed to introduced predators (cats, dogs, rats) and an expanding human population. Dodos had vanished by 1690.

## 28.2e   Little Brown Myotis (*Myotis lucifugus*)

Like many other species of bats living in the temperate zones of the world, little brown myotis (*Myotis lucifugus*) pass the winter hibernating in underground sites, typically caves and abandoned mines. This behaviour and strategy for overwintering was the norm for these bats, but the arrival of a fungus from Europe turned what had been safe sites into deadly places. In March 2006, at sites near Albany, New York, biologists counting bats hibernating in caves and abandoned mines were shocked to find thousands of dead bats where they had expected thousands of live ones. The bats had died from white-nose syndrome (WNS), caused by a cold-loving fungus (*Pseudogymnoascus destructans*; formerly *Geomyces destructans*) that interrupted their rhythm of hibernation. Some infected bats were easy to recognize by the white fungus like structures around their nostrils (**Figure 28.9**). To survive hibernation, bats minimize the number of times they arouse from torpor because of the metabolic cost of waking up (raising the body temperature from 2°C–5°C to over 35°C). At most Canadian hibernation sites, bats normally go about 90 days between arousals because each arousal costs them energy that they would use in 60 days of hibernation. WNS causes them to arouse much more often and exhaust their stores of body fat in January or February, well before spring and the re-appearance of insect prey.

The initial focal area for WNS in North America was specific sites around Albany. By March 2010, WNS had spread to underground hibernation sites in Ontario and Quebec, as well as many other sites in the United States. In March 2016, WNS had been reported from hibernation sites in Washington State. In the intervening years, WNS continued to spread, in Canada arriving at sites at the west end of Lake Superior by March 2015. In March 2016, WNS had not yet been reported from sites in Newfoundland and Labrador.

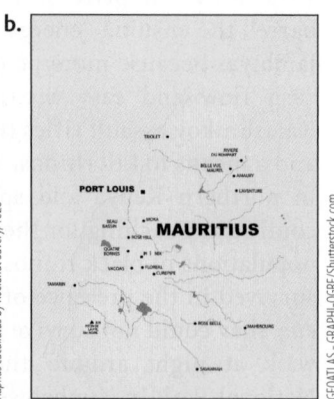

**FIGURE 28.8**  (a) **A reconstruction of a *Raphus cucullatus*, the dodo, an extinct, flightless bird from** (b) **Mauritius**

FIGURE 28.9 **Five little brown myotis, one (middle) showing characteristic signs of infection by the fungus *Pseudogymnoascus destructans* that causes white-nose syndrome (WNS) in bats that hibernate underground in the United States and Canada**

Photo by Lesley Hale

The spread of WNS surely reflects the movements and behaviour of the bats. American bat biologists estimate that, in 2005, there were over 6 million little brown myotis in the American northeast. These bats may well be extirpated (wiped out) from there by 2020.

At known hibernation sites, populations of little brown myotis declined by over 95%. Professor Craig Willis from the University of Winnipeg and his colleagues demonstrated that the strain of the fungus causing WNS in North American bats originated in Europe. It was presumably inadvertently transferred to the sites near Albany by cave explorers or bat biologists. The European strain did not cause WNS in bats there, just as the North American strain did not cause WNS in bat species from North America.

Can the populations of little brown myotis recover? Probably not, because, like most bats, little brown myotis live in the slow life-history lane (see Chapter 29). They reproduce slowly (a single young per year) and, like most species of bats of the temperate regions, up to 60% of young do not survive their first year. The combination of low reproductive output and low survival of first year translates into low potential for increase of their populations.

There are 19 species of bats in Canada but not all are exposed to WNS because only some hibernate underground. So, perhaps WNS does not mean the end of our bats, but likely the loss of more than half the species. WNS is a stark example of how a widespread and abundant species can become endangered.

Other species of fungi put other wildlife at risk. Perhaps best known is *Batrachochytrium dendrobatidis*, a pathogenic fungus apparently responsible for a global decline in populations of amphibians. Still other pathogenic fungi affect snakes, corals, and bees.

## STUDY BREAK QUESTIONS

1. What do ginseng and black rhinos have in common?
2. What harm can pathogenic fungi do?
3. What is causing the extinction of the Mauritian Calvaria tree?
4. What role do AKs play in poaching?

# 28.3 Climate Change Can Cause Extinction

Failure to reproduce can drive a species to extinction. Anything that interferes with reproduction can threaten a species' survival (e.g., Mauritian Calvaria tree). Genetic recombination is a fundamental benefit of sexual reproduction, enabling increases in genetic diversity and elimination of deleterious mutants. Effective sexual reproduction means having male and female systems, sometimes in one individual (hermaphrodites), more often in different individuals. Males and females differ in many fundamental ways: genetically, hormonally, physiologically, and anatomically.

In humans and many other animals, gender is determined by genotype, with males having an X and a Y chromosome and females having two X chromosomes. The reverse is true in many other animals, for example in birds. In many reptiles, gender is determined environmentally. Eggs incubated at some temperatures develop into males; when incubated at other temperatures, they produce females.

In 2008, D. A. Warner and R. Shine reported the results of experiments done with jacky dragons (*Amphibolurus muricatus*; **Figure 28.10**), Australian lizards in which gender is determined by temperature. Eggs incubated at 23°C–26°C or 30°C–33°C produce females; those incubated at 27°C–29°C produce males. Warner and Shine tested the hypothesis that temperature-dependent sex determination ensured production of females when they had an advantage and males when the advantage was to them. Using a combination of temperature and hormonal manipulations, Warner and Shine could produce males or females at any temperature. They analyzed paternity to assess the reproductive output of these males, and observed eggs laid and hatched to document these females' reproductive output.

In female jacky dragons, larger body sizes occur at higher temperatures, and larger females have higher fecundity than smaller ones. Higher temperatures also correlate with larger body size in males. However, males hatched from eggs incubated

FIGURE 28.10 **A jacky (or tree) dragon**

Belle Ciezak/Shutterstock.com

between 27°C and 29°C sired more offspring than those hatched from eggs incubated at lower or higher temperatures.

Change in climate, such as global warming, could put species with temperature-dependent sex determination at risk by effectively eliminating males or females from the population. Eggs incubated at the wrong temperatures would fail to hatch. The importance of variation in temperature during development in ectothermic organisms could explain the prevalence of genotypic-dependent sex determination in euthermic (homeothermic) viviparous animals. Viviparous or ovoviviparous ectotherms (fish, amphibians, reptiles, other animals) could also rely on temperature-dependent gender determination, provided that their developing young experience an appropriate range of temperatures.

Recent work from Mexico reveals that, since 1975, 12% of local populations of lizards have disappeared, likewise 4% of worldwide local populations. Like other ectotherms, lizards have a narrow thermal range in which they thrive, and climate change has altered the thermal niches available to them. This and temperature-dependent gender determination put lizards in double jeopardy.

Long term observations across Europe and North America reveal that, over 110 years, there have been changes in the geographic distributions of 67 species of bumblebees. In both areas, compression of geographic ranges coincides with negative effects of climate change. These changes in the distributions of bumblebees are over and above those caused by the use of insecticides. Climate change also has affected marine vertebrates. The most prevalent mechanisms of change are physiological responses and changes in predator–prey interactions associated with changes in climate.

## STUDY BREAK QUESTIONS

1. What is temperature-dependent sex determination?
2. How does temperature-dependent sex determination relate to climate change?

## 28.4 Protecting Species

The widespread recognition of trademarks such as the World Wildlife Fund (WWF) panda is an example of successfully associating a cause with an icon. It is not surprising that many conservation efforts began with a focus on one species—such as giant pandas (*Ailuropoda melanoleuca*; **Figure 28.11**), polar bears (*Ursus maritimus*), and redwood trees (*Sequoia sempervirens*). The lure of conservation movements that focus on charismatic species is very strong. But some charismatic organisms may not need protection, while other species that are unattractive, dangerous, or mundane desperately need our assistance. Unfortunately, mundane, ugly, and dangerous (to us) species are unlikely to serve as a call to arms (or to attract financial support). Worldwide, the WWF panda is one of the most recognized logos, whether or not pandas are in the neighbourhood.

M.B. Fenton

**FIGURE 28.11 A giant panda**

A critical first step toward conservation is the development and adoption of objective, data-based criteria for assessing the risk posed to different species. This process has been developed on several fronts around the world. Governments and nongovernmental organizations (NGOs) focused on conservation typically use the criteria and assessment procedures perfected by the International Union for Conservation of Nature (IUCN). Conservation actions have sometimes successfully halted the march to extinction, but there are many more examples where we have failed. Making arguments based on data does not guarantee success. Using a data-based approach, some species emerge as being in need of protection, but others do not. Being rare or unusual, by itself, will not warrant protection. The species concept and the Linnaean system of nomenclature (see Chapter 19) are fundamental to conservation.

In Canada, federal and provincial committees are charged with assessing conservation status of species. Federally, recommendations about the conservation status of species involve the Committee on the Status of Endangered Wildlife in Canada (COSEWIC). The definition of wildlife includes plants and animals. Like IUCN, COSEWIC recognizes six categories for assessing species at risk:

- **Extinct** wildlife species no longer exist.
- **Extirpated** species no longer exist in one location/area in the wild but occur elsewhere.
- **Endangered** species face imminent extirpation or extinction.
- **Threatened** species are likely to become endangered if limiting factors are not reversed.
- **Special concern** species may become threatened or endangered because of a combination of biological characteristics and identified threats.
- **Data deficient** is a category used when available information is insufficient either to resolve a wildlife species' eligibility of assessment or to permit an assessment of its risk of extinction.

A seventh category, **not at risk**, identifies species not at risk of extinction under current circumstances.

Members of COSEWIC vote on the appropriate conservation category for each species whose status they review. The members review as many aspects of the situation as possible, including the area of occupancy, an indication of the geographic range of a species, as well as the availability of suitable habitat. They consider data about the population(s) of the species, including trends in the numbers of organisms. This information is corrected for species showing extreme fluctuations in numbers from year to year. Members also consider the demographics of the species and how these vary in the habitat where the species occur. Generation time is also considered, along with specific habitat features essential for the species' survival. The effective population size—the numbers of reproducing adults—is important, as are risks to the survival of the species under consideration.

You may recognize this litany from Chapter 29, on populations. The assessment criteria used by COSEWIC (and similar agencies elsewhere) describe the numbers of individuals in the population, fecundity, mortality, and the intrinsic rate of increase. Carrying capacity is also important, as is the area (range) over which the species occurs. These criteria are designed to support making data-based decisions about the conservation status of species.

### STUDY BREAK QUESTIONS

1. How does extinction differ from extirpation?
2. What is COSEWIC? What does it do?
3. What is the difference between Not at Risk and Data Deficient?

## 28.5  Protecting What?

Before data are used to address questions about the status of species at risk, conservation biologists must decide about eligibility. The conservation jargon for this is "designatable unit." Are the organisms "real" species? Are they subspecies? Are they distinct populations? Are they really Canadian? Do they regularly occur in Canada or perhaps turn up here by accident? If the species does not breed here, is the habitat they use in Canada essential to their survival? Most species of wildlife in Canada occur close to the border with the United States, and many species widespread in the United States just make it

into Canada. In some cases, a distinct population is treated as a designatable unit. Distinct populations may be recognized by their geographic distribution and/or their genetic structure.

Questions about what units are designatable echo those raised in discussions about the definition of species (see Chapter 18). Off the west coast of Canada, biologists use striking differences in behaviour to distinguish among three "kinds" of killer whales. Resident killer whales eat mainly fish and often echolocate. Transient killer whales eat mainly marine mammals and rarely produce echolocation signals. Open-ocean killer whales eat mainly sharks. Individual killer whales often have distinct marks; repeated sightings of recognizable individual whales reveals that different groups of these animals live in different areas along the coast (**Figure 28.12**).

Based on behaviour and geographic distribution, there appear to be three designatable units of killer whales in the Pacific Ocean off Canada's west coast. The different units face different threats to their survival even though they appear to represent a single species.

Questions about what to protect often reflect different realities of biology. Migrating birds may be blown off course and end up in southern Ontario instead of their usual habitat much farther south. Marine birds and mammals may feed in Canadian waters but breed elsewhere. Many organisms commonly hitchhike, using ocean vessels, aircraft, or automobiles as vehicles of dispersal. But some hitchhikers, for example, some snails, travel with birds, making the association and the dispersal more "natural."

People can be quick to try to protect species they consider to be important or distinctive. In 2003, the Ontario Ministry of Natural Resources reported 4–6 white-coloured moose (*Alces alces*) among the approximately 1900 moose in two wildlife management areas near Foleyet, in northeastern Ontario. Should white-coloured moose be protected? There was local

**FIGURE 28.12  Two views of a killer whale (*Orcinus orca*). (a)** A captive animal in Vancouver and **(b)** a wild orca swimming off the Queen Charlotte Islands. The captive orca raises challenging questions about the appropriateness of keeping captive animals as part of an overall conservation strategy.

support for protecting the white moose, animals that have cultural and spiritual significance for First Nations communities. White moose also have been reported from other places in northern Ontario, Newfoundland and Labrador, and elsewhere. Although the population of white moose is small and widespread, there is no evidence that they are a designatable unit. In Canada, they have not been accorded special protection.

CITES, the Convention on International Trade in Endangered Species of Wild Fauna and Flora, plays a pivotal role in protecting species at the international level. Here, countries signatory to the CITES agreement enforce bans forbidding international trade in endangered species. International trade in wildlife is an important threat to biodiversity. In addition to directly affecting local populations of threatened species, it can also spread infectious diseases and promote the spread of invasive species. Membership in CITES includes 180 countries, and CITES tries to regulate trade in almost 36 000 species. Basic, accurate, and reliable biological data about species are essential for informing decisions about which species should be protected. Yet, decisions about what species are protected by CITES are political and not necessarily uniformly acclaimed. Between 2014 and 2016, the annual budget of the secretariat of CITES averaged US$6.2 million, coming from donations. But budget restrictions still influenced the effectiveness of CITES at the secretariat level by affecting capacity for detailed collection and analysis of basic data.

The Linnaean system of nomenclature is used to name species (see Chapter 19). Once a species has a name, however acquired, it may benefit from protection under CITES. But will data-based decisions about what counts as endangered be consistent and predictable? The answer is "yes and no." Black rhinos were not effectively protected under CITES, even though horns and products from the horns were moved across international borders to markets outside Africa.

## 28.5a Leopards and CITES

In Africa, the leopard (*Panthera pardus*; **Figure 28.13**) was protected under CITES. This effectively banned importation of

**FIGURE 28.13  A leopard photographed in a game reserve in South Africa**

leopard skins to the United States after passage of the Endangered Species Act there. The ban extended to the trophy skins of leopards shot by Americans on safari. The safari hunts were legal in the countries where the leopards had been shot. The CITES listing reflected the belief that leopards were endangered and that hunting threatened their survival.

Two groups immediately reacted negatively to the ban. First, predictably, were the hunting and related associations and lobbies. They objected to the ban because their members were anxious to import the trophies they had acquired on safari. Second were leaders and governments in many African countries. They objected to the ban because safaris were (and still are) an important source of foreign exchange. In many of these countries, large tracts of land, "safari hunting areas," have been set aside to accommodate visitors. These areas also protected populations of nongame species as well as appropriate habitat.

What did the data show? Leopards are 40 to 80 kg solitary cats that hunt by stealth. They are widespread in Africa. The estimate is that there are more than 700 000 leopards in the wild in Africa, with resident populations in all but very small countries with high human population densities. In 2000, Zimbabwe alone had a population of more than 16 000 leopards in the wild. The 1969 safari harvest of 6100 leopards throughout Africa and the export of their skins were no threat to the population in Zimbabwe, let alone to leopards in the whole continent.

Ecologists studied the population of leopards in the Matetsi Safari Area in Zimbabwe. Before 1974, the 4300 km² area had been a cattle ranch whose operators made strong efforts to eradicate leopards to protect their livestock. After conversion to a hunting area, people on the first safaris rarely shot leopards. By 1984, the leopard population in this safari area was 800–1000; in 1988, the annual safari quota was 12–28 leopards (3.6% of the estimated population). There was no change in the sizes of leopards shot in the mid-1980s compared with those taken in the 1970s. But by 1986, the average age of leopards taken as trophies was 5.4 years, compared with 3.2 years from the earlier period. These data show that leopards can persist even when subjected to heavy hunting pressure. On average, leopards live longer in a safari hunting regime than when they are hunted in the context of predator control operations. Other evidence suggests that populations of leopards persist even in urban areas; trapping evidence, for example, suggests that resident leopards live in Nairobi, the capital of Kenya.

Leopards are an interesting example of human responses to conservation. Hunting or some other form of harvesting is not necessarily a threat to their survival. Indeed, some harvesting may be critical to the livelihood of some people, and can advance efforts to protect some species. But decisions about harvesting made in one part of the world can influence what happens elsewhere.

Today, there are quotas for the numbers of leopards that can be harvested in different countries in Africa. Safari hunters

FIGURE 28.14  **A polar bear**

In the European Economic Community, setting aside 5% of agricultural land as natural habitat is an effective way to conserve biodiversity. Set-asides can be an important part of worldwide efforts to advance conservation. Mosaics of land use often provide suitable habitat for many organisms, with smaller species probably benefitting more than larger ones. Comparing bat communities between islands in water and those in agricultural landscapes revealed interesting

a.

b.

c.

FIGURE 28.15  **Agricultural landscapes in southwestern Ontario** (a) **and Orange Walk County in Belize** (b, c)**.** In (a) and (b), note the mosaic of land use and forest cover. In (c), note ongoing slash-and-burn land clearing.

must obtain licences to take trophies, and skins exported must be accompanied by paperwork showing that the harvest was legal. The documentation allows a citizen, for example, of Canada or of a European Union country, to import a leopard skin. This was not possible in the United States in the 1970s, but it is now. In Africa, local farmers are permitted to kill "problem" animals that threaten their livestock or themselves and their families. These actions may be supported by government officials.

Key elements in the success of harvesting include having data about the population of organisms, the rates of reproduction, and the rates of harvest. Enforcement of quotas is essential if this approach is to succeed. Legal harvest quotas do not require people who object to hunting to be hunters. Trophy hunting is not the exclusive preserve of countries in Africa. On 3 April 2007, *The Globe and Mail* reported that the economy of Nunavut received C$3.9 million from polar bear **(Figure 28.14)** hunting; hunters can pay US$20 000 for a polar bear hunt.

### STUDY BREAK QUESTIONS

1. Are species the same as designated units? Explain.
2. What is CITES? How did it figure in the conservation of leopards? Did it work in the conservation of black rhinos?
3. Does hunting threaten the survival of leopards?

## 28.6  Conservation and Agriculture

Using land to grow crops to feed people was a reality long before the "beginning" of the Anthropocene, arguably 500 years ago. In some situations, for example in southwestern Ontario **(Figure 28.15a)** or in Belize (Figure 28.15b), agricultural landscapes may be a mosaic of habitats. In many other cases, land is cleared and devoted to growing crops (e.g., Figure 28.15c).

differences. For 66 species of bats, degrees of the evenness and species richness was high among islands in agricultural systems. This was significantly different from prevailing data for islands in lakes.

The proliferation and diversity of edge habitats can both enrich opportunities for some species and threaten those of others. For example, in eastern Canada, songbirds that breed in continuous forest (e.g., hooded warblers, *Wilsonia citrina*; **Figure 28.16a**) are more exposed to nest parasitism by brown-headed cowbirds (*Molothrus ater*; Figure 28.16b) when they nest closer to forest edges.

As important as set-asides can be, they often involve a direct cost to the landowner. For the Brazilian Atlantic forest, a widely recognized system under pressure from expanding human populations and operations, annually spending about 6.5% of what Brazil spends on subsidies to agriculture would greatly enhance conservation efforts there. Set-asides also can be important jumping-off points for restoring threatened habitats in agricultural landscapes.

In September 2014, at the climate summit convened by the United Nations, there was general agreement with the New York Declaration on Forests. This document identified restoration of degraded ecosystems as one approach to dealing with climate change. There are four basic principles associated with restoration. First, the reality that restoration can increase ecological integrity. Second, restoration can be sustainable over a longer term. Third, restoration draws heavily on historical information, which can guide specific goals. Fourth, restoration provides general benefits and leads to societal engagement. Many human activities cause habitat degradation, but starting with agricultural impacts overtly recognizes this operation as a fundamental contributor.

**STUDY BREAK QUESTIONS**

1. What are set-asides? How do they serve conservation?
2. What is restoration?

## 28.7 Contaminating Natural Systems

Contamination of natural systems is one obvious by-product of the spread of humans in the world. This impact is compounded by population growth, habitat destruction, and the demand for resources. Further complicating the picture is our use of technology. To some extent, the resiliency of natural systems dampens some of our negative impact. Resiliency is one of the most impressive features of life at the species and/or ecosystem levels. In one respect, this feature complicates the challenges of conserving biodiversity. Introduced species are a form of contamination, and some of them are very invasive and adaptable and have huge negative impacts where they are released.

### 28.7a 2,4-Dichlorophenoxyacetic Acid (2,4-D)

Humans first identified 2,4-D (**Figure 28.17**) in 1942, and from 1944, it was marketed as a herbicide. Technically, 2,4-D is a hormone absorbed by the plant and translocated to the growing points of roots and shoots. 2,4-D kills weeds by inhibiting growth. The global market for 2,4-D is probably more than US$300 million, and it is used mainly to control broad-leaved weeds in cereal crops. According to the World Health Organization (WHO), 2,4-D is a "moderately hazardous pesticide" known to affect a variety of animals (e.g., dogs but not rats). Curiously, it turns out that other animals use 2,4-D for their own ends.

**FIGURE 28.16** **A hooded warbler (a) and a brown-headed cowbird (b)**

2, 4-D

(2,4-dichlorophenoxy)acetic acid

**FIGURE 28.17** **2,4-Dichlorophenoxyacetic acid (2,4-D)**

In 1971, Thomas Eisner and colleagues reported that a grasshopper (*Romalea microptera*; **Figure 28.18**) produced a froth of chemicals (**Figure 28.19**) for protection against ants. One of the main ingredients in the froth was 2,5-dichlorophenol, apparently derived from 2,4-D. This is an astonishing demonstration of adaptability that can underlie resiliency.

Resiliency and the recuperative powers of ecosystems are demonstrated by stories of "lost cities," for example, structures built by Maya in Central America, being found in a jungle. Archaeological evidence reveals that, in some habitats, these buildings and pyramids were overgrown by the rain forest in about 100 years. The Great Zimbabwe Ruins in southern Africa were overgrown by savannah woodland in a period of 100–200 years and only latterly "discovered" by European explorers.

## 28.7b Plastic Microbeads

Plastics are another example of contamination. Worldwide, polyethylene terephthalate (PET) is used in plastic products, and over 55 million tons of PET was produced in 2013 alone. Many plastics persist in the environment because they are chemically inert. Huge quantities of PET have been released into the environment as microbeads, used in consumer products such as facial soaps and toothpastes. These tiny (< 2 mm diameter) particles of plastic pose an immediate threat to many living species (**Figure 28.20**). Persistence in the environment makes plastics, including those made of PET, chemically inert and resistant to microbial degradation.

In 2016, a team of Japanese scientists described *Ideonella sakaiensis 201-F6*, a species of bacteria new to science. This is an important discovery because *I. sakaiensis 201-F6* produces enzymes that can hydrolyze PET and convert it to terephthalic acid and ethylene glycol, two environmentally benign monomers. The researchers collected samples of debris contaminated with PET at a bottle recycling site. In this case, resiliency of a natural system resulted in what could be the first step in reducing environmental persistence of PET. Investigation of the evolutionary history of the capacity of *I. sakaiensis 201-F6* to digest PET suggested that this species emerged at the contaminated site through lateral gene transfer and natural selection favouring its ability to exploit a new energetic opportunity.

## 28.7c Alien Species

Humans cause extinction through overexploitation of food species and by introducing other species. House cats, *Felis catus*, are among the worst introductions

**FIGURE 28.18** *Romalea microptera*, a grasshopper that uses an ant repellent with a 2,4-D derivative

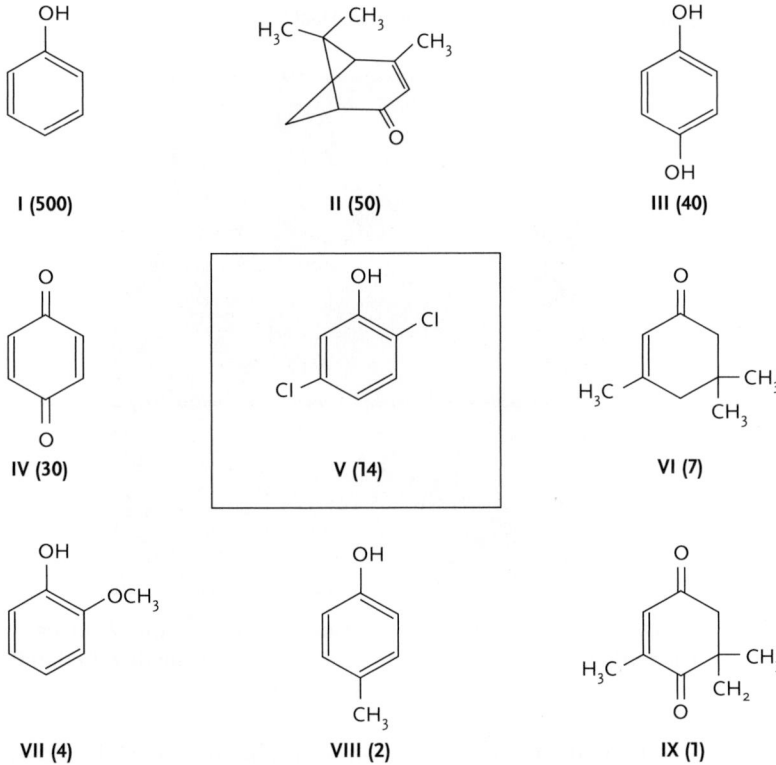

**FIGURE 28.19** Active ingredients in the defensive froth of the grasshopper *Romalea microptera*. 2,5-Dichlorophenol (boxed) is apparently derived from 2,4-D.

I (500)  II (50)  III (40)  IV (30)  V (14)  VI (7)  VII (4)  VIII (2)  IX (1)

**FIGURE 28.20** A cartoon about plastic microbeads

FIGURE 28.21 **Stephen's Island wren, _Xenicus lyalli_.** This species was exterminated by one cat.

a.

b.

FIGURE 28.22 **(a)** Shells of zebra mussels (Dreissena polymorpha) on a beach on Pelee Island in Lake Erie. These mussels were introduced to the Great Lakes in North America, where they have spread rapidly. Their arrival coincided with steep declines in populations of native mussels such as, in **(b)** from left front to right back, kidneyshell (_Ptychobranchus fasciolaris_), eastern pondmussel (_Ligumia nasuta_), rainbow mussel (_Villosa iris_), round pigtoe (_Pleurobema sintoxia_), and maple leaf (_Quadrula quadrula_).

people have made (and continue to make). Anecdotal records suggest that, in 1894, one house cat named Tibbles exterminated an entire population of flightless wrens **(Figure 28.21)** on Stephen's Island, a 2.6 km² island off the north shore of New Zealand. Fossils indicate that the wrens had occurred widely in New Zealand. This record stands for one individual, Tibbles, taking out the remaining approximately 10 pairs and exterminating the species.

The negative impacts occur whether the introductions were intentional or accidental, and whether the anticipated outcome was positive or negative. The invaders, once arrived and established, may outcompete resident species, devastating native species and ecosystems. The list of introduced organisms is very long and includes many domesticated or commensal species of animals and plants. Zebra mussels **(Figure 28.22a)** provide an example. These immigrant mussels outcompeted and overgrew the native ones, reducing their range and populations to levels that threatened the survival of several endemic species (Figure 28.22b).

Meanwhile, in parts of the British Isles, flatworms (_Arthurdendyus triangulatus_; **Figure 28.23**; see also Chapters 39 and 45) introduced from New Zealand in the soil plant pots, are deadly predators of earthworms. Since their arrival the flatworms have thrived and spread rapidly, coinciding with the demise of earthworms. We may think of gardeners as individuals in touch with nature; unfortunately, their propensity to introduce exotic species often conflicts with conservation.

Some organisms move about in ballast water in ships. Since about 1880, ships have regularly used water for ballast. Ships without cargo tend to ride high on the water, resulting in low fuel efficiency. Ballast keeps unladen ships riding lower in the

FIGURE 28.23 **This earthworm-eating planarian (_Arthurdendyus triangulatus_) was introduced to the British Isles from New Zealand.** It has had a devastating effect on local populations of earthworms.

water, reducing their fuel consumption. In the early 1990s, biologists surveyed ballast water in 159 cargo ships in Coos Bay, Oregon. They found 367 taxa representing 16 animal and 3 protist phyla, as well as 3 plant divisions. The samples included all major and most minor phyla. Organisms in the ballast water included carnivores, herbivores, omnivores, deposit feeders, scavengers, suspension feeders, primary producers, and parasites. Ballast water is taken on in one port and discharged in another, providing many species with almost open access to waters around the world.

Meanwhile, introduced diseases (and the organisms that cause them) have decimated, if not obliterated, resident species. When Europeans arrived in the New World, *Castanea dentata*, the American chestnut tree, was widespread in forests from southern Ontario to Alabama. This large tree of the forest canopy grew to heights of 30 m. Often most abundant on prime agricultural soils, the species' distribution and density were reduced as settlers from Europe cleared more and more land for agriculture. *Endothia parasitica*, the chestnut blight, was introduced around 1904 from Asian nursery stock. This introduced blight killed the American chestnut trees by the 1930s. By 2000, only scattered American chestnut trees remained, most of them sprouts from stumps.

Why are invading species so successful? Does the spread of starlings (*Sturnus vulgaris*; **Figure 28.24**) or dandelions (*Taraxacum officinale*) after introduction to new continents suggest that they moved into vacant niches? Does it mean that they are better competitors? In the case of starlings, 13 birds were introduced to Central Park in New York City in 1890, and they have spread far and wide. Once established, invading or introduced species can pose huge conservation problems because of their impact on ecosystems and diversity.

Although many invaders arrive, only a few are widely successful and become large-scale problems in their new settings. Invading plants are most often successful in nutrient-rich habitats, where they can achieve high growth rates, early reproduction, and maximal production of offspring. What happens in resource-poor settings? In the past, conventional wisdom had suggested that low-resource settings could be reservoirs for native species that could outcompete invaders.

However, an experimental examination of the responses of native and introduced species to challenging conditions revealed that invasive plant species almost always fared better (**Figure 28.25**). Resource use efficiency (RUE), calculated by measuring carbon assimilation per unit of resource, is an indicator of success. Many invasive species, such as ferns, $C_3$ and $C_4$ grasses, herbs, shrubs, and trees, were more successful in low-resource systems than native species were.

This research was conducted in Hawaii, where there are many invasive species. Among the invaders were *Bromus tectorum* (cheatgrass), *Heracleum mantegazzianum* (cartwheel flower or giant hogweed), and *Pinus radiata* (Monterey pine). Humans have introduced these plants for gardening (cheatgrass and cartwheel flower) or commercial timber production (Monterey pine). The data demonstrate that attempting to restore ecosystems and exclude invading species by reducing resource availability does not succeed because of the efficiency with which some species use resources.

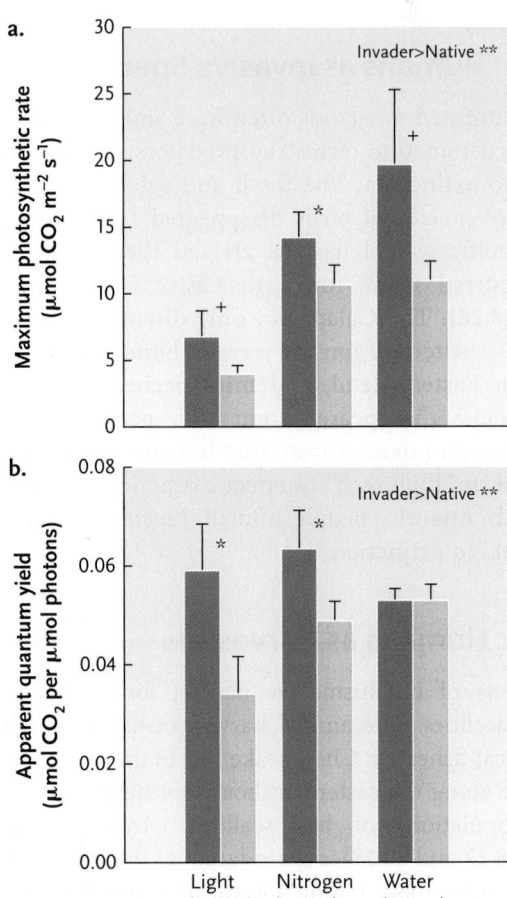

**FIGURE 28.25** (a) **Photosynthetic rates (RUE) and** (b) **light-use efficiency of invasive plant species (blue bars) make them more competitive than native species (yellow bars).** The plants were from three different habitats in Hawaii. In the graphs, + denotes P < 0.01; *denotes P < 0.05. **Indicates that, in both instances, invaders are significantly more efficient than native species.

**FIGURE 28.24  A starling, photographed in Toronto, introduced from Europe**

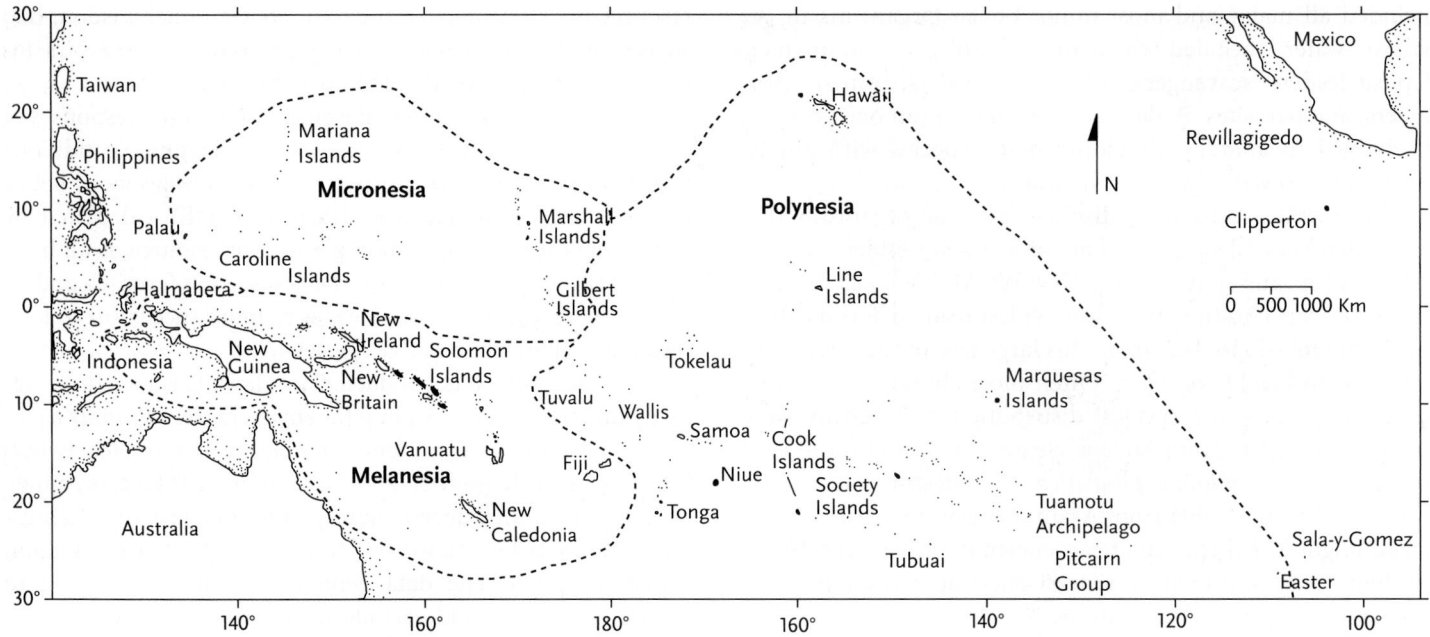

**FIGURE 28.26** Islands in the South Pacific where the arrival of Polynesians coincided with the extinction of many island species of birds

*Source:* From David W. Steadman, "Prehistoric Extinctions of Pacific Island Birds: Biodiversity Meets Zooarchaeology," *Science*, vol. 267, Feb 24, 1995, pp. 1123 - 1131. *Science* by American Association for the Advancement of Science Reproduced with permission of AMERICAN ASSOCIATION FOR THE ADVANCEMENT OF SCIENCE in the format Republish in a book via Copyright Clearance Center.

## 28.7d Humans as Invasive Species

Species confined to islands often have small populations and are unaccustomed to terrestrial predators, making them vulnerable to extinction. The fossil and subfossil records show that many species of birds disappeared from islands in the South Pacific as Polynesians arrived there from the west. This occurred from Tonga to Easter Island and beyond (**Figure 28.26**). The Galápagos, only discovered by people in 1535, was sheltered from the wave of human-induced extinctions. On Easter Island, **endemic species** of sea birds and other species disappeared soon after people settled there. These examples demonstrate that humans do not have to be industrial or "high tech" to effect extinctions. Meanwhile, in the North Atlantic, people hunted *Pinguinus impennis*, the Great Auk, to extinction.

## 28.7e Humans as Harvesters

Populations of organisms we harvest for food often show marked declines. The annual harvest of bivalve molluscs has been a local fishery in Chesapeake Bay in the United States and elsewhere along the eastern seaboard for hundreds of years. In 1999, populations of bay scallops (*Argopecten irradians*; **Figures 28.27** and **28.28**), a main target of the fishery, were very low. The immediate reason for the low populations was the impact of predation by skates and rays that feed heavily on bivalve molluscs. Skates and rays are tertiary consumers and in turn are eaten by larger elasmobranchs, specifically various species of sharks.

Among tertiary consumers, the cownose ray (**Figure 28.29**) shows a marked increase in population. Evidence from surveys

**FIGURE 28.27** A handful of bay scallops (*Argopecten irradians*)

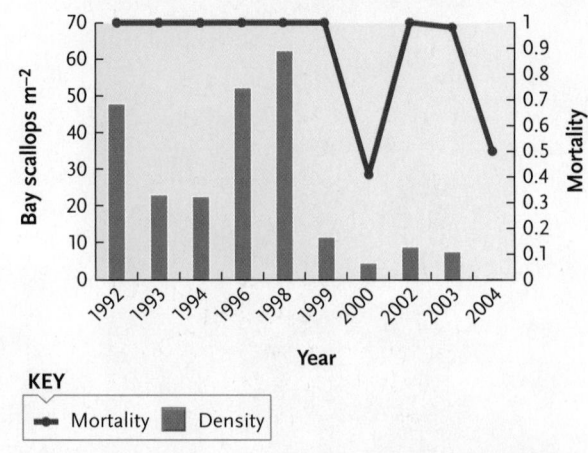

**FIGURE 28.28** Numbers of bay scallops off the east coast of the United States

*Source:* From Ransom A. Myers, Julia K. Baum, Travis D. Shepherd, Sean P. Powers, Charles H. Peterson, "Cascading Effects of the Loss of Apex Predatory Sharks from a Coastal Ocean," *Science*, vol. 315, Mar 30, 2007, pp. 1846 - 1850. *Science* by American Association for the Advancement of Science Reproduced with permission of AMERICAN ASSOCIATION FOR THE ADVANCEMENT OF SCIENCE in the format Republish in a book via Copyright Clearance Center.

**FIGURE 28.29  A cownose ray (*Rhinoptera bonasus*)**

NOAA

The picture becomes clearer when the population data for the local great sharks are added to the mix (**Figure 28.30**). Prolonged and intensive fishing of 12 species of sharks accounts for a 35-year decline in their populations (see Figure 28.30, top row). The sharks have been taken primarily for their fins and meat. In some parts of the world, shark fins sell for around US$700 per kilogram and are used to make shark fin soup.

The data demonstrate how removal of a top predator (sharks) destroyed a century-old scallop fishery. Fewer sharks meant increased predation by tertiary consumers, whose populations, in turn, increased (see Figure 28.30, middle row). The data illustrate a cascading ecological effect and demonstrate the potential long-term harm that our species can do to ecosystems and the species inhabiting them. The demise of bay scallops and other bivalves can be attributed to the impact of large-scale harvesting of marine resources. The late Ransom Myers and his colleagues documented this cascade of effects.

*Bycatch:* One unfortunate reality of harvesting is collateral damage. People fishing for one species may catch another, with unfortunate consequences. Changes in hook design may reduce some incidences of bycatch. Altering the curvature of a hook

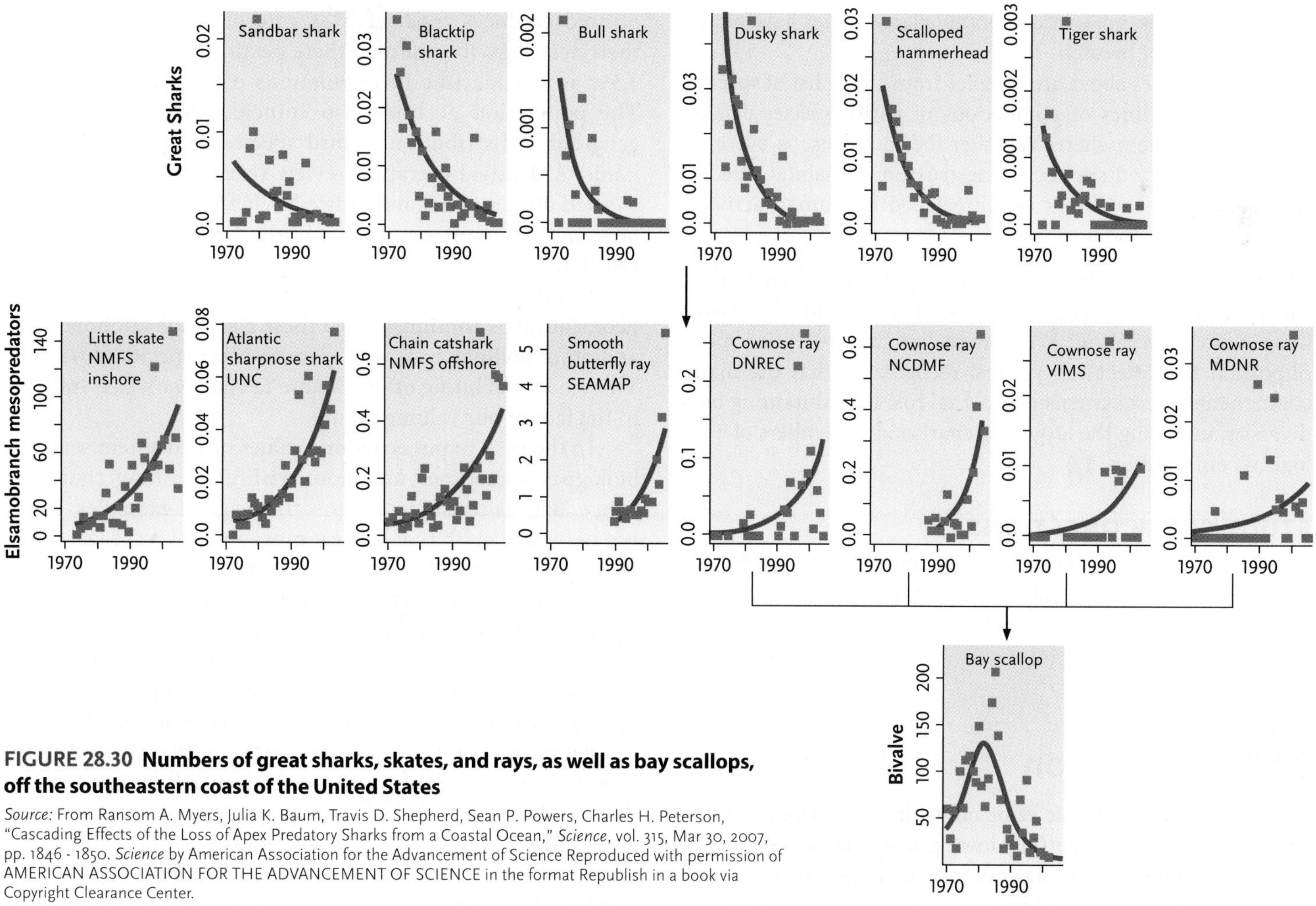

on the U.S. Atlantic coast estimates an order-of-magnitude increase in populations of cownose rays, and that the total population of 14 species of rays and skates exceeds 40 million. So, the decline in scallop (and other bivalve) populations can be explained by the increase in predation by tertiary consumers, especially skates and rays.

**FIGURE 28.30  Numbers of great sharks, skates, and rays, as well as bay scallops, off the southeastern coast of the United States**

*Source:* From Ransom A. Myers, Julia K. Baum, Travis D. Shepherd, Sean P. Powers, Charles H. Peterson, "Cascading Effects of the Loss of Apex Predatory Sharks from a Coastal Ocean," *Science*, vol. 315, Mar 30, 2007, pp. 1846 - 1850. *Science* by American Association for the Advancement of Science Reproduced with permission of AMERICAN ASSOCIATION FOR THE ADVANCEMENT OF SCIENCE in the format Republish in a book via Copyright Clearance Center.

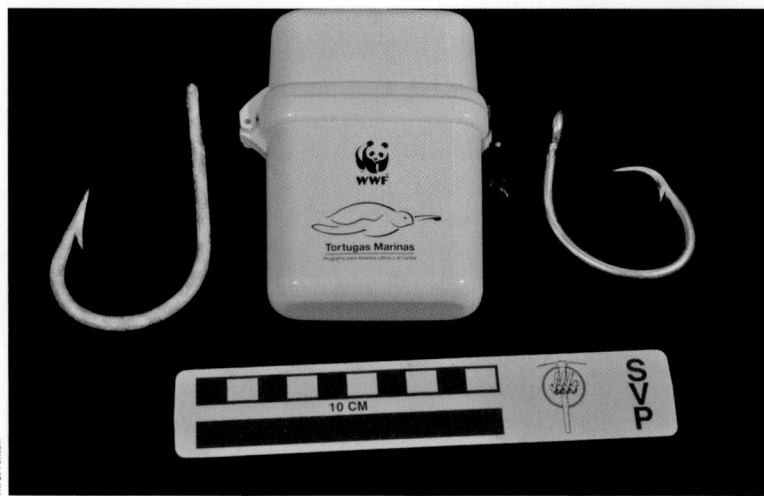

**FIGURE 28.31 Sea turtles and longlining.** Conventional longline hooks (left) readily catch sea turtles, whereas the hook on the right does not. The World Wildlife Fund is promoting the use of hooks (right) that are friendly to sea turtles in an effort to reduce their losses to longline fishing.

can make it less likely to catch sea turtles and not interfere with catching the target fish (**Figure 28.31**). The demise of barndoor skates (*Dipterus laevis*), a species formerly widespread in the North Atlantic, from Canada to Europe, is an example of the damage that bycatch can do. Although never a commercially harvested species, populations of these large skates have plummeted because of bycatch.

The examples above are samples from a long list of species. Evidence of declines of populations of native species can be found almost everywhere. Whether the root cause is overharvesting, introduced species, or destruction of habitat, species from whales to songbirds are threatened by human activity. What can we do about it?

**CONCEPT FIX** Should we focus conservation efforts on large, charismatic animals and plants because these can be the poster images of conservation? We now realize that it is often more important to protect ecosystems, recognizing that the many components of ecosystems play a vital role in maintaining biodiversity, including the large and charismatic members of ecological communities.

## STUDY BREAK QUESTIONS

1. What is bycatch? Why is it important in conservation?
2. How do sharks affect populations of scallops?
3. Are humans an invasive species?
4. What is RUE?

## 28.8 Motivation

Trying to put an economic value on nature is challenging if one wants to move beyond cutting down and selling trees or paying to shoot an animal that is big and/or fierce. Some aspects of biodiversity and ecological interactions make it relatively easy to

appreciate the value-added involved with nature and ecosystems services. Others do not.

Data on the value of pollination to many agricultural enterprises illustrate why we should protect pollinators. It is easy to think of honeybees (*Apis mellifera*) as producers of honey, but the value of the crops they pollinate vastly exceeds revenue from honey and related products. Treatment with neonicotinoid pesticides (e.g., imidacloprid and clothianidin) caused a significant reduction in the number of visits by bumblebees to apple blossoms. Apples are grown commercially in 95 countries, and in 2012 the apple crop was estimated to be worth over US$350 billion.

Many insects visit flowers and, in doing so, pollinate plants and contribute directly to their reproduction. Somehow, bees are champion pollinators even though other insects also are involved. Bee–plant relationships are the product of over 200 million years of coevolution. These interactions provide some of the most exquisite examples of interactive diversification, partly accounting for the over 20 000 species of bees in the world. But the survival of bees is threatened by human activity. For example, 23 species of bees had disappeared from Britain by 2013.

Neonicotinoids also are harmful to many species of vertebrate wildlife. In the Netherlands, treatment with neonicotinoids reduces food such as caterpillars that birds feed their nestlings. Exposure to these pesticides coincided with a 3.5% annual decline in populations of insectivorous birds. The population declines also coincide with reductions in geographic distribution of bird species, especially in farmlands. A detailed literature review revealed that 150 studies showed direct (toxic) and indirect (via the food chain) effects on populations of mammals, birds, fish, amphibians, and reptiles.

It is difficult to understand why using insecticides such as neonicotinoids continues when these chemicals kill honeybees and other pollinators as well as many other species of wildlife. This smacks of biting off one's nose to spite one's face and flies in the face of our valuing nature.

In the rush to put economic values on ecosystem services, biologists sometimes use more wishful thinking than evidence. Bats as consumers of insects are good examples. There is a pervasive myth that bats eat mosquitoes. Use of DNA barcode analysis to identify the insect species eaten by bats revealed that two North American species, big brown bats (*Eptesicus fuscus*) and little brown myotis, rarely eat mosquitoes. The idea that bats are big consumers of mosquitoes comes from work on bat echolocation. In 1960, Donald R. Griffin and colleagues demonstrated that, in the laboratory, bats used echolocation to detect and track insects. In the lab, the targets were mosquitoes and fruit flies. The research had nothing to do with the normal prey of the bats. To demonstrate that predators reduce populations of prey requires actual evidence of consumption and associated reduction in target populations. For Brazilian free-tailed bats (*Tadarida brasiliensis*) in Texas, there is the necessary evidence of the impact of these of bats on populations of insects that are pests of corn and cotton. The fact that these bats live in colonies of millions of individuals probably explains the population control the bats effect. Comparable evidence is rarely available for the effects of other bats on other insects.

One robust example of ecosystem services is provided from coffee plantations in Costa Rica. There, forest patches in coffee plantations provide a reservoir of insectivorous birds that eat the coffee berry borer beetles (*Hypothenemus hampei*), providing a valuable service to coffee growers. In the end, choosing to support conservation activities is more a political than an economic undertaking. Ecosystem service is one argument in support of conservation.

## STUDY BREAK QUESTIONS

1. What are ecosystem services?
2. What are neonicotinoids? Why are they important in conservation?

## 28.9 Effecting Conservation

Today we face many challenges when trying to protect biodiversity. Too many of the immediate threats are the direct or indirect consequences of human activities. We must protect species by acting at levels ranging from species to populations and habitats. Sometimes the route to saving one species appears to necessitate killing another.

Across northern Canada and the United States, many populations of caribou (*Rangifer tarandus caribou*; **Figure 28.32a**) are in sharp decline. Herds that had numbered in the thousands have dwindled to hundreds of individuals. Some isolated populations in southern Canada have disappeared, and none seems to have a secure future. Operations associated with oil and gas exploration in Alberta directly threaten the survival of caribou through habitat destruction and fragmentation. But there, predation by grey wolves (*Canis lupus*; Figure 28.32b) is the immediate cause of caribou mortality.

To assess the impact of wolf predation on populations of caribou, Dave Hervieux and four other biologists compared two herds of caribou in west-central Alberta. The Little Smoky Mountain and the Red Rock Prairie Creek herds were studied from 2000 to 2012. Wolf populations in the area of the Little Smoky Mountain caribou herd were reduced by hunting and poisoning wolves. This did not happen in the area of the Red Rock Prairie Creek herd. Reducing populations of grey wolves coincided with a 4.6% increase in the Little Smoky Mountain herd, while the Red Rock Prairie Creek herd declined by 4.7% during the same period. Survival of calves appeared to explain the differences in the two populations. The results of the wolf cull on the Little Smoky Mountain herd were clear, but would it ensure the long-term survival of the caribou? Does the end justify the means?

**FIGURE 28.32 A woodland caribou** (a) **and a grey wolf** (b)

Earlier, in Baja California, biologists resorted to culling golden eagles (*Aquila chrysaetos*) to preserve populations of Channel Island foxes (*Urocyon littoralis*). In that situation, the eagles had increased their predation on the foxes in the wake of reduced food supply caused by culling feral pigs (*Sus scrofa*). Use of words such as "killing" somewhat minimizes the extent of the killing that is involved, however.

The survival of predators is a matter of great concern for those interested in conservation (e.g., leopards). At least one-third of the countries in Europe have wild populations of at least one large carnivore: brown bears (*Ursus arctos*), grey wolves, Eurasian lynx (*Lynx lynx*), or wolverines (*Gulo gulo*). In Sweden this survival is achieved by various actions, including electric fencing to exclude predators as well as paying subsidies to those who harbour large carnivores on their land. In some jurisdictions in the United States, grey wolves can be hunted

FIGURE 28.33 **Observational Research**

## Near-Complete Extinction of Small Mammals in Tropical Forest Fragments

**Question:** How long do populations of small mammals persist in small fragments of tropical forests?

**Hypothesis:** Populations of small mammals will eventually become extinct on small islands that were created when a large patch of forest was flooded to establish a reservoir **(a).**

**Prediction:** Using principles from the theory of island biogeography, Gibson and his colleagues predicted that extinctions would be more rapid in small forest fragments than in large fragments.

**Method:** The researchers conducted on-the-ground surveys on 16 small islands (red) of varying size (0.3–56.3 ha) five times over a period of 20 years, recording all the small mammal species they encountered. The first surveys took place 5–7 years after the forest fragments were formed.

**a. Islands in Chiew Larn Reservoir**

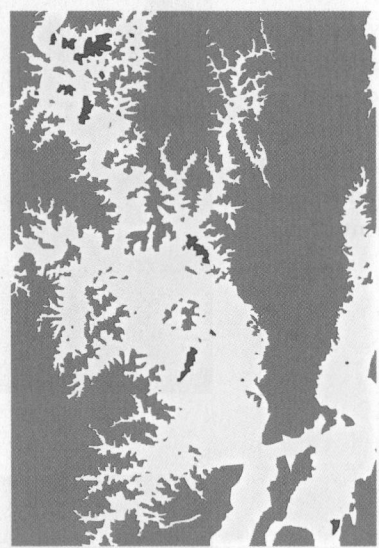

**b. Extinction of small mammals**

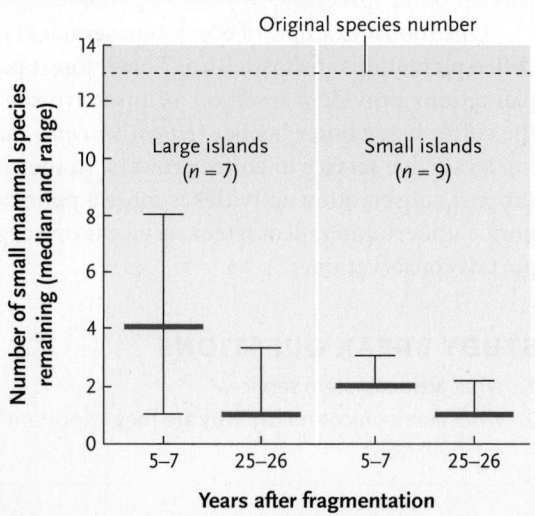

L. Gibson et al. 2013. "Near-complete extinction of native small mammal fauna 25 years after forest fragmentation," *Science* 341:1508—1510. *Science* by American Association for the Advancement of Science Reproduced with permission of AMERICAN ASSOCIATION FOR THE ADVANCEMENT OF SCIENCE in the format Republish in a book via Copyright Clearance Center.

**Result:** Small mammal populations quickly became extinct in the habitat fragments **(b).** Extinction varied with the size of habitat fragments such that most species disappeared from small islands within the first 5–7 years after fragmentation. By 25 years after forest fragmentation, nearly all small native mammals had become extinct on islands of any size. The Malayan field rat (*Rattus tiomanicus*) was the only mammal that persisted in all fragments; researchers believe that it colonized the fragments after they were separated from each other and from the surrounding forest.

**Conclusion:** Habitat fragments experienced size-dependent rates of extinction, but all habitat fragments in this study eventually lost all their native small mammals.

---

legally but there is considerable concern about the levels harvested.

Reactions to the paper about wolves and caribou focused mainly on the means of culling. These included using strychnine and shooting wolves from helicopters. Hervieux and his coauthors did not contend that culling wolves would ensure the future of caribou. Their data did, however, demonstrate that managing populations of predators could have a positive effect on populations of prey. Everyone seemed to acknowledge that, until there are changes in policies about land use, habitat destruction, and disturbance, killing wolves will not save caribou.

The survival of populations of Pacific water shrews in Canada was more a matter of habitat destruction than direct mortality. Fragmentation of populations is an important factor in conservation. Mountain lions (*Felis concolor*) provide an excellent example.

Mountain lions are large predators (130 kg) that once occurred widely in North and South America. Today, there is a small population of mountain lions in the Santa Monica Mountains in California, and their range occurs within

Greater Los Angeles. A genetic analysis combined with data about the movements of tagged individuals revealed that these mountain lions are genetically isolated and show inbreeding depression. The combination of urban development and large freeways effectively contains the Santa Monica Mountain population of mountain lions. Here the immigration of a single male in 2009 increased the genetic diversity of the population. This situation provides at least one solution to isolated populations.

Issues surrounding conservation continue to generate considerable debate. It seems obvious that one size does not fit all when it comes to protecting species and habitats **(Figure 28.33).**

### STUDY BREAK QUESTIONS

1. How can culling wolves help populations of caribou?
2. What is fragmentation of habitat? How is it important in conservation?

## 28.10 Human Population: A Root Problem for Conservation

The increasing human population is a fundamental root cause of declining biodiversity. Visit the website http://www.ined.fr/en/everything_about_population/population-games/world-population-me/ and use it to determine the estimated human population in the year you were born, and then for the years in which your parents and grandparents were born. Even when many people are killed, the momentum of our population increase does not slow down. The December 2004 tsunami killed approximately 250 000 people at a time when the world population was estimated at 6 billion. By comparison, the 1883 explosion of Krakatoa (and resulting tsunamis) is thought to have killed 35 000 people when the global human population was about 1.5 billion. If these estimates are correct, $4.1 \times 10^{-3}\%$ of the human population at the time was killed by the 2004 tsunami and $2.3 \times 10^{-3}\%$ by the explosion of Krakatoa. Neither calamity caused the human population growth curve (see Chapter 29) to waver.

If human population growth continues at the same rate it is growing now, it will double in 40 years. However, studies show that our population is not growing as quickly as it did during much of the twentieth century. The United Nations Development Program (UNDP) has released data on human fertility (the total number of births per woman) for 162 countries (**Table 28.1**). Compared with 1970–1975, 152 countries had lower human fertility in 2000–2005, 3 countries showed increases in fertility, and 7 showed no change.

Concerned about the global population and its effect on Earth, world leaders adopted the United Nations Millennium Development Goals in 2000, committing their nations to achieving the following goals by 2015:

- end poverty and hunger
- universal education
- gender equality
- child health
- maternal health
- combat HIV/AIDS
- environmental sustainability
- global partnerships

These goals can be achieved only if reproduction is controlled (see Chapter 29). Go to the United Nations Millennium Goals website at http://www.un.org/millenniumgoals/bkgd.shtml to see how we are faring. In 1994, the United Nations held the International Conference on Population and Development (ICPD), which set a target for global investment in family planning. By 2004, the amount spent had fallen to 13% of this target. Consequently, family planning information and devices (usually for fertility control) are not readily available in many of the lowest-income countries. In 1950, Sri Lanka and Afghanistan had the same population. Sri Lanka began strong efforts to make family planning available in culturally acceptable ways. This did not happen in Afghanistan. By 2050, Afghanistan will have four times as many people as Sri Lanka. The solution centres around controlling the fertility of women, but more particularly on giving them the power to control their own fertility in culturally acceptable ways. As seen in Chapter 29, the growth potential of a population is determined by the numbers of females of reproductive age. Why females? Because in mammals, females are the limiting step in reproduction—the ones who produce the eggs and young and milk as food.

### STUDY BREAK QUESTIONS

1. What is HDI? What can we learn from it?
2. Why is education important in the dynamics of human populations?

| TABLE 28.1 | Variations in Fertility Rate (Total Births per Woman): A Sample of UNDP Data for 162 Countries | | |
|---|---|---|---|
| Country | Human Development Index (HDI) Rank | 1970–1975 | 2000–2005 |
| Norway | 2 | 2.2 | 1.8 |
| Canada | 4 | 2.0 | 1.5 |
| United States | 12 | 2.0 | 2.0 |
| Portugal | 29 | 2.7 | 1.5 |
| Brazil | 70 | 4.7 | 2.3 |
| China | 81 | 4.9 | 1.7 |
| Indonesia | 107 | 5.2 | 2.4 |
| India | 128 | 5.4 | 3.1 |

## 28.11 Signs of Stress: Systems and Species

People's demand for food, water, and energy puts thousands of other species at risk. We do not have to look far to see examples of species and ecosystems under stress (see Chapter 31). For example, we are losing birds. We know this because for years, birdwatchers and ornithologists have counted them and monitored their behaviour and activity. Locally, birds are affected by changes in habitat availability as cities and towns and their suburbs expand into adjoining land. Birds also lose habitat when agricultural operations expand to increase productivity. Birds that make annual migrations from temperate areas of the world to tropical and subtropical ones must survive the changes that accumulate across their entire circuit of habitats, each one essential to their survival.

Avian influenza (also called *bird flu*) is a looming crisis for humans, one that appears to involve birds as central players. The issue here is another one involving basic biology, namely, the outcome when a disease-causing organism jumps from one species (host) to another. Bird flu could have as much to do with our insatiable demand for poultry as food as it does with birds. In 2006, 12 billion chickens were farmed in China. Worldwide, poultry farms housed over 100 billion broiler chickens. Raising organisms at very high densities (see Chapter 29) provides an ideal setting for the spread of disease. Humans have responded to the threat of bird flu by wholesale slaughter of fowl, raising concerns about the roles played by migrating birds, and efforts to develop a vaccine that will protect humans from bird flu. All involve basic biology.

Drylands are arid, semiarid, and subhumid areas where precipitation is scarce and more or less unpredictable. In drylands, the combination of high temperatures, low relative humidities, and abundant solar radiation means high potential evapotranspiration. Drylands cover approximately 41% of Earth's land surface and are home to about 38% of the human population. Drylands are not just a problem of deserts but cover large expanses, for example, of Canada's Prairie Provinces. However, between 10% and 20% of the drylands are subject to some form of severe land degradation, directly affecting the lives of at least 250 million people. Climate change, combined with increasing pressure on water resources for these people, their crops, and their animals, compounds the problems that confront them. Competition for limited resources, such as water, can generate local and international strife.

We have seen that complexity is an important and pervasive feature of ecosystems. Biodiversity is intimately associated with complexity, and disruption of this complexity often translates into reduced biodiversity and decay of ecosystems. Ironically, many social and economic systems that humans have developed are also subject to disruption by stress. This places the onus on our species to develop sustainable operations, whether in the area of agriculture, resource use and exploitation, or conservation.

## STUDY BREAK QUESTIONS

1. How is reproductive effort different between males and females in birds and in mammals?
2. How are drylands at risk?

## 28.12 Taking Action

Do individuals have the power to effect change? Think of things that have changed dramatically in a relatively short time. Two good examples are the abolition of slavery and the emancipation of women. In a way, these demonstrate humans' capacity for effecting change. On a more local level, the acceptance of the use of tobacco in public has declined remarkably in the past 20 years—in Canada and elsewhere. We also have seen the abolition of capital punishment and much more ready access to abortion in Canada.

But none of these changes is universal. In the daily news we find stories about people living in virtual slavery, of people executed in public, of women with few or no rights in their home countries. To complicate the matter, not everyone agrees that the changes listed above are for the better.

Effecting changes in our approach to conservation means identifying the root causes for the erosion of biodiversity and the things that are impediments to conservation. This means starting by changing our own lifestyles, including the food we eat and our use of energy. We must be wary of simple, and often misleading, solutions and avoid blaming someone else as a way of self-exoneration. We must respect the rights of others; use education and training to become informed; and learn to be objective, to examine and evaluate data or evidence. The outpouring of support for victims of the 2004 tsunami demonstrated that humans have great empathy for their fellows, and we need to extend this concern to the other species with whom we share the planet.

We have seen that action is needed at the species and the habitat level, and there is a propensity to focus more on species. But in the human view, all species are not equal. The 2006 IUCN list of threatened species shows that, whereas 20% of the described species of mammals were listed as threatened, only 0.07% of the insect species received this level of attention. Other interesting numbers from this table are 12% of described species of birds listed as threatened, 4% of fish species, 3.5% of dicotyledonous plants, and 0.006% of species of mushrooms. In Canada, the same situation prevails, with mammals and birds dominating the list of threatened species, with other taxa receiving less attention. Do these data about threatened species mean that mammals are more vulnerable than insects? That we care more about mammals than about insects? Or does it mean that there are more "experts" to offer opinions and data about mammals than about insects? Are the possibilities mutually exclusive?

The success of some native species, for example, Canada geese (**Figure 28.34**), is encouraging for many reasons. However, there can be downsides to large numbers of geese. Anyone who has walked barefoot on the grass in a park with lots of geese

**FIGURE 28.34 Three Canada geese (*Branta canadensis*) landing on the Humber River in Toronto**

will be familiar with one obvious problem posed by geese. Effective population management means finding humane ways to control populations of Canada geese and other species (e.g., raccoons, *Procyon lotor*) that thrive in urban and suburban habitats. In Toronto, Canada, there are ongoing biodiversity programs about native flora and fauna, from bats to bees, from native plants to restoration operations.

Biology can be at the centre of the movement to achieve conservation of biodiversity while being part of our efforts to achieve sustainable use of the resources we need as a species. Conservation begins at home when we modify our lifestyles and become active on any front, from protecting local habitat and species to protecting charismatic species elsewhere.

Our ability to make data-based decisions about conservation can increase the credibility of initiatives and the chances of their being successful. It is important to remember that one size does not fit all when it comes to conservation, whether focused at the species, habitat, or ecosystem level.

## STUDY BREAK QUESTIONS

1. Name three things you could change in your lifestyle to improve your impact on biodiversity.
2. Name three things that your local member of parliament might do to advance conservation of biodiversity.
3. What about the prime minister?

# Summary Illustration

Before humans, the conservation of any one species depended on that species surviving whatever environmental challenges came its way (survival of the fittest). Human population growth and technological advances have superimposed onto this dynamic additional stressors to species. Species are now disappearing at exacerbated rates due to land development (habitat destruction), climate change, overhunting, and other human-induced causes.

Early humans essentially lived in harmony with nature.

**Humans arrive**

## Extinction Events

Ordovician crisis
Devonian crisis
Permian crisis
Triassic crisis
Jurassic crisis
Cretaceous crisis

Number of families (y-axis: 0, 100, 200, 300, 400, 500, 600, 700, 800, 900)

Time (million years) (x-axis: 600, 500, 400, 300, 200, 100, 0)

Before humans, species came and went with radiations and extinction events (e.g., asteroids, volcanoes, ice ages).

**Pollution**

**Wastes**

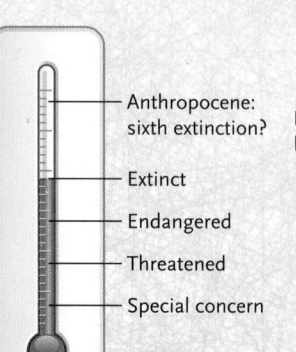

Anthropocene: sixth extinction? — Heats up threats to habitats and species

Extinct

Endangered

Threatened

Special concern

Globalization and transportation of goods facilitates invasive species.

$CO_2$

Conservationists can try to work outside of all of the cumulative impacts to conserve species, but will this stop extinctions?

(Background) Hotcriki0/Shutterstock.com

M.B. Fenton

rviewfinder/Shutterstock.com

NPS Photo

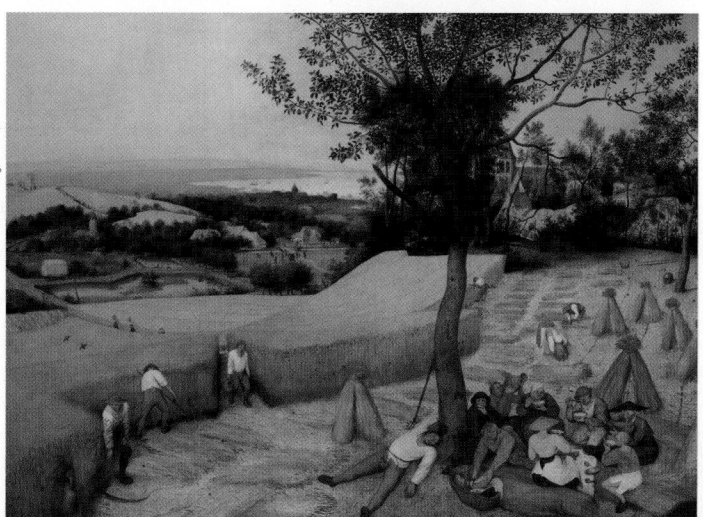

As human populations grew, the threat to biological conservation began.

The Harvesters, Pieter Bruegel the Elder. Metropolitan Museum of Art. Rogers Fund, 1919.

As human culture evolved, so did humans' ability to "tame" the land for their own purposes—the threat to biological conservation began to grow.

## Cumulative Impacts Threaten Biological Conservation

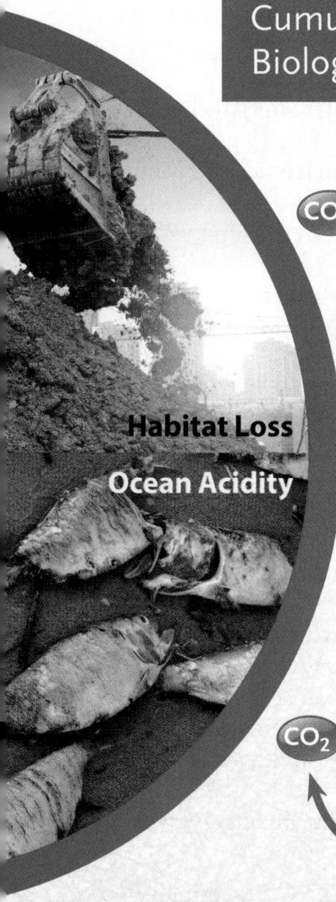
Habitat Loss
Ocean Acidity

$CO_2$

$CO_2$

$CO_2$

Overhunting results in extinctions.

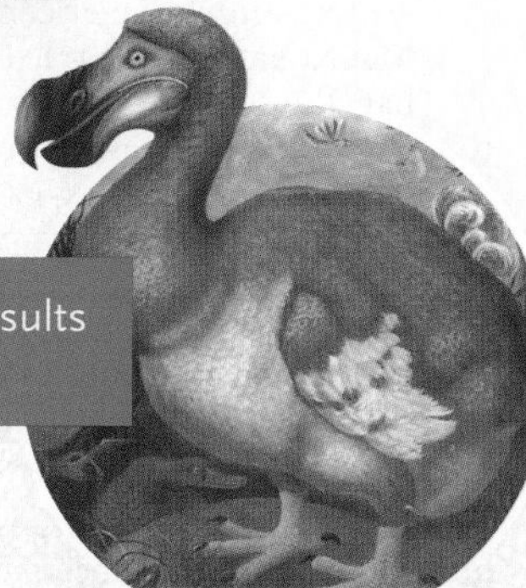

Raphus cucullatus by Roelandt Savery, 1626

Destroy habitat → Carbon

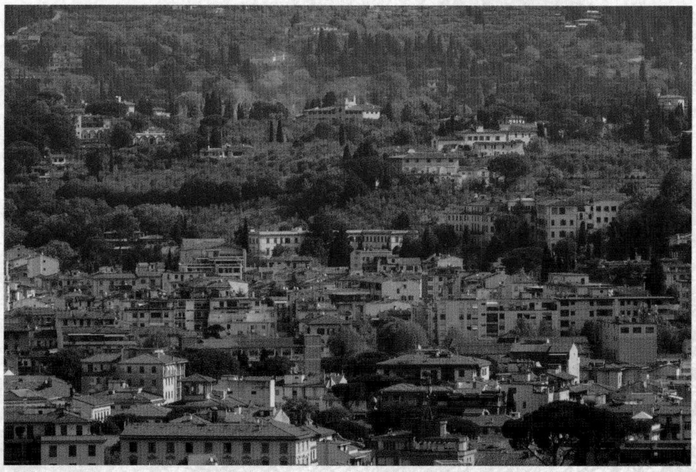

Kiattisak Anoochitarom/Shutterstock.com

Refinements in human culture and technological advances coincided with population growth, land development, and resource extraction.

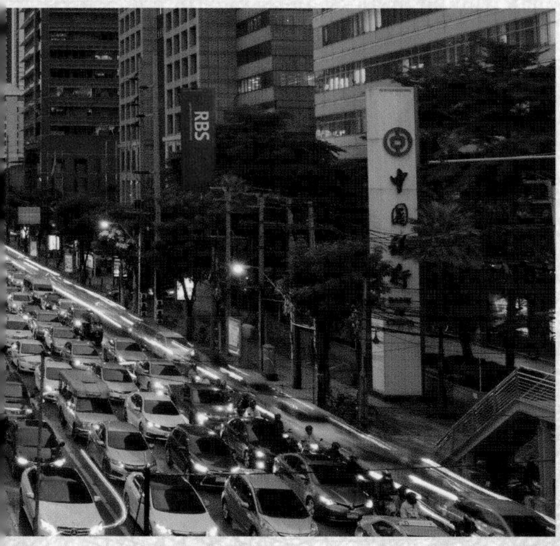
RBS

More humans leads to more habitat conversion and more resource extraction, which threatens more species.

Global warming results in physiological changes to some animals that can influence reproductive capacity.

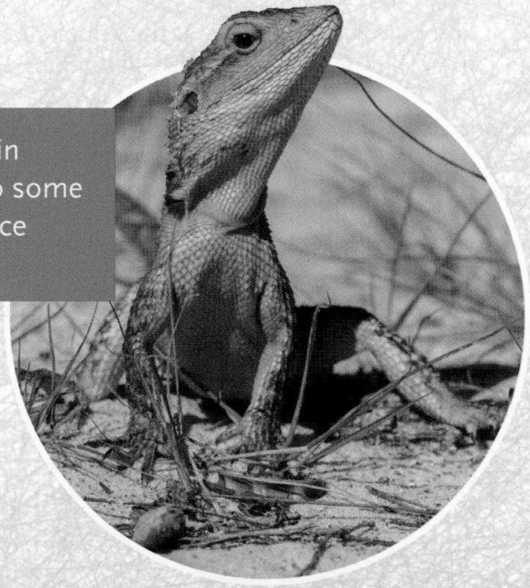

Belle Ciezak/Shutterstock.com

## Recall/Understand

1. How many mass extinctions were in Earth's history before the Anthropocene?
   a. 1
   b. 3
   c. at least 5
   d. at least 8

2. Which of these groups is an example of organisms pending imminent extinction or recently extinct?
   a. Pacific water shrew (*Sorex bendirii*), black rhino (*Diceros bicornis*), American ginseng (*Panax quinquefolius*), Mauritian Calvaria tree (*Sideroxylon majus*), Egyptian fruit bat (*Rousettus aegyptiacus*)
   b. Pacific water shrew (*Sorex bendirii*), white rhino (*Ceratotherium simum*), American ginseng (*Panax quinquefolius*), Mauritian Calvaria tree (*Sideroxylon majus*), Egyptian fruit bat (*Rousettus aegyptiacus*)
   c. Pacific water shrew (*Sorex bendirii*), black rhino (*Diceros bicornis*), American ginseng (*Panax quinquefolius*), Mauritian Calvaria tree (*Sideroxylon majus*), little brown myotis (*Myotis lucifugus*)
   d. Pacific water shrew (*Sorex bendirii*), white rhino (*Ceratotherium simum*), American ginseng (*Panax quinquefolius*), Mauritian Calvaria tree (*Sideroxylon majus*), little brown myotis (*Myotis lucifugus*)

3. Which of the following makes leopards an interesting example of human responses to conservation?
   a. Humans do not hunt leopards.
   b. Leopards are not a vulnerable species.
   c. Leopards live only in Africa.
   d. Hunting is not necessarily a threat to the survival of leopards as a species.

4. Which of these action steps is an effective way to conserve biodiversity in the European Economic Community?
   a. turning natural habitats completely into human-controlled land
   b. creating islands artificially
   c. setting aside 5% of agricultural land as natural habitat
   d. breaking landscapes into smaller areas of land

5. What is the significance of ballast water in ships?
   a. Ballast water is stagnant water, which provides life to a variety of organisms, allowing us to learn about their biodiversity.
   b. Ballast water is taken on in one port and discharged in another, providing many species with great opportunities to move around the world.
   c. Ballast water is a great source of preserved animal and plant remains.
   d. Ballast water is a great source of viruses.

6. If human population growth continues at the same rate as it is growing now, when is it most likely that it will double?
   a. in 20 years
   b. in 40 years
   c. in 60 years
   d. in 80 years

7. CITES is designed to stop international trade of endangered species. Which of these species was effectively protected by CITES?
   a. passenger pigeons
   b. black rhinos
   c. Canada geese
   d. leopards

8. In 1950, Sri Lanka and Afghanistan had the same population. By 2050, Afghanistan will have four times as many people as Sri Lanka. What is the main reason for this?
   a. Afghanistan began strong efforts to make family planning available.
   b. Sri Lanka began strong efforts to make family planning available.
   c. The Sri Lankan government imposed a rule of one child per family.
   d. Afghanistan males have not undergone sterilization.

9. Which of these pairs of species were common about 50 years ago, but by 2008 both demonstrated risks of being rare and vulnerable?
   a. African savannah elephant (*Loxodonta Africana*) and white rhino (*Ceratotherium simum*)
   b. African savannah elephant (*Loxodonta Africana*) and Mauritian Calvaria tree (*Sideroxylon majus*)
   c. black rhino (*Diceros bicornis*) and American ginseng (*Panax quinquefolius*)
   d. white rhino (*Ceratotherium simum*) and American ginseng (*Panax quinquefolius*)

## Apply/Analyze

10. What is the connection between iridium and dinosaur extinction?
    a. Iridium ended up in the water on early Earth, which poisoned all the dinosaurs.
    b. Iridium dust is flammable, and it probably caused massive fires on Earth, which drove dinosaurs to extinction.
    c. Iridium is rare on Earth but common in asteroids, which suggests that an iridium-laden asteroid could have hit Earth, causing dinosaur extinction.
    d. Iridium is radioactive, suggesting that its radioactivity was enough to kill all dinosaurs on Earth.

11. Which of the following is good evidence that the Cretaceous mass extinction was caused by an asteroid impact?
    a. high concentration of iridium in rocks and a crater off the coast of Mexico
    b. earthquakes and volcano eruptions
    c. floods and fires
    d. dust, darkness, and cooling

12. Which tertiary consumers have experienced increases in populations that may explain the demise of scallops off the southeastern coast of the United States?
    a. skates and rays
    b. sharks
    c. killer whales
    d. pelagic seabirds

13. Which of these environmental factors is particularly important for reptiles, and why?
    a. humidity, because it determines their body temperature
    b. humidity, because it determines their food quality
    c. temperature, because it determines their gender
    d. temperature, because it determines their nesting sites

## Create/Evaluate

14. Suppose that a species no longer occurs in Canada but still lives in the United States. Which of these terms best describes the status of this species?
    a. extinct
    b. extirpated
    c. highly endangered
    d. not at risk

15. What is the difference between an extirpated species and an endangered species?

# Chapter Roadmap

**Population Ecology**

The realities of population biology underlie many of the challenges facing our species in general, and biologists in particular.

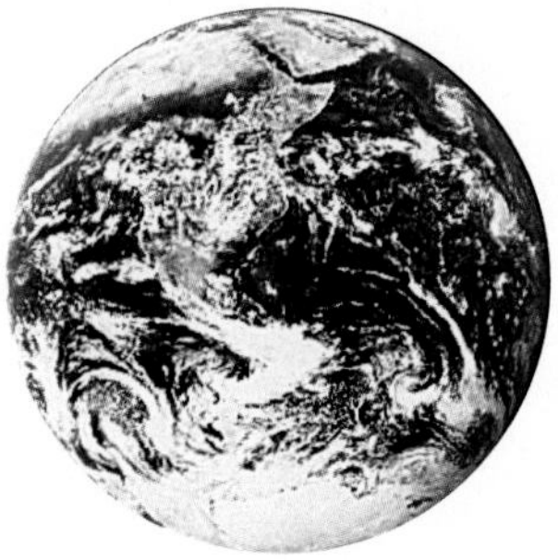

NASA

**29.1 Introduction**

↓

**29.2 Population Characteristics**

↓

**29.3 Demography**

↓

**29.4 Evolution of Life Histories**

↓

**29.5 Models of Population Growth**

↓

**29.6 Population Regulation** → **To Chapter 30**

↓

**29.7 Human Administered Population Control**

↓

**29.8 Human Population Growth**

↓

**29.9 The Future: Where Are We Going?**

↓

**29.10 The Pill**

M.B. Fenton

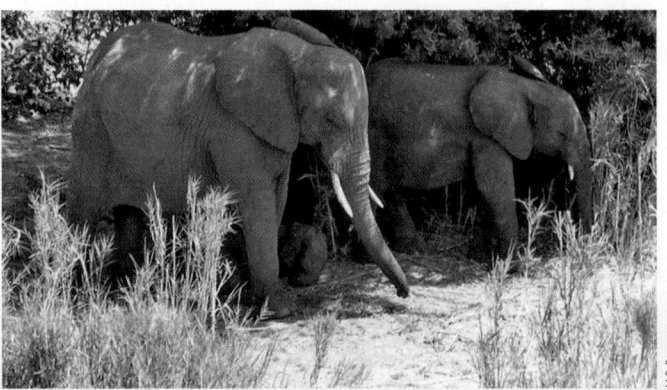

Populations have characteristics that transcend those of the individuals comprising the populations.

# Population Ecology

# 29

**Why it matters . . .** The realities of population ecology underlie many of the challenges facing our species in general, and biologists in particular. Malaria is a good example of the range of realities for at least three reason: first, its impact on millions of humans; second, the resilience of the parasites (mainly *Plasmodium falciparum* and *Plasmodium vivax*) that cause malaria; third, the ubiquity and resilience of the blood-eating insects (the vectors: mosquitoes, mainly *Anopheles* spp.) that move the parasites among prey. Malaria is mainly a disease of the tropics and subtropics **(Figure 29.1)**. One indication of the importance of malaria is that human deaths from malaria have affected the outcomes of wars in many parts of the world.

In 2015, the WHO (World Health Organization) estimated that almost half the world's human population is at risk of being exposed to malaria. Children, pregnant women, and travellers from more temperate parts of the world are most often severely affected by malaria. Today, malaria has the greatest impact on humans in Africa. In 2015, 89% of 214 million cases of malaria occurred there, as well as 91% of 438 000 human deaths from the disease. The numbers side of the impact of malaria on human mortality is clear.

What can we do about this life-threatening disease that is both preventable and curable? The simplest way to avoid exposure to malaria is to ensure that you are not bitten by a mosquito carrying the parasite. Virtually all the vector species bite between dusk and dawn. This means that using an insect repellent and sleeping under an insect net treated with insecticide are good preventative measures. But, as anyone who has worked or slept in areas with mosquitoes will know, neither approach is guaranteed to provide protection. The nets have to be treated and maintained and the repellent applied repeatedly.

Controlling populations of mosquitoes is another avenue of defence against malaria. This may mean minimizing sites for them to breed (females lay eggs in stagnant water) or spraying

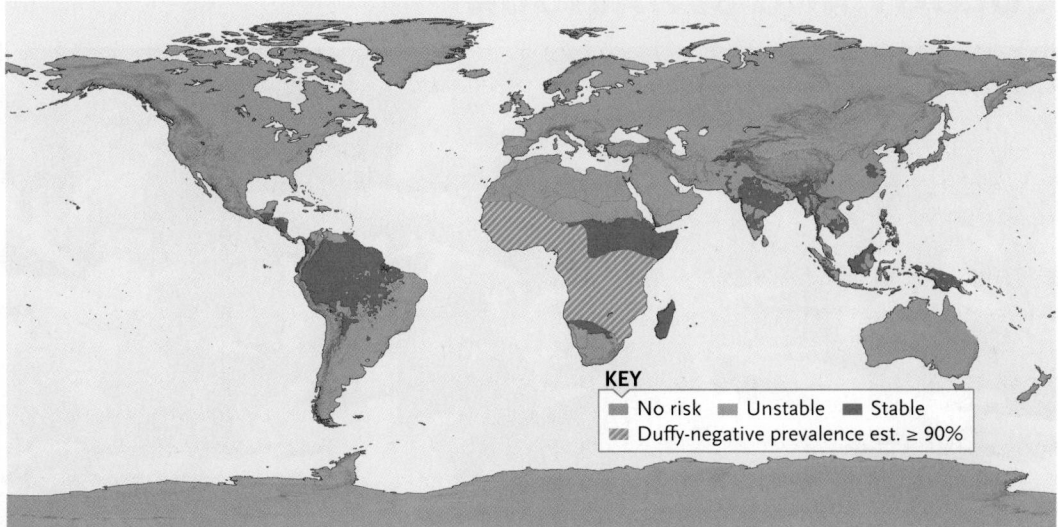

**FIGURE 29.1  An estimation of the risks of exposure to vivax malaria.** Duffy-negative prevalence is an indication of infection by vivax malaria.

Source: Guerra CA, Howes RE, Patil AP, Gething PW, Van Boeckel TP, Temperley WH, et al. (2010) The International Limits and Population at Risk of Plasmodium vivax Transmission in 2009. *PLoS Negl Trop Dis* 4(8): e774. https://doi.org/10.1371/journal.pntd.0000774

them with insecticides. Increasing incidences of mosquito resistance to insecticides, including those in bed nets, erodes the effectiveness of control by insecticides.

Malaria is treatable, usually with an artemisinin-based combination therapy (ACT), but resistance to ACTs and other treatments poses an ongoing problem for this line of defence. Antimalarial medicines suppress the blood stage of the *Plasmodium* and, again, resistance to these drugs makes this approach less effective. Furthermore, antimalarial drugs have significant side effects, another weakness of this approach to controlling malaria.

Dealing with malaria is an ongoing challenge for public health authorities because it requires engaging on the level of treating the disease, controlling the vector, and reducing

human exposure to the vector. The need for continuous vigilance and treatment places a large burden on the economies of some of the countries hardest hit by malaria. Indeed, malaria control is an example of a Sisyphean problem.

According to the myth, Zeus, the supreme Greek God, punished Sisyphus, the King of what is now Corinth, for craftiness and deceitfulness. In Hades, Sisyphus faced a life of eternal frustration because the boulder he had to push up a hill always rolled back down. Sisyphean problems are common in population ecology. Controlling malaria is an example of a Sisyphean problem.

For example, consider the incidence of malaria in Zanzibar **(Figure 29.2)**. Zanzibar, an archipelago of several islands off the east coast of Africa, has a population of 1.3 million people,

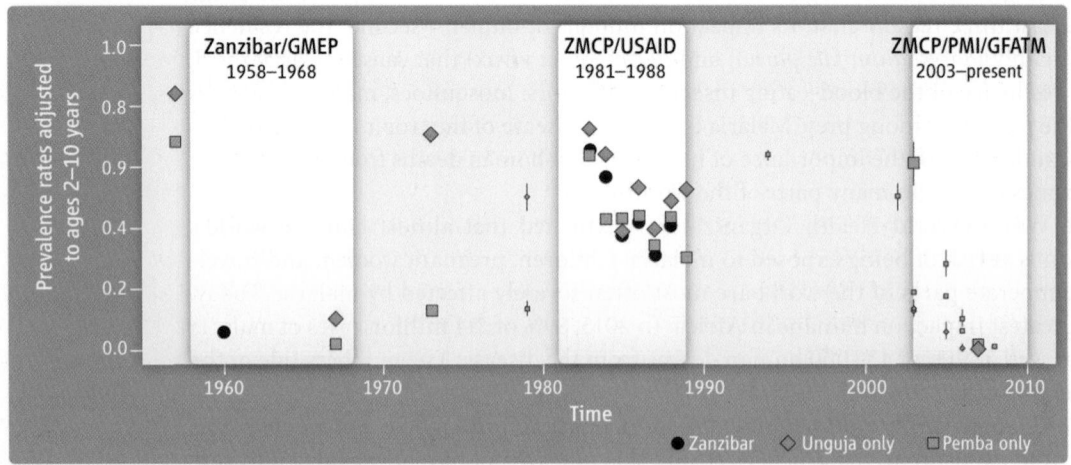

**FIGURE 29.2  Incidence of malaria parasites in children between 1958 and 2010.** During periods of concerted efforts to reduce or eliminate malaria, the incidence of parasites in children drops, only to rebound when control measures are stopped. Large symbols represent regional and national surveys; smaller symbols, smaller-scale surveys. GMEP was part of the Global Malaria Eradication Programme, ZMCP was the Zanzibar Malaria Control Programme assisted by USAID, and ZMCP/PMI/GFATM is the Zanzibar Malaria Control Programme assisted by the U.S. President's Malaria Initiative and the Global Fund to Fight AIDS, Tuberculosis, and Malaria. Here, Zanzibar refers to all the islands; Pemba and Unguja are specific islands in the archipelago.

Source: From Smith, D.L., J.M. Cohen, B. Moonen, A.J. Tatem, O.J. Sabot, A. Ali and S.M. Mugheiry. 2011. "Solving the Sisyphean problem of malaria in Zanzibar." *Science*, vol. 332: 1384–1385. *Science* by American Association for the Advancement of Science Reproduced with permission of AMERICAN ASSOCIATION FOR THE ADVANCEMENT OF SCIENCE in the format Republish in a book via Copyright Clearance Center.

compared to 1.1 billion in Africa. Annual antimalarial efforts in Zanzibar prevent about 600 000 cases of, and about 3300 deaths from, malaria. The cost is about US$1183 per death averted and US$34.50 per impact of reducing the incidence of the disease.

Data on the prevalence of the malarial parasite in children (Figure 29.2) demonstrate why it is essential to maintain antimalarial programs. This is vital even in the face of success measured as fewer cases of malaria and fewer deaths from it. Arrival of people already infected with the malarial parasite in Zanzibar results in new cases of the disease and is part of the problem. This problem is Sisyphean because, as soon as efforts to control malaria are cut back, the incidence of disease increases, along with deaths from it.

To further complicate the situation, malaria caused by *Plasmodium falciparum* has received more attention than the apparently less lethal malaria caused by *Plasmodium vivax*. Vivax malaria is widespread (Figure 29.1) and any overall program to control malaria must consider both variants of the disease. Global warming adds another dimension to issues related to malaria. An obvious example is the consequences of warming that allows vector species to overwinter in areas that used to be too cold.

## 29.1 Introduction

The population ecology roots of such problems lie in patterns of population growth: the impact of $r$ (intrinsic rate of increase), $N$ (population size), and $K$ (carrying capacity). Perhaps Sisyphus's challenge was modest compared to that posed by some problems in population ecology! As we shall see, the growing population of humans remains an urgent and pressing problem.

## 29.2 Population Characteristics

We can describe at least eight characteristics of any population, including geographic range, size, density, dispersion, age structure, generation time, sex ratio, and incidence of reproducing individuals. Populations have characteristics that transcend those of the individuals comprising the populations. Every population has a **geographic range** (the overall space in which it lives) and this can vary considerably. A population of snails might inhabit a small tide pool, whereas a population of marine phytoplankton might occur over a much, much larger area. Every population also occurs in a **habitat** or range of habitats that offers the necessary biotic and abiotic features. Some animals occupy widely separated habitats and migrate between them.

**Population size** is the number of individuals making up the population at a specified time ($N_t$). **Population density** is the number of individuals per unit area or per unit volume of habitat. Species with a large body size generally have lower population densities than those with a small body size **(Figure 29.3)**. Although population size and density are related measures, knowing a population's density provides more information about its relationship to the resources it uses. If a population of 200 oak trees occupies one hectare (ha; 10 000 m²), the population density

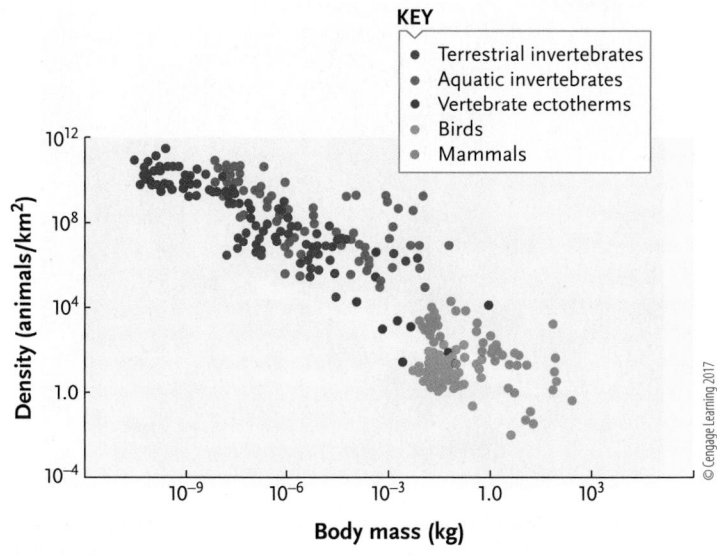

**FIGURE 29.3 Population density and body size.** Population density generally declines with increasing body size among animal species. There are similar trends for other organisms.

is 200 × 10 000 m⁻², or 1 tree per 50 m². But if 200 oaks are spread over 5 ha, the density is 1 tree per 250 m². Clearly, the second population is less dense than the first, and its members will have greater access to sunlight, water, and other resources.

Ecologists use population size and density to monitor and manage populations of endangered species, economically important species, and agricultural pests. For large-bodied species, a simple head count may provide accurate information about population size. For example, ecologists survey the size and density of populations of African elephants by flying over herds and counting individuals **(Figure 29.4)**. Researchers use a variation on that technique to estimate population size in tiny organisms that live at high population densities. To estimate the density of aquatic phytoplankton, for example, you might collect water samples of known volume from representative areas in a lake and count them by looking through a microscope. These data allow you to estimate population size and density based on the estimated volume of the entire lake. One ongoing challenge is measuring population size in organisms that are clones, for example, stands of poplar trees (*Populus* spp.).

Populations can vary in their **dispersion** (the spatial distribution of individuals within the geographic range). Some populations are clumped, reflecting different situations. Clumped populations may reflect the distribution of essential resources. Certain pasture plants, for instance, are clumped in small, scattered areas where cowpats had fallen and locally enriched the soil. Some animals are social, occurring together in groups of varying size. In some cases the essential resources are food or shelter, or sometimes mates. Social individuals may cooperate in rearing offspring, feeding, or defence against predators. Other clumped distributions occur in species that reproduce by asexual clones and remain attached to the parents. Aspen trees and sea anemones reproduce this way and often occur in large aggregations (see Chapter 18). Clumping may also occur in species in

FIGURE 29.4 **Counting elephants.** It is easy to think that large animals such as African elephants (*Loxodonta africana*) would be easy to count from the air **(a)**. This may or may not be true, depending on vegetation. But it can be easy to overlook animals, particularly young ones **(b)**, in the shade.

which seeds, eggs, or larvae lack dispersal mechanisms and offspring grow and settle near their parents **(Figure 29.5)**.

Uniform distributions can occur when individuals repel or avoid one another because resources are in short supply. Creosote bushes are uniformly distributed in the dry scrub deserts of the U.S. Southwest. Mature bushes deplete the surrounding soil of water and secrete toxic chemicals, making it impossible for seedlings to grow. This chemical warfare is called *allelopathy*. Moreover, seed-eating ants and rodents living at the bases of mature bushes eat any seeds that fall nearby. In these situations, the distributions of species of plants and animals can be uniform and interrelated. Territorial behaviour (the defence of an area and its resources) can also produce **uniform dispersion** in some species of animals, such as nests in colonies of colonial birds (see Chapter 32).

FIGURE 29.5 **(a)** Populations of the mushroom *Craterellus tubaeformis* are associated with pitcher plants (*Sarracenia purpurea*) in bogs. Both tend to be clumped. **(b)** Other species, such as toque macaques (*Macaca sinica*), are social. **(c)** In other species, aggregations of individuals reflect the availability of food and water (ducks, *Anas platyrhynchos*).

**Random dispersion** occurs when environmental conditions do not vary much within a habitat, and individuals are neither attracted to nor repelled by others of their species (conspecifics). Ecologists use formal statistical definitions of *random* to establish a theoretical baseline for assessing the pattern of distribution. In cases of random dispersion, individuals are distributed unpredictably. Some spiders, burrowing clams, and rainforest trees exhibit random dispersion.

Whether the spatial distribution of a population appears to be clumped, uniform, or random depends partly on the size of the organisms and of the study area. Oak seedlings may be randomly dispersed on a spatial scale of a few square metres, but over an entire mixed hardwood forest, they are clumped under the parent trees. Therefore, dispersion of a population depends partly on the researcher's scale of observation.

In addition, the dispersion of animal populations often varies through time in response to natural environmental rhythms. Few habitats provide a constant supply of resources throughout the year, and many animals move from one habitat to another on a seasonal cycle, reflecting the distribution of resources such as food. Tropical birds and mammals are often widely dispersed in deciduous forests during the wet season, when food is widely available. During the dry season, these species crowd into narrow gallery forests along watercourses, where evergreen trees provide food and shelter.

All populations have an **age structure**, a statistical description of the relative numbers of individuals in each age class (see also Section 29.8). Individuals can be categorized generally as pre-reproductive (younger than the age of sexual maturity), reproductive, or post-reproductive (older than maximum age of reproduction). The age structure of a population reflects its recent growth history and can be used to predict future growth. Populations composed of many pre-reproductive individuals must have grown rapidly in the recent past. These populations will continue to grow as individuals mature and reproduce.

**Generation time** also influences a population's potential for growth or decline. Generation time is the average time between the birth of an organism and the birth of its offspring. Generation time usually is short in species that reach sexual maturity at a small body size **(Figure 29.6)**. Their populations often grow rapidly because of the speedy accumulation of reproducing individuals.

The proportions of males and females may vary in populations of sexually reproducing organisms. In a species where only females produce young, the number of females has a larger impact on population growth than the number of males. Moreover, in many species, one male can mate with several females, and the number of males may have little effect on the population's reproductive output. In northern elephant seals (see Chapter 17), mature bulls fight for dominance on the beaches

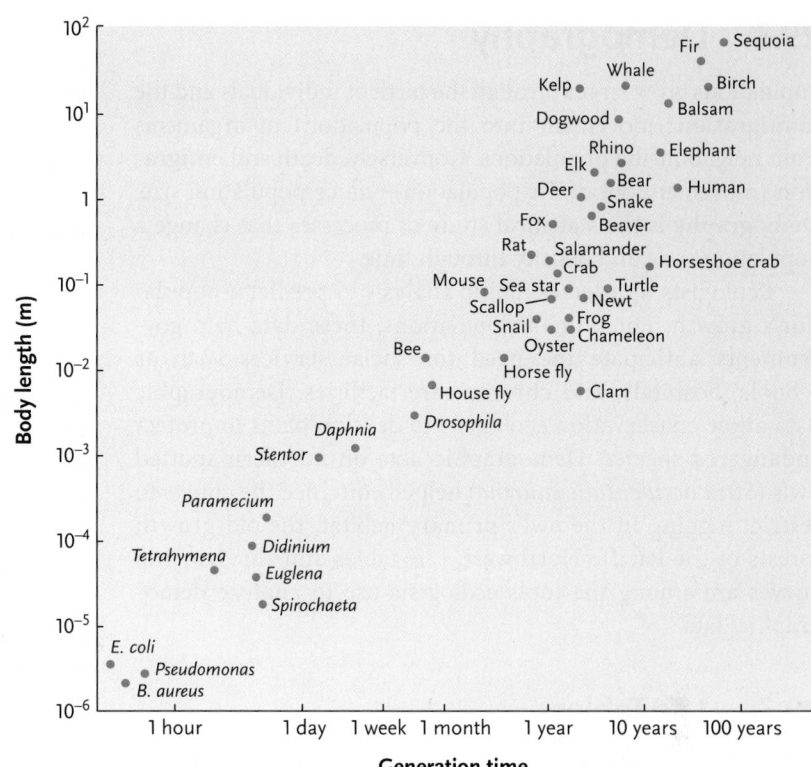

**FIGURE 29.6 Generation time and body size.** Generation time increases with body size among bacteria, protists, plants, and animals. The logarithmic scale on both axes compresses the data into a straight line.

where the seals mate. While a few males each may inseminate many females and sire many young, most males do not. Thus, the presence of other males in the group may have little effect on the size of future generations. In animals that form lifelong pair bonds, such as geese and swans, the number of pairs influences reproduction in the population.

Population ecologists try to determine the **proportion of reproducing individuals** in a population. This issue is particularly relevant to the conservation of any species in which individuals are rare or widely dispersed (see Chapter 32).

**CONCEPT FIX** Many people believe that the sizes of populations of animals and plants will increase until net demands for food (and other resources) exceed the supply. This crisis of carrying capacity leads to crashes in populations and even to extinction. Under natural conditions, however, interactions among individuals (of the same or different species) usually cause populations to stop growing well before they reach carrying capacity. In many populations, there are natural cycles of numbers. ⬡

## STUDY BREAK QUESTIONS

1. What is the difference between geographic range and habitat?
2. What are the three types of dispersion? What is the most common pattern found in nature? Why?
3. What is the common pattern of generation time among bacteria, protists, plants, and animals?

## 29.3 Demography

Populations grow larger through the birth of individuals and the **immigration** (movement into the population) of organisms from neighbouring populations. Conversely, death and **emigration** (movement out of the population) reduce population size. **Demography** is the statistical study of processes that change a population's size and density through time.

Ecologists use demographic analysis to predict a population's growth. For human populations, these data help governments anticipate the need for social services such as schools, hospitals, and chronic care facilities. Demographic data allow conservation ecologists to develop plans to protect endangered species. Demographic data on northern spotted owls (*Strix occidentalis caurina*) helped convince the courts to restrict logging in the owl's primary habitat, the old-growth forests of the Pacific Northwest. Life tables and survivorship curves are among the tools ecologists use to analyze demographic data.

### 29.3a Life Tables

Although every species has a characteristic lifespan, few individuals survive to the maximum age possible. Mortality results from starvation, disease, accidents, predation, or inability to find a suitable habitat. Life insurance companies first developed techniques for measuring mortality rates (known as *actuarial science*), and ecologists adapted these approaches to study populations of other organisms.

A **life table** summarizes the demographic characteristics of a population **(Table 29.1)**. To collect life table data for short-lived organisms, demographers typically mark a **cohort** (a group of individuals of similar age) at birth and monitor their survival until all members of the cohort die. For organisms that live more than a few years, a researcher might sample the population for one or two years, recording the ages at which individuals die and then extrapolating these results over the species' lifespan. The approach to the timing of collection of data about reproduction and longevity will depend on the details of the species under study.

In any life table, lifespans of organisms are divided into age intervals of appropriate length. For short-lived species, days, weeks, or months are useful, whereas for longer-lived species, years or groups of years will be better. Mortality can be expressed in two complementary ways: **age-specific mortality** is the proportion of individuals alive at the start of an age interval that died during that age interval. Its more cheerful reflection, **age-specific survivorship**, is the proportion of individuals alive at the start of an age interval that survived until the start of the next age interval. Thus, for the data shown in Table 29.1, the age-specific mortality rate during the three- to six-month age interval is $195/722 = 0.270$, and the age-specific survivorship rate is $527/722 = 0.730$. For any age interval, the sum of age-specific mortality and age-specific survivorship must equal 1. Life tables also summarize the proportion of the cohort that survived to a particular age, a statistic identifying the probability that any randomly selected newborn will still be alive at that age. For the three- to six-month age interval in Table 29.1, this probability is $722/843 = 0.856$.

Life tables also include data on **age-specific fecundity**, the average number of offspring produced by surviving females during each age interval. Table 29.1 shows that plants in the three- to six-month age interval produced an average of 300 seeds each. In some species, including humans, fecundity is highest in individuals of intermediate age. Younger individuals have not yet reached sexual maturity, and older individuals are past their reproductive prime. However, fecundity increases steadily with age in some plants and animals.

| TABLE 29.1 | Life Table for a Cohort of 843 Individuals of the Grass *Poa annua* (Annual Bluegrass) | | | | | |
|---|---|---|---|---|---|---|
| Age Interval (in months) | Number Alive at Start of Age Interval | Number Dying during Age Interval | Age-Specific Mortality Rate | Age-Specific Survivorship Rate | Proportion of Original Cohort Alive at Start of Age Interval | Age-Specific Fecundity (Seed Production) |
| 0–3 | 843 | 121 | 0.144 | 0.856 | 1.000 | 0 |
| 3–6 | 722 | 195 | 0.270 | 0.730 | 0.856 | 300 |
| 6–9 | 527 | 211 | 0.400 | 0.600 | 0.625 | 620 |
| 9–12 | 316 | 172 | 0.544 | 0.456 | 0.375 | 430 |
| 12–15 | 144 | 90 | 0.625 | 0.375 | 0.171 | 210 |
| 15–18 | 54 | 39 | 0.722 | 0.278 | 0.064 | 60 |
| 18–21 | 15 | 12 | 0.800 | 0.200 | 0.018 | 30 |
| 21–24 | 3 | 3 | 1.000 | 0.000 | 0.004 | 10 |
| 24– | 0 | — | — | — | — | — |

Source: *Population Ecology : A Unified Study of Animals and Plants* by BEGON, MICHAEL ; MORTIMER, MARTIN Reproduced with permission of BLACKWELL SCIENCE in the format Book via Copyright Clearance Center.

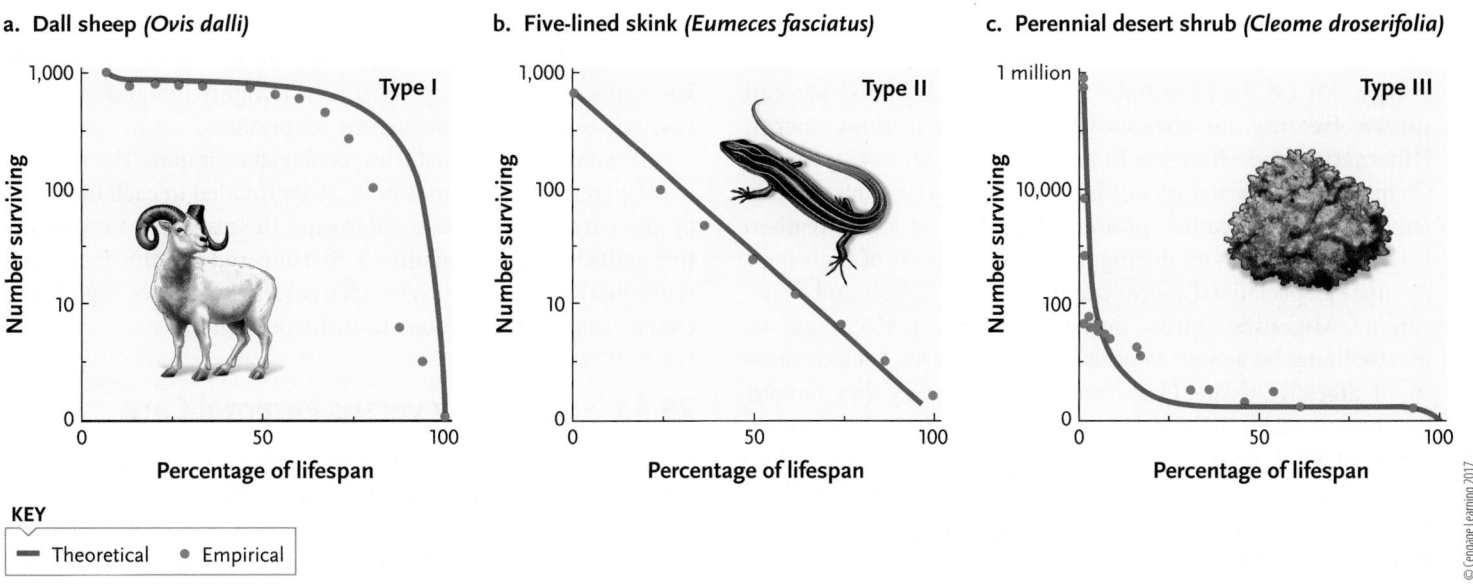

**a. Dall sheep (Ovis dalli)**  Type I

**b. Five-lined skink (Eumeces fasciatus)**  Type II

**c. Perennial desert shrub (Cleome droserifolia)**  Type III

**KEY**
— Theoretical  • Empirical

© Cengage Learning 2017

**FIGURE 29.7 Survivorship curves.** The survivorship curves of many organisms (pink) roughly match one of three idealized patterns (blue).

## 29.3b Survivorship Curves

Survivorship data are depicted graphically in a **survivorship curve**, which displays the rate of survival for individuals over the species' average lifespan. Ecologists have identified three generalized survivorship curves (blue lines in **Figure 29.7**), although most organisms exhibit survivorship patterns falling between these idealized patterns.

Type I curves reflect high survivorship until late in life (see Figure 29.7a). They are typical of large animals that produce few young and reduce juvenile mortality with extended care. Large mammals, such as Dall mountain sheep, produce only one or two offspring at a time and nurture them through their first year. At that time, the young are better able to fend for themselves and are at lower risk for mortality (compared with younger animals). The picture of survivorship in mammals could change if one starts with the time of conception, as opposed to birth. The change would reflect problems of pregnancy (see Chapter 44) and health of mothers.

Type II curves reflect a relatively constant rate of mortality in all age classes, a pattern that produces steadily declining survivorship (see Figure 29.7b). Many lizards, such as the five-lined skink, as well as songbirds and small mammals face a constant probability of mortality from predation, disease, and starvation and show a type II pattern.

Type III curves reflect high juvenile mortality, followed by a period of low mortality once offspring reach a critical age and size (see Figure 29.7c, in which the vertical scale is logarithmic). *Cleome droserifolia*, a desert shrub from the Middle East, experiences extraordinarily high mortality in its seed and seedling stages. Researchers estimate that, for every 1 million seeds produced, fewer than 1000 germinate, and only about 40 individuals survive their first year. Once a plant becomes established, however, its likelihood of future survival is higher, and the survivorship curve flattens out. Many plants, insects, marine invertebrates, and fishes exhibit type III survivorship.

### STUDY BREAK QUESTIONS

1. What is the relationship between age-specific mortality and age-specific survivorship? If the age-specific mortality is 0.384, what is the age-specific survivorship?
2. What is age-specific fecundity?
3. Describe three survivorship curves. Which curve describes humans? Songbirds? Insects?

## 29.4 Evolution of Life Histories

Analysis of life tables reveals how natural selection affects an organism's life history, which includes the lifetime patterns of growth, maturation, and reproduction. Ecologists study life histories to understand trade-offs in the allocation of resources to these three activities. The results of their research suggest that natural selection adjusts the allocation of resources to maximize an individual's number of surviving offspring.

Every organism is constrained by a finite **energy budget**, the total amount of energy it can accumulate and use to fuel its activities. An organism's energy budget is like a savings account. When the individual accumulates more energy than it needs, it makes deposits to this account, storing energy as starch, glycogen, or fat. When the individual expends more energy than it harvests, it makes withdrawals from its energy stores. But unlike a bank account, an organism's energy budget cannot be overdrawn, and no loans against future "earnings" are possible.

Just as humans find clever ways to finance their schemes, many organisms use different ways to mortgage their operations. Organisms that enter states of inactivity or dormancy can maximize the time over which they use stored energy. An extreme example is animals and plants that can survive freezing, an obvious strategy for conserving energy. Hibernation and estivation in animals are other examples (see Chapter 42). Hibernating animals use periods of reduced body temperature to weather prolonged periods of cold weather. Estivation is inactivity during prolonged periods of high temperatures. Specialized spores can be resistant to heat and desiccation. Migrating birds on long flights get energy by metabolizing fat as well as other body structures, such as muscle or digestive tissue. Organisms use the energy they harvest for three broadly defined functions: maintenance (the preservation of good physiological condition), growth, and reproduction. When an organism devotes energy to any one of these functions, the balance in its energy budget is reduced, leaving less energy for other functions.

A fish, a deciduous tree, and a mammal illustrate the dramatic variations existing in life history patterns. Larval coho salmon (*Oncorhynchus kisutch*) hatch in the headwaters of a stream, where they feed and grow for about a year before assuming their adult body form and swimming to the ocean. They remain at sea for a year or two, feeding voraciously and growing rapidly. Eventually, using a Sun compass and geomagnetic and chemical cues, salmon return to the rivers and streams where they hatched. The fishes swim upstream. Males prepare nests and try to attract females. Each female lays hundreds or thousands of relatively small eggs. After breeding, the body condition of males and females deteriorates, and they die.

Most deciduous trees in the temperate zone, such as oaks (genus *Quercus*), begin their lives as nuts (acorns) in late summer. The acorns remain metabolically inactive until the following spring or a later year. After germinating, seedling trees collect nutrients and energy and continue to grow throughout their lives. Once they achieve a critical size, they may produce thousands of acorns annually for many years. Thus, growth and reproduction occur simultaneously through much of the trees' life.

European red deer (*Cervus elaphus*) are born in spring and the young remain with their mothers for an extended period, nursing and growing rapidly. After weaning, the young feed on their own. Female red deer begin to breed after reaching adult size in their third year, producing one or two offspring annually until they die at about 16 years of age, the usual maximum lifespan.

How can we summarize the similarities and differences in the life histories of these organisms? All three species harvest energy throughout their lives. Salmon and deciduous trees continue to grow until old age, whereas deer reach adult size fairly early in life. Salmon produce many offspring in a single reproductive episode, whereas deciduous trees and deer reproduce repeatedly. However, most trees produce thousands of seeds annually, whereas deer produce only one or two young each spring.

What factors have produced these variations in life history patterns? Life history traits, like all population characteristics,

are modified by natural selection. Thus, organisms exhibit evolutionary adaptations that increase the fitness of individuals. Each species' life history is, in fact, a highly integrated "strategy," or suite of selection-driven adaptations.

In analyzing life histories, ecologists compare the number of offspring with the amount of care provided to each offspring by the parents. They also determine the number of reproductive episodes in the organism's lifetime and the timing of first reproduction. Because these characteristics evolve together, a change in one trait is likely to influence others.

## 29.4a Fecundity versus Parental Care

A female with a fixed amount of energy for reproduction can package it in various ways. A female duck with 1000 units of energy for reproduction might lay 10 eggs, each with 100 units of energy. A salmon, which has higher fecundity, might lay 1000 eggs each with 1 unit of energy. Energy invested in each offspring before birth is **passive parental care**, usually provided by the female. Passive parental care is provided through yolk in an egg; endosperm in a seed; or, in mammals, nutrients that cross the placenta.

Many animals also provide **active parental care** after birth. In general, species producing many offspring in a reproductive episode (e.g., the coho salmon) provide relatively little active parental care to each offspring. In fact, female coho salmon, each producing 2400 to 4500 eggs, die before their eggs even hatch. Conversely, species producing few offspring at a time (e.g., European red deer) provide much more care to each one. A red deer doe nurses its single fawn for up to eight months before weaning it.

## 29.4b How Often to Breed

The number of reproductive episodes in an organism's lifespan is a second life history characteristic acted on by natural selection. Some organisms, such as coho salmon, devote all their stored energy to a single reproductive event. Any adult that survives the upstream migration is likely to leave some surviving offspring. Other species, such as deciduous trees and red deer, reproduce more than once. In contrast to salmon, individuals of these species devote only some of their energy budget to reproduction at any time, with the balance allocated to maintenance and growth. Moreover, in some plants, invertebrates, fishes, and reptiles, larger individuals produce more offspring than smaller ones. Thus, one advantage of using only part of the energy budget for reproduction is that continued growth may result in greater fecundity at a later age. But organisms that do not survive until the next breeding season lose the potential advantage of putting energy into maintenance and growth.

## 29.4c Age at First Reproduction

Individuals that first reproduce at the earliest possible age may have a good chance of leaving some surviving offspring. But the energy they use in reproduction is not available for maintenance and growth. Thus, early reproducers may be smaller and less healthy than individuals that delay reproduction in favour of other functions. Conversely, an individual that delays reproduction may increase its chance of survival and its future fecundity by becoming larger or more experienced. But there is always a chance that it will die before the next breeding season, leaving no offspring at all. Therefore, a finite energy budget and the risk of mortality establish a trade-off in the timing of first reproduction. Mathematical models suggest that delayed reproduction will be favoured by natural selection, when a sexually mature individual is likely to survive to an older age. This can be correct if organisms grow larger as they age and if larger organisms have higher fecundity. Early reproduction will be favoured if adult survival rates are low, if animals do not grow larger as they age, or if larger size does not increase fecundity. These characteristics apply more readily to some animals and plants than they do to others. Among animals, the features discussed above apply more readily to vertebrate than to invertebrate animals. Parasitic organisms may have quite different patterns of life history.

**GUPPY LIFE HISTORY** Life history characteristics vary from one species to another, and they can vary among populations of a single species. Predation differentially influences life history characteristics in natural populations of guppies (*Poecilia reticulata*) in Trinidad. Some years ago, drenched with sweat and with fishnets in hand, two ecologists studied guppies and fish communities on the Caribbean island of Trinidad. In their native habitats, guppies bear live young in shallow mountain streams, and John Endler and David Reznick were studying the environmental variables influencing the evolution of their life history patterns.

Male guppies are easy to distinguish from females. Males stop growing at sexual maturity; they are smaller and their scales have bright colours that serve as visual signals in intricate courtship displays. Females are drably coloured and continue to grow larger throughout their lives. In the mountains of Trinidad, guppies live in different streams, even in different parts of the same stream. Two other species of fish eat guppies **(Figure 29.8)**. In some streams, a small killifish (*Rivulus hartii*) preys on immature guppies but does not have much success with the larger adults. In other streams, a large pike–cichlid (*Crenicichla alta*) prefers mature guppies and rarely hunts small, immature ones.

Reznick and Endler found that the life history patterns of guppies vary among streams with different predators. In streams with pike–cichlids, male and female guppies mature faster and begin to reproduce at a smaller size and younger age than their counterparts in streams where killifish live. Female guppies from pike–cichlid streams reproduce more often, producing smaller and more numerous young. These differences allow guppies to avoid some predation. Those in pike–cichlid streams begin to reproduce when they are smaller than the size preferred by that predator. Those from killifish streams grow quickly to a size that is too large to be consumed by killifish.

Male guppy (right) that shared a stream with pike–cichlids (below)

a.

Male guppy (right) that shared a stream with killifish (below)

b.

**FIGURE 29.8** **Male guppies from streams where pike–cichlids live** (a) **are smaller and more streamlined, and have duller colours than those from streams where killifish live** (b). The pike–cichlid prefers to eat large guppies; the killifish feeds on small guppies. Guppies are shown approximately life sized; adult pike–cichlids grow to 16 cm in length; adult killifish grow to 10 cm.

Although these life history differences were correlated with the distributions of the two predatory fishes, they might result from some other, unknown differences between the streams. Endler and Reznick investigated this possibility with controlled laboratory experiments. They shipped groups of live guppies to California, where they bred guppies from each kind of stream for two generations. Both types of experimental populations were raised under identical conditions in the absence of predators. Even in the absence of predators, the two types of experimental populations retained their life history differences. These results provided evidence of a genetic (heritable) basis for the observed life history differences.

Endler and Reznick also examined the role of predators in the *evolution* of the size differences. They raised guppies for many generations in the laboratory under three experimental conditions: some alone, some with killifish, and some with pike–cichlids. As predicted, the guppy lineage subjected to predation by killifish became larger at maturity. Individuals that were small at maturity were frequently eaten, and their reproduction was limited. The lineage raised with pike–cichlids showed a trend toward earlier maturity. Individuals that matured at a larger size faced a greater likelihood of being eaten before they had reproduced.

## STUDY BREAK QUESTIONS

1. Organisms use energy for what three main operations?
2. Explain passive and active parental care in humans.
3. When would early reproduction be favoured?

## 29.5 Models of Population Growth

Now we move to exponential and logistic growth, two mathematical models of population growth. **Exponential** models apply when populations experience unlimited growth. **Logistic** models apply when population growth is limited, often because available resources are finite. These simple models are tools that help ecologists refine their hypotheses, but neither provides entirely accurate predictions of population growth in nature. In the simplest versions of these models, ecologists define births as the production of offspring by any form of reproduction and ignore the effects of immigration and emigration.

### 29.5a Exponential Models

Populations sometimes increase in size for a period of time with no apparent limits on their growth. In models of exponential growth, population size increases steadily by a constant ratio. Populations of bacteria and prokaryotes provide the most obvious examples, but multicellular organisms also sometimes exhibit exponential population growth.

Bacteria reproduce by binary fission. A parent cell divides in half, producing two daughter cells, and each can divide to produce two granddaughter cells. When bacteria all survive and generation time is the time between successive cell divisions, when no bacteria die, the population doubles in size in each generation.

Bacterial populations grow quickly under ideal temperatures and with unlimited space and food. Consider a population of the human intestinal bacterium *Escherichia coli*, for which the generation time could be 20 minutes. If we start with one bacterium, the population doubles to two cells after one generation (20 minutes), to four cells after two generations (40 minutes), and to eight cells after three generations (**Figure 29.9**). After 8 hours (24 generations), the population will number almost 17 million. And after one day (72 generations), the population will number nearly $5 \times 10^{21}$ cells. Although other bacteria grow more slowly than *E. coli*, it is no wonder that pathogenic bacteria, such as those causing cholera or plague, can quickly overtake the defences of an infected animal.

When populations of multicellular organisms are large, they can grow exponentially, as we shall see below for our own species. In any event, over a given time period, change in population size = number of births − number of deaths. We express this relationship mathematically by defining $N$ as the population size; $\Delta N$ (pronounced "delta $N$") as the change in population size; $\Delta t$ as the time period during which the change occurs; and $B$ and $D$ as the numbers of births and deaths, respectively, during that time period. Thus, $\Delta N/\Delta t$ symbolizes the change in population size over time, and

$$\Delta N/\Delta t = B - D.$$

The above equation applies to any population for which we know the exact numbers of births and deaths. Ecologists usually express births and deaths as per capita (per individual) rates,

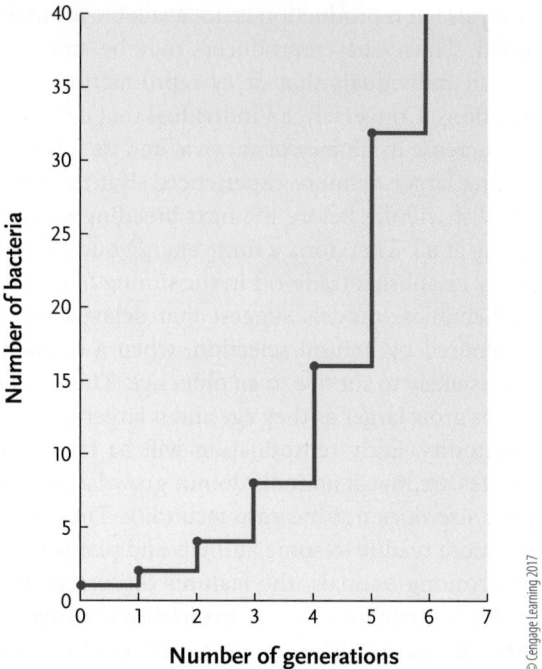

**FIGURE 29.9 Bacterial population growth.** If all members of a bacterial population divide simultaneously, a plot of population size over time forms a stair-stepped curve in which the steps get larger as the number of dividing cells increases.

allowing them to apply the model to a population of any size. The per capita birth rate ($b$) is the number of births in the population during the specified time period divided by the population size: $b = (B/N)$. Similarly, the per capita death rate ($d$) is the number of deaths divided by the population size: $d = (D/N)$.

If in a population of 2000 field mice, 1000 mice are born and 200 mice die during one month: $b = 1000/2000 = 0.5$ births per individual per month, and $d = 200/2000 = 0.1$ deaths per individual per month. Of course, no mouse can give birth to half an offspring, and no individual can die one-tenth of a death. But these rates tell us the per capita birth and death rates averaged over all mice in the population. Per capita birth and death rates are always expressed over a specified time period. For long-lived organisms, such as humans, time is measured in years. For short-lived organisms, such as fruit flies, time is measured in days. We can calculate per capita birth and death rates from data in a life table.

Now we can revise the population growth equation to use per capita birth and death rates instead of the actual numbers of births and deaths. The change in a population's size during a given time period ($\Delta N/\Delta t$) depends on the per capita birth and death rates, as well as on the number of individuals in the population. Mathematically, we can write

$$\Delta N/\Delta t = B - D = bN - dN = (b - d)N$$

or, in the notation of calculus,

$$dN/dt = (b - d)N.$$

This equation describes the **exponential model of population growth**. (Note that, in calculus, $dN/dt$ is the notation for the population growth rate. The $d$ in $dN/dt$ is not the same $d$ we use to symbolize the per capita death rate.)

The difference between the per capita birth rate and the per capita death rate, $b - d$, is the **per capita growth rate** of the population, symbolized by $r$. Like $b$ and $d$, $r$ is always expressed per individual per unit time. Using the per capita growth rate, $r$, in place of $b - d$, the exponential growth equation is written

$$dN/dt = rN.$$

If the birth rate exceeds the death rate, $r$ has a positive value ($r > 0$), and the population is growing. In our example with field mice, $r$ is $0.5 - 0.1 = 0.4$ mice per mouse per month. When the birth rate is lower than the death rate, $r$ has a negative value ($r < 0$) and the population is shrinking. In populations in which the birth rate equals the death rate, $r$ is zero and the population's size is not changing, a situation known as **zero population growth** (ZPG). Even under ZPG, births and deaths still occur, but the numbers of births and deaths may cancel each other out.

Populations will grow as long as the per capita growth rate is positive ($r > 0$). In our hypothetical population of field mice, we started with $N = 2000$ mice and calculated a per capita growth rate of 0.4 mice per individual per month. In the first month, the population grows by $0.4 \times 2000 = 800$ mice **(Figure 29.10)**. At the start of the second month, $N = 2800$ and $r$ is still 0.4. Thus, in the second month, the population grows by $0.4 \times 2800 = 1120$ mice. Notice that, even though $r$ remains constant, the increase in population size grows each month because more individuals are reproducing. In less than two years, the mouse population will be more than one million! A graph of exponential population growth has a characteristic J shape, getting steeper through time. The population grows at an ever-increasing pace because the change in a population's size depends on the number of individuals in the population and its per capita growth rate.

Imagine a hypothetical population living in an ideal environment with unlimited food and shelter; no predators, parasites, or disease; and a comfortable abiotic environment. Under such circumstances (admittedly unrealistic), the per capita birth rate is very high; the per capita death rate is very low; and the per capita growth rate, $r$, is as high as it can be. This maximum per capita growth rate, symbolized $r_{max}$, is the population's **intrinsic rate of increase**. Under these ideal conditions, our exponential growth equation is

$$dN/dt = r_{max}N.$$

When populations grow at their intrinsic rate of increase, population size increases very rapidly. Across a wide variety of protists and animals, $r_{max}$ varies inversely with generation time: species with a short generation time have higher intrinsic rates of increase than those with a long generation time **(Figure 29.11)**.

The exponential model predicts unlimited population growth. But we know from even casual observations that population sizes of most species are somehow limited. We are not knee-deep in bacteria, rosebushes, or garter snakes. What factors limit the growth of populations? As a population gets larger, it uses more vital resources, perhaps leading to a shortage of resources. In this situation, individuals may have less energy available for maintenance and reproduction, causing decreases in per capita birth rates and increases in per capita death rates. Energy in food is not always equally available, and when an animal spends time handling food to eat it, the ratio of cost (handling) to benefit (energy in the food) diminishes, affecting return on investment. Such rate changes can affect a population's per capita growth rate, causing population growth to slow or stop.

| Month | Old Population Size | | Net Monthly Increase | | New Population Size |
|---|---|---|---|---|---|
| 1 | 2 000 | + | 800 | = | 2 800 |
| 2 | 2 800 | + | 1 120 | = | 3 920 |
| 3 | 3 920 | + | 1 568 | = | 5 488 |
| 4 | 5 488 | + | 2 195 | = | 7 683 |
| 5 | 7 683 | + | 3 073 | = | 10 756 |
| 6 | 10 756 | + | 4 302 | = | 15 058 |
| 7 | 15 058 | + | 6 023 | = | 21 081 |
| 8 | 21 081 | + | 8 432 | = | 29 513 |
| 9 | 29 513 | + | 11 805 | = | 41 318 |
| 10 | 41 318 | + | 16 527 | = | 57 845 |
| 11 | 57 845 | + | 23 138 | = | 80 983 |
| 12 | 80 983 | + | 32 393 | = | 113 376 |
| 13 | 113 376 | + | 45 350 | = | 158 726 |
| 14 | 158 726 | + | 63 490 | = | 222 216 |
| 15 | 222 216 | + | 88 887 | = | 311 102 |
| 16 | 311 102 | + | 124 441 | = | 435 543 |
| 17 | 435 543 | + | 174 217 | = | 609 760 |
| 18 | 609 760 | + | 243 904 | = | 853 664 |
| 19 | 853 674 | + | 341 466 | = | 1 195 1340 |

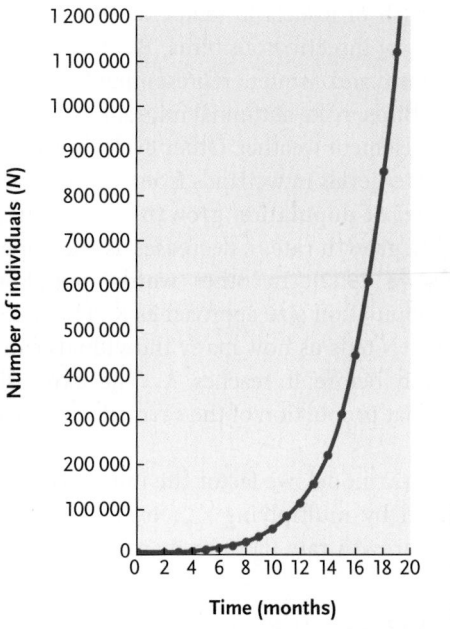

**FIGURE 29.10 Exponential population growth.** Exponential population growth produces a J-shaped curve when population size is plotted against time. Although the per capita growth rate ($r$) remains constant, the increase in population size gets larger every month because more individuals are reproducing.

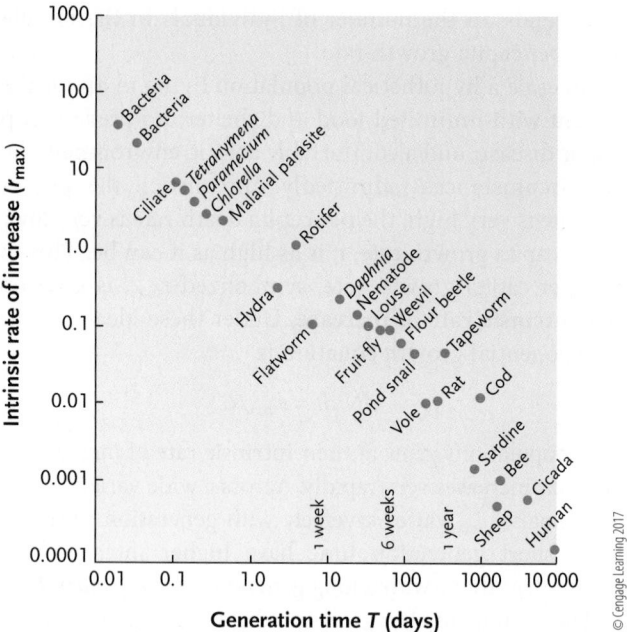

FIGURE 29.11 **Generation time and $r_{max}$.** The intrinsic rate of increase ($r_{max}$) is high for protists and animals with short generation times and low for those with long generation times.

## 29.5b Logistic Models: Populations and Carrying Capacity (*K*)

Environments may provide enough resources to sustain only a finite population of any species. The maximum number of individuals that an environment can support indefinitely is termed its **carrying capacity**, symbolized as *K*. *K* is defined for each population. It is a property of the environment that can vary from one habitat to another and in a single habitat over time. The spring and summer flush of insects in temperate habitats supports large populations of insectivorous birds. But fewer insects are available in autumn and winter, representing a seasonal decline in *K* for birds. Birds make autumnal migrations in search of food and to avoid inclement weather. Other cycles are annual, such as variation in water levels in wetlands from year to year.

The **logistic model of population growth** assumes that a population's per capita growth rate, *r*, decreases as the population gets larger (**Figure 29.12**). In other words, population growth slows as the population size approaches *K*. The mathematical expression *K* − *N* tells us how many individuals can be added to a population before it reaches *K*. The expression (*K* − *N*)/*K* indicates what proportion of the carrying capacity is still available.

To create the logistic model, we factor the impact of *K* into the exponential model by multiplying $r_{max}$ by (*K* − *N*)/*K* to reduce the per capita growth rate (*r*) from its maximum value ($r_{max}$) as *N* increases:

$$dN/dt = r_{max}N(K - N)/K.$$

Calculating how *r* varies with population size is straightforward (**Table 29.2**). In a very small population (*N* much

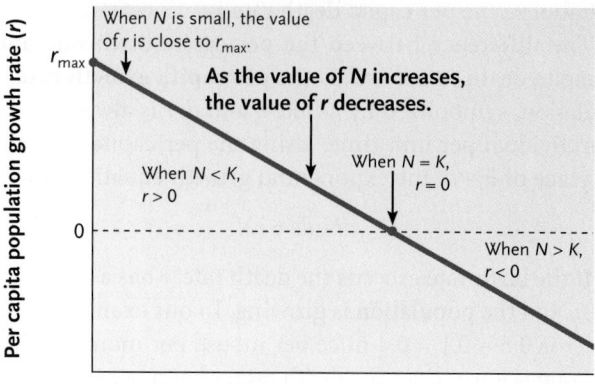

a. **The predicted effect of *N* on *r***

When *N* is small, the value of *r* is close to $r_{max}$.

**As the value of *N* increases, the value of *r* decreases.**

When *N* < *K*, *r* > 0

When *N* = *K*, *r* = 0

When *N* > *K*, *r* < 0

b. **Population size through time**

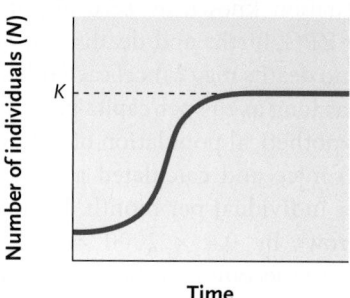

FIGURE 29.12 **The logistic model of population growth.** The logistic model **(a)** assumes that the per capita population growth rate (*r*) decreases linearly as population size (*N*) increases. The logistic model also predicts that population size **(b)** increases quickly at first but then slowly approaches carrying capacity (*K*).

**TABLE 29.2** The Effect of *N* on *r* and Δ*N*\* in a Hypothetical Population Exhibiting Logistic Growth in which *K* Equals 2000 and $r_{max}$ Is 0.04 per Capita per Year

| *N* (population size) | (*K* − *N*)/*K* (% of *K* available) | $r = r_{max}(K - N/K)$ (per capita growth rate) | Δ*N* = *rN* (change in *N*) |
|---|---|---|---|
| 50 | 0.975 | 0.0390 | 2 |
| 100 | 0.950 | 0.0380 | 4 |
| 250 | 0.875 | 0.0350 | 9 |
| 500 | 0.750 | 0.0300 | 15 |
| 750 | 0.625 | 0.0250 | 19 |
| 1000 | 0.500 | 0.0200 | 20 |
| 1250 | 0.375 | 0.0150 | 19 |
| 1500 | 0.250 | 0.0100 | 15 |
| 1750 | 0.125 | 0.0050 | 9 |
| 1900 | 0.050 | 0.0020 | 4 |
| 1950 | 0.025 | 0.0010 | 2 |
| 2000 | 0.000 | 0.0000 | 0 |

\*Δ*N* rounded to the nearest whole number

smaller than $K$), plenty of resources are available and the value of $(K - N)/K$ is close to 1. Here the per capita growth rate ($r$) approaches the maximum possible ($r_{max}$). Under these conditions, population growth is close to exponential. If a population is large ($N$ close to $K$), few additional resources are available. Now the value of $(K - N)/K$ is small, and the per capita growth rate ($r$) is very low. When the size of the population exactly equals $K$, $(K - N)/K$ becomes 0, as does the population growth rate, the situation defined as ZPG.

The logistic model of population growth predicts an S-shaped graph of population size over time, with the population slowly approaching $K$ and remaining at that level **(Figure 29.13)**. According to this model, the population grows slowly when the population size is small because few individuals are reproducing. It also grows slowly when the population size is large because the per capita population growth rate is low. The population grows quickly ($dN/dt$ is highest) at intermediate population sizes, when a sizable number of individuals are breeding and the per capita population growth rate ($r$) is still fairly high (see Table 29.2).

The logistic model assumes that vital resources become increasingly limited as a population grows. Thus, the model is a mathematical portrait of **intraspecific** (within species) **competition**, the dependence of two or more individuals in a population on the same limiting resource. For mobile animals, limiting resources could be food, water, nesting sites, and refuges from predators. For sessile species, space can be a limiting resource. For plants, sunlight, water, inorganic nutrients, and growing space can be limiting. The pattern of uniform dispersion described earlier often reflects intraspecific competition for limited resources.

In some very dense populations, accumulation of poisonous waste products may reduce survivorship and reproduction. Most natural populations live in open systems where wastes are consumed by other organisms or flushed away. But the buildup of toxic wastes is common in laboratory cultures of microorganisms. For example, yeast cells ferment sugar and produce ethanol as a waste product. Thus, the alcohol content of wine usually does not exceed 13% by volume, the ethanol concentration that poisons yeasts that are vital to the wine-making process.

How well do species conform to the predictions of the logistic model? In simple laboratory cultures, relatively small organisms, such as *Paramecium* spp., some crustaceans, and flour beetles, often show an S-shaped pattern of population growth (Figure 29.13, left, middle). Moreover, large animals introduced into new environments sometimes exhibit a pattern of population growth that matches the predictions of the logistic model (Figure 30.13, right).

Nevertheless, some assumptions of the logistic model are unrealistic. For example, the model predicts that survivorship and fecundity respond immediately to changes in a population's density. Many organisms exhibit a delayed response (a **time lag**) because fecundity has been determined by resource availability sometime in the past. This may reflect conditions that prevailed when individuals were adding yolk to eggs or endosperm to seeds. Moreover, when food resources become scarce, individuals may survive and reproduce using reserves of stored energy. This delays the impact of crowding until stored reserves are depleted and means that population size may overshoot $K$ (see Figure 29.13, middle). When deaths outnumber births, the population size drops below $K$, at least temporarily. Time lags often cause a population to oscillate around $K$.

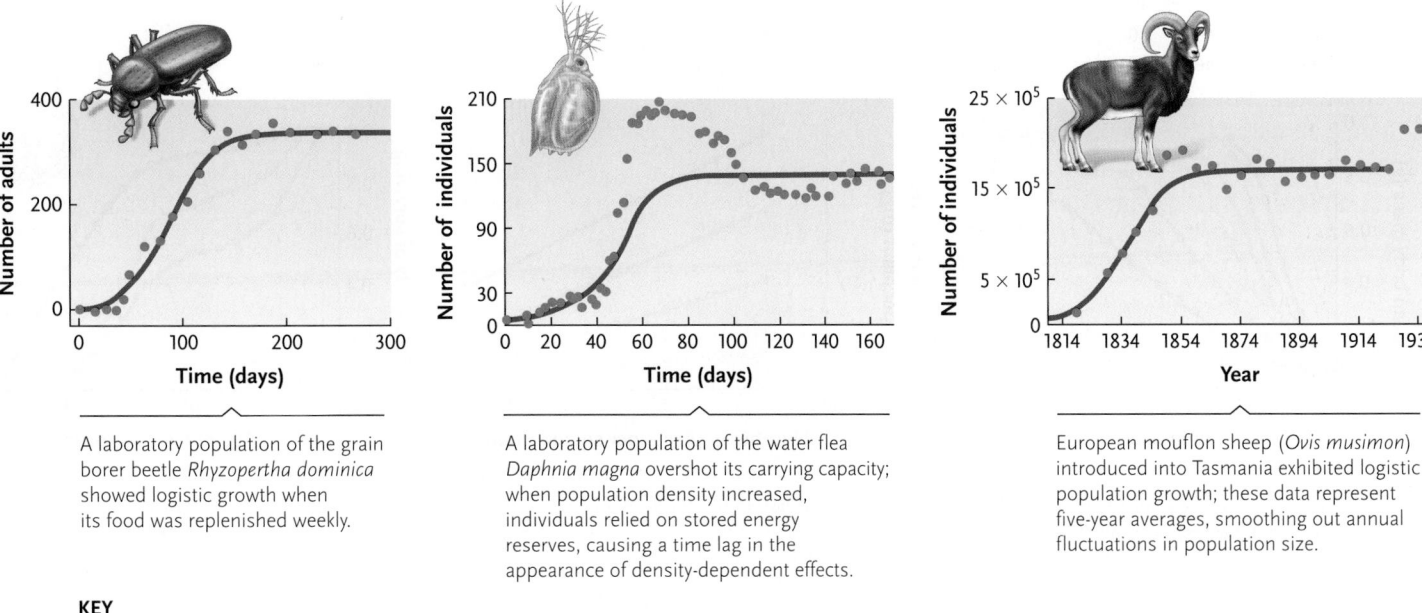

A laboratory population of the grain borer beetle *Rhyzopertha dominica* showed logistic growth when its food was replenished weekly.

A laboratory population of the water flea *Daphnia magna* overshot its carrying capacity; when population density increased, individuals relied on stored energy reserves, causing a time lag in the appearance of density-dependent effects.

European mouflon sheep (*Ovis musimon*) introduced into Tasmania exhibited logistic population growth; these data represent five-year averages, smoothing out annual fluctuations in population size.

**KEY**

— Theoretical   • Data

**FIGURE 29.13  Examples of logistic population growth**

The assumption that the addition of new individuals to a population always decreases survivorship and fecundity is unrealistic. In small populations, modest population growth may not have much impact on survivorship and fecundity. In fact, most organisms probably require a minimum population density to survive and reproduce. Some plants flourish in small clumps that buffer them from physical stresses, whereas a single individual living in the open would suffer adverse effects. In some animal populations, a minimum population density is necessary for individuals to find mates. Determining the minimum viable population for a species is an important issue in conservation biology (see Chapter 28).

### STUDY BREAK QUESTIONS

1. When do you use an exponential model rather than a logistic one?
2. Define the terms in the equation $dN/dt = (b - d)N$.
3. What does it mean when $r < 0$, $r > 0$, or $r = 0$? What is $r_{max}$, and how does it vary with generation time?

## 29.6 Population Regulation

What environmental factors influence population growth rates and control fluctuations in population size? The influence of **density dependent** factors can increase or decrease with population density; either way can be an example of a density-dependent environmental factor. The logistic model includes the effects of

density dependence in its assumption that per capita birth and death rates change with population density.

Numerous laboratory and field studies have shown that crowding (high population density) decreases individual growth rate, adult size, and survival of plants and animals **(Figure 29.14)**. Organisms living in very dense populations are unable to harvest enough resources; they grow slowly and tend to be small, weak, and less likely to survive. Gardeners understand this relationship and thin out their populations of plants to achieve a density that maximizes the number of vigorous individuals available for harvest.

Crowding has a negative effect on reproduction **(Figure 29.15)**. When resources are in short supply, each individual has less energy for reproduction after meeting its basic needs for maintenance. Hence, females in crowded populations produce either fewer offspring or smaller offspring that are less likely to survive.

In some species, crowding stimulates developmental and behavioural changes that can influence population density. Migratory locusts can develop into either solitary or migratory forms in the same population. Migratory individuals have longer wings and more body fat, characteristics that allow long-distance dispersal. High population density increases the frequency of the migratory form, so many locusts move away from the area of high density **(Figure 29.16)**, reducing the size and thus the density of the original population.

Although these data about locusts confirm the assumptions of the logistic equation, they do not prove that natural populations are regulated by density-dependent factors. Experimental evidence is necessary to provide a convincing

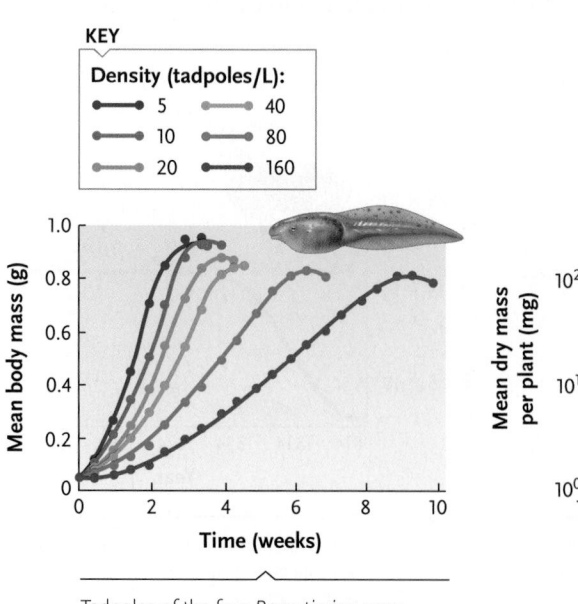

Tadpoles of the frog *Rana tigrina* grew faster and reached larger adult body size at low densities than at high densities.

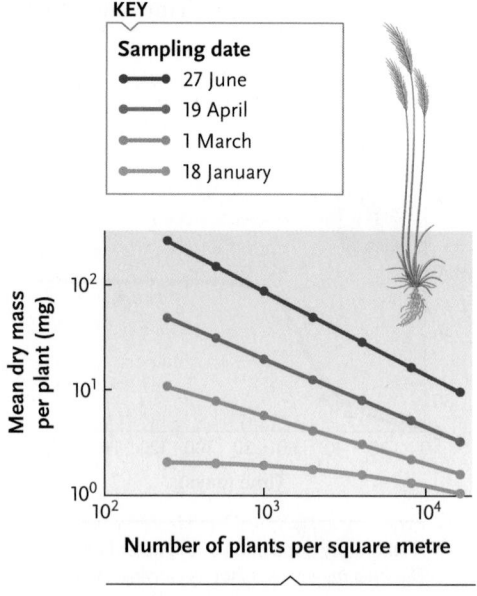

The size of the annual dune grass *Vulpia fasciculata* decreased markedly when plants were grown at high density. Density effects became more accentuated through time as the plants grew larger (indicated by the progressively steeper slopes of the lines).

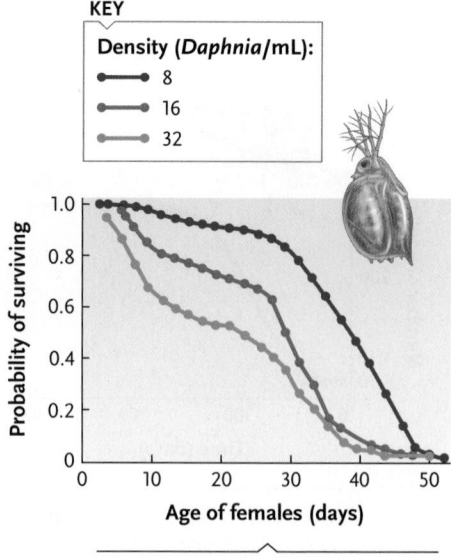

The water flea *Daphnia pulex* had higher survivorship at a density of 8/mL than at densities of 16/mL or 32/mL.

**FIGURE 29.14 Effects of crowding on individual growth, size, and survival**

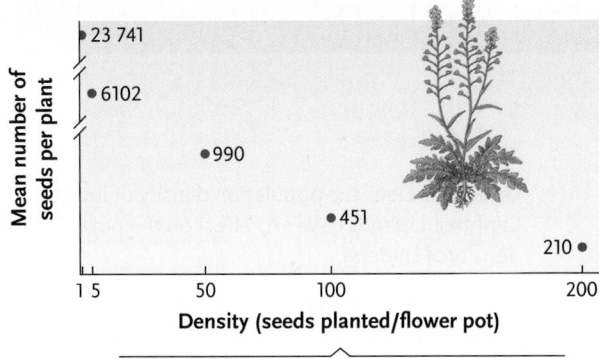

The number of seeds produced by shepherd's purse (*Capsella bursa-pastoris*) decreased dramatically with increasing density in experimental plots.

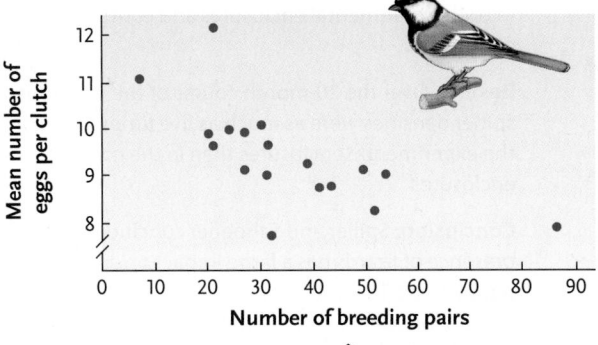

The mean number of eggs produced by the Great Tit (*Parus major*), a woodland bird, declined as the number of breeding pairs in Marley Wood increased.

© Cengage Learning 2017

**FIGURE 29.15  Effects of crowding on fecundity**

Gianni Tortoli/Science Source

**FIGURE 29.16  A swarm of locusts.** Migratory locusts (*Locusta migratoria*) moving across an African landscape can devour their own weight in plant material every day.

demonstration that an increase in population density causes population size to decrease, whereas a decrease in density causes it to increase.

In the 1960s, Robert Eisenberg experimentally increased the numbers of aquatic snails (*Lymnaea elodes*) in some ponds and decreased them in others. He also maintained natural densities in control ponds. Adult survivorship did not differ between experimental and control treatments. But there was a gradient in egg production, from few eggs (snails in high-density ponds) to more (control density) to most (low density). Furthermore, survival rates of young snails declined as density increased. After four months, densities in the two experimental groups converged on those in the control, providing strong evidence of density-dependent population regulation.

At this stage, intraspecific competition appears to be the primary density-dependent factor regulating population size. Competition between populations of different species can also exert density-dependent effects on population growth (see Chapter 30). The Allee effect occurs when *r* begins to decline after *N* falls below some threshold. This is another example of a density-dependent regulator.

Predation can also cause density-dependent population regulation. As a particular prey species becomes more numerous, predators may consume more of it because it is easier to find and catch. Once a prey species exceeds some threshold density, predators may consume a larger percentage of its population, amounting to a density-dependent effect. On rocky shores in California, sea stars feed mainly on the most abundant available invertebrates. When one prey species becomes common, predators feed on it disproportionately, reducing its numbers. Then they switch to now more abundant alternative prey.

Sometimes several density-dependent factors influence a population at the same time. On small islands in the West Indies, spiders are rare wherever lizards (*Ameiva festiva*, *Anolis carolinensis*, and *Anolis sagrei*) are abundant, but common where the lizards are rare or absent. To test whether the presence of lizards limits the abundance of spiders, David Spiller and Tom Schoener built fences around plots on islands where these species occur. They eliminated lizards from experimental plots but left them in control plots. After two years, spider populations in some experimental plots were five times denser than those in control plots, suggesting a strong impact of lizard populations on spider populations **(Figure 29.17)**. In this situation, lizards had two density-dependent effects on spider populations. First, lizards ate spiders; second, they competed with them for food. Experimental evidence made it possible for biologists to better understand the situation.

Predation, parasitism, and disease can cause density-dependent regulation of plant and animal populations. Infectious microorganisms (e.g., those causing malaria) can spread quickly in a crowded population. In addition, if crowded individuals are weak or malnourished, they are more susceptible

FIGURE 29.17 **Experimental Research**

## Evaluating Density-Dependent Interactions between Species

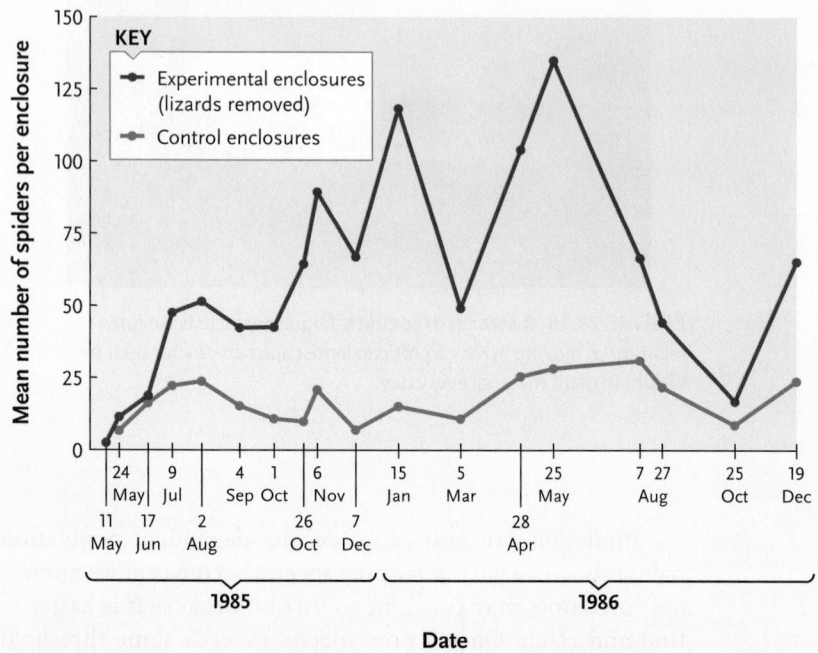

**Date**

Source: D. A. Spiller and T. W. Schoener. 1998. An experimental study of the effects of lizards on web-spider communities. Ecological Monographs 58:57–77. Ecological monographs by ECOLOGICAL SOCIETY OF AMERICA Copyright 1988. Reproduced with permission of ECOLOGICAL SOCIETY OF AMERICA in the format Textbook via Copyright Clearance Center.

**Question:** Does the population density of lizards on Caribbean islands have any effect on the population density of spiders?

**Experiment:** Spiller and Schoener built fences to enclose a series of study plots on a small island in the Bahamas. They excluded all individuals of three lizard species from the experimental enclosures, but left resident lizards undisturbed in the control enclosures. They then made monthly measurements of population densities of the web-building spider *Metepeira daytona* in both experimental enclosures and control enclosures.

**Results:** Over the 20-month course of the experiment, spider densities were as much as five times higher in the experimental enclosures than in the control enclosures.

**Conclusion:** Spiller and Schoener concluded that the presence of lizards has a large impact on spider populations. The lizards not only compete with the spiders for insect food, but they also appear to prey on the spiders.

to infection and may die from diseases that healthy organisms would survive. Effects on survival can be direct or indirect.

## 29.6a Populations and Density

Some populations are affected by **density-independent** factors that reduce the size of a population regardless of its density. If an insect population is not physiologically adapted to high temperature, a sudden hot spell may kill 80% of them, whether they number 100 or 100 000. Fires, earthquakes, storms, and other natural disturbances can contribute directly or indirectly to density-independent mortality. Because such factors do not cause a population to fluctuate around its $K$, these density-independent factors can reduce but do not regulate population size.

Density-independent factors have a particularly strong effect on populations of small-bodied species that cannot buffer themselves against environmental change. Their populations may grow exponentially for a time, then shifts in climate or random events may cause high mortality before populations reach a size at which density-dependent factors would regulate their numbers. When conditions improve, populations grow exponentially, at least until another density-independent factor

causes them to crash again. A small Australian insect, a thrip (*Thrips imaginis*), eats the pollen and flowers of plants in the rose family. These thrips can be abundant enough to damage blooms. Populations of thrips grow exponentially in spring, when many flowers are available and the weather is warm and moist **(Figure 29.18)**. But their populations crash predictably during summer because thrips do not tolerate hot and dry conditions. After the crash, a few individuals survive in remaining flowers, and they are the stock from which the population grows exponentially the following spring.

## 29.6b Density-Dependent and Density-Independent Factors

Density-dependent factors can interact with density-independent factors and limit population growth. Food shortage caused by high population density (a density-dependent factor) may lead to malnourishment. Malnourished individuals may be more likely to succumb to the stress of extreme weather (a density-independent factor).

Populations can be affected by density-independent factors in a density-dependent manner. Some animals retreat into

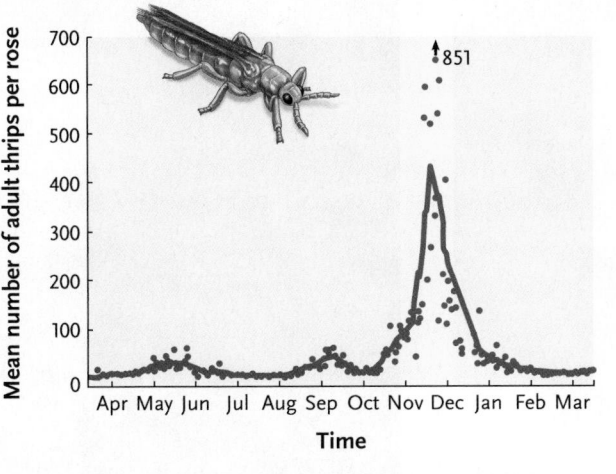

**FIGURE 29.18 Booms and busts in a population of thrips.** Populations of the Australian insect *Thrips imaginis* grow exponentially when conditions are favourable during spring (which begins in September in the southern hemisphere). But the populations crash in summer when hot and dry conditions cause high mortality.

**TABLE 29.3 Characteristics of *r*-Selected and *K*-Selected Species**

| Characteristic | *r*-Selected Species | *K*-Selected Species |
| --- | --- | --- |
| Maturation time | Short | Long |
| Lifespan | Short | Long |
| Mortality rate | Usually high | Usually low |
| Reproductive episodes | Usually one | Usually several |
| Time of first reproduction | Early | Late |
| Clutch or brood size | Usually large | Usually small |
| Size of offspring | Small | Large |
| Active parental care | Little or none | Often extensive |
| Population size | Fluctuating | Relatively stable |
| Tolerance of environmental change | Generally poor | Generally good |

© Cengage Learning 2017

shelters to escape environmental stresses, such as floods or severe heat. If a population is small, most individuals can be accommodated in available refuges. But if a population is large (exceeds the capacity of shelters), only some individuals will find suitable shelter. The larger the population, the greater the percentage of individuals exposed to the stress(es). Thus, although the density-independent effects of weather limit populations of thrips, the availability of flowers in summer (a density-dependent factor) regulates the size of the starting populations of thrips the following spring. Thus both density-dependent and density-independent factors influence the size of populations of thrips.

Other explanations focus on extrinsic control, such as the relationship between a cycling species and its food or predators. A dense population may exhaust its food supply, increasing mortality and decreasing reproduction. The die-off of large numbers of African elephants in Tsavo National Park in Kenya is an example of the impact of overpopulation. There, elephants overgrazed vegetation in most of the Park habitat. In 1970, the combination of overgrazing and a drought caused high mortality of elephants. The picture is not always clear because experimental food supplementation does not always prevent decline in mammal populations, suggesting some level of intrinsic control.

## 29.6c Strategies for Population Growth

Even casual observation reveals considerable variation in the rapidity of changes in sizes of populations in different species. New weeds often appear in a vegetable garden overnight, whereas the number of oak trees in a forest may remain relatively stable for years. Why do some species have the potential for explosive population growth? The answer lies in how natural selection has moulded life history strategies adapted to different ecological conditions. Some ecologists recognize two quite different life history patterns: ***r*-selected** species and ***K*-selected** species (**Table 29.3** and **Figure 29.19**).

On the face of it, *r*-selected species are adapted to rapidly changing environments, and many have at least some of the features outlined in Table 29.3. The success of an *r*-selected life history depends on flooding the environment with a large quantity of young because only some may be successful. Small body size means that, compared with larger-bodied species, *r*-selected species lack physiological mechanisms to buffer themselves from environmental variation. Populations of *r*-selected species can be reduced by changes in abiotic environmental factors (e.g., temperature or moisture) so that they may never grow large enough to reach *K* and face a shortage of limiting resources. In these cases, *K* cannot be estimated by researchers, and changes in population size are not accurately described by the logistic model of population growth. Although *r*-selected species appear to have poor tolerance of environmental change, they appear adaptable to rapidly changing environments.

At the same time, *K*-selected species have at least some of the features outlined for them in Table 29.3. These organisms survive the early stages of life (type I or type II survivorship), and a low $r_{max}$ means that their populations grow slowly. The success of a *K*-selected life history is linked to the production of a relatively small number of high-quality offspring that join an already well-established population. Generalizations about *r*-selected and *K*-selected species are misleading. We can recognize this when we compare two species of small mammals.

*Peromyscus maniculatus*, deer mice, occur widely in North America. In southern Ontario, adults weigh 12–31 g, females produce average litters of four (range two to eight), and each can bear four or five litters a year. Females become sexually mature at age two months and breed in their first year. Occasionally, deer mice live to age three years in the wild.

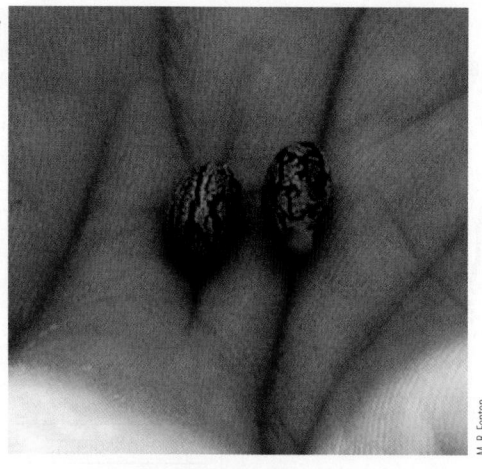

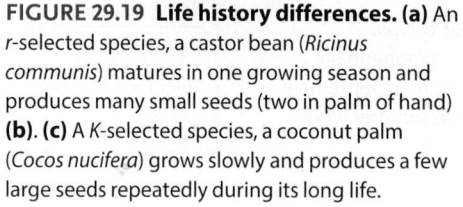

**FIGURE 29.19 Life history differences. (a)** An *r*-selected species, a castor bean (*Ricinus communis*) matures in one growing season and produces many small seeds (two in palm of hand) **(b)**. **(c)** A *K*-selected species, a coconut palm (*Cocos nucifera*) grows slowly and produces a few large seeds repeatedly during its long life.

Throughout their extensive range in North America, *Myotis lucifugus*, little brown myotis, weigh 7–12 g. Females bear a single young per litter and have one litter per year. Females may breed a year after they are born, but many wait until they are two years old. In the wild, little brown myotis can live over 30 years. Using these data, one small mammal (deer mouse) is an *r*-strategist, whereas another (little brown bat) is a *K*-strategist. To complicate matters, deer mice living in Kananaskis in the mountains near Calgary mature at one year and may have two litters per year, typically five young per litter. Compared to little brown bats, Kananaskis deer mice are *r*-strategists. Compared to Ontario deer mice, they are more like *K*-strategists.

Biologists may find the idea of *r*-strategists and *K*-strategists useful, but too often the idea means imposing some human view of the world on a natural system. *K*-strategists and *r*-strategists may be more like beauty, defined by the eye of the beholder. Elephants (*Loxodonta africana, Loxodonta cyclotis, Elephas maximus*) are big and meet all *K*-strategist criteria. Many insects are small but in all other respects meet the criteria considered typical of *K*-strategists because of their patterns of reproduction. Codfish (*Gadus morhua*) are big (compared to insects or bats) but meet most of the criteria used to identify *r*-strategists, such as their patterns of reproduction.

## 29.6d Population Cycles

Population densities of many insects, birds, and mammals in the northern hemisphere fluctuate between species-specific lows and highs in a multiyear cycle. Arctic populations of small rodents (*Lemmus lemmus*) vary in size over a 4-year cycle, whereas snowshoe hares (*Lepus americanus*), ruffed grouse (*Bonasa umbellus*), and lynx have 10-year cycles. Ecologists documented these cyclic fluctuations more than a century ago, but none of the general hypotheses proposed to date explain cycles in all species. Availability and quality of food, abundance of predators, prevalence of disease-causing microorganisms, and variations in weather can influence population growth and declines. Furthermore, food supply and predators for a cycling population are themselves influenced by a population's size.

Theories of intrinsic control suggest that, as an animal population grows, individuals undergo hormonal changes that increase aggressiveness, reduce reproduction, and foster dispersal. The dispersal phase of the cycle may be dramatic. When populations of Norway lemming (*Lemmus lemmus*), a rodent that lives in the Scandinavian Arctic, reach their peak density, aggressive interactions drive younger and weaker individuals to disperse. The dispersal of many thousands of lemmings during periods of population growth has sometimes been incorrectly portrayed in nature films as a suicidal mass migration.

Cycles in populations of predators could be induced by time lags between populations of predators and prey, and vice versa **(Figure 29.20)**. The 10-year cycles of snowshoe hares and their feline predators, Canada lynx, were often cited as a classic example of such an interaction. But snowshoe hare populations can exhibit a 10-year fluctuation even on islands where lynx are absent. Thus, lynx are not solely responsible for population cycles in snowshoe hares. To further complicate matters, the database demonstrating fluctuations was often the numbers of pelts purchased by the Hudson's Bay Company. Here, fur price

FIGURE 29.20 **The predator–prey model.** Predator–prey interactions may contribute to density-dependent regulation of both populations. **(a)** A mathematical model predicts cycles in the numbers of predators and prey because of time lags in each species' responses to changes in the density of the other. (Predator population size is exaggerated in this graph.) **(b)** Canada lynx (*Lynx canadensis*) and snowshoe hare (*Lepus americanus*) were often described as a typical cyclic predator–prey interaction. The abundances of lynx (red line) and snowshoe hares (blue line) are based on counts of pelts that trappers sold to the Hudson's Bay Company over a 90-year period. Recent research shows that population cycles in snowshoe hares are caused by complex interactions between the snowshoe hare, its food plants, and its predators.

**a. Predictions of a predator–prey model**

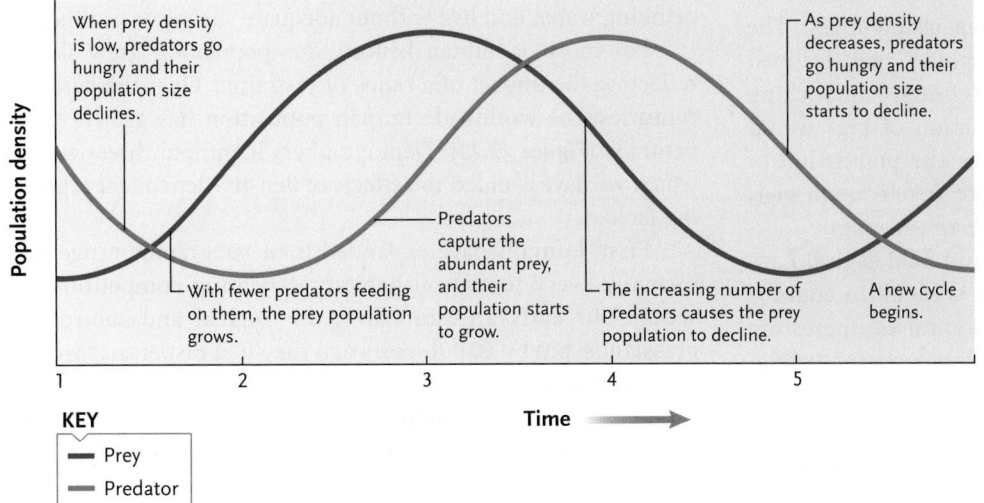

**b. Lynx and hare population sizes through time**

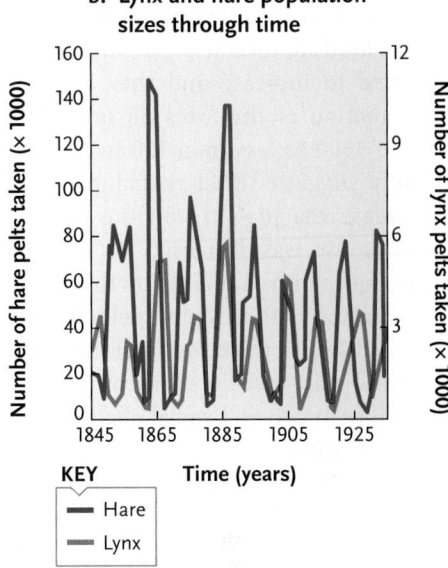

influenced the trapping effort and the numbers of animals harvested. This economic reality brought into question the relationship between the numbers of pelts and actual population densities of lynx and snowshoe hares.

Charles Krebs and his colleagues studied hare and lynx interactions with a large-scale, multiyear experiment in Kluane, in the southern Yukon. Using fenced experimental areas, they could add food for snowshoe hares, exclude mammalian predators, or apply both experimental treatments while monitoring unmanipulated control plots. When mammalian predators were excluded, densities of snowshoe hares approximately doubled relative to controls. Where food was added, densities of snowshoe hares tripled relative to controls. In plots where food was added and predators were excluded, densities of snowshoe hares increased 11-fold compared with controls. Krebs and his colleagues concluded that neither food availability nor predation is solely responsible for population cycles in snowshoe hares. They postulated that complex interactions between snowshoe hares, their food plants, and their predators generate cyclic fluctuations in populations of snowshoe hares.

## STUDY BREAK QUESTIONS

1. What are density-dependent factors? Why do dense populations tend to decrease in size?
2. Define *density-independent factors* and give some examples.
3. Describe two key differences between *r*-selected species and *K*-selected species.

## 29.7 Human Administered Population Control

People commonly expect that predators play an active role in controlling populations of prey. This misconception was one reason that mongooses (*Herpestes auropunctatus*) were introduced from India to Central America. In this case, the mongoose's reputation as a killer of snakes appeared to offer the promise that mongooses would at least reduce populations of fer-de-lances (*Bothrops asper*). These venomous relatives of rattlesnakes were a hazard to cane workers. The mongooses thrived in the New World but did not do well against fer-de-lances, whose strikes were faster than those of cobras. The mongooses were very effective predators of other snakes as well as ground-nesting birds, leading to the extinction of several species. This made the introductions disastrous from a conservation standpoint.

Predators can seriously deplete populations of prey, and this can precipitate dilemmas about conservation and the management of wildlife. One well-known example is the decline of island foxes (*Urocyon littoralis*), a species endemic to the Channel Islands in California. Each of the six islands had a distinct population (subspecies) of foxes. Island foxes were considered to be threatened with imminent extinction, partly reflecting the impact of feral pigs (*Sus scrofa*) that had been introduced to the islands.

After golden eagles (*Aquila chrysaetos*) colonized the Channel Islands, their numbers increased, reflecting the abundant food supply, the pigs. The population of golden eagles continued to increase and they began eating island foxes. The population of the foxes on one island (Santa Cruz) declined from 1500 to less than 100 in less than 10 years. A modelling study suggested that reducing the population of pigs would increase the pressure on the foxes unless the population of eagles also was decreased. As long as there were enough pigs, the eagles preyed mainly on them rather than the foxes.

In the United States, golden eagles (and bald eagles) have special legal protection, making it legally difficult to translocate or otherwise harass them. This situation raised interesting legal, political, and social challenges to those concerned about conservation.

In Alberta, Canada, human disruptions of ecosystems, largely associated with exploration for oil and gas, are largely responsible for drastic declines in herds of woodland caribou (*Rangifer tarandus caribou*). Roadways associated with exploration operations offer wolves (*Canis lupus*) linear features for travel but also facilitate human harvesting of caribou. A study published in 2014 reported the results of monitoring adult survival in a herd of 172 adult female caribou from 2000 to 2012. During the winters of 2005–2006, the researchers reduced populations of wolves, which coincided with a 4.6% increase in the growth rate of the herd of caribou. In a comparable control area where there was no focused reduction of populations of wolves, another herd of caribou declined by 4.7% in the same period.

Unfortunately, human activities in much of the world negatively affect ecosystems and wild populations of organisms. In some cases, control of predators may be one of the main options open to those trying to conserve wild systems.

Actions associated with predator control often stir heated debates. In Canada, we can expect more confrontations around predator control, which often are intended to protect woodland caribou. But population control by culling can be as contentious when the targets are other animals, from white-tailed deer (*Odocoileus virginianus*) to double-crested cormorants (*Phalacrocorax auritus*). There is less contention about the control of weeds.

## 29.8  Human Population Growth

How do human populations compare with those of other species? The worldwide human population was over 7 billion in 2014. Like many other species, humans live in somewhat isolated populations that vary in their demographic traits and access to resources. Although many live comfortably, at least a billion people are malnourished or starving, lack access to clean drinking water, and live without adequate shelter or healthcare.

For most of human history, our population grew slowly, reflecting the impact of a range of restraints. Over the past two centuries, the worldwide human population has grown exponentially **(Figure 29.21)**. Demographers identified three ways in which we have avoided the effects of density-dependent regulating factors.

First, humans have expanded their geographic range into virtually every terrestrial habitat, alleviating competition for space. Our early ancestors lived in tropical and subtropical grasslands, but by 40 000 years ago they had dispersed through much of the world. Humans' success resulted from their ability to solve ecological problems by building fires, assembling shelters, making clothing and tools, planning community hunts,

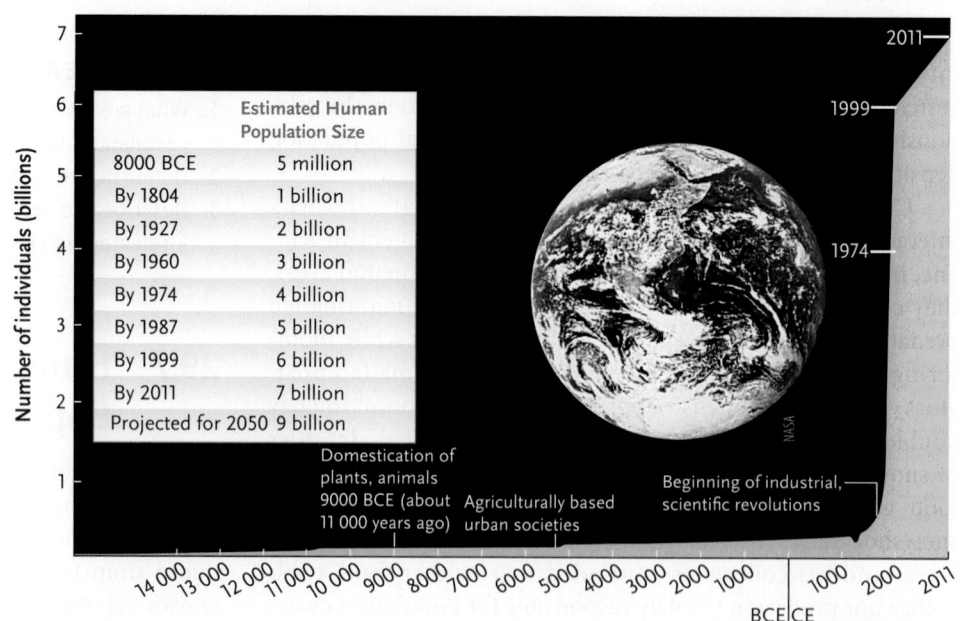

| Estimated Human Population Size | |
|---|---|
| 8000 BCE | 5 million |
| By 1804 | 1 billion |
| By 1927 | 2 billion |
| By 1960 | 3 billion |
| By 1974 | 4 billion |
| By 1987 | 5 billion |
| By 1999 | 6 billion |
| By 2011 | 7 billion |
| Projected for 2050 | 9 billion |

**FIGURE 29.21  Human population growth.** The worldwide human population grew slowly until 200 years ago, when it began to increase explosively. The dip in the mid-fourteenth century represents the death of 60 million Asians and Europeans from the bubonic plague. The table shows how long it took for the human population to add each billion people.

and sharing information. Vital survival skills spread from generation to generation and from one population to another because language allowed communication of complex ideas and knowledge.

Second, we have increased K in habitats we occupy, isolating us, as a species, from restrictions associated with access to resources. This change began to occur about 11 000 years ago, when populations in different parts of the world began to shift from hunting and gathering to agriculture. At that time, our ancestors cultivated wild grasses and other plants, diverted water to irrigate crops, and used domesticated animals for food and labour. Innovations such as these increased the availability of food, raising both K and rates of population growth. In the mid-eighteenth century, people harnessed the energy in fossil fuels, and industrialization began in Western Europe and North America. Food supplies and K increased again, at least in industrialized countries, largely through the use of synthetic fertilizers, pesticides, and efficient methods of transportation and food distribution.

Third, advances in public health reduced the effects of critical population-limiting factors such as malnutrition, contagious diseases, and poor hygiene. Over the past 300 years, modern plumbing and sewage treatment, removal of garbage, and improvements in food handling and processing, as well as medical discoveries, have reduced death rates sharply. Births now greatly exceed deaths, especially in more industrialized countries, resulting in rapid population growth. Note, however, that problems of hygiene and access to fresh water and food had been solved in some societies at least hundreds of years ago. Rome, for example, had a population of about 1 million people by 2 CE, and this was supported by an excellent infrastructure for importing and distributing food, providing fresh water, and dealing with human wastes.

## 29.8a Age Structure and Economic Growth

Where have our migrations and technological developments taken us? It took about 2.5 million years for the human population to reach 1 billion, 80 years to reach the second billion, and only 12 years to jump from 5 billion to 6 billion, and another 12 years to reach 7 billion (see the inset table in Figure 29.21). Rapid population growth now appears to be an inevitable consequence of our demographic structure and economic development.

## 29.8b Population Growth and Age Structure

In 2011, the worldwide annual growth rate for the human population averaged about 1.15% ($r$ = 0.0115 new individuals per individual per year). Population experts expect that rate to decline, but even so, the human population will probably exceed 9 billion before 2050.

In 2000, population growth rates of individual nations varied widely, ranging from much less than 1% to more than 3% **(Figure 29.22)**. Industrialized countries of Western Europe have achieved nearly ZPG, but other countries, particularly those in Africa, Latin America, and Asia, will experience huge increases over the next 20 or 25 years (Figure 29.22b).

For all long-lived species, differences in age structure are a major determinant of differences in population growth rates **(Figure 29.23)**. There are three basic patterns in the graphs in

**a. Mean annual population growth rates, 2013**

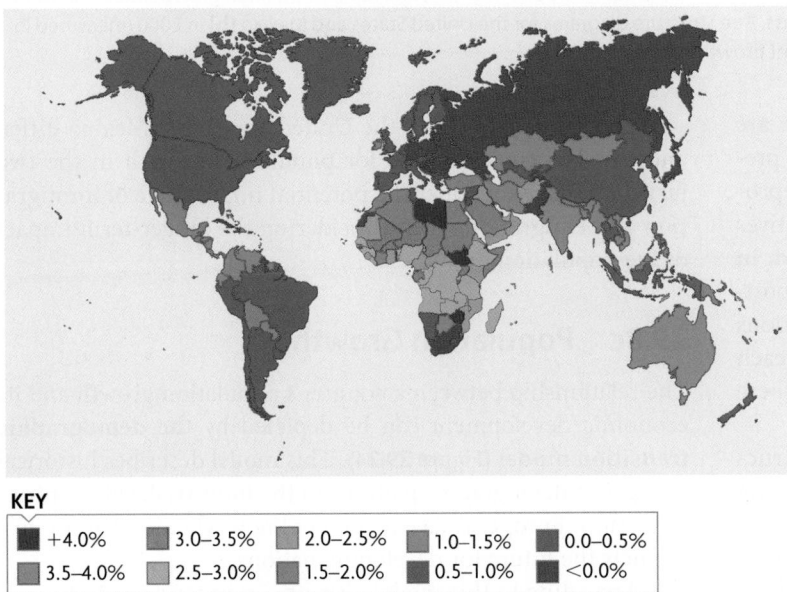

KEY

| | | | | |
|---|---|---|---|---|
| ■ +4.0% | ■ 3.0–3.5% | ■ 2.0–2.5% | ■ 1.0–1.5% | ■ 0.0–0.5% |
| ■ 3.5–4.0% | ■ 2.5–3.0% | ■ 1.5–2.0% | ■ 0.5–1.0% | ■ <0.0% |

**b. Actual and projected population sizes for major world regions**

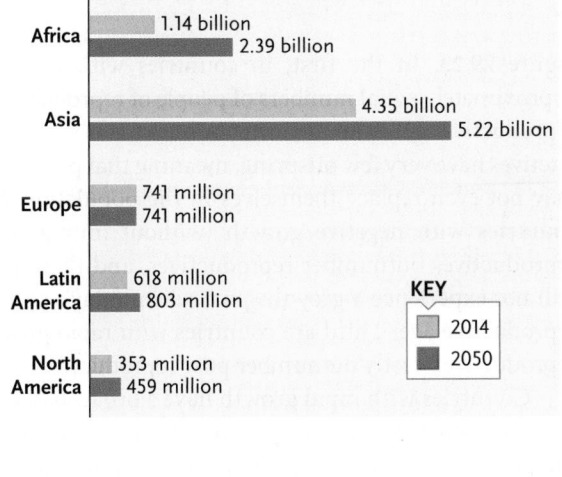

Africa — 1.14 billion / 2.39 billion
Asia — 4.35 billion / 5.22 billion
Europe — 741 million / 741 million
Latin America — 618 million / 803 million
North America — 353 million / 459 million

KEY
■ 2014
■ 2050

**FIGURE 29.22 Local variation in human population growth rates.** In 2001, **(a)** average annual population growth rates varied among countries and continents. In some regions **(b)**, the population is projected to increase greatly by 2025 (red) compared with the population size in 2001 (orange). The population of Europe is likely to decline.

## a. Hypothetical age distributions for populations with different growth rates

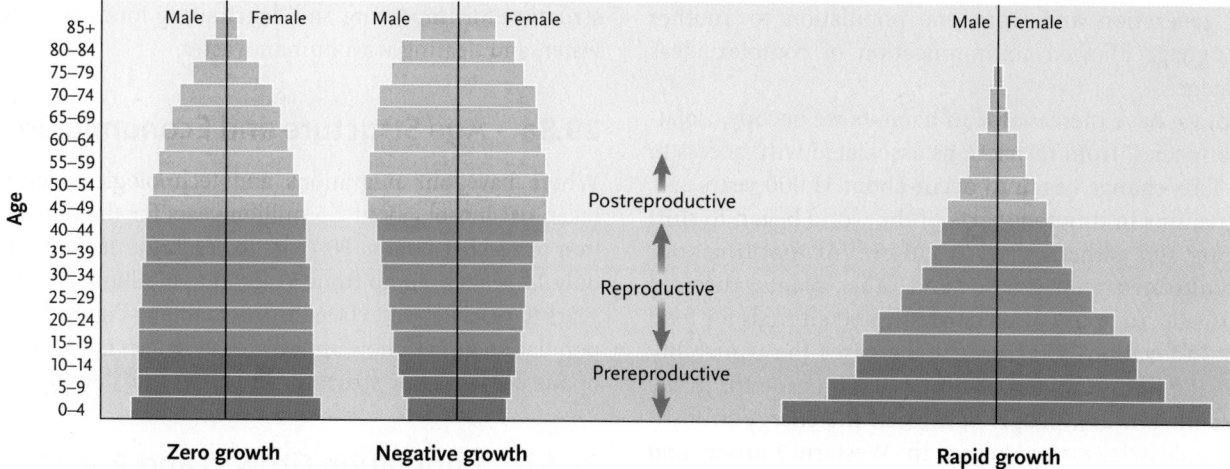

Zero growth  Negative growth  Rapid growth

## b. Age pyramids for the United States and Mexico in 2000

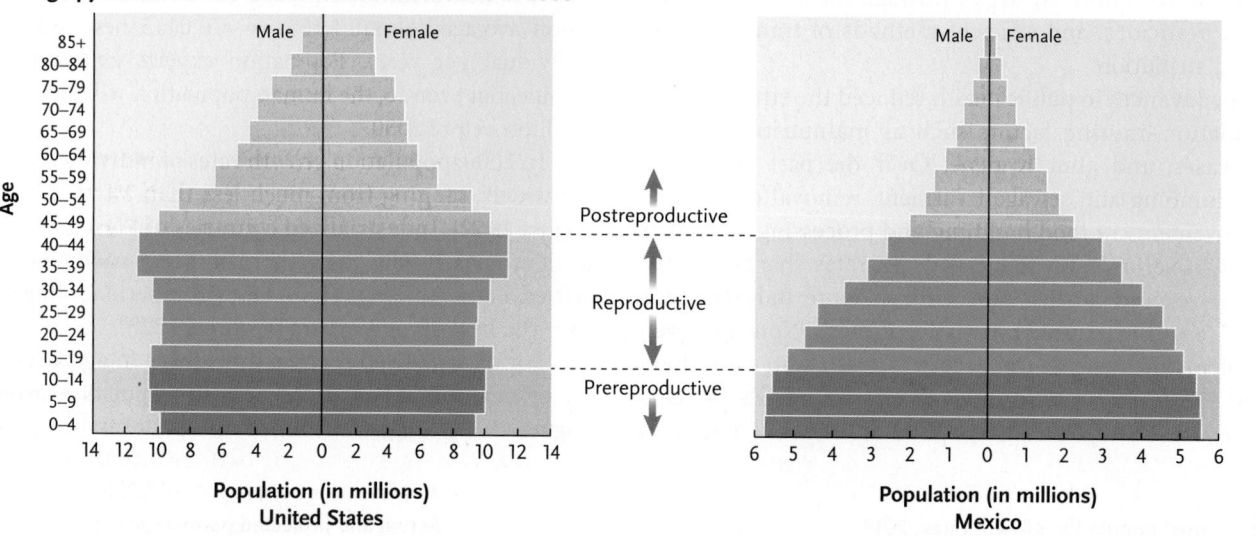

Population (in millions)
United States

Population (in millions)
Mexico

© Cengage Learning 2017

**FIGURE 29.23 Age structure diagrams.** Age structure diagrams **(a)** differ for countries with zero, negative, and rapid population growth rates. The width of each bar represents the proportion of the population in each age class. Age structure diagrams for the United States and Mexico **(b)** in 2000 (measured in millions of people) suggest that these countries will experience different growth rates.

Figure 29.23. In the first, in countries with ZPG, there are approximately equal numbers of people of reproductive and pre-reproductive ages. The ZPG situation is exacerbated when reproductives have very few offspring, meaning that pre-reproductives may not even replace themselves in the population. Second, in countries with negative growth (without immigration), post-reproductives outnumber reproductives, and these populations will not experience a growth spurt when today's children reach reproductive age. Third are countries with rapid growth, where reproductives vastly outnumber post-reproductives.

Countries with rapid growth have a broad-based age structure (pattern three, above), with many youngsters born during the previous 15 years. Worldwide, more than one-third of the human population falls within this pre-reproductive base. This age class will soon reach sexual maturity. Even if each woman produces only two offspring, populations will continue to grow rapidly because so many individuals are reproducing. This situation is a population bomb.

The age structures of the United States and Mexico differ, and this has consequences for population growth in the two jurisdictions. Remember the potential importance of immigration and emigration when considering the longer-term impact of the population bomb.

## 29.8c Population Growth

The relationship between a country's population growth and its economic development can be depicted by the **demographic transition model (Figure 29.24)**. This model describes historical changes in demographic patterns in the industrialized countries of Western Europe. Today, we do not know whether it accurately predicts the future for developing nations.

According to this model, during a country's pre-industrial stage, birth and death rates are high, and the population grows slowly. Industrialization begins a transitional stage, when food production rises and healthcare and sanitation improve, and

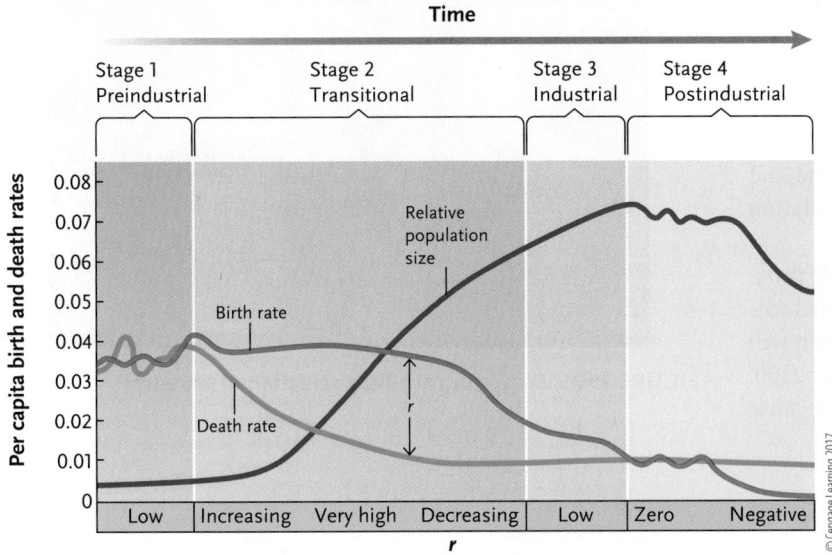

**FIGURE 29.24 The demographic transition.** The demographic transition model describes changes in the birth and death rates and relative population size as a country passes through four stages of economic development. The bottom bar describes the net population growth rate, *r*.

death rates decline, resulting in increased rates of population growth. Later, as living conditions improve, birth rates decline, causing a drop in rates of population growth. When the industrial stage is in full swing, population growth slows dramatically. Now people move from countryside to cities, and urban couples often choose to accumulate material goods instead of having large families. ZPG is reached in the post-industrial stage. Eventually, the birth rate falls below the death rate, *r* falls below zero, and population size begins to decrease.

Today, the United States, Canada, Australia, Japan, Russia, and most of Western Europe are in the industrial stage: their growth rates are slowly decreasing. In Germany, Bulgaria, and Hungary (and other European countries), birth rates are lower than death rates and populations are shrinking, indicating entry into the post-industrial stage. Kenya and other less-industrialized countries are in the transitional stage, but they may not have enough skilled workers or enough capital to make the transition to an industrialized economy. For these reasons, many poorer nations may be stuck in the transitional stage. Developing countries experience rapid population increase because they experience declines in death rates associated with the transitional stage without the decreases in birth rates typical of industrial and post-industrial stages.

Stable population in humans can be achieved with an average of 2.1 births per woman, the replacement level. A study published in 2014 reported that, in at least 40 countries, the rate exceeded 2.1 births per woman. Another important factor in a human population is the potential support ratio (PSR). This depicts the ratio of working people (number aged 20–64 years) to older people (number older than 65 years). The economic and social implications of the PSR are becoming more and more apparent.

## 29.8d Controlling Reproductive Output

Most governments realize that increased population size is now the major factor causing resource depletion, excessive pollution, and an overall decline in quality of life. The principles of population ecology demonstrate that slowing the rate of population growth and effecting an actual decline in population size can be achieved only by decreasing the birth rate and/or increasing the death rate. Increasing mortality is neither a rational nor a humane means of population control. Some governments use **family planning programs** in an attempt to lower birth rates. In other countries, any form of family planning is unlawful. This topic is discussed further in Chapter 28, where we will see that education of women is a vital undertaking.

To achieve ZPG, the average replacement rate should be just slightly higher than two children per couple. This is necessary because some female children die before reaching reproductive age. Today's replacement rate averages about 2.5 children in less industrialized countries with higher mortality rates in pre-reproductive cohorts, and 2.1 in more industrialized countries. However, even if each couple on Earth produced only two children, the human population would continue to grow for at least another 60 years (the impact of the population bomb). Continued population growth is inevitable because today's children, who outnumber adults, will soon mature and reproduce. The worldwide population will stabilize only when the age distributions of all countries resemble that for countries with ZPG.

Family planning efforts encourage women to delay their first reproduction. Doing so reduces the average family size and slows population growth by increasing generation time (see Figure 29.10). Imagine two populations in which each woman produces two offspring. In the first population, women begin reproducing at age 32 years, and in the second they begin reproducing at age 16 years. We can begin with a cohort of newborn baby girls in each population. After 32 years, women in the first population will be giving birth to their first offspring, but women in the second population will be new grandmothers. After 64 years, women in the first population will be new grandmothers, but women in the second population will witness the birth of their first great-great grandchildren (if their daughters also bear their first children at age 16 years). Obviously, the first population will grow much more slowly than the second.

Age at menarche (first menstruation) is an important factor in determining the trajectory of growth of human populations. There is evidence of selection for age at menarche in some human populations. In 2015, analysis of 182 416 European women performed in the course of 57 separate studies confirmed that at least 123 signals at 106 genetic loci were involved in determining age at menarche. Furthermore, there is evidence that parasitic infections by roundworms (*Ascaris lumbricoides*) are associated with earlier first births and shorter interbirth intervals. In contrast, infections by hookworms (*Ancylostoma duodenale* and *Necator americanus*) coincide with delayed first birth and longer interbirth intervals. This evidence illustrates the importance of health and hygiene and the role that helminth parasites can play in population ecology.

A 2014 analysis of data collected to 2012 offered little prospect of stabilization of human populations. The analysis indicated an 80% probability that the human global population will grow from 7.2 billion to between 9.6 and 12.3 billion by 2100. The population in Africa is central to these projections because of higher fertility there. The prospect is daunting.

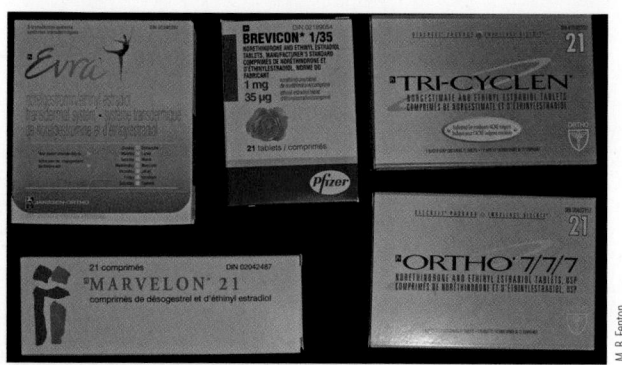

FIGURE 29.25 **Birth control pills, a selection of products**

## 29.9 The Future: Where Are We Going?

*Homo sapiens* has arrived at a turning point in our cultural evolution and in our ecological relationship with Earth. Hard decisions await us, and we must make them soon. All species face limits to their population growth, and it is naive to assume that our unique abilities exempt us from the laws of population growth. We have postponed the action of most factors that limit population growth, but no amount of invention and intervention can expand the ultimate limits set by resource depletion and a damaged environment. We now face two options for limiting human population growth: we can make a global effort to limit our population growth, or we can wait until the environment does it for us.

**STUDY BREAK QUESTIONS**

1. In what three ways have humans avoided the effects of density-dependent regulation factors?
2. What is a population bomb?
3. What does family planning encourage women to do?

## 29.10 The Pill

The advent of birth control pills **(Figure 29.25)** had a great impact on the behaviour of people. Women using birth control pills had more control over their fertility than others. Central to the development of an effective oral contraceptive was a change in the molecular structure of progesterone **(Figure 29.26)**. Specifically, the addition of a $CH_3$ group (Figure 29.26b) meant that the new molecule, megestrol, had the same effect on a woman's reproductive system, but it was not quickly metabolized and remained in the system long enough to have the desired effect (suppressing ovulation). Similarly, slight modifications to the estradiol molecule turned it into ethinylestradiol **(Figure 29.27)**. Megestrol is an analogue of progesterone, and ethinylestradiol is an analogue of estradiol.

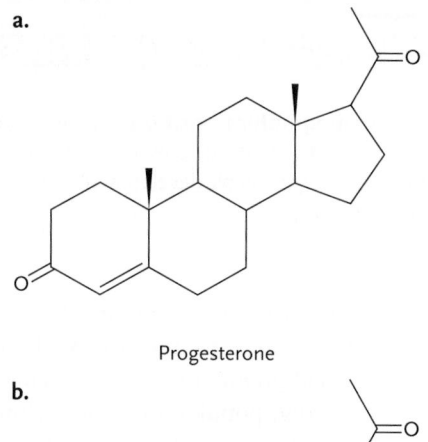

a.

Progesterone

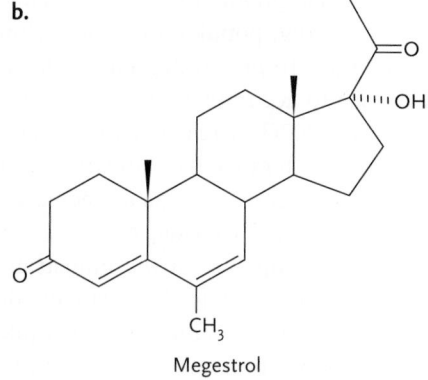

b.

$CH_3$

Megestrol

FIGURE 29.26 **Progesterone and the synthetic megestrol**
Source: Professor John Wiebe

For animals whose populations are growing at a rapid pace, birth control gives keepers the chance to control growth of the populations. The same principles apply to working with organisms in the wild, but getting African elephants to take their birth control pills has not proven to be easy.

Hormones and their analogues are common in untreated municipal wastewaters. But the pill can have unexpected consequences. In some cases, male fish exposed to these wastewaters are feminized. Specifically, some male fish produce vitellogenin mRNA and protein, substances normally associated with the maturation of oocytes in females. Males thus exposed produce early-stage eggs in their testes. This feminization occurs in the presence of estrogenic substances, including

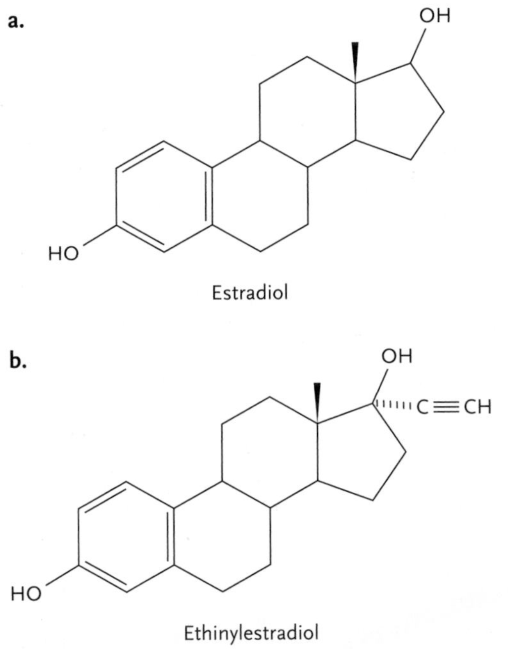

**a.**

Estradiol

**b.**

Ethinylestradiol

**FIGURE 29.27 Estradiol and the synthetic ethinylestradiol**

Source: Professor John Wiebe

**FIGURE 29.28** *Pimephales promelas*, **the fathead minnow**

natural estrogen (17b-estradiol) and the synthetic estrogen 17a-ethynylestradiol.

Do a few feminized male fish in the population matter? Karen A. Kidd and six colleagues conducted a seven-year, whole-lake experiment in northwestern Ontario (the Experimental Lakes Area). Male fathead minnows (*Pimephales promelas*) **(Figure 29.28)** chronically exposed to low levels (5–6 ng/L) of estrogenic substances showed feminizing effects and the development of intersex males, whereas females had altered oogenesis. The situation led to the near-extinction of fathead minnows in the experimental lake.

# Summary Illustration

Population ecology is rooted in patterns of population growth—represented by the equation at the centre of the illustration. At least eight characteristics (shown here encircling the equation) define populations and influence the parameters of the equation. These characteristics in turn are influenced by climate and weather, food, immigration and emigration, predation and parasites, and disease.

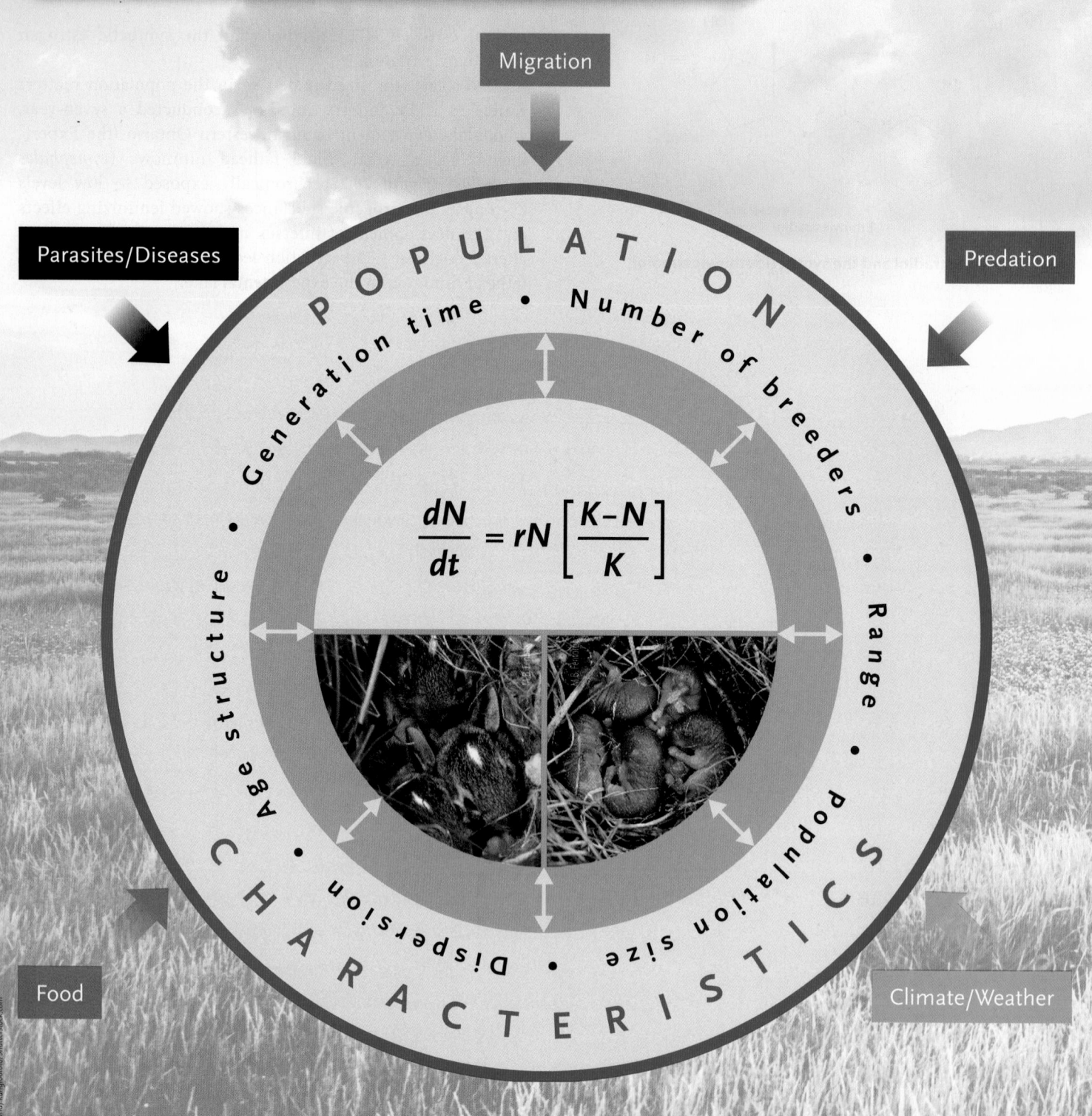

Migration

Parasites/Diseases

Predation

Food

Climate/Weather

POPULATION CHARACTERISTICS

Generation time • Number of breeders • Range • Population size • Dispersion • Age structure

$$\frac{dN}{dt} = rN \left[ \frac{K-N}{K} \right]$$

**Migration**
Population size is increased when animals move into the population (immigration) and is decreased when they move out (emigration).

**Predation**
Population size is decreased with increased predation and is increased when predation pressures relax.

**Climate/Weather**
Shifts in climate and/or adverse weather conditions can cause high mortality events or add stress to population health, which can influence reproductive productivity.

**Food**
When food resources are sufficient, competition for food is reduced. When food is limited, competition reduces the amount of food available for individuals, leading to reduced individual health, reduced reproductive rates, and even starvation.

**Parasites/Diseases**
Populations contract with increased incidence of disease and with elevated parasite loads, and expand when parasites and disease are reduced.

# SELF-TEST QUESTIONS

## Recall/Understand

1. Which of these factors refers to the number of individuals making up the population at a specified time?
   a. size
   b. density
   c. dispersion pattern
   d. age structure

2. Which of these terms can be used to describe the number of individuals per unit area or volume of habitat?
   a. dispersion pattern
   b. density
   c. size
   d. age structure

3. Half the world's human population is at risk of being exposed to which of these diseases?
   a. malaria
   b. HIV
   c. disease caused by Zika virus
   d. disease caused by West Nile virus

4. Which of the following is paired according to what it stands for?
   a. $K$ and population size
   b. $K$ and carrying capacity
   c. $r$ and carrying capacity
   d. $r$ and population size

## Apply/Analyze

5. Suppose that one day you caught and marked 90 butterflies in a population. A week later, you returned to the population and caught 80 butterflies, including 16 that had been marked previously. What is the size of the butterfly population?
   a. 154
   b. 170
   c. 450
   d. 486

6. Which of these statements describes what a uniform dispersion pattern implies about the members of a population?
   a. They work together to escape from predators.
   b. They use resources that are patchily distributed.
   c. They may experience intraspecific competition for vital resources.
   d. They have no ecological interactions with each other.

7. Which of these statements does the model of exponential population growth predict about the per capita population growth rate ($r$)?
   a. $r$ does not change as a population gets larger.
   b. $r$ gets larger as a population gets larger.
   c. $r$ gets smaller as a population gets larger.
   d. $r$ is always at its maximum level ($r_{max}$).

8. If a population of 1000 individuals experiences 452 births and 380 deaths in 1 year, what is the value of $r$ for this population?
   a. 0.009/individual/year
   b. 0.072/individual/year
   c. 0.380/individual/year
   d. 0.452/individual/year

9. According to the logistic model of population growth, which of the following happens to the absolute number of individuals by which a population grows during a given time period?
   a. It gets steadily larger as the population size increases.
   b. It gets steadily smaller as the population size increases.
   c. It remains constant as the population size increases.
   d. It is highest when the population is at an intermediate size.

10. Which of these patterns is a $K$-selected species likely to exhibit?
    a. a type I survivorship curve and a short generation time
    b. a type II survivorship curve and a short generation time
    c. a type III survivorship curve and a short generation time
    d. a type I survivorship curve and a long generation time

11. Suppose that you are researching populations of king penguins (*Aptenodytes patagonicus*) and their predator, leopard seals (*Hydrurga leptonyx*). How would you expect the populations to change in relation to each other?
    a. When the king penguin population density is low, the leopard seal population size increases.
    b. When the king penguin population density is stable, the leopard seal population size increases.
    c. When the king penguin population density is stable, the leopard seal population size decreases.
    d. When the king penguin population density is low, the leopard seal population size also decreases.

## Create/Evaluate

12. Suppose that you observe an animal that gives birth to many young, but does not care for them. Which survivorship curve is it most likely that this animal represents?
    a. type I or type II
    b. type II or type III
    c. type I
    d. type III

13. Which of these examples might reflect density-dependent regulation of population size?
    a. An exterminator uses a pesticide to eliminate carpenter ants from a home.
    b. Mosquitoes disappear from an area after the first frost.
    c. Northeast storms blow over and kill all willow trees along a lake.
    d. A clam population declines in numbers in a bay as the number of predatory herring gulls increases.

14. Which one of these statements is *most* likely a reason that human populations have sidestepped factors that usually control population growth?
    a. Agriculture and industrialization have increased the carrying capacity for our species.
    b. The population growth rate ($r$) for the human population has always been small.
    c. The age structure of human populations has no impact on its population growth.
    d. Plagues have killed off large numbers of humans at certain times in the past.

15. Compare survivorship curves I, II, and III.

# Chapter Roadmap

**Species Interactions and Community Ecology**

Earth is a huge ecosystem consisting of many communities of sympatric organisms interconnected by the flow of energy and wastes.

From Chapter 28 → **30.1 Introduction** → To Chapter 31

**30.2 Symbiosis: Close Associations**

**30.3 Energy Intake**

**30.4 Defence**

From Chapter 29 → **30.5 Competition**

**30.6 The Nature of Ecological Communities**

**30.7 Community Characteristics** → To Chapter 31

**30.8 Effects of Population Interactions on Community Structure**

**30.9 Succession**

**30.10 Variations in Species Richness among Communities**

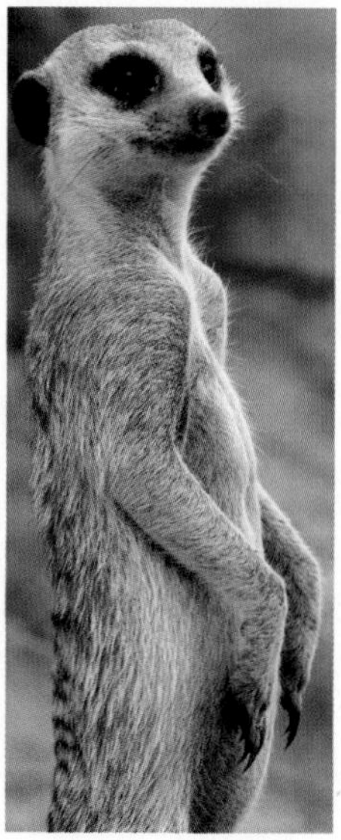

M.B. Fenton

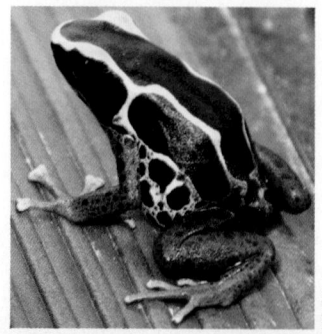

M.B. Fenton

**Five red-billed oxpeckers (*Buphagus erythrorhynchus*) moving around on a giraffe (*Giraffa camelopardalis*).** Oxpeckers, also known as tick birds, remove ticks and other ectoparasites from some large mammals. But is the relationship between oxpeckers and large mammals mutually beneficial?

# Species Interactions and Community Ecology

# 30

**Why it matters . . .** Mutualism describes interactions between organisms that benefit both participants. One commonly cited example is tickbirds, the oxpeckers that eat the ticks they find on their hosts, large mammals such as giraffes. Do the oxpeckers benefit the host? Paul Weeks, a zoologist at Cambridge University, set out to answer this question using experimental manipulation of oxpeckers' access to cattle. He expected that, if hosts, in his case cattle, were well served by oxpeckers, the incidence of ticks would be higher on cattle without the services of oxpeckers. Working in Zimbabwe, Paul Weeks found that exposure to oxpeckers did not coincide with lower tick infestations in cattle. Furthermore, he observed that wounds on cattle exposed to these birds took longer to heal than those on cattle not so exposed. This raised the possibility that oxpeckers feed at wounds where their actions would give them access to blood and this would result in slower healing. The oxpeckers also could obtain insects at wounds. Weeks' data do not support the suggestion that the hosts benefit from the interaction with oxpeckers.

Many other animals use ectoparasites of other animals as a source of food. Cleaner fish are one of the best known. As the name implies, cleaner fish **(Figure 30.1)** remove parasites from the bodies and gills of other fish. On coral reefs, cleaner stations are sites where fish find the cleaner fish and benefit from their feeding activity. The interaction between cleaner fish and their hosts is mutualistic because both appear to benefit from the cleaning behaviour. But, if oxpeckers do not reduce tick infestations and even eat the host's blood, the situation is not mutualistic because there is little if any benefit to the host.

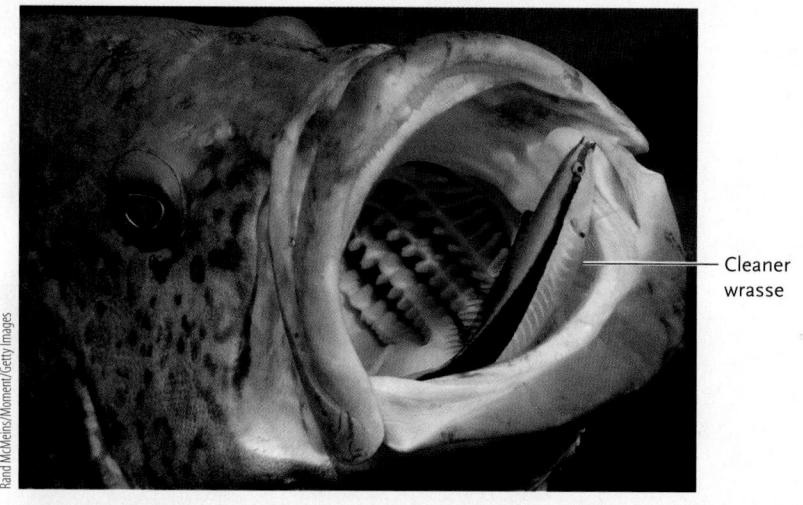

Cleaner wrasse

**FIGURE 30.1 Mutualism between animal species.** A large potato cod (*Epinephelus tukula*) from the Great Barrier Reef in Australia remains nearly motionless in the water while a striped cleaner wrasse (*Labroides dimidiatus*) carefully removes and eats ectoparasites attached to its lip. The potato cod is a predator; the striped cleaner wrasse is a potential prey. Here the mutualistic relationship supersedes the possible predator–prey interaction.

To determine the nature of the relationship between oxpeckers and their host requires knowledge of exactly what oxpeckers eat. Modern techniques for analyzing isotopes in the birds' feathers could shed light on the importance of blood in oxpeckers' diets. DNA barcode analysis (see Section 30.1a) could provide details of what species of arthropods the birds eat. To get answers means catching some oxpeckers, taking some feathers to analyze for isotopes, and some of their droppings to learn just what arthropods they ate. Stay tuned; perhaps we will learn the answer.

## 30.1 Introduction

Earth is a huge ecosystem consisting of many communities of sympatric organisms interconnected by the flow of energy and wastes that are by-products of energy production and use. Ironically, DDT (see Chapter 31) provided an early demonstration of connectivity among Earth's ecosystems and communities. The diversity of Earth's biological communities is astonishing, reflecting a wide range of conditions from bright, hot, and humid to cold, dark, and dry. In most communities, photosynthetic autotrophs (plants and cyanobacteria) are the **primary producers** of energy and oxygen. Exceptionally, other sources of energy are found around hydrothermal vents in the ocean floor; and, as we have seen in caves, bats (their droppings) are the principal energy source for specialized ecosystems (see Chapter 31).

Organisms can be generally classified according to the trophic role they play in an ecosystem. Primary producers supply energy (e.g., a plant), **primary consumers** eat primary producers (e.g., a rabbit), and **secondary consumers** eat primary consumers (e.g., a lynx). Animals are generally **herbivores** because

they eat primary producers or **predators** that eat other animals. Both predators and herbivores have characteristics allowing them to feed effectively and catch food or avoid being caught and eaten. Meat eaters use sensory systems to locate animal prey and specialized behaviours and anatomical structures to capture and consume it. Herbivores use sensory systems to identify preferred food or to avoid food that is toxic. Their anatomical specializations for feeding often are associated with obtaining and chewing food. **Detritus** feeders and **decomposers** are other main components in food chains, and also exhibit a range of specializations.

Although sometimes neutral, interactions among species typically benefit or harm the organisms involved (**Table 30.1**). Furthermore, where interactions with other species affect individuals' survival and reproduction, many relationships we witness today are the products of long-term evolutionary modification. Remember that interactions among species occur at the individual level. Some individuals of a species may be better adapted to survive when individuals of another species exert selection pressure on them. **Co-evolution** occurs when genetically based, reciprocal adaptation occurs in two or more interacting species. Many good examples of co-evolution are provided by interactions among plants and their animal pollinators.

Ecologists describe the co-evolutionary interactions between some predators and their prey as a race in which each species evolves adaptations that temporarily allow it to outpace another. When antelope populations suffer predation by cheetahs, natural selection fosters the evolution of faster antelopes. Faster cheetahs may be the result of this situation; and if their offspring are also fast, then antelopes will also become more fleet of foot. Other co-evolved interactions provide benefits to both partners. Flower structures of different monkey-flower species have evolved characteristics that allow them to be visited by either bees or hummingbirds (see Figure 18.6, Chapter 18).

| TABLE 30.1 | Population Interactions and Their Effects | |
|---|---|---|
| Interaction | | Effects on Interacting Populations |
| Predation | +/− | Predators gain nutrients and energy; prey are killed or injured. |
| Parasitism | +/− | Parasites gain nutrients and energy; hosts are injured or killed. |
| Herbivory | +/− | Herbivores gain nutrients and energy; plants are killed or injured. |
| Competition | −/− | Both competing populations lose access to some resources. |
| Commensalism | −/0 | One population benefits; the other population is unaffected. |
| Mutualism | +/+ | Both populations benefit. |

© Cengage Learning 2017

Rand McMeins/Moment/Getty Images

One can hypothesize a co-evolutionary relationship between any two interacting species, but it can be challenging to document the evolution of reciprocal adaptations. Co-evolutionary interactions often involve more than two species, and most organisms experience complex interactions with numerous other species in their communities. Cheetahs take several prey species. Antelopes are prey for many species of predators, from cheetahs to lions, leopards, and hyenas, as well as some larger birds of prey. Not all predators use the same hunting strategy; therefore, the simple portrayal of co-evolution as taking place between two species rarely does justice to the complexity of these relationships.

## 30.1a The CO1 Gene: Barcode of Life

Whether the challenge is answering a question such as, How many species are there in my sample? or What did that bat actually eat?, the Barcode of Life work with the CO1 gene has provided a means to obtain accurate answers (**Figure 30.2**). The diversity of species can be overwhelming, so it is difficult to provide a confident estimate of how many species remain undescribed. For many groups of organisms, there may be very few authorities able to identify species and provide descriptions of "new" species, the ones not yet described and therefore nameless. The Barcode of Life Data Systems, based in Guelph, Ontario, offers one alternative to the challenge of knowing how many species are in the sample you have just acquired, or the origin of a mystery mouse found in a shipment of frozen chickens from Thailand.

The Barcode of Life project depends upon variation in the mitochondrial cytochrome *c oxidase 1* (CO1) gene consisting of about 650 nucleotides. This genetic barcode is embedded in almost every cell and offers biologists a chance to identify a species even if they have only a small sample of feathers or fur, a leaf, a seed, or a caterpillar. Since identification of some species depends upon having a whole adult specimen, being able to make an identification from an egg, a larva, or a hair offers enormous potential. Identification of organisms with different life stages can be particularly challenging. Using morphology, it can be easy to identify a butterfly or a frog, but much more difficult to identify its caterpillar or its tadpole.

The Barcode of Life project is based on polymerase chain reaction (PCR) technology, which allowed biologists to process 100 samples every three hours. Subsequent advances in genomic technology have increased our capacity for efficient sequencing of DNA. The combination of this potential, an army of researchers collecting specimens, and Global Positioning Satellite (GPS) technology to document locations means that the Barcode of Life project can deliver accurate (to 97.5%) identifications of specimens in a short time. Further developments could see biologists and naturalists armed with appropriately programmed handheld devices to obtain in-field identifications.

One important consequence of this project is that biologists will have a fighting chance to document more fully the diversity of life on Earth. On one hand, this means realizing that one species of the butterfly *Astraptes fulgerator* is actually 10 species, or that what people had thought were several species is, in fact, one. Protecting species through CITES, the Convention on International Trade in Endangered Species, means being able to name them so that they can be placed on a protected list. The Barcode of Life project should allow a merchant to be sure that the ivory being sold in her shop is from an extinct mammoth, rather than a living species said to be endangered. The same applies to food species in a market: Is that fish really what the label says?

Everyone has experience with barcode operations because they are used in many retail outlets and therefore we all know that barcodes and readers do not always work. These limitations, as well as biological ones associated with genetics of different species, make some organisms more appropriate for Barcode of Life approaches than others.

### STUDY BREAK QUESTIONS

1. What are the basic components of biological communities?
2. What is co-evolution? Is it usually restricted to two species?

a.

International Barcode of Life

b.

M. B. Fenton

**FIGURE 30.2 Shown here is** (a) **the bar code of** (b) **a flying fringe-lipped bat** (*Trachops cirrhosus*).

## 30.2 Symbiosis: Close Associations

Symbiosis occurs when one species has a physically close ecological association with another (*sym* = together; *bio* = life; *sis* = process). Biologists define three types of symbiotic interactions: commensalism, mutualism, and parasitism (see Table 30.1). Oxpeckers are a good introduction to the problem of drawing boundaries among different types of interactions.

In **commensalism**, one species benefits from and the other is unaffected by the interactions. Commensalism appears to be rare in nature because few species are unaffected by interactions with another. If oxpeckers eat mainly ectoparasites that they remove from their hosts, and cause no harm to the hosts, the relationship would be commensal.

In **mutualism**, both partners benefit. Mutualism appears to be common and includes co-evolved relationships between flowering plants and animal pollinators. Animals that feed on a plant's nectar or pollen carry the plant's pollen from one flower to another. Similarly, animals that eat fruits disperse the seeds and "plant" them in piles of nutrient-rich feces. Mutualistic relationships between plants and animals do not require active cooperation, as each species simply exploits the other for its own benefit. Some associations between bacteria and plants are mutualistic. The association between *Rhizobium* and leguminous plants such as peas, beans, and clover is very important for agricultural operations (see Chapter 36).

Mutualistic relationships among animal species are common, as are mutualistic relationships between animals and plants. One example of mutualism is the relationship between the bull's horn acacia tree (*Acacia cornigera*) of Central America and small ants (*Pseudomyrmex ferruginea*) (**Figure 30.3**). Each acacia is inhabited by an ant colony that lives in hollows in the tree's swollen thorns. Ants swarm out of the thorns to sting, and sometimes kill, herbivores that touch the tree. Ants also clip any vegetation that grows nearby. Acacia trees colonized by ants grow in a space free of herbivores and competitors, and occupied trees grow faster and produce more seeds than unoccupied trees. In return, the plants produce sugar-rich nectar consumed by adult ants and protein-rich structures that the ants feed to their larvae. Ecologists describe the co-evolved mutualism between these species as obligatory, at least for the ants, because they cannot subsist on any other food sources.

Many animals eat honey and sometimes the bees that produce it. In Africa, greater honeyguide birds (*Indicator indicator*) use a special guiding display to lead humans to beehives. Individuals in one tribe of Kenyans, the honey-gathering Borans, call honeyguides with a special whistle. Boran honey gatherers that follow greater honeyguides are much more efficient at finding beehives than those working alone. When the honey gatherer goes to the hive and raids it to obtain honey, greater honeyguides help themselves to bee larvae, left-over honey, and wax. Although greater honeyguides are said to guide ratels (honey badgers, *Mellivora capensis*) to beehives, there are no firm data supporting this position.

If oxpeckers benefit from eating ectoparasites taken from their hosts, and if the hosts benefit by incurring fewer ectoparasites, then the relationship would be mutualistic. But if the oxpeckers benefit at the hosts' expense, then the relationship is more parasitic.

In **parasitism**, one species, the parasite, uses another, the host, in a way that harms the host. A parasite is an organism whose survival depends upon exploitation of its host. Parasite–host interactions can be considered to be specialized predator–prey relationships because one population of organisms feeds on another. Parasites differ from predators because they do not directly kill their prey. A dead host typically is not a continuing source of nourishment such as blood.

Many animals eat blood (**Figure 30.4**). Ticks, leeches, insects, and vampire bats are on the list. Blood-feeding insects include mosquitoes, black flies, bed bugs, fleas, and kissing bugs among others and number about 10 000 species. This is less than 1% of all species of insects. Are blood feeders parasites or just crafty predators? The three species of vampire bats stand out among blood feeders because they are warm blooded. This means that they must ingest larger quantities of blood than cold-blooded blood feeders. One species of Darwin's finches, the vampire finch (*Geospiza difficilis septentrionalis*), eats blood. The vampire bats are parasites because their survival depends upon obtaining blood from their host(s). This may or may not be true of vampire finches. Interestingly it is true of many female mosquitoes, but not the males that eat nectar.

While blood is arguably an ideal food and a renewable resource, various defence mechanisms protect animals' blood. Blood feeders typically have chemicals in their saliva that prevent clotting. For example, a leech bite typically bleeds for some time after the leech stops feeding (Figure 30.4e). Digesting blood also is a challenge, and it is interesting to see that leeches and vampire bats have similar bacteria in their digestive tracts. To obtain a blood meal, blood feeders must overcome clotting and clustering of red blood cells, and counter peripheral

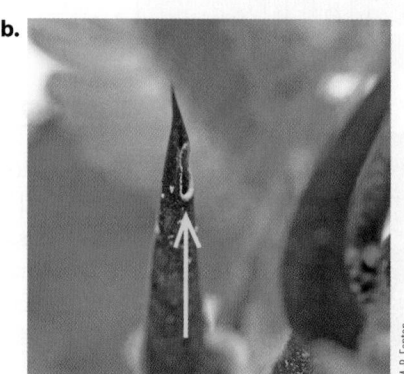

**FIGURE 30.3 Highly co-evolved mutualisms. (a)** Bull's horn acacia trees (*Acacia cornigera*) provide colonies for small ants (*Pseudomyrmex ferruginea*). In addition to providing homes (domatia: yellow arrow in **(b)**) in hollow thorns, the acacia also provides food for ants (nectar: yellow arrow in **(c)**).

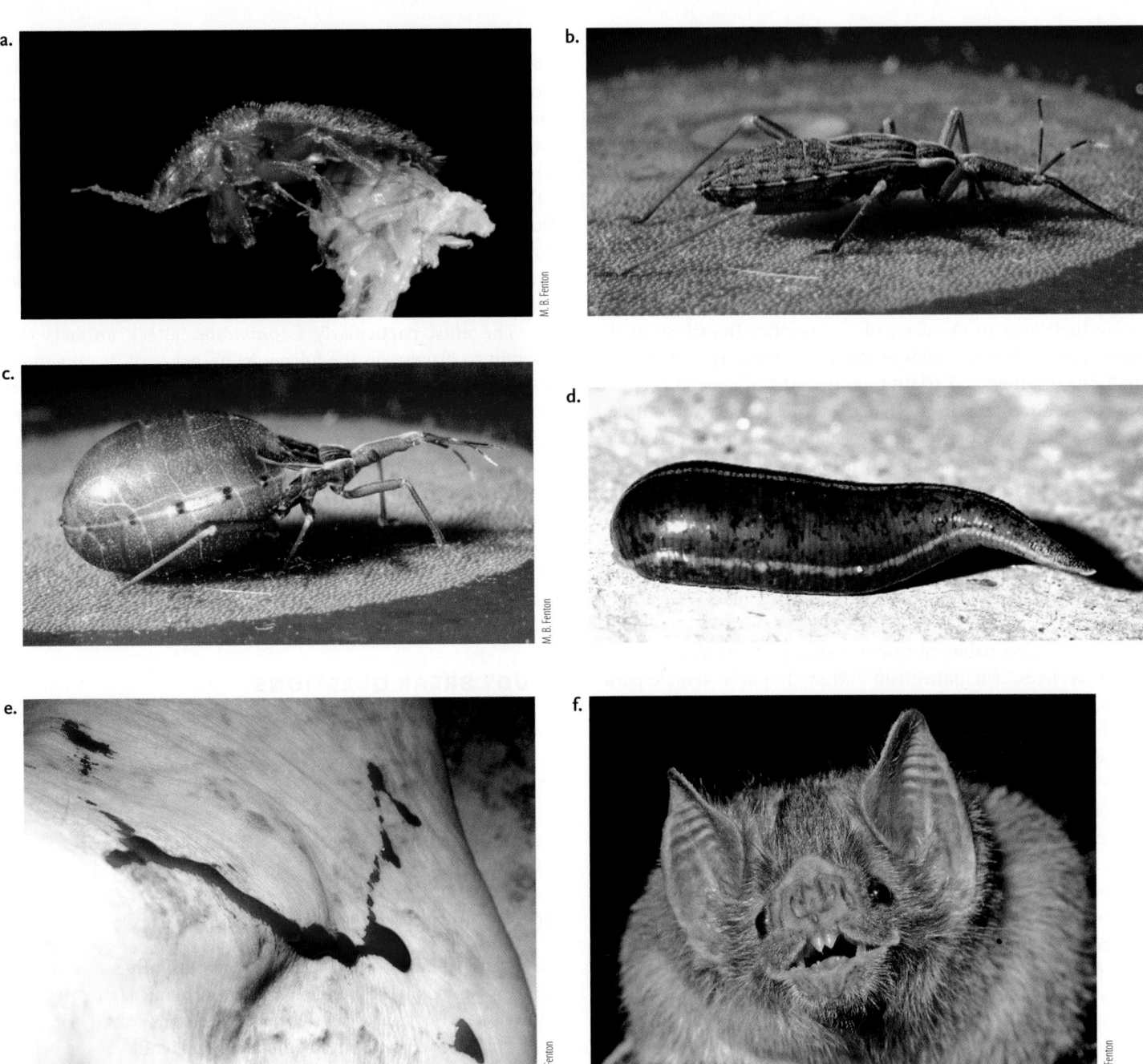

**FIGURE 30.4** A sample of blood feeders including a bat bug **(a)**; two kissing bugs (*Rhodnius prolixus*), one unfed **(b)** and one fed **(c)**; an engorged land leech and **(d)** blood marking the site of a bite from the land leech **(e)**; and a vampire bat (*Desmodus rotundus* **(f)**). A comparison of the two pictures of the kissing bug (b, c) and the distended leech (d) illustrate just how much blood may be consumed at one time.

vasoconstriction that reduces blood flow to a wounded area. The limitations appear to more directly affect warm-blooded blood feeders, which must ingest more blood. A vampire bat (30 g) eats about 25 g of blood a day and cannot go two days without feeding. Vampire bats appear to be one stop shoppers, getting their daily blood meal from one prey.

Diseases can complicate the relationship of blood feeders to their hosts. A mosquito taking a blood meal can transfer a disease such as malaria that may kill the host. There are many examples of disease-causing agents being transmitted by blood-feeding animals. But this situation does not address the issue of whether the victim is a prey or a host.

**Endoparasites**, such as tapeworms, flukes, and roundworms, live within a host. Many endoparasites acquire their hosts passively when a host accidentally ingests the parasites' eggs or larvae. Endoparasites generally complete their life cycle in one or two host individuals. Ectoparasites, such as leeches, aphids, and mosquitoes, feed on the exterior of the host. Most animal ectoparasites have elaborate sensory and behavioural mechanisms, allowing them to locate specific hosts, and they

CHAPTER 30 SPECIES INTERACTIONS AND COMMUNITY ECOLOGY | **781** feed on numerous host individuals during their lifetimes. Plants such as mistletoes (genus *Phoradendron*) live as ectoparasites on the trunks and branches of trees; their roots penetrate the host's xylem and extract water and nutrients. These differ from epiphytes, such as bromeliads or Spanish moss, that use the host only as a base. Other plants are root parasites, for example, *Conopholis americana*.

Not all parasites eat a host's tissues. Some bird species are brood parasites, laying their eggs in the host's nest. It is quite common for female birds such as canvasback ducks (*Aythya valisineria*), brown-headed cowbirds, and Kirtland's warblers to lay their eggs in the nests of conspecifics (members of the same species). Some species of songbirds often lay some eggs in the nests of others, a variation on hedging of genetic bets and on extra-pair copulations (see Chapter 32 respectively). Brood parasitism is the next level of escalation in this spectrum of parasitism. Brown-headed cowbirds (*Molothrus ater*), like other brood parasites, always lay their eggs in the nest of other species, leaving it to the host parents to raise their young. This behaviour can have drastic repercussions for host species. Brown-headed cowbirds, for instance, have played a large role in the near-extinction of Kirtland's warblers (*Dendroica kirtlandii*).

The feeding habits of insects called *parasitoids* fall somewhere between true parasitism and predation. A female parasitoid lays her eggs in a larva or pupa of another insect species, and her young consume the tissues of the living host. But the parasitoid spends part of its life cycle as free living. The larval stage usually kills the host. Because the hosts chosen by most parasitoids are highly specific, agricultural ecologists often try to use parasitoids to control populations of insect pests.

One of the most striking and perhaps startling example of symbioses is the rich biota of prokaryotes and Protozoa that inhabit our digestive tracts. This biota significantly expands our capacity for extracting nutrients and other important factors from the food we ingest. The producers of "probiotic" foods depend upon our being impressed by the importance of our symbionts.

## 30.2a   Some Perils of Mutualism

Living organisms offer many examples of mutualistic interactions in which one species (or group of species) shows varying levels of dependence on another or others. Mutualistic situations can place species on the edge of survival. Where one species depends entirely on another, the extinction of one must lead to change or the extinction of both (e.g., dodos, discussed in Chapter 28, and yucca plants and their moths). There are many other examples of close relationships, including a desert melon (*Cucumis humifructus*) that depends perhaps entirely on aardvarks (*Orycteropus afer*) for dispersal of its seeds. Aardvarks sniff out the underground melons, dig them up, and eat them to obtain water. When aardvarks bury their dung, they plant the melon's seeds and fertilize them. The survival of the melon depends on the aardvark but not vice versa.

Mutualistic interactions between species can be even more complex. In the African **savannah**, ants often live in mutualistic relationships with trees. In east Africa, whistling thorn acacia trees (*Acacia drepanolobium*) are host to four species of ants (see Figure 30.4). One species of ant (*Crematogaster mimosae*) in particular depends on room (hollows in swollen thorns, called *domatia*) and board (carbohydrates secreted from extrafloral glands and the bases of leaves) provided by the trees. Another species of ant (*Crematogaster sjostedti*) also lives on the trees but usually nests in holes made by cerambycid beetles that burrow into and harm the trees.

The ants, particularly *C. mimosae*, attack animals that attempt to browse on the foliage or branches of *A. drepanolobium*. They deter many herbivores, from large mammals to wood-boring beetles (such as cerambycids). If large, browsing mammals are excluded from the area, *A. drepanolobium* produce fewer domatia and fewer carbohydrates for *C. mimosae*. The decline in this species of ant leads to higher damage by cerambycid beetles and increases in populations of *C. sjostedti*.

Many other plants also use ants as mercenaries (see Figure 30.4), and it is becoming clear that survival of these systems depends on the continued presence of participating species.

**STUDY BREAK QUESTIONS**

1. How do commensalism, mutualism, and parasitism differ?
2. Give examples of each. What sets the boundaries among them?
3. How do parasites differ from predators?
4. Why is blood often exploited as food? Give examples of blood-feeding animals.

# 30.3   Energy Intake

Plants and some other organisms use photosynthesis to trap the sun's rays and convert them from light to chemical energy. Some animals harvest chloroplasts; for example, solar sea slugs harvest chloroplasts and use them to emulate green plants. Some plants, notably pitcher plants, use photosynthesis to obtain energy and obtain nitrogen from animal excretory products. This includes rotifers living in pitchers of pitcher plants (**Figure 30.5**).

In Borneo, biologists have discovered two astonishing variations on the pitcher plant story. Specifically, one species, *Nepenthes lowii*, provides pit toilets for tree shrews (*Tupaia* spp.). Nectaries around the pitcher attract the shrews and provide them with a snack as they deposited feces and urine in the pitcher. Another species, *Nepenthes hemsleyana*, has pitchers modified to accommodate roosting bats (*Kerivoula hardwickii*), which urinate and defecate into the pitcher. In both cases, isotopic analysis reveals that nitrogen from the tree shrews and the bats is used by the plants.

Animals typically select food from a variety of potential items. Some species, specialists, eat one or just a few types of food. Among birds, Everglades kites (*Rostrhamus sociabilis*) eat

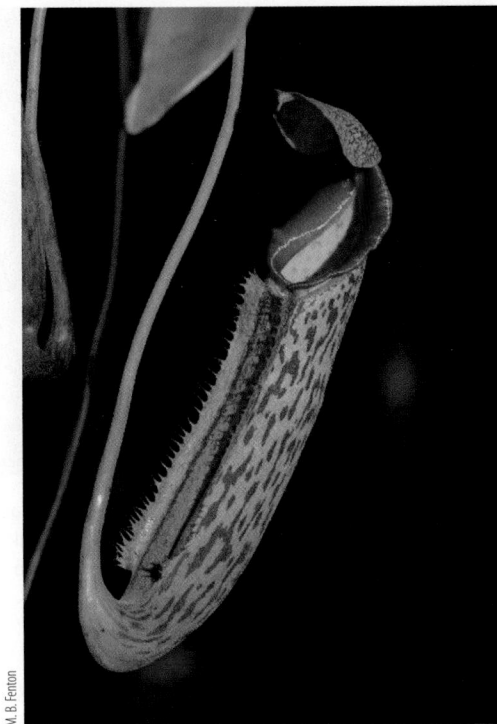

**FIGURE 30.5 Pitcher of a *Nepenthes* spp.**

only apple snails (*Pomacea paludosa*). Koalas (see Figure 27.119b, Chapter 27) eat the leaves of only a few of the many available species of *Eucalyptus*. Other species, generalists, have broader tastes. Crows (genus *Corvus*) take food ranging from grain to insects to carrion. Bears (genus *Ursus*) and pigs (genus *Sus*) are as omnivorous as humans.

Herbivores are adapted to locate and process their food plants. Insects use chemical sensors on their legs and mouthparts to identify edible plants, and sharp mandibles or sucking mouthparts to consume plant tissues or sap. Herbivorous mammals have specialized teeth to harvest and grind tough vegetation (see Chapter 27). Herbivores such as farmer ants, ruminants, and termites (see "Digesting Cellulose: Fermentation," Chapter 39) may co-opt other species to gain access to nutrients locked up in plant materials.

How does an animal select its food? Why eat pizza rather than salad? Mathematical models, collectively described as **optimal foraging theory**, predict that an animal's diet is a compromise between the costs and benefits associated with different types of food. Assuming that animals try to maximize their energy intake at any meal, their diets should be determined by the ratio of costs to benefits; in short, the costs of obtaining the food versus the benefits of consuming it. Costs are the time and energy it takes to pursue, capture, consume, and digest a particular kind of food. Benefits are the energy provided by that food. A cougar (*Felis concolor*) will invest more time and energy hunting and attacking a mountain goat (*Oreamnos americanus*) than a jackrabbit (*Lepus townsendii*), but the payoff for the cat is a bigger meal. One important element in food choice is the relative abundance of prey, referred

to as encounter rate. This usually is influenced by population density of prey and can influence a predator's diet. For the cougar, encounter rate determines the time between jackrabbits, and when they are abundant, they can be a more economical meal than larger, scarcer prey.

Food abundance affects food choice. When prey are scarce, animals often take what they can get, settling for food with a higher cost-to-benefit ratio. When food is abundant, they may specialize, selecting types that provide the largest energetic return. Bluegill sunfishes eat *Daphnia* spp. and other small crustaceans. When crustacean density is high, these fishes take mostly large *Daphnia*, which provide a higher energetic return than small ones. When prey density is low, bluegills eat *Daphnia* of all sizes (**Figure 30.6**).

Think of yourself at a buffet. The array of food can be impressive, if not overwhelming. But your state of hunger, the foods you like, the ones you do not like, and any to which you are allergic all influence your selection. You may also be influenced by choices made by others. In your feeding behaviour, you betray your animal heritage.

For predators, finding food is one thing, capturing and subduing it is another. Rattlesnakes, such as species in the genus *Crotalus*, use heat sensors in pits in their faces (see Figure 45.39, Chapter 45) to detect warm-blooded prey. The snakes deliver venom through fangs (hollow teeth) by open-mouthed strikes

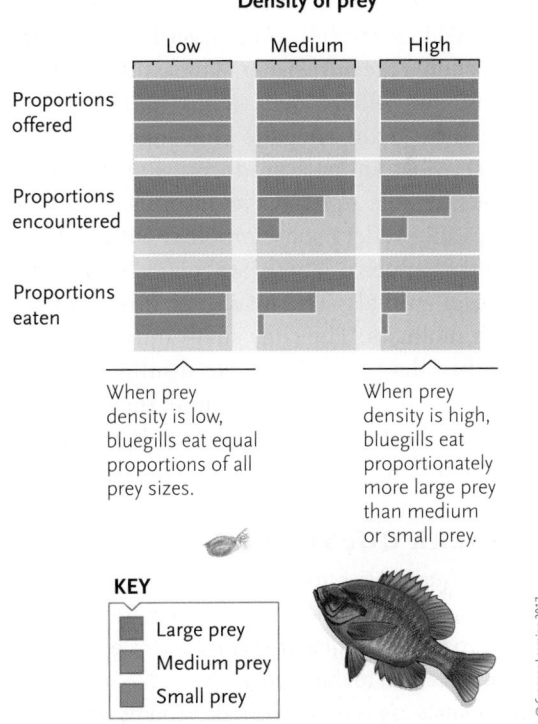

**FIGURE 30.6 An experiment demonstrating that prey density affects predator food choice.** Bluegill sunfishes (*Lepomis macrochirus*) were offered equal numbers of small, medium, and large prey (*Daphnia magna*) at three different total densities of prey. Because large prey are easy to find, the fishes encountered them more often, especially at the highest prey densities, than either medium-sized or small prey. The fishes' choice of prey varied with prey density, but they always chose the largest prey available.

FIGURE 30.7  **Shells of cone snails (*Conus* spp.)**

FIGURE 30.8  **Protective latex sap.** Milky sap laced with cardiac glycosides oozes from a cut milkweed (*Asclepias* species) leaf. Milky sap does not always mean dangerous chemicals; for example, the sap of dandelions is benign.

on prey. After striking, the snakes wait for the venom to take effect and then use chemical sensors on the roofs of their mouths to follow the scent trail left by the dying prey. Venom is produced in the snakes' salivary glands. Venom typically is a cocktail of proteins, including neurotoxins that paralyze prey and protease enzymes that begin to digest it. The specific components vary among venomous species. Elastic ligaments connecting the bones of the snakes' jaws (mandibles) to one another and the mandibles to the skull allow snakes to open their mouths very wide to swallow prey larger than their heads.

Some venoms are surprising. At least two species of cone snails (*Conus geographus* and *Conus tulipa*) use insulin to immobilize fish, facilitating the challenge of catching them (**Figure 30.7**). Most animals produce insulin, a hormone, but there is considerable diversity in insulins. Diseases such as diabetes typically reflect some problem with insulin production and management. There are many different kinds of insulin among animals. The insulin of fish is quite different from that of molluscs. The cone snails immobilize fish with a fish-like rather than a mollusc-like insulin. The cone snails release insulin into the water around the fish; the insulin enters the fish through its gills, causing hypoglycemic shock and immobilizing it.

### STUDY BREAK QUESTIONS

1. How do predators differ from herbivores? How are they similar?
2. Is a koala a generalist or a specialist? What is the difference?
3. What does optimal foraging theory predict? Describe the costs and benefits central to this theory.
4. How do animals use venoms? How do venoms work?

## 30.4  Defence

**CONCEPT FIX** Some people believe that "natural" products (chemicals) are beneficial to us, while artificial ones are potentially

harmful. In reality, many plants produce chemicals (natural products) that are dangerous and even deadly, to humans and to other animals and to some plants. Contact with the leaves (or stems, roots, flowers, or berries) of poison ivy may be enough to convince you that not all plant products are beneficial. If not, you can read about coniine, an active ingredient in poison hemlock, the poison that killed Socrates. ⬡

Predation and herbivory negatively affect the species being eaten, so it is no surprise that animals and plants have evolved mechanisms to avoid being caught and eaten. Some plants use spines, thorns, and irritating hairs to protect themselves from herbivores. Plant tissues often contain poisonous chemicals that deter herbivores from feeding. When damaged, milkweed plants (family Asclepiadaceae) exude a milky, irritating sap (**Figure 30.8**) that contains poisons that affect the heart (cardiac glycosides). Even small amounts of cardiac glycosides are toxic to the heart muscles of some vertebrates. Other plants have compounds that mimic the structure of insect hormones, disrupting the development of insects that eat them. Most poisonous compounds are volatile, giving plants their typical aromas. Some herbivores recognize these odours and avoid toxic plants. Some plants increase their production of toxic compounds in response to herbivore feeding. Potato and tomato plants damaged by herbivores have higher levels of protease-inhibiting chemicals. These compounds prevent herbivores from digesting the proteins they have eaten, reducing the food value of these plants.

### 30.4a  Be Too Big to Tackle

Size can be a defence. At one end of the spectrum, this means being too small to be considered food. At the other end, it means being so big that few predators can succeed in attacking and killing the prey. Relative size of predator and prey is central to this situation. Today, elephants and some other large herbivores (megaherbivores) are species with few predators (other than humans). But 50 thousand years ago, there were larger predators, including one species of "lion" that was one-third larger than an African lion.

## 30.4b   Eternal Vigilance: Always Be Alert

A first line of defence of many animals is avoiding detection. This often means not moving, as well as keeping a sharp lookout for the danger presented by approaching predators (**Figure 30.9**). Animals that live in groups benefit from the multitude of eyes and ears that can detect approaching danger, so the risk of predation influences group size and social interactions.

## 30.4c   Avoid Detection: Freeze—Movement Invites Discovery

Many animals are cryptic, camouflaged so that a predator does not distinguish them from the background (**Figure 30.10**). Patterns such as the stripes of a zebra (*Equus burchellii*) make the animal conspicuous at close range, but at a distance, patterns break up the outline, rendering the animals almost invisible.

**FIGURE 30.10  A camouflaged praying mantis is almost invisible on the trunk of a tree in Belize.**

Many other animals look like something that is not edible. Some caterpillars look like bird droppings, whereas other insects look like thorns or sticks. Neither bird droppings nor thorns are usually eaten by insectivores.

## 30.4d   Thwarting Attacks: Take Evasive Action

Animals resort to other defensive tactics once they have been discovered and recognized. Running away is a typical next line of defence. Taking refuge in a shelter and getting out of a predator's reach are alternatives. African pancake tortoises (*Malacochersus tornieri*) are flat, as the name implies. When threatened, they retreat into rocky crevices and puff themselves up with air, becoming so tightly wedged that predators cannot extract them.

If cornered by a predator, offence is the next line of defence. This can involve displays intended to startle or intimidate by making the prey appear large and/or ferocious. Such a display might dissuade a predator or confuse it long enough to allow the potential victim to escape. Many animals use direct attack in these situations, engaging whatever weapons they have (biting, scratching, stinging, etc.). Direct attacks are not usually a good primary defence because they involve getting very close to the predator, something prey usually avoid doing.

## 30.4e   Spines and Armour: Be Dangerous or Impossible to Attack

Other organisms use active defence in the form of spines or thorns (**Figure 30.11**). North American porcupines (genus *Erethizon*) release hairs modified into sharp, barbed quills that, when stuck into a predator, cause severe pain and swelling. The spines detach easily from the porcupine, and the nose, lips, and tongue of an attacker are particularly vulnerable. In Israel, there are records of leopards (*Panthera pardus*) being killed by

**FIGURE 30.9  Eternally vigilant.** The sentry of a group of meerkats (*Suricata suricatta*)

CHAPTER 30   SPECIES INTERACTIONS AND COMMUNITY ECOLOGY     **785**

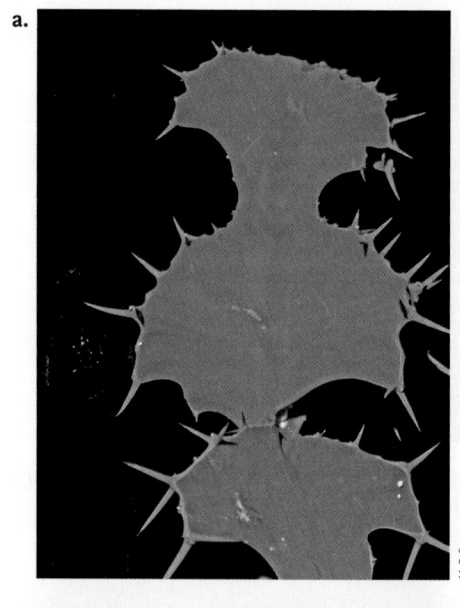

a.

b.

c.

d.

FIGURE 30.11 **Defensive spines.** Plants such as **(a)** the cow horn euphorb (*Euphorbia grandicornis*) and **(b)** crown of thorns (*Euphorbia milii*), and animals such as **(c)** spiny anteaters (*Tachyglossus* species) and **(d)** porcupines (*Hystrix* species) use thorns or spines in defence. Pen shown for scale with quills in (d)

## 30.4f Chemical Defence Ranges from Bad Taste to Deadly

Like plants that produce chemicals to repel herbivores, many animals make themselves chemically unattractive. At one level, this can be as simple as smelling or tasting bad. Have you ever had a dog or a cat that was sprayed by a skunk (*Mephitis mephitis*)? Many animals vomit and defecate on their attackers. Skunks and bombardier beetles escalate this strategy by producing and spraying a noxious chemical. Other animals go beyond spraying. Many species of cnidarians, annelids, arthropods, and chordates produce dangerous toxins and deliver them directly into their attackers. These toxins may be synthesized by the user or sequestered from other sources, often plants or other animals (see "Nematocysts"; Chapter 27). Caterpillars of monarch butterflies are immune to the cardiac glycosides in the milkweed leaves they eat. They extract, concentrate, and store these chemicals, making the caterpillars themselves poisonous to potential predators. The concentrations of defensive chemicals may be higher in the animal than they were in its food. Cardiac glycosides persist through metamorphosis, making adult monarchs poisonous to vertebrate predators.

porcupine spines. In these instances, the damage to the leopards' mouths, combined with infection, was probably the immediate cause of death. Many other mammals, from monotremes (spiny anteaters) to tenrecs (insectivores from Madagascar, *Tenrec* species and *Hemicentetes* species), hedgehogs (*Erinaceus* species), and porcupines in the Old World, use the same defence. So do some fishes and many plants.

Other organisms are armoured (**Figure 30.12**). Examples include bivalve and gastropod molluscs, chambered nautiluses, arthropods such as horseshoe crabs (*Limulus* species), trilobites (see Chapter 27), fishes such as catfish (Siluriformes), reptiles (turtles; see Figure 27.106, Chapter 27), and mammals (armadillos, scaly anteaters). We know a great deal about extinct species that were armoured (see Chapter 19) because they often made good fossils.

FIGURE 30.12 **Even life in a shell does not make leopard tortoises immune to mishaps.** Turtles and their allies live inside shells. This leopard tortoise (*Stigmochelys pardalis*) is inspecting the remains of a conspecific. Armour does not guarantee survival.

a.
b.
c.

**FIGURE 30.13 Warning colours. (a)** This arrowhead frog (*Dendrobates tinctorius*) gets its name from toxins in its skin that were used to poison arrowheads. **(b)** Three wasps on their nest; their black and yellow colouring advertises their ability to sting. **(c)** The grasshopper nymph also is black and yellow, but to date we do not know whether this is an aposematic signal or false advertising.

## 30.4g Warnings Are Danger Signals

Many noxious or dangerous animals are **aposematic**: they advertise their unpalatability with an appropriate display (**Figure 30.13**; see Chapter 17). Aposematic displays are designed to "teach" predators to avoid the signaller, reducing the chances of harm to would-be predators and prey. Predators that attack a brightly coloured bee or wasp and are stung learn to associate the aposematic pattern with the sting. Many predators quickly learn to avoid black-and-white skunks, yellow-banded wasps, or orange monarch butterflies because they associate the warning display with pain, illness, or severe indigestion.

But for every ploy there is a counter-ploy, and some predators eat mainly dangerous prey. Bee-eaters (family Meropidae) are birds that eat hymenopterans (bees and wasps). Some individual African lions specialize in porcupines, and animals such as hedgehogs (genus *Erinaceus*) seem able to eat almost anything and show no ill effects. Indeed, some hedgehogs first lick toads and then their own spines, anointing them with toad venom. Hedgehog spines treated with toad venom are more irritating (at least to people) than untreated ones, enhancing their defensive impact.

## 30.4h Mimicry Is Advertising, Whether True or False

If predators learn to recognize warning signals, it is no surprise that many harmless animals' defences are based on imitating (mimicking) dangerous or distasteful species. Mimicry occurs when one species evolves to resemble another (**Figure 30.14**). Batesian mimicry, named for English naturalist Henry W. Bates, occurs when a palatable or harmless species (the mimic) resembles an unpalatable or poisonous one (the model). Any predator that eats the poisonous model and suffers accordingly will subsequently avoid other organisms that resemble it. However, the predator must survive the encounter. Müllerian mimicry, named for German zoologist Fritz Müller, involves two or more unpalatable species looking the same, presumably to reinforce lessons

learned by a predator that attacks any species in the mimicry complex.

For mimicry to work, the predator must learn (see Chapter 32) to recognize and then avoid the prey. The more deadly the toxin, the less likely an individual predator is to learn by its experience. In many cases, predators learn by watching the discomfort of a conspecific that has eaten or attacked an aposematic prey.

Plants often use toxins to protect themselves against herbivores. Is this also true of toxins in mushrooms (see Chapter 18)?

## 30.4i There Is No Perfect Defence

Helmets protect soldiers, skiers, motorcyclists, and cyclists, but not completely; no defence provides perfect protection. Some predators learn to circumvent defences. Many predators learn to deal with a diversity of prey species and a variety of defensive tactics. Orb web spiders confronting a captive in a web adjust their behaviour according to the prey. They treat moths differently from beetles, and they treat bees in yet another way. When threatened by a predator, headstand beetles raise their rear ends and spray a noxious chemical from a gland at the tip of the abdomen. This behaviour deters many would-be predators. But experienced grasshopper mice from western North America circumvent this defence. An experienced mouse grabs the beetle, averts its face (to avoid the spray), turns the beetle upside down so that the gland discharges into the ground, and eats the beetle from the head down.

### STUDY BREAK QUESTIONS

1. List the eight defence techniques used by animals and/or plants. Provide an example of each.
2. How do animals obtain the chemicals they use in chemical defences?
3. What is the purpose of aposematic displays?
4. What do aposematic displays depend upon?

**FIGURE 30.14  If you closely watch insects visiting goldenrod (*Solidago* spp.) flowers, you can see both Batesian and Müllerian mimics.** Stinging hymenoptera that visit flowers include wasps **(a)**, bumblebees **(b)**, and honey bees **(c)**. These are Müllerian mimics. Syrphid flies **(d)** are stingless Batesian mimics whose general behaviour and colour resembles stinging hymenoptera. Note the differences in the eyes, antennae, and heads. A fly that does not mimic hymenoptera **(e)** does not have black and yellow colouring. The ambush bug **(f)** hunts other insects, including bees, at flowers.

## 30.5   Competition

When access to resources limits populations (Chapter 32), individuals of the same species (**intraspecific**) may compete among themselves for limiting resources such as food and shelter. Individuals of different species using the same limiting resources experience **interspecific** competition (competition between species). Competing individuals may experience increased mortality and decreased reproduction, responses similar to the effects of intraspecific competition. Interspecific competition can reduce the size and population growth rate of one or more of the competing populations.

Community ecologists identify two main forms of interspecific competition. In **interference competition**, individuals of one species directly harm individuals of another species. Here animals may fight for access to resources, as when lions chase smaller predators, such as hyenas, jackals, and vultures, from their kills. Many plant species, including creosote bushes, release toxic chemicals into the soil, preventing other plants from growing nearby.

In **exploitative competition**, two or more populations use (exploit) the same limiting resource, and the presence of one species reduces resource availability for others. Exploitative competition need not involve snout-to-snout or root-to-root confrontations. In the deserts of the U.S. Southwest, many bird and ant species eat mainly seeds, and each seed-eating species may deplete the food supply available to others without necessarily encountering each other.

To further explore the role of competition, ecologists undertook field experiments on competition in natural populations. The experiment on barnacles (**Figure 30.15**) is typical of this approach: the impact on one species' potential competitors of adding or removing another species changed patterns of distribution or population size. The picture that emerges from the results of these experiments is not clear, even to ecologists. In the early 1980s, Joseph Connell surveyed 527 published experiments on 215 species. He found that competition was demonstrated in roughly 40% of the experiments and more than 50% of species. At the same time, Thomas W. Schoener used different criteria to evaluate 164 experiments on approximately 400 species. He found that competition affected more than 75% of species.

Data on resource partitioning and character displacement suggest, but do not prove, that interspecific competition is an

FIGURE 30.15 **Experimental Research**

## Demonstration of Competition between Two Species of Barnacles

**Question:** Do two barnacle species limit one another's realized niches in habitats where they coexist?

**Experiment:** Connell observed a difference in the distributions of two barnacle species on a rocky coast: *Chthamalus stellatus* occupies shallow water, and *Balanus balanoides* lives in deeper water. He then determined the fundamental niche of each species by removing either *Chthamalus* or *Balanus* from rocks and monitoring the distribution of each species in the absence of the other.

**Results:** When Connell removed *Balanus* from rocks in deep water, larval *Chthamalus* colonized the area and produced a flourishing population of adults. By contrast, the removal of *Chthamalus* from rocks in shallow water did not result in colonization by *Balanus*.

**Control:** No treatment. *Chthamalus* occupies only shallow water and *Balanus* occupies only deep water.

**Treatment 1:** Remove *Balanus*. In the absence of *Balanus*, *Chthamalus* occupies both shallow water and deep water.

**Treatment 2:** Remove *Chthamalus*. In the absence of *Chthamalus*, *Balanus* still occupies only deep water.

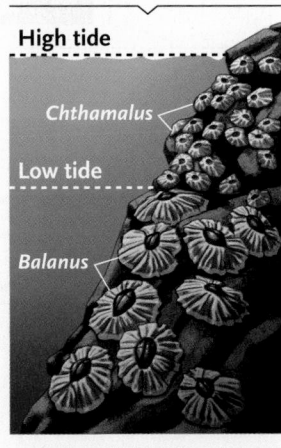
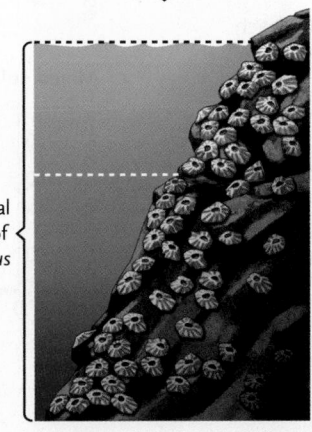
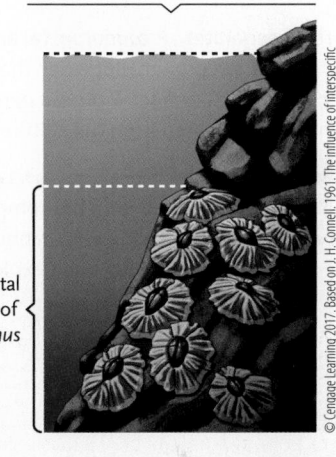

© Cengage Learning 2017. Based on J. H. Connell. 1961. The influence of interspecific competition and other factors on the distribution of the barnacle *Chthamalus stellatus*. *Ecology* 42:710–723.

**Conclusion:** In habitats where *Balanus* and *Chthamalus* coexist, the realized niche (see Section 30.5a) of *Chthamalus* is smaller than its fundamental niche (see Section 30.5a) because of competition from *Balanus*. The realized niche of *Balanus* is similar to its fundamental niche because it is not affected by the competitive interaction.

important selective force in nature. To demonstrate conclusively that interspecific competition limits natural populations, one must show that the presence of one population reduces the population size or density of its presumed competitor. In a classic field experiment, Joseph Connell examined competition between two barnacle species (Figure 30.15). Connell first observed the distributions of both species of barnacles in undisturbed habitats to establish a reference baseline. *Chthamalus stellatus* is generally found in shallow water on rocky coasts, where it is periodically exposed to air. *Balanus balanoides* typically lives in deeper water, where it is usually submerged.

In the absence of *Balanus* on rocks in deep water, larval *Chthamalus* colonized the area and produced a flourishing population of adults. *Balanus* physically displaced *Chthamalus* from these rocks. Thus, interference competition from *Balanus* prevents *Chthamalus* from occupying areas where it would

otherwise live. Removal of *Chthamalus* from rocks in shallow water did not result in colonization by *Balanus*. *Balanus* apparently cannot live in habitats that are frequently exposed to air. Connell concluded that there was competition between the two species. But competition was asymmetrical because *Chthamalus* did not affect the distribution of *Balanus*, whereas *Balanus* had a substantial effect on *Chthamalus*.

Not surprisingly, there is no single answer to the question about how competition works in and influences communities. Plant and vertebrate ecologists working with *K*-selected species generally believe that competition has a profound effect on species distributions and resource use. Insect and marine ecologists working with *r*-selected species argue that competition is not the major force governing community structure, pointing instead to predation or parasitism and physical disturbance. We know that even categorizing a species as *r*- or *K*-selected is open to discussion (see Chapter 29).

FIGURE 30.16 **Experimental Research**

## Gause's Experiments on Interspecific Competition in *Paramecium*

**Question:** Can two species of *Paramecium* coexist in a simple laboratory environment?

**Experiment:** Gause grew populations of two species, *Paramecium aurelia* and *Paramecium caudatum,* alone (single species cultures) or together (mixed cultures) in small bottles in his laboratory. To determine whether the growth of these populations followed the predictions of the logistic equation, Gause had to maintain a reasonably constant carrying capacity in each culture. Thus, he fed the cultures a broth of bacteria, and he eliminated their waste products (by centrifuging the cultures and removing some of the culture medium) on a regular schedule. He then monitored their population sizes over time.

**Results:** When grown separately, *P. caudatum* **(a)** and *P. aurelia* **(b)** each exhibited logistic population growth. But when the two species were grown together in a mixed culture **(c)**, *P. aurelia* persisted and *P. caudatum* was nearly eliminated from the culture.

**Conclusion:** Because one species was almost always eliminated from mixed species cultures, Gause formulated the competitive exclusion principle: Populations of two or more species cannot coexist indefinitely if they rely on the same limiting resources and exploit them in the same way.

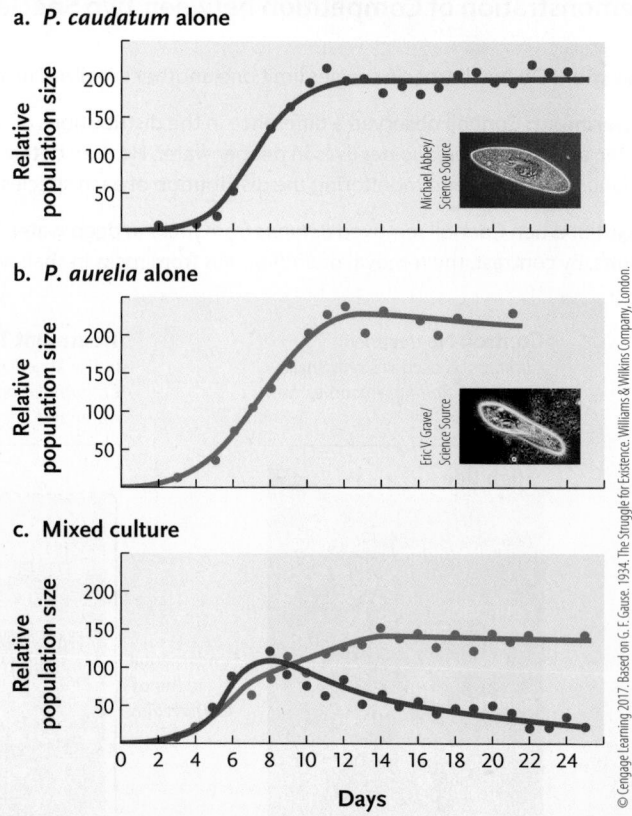

## 30.5a Competition and Niches: When Resources Are Limited

In the 1920s, the Russian mathematician Alfred J. Lotka and the Italian biologist Vito Volterra independently proposed a model of interspecific competition, modifying the logistic equation (see Chapter 29) to describe the effects of competition between two species. In their model, an increase in the size of one population reduces the population growth rate of the other.

In the 1930s, Russian biologist G. F. Gause tested the model experimentally. He grew cultures of two *Paramecium* species (ciliate protozoans) under constant laboratory conditions, regularly renewing food and removing wastes. Both species ate bacteria suspended in the culture medium. When grown alone, each species exhibited logistic growth. When grown together in the same dish, *Paramecium aurelia* persisted at high density, but *Paramecium caudatum* was almost eliminated **(Figure 30.16)**. These results inspired Gause to define the **competitive exclusion principle**. Populations of two or more species cannot coexist indefinitely if they rely on the same limiting resources and exploit them in the same way. One species inevitably harvests resources more efficiently; produces more offspring than the other; and, by its actions, negatively affects the other species.

Ecologists developed the concept of the **ecological niche** to visualize resource use and the potential for interspecific competition in nature. They define a species' niche by the resources it uses and the environmental conditions it requires over its lifetime. In this context, niche includes food, shelter, and nutrients, as well as non-depletable abiotic conditions such as light intensity and temperature. In theory, an almost infinite variety of conditions and resources could contribute to a species' niche. In practice, ecologists usually identify the critical resources for which populations might compete. Sunlight, soil moisture, and inorganic nutrients are important resources for plants, so differences in leaf height and root depth, for example, can affect plants' access to these resources. Food type, food size, and nesting sites are important for animals. When several species coexist, they often use food and nest resources in different ways.

Ecologists distinguish the **fundamental niche** of a species, the range of conditions and resources it could tolerate and use, from its **realized niche**, the range of conditions and resources it actually uses in nature. Realized niches are smaller than fundamental niches, partly because all tolerable conditions are not always present in a habitat and partly because some resources are used by other species. We can visualize competition between two populations by plotting their fundamental and realized niches with respect to one or more resources

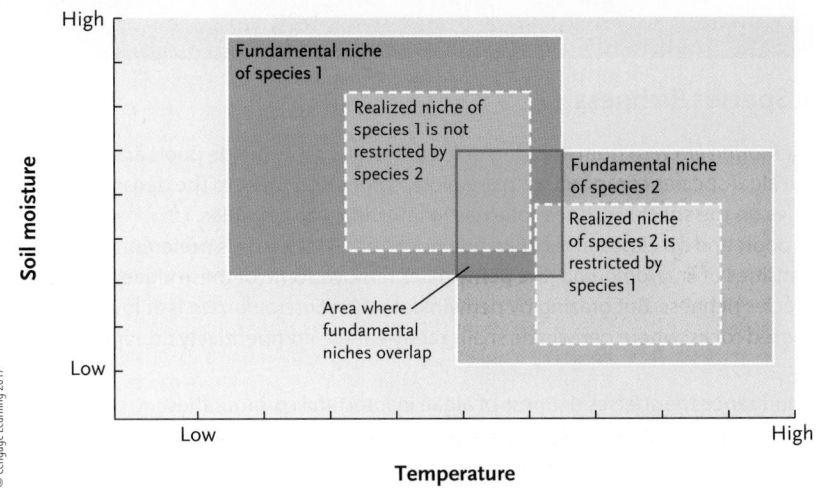

© Cengage Learning 2017

**FIGURE 30.17 Fundamental versus realized niches.** In this hypothetical example, both species 1 and species 2 can survive intermediate temperature conditions, as indicated by the shading where their fundamental niches overlap. Because species 1 actually occupies most of this overlap zone, its realized niche is not much affected by the presence of species 2. In contrast, the realized niche of species 2 is restricted by the presence of species 1, and species 2 occupies warmer and drier parts of the habitat.

**(Figure 30.17)**. If the fundamental niches of two populations overlap, they might compete in nature.

Observing that several species use the same resource does not demonstrate that competition occurs (or does not occur). All terrestrial animals consume oxygen but do not compete for oxygen because it is usually plentiful. Nevertheless, two general observations provide indirect evidence that interspecific competition may have important effects.

**Resource partitioning** occurs when several sympatric (living in the same place) species use different resources or the same resources in different ways. Although plants might compete for water and dissolved nutrients, they may avoid competition by partitioning these resources, collecting them from different depths in the soil **(Figure 30.18)**. This allows coexistence of different species.

**Character displacement** can be evident when comparing species that are sometimes sympatric and sometimes allopatric (living in different places). Allopatric populations of some animal species are morphologically similar and use similar resources, whereas sympatric populations are morphologically different and use different resources. Differences between sympatric species allow them to coexist without competing. To illustrate this situation, Allen Keast studied honeyeaters (family Meliphagidae), a group of birds from Australia. In mainland Australia, up to six species in the genus *Melithreptus* occur in some habitats. On the coast of Kangaroo Island, there are two species. When two species are sympatric, each feeds in a wider range of situations than when six species live in the same area, reflecting the use of broader niches. Behavioural and morphological differences are evident when species are compared between the different situations. Although well known for his work on birds, Keast also studied communities of fish. He spent most of his academic career at Queen's University in Kingston, Ontario.

Which might be more important, competition or predation? In 2010, Ryan Calsbeek and Robert M. Cox reported their work with lizards (*Anolis* spp.) on islands in the Caribbean. In this system, competition between species altered their morphological traits, while predation did not.

Predators can influence the species richness and structure of communities by reducing the sizes of prey populations. On the rocky coast of British Columbia, different species that fill different trophic roles compete for attachment sites on rocks, a requirement for life on a wave-swept shore. Mussels are the strongest competitors for space, eliminating other species from the community. At some sites, predatory sea stars preferentially eat mussels, reducing their numbers and creating space for other species to grow. Because the interaction between *Pisaster* and *Mytilus* affects other species as well, it qualifies as a strong interaction.

In the 1960s, Robert Paine used removal experiments to evaluate the effects of predation by *Pisaster*. In predator-free experimental plots, mussels outcompeted barnacles, chitons, limpets, and other invertebrate herbivores, reducing species richness from 15 species to 8. In control plots containing predators, all 15 species persisted. Ecologists describe predators such as *Pisaster* as **keystone species**, defined as species with a greater effect on community structure than their numbers might suggest. Snowshoe hares (Chapter 29) are candidates to be keystone species in boreal forest ecosystems because they are prey for a range of predators. Pallas' long-tongued bats may emerge as keystone species because, as we have seen, they eat insects and fruit as well as nectar and pollen.

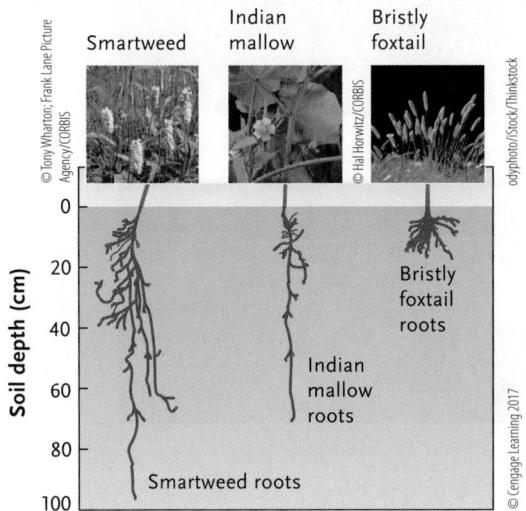

**FIGURE 30.18 Resource partitioning.** The root systems of three plant species that grow in abandoned fields partition water and nutrient resources in soil. Bristly foxtail grass (*Setaria faberi*) has a shallow root system, Indian mallow (*Abutilon theophrasti*) has a moderately deep taproot, and smartweed (*Polygonum pensylvanicum*) has a deep taproot that branches at many depths.

FIGURE 30.19 **Experimental Research**

## The Complex Effects of a Herbivorous Snail on Algal Species Richness

Jane Lubchenco made enclosures that prevented periwinkle snails (*Littorina littorea*) from entering or leaving study plots in tide pools and on exposed rocks in rocky intertidal habitat **(a)**. She then monitored the algal species composition in the plots, comparing them to the density of the periwinkles. In this way, she examined the influence of the periwinkles on the species richness of algae in intertidal communities.

The results varied dramatically between the study plots in tide pools and on exposed rocks. In tide pools, periwinkle snails preferentially ate *Enteromorpha*, the competitively dominant alga. At intermediate densities of *Enteromorpha*, the periwinkles remove some of these algae, allowing weakly competitive species to grow. The snails' grazing increases species richness. But grazing by periwinkles when *Enteromorpha* is at low or high densities reduces the species richness of algae in tide pools. On exposed rocks, where periwinkle snails rarely eat the competitively dominant alga Chondrus, feeding by snails reduces algal species richness **(b)**.

**Question:** How does feeding by periwinkle snails (*Littorina littorea*) influence the species richness of algae in intertidal communities?

**Experiment:** Lubchenco manipulated the densities of periwinkle snails in tidepools and on exposed rocks in a rocky intertidal habitat by creating enclosures that prevented snails from either entering or leaving her study plots. She then monitored the species composition of algae in the study plots and graphed them against periwinkle density.

### a. The distribution of periwinkle snails and two kinds of algae

**Periwinkle snails (*Littorina littorea*)**

*Enteromorpha* growing in tide pools

*Chondrus* growing on exposed rocks

**Results:** The effects of periwinkle density on algal species richness varied dramatically between study plots in tidepools and on exposed rocks.

**Conclusion:** Grazing by periwinkle snails has complex effects on the species richness of competing algae. In tidepools, where periwinkle snails preferentially feed on *Enteromorpha*, the competitively dominant alga, snails at an intermediate density remove some *Enteromorpha*, which allows weakly competitive algae to grow, increasing species richness. Feeding by snails at either low or high densities reduces algal species richness. On exposed rocks, where periwinkle snails rarely eat the competitively dominant alga *Chondrus*, feeding by snails reduces algal species richness.

### b. Density of periwinkles versus algal species richness in tide pools and on exposed rocks

**In tide pools**

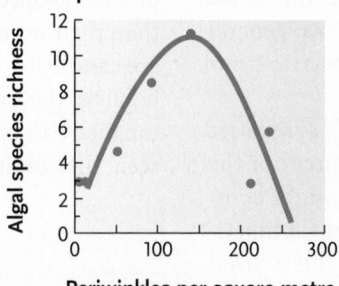

In tide pools, snails at low densities eat little algae and *Enteromorpha* competitively excludes other algal species, reducing species richness. At high snail densities, heavy feeding on all species reduces algal species richness. At intermediate snail densities, grazing eliminates some *Enteromorpha*, allowing other species to grow.

**On exposed rocks**

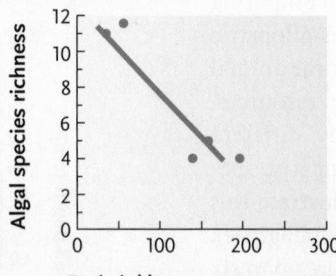

On exposed rocks, periwinkles don't eat much *Chondrus*, but they consume the tender, less successful competitors. Thus, feeding by periwinkles reinforces the competitive superiority of *Chondrus*: as periwinkle density increases, algal species richness declines.

Herbivores also exert complex effects on communities. In the 1970s, Jane Lubchenco studied herbivory in a periwinkle snail, believed to be a keystone species on rocky shores in Massachusetts **(Figure 30.19)**. The features of plants and algae and the food preferences of animals that eat them can influence community structure.

### STUDY BREAK QUESTIONS

1. How does the importance of competition vary between *K*-selected and *r*-selected species?
2. Does predation or herbivory increase or decrease species richness? Explain.
3. What is a keystone species?

## 30.6 The Nature of Ecological Communities

The interactions among species in an ecological community can be broadly categorized as antagonistic or mutually beneficial (Table 30.1; **Figure 30.20**). Trophic interactions are associated with consumption (antagonistic; one species eating another), the usual situation portrayed in food webs. Mutually beneficial interactions include, for example, those between flowering plants and their insect pollinators. Understanding community dynamics requires knowledge of the structure of community networks (e.g., food webs; see Chapter 31) as well as information about how structure influences the extinction or persistence of species. An overview of the dynamics of an ecological community is obtained through a combination of fieldwork and attendant statistical analysis of data to document ecosystem architecture. The second element, knowledge of the influence of architecture on species persistence, emerges from mathematical modelling.

To explore the nature of ecosystems, Elisa Thébault and Colin Fontaine examined pollination (mutualistic) and plant–herbivore (trophic) systems (Figure 30.20). They found that the structure of the network favouring ecosystem **stability** differs between trophic (herbivore) and mutually beneficial (pollination) networks. In pollination networks, the elements are highly connected and nested, promoting stability of communities. In herbivore networks, stability is greater in structures that are compartmentalized and weakly connected. The work identifies features that affect the stability of ecosystems, potentially informing those working to effect conservation at the system level.

**Ecotones**, the borders between communities, are sometimes wide transition zones. Ecotones are generally species rich because they include plants and animals from both neighbouring communities, as well as some species that thrive only under transitional conditions. Although ecotones are usually relatively broad, places where there is a discontinuity in a critical resource or important abiotic factor may have a sharp community boundary. Chemical differences between soils derived from serpentine rock and sandstone establish sharp boundaries between communities of native California wildflowers and introduced European grasses (See **Figure 30.21**).

### STUDY BREAK QUESTIONS

1. Distinguish between antagonistic and mutualistic architectural structures in ecosystems.
2. Are ecotones generally species rich or species poor?

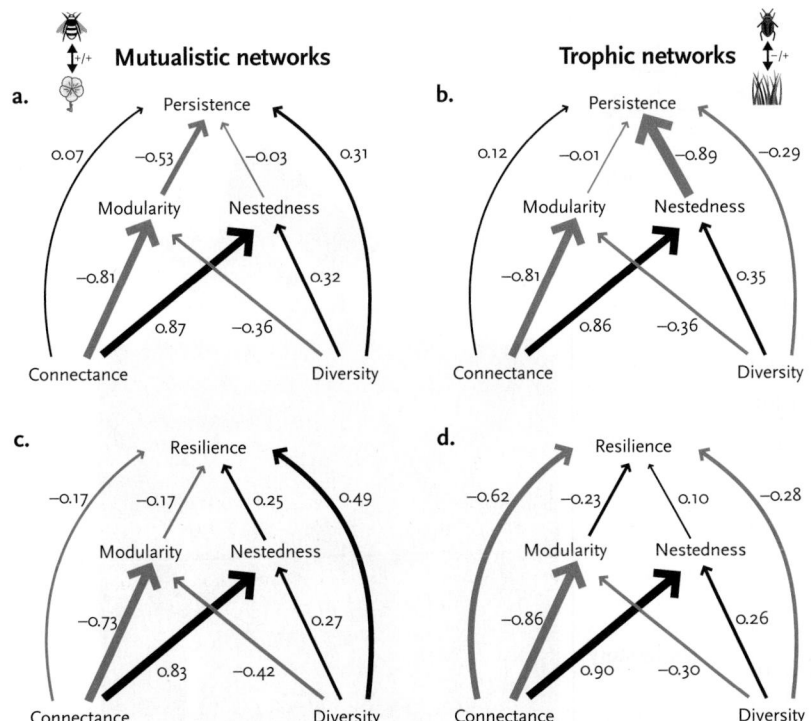

**FIGURE 30.20  The persistence** (a, b) **and resilience** (c, d) **of pollinating and herbivore ecosystem patterns are summarized, revealing important differences.** The thickness of arrows, scaled to standardized coefficients, illustrates the relative strength of the effects. Red identifies negative effects; black, positive ones. There is a further comparison of the effects of connectance and diversity, comparing direct and indirect effects, considering modularity and nestedness. The numbers in each diagram indicate the coefficients along the path.

Source: From Elisa Thébault, Colin Fontaine, "Stability of Ecological Communities and the Architecture of Mutualistic and Trophic Networks," *Science* 13 August 2010, Vol. 329 no. 5993 pp. 853-856. *Science* by American Association for the Advancement of Science Reproduced with permission of AMERICAN ASSOCIATION FOR THE ADVANCEMENT OF SCIENCE in the format Republish in a book via Copyright Clearance Center.

## 30.7 Community Characteristics

Growth forms (sizes and shapes) of plants vary markedly in different environments, so the attributes of plants often can be used to characterize communities. Warm, moist environments support complex vegetation with multiple vertical layers. Tropical forests include a canopy formed by the tallest trees, an understory of shorter trees and shrubs, and a herb layer under openings in the canopy. Vinelike lianas and epiphytes grow on the trunks and branches of trees (**Figure 30.22**). In contrast, physically harsh environments are occupied by low vegetation with simple structure. Trees on mountainsides buffeted by cold winds are short, and the plants below them cling to rocks and soil. Other environments support growth forms between these extremes.

In 2016, there were important advances in the study of vascular plants. Sandra Diaz and colleagues reported the results of a global look at plant form and function. They used an analysis of six major traits critical to the growth, survival, and reproduction of vascular plants to show the importance of coordination and trade-offs. About 75% of the variation in traits related directly to plant form and function. One important element is the sizes of plants and their parts. Another involves leaf operations, as

**a. Interactive hypothesis**

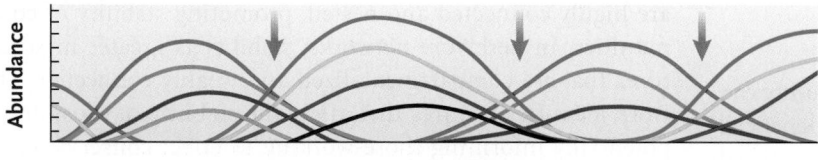

The interactive hypothesis predicts that species within communities exhibit similar distributions along environmental gradients (indicated by the close alignment of several curves over each section of the gradient) and that boundaries between communities (indicated by arrows) are sharp.

**b. Individualistic hypothesis**

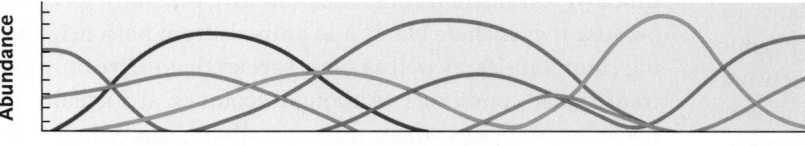

The individualistic hypothesis predicts that species distributions along the gradient are independent (indicated by the lack of alignment of the curves) and that sharp boundaries do not separate communities.

**c. Siskiyou Mountains**

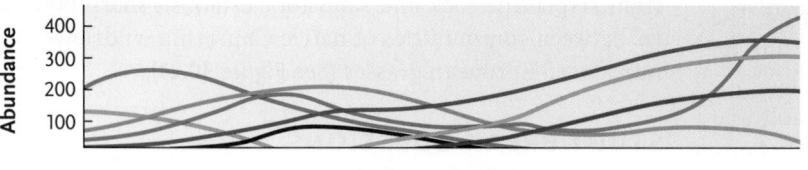

**d. Santa Catalina Mountains**

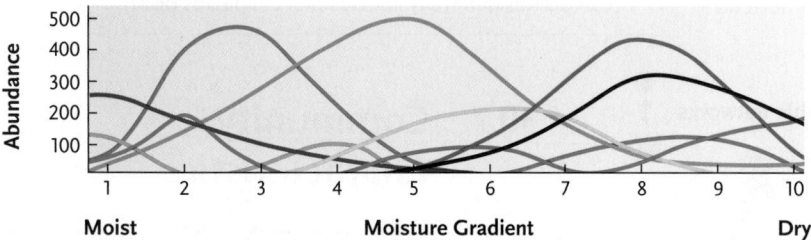

Most gradient analyses support the individualistic hypothesis, as illustrated by distributions of tree species along moisture gradients in Oregon's Siskiyou Mountains and Arizona's Santa Catalina Mountains.

**FIGURE 30.21 Two views of ecological communities.** Each graph line indicates a different species.

they reflect the cost of development relative to growth potential. Meanwhile, Kunstler and colleagues used data from more than 3 million trees to show how the outcome of wood density, leaf area, and maximum height affect the outcome of competition among species. Their analysis revealed that intraspecific competition was more important than interspecific competition. Farrior and colleagues examined the size distributions of tropical trees. Faster-growing species fill gaps in the forest canopy, and the species forming the understory scale themselves to fit within the relationship of the ratio of diameters of crown to trunk.

Collectively these species illustrate the importance of modelling to understand the dynamics of communities of plants.

Communities differ greatly in **species richness**, the number of species that live within them. The harsh environment on a low desert island may support just a few species of microorganisms, fungi, algae, plants, and arthropods. In contrast, tropical forests that grow under milder physical conditions include many thousands of species. Ecologists have studied global patterns of species richness (see Chapter 28) for decades. Today, as human disturbance of natural communities has reached a crisis point, conservation biologists try to understand global

**FIGURE 30.22 Layered forests.** Tropical forests, such as one near the Mazaruni River in Guyana (South America), include a canopy of tall trees and an understorey of short trees and shrubs. Huge vines (lianas) climb through the trees, eventually reaching sunlight in the canopy. Epiphytic plants grow on trunks and branches, increasing the structural complexity of the habitat.

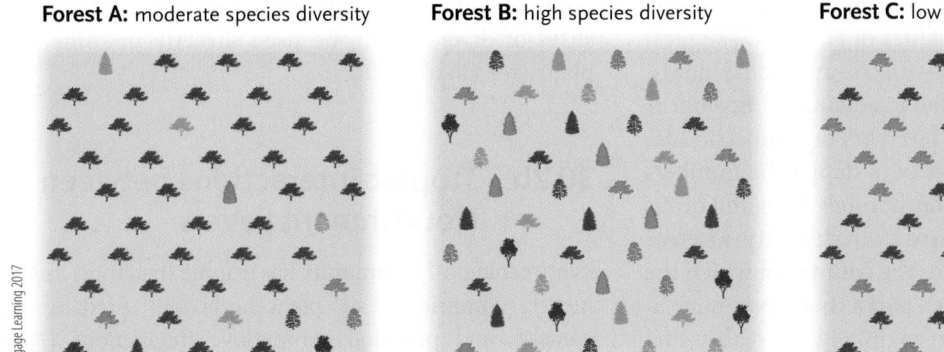

**Forest A:** moderate species diversity    **Forest B:** high species diversity    **Forest C:** low species diversity

© Cengage Learning 2017

**FIGURE 30.23  Species diversity.** In this hypothetical example, each of the 3 samples of forest communities (A, B, and C) contains 50 trees. Indices allow biologists to express the diversity of species and evenness of numbers (see Table 30.2).

patterns of species richness to determine which regions of Earth are most in need of preservation.

The relative abundances of species vary across communities. Some communities have one or two abundant species and a number of rare species. In others, the species are represented by more equal numbers of individuals. In a **temperate deciduous forest** in southern Quebec, red oak trees (*Quercus rubra*) and sugar maples (*Acer saccharum*) might together account for nearly 85% of the trees. A tropical forest in Costa Rica may have more than 200 tree species, each making up a small percentage of the total.

The factors underlying diversity and community structure can be expected to vary among groups of organisms, and the interactions between very different groups of organisms can have positive effects on both. Using an experimental mycorrhizal plant system (see Chapter 25), H. Maherali and J. N. Klironomos found that, after one year, the species richness of mycorrhizal fungi correlated with higher plant productivity. In turn, the diversity and species richness of mycorrhizal fungi were highest when their starting community had more distinct evolutionary lineages. This example illustrates the importance of diversity and interactions.

### 30.7a  Measuring Species Diversity and Evenness: Calculating Indices

The number of species is the simplest measure of diversity, so a forest with four tree species has higher **species diversity** than one with two tree species. But there can be more to measuring diversity than just counting species. Biologists use indices of diversity to facilitate comparison of data sets documenting the numbers of species and of individuals. Shannon's index of diversity ($H'$), one commonly used measure, is calculated using the formula

$$H' = -\sum_{i=1}^{s} p_i \ln p_i$$

where $S$ is the total number of species in the community (richness), $p_i$ is the proportion of $S$ made up by species $i$, and ln is the natural logarithm.

Another index, Shannon's evenness index ($E_H$), is calculated using the formula

$$E_H = \frac{H'}{\ln S}$$

where ln $S$ is the natural logarithm of the number of species. Evenness is an indication of the mixture of species. Indices of diversity and evenness allow population biologists to objectively portray and compare the diversity of communities.

Use the two indices to compare the 3 forests of 50 trees each in **Figure 30.23**. The number of species and the number of individuals of each species in each forest are shown in **Table 30.2**. In Table 30.2, the values of $H'$ and $E_H$ indicate the diversity of the three hypothetical forests and the evenness of species representations. Lower values of $H'$ and $E_H$ suggest

| TABLE 30.2 | Shannon's Indices for Measuring Diversity and Evenness | | |
|---|---|---|---|
| **Numbers of Individuals per Species** | | | |
| | Forest A* | Forest B* | Forest C* |
| Species 1 | 39 | 5 | 25 |
| Species 2 | 2 | 5 | 25 |
| Species 3 | 2 | 5 | 0 |
| Species 4 | 1 | 5 | 0 |
| Species 5 | 1 | 5 | 0 |
| Species 6 | 1 | 5 | 0 |
| Species 7 | 1 | 5 | 0 |
| Species 8 | 1 | 5 | 0 |
| Species 9 | 1 | 5 | 0 |
| Species 10 | 1 | 5 | 0 |
| **Shannon Indices** | | | |
| $H'$ diversity | 0.6 | 2.3 | 0.7 |
| $E_H$ evenness | 0.26 | 1.0 | 1.0 |

*Forests from Figure 30.23

communities with few species (low $H'$ values) or uneven distribution (low $E_H$ values). Higher values of $H'$ and $E_H$ suggest a richer array of species with evenly distributed individuals.

Measures of diversity can be used to advantage. Ecologists refer to α diversity to represent the numbers of sympatric species in one community, and β diversity to depict the numbers in a collection of communities. The number of herbivorous Lepidoptera species in one national park is α diversity, whereas β diversity is the number of species in the country in which the park is located. The trend to establish parks that cross international boundaries is a step toward recognizing the reality that political and biological boundaries can be quite different. Measures of diversity can be used directly in some conservation plans (see Chapter 28).

## 30.7b Trophic Interactions between Nourishment Levels

Every ecological community has trophic structure (*troph* = nourishment), comprising all plant–herbivore, predator–prey, host–parasite, and potential competitive interactions (**Figure 30.24**).

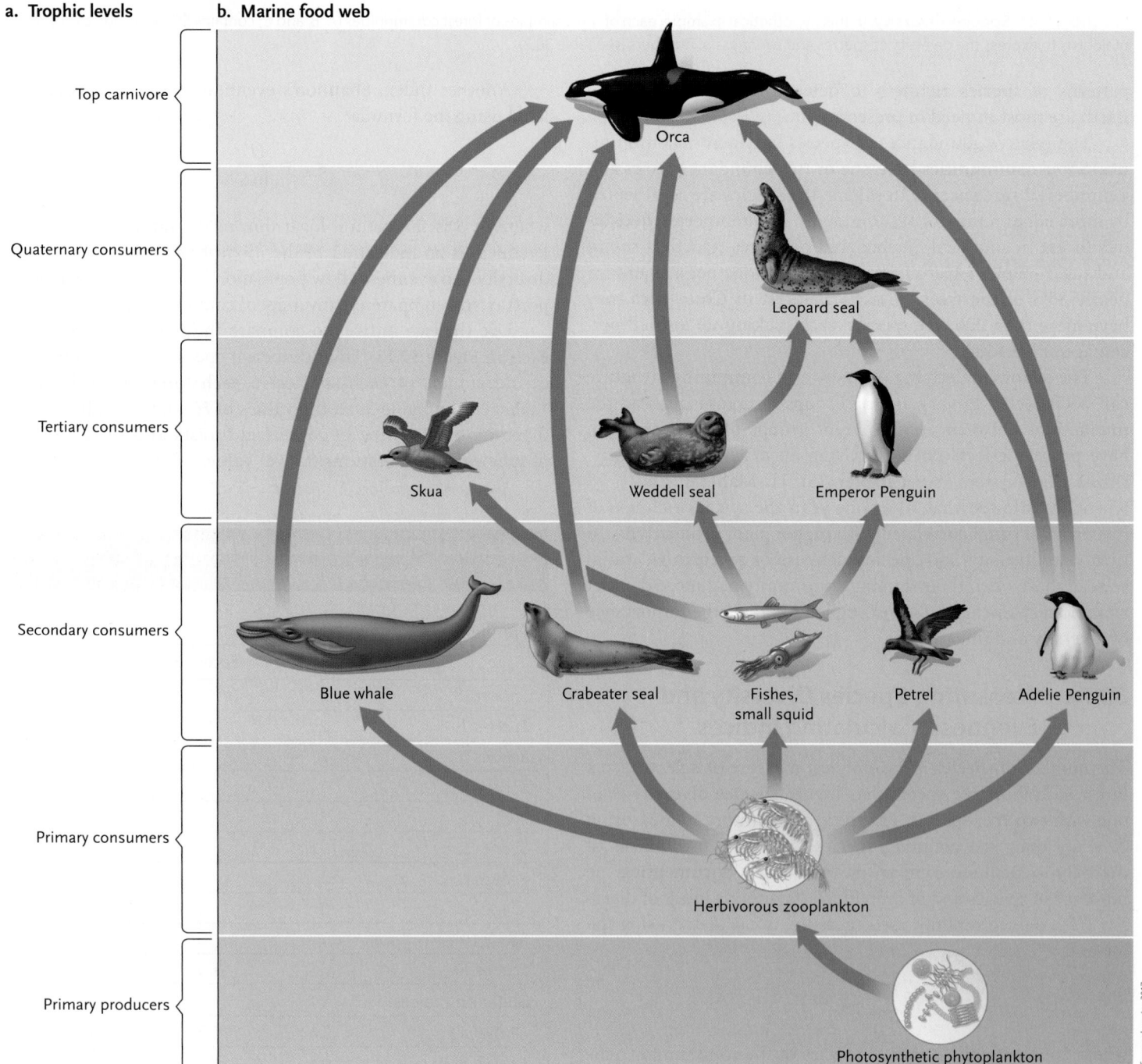

**FIGURE 30.24 The marine food web off the coast of Antarctica**

We can visualize the trophic structure of a community as a hierarchy of **trophic levels**, defined by the feeding relationships among its species (see Figure 30.24a). Photosynthetic organisms are primary producers, the first trophic level. Primary producers are photoautotrophs (*auto* = self) because they capture sunlight and convert it into chemical energy, which is used to make larger organic molecules that plants can use directly. Plants are the main primary producers in terrestrial communities. Multicellular algae and plants are the major primary producers in shallow freshwater and marine environments, whereas photosynthetic protists and cyanobacteria play that role in deep open water.

All **consumers** in a community (animals, fungi, and diverse microorganisms) are heterotrophs (*hetero* = other) because they acquire energy and nutrients by eating other organisms or their remains. Animals are consumers. Herbivores (primary consumers) feed directly on plants and form the second trophic level. Secondary consumers (mesopredators) eat herbivores and form the third trophic level. Animals that eat secondary consumers make up the fourth trophic level, the **tertiary consumers**. In one meal, animals that are omnivores (e.g., humans, pigs, and bears) can act as primary, secondary, and tertiary consumers.

Detritivores (scavengers) form a separate and distinct trophic level. These organisms extract energy from organic detritus produced at other trophic levels. Detritivores include fungi, bacteria, and animals such as earthworms and vultures that ingest dead organisms, digestive wastes, and cast-off body parts such as leaves and exoskeletons. Decomposers, a type of detritivore, are small organisms, such as bacteria and fungi, that feed on dead or dying organic material. Detritivores and decomposers serve a critical ecological function because their activity reduces organic material to small inorganic molecules that producers can assimilate (see Chapter 23).

Although omnivores obviously do not fit exclusively into one trophic level, this can also be true of other organisms. Carnivorous plants and sea slugs that use chloroplasts are examples of species that do not fit readily into trophic categories.

## 30.7c Food Chains and Webs: Connections In Ecosystems

Ecologists use food chains and webs to illustrate the trophic structure of a community. Each link in a food chain is represented by an arrow pointing from food to consumer (see Figure 30.24b). Simple, straight-line food chains are rare in nature because most consumers feed on more than one type of food and because most organisms are eaten by more than one type of consumer. Complex relationships are portrayed as food webs—sets of interconnected food chains with multiple links.

In the food web for the waters off the coast of Antarctica (see Figure 30.24), primary producers and primary consumers are small organisms occurring in vast numbers. Microscopic diatoms (phytoplankton) are responsible for most photosynthesis, and small shrimplike krill (zooplankton) are the major primary consumers. These tiny organisms, in turn, are eaten by larger species such as fish and seabirds, as well as by suspension-feeding baleen whales. Some secondary consumers are eaten by birds and mammals at higher trophic levels. The top carnivore in this ecosystem, the orca, feeds on carnivorous birds and mammals.

Ideally, depictions of food webs would include all species in a community, from microorganisms to top consumer. But most ecologists simply cannot collect data on every species, particularly those that are rare or very small. Instead, they study links between the most important species and simplify analysis by grouping trophically similar species. Figure 30.24 categorizes the many different species of primary producers and primary consumers as phytoplankton and zooplankton respectively.

Many biological hot spots (areas with many species) exist, from thermal vents on the floor of some oceans to deposits of bat guano in some caves. A more recently described example is icebergs drifting north from Antarctica. The icebergs can be hot spots of enrichment because of the nutrients and other materials they shed into surrounding waters. The water around two free-drifting icebergs (0.1 km$^2$ and 30.8 km$^2$ in area) was sampled in the Weddell Sea. High concentrations of chlorophyll, krill, and seabirds extended about 3.7 km around each iceberg. These data, reported by K. L. Smith Jr. and seven colleagues, demonstrate that icebergs can have substantial effects on pelagic ecosystems.

In the late 1950s, Robert MacArthur analyzed food webs to determine how the many links between trophic levels may contribute to a community's stability. The stability of a community is defined as its ability to maintain **species composition** and relative abundances when environmental disturbances eliminate some species from the community. MacArthur hypothesized that, in species-rich communities, where animals feed on many food sources, the absence of one or two species would have only minor effects on the structure and stability of the community as a whole. He proposed a connection between species diversity, food web complexity, and community stability.

Subsequent research has confirmed MacArthur's reasoning. The average number of links per species generally increases with increasing species richness. Comparative food web analysis reveals that the relative proportions of species at the highest, middle, and lowest trophic levels are reasonably constant across communities. In 92 communities, MacArthur found two or three prey species per predator species, regardless of species richness.

Interactions among species in most food webs can be complex, indirect, and hard to unravel. In contrast, rodents and ants living in desert communities of the U.S. Southwest potentially compete for seeds, their main food source. Plants that produce the seeds compete for water, nutrients, and space. Rodents generally prefer to eat large seeds, whereas ants prefer small seeds. Thus, feeding by rodents reduces the potential population sizes of plants that produce large seeds. As a result, the population sizes of plants that produce small seeds may increase, ultimately providing more food for ants (see Chapter 39). Compared with the Antarctic system described above (see Figure 30.24), this community is not particularly complex.

(see Chapter 39)

## STUDY BREAK QUESTIONS

1. Why are indices important for population biologists? What do Shannon's indices measure?
2. Differentiate between α and β diversity.
3. Are herbivores primary or secondary consumers? Which trophic level do they form? Where do omnivores belong?

# 30.8 Effects of Population Interactions on Community Structure

Observations of resource partitioning and character displacement suggested that some process had fostered differences in resource use among coexisting species, and competition provided the most straightforward explanation of these patterns.

Interspecific competition can cause local extinction of species or prevent new species from becoming established in a community, reducing its species richness. During the 1960s and early 1970s, ecologists emphasized competition as the primary factor structuring communities.

## 30.8a Effects of Disturbance on Community Characteristics

Recent research tends to support the individualistic view that many communities are not in equilibrium and that species composition changes frequently. Environmental disturbances such as storms, landslides, fires, floods, avalanches, and cold spells often eliminate some species and provide opportunities for others to become established. Frequent disturbances keep some ecological communities in a constant state of flux.

Physical disturbances are common in some environments. Lightning-induced fires commonly sweep through grasslands, powerful hurricanes often demolish patches of forest and coastal habitats, and waves wash over communities at the edge of the sea and sweep away organisms as well as landforms and other structures.

Joseph Connell and his colleagues conducted an ambitious long-term study of the effects of disturbance on coral reefs, shallow tropical marine habitats that are among the most species-rich communities on Earth. In some parts of the world, reefs are routinely battered by violent storms that wash corals off the substrate, creating bare patches in the reef. The scouring action of storms creates opportunities for coral larvae to settle on bare substrates and start new colonies.

From 1963 to 1992, Connell and his colleagues tracked the fate of the Heron Island Reef at the south end of Australia's Great Barrier Reef (**Figure 30.25**). The inner flat and protected crests of the reef are sheltered from severe wave action during storms, whereas some pools and crests are routinely exposed to physical disturbance. Because corals live in colonies of variable size, the researchers monitored coral abundance by measuring the percentage of the substrate (i.e., the sea floor) that colonies covered. They revisited marked study plots at intervals, photographing and identifying individual coral colonies.

Five major cyclones crossed the reef during the 30-year study period. Coral communities in exposed areas of the reef were in a nearly continual state of flux. In exposed pools, four of the five cyclones reduced the percentage of cover, often drastically. On exposed crests, the cyclone of 1972 eliminated virtually all corals, and subsequent storms slowed the recovery of these areas for more than 20 years. In contrast, corals in sheltered areas suffered much less storm damage. Nevertheless, their coverage also declined steadily during the study as a natural consequence of the corals' growth. As colonies grew taller and closer to the ocean's surface, their increased exposure to air resulted in substantial mortality.

Connell and his colleagues also documented recruitment, the growth of new colonies from settling larvae, in their study plots. They discovered that the rate at which new colonies developed was almost always higher in sheltered than in exposed areas. Recruitment rates were extremely variable, depending in part on the amount of space that storms or coral growth had made available.

This long-term study of coral reefs illustrates that frequent disturbances prevent some communities from reaching an equilibrium determined by interspecific interactions. Changes in the coral reef community at Heron Island result from the effects of external disturbances that remove coral colonies from the reef, as well as internal processes (growth and recruitment) that either eliminate colonies or establish new ones. In this community, growth and recruitment are slow processes and disturbances are frequent. Thus, the community never attains equilibrium, and moderate levels of disturbance can foster high species richness.

The **intermediate disturbance hypothesis**, proposed by Connell in 1978, suggests that species richness is greatest in communities experiencing fairly frequent disturbances of moderate intensity. Moderate disturbances create openings for $r$-selected species to arrive and join the community while allowing $K$-selected species to survive. Thus, communities that experience intermediate levels of disturbance contain a rich mixture of species. Where disturbances are severe and frequent, communities include only $r$-selected species that complete their life cycles between catastrophes. Where disturbances are mild and rare, communities are dominated by long-lived $K$-selected species that competitively exclude other species from the community.

Several studies in diverse habitats have confirmed the predictions of the intermediate disturbance hypothesis. Colin R. Townsend and his colleagues studied the effects of disturbance at 54 stream sites in the Taieri River system in New Zealand.

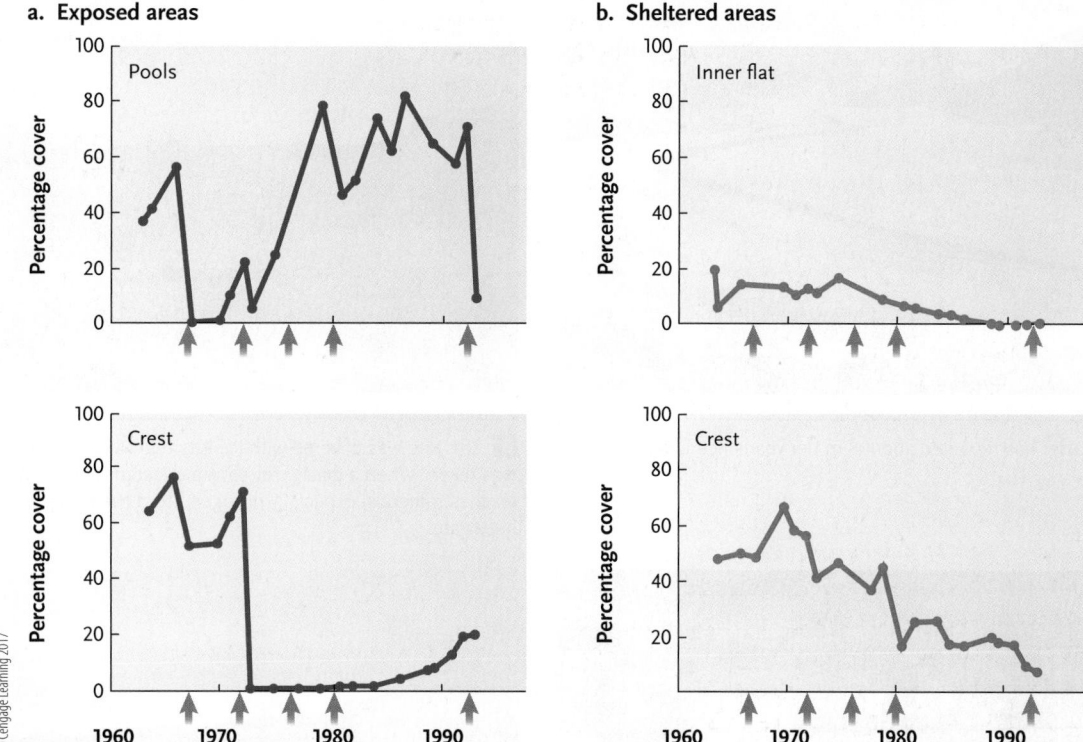

a. Exposed areas    b. Sheltered areas

**FIGURE 30.25 Major hydrodynamic disturbances to coral reefs, such as tsunamis and severe storms, have important impacts on coral reefs.** Using oceanographic and engineering models, it is possible to predict the degree of dislodgement of benthic reef corals and, in this way, predict how coral shape and size indicate vulnerability to major disturbances. The use of these models is particularly important during times of climate change. The graphs show the effects of storms on corals. Five tropical cyclones (marked by grey arrows) damaged corals on the Heron Island Reef during a 30-year period. Storms reduced the percentage cover of corals in **(a)** exposed parts of the reef much more than in **(b)** sheltered parts of it. These data show that the 1970 event had the largest impact on some exposed and sheltered areas.

Disturbance occurs in these communities when water flow from heavy rains moves rocks, soil, and sand in the streambed, disrupting animal habitats. Townsend and his colleagues measured how much the substrate moved in different streambeds to develop an index of the intensity of disturbance. Their results indicate that species richness is highest in areas that experience intermediate levels of disturbance (**Figure 30.26**).

Some ecologists have suggested that species-rich communities recover from disturbances more readily than less diverse communities. In the United States, David Tilman and his colleagues conducted large-scale experiments in Midwestern grasslands. They examined relationships between species number and the ability of communities to recover from disturbance. Grassland plots with high species richness recover from drought faster than plots with fewer species.

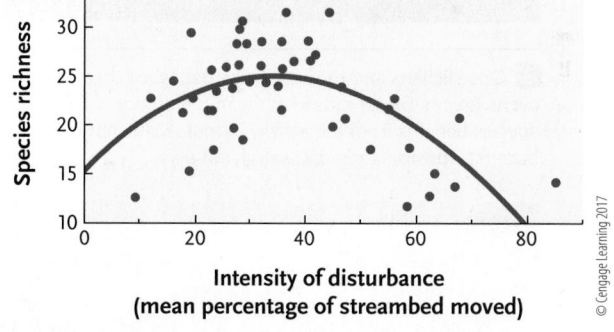

**FIGURE 30.26 An observational study that supports the intermediate disturbance hypothesis.** In the Taieri River system in New Zealand, species richness was highest in stream communities that experienced an intermediate level of disturbance.

## 30.9 Succession

Ecosystems change over time in a process called **succession**, the change from one community type to another.

### 30.9a Primary Succession: The First Steps

**Primary succession** begins when organisms first colonize habitats without soil, such as those created by erupting volcanoes and retreating glaciers (**Figure 30.27**). Lichens are often among

---

**STUDY BREAK QUESTIONS**

1. What did Connell's 30-year study of coral reefs illustrate about the ability of communities to reach a state of equilibrium?
2. What is the intermediate disturbance hypothesis? Describe one study that supports this hypothesis.
3. How does species richness affect the rate of recovery following a disturbance?

**1** The glacier has retreated about 8 m per year since 1794.

**2** This site was covered with ice less than 10 years before this photo was taken. When a glacier retreats, a constant flow of melt water leaches minerals, especially nitrogen, from the newly exposed substrate.

**3** Once lichens and mosses have established themselves, mountain avens (genus *Dryas*) grows on the nutrient-poor soil. This pioneer species benefits from the activity of mutualistic nitrogen-fixing bacteria, spreading rapidly over glacial till.

**4** Within 20 years, shrubby willows (genus *Salix*), cottonwoods (genus *Populus*), and alders (genus *Alnus*) take hold in drainage channels. These species are also symbiotic with nitrogen-fixing microorganisms.

**5** In time, young conifers, mostly hemlocks (genus *Tsuga*) and spruce (genus *Picea*), join the community.

**6** As the years progress, the smaller trees and shrubs are gradually replaced by larger trees.

**FIGURE 30.27 Primary succession following glacial retreat.** The retreat of glaciers at Glacier Bay, Alaska, has allowed ecologists to document primary succession on newly exposed rocks and soil.

the very first colonists (see Chapter 25), deriving nutrients from rain and bare rock. They secrete mild acids that erode rock surfaces, initiating the slow development of soil, which is enriched by the organic material lichens produce. After lichens modify a site, mosses (see Chapter 26) colonize patches of soil and grow quickly.

As soil accumulates, hardy, opportunistic plants (grasses, ferns, and broad-leaved herbs) colonize the site from surrounding areas. Their roots break up rock, and when they die, their decaying remains enrich the soil. Detritivores and decomposers facilitate these processes. As the soil becomes deeper and richer, increased moisture and nutrients support bushes and, eventually, trees. Late successional stages are often dominated by K-selected species with woody trunks and branches that position leaves in sunlight and large root systems that acquire water and nutrients from soil.

In the classical view of ecological succession, long-lived species, which replace themselves over time, eventually dominate a community, and new species join it only rarely. This relatively stable, late successional stage is called a **climax community** because the dominant vegetation replaces itself and persists until an environmental disturbance eliminates it and allows other species to invade. Local climate and soil conditions, the surrounding communities where colonizing species originate, and chance events determine the species composition of climax communities. We now know that even climax communities change slowly in response to environmental fluctuations.

## 30.9b Secondary Succession: Changes after Destruction

**Secondary succession** occurs after existing vegetation is destroyed or disrupted by an environmental disturbance, such as a fire, a storm, or human activity. The presence of soil makes disturbed sites ripe for colonization and may contain numerous seeds that germinate after disturbance. Early stages of secondary succession proceed rapidly, but later stages parallel those of primary succession.

## 30.9c Climax Communities: The Ultimate Ecosystems until Something Changes

Similar climax communities can arise from several different successional sequences. Hardwood forests can also develop in sites that were once ponds. During **aquatic succession**, debris from rivers and runoff accumulates in a pond, filling it to its margins. Ponds are first transformed into swamps, inhabited by plants adapted to a semisolid substrate. As larger plants get established, their high transpiration rates dry the soil, allowing other plant species to colonize.

Given enough time, the site may become a meadow or forest in which an area of moist, low-lying ground is the only remnant of the original pond.

Because several characteristics of communities can change during succession, ecologists try to document how patterns change. First, because r-selected species are short lived and K-selected species are long lived, species composition changes rapidly in the early stages and more slowly in the later stages of succession. Second, species richness increases rapidly during early stages because new species join the community faster than resident species become extinct. In later stages, species richness stabilizes or may even decline. Third, in terrestrial communities receiving sufficient rainfall, the maximum height and total mass of the vegetation increase steadily as large species replace small ones, creating the complex structure of the climax community.

Because plants influence the physical environment below them, the community itself increasingly moderates its **microclimate**. The shade cast by a forest canopy helps retain soil moisture and reduce temperature fluctuations. The trunks and canopy also reduce wind speed. In contrast, the short vegetation in an early successional stage does not effectively shelter the space below it.

Although ecologists usually describe succession in terms of vegetation, animals can show similar patterns. As the vegetation shifts, new resources become available, and animal species replace each other over time. Herbivorous insects, often with strict food preferences, undergo succession along with their food plants. And as herbivores change, so do their predators, parasites, and parasitoids. In old-field succession in eastern North America, different vegetation stages harbour a changing assortment of bird species (**Figure 30.28**).

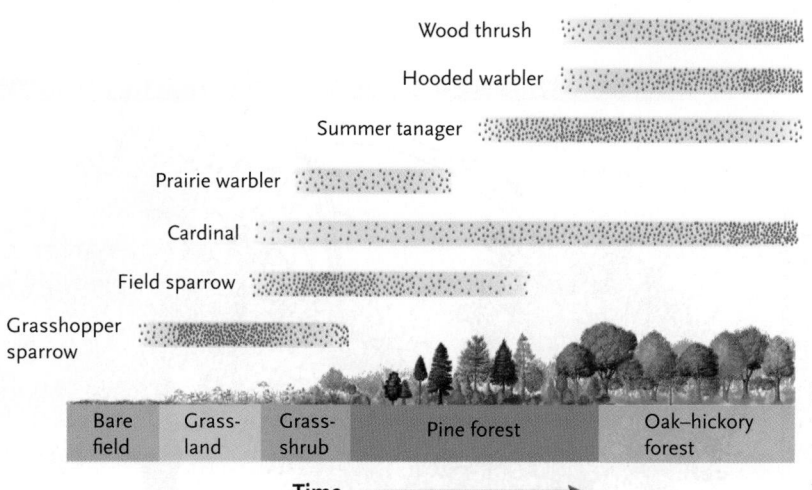

**FIGURE 30.28 Succession in animals.** Successional changes in bird species composition in an abandoned agricultural field in eastern North America parallel the changes in plant species composition. The residence times of several representative species are illustrated. The density of stippling inside each bar illustrates the density of each species through time.

Differences in dispersal abilities (see "Dispersal," Section 30.9e), maturation rates, and life spans among species are partly responsible for ecological succession. Early successional stages harbour many *r*-selected species because they produce numerous small seeds that colonize open habitats and grow quickly. Mature successional stages are dominated by *K*-selected species because they are long lived. Nevertheless, coexisting populations inevitably affect one another. Although the role of population interactions in succession is generally acknowledged, ecologists debate the relative importance of processes that either facilitate or inhibit the turnover of species in a community.

## 30.9d Facilitation Hypothesis: One Species Makes Changes That Help Others

The **facilitation hypothesis** suggests that species modify the local environment in ways that make it less suitable for themselves but more suitable for colonization by species typical of the next successional stage. When lichens first colonize bare rock, they produce a small quantity of soil that is required by mosses and grasses that grow there later. According to this hypothesis, changes in species composition are both orderly and predictable because the presence of each stage facilitates the success of the next one. Facilitation is important in primary succession, but it may not be the best model of interactions that influence secondary succession.

## 30.9e Inhibition Hypothesis: One Species Negatively Affects Others

The **inhibition hypothesis** suggests that new species are prevented from occupying a community by species that are already present. According to this hypothesis, succession is neither orderly nor predictable because each stage is dominated by the species that happened to have colonized the site first. Species replacements occur only when individuals of dominant species die of old age or when an environmental disturbance reduces their numbers. Eventually, long-lived species replace short-lived species, but the precise species composition of a mature community is open to question. Inhibition appears to play a role in some secondary successions. The interactions among early successional species in an old field are highly competitive. Horseweed inhibits the growth of asters that follow them in succession by shading aster seedlings and releasing toxic substances from their roots. Experimental removal of horseweed enhances the growth of asters, confirming the inhibitory effect.

DISPERSAL In other situations, plants disperse with the assistance of animals through pollination and seeds. Using the Mahaleb cherry (*Prunus mahaleb*) and genetic techniques, P. Jordano and two colleagues examined the role of birds and mammals in pollination and the dispersion of seeds (**Figure 30.29**). Small passerine birds dispersed seeds short distances (most less than 50 m) from the parent tree, whereas medium-sized birds (*Corvus corone* and *Turdus viscivorus*) usually dispersed seeds over longer distances (more than 110 m). Mammals (usually *Martes foina* and *Vulpes vulpes* but sometimes *Meles meles*) dispersed seeds about 500 m. The genetic work also indicated the extent of gene flow during pollination.

It is obvious that plants capable of self-fertilization or vegetative reproduction can be more effective colonists than those depending on outcrossing, especially with the help of animal pollinators.

From Katriona Shea, "How the Wood Moves", *Science*, vol. 315, Mar. 2, 2007, pp. 1231 – 1232. *Science* by American Association for the Advancement of Science. Reproduced with permission of AMERICAN ASSOCIATION FOR THE ADVANCEMENT OF SCIENCE in the format Republish in a book via Copyright Clearance Center.

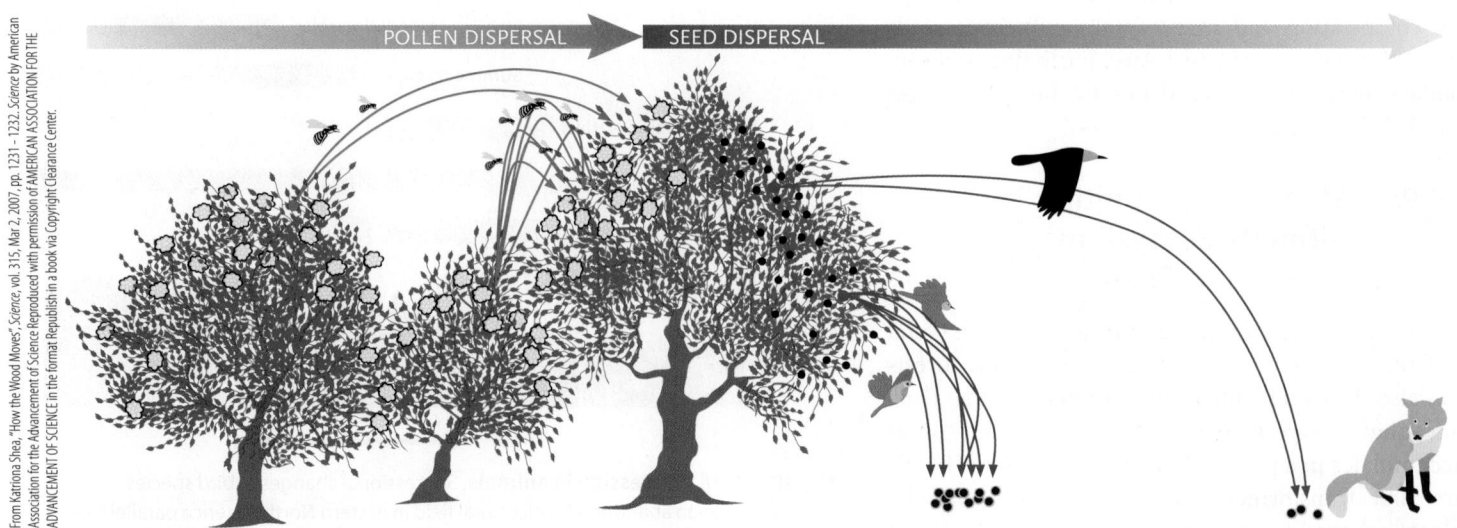

**FIGURE 30.29 The movement of pollen and seeds from Mahaleb cherry trees.** Gene flow occurs through pollination and seed dispersal (see Chapter 17).

## 30.9f Tolerance Hypothesis: Species Tolerate One Another

The **tolerance hypothesis** asserts that succession proceeds because competitively superior species replace competitively inferior ones. According to this model, early-stage species neither facilitate nor inhibit the growth of later-stage species. Instead, as more species arrive at a site and resources become limiting, competition eliminates species that cannot harvest scarce resources successfully. In the Piedmont region of North America, young hardwood trees are more tolerant of shade than are young pine trees, and hardwoods gradually replace pines during succession. Thus, the climax community includes only strong competitors. Tolerance may explain the species composition of many transitional and mature communities.

At most sites, succession probably results from some combination of facilitation, inhibition, and tolerance, coupled with interspecific differences in dispersal, growth, and maturation rates. Moreover, within a community, the patchiness of abiotic factors strongly influences plant distributions and species composition. In deciduous forests of eastern North America, maples (*Acer* species) predominate on wet, low-lying ground, but oaks (*Quercus* species) are more abundant at higher and drier sites. Thus, a mature deciduous forest is often a mosaic of species and not a uniform stand of trees.

Disturbance and density-independent factors play important roles, in some cases speeding successional change. Moose (*Alces alces*) prefer to feed on deciduous shrubs in northern forests. This disturbance accelerates the rate at which conifers replace deciduous shrubs. On Isle Royale in Lake Superior, however, grazing by moose strongly affects balsam fir (*Abies balsamea*), their preferred food there. The net effect is a severe reduction in conifers and an increase in deciduous shrubs. Disturbance can also inhibit successional change, establishing a **disturbance climax** or **disclimax community.** In many grassland communities, periodic fires and grazing by large mammals kill seedlings of trees that would otherwise become established. Thus, disturbance prevents the succession from grassland to forest, and grassland persists as a disclimax community.

Animals such as moose can alter patterns of succession and vegetation in some communities, but the effect also extends to small mammals. Removal experiments involving kangaroo rats and plots of shrubland in the Chihuahuan Desert (southeastern Arizona) allowed J. H. Brown and E. J. Heske to demonstrate that these rodents were keystones in some systems where they occur. Kangaroo rats affect the plants in several ways. They are seed predators, and their burrowing activities disturb soils. Excluding kangaroo rats from experimental plots led to a threefold increase in the density of tall perennials and annual grasses **(Figure 30.30)**, suggesting that, by predation on seeds and burrowing, these rodents affected the vegetation in the experimental areas.

On a local scale, disturbances often destroy small patches of vegetation, returning them to an earlier successional stage. A hurricane, tornado, or avalanche may topple trees in a forest, creating small, sunny patches of open ground. Locally occurring *r*-selected species take advantage of newly available resources and quickly colonize the openings. These local patches then undergo succession that is out of step with the immediately surrounding forest. Thus, moderate disturbance, accompanied by succession in local patches, can increase species richness in many communities.

**FIGURE 30.30 Predation and succession.** Kangaroo rats (*Dipodomys*) were removed from the left side of the fence, which excluded them from the plot on the left. The top photograph was taken 5 years after the removal and the bottom one 13 years after. A large-seeded annual (after 5 years) and tall grasses are present in the *Dipodomys*-free plots.

From James H. Brown, Edward J. Heske, "Control of a Desert-Grassland Transition by a Keystone Rodent Guild," *Science*, vol. 250, Dec 21, 1990, pp. 1705–1707. *Science* by American Association for the Advancement of Science. Reproduced with permission of AMERICAN ASSOCIATION FOR THE ADVANCEMENT OF SCIENCE in the format Republish in a book via Copyright Clearance Center.

1. What are the two types of succession? How do they differ?
2. What is a climax community? What determines the species composition of a climax community?
3. Identify and briefly describe the three hypotheses used to explain how succession proceeds.

## 30.10 Variations in Species Richness among Communities

Species richness often varies among communities according to a recognizable pattern. Two large-scale patterns of species richness—latitudinal trends and island patterns—have captured the attention of ecologists for more than a century.

### 30.10a Latitudinal Effects: From South to North

Ever since Darwin and Wallace travelled the globe (see Chapter 16), ecologists have recognized broad latitudinal trends in species richness. For many but not all plant and animal groups, species richness follows a latitudinal gradient, with the most species in the tropics and a steady decline in numbers toward the poles (**Figure 30.31**). Several general hypotheses may explain these striking patterns.

Some hypotheses propose historical explanations for the *origin* of high species richness in the tropics. The benign climate in tropical regions allows some tropical organisms to have more generations per year than their temperate counterparts. Small seasonal changes in temperature mean that tropical species may be less likely than temperate species to migrate from one habitat to another, reducing gene flow between geographically isolated populations (see Chapter 17). These factors may have fostered higher speciation rates in the tropics, accelerating the accumulation of species. Tropical communities may also have experienced severe disturbance less often than communities at higher latitudes, where periodic glaciations have caused repeated extinctions. Thus, new species may have accumulated in the tropics over longer periods of time.

Other hypotheses focus on ecological explanations for the *maintenance* of high species richness in the tropics. Some resources are more abundant, predictable, and diverse in tropical communities. Tropical regions experience more intense sunlight, warmer temperatures in most months, and higher annual rainfall than temperate and polar regions (see *The Purple Pages*). These factors provide a long and predictable growing season for the lush tropical vegetation that supports a rich assemblage of herbivores and, through them, many carnivores and parasites. Furthermore, the abundance, predictability, and year-round availability of resources allow some tropical animals to have specialized diets. Tropical forests support many species of fruit-eating bats and birds that could not survive in temperate forests where fruits are not available year-round.

Species richness may be a self-reinforcing phenomenon in tropical communities. Complex webs of population interactions and interdependency have co-evolved in relatively stable and predictable tropical climates. Predator–prey, competitive, and symbiotic interactions may prevent individual species from dominating communities and reducing species richness.

**FIGURE 30.31 Latitudinal trends in species richness.** The species richness of many animals and plants varies with latitude **(c)** as illustrated here for **(a)** ants in North, Central, and South America and **(b)** birds in North and Central America. The species richness data used in (b) are based on records of where these birds breed.

## 30.10b Equilibrium Theory of Island Biogeography

In 1883, a volcanic eruption virtually obliterated the island of Krakatoa. Within 50 years, what was left of Krakatoa had been recolonized by plants and animals, providing biologists with a clear demonstration of the dispersal powers of many living species. The colonization of islands and the establishment of biological communities there have provided many natural experiments that have advanced our knowledge of ecology and populations. Islands are attractive sites for experiments because, although the species richness of communities may be stable over time, the species composition is often in flux as new species join a community and others drop out. In the 1960s, Robert MacArthur and Edward O. Wilson used islands as model systems to address the question of why communities vary in species richness. Islands provide natural laboratories for studying ecological phenomena, just as they do for evolution (see Chapter 16). Island communities can be small, with well-defined boundaries, and are isolated from surrounding communities.

MacArthur and Wilson developed the **equilibrium theory of island biogeography** to explain variations in species richness on islands of different size and different levels of isolation from other landmasses. They hypothesized that the number of species on any island was governed by give and take between two processes: the immigration of new species to an island and the extinction of species already there (**Figure 30.32**).

According to their model, the mainland harbours a *species pool* from which species immigrate to offshore islands.

Seeds and small arthropods are carried by wind or floating debris. Animals such as birds arrive under their own power. When only a few species are on an island, the rate at which new species immigrate to the island is high. But as more species inhabit the island over time, the immigration rate declines because fewer species in the mainland pool can still arrive on the island as *new* colonizers (see Chapter 16). Once some species arrive on an island, their populations grow and persist for variable lengths of time. Other immigrants die without reproducing. As the number of species on an island increases, the rate of species extinction also rises. Extinction rates increase over time partly because more species can go extinct there. In addition, as the number of species on the island increases, competition and predator–prey interactions can reduce the population sizes of some species and drive them to extinction.

According to MacArthur and Wilson's theory, an equilibrium between immigration and extinction determines the number of species that ultimately occupy an island (see Figure 30.32a). Once that equilibrium has been reached, the number of species remains relatively constant because one species already on the island becomes extinct in about the same time it takes a new one to arrive. The model does not specify which species immigrate or which ones already on the island become extinct. It simply predicts that the number of species on the island is in equilibrium, although species composition is not. The ongoing processes of immigration and extinction establish a constant turnover in the roster of species that live on any island.

The MacArthur–Wilson model also explains why some islands harbour more species than others. Large islands have

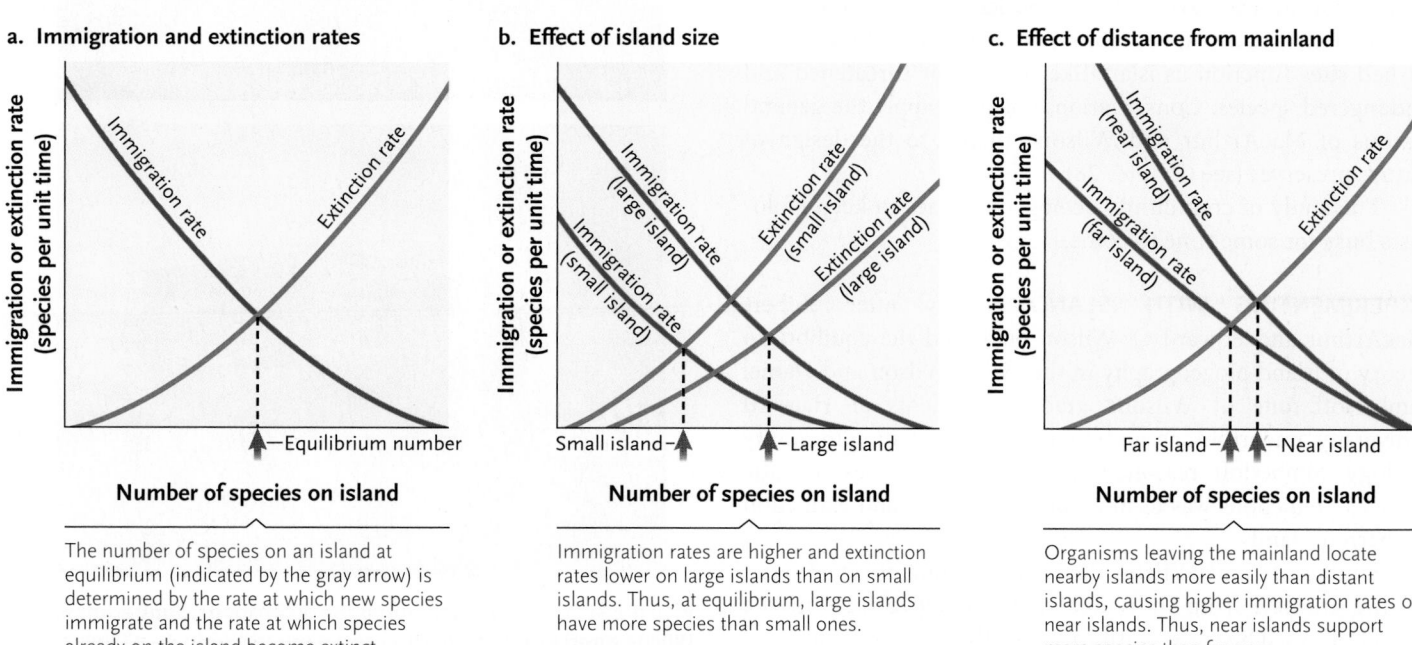

**a. Immigration and extinction rates**

The number of species on an island at equilibrium (indicated by the gray arrow) is determined by the rate at which new species immigrate and the rate at which species already on the island become extinct.

**b. Effect of island size**

Immigration rates are higher and extinction rates lower on large islands than on small islands. Thus, at equilibrium, large islands have more species than small ones.

**c. Effect of distance from mainland**

Organisms leaving the mainland locate nearby islands more easily than distant islands, causing higher immigration rates on near islands. Thus, near islands support more species than far ones.

© Cengage Learning 2017

**FIGURE 30.32 Predictions of the theory of island biogeography.** The horizontal axes of the graphs are time.

higher immigration rates than small islands because they are larger targets for dispersing organisms. Moreover, large islands have lower extinction rates because they can support larger populations and provide a greater range of habitats and resources. At equilibrium, large islands have more species than small islands do (see Figure 30.32b). Islands near the mainland have higher immigration rates than distant islands because dispersing organisms are more likely to arrive at islands close to their point of departure. Distance does not affect extinction rates, so, at equilibrium, nearby islands have more species than distant islands (see Figure 30.32c).

The equilibrium theory's predictions about the effects of area and distance are generally supported by data on plants and animals (Figure 30.32). Experimental work has verified some of the theory's basic assumptions. Amy Schoener found that more than 200 species of marine organisms colonized tiny artificial islands (plastic kitchen scrubbers) within 30 days after she placed them in a Bahamian lagoon. Her research also confirmed that immigration rate increases with island size. Daniel Simberloff and Edward O. Wilson exterminated insects on tiny islands in the Florida Keys and monitored subsequent immigration and extinction (see next section, "Experimenting with Islands"). Their research confirmed the equilibrium theory's predictions that an island's size and distance from the mainland influence how many species will occupy it.

The equilibrial view of species richness can also apply to mainland communities that exist as islands in a metaphorical sea of dissimilar habitat. Lakes are "islands" in a "sea" of dry land, and mountaintops are habitat "islands" in a "sea" of low terrain. Species richness in these communities is governed partly by the immigration of new species from distant sources and partly by the extinction of species already present. As human activities disrupt environments across the globe, undisturbed sites function as islandlike refuges for threatened and endangered species. Conservation biologists apply the general lessons of MacArthur and Wilson's theory to the design of nature preserves (see Chapter 28).

The study of community ecology promises to keep biologists busy for some time to come.

**EXPERIMENTING WITH ISLANDS** Shortly after Robert MacArthur and Edward O. Wilson published the equilibrium theory of island biogeography in the 1960s, Wilson and Daniel Simberloff, one of Wilson's graduate students at Harvard University, undertook an ambitious experiment in community ecology. Simberloff reasoned that the best way to test the theory's predictions was to monitor immigration and extinction on barren islands.

Simberloff and Wilson devised a system for removing all the animals from individual red mangrove trees in the Florida Keys. The trees, with canopies that spread from 11 to 18 m in diameter, grow in shallow water and are isolated from their neighbours. Thus, each tree is an island that harbours an arthropod community. The species pool on the Florida mainland includes about 1000 species of arthropods, but each mangrove island contains no more than 40 species at one time.

After cataloguing the species on each island, Simberloff and Wilson hired an extermination company to erect large tents over each mangrove island and fumigate them to eliminate all arthropods on them (**Figure 30.33**). The exterminators used methyl bromide, a pesticide that does not harm trees or leave any residue. The tents were then removed.

Simberloff then monitored both the immigration of arthropods to the islands and the extinction of species that became established on them. He surveyed four islands regularly for two years and at intervals thereafter.

The results of this experiment confirm several predictions of MacArthur and Wilson's theory (**Figure 30.34**): Arthropods rapidly recolonized the islands, and within eight or nine months the number of species living on each island had reached an

**FIGURE 30.33 After cataloguing the arthropods, Simberloff and Wilson hired an extermination company to eliminate all living arthropods.**

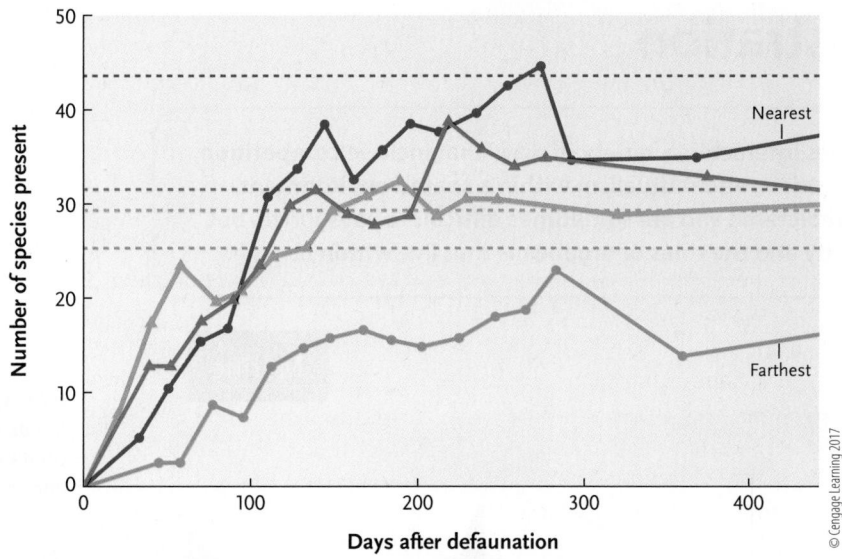

**FIGURE 30.34 On three of four islands, species richness slowly returned to the pre-defaunation level (indicated by colour-coded dotted lines).** The most distant island had not reached its pre-defaunation species richness after two years.

equilibrium that was close to the original species number. The island nearest the mainland had more species than the most distant island. However, immigration and extinction were rapid, and Simberloff and Wilson suspected that some species went extinct even before they had noted their presence. The researchers also discovered that three years after the experimental treatments, the species composition of the islands was still changing constantly and did not remotely resemble the species composition on the islands before they were defaunated.

Simberloff and Wilson's research was a landmark study in ecology because it tested the predictions of an important theory using a field experiment. Although such efforts are now almost routine in ecological studies, this project was one of the first to demonstrate that large-scale experimental manipulations of natural systems are feasible and that they often produce clear results.

## STUDY BREAK QUESTIONS

1. How does species richness change with increasing latitude?
2. In the island biogeography model proposed by MacArthur and Wilson, what processes govern the number of species on an island? What happens to the number of species once equilibrium is reached?
3. What effect do island size and distance from the mainland have on immigration and extinction of colonizing species?

# Summary Illustration

Species within communities interact in a variety of ways that include competition, predation, herbivory, parasitism, and mutualism within a shared environment. All interactions are not predictable and are sometimes difficult to categorize, but these define the community and the roles of organisms that live within it.

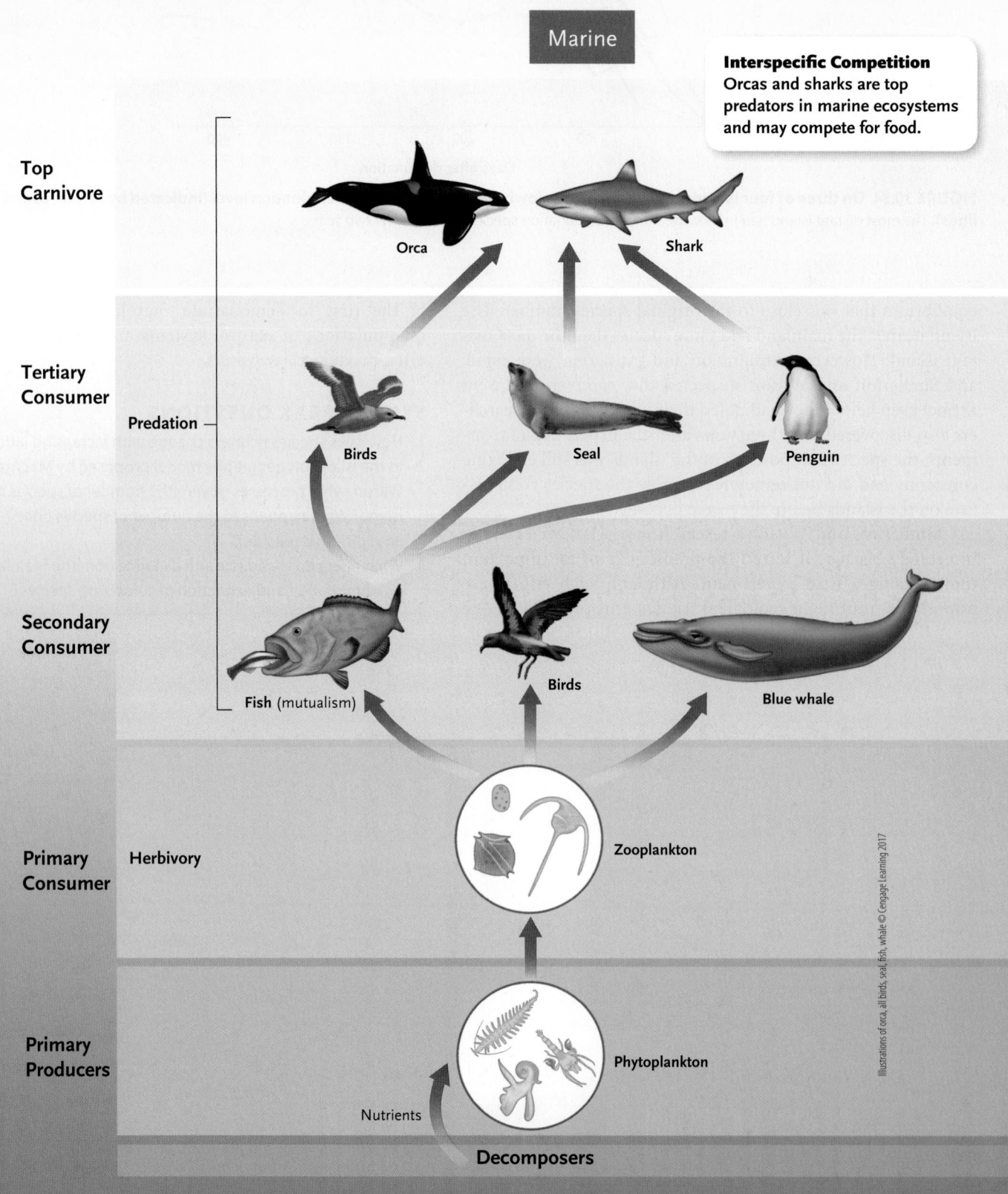

Marine

**Interspecific Competition**
Orcas and sharks are top predators in marine ecosystems and may compete for food.

Top Carnivore

Orca

Shark

Tertiary Consumer

Predation

Birds

Seal

Penguin

Secondary Consumer

Fish (mutualism)

Birds

Blue whale

Primary Consumer

Herbivory

Zooplankton

Primary Producers

Phytoplankton

Nutrients

Decomposers

Illustrations of orca, all birds, seal, fish, whale © Cengage Learning 2017

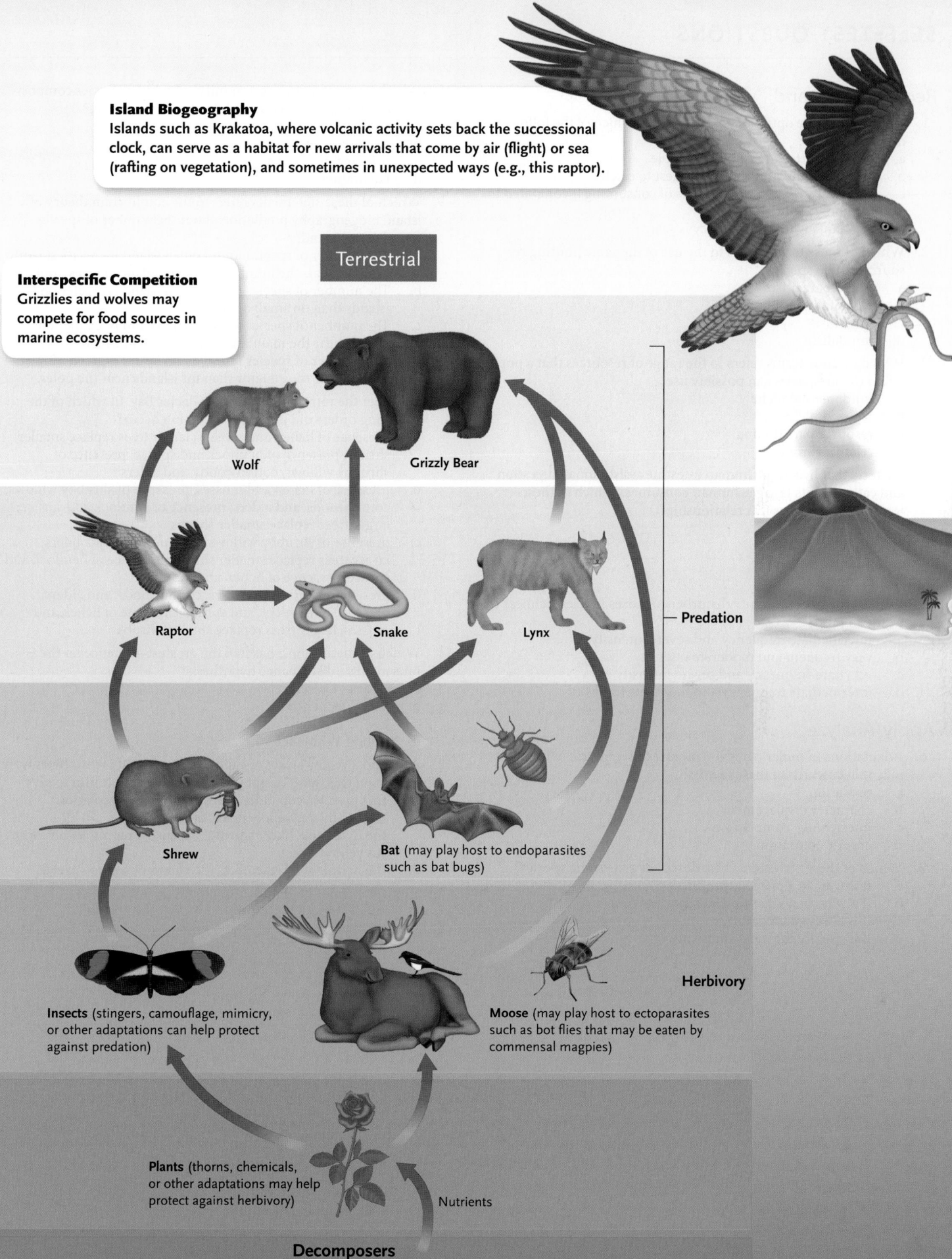

**Island Biogeography**
Islands such as Krakatoa, where volcanic activity sets back the successional clock, can serve as a habitat for new arrivals that come by air (flight) or sea (rafting on vegetation), and sometimes in unexpected ways (e.g., this raptor).

**Interspecific Competition**
Grizzlies and wolves may compete for food sources in marine ecosystems.

Terrestrial

Wolf

Grizzly Bear

Raptor

Snake

Lynx

— Predation

Shrew

**Bat** (may play host to endoparasites such as bat bugs)

**Insects** (stingers, camouflage, mimicry, or other adaptations can help protect against predation)

**Moose** (may play host to ectoparasites such as bot flies that may be eaten by commensal magpies)

Herbivory

**Plants** (thorns, chemicals, or other adaptations may help protect against herbivory)

Nutrients

**Decomposers**

# SELF-TEST QUESTIONS

## Recall/Understand

1. According to the optimal foraging theory, which of the following do predators do?
   a. always eat the largest prey possible
   b. always eat the prey that are easiest to catch
   c. choose prey based on the costs of consuming it compared to the energy it provides
   d. eat plants when animal prey is scarce

2. Which of these terms refers to the use of the same limiting resource by two species?
   a. brood parasitism
   b. exploitative competition
   c. symbiosis
   d. mutualism

3. Which of these terms refers to the range of resources that a population of one species can possibly use?
   a. fundamental niche
   b. realized niche
   c. resource partitioning
   d. relative abundance

4. Bacteria that live in the human intestine assist human digestion and eat nutrients that the human consumes. Which of these terms best describes this relationship?
   a. commensalism
   b. mutualism
   c. endoparasitism
   d. ectoparasitism

5. Which type of community disturbance causes species richness to be the highest?
   a. intermediate frequency and severe intensity
   b. very frequent and moderate intensity
   c. very rare frequency and severe intensity
   d. intermediate frequency and moderate intensity

## Apply/Analyze

6. Adaptations in molar (tooth) structure of sympatric mammals may reflect which of these factors?
   a. predation
   b. character displacement
   c. interference competition
   d. cryptic coloration

7. Which of these statements best describes a keystone species?
   a. It is usually a primary producer.
   b. It always plays a critically important role.
   c. It is always a predator.
   d. It is usually the most abundant.

8. Which term refers to a community's change in species composition from bare and lifeless rock to climax vegetation?
   a. competition
   b. secondary succession
   c. primary succession
   d. facilitation

9. Which of these statements refers to the equilibrium theory of island biogeography prediction about the number of species found on an island?
   a. The number of species found on an island increases steadily until it equals the number in the mainland species pool.
   b. The number of species found on an island is greater on large islands than on small ones.
   c. The number of species found on an island is smaller on islands near the mainland than on distant islands.
   d. The number of species found on an island is greater for islands near the equator than for islands near the poles.

10. Consider the retreat of glaciers at Glacier Bay. In which of the following orders did primary succession occur?
    a. presence of lichen and mosses; larger trees replace smaller shrubs; presence of hemlock and spruce; presence of shrubby willows, cottonwoods, and alders
    b. presence of lichen and mosses; presence of shrubby willows, cottonwoods, and alders; presence of hemlock and spruce; larger trees replace smaller shrubs
    c. presence of shrubby willows, cottonwoods, and alders; larger trees replace smaller shrubs; presence of hemlock and spruce; presence of lichen and mosses
    d. presence of shrubby willows, cottonwoods, and alders; presence of hemlock and spruce; presence of lichen and mosses; larger trees replace smaller shrubs

11. Which of these people has had the greatest influence on the intermediate disturbance hypothesis?
    a. Charles Darwin
    b. Jane Lubchenco
    c. Joseph Connell
    d. Robert Whittaker

12. A fly and a yellow jacket resemble each other. If Henry Bates were told about this, what might you reasonably expect him to say?
    a. This is only a coincidence resulting from a mutation.
    b. Neither fly nor yellow jacket is venomous.
    c. The fly is most likely harmful because it resembles a venomous yellow jacket.
    d. The harmless fly resembles the venomous yellow jacket.

## Create/Evaluate

13. In the table below, the letters refer to four communities, and the numbers indicate how many individuals were recorded for each of five species in those communities. Which of the four communities has the highest species diversity?

|     | Species 1 | Species 2 | Species 3 | Species 4 | Species 5 |
| --- | --------- | --------- | --------- | --------- | --------- |
| a.  | 80        | 10        | 10        | 0         | 0         |
| b.  | 25        | 25        | 25        | 25        | 0         |
| c.  | 0         | 4         | 6         | 8         | 80        |
| d.  | 20        | 20        | 20        | 20        | 20        |

14. Compare realized niche and fundamental niche.

15. Describe Gause's experiments and explain the principle behind their results.

# Chapter Roadmap

### Ecosystems

Ecosystems are based on connections among the diversity of species comprising the systems. Ecosystems can be studied by following the movement of energy from one level to another.

### 31.1 Connections Within and Among Ecosystems

Natural systems provide many examples of biological magnification. DDT, mercury, and pesticides are examples of contaminants that undergo biological magnification.

**From Chapter 30**

M.B. Fenton

### 31.2 Ecosystems and Energy

Food webs define the pathways by which energy and nutrients move through an ecosystem's biotic components.

### 31.3 Nutrient Cycling in Ecosystems

The availability of nutrients is as important to ecosystem function as the input of energy. Earth is essentially a closed system with respect to matter; nutrients constantly circulate between biotic and abiotic organisms.

**To Chapter 36**

### 31.4 Carbon: A Disrupted Cycle

$CO_2$ and other compounds act like a pane of glass in a greenhouse, trapping much of their energy as heat. The rising atmospheric levels of $CO_2$ could change the composition and dynamics of communities.

### 31.5 Ecosystem Modelling

Ecologists use modelling to make predictions about how an ecosystem will respond to specific changes in physical factors, energy flow, or nutrient availability.

### 31.6 Scale, Ecosystems, Species

The complex interactions between and among species combine with abiotic and biotic factors to produce even more complex situations.

### 31.7 Three Sample Ecosystems

M.B. Fenton

**Clumps of white seedlings on the floor of a cave in Cuba mark the areas under roosts used by Jamaican fruit bats.** The seedlings and bat droppings are the main energy input into a totally dark system. Guano and seedlings support a community of cave-loving organisms, including detritivores as well as primary and secondary consumers.

# Ecosystems

# 31

**Why it matters...** Photosynthetic organisms are absent from places with perpetual darkness, such as ocean depths and caves. In caves of the tropics and subtropics, bat droppings are the primary energetic (and biomass) inputs. Caves with large populations of active bats are showered with bat guano and often support considerable biomass, diversity, and well-developed food webs. Caves of the cooler temperate regions are typically too cold for active bats, lack bat guano-driven systems, and have much less diversity and biomass. Caves in glaciers and those with year-round ice support even lower levels of biomass. These are, effectively, refrigerated dark systems with very low biodiversity. In intermediate areas, probably best defined by temperature, there are cave ecosystems with low biomass and low energy.

Caves are interesting natural laboratories for studying ecosystems, communities, diversity, and energy flow. The topic is enriched by variation in cave size and the degree of isolation from the surrounding surface habitat. The spectrum of cave-dwelling organisms reflects levels of specialization for life in the dark. Troglobites are obligatory cave dwellers that complete their entire life cycles underground. Many troglobitic species lack eyes and pigments. Troglophiles, cave lovers, use caves but do not complete their life cycles underground. Trogloxenes are animals that visit caves. Worldwide, there are many species of troglobitic arthropods, fish, and amphibians; some bats and cave crickets are examples of troglophiles. Many other organisms, including humans, are trogloxenes, occasionally visiting caves. As usual in biology, the differences among categories are subjective.

**FIGURE 31.1  Two species of cavefishes, one from Mexico** (a) **and the other from the south central United States** (b)**.** Both species are troglobitic, obligatory, cave dwellers but they are classified in two different families (Characidae and Amblyopsidae respectively); they are not closely related in an evolutionary sense. These troglobites lack eyes and pigment.

Mexican cavefish (*Astyanax mexicanus*; **Figure 31.1a**) are often sold in pet stores. These fish occur in caves in Mexico where they live in a soup of bat droppings and the many organisms supported by this input. In some cases, cave and surface waters are connected and there is a spectrum of Mexican cavefish from individuals with well-developed eyes to eyeless fish. Mexican cavefish swim continuously propelled by lateral movements of their tail (caudal) fins. They appear to find food by random searching, an effective strategy when you live in an energy-rich soup of bat droppings.

Other species of cavefish occur elsewhere in the world. In the central United States (e.g., Kentucky, Indiana), there is no bat enrichment of the waters. The troglobitic southern cavefish (*Typhlichthys subterraneus*; Figure 31.1b) eat mainly aquatic crustaceans such as amphipods. These fish use specialized sensory cells to detect the vibrations generated by swimming prey. They are slow and deliberate swimmers, propelling themselves with enlarged pectoral fins.

Perhaps as interesting are communities of eukaryotes living in biofilms, in the dark, in rocks 1.4 km below Earth's surface. These communities were discovered in the depths of gold mines in South Africa. The fissure waters in which they live are up to 12 300 years old. These biofilm communities include protozoans and fungi as well as species of platyhelminths, rotifers, annelids, and arthropods. The organisms all appear to have originated from surface waters, and their populations are limited by access to food rather than oxygen.

Caves and deep subsurface biofilms are examples of life in the dark. These systems illustrate the diversity of life and the different situations in which some forms of life can thrive. The deep subsurface biofilms may set the stage for different approaches to searches for life on other planets.

**Ecosystems** are based on connections among the diversity of species comprising the systems. In a setting as large as planet Earth, it could be easy to dismiss the proposal that different species are connected in ecosystems. Ironically, the prevalence and importance of the connections was forcefully illustrated by a poison named DDT (dichloro-diphenyl-trichloroethane).

Originally formulated in 1873, DDT's potential as an insecticide was recognized in 1939. DDT (**Figure 31.2**), the first of the chlorinated insecticides, was used extensively in some theatres of World War II. In 1943 in southern Italy, DDT was instrumental in controlling populations of lice that plagued Canadian troops there. Widespread application of DDT in Burma (now Myanmar) reduced the incidence of malaria by killing mosquitoes, the vectors of the disease. After World War II, the use of DDT spread rapidly, and the World Health Organization (WHO) credited this molecule with saving 25 million human lives (mainly through control of mosquitoes that carry malaria). As we shall see, DDT rapidly spread well beyond the locations where it had been used, directly illustrating connections among species.

Ecosystems can be studied by following the movement of energy from one level to another. Photosynthetic organisms form the energetic basis for ecosystems, providing sources of food for other organisms (usually animals). Levels of biomass at different trophic levels (primary producers; primary, secondary, and tertiary consumers) generally reflect the movement of energy.

**FIGURE 31.2  A molecule of DDT**

# 31.1 Connections Within and Among Ecosystems

At first, DDT seemed an ideal insecticide. In addition to being inexpensive to produce, it had low toxicity to mammals. For mammals, 300–500 mg/kg is the $LD_{50}$ of DDT, the amount required to kill half the target population. But many insects subsequently developed immunity to DDT, reducing its effectiveness.

DDT is chemically stable and soluble in fat. Mammals store DDT in their fat rather than metabolizing it. The biological half-life of DDT is approximately eight years. It takes about eight years for a mammal to metabolize half the amount of DDT it has assimilated. DDT is released when fat is metabolized, so when mammals metabolize fat (e.g., when humans go on a diet), they are exposed to higher concentrations of DDT in their blood. DDT had dramatic effects on some birds, notably those higher up the food chain. Eggshell thinning was a consequence of exposure to DDT. Populations of birds such as peregrine falcons (*Falco peregrinus*) and bald eagles (*Haliaeetus leucocephalus*) plummeted.

DDT provided a graphic example of **biological magnification**. Consumers accumulate DDT from all the organisms they eat in their lifetimes. Primary consumers, such as herbivorous insects, may ingest relatively small amounts of DDT. But a songbird that eats many of these insects accumulates all the collected DDT consumed by its prey. A predator such as a raptor that eats songbirds accumulates even more DDT. This biomagnification occurs whether the food chain (web) is aquatic or terrestrial. The net effect on higher-level consumers is the same **(Figure 31.3)** and can be debilitating or lethal.

Natural systems provide many examples of biological magnification. In cities where DDT was used to control the spread of Dutch elm disease, songbirds died from DDT poisoning after eating insects that had been sprayed (whether or not they were involved in spreading the disease). In forests, DDT was used in an effort to control spruce budworm moths (*Choristoneura occidentalis*). Here the salmon died because runoff carried DDT into their streams and rivers, where their herbivorous prey consumed it.

Despite the ban on the use of DDT in the United States in 1973, in 1990, the California State Department of Health recommended closing a fishery off the coast of California because of DDT accumulating there. DDT discharged in industrial waste 20 years earlier was still moving through the ecosystem.

Biological magnification occurs with other contaminants. Mercury contamination is a common by-product of the pulp and paper industry. Minamata, the disease humans get from

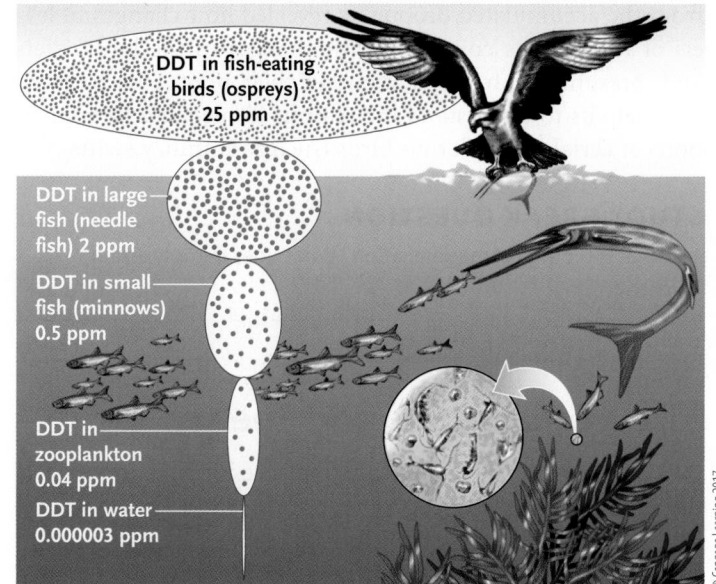

**FIGURE 31.3 Biological magnification.** In this marine food web in northeastern North America, DDT concentration (measured in parts per million, ppm) was magnified nearly 10 million times between zooplankton and the osprey (*Pandion haliaetus*).

mercury poisoning, is usually linked to the consumption of fish taken from contaminated watersheds. Eating fish contaminated with mercury can result in mercury concentrations in people's hair (0.9–94 mg/kg) and in otters' fur (*Lontra canadensis*; 0.49–54.37 mg/kg). In southern Ontario, hair of bats that eat insects that emerge from mercury-contaminated sediments contain concentrations up to 13 mg/kg. These data illustrate that fish are not essential to this chain of biomagnification.

Since 1985, the use of DDT has been totally banned in Canada, and it is now banned in many other countries. But DDT is still produced in countries such as the United States, and still used where malaria is a prominent problem because the ecological costs of DDT are considered secondary to the importance of controlling the mosquitoes. By the early 1970s, cetaceans in the waters around Antarctica had DDT in their body fat even though DDT had never been used there. The movement of DDT up the food chain and through food webs demonstrated the interconnections in biological systems. The movement of DDT also provides a graphic demonstration of the transfer of materials from one trophic level to another.

Removing DDT from the arsenal of products used to control insects had other impacts. For example, an upsurge in the number of houses, apartments, and hotel rooms infested by bedbugs (*Cimex lectularius*). DDT had been very effective in the control of bedbugs but, in its absence, populations of these insects have rebounded, renewing old challenges that our grandparents experienced.

Evidence for the impact of pesticides often comes from unexpected sources. An excellent example is the accumulation of chimney swift (*Chaetura pelagica*) droppings at the bottom of a chimney in Kingston, Ontario. As their name implies, chimney swifts often nest in chimneys, and analysis of samples from the accumulated droppings revealed how changes in levels of insecticides coincided with changes in the birds' diets and, presumably, in populations of their prey. This research may help us to understand the reasons for declines in populations of aerial insectivorous birds (such as chimney swifts).

## STUDY BREAK QUESTION

1. What is biological magnification? What does it imply about ecosystems?

## 31.2 Ecosystems and Energy

Ecosystems receive input of energy from an external source, usually the Sun. Energy flows through an ecosystem but, as dictated by the laws of thermodynamics (see Chapter 3), much of it is lost without being used by organisms. In contrast, materials cycle between living and nonliving reservoirs, both locally and on a global scale. The flow of energy through, and the cycling of materials around, an ecosystem make resident organisms highly dependent on one another and on their physical surroundings.

Food webs define the pathways by which energy and nutrients move through an ecosystem's biotic components. In most ecosystems, nutrients and energy move simultaneously through a grazing food web and a detrital food web (**Figure 31.4**). The grazing food web includes the producer, herbivore, and secondary consumer trophic levels. The detrital food web includes detritivores and decomposers. Because detritivores and decomposers subsist on the remains and waste products of organisms at every trophic level, the two food webs are closely interconnected. Detritivores also contribute to the grazing food web when carnivores eat them.

All organisms in a particular trophic level are the same number of energy transfers away from the ecosystem's ultimate energy source. Photosynthetic plants are one energy transfer removed from sunlight, herbivores (primary consumers) are two, secondary consumers are three, and tertiary consumers are four.

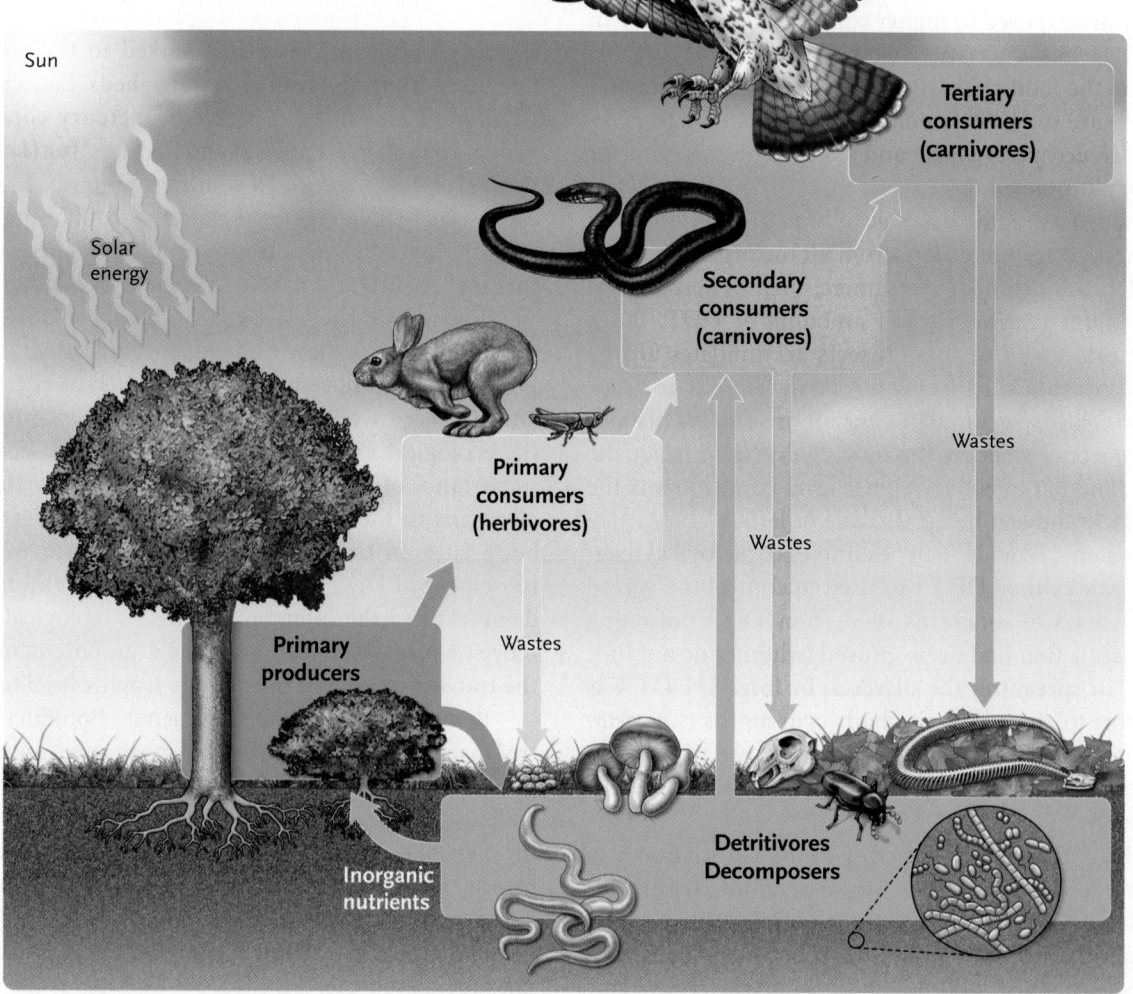

**FIGURE 31.4 Grazing and detrital food webs.** Energy and nutrients move through two parallel food webs in most ecosystems. The grazing food web includes producers, herbivores, and carnivores. The detrital food web includes detritivores and decomposers. Each box in this diagram represents many species, and each arrow represents many arrows.

## 31.2a Primary Productivity Involves Fixing Carbon

Almost all life on Earth depends directly or indirectly on the input of solar energy. Every minute of every day, Earth's atmosphere intercepts roughly 80 kJ (kilojoules) of energy per square metre (see Chapter 1). About half that energy is absorbed, scattered, or reflected by gases, dust, water vapour, and clouds before it reaches the planet's surface (see *The Purple Pages*). Most energy reaching the surface falls on bodies of water or bare ground, where it is absorbed as heat or reflected back into the atmosphere. Reflected energy warms the atmosphere. Only a small percentage contacts primary producers, and most of that energy evaporates water, driving transpiration in plants (see Chapter 6).

Ultimately, photosynthesis converts less than 1% of the solar energy arriving at Earth's surface into chemical energy. But primary producers still capture enough energy to produce an average of several kilograms of dry plant material per square metre per year. On a global scale, they produce more than 150 billion tonnes of new biological material annually. Some of the solar energy that producers convert into chemical energy is transferred to consumers at higher trophic levels.

The rate at which producers convert solar energy into chemical energy is an ecosystem's **gross primary productivity**. But, like other organisms, producers use energy for their own maintenance functions. After deducting energy used for these functions (see Chapter 5), the remaining chemical energy is the ecosystem's **net primary productivity**. In most ecosystems, net primary productivity is 50%–90% of gross primary productivity. In other words, producers use between 10% and 50% of the energy they capture for their own respiration.

Ecologists usually measure primary productivity in units of energy captured ($kJ/m^2/year$) or in units of biomass created ($kg/m^2/year$). **Biomass** is the dry mass of biological material per unit area or volume of habitat. Do not confuse an ecosystem's productivity with its **standing crop biomass**, the total dry mass of plants present at a given time. Net primary productivity is the *rate* at which the standing crop produces *new* biomass (see Chapter 6).

Energy captured by plants is stored in biological molecules, mostly carbohydrates, lipids, and proteins. Ecologists can convert units of biomass into units of energy or vice versa as long as they know the total amounts of carbohydrate, protein, and lipid in a sample of biological material. For reference, 1 g of carbohydrate and 1 g of protein each contains about 17.5 kJ of energy. Thus, net primary productivity indexes the rate at which producers accumulate energy as well as the rate at which new biomass is added to an ecosystem. Ecologists measure changes in biomass to estimate productivity because it

is far easier to measure biomass than energy content. New biomass takes at least three forms, including:

- growth of existing producers,
- creation of new producers by reproduction, and
- storage of energy as carbohydrates.

Because herbivores eat all three forms of new biomass, net primary productivity also measures how much new energy is available for primary consumers.

The potential rate of photosynthesis in any ecosystem is proportional to the intensity and duration of sunlight, which varies geographically and seasonally (see Chapter 5, Chapter 6, and *The Purple Pages*). Sunlight is most intense and day length is least variable near the equator. In contrast, the intensity of sunlight is weakest and day length is most variable near the poles. This means that producers at the equator can photosynthesize for nearly 12 hours a day, every day of the year, whereas near the poles, photosynthesis is virtually impossible during the long dark winter. In summer, however, photosynthesis occurs virtually around the clock.

Sunlight is not the only factor influencing the rate of primary productivity. Temperature and the availability of water and nutrients also affect this rate. Many of the world's **deserts** receive plenty of sunshine but have low rates of productivity because water is in short supply and the soil is poor in nutrients. Mean annual primary productivity varies greatly on a global scale (**Figure 31.5**), reflecting variations in these environmental factors (see *The Purple Pages*).

On a finer geographic scale, within a particular terrestrial ecosystem, mean annual net productivity often increases with the availability of water (**Figure 31.6**). In systems with sufficient water, a shortage of mineral nutrients may be limiting. All plants need specific ratios of macronutrients and micronutrients for maintenance and photosynthesis (see Chapter 6). But plants withdraw nutrients from soil, and if nutrient concentration drops below a critical level, photosynthesis may decrease or stop altogether. In every ecosystem, one nutrient inevitably runs

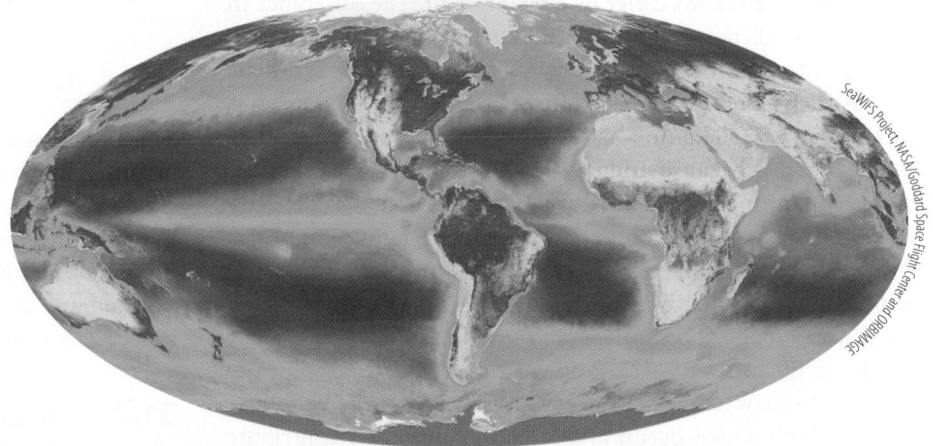

**FIGURE 31.5 Global variation in primary productivity.** Satellite data from 2002 provide a visual portrait of net primary productivity across Earth's surface. High-productivity regions on land are dark green; low-productivity regions are yellow. For aquatic environments, the highest productivity is red, down through orange, yellow, green, blue, and purple (lowest).

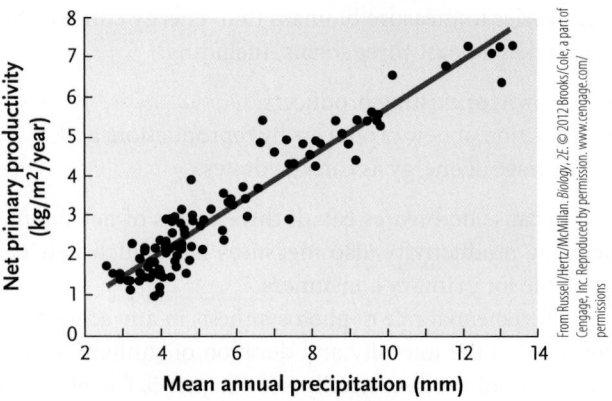

From Russell/Hertz/McMillan. *Biology, 2E.* © 2012 Brooks/Cole, a part of Cengage, Inc. Reproduced by permission. www.cengage.com/permissions

**FIGURE 31.6 Water and net primary productivity.** Mean annual precipitation at 100 sites in the Great Plains of North America. These data include only above-ground productivity.

out before the supplies of other nutrients are exhausted. The element in shortest supply is a **limiting nutrient** because its absence curtails productivity. Productivity in agricultural fields is subject to the same constraints as productivity in natural ecosystems. Farmers increase productivity by irrigating (adding water to) and fertilizing (adding nutrients to) their crops.

In freshwater and marine ecosystems, depth of water and combined availability of sunlight and nutrients govern the rate of primary productivity. Productivity is high in near-shore ecosystems, where sunlight penetrates shallow nutrient-rich waters. Kelp beds and coral reefs along temperate and tropical marine coastlines, respectively, are among the most productive ecosystems on Earth (**Table 31.1**). In contrast, productivity is low in the open waters of a large lake or ocean. There, sunlight penetrates only the upper layers, and nutrients sink to the bottom; thus, the two requirements for photosynthesis—sunlight and nutrients—are available in different places.

Although ecosystems vary in their rates of primary productivity, these differences are not always proportional to variations in their standing crop biomass (see Table 31.1). For example, biomass amounts in temperate deciduous forests and **temperate grasslands** differ by a factor of 20. The difference in their rates of net primary productivity, however, is much smaller. Most biomass in trees is present in non-photosynthetic tissues such as wood, so their ratio of productivity to biomass is low ($12 \text{ kg/m}^2/300 \text{ kg/m}^2 = 0.04$). Grasslands do not accumulate much biomass because annual mortality, herbivores, and fires remove plant material as it is produced. Here the productivity to biomass ratio is much higher ($6.0 \text{ kg/m}^2/16 \text{ kg/m}^2 = 0.375$).

Some ecosystems contribute more than others to overall net primary productivity (**Figure 31.7**). Ecosystems covering large areas make substantial total contributions, even if their productivity per unit area is low. Conversely, geographically restricted ecosystems make large contributions if their productivity is high. Open ocean and tropical rainforests contribute about equally to total global productivity, but for different reasons. Open oceans have low productivity, but they cover nearly two-thirds of Earth's surface. Tropical rainforests are highly productive but cover only a relatively small area.

**TABLE 31.1** | **Standing Crop Biomass and Net Primary Productivity of Different Ecosystems**

| Ecosystem | Mean Standing Crop Biomass (kg/m²) | Mean Net Primary Productivity (kg/m²/y) |
|---|---|---|
| **Terrestrial Ecosystems** | | |
| Tropical rainforest | 450 | 22.0 |
| **Tropical deciduous forest** | 350 | 16.0 |
| Temperate rainforest | 350 | 13.0 |
| Temperate deciduous forest | 300 | 12.0 |
| Savannah | 40 | 9.0 |
| Boreal forest (**taiga**) | 200 | 8.0 |
| Woodland and shrubland | 60 | 7.0 |
| Agricultural land | 10 | 6.5 |
| Temperate grassland | 16 | 6.0 |
| Tundra and Alpine tundra | 6.0 | 1.4 |
| Desert and thornwoods | 7.0 | 0.9 |
| Extreme desert, rock, sand, ice | 0.2 | 0.03 |
| **Freshwater Ecosystems** | | |
| Swamp and marsh | 150 | 20 |
| Lake and stream | 0.2 | 2.5 |
| **Marine Ecosystems** | | |
| Open ocean | 0.03 | 1.3 |
| Upwelling zones | 0.2 | 5.0 |
| Continental shelf | 0.1 | 3.6 |
| Kelp beds and reefs | 20 | 25 |
| Estuaries | 10 | 15 |
| **World Total** | **36** | **3.3** |

Source: Based on Whittaker, R.H. 1975. Communities and Ecosystems. 2nd ed. Macmillan.

Net primary productivity ultimately supports all consumers in grazing and detrital food webs. Consumers in the grazing food web eat some biomass at every trophic level except the highest. Uneaten biomass eventually dies and passes into detrital food webs. Moreover, consumers assimilate only a portion of the material they ingest, and unassimilated material passed as feces also supports detritivores and decomposers.

### 31.2b Secondary Productivity: Animals Eating Plants

As energy is transferred from producers to consumers, some is stored in new consumer biomass, **secondary productivity**. Nevertheless, two factors cause energy to be lost from the

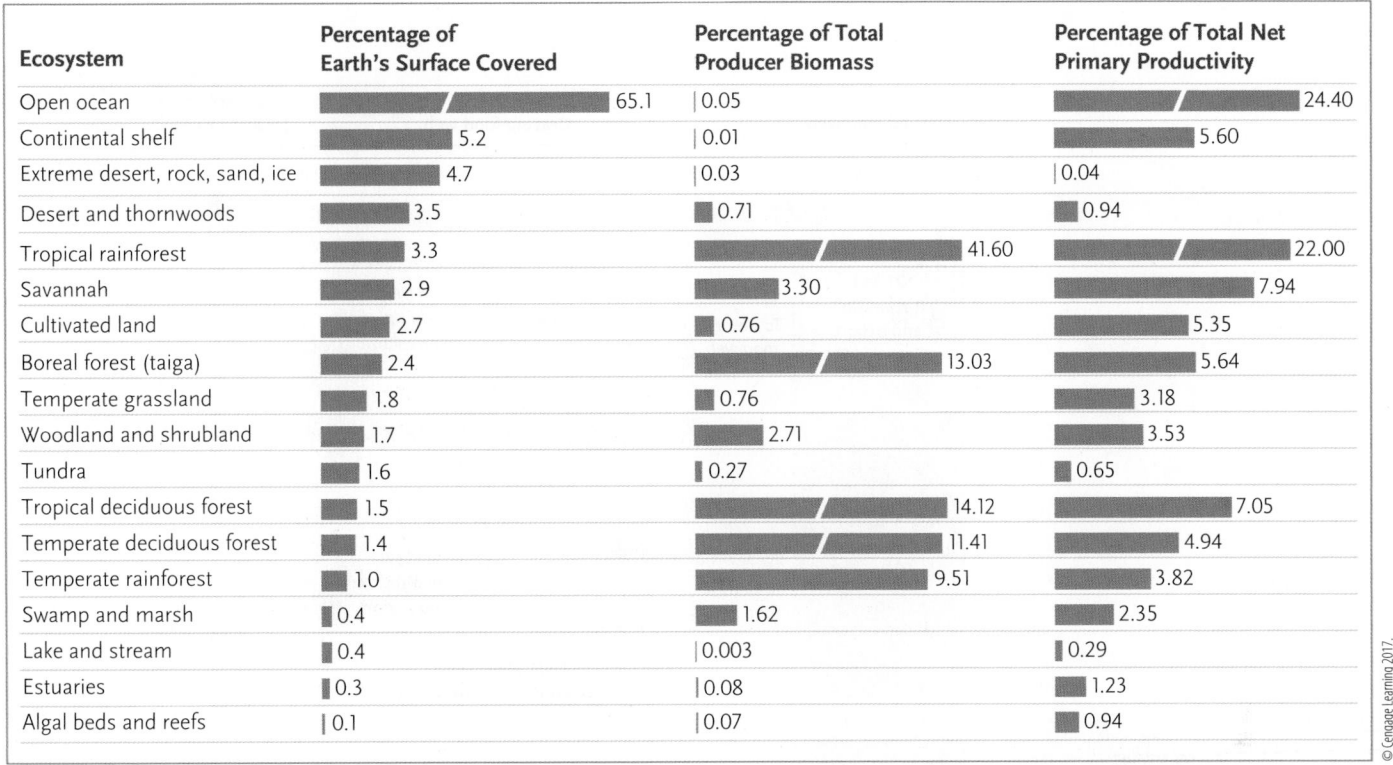

| Ecosystem | Percentage of Earth's Surface Covered | Percentage of Total Producer Biomass | Percentage of Total Net Primary Productivity |
|---|---|---|---|
| Open ocean | 65.1 | 0.05 | 24.40 |
| Continental shelf | 5.2 | 0.01 | 5.60 |
| Extreme desert, rock, sand, ice | 4.7 | 0.03 | 0.04 |
| Desert and thornwoods | 3.5 | 0.71 | 0.94 |
| Tropical rainforest | 3.3 | 41.60 | 22.00 |
| Savannah | 2.9 | 3.30 | 7.94 |
| Cultivated land | 2.7 | 0.76 | 5.35 |
| Boreal forest (taiga) | 2.4 | 13.03 | 5.64 |
| Temperate grassland | 1.8 | 0.76 | 3.18 |
| Woodland and shrubland | 1.7 | 2.71 | 3.53 |
| Tundra | 1.6 | 0.27 | 0.65 |
| Tropical deciduous forest | 1.5 | 14.12 | 7.05 |
| Temperate deciduous forest | 1.4 | 11.41 | 4.94 |
| Temperate rainforest | 1.0 | 9.51 | 3.82 |
| Swamp and marsh | 0.4 | 1.62 | 2.35 |
| Lake and stream | 0.4 | 0.003 | 0.29 |
| Estuaries | 0.3 | 0.08 | 1.23 |
| Algal beds and reefs | 0.1 | 0.07 | 0.94 |

© Cengage Learning 2017.

**FIGURE 31.7 Biomass and net primary productivity.** An ecosystem's percentage coverage of Earth's surface is not proportional to its contribution to total biomass of producers or its contribution to the total net primary productivity.

ecosystem every time it flows from one trophic level to another. First, animals use much of the energy they assimilate for maintenance and locomotion rather than for production of new biomass. Second, as dictated by the second law of thermodynamics, no biochemical reaction is 100% efficient, so some of the chemical energy liberated by cellular respiration is converted to heat, which most organisms do not use.

### 31.2c Ecological Efficiency Is Measured by Use of Energy

**Ecological efficiency** is the ratio of net productivity at one trophic level to net productivity at the trophic level below. If plants in an ecosystem have a net primary productivity of 1.0 kg/m$^2$/year of new tissue, and the herbivores that eat these plants produce 0.1 kg of new tissue per square metre per year, the ecological efficiency of the herbivores is 10%. The efficiencies of three processes (harvesting food, assimilating ingested energy, and producing new biomass) determine the ecological efficiencies of consumers.

**Harvesting efficiency** is the ratio of the energy content of food consumed to the energy content of food available. Predators harvest food efficiently when prey are abundant and easy to capture (see Chapter 30).

**Assimilation efficiency** is the ratio of the energy absorbed from consumed food to the total energy content of the food. Because animal prey is relatively easy to digest, carnivores absorb between 60% and 90% of the energy in their food.

Assimilation efficiency is lower for prey with indigestible parts such as bones or exoskeletons. Herbivores assimilate only 15% to 80% of the energy they consume because cellulose is not very digestible. Herbivores lacking cellulose-digesting systems are on the low end of the scale, whereas those that can digest cellulose are at the higher end.

**Production efficiency** is the ratio of the energy content of new tissue produced to the energy assimilated from food. Production efficiency varies with maintenance costs. Endothermic animals often use less than 10% of their assimilated energy for growth and reproduction because they use energy to generate body heat (see Chapter 42). Ectothermic animals channel more than 50% of their assimilated energy into new biomass.

The overall ecological efficiency of most organisms is 5%–20%. As a rule of thumb, only about 10% of energy accumulated at one trophic level is converted into biomass at the next higher trophic level. This is illustrated by energy transfers at Silver Springs, Florida (**Figure 31.8**), an ecosystem studied for many years. Producers in the Silver Springs ecosystem convert 1.2% of the solar energy they intercept into chemical energy (represented by 86 986 kJ/m$^2$/year of gross primary productivity). However, plants use about two-thirds of this energy for respiration, leaving a net primary productivity, one-third of which is to be included in new plant biomass. All consumers in the grazing food web (on the right in Figure 31.8) ultimately depend on this energy source, which diminishes with each transfer between trophic levels. Energy is lost to respiration and export at each trophic level. In addition, organic wastes

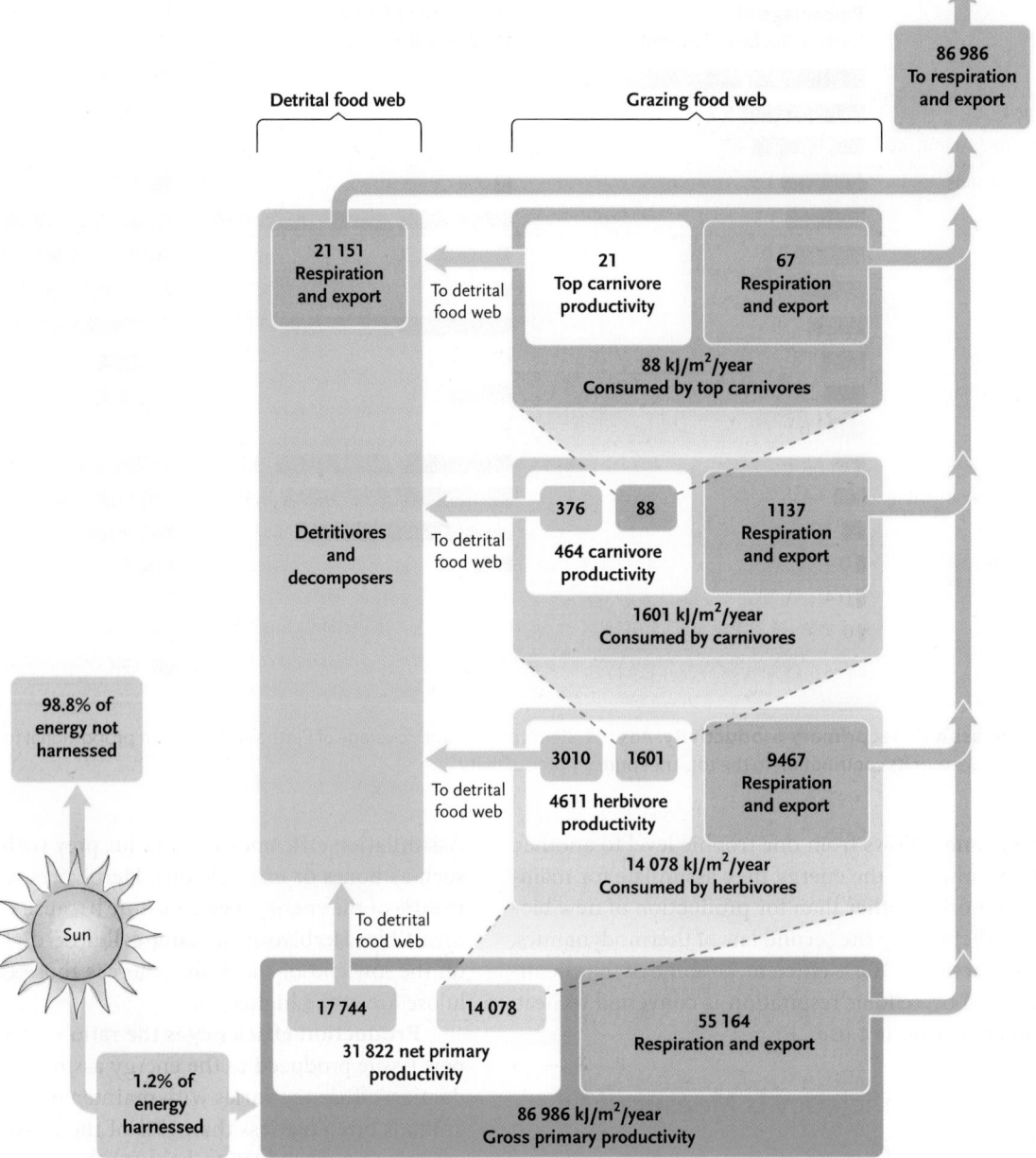

**FIGURE 31.8  Energy flow through the Silver Springs ecosystem**

and uneaten biomass represent substantial energy that flows into the detrital food web (on the left in Figure 31.8). To determine the ecological efficiency of any trophic level, we divide its productivity by the productivity of the level below it. The ecological efficiency of midlevel carnivores at Silver Springs is 10.06%: 464 kJ/m²/year/4611 kJ/m²/year.

## 31.2d  Pyramids in Ecosystems: Energy, Biomass, and Numbers

As energy works its way up a food web, energy losses are multiplied in successive energy transfers (**Figure 31.9**). Consider a hypothetical example with ecological efficiency of 10% for all consumers. Assume that the plants in a small field annually

produce new tissues containing 100 kJ of energy. Because only 10% of that energy is transferred to new herbivore biomass, the 100 kJ in plants produces 10 kJ of new herbivorous insects, 1 kJ of new songbirds that eat insects, and only 0.1 kJ of new falcons that eat songbirds. About 0.1% of the energy from primary productivity remains after three trophic levels of transfer. If the energy available to each trophic level is depicted graphically, the result is a **pyramid of energy**, with primary producers on the bottom and higher-level consumers on the top (Figure 31.9).

The low ecological efficiencies that characterize most energy transfers illustrate one advantage of eating "lower on the food chain." This reality accounts for major adaptive radiations of lineages of animals where ancestors were secondary

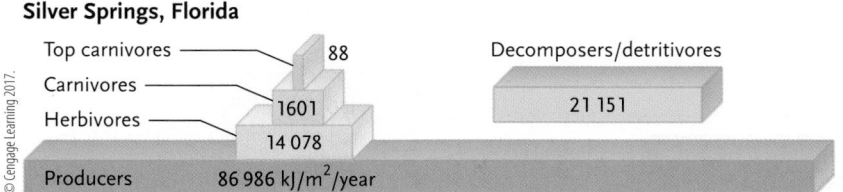

**Silver Springs, Florida**

**FIGURE 31.9 Pyramids of energy.** The pyramid of energy for Silver Springs, Florida, shows that the amount of energy (kJ/m²/year) passing through each trophic level decreases as it moves up the food web.

consumers that then switched to being primary consumers. Good examples of such radiations occur, for example, among insects, fish, dinosaurs, and mammals.

Humans digest and assimilate meat more efficiently than vegetables. But we could feed more people if we ate more primary producers rather than secondary consumers. Being a secondary consumer means passing carbohydrates through another trophic level, such as cattle or chickens. Production of animal protein is costly because much of the energy fed to livestock is used for their own maintenance rather than production of new biomass. But despite the economic and health-related logic of a more vegetarian diet, changing our eating habits alone will not eliminate food shortages or the frequency of malnutrition. Many regions of Africa, Australia, North America, and South America support vegetation that is suitable only for grazing by large herbivores. These areas could not produce significant quantities of edible grains and vegetables without significant additions of water and fertilizer (see Chapter 36).

Inefficiency of energy transfer from one trophic level to the next has profound effects on ecosystem structure. Ecologists illustrate these effects in diagrams called **ecological pyramids**. Trophic levels are drawn as stacked blocks, with the size of each block proportional to the energy, biomass, or numbers of organisms present. Pyramids of energy typically have wide bases and narrow tops (Figure 31.9) because each trophic level contains only about 10% as much energy as the trophic level below it.

Progressive reduction in productivity at higher trophic levels usually establishes a **pyramid of biomass (Figure 31.10)**. The biomass at each trophic level is proportional to the amount of chemical energy temporarily stored there. Thus, in terrestrial

ecosystems, the total mass of producers is generally greater than the total mass of herbivores, which, in turn, is greater than the total mass of predators (Figure 31.10a). Populations of top predators, from killer whales to lions and crocodiles, contain too little biomass and energy to support another trophic level; thus, they have no nonhuman predators.

Freshwater and marine ecosystems sometimes exhibit inverted pyramids of biomass (Figure 31.10b). In the open waters of a lake or ocean, primary consumers (zooplankton) eat primary producers (phytoplankton) almost as soon as they are produced. As a result, the standing crop of primary consumers at any time is actually larger than the standing crop of primary producers. Food webs in these ecosystems are stable because producers have exceptionally high **turnover rates**. In other words, producers divide and their populations grow so quickly that feeding by zooplankton does not endanger their populations or reduce the producers' productivity. However, on an annual basis, the cumulative total biomass of primary producers far outweighs that of primary consumers.

The reduction of energy and biomass affects sizes of populations of organisms at the top of a food web. Top predators can be relatively large animals, so the limited biomass present in the highest trophic levels is concentrated in relatively few animals **(Figure 31.11)**. The extremely narrow top of this **pyramid of numbers** has grave implications for conservation biology (see Chapter 28). Top predators tend to be large animals with small population sizes. And because each individual must patrol a large area to find sufficient food, members of a population are often widely dispersed within their habitats. As a result, they are subject to genetic drift (see Chapter 17) and are highly sensitive to hunting, habitat destruction, and random events that can lead to extinction. Top predators may also suffer from the accumulation of poisonous materials that move through food webs (biomagnification). Even predators that feed below the top trophic level often suffer the ill effects of human activities. Consumers sometimes regulate ecosystem processes.

Numerous abiotic factors, such as the intensity and duration of sunlight, rainfall, temperature, and the availability of nutrients, significantly affect primary productivity. Primary productivity, in turn, profoundly affects the populations of herbivores

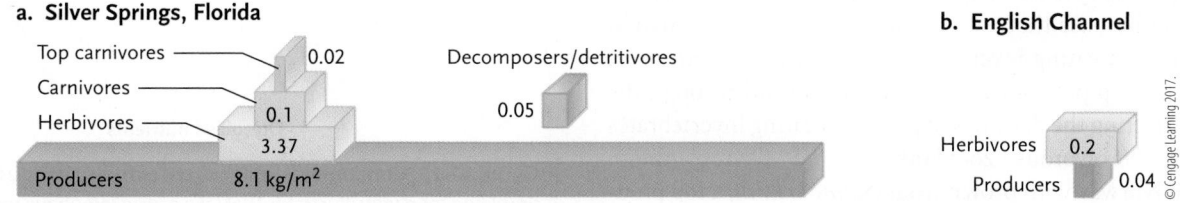

**FIGURE 31.10 Pyramids of biomass. (a)** The pyramid of standing crop biomass for Silver Springs is bottom heavy, as it is for most ecosystems. **(b)** Some marine ecosystems, such as that in the English Channel, have an inverted pyramid of biomass because producers are quickly eaten by primary consumers. Only the producer and herbivore trophic levels are illustrated here. The data for both pyramids are given in kilograms per square metre of dry biomass.

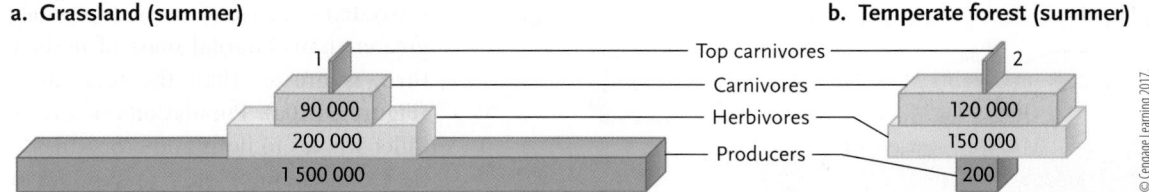

a. **Grassland (summer)**                                     b. **Temperate forest (summer)**

| Top carnivores | 1 | | 2 |
| Carnivores |
| Herbivores |
| Producers |

90 000     120 000

200 000     150 000

1 500 000     200

© Cengage Learning 2017.

**FIGURE 31.11 Pyramids of numbers. (a)** The pyramid of numbers (numbers of individuals per 1000 m²) for temperate grasslands is bottom heavy because individual producers are small and very numerous. **(b)** The pyramid of numbers for forests may have a narrow base because herbivorous insects usually outnumber the producers, many of which are large trees. Data for both pyramids were collected during summer. Detritivores and decomposers (soil animals and microorganisms) are not included because they are difficult to count. Parasites are another example of an inverted pyramid.

and the predators that feed on them. But what effect does feeding by these consumers have on primary productivity?

Consumers sometimes influence rates of primary productivity, especially in ecosystems with low species diversity and relatively few trophic levels. Food webs in lake ecosystems depend primarily on the productivity of phytoplankton **(Figure 31.12)**. Phytoplankton, in turn, are eaten by herbivorous zooplankton, which themselves consumed by predatory invertebrates and fishes. The top nonhuman carnivore in these food webs is usually a predatory fish.

Herbivorous zooplankton play a central role in regulation of lake ecosystems. Small zooplankton species consume only small phytoplankton. Thus, when small zooplankton are especially abundant, large phytoplankton escape predation and survive, and the lake's primary productivity is high. Large zooplankton are voracious, eating both small and large phytoplankton. When large zooplankton are abundant, they reduce the overall biomass of phytoplankton and lower the ecosystem's primary productivity.

In this **trophic cascade**, predator–prey effects reverberate through population interactions at two or more trophic levels. Feeding by plankton-eating invertebrates and fishes directly affects populations of herbivorous zooplankton and indirectly affects populations of phytoplankton (the ecosystem's primary producers). Invertebrate predators prefer small zooplankton, and when they dominate an ecosystem, large zooplankton become more abundant. In turn, the larger zooplankton eat many phytoplankton and cause a decrease in productivity in the ecosystem. But plankton-eating fishes prefer to eat large zooplankton (Figure 31.12), so when they are abundant, small zooplankton become the dominant herbivores. This leads to more numerous large phytoplankton, which in turn raises the lake's productivity.

Large predatory fishes may add an additional level of control to the system because they eat and thus regulate the population sizes of plankton-eating invertebrates and fishes. The effects of feeding by the top predator can cascade downward through the food web, affecting the densities of plankton-eating invertebrates and fishes, herbivorous zooplankton, and phytoplankton. Research in Norway with brown trout (*Salmo trutta*), a top predator, and Arctic char (*Salvelinus alpinus*), the prey, demonstrated how culling prey can promote the recovery of top predators. Removal of older, stunted, prey individual Arctic char from Lake

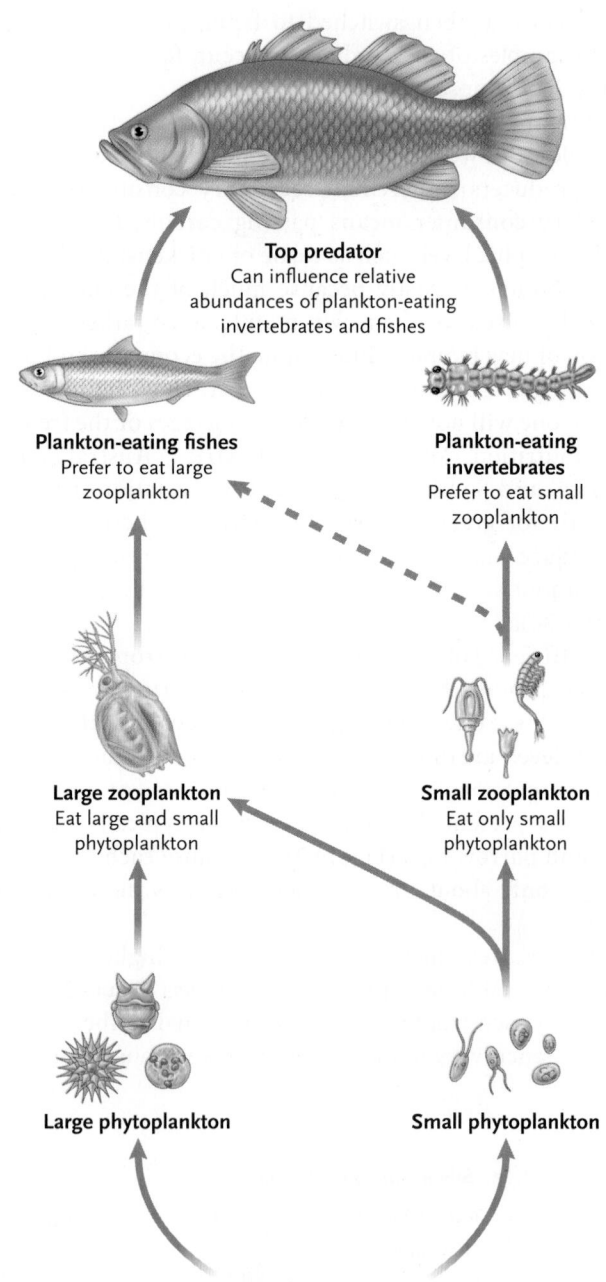

**Top predator**
Can influence relative abundances of plankton-eating invertebrates and fishes

**Plankton-eating fishes**
Prefer to eat large zooplankton

**Plankton-eating invertebrates**
Prefer to eat small zooplankton

**Large zooplankton**
Eat large and small phytoplankton

**Small zooplankton**
Eat only small phytoplankton

**Large phytoplankton**

**Small phytoplankton**

**Dissolved nutrients**

**FIGURE 31.12 Consumer regulation of primary productivity.** A simplified food web illustrates that lake ecosystems have relatively few trophic levels. The effects of feeding by top carnivores can cascade downward, exerting an indirect effect on the phytoplankton and thus on primary productivity.

Takvatn resulted in an increase in the availability of prey and recovery of the predator. Here brown trout were the top predators. Culling Arctic char, an introduced species, rejuvenated the lake ecosystem. This example shows how addition of a fish-eating fish to a lake successfully restored ecosystem balance.

## STUDY BREAK QUESTIONS

1. What are primary producers? Secondary producers? Detritivores?
2. What is gross primary productivity?
3. What is standing crop biomass?
4. What is a limiting nutrient?
5. What is secondary productivity?
6. What are the differences between harvesting efficiency, assimilation efficiency, and production efficiency?
7. What are the differences between energy, biomass, and numbers pyramids?
8. How is the pyramid for the English Channel different from that of a grassland community?
9. How do these pyramids relate to biomagnification?

# 31.3 Nutrient Cycling in Ecosystems

The availability of nutrients is as important to ecosystem function as the input of energy. Photosynthesis requires carbon, hydrogen, and oxygen, which producers acquire from water and air. Primary producers also need nitrogen, phosphorus, and other minerals. A deficiency in any of these minerals can reduce primary productivity.

Earth is essentially a closed system with respect to matter, even though cosmic dust enters the atmosphere. Thus, unlike energy, for which there is a constant cosmic input, virtually all the nutrients that will ever be available for biological systems are already present. Nutrient ions and molecules constantly circulate between the abiotic environment and living organisms in **biogeochemical cycles**. And, unlike energy, which flows through ecosystems and is gradually lost as heat, matter is conserved in biogeochemical cycles. Although there may be local shortages of specific nutrients, Earth's overall supplies of these chemical elements are never depleted or increased.

Nutrients take various forms as they pass through biogeochemical cycles. Materials such as carbon, nitrogen, and oxygen form gases that move through global atmospheric cycles. Geologic processes move other materials, such as phosphorus, through local sedimentary cycles, carrying them between dry land and the sea floor. Rocks, soil, water, and air are the reservoirs where mineral nutrients accumulate, sometimes for many years.

Ecologists use a **generalized compartment model** to describe nutrient cycling (**Figure 31.13**). Two criteria divide ecosystems into four compartments in which nutrients accumulate: (1) Nutrient molecules and ions are either *available* or *unavailable*, depending on whether they can be assimilated by organisms.

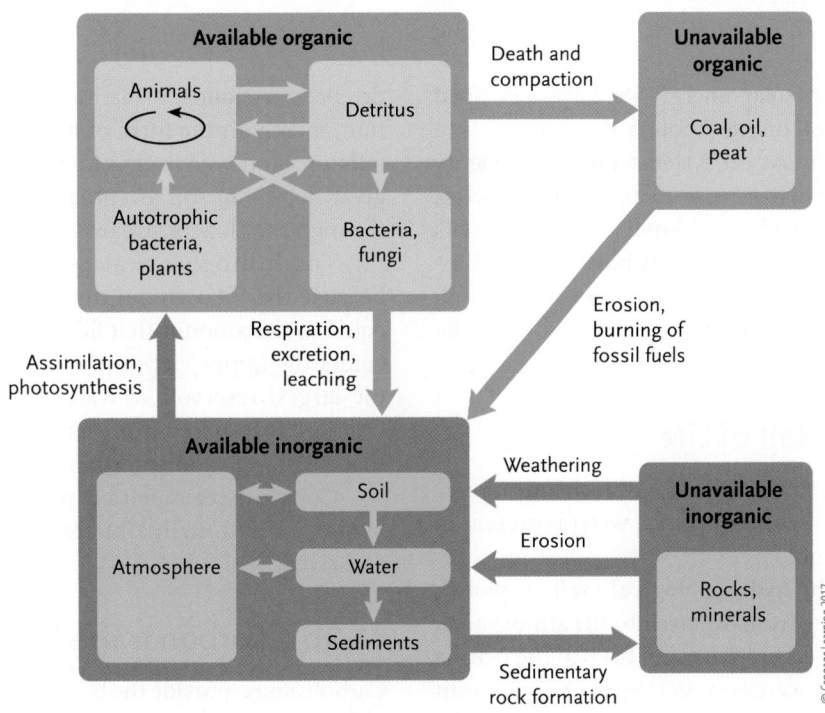

**FIGURE 31.13 A generalized compartment model of nutrient cycling.** Nutrients cycle through four major compartments within ecosystems. Processes that move nutrients from one compartment to another are indicated on the arrows. The circular arrow under "Animals" represents animal predation on other animals.

(2) Nutrients are present in either *organic* material, such as living or dead tissues of organisms, or *inorganic* material, such as rocks and soil. Minerals in dead leaves on the forest floor are in the available–organic compartment because they are in the remains of organisms that can be eaten by detritivores. Calcium ions in limestone rocks are in the unavailable–inorganic compartment because they are in a non-biological form that producers cannot assimilate.

Nutrients move rapidly within and between the available compartments. Living organisms are in the available–organic compartment, and whenever heterotrophs consume food, they recycle nutrients within that reservoir (indicated by the circular arrow in the upper left of Figure 31.13). Producers acquire nutrients from the air, soil, and water of the available–inorganic compartment. Consumers acquire nutrients from the available–inorganic compartment when they drink water or absorb mineral ions through their integument. Several processes routinely transfer nutrients from organisms to the available–inorganic compartment. Respiration releases carbon dioxide, moving both carbon and oxygen from the available–organic compartment to the available–inorganic compartment.

The exchange of materials into and out of the unavailable compartments is generally slow. Sedimentation, a long-term geologic process, converts ions and particles of the available–inorganic compartment into rocks of the unavailable–inorganic compartment. Materials are gradually returned to the available–inorganic compartment when rocks are uplifted and eroded or weathered. Similarly, over millions of years, the remains of organisms in the available–organic compartment were converted into the coal, oil, and peat of the unavailable–organic compartment. In many systems, fire plays an essential role in nutrient cycling **(Figure 31.14)**.

Except for the input of solar energy, we have described energy flow and nutrient cycling as though ecosystems were closed systems. In reality, most ecosystems exchange energy and nutrients with neighbouring ecosystems. Rainfall carries nutrients into a forest ecosystem, and runoff carries nutrients from a forest into a lake or river. Ecologists have mapped biogeochemical cycles of important elements, often by using radioactively labelled molecules that they can follow in the environment.

## 31.3a Water Is the Staff of Life

Water is the universal intracellular solvent for biochemical reactions, but only a fraction of 1% of Earth's total water is present in biological systems at any time.

The cycling of water, the **hydrogeological cycle**, is global, with water molecules moving from oceans into the atmosphere, to land, through freshwater ecosystems, and back to the oceans **(Figure 31.15)**. Solar energy causes water to evaporate from oceans, lakes, rivers, soil, and living organisms, entering the atmosphere as a vapour and remaining aloft as a gas, as

M. B. Fenton

**FIGURE 31.14 A ghostly heap of ash starkly demonstrates the importance of fire in releasing materials, in this case locked up in a tree trunk.** Regular fires are part of the cycle in ecosystems like this savanna in South Africa.

droplets in clouds, or as ice crystals. Water falls as precipitation, mostly in the form of rain and snow. When precipitation falls on land, water flows across the surface or percolates to great depths in soil, eventually reentering the ocean reservoir through the flow of streams and rivers.

The hydrogeological cycle maintains its global balance because the total amount of water entering the atmosphere is equal to the amount that falls as precipitation. Most water that enters the atmosphere evaporates from the oceans, which are the largest reservoir of water on the planet. A much smaller fraction evaporates from terrestrial ecosystems, and most of that is through transpiration by green plants.

Constant recirculation provides fresh water to terrestrial organisms and maintains freshwater ecosystems such as lakes and rivers.

## 31.3b Carbon Is the Backbone of Life

Carbon atoms provide the backbone of most biological molecules, and carbon compounds store the energy captured by photosynthesis (see Chapter 6). Carbon enters food webs when producers

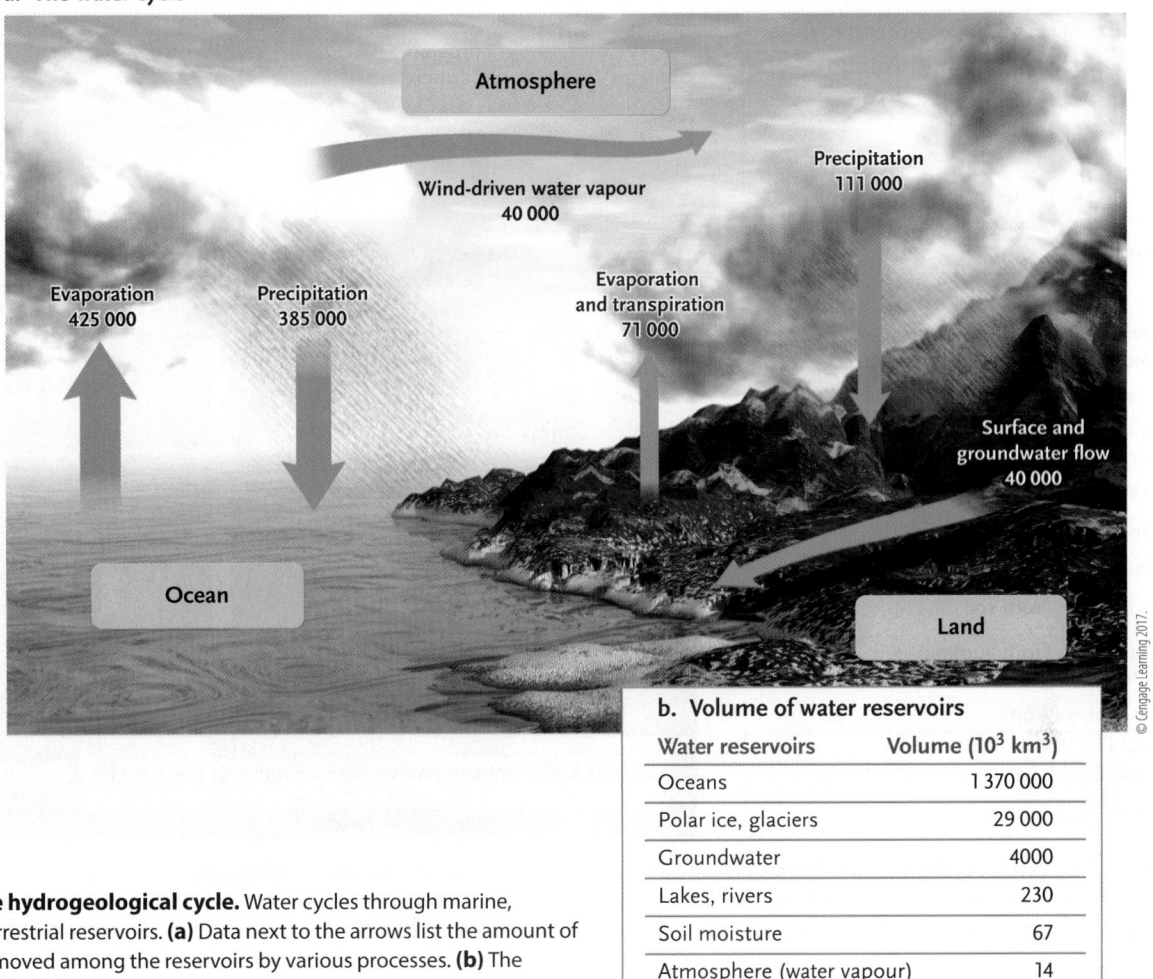

**a. The water cycle**

Atmosphere

Wind-driven water vapour
40 000

Precipitation
111 000

Evaporation
425 000

Precipitation
385 000

Evaporation
and transpiration
71 000

Surface and
groundwater flow
40 000

Ocean

Land

© Cengage Learning 2017.

**b. Volume of water reservoirs**

| Water reservoirs | Volume ($10^3$ $km^3$) |
|---|---|
| Oceans | 1 370 000 |
| Polar ice, glaciers | 29 000 |
| Groundwater | 4000 |
| Lakes, rivers | 230 |
| Soil moisture | 67 |
| Atmosphere (water vapour) | 14 |

**FIGURE 31.15 The hydrogeological cycle.** Water cycles through marine, atmospheric, and terrestrial reservoirs. **(a)** Data next to the arrows list the amount of water (in $km^3$/year) moved among the reservoirs by various processes. **(b)** The oceans are by far the largest of the six major reservoirs of water on Earth.

convert atmospheric carbon dioxide ($CO_2$) into carbohydrates. Heterotrophs acquire carbon by eating other organisms or detritus. Although carbon moves somewhat independently in sea and on land, a common atmospheric pool of $CO_2$ creates a global **carbon cycle (Figure 31.16).**

The largest reservoir of carbon is sedimentary rock, such as limestone. Rocks are in the unavailable–inorganic compartment, and they exchange carbon with living organisms at an exceedingly slow pace. Most available carbon is present as dissolved bicarbonate ions ($HCO_3^-$) in the ocean. Soil, atmosphere, and plant biomass are significant, but much smaller, reservoirs of available carbon. Atmospheric carbon is mostly in the form of molecular $CO_2$, a product of aerobic respiration. Volcanic eruptions also release small quantities of $CO_2$ into the atmosphere.

Carbon atoms sometimes leave organic compartments for long periods of time. Some organisms in marine food webs build shells and other hard parts by incorporating dissolved carbon into calcium carbonate ($CaCO_3$) and other insoluble salts. When shelled organisms die, they sink to the bottom and

are buried in sediments. Other animals, notably vertebrates, store calcium in bone. Insoluble carbon that accumulates as rock in deep sediments may remain buried for millions of years before tectonic uplifting brings it to the surface, where erosion and weathering dissolve sedimentary rocks and return carbon to an available form.

Carbon atoms are also transferred to the unavailable–organic compartment when soft-bodied organisms die and are buried in habitats where low oxygen concentration prevents decomposition. In the past, under suitable geologic conditions, these carbon-rich tissues were slowly converted to gas, petroleum, or coal, which we now use as fossil fuels. Human activities, especially burning fossil fuels, are transferring carbon into the atmosphere at an unnaturally high rate. The resulting change in the worldwide distribution of carbon is having profound consequences for Earth's atmosphere and climate, including a general warming of the climate and a rise in sea level.

Changes in land use can affect carbon cycles. An analysis of above-ground biomass at 45 forest sites in the

## c. The global carbon cycle

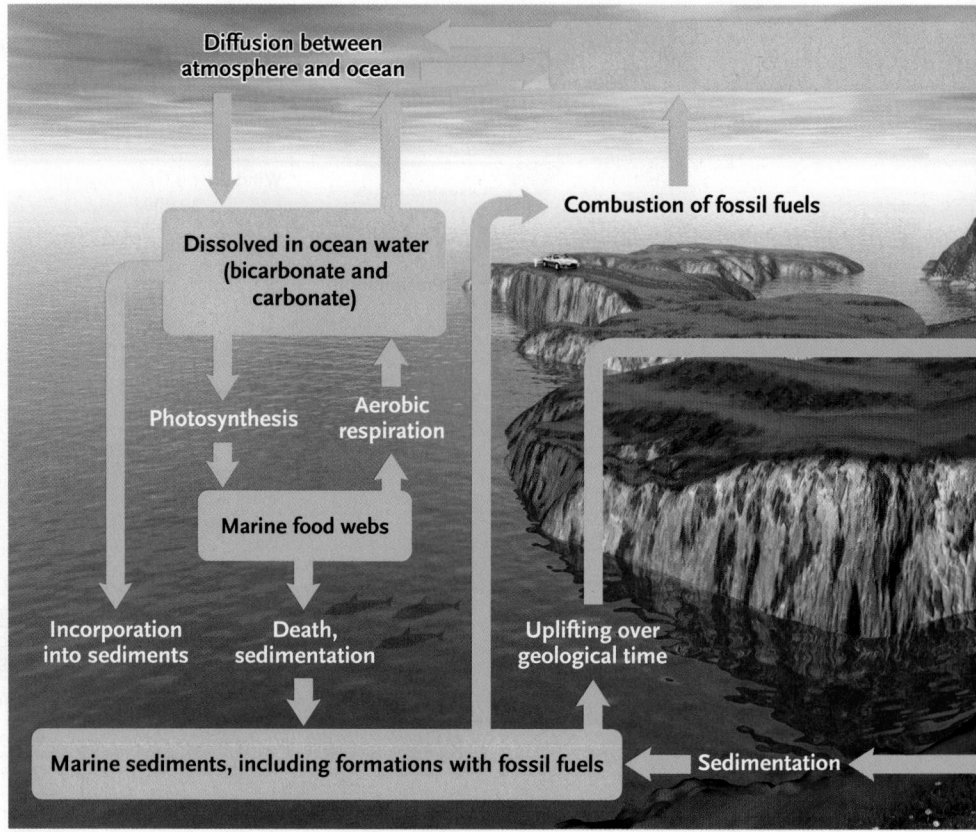

### a. Amount of carbon in major reservoirs

| Carbon Reservoirs | Mass ($10^{12}$ g) |
|---|---|
| Sediments and rocks | 770 000 000 |
| Ocean (dissolved forms) | 397 000 |
| Soil | 15 000 |
| Atmosphere | 7 500 |
| Biomass on land | 7 150 |

### b. Annual global carbon movement between reservoirs

| Direction of Movement | Mass ($10^{12}$ kg) |
|---|---|
| From atmosphere to plants (carbon fixation) | 1200 |
| From atmosphere to ocean | 1070 |
| To atmosphere from ocean | 1050 |
| To atmosphere from plants | 600 |
| To atmosphere from soil | 600 |
| To atmosphere from burning fossil fuel | 50 |
| To atmosphere from burning plants | 20 |
| To ocean from runoff | 4 |
| Burial in ocean sediments | 1 |

**FIGURE 31.16 The carbon cycle.** Marine and terrestrial components of the global carbon cycle are linked through an atmospheric reservoir of carbon dioxide. **(a)** By far the largest amount of Earth's carbon is found in sediments and rocks. **(b)** Earth's atmosphere mediates most of the movement of carbon. **(c)** In this illustration of the carbon cycle, boxes identify major reservoirs, and labels on arrows identify the processes that cause carbon to move between reservoirs.

Neotropics was published in 2016. During the development of second-growth (secondary; **Figure 31.17**) forests, the rate of carbon uptake was 11 times higher than in old-growth forest. After 20 years, recovery of above-ground biomass averaged 122 Mg per hectare. These results have important implications for conservation and patterns of land use. Promoting

**FIGURE 31.17 A Mayan temple emerges from partly cleared, second-growth forest in Belize.** At the time the temple was built, about 800 years ago, much of the surrounding area would have been cleared for human habitation and agricultural operations.

regeneration and restoration of second-growth forest is an important positive strategy.

### 31.3c Nitrogen Is a Limiting Element

All organisms require nitrogen to construct nucleic acids, proteins, and other biological molecules (see Chapter 39). Earth's atmosphere had a high nitrogen concentration long before life began. Today, a global **nitrogen cycle** moves this element between the huge atmospheric pool of gaseous molecular nitrogen ($N_2$) and several much smaller pools of nitrogen-containing compounds in soils, marine and freshwater ecosystems, and living organisms **(Figure 31.18)**.

Molecular nitrogen is abundant in the atmosphere, but triple covalent bonds bind its two atoms so tightly that most organisms cannot use it. Only certain microorganisms, volcanic action, and lightning can convert $N_2$ into ammonium ($NH_4^+$) and nitrate ($NO_3^-$) ions. This conversion is called **nitrogen fixation** (see Chapter 36). Once nitrogen is fixed, primary producers can incorporate it into biological molecules such as proteins and nucleic acids. Secondary consumers obtain nitrogen by consuming these molecules.

Several biochemical processes produce different nitrogen-containing compounds and thus move nitrogen through

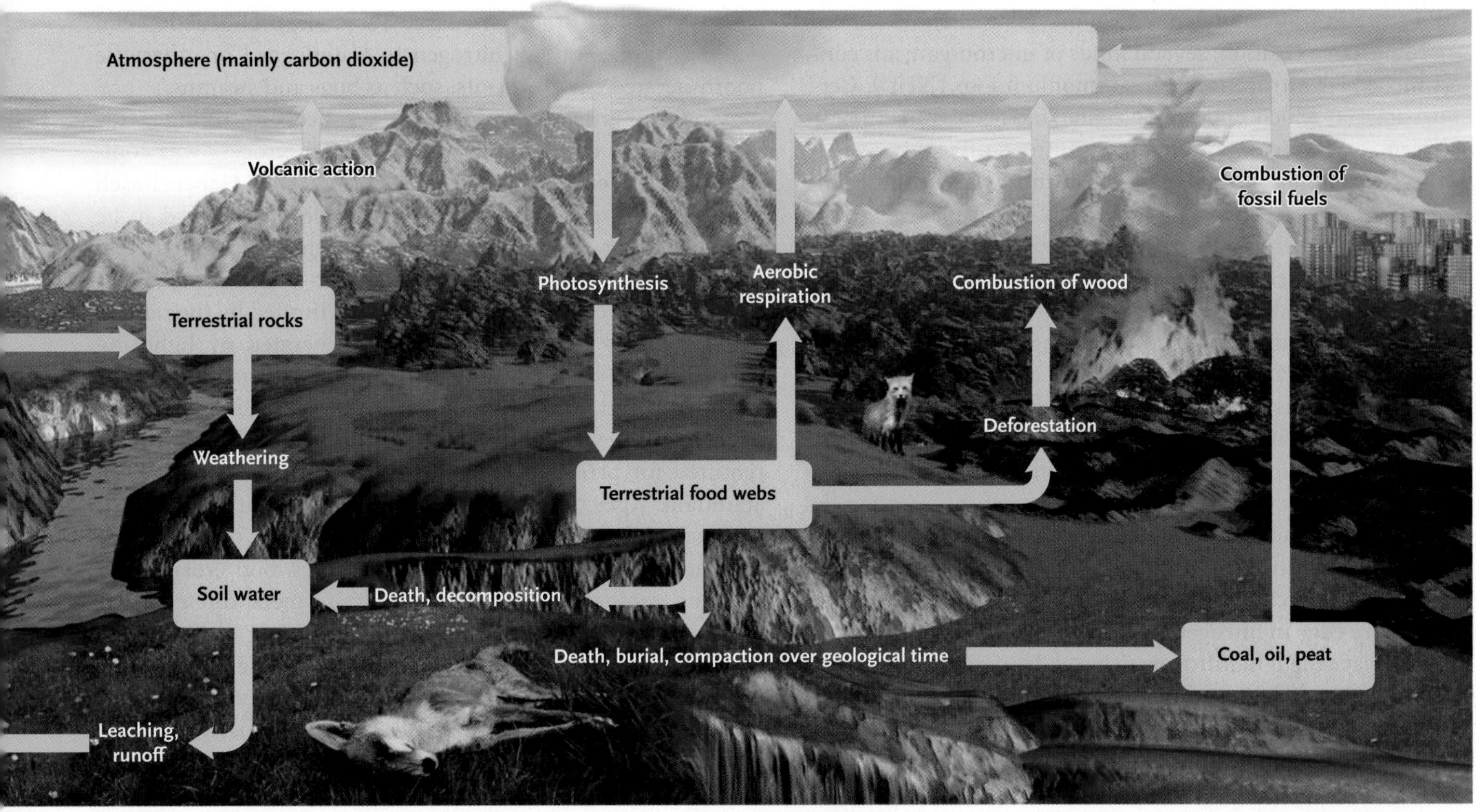

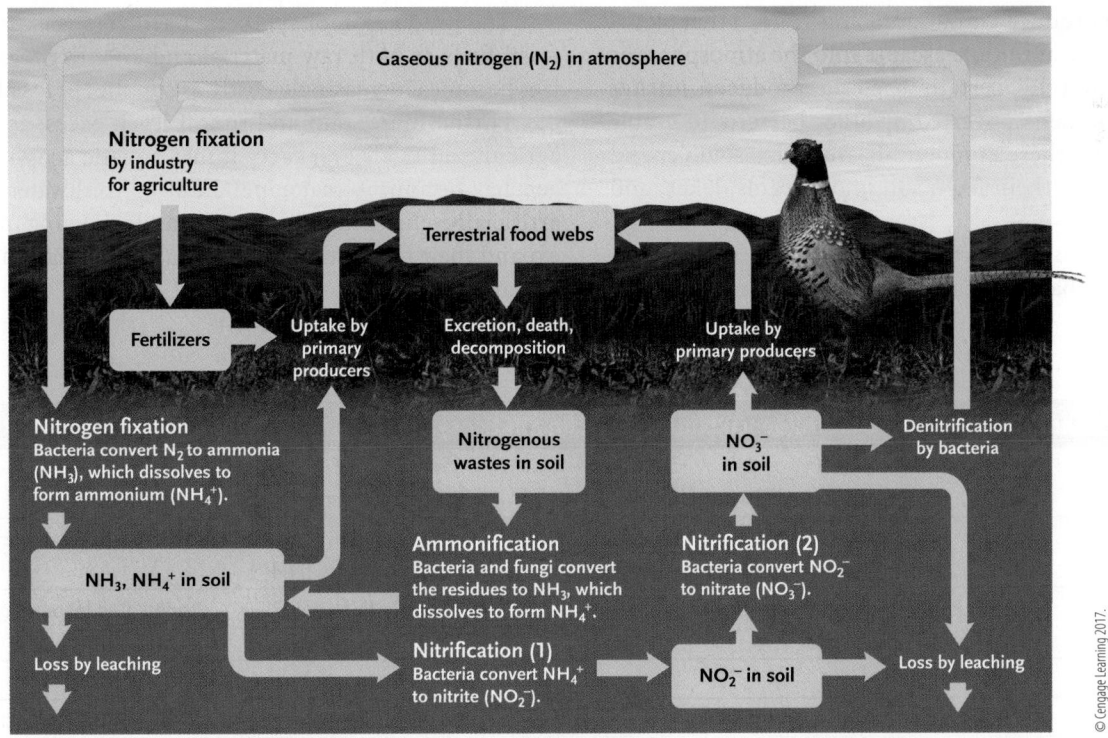

**FIGURE 31.18 The nitrogen cycle in a terrestrial ecosystem.** Nitrogen-fixing bacteria make molecular nitrogen available in terrestrial ecosystems. Other bacteria recycle nitrogen within the available–organic compartment through ammonification and two types of nitrification, converting organic wastes into ammonium ions and nitrates. Denitrification converts nitrate to molecular nitrogen, which returns to the atmosphere. Runoff carries nitrogen from terrestrial ecosystems into aquatic ecosystems, where it is recycled in freshwater and marine food webs.

ecosystems. These processes are nitrogen fixation, ammonification, nitrification, and denitrification (**Table 31.2**).

In nitrogen fixation, several kinds of microorganisms convert molecular nitrogen ($N_2$) to ammonium ions ($NH_4^+$). Certain bacteria, which collect molecular nitrogen from the air between soil particles, are the major nitrogen fixers in terrestrial ecosystems (see Table 31.2). The cyanobacteria partners in some lichens (see Chapter 25) also fix molecular nitrogen. Other cyanobacteria are important nitrogen fixers in aquatic ecosystems, whereas the water fern (genus *Azolla*) plays that role in rice paddies. Collectively, these organisms fix an astounding 200 million tonnes of nitrogen each year. Plants and other primary producers assimilate and use this nitrogen in the biosynthesis of amino acids, proteins, and nucleic acids, which then circulate through food webs.

Some plants, including legumes (such as beans and clover), alders (*Alnus* species), and some members of the rose family (Rosaceae), are mutualists with nitrogen-fixing bacteria. These plants acquire nitrogen from soils much more readily than plants that lack such mutualists. Although these plants have the competitive edge in nitrogen-poor soil, non-mutualistic species often displace them in nitrogen-rich soil. In an interesting twist on the usual predator–prey relationships, several species of flowering plants living in nitrogen-poor soils capture and digest insects.

In addition to nitrogen fixation, other biochemical processes make large quantities of nitrogen available to producers. **Ammonification** of detritus by bacteria and fungi converts organic nitrogen into ammonia ($NH_3$), which dissolves in water to produce ammonium ions ($NH_4^+$) that plants can assimilate. Some ammonia escapes into the atmosphere as a gas. **Nitrification** by certain bacteria produces nitrites ($NO_2^-$), which are then converted by other bacteria to usable nitrates ($NO_3^-$). All these compounds are water soluble, and water rapidly leaches them from soil into streams, lakes, and oceans.

Under conditions of low oxygen availability, **denitrification** by still other bacteria converts nitrites or nitrates into nitrous oxide ($N_2O$) and then into molecular nitrogen ($N_2$), which enters the atmosphere (see Table 31.2). This action can deplete supplies of soil nitrogen in waterlogged or otherwise poorly aerated environments, such as bogs and swamps.

In 1909, Fritz Haber developed a process for fixing nitrogen and, with the help of Carl Bosch, the process was commercialized for fertilizer production. The Haber–Bosch process has altered Earth's nitrogen cycles and is said to be responsible for the existence of 40% of the people on Earth. Before the implementation of the Haber–Bosch process, the amount of nitrogen available for life was limited by the rates at which $N_2$ was fixed by bacteria or generated by lightning strikes. Today, spreading fertilizers rich in nitrogen is the basis for most of agriculture's productivity. This practice has quadrupled some yields over the past 50 years. Of all nutrients required for primary production, nitrogen is often the least abundant. Agriculture routinely depletes soil nitrogen, which is removed from fields through the harvesting of plants that have accumulated nitrogen in their tissues. Soil erosion and leaching remove more. Traditionally, farmers rotated their crops, alternately planting legumes and other crops in the same fields. In combination with other soil conservation practices, crop rotation stabilized soils and kept them productive, sometimes for hundreds of years. Some of the most arable land in New York State was farmed by members of the Mohawk Iroquois First Nations. The evidence of this comes from the locations of palisaded villages. The people moved their villages and farming operations every 10–20 years, changing fields repeatedly over hundreds of years.

The production of synthetic fertilizers is expensive, using fossil fuels as both raw material and an energy source. Fertilizer becomes increasingly costly as supplies of fossil fuels dwindle. Furthermore, rain and runoff leach excess fertilizer from agricultural fields and carry it into aquatic ecosystems. Nitrogen has become a major pollutant of freshwater ecosystems, artificially enriching the waters and allowing producers to expand their populations. Human activities have disrupted the global nitrogen cycle (**Figure 31.19**).

| TABLE 31.2 | Biochemical Processes That Influence Nitrogen Cycling in Ecosystems | | |
|---|---|---|---|
| Process | Organisms Responsible | Products | Outcome |
| Nitrogen fixation | Bacteria: *Rhizobium, Azotobacter, Frankia* Cyanobacteria: *Anabaena, Nostoc* | Ammonia ($NH_3$), ammonium ions ($NH_4^+$) | Assimilated by primary producers |
| Ammonification of organic detritus | Soil bacteria and fungi | Ammonia ($NH_3$), ammonium ions ($NH_4^+$) | Assimilated by primary producers |
| Nitrification | | | |
| (1) Oxidation of $NH_3$ | Bacteria: *Nitrosomonas, Nitrococcus* | Nitrite ($NO_2^-$) | Used by nitrifying bacteria |
| (2) Oxidation of $NO_2^-$ | Bacteria: *Nitrobacter* | Nitrate ($NO_3^-$) | Assimilated by primary producers |
| Denitrification of $NO_3^-$ | Soil bacteria | Nitrous oxide ($N_2O$), molecular nitrogen ($N_2$) | Released to atmosphere |

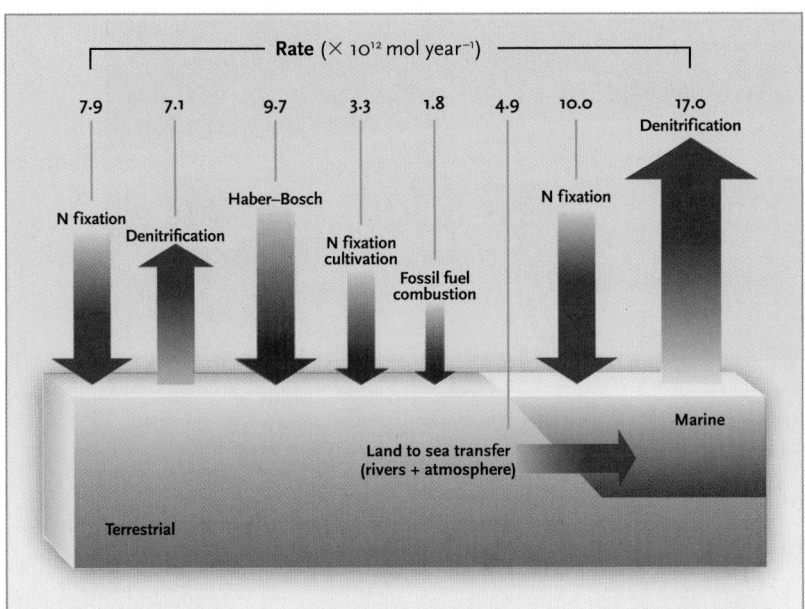

Rate (× 10¹² mol year⁻¹)

7.9   7.1   9.7   3.3   1.8   4.9   10.0   17.0
                                            Denitrification

N fixation
        Denitrification
              Haber–Bosch
                    N fixation
                    cultivation
                          Fossil fuel
                          combustion
                                      N fixation

Marine

Land to sea transfer
(rivers + atmosphere)

Terrestrial

**FIGURE 31.19 Modern global nitrogen flux depends upon the efficiency of transfer of N between reservoirs.** Thickness of arrows indicates relative size of flux. Anthropogenic inputs are shown as dark brown arrows.

Source: From Canfield, D.E., A.N. Glazer and P.G. Falkowski. "The evolution and future of Earth's nitrogen cycle," *Science* 8 October 2010, Vol. 330 no. 6001 pp. 192-196. *Science* by American Association for the Advancement of Science Reproduced with permission of AMERICAN ASSOCIATION FOR THE ADVANCEMENT OF SCIENCE in the format Republish in a book via Copyright Clearance Center.

## 31.3d  Phosphorus Is Another Essential Element

Phosphorus compounds lack a gaseous phase, and this element moves between terrestrial and marine ecosystems in a sedimentary cycle (**Figure 31.20**). Earth's crust is the main reservoir of phosphorus, as it is for other minerals, such as calcium and potassium, that also undergo sedimentary cycles.

Phosphorus is present in terrestrial rocks in the form of phosphates ($PO_4^{3-}$). In the **phosphorus cycle**, weathering and erosion add phosphate ions to soil and carry them into streams and rivers, which eventually transport them to the ocean. Once there, some phosphorus enters marine food webs, but most of it precipitates out of solution and accumulates for millions of years as insoluble deposits, mainly on continental shelves. When parts of the sea floor are uplifted and exposed, weathering releases the phosphates.

Plants absorb and assimilate dissolved phosphates directly, and phosphorus moves easily to higher trophic levels. All heterotrophs excrete some phosphorus as a waste product in urine and feces; the phosphorus becomes available after decomposition. Primary producers readily absorb the phosphate ions, so phosphorus cycles rapidly *within* terrestrial communities.

Supplies of available phosphate are generally limited, however, and plants acquire it so efficiently that they reduce soil phosphate concentration to extremely low levels. Thus, like nitrogen, phosphorus is a common ingredient in agricultural fertilizers, and excess phosphates are pollutants of freshwater ecosystems. A particularly good example is Lake Erie, a Great Lake that was heavily affected by accumulations of phosphorus. The example here is more convincing because the problem has largely been resolved over the years.

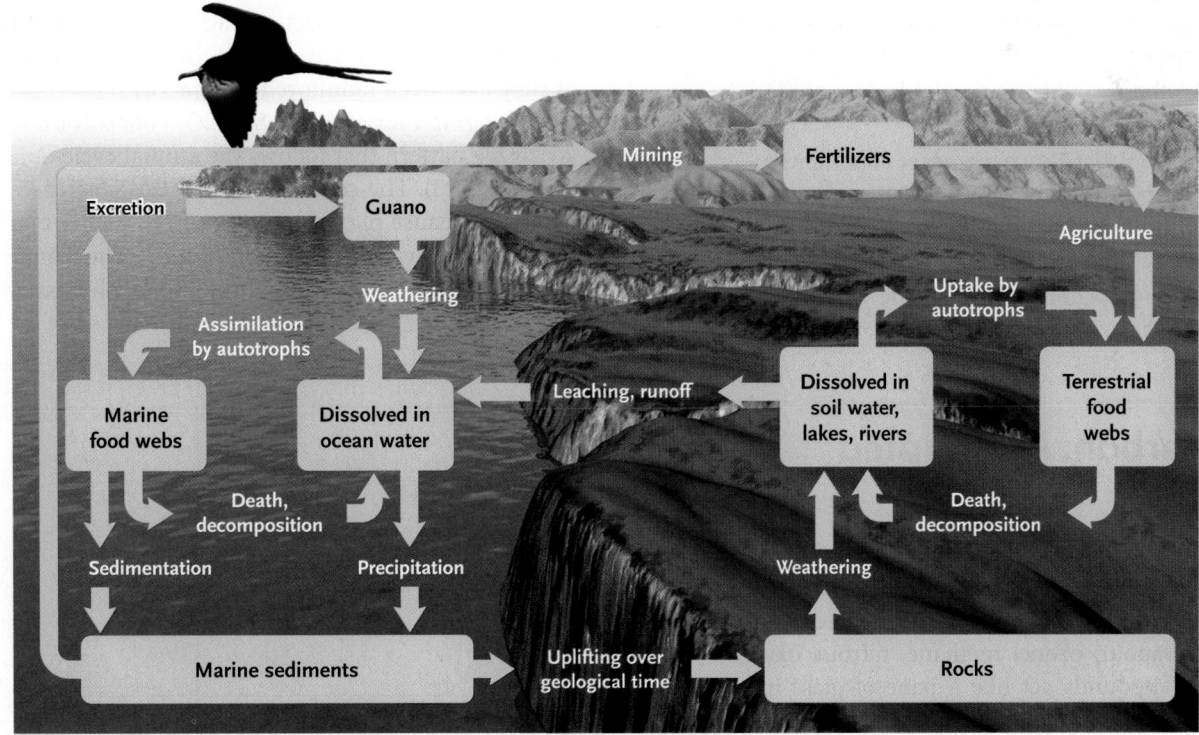

**FIGURE 31.20 The phosphorus cycle.** Phosphorus becomes available to biological systems when wind and rainfall dissolve phosphates in rocks and carry them into adjacent soil and freshwater ecosystems. Runoff carries dissolved phosphorus into marine ecosystems, where it precipitates out of solution and is incorporated into marine sediments.

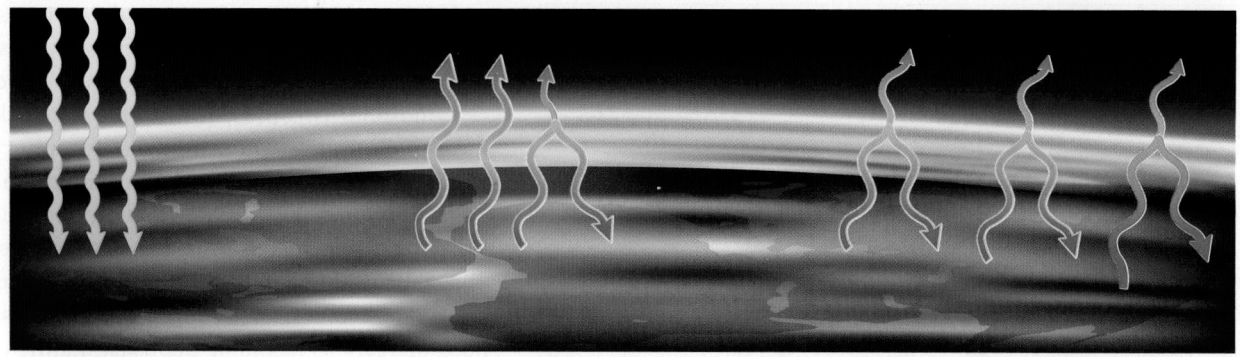

Sunlight penetrates the atmosphere and warms Earth's surface.

Earth's surface radiates heat (infrared wavelengths) to the atmosphere. Some heat escapes into space. Greenhouse gases and water vapour absorb some infrared energy and reradiate the rest of it back toward Earth.

When atmospheric concentrations of greenhouse gases increase, the atmosphere near Earth's surface traps more heat. The warming causes a positive feedback cycle in which rising ocean temperatures cause increased evaporation of water, which further enhances the greenhouse effect.

**FIGURE 31.21  The greenhouse effect**

For many years, phosphate for fertilizers was obtained from guano (the droppings of seabirds that consume phosphorus-rich food), which was mined on small islands that hosted seabird colonies, for example, in Polynesia and Micronesia. We now obtain most phosphate for fertilizer from phosphate rock mined in places such as Saskatchewan that have abundant marine deposits.

### STUDY BREAK QUESTIONS

1. What is a generalized compartment model?
2. How does evaporation play into the hydrogeological cycle?
3. What is secondary forest? Why is it important in the Neotropics?
4. Why is carbon referred to as "the backbone of life"?
5. What is nitrification?
6. Why was the Haber–Bosch process so important?
7. What is nitrogen fixation?
8. Why is phosphorus important?
9. Why were accumulations of phosphorus lethal?
10. What is the role of cyanobacteria in the nitrogen cycle?

## 31.4  Carbon: A Disrupted Cycle

Concentrations of gases in the lower atmosphere have a profound effect on global temperature, in turn affecting global climate. Collectively, molecules of $CO_2$, water vapour, ozone, methane, nitrous oxide, and other compounds act like a pane of glass in a greenhouse. These "greenhouse gases" allow short wavelengths of visible light to reach Earth's surface while impeding the escape of longer, infrared wavelengths into space, trapping much of their energy as heat (**Figure 31.21**). Greenhouse gases foster the accumulation of heat in the lower atmosphere, a warming action known as the **greenhouse effect**. This natural process prevents Earth from being a cold and lifeless planet.

Data from air bubbles trapped in glacial ice indicate that atmospheric $CO_2$ concentrations have fluctuated widely over Earth's history (**Figure 31.22**). Since the late 1950s, scientists have measured atmospheric concentrations of $CO_2$ and other greenhouse gases at remote sampling sites such as the top of Mauna Loa in the Hawaiian Islands. These sites are free of local contamination and reflect average global conditions. Concentrations of greenhouse gases have increased steadily for as long as they have been monitored (**Figure 31.23**).

The graph for atmospheric $CO_2$ concentration has a regular zigzag pattern that follows the annual cycle of plant growth (Figure 31.23). The concentration of $CO_2$ decreases during the summer because photosynthesis withdraws so much from the atmospheric available–inorganic pool. The concentration of $CO_2$ is higher during the winter when photosynthesis slows

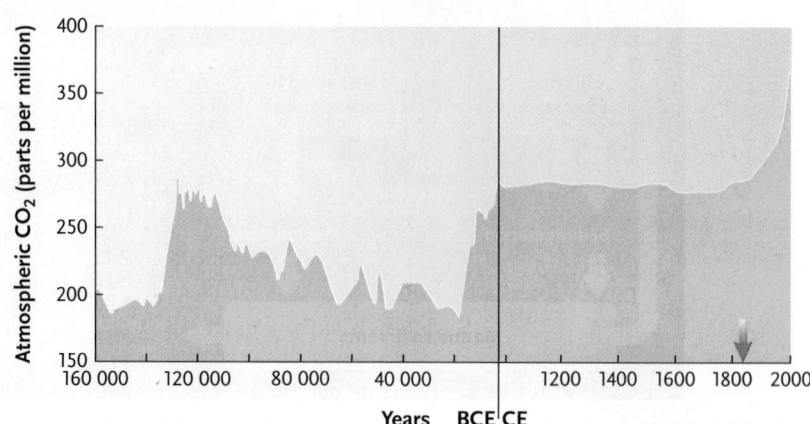

**FIGURE 31.22  Carbon dioxide levels over time.** The amount of atmospheric $CO_2$ has risen dramatically since about 1850 (arrow).

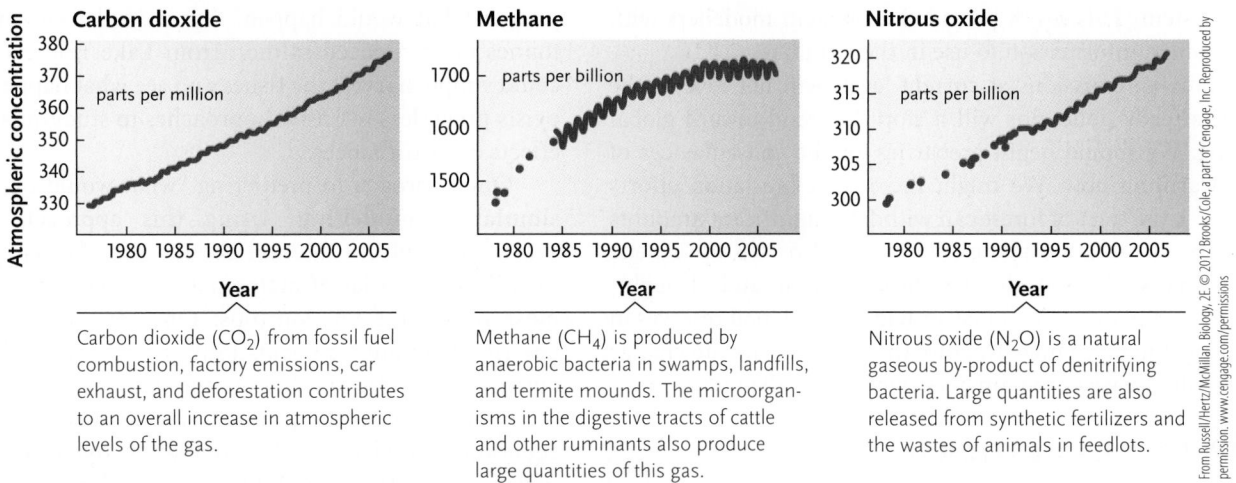

**Carbon dioxide**

Atmospheric concentration

380
370
360
350
340
330

parts per million

1980 1985 1990 1995 2000 2005

Year

Carbon dioxide ($CO_2$) from fossil fuel combustion, factory emissions, car exhaust, and deforestation contributes to an overall increase in atmospheric levels of the gas.

**Methane**

1700
1600
1500

parts per billion

1980 1985 1990 1995 2000 2005

Year

Methane ($CH_4$) is produced by anaerobic bacteria in swamps, landfills, and termite mounds. The microorganisms in the digestive tracts of cattle and other ruminants also produce large quantities of this gas.

**Nitrous oxide**

320
315
310
305
300

parts per billion

1980 1985 1990 1995 2000 2005

Year

Nitrous oxide ($N_2O$) is a natural gaseous by-product of denitrifying bacteria. Large quantities are also released from synthetic fertilizers and the wastes of animals in feedlots.

**FIGURE 31.23 Increases in atmospheric concentrations of three greenhouse gases, mid-1970s through 2004.** The data were collected at a remote monitoring station in Australia (Cape Grim, Tasmania) and compiled by scientists at the Commonwealth Scientific and Industrial Research Organization, an agency of the Australian government.

while aerobic respiration continues, returning carbon to the atmospheric available–inorganic pool. Whereas the zigs and zags in the data for $CO_2$ represent seasonal highs and lows, the midpoint of the annual peaks and troughs has increased steadily for 40 years. These data are evidence of a rapid buildup of atmospheric $CO_2$, representing a shift in the distribution of carbon in the major reservoirs on Earth. The best estimates suggest that $CO_2$ concentration has increased by 35% in the past 150 years, and by more than 10% in the past 30 years.

The increase in the atmospheric concentration of $CO_2$ appears to result from combustion, whether we burn fossil fuels or wood. Today, humans burn more wood and fossil fuels than ever before. Vast tracts of tropical forests are being cleared and burned (see Chapter 28). To make matters worse, deforestation reduces the world's biomass of plants that assimilate $CO_2$ and help maintain the carbon cycle as it existed before human activities disrupted it.

The increase in the concentration of atmospheric $CO_2$ is alarming because plants with $C_3$ metabolism respond to increased $CO_2$ concentrations with increased growth rates. This is not true of $C_4$ plants (see Chapter 6). Thus, rising atmospheric levels of $CO_2$ will probably alter the relative abundances of many plant species, changing the composition and dynamics of their communities.

Simulation models suggest that increasing concentrations of any greenhouse gas may intensify the greenhouse effect, contributing to a trend of global warming. Should we be alarmed about the prospect of a warmer planet? Some models predict that the mean temperature of the lower atmosphere will rise by 4°C, enough to increase ocean surface temperatures. In some areas, such as the Canadian Arctic and the Antarctic, warming has occurred much more rapidly than predicted or expected. Water expands when heated, and global sea levels could rise as much as 0.6 m just from this expansion. In addition, atmospheric temperature is rising fastest near the poles. Thus, global warming may also foster melting of glaciers and

the Antarctic ice sheet, which might raise sea levels as much as 50–100 m, inundating low coastal regions. Waterfronts in Vancouver, Los Angeles, Hong Kong, Durban, Rio de Janeiro, Sydney, New York, and London would be submerged. So would agricultural lands in India, China, and Bangladesh, where much of the world's rice is grown. Moreover, global warming could disturb regional patterns of precipitation and temperature. Areas that now produce much of the world's grains would become arid scrub or deserts, and the now-forested areas to their north would become dry grasslands.

Many scientists believe that atmospheric levels of greenhouse gases will continue to increase at least until the middle of the twenty-first century, and that global temperature may rise by several degrees. At the Earth Summit in 1992, leaders of the industrialized countries agreed to try to stabilize $CO_2$ emissions by the end of the twentieth century. We have already missed that target, and some countries, including the United States (then the largest producer of greenhouse gases), have now forsaken that goal as too costly.

Marked seasonal variation in $CO_2$ occurs in many parts of the world, especially in northern terrestrial ecosystems. Since 1960, the marked increase in the amplitude of seasonal variation in $CO_2$ reflects upward trends in $CO_2$ because of climate warming. Changes in vegetation cover in northern ecosystems appear to be responsible for the increasing amplitude. This reality emphasizes the importance of feedbacks between climate, vegetation, and carbon cycle at high latitudes. The change in amplitude informs us that photosynthetic carbon uptake has reacted more strongly than processes that release carbon.

Seasonality of photosynthesis in evergreen forests of the Amazon basin have been a matter of some discussion. In 2016, the results of a detailed analysis of photographic observations and measures of fluctuations in $CO_2$ revealed an unexpected reality. Changes in the patterns of leaf development and demography explained the large changes (27%) in photosynthesis in the ecosystem. This result provided ecosystem modellers with more detailed information to use in their studies.

Stabilizing emissions at current levels will not reverse the damage already done, nor will it stop the trend toward global warming. We should begin preparing for the consequences of global warming now. We might increase reforestation efforts because a large tract of forest can withdraw significant amounts of $CO_2$ from the atmosphere. We might also step up genetic engineering studies to develop heat-resistant and drought-resistant crop plants, which may provide crucial food reserves in regions of climate change. In 2016, the issues of climate change and greenhouse gases remain persistent and challenging.

## STUDY BREAK QUESTIONS

1. What is the greenhouse effect? How does it relate to global warming?
2. What is a greenhouse gas?
3. Is *climate warming* synonymous with *climate change*?

# 31.5 Ecosystem Modelling

Ecologists use modelling to make predictions about how an ecosystem will respond to specific changes in physical factors, energy flow, or nutrient availability. Analyses of energy flow and nutrient cycling allow us to create a conceptual model of how ecosystems function (**Figure 31.24**). Energy that enters ecosystems is gradually dissipated as it flows through a food web. By contrast, nutrients are conserved and recycled among the system's living and nonliving components. This general model does not include processes that carry nutrients and energy out of one ecosystem and into another.

More important, the model ignores the nuts-and-bolts details of exactly how specific ecosystems function. Although it is a useful tool, a conceptual model does not really help us

predict what would happen, say, if we harvested 10 million tonnes of introduced salmon from Lake Erie every year. We could simply harvest the fishes and see what happens. But ecologists prefer less intrusive approaches to studying the potential effects of disturbances.

One approach to predicting "what would happen if..." is **simulation modelling**. Using this approach, researchers gather detailed information about a specific ecosystem. They then derive a series of mathematical equations that define its most important relationships. One set of equations might describe how nutrient availability limits productivity at various trophic levels. Another might relate the population growth of zooplankton to the productivity of phytoplankton. Other equations would relate the population dynamics of primary carnivores to the availability of their food, and still others would describe how the densities of primary carnivores influence reproduction in populations at both lower and higher trophic levels. Thus, a complete simulation model is a set of interlocking equations that collectively predict how changes in one feature of an ecosystem might influence other features.

Creating a simulation model is a challenge because the relationships within every ecosystem are complex. First you must identify the important species, estimate their population sizes, and measure the average energy and nutrient content of each. Next you must describe the food webs in which they participate, measure the quantity of food each species consumes, and estimate the productivity of each population. And, for the sake of completeness, you must determine the ecosystem's energy and nutrient gains and losses caused by erosion, weathering, precipitation, and runoff. You must repeat these measurements seasonally to identify annual variation in these factors. Finally, you might repeat the measurements over several years to determine the effects of year-to-year variation in climate and chance events.

After collecting these data, you must write equations that quantify the relationships in the ecosystem, including information about how temperature and other abiotic factors influence the ecology of each species. Having completed that job, you would begin to predict, for example, possibly in great detail, the effects of adding 1000 new housing units to an area of native prairie or boreal forest. Of course, you must refine the model whenever new data become available.

Some ecologists devote their professional lives to studying ecosystem processes and creating simulation models. Modelling becomes an increasingly important tool as we attempt to understand larger and more complex ecosystems. These systems bring more challenging environmental problems. A model based on well-defined ecological relationships and good empirical data can allow us to make accurate predictions about

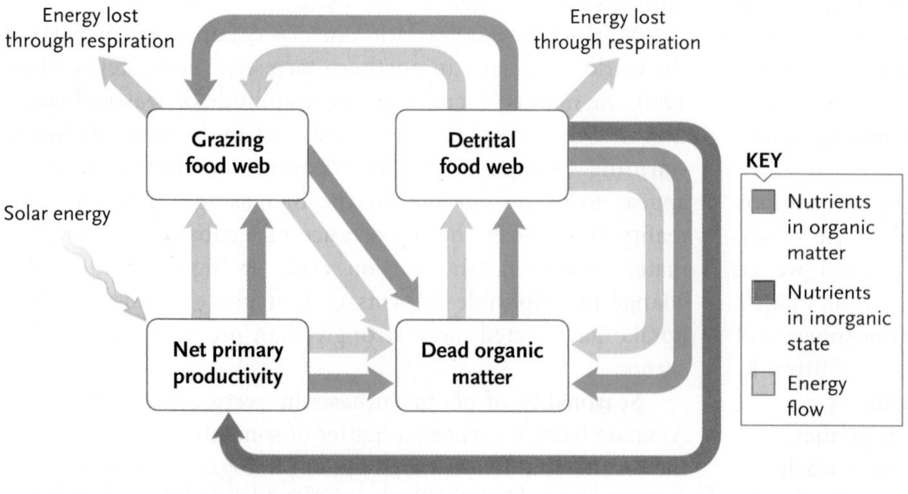

**FIGURE 31.24 A conceptual ecosystem model.** A simple conceptual model of an ecosystem illustrates how energy flows through the system and is lost from both detrital and grazing food webs. Nutrients are recycled and conserved.

KEY
- Nutrients in organic matter
- Nutrients in inorganic state
- Energy flow

Energy lost through respiration

Energy lost through respiration

Solar energy

Grazing food web

Detrital food web

Net primary productivity

Dead organic matter

ecosystem changes without the need for costly and environmentally damaging experiments. But, like all ideas in science, a model is only as good as its assumptions, and models must constantly be adjusted to incorporate new ideas and recently discovered facts.

## STUDY BREAK QUESTIONS

1. Briefly describe the process of simulation modelling.
2. Why is simulation modelling necessary?

## 31.6 Scale, Ecosystems, Species

As we have seen, the complex interactions between and among species combine with abiotic and biotic factors to produce even more complex situations. Several questions emerge from this situation: What determines which species occur in an ecosystem? What controls the size of the populations of species in an ecosystem? How do species in an ecosystem interact? What effect does scale have on the situation?

Ecosystems span scales from millimetres to kilometres. Consider the microorganisms in a biofilm of water compared to the species, some of them microorganisms, in the water contained in the pitcher of a pitcher plant. Furthermore, the community of organisms may vary among pitchers on one plant. Like the pitcher-based community, terrestrial organisms living on an island may be relatively isolated. Consider the differences among islands, such as the British Isles, the Hawaiian Islands, or the Galapagos Islands, with respect to the combination of size (area), degree of isolation (distance from mainland), and range of habitats.

Variations in the scale of interactions (**Figure 31.25**) help to put the nature of ecosystems in context. Compare Figure 31.25 to Figure 30.29—about pollen and seed dispersal. More obvious in the latter is the influence of mobility on patterns of dispersal and connections. Large animals disperse seeds farther than small ones. Animals that can fly have greater potential as dispersers of seeds and pollen than those that walk or run. Data on the distribution and habitat associations of terrestrial birds in Denmark reveal how species in the same genus and those filling similar niches have more influence on the patterns of distribution of one another than less similar species.

Studies of salmon along the northwest coast of North America (Great Bear Rainforest in British Columbia and sites around Bristol Bay in Alaska) reveal how salmon, fish in the genus *Oncorhynchus*, can influence the plant communities bordering the streams in which they spawn. Nutrients from salmon enter these communities when salmon die after spawning and/or when they are taken and eaten by predators such as bears. Healthy populations of salmon affect the nutrient loading in terrestrial plants along the rivers and streams. The density of salmon and the characteristics of the watershed (steep versus shallow banks) influence the situation. Nutrient input from

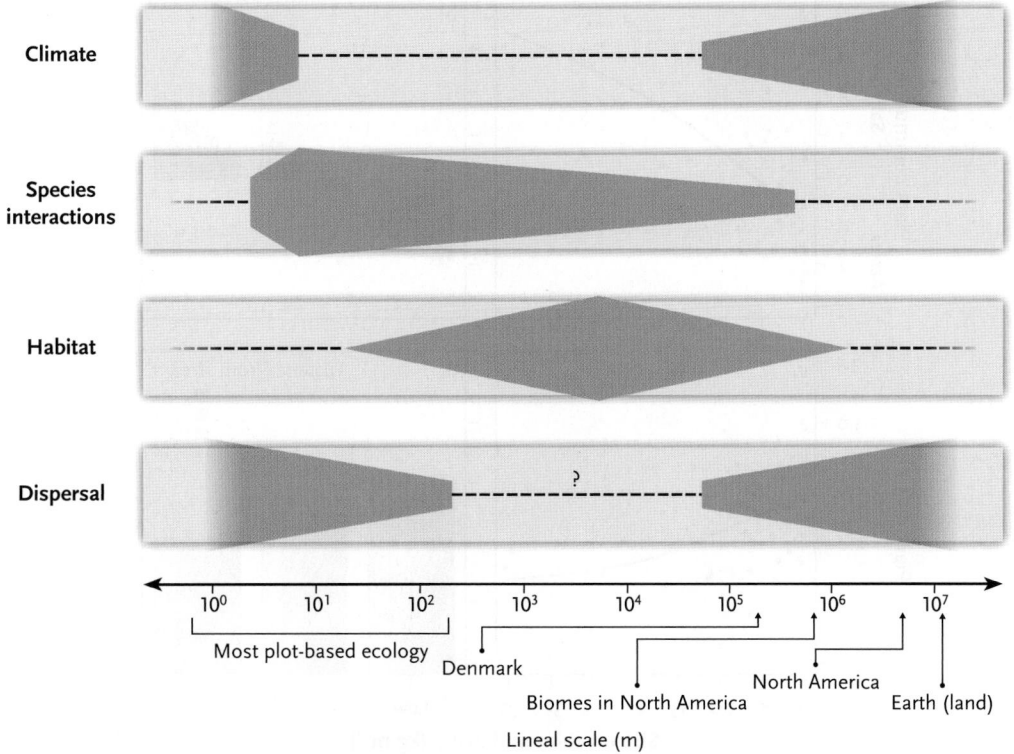

**FIGURE 31.25 Climate, species interactions, habitat, and dispersal are four main factors controlling the distribution of species (vertical axis).** Note the variation in scale (horizontal axis) across which these factors can act.

Source: From McGill, B.J., "Matters of scale," *Science* 30 April 2010, Vol. 328 no. 5978 pp. 575-576. *Science* by American Association for the Advancement of Science Reproduced with permission of AMERICAN ASSOCIATION FOR THE ADVANCEMENT OF SCIENCE in the format Republish in a book via Copyright Clearance Center.

salmon leads to an increase in plants, such as salmonberry, associated with nutrient-rich soils. Lower input from salmon is associated with plants associated with nutrient-poor soils (e.g., blueberries). Increases in nutrient-rich soils coincide with decreases in plant diversity (**Figure 31.26**).

The above data from salmon at sites along 50 watersheds in British Columbia demonstrate the local impact that species in one genus can have. Work from sites in Alaska shows how the inherent diversity of populations of sockeye salmon (*Oncorhynchus nerka*) is vital to the survival of the species and, by extension, the ecosystem. The data from sockeye salmon show how damping variance in the population provides stability. One example of variance is the timing of returns of salmon to the streams in which they hatched. The diversity is part of the portfolio effect, named because it is analogous to the impact of asset diversity on the stability of financial portfolios.

The diversity inherent in several hundred discrete watershed-based populations of sockeye is less than half the diversity that would occur if the sockeye were a single homogeneous population. The diversity also makes sockeye more resilient to pressures of fishing. Studies of food webs in the watersheds provide further evidence of diversity and extend the portfolio effect.

In short, work with salmon advances our knowledge of the fundamental nature of ecosystems and helps us to appreciate the importance of maintaining biodiversity, which sets the stage for Chapter 28.

## STUDY BREAK QUESTIONS

1. Why do ecosystems range so greatly in scale?
2. How do salmon have such a great influence on ecosystems around the streams in which they spawn?

## 31.7 Three Sample Ecosystems

Now we use three sample ecosystems to illustrate the guiding points presented above. We will move across a scale from individual leaves, to caves and to cityscapes.

### 31.7a Pitcher Plant Ecosystems

Pitcher plants have modified leaves (pitchers) that act as pitfall traps for drowning and digesting insect prey. Pitchers have developed in at least five different evolutionary lines of vascular plants (see Chapter 34). Throughout much of North America,

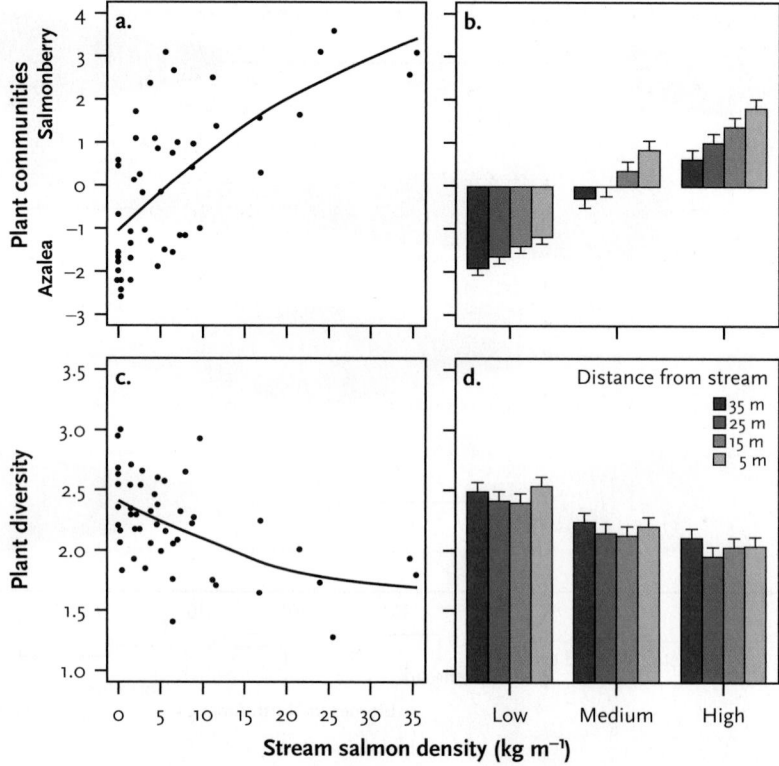

**FIGURE 31.26** **The influence of stream level density of spawning salmon (horizontal axis) on the structure of the community of understorey plants** (a, b) **and on the diversity of plants** (c, d; vertical axis). **Note the impact of distance from the stream.**

Source: From Hocking, M.D. and J.D. Reynolds, "Impacts of salmon on riparian plant diversity," *Science* 25 March 2011, Vol. 331 no. 6024 pp. 1609-1612. *Science* by American Association for the Advancement of Science Reproduced with permission of AMERICAN ASSOCIATION FOR THE ADVANCEMENT OF SCIENCE in the format Republish in a book via Copyright Clearance Center.

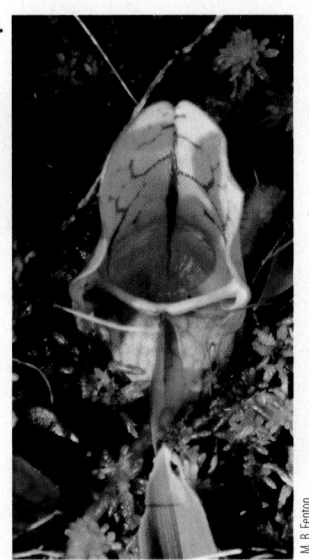

**FIGURE 31.27** *Sarracenia purpurea*, **a pitcher plant, showing the flower** (a) **on the end of a long stalk, and a pitcher** (b)**.** Note the water in the pitcher.

pitcher plants (the provincial flower of Newfoundland and Labrador; **Figure 31.27**) are common in bogs. *Sarracenia purpurea*, like other carnivorous plants, obtain much of their nitrogen from the insects they capture.

The captured arthropod prey, mainly ants and flies, is the base of a food web inside the pitchers (**Figure 31.28**). These are shredded and partly consumed by larvae of midges (*Metriocnemus knabi*) and sarcophagid flies. A soup of bacteria and protozoa processes shredded prey, which are eaten by filter-feeding rotifers (*Habrotrocha rosa*; **Figure 31.29**) and mites (*Sarraceniopus gibsonii*). Mosquito larvae (*Wyeomyia smithii*) eat the bacteria, protozoa, and rotifers, whereas the larger sarcophagid fly larvae eat the rotifers and smaller mosquito larvae. Populations of bacteria, protozoa, and rotifers grow much more rapidly than populations of mosquito or midge larvae, making the system sustainable.

Pitchers are essential to the life cycles of two species of insects whose larvae live in them. A mosquito and a midge coexist in the same pitchers, and their populations are limited by the availability of insect carcasses. In any pitcher, growth in populations of the midge larvae is not affected by increases in the numbers of mosquito larvae. But, as shown in Figure 31.28 populations of mosquito larvae increase as populations of midge larvae increase.

The situation is an example of processing-chain commensalism (see also Chapter 30) because the action of one species creates opportunities for another. In this case, midge larvae feed on the hard parts of insect carcasses and break them up in the process. Mosquito larvae are filter feeders, consuming particles derived from the decaying matter. The feeding of the midges generates additional food for the mosquito larvae. Although the populations of midge and mosquito larvae can be large in any pitcher, only a single sarcophagid fly larva occurs in any pitcher. *Fletcherimyia fletcheri* is a *K*-strategist (see Chapter 29) and gives birth to larvae. If you place more than one *F. fletcheri* larva in a pitcher, a fight ensues. The larger larva either wins or leaves the pitcher to pupate in the sphagnum around it.

These insects do not appear to compete with their hosts, the pitcher plants. The abundance of rotifers living in the pitchers of *S. purpurea* is negatively associated with the presence of midge and mosquito larvae (which eat the rotifers). Rotifers are detritivores, and their excretory products ($NO_3^--N$, $NH_4OH$, P) account for a major portion of the N acquired by the plants from their insect prey.

Two species of moths also exploit *S. purpurea* (**Figure 31.30**). *Exyra fax* and *Papaipema appassionata* do not live in the pitchers. *Exyra fax* caterpillars eat the interior surface of the pitcher chambers, whereas *P. appassionata* caterpillars consume the rhizomes. Although predation by *E. fax* caterpillars does not kill the plants, predation by *P. appassionata* does. To what trophic level does one

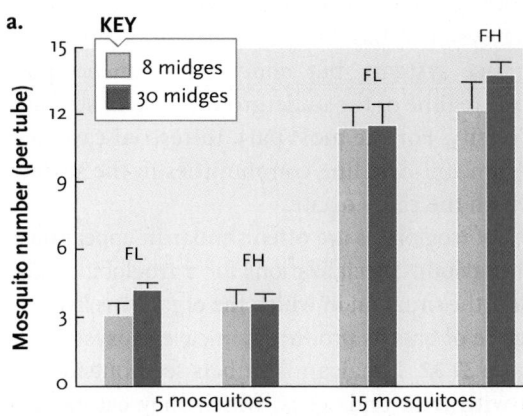

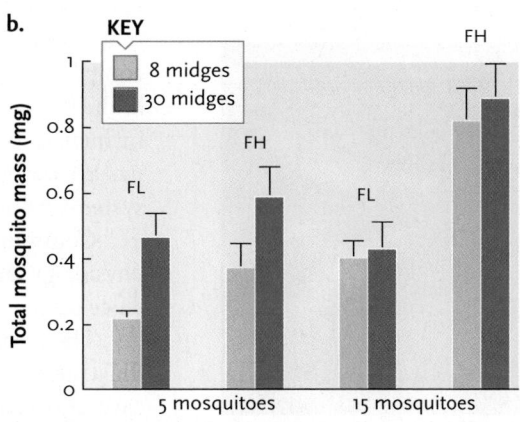

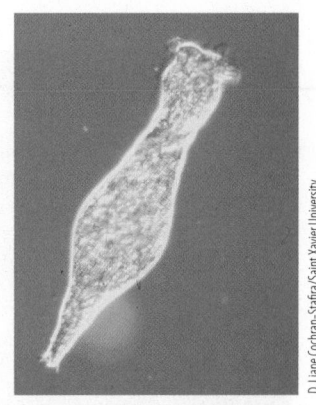

**FIGURE 31.28 Midge and mosquito larvae in pitchers. (a)** The density and **(b)** total dry mass of mosquito larvae are the same whether the population of midges is low (8 midges) or high (30 midges). FH = high food availability; FL = low food availability. Error bars show standard errors of the mean.

**FIGURE 31.29 A bdelloid rotifer,** *Habrotrocha rosa*, **from a** *Sarracenia purpurea* **pitcher**

a.

Courtesy of the Biodiversity Institute of Ontario

b.

Courtesy of Daniel Handfield

**FIGURE 31.30 Moths whose caterpillars eat *Sarracenia purpurea*.** The caterpillars of **(a)** *Exyra fax* and **(b)** *Papaipema appassionata* feed on pitcher plants, either (a) the lining of pitchers or (b) the rhizomes.

assign moths whose caterpillars are herbivores feeding on primary producers that eat insects?

At this point, remember other interactions involving pitcher plants and tree shrews and bats (see Chapter 30). The leaves of pitcher plants provide an excellent illustration of the complexity of a small, self-contained ecosystem.

## 31.7b Cave Ecosystems

Mexican cavefish and southern cavefish (Figure 31.1) illustrate two quite different energy regimes that can occur in cave ecosystems. The tendency for troglobitic species to lack pigment and vision appears to reflect the costs of maintaining these features in situations where they serve no purpose. Mexican cavefish are part of a species complex that includes both cave and surface populations occurring in several neighbouring systems in the area of Sierra de El Abra in south central Mexico. Lineages of these fish have lost eyes at least three times in the last one million years, and there is a range of eye conditions in today's populations (**Figure 31.31**).

M. B. Fenton

**FIGURE 31.31 This grouping of captive Mexican cavefish photographed in a pet store illustrates the range of eye development.**

The situation in cavefish supports the view that the cost of maintaining eyes (for example) explains the lack of eyes for organisms living in perpetual darkness. Expression of *Pax6* genes (see Chapter 1) as well as fate determination of the optic primordia are responsible for the loss of eyes in different populations of Mexican cavefish. It appears that both natural selection and neutral mutations are responsible for loss of eyes in these fish.

A comparison of eyed and eyeless populations of Mexican cavefish revealed that, while the eyed fish showed a typical circadian rhythm, the eyeless fish did not. Circadian rhythms are daily patterns of activity and energy expenditure. The blind Mexican cavefish achieve a 27% savings in daily energetic expenditure compared to eyed forms.

Compared to surface ecosystems, cave ecosystems have truncated food webs. They lack primary producers and consumers and they have few strictly top level predators. This means that cave systems depend upon input from elsewhere. This input is known as **allochthonous** and could be considered a subsidy. Allochthonous input can be bat guano or material washed in by floods. Cave ecosystems are isolated from surface systems and appear protected from environmental changes that affect surface systems. Biodiversity of cave systems is low compared to surface systems, but nonetheless can be quite high. The energetic regime of the underground system strongly influences biodiversity. For the most part, terrestrial cave faunas are derived from soil-dwelling communities in the surface systems below which the caves occur.

Communities of troglobites are often similar in appearance, physiology, and behaviour. Specializations for a troglobitic existence usually reflect the situation in which the organisms live.

The importance of bats as producers in cave ecosystems is illustrated in **Figure 31.32**. Jamaican fruit bats feed outside the cave and return with fruit and seeds, which they eat as they roost. In some cases the bats deposit only guano (**Figure 31.33a**), or a mixture of guano, pellets of chewed fruit fibre, and seeds (Figure 31.33b).

FIGURE 31.32 **Guano and pellets of fruit fibre (each about 1 cm long) cover the floor of a cave room where Jamaican fruit bats (inset:** *Artibeus jamaicensis*) **roost.**

a.

b.

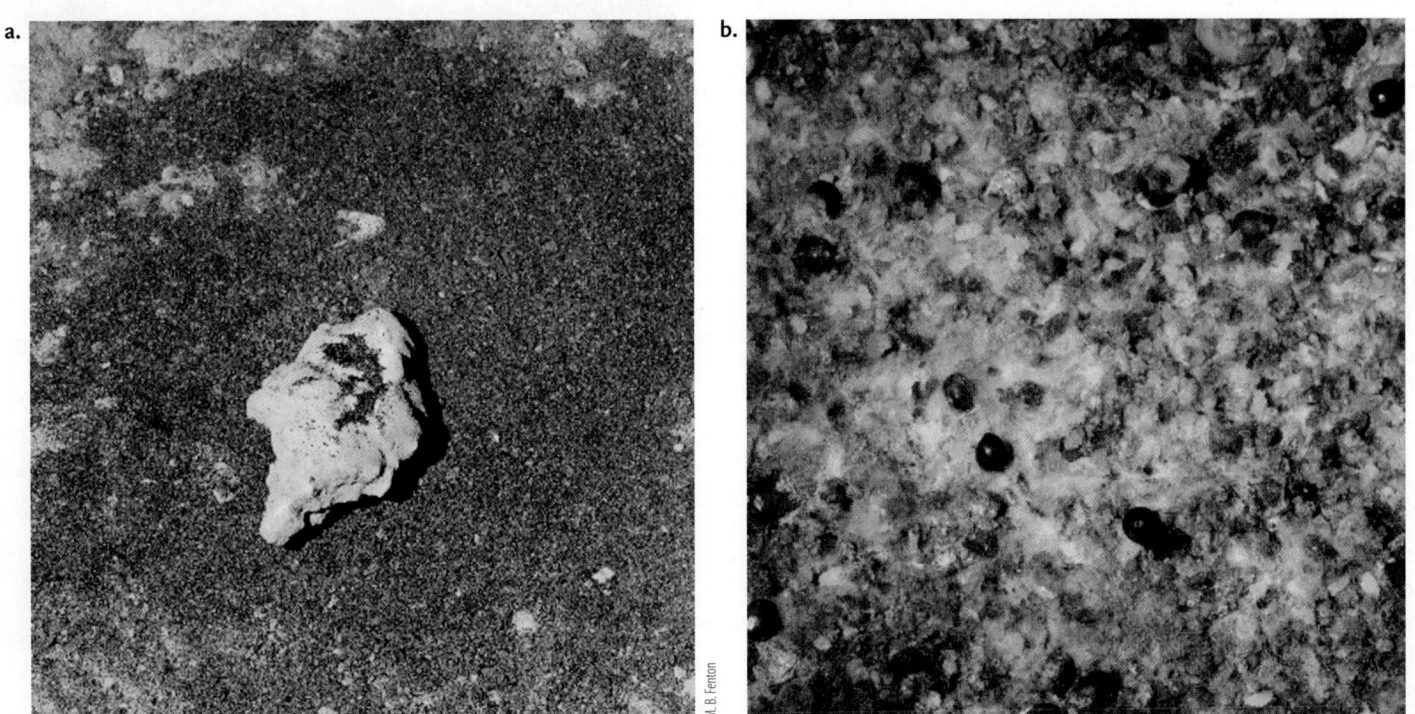

FIGURE 31.33 **Detail of bat guano (a., from an insectivorous bat) or a mixture of guano, seeds, and pellets of fruit fibre** (b). In (a), Waterhouse's leaf-nosed bat (*Macrotus waterhousii*) produces pellets consisting of insect fibres. In (b), Jamaican fruit bats drop guano, seeds (black and shiny), and pellets of fruit fibre (yellowish). The bats make the pellets by chewing on the fruit while sucking out the pulp and juices. The bats then spit out the pellets.

Cave communities include many detritivores, and species that are usually herbivorous (e.g., cave crickets: *Amphiacusta* spp.) also may eat fresh bat guano. Predatory troglobitic grotto salamanders (*Eurycea spelaea*) also feed on bat guano; isotopic analysis reveals that material from the guano is assimilated into muscle.

Bats themselves are important food resources for scavengers and detritivores living in caves. They also serve as food for opportunistic predators, ranging from feral cats (*Felis catus*) to snakes that live in caves (**Figure 31.34**). Around the world, especially in the tropics and subtropics, concentrations of bats attract predators such as snakes. None of the bat-eating snakes is troglobitic.

The other major energetic input to caves is materials swept in by floods, or that fall into entrances. This input can include materials brought into caves by animals, including humans, taking shelter there.

**FIGURE 31.34** Cuban dwarf boa (*Epicrates angulifer*) photographed in a cave where it preyed on passing bats

Four features appear to account for the patterns of biodiversity in caves and thus the structures of the ecosystems that occur there. First is environmental harshness, reflecting mainly darkness. Second is a high level of endemic species and allopatric vicariant species usually associated with habitat fragmentation and isolation. Third is a high level of relict taxa, which reflects the relative stability and antiquity of cave environments. Fourth is the truncated ecosystem. Some of these features also occur in other systems, such as the depths of Lake Baikal.

In any event, cave ecosystems provide a clear demonstration of how energy input affects biodiversity and food webs. Of special note is the fact that a cave in southern Romania has chemoautotrophic bacteria that can fix inorganic carbon. These bacteria use hydrogen sulfide as an energy source. Isotopic analysis reveals that production from these bacteria provides a food base for troglobitic animals. It seems that not all cave ecosystems are created equal.

## 31.7c Cities: Urban Ecosystems

In a 2013 model, Luís Bettencourt identified four simple assumptions that could be used to advantage in understanding the dynamics of cities. First, cities have the capacity for mixing populations of citizens that live there. This presumes that citizens can afford to fully explore the city and use it to advantage. Second, infrastructure develops gradually and incrementally, accommodating the expanding population. The mainstay of this assumption is a city's network of roads. Third, $G$ (the product of gross domestic product and road volume per capita) is mainly independent of $N$ (population size). $G$ reflects an increasing demand by cities on the mental and physical efforts of their citizens. This also involves communication networks. Fourth, socioeconomic outputs are proportional to local social interactions. In other words, cities are concentrations of social interactions, not just of people. Unlike biological systems that appear to minimize dissipation of energy, cities are systems in which the opposite is true: energy dissipation is maximized. This reflects ongoing processes such as transportation, as well as heating and cooling.

Waste disposal is one harsh reality of the energy side of cities (**Figure 31.35**). Landfill sites attract large numbers of animals searching for food. At the Thunder Bay site, gulls and ravens are both conspicuous and numerous. Rats also abound at the site, but are less visible. In December 2015, about 100 bald eagles also converged on the landfill site (**Figure 31.36**). These birds showed little interest in the other

**FIGURE 31.35** Operations at a landfill site near Thunder Bay, Ontario, illustrate the scale of the accumulated refuse as well as fuel consumption associated with maintaining the site. The attendant birds hint at another side of the garbage we produce.

**FIGURE 31.36** Eight of approximately 100 bald eagles (*Haliaeetus leucocephalus*) loitering at a landfill in Thunder Bay in December 2015

birds and appeared to scavenge a living from the accumulated garbage.

Cities share many features with more biological ecosystems, and thinking of them in this way may teach us more about these different kinds of systems and how they operate. Just as intriguing are the reasons that some organisms thrive in cities (**Figure 31.37**) while others do not. This is a critical problem in conservation biology because cities are the fastest growing ecosystems in the world.

## STUDY BREAK QUESTIONS

1. What do pitcher plant, cave, and city ecosystems have in common?
2. How do they differ?
3. Which would you choose as a "model" system?

**FIGURE 31.37  A view of an urban techno ecosystem, specifically the campus of Western University as seen in 2007.** The expanses of woodland may be more extensive in cities than they are in agroecosystems.

# Summary Illustration

Pyramids of energy biomass and numbers have the same basic shape. Each category of organism in these pyramids is part of an ecosystem and plays a role in the cycling of ecosystem nutrients. Consider the role of each category of organism in each of these cycles.

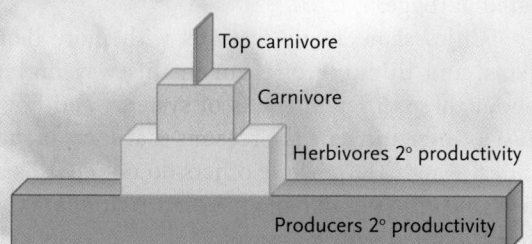

## Water Cycle

Water cycles through marine, atmospheric, and terrestrial reservoirs. The numbers next to the arrows indicate the amount of water (in km³/year) moved among the reservoirs by various processes.

The six major reservoirs of water are the oceans, polar ice and glaciers, groundwater, lakes and rivers, soil moisture, and the atmosphere. The oceans are by far the largest of the major reservoirs.

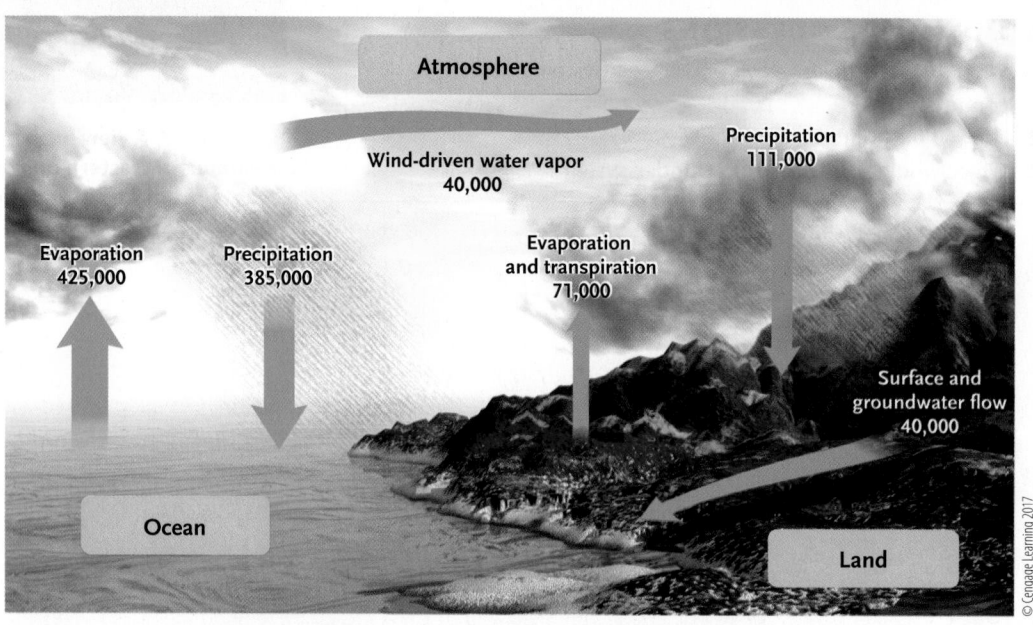

## Carbon Cycle

Marine and terrestrial components of the global carbon cycle are linked through an atmospheric reservoir of carbon dioxide. The largest amount of Earth's carbon is found in sediments and rocks. Earth's atmosphere mediates most of the movement of carbon.

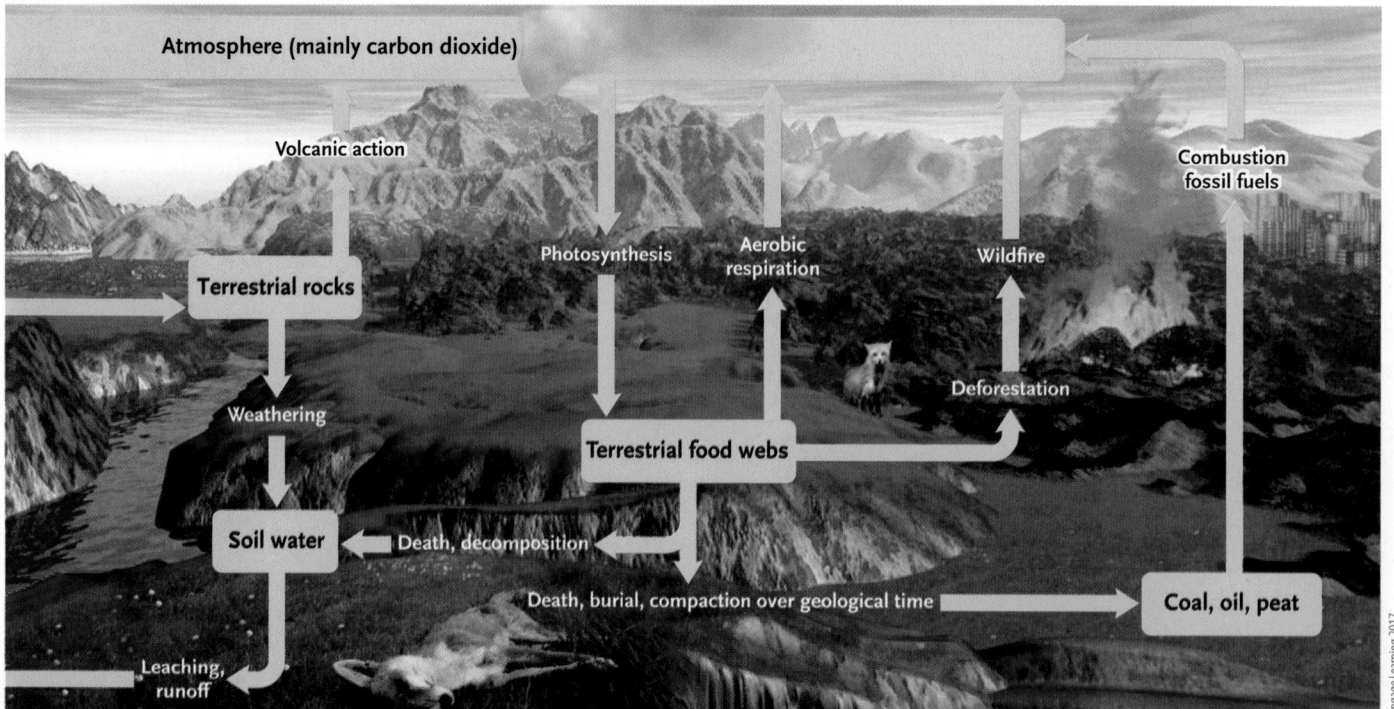

## Nitrogen Cycle

Nitrogen-fixing bacteria produce molecular nitrogen. Other bacteria recycle nitrogen through ammonification and two types of nitrification. Denitrification converts nitrate to molecular nitrogen. Runoff carries nitrogen from terrestrial ecosystems into aquatic ecosystems.

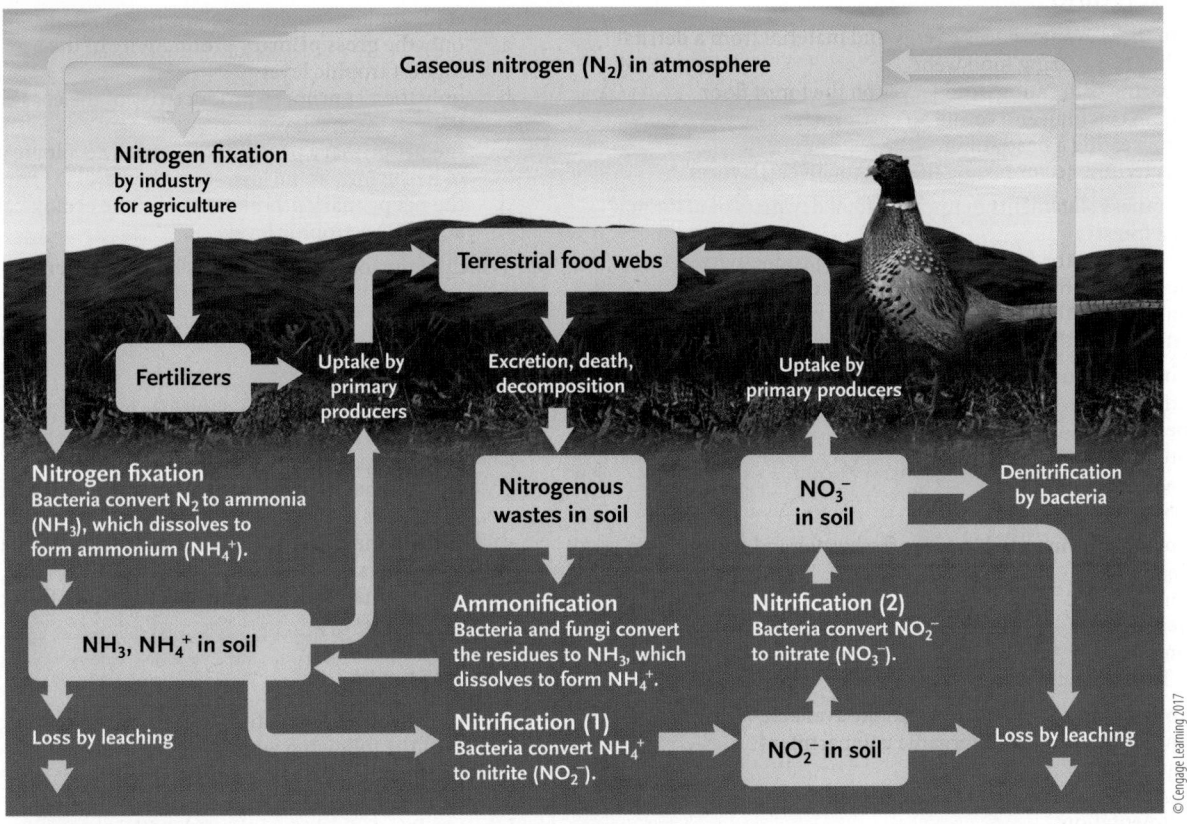

**Gaseous nitrogen ($N_2$) in atmosphere**

**Nitrogen fixation**
by industry
for agriculture

**Terrestrial food webs**

**Fertilizers**

Uptake by primary producers

Excretion, death, decomposition

Uptake by primary producers

**Nitrogen fixation**
Bacteria convert $N_2$ to ammonia ($NH_3$), which dissolves to form ammonium ($NH_4^+$).

**Nitrogenous wastes in soil**

**$NO_3^-$ in soil**

Denitrification by bacteria

**$NH_3$, $NH_4^+$ in soil**

**Ammonification**
Bacteria and fungi convert the residues to $NH_3$, which dissolves to form $NH_4^+$.

**Nitrification (2)**
Bacteria convert $NO_2^-$ to nitrate ($NO_3^-$).

Loss by leaching

**Nitrification (1)**
Bacteria convert $NH_4^+$ to nitrite ($NO_2^-$).

**$NO_2^-$ in soil**

Loss by leaching

© Cengage Learning 2017

## Phosphorous Cycle

Phosphorus becomes available when wind and rainfall dissolve phosphates in rocks and carry them into soil and freshwater ecosystems. Runoff carries dissolved phosphorus into marine ecosystems, where it precipitates and is incorporated into marine sediments.

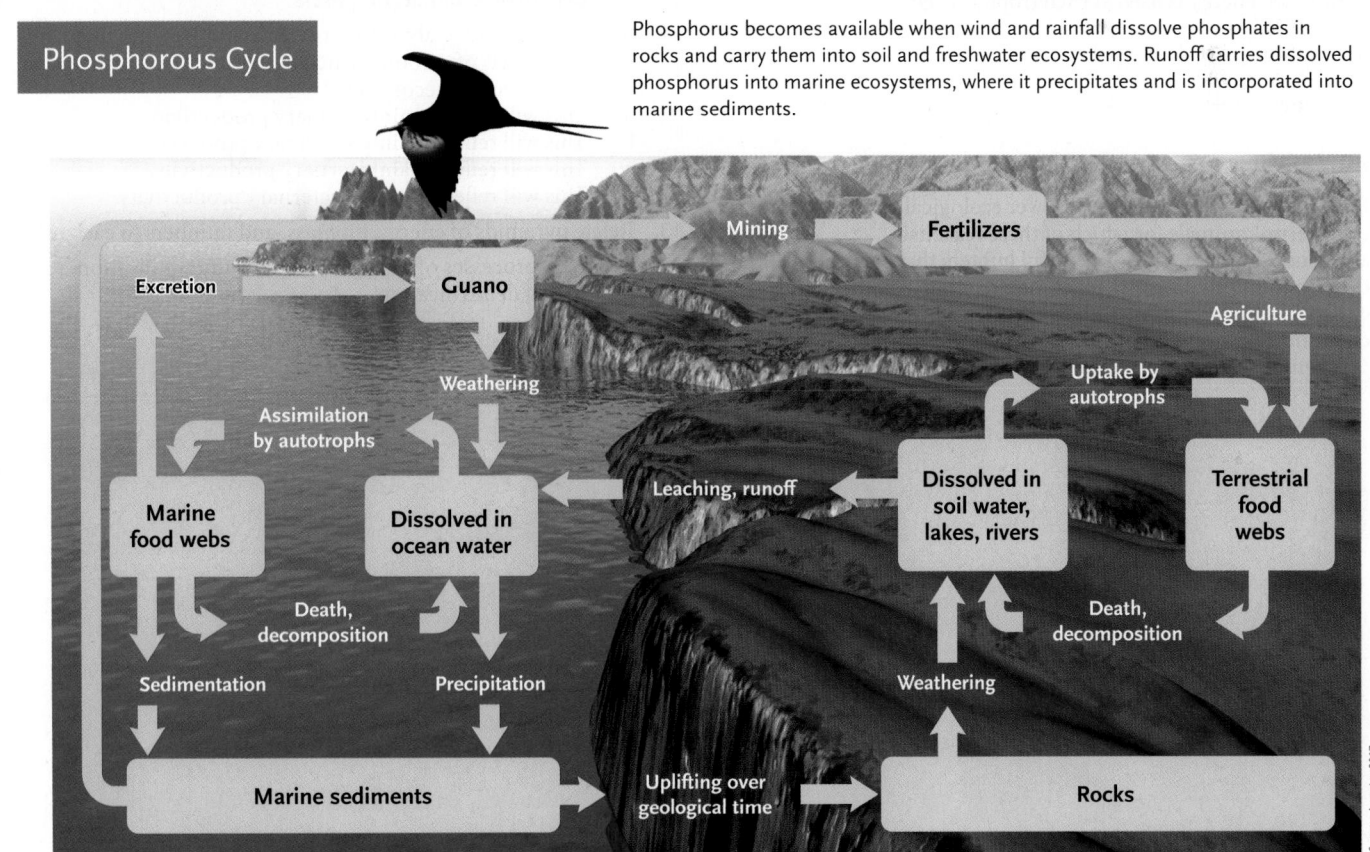

Mining

**Fertilizers**

Excretion

**Guano**

Agriculture

Weathering

Uptake by autotrophs

Assimilation by autotrophs

**Marine food webs**

**Dissolved in ocean water**

Leaching, runoff

**Dissolved in soil water, lakes, rivers**

**Terrestrial food webs**

Death, decomposition

Death, decomposition

Sedimentation

Precipitation

Weathering

**Marine sediments**

Uplifting over geological time

**Rocks**

© Cengage Learning 2017

# SELF-TEST QUESTIONS

## Recall/Understand

1. Which of these events moves energy and material from a detrital food web into a grazing food web?
   a. an earthworm eating dead leaves on the forest floor
   b. a robin catching and eating an earthworm
   c. a crow eating a dead robin
   d. a bacterium decomposing the feces of an earthworm

2. Which of these statements defines the total dry mass of plant material in a forest?
   a. a measure of the forest's gross primary productivity
   b. a measure of the forest's net primary productivity
   c. a measure of the forest's standing crop biomass
   d. a measure of the forest's ecological efficiency

3. Which of these ecosystems has the highest rate of net primary productivity?
   a. open ocean
   b. temperate deciduous forest
   c. tropical rainforest
   d. agricultural land

4. Which pyramid is inverted in some freshwater and marine ecosystems?
   a. biomass
   b. energy
   c. numbers
   d. ecological efficiency

5. Which process moves nutrients from the available–organic compartment to the available–inorganic compartment?
   a. respiration
   b. assimilation
   c. sedimentation
   d. photosynthesis

6. How much energy is used at each trophic level?
   a. ~10%
   b. ~30%
   c. ~50%
   d. ~90%

## Apply/Analyze

7. Endothermic animals exhibit a lower ecological efficiency than ectothermic animals for which of these reasons?
   a. Endotherms are less successful hunters than ectotherms.
   b. Endotherms eat more plant material than ectotherms eat.
   c. Endotherms are larger than ectotherms.
   d. Endotherms use more of their energy to maintain body temperature than ectotherms.

8. Which of these factors determines the amount of energy available at the highest trophic level in an ecosystem?
   a. only the gross primary productivity of the ecosystem at the highest trophic level
   b. only the net primary productivity of the ecosystem at the highest trophic level
   c. the net primary productivity and the ecological efficiencies of herbivores at the lowest trophic level
   d. the net primary productivity and the ecological efficiencies at all lower trophic levels

9. Which of the following materials has a sedimentary cycle?
   a. oxygen
   b. nitrogen
   c. phosphorus
   d. carbon

10. Which of these phenomena describes biological magnification?
    a. Certain materials become increasingly concentrated in the tissues of animals at higher trophic levels.
    b. Certain materials become most concentrated in the tissues of animals at the lowest trophic levels.
    c. Certain materials accumulate only in the tissues of tertiary consumers.
    d. Certain materials accumulate only in the tissues of detritivores.

## Create/Evaluate

11. Suppose you want to create an experimental grazing food web. Which of the following would you need to include so that it closely resembles a real grazing food web?
    a. carnivores and decomposers
    b. producers, herbivores, and detritivores
    c. producers, herbivores, and carnivores
    d. detritivores and decomposers

12. Suppose that you analyze an ecosystem and you find that it has declining levels of carbon. Which of these statements may you conclude about this ecosystem?
    a. This will reflect mainly primary productivity.
    b. This will reflect mainly secondary productivity.
    c. This will reflect mainly tertiary productivity.
    d. This will reflect mainly quaternary productivity.

13. Relate pyramids of energy, biomass, and numbers to each other.

14. Compare processes of nitrogen fixation, ammonification, nitrification, and denitrification.

15. Using the figure below, provide an overview the phosphorus cycle.

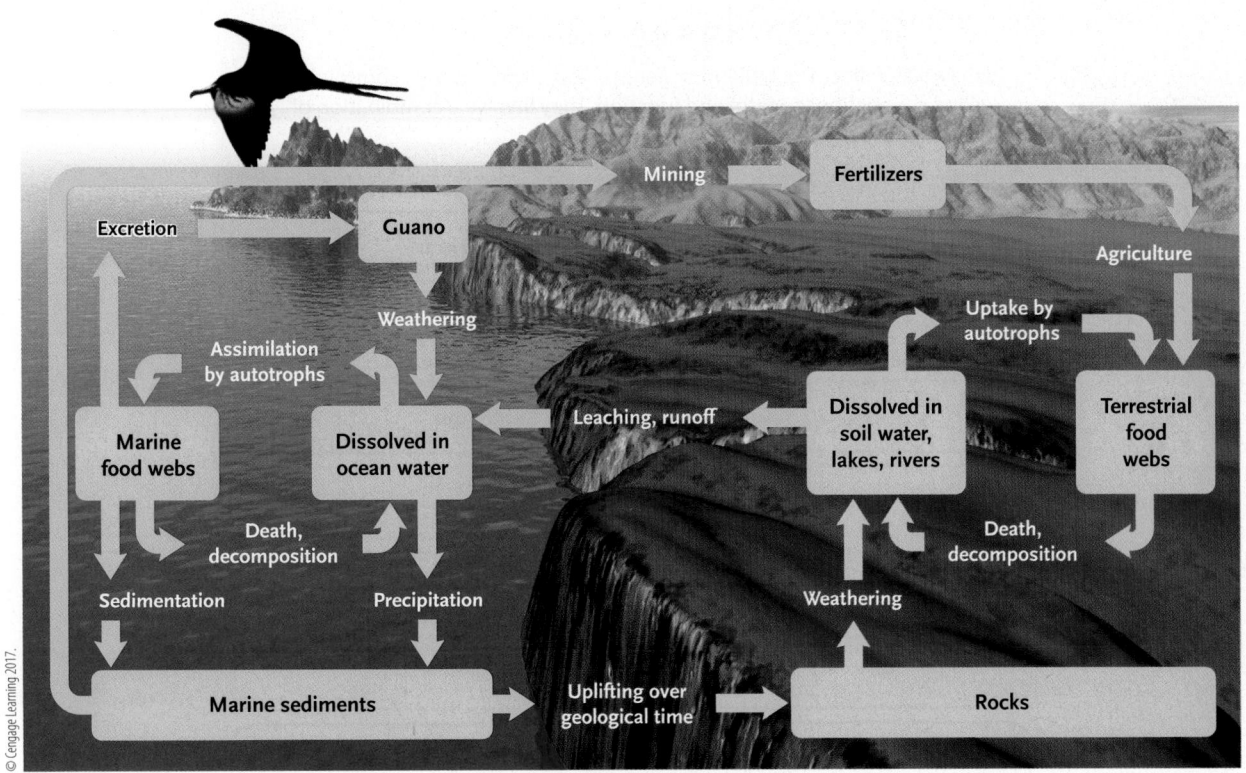

# Chapter Roadmap

## Animal Behaviour

Behaviours reflect a rich blend of genetic and environmental control as well as connections to form and function. They involve a combination of instinct and learning.

**32.1 Genes, Environment, and Behaviour**

**32.2 Instinct**

**32.3 Knockouts: Genes and Behaviour**

**32.4 Learning**

**32.5 Neurophysiology and Behaviour**

**32.6 Hormones and Behaviour**

**32.7 Neural Anatomy and Behaviour**

**32.8 Communication**

**32.9 Language: Syntax and Symbols**

**32.10 Space**

**32.11 Home Range and Territory**

**32.12 Migration**

**32.13 Mates as Resources**

**32.14 Sexual Selection**

**32.15 Social Behaviour**

**32.16 Kin Selection and Altruism**

**32.17 Eusocial Animals**

**32.18 Human Social Behaviour**

A flying western sandpiper (*Calidris mauri*)

# Animal Behaviour

# 32

**Why it matters . . .** Like many other birds, western sandpipers migrate considerable distances from their breeding grounds along the coast of western Alaska to their wintering grounds in the southern United States. Migration is a recurring theme among animals, and questions about how they navigate continue to intrigue biologists. Considerable experimental and observational evidence has indicated that animals orient using variations in Earth's magnetic field. Until recently, however, we have lacked information about how animals sense magnetic fields.

In 2015, biophysicist Xie Can and his colleagues used an electron microscope to observe assemblies of rod-shaped cryptochromes, proteins sensitive to magnetic fields. They named the proteins MagR and proposed them as the missing biocompass, a receptor that animals could use as a magnetic sensor. Experiments with fruit flies (*Drosophila melanogaster*) revealed that flies missing MagR lost their magnetic sense, supporting the hypothesis. Cryptochromes are blue-light absorbing flavoproteins and homologous proteins that also occur in other animals. Many animals from humans to bees, whales to birds, butterflies to pigeons appear to have the capacity to sense magnetic fields. Understanding how these animals sense magnetic fields was a fundamental discovery in animal behaviour.

Moving animals also use other mechanisms to find their way during migration. There are three categories of way-finding mechanisms: piloting, compass orientation, and navigation. Most species use some combination of these mechanisms to guide their movements. Arctic terns are seabirds that make annual round-trip migrations of 40 000 km **(Figure 32.1)**. Light-sensing geolocators allowed biologists to document the details of their movement paths. The exact mechanisms these birds use to navigate are still under investigation.

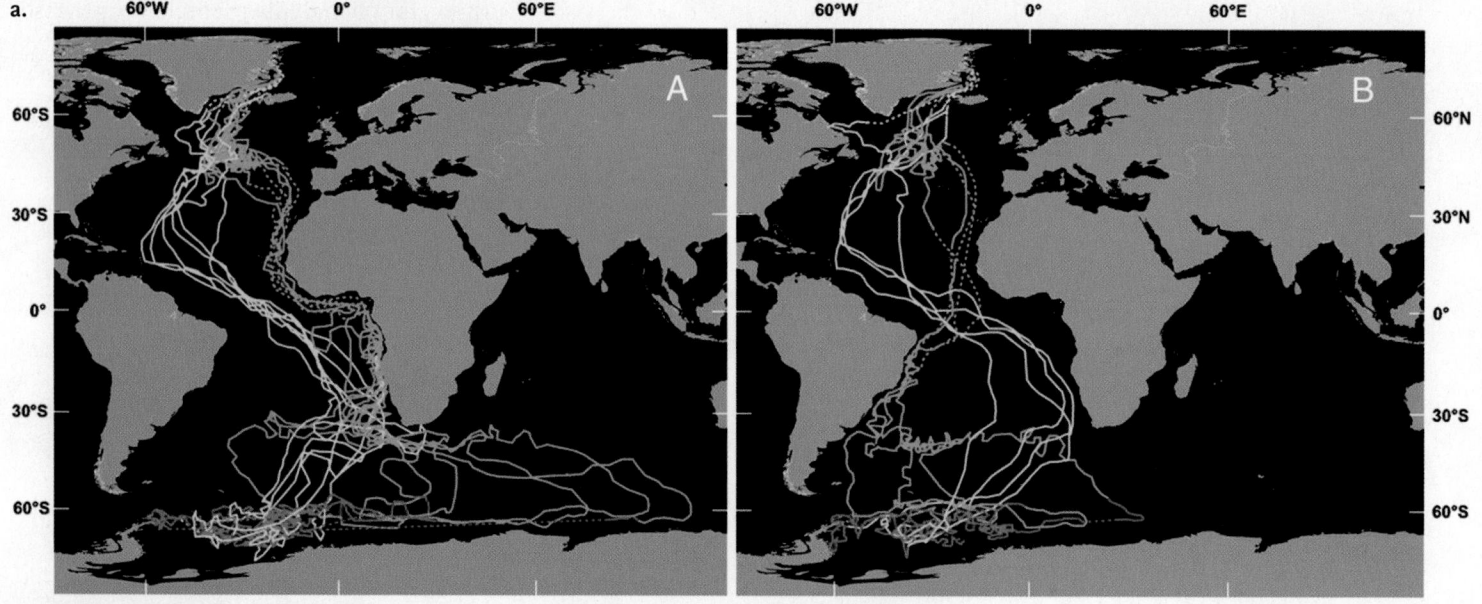

a.

"Tracking of Arctic terns *Sterna paradisaea* reveals longest animal migration." Carsten Egevang, Iain J. Stenhouse, Richard A. Phillips, Aevar Petersen, James W. Fox, and Janet R. D. Silk. *PNAS* February 2, 2010 vol. 107 no. 5 2078–2081.

b.

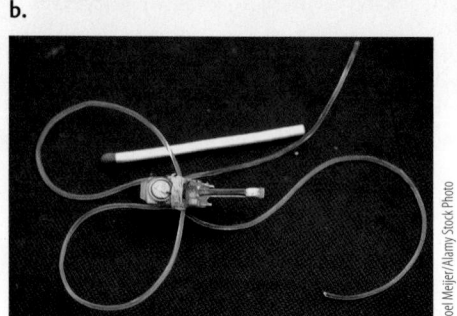

Roel Meijer/Alamy Stock Photo

c.

Photos.com

**FIGURE 32.1** **(a)** Geolocators provided details of the movements of 11 Arctic terns tagged at breeding colonies in Greenland (10 terns) and Iceland (1 tern). Two migration routes emerged, one along the coast of Africa (A) and the other along the coast of South America (B). **(b)** A small geolocator. **(c)** an Arctic tern

The purpose of this chapter is to introduce **animal behaviour**. Behaviours, such as migration, reflect a rich blend of genetic and environmental control as well as connections to form and function. They involve a combination of instinct and learning. Hormones exert a strong influence over an animal's behaviour. The nervous system and, by extension, the sensory system mediate behaviour. Some animals are territorial, defending all or part of their home range, usually in association with reproduction. Migration involves movements to and from different areas, usually between seasons, and implies the use of navigational cues. Animals show rich repertoires of behaviour around mating and reproduction. A few species live in large groups and others exhibit complex social behaviour. As we will see in what follows, animal behaviour covers this broad range of topics.

## 32.1 Genes, Environment, and Behaviour

Nature versus nurture is a long-standing topic of curiosity and discussion. How much of our behaviour is a function of what we inherited (nature) as opposed to the environment and setting in which we grow up and live (nurture). And in this regard, how different are humans from other animals? Consider this in the

context of the following five examples of food-associated learning in other animals.

First, in Canada, moose (*Alces alces*) and deer (*Odocoileus virginiana*) respond to the sound of chainsaws to feed on the foliage of felled trees. The upper foliage is less chemically defended than the lower leaves.

Second, during the Vietnam War (1959–1975), tigers (*Panthera tigris*; **Figure 32.2**) learned to associate the sound of gunfire with an opportunity to eat. The tigers' behaviour meant that some wounded soldiers waiting for treatment received a different kind of attention than what they expected. During World War II, wolves (*Canis lupus*) showed the same behaviour in some areas of Poland. A food reward is a strong re-enforcer of behaviour.

In the 1970s, Kim McCleneghan and Jack Ames were studying sea otters (*Enhydra lutris*) in California coastal waters. These otters dive and collect food (sea urchins, *Pisaster brevispinus*, and clams, *Saxidomus nuttalli*) from the bottom and bring their catch to the surface to eat it. Some otters resurfaced with empty beverage cans. These otters would lie on their backs in the ocean swells, take a can and bite it open. In some cases they removed and ate something before discarding the can. Some cans appeared to be empty and were discarded after opening. The biologists collected their own beverage cans and

**FIGURE 32.2  A tiger (*Panthera tigris*)**

discovered that many harboured young octopods (*Octopus* species). Populations of these cephalopods are limited by the number of shelters available. Young octopods were exploiting new opportunities for shelter, and the sea otters, in turn, were exploiting the molluscs' behaviour.

Meanwhile, in savannah woodlands in Senegal (West Africa), Jill Pruetz and Paco Bertolani observed chimpanzees (*Pan troglodytes*) hunting Senegal galagos (*Galago senegalensis*; Figure 32.3). Chimps are not vegetarians. They had been reported using grass stalks to fish for termites and working in gangs to hunt and kill young baboons (*Papio ursinus*). The discovery that savannah chimps in Senegal used "spears" to impale Senegal galagos hidden in tree hollows further demonstrated chimps' repertoire of tool use. Pruetz and Bertolani watched chimps bite branches to sharpen them before using them against Senegal galagos. The chimps that Pruetz and Bertolani studied appeared to plan their hunts in advance.

Western scrub-jays (*Aphelocoma californica*) cache food in preparation for the next day's breakfast. Proving that animals consciously plan ahead means that the experimenters have to demonstrate that the animal executes a novel action or combination of actions anticipating an emotional state different from the one at the time of planning. These two conditions rule out such anticipatory behaviours that are genetically based, such as

**FIGURE 32.3  A Senegal galago (*Galago senegalensis*)**

those associated with migration and hibernation or those associated with meeting an immediate need for food.

These examples illustrate how some behaviour patterns are acquired rather than inherited. But are all behaviours acquired? Animal behaviourists have long debated whether animals are born with the ability to perform behaviours completely and whether experience is necessary to shape their actions. This was addressed in a classic study from a different perspective. White-crowned sparrows sing a song that no other species sings (Figure 32.4). Is this behaviour innate (inborn)? If so, young sparrows should have the ability to produce their particular song from birth, an ability so reliable that young males should sing the "right" song the first time they try. According to this hypothesis, their distinctive song would be an **instinctive behaviour**, genetically or developmentally "programmed," that appears in complete and functional form the first time it is used. An alternative hypothesis is that they acquire the song through experiences such as hearing the songs of adult male white-crowned sparrows that live nearby. If so, this species' distinctive song might be a **learned behaviour** that depends on having a particular kind of experience during development.

How can one determine which of these two hypotheses is correct? If the white-crowned sparrow's song is instinctive, isolated male nestlings that have never heard other members of their species should sing their species' song when they mature. If the learning hypothesis is correct, young birds deprived of hearing other members of their species sing should not sing "properly" when they become adults.

Peter Marler tested these two hypotheses. He took newly hatched white-crowned sparrows from nests in the wild and reared them individually in soundproof cages in his laboratory. Some of the chicks heard recordings of a male white-crowned sparrow's song when they were 10–50 days of age. Others did not. Juvenile males in both groups first started to vocalize at about 150 days of age. For many days, these birds produced whistles and twitters that only vaguely resembled the songs of adults. Gradually, the young males that had listened to tapes of their species' song began to sing better and better approximations of that song. At about 200 days of age, these males were right on target, producing a song that was nearly indistinguishable from the one they had heard months before. Captive-raised males that had not heard recordings of white-crowned sparrow songs never sang anything close to the songs typical of wild males.

These results show that learning is essential for a young male white-crowned sparrow to acquire the full song of its species. Although birds isolated as nestlings sang instinctively, they needed the acoustical experience of listening to their species' song early in life if they were to reproduce it months later. These data allow us to reject the hypothesis that white-crowned sparrows hatch from their eggs with the ability to sing the "right" song. Their species-specific song, and perhaps the songs of many other songbirds, includes both instinctive and learned components.

**White-crowned sparrow**
*(Zonotrichia leucophrys)*

**Song sparrow**
*(Melospiza melodia)*

**Swamp sparrow**
*(Melospiza georgiana)*

Frequency (kHz)

Time

Time

Time

**FIGURE 32.4 Songbirds and their songs.** Sound spectrograms (visual representations of sound graphed as frequency versus time) illustrate differences in the songs of the white-crowned sparrow (*Zonotrichia leucophrys*), song sparrow (*Melospiza melodia*), and swamp sparrow (*Melospiza georgiana*).

In the past, researchers generally classified behaviours as either instinctive or learned; the current belief is that many behaviours include both instinctive and learned components. The emerging picture is that few behaviours are determined entirely by genetics or entirely by environmental factors. Rather, most behaviours develop through complex gene–environment interactions. Some behaviours have a stronger instinctive component than others, and these will be discussed next.

### STUDY BREAK QUESTIONS

1. Is behaviour learned? How has the study of bird song advanced our understanding of the influence of learning versus genes on behaviour?
2. Give any example of your choice that demonstrates that behaviour in animals is learned.

## 32.2 Instinct

Instinctive behaviours can be performed without the benefit of previous experience. They can be grouped into functional categories such as feeding, defence, mating, and parental care. We assume that they have a strong genetic basis, and that natural selection has preserved them as adaptive behaviours.

These instinctive behaviours are highly stereotyped. When an animal is triggered by a specific cue, it performs the same response over and over in almost exactly the same way. These **fixed action patterns** are triggered by **sign stimuli**. Very young herring gull chicks use a begging response **(Figure 32.5a)**, a fixed action pattern, to secure food from their parents. Begging

chicks peck at the red spot on the parent's bill, and the tactile stimulus serves as a sign stimulus inducing the adult to regurgitate food from its crop. Baby gulls eat the chunks of fish, clams, or other food that have been regurgitated for them. We know that the spot on the parent's bill elicits the begging response of the young gull because the same response is triggered by an artificial bill that looks only vaguely like an adult bill, provided that it has a dark contrasting spot near the tip (Figure 32.5b). Simple cues can activate fixed action patterns. A nestling herring gull, is not reacting to every feature of a face but rather to simple cues that function as sign stimuli releasing a fixed behavioural response.

Natural selection has moulded the behaviour of some parasitic species to exploit the relationship between sign stimuli and fixed action patterns for their own benefit. In effect, they have broken another species' code. Birds that are brood parasites lay their eggs in the nests of other species of birds. When the brood parasite's egg hatches, the nestling mimics sign stimuli ordinarily exhibited by its host's own chicks. The parasitic chick begs for food by opening its mouth, bobbing its head, and calling more vigorously than the host's chicks. These exaggerated behaviours elicit feeding by the foster parents, and the young brood parasite often receives more food than the hosts' own young **(Figure 32.6)**.

The situation is more complicated when birds such as honeyguides (African family Indicatoridae) are the parasites. Female greater honeyguides (*Indicator indicator*) lay their eggs in the nests of several host species that nest in dark hollows. Greater honeyguides are not territorial, so more than one female may lay her eggs in the nest of a host. When laying her eggs, a female greater honeyguide minimizes future

FIGURE 32.5 **Experimental Research**

## The Role of Sign Stimuli in Parent–Offspring Interactions

**a.**

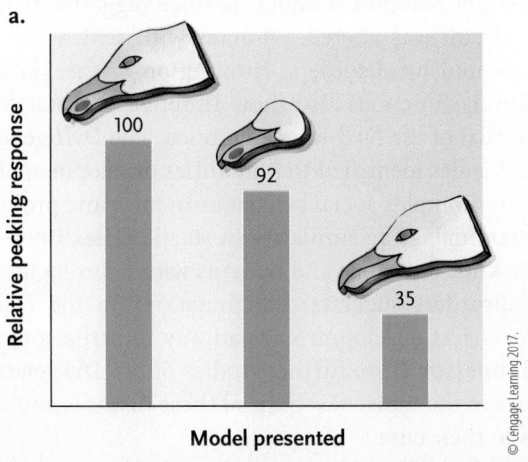

*Relative pecking response* (y-axis)

100

92

35

Model presented (x-axis)

© Cengage Learning 2017.

**b. Herring gulls (Larus argentatus)**

Johner Images/Alamy Stock Photo

**Question:** What feature of the parent's head triggers pecking behaviour in young herring gulls?

**Experiment:** Niko Tinbergen and A. C. Perdeck tested the responses of young herring gull *(Larus argentatus)* chicks to cardboard cutouts of an adult herring gull's head and bill. They waved these models in front of the chicks and recorded how often a particular model elicited a pecking response from the chicks. One cutout included an entire gull's head with a red spot near the tip of the bill, another cutout included just the bill with the red spot, and the third cutout included the entire head but lacked the red spot.

**Result:** Young herring gulls pecked at the model of the bill with a red spot almost as often as they pecked at the model of an entire head with a red spot, but they pecked much less frequently at the model of an entire head that lacked a red spot.

**Conclusion:** Begging behaviour by young herring gulls is triggered by a simple sign stimulus, the red spot on the parent's bill. Experimental tests revealed that herring gull chicks respond more to the presence of the contrasting spot than they do to the outline of an adult's head.

Stephen Dalton/Science Source

**FIGURE 32.6 This European cuckoo (*Cuculus canorus*) is a brood parasite that stimulates food delivery by its foster parent, a hedge sparrow (*Prunella modularis*).** The cuckoo elicits food delivery by displaying exaggerated versions of the sign stimuli used by the host offspring. The exaggerated stimuli are releasers, initiating the appropriate behaviour from a parent with food.

competition among nestlings by selectively piercing the eggs of other greater honeyguides (conspecifics) in the nest. After hatching, greater honeyguide chicks kill other nestlings, whether conspecifics or young of the hosts. Both egg piercing and killing nestlings increase the chances of the chick surviving and reproducing.

Although instinctive behaviours are often performed completely the first time an animal responds to a stimulus, they can be modified by an individual's experiences, as described in the previous section. The fixed action patterns of a young herring gull change over time. Although the youngster initially begs by pecking at almost anything remotely similar to an adult gull's bill, it eventually learns to recognize the distinctive visual and vocal features associated with its parents. The chick uses this information to become increasingly selective about which stimuli elicit its begging behaviour. During their early performances, instinctive behaviours can be modified in response to particular experiences.

Many other experiments have confirmed that genetic differences between individuals can translate into behavioural differences between them. Bear in mind, however, that single genes do not directly control complex behaviour patterns. Rather, the alleles determine the kinds of enzymes that cells can produce, influencing biochemical pathways involved in the development of an animal's nervous system. The resulting neurological differences translate into behavioural differences between individuals that have certain alleles and those that do not. In the following section we explore one way in which this has been demonstrated.

**STUDY BREAK QUESTIONS**

1. What are the differences between instinctive and learned behaviours?
2. What are fixed action patterns and sign stimuli?

## 32.3 Knockouts: Genes and Behaviour

Manipulating genes provides one way to assess the role of genetics in behaviour. The pathway called *wingless/Wnt* controls a series of development interactions shared by almost all eukaryotic organisms. Named after the original discovery in the fruit fly *Drosophila melanogaster*, mutant genes of the pathway cause alterations in the wings and other segmental structures. Three genes closely related to *wingless/Wnt* have been identified in mice but, as yet, we do not know which proteins are encoded in the mouse genes that are highly active in embryos and adults. Their function must be important, but what could it be?

Nardos Lijam and his co-workers developed a line of mice lacking *dishevelled* (*Dvl1* in genetic shorthand), one of the genes in the pathway. First, they constructed an artificial copy of the *Dvl1* gene with the central section scrambled so that no functional proteins could be made from its encoded directions. Next, they introduced the artificial gene into embryonic mouse cells. Cells that successfully incorporated the gene were injected into very early mouse embryos. Some mice grown from these embryos were heterozygotes, with one normal copy of the *Dvl1* gene and one dysfunctional copy. Interbreeding the heterozygotes produced some individuals that carried two copies of the altered *Dvl1* gene and no normal copies. Individuals lacking any copies of the normal gene are called *knockout* mice because the normal gene is completely missing.

Knockout mice grew to maturity with no apparent morphological defects in any tissue examined, including the brain. Their motor skills, sensitivity to pain, cognition, and memory all appeared normal. However, their social behaviour differed from that of control mice—mice with at least one copy of the normal gene. When placed in cages with control mice, knockout mice did not participate in activities common in mouse social groups, for example social grooming, tail pulling, mounting, and sniffing. While normal mice built nests and slept in huddled groups, knockout mice tended to sleep alone, and did not construct full nests. Mice heterozygous for the *Dvl1* gene (those with one normal and one altered copy of the gene) behaved normally in all these social activities.

Furthermore, knockout mice jumped around wildly in response to a startling sound. Normal mice did not. It appears that a neural circuit of the brain inhibits the startle response of normal mice, and the reaction of knockout mice suggested that this inhibitory circuit was altered. Humans with schizophrenia, obsessive-compulsive disorders, Huntington disease, and some other brain dysfunctions also show an intensified startle reflex similar to that of the *Dvl1* knockout mice. The *Dvl1* gene is one of the first genes identified that modifies developmental pathways affecting complex social behaviour in mice and probably in other mammals. The similarity in startle reflex intensity between the knockout mice and humans with neurological or psychiatric disorders suggests that mutations in the *Dvl* genes and the *wingless* developmental pathway underlie some human mental illnesses. If so, further studies of the *Dvl* genes may give us clues to the molecular basis of these diseases and a possible means to their cure.

The ability to knockout single genes has become a powerful tool that can be used to explore the genetic differences between individuals that translate into behavioural differences between them.

**STUDY BREAK QUESTION**

1. What are knockout experiments? What can they reveal?

## 32.4 Learning

Unlike instinctive behaviours, learned behaviours are not performed accurately or completely the first time an animal responds to a specific stimulus. Behavioural responses change in response to the environmental stimuli an individual experiences as it develops. Behavioural scientists generally define learning as a process in which experiences change an animal's behavioural responses. Different types of learning occur under different environmental circumstances.

**Imprinting** occurs when animals learn the identity of a caregiver or the key features of a suitable mate during a **critical period**, a stage of development early in life. Newly hatched geese imprint on their mother's appearance and identity, staying near her for months. When they reach sexual maturity, young geese try to mate with other geese exhibiting the visual and behavioural stimuli on which they had imprinted as youngsters. When Konrad Lorenz, a founder of **ethology** (the study of animal behaviour), tended a group of newly hatched greylag geese (*Anser anser*), they imprinted on him rather than on an adult of their own species. Male geese not only followed Lorenz, at sexual maturity they also courted humans.

Other forms of learning can occur throughout an animal's lifetime. Ivan Pavlov, a Russian physiologist, demonstrated

**classical conditioning** in experiments with dogs. Like many other animals, dogs can develop a mental association between two phenomena that are usually unrelated. Dogs typically salivate when they eat. Food is an unconditioned stimulus because the dogs instinctively salivate when presented with food. Pavlov rang a bell just before offering food to dogs. After about 30 trials in which dogs received food immediately after the bell rang, the dogs associated the bell with feeding time and drooled profusely whenever it rang, even when no food was forthcoming. The bell was a conditioned stimulus that elicited a particular learned response. In classical conditioning, an animal learns to respond to a conditioned stimulus (e.g., the bell) when it precedes an unconditioned stimulus (e.g., food) that normally triggers the response (e.g., salivation). If your pet cat becomes exceptionally friendly whenever it hears the sound of a can opener, its behaviour is the result of classical conditioning.

**Operant conditioning**, trial-and-error learning, is another form of associative learning. Here animals learn to link a voluntary activity, an **operant**, with its favourable consequences, a **reinforcement**. A laboratory rat will explore a new cage randomly. If the cage was equipped with a bar that released food when it was pressed by accident (the operant) and the rat immediately received a morsel of food (the reinforcement), after a few such experiences, a hungry rat learned to press the bar in its cage more frequently, provided that the bar-pressing behaviour was followed by access to food. Laboratory rats have also learned to press bars to turn off disturbing stimuli, such as bright lights.

**Insight learning** occurs when an animal abruptly learns to solve problems without apparent trial-and-error attempts at the solution. As an example, captive chimpanzees solved a novel problem: how to get bananas hung far out of reach. The chimps studied the situation and then stacked several boxes, stood on them, and used a stick to knock the fruit to the floor.

**Habituation** occurs when animals lose their responsiveness to frequent stimuli not immediately followed by the usual reinforcement. Habituation can save the animal the time and energy of responding to stimuli that are no longer important. Sea hares (*Aplysia* species) are shell-less molluscs that typically retract their gills when touched on the side. Gill retraction helps protect sea hares from approaching predators. But a sea hare stops retracting its gills when it is touched repeatedly over a short period of time with no harmful consequences.

## 32.4a Changing Behaviour

Animals often learn to exploit important resources. For example, salting of highways often is used to prevent dangerous buildups of ice on road surfaces. After snowplowing and runoff, the salt usually accumulates in roadside ditches. Moose (*Alces alces*) use these salty pools (salt licks) to supplement their mineral intake. Moose at roadsides often come dangerously close to high speed traffic, endangering themselves and the motoring public **(Figure 32.7)**.

Roy Rea and his students at the University of Northern British Columbia work closely with the B.C. Ministry of Transportation and Infrastructure to decrease the attractiveness of roadside salt pools. For over five years, trail cameras installed

**FIGURE 32.7 Aftermath of a moose–car collision that occurred on 4 July 2014 in Maine**

at 15 pools (also known as *mineral licks*) and at multiple control sites have provided many pictures of roadside moose. One way to reduce the problem is to "decommission" the salt pools **(Figure 32.8)**. This can be accomplished by digging out and removing the salty soils, altering drainage patterns, and filling pool sites with materials such as rock and cedar mulch. In one case, human and dog hair were mixed and rototilled into the soils to make a lick unattractive to moose.

The salt licks attract moose, and individuals repeatedly visit the same licks and even bring their young to use the same sites. Furthermore, moose repeatedly visit decommissioned sites shortly after decommissioning, but spend less and less time there. Eventually, however, the absence of mineral soils and water drives moose from these roadside areas to seek natural salt licks outside the road corridor. This makes the highways safer for moose and for motorists.

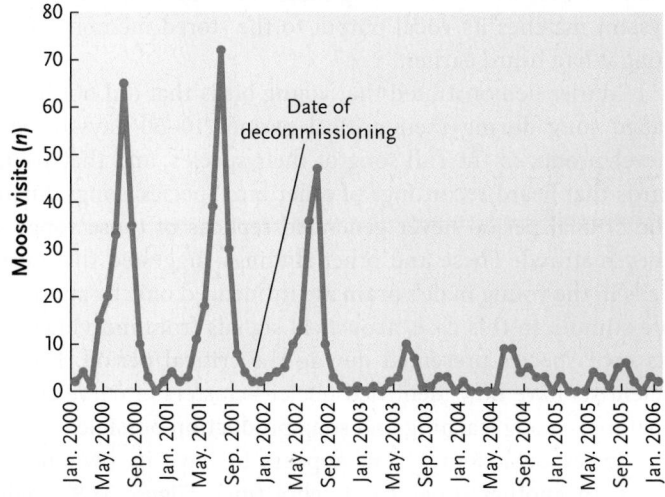

**FIGURE 32.8 Number of moose visits to a series of salt pools, showing the change in behaviour after the site was decommissioned.** Moose continued to visit the lick sites in the first summer after decommissioning. The number of moose visits then declined.

Source: Courtesy of Roy Rea

Until the practice of decommissioning roadside licks becomes more widespread, it will be up to road safety engineers to alter driver behaviours through education and increased warning signage in areas known to be visited regularly by moose. Interestingly, altering driver behaviour, may prove a much more difficult task than altering the behaviours of salt-hungry moose!

## STUDY BREAK QUESTIONS

1. How do the examples of feeding behaviour (see also *Why It Matters*) inform us about learning?
2. Distinguish between instinctive and learned behaviours. Give examples of each.
3. How do collisions between moose and vehicles reflect behaviour?

**FIGURE 32.9** **Zebra finches (*Taeniopygia guttata*) are native to Indonesia.** They have played an important role in studies of the physiological basis of song learning. The male has the striped throat.

# 32.5 Neurophysiology and Behaviour

All behavioural responses, whether mostly instinctive or mostly learned, depend on an elaborate physiological foundation. This is provided by the biochemistry and structure of nerve cells. This is where genetic information and environmental contributions intertwine. The anatomical and physiological basis for some behaviours is present at birth but when an individual's experiences alters the cells of its nervous system, these alterations produce changes in patterns of behaviour.

Marler's experiments described earlier (see Section 32.1) help explain the physiological underpinnings of singing behaviour in male white-crowned sparrows. Acoustical experience shaped singing, suggesting that a sparrow chick's brain must acquire and store information present in the songs of other males. Later, when the young male starts to sing, its nervous system matches its vocal output to the stored memory of the song it had heard earlier.

Marler demonstrated that young birds that did not hear a taped song during their critical period (10–50 days of age), never produced the full song of their species, and that young birds that heard recordings of other bird species' songs during the critical period never generated replicas of those songs as they matured. These and other findings suggested that nerve cells in the young male's brain are influenced only by appropriate stimuli, in this case, acoustical signals from individuals of its own species presented during the critical period. Neuroscientists have now identified nuclei—clusters of nerve cells—that make song learning and song production possible.

Every behavioural trait appears to have its own neural basis. In another songbird, a zebra finch **(Figure 32.9)**, males discriminate between the songs of strangers and those of neighbours. These finches live in **territories** (see Section 32.10), spaces defended by individual males or breeding pairs. Defence of the territory ensures that the residents there have exclusive access to food and other necessary resources.

A nucleus in the forebrain allows zebra finches to discriminate between the songs of neighbours and those of strangers. Cells in this nucleus fire frequently the first time the zebra finch hears the song of a new conspecific. As the song is played again and again, the cells of this nucleus cease to respond, as the bird is habituated to a now familiar song. The same bird still reacts to the songs of strangers. Neurophysiological networks that make this selective learning possible enable male zebra finches to behave differently toward familiar neighbours, which they largely ignore, than they do to unfamiliar singers, which they attack and drive away. In 2016, Daniela Vallentin and her colleagues reported that adult and young zebra finches may show different responses. Here exposure of a young zebra finch to a tutor's song resulted in learning that occurs through stimulation of premotor neurons. But in adults, the same stimuli suppress learning. This finding indicates that, during development, suppression can be as important as stimulation and that adults and young may respond.

Researchers have used molecular and cellular techniques to identify the role of specific genes in this learning. When a zebra finch is exposed to songs of potential rivals of conspecifics, the gene called *ZENK* rapidly becomes active within neurons in the song-controlling nuclei of the bird's brain. This produces an enzyme that changes the structure and function of those neurons. The events that trigger additional changes in the bird's brain enhance its ability to detect and respond to new intruding conspecifics. These intruders can pose a real threat to the individual's continued control of its territory.

## STUDY BREAK QUESTIONS

1. What role does the *ZENK* gene play?
2. How do nerve connections influence behaviour?
3. What makes zebra finches a good model organism for studying song learning?
4. What is a conspecific?

## 32.6 Hormones and Behaviour

Hormones are chemical signals that underlie the performance of specific behaviours. Hormones often work by regulating the development of neurons and neural networks, or by stimulating cells within endocrine organs to release chemical signals.

An example of how hormones alter the development of neurons and neural networks can be seen in the singing of courtship songs in male zebra finches. Normally, female zebra finches do not sing. Males do, and very early in life certain cells in their brains produce estrogen, which acts on target neurons in the higher vocal centre of the developing brain. Estrogen invokes a complex series of biochemical changes resulting in the production of more nerve cells in the parts of the brain regulating singing. Brains of developing females do not produce estrogen and females do not sing courtship songs. In the absence of estrogen, the number of neurons in the higher vocal centre of females declines over time **(Figure 32.10)**. If young, female zebra finches are given estrogen, they produce more nerve cells in the higher vocal centre and they can sing. Specific stimuli, such as the songs of familiar or unfamiliar males, alter the genetic activity of the nerve cells controlling adult birds' behaviour.

Changes in the concentrations of hormones over time also affect behaviour. For example, as honeybees age, workers perform different tasks. Nurse bees—adults younger than 15 days—tend to care for larvae and maintain the hive; forager bees—adults older than 15 days—make foraging excursions from the hive to collect food (nectar and pollen) **(Figure 32.11)**. This behavioural change is induced by rising concentrations of juvenile hormone (see Chapter 43) released by a gland near the bee's brain. Despite its name, circulating levels of juvenile hormone increase as a honeybee ages.

Juvenile hormone affects bee behaviour by stimulating genes in certain brain cells to produce proteins such as octopamine that affect the nervous system. Octopamine stimulates neural transmissions and reinforces memories. It is concentrated in the antennal lobes, the parts of the bee's brain that contribute to analysis of chemical scents in the external environment, and occurs at higher concentrations in older, foraging bees, those with higher levels of juvenile hormone. Experimentally delivered extra juvenile hormone causes bees to increase their production of octopamine. This, in turn, increases octopamine levels in the antennal lobes and helps the foraging bee recognize the odours of flowers where it can collect nectar and pollen.

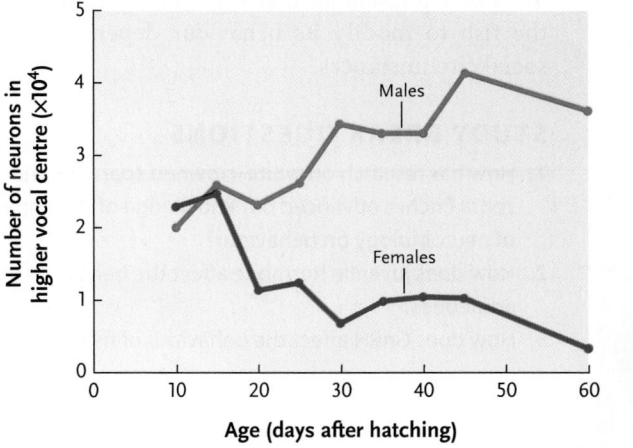

**FIGURE 32.10 Hormonally induced changes in brain structure.** The brains of young male zebra finches secrete estrogen, which stimulates production of additional neurons in the higher vocal centre. Lacking estrogen, young female zebra finches have fewer neurons in this region of the brain.

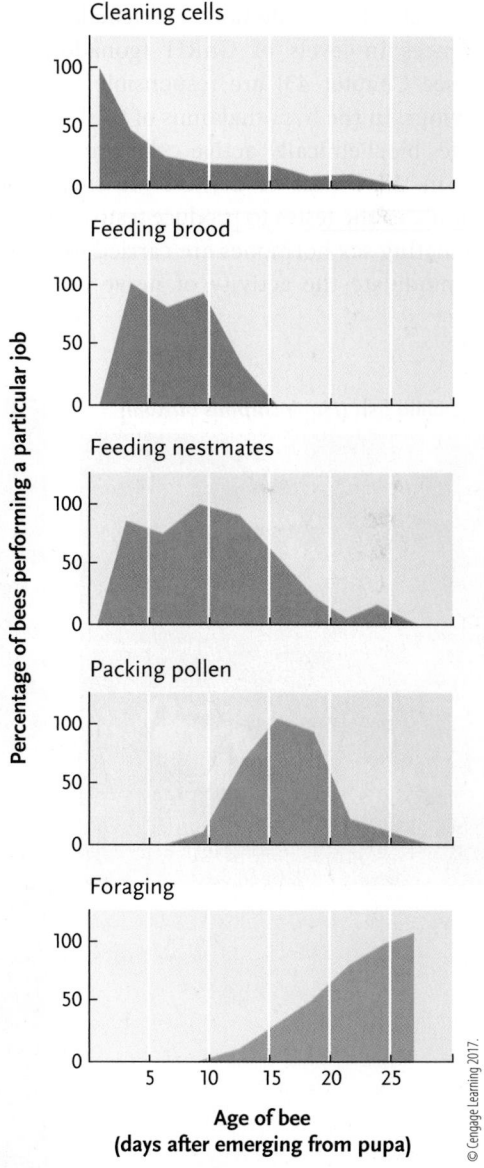

**FIGURE 32.11 Age and task specialization in honeybee (*Apis mellifera*) workers.** Newly emerged adult bees (nurses) typically clean cells and feed the brood, whereas older workers (foragers) leave the hive to forage for food.

The honeybee example illustrates how genes and hormones interact in the development of behaviour. Genes code for the production of hormones that become part of the intracellular environment of their target cells. Hormones then directly or indirectly change genetic activity and enzymatic biochemistry in these cells. When the target cells are neurons, changes in biochemistry translate into changes in the animal's behaviour.

An African cichlid fish illustrates how hormones regulate reproductive behaviour. Some adult male cichlids maintain nesting territories on the bottom of Lake Tanganyika in East Africa (**Figure 32.12**). Territory holders are relatively brightly coloured and attract egg-laden females with elaborate behavioural displays. These males aggressively defend their territories against neighbouring territory holders and incursions by non-territorial males. Non-territorial males (drifters) are much less colourful and aggressive and do not control a patch of suitable nesting habitat. They do not court females.

Differences in levels of GnRH (gonadotropin-releasing hormone; see Chapter 43) are responsible for differences in male behaviour. In the hypothalamus of the brain of territorial males, large, biochemically active cells produce GnRH. The same cells in the brains of drifters are small and inactive. GnRH stimulates the testes to produce testosterone and sperm. When circulating sex hormones are carried to the brain of the fish, they modulate the activity of nerve cells that regulate sexual and aggressive behaviour. In the absence of GnRH, male fish do not court females or attack other males.

What causes the differences in the neuronal and hormonal physiology of the two types of male fish? Russell Fernald and his students manipulated the territorial status of males. Some territorial males were stripped of their territories and some non-territorial males were provided with territories. As a control, the territorial status of other males was unaltered. Four weeks after the changes, Fernald and his students compared experimental and control fishes. They considered coloration and behaviour, as well as the size of the GnRH-producing cells in the brains. Territorial males that had been changed to non-territorial males had lost their bright colours and stopped being combative. Moreover, their GnRH-producing cells were smaller than those of the territory-holding controls. Conversely, males that gained a territory had developed bright colours and displayed aggressive behaviours toward other males. GnRH-producing cells in their brains were larger than those of control fish.

This example shows that hormonal changes affect the fishes' success or failure at gaining and holding a territory. Fish can detect and store information about their aggressive interactions. Neurons that process this information transmit their input to the hypothalamus. There it affects the size of cells producing GnRH, in turn dictating the hormonal state of the male. A decrease in GnRH production turns a feisty territorial male into a subdued drifter. Drifters bide their time and build energy reserves for a future attempt at defeating a weaker male and taking over his territory. Males that regain territorial status develop higher levels GnRH, and show vigorous sexual and aggressive behaviour.

Note the general similarity of these processes to those described for song learning by white-crowned sparrows. The fish's brain has cells that secrete hormones that can change its biochemistry, structure, and function in response to well-defined social stimuli. These physiological changes make it possible for the fish to modify its behaviour depending on its social circumstances.

### STUDY BREAK QUESTIONS

1. How has research on white-crowned sparrows and zebra finches advanced our knowledge of the impact of neurobiology on behaviour?
2. How does juvenile hormone affect the behaviour of adult bees?
3. How does GnRH affect the behaviour of fish?

**a. African cichlid fish (*Haplochromis burtoni*)**

Nonterritorial male

Territorial male

Russell Fernald, Stanford University

**b.**

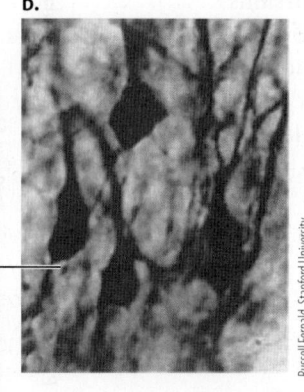

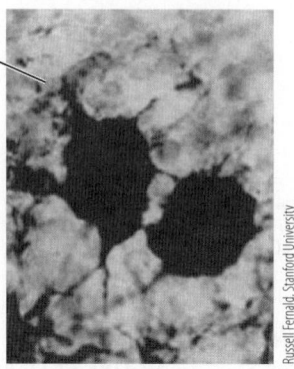

Russell Fernald, Stanford University

**FIGURE 32.12** Photograph **(a)** compares a non-territorial male *Haplochromis burtoni* (top) with a territorial one. Photomicrographs **(b)** compare gonadotropin-releasing hormone (GnRH) cells in the corresponding non-territorial and territorial males.

## 32.7 Neural Anatomy and Behaviour

Sensory systems are often structured to acquire a disproportionately large amount of information about the stimuli that are most important to the survival and reproductive success of a species. In many cases, sensory information can be relayed directly to motor neurons with little central processing decreasing the time required to produce a response. For instance, insects such as crickets fly mainly at night and avoid most predatory birds. But nocturnal flight exposes them to hunting insectivorous bats. Most insectivorous bats hunt at night and rely on echolocation to detect, identify, and track flying prey (see Chapter 45). The echolocation calls of these bats are usually intense, about 130 dB at 10 cm distance, making the calls stronger than the sound of a smoke detector alarm. The echolocation calls of most bats, however, are beyond the range of human hearing (nominally 20 kHz). While bats use echolocation to obtain information about surroundings and potential prey, these calls can also warn crickets and other insects of an approaching bat.

Many orthopteran insects (grasshoppers and their relatives) have ears on their front legs **(Figure 32.13)** usually used to hear the advertising calls of males. Black field crickets also use these ears to listen to echolocating bats, and then initiate defensive behaviour. Sensory neurons connected to the ears fire in response to bats' echolocation calls, and the information is immediately translated into evasive action. When a bat attacks from the cricket's right side, the right ear receives stronger stimulation than the left ear. The cricket's nervous system relays incoming messages from the right ear to the motor neurons controlling the left hind leg. This stimulation induces firing of motor neurons that control the left hind leg, causing it to jerk up. This, in turn, blocks the movement of the left hindwing, reducing flight power generated on the cricket's left side. Now the cricket swerves sharply to the left and loses altitude, effectively diving down and away from the approaching bat **(Figure 32.14)**.

The structure and neural connections of sensory systems also allow some animals to distinguish potentially life-threatening from more mundane stimuli. Fiddler crabs live and feed on mud flats. They dig burrows providing safe refuge from predators such as gulls and shorebirds. Distinguishing between

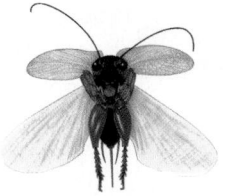

A flying cricket usually holds its hind legs close to the body so that they don't get in the way of its wings.

Sound waves from a predatory bat

When a cricket hears the ultrasonic call of a bat coming from its left side, it automatically lifts its right hind leg.

The raised leg interrupts the right wing's movement, causing the insect to swerve down to the right and away from the approaching predator.

**FIGURE 32.14 A neural mechanism for escape behaviour in the black field cricket (*Teleogryllus oceanicus*).**

Source: May, M. 1991. Aerial defense tactics of flying insects. *American Scientist*, Volume 79, Issue 4, pp. 316–328

predators and other crabs allows a fiddler crab to use its burrow to best advantage. The crab does not dash for cover whenever anything moves in its field of vision, only when it sees a gull or shorebird.

Fiddler crabs have long-stalked eyes that they hold perpendicular to the ground **(Figure 32.15)**. John Layne wondered whether these crabs have a divided field of view to distinguish dangerous predators from fellow crabs. If so, an approaching large gull would stimulate receptors on the upper part of the eye. Movements of other crabs would stimulate receptors below the midpoint of the eyes. Receptors above and below the retinal equator would relay signals to different groups of neurons, effectively wiring the crab's nervous system for a split field of view. If this were correct, stimulation of receptors above the

**FIGURE 32.13 A great grig (*Cyphoderris monstrosa*), an orthopteran with ears located on its forelegs (arrow shows grig's right ear)**

**FIGURE 32.15 A fiddler crab (*Uca pugilator*)**

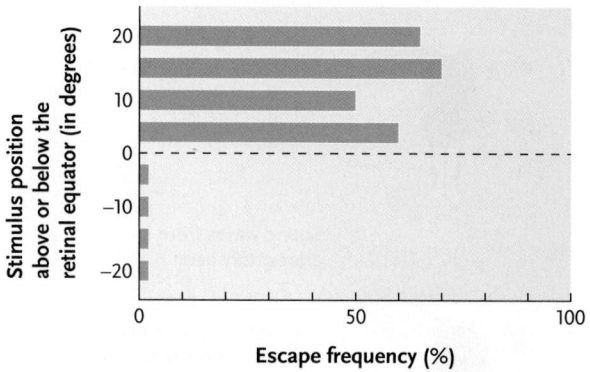

**FIGURE 32.16 Stimuli that activated the upper part of the retinae of *Uca pugilator* elicited escape behaviour much more often than those activating the lower retinas.**

midline of the eye would activate neurons controlling an escape response, triggering a dash for the burrow. A moving stimulus at or below eye level would not.

Layne placed crabs individually in a glass jar on an elevated platform. He presented a black square to each crab from two different heights. The stimulus circled the jar above or below the crab's eyes. Stimuli activating the upper part of the retina induced escape behaviour; those below the retinal equator were usually ignored **(Figure 32.16)**. Specific nervous system connections between a fiddler crab's eyes and brain provide appropriate responses to different specific stimuli.

The match between the structure of an animal's nervous system and the real-world challenges it faces extends beyond the ability to avoid predators. Star-nosed moles live in wet tunnels in North American marshlands and spend almost all their lives in complete darkness. Like bats, its receptor–perceptual system enables it to find food in the dark. A star-nosed mole eats mainly earthworms it locates with its nose, but not by smell. As the mole proceeds down its tunnel, 22 fingerlike tentacles on its nose sweep the area directly ahead of it. Each tentacle is covered with thousands of Eimer's organs (touch receptors; **Figure 32.17**). Sensory nerve terminals in Eimer's organs generate complex and detailed patterns of signals about the objects they contact. These messages are relayed by neurons to the cortex of the mole's brain, much of which is devoted to the analysis of information received from the nose's touch receptors.

The structural basis of the mole's sensory analysis is reflected by the amount of brain tissue responding to signals from its nose. The mole's brain contains many more cells decoding input from Eimer's glands than the combined input received from all other parts of the animal's body (Figure 32.17b). Moreover, the brain does not treat inputs from all 22 of the mole's "nose fingers" equally. Instead, the brain devotes more cells to input from tentacles closest to the mouth. Fewer cells analyze messages from those farther away. The extra attention given to signals from tentacles closest to the mouth helps the star-nosed mole locate prey that are close to its mouth, in turn allowing it to feed more efficiently.

Animals' nervous systems do not offer neutral and complete pictures of the environment. Instead, the pictures are distorted, but the unbalanced perceptions of the world are advantageous because certain types of information are far more important than others for the animals' survival and reproductive success.

### STUDY BREAK QUESTIONS

1. How do crickets hear the echolocation calls of bats?
2. How does what they see influence the behaviour of fiddler crabs?
3. What function is played by the star of a star-nosed mole?

## 32.8 Communication

In animal communication, one individual produces a signal that is received by another. This can change the behaviour of one or both individuals in a way that benefits the signaller and/or the signal receiver. The signaller is the individual transmitting information (the signal), and the signal receiver **(Figure 32.18)** is the one receiving the signal. Behaviour such as mimicry (see Section 30.4) and the success of nest parasites (see above) occurs when one species breaks the signal codes of another, exploiting them to advantage.

Animals use a variety of sensory modalities to transmit signals, including acoustical, chemical, electrical, vibrational, and visual. Some signals combine modalities. Sometimes the animal itself is a signal; in other situations, the animal's excretory or eliminated products are signals.

Bird songs are acoustical signals. The song of a male whippoorwill (*Caprimulgus vociferus*) or grey vireo, advertises his presence to females and may help him secure a mate. The same song is heard by other males, who recognize it as a territorial display. After the eggs have been laid, the same song is heard by the young developing in the eggs. This exposure influences the songs to which the animals respond when they mature. Other birds, such as male club-winged manakins (*Machaeropterus deliciosus*) and some hummingbirds, use courtship sounds produced by feather stridulations, rubbing one feather against another. Many other animals, from insects to rattlesnakes, use sounds as signals. Pacific herring (*Clupea pallasii*) communicate with conspecifics through the noise generated with little bursts of gas (known colloquially as "farts") passed from the anus.

A striped skunk's (*Mephitis mephitis*; **Figure 32.19a**) black and white stripes constitute a **visual signal**. Other examples of visual signals are humans' facial expressions and body language. These visual signals are available to anyone viewing them. Visual signals can be enhanced by morphological features, such as the erectile crest of a royal kingbird (*Onychorhynchus coronatus*; Figure 32.19b), or bioluminescent signals in animals living in darkness (e.g., Figure 39.4, Chapter 39). In many animals, visual signals are ritualized—exaggerated and stereotyped to enhance their function as signals, such as the swaggering gait of a striped skunk.

### a. Sensory organs on the tentacle of a star-nosed mole

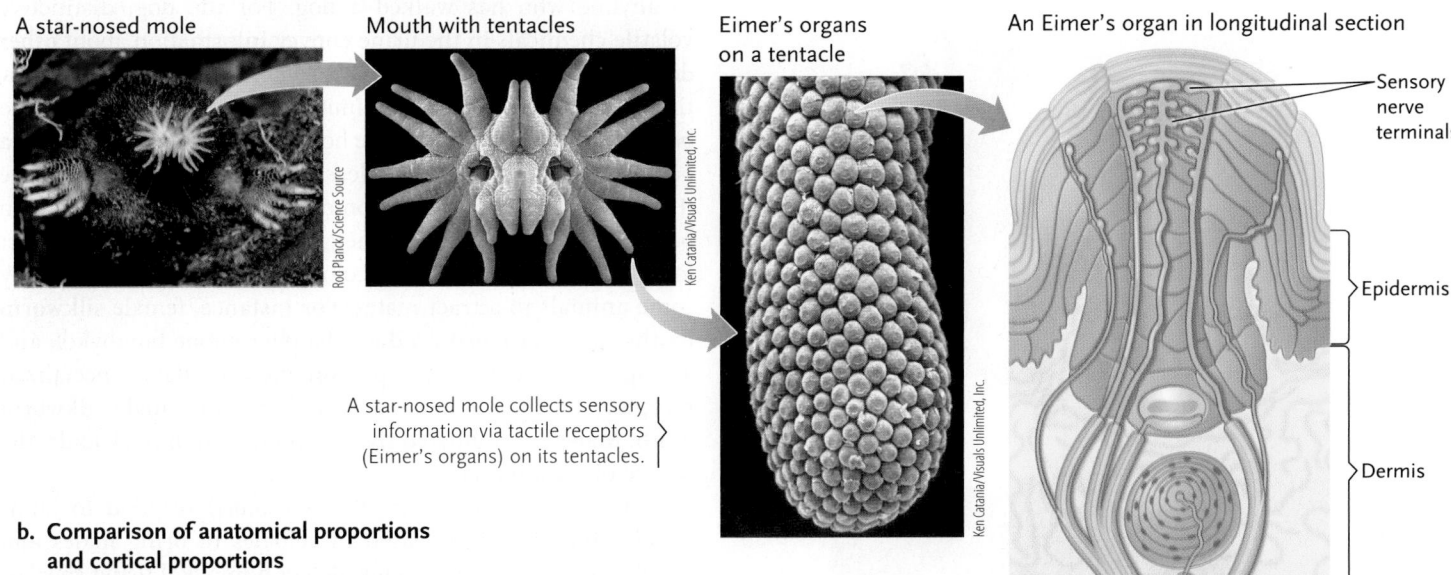

A star-nosed mole

Mouth with tentacles

Eimer's organs on a tentacle

An Eimer's organ in longitudinal section

Sensory nerve terminals

Epidermis

Dermis

Rod Planck/Science Source

Ken Catania/Visuals Unlimited, Inc.

Ken Catania/Visuals Unlimited, Inc.

A star-nosed mole collects sensory information via tactile receptors (Eimer's organs) on its tentacles.

### b. Comparison of anatomical proportions and cortical proportions

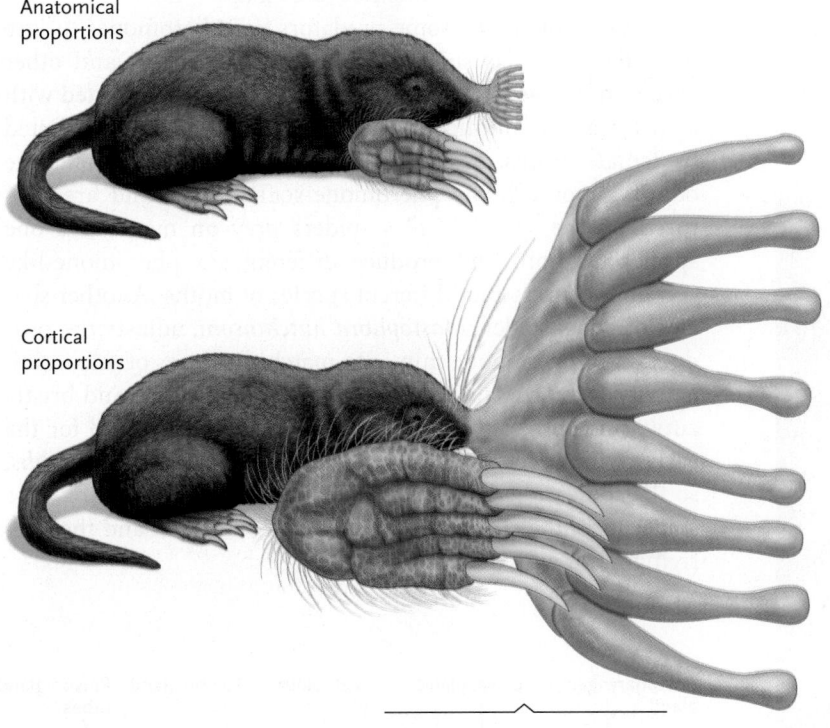

Anatomical proportions

Cortical proportions

Most of the mole's cerebral cortex is devoted to the tentacles and front, digging feet.

**FIGURE 32.17 The collection and analysis of sensory information by the star-nosed mole (*Condylura cristata*). (a)** The mole's nose has 22 fleshy tentacles covered with cylindrical tactile receptors called *Eimer's organs*. Each Eimer's organ contains sensory nerve terminals. **(b)** The mole's cerebral cortex devotes far more space and neurons to analysis of input from the tentacles than from elsewhere on the body. These drawings compare the relative amounts of sensory information coming from different parts of a mole's body.

M. B. Fenton

**FIGURE 32.18 Song birds, such as this grey vireo (*Vireo vicinior*), use songs to advertise their presence to unmated females and to other males**

a.

b.

**FIGURE 32.19** **(a)** The distinctive black and white pattern of a striped skunk (*Mephitis mephitis*) warns predators about its chemical defence. **(b)** The distinctive crest of a female royal kingbird is a sexually dimorphic character: males have red crests; females have yellow crests.

Many species produce chemical signals, as is well known to anyone who has walked a dog. For the dog, distinctive volatile chemicals in the urine convey information about other dogs that have urinated there. Pheromones are distinctive volatile chemicals released in minute amounts to influence the behaviour of conspecifics. The body of a worker ant contains a battery of glands, each releasing a different pheromone **(Figure 32.20)**. One set of pheromones recruits fellow workers to battle colony invaders. Another stimulates workers to collect food discovered outside the colony. Pheromones are used by some animals to attract mates. For instance, female silkworm moths (*Bombyx mori*) produce the pheromone bombykol, and a single molecule of this pheromone stimulates specialized receptors on the antennae of any downwind, male silkworm moth. Males so stimulated fly upwind in search the female, the source of the stimulus.

Male silkworm moths (*Bombyx mori*) respond to bombykol produced and released by females to bring males and females together. Male *B. mori* detect bombykol using specialized receptors on their antennae (see Chapter 45).

Not surprisingly, some predators use pheromones to lure prey. Female bolas spiders (*Mastophora cornigera* and other species in the genus) use a sticky ball of web impregnated with a chemical that mimics the odour of sex pheromones secreted by female moths. Male moths respond to the lure of these odours, approach the pheromone-soaked web, and are captured by the spiders. Bolas spiders prey on more than one species of moth and produce different sex pheromone-like compounds to attract different species of moths. Another species of bolas spider, *Mastophora hutchinsoni*, adjusts the production of pheromone mimic to match the times of maximum activity by smoky tetanolita (*Tetanolita mynesalis*) and bristly cutworm (*Lacinipolia renigera*). The pheromone blend for the early-flying *L. renigera* does not attract late-flying *T. mynesalis*, so the spider adjusts the blend of pheromones on its lure. This spider lures the early-flying moth with one blend and the late-flying moth with another.

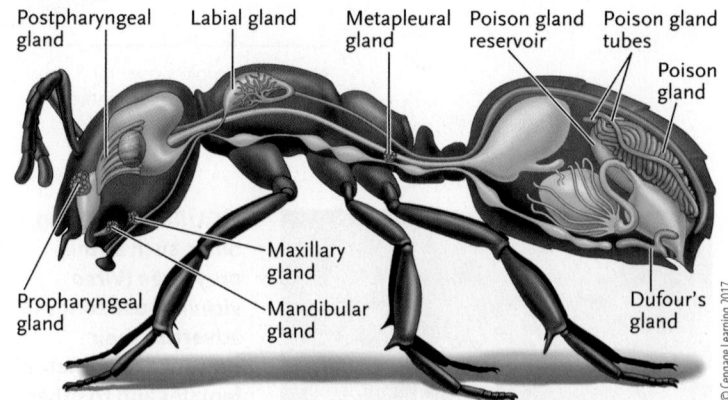

**FIGURE 32.20** **Chemical signals.** An ant's body contains a host of pheromone-producing glands, each of which manufactures and releases its own volatile chemical or chemicals.

In many species, touch conveys important messages from a signaller to a receiver. **Tactile signals** can operate only over very short distances, but for social animals living in close company, they play a significant role in the development of friendly bonds between individuals **(Figure 32.21)**.

Some freshwater fish species use weak **electric signals** to communicate. This is especially true of species living in murky tropical rivers where visual signals cannot be seen (see Figure 45.41, Chapter 45). These fish have electric organs that produce electric signals that vary in intensity, duration, and frequency. This gives the fish a considerable repertoire of signals. Among the New World knifefish (order Gymnotiformes), including the electric eel (Figure 45.41, Chapter 45), electrical discharges can signal threats, submission, or a readiness to breed.

Karl von Frisch demonstrated that the famous dance of the honeybee involves tactile, acoustical, and chemical signals **(Figure 32.22)**. When a foraging honeybee discovers a source of pollen or nectar, it returns to its colony. There, in the darkness of the hive, it dances on the vertical surface of the honeycomb. The dancer moves in a circle, attracting a crowd of workers. Some workers follow and maintain physical contact with the dancer. The dance delivers information about the food source, its quality, and the distance and direction observers will need to fly to locate it.

The bee performs a round dance when the food source is less than 75 m from the hive (Figure 32.22a). Here the bee moves in tight circles, swinging its abdomen back and forth. Bees surrounding the dancer produce a brief acoustical signal that stimulates the dancer to regurgitate a sample of the food it discovered. The regurgitated sample serves as a chemical cue for other workers that search for the food. The bee uses a waggle dance when the food is farther away. This involves a half-circle in one direction, then a straight line while waggling its abdomen, and finally a half-circle in the other direction (see Figure 32.22b). With each waggle, the dancer produces a brief buzzing sound. The angle of the waggle run relative to the vertical honeycomb indicates the direction of the food source relative to the position of the Sun (see Figure 32.22c). The duration of the waggles and buzzes carries information about distance to the food. The more time spent waggling and buzzing, the farther away the food is from the hive. Some people were loath to accept a "dance language" in bees, perhaps in the hopes that language was a feature unique to humans. Bees and many other insects use "simple eyes" (ocelli) to measure light intensity. By blackening the ocelli of dancing bees, James L. Gould manipulated their perception of the Sun. This affected the messages in the dances, effectively lying to other bees about the location of food. The bees observing the dance did not have blackened ocelli and went to find flowers in the location indicated by the dance. In reality, this was the wrong location because of differences in the dancing and observer bees' perceptions of the position of the Sun.

**An echolocating animal** stores the outgoing signal in its brain for comparison with returning echoes. The differences between what the animal "says" and what it hears are the data used in echolocation. However, when an echolocating bat or dolphin produces echolocation signals, the signals are audible

**a. Round dance**

**b. Waggle dance**

**c. Coding direction in the waggle dance**

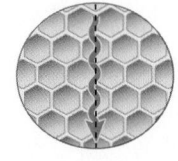

When the bee moves straight down the comb, other bees fly to the source directly away from the Sun.

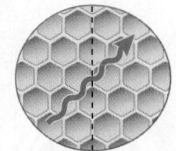

When the bee moves 45° to the right of vertical, other bees fly at a 45° angle to the right of the Sun.

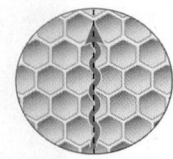

When the bee moves straight up the comb, other bees fly straight toward the Sun.

© Cengage Learning 2017.

**FIGURE 32.22 Dance communication by honeybees (*Apis mellifera*).** Foraging honeybees transmit information about the location and quality of a food source by dancing on a vertical honeycomb. **(a)** If the food source is close to the hive, the forager performs a *round dance*. **(b)** When food is farther from the hive, the honeybee performs a *waggle dance*. **(c)** The dancing bee indicates the direction to the distant food source by the angle of the waggle run.

M. B. Fenton

**FIGURE 32.21 Tactile signals.** Grooming by hyacinth macaws (*Anodorhynchus hyacinthinus*) removes ectoparasites and dirt from feathers. The close physical contact promotes friendly relationships between groomer and groomee.

to some other animals as well. When the bat or dolphin is foraging, potential prey (certain insects for the bat; certain fish for the dolphin) hear the signals and move away from the sound source (= negative phonotaxis) in an effort to evade the approaching predator. When the bat is close (strong echolocation signals), moths with ears dive to the ground or use erratic flight to evade the bats. Moths with ears sensitive to bat echolocation calls evade bat attacks 40% of the time. Insects lacking bat detectors are caught at much higher rates, sometimes >90% of the time. Acoustic warfare between bats and insects and dolphins and fish intrigues biologists because of the measures and countermeasures used by both predator and prey.

The same echolocation calls that alert potential prey are available to any other animals within earshot, provided that their ears are sensitive to the frequencies in the signals. Little brown myotis **(Figure 32.23a)** eavesdrop on the calls of conspecifics to locate concentrations of prey. Spotted bats (*Euderma maculatum*; Figure 32.23b) either approach a calling conspecific, apparently to chase it away, or turn and leave the area. Resident killer whales (*Orcinus orca*) in the Pacific Ocean off the west coast of Canada typically use echolocation to detect, track, and locate the salmon they eat. Transient killer whales in the same area feed mainly on marine mammals. These killer whales rarely echolocate. Local marine mammals, such as seals, quickly leave the water when they hear the echolocation calls of approaching killer whales.

The study of echolocation is a rich source of information about signals, signal design, hearing systems, and behaviour. Signal receivers often respond to communications from signallers in predictable ways. A male white-crowned sparrow generally avoids entering a neighbouring territory when it hears the song of the resident male. Similarly, young male baboons and mandrills often retreat without a fight when they see an older male's visual threat display **(Figure 32.24)**, even when retreat means loss of a chance to mate with a female. Why do these individuals behave in ways that appear to benefit their rivals but not themselves?

Explaining behavioural interactions often means considering how an animal's actions affect its reproductive output. The retreating white-crowned sparrow avoids wasting time and energy on a battle it is likely to lose. By retreating, the would-be intruder minimizes the chances of being injured or killed by a resident male. Moreover, ousting the current resident might be more tiring and risky than finding a suitable unoccupied breeding site. Resident males usually win physical contests, and intruders typically succeed in gaining a territory from a resident only after a prolonged series of exhausting clashes. Observations of territorial species such as birds, lizards, frogs, fish, and insects generally support these predictions.

a.

b.

M. B. Fenton

**FIGURE 32.23  A little brown myotis** (a) **and a spotted bat** (b)

Courtesy of Naas Rautenbach

**FIGURE 32.24  The open-mouth threat display of a male chacma baboon (*Papio ursinus*) almost looks like a yawn but is much more menacing.**

Applying a similar argument to competition among male baboons, smaller or younger males will concede females to threatening older rivals without fighting. Retreating means reducing the risk of losing a fight and being injured. Evolutionary analyses suggest that the signaller and signal receiver benefit from the exchange of signals. Here, both individuals avoid a physical altercation that might be damaging or fatal.

In winter, common ravens (*Corvus corax*) sometimes emit a "yell" call upon finding the carcass of a deer. The yell attracts a crowd of hungry ravens. The calling behaviour puzzled Bernd Heinrich, who noted that, when paired territory-holding adult ravens found a carcass, they fed quietly and did not yell. He noted young ravens without territories yelled when they happened upon a carcass in another bird's territory. The yells attracted other ravens, which collectively overwhelmed the residents' efforts to defend the carcass and their territory. Non-territorial ravens used yells to exploit the food supply, whereas residents just ate. Heinrich concluded that the reproductive benefit of resident ravens was enhanced by uninterrupted feeding. Non-territorial ravens succeeded in their trespassing only when they attracted others.

## STUDY BREAK QUESTIONS

1. What sensory modalities do animals use in communication?
2. How do "yells" influence the behaviour of ravens? Explain.
3. What is echolocation? Which animals echolocate?

## 32.9 Language: Syntax and Symbols

Although language is communication, not all communication is language. Many people believe that language is the exclusive domain of humans, but the basis for the distinction between humans and other animals is not clear. The round and waggle dances of honeybees contain both syntax (the order in which information is presented) and symbols (a display that represents something else), and many consider them to meet the criteria for language.

Vervet monkeys also have a repertoire of signals to alert conspecifics to different predators. These monkeys use one signal for snakes, another for leopards, and still another for raptors. Furthermore, they show different predator-specific defensive behaviours. Chickadees (*Poecile atricapillus*) also use different alarm calls to alert others to approaching danger. Captive, trained chimpanzees and gorillas (*Gorilla gorilla*) have been reported to be able to learn and use American Sign Language (ASL).

When it comes to communication, humans are not as distinct from other animals as some people would like to believe. For example, like most other animals, humans used body language. To appreciate this, and redundancy in animal communication, observe the body language and facial expressions of someone talking on a telephone. The eloquence of these signals is not conveyed to the signal receiver at the other end of the phone!

As in the case of the songs of some birds, humans also show sex-specific transmission of language. In 2011, Peter Forster and Colin Renfrew reported that, in several parts of the world **(Figure 32.25)**, immigrant men are central to producing changes in local languages. Note that this has been documented in North America, Iceland, Africa, India, and the Malayo–Polynesian areas. The finding is based on the relationship between the incidence of Y-chromosome types (male lineages) on language change, while mtDNA types (female lineages) reflect the persistence of the more ancient language. The movement of animals—in this case people—influences the spread of behaviour, culture, and social norms.

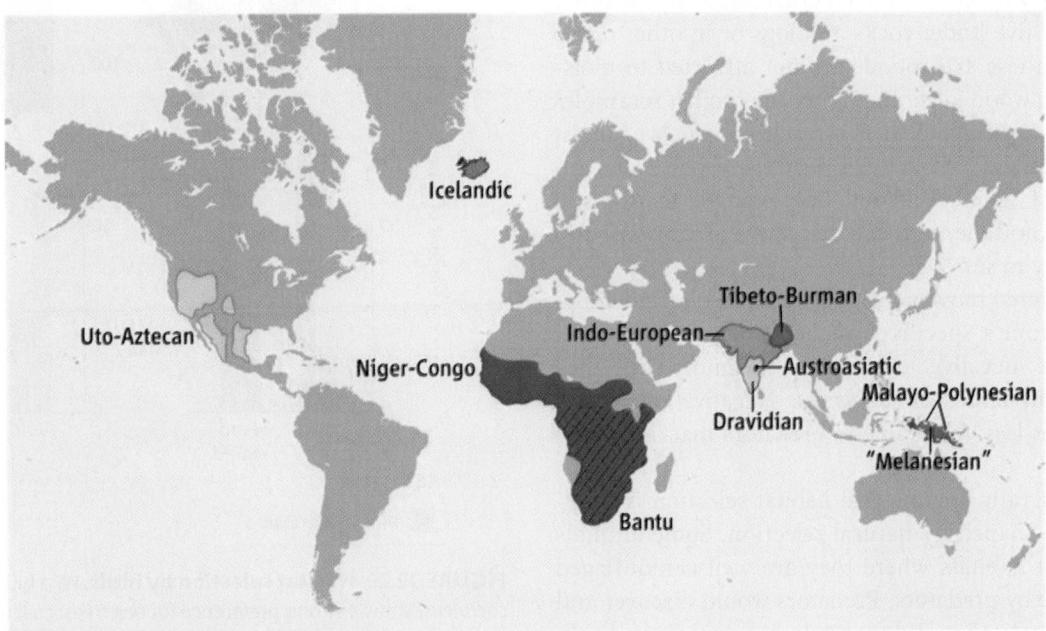

**FIGURE 32.25 The relationship between Y-chromosome DNA types and language.** This pattern does not emerge from mtDNA derived from the mother. Here, "Melanesian" indicates non–Malayo-Polynesian languages (New Guinea). The Niger–Congo language family includes Bantu (the hatched area).

Source: From Forster and Renfrew. 2011. "Mother Tongue and Y Chromosomes," *Science* Volume 333, page 1390. *Science* by American Association for the Advancement of Science Reproduced with permission of AMERICAN ASSOCIATION FOR THE ADVANCEMENT OF SCIENCE in the format Republish in a book via Copyright Clearance Center.

**STUDY BREAK QUESTIONS**

1. What is the meaning and importance of syntax and symbols in signalling?
2. What are the social implications of findings about the appearances of new languages in humans?
3. What other animals use language?

## 32.10 Space

The geographic range of many animal species includes a mosaic of habitat types. The breeding ranges of white-crowned sparrows can encompass forests, meadows, housing developments, and city dumps. Other animals have a limited geographic range; for example, a Kirtland's warbler (*Dendroica kirtlandii*) is found only in young jack pine forests. At the individual level, an animal's home range, its choice of habitat, is critically important because the habitat provides food, shelter, nesting sites, and the other organisms with which it interacts. If an animal chooses a habitat that does not provide appropriate resources, it will not survive and reproduce.

On a large spatial scale, animals almost certainly use multiple criteria to select the habitats they occupy, but we do not know the general principles about how animals make these choices. When a migrating bird arrives at its breeding range, it probably cues on large-scale geographic features, such as a pond or a patch of large trees. If the bird does not find the food or nesting resources it needs, or if other individuals already occupy the space, it may move to another habitat patch.

Thus, on a finer spatial scale, basic responses to physical factors enable animals to find suitable habitats. **Kinesis** (*kine* = movement; *es* = inward) is a change in the rate of movement or the frequency of turning movements in response to environmental stimuli. Wood lice (terrestrial crustaceans in the order Isopoda) typically live under rocks and logs or in other damp places. Although these arthropods are not attracted to moisture per se, when a wood louse encounters dry soil, it scrambles around, turning frequently. When it reaches a patch of moist soil, it moves much less. This kinesis results in wood lice accumulating in moist habitats. Wood lice exposed to dry soil quickly dehydrate and die, so those that move to moister habitats are more likely to survive.

A **taxis** (= ordered movement) is a response directed either toward or away from a specific stimulus. Cockroaches (order Blattodea) exhibit negative phototaxis, meaning that they actively avoid light and seek darkness. Negative phototaxis makes cockroaches less vulnerable to predators that use vision to find their food.

Biologists generally assume that habitat selection is adaptive and has been shaped by natural selection. Some animals instinctively select habitats where they are well camouflaged and less detectable by predators. Predators would discover and eliminate individuals that did not select a matching background, along with any alleles responsible for the mismatch.

Many insects have inherited preferences for the plants they eat as larvae (e.g., caterpillars). Adults often lay their eggs only on appropriate food plants, effectively selecting the habitats where their offspring will live and feed.

Vertebrates sometimes exhibit innate preferences, as demonstrated by two closely related species of European birds, blue tits (*Cyanistes caeruleus*) and coal tits (*Periparus ater*). Adult blue tits forage mainly in oak trees; coal tits in pine trees. When researchers reared the young of both species in cages without any vegetation and then offered them a choice between oak branches and pine branches, coal tits immediately gravitated toward pine branches and blue tits toward oak branches, suggesting an innate preference **(Figure 32.26)**. Each species feeds most efficiently in the tree species it prefers.

**STUDY BREAK QUESTION**

1. Define *kinesis* and *taxis*.

## 32.11 Home Range and Territory

Space is an important resource for animals. Although many animals are motile, moving about in space, others are sessile. Sessile species such as barnacles (see Chapter 27) anchor themselves to the substrate but are motile as larvae. Barnacles that live on whales or the hulls of ships are sessile but mobile because of the substrate they selected. Motile animals have a home range, the

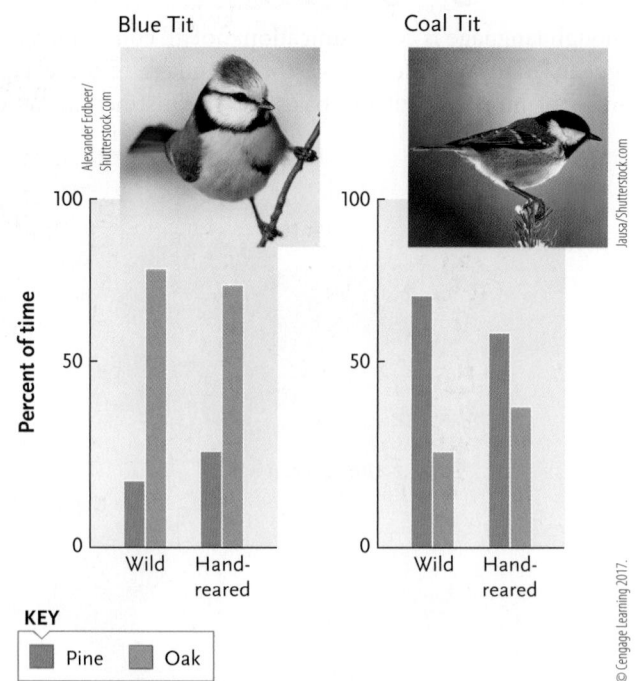

**FIGURE 32.26 Habitat selection by birds.** Wild blue tits (*Cyanistes caeruleus*) show a strong preference for oak trees; coal tits (*Periparus ater*) show a strong preference for pines. Hand-reared birds raised in a vegetation-free environment showed identical but slightly weaker responses.

space they regularly traverse during their lives. Home ranges or parts of home ranges become territories when they are defended. In species such as pronghorn antelopes **(Figure 32.27)**, some males hold territories. Female pronghorns are not usually territorial. There is a direct connection between territory quality and male reproductive success. Male pronghorn antelopes defending the "best" territories (those with the best food resources) attract the most females, offering the male the most opportunities to mate with the most females.

Territorial defence is always a costly activity. Patrolling territory borders, performing displays hundreds of times per day, and chasing intruders take time and energy. Moreover, territorial displays increase an animal's likelihood of being injured or detected and captured by a predator. But territorial behaviour has its benefits, such as access to females. Territorial surgeonfish (*Acanthurus lineatus*) living in coral reefs around American Samoa may engage in as many as 1900 chases per day, defending their small territories from incursions by other algae-eating fish. However, territorial surgeonfish eat five times as much food as non-territory-holders because they have more exclusive access to the food in their territories.

## STUDY BREAK QUESTIONS

1. What is the difference between a home range and a territory?
2. How are home ranges and territories different from a species' range?

## 32.12 Migration

**CONCEPT FIX** Many people think that migrating animals travel in groups. But we now know that many animals migrate alone, including birds, bats, fur seals, and sea turtles. We know relatively little about the details of the migrations and migratory behaviour of most animals. ⬢

**FIGURE 32.27 Pronghorn antelopes (*Antilocapra americana*)**

Many animal species migrate. Seasonal migrations involve individuals travelling from the area where they were born or hatched to a distant and initially unfamiliar destination. The migration is complete when the same individuals later return to their natal site. Defining migration as seasonal movements of individuals to and from different areas readily applies to many birds and other animals. This definition does not, however, describe the migrations of other animals such as monarch butterflies (*Danaus plexippus*). Here, different individuals are involved in the migration. Seasonal changes in food supply underlie the migration of monarch butterflies, which eat milkweed leaves as caterpillars and milkweed nectar as adults **(Figure 32.28)**. In eastern North America, milkweed plants grow only during spring and summer. Many adult monarchs head south in late summer, when the plants begin to die. Some migrate as much as 4000 km from eastern and central North America to central Mexico, where they cluster in spectacular numbers (Figure 32.28b and c). They appear to use olfactory cues to find preferred resting places. Unlike migrant birds, these insects do not feed at their overwintering grounds. Instead, their metabolic rate decreases in the cool mountain air. The butterflies are inactive for months, conserving their energy reserves.

With the arrival of spring, the butterflies become active and begin the return migration to northern breeding habitats. The northward migration is slow, however, and many individuals stop along the way to feed and lay eggs. Their offspring, and their offspring's offspring, continue the northward migration through the summer. Some descendants of these migrants eventually reach Canada for a final round of breeding. The summer's last generation then returns south to the spot where their ancestors, two to five generations removed, spent the previous winter.

As we have seen there are many interesting facets to migration. What is the underlying physiology of the migrants? What determines the routes that migrants follow? What cues are used in orientation and navigation?

Fuel selection is an important aspect of migration physiology. For the most part, migrating birds appear to burn fat to fuel flight, and they are able to do this because they laid down fat stores in the period leading up to migration. In 2011, however, Alex Gerson and Chris Guglielmo reported their work on Swainson's thrushes (*Catharus ustulatus*). They flew birds in a wind tunnel continuously for up to five hours **(Figure 32.29)**. The birds flew in high or in low relative humidity. When flying in drier air, the birds increased their rates of loss of lean mass (i.e., turned to using protein stores for fuel). This increased production of endogenous water and increased the concentrations of uric acid in blood plasma (a method of conserving water). Humidity clearly influences the composition of fuel consumed by flying Swainson's thrushes. Understanding the physiology of migration is an intriguing area of research.

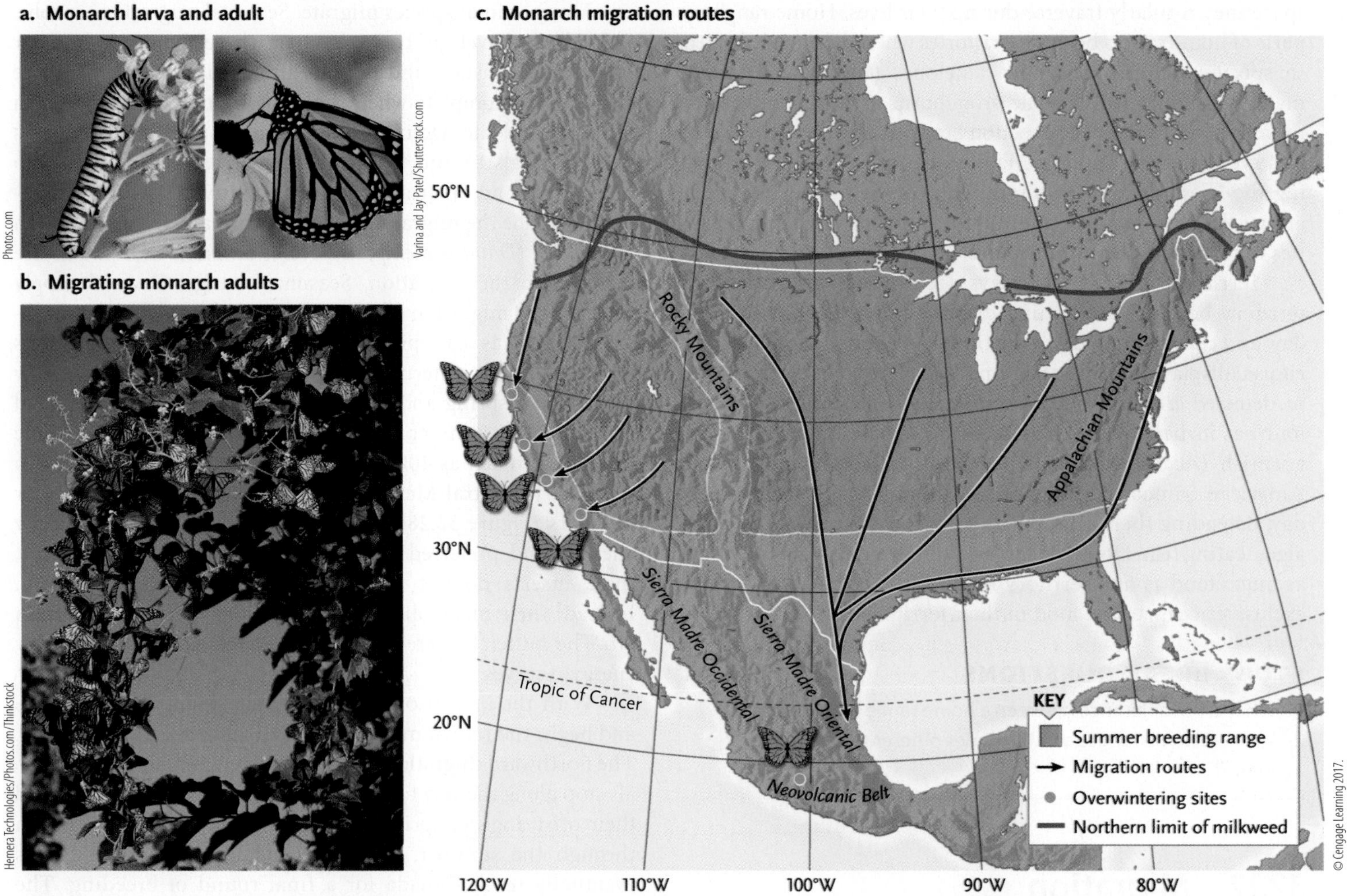

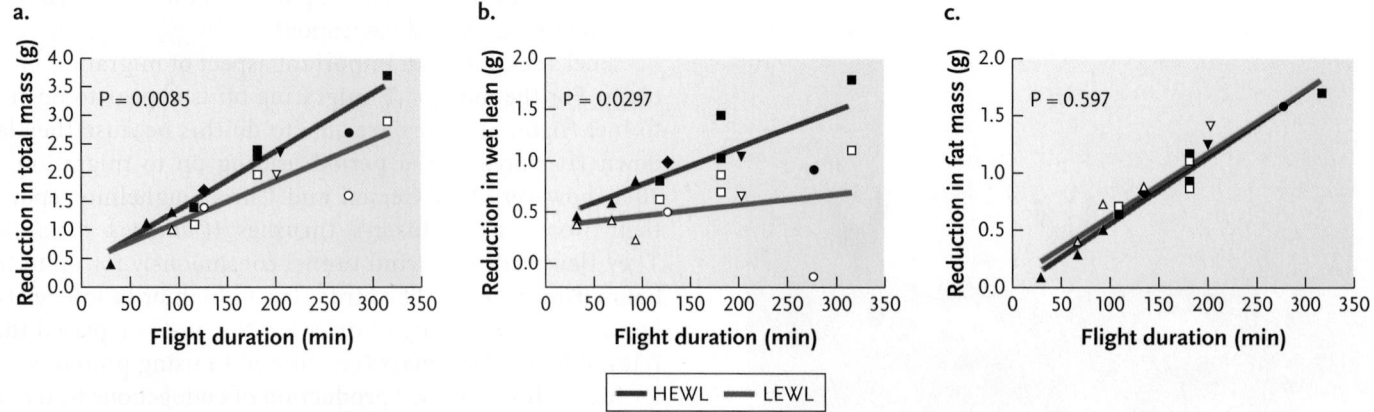

a. Monarch larva and adult
Photos.com
Varina and Jay Patel/Shutterstock.com
b. Migrating monarch adults
Hemera Technologies/Photos.com/Thinkstock
c. Monarch migration routes
50°N
30°N
20°N
Rocky Mountains
Appalachian Mountains
Sierra Madre Occidental
Sierra Madre Oriental
Tropic of Cancer
Neovolcanic Belt
KEY
Summer breeding range
Migration routes
Overwintering sites
Northern limit of milkweed
120°W
110°W
100°W
90°W
80°W
© Cengage Learning 2017.

**FIGURE 32.28 Migrating monarch butterflies. (a)** Monarch butterflies eat milkweed plants as caterpillars. **(b)** When milkweed plants in their breeding range die back at the end of summer, monarchs migrate south. The following spring, after passing the winter in a semidormant state, they migrate north. **(c)** Monarchs that live and breed east of the Rocky Mountains migrate to Mexico. Those living west of the Rocky Mountains overwinter in coastal California.

a.
P = 0.0085
Reduction in total mass (g)
Flight duration (min)
b.
P = 0.0297
Reduction in wet lean (g)
Flight duration (min)
c.
P = 0.597
Reduction in fat mass (g)
Flight duration (min)
HEWL
LEWL

**FIGURE 32.29** **Loss of mass** (a)**, wet lean mass** (b)**, and fat mass** (c) **by flying Swainson's thrushes differed significantly, depending upon humidity.** Closed symbols and red lines show data from high relative humidity (high evaporative water loss: HEWL); open symbols and blue lines are from low relative humidity (low evaporative water loss: LEWL).

Source: From Gerson, "Flight at Low Ambient Humidity Increases Protein Catabolism in Migratory Birds," *Science* 09 Sep 2011: Vol. 333, Issue 6048, pp. 1434-1436. *Science* by American Association for the Advancement of Science Reproduced with permission of AMERICAN ASSOCIATION FOR THE ADVANCEMENT OF SCIENCE in the format Republish in a book via Copyright Clearance Center.

How do young animals learn migration routes and destinations? In some cases, young migrate with adults, but this is not always the case. For most migrating animals, we do not know the details of what is involved. For instance, in North America, some bats appear to migrate between summer and winter ranges. For the most part, hoary bats (*Lasiurus cinereus*; **Figure 32.30a**) and silver-haired bats (*Lasionycteris noctivagans*; Figure 32.30b) are not found in the northern parts of their range in winter. Isotopic and other evidence suggests that these bats undertake seasonal north–south migrations but, to date, there are few records of the movements of tagged individuals.

Erin Baerwald and Robert Barclay (University of Calgary) assessed the possibility that young hoary and silver-haired bats migrated with their mothers. They analyzed microsatellite genotypes and stable isotopic values ($\delta^{13}$C, $\delta^{15}$N, and $\delta^{2}$H) in tissues obtained from bats killed (133 hoary bats and 87 silver-haired bats) at turbines on wind farms. They found no evidence that bats killed at the same time at the same turbines were close genetic relatives, or had spent the summer in the same geographic locations. These data indicate that at least hoary bats and silver-haired bats do not migrate with genetic relatives or with animals that might have been their summer neighbours.

What cues are used in orientation and navigation? Moving animals use three main categories of way-finding mechanisms: **piloting**, **compass orientation**, and **navigation**. Many species probably use some combination of these mechanisms to guide their movements.

## 32.12a Piloting

Piloting is the simplest way-finding mechanism; it involves the use of familiar landmarks to guide the journey. Grey whales migrate from Alaska to Baja California and back using visual cues provided by the Pacific coastline of North America. When it is time to breed and lay eggs, Pacific salmon use olfactory cues to pilot their way from the ocean back to the stream in which they hatched.

Often, animals that do not migrate use specific landmarks to identify their nest site or places where they have stored food. Female digger wasps (*Philanthus triangulum*) nest in soil. In 1938, Niko Tinbergen showed that, after foraging flights, these wasps used visual landmarks to find their nests **(Figure 32.31)**. While the female wasp was in the nest, Tinbergen arranged pinecones in a circle around it. As she left, the wasp flew around the area, apparently noting nearby landmarks. Tinbergen then moved the circle of pinecones a short distance away. Each time the female returned, she searched for her nest within the pinecone circle. She never once found her nest unless the pinecones were returned to their original position. Later, Tinbergen rearranged the pinecones into a triangle after females left their nests and added a ring of stones nearby. The returning females looked for their nest in the stone circle. Tinbergen concluded that digger wasps respond to the general outline or geometry of landmarks around their nests and not to the specific objects making up the landmarks.

a.

b.

**FIGURE 32.30  A hoary bat** (a) **and a silver-haired bat** (b)

Some birds that migrate at night determine their direction by using **celestial navigation**: the positions of stars. The indigo bunting flies about 3500 km from the northeastern United States to the Caribbean or Central America each fall and makes the return journey each spring. Stephen Emlen demonstrated that indigo buntings direct their migration using celestial cues

Nest

**FIGURE 32.31  Female digger wasps find their nest.** A ring of pinecones serves as a landmark for a female digger wasp (*Philanthus triangulum*). By moving landmarks, Niko Tinbergen demonstrated the role they serve in the wasp's orientation behaviour.

(**Figure 32.32**). Emlen confined individual buntings in cone-shaped test cages whose sides were lined with blotting paper. He placed inkpads on the cage bottoms and kept the cages in an outdoor enclosure so that the birds had a full view of the night sky. Whenever a bird made a directed movement, its inky footprints indicated the direction in which it was trying to move. On clear nights in fall, the footprints pointed to the south, but in spring, they pointed north. On cloudy nights, when the buntings could not see the stars, Emlen recorded that their footprints were evenly distributed in all directions. The data indicated that the compass of indigo buntings required a view of the stars.

## 32.12b  Navigation

Navigation is the most complex way-finding mechanism. It occurs when an animal moves toward a specific destination, using both a compass and a mental map of where it is in relation to the destination. Hikers in unfamiliar surroundings routinely use navigation to find their way home. They use a map to determine their current position and the necessary direction of movement, as well as a compass to orient themselves in that direction.

To document navigation, biologists often use animals carrying radio transmitters, sometimes with GPS (Global Positioning System) capability. By releasing the animals from distant locations and following them, researchers obtain evidence of migration. This is true for homing pigeons (*Columba livia*), birds that can navigate to their home coops from any direction. Homing pigeons appear to use the Sun's position as their compass and olfactory cues as their map. In Israel, biologists demonstrated that Egyptian rousette bats (*Rousettus aegyptiacus*; **Figure 32.33**) have a mental map of their home

ranges. These bats locate preferred roosts and sources of food even when released 10s of kilometres outside their home range.

Genetic analyses of populations of dragonflies (the wandering glider; *Pantala flavescens*) from different parts of the world (North America, South America, and Asia) suggest one interbreeding (panmictic) population. This raises interesting questions about the physiology of these dragonflies on flights of several thousand kilometres, as well as others about navigational cues and performance.

## 32.12c  Why Migrate?

Migrations by white-crowned sparrows and many other species are triggered by changes in day length. Shortening day length indicates approaching fall and winter; lengthening day length indicates spring. Day length changes the anterior pituitary of the bird's brain to generate a series of hormonal changes. In response, birds feed heavily and accumulate the fat reserves necessary to fuel their long journey. Sparrows also become increasingly restless at night until, one evening, they begin their nocturnal migration. Their ability to adopt and maintain a southerly orientation in autumn (and a northerly one in spring) rests in part on their capacity to use the positions of stars to provide directional information.

Not all animal species migrate and, in some species, individuals in some populations migrate, while others do not, for example, different populations of Brazilian free-tailed bats (*Tadarida brasiliensis*). Advantages to staying put can include effective exploitation of local resources, reflecting detailed local knowledge. This can be a combination of food, nest sites, mates, and local communities of predators and parasites.

Migratory behaviour entails obvious costs, such as the time and energy devoted to the journey and the risk of death

FIGURE 32.32 **Experimental Research**

## Experimental Analysis of the Indigo Bunting's Star Compass

**Indigo Bunting**

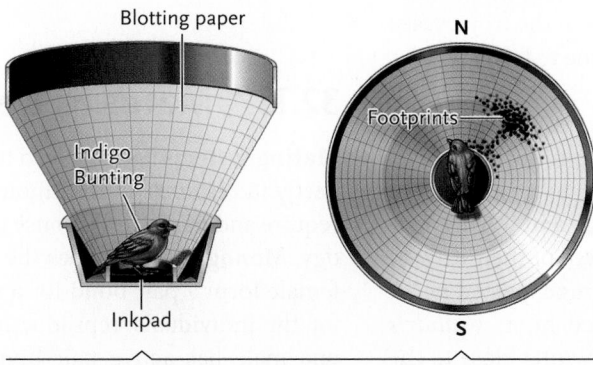

Side (left) and overhead (right) views of the test cage with blotting paper on the sides and an inkpad on the bottom.

In autumn, the bunting footprints indicated that they were trying to fly south.

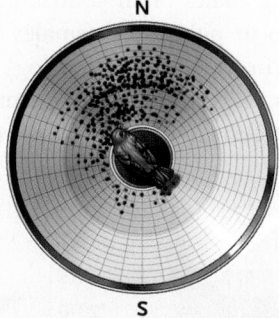

In spring, the bunting footprints indicated that they were trying to fly north.

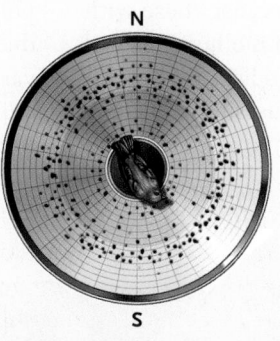

On cloudy nights, when buntings could not see the stars, their footprints indicated a random pattern of movement.

**Question:** Do indigo buntings (*Passerina cyanea*) use the positions of stars in the night sky to orient their migrations?

**Experiment:** Emlen placed individual buntings in cone-shaped test cages. He lined the sides of the cages with blotting paper, placed inkpads on the bottom, and kept the cages in an outdoor enclosure so that the birds had a full view of the sky. Whenever a bird made a directed movement, its inky footprints indicated the direction in which it was trying to fly. Emlen predicted that the footprints would show the buntings' inclination to migrate south in autumn and north in spring.

**Results:** On clear nights in autumn, the footprints pointed to the south; on clear nights in spring, they pointed north. On cloudy nights, when buntings could not see the stars, their footprints were evenly distributed in all directions.

**Conclusion:** Indigo buntings use the positions of the stars to direct their seasonal migrations. When they could see the stars above their test cages, they moved in the predicted direction; but when clouds obscured their view of the stars, they moved in random directions.

Source: © Cengage Learning 2017. Based on S. T. Emlen. 1967. "Migratory orientation of the indigo bunting, *Passerina cyanea*. Part I: Evidence for use of celestial cues." *The Auk* 84: 309–342.

**FIGURE 32.33 A flying Egyptian rousette**

from exhaustion or predation. Migratory behaviour is not universal: many animals never migrate, spending their lives in one location. Why do some species migrate? What ecological pressures give migrating individuals higher fitness than individuals that do not migrate? Remember that many species of terrestrial animals migrate, such as wildebeest and caribou.

For migratory birds, seasonal changes in food supply are the most widely accepted hypothesis to explain migratory behaviour. Insects can be abundant in higher-latitude (greater than 50 degrees north or south) habitats during the warm spring and summer, providing excellent resources for birds to raise offspring. As summer wanes and fall and winter approach, insects all but disappear. Bird species that remain in temperate habitats over winter eat mainly seeds and dormant insects.

When it is winter at higher latitudes, energy supplies are more predictably available in the tropical grounds used by overwintering migratory birds.

Two-way migratory journeys may provide other benefits. Avoiding the northern winter is probably adaptive because endotherms must increase their metabolic rates just to stay warm in cold climates (see Chapter 42). Moreover, summer days are longer at high latitudes than they are in the tropics (see *The Purple Pages*), giving adult birds more time to feed and rear a brood.

For other animals, migration to breeding grounds may provide the special conditions necessary for reproduction. Grey whales migrate south, where females give birth to their young in quiet, shallow lagoons where predators are rare and warm water temperatures are more conducive to the growth of their calves.

Global warming can have what may be unexpected negative effects on some migrating animals. Red knots (*Calidris canutus canutus*) summer in the Arctic and winter close to the equator **(Figure 32.34)**. Young red knots raised in the far north and exposed to global warming are malnourished because of the warmer habitats. Malnourished red knots have shorter bills and smaller body size, and are vulnerable because those with shorter bills eat more seagrass rhizomes than molluscs. Global warming produces red knots with smaller bodies and shorter bills; they are less effective at obtaining molluscs buried in the mud and suffer higher overwinter mortality.

**STUDY BREAK QUESTIONS**

1. Define *migration*. Give examples of migratory animals, including some not mentioned in the text. Do any humans migrate?
2. How do migrating animals find their way? Distinguish between navigation and compass orientation.

## 32.13 Mates as Resources

**Mating systems** have evolved to maximize reproductive success, partly in response to the amount of parental care that offspring require and partly in response to other aspects of a species' ecology. **Monogamy** describes the situation in which a male and a female form a pair bond for a mating season or, in some cases, for the individuals' reproductive lives. **Polygamy** occurs when one male has active pair bonds with more than one female **(polygyny)**, or one female has active pair bonds with more than one male **(polyandry)**. **Promiscuity** occurs when males and females have no pair bonds beyond the time it takes to mate. In polygyny, males often contribute nothing but sperm to reproduction; in polyandry, females nothing but eggs. The details vary according to the physiology of reproduction. In viviparous animals, the animals that get pregnant (usually females) may bear the costs of housing and feeding developing young.

**FIGURE 32.34 Red knots, their summer and winter ranges** (a), **and effects of ice melt on body size** (b)

Source: From van Gils, "Body shrinkage due to Arctic warming reduces red knot fitness in tropical wintering range," *Science* 13 May 2016: Vol. 352, Issue 6287, pp. 819-821. *Science* by American Association for the Advancement of Science Reproduced with permission of AMERICAN ASSOCIATION FOR THE ADVANCEMENT OF SCIENCE in the format Republish in a book via Copyright Clearance Center.

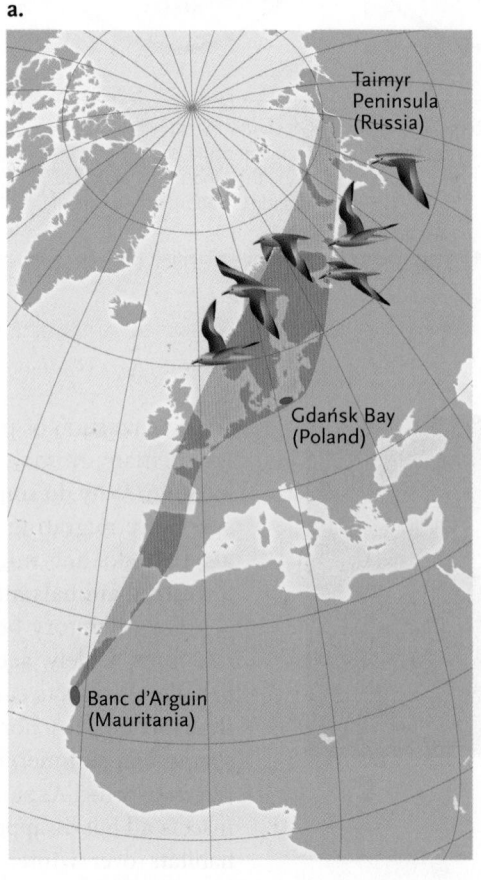

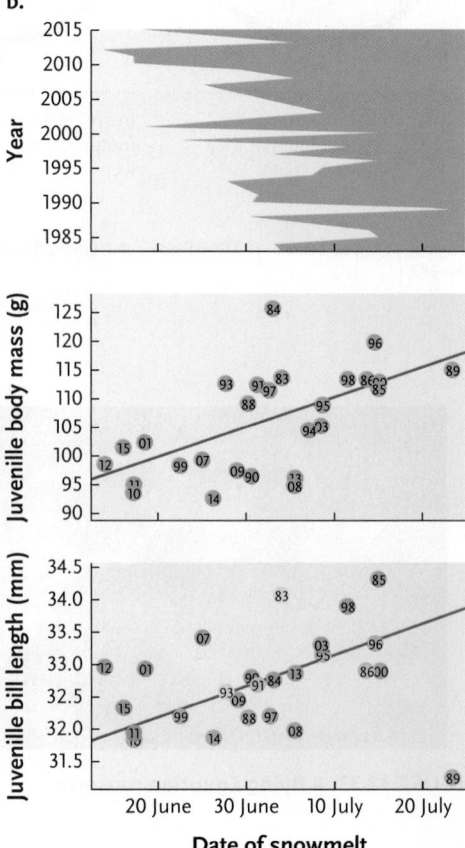

When young require a great deal of care that both parents can provide, monogamy often prevails. Songbirds, such as the white-crowned sparrow **(Figure 32.35)**, are altricial (naked and helpless) when they hatch. They beg for food, and both parents can bring it to them. Males and females achieve higher rates of reproduction when both parents are actively involved with raising young. In mammals, the situation is different because females provide the food (milk). Monogamy occurs in species in which males indirectly feed the young by bringing food to the mother.

If males have high-quality territories, the females living there may be able to raise young on their own. These males may be polygynous (mate with several females). The male's role is that of sperm donor and protector of the space rather than that of an active parent to all of his young. In birds such as red-winged blackbirds (*Agelaius phoeniceus*), some males hold large, resource-filled territories that support several females. These males will be attractive to females even if a female (or females) already lives on the territory. Polygyny is prevalent among mammals because, compared with males, females make a much larger investment in raising young (through egg development and care of the young).

Promiscuous mating systems occur when females are with males only long enough to receive sperm and there is no pair bond. These males make no contribution to raising young. Sage grouse **(Figure 32.36)** and hammer-headed bats (*Hypsignathus monstrosus*) are examples of this approach. Both species form **leks**, congregations of displaying males, where females come only to mate. There are more details about sage grouse below.

**FIGURE 32.36 Lekking behaviour.** Male sage grouse (*Centrocercus urophasianus*) use their ornamental feathers in visual courtship displays performed at a lek. There, each male has his own small territory. The smaller brown females observe the performing males before picking a mate.

**STUDY BREAK QUESTION**

1. What do the terms *monogamy*, *polygamy*, and *promiscuity* mean? How do they differ?

## 32.14  Sexual Selection

Given the drive to reproduce (see Chapter 44), competition for access to mates coupled with mate choice sets the stage for sexual selection. **Sexual dimorphism**, in which one gender is larger or more colourful than the other, can be an outcome of sexual selection. When males compete for females, males are often larger than females and may have ornaments and weapons, such as horns and antlers, for attracting females and for butting, stabbing, or intimidating rival males. Displays of adornments or weapons can simultaneously warn off other males and attract the attention of females. Peacocks strut in front of peahens while spreading a gigantic fan of tail feathers, which they shake, rattle, and roll.

Why should females choose males with exaggerated structures conspicuously displayed? A male's large size, bright feathers, or large horns might indicate that he is particularly healthy. His appearance could indicate that he can harvest resources efficiently or simply that he has managed to survive to an advanced age. The features are, in effect, signals of male quality, and if they reflect a male's genetic makeup, he is likely to fertilize a female's eggs with sperm containing successful alleles. Large showy males may hold large, rich territories. Females that choose these males can gain access to the resources their territories contain.

**FIGURE 32.35 Reproductive success.** Parental care is just one of the many behaviours required for successful reproduction in white-crowned sparrows and in many other animal species. The number of surviving nestlings will determine the reproductive success of their parents and the representation of their genes in the next generation.

The degree to which females actively choose genetically superior mates varies among species. In northern elephant seals, female choice is more or less passive. Large numbers of females gather on beaches to give birth to their pups before becoming sexually receptive again (see "Delaying Reproduction," Chapter 44). Males locate clusters of females and fight to keep other males away. Males that win have exceptional reproductive success because they mate with many females, but only after engaging in violent and relentless combat with rival males. In this mating system, the females struggle during a male's attempts to mate with them. A female's struggles attract other males, who try to interrupt the attempted mating. Only the largest and most powerful males are not interrupted in their copulations, and they inseminate the most females. These attributes may be associated with alleles that will increase their offspring's chances of living long enough to reproduce.

In other species, females exercise more active mate choice, mating only after inspecting several potential partners. Among birds, active female mate choice is most apparent at leks, display grounds where each male holds a small territory from which it courts attentive females. The male is the only resource on the territory. Male sage grouse in western North America gather in open areas among stands of sagebrush. Each male defends a few square metres, where it struts in circles while emitting booming calls and showing off its elegant tail feathers and big neck pouches (see Figure 32.36). Females wander among displaying males, presumably observing the males' visual and acoustical displays. Eventually, each female selects one mate from among the dozens of males that are present. Females repeatedly favour males that come to the lek daily, defend their small area vigorously, and display more frequently than the average lek participant. Males preferred by females sustain their territorial defence and high display rate over long periods, abilities that may correlate with other useful genetic traits. Ultimately, the male holding the "best" position in the lek mates with the most females.

The results of experiments with peafowl suggest that the top peacocks (*Pavo cristatus*) supply advantageous alleles to their offspring. In nature, peahens prefer males whose tails have many ornamental eyespots **(Figure 32.37)**. In an experiment on captive birds, some peahens were mated to peacocks with highly attractive tails, but others were paired with males with less impressive tails. The offspring of both groups were reared under uniform conditions for several months and then released into an English woodland. After three months on their own, the offspring of fathers with impressive tails survived better and weighed significantly more than did those whose fathers had less-attractive tails. The evidence demonstrates that a peahen's mate choice influences her offspring's chances of survival.

According to the handicap hypothesis, females select males that are successful: the ones with ornate structures. These structures may impede their locomotion, and their elaborate displays may attract the attention of predators. Females select ornate males because they have survived *despite* carrying such a handicap. Successful alleles responsible for the ornamental handicap are passed to the female's offspring.

**FIGURE 32.37 Sexual selection for ornamentation.** The attractiveness of a peacock to peahens depends in part on the number of eyespots in his extraordinary tail. The offspring of males with elaborate tails are more successful than the offspring of males with plainer tails.

In a study of ~6000 species of birds, James Dale and his colleagues examined the relationships between coloration of plumage of males and females and how this related to sexual selection and life history. In general, larger species of birds and tropical species are more ornamented. Females, but not males, are more colourful in species that breed cooperatively. This probably reflects female–female competition. Bird species in which males are more colourful than females typically show strong sexual selection and male–male competition. Here, females tend to be much less colourful than males. Dale and his colleagues conclude that there may be genetic constraints on the evolution of colourful plumage in birds.

**STUDY BREAK QUESTIONS**

1. What are the distinguishing features of a lek?
2. What is the handicap hypothesis?
3. Where are the most colourful birds found?

# 32.15   Social Behaviour

Social behaviour interactions among members of a species have profound effects on an individual's reproductive success. Some animals are solitary, getting together only briefly to mate (e.g., houseflies and leopards). Others spend most of their lives in small family groups (e.g., gorillas). Still others live in groups with thousands of relatives (e.g., termites and honeybees). Some species, such as caribou and humans, live in large social units composed primarily of nonrelatives. In many species, the level of social interactions varies seasonally, usually reflecting the timing of reproduction. This, in turn, is influenced by changes in day length. What follows are a few examples of social interactions.

## 32.15a   African Lions and Infanticide

African lions (*Panthera leo*) usually live in prides, one adult male with several females and their young. Males typically sire the young born to the females in their pride and so achieve a high reproductive output. Females benefit from the support of the others in the group, which includes caring for young and cooperating in foraging. Female lions living in prides wean more young per litter than females living alone. The females in a pride are often genetically related, and their estrus cycles are usually synchronized. Male lions are bigger (~200 kg) than females (~150 kg), and males fight vigorously for the position of pride male. Males protect their females from incursions by other males.

When a new male takes over a pride, he kills all nursing young, bringing the females into estrus. At first, this infanticide seems counterproductive. However, it benefits the male because it increases the chances of his reproducing. Were he to wait until the females had weaned their young, his reproductive contributions could be delayed for some time, perhaps for a year or more. Furthermore, in the intervening period he could lose the opportunity to sire any young at all.

Females are not large enough to protect their young from the male. If a female takes her nursing young and leaves the pride, her efficiency as a hunter declines, and she is less able to protect and feed her young. Her reproductive success plummets. Females are more productive (measured by output of young) when they are part of a pride.

But why live in a group in the first place? By hunting together, lions are more efficient foragers than when they hunt alone. They raise more young. Perhaps more important is the threat posed by spotted hyenas **(Figure 32.38)**, which live in large groups (clans). Although individually smaller (~60 kg), when spotted hyenas outnumber lions, they can chase lions from their kills. Furthermore, many of the lion's main prey also live in groups, and group defences affect lions' hunting success.

The situation in lions exemplifies some biological realities. Males and females do not have the same strategies when it comes to reproduction. Understanding behaviour means considering genetic relatedness and production of offspring, as well as the setting in which the animals live.

## 32.15b   Costs and Benefits of Group Living

Ecological factors have a large impact on the reproductive benefits and costs of social living. Group living brings both costs and benefits. Groups of cooperating predators frequently capture prey more effectively than they would on their own. White pelicans (*Pelecanus erythrorhynchos*) often encircle a school of fish before attacking, so being part of a group provides a better yield to individuals than working alone. On the other hand, prey subject to intense predation may benefit from group defence. This can mean more pairs of watchful eyes or ears to detect an approaching danger. It may also translate into multiple lures so that, when a predator attacks, it is more difficult to focus on an individual. When you are part of a group that is attacked, it may be someone other than you that is captured, diluting the risk to any one group member.

When attacked by wolves, adult muskoxen form a circle around the young, so attackers are always confronted by horns and hooves **(Figure 32.39)**. Insects such as Australian sawfly caterpillars also show cooperative defensive behaviour. When predators disturb the caterpillars, all group members rear up, writhe about, and regurgitate sticky, pungent oils. The caterpillars collect the oils from the eucalyptus leaves they eat. The oils do not harm the caterpillars but are toxic and repellent to birds.

Living in groups, however, can also be expensive. One cost can be increased competition for food. When thousands of royal penguins crowd together in huge colonies **(Figure 32.40)**, the pressure on local food supplies is great, increasing the risk of starvation. Communal living may facilitate the spread of contagious diseases and parasites. Nestlings in large colonies of cliff swallows (*Petrochelidon pyrrhonota*) are often stunted in growth because the nests swarm with blood-feeding, bedbug-like parasites, *Oeciacus vicarius*. The parasites move readily from nest to nest in crowded conditions. Some social animals learn to recognize and avoid diseased group members. Caribbean spiny lobsters live in groups but avoid conspecifics infected by a lethal virus (PaV1). In 2016, Quinn Webber and his colleagues reported that big brown bats (*Eptesicus fuscus*) using buildings as summer roosts were more vulnerable to transmission of pathogens than individuals roosting in trees. The big difference between the two situations is that, on any given night, most of the bats in a building roost are more clustered than those spread among hollows in different trees.

Social animals usually live in groups characterized by some form of structure. Some individuals may dominate others (a **dominance hierarchy**), manifested in access to resources. Dominant (alpha, or α) individuals get priority access to food (or mates or sleeping sites). In some situations, only dominant individuals (a male and a female) reproduce. Dominance hierarchies may be absolute, such as when the same individual always has priority access to any resource. In relative dominance hierarchies, an individual's status depends on the circumstance. One individual may dominate at a food source, while another may dominate in access to mates.

Dominance brings its costs. In animals such as wild dogs (*Lycaon pictus*) and grey wolves, dominant animals must constantly defend their status. Dominants often have high levels of cortisol and other stress-related hormones in their blood (see Chapter 43) compared with subordinates. Elevated cortisol levels may induce high blood pressure, disruption of sugar metabolism, and other pathological conditions.

**FIGURE 32.38   These three spotted hyenas are part of a clan living in Kruger National Park**

FIGURE 32.39 **Muskoxen**

FIGURE 32.40 **Colonial living.** Royal penguins (*Eudyptes schlegeli*) on Macquarie Island between New Zealand and Antarctica experience benefits and costs from living together in huge groups.

Subordination brings its benefits. Subordinate group members, like all members of the group, gain protection from predators. They may also gain experience by helping dominant individuals raise young. Over time, subordinate individuals can rise in a dominance hierarchy and avoid some of the side effects of dominance. Many social animals cannot survive on their own.

Not all animals that live in groups are social, a term implying some organization of the group. The 10 million Brazilian free-tailed bats emerging from a cave roost near San Antonio, Texas,

are no more a social group than the dozens of people leaving a high-rise apartment or university residence. Within the aggregation, there may be social units, but the aggregation itself is not necessarily a social unit.

**STUDY BREAK QUESTIONS**

1. What is infanticide? Why does it occur?
2. Give some examples of the advantages and disadvantages of group living.

## 32.16 Kin Selection and Altruism

Behavioural ecologist William D. Hamilton recognized that helping genetic relatives effectively propagates the helper's genes because family members share alleles inherited from their ancestors. By calculating the degree of relatedness, we can quantify the average percentage of alleles shared by relatives **(Figure 32.41)**. Individuals should be more likely to help close relatives because increasing a close relative's fitness means that the individual is helping to propagate some of its own alleles. This is **kin selection**.

### 32.16a Degrees of Relatedness

The kin selection hypothesis suggests that the extent of altruistic behaviour exhibited by one individual to another is directly proportional to the percentage of alleles they share. The hypothesis predicts that individuals are more likely to help close relatives because, by increasing a close relative's fitness, the individual is helping to propagate some of its own alleles. To test this prediction, we must calculate the degrees of relatedness among individuals.

To do this between any two individuals, we first draw a family tree showing all the genetic links between them. The alleles of a parent are shuffled by recombination and independent assortment in the gametes they produce, so we can calculate only the average percentage of a parent's alleles that offspring are likely to share.

Half siblings share only one genetic parent. Each sibling receives half its alleles from its mother. Because a parent has only two alleles at each gene locus, the probability of sibling A getting a particular allele from its mother is 0.5, or 50%, as is the probability for sibling B. Statistically, the probability that two independent events—in this case, the transfer of an allele to sibling A and the transfer of the same allele to sibling

**Half siblings**

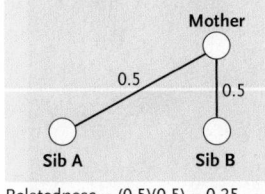

Relatedness = (0.5)(0.5) = 0.25

**First cousins**

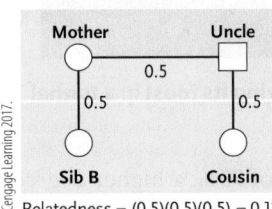

Relatedness = (0.5)(0.5)(0.5) = 0.125

© Cengage Learning 2017.

**Full siblings**

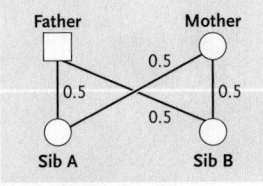

Relatedness
Through mother = (0.5)(0.5) = 0.25
Through father = (0.5)(0.5) = 0.25
Total relatedness = 0.25 + 0.25 = 0.5

**FIGURE 32.41 Calculating degrees of relatedness**

B—will both occur is the product of their separate probabilities. Thus, the likelihood that both siblings receive the same allele from their mother is 0.5 × 0.5 = 0.25. Two full siblings share 50% of their mother's and father's alleles. The degree of relatedness for full siblings is 0.50.

Each link drawn between a parent and an offspring or between full siblings indicates two individuals sharing, on average, 50% of their alleles. We can calculate the total relatedness (r) between any two individuals by multiplying out the probabilities across all of the links between them. The degree of relatedness between a nephew or niece and an aunt or an uncle is 0.25, and between first cousins it is 0.125.

A male grey wolf helps his parents rear four pups to adulthood, pups that would have died without the extra assistance he provided. The pups are his younger full siblings, sharing 0.5 of his genes, so, on average, the helper has created "by proxy" two (0.50 × 4 = 2) copies of any allele they shared. However, the costs of his helping must be measured against this indirect reproductive success. If he had found a mate, sired offspring, and raised two of them, each would have carried half his alleles, preserving only one (0.50 × 2 = 1) copy of a given allele. In this situation, reproducing on his own would have produced fewer copies of his alleles in the next generation than helping to raise his siblings. Sibling helpers have been documented in many species of birds and mammals. The phenomenon is especially common among animals in which inexperienced parents are not very successful at reproducing offspring on their own. By helping, they gain experience and realize some genetic benefit.

Among the many features of social animals, the evolution of cooperative behaviour can be one of the most challenging to understand. Why has cooperative behaviour arisen in populations of animals? How does it arise? And how is it maintained in populations? **Altruism** involves doing something that costs the actor while enhancing the situation of another individual (the receiver). Hamilton's kin selection theory demonstrates why parental behaviour (or helping parents raise siblings) is genetically selfish, not altruistic. Therefore, the behaviour of

the wolf mentioned above is not altruistic. Robert Trivers proposed that individuals will help nonrelatives if they are likely to return the favour in the future. Trivers called this **reciprocal altruism** because each member of the partnership can potentially benefit from the relationship. Trivers hypothesized that reciprocal altruism would be favoured by natural selection as long as cheaters—individuals that do not reciprocate—are denied future aid.

Many species of dolphins are long lived and social, living in groups. Dolphins and other cetaceans show many forms of aid-giving behaviour, from attending injured group members to assisting with difficult births. They also use group behaviour to protect themselves from attacks by sharks. Richard Connor and Kenneth Norris proposed that the persistent threat of attacks by sharks and the perils of living in the ocean combined to provide dolphins with many opportunities to help one another, or even members of other species. Connor and Norris did not have specific details of genetic relationships among group members, but they proposed that dolphins are reciprocal altruists.

John M. McNamara and three colleagues wrote about the coevolution of choosiness and cooperation. Using modelling and simulation experiments, these authors examined the consequences arising in situations in which one individual's cooperativeness influences the decisions about actions by other individuals toward group members. They postulated a situation of competitive altruism in which individuals actually compete with one another to be more cooperative.

The results of their analysis suggest that longer-lived species are more likely to develop cooperative behaviour than shorter-lived ones. This is important because the model does not require intermediate situations involving negotiation behaviour. The model helps us understand the appearance of cooperative behaviour in all animals, including in *Homo sapiens*.

The McNamara et al. model of competitive altruism helps explain the evolution of blood-sharing behaviour in vampire bats. Vampire bats are the only warm-blooded blood feeders and, like many other bats, they are long lived in the wild, recorded to at least 19 years of age). The three living species of vampire bats, the common vampire bat (*Desmodus rotundus*; **Figure 32.42**), the white-winged vampire bat (*Diaemus youngi*), and the hairy-legged vampire bat (*Diphylla ecaudata*), all practice food sharing. An individual unsuccessful in foraging can return to its roost and beg blood from a successful forager among its roost mates. The donor bat regurgitates some of its blood meal to the recipient. G. S. Wilkinson's work with common vampire bats demonstrated that individuals roost with both nonrelatives and genetic relatives. Familiarity, not relatedness, was the key to food sharing by these bats.

The selection process for the behaviour can be placed in context by evidence about a bat's success. Adult common vampire bats are typically unsuccessful in obtaining blood one night per month. An adult can survive two days (daytime periods) without feeding, but not three. This means that, on any night in any month in a colony of 30 adult vampire bats, one individual will benefit from the cooperativeness of a roost mate.

Even more important, young bats may be unsuccessful three or four times a week. Blood-feeding bats thus live on the edge of survival and likely depend on a network of cooperation by roost mates. The social network demonstrated for common vampire bats probably applies to white-winged and hairy-legged species as well. The network is based on cooperation and may be the key to being a successful warm-blooded blood-feeder.

## STUDY BREAK QUESTIONS

1. What is the main argument in Hamilton's kin selection theory?
2. Imagine that four of your first cousins, two siblings, and two half-siblings are about to fall from a cliff and die. You have the option of taking their place. In terms of kin selection, which is more beneficial to you, your life or the life of your genetic relatives?
3. Which of the following behaviours is altruistic: parental care, mate selection, courtship feeding, self-defence, and/or helping nonrelatives? Explain your choices.
4. Why do common vampire bats regurgitate blood to others?

## 32.17 Eusocial Animals

Hamilton's insights led to the prediction that self-sacrificing behaviour should be directed to kin. Evidence from many species of animals, particularly bees, ants, termites, and wasps, overwhelmingly supports this prediction. In a colony of **eusocial** insects, thousands of genetically related individuals, most of them sterile workers, live and work together for the reproductive benefit of a single queen and her mate(s). The workers may even die in defence of their colonies.

How did this social behaviour evolve, and why does it persist over time? A colony of honeybees may contain 30–50 thousand related individuals, but only the queen bee is fertile. All the workers are her daughters **(Figure 32.43)**. Reproduction is the queen's role in the colony. The workers perform all the other tasks in maintaining the hive, from feeding the queen and her larvae to constructing new honeycomb and foraging for nectar and pollen. They also transfer food to one another (trophallaxis) and sometimes guard the entrance to the hive. Some pay the ultimate sacrifice when they sting intruders because stinging tears open the bee's abdomen, leaving the stinger and the poison sac behind in the intruder's skin and killing the bee.

In bees and other eusocial insects, sex is determined genetically through **haplodiploidy (Figure 32.44)**. Female bees are diploid because they receive a set of chromosomes from each parent. Male bees (drones), however, are haploid because they hatch from unfertilized eggs. All the sperm carried by a drone will be genetically identical because he has just one set of chromosomes. When a queen bee mates with just one male, all her worker offspring will inherit exactly the same set of alleles from their male parent, ensuring at least a 50% degree of relatedness among them. Like other diploid organisms, workers are related to each other by an average of 25% through their female parent. Adding these two components of relatedness, workers

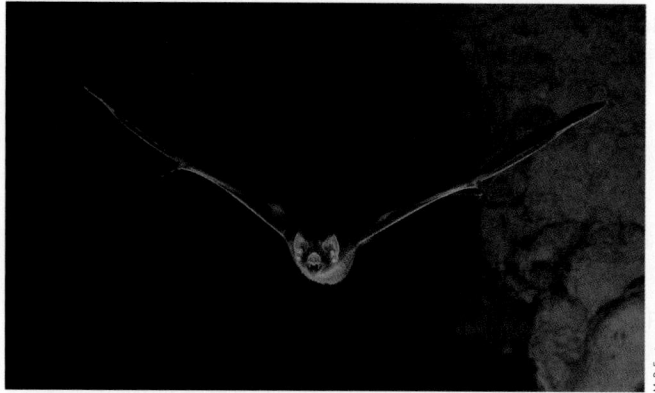

**FIGURE 32.42 A common vampire bat leaving its roost in a tunnel in Belize**

are related to each other by an average of 75%, a higher degree of relatedness than they would have to any offspring they would have produced had they been fertile.

The high degree of relatedness among workers in some colonies of eusocial insects may explain their exceptional level of cooperation. When Hamilton first worked out this explanation of eusocial behaviour, he suggested that workers devote their lives to caring for their siblings (the queen's other offspring) because a few of those siblings, those carrying 75% of the workers' alleles, may become future queens and produce enormous numbers of offspring themselves.

### 32.17a Naked Mole Rats

Naked mole rats are a mammalian example of eusocial animals with nonbreeding workers. In East Africa, these small, almost hairless animals live in underground colonies of 70–80 individuals. Like eusocial insects, naked mole rats share an exceptionally high proportion of alleles. Naked mole rats are sightless and

a. **Queen with sterile workers**

b. **Workers sharing food and passing pheromones**

**FIGURE 32.43 (a)** In a hive of honeybees, a court of sterile workers (daughters) surround their mother (the queen). **(b)** Worker bees routinely share food (trophallaxis) and transfer pheromones to one another.

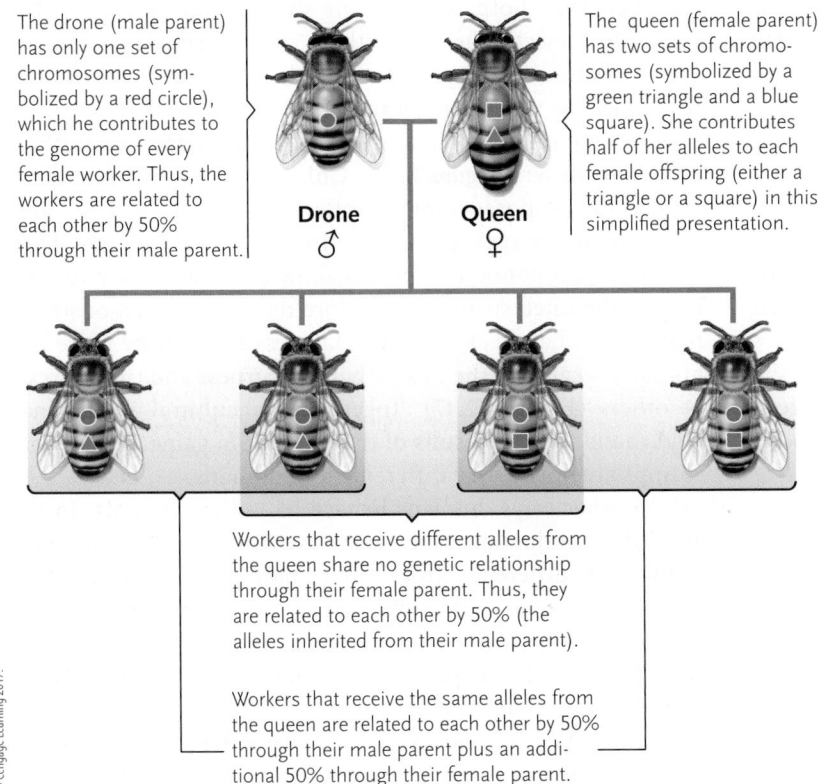

The drone (male parent) has only one set of chromosomes (symbolized by a red circle), which he contributes to the genome of every female worker. Thus, the workers are related to each other by 50% through their male parent.

The queen (female parent) has two sets of chromosomes (symbolized by a green triangle and a blue square). She contributes half of her alleles to each female offspring (either a triangle or a square) in this simplified presentation.

**Drone**
♂

**Queen**
♀

Workers that receive different alleles from the queen share no genetic relationship through their female parent. Thus, they are related to each other by 50% (the alleles inherited from their male parent).

Workers that receive the same alleles from the queen are related to each other by 50% through their male parent plus an additional 50% through their female parent.

© Cengage Learning 2017.

**FIGURE 32.44 Haplodiploidy.** The genetic system of eusocial insects produces full siblings with exceptionally high degrees of relatedness. Although this simplified model ignores recombination between the queen's two sets of chromosomes, it demonstrates how half the workers are related to each other by 50%, and half are related to each other by 100%. On average, the relatedness between workers is 75%.

essentially hairless burrowing mammals **(Figure 32.45)** that live in mazes of subterranean tunnels in parts of Ethiopia, Somalia, and Kenya. Colonies of naked mole rats may number from 25 to several hundred individuals. In each colony, a single "queen" and one to three males are the breeders. All the others, males and females, are nonbreeding workers that, like worker bees, ants, and termites in insect colonies, do all the labour, including digging and defending the tunnels and caring for the queen and her mates. H. Kern Reeve and his colleagues used molecular techniques resembling DNA fingerprint analysis (see Chapter 14) to determine if close kinship could explain the behaviour of worker naked mole rats. The technique depends on a group of repeated DNA sequences that vary to a greater or lesser extent among individuals (e.g., they are polymorphic). No two individuals (except identical twins) are likely to have exactly the same combination of sequences. Brothers and sisters with the same parents have the most closely related sequences, and differences increase as genetic relationships become more distant. Reeve and his colleagues captured mole rats living in four colonies in Kenya. Individuals from the same colony were placed together in a system of artificial tunnels. Samples of the entire DNA complement were extracted from individuals that died naturally in the artificial colonies. The extracted DNA was then "probed" with radioactively labelled DNA sequences that paired with and marked the

three distinct groups of polymorphic sequences in the mole rat DNA (see Chapter 14).

Naked mole rat sequences were then fragmented by treatment with a restriction endonuclease. This procedure produced a group of fragments that, reflecting the variations in polymorphic sequences, is unique for each individual. As a final experimental step, the fragments for each individual were separated into a pattern of bands by gel electrophoresis. The pattern of bands, different for each individual, is the DNA fingerprint.

Reeve and his colleagues compared the DNA fingerprint of each mole rat with those of other members of the same and other colonies. In the comparisons, bands that were the same in two individuals were scored as hits. The number of hits was then analyzed to assign relatedness by noting which individuals shared the greatest number of bands.

Individuals in the same mole rat colony were closely related. They shared an unusually high number of bands, higher than human siblings and approaching the kin similarity of identical twins. The number of bands shared between individuals of different colonies was significantly lower but still higher than that noted between unrelated individuals of other vertebrate species. Close relatedness of even separate colonies may be due to similar selection pressures or to recent common ancestry among colonies in the same geographic region.

In naked mole rats, close genetic relatedness among individuals in a colony could explain the altruistic behaviour of workers. The persistence of the social organization reflects its importance to the survival of individual naked mole rats, rather like the situation in lion prides.

The presence of non-reproductive workers is diagnostic of eusocial animals. Jason Olejarz and his colleagues demonstrated that non-reproductive individuals readily arise in situations where the "queen" has mated with several males

M. B. Fenton

**FIGURE 32.45 Naked mole rat (*Heterocephalus glaber*), a colonial rodent whose colonies contain many workers that are effectively sterile.**

(= polyandrous). The rate at which the colony reproduces and the fractions of non-reproductive workers in a colony emerged as key factors in their model. These observations may provide a clue about the evolution of eusociality among animals.

Animals living in groups, whether they are aggregations or social units, may be at greater risk of inbreeding than those living alone. Dispersal is a mechanism that can reduce the chances of incestuous matings and inbreeding. Although spotted hyenas live in clans, males tend to disperse from their natal units, minimizing the risk of inbreeding. O. P. Höner and colleagues used microsatellite profiling to show that a female preferred mates that had been born into or immigrated into the clan after she was born. As usual, it can be difficult to separate cause from effect. Are clans of spotted hyenas prone to this pattern of social organization, or is the pattern a result of their behaviour?

**STUDY BREAK QUESTIONS**

1. What is haplodiploidy? How does it relate to Hamilton's prediction about self-sacrificing behaviour?
2. Are naked mole rats eusocial?

## 32.18 Human Social Behaviour

Although humans and chimpanzees share 96% of their genomes, compared with humans, both chimpanzees and bonobos (*Pan paniscus*) live in relatively unstructured social groups. The difference has been attributed to brain size. The cultural intelligence hypothesis proposes that large brain size in humans reflects cognitive skill sets absent from great apes. Large brains allow humans to perform many cognitive tasks more rapidly and efficiently than other species with smaller brains. The tasks include those associated with memory, learning time, long-range planning, and complexity of inter-individual interactions.

To test this, Esther Herrmann and her colleagues administered a large battery of cognitive tests to chimpanzees, orangutans (*Pongo pygmaeus*), and two-and-a-half-year-old human children. The children in the experiment were preschool and preliterate. Although the children, chimpanzees, and orangutans had similar cognitive skills for dealing with the physical world, the children had more sophisticated cognitive skills for dealing with the social world **(Figure 32.46)**. The data support the hypothesis that cultural intelligence is an important way to distinguish humans from their closest living relatives.

The ultimatum game is an economic decision-making tool for assessing the responses of individuals to opportunities and the behaviour of others. Responses allow researchers to distinguish between players on the basis of sensitivity and sense of fairness. Keith Jensen and his colleagues used the ultimatum game to compare humans and chimpanzees. Two anonymous individuals can play a round of this game. One, the proposer, is offered a sum of money (or a food reward) and can decide whether to share it with the other, the responder. The responder can accept or reject the proposer's offer. If the responder accepts the offer, then both receive their share of the reward. If the responder rejects the offer, then neither gets any reward. The economic model predicts that the proposer will offer the responder the minimum award.

When humans and chimps play the ultimatum game, their behaviour differs **(Figure 32.47)**. Chimps are rational maximizers because proposers typically offer 40% to 50% of the reward, and responders typically reject offers of less than 20%. They follow the economic model and show little sensitivity to fairness or the interests of others. More recent work demonstrates that chimps have a clear view of fairness and may be more like humans because of their sensitivity to fairness and the interests of others (Figure 32.47). Together, the cultural intelligence hypothesis and the results of the ultimatum game suggest that chimps are not so very different from humans.

In other ways, humans behave like other animals. In the area of reproduction and genetic selfishness, some humans show little difference from their mammalian cousins. Kin selection predicts that humans (and other animals) that are genetic relatives will benefit from assisting the members of their family. What happens when there is no close genetic tie between parents and children?

Margo Wilson and Martin Daly wondered if child abuse might be more common in families with step-parents who are not genetically related to all the children in their care. They examined data on criminal child abuse within families, made available by the police department of a Canadian city. They found that the chance that a young child would be subject to criminal abuse was 40 times as high when children lived with one step-parent and one genetic parent as with children living with both genetic parents **(Figure 32.48)**.

This example illustrates the insights that an evolutionary analysis of human behaviour can provide. Wilson and Daly made the point that humans may have some genetic characteristic that makes it more difficult to invest in children they know are not their own, particularly if they also care for their own genetic children. They did not excuse child abusers or claim that abusive step-parenting is acceptable. These results are not just academic. Most step-parents cope well with the difficulties of their role, but a few do not. Knowing the familial circumstances under which child abuse is more likely to occur may allow us to provide social assistance that could prevent some children from being abused in the future.

Violence and conflict are recurring themes in the behaviour of many animals, including humans. Killing of other members of the same species is widespread. Michael Wilson and his colleagues reported this in chimpanzees and bonobos. Their sample was of 152 killings, most of which involved intergroup interactions. Meanwhile, M. Mirazón Lahr and colleagues presented evidence of inter-group violence from humans living as hunter–gatherers perhaps 14 000–12 000 years ago in what is now Kenya. These data suggest that violence is not a new development in our species.

Intrinsic honesty and a sense of fairness may be fundamental aspects of human societies. Although deception is a common

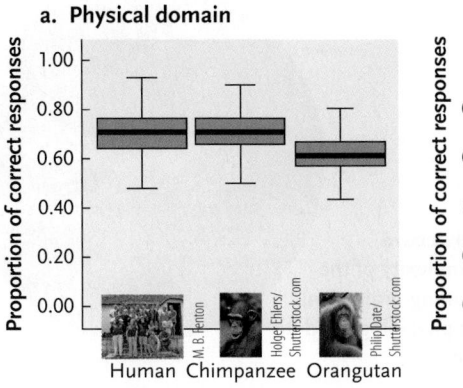

**a. Physical domain**

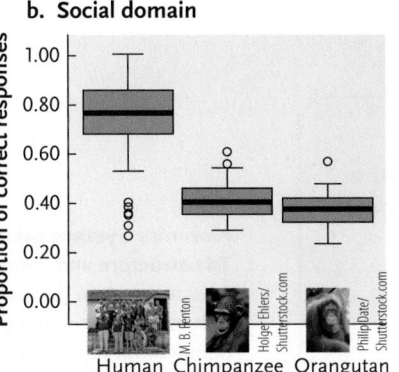

**b. Social domain**

**FIGURE 32.46 Humans, chimpanzees, and orangutans.** Box plots showing the proportion of correct responses to survey questions in the physical and the social domains. In the social domain, outlying data points (circles) were at least 1.5 times the interquartile distances (shown by the error bars).

Source: From Esther Herrmann, Josep Call, Maria Victoria Hernandez-Lloreda, Brian Hare, Michael Tomasello, "Humans Have Evolved Specialized Skills of Social Cognition: The Cultural Intelligence Hypothesis," *Science*, vol. 317, Sep 7, 2007, pp. 1360 - 1366. *Science* by American Association for the Advancement of Science Reproduced with permission of AMERICAN ASSOCIATION FOR THE ADVANCEMENT OF SCIENCE in the format Republish in a book via Copyright Clearance Center.

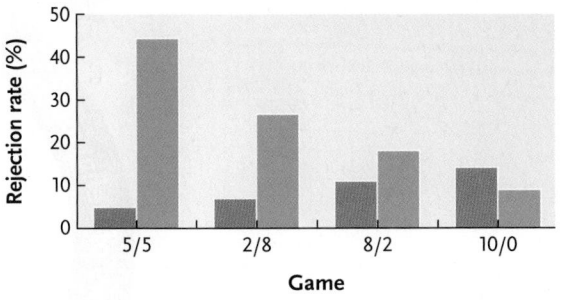

**FIGURE 32.47 The ultimatum game.** Data from chimpanzees (orange bars) and humans (green bars) show rejection rates (percentage of offers) indicating fundamental differences in the way that humans and chimps approach issues of fairness. The chimps are rational maximizers, whereas the humans are not.

Source: From Keith Jensen, Josep Call, Michael Tomasello, "Chimpanzees Are Rational Maximizers in an Ultimatum Game", *Science*, vol. 318, Oct 5, 2007, pp. 107-109. *Science* by American Association for the Advancement of Science Reproduced with permission of AMERICAN ASSOCIATION FOR THE ADVANCEMENT OF SCIENCE in the format Republish in a book via Copyright Clearance Center.

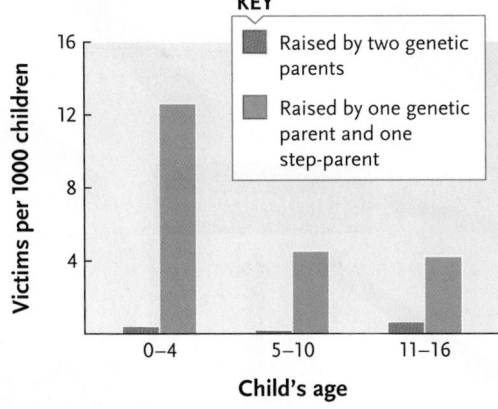

**FIGURE 32.48 Children raised by one genetic parent and one step-parent were 40 times as likely to suffer criminal abuse at home as children living with two genetic parents.**

behaviour among animals, stability in our societies involves some level of intrinsic honesty. Simon Gächter and Jonathan Schulz studied societies in 23 countries, and their sample involved 2568 "young" people. They focused on intrinsic honesty reflected by PRV, the prevalence of rule violations. They found that intrinsic honesty was more common in countries with a low incidence of PRV.

Among humans, there is considerable variation in the level of fairness in resource sharing. P. R. Blake and colleagues examined the development of fairness behaviour in seven human societies. They used a standardized resource decision task to test children from 4 to 15 years of age. They focused on two key aspects: first, where peer received more than self and, second, where self received more than peer. By middle childhood, the first aspect was common throughout the sample. The appearance of the second aspect was more variable, emerging only in later development in three of the societies. The level of fairness and perception of fairness does not appear to be under genetic control.

In recent years, the application of evolutionary thinking to human behaviour has produced research on many kinds of questions. Some questions are interesting or even profound: Why do some tightly knit ethnic groups discourage intermarriage with members of other groups? At other times, the issues may seem frivolous: Why do men often find women with certain physical characteristics attractive? Evolutionary hypotheses about the adaptive value of behaviour can be tested, and the results help us to understand why we behave as we do. Understanding why we get along or fail to get along with each other, and the ability to make moral judgments about our behaviour are uniquely human characteristics that set us apart from other animals.

Returning to behaviour related to food, Carey Morewedge and two colleagues reported how people thinking about eating a food reduced their consumption of that food. Their experiment included over 50 participants and involved different foods (cheese and m&m's). Individuals who thought about eating cheese consumed significantly less cheese when actually eating compared to those who imagined eating less cheese, or eating m&m's. These findings have implications for treating eating disorders, and illustrate how mental representations can lead to habituation. The findings also suggest similarities to other animals when it comes to food and feeding (see above).

## STUDY BREAK QUESTIONS

1. What is the ultimatum game? How does it help us understand behaviour?
2. What genetic reason helps explain the domestic risks to foster children and stepchildren?
3. What is fairness? What is intrinsic honesty?
4. How does PRV vary across the community in which you live?

# Summary Illustration

Animal behaviour is what animals do or how they behave. It is how they interact with conspecifics, other members of their community, and their environment. Animal behaviour is governed by genetic and environmental factors and involves instinct and learning. Nervous and sensory systems integrate internal and external cues and mediate behaviours such as communication, breeding, and foraging.

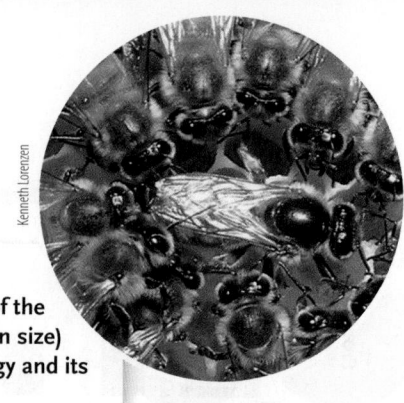

### Nervous System Structure
The structure and complexity of the nervous system (including brain size) influence an animal's physiology and its behavioural repertoire.

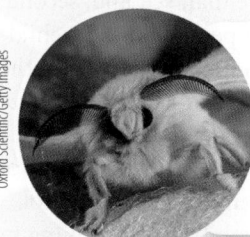

### Hormones and Neurotransmitters
Biochemical pathways within an animal's endocrine and nervous systems allow animals to respond to stimuli.

## Anatomy/Physiology

### Imprinting
Imprinting occurs when an animal learns the identity of a caregiver or features of a suitable mate during a critical period.

## Governors of Behaviour

### Instinctive Behaviours
Highly stereotyped behaviours performed without the benefit of previous experience.

## Genes

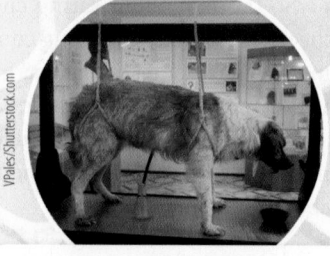

### Fixed Action Patterns
This denotes a response repeated over and over to a specific cue.

### Classical Conditioning
This refers to the development of a mental association between two phenomena that are usually unrelated.

## Environment

### Operant Conditioning
Learning that occurs when animals link an action with a consequence. Example: rat pushing bar to receive food.

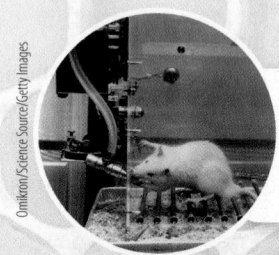

### Insight Learning
Occurs when an animal learns to solve a problem without trial and error. Example: chimp getting bananas after stacking boxes to reach them

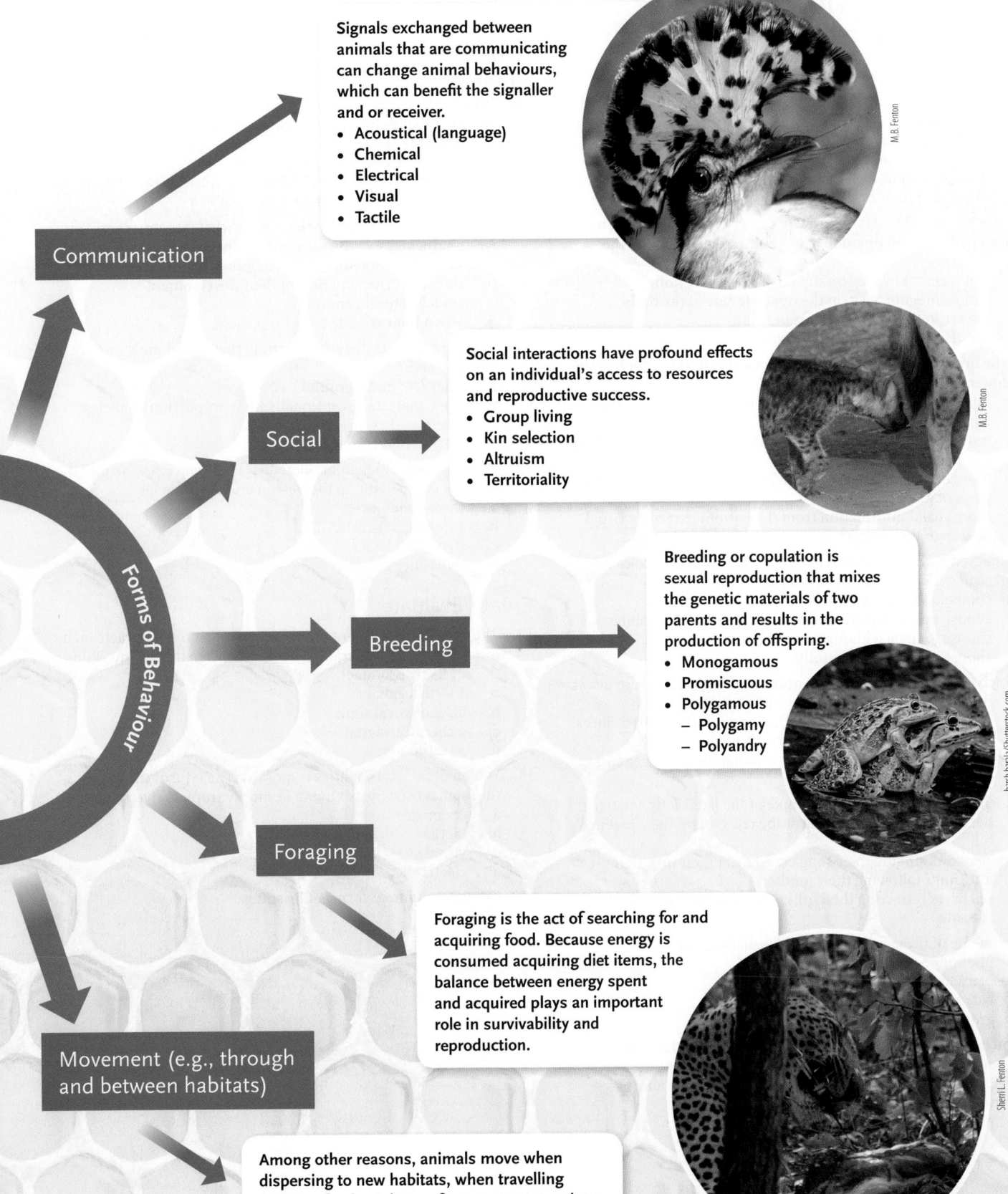

Signals exchanged between animals that are communicating can change animal behaviours, which can benefit the signaller and or receiver.
- Acoustical (language)
- Chemical
- Electrical
- Visual
- Tactile

M.B. Fenton

**Communication**

**Forms of Behaviour**

**Social**

Social interactions have profound effects on an individual's access to resources and reproductive success.
- Group living
- Kin selection
- Altruism
- Territoriality

M.B. Fenton

**Breeding**

Breeding or copulation is sexual reproduction that mixes the genetic materials of two parents and results in the production of offspring.
- Monogamous
- Promiscuous
- Polygamous
  – Polygamy
  – Polyandry

harsh.barala/Shutterstock.com

**Foraging**

Foraging is the act of searching for and acquiring food. Because energy is consumed acquiring diet items, the balance between energy spent and acquired plays an important role in survivability and reproduction.

Sherri L. Fenton

**Movement (e.g., through and between habitats)**

Among other reasons, animals move when dispersing to new habitats, when travelling between food patches or from summer to winter ranges, or when migrating from breeding to feeding grounds.
- Kinesis
- Migration
- Taxis

Alexander Erdbeer/Shutterstock.com

# SELF-TEST QUESTIONS

## Recall/Understand

1. Which of these behaviours occurs in cichlid fish with high levels of the hormone GnRH?
   a. Females are receptive to male attention.
   b. Males are sexually aggressive but not territorial.
   c. A male defends its territory.
   d. Males lose their bright colours.

2. Sensory bias in the nervous system of a cricket ensures that ultrasound perceived on one side of the body causes which of the following?
   a. a movement in a leg on the same side of the body
   b. a movement in a leg on the opposite side of the body
   c. the cricket's response by vocalization
   d. the cricket's flight toward the sound

3. In the brain of a star-nosed mole, more cells decode which of the following?
   a. more tactile information from its feet than from all other parts of its body
   b. more tactile information from the tentacles on its nose than from all other parts of its body
   c. more tactile information from its mouth than from all other parts of its body
   d. more visual information from the bottom part of its visual field than the top part

4. Compared with males, the females of many animal species engage in which of these behaviours?
   a. compete for mates
   b. choose mates that are well camouflaged in their habitats
   c. choose to mate with many partners
   d. choose their mates carefully

5. Which of these statements is an accurate description of altruism?
   a. It advances the welfare of the entire species.
   b. It decreases the number of offspring an individual produces.
   c. It can indirectly spread the altruist's alleles.
   d. It can evolve only in animals with a haplodiploid genetic system.

6. Which of the following is an example of the fixed action pattern?
   a. herring gull chicks pecking at the red spot on their parent's bill
   b. sparrows singing their song correctly at their first attempt
   c. ducklings following their mother
   d. sea hares retracting their gills when repeatedly touched on the side

7. Which one of these is an example of visual signals?
   a. pheromones released by a male
   b. black and white stripes on a skunk
   c. bats spreading their wings while flying
   d. grooming of another individual

8. Which are the three categories of way-finding mechanisms?
   a. sources of food, drinking water, and nesting sites
   b. pheromones, climate, and reproductive behaviours
   c. temperature, humidity, and winds
   d. piloting, compass orientation, and navigation

## Apply/Analyze

9. Which of these people have made the greatest contribution to the proposal that dolphins are reciprocal altruists?
   a. John M. McNamara and three colleagues
   b. Richard Connor and Kenneth Norris
   c. Robert Trivers and Ken Reeve
   d. William D. Hamilton and Xie Can

10. As concluded by Peter Marler, under what circumstances can white-crowned sparrows learn their species' song?
    a. after receiving hormone treatments
    b. during a critical period of their development
    c. under natural conditions
    d. when their genetic father is present

11. Which of these factors demonstrate that naked mole rats are like eusocial bees?
    a. They live underground.
    b. They share an exceptionally high proportion of alleles.
    c. Their workers are only females.
    d. Their workers breed.

12. What is the coefficient of relatedness between a person and their sister in comparison to the person and their uncle?
    a. three times lesser
    b. three times greater
    c. two times lesser
    d. two times greater

## Create/Evaluate

13. The squashing of an ant on a picnic blanket often attracts many other ants to its "funeral." What kind of signal does squashing of the ant likely produce?
    a. a visual signal
    b. an acoustical signal
    c. a chemical signal
    d. a tactile signal

14. Which of these modalities is most likely a type of communication signal used by fish living in murky tropical rivers?
    a. chemical
    b. tactile
    c. visual
    d. electrical

15. Compare different forms of learning.

# The Chemical and Physical Foundations of Biology

## What Are the Purple Pages?

Biology can be complex—incredibly complex! A common concern expressed by students in biology (and indeed in most sciences) is that the terminology and concepts are overwhelming. In fact, learning science is often compared to learning a new language. It's tricky at first and each new word is foreign and awkward. As you progress, however, you grow comfortable with how each word has context, and it fits nicely with the rest of the vocabulary that you're using it with. You learn not to remember each word in isolation, but to integrate them with the larger context of your language.

This textbook includes these Purple Pages which provide you with a place to access fundamental concepts that help you make sense of biology. It's likely you already know a lot of what is in these pages from high-school science, but looking them over now is a good chance for you to remember what you learned—perhaps some time ago—and the way that we're going to use these concepts in this textbook.

You'll also note that much of the Purple Pages is about chemistry! Indeed, the distinction between biology and chemistry is an artificial one. Biology relies on a good chemistry background to make sense. Don't worry, we won't be balancing a lot of equations here. The Purple Pages, as the roadmap image suggests, connect to all concepts and chapters in the book. The unification is largely an example of scale: atoms are small and individually pretty insignificant, but they are the basis of all matter in the universe. Individually, an atom has only a few tricks it can perform. When atoms are combined, however, they acquire new abilities, which themselves contribute to larger levels of complexity and even more abilities. This concept is called **emergent properties**. By understanding the basis of emergent properties, you can dispense with memorizing a lot of facts, and instead build a strategy that makes understanding this discipline more efficient and meaningful. Chapter 21 uses the concept of emergent properties to show how a combination of properties allows for us to define life—and how this definition is complex and elusive! Scientists do not all agree on a single definition of life.

The importance of these concepts should be apparent from how this book is set out. Purple is a striking colour and is different from the other pages in this book, and this section is in the *middle* rather than the beginning of the book. Although you should be comfortable with Purple Pages

concepts even as you read through the starting chapters, this section is positioned to indicate that the fundamentals of biology are the core of all the other concepts.

## Emergent Properties

*New abilities through increasing complexity*, emergent properties, was introduced in the previous section. Exactly how does this work? First, it's important to understand that a **property** is a distinctive attribute of something; a property is the essence of a thing. Next, we know that combining things together leads to increasing levels of complexity. Complexity can thus be viewed as a hierarchy, an ascending ranking. Simpler things are at the bottom, and more complex and massive things are at the top.

Specific properties can be identified for each level of a hierarchy of complexity. If we start with the simple atoms that make up all matter, there are only a few properties and they exert their effect in a very small, localized way. Each atom can exert electronegativity in the way its electrons interact with the nucleus. We use the concept of positive and negative charge to describe how protons and electrons behave with each other. Quantum physics affects atoms, causing certain conformations to have different stabilities. These conformations lead to secure associations between atoms; these are *atomic bonds*, and there are several different ways that atoms can bond. These different bonds are new properties that emerge when atoms combine to form compounds. Molecules are a form of a compound where atoms are joined using fairly fixed bonds called *covalent bonds*. These bonds can be polar or non-polar, and this influences how the molecule will interact with other molecules, such as water. As the hierarchy progresses through macromolecules, organelles, cells, tissues, organs, organisms ... all the way up to the biosphere and culminating in the universe, new properties like ecologies, weather, and planetary orbits pop up, emerge, as complexity increases.

We'll start with a quick look at how scientists gather knowledge and test their ideas, and then work our way through the hierarchy of complexity, starting from atoms and ending with the evolutionary and geologic timescales. Note that all levels of complexity and descriptions of properties are human constructions; nature doesn't automatically fall into the categories we scientists create for our models. Levels of complexity below atoms and above geologic timescales definitely exist, and there are tiers of complexity that can be found between the ones we highlight here. As you read, ask yourself if you'd add any levels of organization or can point out properties that we might not have included.

Before we venture up through the hierarchy of matter, let's take a moment to ponder how scientists come to believe the principles they hold.

# The Scientific Basis of Biology

The information contained in this textbook represents the culmination of hundreds of years of research involving a huge number of experiments carried out by countless scientists. The entire content of this book—every observation, experimental result, and generality—is the product of **biological research,** the collective effort of individuals who have worked to understand every aspect of the living world. This section describes how biologists working today pose and find answers to questions.

## The Scientific Method

Beginning about 500 years ago in Europe, inquisitive people began to understand that direct observation is the most reliable and productive way to study natural phenomena. By the nineteenth century, researchers were using the **scientific method**—an investigative approach to acquiring knowledge in which scientists make observations about the natural world, develop working explanations about what they observe, and then test those explanations by collecting more information.

Application of the scientific method requires both curiosity and skepticism: successful scientists question the current state of our knowledge and challenge old concepts with new ideas and new observations. Explanations of natural phenomena must be backed up by objective evidence rooted in observation and measurement. Most importantly, scientists share their ideas and results by publishing their work.

## Testing a Hypothesis Is Central to the Scientific Method

A **hypothesis** can be defined as a tentative explanation for an observation, phenomenon, or scientific problem that can be tested by further investigation. Scientific hypotheses have two fundamental elements. First, a hypothesis must be *testable*. That is, there must be some set of observations or experiments that can be undertaken to support the hypothesis. For example, you may be studying a gene in yeast that you find is activated when cells are placed under conditions of heat stress. You may hypothesize that the protein encoded by this gene is essential for the yeast to survive short-term exposure to high temperature. Using modern molecular techniques, you can test this hypothesis by inactivating the gene in a population of yeast cells and observing if there is a change in heat tolerance. Today, this hypothesis is easily testable. A scientist may have had a similar idea 30 years ago but, given the lack of molecular techniques, the hypothesis would not have been testable at that time.

The second key to a scientific hypothesis is that it must be *falsifiable*. That is, through observation or experimentation you must be able to show that the original hypothesis may not be correct. Getting back to the yeast analogy, it is possible that your analysis might show that inactivation of the gene does not change the ability of yeast cells to survive high temperatures.

Scientists test the predictions that come from hypotheses with experimental or observational tests that generate relevant data. And if data from just one study refute a scientific hypothesis (i.e., demonstrate that its predictions are incorrect), the scientist must modify the hypothesis and test it again or abandon it altogether.

No amount of data can prove beyond a doubt that a hypothesis is correct; there is always the chance that a contradictory example exists, and it is impossible to test every imaginable example. That is why scientists say that positive results are consistent with, support, or confirm a hypothesis. They do not say the hypothesis is "proven."

## Elements of the Scientific Method

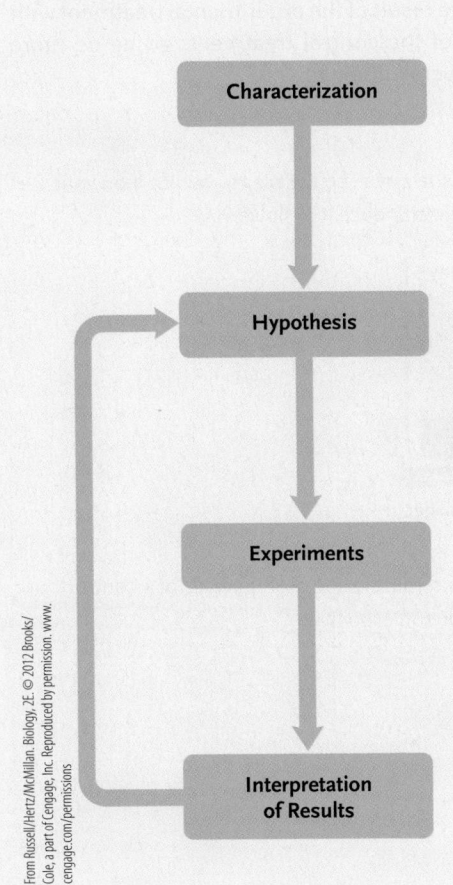

**Characterization**

**Hypothesis**

**Experiments**

**Interpretation of Results**

From Russell/Hertz/McMillan. Biology, 2E. © 2012 Brooks/Cole, a part of Cengage, Inc. Reproduced by permission. www.cengage.com/permissions

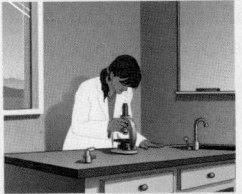

**1** Before a new hypothesis is formulated, researchers today usually know a fair amount about the subject under study. This characterization comes from years of their own experiments as well as the published research of other scientists working in the same discipline.

**2** Based on earlier findings, create a testable and falsifiable explanation (a hypothesis) of the information gathered. Hypotheses may be expressed in words or in mathematical equations.

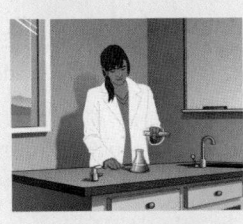

**3** Design and conduct a controlled experiment to test the predictions of the hypothesis, that is, what you would expect to observe if the hypothesis were correct. The experiment must be clearly defined so that it can be repeated by others.

**4** Compare the results of the experiment with those predicted by the hypothesis. If the results do not match the predictions, the hypothesis is refuted, and it must be rejected or revised. If the prediction was correct, the hypothesis is confirmed. The data from one set of experiments are subsequently used to develop additional hypotheses to be tested.

## An Example of Hypothesis Development and Testing

Consider this simple example of hypothesis development and testing. A friend gives you a plant that she grew on her windowsill. Under her care, the plant always flowered. You place the plant on your windowsill and water it regularly, but the plant never blooms. You know that your friend always gave fertilizer to the plant, and you wonder whether fertilizing the plant will make it flower. In other words, you create a hypothesis with a specific **prediction**: "This type of plant will flower if it receives fertilizer." This is a good hypothesis because it is not only testable but also falsifiable. To test the hypothesis, you would simply give the plant fertilizer. If it flowers, your hypothesis is supported. If it does not bloom, the data force you to reject or revise your hypothesis.

With all experiments it is important to include a **control**—a set of individuals that will not be subject to the treatment. To test this specific hypothesis, you need to compare plants that receive fertilizer (the experimental treatment) with plants grown without fertilizer (the control treatment). The presence or absence of fertilizer is the **experimental variable** and, in a controlled experiment, everything except the experimental variable—the flower pots, the soil, the amount of water, and exposure to sunlight—is kept the same between the treated and control individuals. This type of control ensures that any differences in flowering pattern observed between plants that receive the experimental treatment (fertilizer) and those that receive the control treatment (no fertilizer) can be attributed to the experimental variable.

*continued on next page*

Nearly all experiments in biology include **replicates**, multiple subjects that receive either the same experimental treatment or the same control treatment. Scientists use replicates in experiments because individuals typically vary in genetic makeup, size, health, or other characteristics—and because accidents may disrupt a few replicates. By exposing multiple subjects to both treatments, we can use a statistical test to compare the average result of the experimental treatment with the average result of the control treatment, giving us more confidence in the overall findings.

**Question:** Your friend fertilizes a plant that she grows on her windowsill, and it flowers. After she gives you the plant, you put it on your windowsill, but you do not give it any fertilizer and it does not flower. Will giving the plant fertilizer induce it to flower?

Friend added fertilizer.

You did not add fertilizer.

**Experiment:** Establish six replicates of an experimental treatment (identical plants grown with fertilizer) and six replicates of a control treatment (identical plants grown without fertilizer). Put on the same window sill to control for sun exposure.

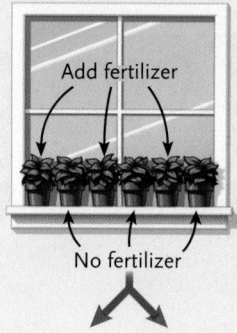

**Possible Result 1:** Neither experimental nor control plants flower.

**Possible Result 2:** Plants in the experimental group flower, but plants in the control group do not.

**Conclusion:** Fertilizer alone does not cause the plants to flower. Consider alternative hypotheses and conduct additional experiments, each testing a different experimental treatment, such as the amount of water or sunlight the plant receives or the temperature to which it is exposed.

**Conclusion:** The application of fertilizer induces flowering in this type of plant, supporting your original hypothesis. Pat yourself on the back and apply to graduate school in plant biology.

## The Scientific Theory

When a hypothesis stands up to repeated experimental tests, it is gradually accepted as an accurate explanation of natural events. This acceptance may take many years, and it usually involves repeated experimental confirmations. When many different tests have consistently confirmed a hypothesis that addresses many broad questions, it may become regarded as a scientific **theory**—a scientifically acceptable, well-substantiated explanation of some aspect of the natural world. Most scientific theories are supported by exhaustive experimentation; thus scientists usually regard them as established truths that are unlikely to be contradicted by future research.

In common usage, the word "theory" most often labels an idea as either speculative or downright suspect, as in the expression "It's only a theory." But when scientists talk about theories, they refer to concepts that have withstood the test of many experiments. Because of the difference between the scientific and the common usage of the word theory, many people fail to appreciate the extensive evidence that supports scientific theories. For example, virtually every scientist accepts the theory of evolution as a fully supported scientific truth: all species change with time, new species are formed, and older species eventually die off. Although evolutionary biologists debate the details of how evolutionary processes bring about these changes, very few scientists doubt that the theory of evolution is essentially correct. Moreover, *no scientist who has tried to cast doubt on the theory of evolution has ever devised or conducted a study that disproves any part of it*. Unfortunately, the confusion between the scientific and the common usage of the word theory has led, in part, to endless public debate about supposed faults and inadequacies in the theory of evolution.

## Experimental versus Observational Science

In some scientific disciplines, the system under study may be too large or too complex to establish controlled experiments. In astronomy, for example, one cannot manipulate stars and galaxies as if they were potted plants. Astronomy is considered an observational science, as are research themes in ecology and evolutionary biology. Observational science relies on sophisticated statistical techniques to analyze detailed observational data in order to test hypotheses. The statistical tools provide a method for researchers to infer pattern and underlying cause from the collected data.

Many scientific disciplines rely on a combination of observational and experimental science. For example, ecology researchers studying global climate change often set up experiments that take place in the environment. These experiments enable a certain level of control of variables under far more realistic conditions than would be possible in a laboratory. These so-called *field experiments* complement the analysis of observational data that may reflect changes to our climate that occurred hundreds of years ago.

# Measurement and Scale

## The SI System of Measurement

Because scientists rely heavily on each other's work, it is critically important that our findings from one experiment can be put into context with other work (see "Why Everyone Should Use SI Units"). The scientific community has therefore adopted a common set of metrics. No doubt you're familiar with metres, degrees Celsius, and litres. Common prefixes such as "kilo-" and "milli-" are well known also, and "giga-," "nano-," and "tera-" are gaining popularity. Scientists frequently deal with the very small and the very large, so when you're exploring the literature you might come across brand new units that you need to look up. With one system of measurements, this is much easier to do.

The International System of Units is the most widely used system of measurement in the world. Its abbreviation, SI, is from the French Système International d'Unités. It was adopted by the eleventh General Conference of Weights and Measures in 1960 and represents the latest modification of the metric

*continued on next page*

system, which was first implemented by the French National Assembly in 1790.

The SI system uses seven base units, each of which measures or describes a different kind of physical quantity. Each unit is strictly defined, although the definitions have been modified (and made more accurate) over time. As an example, the metre was originally defined by the French Academy of Sciences as the length between two marks on a platinum–iridium bar that was designed to represent 1/10 000 000 of the distance from the equator to the North Pole through Paris. This definition was changed in 1983 by the International Bureau of Weights and Measures to become the distance travelled by light in absolute vacuum in 1/299 792 458 of a second.

### The Seven Base Units of SI

| Name | Symbol | Quantity |
|------|--------|----------|
| metre | m | length |
| kilogram | kg | mass |
| second | s | time |
| ampere | A | electric current |
| kelvin | K | temperature |
| mole | mol | amount of substance |
| candela | cd | luminous intensity |

The SI system also uses a series of prefix names and prefix symbols to form the names and symbols of the decimal multiples of the base SI units. Note that the base unit for mass is the kilogram, not the gram. One kilogram equals 1000 g ($1 \text{ kg} = 10^3 \text{ g}$). This list has been extended several times: prefixes now range from yotta, at $10^{24}$ (one septillion), to yocto, at $10^{-24}$ (one septillionth).

| Factor | Prefix | Symbol | Factor | Prefix | Symbol |
|--------|--------|--------|--------|--------|--------|
| $10^{24}$ | yotta | Y | $10^{-1}$ | deci | d |
| $10^{21}$ | zetta | Z | $10^{-2}$ | centi | c |
| $10^{18}$ | exa | E | $10^{-3}$ | milli | m |
| $10^{15}$ | peta | P | $10^{-6}$ | micro | μ |
| $10^{12}$ | tera | T | $10^{-9}$ | nano | n |
| $10^{9}$ | giga | G | $10^{-12}$ | pico | p |
| $10^{6}$ | mega | M | $10^{-15}$ | femto | f |
| $10^{3}$ | kilo | k | $10^{-18}$ | atto | a |
| $10^{2}$ | hecto | h | $10^{-21}$ | zepto | z |
| $10^{1}$ | deca | da | $10^{-24}$ | yocto | y |

### Derived SI Units

Several other units have been derived from combinations of the seven base units of measure. Three of the more common ones concern units of force (newton), pressure (pascal), and energy or heat (joule). The measurement of temperature in degrees Celsius is also considered a derived unit, even though one Celsius degree is the same size as one kelvin. However, $0°C = 273.16 \text{ K}$ (note that no degree symbol is used when expressing temperature in kelvins).

| Name | Symbol | Quantity | Expression |
|------|--------|----------|------------|
| newton | N | force | $m \cdot kg \cdot s^{-2}$ |
| pascal | Pa | pressure | $N \cdot m^{-2}$ |
| joule | J | energy and work | $N \cdot m$ |

### Non-SI Units in Common Usage

A number of units not derived from the base SI units are accepted for use with SI units.

| Name | Symbol | Value in SI Units |
|------|--------|-------------------|
| minute | min | 60 s |
| hour | h | 3 600 s |
| day | d | 86 400 s |
| litre | L | $1 \text{ dm}^3 = 10^{-3} \text{ m}^3$ |
| angstrom | Å | $10^{-10}$ m |
| Calorie, a measure of food energy* | cal | 4.184 J |
| Unified atomic mass unit or Dalton** | u or Da | ~$1.66054 \times 10^{-24}$ kg |

*One food calorie = 1 Cal = 1000 cal
**Value determined experimentally to be 1/12 the mass of an unbound atom of carbon-12

## Scale in Biology

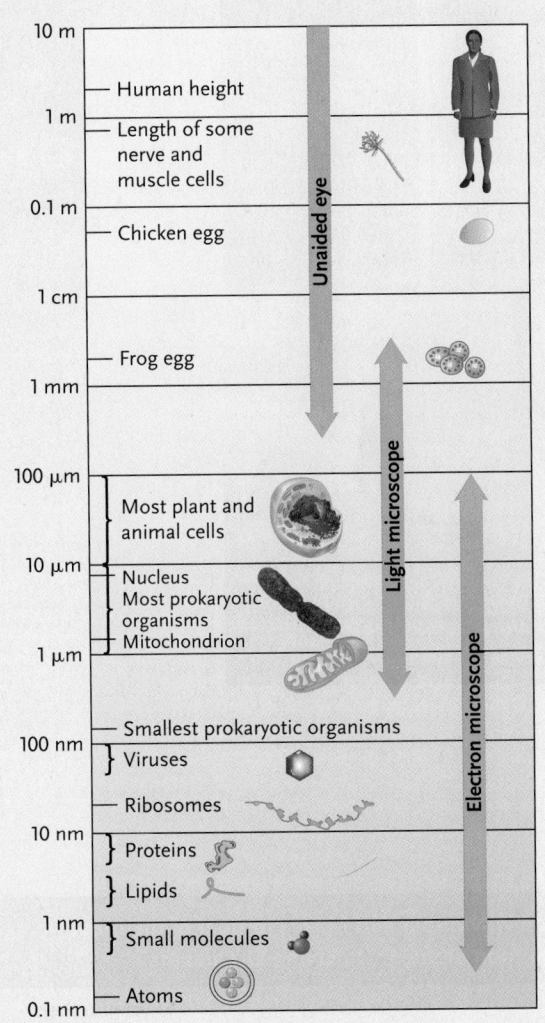

10 m
— Human height
1 m
— Length of some nerve and muscle cells
0.1 m
— Chicken egg
1 cm
— Frog egg
1 mm

Unaided eye

100 μm
Most plant and animal cells
10 μm
Nucleus
Most prokaryotic organisms
Mitochondrion
1 μm
— Smallest prokaryotic organisms
100 nm
} Viruses
— Ribosomes
10 nm
} Proteins
} Lipids
1 nm
} Small molecules
— Atoms
0.1 nm

Light microscope

Electron microscope

*continued on next page*

## The Organization of Matter

Any substance in the universe that has mass and occupies space is defined as **matter**. The fundamental scientific concepts that explain how matter is organized in biological systems are no different from those for non-living forms of matter. Living organisms are built from the same chemical building blocks as non-living systems and abide by the same fundamental laws of chemistry and physics. Because of this, a basic understanding of how all matter is organized is important for a complete picture of the structure and function of organisms.

## Why Everyone Should Use SI Units

In December 1998, NASA launched the Mars Climate Orbiter on a mission to study the Martian weather and climate. As it approached Mars, the spacecraft received instructions from flight control on Earth to fire thruster engines to enter into a proper orbit about 140 to 150 km above the Martian surface. However, as it approached the planet, a navigation error caused the spacecraft to descend into an orbit of only 57 km above the surface. The spacecraft was soon destroyed by the heat caused by atmospheric friction.

The review of the incident found that the root cause was a mix-up between the use of SI units and an older system of measure, imperial units (e.g., inches, feet, and pounds). More specifically, the software that was used to control the thruster engines of the spacecraft from the ground was written using the imperial unit of force, the pound-force, whereas onboard the spacecraft, information was interpreted in terms of newtons, the metric unit of force. Since 1 pound-force equals about 4.45 N, instructions from the ground were thus multiplied by 4.45.

The total cost of the mission was approximately $327 million.

## Elements and Compounds

All matter is composed of elements. An **element** is a pure substance composed of only one type of atom. Ninety-two different elements occur naturally on Earth. Living organisms are composed of about 25 elements, with only 4 elements—carbon, hydrogen, oxygen, and nitrogen—accounting for more than 96% of the mass of an organism. Seven other elements—calcium, phosphorus, potassium, sulfur, sodium, chlorine, and magnesium—contribute most of the remaining 4%. The proportions by mass of different elements differ markedly in sea water, the human body, a fruit, and Earth's crust, as shown below.

| Ocean water | |
|---|---|
| Oxygen | 85.84 |
| Hydrogen | 10.82 |
| Chloride | 1.94 |
| Sodium | 1.08 |
| Magnesium | 0.1292 |
| Sulphur | 0.091 |
| Calcium | 0.04 |
| Potassium | 0.04 |
| Bromide | 0.0067 |
| Carbon | 0.0028 |
| Other | 0.0103 |
| **Total:** | **100** |

| Human | |
|---|---|
| Oxygen | 65 |
| Carbon | 18 |
| Hydrogen | 10 |
| Nitrogen | 3 |
| Calcium | 1.4 |
| Phosphorus | 1.1 |
| Potassium | 0.2 |
| Sulfur | 0.25 |
| Sodium | 0.15 |
| Chlorine | 0.15 |
| Other | 0.75 |
| **Total:** | **100** |

| Earth's crust | |
|---|---|
| Oxygen | 46.73 |
| Silicon [A] | 27.80 |
| Aluminium | 8.15 |
| Iron | 5.01 |
| Calcium | 3.64 |
| Sodium | 2.84 |
| Potassium | 2.60 |
| Magnesium | 2.10 |
| Titanium | 0.44 |
| Hydrogen | 0.14 |
| Other | 0.55 |
| **Total:** | **100** |

| Corn Silage | |
|---|---|
| Oxygen | 45 |
| Carbon | 44 |
| Hydrogen | 6.3 |
| Nitrogen | 1.3 |
| Silicon | 1.2 |
| Potassium | 0.9 |
| Calcium | 0.25 |
| Phosphorus | 0.16 |
| Magnesium | 0.16 |
| Sulfur | 0.15 |
| Other | 1 |
| **Total:** | **100** Dry weight! |

© Cengage Learning 2017

Andriano / Shutterstock.com

oticki / Shutterstock.com

## The Atom

Elements are composed of **atoms**—the smallest units that retain the chemical and physical properties of an element. Each atom has a few properties, most of which are based on the ability to attract electrons (electronegativity) and hold energy in alternative stable states. Any given element has only one type of atom identified by a standard one- or two-letter symbol. The element carbon is identified by the single letter C, which stands for both the carbon atom and the element.

Each atom consists of an atomic nucleus surrounded by one or more, smaller, fast-moving particles called *electrons*. All atomic nuclei contain one or more positively charged particles called **protons**. The number of protons in the nucleus of each kind of atom is referred to as the **atomic number**. This number does not vary and thus specifically identifies the atom. The smallest atom, hydrogen, has a single proton in its nucleus, so its atomic number is 1. Carbon, with six protons, nitrogen, with seven protons, and oxygen, with eight protons, have atomic numbers of 6, 7, and 8, respectively.

With one exception, the nuclei of all atoms also contain uncharged particles called **neutrons**, which occur in variable numbers approximately equal to the number of protons.

### Atomic Number and Mass Number of the Most Common Elements in Living Organisms

| Element | Symbol | Atomic Number | Mass Number of the Most Common Form |
|---|---|---|---|
| Hydrogen | H | 1 | 1 |
| Carbon | C | 6 | 12 |
| Nitrogen | N | 7 | 14 |
| Oxygen | O | 8 | 16 |
| Sodium | Na | 11 | 23 |
| Magnesium | Mg | 12 | 24 |
| Phosphorus | P | 15 | 31 |
| Sulfur | S | 16 | 32 |
| Chlorine | Cl | 17 | 35 |
| Potassium | K | 19 | 39 |
| Calcium | Ca | 20 | 40 |
| Iron | Fe | 26 | 56 |
| Iodine | I | 53 | 127 |

*continued on next page*

The single exception is the most common form of hydrogen, which has a nucleus that contains only a single proton. Atoms are assigned a **mass number** based on the total number of protons and neutrons in the atomic nucleus. Electrons are ignored in determinations of atomic mass because the mass of an electron is very small.

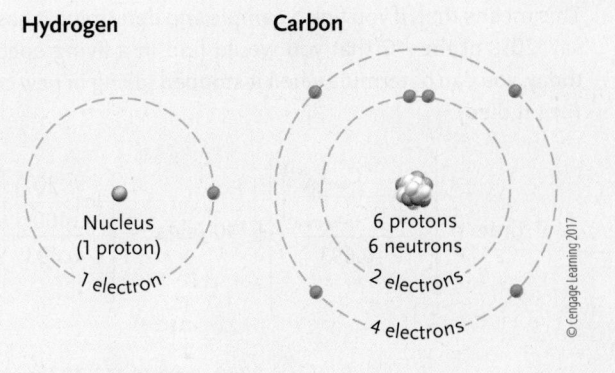

**Hydrogen**

Nucleus
(1 proton)
1 electron

**Carbon**

6 protons
6 neutrons
2 electrons
4 electrons

© Cengage Learning 2017

## Isotopes

All atoms of a specific element have the same number of protons, but they may differ in the number of neutrons. These distinct forms of an element, where atoms have the same atomic number but different atomic masses, are called **isotopes**. The nuclei of some isotopes are unstable and break down, or *decay*, giving off particles of matter and energy that can be detected as radioactivity. The decay transforms the unstable, radioactive isotope—called a *radioisotope*—into an atom of another element. For example, the carbon isotope $^{14}$C is unstable and undergoes radioactive decay in which one of its neutrons splits into a proton and an electron. The electron is ejected from the nucleus, but the proton is retained, giving a new total of seven protons and seven neutrons, which is characteristic of the most common form of nitrogen. Thus, the decay transforms the carbon atom into an atom of nitrogen.

**Isotopes of hydrogen**

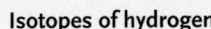

$^{1}$H
1 proton

atomic number = 1
mass number = 1

$^{2}$H (deuterium)
1 proton
1 neutron
atomic number = 1
mass number = 2

$^{3}$H (tritium)
1 proton
2 neutrons
atomic number = 1
mass number = 3

**Isotopes of carbon**

$^{12}$C
6 protons
6 neutrons
atomic number = 6
mass number = 12

$^{13}$C
6 protons
7 neutrons
atomic number = 6
mass number = 13

$^{14}$C
6 protons
8 neutrons
atomic number = 6
mass number = 14

© Cengage Learning 2017

## Use of Radioisotopes

Radioactive decay occurs at a steady, clocklike rate. The length of time it takes for one-half of a sample of a radioisotope to decay is termed its **half-life**. Each type of radioisotope has a characteristic half-life. For example, $^{14}$C decays with a fixed half-life of 5730 years, and $^{238}$U has a half-life of 4.5 billion years. Because unstable isotopes decay at a fixed rate that is not affected by chemical reactions or environmental conditions such as temperature or pressure, they are used to estimate the age of organic material, rocks, and fossils. These radiometric techniques have been vital in dating animal remains and tracing evolutionary lineages.

A living organism takes in $^{12}$C and $^{14}$C at a constant ratio. When an organism dies, it no longer is adding new carbon to itself and the $^{14}$C decays, increasing the $^{12}$C:$^{14}$C ratio. We can look at the ratio of fossils or mummified remains to figure out when the organism stopped incorporating carbon. The rate of decay is fixed, but the loss of the radionuclide decreases with time, making the calculation logarithmic in nature. The formula that can be used for radiocarbon dating is:

$$\text{time} = \left[ \frac{\ln\left(\dfrac{\text{isotope}_{sample}}{\text{isotope}_{reference}}\right)}{-0.693} \right] \text{half-life}$$

*continued on next page*

THE CHEMICAL AND PHYSICAL FOUNDATIONS OF BIOLOGY |

This means that, if you find a sample and determine it has only, say, 20% of the $^{14}C$ that you would find in a living specimen today, you can determine when it stopped taking in new carbon (i.e., it died).

$$time = \left[\frac{\ln\left(\frac{^{14}C_{sample}}{^{14}C_{reference}}\right)}{-0.693}\right] 5730 \text{ years} = \left[\frac{\ln\left(\frac{20}{100}\right)}{-0.693}\right]$$

$$5730 \text{ years} = 13\ 307 \text{ years}$$

These results show that the sample can be dated to over 13 000 years. Note that it's not realistic to pin it down to a specific date.

A number of radioisotopes that have short half-lives are used in medical imaging and in the treatment of diseases.

These isotopes include iodine-123 and thallium-201, which have half-lives of only 13.3 and 3.1 days respectively. Their short half-lives mean that they emit a constant, detectable signal during the test and also can be broken down and cleared from the patient in a reasonable time.

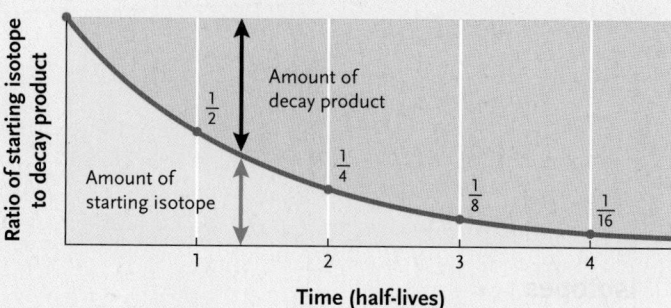

## Electrons and Electron Shells

In an atom, the number of electrons is equal to the number of protons in the nucleus. Because electrons carry a negative charge and protons are positively charged, the total structure of an atom is electrically neutral.

Electrons move around the atomic nucleus in **orbitals**, which are grouped into **electron shells**. These represent the energy states of the electrons; if enough energy is absorbed by an atom, electrons may store that as potential energy by reconfiguring its electrons by, for example, moving them farther from the nucleus. The most stable shells position the electrons closest to the nucleus, and as electrons are added they occupy higher level shells. As shown at right, the first shell (I) may be occupied by a maximum of two electrons. The second (II) and third (III) shells can hold a maximum of eight electrons each. The fourth shell can hold 18 electrons (not all shown). Atoms with more than four electron shells are very rare in biological molecules.

The chemical behaviour of an atom depends primarily on the number of electrons in its outermost shell. This is referred to as the *valence shell*, which holds **valence electrons**. Quantum effects make certain configurations of electrons more stable, so the inner orbitals tend to be completely occupied. The valence electrons tend toward filling the shell. Atoms that naturally have enough protons to support electrons that completely fill the valence shell are inert—the "noble gasses" helium, neon, and argon in the table. They form few important biological compounds. However, when a valence shell is filled by gaining, losing, or sharing electrons, new emergent properties arise from the associations of more than one atom.

Because an unfilled electron shell is less stable than a filled one, atoms with an incomplete outer shell have a strong tendency to interact with other atoms in a way that causes them to either gain or lose enough electrons to achieve a filled valence shell. All elements commonly found in living organisms have valence shells that are not completely filled with electrons (purple balls in figure). Because of this, these atoms readily participate in chemical reactions with other atoms.

# Atoms Interact to Produce New Properties

For this book, it makes sense to be clear about the way our definitions of matter are used. These definitions are not the ones you would find online, but they make understanding emergent properties easier. Standard definitions of compounds and molecules are of little help to distinguish biologically important chemistry, so our definitions are for clarity and precision.

A **compound** is a substance that contains two or more elements. For example, hydrogen and oxygen are the elements that make up the compound water ($H_2O$); sodium and chloride make up table salt (NaCl). The chemical and physical properties of compounds are typically distinct from those of their constituent atoms or elements.

A **molecule** is a group of atoms held together in a particular order through covalent bonds, such as glucose or water. Some molecules may consist of only one element (such as diamond), while some compounds are not molecules (e.g., sodium chloride, which is held together by ionic bonds). In chemistry, bonds can be viewed as a continuum of interactions, with ionic bonds being strongest; but this is not the case, as you'll see.

Why is this important? The basis of biology is chemistry. Biological chemistry is overwhelmingly considered as existing in aqueous solutions, and therefore a molecule—being held together by covalent bonds—is a more permanent arrangement of the atoms involved. If you conceive of water within a glass, would you consider it to be composed of a huge molecule of water, or a collection of about $8 \times 10^{24}$ molecules? In strict chemical analysis, an ionic bond is measured to be the strongest bond, but in an aqueous environment the atoms easily dissociate. Biologically, a covalent bond acts more permanently and we find structures held together by covalent bonds to be the most durable. Hence, calling these entities "molecules" is

a more functional definition. When you find something called a molecule, you often find that its biological function depends on its three-dimensional conformation.

Thus, we can describe a new emergent property when atoms interact: the ability to form bonds.

# Chemical Bonds

An atom with an incomplete valence shell has a strong tendency to interact with other atoms so that they have a completely filled valence shell. These interactions, called **chemical bonds**, are caused by closely associated atoms sharing or transferring electrons to complete the valence shell. Four types of chemical bonds are important in biological molecules: ionic bonds, covalent bonds, hydrogen bonds, and van der Waals forces. Because of their importance in hydrogen bonding, polar molecules are also discussed in this section.

The emergent properties of chemical bonds provide different functions to compounds and molecules that build up to the properties required for life. Ionic bonds dissociate easily in water but still provide essential functions such as aligning protein subunits and setting up gradients. Covalent bonds act more permanently, and molecules in their most meaningful sense—those that are joined firmly—are atoms that are covalently joined. Hydrogen bonds arise from covalently bonded atoms that have very different electronegativities (see "Polarity and Hydrogen Bonding" below). Particles that are held together but must occasionally dissociate (e.g., separation of two molecules of DNA in the double helix, or temporary binding of a hormone to a receptor) are often held together by hydrogen bonds. Although Van der Waals interactions are quite weak, they influence protein folding and interactions within and between molecules to set up three-dimensional structure.

## Ionic Bonds

Ionic bonds form between atoms that gain or lose valence electrons completely. A sodium atom (Na) readily loses a single electron to achieve a full valence shell (see previous section), and chlorine (Cl) readily gains an electron to do the same. After the transfer, the sodium atom, now with 11 protons and 10 electrons, carries a single positive charge. The chlorine atom, now with 17 protons and 18 electrons, carries a single negative charge. In this charged condition, the atoms are called **ions**: sodium, with a positive charge, is a **cation**; chloride, with a negative charge, is an **anion.**

Ionic bonds are common among the forces that hold ions, atoms, and molecules together in living organisms because

these bonds have three key features:

- They exert an attractive force over greater distances than any other chemical bond.
- Their attractive force extends in all directions.
- They vary in strength depending on the presence of other charged substances.

Due to the aqueous environment of cellular chemistry, ionic bonds can dissociate more easily than covalent bonds; thus, as an emergent property, their weaker associations are better suited for only certain interactions, usually those involving temporary associations.

*continued on next page*

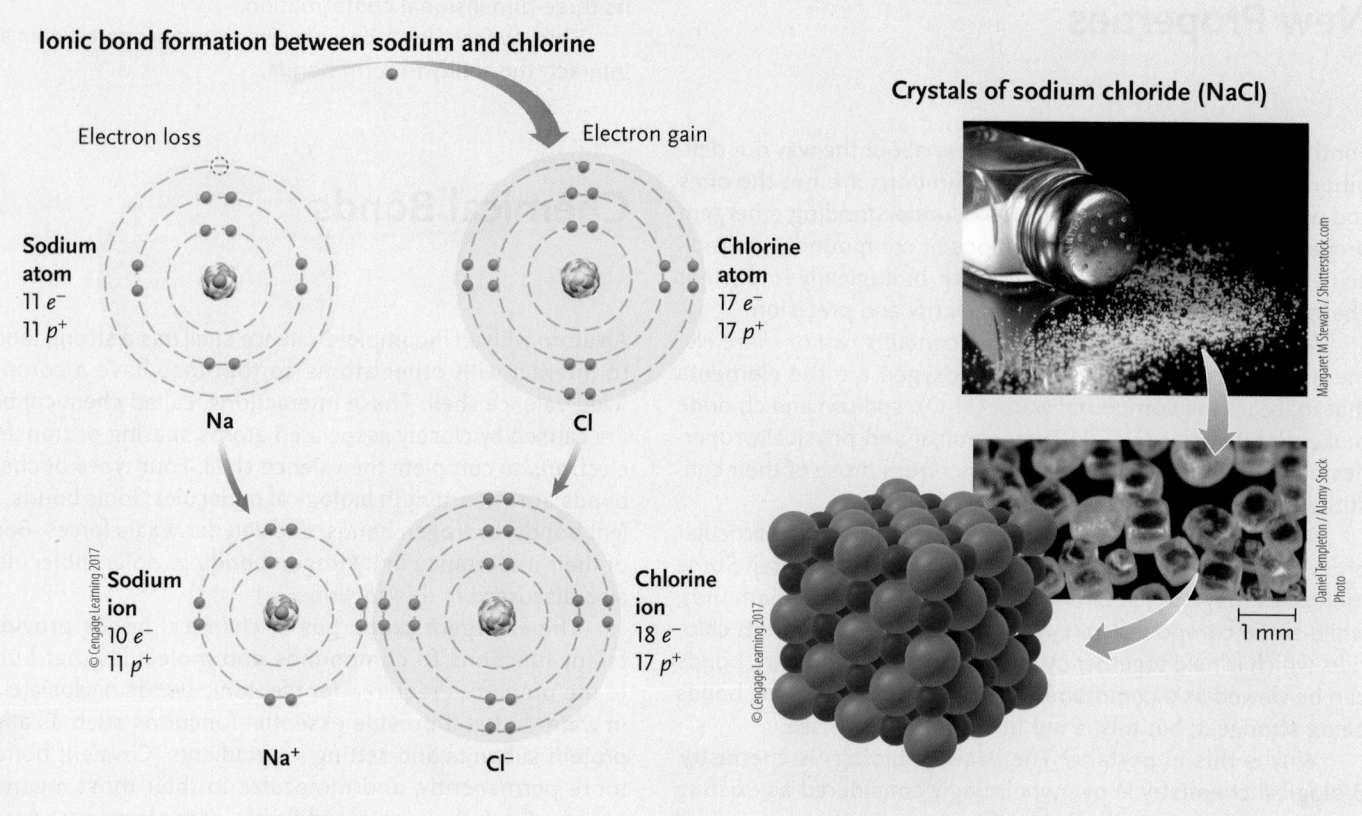

**Ionic bond formation between sodium and chlorine**

Electron loss

Electron gain

**Sodium atom**
11 $e^-$
11 $p^+$

**Na**

**Chlorine atom**
17 $e^-$
17 $p^+$

**Cl**

**Sodium ion**
10 $e^-$
11 $p^+$

**Na$^+$**

**Chlorine ion**
18 $e^-$
17 $p^+$

**Cl$^-$**

© Cengage Learning 2017

**Crystals of sodium chloride (NaCl)**

Margaret M Stewart / Shutterstock.com

Daniel Templeton / Alamy Stock Photo

1 mm

## Covalent Bonds

**Covalent bonds** form between two atoms when they share valence electrons. This is distinct from ionic bonds, where electrons are gained or lost from atoms. In biology, the term molecule usually refers to two or more atoms held together by covalent bonds. The formation of molecular hydrogen ($H_2$) by two hydrogen atoms is the simplest example of a covalent bond. If two hydrogen atoms collide, the single electron of each atom may join in a new, combined, two-electron orbital that surrounds both nuclei. The two electrons fill the orbital; thus the hydrogen atoms tend to remain linked stably together. The linkage formed by the shared orbital is a covalent bond.

A structural formula represents a covalent bond of a pair of shared electrons as a single line. For example, in $H_2$ the covalent bond that holds the molecule together is represented as H:H or H—H. Generally speaking, the covalent bonding capacity of an atom is equal to the number of valence shell electrons necessary to fill the shell: hydrogen, 1; oxygen, 2; nitrogen, 3; and carbon, 4.

As shown below, a single oxygen atom has six valence-shell electrons, and two oxygen atoms form a single molecule.

Carbon, with four unpaired outer electrons, typically forms four covalent bonds to complete its outermost energy level. An example is methane, $CH_4$, the main component of natural gas.

Unlike ionic bonds, which extend their attractive force in all directions, the shared orbitals that form covalent bonds extend between atoms at discrete angles and directions, giving covalently bound molecules distinct, three-dimensional forms. For biological molecules such as proteins, which are held together primarily by covalent bonds, the three-dimensional form imparted by these bonds is critical to their functions.

The four covalent bonds formed by the carbon atom are fixed at an angle of 109.5° from each other, forming a tetrahedron. The tetrahedral arrangement of the bonds allows carbon

*continued on next page*

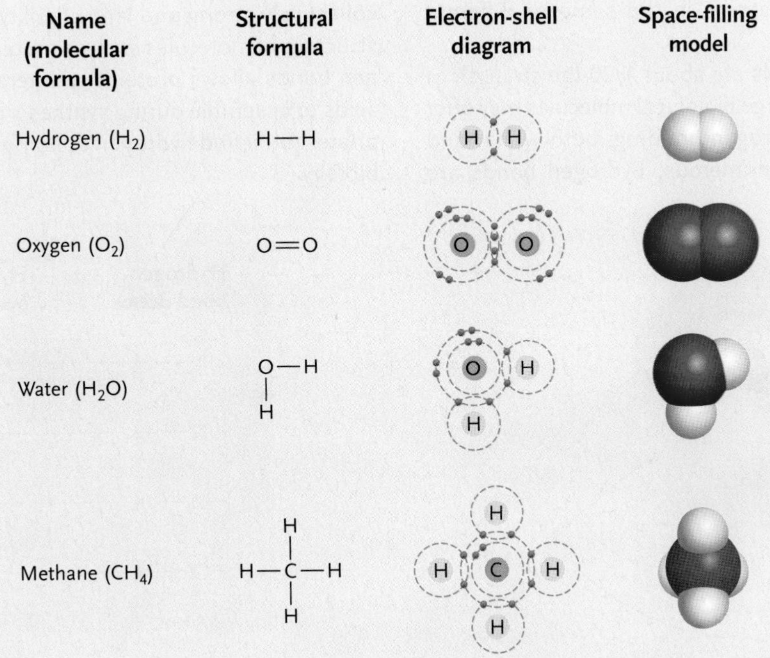

| Name (molecular formula) | Structural formula | Electron-shell diagram | Space-filling model |
| --- | --- | --- | --- |
| Hydrogen (H₂) | H—H | | |
| Oxygen (O₂) | O=O | | |
| Water (H₂O) | O—H<br>  \|<br>  H | | |
| Methane (CH₄) |    H<br>   \|<br>H—C—H<br>   \|<br>   H | | |

atoms to link extensively to each other in chains and rings in both branched and unbranched form. Such structures form the backbones of an almost unlimited variety of molecules. Carbon can also form double bonds, in which atoms share two pairs of electrons, and triple bonds, in which atoms share three pairs of electrons.

The emergent property of covalent bonding arises when atoms share electrons to form a persistent three-dimensional structure that gives function to the form. Without covalent bonding, macromolecules, organelles, and cells would not have their structure and life would be impossible.

## Polarity and Hydrogen Bonding

All covalent bonds involve the sharing of valence electrons between two atoms. Yet the degree of electron sharing between the two atoms can differ widely. **Electronegativity** is the measure of an atom's attraction for the electrons it shares in a chemical bond with another atom. The more electronegative an atom is, the more strongly it attracts shared electrons. Oxygen is the most electronegative atom found in biological molecules, followed by nitrogen and sulfur. By comparison, neither carbon nor hydrogen is considered electronegative.

The unequal sharing of electrons between two atoms that differ in their electronegativity results in a **polar covalent bond**. The atom that attracts the electrons more strongly carries a partial negative charge (denoted by the symbol $\sigma^-$), and the atom deprived of electrons carries a partial positive charge (denoted by the symbol $\sigma^+$). As shown in the molecule of water on the facing page, atoms carrying partial charges give the molecule partially positive and negative ends; this is referred to as *polarity*, and the molecule is termed **polar.**

Polar molecules attract and align themselves with other polar molecules and with charged ions and molecules. Polar molecules that associate readily with water because it is strongly polar are identified as **hydrophilic** (*hydro* = water; *philic* = preferring). Non-polar substances that are excluded by water and other polar molecules are identified as **hydrophobic** (*phobic* = avoiding). Most common non-polar molecules consist primarily of C—H bonds (neither atom being electronegative).

Hydrogen atoms are made partially positive by sharing electrons unequally with oxygen, nitrogen, or sulfur. Because of this, the hydrogen atom may be attracted to other electronegative atoms that it is not directly bonded to (see figure below). This attractive force is the **hydrogen bond**, illustrated by a dotted line in structural diagrams of molecules. Hydrogen

*continued on next page*

THE CHEMICAL AND PHYSICAL FOUNDATIONS OF BIOLOGY |

bonds may form between atoms in the same or different molecules.

Individual hydrogen bonds are about 1/20 the strength of a covalent bond. However, large biological molecules may offer many opportunities for hydrogen bonding, both within and between molecules. When numerous, hydrogen bonds are collectively strong and lend stability to the three-dimensional structure of molecules such as proteins. The property of hydrogen bonds allows proteins to interact reversibly, and nucleic acids to assemble during synthesis and separate when appropriate. You'll find hydrogen bonding plays a ubiquitous role in biology.

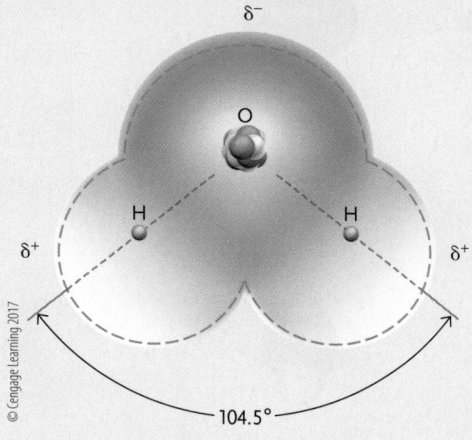

## Van der Waals Forces

**Van der Waals** forces are even weaker than hydrogen bonds. These forces develop between non-polar molecules or regions of molecules when, through their constant motion, electrons accumulate by chance in one part of a molecule or another. This process leads to zones of positive and negative charge, making the molecule polar. If they are oriented in the right way, the polar parts of the molecules are attracted electrically to one another and cause the molecules to stick together briefly. Although an individual bond formed with van der Waals forces is weak and transient, the formation of many bonds of this type can stabilize the shape of a large molecule, such as a protein.

A striking example of the collective power of van der Waals forces concerns the ability of geckos to cling to and walk up vertical smooth surfaces. The toes of the lizard are covered in millions of pads, each one forming a weak interaction—using van der Waals forces—with the molecules on the smooth surface.

## Chemical Reactions

**Chemical reactions** occur when atoms or molecules interact to form new chemical bonds or break old ones. As a result of bond formation or breakage, atoms are added to or removed from molecules, or the linkages of atoms in molecules are rearranged. When any of these alterations occur, molecules change from one type to another, usually with different chemical and physical properties. In biological systems, chemical reactions are accelerated by *enzymes*, which are discussed in Chapter 3.

The atoms or molecules entering a chemical reaction are called the **reactants**, and those leaving a reaction are the **products**. A chemical reaction is written with an arrow showing the direction of the reaction; reactants are placed to the left of the arrow, and products are placed to the right. Both reactants and products are usually written in chemical shorthand as formulas.

For example, the overall reaction of photosynthesis, in which carbon dioxide and water are combined to produce sugars and oxygen (see Chapter 6), is written as follows:

$$6CO_2 + 6H_2O \rightarrow C_6H_{12}O_6 + 6O_2$$

Carbon    Water    A sugar Molecular

dioxide              oxygen

The number in front of each formula indicates the number of molecules of that type among the reactants and products (the number 1 is not written). Notice that there are as many atoms of each element to the left of the arrow as there are to the right, even though the products are different from the reactants. This balance reflects the fact that, in such reactions, atoms may be rearranged but not created or destroyed. Chemical reactions written in balanced form are known as **chemical equations.**

While some chemical reactions result in all the reactant molecules being converted into products, many reactions are reversible; that is, the products of the forward reaction can become the reactants of the reverse reaction. That a reaction is reversible is illustrated by using opposite-headed arrows. As an example, hydrogen and molecular nitrogen can react to produce ammonia, but ammonia can also break down to produce hydrogen and nitrogen:

$$3H_2 + N_2 \rightleftarrows 2NH_3$$

The direction of the reaction is dictated by environmental conditions and is dependent on the energy and stability of the components. The ability to bond is an emergent property arising from combining atoms in different ways and allows energy to be stored and released, cells to replicate, and information to flow. Chemistry is a property that emerges from the level of molecular organization, and is based on the properties atoms individually possess which allow them to interact with each other.

# Water

All living organisms contain water, and many kinds of organisms live directly in water. Even those that live in dry environments contain water in all their structures; different organisms range from 50% to more than 95% water by mass. The water inside organisms is crucial for life: it is required for many important biochemical reactions and plays major roles in maintaining the shape and organization of cells and tissues.

### Hydrogen Bonds and the Properties of Water

The properties of water molecules that make them so important to life depend to a great extent on their polar structure and their ability to link to each other by hydrogen bonds (see "Chemical Bonds").

Hydrogen bonds form readily between water molecules in both liquid water and ice. In liquid water, each water molecule establishes an average of 3.4 hydrogen bonds with its neighbours, forming an arrangement known as the **water lattice**. In liquid water, the hydrogen bonds that hold the lattice together constantly break and re-form, allowing the water molecules to break loose from the lattice, slip past one another, and re-form the lattice in new positions.

In ice, the water lattice is a rigid, crystalline structure in which each water molecule forms four hydrogen bonds with neighbouring molecules. The rigid ice lattice spaces the water molecules farther apart than the water lattice. Because of this greater spacing, water has the unusual property of being about 10% less dense when solid than when liquid. Imagine what Earth would be like if ice sank to the bottom, as most solids do.

Water has behaviours that are different from other molecules and that lead to emergent properties essential for life.

*continued on next page*

Scientists cannot easily conceive of life that does not require water because of these properties. Most molecules become denser as they cool; water becomes less dense. Ice floats to cover bodies of water to insulate the liquid underneath, permitting organisms to survive. Because freezing water expands, it can fit in crevices and grind stones to create soil. It is water's ability to interact with ions, both positive and negative, stabilize membrane sheets, and dissociate into hydroxyl as well as form hydronium ions that makes the complex chemistry of life possible.

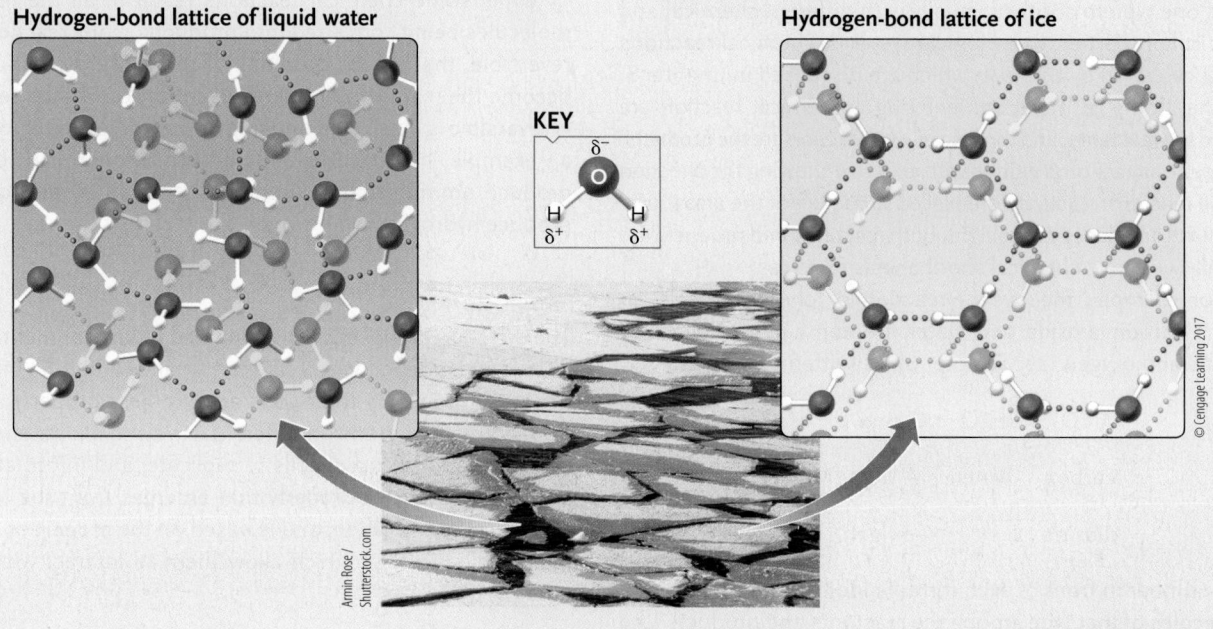

**Hydrogen-bond lattice of liquid water**

**KEY**

**Hydrogen-bond lattice of ice**

Armin Rose / Shutterstock.com

© Cengage Learning 2017

## Specific Heat and Heat of Vaporization

The hydrogen-bond lattice of liquid water retards the escape of individual water molecules as the water is heated. As the heat flows into water, much of it is absorbed in the breakage of hydrogen bonds. As a result, the temperature of water, reflected in the average motion of its molecules, increases relatively slowly as heat is added. This results in water having a high **specific heat**, defined as the amount of heat required to increase the temperature of a given quantity of water. For example, relatively high temperatures and the addition of considerable heat are required to break enough hydrogen bonds to make water boil. The high boiling point maintains water as a liquid over the wide temperature range of 0°C–100°C.

The unusual properties of water are more obvious if you compare it to $H_2S$, a molecule that has a similar molecular mass and structure. Compared to $H_2O$, $H_2S$ boils at an astonishingly low temperature of −60°C. The vast difference in boiling points between these two molecules is explained by oxygen being more electronegative than sulfur. This results in water being a more polar molecule, and in turn being able to form a much stronger hydrogen-bond lattice.

A large amount of heat, 586 cal/g, must be added to give water molecules enough energy of motion to break loose from liquid water and form a gas. This required heat, known as the **heat of vaporization**, allows humans and many other organisms to cool off when hot. In humans, water is released onto the surface of the skin by more than 2.5 million sweat glands; the heat energy absorbed by the water in sweat as the sweat evaporates cools the skin and the underlying blood vessels. The heat loss helps keep body temperature from increasing when environmental temperatures are high. Plants use a similar cooling mechanism as water evaporates from their leaves.

## Surface Tension

The hydrogen-bond lattice of water results in water molecules staying together, a phenomenon called **cohesion**. For example, in land plants, cohesion holds water molecules in unbroken columns in the microscopic conducting tubes that extend from the roots to the highest leaves. As water evaporates from the leaves, water molecules in the columns, held together by cohesion, move upward through the tubes to replace the lost water.

Related to cohesion is **surface tension**, which is a measure of how difficult it is to stretch or break the surface of a liquid. The water molecules at surfaces facing air can form hydrogen bonds with water molecules beside and below them but not on the sides that face the air. This unbalanced bonding produces a force that places the surface water molecules under tension, making them more resistant to separation than the underlying water molecules. This force is strong enough to allow small insects such as spiders (to be consistent with the diagram) to walk on water.

## Hydrophobic Interactions

The tendency for water molecules to neutralize their charges by maximizing hydrogen bonds also plays a role in the famous "oil separating from water" phenomenon. When hydrophobic molecules such as fats are mixed into a polar solvent like water, the fats clump together in what we call "hydrophobic interactions." In reality, there's no particular attraction between the fats; it's the tendency of water molecules to stabilize around the non-polar molecules, forming a pocket of hydrophobic molecules surrounded by a hydration shell. The water molecules hydrogen bond with each other in their most stable way, forcing the lipids to cluster.

This clustering has immense importance in biology. It allows for sheets of phospholipids to form spontaneously in an aqueous environment and creates environments that give proteins their structure. Non-polar amino acids are

Creation of surface tension by unbalanced hydrogen bonding

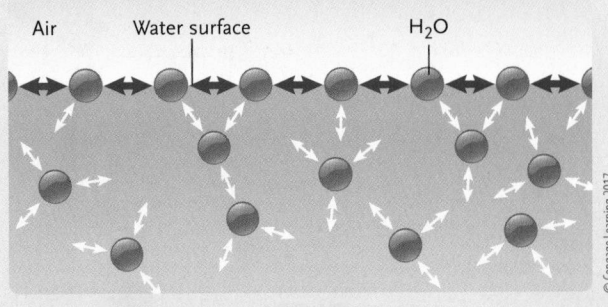

Spider supported by water's surface tension

forced to interact internally to support tertiary protein structure, and the hydrophilic amino acids at the surface of soluble proteins are stabilized by water on the outside (see the facing page).

## Aqueous Solutions

Because water molecules are small and strongly polar, they readily surround other polar and charged molecules and ions. The surface coat, called a **hydration shell**, reduces the attraction between the molecules or ions and promotes their separation and entry into a **solution**, where they are suspended individually, surrounded by water molecules. Once in solution, the hydration shell prevents the polar molecules or ions from reassociating. In such an aqueous solution, water is called the **solvent**, and the molecules of a substance dissolved in water are called the *solute*.

Sodium chloride (salt) dissolves in water because water molecules quickly form hydration layers around the $Na^+$ and $Cl^-$ ions in the salt crystals, reducing the attraction between the ions so much that they separate from the crystal and enter the surrounding water lattice as individual ions. In much the same way, hydration shells surround macromolecules such as nucleic acids and proteins, reducing their electrostatic interaction with other molecules.

*continued on next page*

Salt

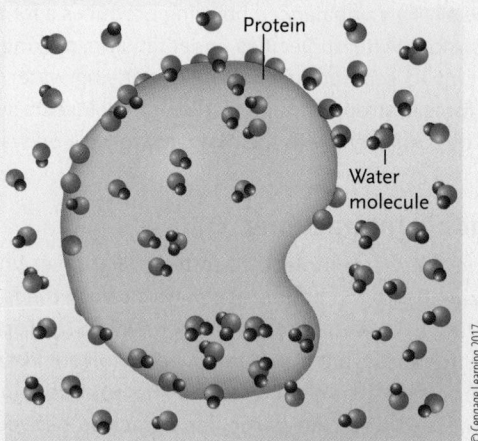

Protein

Water molecule

© Cengage Learning 2017

## Calculating Solute Concentrations

In the cell, chemical reactions depend on solutes dissolved in aqueous solutions. To understand these reactions, you need to know the number of atoms and molecules involved. **Concentration** is the number of molecules or ions of a sub-stance in a unit volume of space, such as 1 mL or 1 L. The number of molecules or ions in a unit volume cannot be counted directly, but it can be calculated indirectly by using the mass number of atoms as the starting point.

*continued on next page*

The mass number of an atom is equivalent to the number of protons and neutrons in its nucleus. From the mass number, and the fact that neutrons and protons have approximately the same mass (i.e., $1.66 \times 10^{-24}$ g), you can calculate the mass of an atom of any substance. For an atom of the most common form of carbon, with six protons and six neutrons in its nucleus, the total mass is

$$12 \times (1.66 \times 10^{-24} \text{ g}) = 1.992 \times 10^{-23} \text{ g}$$

For an oxygen atom, with eight protons and eight neutrons in its nucleus, the total mass is

$$16 \times (1.66 \times 10^{-24} \text{ g}) = 2.656 \times 10^{-23} \text{ g}$$

Dividing the total mass of a sample of an element by the mass of a single atom gives the number of atoms in the sample. Suppose you have a carbon sample with a mass of 12 g—a mass in grams equal to the atom's mass number. (In the periodic table, the atomic weight isn't equal to the sum of protons and neutrons because the weight is an average of the proportions of isotopes for that element.) Dividing 12 g by the mass of one carbon atom gives

$$\frac{12}{\left(10.992 \times 10^{-23} \text{ g}\right)} = 6.02 \times 10^{-23} \text{ atoms}$$

If you divide the atomic weight of oxygen (16 g) by the mass of one oxygen atom, you get the same result:

$$\frac{16}{\left(2.656 \times 10^{-23} \text{ g}\right)} = 6.02 \times 10^{-23} \text{ atoms}$$

In fact, dividing the atomic weight of any element by the mass of an atom of that element always produces the same number: $6.02 \times 10^{23}$. This number is called **Avogadro's number**, after Amedeo Avogadro, the nineteenth-century Italian chemist who first discovered the relationship.

The same relationship holds for molecules. The **molecular weight** of any molecule is the mass in grams equal to the total mass number of its atoms. For NaCl, the total mass number is $23 + 35 = 58$ (a sodium atom has 11 protons and 12 neutrons, and a chlorine atom has 17 protons and 18 neutrons). The mass of one NaCl molecule is therefore

$$58 \times (1.66 \times 10^{-24} \text{ g}) = 9.628 \times 10^{-23} \text{ g}$$

Dividing the molecular weight of NaCl (58 g) by the mass of a single NaCl molecule gives

$$\frac{58}{\left(9.628 \times 10^{-23} \text{ g}\right)} = 6.02 \times 10^{-23} \text{ atoms}$$

When concentrations are described, the atomic weight of an element or the molecular weight of a compound—the amount that contains $6.02 \times 10^{23}$ atoms or molecules—is known as a **mole** (abbreviated mol). The number of moles of a substance dissolved in 1 L of solution is known as the **molarity** (abbreviated M) of the solution. This relationship is highly useful in chemistry and biology because we know that two solutions with the same volume and molarity but composed of different substances will contain the same number of molecules of the substances.

## Dissociation of Water and pH

The most critical property of water that is unrelated to its hydrogen-bond lattice is its ability to separate, or dissociate. This occurs when a hydrogen atom that is involved in a hydrogen bond between two water molecules moves from one molecule to the other. The proton ($H^+$) is what actually leaves; the electron is left behind. This proton switch results in the formation of a hydroxide ion ($OH^-$) and a hydronium ion ($H_3O^+$).

It is convention to simply use $H^+$ (the hydrogen ion) to denote the hydronium ion. The proportion of water molecules that dissociate to release hydrogen and hydroxide ions is small. However, because of the dissociation, water always contains some $H^+$ and $OH^-$ ions.

In pure water, the concentrations of $H^+$ and $OH^-$ ions are equal. However, adding other substances may alter the relative concentrations of $H^+$ and $OH^-$, making them unequal. Some substances, called **acids**, are proton donors, which release hydrogen ions (and anions) when they are dissolved in water, effectively increasing the $H^+$ concentration. For example, hydrochloric acid (HCl) dissociates into $H^+$ and $Cl^-$ when dissolved in water:

$$HCl \rightarrow H^+ + Cl^-$$

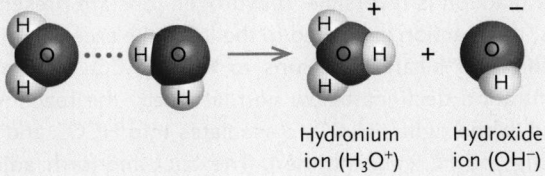

Hydronium ion ($H_3O^+$)   Hydroxide ion ($OH^-$)

*continued on next page*

Other substances, called **bases**, are proton acceptors, which reduce the $H^+$ concentration of a solution. Most bases dissociate in water into hydroxide ions ($OH^-$) and cations. The hydroxide ion can act as a base by accepting a proton to produce water. For example, sodium hydroxide (NaOH) separates into $Na^+$ and $OH^-$ ions when dissolved in water:

$$NaOH \rightarrow Na^+ + OH^-$$

The excess $OH^-$ combines with $H^+$ to produce water

$$OH^- + H^+ \rightarrow H_2O$$

thereby reducing the $H^+$ concentration. Basic solutions are also called *alkaline* solutions.

Other bases do not dissociate to produce hydroxide ions directly. For example, ammonia ($NH_3$), a poisonous gas, acts as a base when dissolved in water, directly accepting a proton from water, producing an ammonium ion, and releasing a hydroxide ion:

$$NH_3 + H_2O \rightarrow NH_4^+ + OH^-$$

The concentration of $H^+$ is measured on a numerical scale from 0 to 14, called the pH scale. Because the number of $H^+$ ions in solution increases exponentially as the acidity increases, the scale is based on logarithms of this number to make the values manageable:

$$pH = -\log_{10}[H^+]$$

In this formula, the brackets indicate concentration in moles per litre. The negative of the logarithm is used to give a positive number for the pH value. For example, in a water solution that is *neutral*—neither acidic nor basic—the concentration of *both* $H^+$ and $OH^-$ ions is $1 \times 10^{-7}$ M (0.000 000 1 M). The base 10 logarithm of $1 \times 10^{-7}$ is $-7$. The negative of the logarithm $-7$ is 7. Acidic solutions have pH values less than 7, while basic solutions have pH values greater than 7. Each whole number on the pH scale represents a value 10 times or one-tenth the next number.

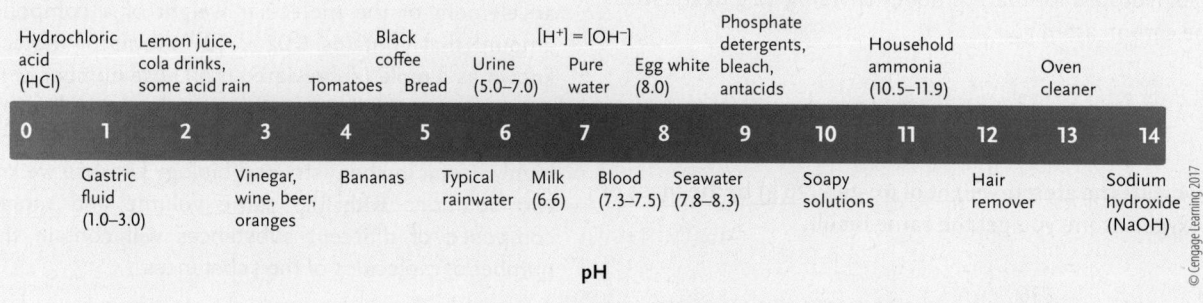

© Cengage Learning 2017

## Buffers Keep pH within Limits

Acidity is important to cells because even small changes, on the order of 0.1 or even 0.01 pH unit, can drastically affect biological reactions. In large part, a small change in pH can cause structural changes in proteins that can damage or destroy the proteins' function. Consequently, all living organisms have elaborate systems that control their internal acidity by regulating $H^+$ concentration near the neutral value of pH 7.

Living organisms control the internal pH of their cells with *buffers*—substances that compensate for pH changes by absorbing or releasing hydrogen ions. When hydrogen ions are released in excess by biological reactions, buffers combine with them and remove them from the solution; if the concentration of hydrogen ions decreases, buffers release $H^+$ to restore the balance. Most buffers are weak acids, weak bases, or combinations of these substances that dissociate reversibly in water solutions to release or absorb $H^+$ or $OH^-$. (Weak acids, such as acetic acid, or weak bases, such as ammonia, release relatively few $H^+$ or $OH^-$ ions in an aqueous solution, whereas

strong acids or bases dissociate extensively. HCl is a strong acid; NaOH is a strong base.)

The buffering mechanism that maintains blood pH near neutral values is a good example. In humans and many other animals, blood pH is buffered by a chemical system based on carbonic acid ($H_2CO_3$), a weak acid. In water solutions, carbonic acid dissociates readily into bicarbonate ions ($HCO_3^-$) and $H^+$:

$$H_2CO_3 \rightarrow HCO_3^- + H^+$$

The reaction is reversible. If hydrogen ions are present in excess, the reaction is pushed to the left—the excess $H^+$ ions combine with bicarbonate ions to form $H_2CO_3$. If the $H^+$ concentration declines below normal levels, the reaction is pushed to the right—$H_2CO_3$ dissociates into $HCO_3^-$ and $H^+$, restoring the $H^+$ concentration. The back-and-forth adjustments of the buffer system help keep human blood close to its normal pH of 7.4.

# Carbon Compounds

## Carbon Bonding

Compounds that contain carbon form the structures of living organisms and take part in all biological reactions as well as serving as energy sources. Collectively, molecules based on carbon are known as *organic molecules*. All other substances, that is, those without carbon atoms in their structures, are **inorganic molecules**. A few of the smallest carbon-containing molecules that occur in the environment as minerals or atmospheric gases, such as $CaCO_3$ and $CO_2$, are also considered inorganic molecules.

Carbon's central role in life's molecules arises from its bonding properties: it can assemble into an astounding variety of chain and ring structures that form the backbones of all biological molecules. This is because carbon has four unpaired outer electrons that it readily shares to complete its outermost energy level, forming four covalent bonds. With different combinations of single, double, and even triple bonds, an almost limitless array of molecules is possible. Carbon atoms bond covalently to each other and to other atoms, chiefly hydrogen, oxygen, nitrogen, and sulfur, in molecular structures that range in size from a few to thousands or even millions of atoms. Molecules consisting of carbon linked only to hydrogen atoms are called *hydrocarbons* (*hydro*- refers to hydrogen, not water). The simplest hydrocarbon, $CH_4$ (methane), consists of a single carbon atom bonded to four hydrogen atoms. Removing one hydrogen atom from methane leaves a methyl group, which occurs in many biological molecules:

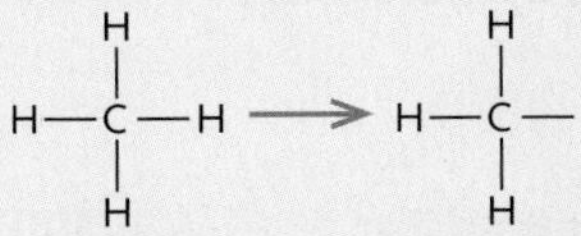

Methane     Methyl group

Now imagine bonding two methyl groups together. Removing a hydrogen atom from the maximum of four bonds, the number of hydrogen atoms in a molecule decreases as the resulting structure, ethane, produces an ethyl group:

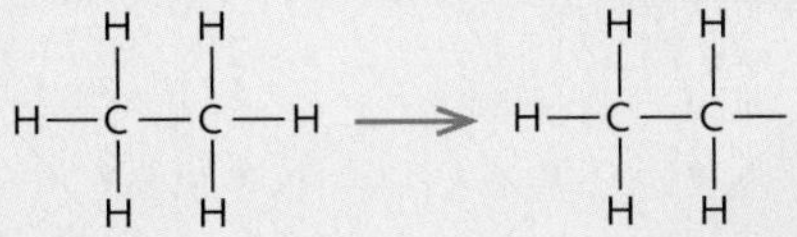

Ethane     Ethyl group

Repeating this process builds a linear hydrocarbon chain:

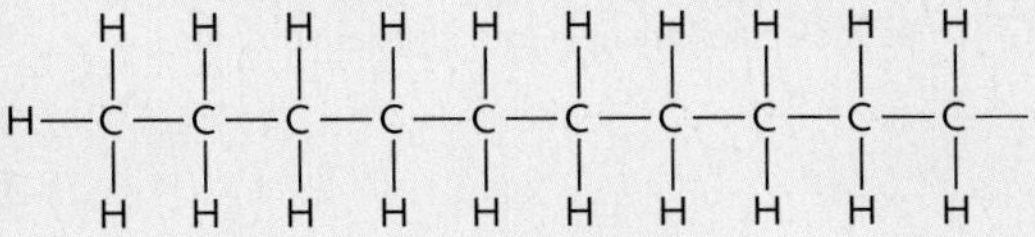

© Cengage Learning 2017

Branches can be added to produce a branched hydrocarbon chain:

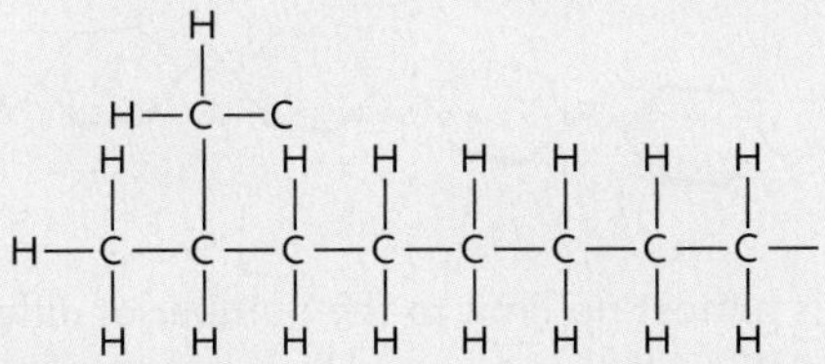

A chain can loop back on itself to form a ring. For example, cyclohexane, $C_6H_{12}$, has single covalent bonds between each pair of carbon atoms and two hydrogen atoms attached to each carbon atom:

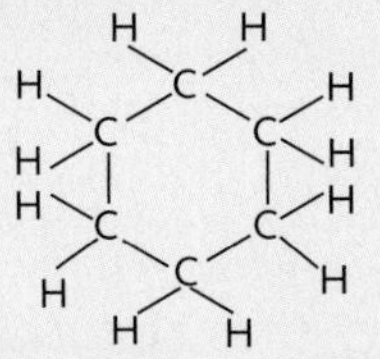

$C_6H_{12}$, cyclohexane

To simplify things, the ring structure above is often simply depicted like this:

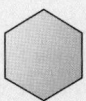

Hydrocarbons gain added complexity when neighbouring carbon atoms form double or triple bonds. Because each carbon atom can form a maximum of four bonds, the number of hydrogen atoms in a molecule decreases as the number of bonds between any two carbon atoms increases:

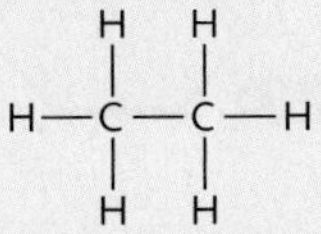

Single bonding: $C_2H_6$, ethane

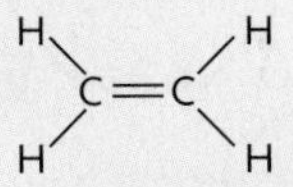

Double bonding: $C_2H_4$, ethene (ethylene)

Triple bonding: $C_2H_2$, ethyne (acetylene)

Double bonds between carbon atoms are also found in carbon rings:

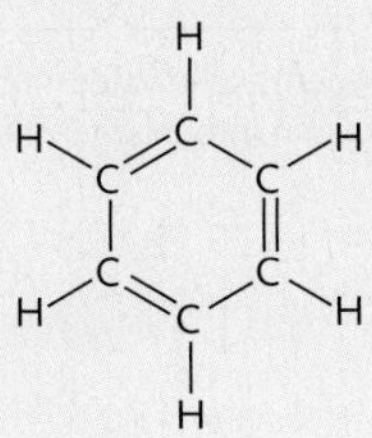

*continued on next page*

Notice how each carbon in this ring still maintains four covalent bonds.

Many carbon rings can join together to produce larger molecules, as in the string of sugar molecules that makes up a polysaccharide chain:

There is almost no limit to the number of different hydrocarbon structures that carbon and hydrogen can form; however, the molecules of living systems typically contain other elements in addition to carbon and hydrogen. These other elements confer functional properties on organic molecules, producing the four major classes of organic molecules: *carbohydrates, lipids, proteins,* and *nucleic acids*.

Carbon is the atom most associated with life. Chemistry involving carbon is called "organic chemistry," even if the molecules being investigated are not involved in biology. Bonds made by carbon atoms have emergent properties that make them able to interact well in three dimensions due to their tetrahedral arrangement. In addition, because carbon and hydrogen are equally electronegative, their covalent bonds are non-polar; they do not interact well with water. This means that some organic molecules, usually hydrocarbons, form vital hydrophobic materials. When oxygen, sulfur, and nitrogen associate with carbon they form polar bonds, setting up opportunities for hydrogen bonding.

## Dehydration and Hydrolysis Reactions

In many of the reactions that involve functional groups, the components of a water molecule, —H and —OH, are removed from or added to the groups as they interact. When the components of a water molecule are *removed* during a reaction, usually as part of the assembly of a larger molecule from smaller subunits, the reaction is called a **dehydration synthesis reaction** or a *condensation reaction*. For example, this type of reaction occurs when individual sugar molecules combine to form a starch molecule. In **hydrolysis**, the reverse reaction, the components of a water molecule are *added* to functional groups as molecules are broken into smaller subunits. For example, the breakdown of a protein molecule into individual amino acids occurs by hydrolysis.

**Dehydration synthesis reactions**

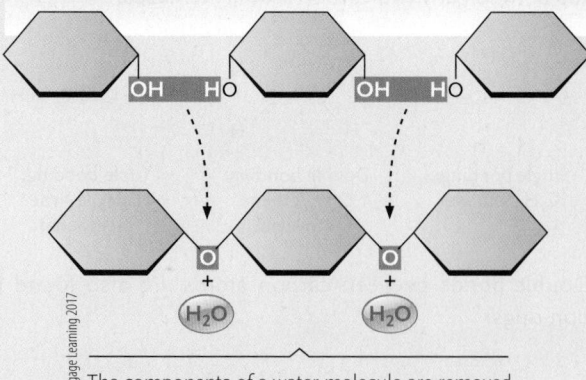

© Cengage Learning 2017

The components of a water molecule are removed as subunits join into a larger molecule.

**Hydrolysis**

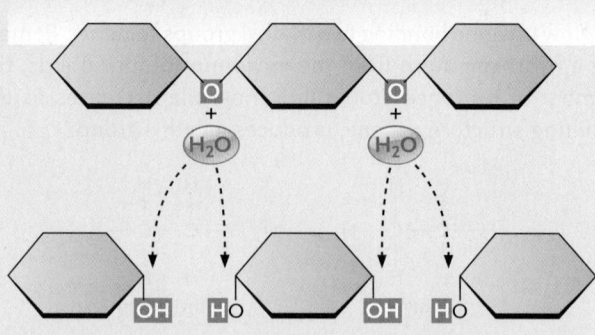

The components of a water molecule are added as molecules are split into smaller subunits.

# Functional Groups

Carbohydrates, lipids, proteins, and nucleic acids are synthesized and degraded in living organisms through interactions between small reactive groups of atoms attached to the organic molecules. The atoms in these reactive groups, called **functional groups**, occur in positions in which their covalent bonds are more readily broken or rearranged than the bonds in other parts of the molecules.

The functional groups that enter most frequently into biological reactions are the *hydroxyl, carbonyl, carboxyl, amino, phosphate,* and *sulfhydryl* groups. The unconnected covalent bonds written to the left of each structure link these functional groups to other atoms in biological molecules, usually carbon atoms. The symbol R is used to represent a chain of carbon atoms.

### Common Functional Groups of Organic Molecules

| Functional Group | Major Classes of Molecules | Example |
|---|---|---|
| Hydroxyl  R—OH | Alcohols | Ethyl alcohol (in alcoholic beverages) |

A hydroxyl group (—OH) consists of an oxygen atom linked to a hydrogen atom. Hydroxyl groups are polar and confer polarity on the parts of the molecules that contain them. The presence of the hydroxyl group enables an alcohol to form linkages to other organic molecules through dehydration synthesis reactions.

| Carbonyl  R—C=O (H) | Aldehydes | Acetaldehyde |
|---|---|---|
| Carbonyl  R—C=O (C) | Ketones | Acetone (a solvent) |

A carbonyl group (C=O) consists of an oxygen atom linked to a carbon atom by a double bond. Carbonyl groups are the reactive parts of aldehydes and ketones, molecules that act as major building blocks of carbohydrates, and also take part in the reactions supplying energy for cellular activities. In an aldehyde, the carbonyl group is linked, along with a hydrogen atom, to a carbon atom at the end of a carbon chain, as in acetaldehyde. In a ketone, the carbonyl group is linked to a carbon atom in the interior of a carbon chain, as in acetone.

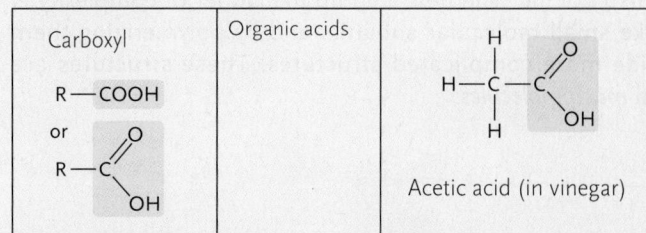

| Carboxyl  R—COOH  or  R—C=O (OH) | Organic acids | Acetic acid (in vinegar) |
|---|---|---|

A carboxyl group (—COOH) is formed by the combination of a carbonyl group and a hydroxyl group. The carboxyl group is the characteristic functional group of organic acids (also called *carboxylic acids*). The carboxyl group gives organic molecules acidic properties because its —OH group readily releases the hydrogen as a proton ($H^+$) in solution.

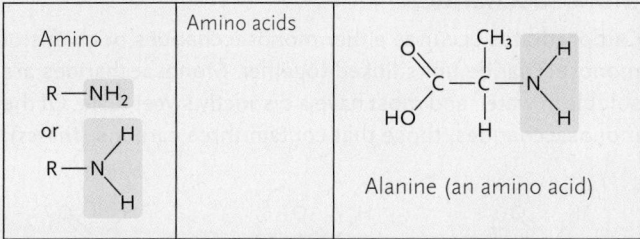

| Amino  R—NH₂  or  R—N (H)(H) | Amino acids | Alanine (an amino acid) |
|---|---|---|

The amino group ($—NH_2$) consists of a nitrogen atom bonded on one side to two hydrogen atoms; in a molecule it is linked to an R group on the other side, as in the amino acid alanine and all other amino acids.

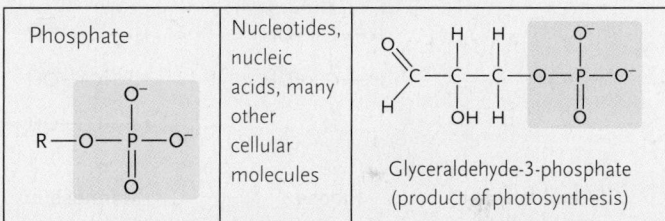

| Phosphate  R—O—P—O⁻ (O⁻)(O) | Nucleotides, nucleic acids, many other cellular molecules | Glyceraldehyde-3-phosphate (product of photosynthesis) |
|---|---|---|

The phosphate group ($—OPO_3^{2-}$) consists of a central phosphorus atom bonded to four oxygen atoms, as shown at left. Among the large biological molecules linked by phosphate groups is the nucleic acid DNA. Phosphate groups are added to or removed from biological molecules as part of reactions that conserve or release energy. In addition, they control biological activity—the activity of many proteins is turned on or off by the addition or removal of phosphate groups.

| Sulfhydryl  R—SH | Many cellular molecules | Mercaptoethanol |
|---|---|---|

In the sulfhydryl group (—SH), a sulfur atom is linked on one side to a hydrogen atom; in a molecule, the other side is linked to an R group. The sulfhydryl group is easily converted into a covalent linkage in which it loses its hydrogen atom as it binds. In many of these linking reactions, two sulfhydryl groups interact to form a disulfide linkage (—S—S—). In proteins, the disulfide bond contributes to tertiary structure.

Bonds between atoms are an emergent property that can happen only when complexity is increased from single atoms to interactions between atoms. These new properties drive the chemistry of life. The next step up the ladder of complexity is to take small molecular subunits and by polymerizing them provide more complicated structures. These structures are called *macromolecules*.

# Carbohydrates

Carbohydrates, the most abundant biological molecules, serve many functions. Together with fats, they act as the major fuel substances providing chemical energy for cellular activities. Chains of carbohydrate subunits also form structural molecules such as cellulose, one of the primary constituents of plant cell walls. Carbohydrates get their name because they contain carbon, hydrogen, and oxygen atoms, with the approximate ratio of the atoms being 1 carbon : 2 hydrogens : 1 oxygen ($CH_2O$).

## Monosaccharides

Carbohydrates occur as either monosaccharides or chains of monosaccharide units linked together. Monosaccharides are soluble in water, and most have a distinctly sweet taste. Of the monosaccharides, those that contain three carbons (*trioses*), five carbons (*pentoses*), and six carbons (*hexoses*) are most common in living organisms. All monosaccharides can occur in the linear form, where each carbon atom in the chain except one has both a —H and a —OH group attached to it.

Monosaccharides with five or more carbons can fold back on themselves to assume a ring form. Folding into a ring occurs through a reaction between two functional groups in the same monosaccharide, as occurs in glucose. The ring form of most five- and six-carbon sugars is much more common in cells than the linear form.

When glucose forms into a ring, two alternative arrangements are possible (α-glucose and β-glucose) that differ in the arrangements of the —OH group bound to the carbon at position 1. These two different forms of glucose are called *isomers*.

Glyceraldehyde
(3 carbons;
a triose)

Ribose
(5 carbons;
a pentose)

Mannose
(6 carbons;
a hexose)

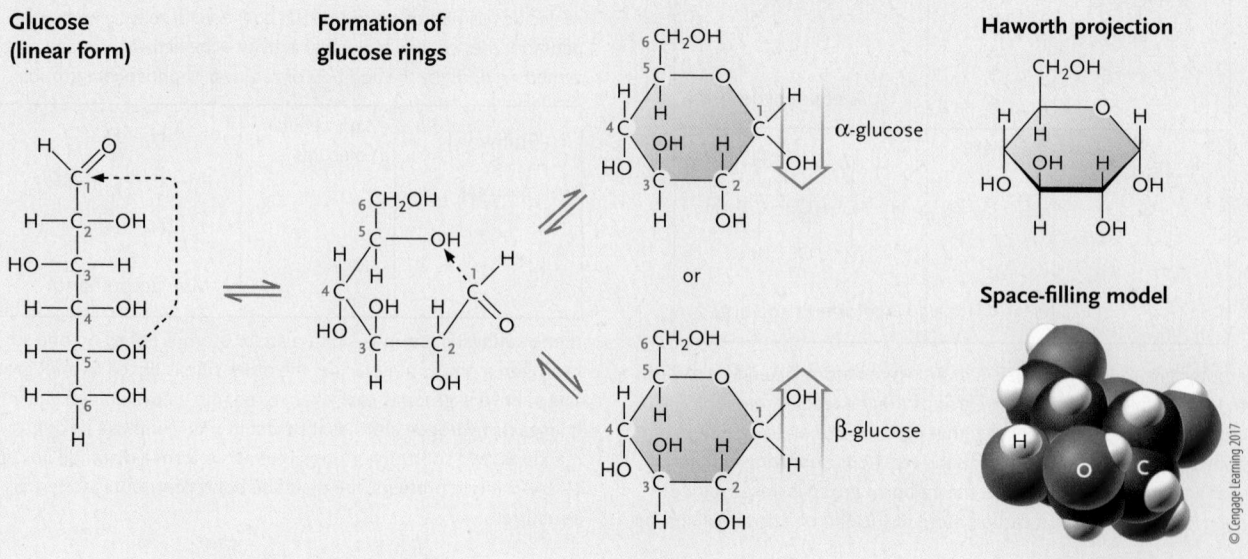

Glucose
(linear form)

Formation of
glucose rings

α-glucose

or

β-glucose

Haworth projection

Space-filling model

© Cengage Learning 2017

## Isomers of the Monosaccharides

Typically, one or more of the carbon atoms in a monosaccharide links to four different atoms or chemical groups. Carbons linked in this way are called *asymmetric* carbons; they have important effects on the structure of a monosaccharide because they can take either of two fixed positions with respect to other carbons in a carbon chain. For example, the middle carbon of the three-carbon sugar glyceraldehyde is asymmetric because it shares electrons in covalent bonds with four different atoms or groups: —H, —OH, —CHO, and —CH$_2$OH. The —H and —OH groups can take either of two positions, with the —OH extending to either the left or the right of the carbon chain relative to the —CHO and —CH$_2$OH groups:

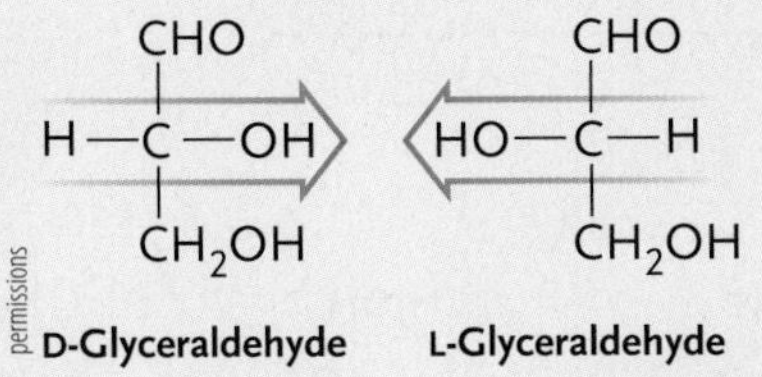

From Russell/Hertz/McMillan. Biology, 2E. © 2012 Brooks/Cole, a part of Cengage, Inc. Reproduced by permission. www.cengage.com/permissions

D-Glyceraldehyde    L-Glyceraldehyde

Note that the two forms of glyceraldehyde have the same chemical formula, C$_3$H$_6$O$_3$. The difference between the two forms is similar to the difference between your two hands. Although both hands have four fingers and a thumb, they are not identical; rather, they are mirror images of each other. That is, when you hold your right hand in front of a mirror, the reflection looks like your left hand, and vice versa.

Two or more molecules with the same chemical formula but different molecular structures are called *isomers*. Isomers that are mirror images of each other, like the two forms of glyceraldehyde, are called *enantiomers*, or *optical isomers*. One of the enantiomers—the one in which the hydroxyl group extends to the left in the view just shown—is called the *l-form* (*laevus* = left). The other enantiomer, in which the —OH extends to the right, is called the *d-form* (*dexter* = right). The difference between l- and d-enantiomers is critical to biological function. Typically, one of the two forms enters much more readily into cellular reactions; just as your left hand does not fit readily into a right-hand glove, enzymes (proteins that accelerate chemical reactions in living organisms) fit only one of the two forms of an enantiomer. For example, most of the enzymes that catalyze the biochemical reactions of monosaccharides react exclusively with the D-form, making this form much more common among cellular carbohydrates than the L-form. Many other kinds of biological molecules besides carbohydrates form enantiomers; an example is the amino acids.

In the ring form of many five- or six-carbon monosaccharides, including glucose, the carbon at the 1 position of the ring is asymmetric because its four bonds link to different groups of atoms. This asymmetry allows monosaccharides such as glucose to exist as two different enantiomers. The glucose enantiomer with a —OH group pointing below the plane of the ring is known as *alpha-glucose* or *α-glucose*; the enantiomer with a —OH group pointing above the plane of the ring is known as *beta-glucose* or *β-glucose*. Other five- and six-carbon monosaccharide rings have similar α- and β-configurations.

The α- and β-rings of monosaccharides can give the polysaccharides assembled from them vastly different chemical properties. For example, starches, which are assembled from α-glucose units, are biologically reactive polysaccharides easily digested by animals; cellulose, which is assembled from β-glucose units, is relatively unreactive and, for most animals, completely indigestible.

Another form of isomerism is found in monosaccharides, as well as in other molecules. Two molecules with the same chemical formula but atoms that are arranged in a different order are called *structural isomers*. The sugars glucose and fructose are examples of structural isomers.

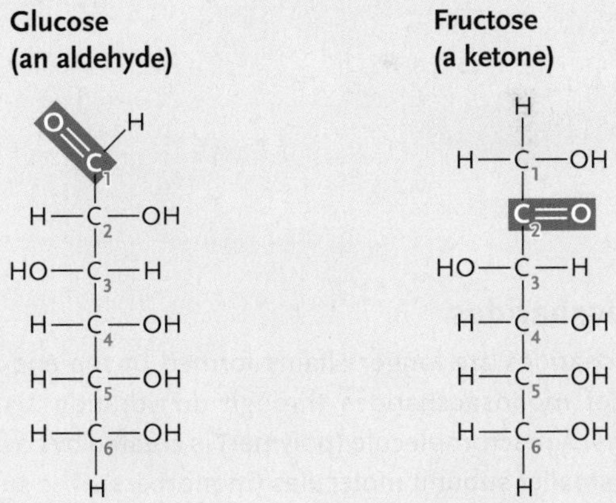

Glucose
(an aldehyde)

Fructose
(a ketone)

© Cengage Learning 2017

## Disaccharides

Disaccharides are typically assembled from two monosaccharides linked by a dehydration synthesis reaction. For example, the disaccharide maltose is formed by the linkage of two α-glucose molecules, with oxygen as a bridge between the number 1 carbon of the first glucose unit and the number 4 carbon of the second glucose unit. Bonds of this type, which commonly link monosaccharides into chains, are known as

*continued on next page*

*glycosidic bonds.* A glycosidic bond between a 1 carbon and a 4 carbon is written in chemical shorthand as a 1 → 4 linkage. Linkages such as 1 → 2, 1 → 3, and 1 → 6 are also common in carbohydrate chains. The linkages are designated as α or β depending on the orientation of the—OH group at the 1 carbon that forms the bond. In maltose, the—OH group is in the α position; therefore, the link between the two glucose subunits of maltose is written as an α (1 → 4) linkage. Maltose, sucrose, and lactose are common disaccharides.

**Formation of maltose**

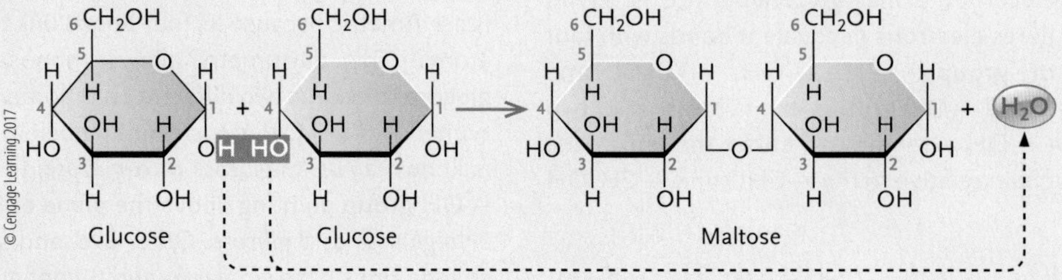

Glucose + Glucose → Maltose + $H_2O$

**Sucrose**

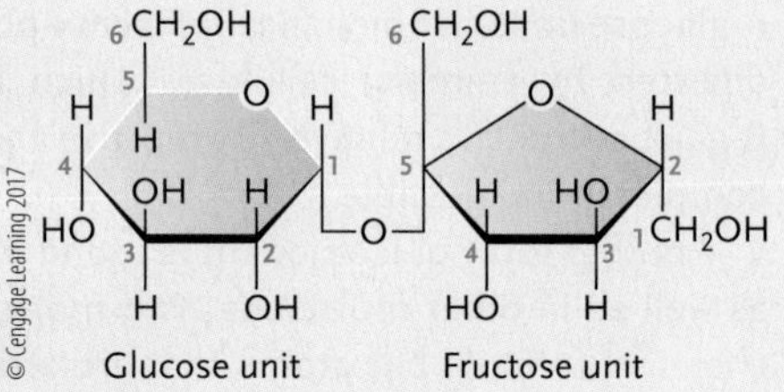

Glucose unit    Fructose unit

**Lactose**

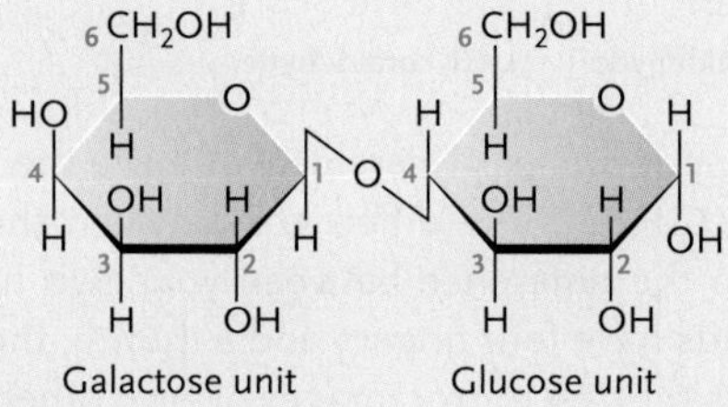

Galactose unit    Glucose unit

© Cengage Learning 2017

## Polysaccharides

Polysaccharides are longer chains formed by the end-to-end linking of monosaccharides through dehydration synthesis reactions. A macromolecule (polymer) is created by covalently linking smaller subunit molecules (monomers). The subunits for the macromolecule class of polysaccharides are the monosaccharides.

The dehydration synthesis reactions that assemble polysaccharides from monosaccharides are examples of polymerization, in which identical or nearly identical subunits, called the *monomers* of the reaction, join like links in a chain to form a larger molecule called a *polymer*. Linkage of a relatively small number of non-identical subunits can create highly diverse and varied biological molecules. Many kinds of polymers, not just polysaccharides, are found in cells. DNA is a primary example of a highly diverse polymer assembled from various sequences of only four different types of monomers.

All the most common polysaccharides—the plant starches, glycogen, and cellulose—are assembled from hundreds or thousands of glucose units. Other polysaccharides are built up from a variety of different sugar units. Polysaccharides may be linear, unbranched molecules, or they may contain one or more branches in which side chains of sugar units are attached to a main chain.

*continued on next page*

Amylose, formed from α-glucose units joined end to end in α (1 → 4) linkages. The coiled structures are induced by the bond angles in the α-linkages.

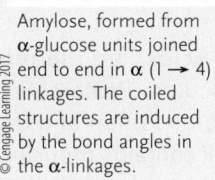

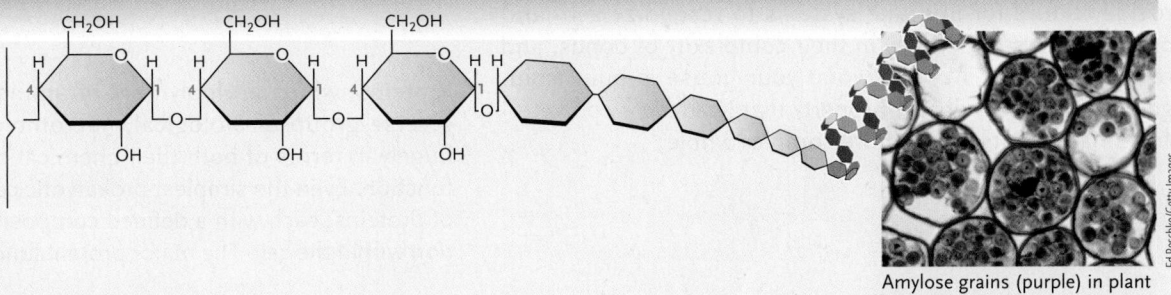

Amylose grains (purple) in plant root tissue

Glycogen, formed from glucose units joined in chains by α (1 → 4) linkages; side branches are linked to the chains by α (1 → 6) linkages (boxed in blue).

Glycogen particles (blue) in liver cell

Cellulose, formed from glucose units joined end to end by β (1 → 4) linkages. Hundreds to thousands of cellulose chains line up side by side, in an arrangement reinforced by hydrogen bonds between the chains, to form cellulose microfibrils in plant cells.

Glucose subunit

Cellulose molecule

Cellulose microfibril

Cellulose microfibrils in plant cell wall

Chitin, formed from β-linkages joining glucose units modified by the addition of nitrogen-containing groups. The external body armour of the tick is reinforced by chitin fibres.

Carbohydrates have a variety of arrangements for their subunits and can form linear or networked molecules. These provide texture for immune systems to recognize self- and non-self cells, store energy in their complexity of bonds, and provide structure, like the wood your house is built from. Again, this is an emergent property that is added by polymerizing smaller units into a more complex whole.

# Proteins

Proteins, which are polymers of amino acids, are the most diverse group of biological macromolecules. Proteins vary hugely in terms of both their chemical composition and their function. Even the simplest prokaryotic cell contains thousands of proteins, each with a defined composition and specific function within the cell. The major protein functions are listed below.

| Protein Type | Function | Examples |
| --- | --- | --- |
| Structural proteins | Support | Microtubule and microfilament proteins form supporting fibres inside cells; collagen and other proteins surround and support animal cells; cell wall proteins support plant cells. |
| Enzymatic proteins | Increase the rate of biological reactions | Among thousands of examples, DNA polymerase increases the rate of duplication of DNA molecules; RuBP (ribulose-1,5-bisphosphate) carboxylase/oxygenase increases the rates of the first synthetic reactions of photosynthesis; the digestive enzymes lipases and proteases increase the rate breakdown of fats and proteins respectively. |
| Membrane transport proteins | Speed up movement of substances across biological membranes | Ion transporters move ions such as $Na^+$, $K^+$, and $Ca^{2+}$ across membranes; glucose transporters move glucose into cells; aquaporins allow water molecules to move across membranes. |
| Motile proteins | Produce cellular movements | Myosin acts on microfilaments (called *thin filaments* in muscle) to produce muscle movements; dynein acts on microtubules to produce the undulating movements of flagella and cilia (the whiplike appendages on the surfaces of many eukaryotic cells); kinesin and dynein act on microtubules of the cytoskeleton (the three-dimensional scaffolding of eukaryotic cells responsible for cellular movement, cell division, and the organization of organelles). |
| Regulatory proteins | Promote or inhibit the activity of other cellular molecules | Nuclear regulatory proteins turn genes on or off to control the activity of DNA; protein kinases add phosphate groups to other proteins to modify their activity. |
| Receptor proteins | Bind molecules at cell surface or within cell; some trigger internal cellular responses | Hormone receptors bind hormones at the cell surface or within cells, and trigger cellular responses; cellular adhesion molecules help hold cells together by binding molecules on other cells; LDL receptors bind cholesterol-containing particles to cell surfaces. |
| Hormones | Carry regulatory signals between cells | Insulin regulates sugar levels in the bloodstream; growth hormone regulates cellular growth and division. |
| Antibodies | Defend against invading molecules and organisms | Antibodies recognize, bind, and help eliminate essentially any protein of infecting bacteria and viruses, and many other types of molecules, both natural and artificial. |
| Storage proteins | Hold amino acids and other substances in stored form | Ovalbumin is a storage protein of eggs; apolipoproteins hold cholesterol in stored form for transport through the bloodstream. |
| Venoms and toxins | Interfere with competing organisms | Ricin is a castor bean protein that stops protein synthesis; bungarotoxin is a snake venom that causes muscle paralysis. |

## Amino Acids

All proteins are polymers of amino acids. The generalized structure of an amino acid has a central carbon atom attached to an amino group ($-NH_2$), a carboxyl group ($-COOH$), and a hydrogen atom:

$$H_2N-\underset{\underset{H}{|}}{\overset{\overset{R}{|}}{C}}-COOH$$

The remaining bond of the central carbon is to 1 of 20 different side groups represented by the R. The R group, also called the *side chain*, ranges from a single hydrogen atom in the amino acid glycine to complex carbon chains or rings in some others. Differences in the side groups give the amino acids their individual properties. When discussing protein structure, amino acids are commonly referred to as *amino acid residues*, or simply *residues*.

*continued on next page*

Proteins are synthesized from 20 different amino acids. These 20 are most commonly grouped according to the properties of their side chains. Here, the amino acids are shown in the ionic form common at the pH typical of a cell, 7.2.

**Non-polar amino acids**

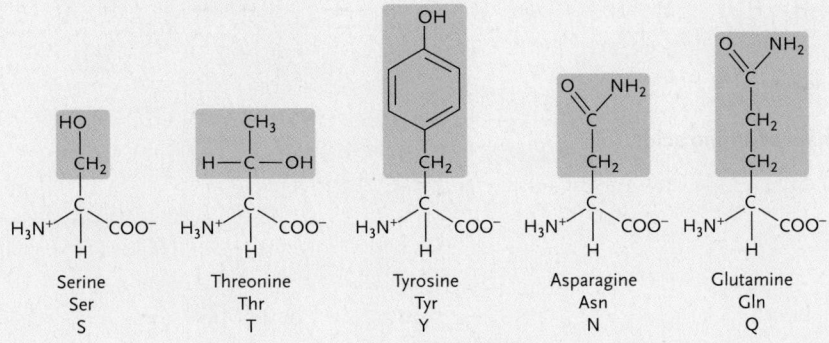

| Alanine Ala A | Valine Val V | Leucine Leu L | Isoleucine Ile I | Glycine Gly G |

| Cysteine Cys C | Phenylalanine Phe F | Tryptophan Trp W | Methionine Met M | Proline Pro P |

**Uncharged polar amino acids**

Serine Ser S — Threonine Thr T — Tyrosine Tyr Y — Asparagine Asn N — Glutamine Gln Q

**Negatively charged (acidic) polar amino acids**

**Positively charged (basic) polar amino acids**

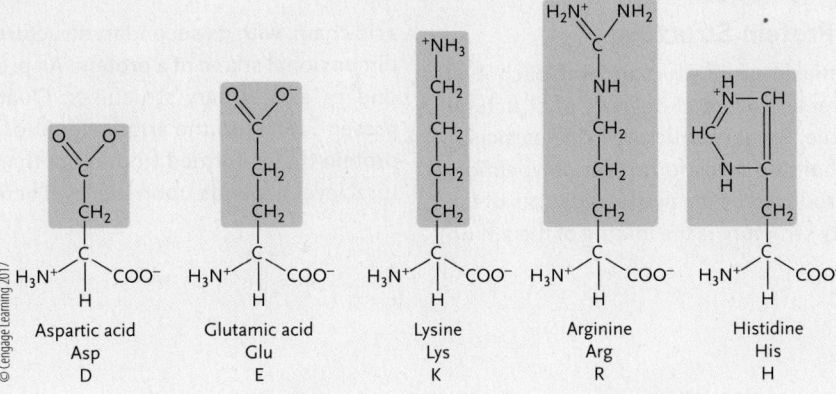

Aspartic acid Asp D — Glutamic acid Glu E — Lysine Lys K — Arginine Arg R — Histidine His H

## Polypeptides

Covalent bonds link amino acids into chains called **polypeptides**. The link between each pair of amino acids in a polypeptide, a peptide bond, is formed by a dehydration synthesis reaction between the —NH$_2$ group of one amino acid and the —COOH group of a second. An amino acid chain always has an —NH$_2$ group at one end, called the *N-terminal end*, and a —COOH group at the other end, called the *C-terminal end*. In cells, amino acids are added only to the —COOH end of the growing peptide strand.

The distinction between a polypeptide and a protein is that a polypeptide is simply a string of amino acids. A protein is a polypeptide that has folded into the specific three-dimensional shape that is required for most proteins to be functional. The following figure shows the formation of a peptide bond.

The backbone of the polypeptide is highlighted in blue in the figure. The amino end of the polypeptide is called the *N-terminus*, and the carboxyl end is called the *C-terminus*.

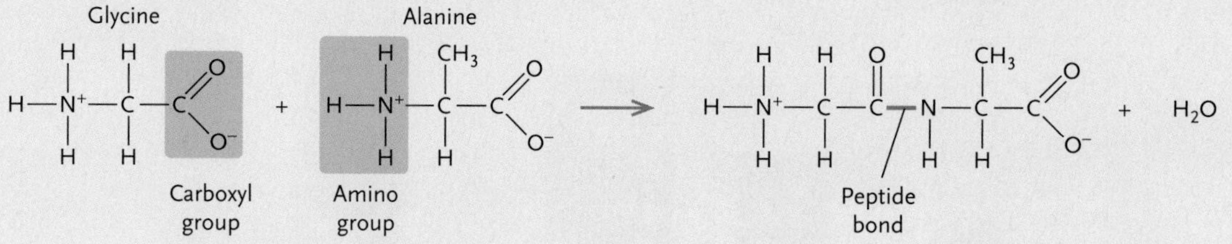

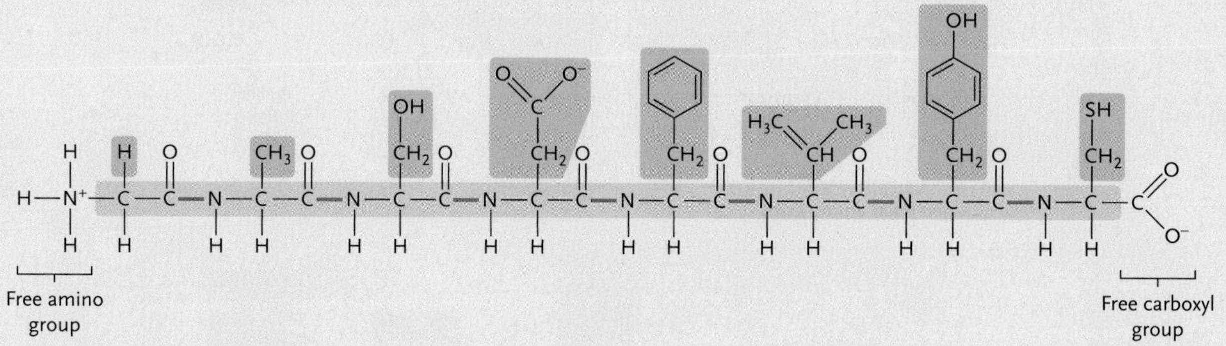

**A polypeptide is a linear chain of amino acids.**

## The Four Levels of Protein Structure

Proteins have four potential levels of structure, with each level imparting different characteristics and degrees of structural complexity to the molecule. **Primary structure** is the particular and unique sequence of amino acids forming a polypeptide; **secondary structure** is produced by the twists and turns of the amino acid chain. Tertiary structure is the folding of the amino acid chain, with its secondary structures, into the overall three-dimensional shape of a protein. All proteins have primary, secondary, and tertiary structures. Quaternary structure, when present, refers to the arrangement of polypeptide chains in a protein that is formed from more than one chain. Each structural level depends upon the level before it.

*continued on next page*

Primary structure:
the sequence of amino
acids in a protein

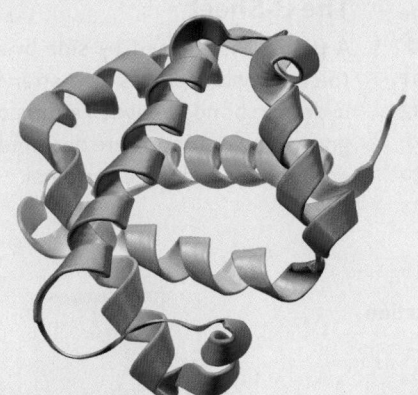

Secondary structure:
regions of an alpha
helix or beta sheet, and
in some cases a particular
loop or coil.

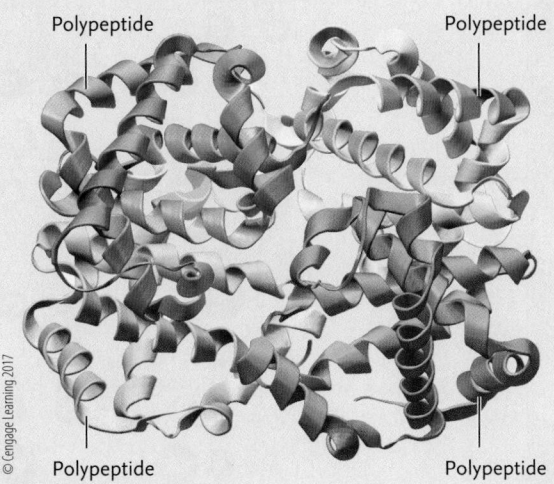

Tertiary structure:
overall three-dimensional
folding of a polypeptide
chain.
This diagram shows a
β-globin polypeptide, of
the subunits required for
the hemoglobin protein.

Polypeptide          Polypeptide

Quaternary structure:
the arrangement of
polypeptide chains in a
protein that contains more
than one chain.
This is an example of the
hemoglobin protein
consisting of two α-globin
and two β-globin
polypeptides. The protein
requires all four
polypeptides to be
functional.

Polypeptide          Polypeptide

© Cengage Learning 2017

## Primary Structure

The primary structure of a protein is simply its complete amino acid sequence. The primary sequence is determined by the nucleotide sequence of the coding region of the protein's corresponding gene. The amino acid subunits are joined covalently (a peptide bond), giving rise to persistent associations that hold together well in the cell's aqueous environment in which ionic and hydrogen bonds would dissociate.

$H_3N^+$ — Phe Val Asn Gln His Leu Cys Gly Ser His Leu Val Glu Ala Leu Tyr Leu Val Cys Gly Glu Arg Gly Phe Phe Tyr Thr Pro Lys Ala — $COO^-$

## Secondary Structure

The amino acid chain of a protein, rather than being stretched out in linear form, is folded into arrangements that form the protein's secondary structure. Secondary structure is based on hydrogen bonds between atoms of the backbone. More precisely, the hydrogen bonds form between the hydrogen atom attached to the nitrogen of the backbone and the oxygen attached to one of the carbon atoms of the backbone. Two highly regular secondary structures are the alpha helix and the beta sheet. In the alpha helix, side chains project outward, supporting the tertiary level of structure. Beta sheets have the side chains sticking out from the plane of the sheet alternating to either side, again supporting the overall structure. A third, less regular arrangement, the coil or loop, imparts flexibility to certain regions of the protein. Most proteins have segments of all three arrangements.

## The α-Helix

A model of the α-helix (below, left), a coil shape formed when hydrogen bonds form between every N—H group of the backbone and the C=O group of the amino acid four residues earlier. In protein diagrams (below, right), the α-helix is depicted as a cylinder or barrel.

## The β-Sheet

A β-sheet is formed by side-by-side alignment of β-strands (picture below shows two strands). The sheet is formed by hydrogen bonds between atoms of each strand. In protein diagrams, the β-strands are depicted as ribbons with arrowheads pointing toward the C-terminal.

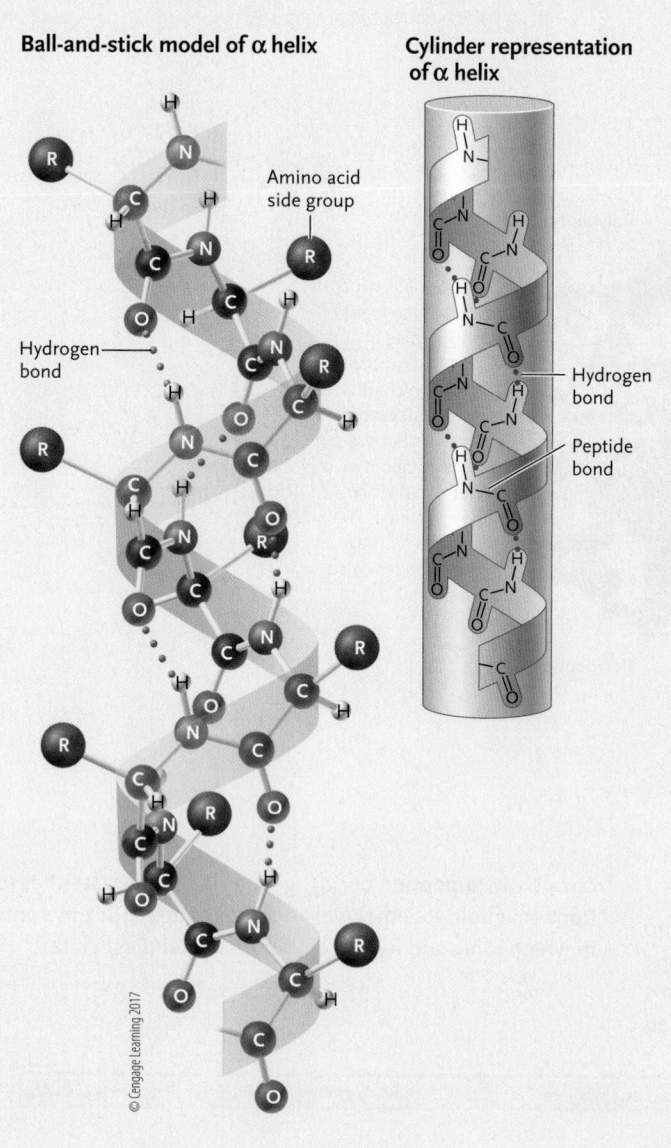

**Ball-and-stick model of α helix**

**Cylinder representation of α helix**

Amino acid side group

Hydrogen bond

Hydrogen bond

Peptide bond

© Cengage Learning 2017

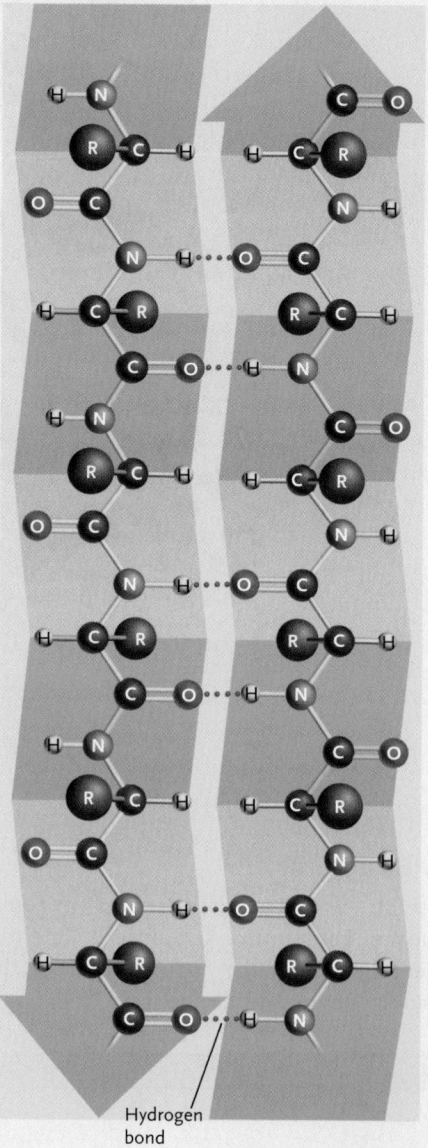

Hydrogen bond

## Tertiary Structure

The four major interactions between R groups that contribute to tertiary structure are shown on the right: (1) ionic bonds, (2) hydrogen bonds, (3) hydrophobic interactions, and (4) disulfide bridges. The tertiary structure of most proteins is flexible, allowing them to undergo limited alterations in three-dimensional shape known as *conformational changes*. These changes contribute to the function of many proteins, particularly enzymes, as well as other proteins involved in cellular movements or in the transport of substances across cell membranes.

Below are two representations of the three-dimensional structure of the enzyme lysozyme. In a ribbon diagram, α-helices are shown as a cylinder, β-strands are depicted as flat arrows, and random coils are shown as thin ropes. In a space-filling model, spheres represent different atoms. The sizes of the spheres and the intersphere distances are proportional to the actual dimensions. Atoms of different elements are represented by different colours. Disulfide bonds are shown in yellow.

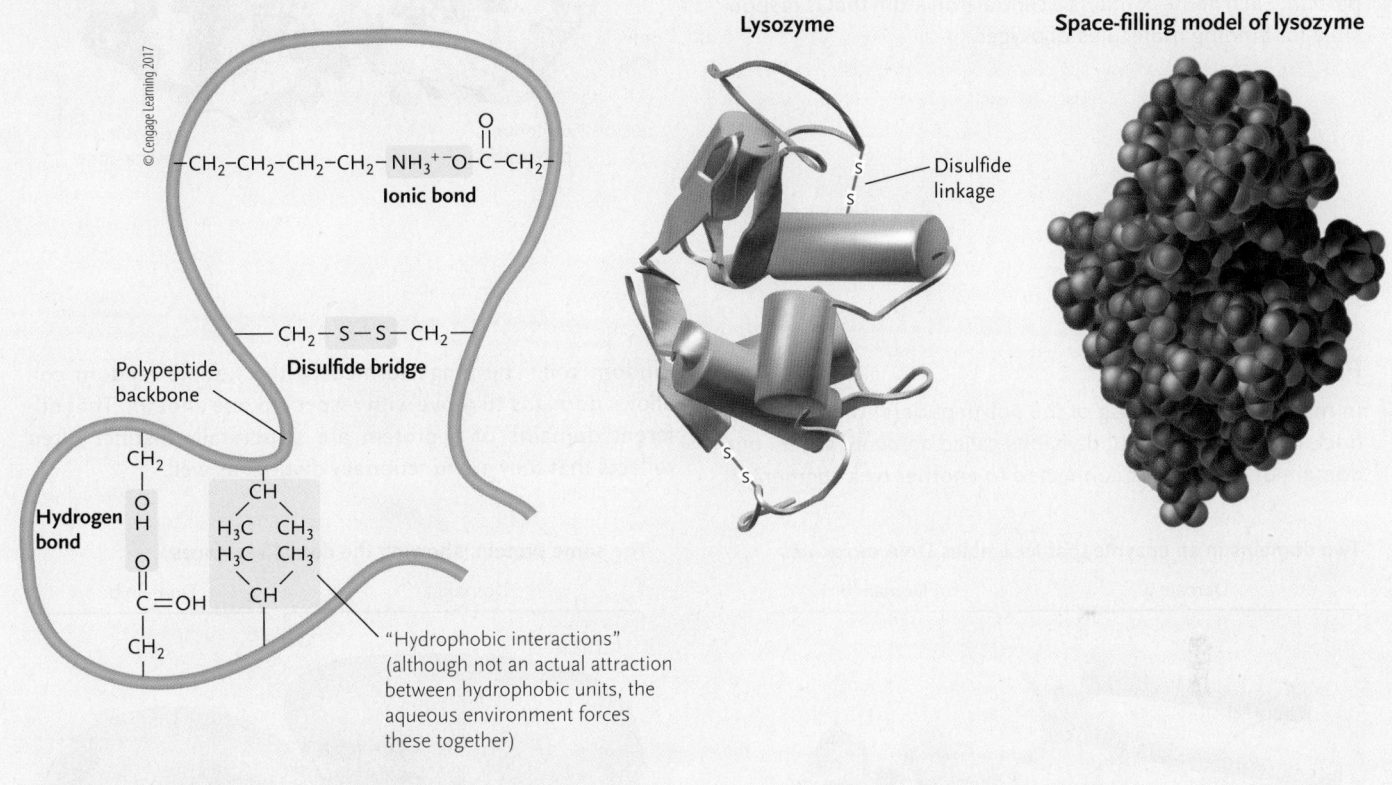

**Lysozyme**

**Space-filling model of lysozyme**

© Cengage Learning 2017

Ionic bond

Disulfide bridge

Polypeptide backbone

Hydrogen bond

Disulfide linkage

"Hydrophobic interactions" (although not an actual attraction between hydrophobic units, the aqueous environment forces these together)

## Quaternary Structure

Some proteins consist of two or more polypeptides that come together to form a functional protein. An example of a protein that exhibits quaternary structure is collagen. The collagen molecule consists of three helical polypeptides that aggregate to form a triple-helix structure. Collagen is a major component of the connective tissue, is found exclusively in animals, and is the most abundant protein in mammals.

Polypeptide chain

Collagen fibre

## Cofactors/Prosthetic Groups

A cofactor (also called a *prosthetic group*) is a nonprotein chemical compound that is bound to a protein and is required for the protein to function. Many enzymes require cofactors, which can be either organic or inorganic molecules. Organic cofactors are often called *coenzymes*, reflecting their organic, non-protein status. Many vitamins are essential to life because they act as key cofactors. A good example of a prosthetic group is the molecule heme, which is a key component of the oxygen-carrying protein hemoglobin. Each molecule of hemoglobin contains four heme molecules—one attached to each globin protein. Each heme contains a central iron atom that is responsible for binding molecules of oxygen.

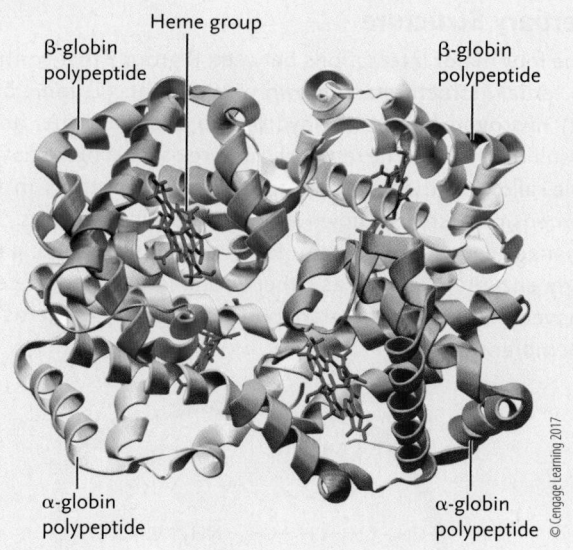

## Protein Domains

In many proteins, folding of the polypeptide(s) produces distinct, large structural subdivisions called *domains*. Often, one domain of a protein is connected to another by a segment of random coil. The hinge formed by the flexible random coil allows domains to move with respect to one another. That different domains of a protein are structurally distinct often reflects that they are functionally distinct as well.

**Two domains in an enzyme that assembles DNA molecules**

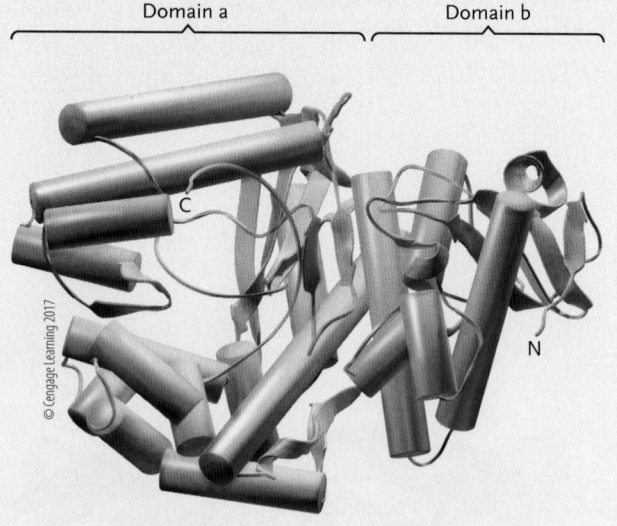

**The same protein, showing the domain surfaces**

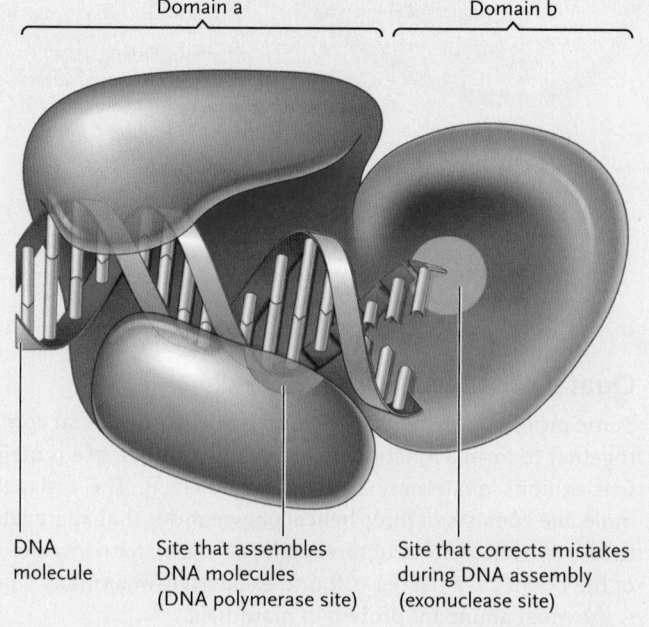

## Protein Folding and Denaturation

A fundamental biochemical question is, "What determines how a protein will fold into the correct functional conformation?" The first insight came from a classic experiment published by Christian Anfinsen and Edgar Haber in 1962. The researchers studied ribonuclease, an enzyme that hydrolyzes RNA.

When they treated the enzyme chemically to break the disulfide linkages holding the protein in its functional state, the protein unfolded and had no enzyme activity. Unfolding a protein from its active conformation so that it loses its structure and function is called **denaturation**. This most often involves the use of specific chemicals or heat.

When they removed the denaturing chemicals, the ribonuclease slowly regained full activity because the disulfide linkages re-formed, enabling the protein to reassume its functional conformation. The reversal of denaturation is called **renaturation**.

The key conclusion from this experiment was that the amino acid sequence itself specifies the tertiary structure of a protein. Nothing else is required. For this work, Christian Anfinsen received a Nobel Prize in 1972.

Within the cell, the high density of newly synthesized proteins may impede the proper folding of individual proteins. For many proteins, correct folding is helped by a group of proteins called **chaperone proteins** or **chaperonins** (see figure above).

They function by temporarily binding with newly synthesized proteins, directing their conformation toward the correct tertiary structure and inhibiting incorrect arrangements as the new proteins fold.

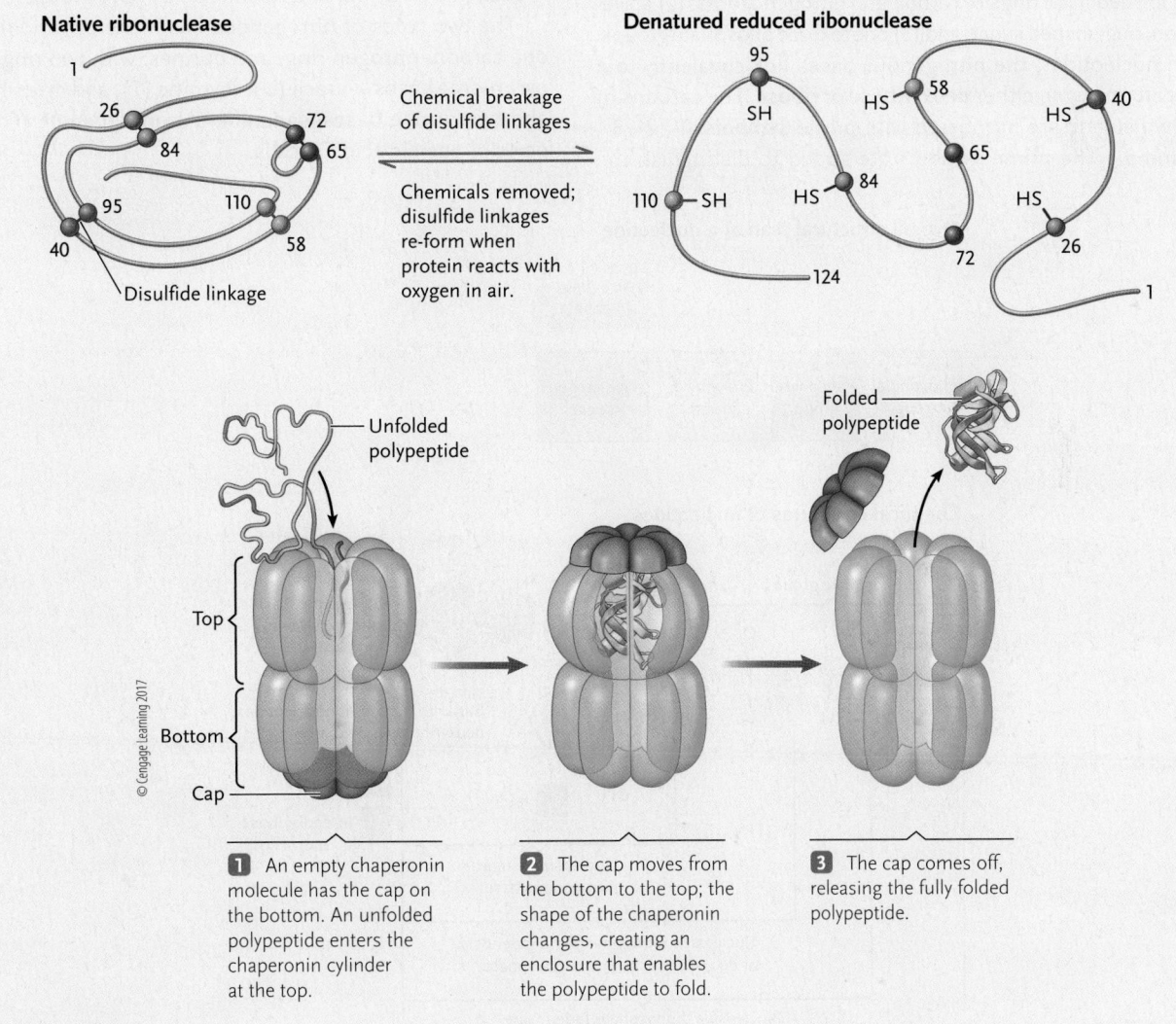

**Native ribonuclease**

Disulfide linkage

Chemical breakage of disulfide linkages

Chemicals removed; disulfide linkages re-form when protein reacts with oxygen in air.

**Denatured reduced ribonuclease**

© Cengage Learning 2017

Unfolded polypeptide

Folded polypeptide

Top

Bottom

Cap

**1** An empty chaperonin molecule has the cap on the bottom. An unfolded polypeptide enters the chaperonin cylinder at the top.

**2** The cap moves from the bottom to the top; the shape of the chaperonin changes, creating an enclosure that enables the polypeptide to fold.

**3** The cap comes off, releasing the fully folded polypeptide.

Proteins are composed of subunits with a wide variety of chemical properties and shapes. These provide a set of emergent properties that lead to complex structures capable of support and that can catalyze reactions. Amino acids are like LEGO blocks of varied shape that can be assembled to form sophisticated sculptures. Without proteins, life as we know it cannot exist.

# Nucleic Acids

Two types of nucleic acids exist: DNA and RNA. Deoxyribonucleic acid (DNA) stores the hereditary information in all eukaryotes, bacteria, and archaea. Ribonucleic acid (RNA) carries out a diversity of functions in all organisms. RNA carries the instructions for assembling proteins from DNA to the site of protein synthesis, the ribosome, which is itself composed partially of RNA. Another type of RNA serves to bring amino acids to the ribosome for their assembly into proteins.

## Nucleotides

All nucleic acids are polymers of nucleotides. A **nucleotide** consists of three parts linked by covalent bonds: (1) a nitrogenous base formed from rings of carbon and nitrogen atoms; (2) a five-carbon, ring-shaped sugar; and (3) one to three phosphate groups.

In nucleotides, the nitrogenous bases link covalently to a five-carbon sugar, either **deoxyribose** or **ribose**. The carbons of the two sugars are numbered with prime symbols: 1′, 2′, 3′, 4′, and 5′. The prime symbols are added to distinguish the carbons in the sugars from those in the nitrogenous bases, which are written without primes. The two sugars differ only in the chemical group bound to the 2′ carbon: deoxyribose has a —H at this position, and ribose has a—OH group.

The two types of nitrogenous bases are pyrimidines, with one carbon–nitrogen ring, and purines, with two rings. Three pyrimidine bases—uracil (U), thymine (T), and cytosine (C)— and two purine bases—adenine (A) and guanine (G)—form parts of nucleic acids in cells.

### Overall structural plan of a nucleotide

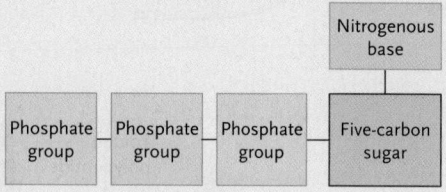

### Chemical structures of nucleotides

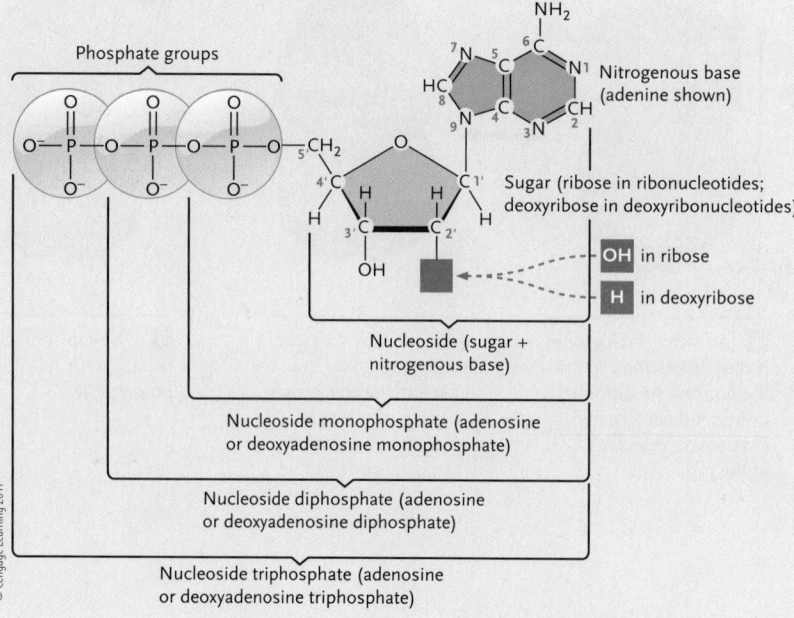

© Cengage Learning 2017

## Pyrimidine and Purine Bases of Nucleic Acids

The figure shows the three single-ring pyrimidines and two double-ring purines that are the nitrogenous bases of nucleotides. The red arrows indicate where the bases link to ribose or deoxyribose sugars to form nucleotides.

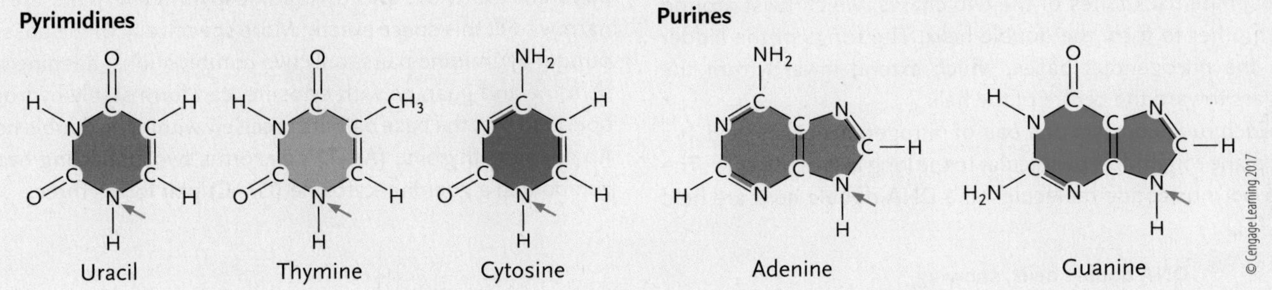

Pyrimidines
Uracil
Thymine
Cytosine
Purines
Adenine
Guanine
© Cengage Learning 2017


## DNA and RNA Structure

Nucleotides in DNA and RNA are linked by a bridging phosphate group between the 5′ carbon of one sugar and the 3′ carbon of the next sugar in line. This linkage is called a *phosphodiester bond.* This arrangement of alternating sugar and phosphate groups forms the backbone of a nucleic acid. The nitrogenous bases of the nucleotides project from this backbone. Note that the nucleotide thymine (T) in DNA is not found in RNA; it is replaced by uracil (U).

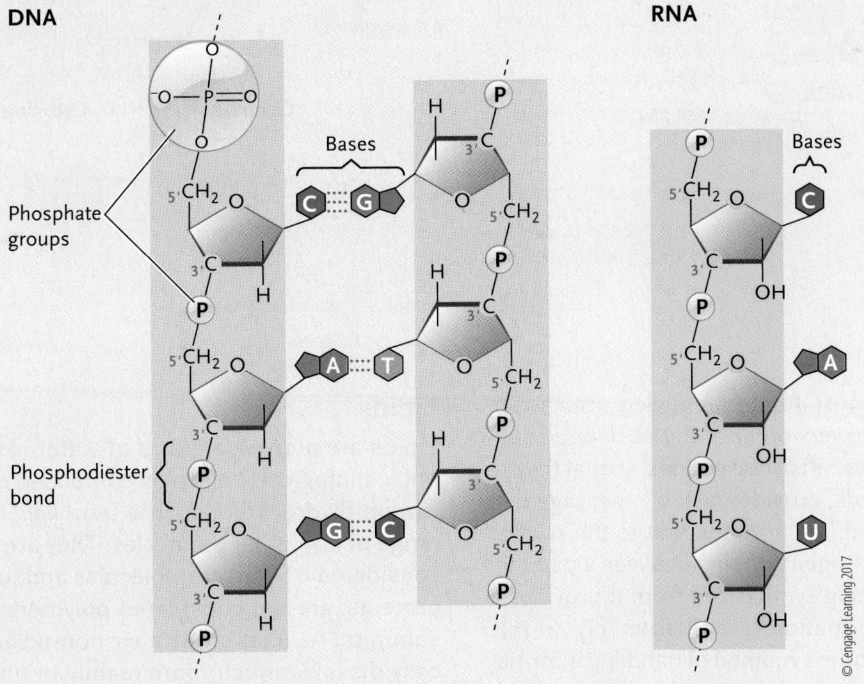

DNA
RNA
Bases
Phosphate groups
Phosphodiester bond
© Cengage Learning 2017

## DNA Double Helix

In cells, DNA takes the form of a double helix: two molecules wrapped around each other in a spiral that resembles a twisted ladder. As shown below, the sides of the ladder are the sugar–phosphate backbones of the two chains, which twist around each other to form the double helix. The rungs of the ladder are the nitrogenous bases, which extend inward from the sugars toward the centre of the helix.

Each rung consists of a pair of nitrogenous bases held in a flat plane roughly perpendicular to the long axis of the helix. The two polynucleotide molecules of a DNA double helix are held together by hydrogen bonds between the base pairs. The space separating the sugar–phosphate backbones of a DNA double helix is just wide enough to accommodate a base pair that consists of one purine and one pyrimidine. Purine–purine base pairs are too wide, and pyrimidine–pyrimidine pairs are too narrow to fit this space exactly. More specifically, of the possible purine–pyrimidine pairs, only two combinations, adenine with thymine and guanine with cytosine, can form stable hydrogen bonds so that the base pair fits precisely within the double helix. An adenine–thymine (A—T) pair forms two stabilizing hydrogen bonds; a guanine–cytosine (G—C) pair forms three.

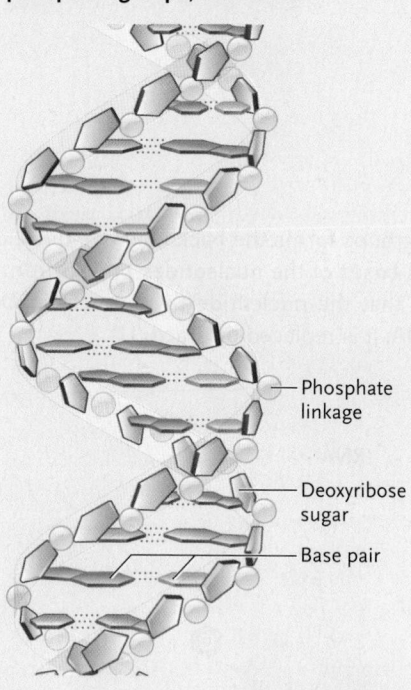

**DNA double helix, showing arrangement of sugars, phosphate groups, and bases**

Phosphate linkage

Deoxyribose sugar

Base pair

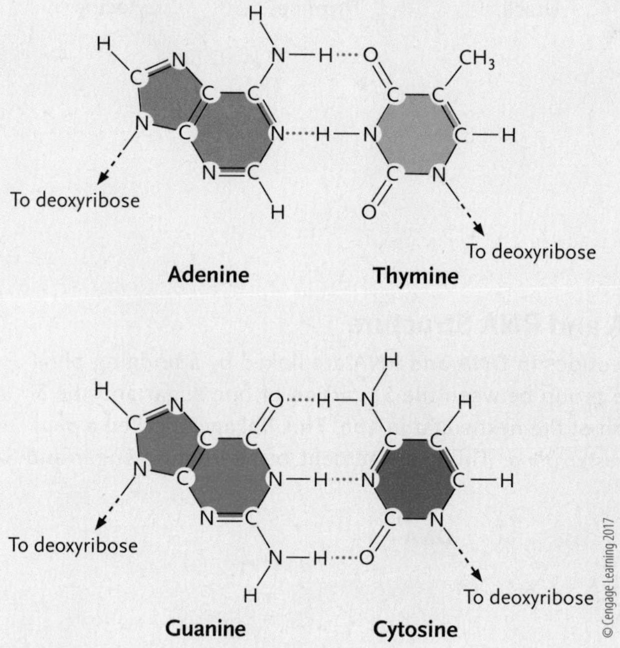

Adenine   Thymine

Guanine   Cytosine

To deoxyribose

© Cengage Learning 2017

The emergent property most notable in nucleic acids is the information that's held in the very order of the nucleotide subunits. Note that the polymerization of nucleotides, so that they're held in order by covalent bonds, provides a stable message that can be passed in an unbroken line from the first to the current generation of organisms. Hydrogen bonding between a parental template of DNA and one being synthesized from it provides a mechanism to replicate information (see Chapter 11). In this way, the hydrogen bonds become a method of handling information in a way not possible from the subunits alone.

## Lipids

Lipids are a diverse group of water-insoluble, primarily non-polar, biological molecules composed mostly of hydrogen and carbon (hydrocarbons). The term *lipid* is a catch-all word for a range of non-polar molecules. They are not large enough to be considered true macromolecules and, unlike nucleic acids and proteins, are not considered polymers of defined monomeric subunits. As a result of their non-polar character, lipids typically dissolve much more readily in non-polar solvents, such as acetone and chloroform, than in water. Their insolubility in water underlies their ability to form cell membranes (see Chapter 4). In addition, some lipids are stored and used in cells as an energy source. Other lipids serve as hormones that regulate cellular activities. Lipids in living organisms can be grouped into one of three categories: fats, phospholipids, or steroids.

## Isoprenes and Fatty Acids

The structural backbone of all lipids is derived from one of two hydrocarbon molecules: isoprene and fatty acids. Isoprenes are five-carbon molecules that, when linked together, can form long hydrocarbon chains. Isoprenes are the structural unit in steroids and a number of phospholipids. A fatty acid consists of a single hydrocarbon chain with a carboxyl group (—COOH) linked at one end. The carboxyl group gives the fatty acid its acidic properties. The fatty acids in living organisms contain four or more carbons in their hydrocarbon chain, with the most common forms having even-numbered chains of 14–22 carbons. As their chain length increases, fatty acids become progressively less water soluble and more solid.

If the hydrocarbon chain of a fatty acid binds the maximum possible number of hydrogen atoms, so that only single bonds link the carbon atoms, the fatty acid is said to be saturated with hydrogen atoms. If one or more double bonds link the carbons, reducing the number of bound hydrogen atoms, the fatty acid is unsaturated. Fatty acids with one double bond are monounsaturated; those with more than one double bond are polyunsaturated. Unlike saturated fatty acids, the presence of double bonds imparts a "kink" in the molecule.

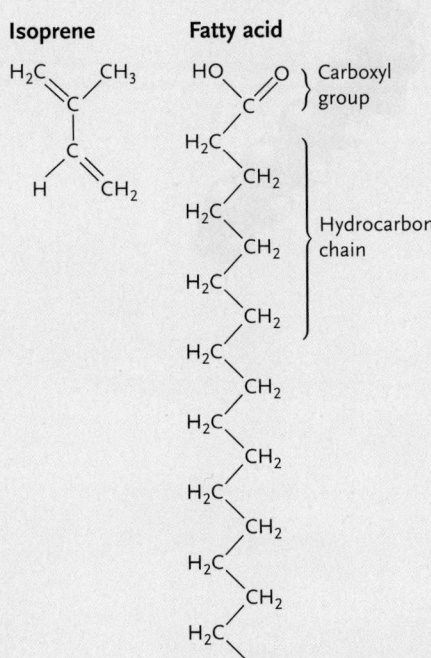

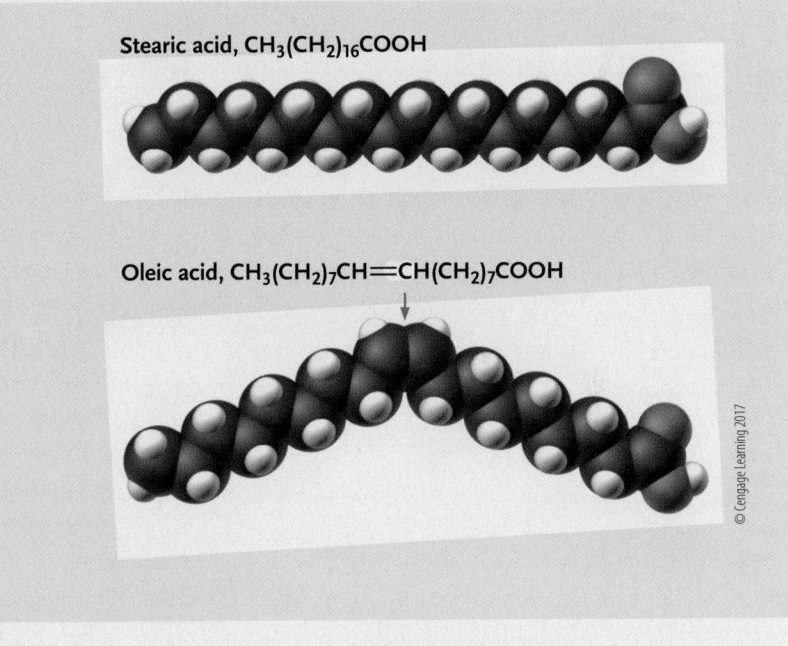

## Phospholipids

Phosphate-containing lipids, or phospholipids, are the primary lipids of cell membranes. In the most common phospholipids, glycerol forms the backbone for the molecule as in triglycerides, but only two of its binding sites are linked to fatty acids. The third site is linked to a polar phosphate group that also binds to another polar unit. Thus, a phospholipid contains two hydrophobic fatty acids at one end, attached to a hydrophilic polar group, often called the *head group*. Molecules that contain both hydrophobic and hydrophilic regions are called *amphipathic molecules*.

*continued on next page*

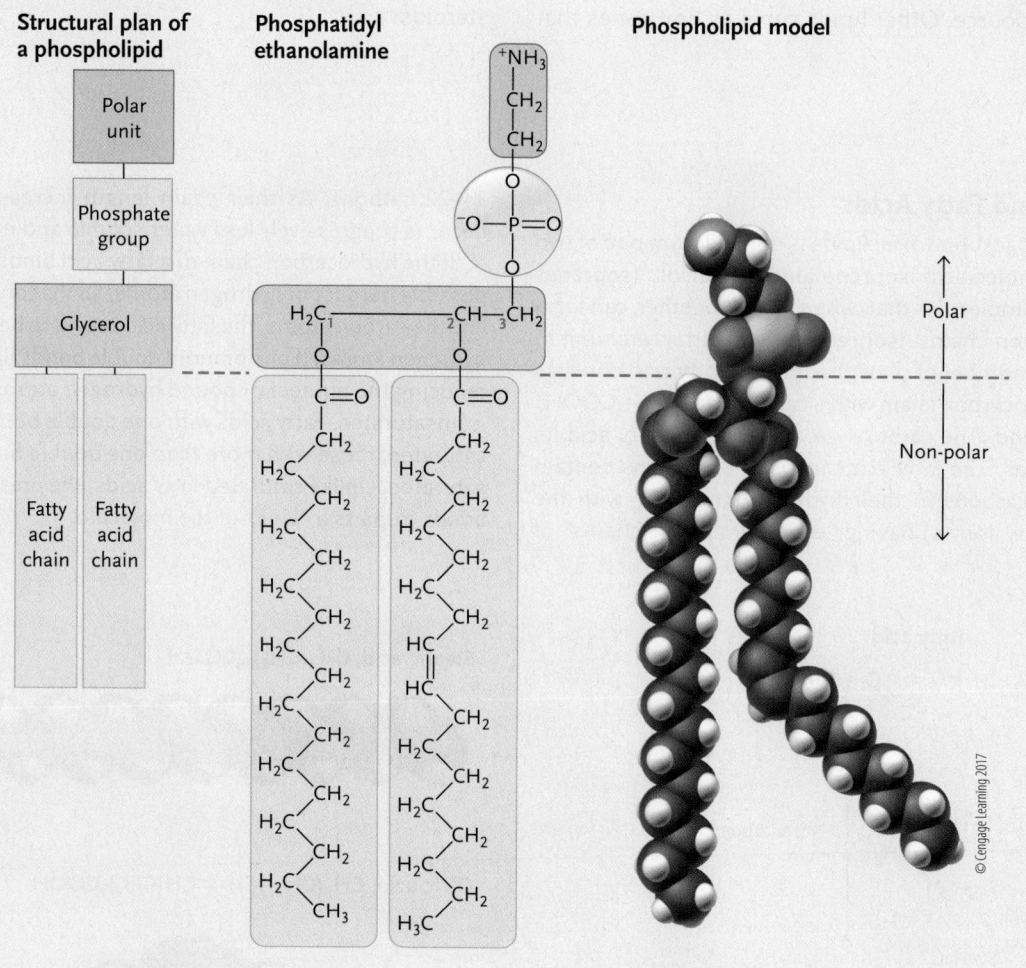

**Structural plan of a phospholipid** · **Phosphatidyl ethanolamine** · **Phospholipid model**

## Fats

A fat consists of three fatty acid chains linked to a single molecule of glycerol. Because of this, fats are also often referred to as *triacylglycerols* or *triglycerides*. The three fatty acids linked to the glycerol may be different or the same. Different organisms usually have distinctive combinations of fatty acids in their triglycerides. As with individual fatty acids, triglycerides generally become less fluid as the length of their fatty acid chains increases; those with shorter chains remain liquid as oils at biological temperatures, and those with longer chains solidify.

Triglycerides are used widely as stored energy in animals. Gram for gram, they yield more than twice as much energy as carbohydrates. Therefore, fats are an excellent source of energy in the diet. Storing the equivalent amount of energy as carbohydrates rather than fats would add more than 45 kg to the mass of an average man or woman. A layer of fatty tissue just under the skin also serves as an insulating blanket in humans, other mammals, and birds. Triglycerides secreted from special glands in waterfowl and other birds help make feathers water repellent.

*continued on next page*

**Formation of a triglyceride**

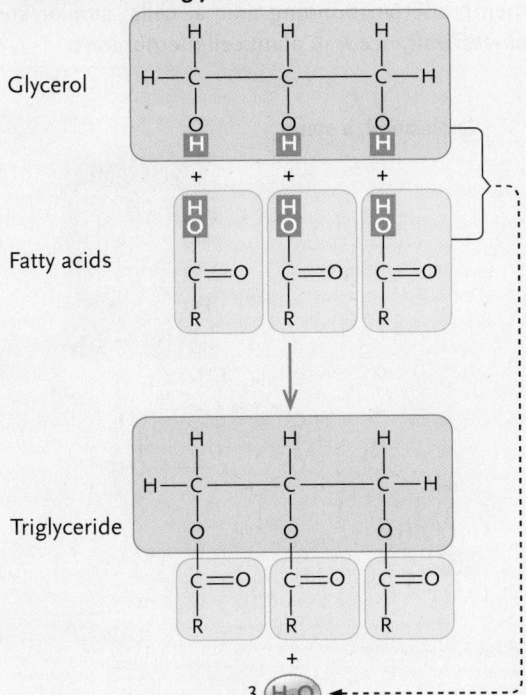

Glycerol

Fatty acids

Triglyceride

$3$ $H_2O$

**Glyceryl palmitate**

**Triglyceride model**

© Cengage Learning 2017

## Steroids

Steroids are a group of lipids with structures based on a frame-work of four carbon rings that are derived from isoprene units. Small differences in the side groups attached to the rings distinguish one steroid from another. The most abundant steroids, the sterols, have a single polar—OH group linked to one end of the ring framework and a complex, non-polar, hydrocarbon chain at the other end. Although sterols are almost completely hydrophobic, the single hydroxyl group gives one end of the molecules a slightly polar, hydrophilic

*continued on next page*

THE CHEMICAL AND PHYSICAL FOUNDATIONS OF BIOLOGY |

character. As a result, sterols also have dual solubility properties and, like phospholipids, tend to assume positions that satisfy these properties.

Cholesterol is an important component of the plasma membrane surrounding animal cells; similar sterols, called *phytosterols*, occur in plant cell membranes.

**Arrangement of carbon rings in a steroid**

**Cholesterol, a sterol**

**Cholesterol model**

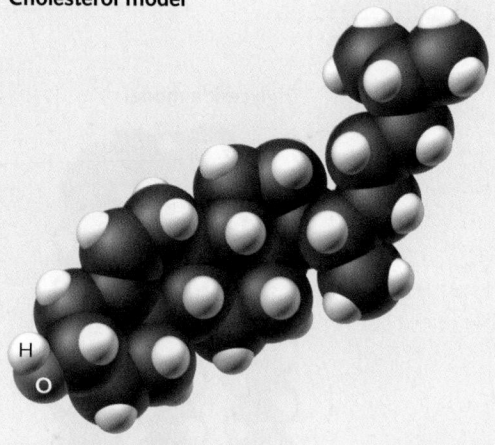

Note that the emergent property of lipids is based on their hydrocarbon construction. These molecules form partitions within cells and provide lightweight, compact energy reserves.

# History of Earth

Atoms lead to molecules, which lead to macromolecules. Macromolecules combine to form organelles, and a variety of organelles are needed to fulfill a cell's functions (see Chapter 2). A collection of cells forms a tissue, and tissues make up organs, which contribute to complete organ systems (Chapters 33 and 38). This layering of complexity leads to organisms, populations, communities, ecosystems, and eventually the biosphere (Chapters 29–32). This can continue to the level of the universe. As an exercise, consider what new properties emerge as we move from one level of complexity to the next. Entire courses can focus not only on each level of complexity and the properties that emerge from it, they can also zero in on a single small aspect, such as a single type of amino acid for instance.

The grandeur of life arose from the primordial Earth (see Chapter 21). Emergent properties from the atoms and molecules that condensed from the debris of the Big Bang set up an environment from which simple molecules, and later macromolecules, and then cells, could form.

Thus it is fitting to present a timescale to consider. Note that complexity has arisen and has been shaped through natural selection; the chemicals themselves accumulated when the emergent properties of lone amino acids allowed the amino end of one molecule to bind with the carboxylic acid end of a neighbour. Some of these proteinoids aggregated. Some had catalytic capabilities. At each step of the way, conditions favoured certain types of complexity. Energy from the Sun and from Earth itself was trapped in a variety of bonds available from precursor molecules. Ecosystems naturally arose; as some protobionts (primitive cells) assembled from constituents, they competed with each other and fed off each other.

The figure below shows the emergence of complexity from Earth's materials. Life is based on chemistry. Life itself is an emergent property that arises when the environment—collections of lipids, carbohydrates, proteins, nucleic acids, and other chemicals—interacts with an energy source to go from a spark to the biosphere that surrounds us today.

## Geological Time Scale and Major Evolutionary Events

### The Geological Time Scale and Major Evolutionary Events

| Eons (duration drawn to scale) | Eon | Era | Period | Epoch | Millions of Years Ago | Major Evolutionary Events |
|---|---|---|---|---|---|---|
| Phanerozoic — Cenozoic / Mesozoic / Paleozoic; Proterozoic | Phanerozoic | Cenozoic | Quaternary | Holocene | | |
| | | | | | 0.01 | |
| | | | | Pleistocene | | Origin of humans; major glaciations |
| | | | | | 1.7 | |
| | | | | Pliocene | | Origin of apelike human ancestors |
| | | | | | 5.2 | |
| | | | | Miocene | | Angiosperms and mammals further diversify and dominate terrestrial habitats |
| | | | | | 23 | |
| | | | Tertiary | Oligocene | | Divergence of primates; origin of apes |
| | | | | | 33.4 | |
| | | | | Eocene | | Angiosperms and insects diversify; modern orders of mammals differentiate |
| | | | | | 55 | |
| | | | | Paleocene | | Grasslands and deciduous woodlands spread; modern birds and mammals diversify; continents approach current positions |
| | | | | | 65 | |

*continued on next page*

| Eons (duration drawn to scale) | Eon | Era | Period | Epoch | Millions of Years Ago | Major Evolutionary Events |
|---|---|---|---|---|---|---|
| Proterozoic | Phanerozoic | Mesozoic | Cretaceous | | | Many lineages diversify: angiosperms, insects, marine invertebrates, fishes, dinosaurs; asteroid impact causes mass extinction at end of period, eliminating dinosaurs and many other groups |
| | | | | | 144 | |
| | | | Jurassic | | | Gymnosperms abundant in terrestrial habitats; first angiosperms; modern fishes diversify; dinosaurs diversify and dominate terrestrial habitats; frogs, salamanders, lizards, and birds appear; continents continue to separate |
| | | | | | 206 | |
| | | | Triassic | | | Predatory fishes and reptiles dominate oceans; gymnosperms dominate terrestrial habitats; radiation of dinosaurs; origin of mammals; Pangaea starts to break up; mass extinction at end of period |
| | | | | | 251 | |
| | | Paleozoic | Permian | | | Insects, amphibians, and reptiles abundant and diverse in swamp forests; some reptiles colonize oceans; fishes colonize freshwater habitats; continents coalesce into Pangaea, causing glaciation and decline in sea level; mass extinction at end of period eliminates 85% of species |
| | | | | | 290 | |
| | | | Carboniferous | | | Vascular plants form large swamp forests; first seed plants and flying insects; amphibians diversify; first reptiles appear |
| | | | | | 354 | |
| Archaean | | | Devonian | | | Terrestrial vascular plants diversify; fungi and invertebrates colonize land; first insects appear; first amphibians colonize land; major glaciation at end of period causes mass extinction, mostly of marine life |
| | | | | | 417 | |
| | | | Silurian | | | Jawless fishes diversify; first jawed fishes; first vascular plants on land |
| | | | | | 443 | |
| | | | Ordovician | | | Major radiations of marine invertebrates and fishes; major glaciation at end of period causes mass extinction of marine life |
| | | | | | 490 | |
| | | | Cambrian | | | Diverse radiation of modern animal phyla (Cambrian explosion); simple marine communities |
| | | | | | 543 | |
| | | Proterozoic | | | | High concentration of oxygen in atmosphere; origin of aerobic metabolism; origin of eukaryotic cells; evolution and diversification of protists, fungi, soft-bodied animals |
| | | | | | 2500 | |
| | | Archaean | | | | Evolution of prokaryotes, including anaerobic bacteria and photosynthetic bacteria; oxygen starts to accumulate in atmosphere |
| | | | | | 3800 | |
| | | | | | | Formation of Earth at start of era; Earth's crust, atmosphere, and oceans form; origin of life at end of era |
| | | | | | 4600 | |

# SYSTEMS AND PROCESSES

## VOLUME 3

**Larva of a monarch butterfly (*Danaus plexippus*) feeding on milkweed (*Asclepias* sp.)**

In the next two units, we focus on the key characteristics of systems and processes in plants and animals, with an emphasis on land plants and vertebrate animals. The emphasis on these organisms reflects the approach taken in the text and is not meant to downplay the importance of other groups.

Why are plants and animals so different? Plants and animals share many features: Their bodies are composed of eukaryotic cells that form tissues and organs. The ancestors of modern-day plants and animals are thought to have diverged about 1.6 billion years ago, when both groups consisted of unicellular organisms. The earliest known fossils of multicellular land plants and animals date from only about 570 million years ago, indicating that multicellularity evolved independently in plants and animals. The unicellular common ancestor of both plants and animals had already incorporated the endosymbiont that would become mitochondria, which explains why both plants and animals have mitochondria (see Figure 2.18, Chapter 2). However, while both plants and animals inherited mitochondria, the lineage that gave rise to plants also incorporated another endosymbiont, a photosynthetic cyanobacterium that over evolutionary time would become the chloroplast and would set plants on a very different trajectory compared to animals.

The fundamental differences between plants and animals reflect the way in which the presence or absence of chloroplasts has led to very different solutions to the challenges of life on land. If we generalize about "typical" plants and "typical" animals, we get a clearer picture of these two different strategies.

Animals can, and usually must, move. They obtain both energy and carbon from food. Their food sources tend to have fairly high concentrations of nutrients. Almost all terrestrial animals move from one place to another in search of food, water, or a mate. They can also flee from predators or move away from unfavourable conditions.

In contrast, most plants are stationary (because of the presence of chloroplasts, they are "self-feeders"), needing only sunlight, carbon dioxide (available in air), and water and inorganic nutrients (available in soil). These nutrients are usually patchily distributed in low concentrations in the soil. How best to capture diffuse nutrients from soil and air? Large surface area is the answer! Unlike the compact form of animals, plants are highly branched (the term for this form is *dendritic*, meaning "treelike"). To visualize this dendritic growth, think about the branches of a deciduous tree **(Figure 1)**. The root system of the tree is also dendritic, branching and spreading below ground. Thus, the evolutionary response to the challenges posed by life on land has resulted in a plant body consisting of two closely linked but quite different components: a photosynthetic *shoot system* and a non-photosynthetic *root system*.

Obviously, plants cannot just pick up their extensive root system and move around in search of better conditions. They must search for nutrients and water, find mates, and defend themselves from predators while fixed in place (sessile). Adaptations for these differing strategies have resulted in specialized body plans that distinguish plants from animals.

**Figure 1**

**Giraffes feeding on tree leaves.** The features that distinguish plants from animals are seen clearly here and are related to the nutrient requirements of each and how they are obtained.

Of course, not all plants look alike; nor do all animals. Both groups show tremendous variation in **anatomy** (the study of the structures of organisms) and **physiology** (the study of the functions of these structures). Differences in the shapes and forms of organisms reflect differences in function that arise primarily through evolution by natural selection (see Chapter 16). Understanding how basic physiological processes have evolved is a first step in understanding adaptation. The second is understanding how these basic physiological systems have further evolved to allow plants and animals to thrive in different habitats, and in turn understand habitat selection and range distribution of any species. Organisms can live only in areas where they can fulfill the basic essentials of life: growing, developing, and reproducing. This understanding is also essential for evaluating and developing conservation strategies to mitigate the consequences to organisms of environmental changes due to anthropogenic threats (i.e., human activities). Threats to biodiversity arising from human activities are a worldwide problem from which Canada is not exempt **(Figure 2)**. Knowing how plants and animals work is essential for identifying which species, populations, and communities will be most vulnerable to environmental stressors, and for determining ways in which we can rebuild those populations and restore their ecosystems if they are impacted. This information will help determine priorities for conservation measures and could be used to guide policymakers and the public in protecting the environment and its inhabitants.

a.

b.

Plantography/Alamy Stock Photo

CampCrazy Photography/Shutterstock.com

**Figure 2**

**Species at risk in Canada include (a) the white prairie gentian and (b) the beluga whale.**

As you read through the chapters in Units 7 and 8, think about how differences in animal and plant processes relate to the fundamental difference between the need to be motile, obtaining the materials needed to build bodily structures from the food they eat; and being sessile, obtaining the primary material needed to build body structures (carbon) from the air and sunlight that they capture. Think also about how physiological processes have evolved to allow plants and animals to live in different habitats, and how environmental change will impact their existence and distribution.

# Chapter Roadmap

## Organization of the Plant Body

Plants are made up of three systems: shoots, leaves, and roots. All plant structures are derived from these components.

From Chapter 6

From Chapter 25

From Chapter 26

### 33.1 Plant Structure and Growth: An Overview

Meristems give rise to the plant body and are responsible for a plant's lifelong growth. Primary growth originates at apical meristems at root and shoot tips. Some plants have lateral meristems that produce secondary growth.

To Chapter 37

To Chapter 38

From Chapter 26

### 33.2 The Three Plant Tissue Systems

The dermal tissue system covers the plant, offering protection; the tissues of the vascular tissue system circulate water, hormones, and other important materials throughout the plant; and the ground tissue system, found between the other tissue systems, has many roles, including photosynthesis and storage.

To Chapter 35

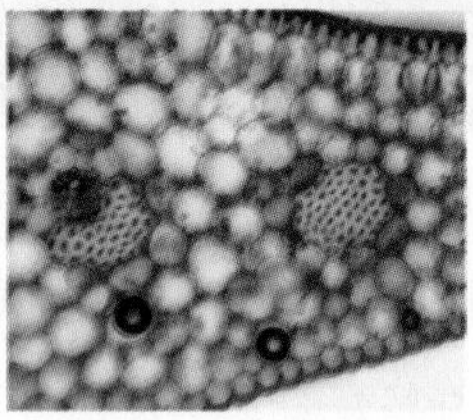

Shona Ellis

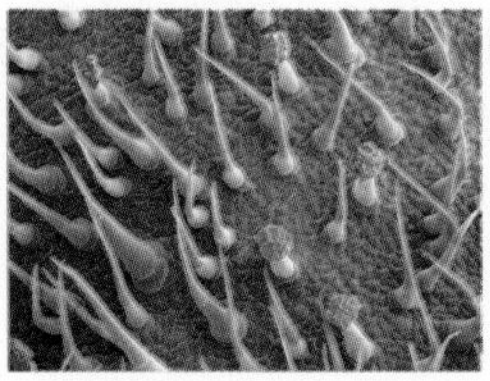

STEVE GSCHMEISSNER/SCIENCE PHOTO LIBRARY

### 33.3 Primary Shoot Systems

Stems are organized into modular segments. Nodes are points where leaves and buds are attached, and internodes are the regions between nodes (Figure 33.13). The terminal bud at a shoot tip consists of shoot apical meristem. Lateral buds occur at intervals along the stem. Meristem tissue in buds gives rise to leaves, flowers, or both.

To Chapter 36

To Chapter 37

To Chapter 38

### 33.4 Root Systems

Roots absorb water and dissolved minerals and conduct them to aerial plant parts. Roots anchor and sometimes support the plant, and often store food.

To Chapter 35

### 33.5 Secondary Growth

Two lateral meristems (vascular cambium and cork cambium) contribute to an increase in girth, producing the wood and bark that we find in stems and roots of many plants.

To Chapter 35

Banyan tree (*Ficus* sp.), one type of "strangler fig"

# Organization of the Plant Body

# 33

**Why it matters ...** What is the largest plant in the world? The answer depends on how we define largest: Is it the tallest? The one with the greatest mass? If we define largest as the plant with the biggest canopy (stem and branches), then the winner of the contest is the banyan tree (see photograph above). The banyan is one of several kinds of figs (*Ficus* species) that are known as *strangler figs* due to their aggressive growth habit. The seeds of strangler figs, dispersed by birds, are often deposited high up on the branches of other tree species in tropical rainforests. The seeds germinate in the bark of their host tree and send thin roots down the trunk of the host plant to the ground. Once the roots enter the ground, they grow and thicken quickly. Roots that cross over each other fuse together, trapping the host plant's trunk in a cage of roots that eventually fuse into a more or less solid mass. Meanwhile, the stem of the fig climbs upward, twining itself around the host's stem, and soon overtops the host, putting out many thick leaves that shade the host plant's leaves. The strangler fig can now outcompete the host plant for sunlight and for water and nutrients from the soil. The network of roots that surround the host's trunk prevents further lateral growth of the host, which eventually starves to death. The host trunk rots away, leaving a hollow cylinder of roots that forms the main trunk of the fig tree. Some of these fig species continue to send down roots from their branches. When these aerial roots reach the ground, they become additional trunks to help support the canopy, which can become massive. In this way, a single fig tree and its numerous, interconnected trunks can spread out over a very large area. The largest banyan tree in the world has a canopy that is 420 m in diameter! This aggressive growth strategy is a definite advantage in rainforests, where competition for light under the dense upper canopy is fierce.

What structures make up the root and shoot systems of a plant? How do the different parts of a plant develop? How do plants grow in height (upward for shoots and downward for roots)? How do some plants, such as strangler figs, become woody? Starting in this chapter and continuing through the next three chapters, we investigate these questions and explore the structure and functioning of plants: their morphology, anatomy, and physiology.

## 33.1 Plant Structure and Growth: An Overview

In this chapter, we focus on the key characteristics of plant structure and growth and make several comparisons between land plants and terrestrial animals. We could compare plants with many other organisms since plants and animals are just two of the many kingdoms of life, but we tend to be most familiar with animals. It is obvious that plants are very different from animals, but why are they so different? We can think of plants and animals as representatives of two very different solutions to the challenges of life on land. If we generalize about "typical" plants and "typical" animals, we can get a clearer picture of these two different strategies. Animals are chemoheterotrophs; that is, they obtain both energy and carbon from the food they eat. Their food sources tend to have fairly high concentrations of nutrients. All terrestrial animals are motile (some aquatic animals are stationary) and can move from one place to another in search of food, water, or a mate. They can also flee from predators or move away from unfavourable conditions. Animal bodies, then, need to be fairly compact to facilitate moving around.

In contrast, most plants are photosynthetic autotrophs (self-feeders) that need sunlight, carbon dioxide (available in air), and water (available in soil). In addition, plants require other nutrients that are usually available only in soil; these nutrients are usually patchily distributed in the soil and often available only at low concentrations. Thus, unlike animals, plants have to gather diffuse nutrients from both air and soil. How best to capture these diffuse nutrients? A large surface area is important, both above ground and below ground, so plant bodies are not compact but spreading and branched in form (the term for this form is *dendritic,* which literally means "treelike"). To visualize this dendritic growth, think about how the branches of an aspen or another poplar tree look in the spring before they have leafed out **(Figure 33.1)**. The root system of the tree is also dendritic, branching and spreading below ground. Thus, the evolutionary response to the challenges posed by life on land has resulted in a plant body consisting of two closely linked but quite different components: a photosynthetic *shoot system* extending upward into the air and a non-photosynthetic *root system* extending downward into the soil **(Figure 33.2)**.

Obviously, a plant cannot just pick up this extensive root system and move around in search of better conditions. Instead, plants are fixed in place (sessile), and they must therefore search for nutrients and water, find mates, and defend themselves from predators—everything that animals have to do—while fixed in one place. As you read through this chapter, think about how plant morphology and growth relate to being sessile photoautotrophs.

### 33.1a Cells of All Plant Tissues Share Some General Features

Both root and shoot systems consist of various **organs**, body structures that contain two or more types of tissues and have a definite form and function. Plant organs include leaves, stems, and roots. A **tissue** is a group of cells and intercellular substances that function together in one or more specialized tasks.

Plant cells share some features with animal cells but differ in that they typically have a cell wall, a large vacuole, and, in many cells, chloroplasts. Chloroplasts function in photosynthesis and are discussed in more detail in Chapter 6. The vacuole may occupy most of the volume in a mature plant cell and plays an important role in cell elongation and maintenance of rigid tissues. Vacuoles may also act as storage compartments. In all plant tissues, the cells have a **primary cell wall** surrounding the plasma membrane and cell contents (cytoplasm and organelles). These cell walls are the "skeleton" of a plant, serving to support the plant's body, as the skeleton for an

**FIGURE 33.1 Dendritic growth shown by the above-ground portion of a tree**

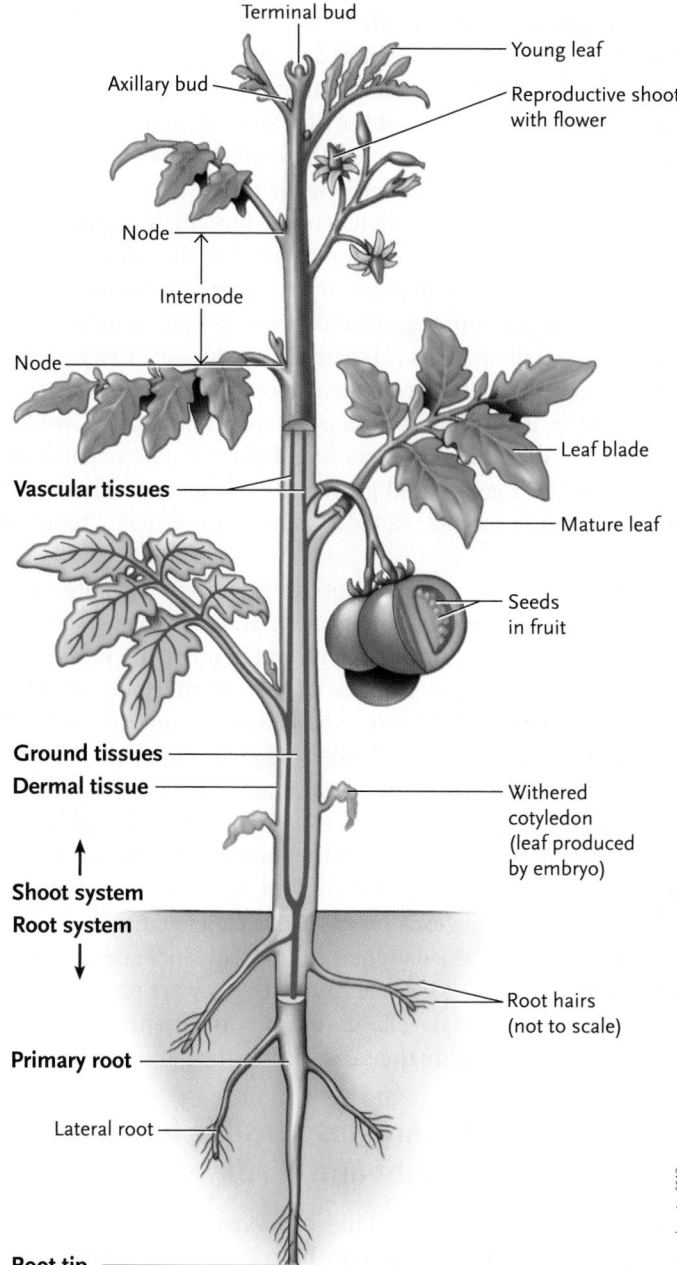

**FIGURE 33.2 Basic body plan for the tomato plant *Solanum lycopersicum*, a typical angiosperm.** Vascular tissues (purple) conduct water, dissolved minerals, and organic substances. They thread through ground tissues, which make up most of the plant body. Dermal tissues (epidermis, in this case) cover the surfaces of the root and shoot systems.

## Primary Plant Cell Wall

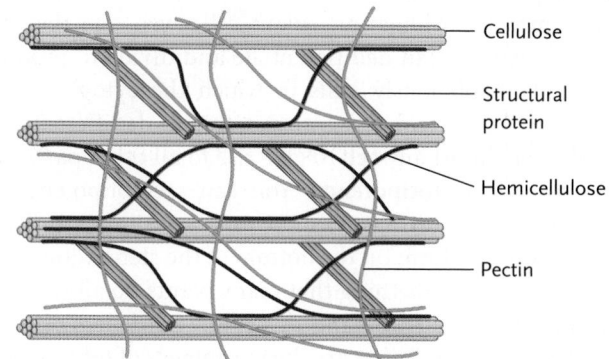

**FIGURE 33.3 Structure of a plant cell wall**

of these are structural proteins that contribute to the wall's strength, whereas others are enzymes that catalyze the formation and modification of the cell wall.

**CONCEPT FIX** Don't think of the cell wall as a solid barrier, like a cement wall, but rather as a semipermeable "mesh" or filter, which allows some molecules (e.g., water) to pass through into the cell. As well, cytoplasmic connections between adjacent cells, called **plasmodesmata** (singular, *plasmodesma*), allow solutes such as amino acids and sugars to move from one cell to the next. The space between the primary cell walls of adjacent cells is filled with a polysaccharide layer called the *middle lamella*. ⬡

As a young plant grows, different types of cells deposit additional cellulose and other materials inside the primary wall, forming a strong **secondary cell wall**. Secondary walls often contain **lignin**, a complex water-insoluble polymer (see Chapter 25) that makes cell walls very strong, rigid, and impermeable to water. As we learned in Chapter 26, the evolution of large vascular plants became possible only after biochemical pathways producing lignin evolved through modification of existing pathways, allowing a plant to produce lignified cells that both provided support and conducted water through the plant body. Lignin is also very resistant to decomposition, so its presence in cell walls makes the cell more resistant to attack by microbes (see Chapter 25).

As in animals, all of a plant's cells have the same genes in their nuclei. So how do specialized cells such as xylem arise in plants? As each cell matures and *differentiates* (becomes specialized for a particular function), specific genes are activated. For the most part, fully differentiated animal cells perform their functions while alive, but some types of plant cells die after differentiating, and their cytoplasm disappears. The walls that remain, however, serve key functions, particularly in xylem.

Most plant cells have a much more flexible differentiation than do animal cells. In general, once an animal cell has

animal does. A primary cell wall is made largely of microfibrils of **cellulose**, a polymer of glucose embedded in a matrix of other polysaccharides (**Figure 33.3**). Cellulose is the most abundant polysaccharide on Earth and is currently being investigated as a source of biofuel. The combination of cellulose fibrils and other polysaccharides gives the cell wall strength and flexibility. Primary cell walls also contain various proteins. Some

differentiated, it cannot easily dedifferentiate or "turn back" into an unspecialized cell (this is why it has proved so difficult to clone animals). Almost any plant cell, even one that has become specialized, can dedifferentiate and divide to produce an entire plant (obviously, cells in which the cytoplasm has been lost, such as xylem cells, are not able to dedifferentiate). This ability of almost any cell to give rise to all other parts of a plant is known as **totipotency**. You can see totipotency in action if you take a cutting of a shoot and place it in water: in a few days, roots will form on the bottom of the stem. Cloning of plants is very easy, something that many plants do all the time as a means of reproduction and that many gardeners use as a means of propagation. What are the advantages of totipotency? It allows plants to heal wounds and, as mentioned above, is also one means of asexual reproduction; for example, in many plants (such as raspberries), if a branch or stem comes into contact with the soil for long enough, roots will develop at the point where the stem touches the ground, forming a new plant.

## 33.1b Shoot and Root Systems Perform Different but Integrated Functions

A flowering plant's **shoot system** typically consists of stems, leaves, buds, and, during part of the plant's life cycle, reproductive organs called *flowers* (see Figure 33.2). A stem with its attached leaves and buds is a *vegetative* (non-reproductive) shoot; a bud eventually gives rise to an extension of the shoot or to a new, branching shoot. A *reproductive* shoot produces flowers, which later develop fruits containing seeds.

The shoot system is highly adapted for photosynthesis. Leaves greatly increase a plant's surface area and thus its exposure to light. Stems are frameworks for upright growth, which favourably positions leaves for light exposure and flowers for pollination. Some parts of the shoot system also store carbohydrates manufactured during photosynthesis. Many plants can change the orientation of their leaves to maximize light absorption or, in arid habitats, to prevent overheating.

The **root system** usually grows below ground. It anchors the plant and supports its upright parts. It also absorbs water and dissolved minerals from soil and stores carbohydrates. Adaptations in the structure and function of plant cells and tissues were an integral part of the evolution of shoots and roots, for example, the development of vascular tissues specialized to serve as internal pipelines that conduct water, minerals, and organic substances throughout the plant. The root hairs illustrated in Figure 33.2 are extensions of cells specialized for absorbing water and nutrients from soil.

## 33.1c Meristems Produce New Tissues Throughout a Plant's Life

Most animals grow to a certain size and then their growth slows dramatically or stops. This pattern is called **determinate growth**. In contrast, plants can grow throughout their lives, a pattern called **indeterminate growth**. Individual plant parts, such as leaves, flowers, and fruits, exhibit determinate growth, but every plant also has self-perpetuating embryonic tissue called *meristem* (*merizein* = to divide) at the tips of shoots and roots. Under the influence of plant hormones, these **meristems** produce new tissues more or less continuously while the plant is alive.

Why do plants have indeterminate growth? A capacity for indeterminate growth gives plants a great deal of flexibility, or what biologists often call *plasticity,* in their possible responses to changes in environmental factors such as light, temperature, water, and nutrients. This plasticity has major adaptive benefits for an organism that cannot move about as most animals can. For example, if external factors (such as a houseplant's owner) change the direction of incoming light for photosynthesis, stems can "shift gears" and grow in that direction. These and other plant movements, called *tropisms*, are a major topic of Chapter 36.

Remember, too, that nutrients are patchily distributed and diffuse in soil. Indeterminate growth allows a root system to extend and grow out of regions in which nutrients have been depleted and forage for patches with more nutrients; if plant root systems were determinate, plants would soon exhaust local nutrient supplies and be unable to forage for more.

As you know, animals grow mainly by mitosis, which increases the number of body cells. Plants, however, grow by two mechanisms: an increase in the number of cells by mitotic cell division in the meristems *and* an increase in the *size* of individual cells. In regions adjacent to the meristems in the tips of shoots and roots, the daughter cells rapidly increase in size—especially in length—for some time after they are produced. In contrast, when animal cells divide mitotically, the daughter cells are usually roughly the same size as the parent cell.

## 33.1d Meristems Are Responsible for Growth in Both Height and Girth

Some plants have only one kind of meristem, whereas others have two (**Figure 33.4**). All plants have **apical meristems**, clusters of self-perpetuating tissue at the tips of their buds, stems, and roots (see Figure 33.4a). Tissues that develop from apical meristems are called **primary tissues** and make up the **primary plant body**. Growth of the primary plant body is called **primary growth**.

Some plants (e.g., herbaceous plants such as grasses) have only primary growth, which occurs at the tips of roots and shoots. Others have **secondary growth** as well as primary growth. Secondary growth originates at cylinders of tissue called **lateral meristems** and increases the diameter of older roots and stems (see Figure 33.4b). Tissues that develop from lateral meristems are called **secondary tissues**. Woody plants such as trees and shrubs all have secondary tissues.

Primary and secondary growth can go on simultaneously in a single plant, with primary growth increasing the length of shoots and roots, and secondary growth adding girth to these

**a. Plants increase in length by cell divisions in apical meristems and by elongation of the daughter cells derived from the apical meristems.**

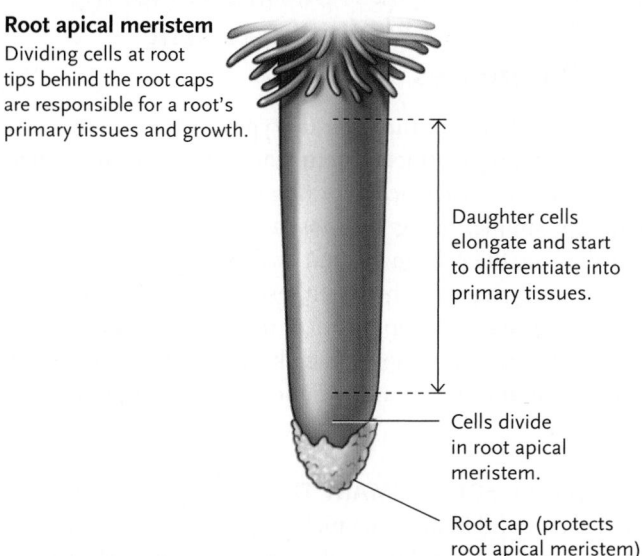

**Shoot apical meristem**
Dividing cells at all shoot tips are responsible for a shoot's primary tissues and growth.

Cells divide in shoot apical meristem.

Daughter cells elongate and start to differentiate into primary tissues.

**Root apical meristem**
Dividing cells at root tips behind the root caps are responsible for a root's primary tissues and growth.

Daughter cells elongate and start to differentiate into primary tissues.

Cells divide in root apical meristem.

Root cap (protects root apical meristem)

**b. The stems of some plants increase in girth by way of cell divisions in lateral meristems: the vascular cambium and cork cambium.**

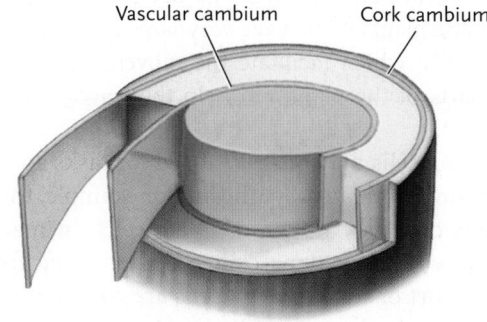

Vascular cambium     Cork cambium

**FIGURE 33.4 Approximate locations of types of meristems that are responsible for increases in the length** (a) **and diameter** (b) **of the shoots and roots of a vascular plant**.

organs. Each spring, for example, a poplar tree undergoes primary growth at each of its root and shoot tips, and secondary growth increases the diameter of its older, woody parts. Plant hormones govern these growth processes and other key events described in Chapter 37.

## 33.1e Monocots and Eudicots Are the Two General Structural Forms of Flowering Plants

Several broad categories of body architecture arose as flowering plants evolved, the two major categories being the **monocot** and **eudicot** lineages. Grasses, lilies, cattails, corn, wheat, and rice are examples of monocots. Eudicots include nearly all familiar angiosperm trees and shrubs, as well as many nonwoody (herbaceous) plants. Examples are poplars, willows, oaks, cacti, roses, poppies, sunflowers, and garden beans and peas.

Monocots and eudicots get their names from the number of *cotyledons*, the first leaves produced by the embryo, sometimes called *seed leaves* (see Chapter 26). Monocot seeds have one cotyledon and eudicot seeds have two. Although monocots and eudicots have similar types of tissues, their body structures differ in distinctive ways **(Table 33.1)**. As we discuss the morphology of flowering plants, we refer frequently to these structural differences.

## 33.1f Flowering Plants Can Be Grouped According to Type of Growth and Lifespan

As you learned above, we can distinguish between flowering plants depending on whether they are herbaceous or woody plants, and whether they are monocots or eudicots. We can also distinguish plants by lifespan. **Annuals** are herbaceous plants in which the life cycle is completed in one growing season with minimal or no secondary growth. Examples are tomatoes (a eudicot) and corn (a monocot). **Biennials**, such as carrots, complete their life cycle in two growing seasons, and limited secondary growth occurs in some species. In the first season, roots, stems, and leaves form; in its second year of growth, the plant flowers, forms fruits and seeds, and dies. (When grown for food, carrots are typically pulled after the first season.) In **perennials**, vegetative growth and reproduction continue year after year. Many perennials, such as trees, shrubs, and some vines, have secondary tissues, although others, such as irises and daffodils, do not.

### STUDY BREAK QUESTIONS

1. Explain how plant cell secondary walls differ from primary walls.
2. Compare the components and functions of a land plant's shoot and root systems.
3. Explain what meristem tissue is, and name and describe the functions of apical and lateral meristems.

| TABLE 33.1 | Comparison between Eudicots and Monocots | |
|---|---|---|

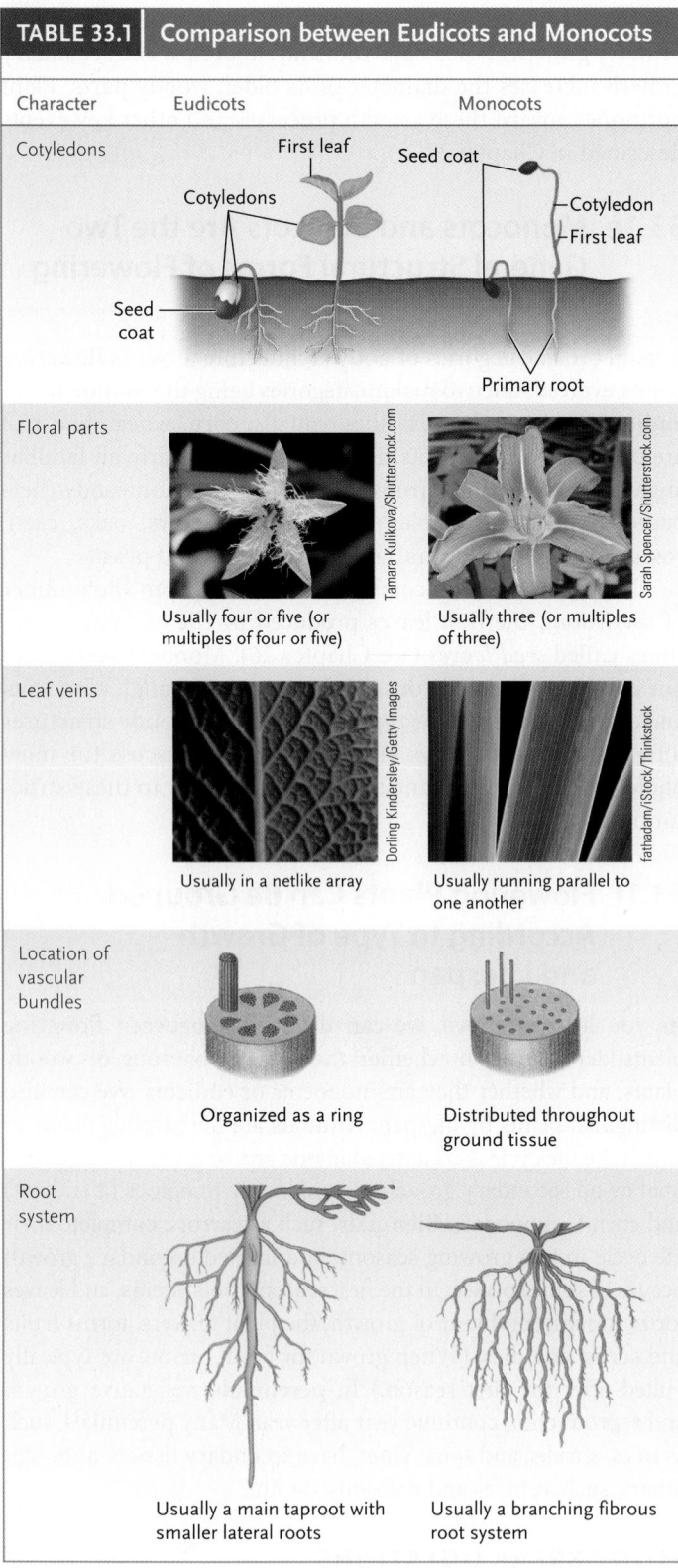

| Character | Eudicots | Monocots |
|---|---|---|
| Cotyledons | First leaf, Cotyledons, Seed coat | Seed coat, Cotyledon, First leaf, Primary root |
| Floral parts | Usually four or five (or multiples of four or five) | Usually three (or multiples of three) |
| Leaf veins | Usually in a netlike array | Usually running parallel to one another |
| Location of vascular bundles | Organized as a ring | Distributed throughout ground tissue |
| Root system | Usually a main taproot with smaller lateral roots | Usually a branching fibrous root system |

© Cengage Learning 2017.

## 33.2 The Three Plant Tissue Systems

As in animals, plant organs are composed of tissue systems. Each tissue system includes several types of tissue, and each tissue is made up of cells with specializations for different functions (**Table 33.2**). *Simple* tissues have only one type of cell. Other tissues are *complex,* with organized arrays of two or more types of cells. **Figure 33.5** will help you interpret images of plant tissues, beginning with the tissues in a transverse section of a stem, shown in **Figure 33.6**.

Unlike animals, which have a wide range of tissues, plant organs are composed of just three tissue systems. The **ground tissue system**, which makes up most of the plant body, functions in metabolism (including photosynthesis), storage, and support. The **vascular tissue system** consists of xylem and phloem, which transport water and nutrients throughout the plant. The cylinders of vascular tissue are embedded in ground tissue. The **dermal tissue system** is a skinlike protective covering for the plant body. As shown in Figure 33.2, these tissues generally have a radial arrangement in the plant body, with dermal tissues surrounding ground tissues, in which vascular tissues are embedded. Below we discuss the key features of each tissue system.

### 33.2a Ground Tissues Are All Structurally Simple But Exhibit Important Differences

Plants have potentially three tissue types in the ground tissue system, each with a distinct structure and function: *parenchyma*, *collenchyma*, and *sclerenchyma* (**Figure 33.7**). Each tissue is structurally simple, being composed of one kind of cell. In a very real sense, the cells in ground tissues are the "worker bees" of plants, carrying out photosynthesis, storing carbohydrates, providing mechanical support for the plant body, and performing other basic functions. Each kind of cell has a distinctive wall structure, and some have variations in the cytoplasmic contents as well.

**PARENCHYMA: SOFT PRIMARY TISSUES** Parenchyma (*para* = around; *chein* = fill in or pour) makes up the bulk of the primary growth of roots, stems, leaves, flowers, and fruits. Most parenchyma cells have only a thin primary wall and so are pliable and permeable to water. Often the cells are spherical or many sided, as in Figure 33.7a. Parenchyma cells typically have air spaces between them, especially in leaves (see Section 33.3). Stems and leaves in aquatic plants often have very large air spaces between parenchyma cells, which facilitate the movement of oxygen to submerged parts of the plant and help the leaves float upward toward the light.

Parenchyma cells may be specialized for tasks as varied as storage, secretion, and photosynthesis. For example, the photosynthetic cells of leaves are parenchyma cells. In many plant species, modified parenchyma cells are specialized for short-distance transport of solutes. Such cells are common in tissues in which water and solutes must be rapidly moved from cell to cell. Parenchyma cells usually remain alive and metabolically active when mature.

**COLLENCHYMA: FLEXIBLE SUPPORT** The "strings" in celery are made up of the flexible ground tissue called **collenchyma** (*kolla* = glue; see Figure 33.7b), which helps strengthen plant

**TABLE 33.2** | **Summary of Flowering Plant Tissues and Their Components**

| Tissue System | Name of Tissue | Cell Types in Tissue | Tissue Function |
|---|---|---|---|
| Ground tissue | Parenchyma | Parenchyma cells | Photosynthesis, respiration, storage, secretion |
| | Collenchyma | Collenchyma cells | Flexible strength for growing plant parts |
| | Sclerenchyma | Fibres or sclereids | Rigid support, deterring herbivores |
| Vascular tissue | Xylem | Conducting cells (tracheids, vessel members), parenchyma cells, fibres, sclereids | Transport of water and dissolved minerals |
| | Phloem | Conducting cells (sieve tube members), parenchyma cells, fibres, sclereids | Sugar transport |
| Dermal tissue | Epidermis | Undifferentiated cells, guard cells, other specialized cells | Control of gas exchange, water loss, protection |
| | Periderm | Cork, cork cambium, phelloderm | Protection |

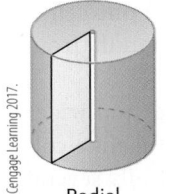 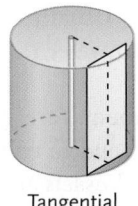 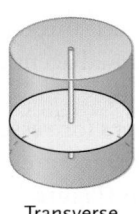

Radial     Tangential     Transverse

© Cengage Learning 2017.

**FIGURE 33.5  Terms that identify how tissue specimens are cut from a plant.** Along the radius of a stem or root, longitudinal cuts give radial sections. Cuts at right angles to a root or stem radius give tangential sections. Cuts perpendicular to the long axis of a stem or root give transverse sections (cross-sections).

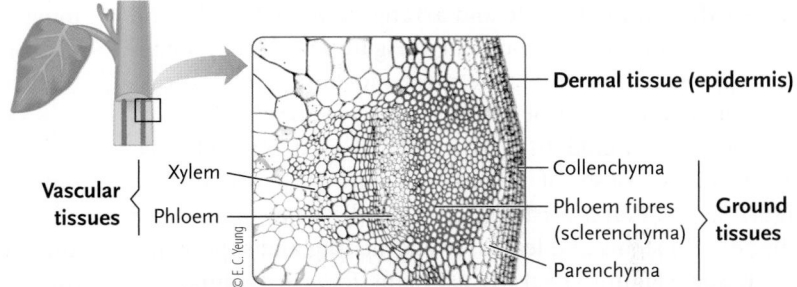

Vascular tissues — Xylem, Phloem

Dermal tissue (epidermis)

Collenchyma

Phloem fibres (sclerenchyma)

Parenchyma

Ground tissues

© E. C. Yeung

**FIGURE 33.6  Locations of ground, vascular, and dermal tissues in one kind of plant stem, transverse section.** Ground tissues are simple tissues, whereas vascular and dermal tissues are complex, containing various types of specialized cells.

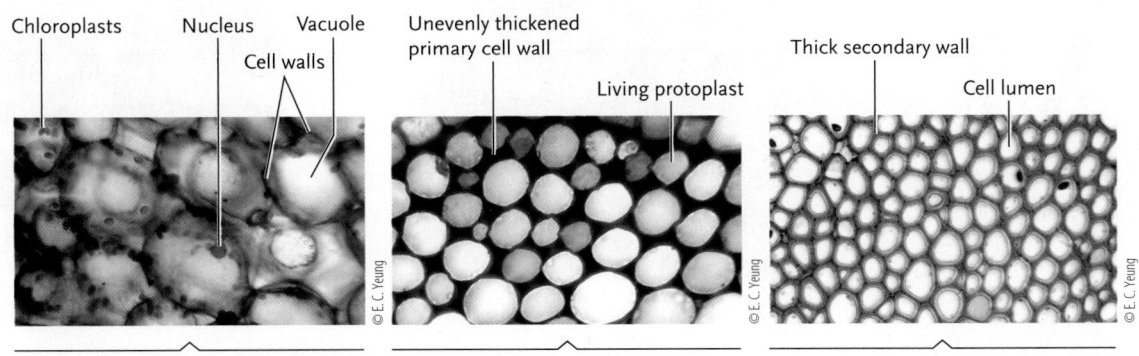

Chloroplasts     Nucleus     Vacuole

Cell walls

**a.** Parenchyma tissues consist of soft, living cells specialized for storage, other functions.

Unevenly thickened primary cell wall

Living protoplast

**b.** Collenchyma tissues provide flexible support.

Thick secondary wall

Cell lumen

**c.** Sclerenchyma tissues provide rigid support and protection.

© E. C. Yeung

**FIGURE 33.7**  (a, b) **Examples of ground tissues from the stem of a pepper plant (*Capsicum*) and** (c) **a sunflower plant (*Helianthus annuus*)**

parts that are still elongating. Collenchyma cells are typically elongated and, collectively, they often form strands under the dermal tissue system of growing structures of the primary plant body.

The primary walls of collenchyma cells are built of alternating layers of cellulose and pectin and are unevenly thickened. These walls can stretch as the cell enlarges, making them very suitable for flexible support of young, growing organs. Mature collenchyma cells are alive and metabolically active, and they continue to synthesize primary wall layers as the plant grows.

### SCLERENCHYMA: RIGID SUPPORT AND PROTECTION

Mature plant parts gain additional mechanical support and protection from **sclerenchyma** (*skleros* = hard) tissue, which is made up of cells with thick, lignified secondary walls (see Figure 33.7c). Regions of the cell wall lack secondary wall material, forming a *pit* where there is primary cell wall that is thinner and more porous than elsewhere. Water and other materials can flow through these pits, which is important when the cell is living and generating a secondary cell wall. After lignification occurs and differentiation is complete, sclerenchyma cells die. The walls of these dead cells provide protection and support.

The two types of sclerenchyma cells—*sclereids* and *fibres*—differ in their shape and arrangement. **Sclereids** tend to be short and are often branched (**Figure 33.8a**); they sometimes aggregate into protective sheets, forming the hard casings of a coconut shell or a peach pit for example. Sclereids can also be scattered in tissue: cube-shaped sclereids dispersed in the flesh of a pear give it its gritty texture (Figure 33.8b). **Fibres** are long, tapered cells. They often occur in bundles in stems and leaves, strengthening and supporting these tissues (Figure 33.8c). We use plant fibres to manufacture rope, paper, and cloth. Rope and twine, for example, are made of fibres extracted from the leaves of the sisal plant (*Agave sisalana*).

## 33.2b Vascular Tissues Are Specialized for Conducting Fluids

The vascular tissue system is made up of two kinds of vascular tissues: *xylem* and *phloem*. Each tissue generally consists of specialized conducting cells, parenchyma cells, and fibres. Xylem and phloem are organized into networks or cylinders of interconnected cells that extend throughout the plant.

**XYLEM: TRANSPORTING WATER AND MINERALS** Xylem (*xylon* = wood) conducts water and dissolved minerals absorbed from the soil upward from a plant's roots to the shoot. The evolution of xylem cells was a key adaptation allowing plants to make the transition to life on land (see Chapter 26). The two types of conducting cells, *tracheids* and *vessel members*, develop thick, lignified secondary cell walls and die at maturity, forming pipelines for water and minerals. Secondary cell wall deposition is highly regulated (**Figure 33.9**).

**Tracheids** are elongated cells, with tapered, overlapping ends (**Figure 33.10a**). As with fibres and sclereids, water can move from cell to cell through pits. Usually, a pit in one cell is opposite a pit of an adjacent cell, so water flows laterally from tracheid to tracheid.

**Vessel members** (or vessel elements) are shorter and wider cells than tracheids and are joined end to end in tubelike columns called *vessels* (Figure 33.10b). **Vessels** are typically several centimetres long, and may even be metres long in some vines and trees. Like tracheids, vessel members have pits. However, they have another adaptation that greatly enhances water flow.

**a.**

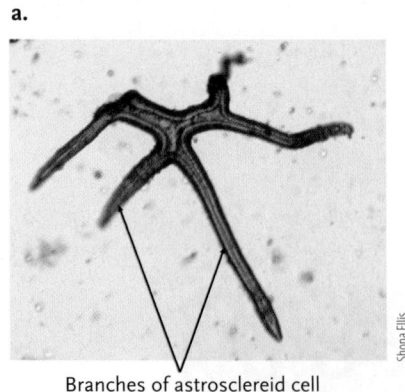

Branches of astrosclereid cell

**b.**

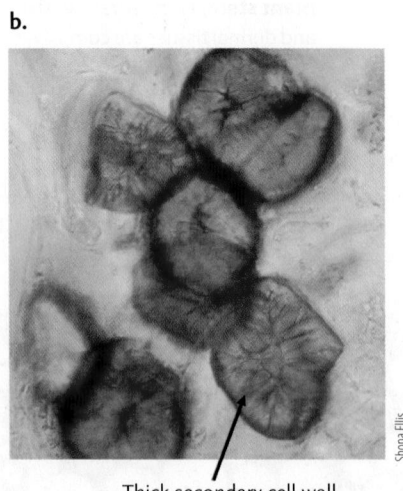

Thick secondary cell wall of sclereid cell

**c.**

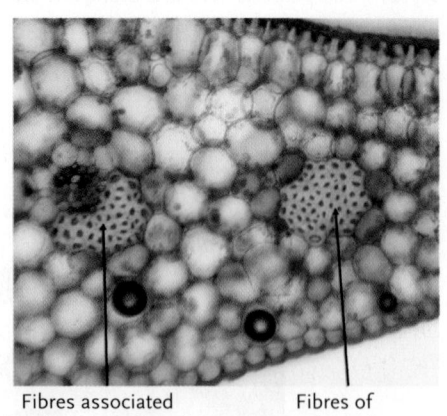

Fibres associated with vascular bundle

Fibres of sclerenchyma

**FIGURE 33.8 Examples of sclerenchyma cells. (a)** Astrosclereid, a radiately branched type of sclereid. **(b)** Cross-section of the flesh of a pear (*Pyrus*) stained with phloroglucinol. Sclereids are distinguished from the surrounding cells by their thick secondary cell walls (stained red in the figure). **(c)** Cross-section of a *Sansevieria* leaf stained with toluidine blue. Note that fibres occur in clusters and, like sclereids, are distinguished from the surrounding cells by their thick secondary cell walls (stained blue in the figure).

FIGURE 33.9  **Experimental Research**

## Networking the Secondary Cell Wall

**Question:** How elaborate is the regulatory network controlling the development of secondary walls of xylem cells?

**Experiments:** The researchers began with available information on transcription factors and their target genes that function in the formation of xylem in developing roots of *Arabidopsis thaliana* (thale cress), a major model organism in plant research and the first plant to have its genome sequenced. The *A. thaliana* genes of interest were mainly those for enzymes associated with the synthesis of lignin and other secondary wall components. Next, the team used laboratory assays to pinpoint which DNA sequences transcription factors bind to, and thus which target genes they regulate. The investigators also used high-resolution microscopy to track the sequence of structural changes that unfolded due to shifts in gene expression as xylem cells arose and differentiated in developing *A. thaliana* rootlets **(Figure 1).** Computerized analysis generated a map of interactions in the regulatory network underlying these sequential changes.

**Results:** Previous work by others had identified 50 transcription factors with roles in *A. thaliana* xylem development. The new experiments uncovered 152 additional transcription factors and an unexpectedly complex regulatory network governing xylem development. Among other findings, computer analysis mapped 617 separate interactions of transcription factors with one another or with regulatory sequences of genes encoding the synthesis of secondary wall components. On average, genes coding for proteins involved in secondary wall development were regulated by five different transcription factors. Using their network analysis, the researchers predicted that a transcription factor called *REV* regulates genes coding for enzymes involved in synthesizing lignin, and they confirmed this prediction in plants with mutations to the gene for REV.

**Conclusions:** The highly interconnected network demonstrates a regulatory arrangement with a large number of possible combinations, which is shown to be important for adaptive responses to environmental stresses. There is also potential to manipulate this system for biotechnological purposes, for example to develop new plant varieties for use in biofuel production.

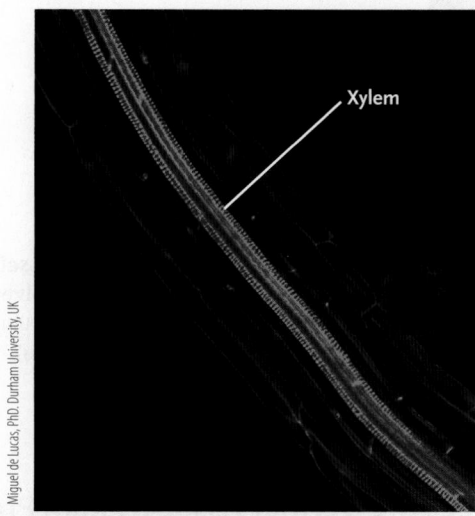

Miguel de Lucas, PhD. Durham University, UK

**Figure 1  Light microscopy of developing root xylem**

Source: © Cengage Learning 2017. Based on M. Taylor-Teeples et al. 2015. an Arabidopsis gene regulatory network for secondary cell wall synthesis. Nature (January, Vol. 517: published online)

As vessel members mature, enzymes break down portions of their end walls, producing perforations (holes). Some vessel members have a single large perforation, so that the end is completely open (see Figure 33.10b). Others have a cluster of small round perforations, or ladderlike bars, extending across the open end. Water moves more efficiently through vessels than tracheids due to their greater diameter and perforated ends.

Fossil evidence shows that the forerunners of modern vascular plants relied solely on tracheids for water transport, and today ferns and most gymnosperms still have only tracheids. Nearly all angiosperms and a few gymnosperms and seedless vascular plants have *both* tracheids and vessel members.

### PHLOEM: TRANSPORTING SUGARS AND OTHER SOLUTES

The vascular tissue **phloem** (*phloios* = tree bark) transports the sugars made in photosynthesis and other organic molecules throughout the plant body. The main conducting cells of phloem are **sieve tube members** in flowering plants **(Figure 33.11)**, which are connected end to end to form a **sieve tube**. As the name implies, the end walls of sieve tubes, called *sieve plates*, contain numerous pores. In flowering plants, phloem tissue often contains fibres and sclereids in addition to conducting cells; these cells strengthen stems.

Immature sieve tube members contain the usual plant organelles. Over time, however, the cell nucleus and internal membranes in plastids break down, mitochondria shrink, the cytoplasm is reduced to a thin layer lining the interior surface of the cell wall, and a sieve plate forms with big pores for movement of substances from cell to cell. Even without a nucleus, the cell lives up to several years in most plants and much longer in some trees.

In flowering plants, specialized parenchyma cells known as **companion cells** are connected to mature sieve tube members by plasmodesmata. Unlike sieve tube members, companion cells retain their nuclei when mature. Companion cells assist sieve tube members with both the uptake of sugars and the unloading of sugars in tissues engaged in food storage or growth. They may also help regulate the metabolism of mature sieve tube members. We will take a deeper look at the functions of xylem and phloem cells in Chapter 34.

**a. Tracheids, tangential section**

**b. A vessel member**

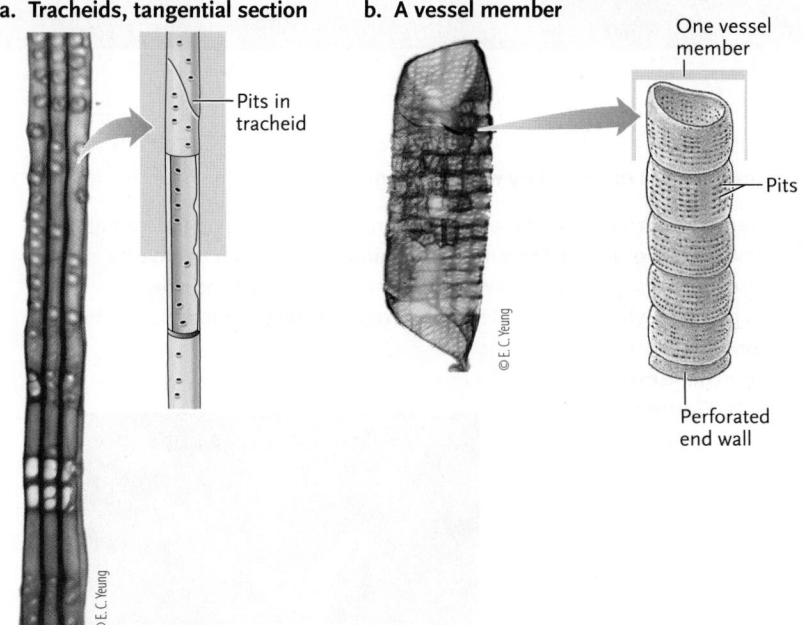

Pits in tracheid

One vessel member

Pits

Perforated end wall

© E. C. Yeung

**FIGURE 33.10 Representative tracheids and vessel members from woody stems, elements in xylem that conduct water and dissolved mineral salts through the body of a vascular plant.** These images show longitudinal views of **(a)** tracheids from pine (*Pinus*) and **(b)** a vessel member from oak (*Quercus*).

© Cengage Learning 2017.

**a. Sieve tube members**

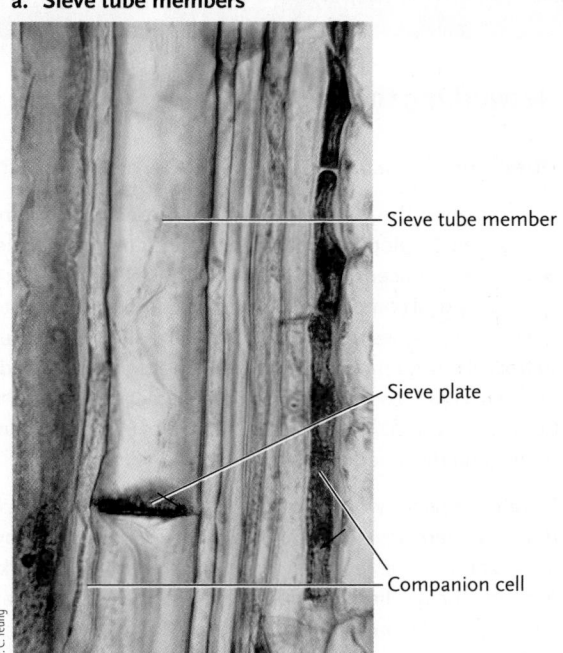

Sieve tube member

Sieve plate

Companion cell

© E. C. Yeung

**b. Sieve plate**

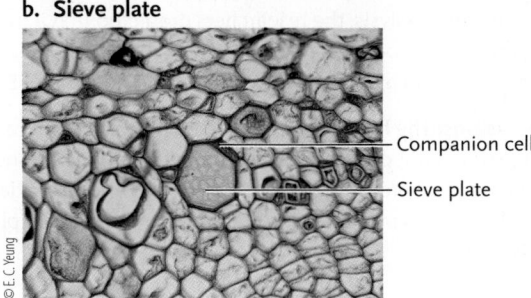

Companion cell

Sieve plate

© E. C. Yeung

**FIGURE 33.11 Structure of sieve tube members. (a)** Micrograph showing sieve tube members of cucumber (*Cucumis*) in longitudinal section. Long tubes of sieve tube members conduct sugars and other organic compounds. **(b)** Sieve plate in a cell in phloem of cucumber (*Cucumis*); cross-section

## 33.2c The Dermal Tissue System Protects Plant Surfaces

A complex tissue called **epidermis** covers the primary plant body in a layer one cell thick (Figure 33.6), or sometimes in multiple layers of tightly packed cells. The external surface of epidermal cell walls is coated with waxes that are embedded in cutin, a network of chemically linked fats. Epidermal cells secrete this coating, or **cuticle** (see **Figure 33.12a**), which resists water loss and helps protect against attacks by microbes. A cuticle coats all plant parts except the very tips of the shoot and the most absorptive parts of roots; other root regions have an extremely thin cuticle.

Most epidermal cells are relatively unspecialized, but some are modified in ways that represent important adaptations for plants. Young stems, leaves, flower parts, and even some roots have pairs of crescent-shaped **guard cells** (see Figure 33.12b). Unlike other cells of the epidermis, guard cells contain chloroplasts and so can carry out photosynthesis. The pore between a pair of guard cells is called a **stoma** (plural, *stomata*). Water vapour, carbon dioxide, and oxygen cross the epidermis through the stomata. Guard cells regulate opening and closing of stomata via mechanisms we consider in Chapter 34.

Other epidermal specializations are the single-celled or multicellular outgrowths collectively called **trichomes** that give the stems or leaves of some plants a hairy appearance. Some trichomes exude sugars that attract insect pollinators. Leaf trichomes of *Urtica*, the stinging nettle, provide protection

by injecting an irritating toxin into the skin of animals that brush against the plant or try to eat it (see Figure 33.18d). **Root hairs**, extensions of the outer wall of root epidermal cells (Figure 33.12c), are also trichomes. Root hairs absorb much of a plant's water and minerals from the soil.

The epidermal cells of flower petals (which are modified leaves) synthesize pigments that are partly responsible for a blossom's colours.

## STUDY BREAK QUESTIONS

1. Describe the defining features, cellular components, and functions of the ground tissue system.
2. What are the functions of xylem and phloem?
3. What are the cellular components and functions of the dermal tissue system?

**a. Leaf epidermis**

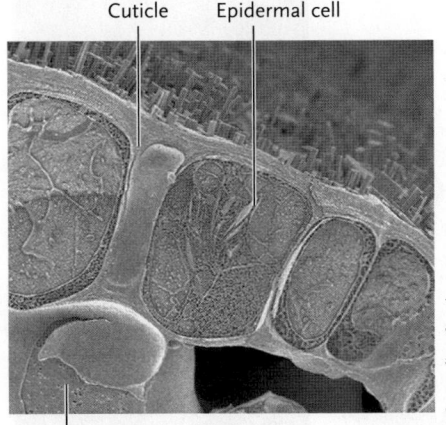

Cuticle    Epidermal cell

Courtesy of Lacey Samuels

Parenchyma cell inside leaf

**b. Secretory trichomes of *Cannabis sativa***

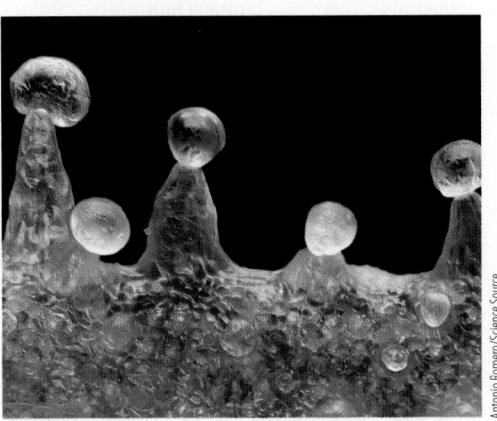

Antonio Romero/Science Source

**c. Root hairs**

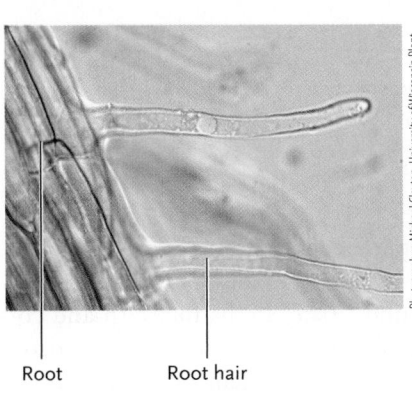

Photographer: Michael Clayton. University of Wisconsin Plant Teaching Collection, http://botit.botany.wisc.edu

Root    Root hair

**d. Stomata**

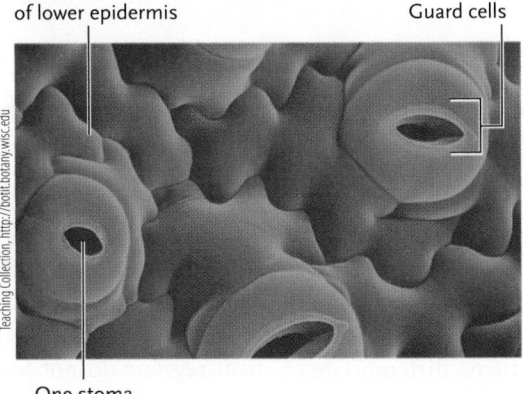

Cuticle-coated cell of lower epidermis                Guard cells

Jeremy Burgess / Science Source

One stoma

**FIGURE 33.12 Structure of epidermal tissue and examples of epidermal specializations. (a)** Cross-section of leaf epidermis from a bush lily (*Clivia miniata*). Cryo scanning electron micrograph of epidermis covered with cuticle. **(b)** Light micrograph of trichomes on a bract (specialized leaf) of marijuana (*Cannabis sativa*). The trichomes secrete various substances, including the resinous psychoactive compound THC (tetrahydrocannabinol). In nature, THC deters insect pests. **(c)** Root hairs, trichomes that develop from root epidermis. **(d)** A scanning electron micrograph of a leaf surface shows stomata among cuticle-covered epidermal cells.

# 33.3 Primary Shoot Systems

A young flowering plant's shoot system consists of the main stem, leaves, and buds, as well as flowers and fruits. Chapter 35 looks more closely at flowers and fruits; here we focus on the growth and organization of stems, buds, and leaves of the primary shoot system.

## 33.3a Stems Are Adapted to Provide Support, Routes for Vascular Tissues, Storage, and New Growth

Stems are structurally adapted for four main functions:

- Stems provide mechanical support, generally along a vertical (upright) axis, for body parts involved in growth, photosynthesis, and reproduction. These parts include meristematic tissues, leaves, and flowers.
- Stems have vascular tissues (xylem and phloem), which transport products of photosynthesis, water and dissolved minerals, hormones, and other substances throughout the plant.
- Stems are often modified to store water and food.

- Buds and specific stem regions contain meristematic tissue that gives rise to new cells of the shoot.

**THE MODULAR ORGANIZATION OF A STEM** A plant stem develops in a pattern that divides the stem into modules, each consisting of a *node* and an *internode*. A **node** is a place on the stem where one or more leaves are attached; the region between two nodes is thus an **internode**. New primary growth occurs in buds: a **terminal bud** at the apex of the main shoot, and **axillary buds**, which produce branches (lateral shoots) at the point where leaves meet the stem. Meristematic tissue in buds gives rise to leaves, flowers, or both **(Figure 33.13)**.

**CONCEPT FIX** Many people think that flowering plants grow from the base of their stems, as if they pushed upward from the soil surface. But this is not true. Shoot growth occurs primarily from the apical meristem, not the base of the stem. In addition to the apical meristem, internode cells divide and elongate. Internode cells nearest the apex are most active, so the most visible new growth occurs at the ends of branches. ⬡

Terminal buds release a hormone (auxin) that inhibits the growth of nearby **lateral buds**, a phenomenon called **apical dominance**. Gardeners who want a bushier plant can stimulate axillary bud growth by periodically cutting off the terminal bud. The flow of hormone signals then dwindles to a level low enough that lateral buds begin to grow. In nature, apical dominance is an adaptation that directs the plant's resources into growing up toward the light (see Chapter 36).

## PRIMARY GROWTH AND STRUCTURE OF A STEM
Primary growth, the cell divisions and enlargement that produce the primary plant body, begins in the shoot and root apical meristems. The sequence of events is shown for a eudicot shoot in **Figure 33.14.**

The shoot apical meristem is a dome-shaped mass of cells at the tip of shoots, surrounded by developing leaves. When a cell of this meristem divides, one of its daughter cells remains part of the meristem, whereas the other begins to differentiate to follow a particular developmental path.

The differentiating cells give rise to three **primary meristems**: *protoderm*, *procambium*, and *ground meristem* (see Figure 33.14a). These primary meristems are relatively unspecialized tissues with cells that, in turn, differentiate into specialized cells and tissues. In eudicots, the primary meristems are also responsible for elongation of the plant body.

The **protoderm**, a primary meristem that gives rise to the stem's epidermis, is the outermost layer of the shoot tip, as shown in Figure 33.14a. Inward from the protoderm is the **ground meristem**, which will give rise to the tissues of the ground tissue system. **Procambium**, which produces the primary vascular tissues (primary xylem and primary phloem), is in strands surrounded by cells of the ground meristem layers. Procambial cells are long and thin, and their spatial orientation foreshadows the function of the tissues they produce. In most plants, inner procambial cells give rise to xylem, and outer procambial cells to phloem. In plants with secondary growth, a thin region of procambium between the primary xylem and phloem remains undifferentiated. Later, this residual procambium will give rise to a lateral meristem (vascular cambium).

The developing vascular tissues are organized into **vascular bundles** of primary xylem and phloem that are sometimes wrapped in sclerenchyma. Eudicot stems have vascular bundles arranged in a circle that separates the ground tissue in the centre of the stem (the **pith**) from the ground tissue between the epidermis and the bundles (the cortex; **Figure 33.15a**). Both cortex and pith often consist of parenchyma cells; in some

**a. Location of nodes and buds**

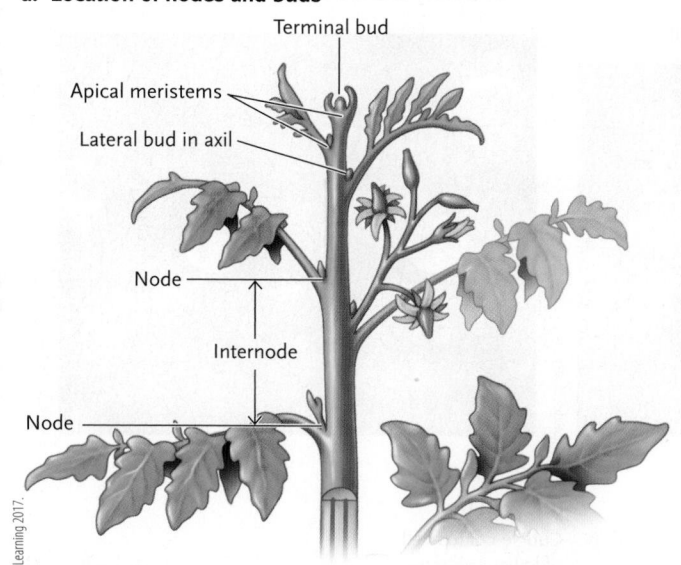

Terminal bud
Apical meristems
Lateral bud in axil
Node
Internode
Node

© Cengage Learning 2017.

**b. Leaves at a terminal bud**

altrendo nature/Altrendo/Getty Images

**FIGURE 33.13 Modular structure of a stem. (a)** The arrangement of nodes and buds on a plant stem. **(b)** Formation of leaves at a terminal bud of a dogwood (genus *Cornus*)

plant species, the pith parenchyma stores starch reserves. Monocot stems also have vascular bundles, but these are scattered throughout the ground tissue, so distinct pith and cortical regions do not form (Figure 33.15b). In some monocots, including bamboo, the centre of the stem of the internodes breaks down, leaving a hollow core. The hollow stems of certain hard-walled bamboo species are used to make bamboo flutes.

As leaves and buds develop along a stem, some vascular bundles in the stem branch off into these tissues. The arrangement of vascular bundles in a plant ultimately depends on the number of branch points to leaves and buds, and on the number and distribution of leaves.

## STEM MODIFICATIONS
Evolution has produced a range of stem specializations, including structures modified for reproduction, food storage, or both **(Figure 33.16)**. An onion or a garlic head is a *bulb*, a modified shoot that consists of a bud with fleshy leaves. *Tubers* are stem regions enlarged by the presence of starch-storing parenchyma cells; the potato is an example of a plant that forms tubers. The "eyes" of a potato are buds at nodes of the modified stem. Many grasses, such as quackgrass (*Elymus repens*), and some weeds are difficult to eradicate because they have *rhizomes*, long underground stems that can extend as much as 50 cm deep into the soil and rapidly produce new shoots when existing ones are pulled out. The pungent, starchy "root" of ginger is also a rhizome. Crocuses and some other ornamental plants develop elongated, fleshy underground stems called *corms*, another starch-storage adaptation. Tubers, rhizomes, and corms

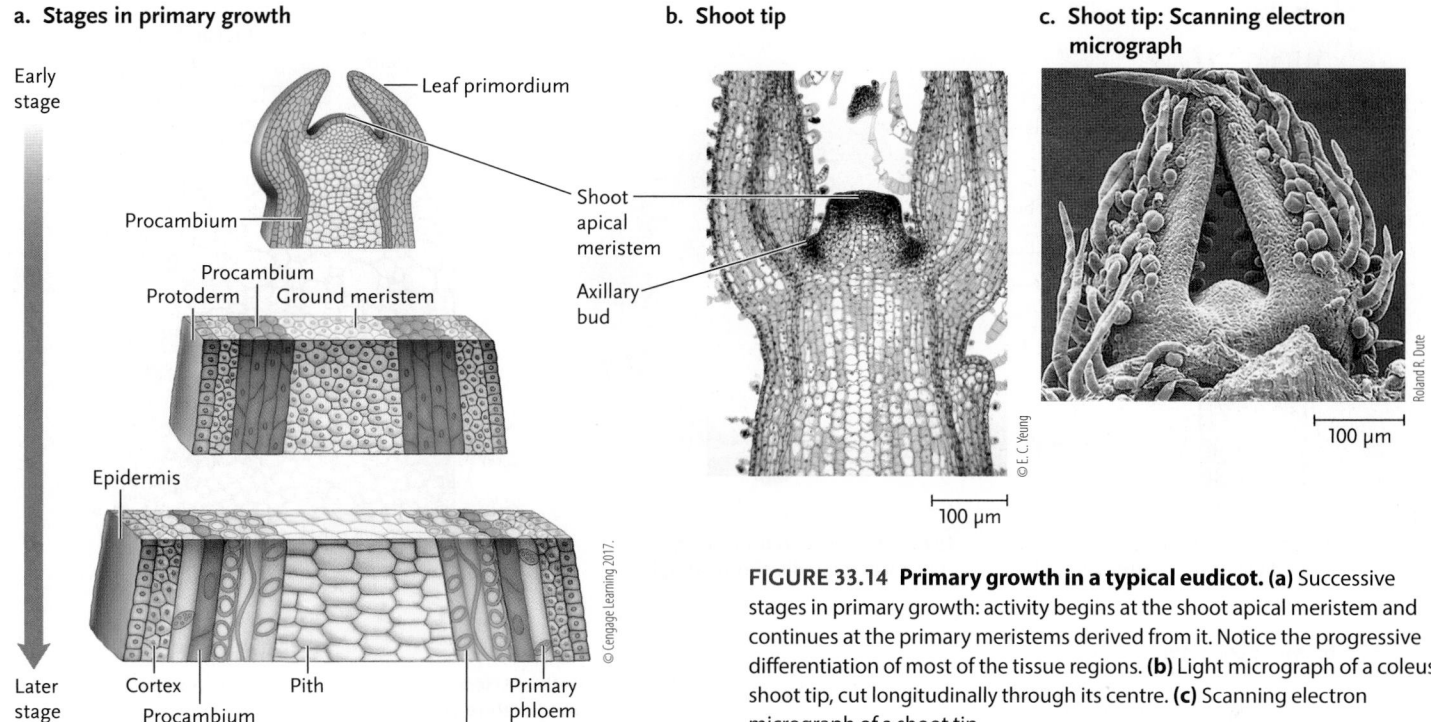

**a. Stages in primary growth**

Early stage

Leaf primordium

Procambium

Procambium
Protoderm | Ground meristem

Epidermis

Later stage

Cortex | Pith
Procambium

Primary xylem

Primary phloem

© Cengage Learning 2017.

**b. Shoot tip**

Shoot apical meristem

Axillary bud

© E. C. Yeung

100 μm

**c. Shoot tip: Scanning electron micrograph**

Roland R. Dute

100 μm

**FIGURE 33.14  Primary growth in a typical eudicot. (a)** Successive stages in primary growth: activity begins at the shoot apical meristem and continues at the primary meristems derived from it. Notice the progressive differentiation of most of the tissue regions. **(b)** Light micrograph of a coleus shoot tip, cut longitudinally through its centre. **(c)** Scanning electron micrograph of a shoot tip

all have meristematic tissue at nodes from which new plants can be propagated—a vegetative (asexual) reproductive mode. Other plants, including strawberries (*Fragaria* spp.), reproduce vegetatively via slender stems called *stolons*, which grow along the soil surface. New plants arise at nodes along the stolon.

## 33.3b  Leaves Carry Out Photosynthesis and Gas Exchange

Each spring, a mature maple tree heralds the new season by unfurling roughly 100 000 leaves. Some other tree species produce leaves by the millions. For these and most other plants, leaves are the main organs of photosynthesis and gas exchange (the movement of carbon dioxide and oxygen into and out of the leaf).

**LEAF MORPHOLOGY AND ANATOMY** In both eudicots and monocots, the leaf **blade** provides a large surface area for absorbing sunlight and carbon dioxide (**Figure 33.17**). Leaves of flowering plants are generally oriented on the stem axis so that they can capture the maximum amount of sunlight; the stems and leaves of some plants change position to follow the Sun's movement during the day (this phenomenon is described in Chapter 37).

Many eudicot leaves, such as those of maples, have a broad, flat blade attached to the stem by a stalklike **petiole** (see Figure 33.17). Celery stalks that we eat are actually petioles. Petioles hold leaves away from the stem and help prevent indi-

vidual leaves from shading one another. In many plant species, petioles allow leaves to move in the breeze—think about trembling aspen (*Populus tremuloides*) leaves rustling in a breeze—enhancing air circulation around leaves, thus replenishing the supply of carbon dioxide for photosynthesis. In most monocot leaves, such as those of grass and corn, the blade is longer and narrower and its base simply forms a sheath around the stem (see Figure 33.17).

As with other plant parts, however, the adaptation of land plants to different environments has produced tremendous variety in leaf morphology. For instance, spiny margins on the leaves of the carnivorous Venus flytrap (*Dionaea muscipula*; **Figure 33.18a**) prevent the escape of insects that become trapped when the seemingly hinged leaves snap shut around them—a movement that takes only about a tenth of a second. Leaves or parts of leaves may also be modified into tendrils, like those of the sweet pea (Figure 33.18b). Cactus leaves are modified as spines, while leaves of other plants have trichomes that take the form of hairs or hooks (Figure 33.18c) that help defend against grazing by herbivores. In some plants, these trichomes seem more aggressive than defensive: the leaves and stem of stinging nettle (*Urtica dioica*) are covered with stinging trichomes (Figure 33.18d). When a herbivore or unlucky passerby brushes against a leaf, the tips of the trichomes break off, converting each trichome into a hypodermic needle that injects the stinging chemicals in the base of the trichome into the victim's skin.

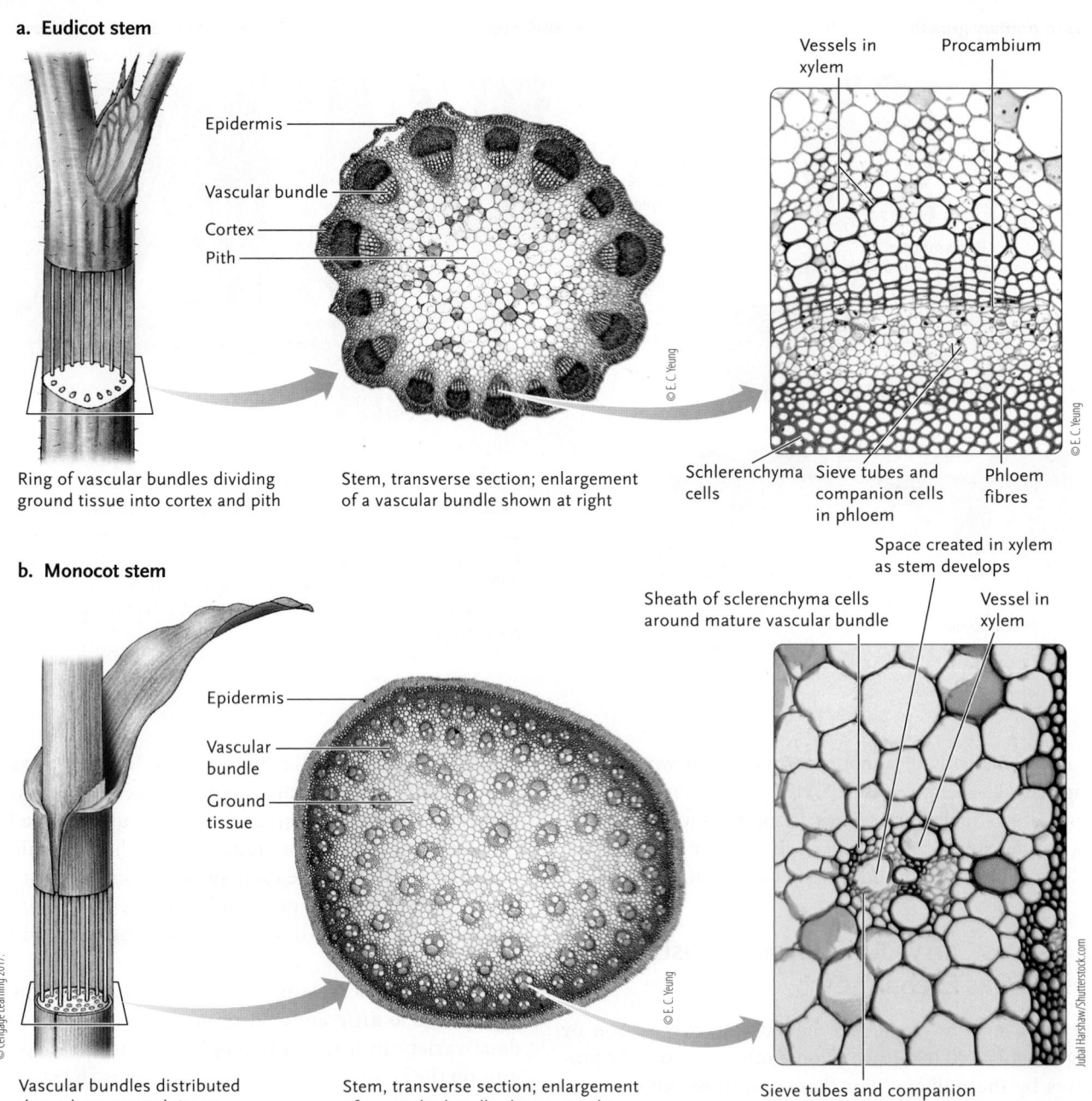

**a. Eudicot stem**

Epidermis

Vascular bundle

Cortex

Pith

Vessels in xylem

Procambium

Ring of vascular bundles dividing ground tissue into cortex and pith

Stem, transverse section; enlargement of a vascular bundle shown at right

Schlerenchyma cells

Sieve tubes and companion cells in phloem

Phloem fibres

**b. Monocot stem**

Space created in xylem as stem develops

Sheath of sclerenchyma cells around mature vascular bundle

Vessel in xylem

Epidermis

Vascular bundle

Ground tissue

Vascular bundles distributed throughout ground tissue

Stem, transverse section; enlargement of a vascular bundle shown at right

Sieve tubes and companion cells in phloem

**FIGURE 33.15 Organization of cells and tissues inside the stem of a eudicot and a monocot. (a)** Part of a stem from sunflower (*Helianthus*), a eudicot. In many species of eudicots and conifers, the vascular bundles develop in a more or less ringlike array in the ground tissue system, as shown here. The enlarged photo at right is of a vascular bundle of a sunflower *(Helianthus).* **(b)** Part of a stem from corn (*Zea mays*), a monocot. In most monocots and some herbaceous eudicots, vascular bundles are scattered through the ground tissue, as shown here.

**LEAF PRIMARY GROWTH AND INTERNAL STRUCTURE** As the shoot apical meristem divides, it produces a series of bumps on its sides, **leaf primordia**, which give rise to leaves (see Figure 33.14a). As the plant grows and the internodes elongate, the leaves that form from leaf primordia become spaced at intervals along the length of the stem or its branches.

A leaf is typically composed of several layers **(Figure 33.19)**. Outermost is the epidermis, with cuticle covering its surface. Between the epidermis and the veins (vascular tissues), the ground tissue system is made up of **mesophyll** (*mesos* = middle; *phyllon* = leaf), composed of loosely packed parenchyma cells that contain chloroplasts. In the leaves of

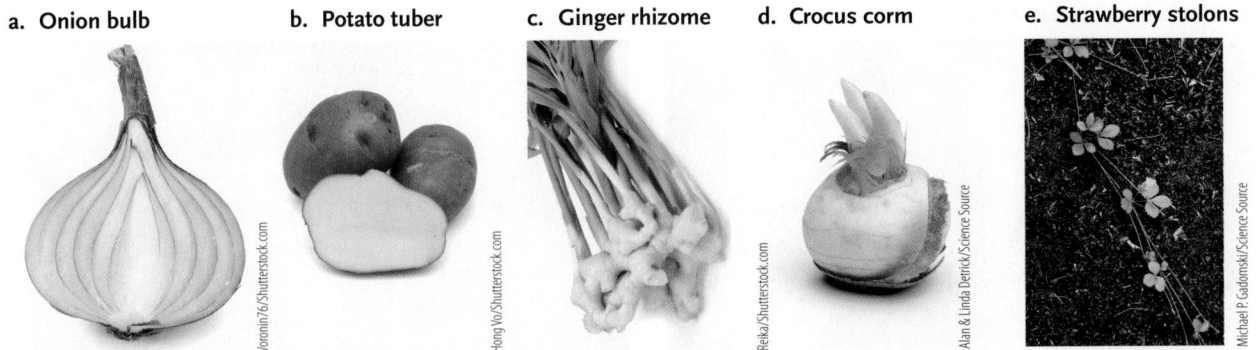

**FIGURE 33.16  A selection of modified shoots. (a)** The fleshy bulbs of onions (*Allium cepa*) are modified shoots with a small stem and many leaves that store sugars. **(b)** A potato (*Solanum tuberosum*), a tuber. **(c)** Ginger "root," the pungent, starchy rhizome of the ginger plant (*Zingiber officinale*). **(d)** Crocus plants (genus *Crocus*) typically grow from a corm. **(e)** A strawberry plant (*Fragaria ananassa*) and stolons

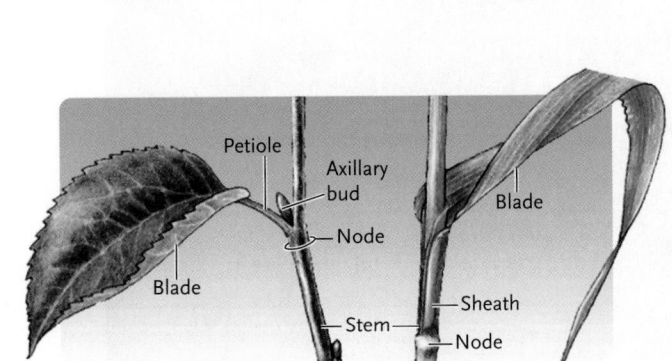

**FIGURE 33.17  Leaf forms.** Common forms of eudicot and monocot leaves

many plants, especially eudicots, the mesophyll is differentiated into palisade mesophyll and spongy mesophyll. *Palisade mesophyll* cells contain more chloroplasts than the spongy mesophyll cells and are arranged in compact columns with smaller air spaces between them, typically toward the upper leaf surface. *Spongy mesophyll*, which tends to be located toward the lower part of a leaf, consists of irregularly arranged cells with a conspicuous network of air spaces—between 15% and 50% of the leaf's volume—that give this layer a spongy appearance. What is the role of these air spaces? They enhance the uptake of carbon dioxide and the release of oxygen during photosynthesis. Mesophyll may also contain collenchyma and sclerenchyma tissues, which provide support for the leaf.

The lower side of the leaf has a cuticle-covered epidermal layer. Except in grasses and a few other plants, this layer contains most of the stomata through which water vapour exits the leaf and gas exchange occurs. For example, the upper surface

of an apple leaf has no stomata, whereas a square centimetre of the lower surface has more than 20 000. A square centimetre of the upper epidermis of a tomato leaf has about 1200 stomata, whereas the same area of the lower epidermis has 13 000. Why are more stomata located on the underside of the leaf? This positioning protects stomata from direct exposure to sunlight, thus limiting water loss by evaporation through stomatal openings.

Vascular bundles form a lacy network of **veins** throughout the leaf. Eudicot leaves typically have a branching vein pattern; in monocot leaves, veins tend to run in parallel along the length of the leaf (see Table 33.1).

In temperate regions, most leaves are temporary structures. In deciduous species such as birches and maples, hormonal signals cause the leaves to drop from the stem as the days shorten in autumn. Other temperate plants, such as most conifers, also drop their leaves (which are modified into needles in conifers), but they appear "evergreen" because the leaves may persist for several years and do not all drop at the same time.

## STUDY BREAK QUESTIONS

1. Describe the functions of stems and stem structures.
2. Explain how primary growth occurs in stems. What are the three primary meristems that form, and to what tissues does each give rise?
3. Compare the arrangement of the three primary tissues in monocot and dicot stems.
4. Explain the general function of leaves and how leaf anatomy supports this role in eudicots and monocots.
5. Describe the steps in the primary growth of a leaf and the structures that result from the process.

**a. Interlocking spines of Venus flytrap leaves**

**b. Tendrils of a sweet pea**

50 μm

**c. Hairs and glandular structures on a tomato leaf**

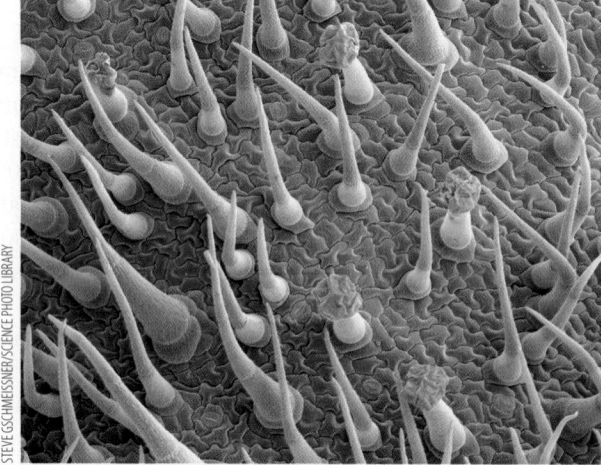

**d. Stinging hairs on nettle leaf**

**FIGURE 33.18  A few adaptations of leaves. (a)** Margins on the leaves of the Venus flytrap (*Dionaea muscipula*) are modified into long, interlocking spines. **(b)** The tendrils of a sweet pea (*Lathyrus odoratus*) help to support the climbing plant's stem. **(c)** Specializations on a tomato leaf include hooklike hairs and lobed glandular structures that release an insect-deterring chemical. **(d)** Stinging hairs (trichomes) on a leaf of *Urtica* (stinging nettle) defend the plant against herbivores.

## 33.4  Root Systems

Plants cannot move around to find water and nutrients when they have depleted supplies in their immediate soil neighbourhood, yet they must be able to forage for new supplies. Once these supplies are found, the plant must absorb enough water and dissolved minerals to sustain growth and perform routine cellular maintenance. These tasks can require a tremendous root surface area, at least part of which is regularly replaced. In one study, rye plants (*Secale cereale*) that had been growing for only four months were measured. One plant's root system had a surface area of more than 700 m² — about 130 times the surface area of its shoot system!

In addition to taking up water and nutrients, roots store nutrients produced by photosynthesis, some of which is used by root cells and some transported later to cells of the shoot. As the root system penetrates downward and spreads out, it also anchors the above-ground parts.

### 33.4a  Taproot and Fibrous Root Systems Are Specialized for Particular Functions

Most eudicots have a **taproot system**: a single main root, or taproot, that is adapted for storage, plus smaller branching roots called **lateral roots** (**Figure 33.20a**). As the main root grows downward, the diameter of the upper, older part of the root increases, and the lateral roots emerge along the length of its older, differentiated regions. The youngest lateral roots are near the root tip. Carrots and dandelions have a taproot system, as do pines and many other conifers. A pine's taproot system can penetrate 6 m or more into the soil.

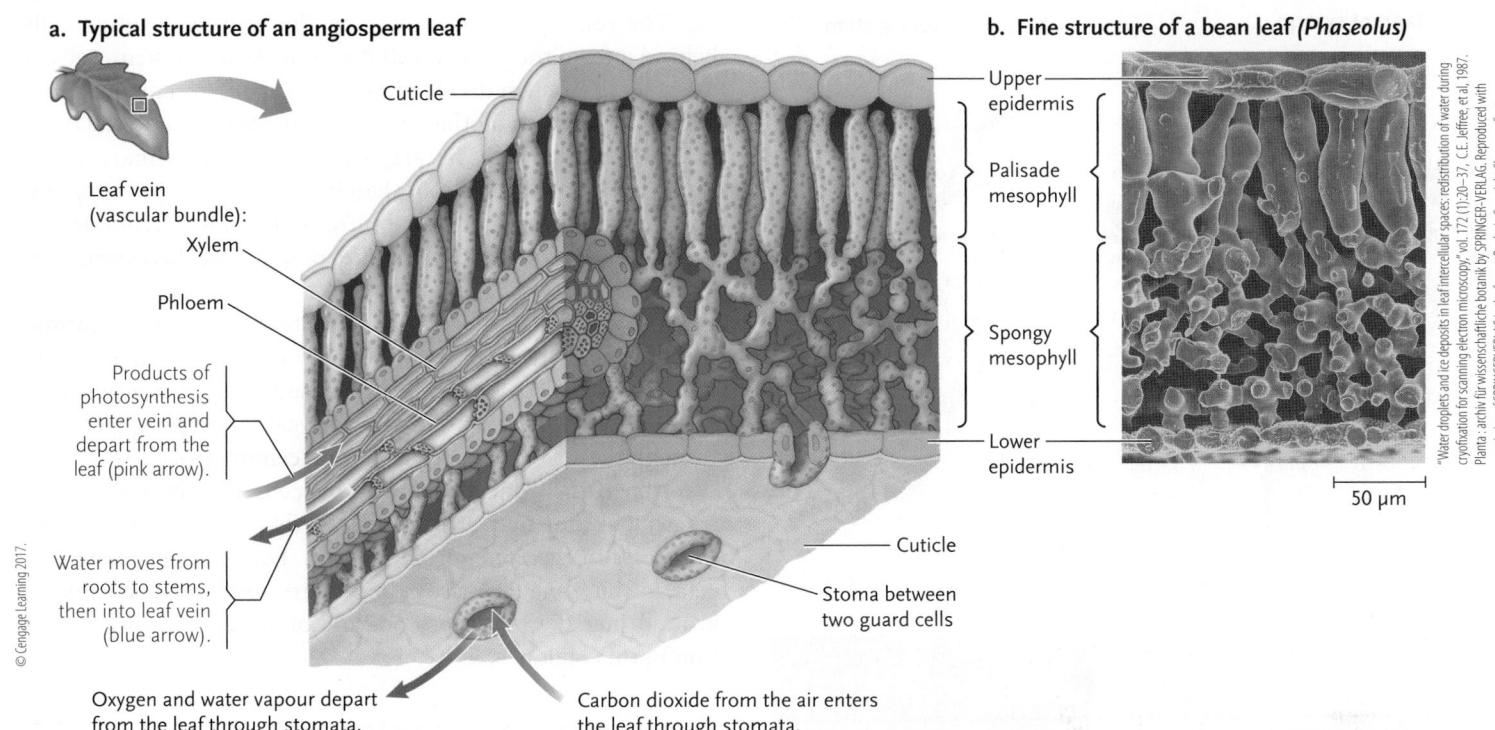

**a. Typical structure of an angiosperm leaf**

Cuticle

Leaf vein
(vascular bundle):

Xylem

Phloem

Products of
photosynthesis
enter vein and
depart from the
leaf (pink arrow).

Water moves from
roots to stems,
then into leaf vein
(blue arrow).

© Cengage Learning 2017.

Oxygen and water vapour depart
from the leaf through stomata.

Carbon dioxide from the air enters
the leaf through stomata.

**b. Fine structure of a bean leaf (*Phaseolus*)**

Upper
epidermis

Palisade
mesophyll

Spongy
mesophyll

Lower
epidermis

Cuticle

Stoma between
two guard cells

50 µm

"Water droplets and ice deposits in leaf intercellular spaces: redistribution of water during cryofixation for scanning electron microscopy," vol. 172 (1):20–37, C.E. Jeffree, et al, 1987. Planta : archiv für wissenschaftliche botanik by SPRINGER-VERLAG. Reproduced with permission of SPRINGER-VERLAG in the format Book via Copyright Clearance Center.

**FIGURE 33.19 Internal structure of a leaf. (a)** Diagram of typical leaf structure for many kinds of flowering plants. (See Figure 33.12d for a scanning electron micrograph of stomata.) **(b)** Scanning electron micrograph of tissue from the leaf of a kidney bean plant (*Phaseolus*), transverse section. Notice the compact organization of epidermal cells.

Grasses and many other monocots develop a **fibrous root system** in which several main roots branch to form a dense mass of smaller roots (Figure 33.20b). Fibrous root systems are adapted to absorb water and nutrients from the upper layers of soil, and tend to spread out laterally from the base of the stem. Fibrous roots are important ecologically because dense root networks help hold topsoil in place and prevent erosion. During the 1930s, overgrazing by livestock and intensive farming in the prairie provinces of Canada and the U.S. Midwest destroyed hundreds of thousands of acres of native prairie grasses, contributing to soil erosion on a massive scale. Swirling clouds of soil particles prompted journalists to name the area the Dust Bowl and gave this decade the name the "Dirty Thirties."

In some plants, **adventitious roots** arise from the stem of the young plant. **Adventitious** refers to any structure arising at an unusual location, such as roots that grow from stems or leaves. Adventitious roots of Virginia creeper (*Parthenocissus quinquefolia*) and some other climbing plants produce a glue-like substance that allows them to cling to vertical surfaces. The *prop roots* of a corn plant are adventitious roots that develop from the shoot node nearest the soil surface; they support the plant and absorb water and nutrients. Mangroves and other trees that grow in marshy habitats often have huge prop roots, which develop from branches and from the main stem (Figure 33.20e).

## 33.4b Root Structure Is Specialized for Underground Growth

Like shoots, roots have distinct anatomical parts, each with a specific function. In most plants, primary growth of roots begins when an embryonic root emerges from a germinating seed and its apical meristem becomes active. **Figure 33.21** shows the structure of a root tip. Notice that the root apical meristem is protected by a dome-shaped cell mass, the **root cap**. Certain cells in the cap respond to gravity, guiding the root tip downward. Cap cells also secrete a polysaccharide-rich substance that lubricates the tip and eases the growing root's passage through the soil. Outer root cap cells are continually abraded off and replaced by new cells at the cap's base.

**ZONES OF PRIMARY GROWTH IN ROOTS** In most plants, root growth is a continuous process that only stops if environmental conditions become unfavourable for growth (e.g., drought).

**a. Taproot system**

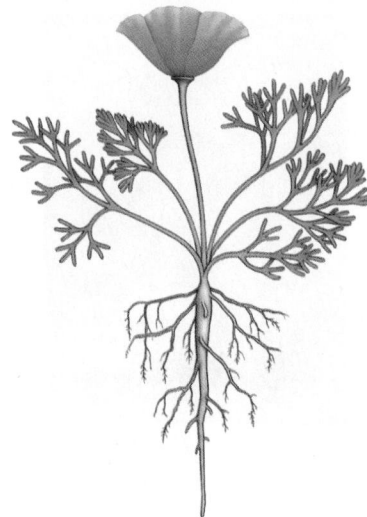

**b. Fibrous root system**

**c. Prop roots**

**d. Buttress roots**

**e. Adventitious roots**

**f. A storage root**

**FIGURE 33.20  Types of roots. (a)** Taproot system of a California poppy (*Eschscholzia californica*). **(b)** Fibrous root system of a grass plant. **(c)** Prop roots of a corn plant. **(d)** A tropical rainforest tree supported by flaring buttress roots. **(e)** The prop roots of mangrove trees (*Rhizophora*), examples of adventitious roots. **(f)** Sweet potatoes are storage roots.
© Cengage Learning 2017

The root apical meristem and the actively dividing cells behind it form the **zone of cell division**. As in the stem, cells of the apical meristem divide to produce cells that remain as part of the meristem, and other cells that differentiate into the three primary meristems. The arrangement of the primary meristems is different in the root than in the stem: the procambium develops as a cylinder in the centre of the root, surrounded by the ground meristem, with the outer layer becoming the protoderm.

The zone of cell division merges into the **zone of elongation**. Most of the increase in a root's length comes from this region, where cells become longer as their vacuoles fill with water. This *hydraulic* elongation pushes the root cap and apical meristem through the soil by as much as several centimetres a day.

Above the zone of elongation, cells do not increase in length, but they may differentiate further and take on specialized roles in the **zone of maturation**. For example, epidermal cells in this zone give rise to root hairs, and the procambium, ground meristem, and protoderm complete their differentiation in this region.

**TISSUES OF THE ROOT SYSTEM**  Together with the primary growth of the shoot, primary root growth produces a unified system of vascular pipelines extending from root tip to shoot tip. The root procambium produces cells that mature into the root's xylem and phloem (**Figure 33.22**). Ground meristem gives rise to the root's cortex, its ground tissue of starch-storing parenchyma cells that surround the vascular cylinder (**stele**). In eudicots, the stele runs through the centre of the root (see Figure 33.22a). In corn and some other monocots, the xylem and phloem differentiate in a ring that divides the ground tissue into cortex and pith region (see Figure 33.22b).

The root cortex often contains air spaces that allow oxygen to reach all the living root cells. In many flowering plants, the outer root cortex cells give rise to an **exodermis**, a thin band of cells that, among other functions, may limit water losses from roots and help regulate the absorption of ions. The innermost layer of the root cortex is the **endodermis**, a thin, selectively permeable barrier that helps control the movement of water and dissolved minerals into the stele. We look in more detail at the roles of exodermis and endodermis in Chapter 34.

The outermost part of the stele, between the endodermis and the phloem, is the **pericycle**, consisting of one or more layers of parenchyma cells that have retained the ability to function as meristem. The pericycle initiates the formation of lateral roots (**Figure 33.23**) in response to chemical growth regulators. These lateral roots grow out through the cortex and epidermis, producing enzymes that help break down the intervening cells. The distribution and the frequency of lateral root formation partly control the overall shape of the root system and the extent of the soil area it can penetrate.

The outer surfaces of some cells in the developing root epidermis become elongated into root hairs (see Figure 33.21). Root hairs can be more than a centimetre long and can form in

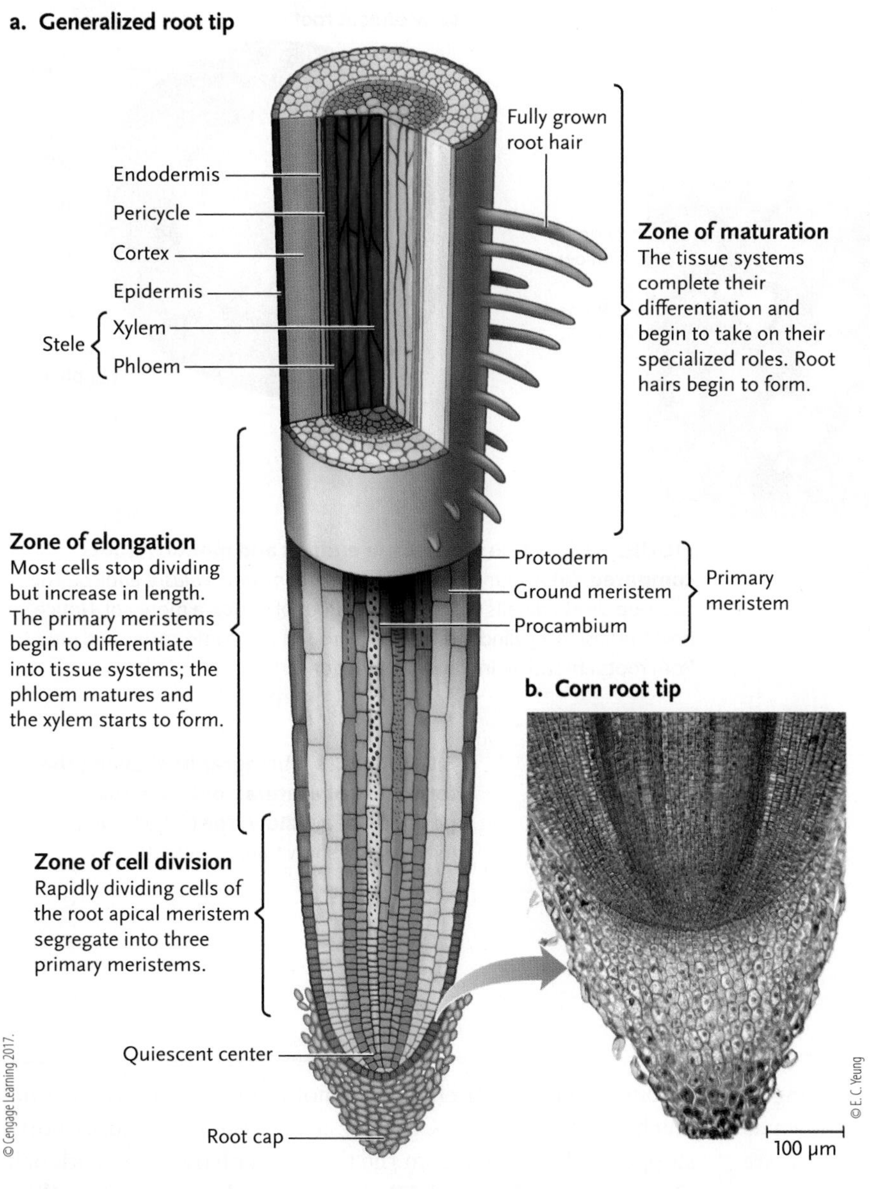

## a. Generalized root tip

Endodermis
Pericycle
Cortex
Epidermis
Stele { Xylem
Phloem

Fully grown root hair

**Zone of maturation**
The tissue systems complete their differentiation and begin to take on their specialized roles. Root hairs begin to form.

**Zone of elongation**
Most cells stop dividing but increase in length. The primary meristems begin to differentiate into tissue systems; the phloem matures and the xylem starts to form.

Protoderm
Ground meristem
Procambium

Primary meristem

### b. Corn root tip

**Zone of cell division**
Rapidly dividing cells of the root apical meristem segregate into three primary meristems.

Quiescent center

Root cap

100 μm

© Cengage Learning 2017.

© E. C. Yeung

**FIGURE 33.21 Tissues and zones of primary growth in a root tip.**
**(a)** Generalized root tip, longitudinal section. **(b)** Micrograph of a corn root tip, longitudinal section.

less than a day. Collectively, the thousands or millions of them on a plant's roots greatly increase the plant's absorptive surface. But it is not just the increased surface area provided by root hairs that increases nutrient uptake: each hair is a slender tube with thin walls made sticky on their surface by a coating of pectin. Soil particles tend to adhere to the walls, providing an intimate association between the hair and the surrounding earth, thus facilitating the uptake of water molecules and mineral ions from soil. When plants are transplanted, rough handling can tear off much of this fragile absorptive surface. Unable to take up enough water and minerals, the transplant may die before new root hairs can form.

1. Compare the two general types of root systems.
2. Describe the zones of primary growth in roots.
3. Describe the various tissues that arise in a root system and their functions.
4. Compare the arrangement of the three primary tissues in a dicot root to the arrangement in a monocot root and in a dicot stem.

## 33.5 Secondary Growth

All plants undergo primary growth of the root and stem. In addition, some plants have secondary growth processes that add girth to roots and stems.

**CONCEPT FIX** Many people think that only woody plants have secondary growth. In reality, many herbaceous plants also have secondary growth; for example, carrot roots are mostly secondary tissues. And if you've ever tried to dig up a dandelion, you'll know how large and tough their taproots are, which is due to secondary growth in these roots. ⬡

In plant species that have secondary growth, older stems and roots become more massive and woody through the activity of two types of lateral meristems called *cambia* (singular, *cambium*). One of these meristems, the **vascular cambium**, produces secondary xylem and phloem. The other, called the **cork cambium**, produces **cork**, a secondary tissue that replaces the original epidermis of the plant. In contrast to the cells of the apical meristems, the cells of the lateral meristems divide perpendicular to the stem's longitudinal axis, so their descendants add girth to the stem instead of length.

### 33.5a Vascular Cambium Gives Rise to Secondary Growth in Stems

Recall that, after the stem of a woody plant completes its primary growth, each vascular bundle contains a layer of undifferentiated cells (residual procambium) between the primary xylem and the primary phloem. These cells, along with parenchyma cells between the vascular bundles, eventually give rise to a continuous cylinder of vascular cambium that surrounds the xylem and pith of the stem (**Figure 33.24**). Secondary growth takes place as the cells of the vascular cambium divide. Division of the vascular cambium produces secondary xylem toward the inside of the stem and secondary phloem toward the outside of the stem.

**a. Eudicot root**

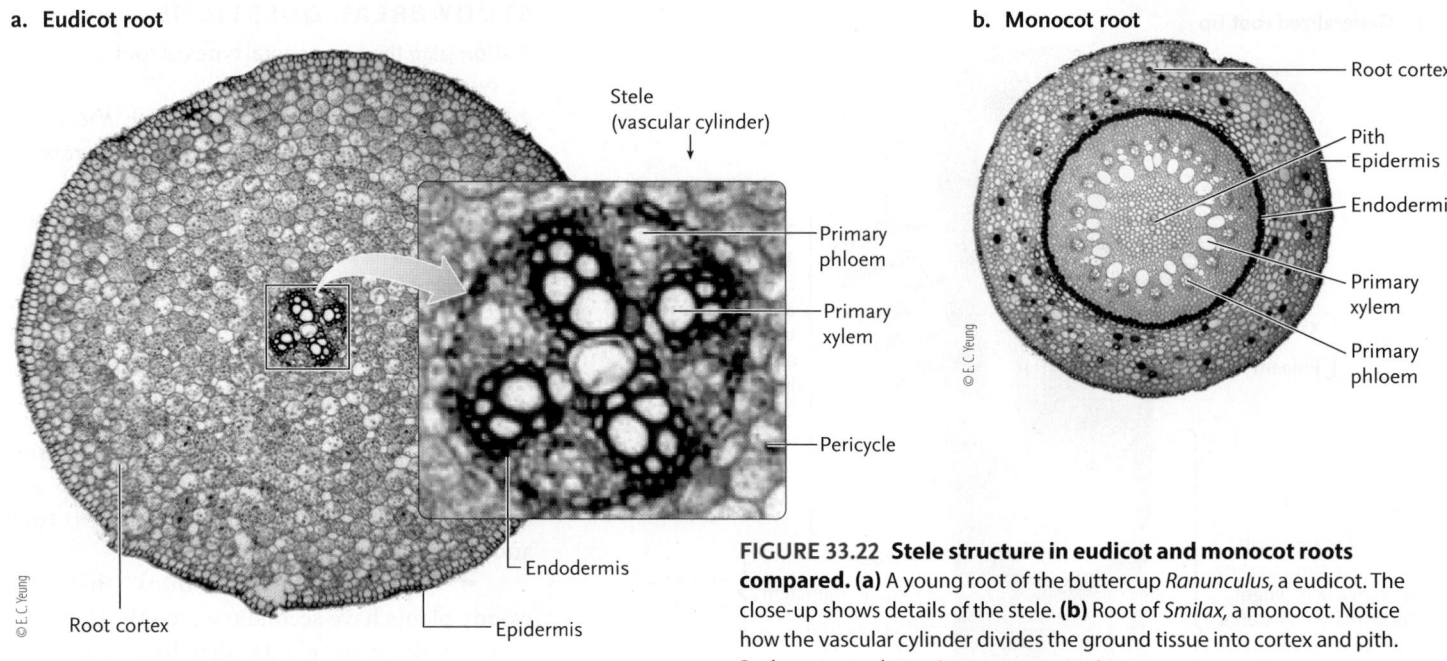

Stele (vascular cylinder)

Primary phloem

Primary xylem

Pericycle

Endodermis

Epidermis

Root cortex

© E. C. Yeung

**b. Monocot root**

Root cortex

Pith

Epidermis

Endodermis

Primary xylem

Primary phloem

© E. C. Yeung

**FIGURE 33.22  Stele structure in eudicot and monocot roots compared. (a)** A young root of the buttercup *Ranunculus*, a eudicot. The close-up shows details of the stele. **(b)** Root of *Smilax*, a monocot. Notice how the vascular cylinder divides the ground tissue into cortex and pith. Both roots are shown in transverse section.

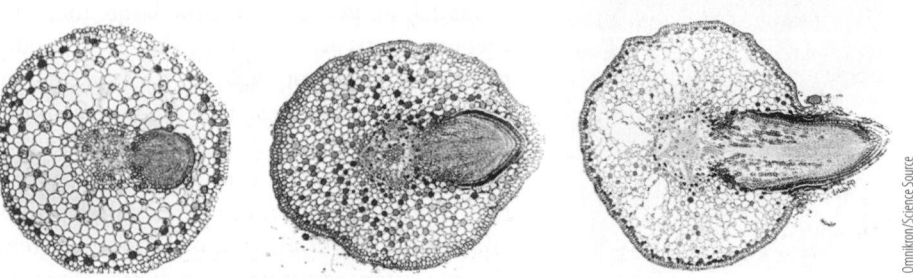

Omnikron/Science Source

**FIGURE 33.23  Micrographs showing the formation of a lateral root from the pericycle of a willow tree (*Salix*).** These micrographs show transverse sections.

With time, the mass of secondary xylem inside the ring of vascular cambium increases, forming the hard tissue known as **wood**. Outside the vascular cambium, secondary phloem cells are also added each year **(Figure 33.25)**. (The primary phloem cells, which are thin walled, are destroyed as they are pushed outward by secondary growth, but fibres often persist.) As a stem increases in diameter, epidermis is stretched and no longer serves as protection for the underlying tissues. Cork cambium is produced early in the stem's secondary development. It is usually initiated from cells in the outer cortex, producing cork cells that replace the epidermis. The walls of cork cells contain lignin and thick layers of **suberin**, a waxy substance that is impermeable to water and gases. Cork cells are dead at maturity. Cork is produced toward the outside of the stem; like the vascular cambium, the cork cambium also produces cells toward the inside of the stem, called *phelloderm*. Together, the cork, cork cambium, and phelloderm make up the **periderm (Figure 33.26)**.

**Bark** encompasses all the tissues outside the vascular cambium; it thus includes the secondary phloem and the periderm (see Figure 33.26). Girdling a tree by removing a strip of bark around the trunk is lethal because it destroys the secondary phloem layer, so nutrients from photosynthesis in leaves cannot reach the tree's roots. Cork for use in flooring and as bottle stoppers is harvested from the thick outer bark of the cork oak, *Quercus suber* **(Figure 33.27)**. Cork can be harvested from these trees once they are 25 years old and can be sustainably harvested every 9 to 12 years thereafter. Some trees can yield about 1 tonne of cork over the course of their lives!

Given that the bark can be very thick on some trees, how do the vascular cambium and other living tissues in a secondary stem obtain oxygen? In some regions of the stem, the cork cambium divides very actively, forming tissue with abundant air spaces (*lenticels*). Lenticels allow the exchange of oxygen and carbon dioxide between the living tissues and the outside air.

As a tree ages, changes also unfold in the appearance and function of the wood itself. In the centre of its older stems and roots is **heartwood** that no longer transports water and solutes and is a storage depot for defensive compounds. In time, these substances—including resins, oils, gums, and tannins—clog and fill in the oldest xylem pipelines. Typically, they darken the heartwood, strengthen it, and make it more aromatic and resistant to decay. **Sapwood** is the xylem located between heartwood

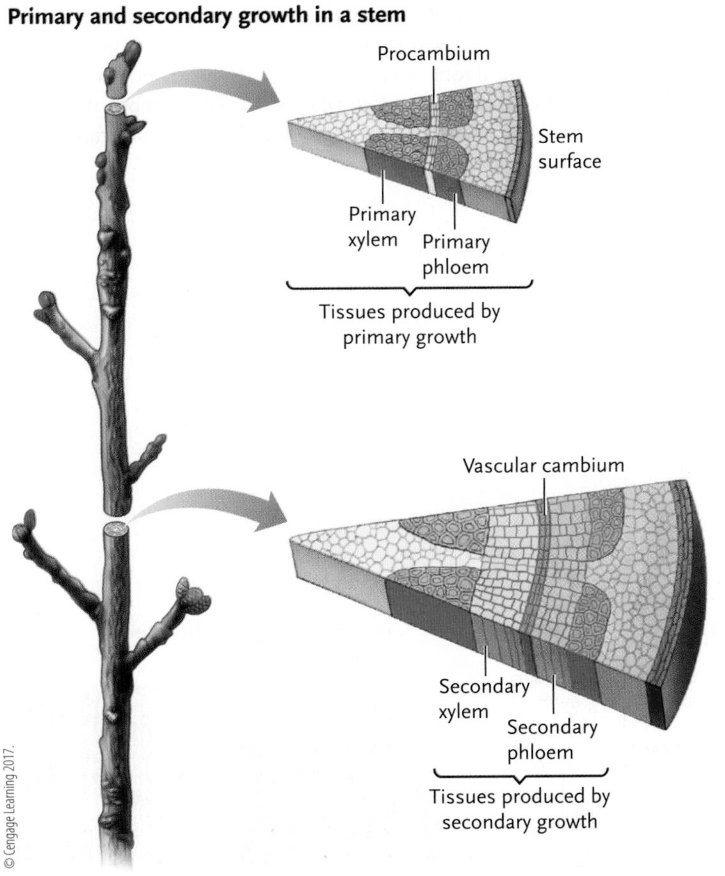

## Primary and secondary growth in a stem

Procambium

Stem surface

Primary xylem    Primary phloem

Tissues produced by primary growth

Vascular cambium

Secondary xylem    Secondary phloem

Tissues produced by secondary growth

**FIGURE 33.24 Secondary and primary growth compared.** In a woody plant, primary growth resumes each spring at the terminal and lateral buds. Secondary growth resumes at the vascular cambium inside the stem.

© Cengage Learning 2017.

and the vascular cambium. Compared with heartwood, it is wet and not as strong (see Figure 33.26).

In temperate climates, trees produce secondary xylem seasonally, with larger-diameter cells produced in spring, when water is generally abundant, and smaller-diameter cells in summer, when less water is available to be transported. The contrasting appearance of "spring wood" and "summer wood" make it is possible to identify them as alternating light and dark bands. The alternating bands represent annual growth layers known as "growth rings" (**Figure 33.28**). The age of a tree can be determined by counting the growth rings.

Growth rings also provide information on past climates: the wider spaced the rings, the more growth a tree was able to put on in one year, so the better the conditions (i.e., warmer and wetter). Dendroclimatologists use tree rings and other biological information to reconstruct past environments. This line of research is making significant contributions to our understanding of how the global climate has changed over time.

## 33.5b Secondary Growth Occurs in Roots

Like in stems, roots of grasses, palms, and other monocots are almost always produced by primary growth alone. Plants with secondary growth in their stems also have secondary growth in their roots. The basic arrangement is similar to the production of secondary phloem to the outside and secondary xylem to the inside of the dividing vascular cambium. There is also heartwood and sapwood as well as early and late wood. In a root, initiation of the lateral meristems is different than in stems. The vascular cambium of roots arises in part from the residual procambium between the primary xylem and primary phloem (**Figure 33.29**, step 1) and in part from the pericycle (step 2). The combined meristematic activity of these cells forms a complete cylinder of vascular cambium (step 3). The vascular cambium functions in roots as it does in stems, producing secondary

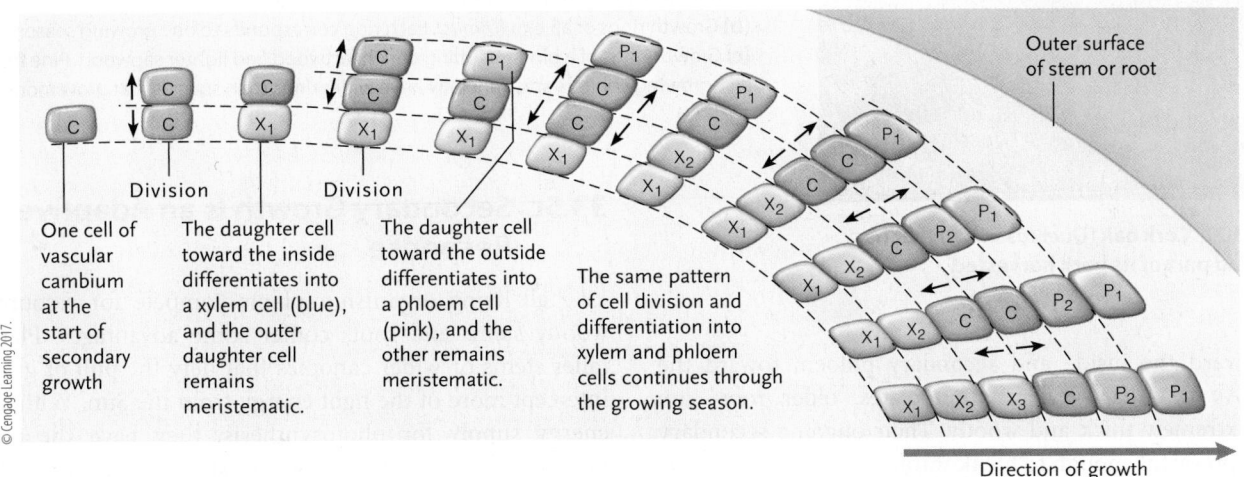

One cell of vascular cambium at the start of secondary growth

The daughter cell toward the inside differentiates into a xylem cell (blue), and the outer daughter cell remains meristematic.

The daughter cell toward the outside differentiates into a phloem cell (pink), and the other remains meristematic.

The same pattern of cell division and differentiation into xylem and phloem cells continues through the growing season.

Outer surface of stem or root

Direction of growth

© Cengage Learning 2017.

**FIGURE 33.25 Relationship between the vascular cambium and its derivative cells (secondary xylem and phloem).** The drawing shows stem growth through successive seasons. Notice how the ongoing divisions displace the cambial cells, moving them steadily outward even as the core of xylem increases the stem or root thickness.

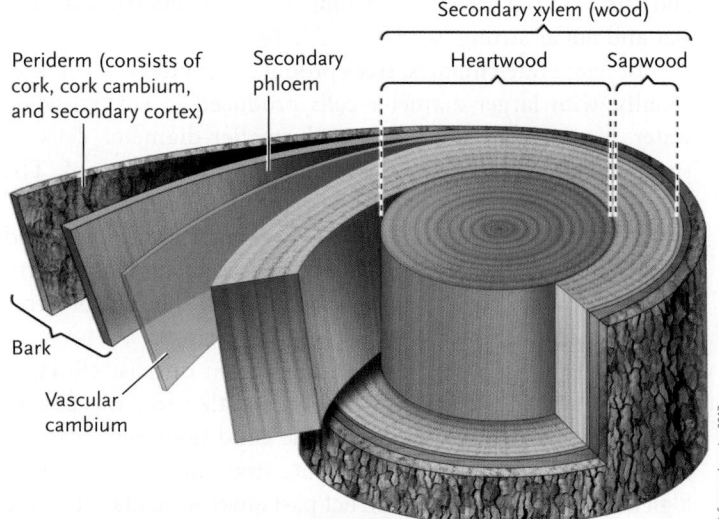

Periderm (consists of cork, cork cambium, and secondary cortex)

Secondary phloem

Secondary xylem (wood)

Heartwood

Sapwood

Bark

Vascular cambium

© Cengage Learning 2017.

**FIGURE 33.26 Structure of a woody stem showing extensive secondary growth.** Heartwood, the mature tree's core, has no living cells. Sapwood, the cylindrical zone of xylem between the heartwood and vascular cambium, contains some living parenchyma cells among the non-living vessels and tracheids. Everything outside the vascular cambium is bark. Everything inside it is wood.

**FIGURE 33.27 Cork oak (*Quercus suber*) that has recently had part of its bark harvested**

adrian davies/Alamy Stock Photo

**a. A woody stem**

Primary growth, some secondary growth

Secondary growth

Year 1    2    3

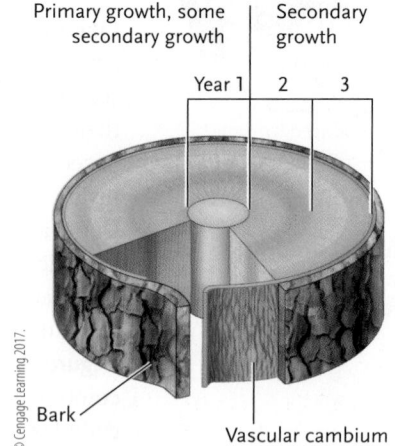

Bark

Vascular cambium

© Cengage Learning 2017.

**b. Growth rings of American elm (*Ulmus americana*)**

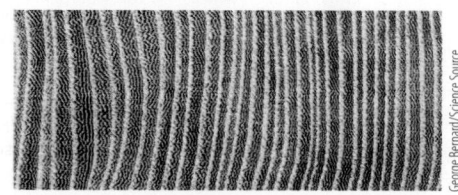

George Bernard/Science Source

**c. *Pinus* growth rings**

Christopher Kolaczan/Shutterstock.com

**FIGURE 33.28 Secondary growth and tree ring formation. (a)** Radial cut through a woody stem that has three annual rings, corresponding to secondary growth in years 2 to 4. **(b)** Growth rings of an elm (*Ulmus*). Each ring corresponds to one growing season. **(c)** Growth rings of a pine, including dark heartwood and lighter sapwood. Pine trees are fast-growing conifers and generally have wider rings than species that grow more slowly.

## 33.5c Secondary Growth Is an Adaptive Response

Like all living organisms, plants compete for resources, and woody stems and roots confer some advantages. Plants with taller stems or wider canopies that defy the pull of gravity can intercept more of the light energy from the Sun. With a greater energy supply for photosynthesis, they have the metabolic means to increase their root and shoot systems, and thus are better able to acquire resources—and ultimately to reproduce successfully.

In every stage of a plant's growth cycle, growth maintains a balance between the shoot system and the root system. Leaves and other photosynthetic parts of the shoot must supply

xylem toward the inside and secondary phloem toward the outside. As secondary xylem accumulates, older roots can become extremely thick and woody. Their ongoing secondary growth is powerful enough to break through concrete sidewalks and even dislodge the foundations of homes.

The outer layers of the pericycle also produce cork cambium in roots. In many woody eudicots and in all gymnosperms, most of the root epidermis and cortex falls away as the periderm develops (see Figure 33.29, step 4).

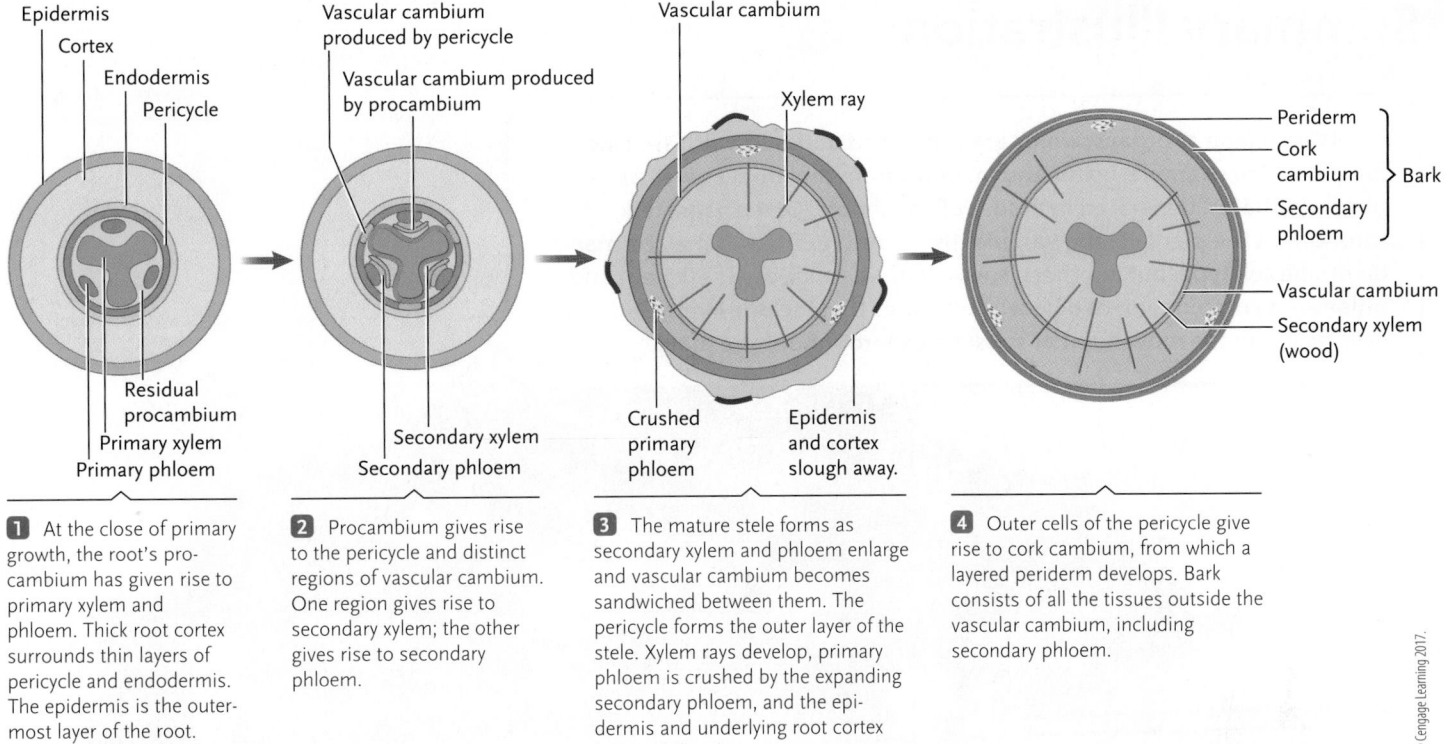

**Epidermis**
**Cortex**
**Endodermis**
**Pericycle**

**Residual procambium**
**Primary xylem**
**Primary phloem**

**Vascular cambium produced by pericycle**
**Vascular cambium produced by procambium**

**Secondary xylem**
**Secondary phloem**

**Vascular cambium**

**Xylem ray**

**Crushed primary phloem**
**Epidermis and cortex slough away.**

**Periderm**
**Cork cambium**
**Secondary phloem**
} **Bark**

**Vascular cambium**
**Secondary xylem (wood)**

**1** At the close of primary growth, the root's pro-cambium has given rise to primary xylem and phloem. Thick root cortex surrounds thin layers of pericycle and endodermis. The epidermis is the outer-most layer of the root.

**2** Procambium gives rise to the pericycle and distinct regions of vascular cambium. One region gives rise to secondary xylem; the other gives rise to secondary phloem.

**3** The mature stele forms as secondary xylem and phloem enlarge and vascular cambium becomes sandwiched between them. The pericycle forms the outer layer of the stele. Xylem rays develop, primary phloem is crushed by the expanding secondary phloem, and the epidermis and underlying root cortex begin to slough away.

**4** Outer cells of the pericycle give rise to cork cambium, from which a layered periderm develops. Bark consists of all the tissues outside the vascular cambium, including secondary phloem.

**FIGURE 33.29 Secondary growth in the root of a woody plant**

root cells with enough sugars to support their metabolism, and roots must provide the shoot structures with water and minerals. As long as a plant is growing, this balance is maintained even as the complexity of the root and shoot systems increases. This happens in all plants, whether they live only a few months or, like some bristlecone pines, for 6000 years.

In this chapter, we've established the basic anatomy and morphology of the plant body, with an emphasis on angiosperms. We will continue to examine the vascular tissues and how water and nutrients are transported throughout the plant in Chapter 34. In Chapter 35 we will explore flowering plant reproduction and how the basic plan of a plant is established in the embryo and seedling, and then examine plant nutrition and adaptations for obtaining nutrients in Chapter 36. In Chapter 37 we will look at how plants control the patterns of growth and development described in this chapter.

## STUDY BREAK QUESTIONS

1. Define *secondary growth*, explaining how it is similar to and different from primary growth, and where it typically occurs in plants.

2. Explain how the vascular cambium produces secondary xylem and phloem. How does division of cambial cells maintain the vascular cambium?

3. What is cork and how is it formed? What are the differences between cork, bark, periderm, and wood?

4. Compare secondary growth in stems and roots.

# Summary Illustration

Plants are made of organs, which are composed of tissues with specific functions. For example, water and minerals from the roots as well as photosynthates, generated in tissues of the shoots, are transported throughout the plant via the vascular tissue system. Tissues may be made up of one cell type, but in others, such as the vascular tissues (xylem and phloem), a combination of different cell types that include living and dead cells facilitate the movement of substances throughout the plant.

$O_2$

$CO_2$

Photosynthates (sucrose)

Xylem

Phloem

Leaves

Shoots

Stem

$H_2O$ + minerals

Roots

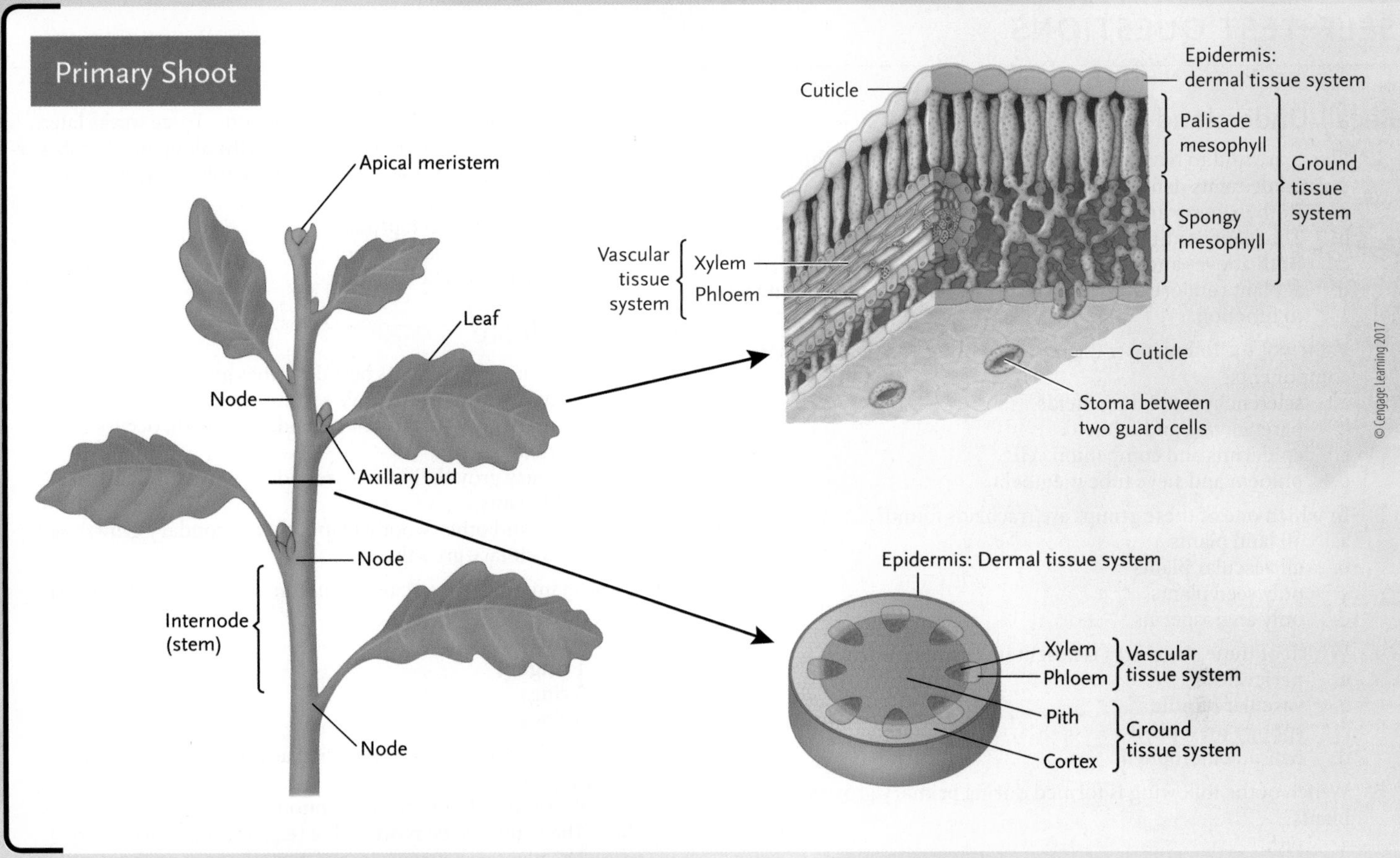

## Primary Shoot

Apical meristem

Leaf

Node

Axillary bud

Node

Internode (stem)

Node

Cuticle

Epidermis: dermal tissue system

Palisade mesophyll

Spongy mesophyll

Ground tissue system

Vascular tissue system
- Xylem
- Phloem

Cuticle

Stoma between two guard cells

Epidermis: Dermal tissue system

Xylem — Vascular tissue system
Phloem

Pith — Ground tissue system
Cortex

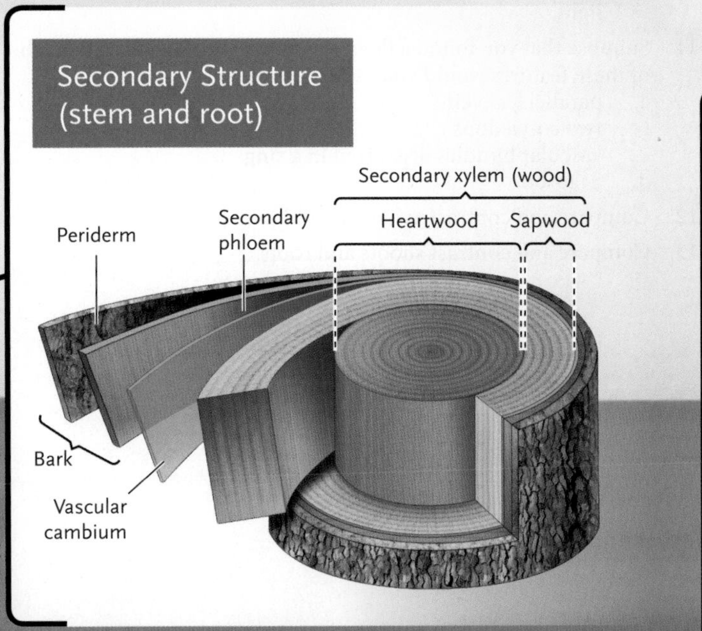

## Secondary Structure (stem and root)

Secondary xylem (wood)

Periderm

Secondary phloem

Heartwood

Sapwood

Bark

Vascular cambium

## Primary Root

Dermal Tissue System — Epidermis

Ground Tissue System
- Endodermis
- Cortex

Vascular Tissue System
- Pericycle
- Xylem
- Phloem

Fully grown root hair

Zone of maturation

Protoderm

**Zone of elongation**

Ground meristem

Primary meristem

Procambium

**Zone of cell division**

Root cap

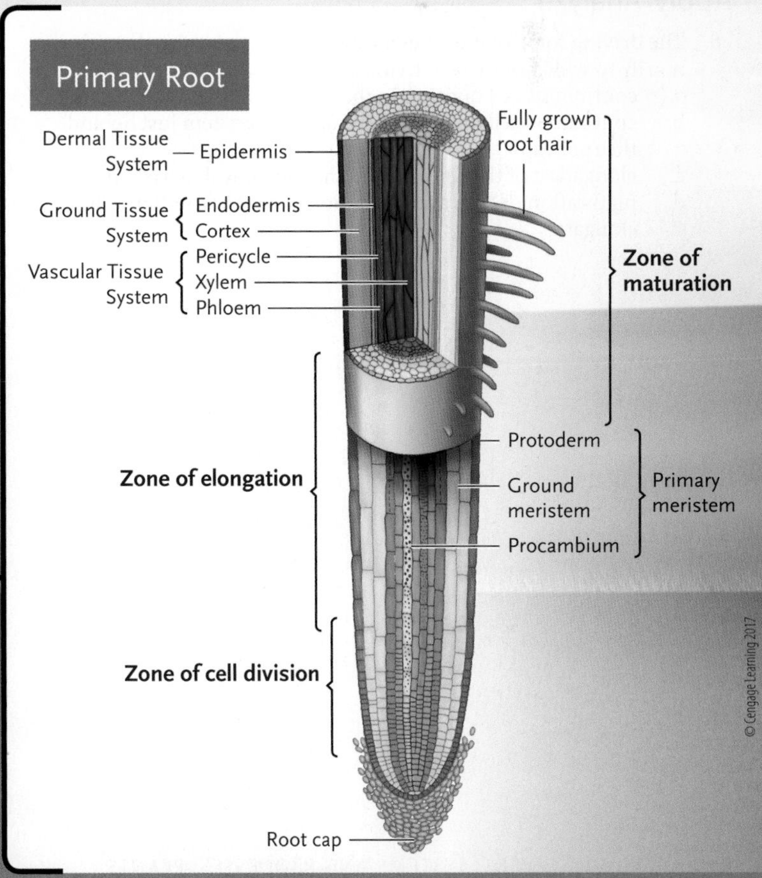

© Cengage Learning 2017

## Recall/Understand

1. Plants are said to have a dendritic pattern of growth. Which of these statements defines a "dendritic growth pattern"?
   a. Both primary and secondary growth occurs.
   b. The plant continues to grow throughout its lifetime.
   c. Both above- and below-ground parts are highly branched.
   d. A plant can lose individual roots, leaves, etc., and continue to function.

2. Which of the following is the correct pairing of a tissue with its components?
   a. sclerenchyma and tracheids
   b. parenchyma and sclereids
   c. epidermis and companion cells
   d. phloem and sieve tube members

3. In which one of these groups are tracheids found?
   a. all land plants
   b. all vascular plants
   c. only seed plants
   d. only angiosperms

4. Which of these structures is absent in a eudicot leaf?
   a. pericycle
   b. vascular bundle
   c. spongy mesophyll
   d. palisade mesophyll

5. Which of the following is formed during primary growth in plants?
   a. pith
   b. cork
   c. periderm
   d. heartwood

## Apply/Analyze

6. The driving force that pushes a root through the soil is due primarily to which of these activities?
   a. continuous cell division in the root cap at the tip of the root
   b. continuous cell division of the apical meristem just behind the root cap
   c. elongation of the cells behind the root apical meristem
   d. maturation of cells and formation of root hairs after cells elongate

7. A student leaves a carrot in her refrigerator. Three weeks later, she notices long, slender, white outgrowths along most of its surface. They are not a fungus. Which of the following are they?
   a. adventitious roots
   b. lateral roots on a taproot
   c. root hairs on a lateral root
   d. root hairs on a fibrous root

## Create/Evaluate

8. Which of these statements best describes growth in plants?
   a. Stems, but not roots, have secondary growth.
   b. Primary growth, but not secondary growth, occurs at meristems.
   c. Primary growth, but not secondary growth, occurs in all seed plants.
   d. Trees and other woody plants have secondary growth but not primary growth.

9. How many rings of vascular cambium would be found in a tree that is six years old?
   a. 0 rings
   b. 1 ring
   c. 3 rings
   d. 6 rings

10. Which of the following is a specific advantage of a dendritic growth pattern?
    a. Roots and shoots can continuously grow into new spaces.
    b. The plant will be more stable (e.g., less likely to tip over).
    c. The plant can survive loss of part of a root or shoot system.
    d. It provides a large surface area for uptake of nutrients and light.

11. Suppose that you found a flowering plant with six petals. Which of these features would you expect to see on the plant?
    a. parallel leaf veins
    b. two cotyledons
    c. vascular bundles organized in a ring
    d. a taproot

12. Compare and contrast xylem and phloem.

13. Compare and contrast shoots and roots.

# Chapter Roadmap

### Transport in Plants

Plants have a circulatory system called a *vascular system* that is made up of two tissues. Xylem tissue carries water and solutes, which are absorbed through the roots, to all parts of the plant. Phloem tissue is responsible for distributing photosynthates and other substances

**From Chapter 4** →

### 34.1 Principles of Water and Solute Movement in Plants

Both passive and active transport mechanisms move substances across plant cell membranes. Water crosses plant cell membranes by osmosis, which is driven by differences in water potential ($\psi_w$) between a cell and its surroundings. Water tends to move from regions where water potential is higher to regions where it is lower.

**To Chapter 34** →

**From Chapter 4** →

### 34.2 Uptake and Transport of Water and Solutes by Roots

Water and mineral ions entering roots travel laterally through the root cortex to the xylem, following three pathways. The endodermis, the innermost layer of cortex, regulates the movement of ions into the stele.

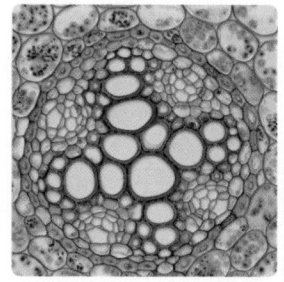

Ed Reschke/Photolibrary/Getty Images

**From Chapter 6** →

### 34.3 Long-Distance Transport of Water and Minerals in the Xylem

Transpiration, the evaporation of water from leaves and shoots, creates tension (negative pressure) on the water in the xylem. Cohesion between water molecules creates a continuous column of water molecules that is pulled by the tension created as water exits a plant's leaves.

Dr. John D. Cunningham/Visuals Unlimited, Inc

### 34.4 Transport of Organic Substances in the Phloem

Phloem sap carries much more than just sugars; it also transports amino acids, organic acids, organic nitrogen compounds, hormones, and other signal molecules. Differences in pressure between source and sink regions drive the flow.

**To Chapter 34** →

**To Chapter 38** →

**Giant Sitka Spruce (*Picea sitchensis*), such as these trees growing in the coastal forests of Vancouver Island, can grow to be more than 70 m tall and can live to be several hundred years old.** Such extremely tall trees exemplify the ability of plants to move water and solutes from roots to shoots over amazingly long distances.

Chris Cheadle/Alamy Stock Photo

# Transport in Plants

# 34

**Why it matters . . .** Conifer trees growing in the coastal rainforests of British Columbia take life to extremes. Many of these giant trees can live for more than 400 years and, like those shown above, they can grow very tall. In fact, Vancouver Island is home to two of the tallest trees on Earth: the Red Creek Fir is the tallest Douglas fir (*Pseudotsuga menziesii*) in the world, measuring 73 m high and over 13 m in circumference. Larger still, the tallest spruce tree on Earth is the Carmanah Giant, a Sitka spruce (*Picea sitchensis*) tree that soars 95 m above the forest floor. Such massive plants consume thousands of litres of water each day to survive. And that water—with its cargo of dissolved nutrients—must be transported the great distances between roots and leaves.

At first, movement of fluids and solutes 70 m or more from a tree's roots to its leafy crown may seem to challenge the laws of physics. If you wanted to raise water that high above ground in a pipe, you would need a powerful mechanical pump at the base and substantial energy to move the water against the pull of gravity. You also require a pump—your heart—to move fluid over a vertical distance of (usually) less than 2 m in your body. Yet a giant tree has no pump, so how does it move water from its roots to its leaves? In addition to moving water, plants must also move the sugars produced in their leaves to the rest of the plant—how do they manage to do this without a pump to circulate fluids? As you'll learn in this chapter, plants are able to move large volumes of fluid over great distances by harnessing the cumulative effects of seemingly weak interactions such as cohesion, the effects of solutes on the tendency of water to move across membranes, and the tremendous tension that can be created by the evaporation of water from plant leaves. Overall, plant transport mechanisms solve a fundamental biological problem—the need to acquire materials from the environment and distribute them throughout the plant body.

Our discussion begins with a brief review of the principles of water and solute movement in plants, a topic introduced in Chapter 4. Then we examine how these principles apply to the movement of water and solutes into and throughout a plant's vascular system.

# 34.1 Principles of Water and Solute Movement in Plants

Plants require large volumes of water to maintain the turgor pressure necessary to support their tissues and drive cell expansion, as well as for cooling by transpiration. Water is also required for photosynthesis and other metabolic processes. Plants must move water and nutrients long distances throughout their bodies in response to changing demands for those substances **(Figure 34.1a)**, which involves their specialized transport systems: the vascular tissues called *xylem* and *phloem* (Figure 34.1b). In long-distance transport, water and dissolved minerals travel in the xylem from roots to shoots and leaves, and the products of photosynthesis move via the phloem from the leaves and stems into roots and other structures **(Figure 34.2)**. However, in plants, as in all organisms, the movement of water and solutes begins at the level of individual cells and relies on short-distance transport mechanisms that move substances across membranes. Examples of short-distance transport are water and soluble minerals entering roots by crossing the cell membranes of root hairs (Figure 34.1c), or sugars in the phloem crossing plasma membranes into metabolically active cells. Ultimately, the movement of materials throughout a plant results from the integrated activities of individual cells, tissues, and organs.

We will look at long-distance transport processes in the xylem and phloem later in this chapter. First, we will focus on short-distance mechanisms that move water and solutes into and out of specific cells in roots, leaves, and stems. Keep in mind that, although the plant cell wall is very strong, it is also porous, meaning that it is not a barrier to the flow of water and solutes to and from the semipermeable cell membrane. Water and solutes can also move from one cell to another through cytoplasmic connections (plasmodesmata) between adjacent cells (see Chapter 33).

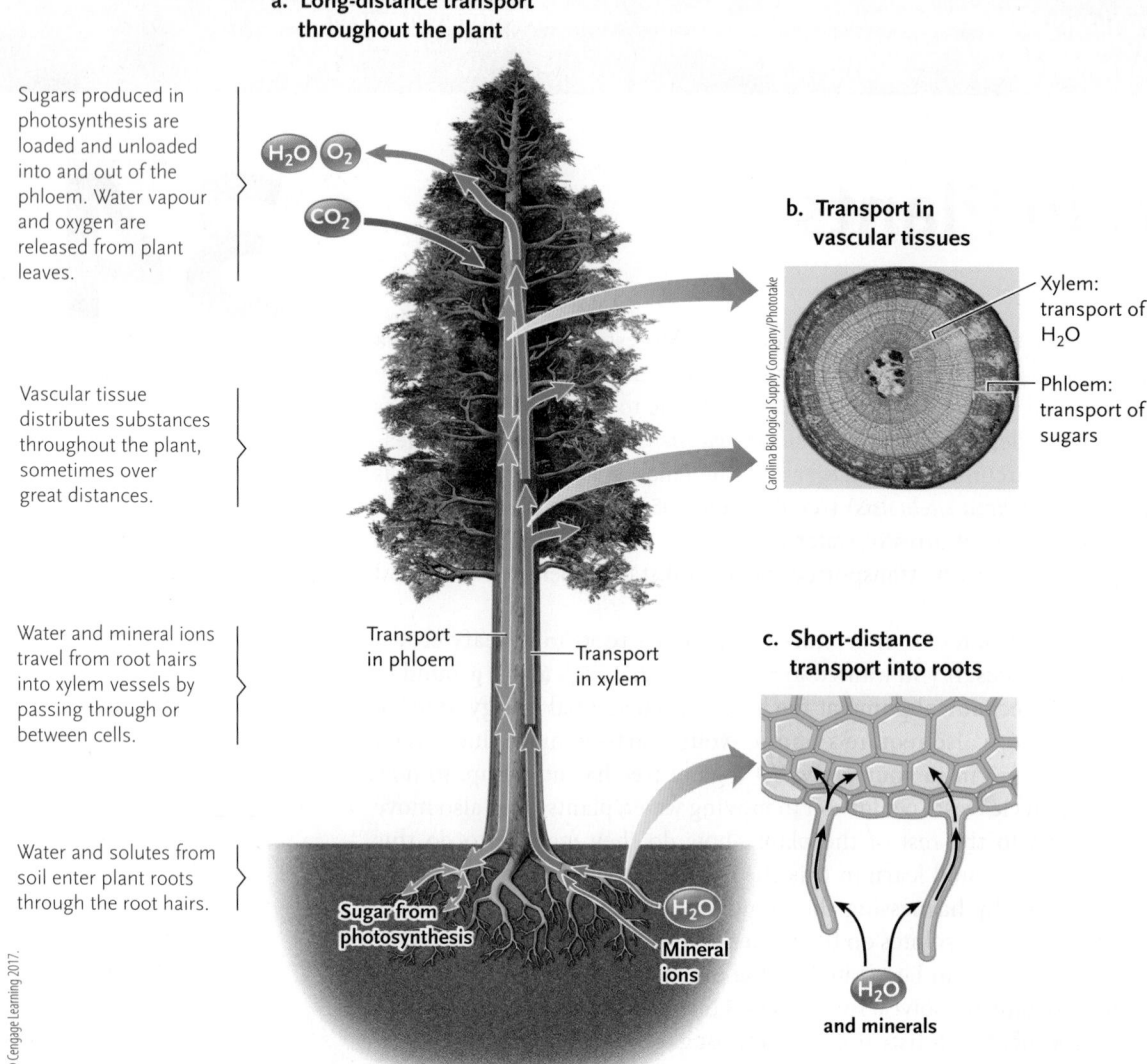

**a. Long-distance transport throughout the plant**

Sugars produced in photosynthesis are loaded and unloaded into and out of the phloem. Water vapour and oxygen are released from plant leaves.

Vascular tissue distributes substances throughout the plant, sometimes over great distances.

Water and mineral ions travel from root hairs into xylem vessels by passing through or between cells.

Water and solutes from soil enter plant roots through the root hairs.

$H_2O$  $O_2$

$CO_2$

Transport in phloem

Transport in xylem

Sugar from photosynthesis

$H_2O$ Mineral ions

**b. Transport in vascular tissues**

Carolina Biological Supply Company/Phototake

Xylem: transport of $H_2O$

Phloem: transport of sugars

**c. Short-distance transport into roots**

$H_2O$

**and minerals**

FIGURE 34.1 **Overview of transport routes in plants. (a)** Water and minerals are transported upward in xylem from roots to leaves, where some of the water evaporates into the air. Sugars are transported in phloem from sites where they are made or stored to sites where they are needed. **(b)** Vascular tissues are involved in long-distance transport. Long-distance transport of water and minerals throughout the plant occurs in the xylem. Long-distance transport of carbohydrates, hormones, and other compounds from leaves and stems into other tissues occurs in the phloem. **(c)** Short-distance transport of water and minerals into and between cells of the root. Short-distance transport also includes movement of water, minerals, sugars, and other materials through and between cells of other tissues, and into and out of xylem and phloem.

© Cengage Learning 2017.

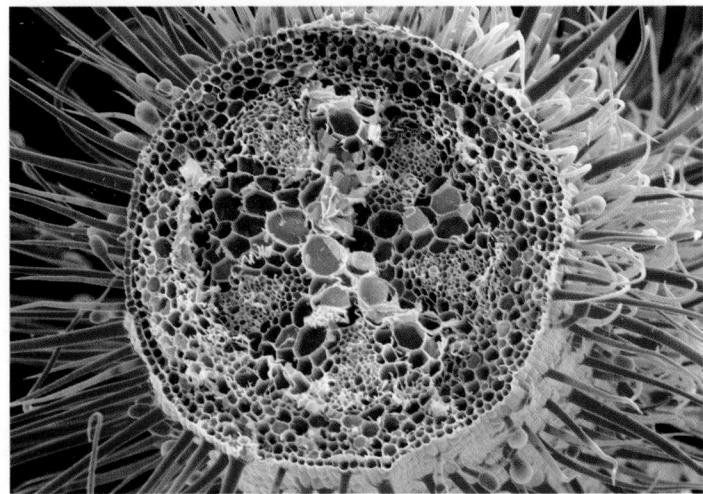

**FIGURE 34.2 Cross-section of the stem of geranium (*Pelargonium*).** This false-colour image shows large-diameter xylem vessels, which carry water and minerals, as whitish cells in the centre and radiating out from the centre. Phloem cells, which transport sugars and other organic molecules, are shown in pale green and are located between the "arms" of xylem. Layers of parenchyma cells (pink) surround the vascular tissue; epidermal cells form the outermost layer.

## 34.1a Short-Distance Transport Mechanisms Move Molecules Across Plant Cell Membranes

Recall from Chapter 4 that there are two general mechanisms for transporting molecules across a plasma membrane: passive transport and active transport. In **passive transport**, a substance moves with its concentration gradient or, if the substance is an ion, with its electrochemical gradient (see Figure 4.12), which means that cells do not need to expend energy. Passive transport includes both simple diffusion (transport of non-polar molecules and small polar molecules that can readily diffuse across the lipid portion of a membrane) and facilitated diffusion (transport of polar and charged molecules that move across the membrane via transport proteins). Like facilitated diffusion, **active transport** moves ions and large molecules across membranes via transport proteins but, because these solutes are being moved against their concentration gradient, cells must expend energy. The energy for active transport can be provided by either ATP hydrolysis (for primary active transport) or by harnessing the energy in a concentration gradient (for secondary active transport).

Our focus in this section is on understanding the movement of water across cell membranes, as this is one of the most important aspects of plant physiology. You'll recall from Chapter 4 that individual cells gain and lose water by **osmosis**, the passive transport of water across a selectively permeable membrane by either simple diffusion or facilitated diffusion through water-conducting channel proteins called **aquaporins**, which allow rapid movement of water across a membrane. Osmosis occurs in response to solute concentration gradients, a pressure gradient, or both (see Chapter 4). The combined influence of solute concentration and pressure on the movement of water is captured by the parameter of **water potential**. Water potential refers to the potential energy of water, or its tendency to move from one place to another.

## 34.1b The Relationship between Osmosis and Water Potential

Water potential is symbolized by the Greek letter psi ($\psi_w$) and is measured in units of pressure (**megapascals**; MPa). Water potential is a relative value that is defined in reference to pure water at atmospheric pressure (such as water in an open container), which has a $\psi_w$ value of 0 MPa. Two factors that determine water potential in living plants are the presence of solutes and physical pressure.

The movement of water across a membrane is strongly influenced by the concentration of solutes on either side of the membrane. The effect of dissolved solutes on water potential is called *solute potential*, symbolized by $\psi_s$. When solutes are added to water, they disrupt some of the hydrogen bonding between water molecules, and the polar water molecules then interact with the solutes, forming a hydration shell that surrounds the solute molecules (see *The Purple Pages*). Water molecules in a hydration shell are constrained from moving, and thus addition of solutes decreases the free energy of the water in the solution. Thus, water potential is *lower* in a solution with more solutes than in pure water; pure water has a $\psi_s$ of 0 MPa, and solutions containing solutes will have $\psi_s$ values less than zero. The relationship between water potential and solute potential is vital to understanding transport in plants because water moves by osmosis from regions where water potential is higher (closer to zero, or less negative) to regions where it is lower (farther from zero, or more negative), as shown in **Figure 34.3**. Solutes are usually more concentrated inside plant cells than in the fluid surrounding them. This means that the water potential is higher outside plant cells than inside them, so water tends to enter the cells by osmosis; this is the process by which soil water is drawn into a plant's roots.

Pressure can also change how water moves. We can investigate how changes in pressure influence the movement of water by considering a simple U-tube experiment in which the solutions on either side of the U-tube are separated by a membrane that is permeable to water but not to solutes. We can change the movement of water between the two sides of the U-tube by pushing or pulling on a plunger inserted in one side of the tube. If we push on the plunger, we will exert a positive pressure on the water, giving it more potential energy than the water in the other side of the U-tube, causing water to flow to that side. In contrast, if we pull on the plunger, we put the water under negative pressure (or tension), reducing its potential energy, thus effectively pulling water from the other side of the U-tube to the side under tension. Pressure potential is symbolized as $\psi_p$ and can be positive (greater than 0 MPa) if water is under positive pressure, negative (less than 0 MPa) if water is under tension, or equal to 0 MPa (at atmospheric pressure).

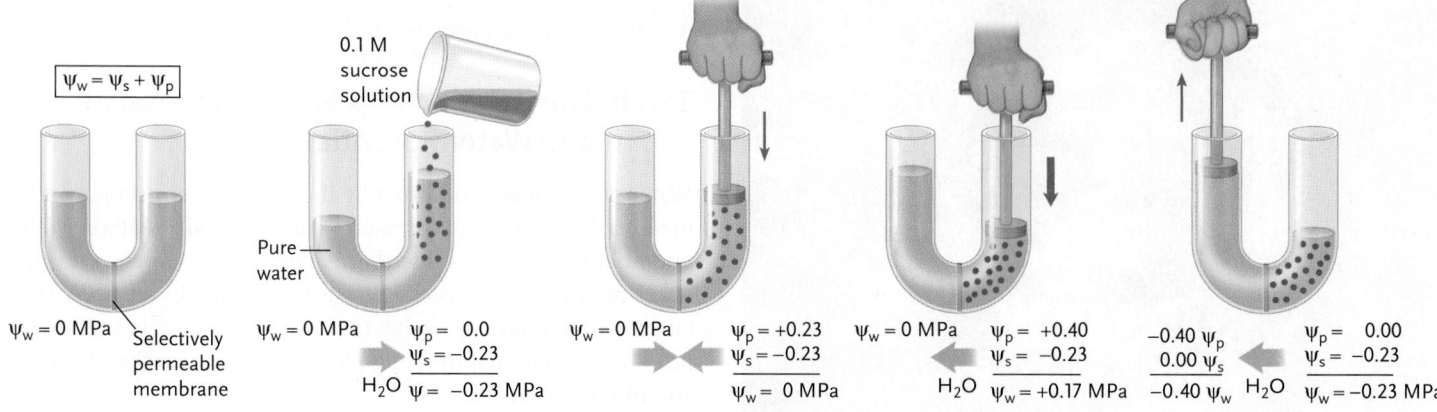

$$\psi_w = \psi_s + \psi_p$$

$\psi_w = 0$ MPa — Selectively permeable membrane

0.1 M sucrose solution

Pure water

$\psi_w = 0$ MPa

$\psi_p = 0.0$
$\psi_s = -0.23$
$H_2O$ $\quad \psi = -0.23$ MPa

$\psi_w = 0$ MPa

$\psi_p = +0.23$
$\psi_s = -0.23$
$\psi_w = 0$ MPa

$\psi_w = 0$ MPa

$\psi_p = +0.40$
$\psi_s = -0.23$
$H_2O$ $\quad \psi_w = +0.17$ MPa

$-0.40 \; \psi_p$
$0.00 \; \psi_s$
$-0.40 \; \psi_w$

$\psi_p = 0.00$
$\psi_s = -0.23$
$H_2O$ $\quad \psi_w = -0.23$ MPa

Pure water is poured into a curved tube with compartments separated by a selectively permeable membrane.

When sucrose is added to the water on one side to form a 0.1 M sucrose solution, the water potential on that side falls. Water moves into the solution by osmosis.

By applying enough pressure ($\psi_p$) to the solution to balance the osmotic pressure, water potential can be increased to zero, equalling that on the pure-water side of the membrane. Now there is no net movement of water across the membrane.

Increasing pressure further increases the water potential of the sucrose solution, so water moves back across the membrane into the compartment containing pure water.

Water potential in a system decreases under tension (negative pressure)—suggested here by pulling up on the plunger. As the $\psi_w$ of the pure water falls, even more water leaves the sucrose solution.

Plant physiologists assign a value of 0 MPa to the water potential ($\psi_w$) of pure water in an open container under normal atmospheric pressure and temperature.

© Cengage Learning 2017.

**FIGURE 34.3 The relationship between osmosis and water potential ($\psi$).** As discussed in more detail in the text, water potential in plant cells is determined by physical pressure (p) and the concentration of solutes (s). If the water potential is higher on one side of a membrane that is permeable to water and not to solutes, water will cross the membrane to the side with lower water potential. This diagram shows pure water on one side of a selectively permeable membrane and a simple sucrose solution on the other side. In an organism, however, the selectively permeable membranes of cells are rarely, if ever, in contact with pure water.

Together, solute potential and pressure potential determine a cell's water potential; the equation to express this relationship is $\psi_w = \psi_s + \psi_p$. In all cases, water will move from a solution of higher (less negative) potential to a solution of lower (more negative) potential.

## 34.1c Osmosis in Plant Cells Creates Turgor Pressure, Which Is Necessary for Plant Support

The movement of water in cells is more complex than in a simple U-tube, of course. Most of the volume of a mature plant cell is occupied by a large **central vacuole**, which is surrounded by a vacuolar membrane (**tonoplast**) and contains a dilute solution of sugars, proteins, other organic molecules, and salts. The cell cytoplasm is confined to a thin layer between the tonoplast and the plasma membrane. Many solutes that enter a plant cell are actively transported from the cytoplasm into the central vacuole through ion channels in the tonoplast. As the solutes accumulate in the vacuole, water follows by osmosis. Recall from Chapter 4 that, when animal cells are placed in a hypotonic solution, they may swell to the point of bursting. In plants, bursting is prevented by the cell wall, which resists the further

inward movement of water. The pressure of the water-filled vacuole and cytoplasm against the wall keeps the cell firm, or **turgid**, so we refer to the pressure of the cytoplasm on the wall as **turgor pressure**. Turgor pressure develops as a result of osmosis, and increases until it is high enough to prevent more water from entering a cell by osmosis. Turgor pressure in many plant cells is in the area of 0.6 MPa, which is more than three times the pressure in a car tire!

The water mechanics we have been discussing have major implications for land plants, which obtain water and mineral nutrients from the soil surrounding their roots. As long as the $\psi_w$ of soil is higher than that of the root epidermal cells, water will follow the $\psi_w$ gradient and flow into root cells, making them turgid. However, if the soil around the roots dries out, the soil water potential becomes more negative than that of root epidermal cells, and water no longer flows into the roots from the soil. The turgor pressure inside plant cells falls, and the protoplasts shrink away from the cell walls. This disruption in water uptake from the soil can lead to the drooping of leaves and stems called **wilting**, which occurs when turgor pressure in the cells of leaves and stems drops to very low levels. We can mimic these changes in water potential by placing plant cells in solutions of different water potentials **(Figure 34.4)**.

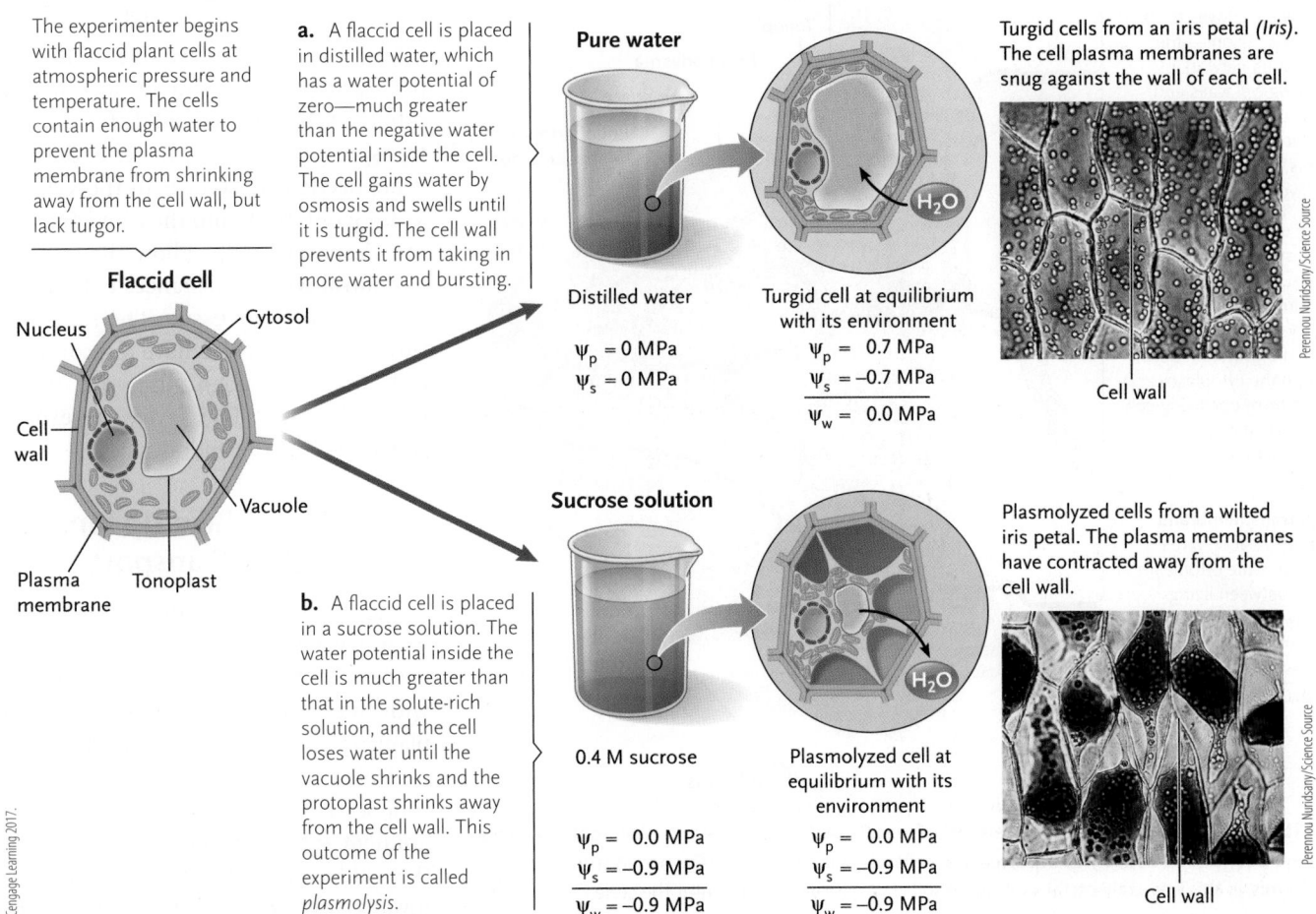

**FIGURE 34.4 An experiment to test the effects of different osmotic environments on plant cells.** Notice that in both **(a)** and **(b)**, the final condition is the same: the water potentials of the plant cell and its environment become equal.

## STUDY BREAK QUESTIONS

1. How is facilitated diffusion similar to active transport? How are the two processes different?
2. What are the two components of water potential in plant cells?
3. Explain how adding more dissolved solutes to the cytoplasm of a plant cell would affect the cell's water potential.
4. What is turgor pressure? How is it generated, and why is it important in plant cells?

## 34.2 Uptake and Transport of Water and Solutes by Roots

As mentioned above, land plants obtain water and mineral nutrients from the soil surrounding their roots. In this section, we will investigate how water and minerals enter roots, and how they move across the root to the xylem, which will transport them to the rest of the plant.

### 34.2a Water Travels across the Root to the Root Xylem by Three Pathways

Soil water and the minerals dissolved in it always enter a root through the root epidermis but can then travel by different paths across the root to the xylem, either through interconnected cytoplasm of living cells, through cell walls and intercellular spaces, or across membranes **(Figure 34.5)**. The living cells make up the **symplast** (*sym* = with, together; *plast* refers to the cytoplasm) and are interconnected by plasmodesmata, allowing water to flow from the cytoplasm of one cell to the next via the **symplastic pathway**. In contrast, the continuous network of cell walls and spaces between cells makes up the non-living areas of the root, or the **apoplast** (*apo* = away from). Water moves through the **apoplastic pathway** as it flows through these non-living spaces without crossing plasma membranes. The transmembrane is short-distance transport; water diffuses across plasma membranes, tonoplasts, or through membrane aquaporins.

In the **apoplastic pathway** (red), water moves through nonliving regions—the continuous network of adjoining cell walls and tissue air spaces. However, when it reaches the endodermis, it passes through one layer of living cells.

In the **symplastic pathway** (green), water passes into and through living cells. After being taken up into root hairs, water diffuses through the cytoplasm and passes from one living cell to the next through plasmodesmata.

In the **transmembrane pathway** (black), water that enters the cytoplasm moves between living cells by diffusing across cell membranes, including the plasma membrane and perhaps the tonoplast.

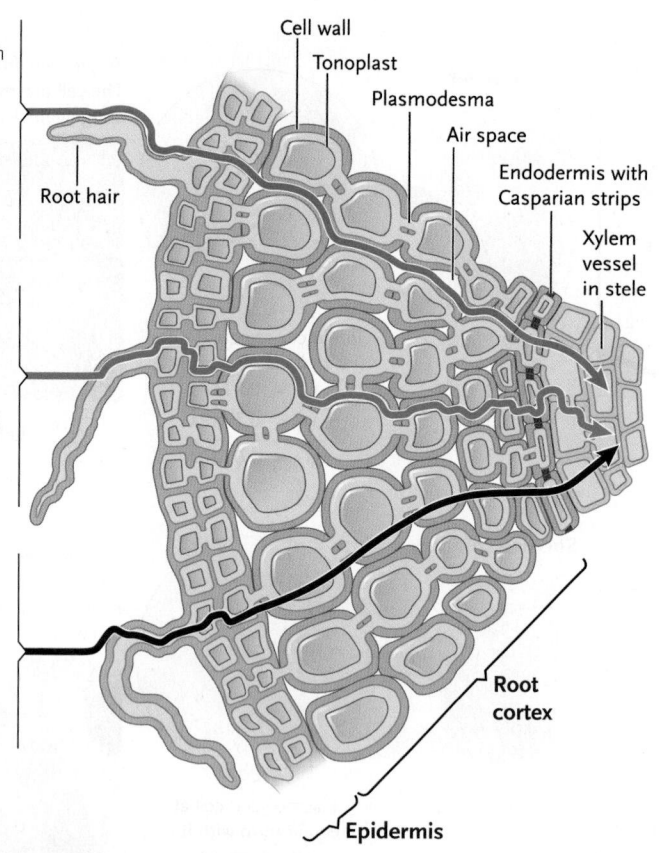

**FIGURE 34.5 Pathways for the movement of water into roots.** Ions also enter roots via these pathways but must be actively transported into cells when they reach the Casparian strip of the endodermis. In this way, only certain solutes in soil water are allowed to enter the stele.

When water enters a root **(Figure 34.6a)**, some diffuses across the plasma membranes of epidermal cells, entering the symplast, but most moves into the apoplast, flowing through cell walls and intercellular spaces. This apoplastic water (and any solutes dissolved in it) travels rapidly inward until it encounters the **endodermis**, the innermost layer of the cortex. Cells in the root cortex generally have air spaces between them (which helps aerate the tissue), but endodermal cells are tightly packed (Figure 34.6b). Each endodermal cell also has a ribbon-like **Casparian strip** in its radial and transverse walls, positioned somewhat like a ribbon of packing tape around a rectangular package (Figure 34.6c). The Casparian strip is impregnated with **suberin**, a waxy substance that is impermeable to water and blocks the apoplastic movement of water at the endodermis. What happens when apoplastic water and solutes reach the Casparian strip? They are forced to detour from the apoplast, moving across the plasma membrane of endodermal cells and into the symplastic pathway, which is not blocked by the Casparian strips. Water and solutes then pass through plasmodesmata to cells in the outer layer of the stele.

What is the benefit of blocking the apoplastic pathway so that water and solutes can't just flow automatically into the xylem? Although water molecules can easily cross an endo-dermal cell's plasma membrane, the semipermeable membrane allows only certain solutes to cross. Undesirable solutes may be barred, whereas desirable ones may move into the cell by facilitated diffusion or active transport. Conversely, the endodermis prevents needed substances in the xylem from leaking out, back into the root cortex. Thus, the Casparian strips allow the endodermis to control which substances enter and leave a plant's vascular tissue. The roots of most flowering plants also have a second layer of cells with Casparian strips just inside the root epidermis. This layer, the exodermis, functions like the endodermis.

## 34.2b Roots Take Up Ions by Active Transport

As described above, mineral ions dissolved in soil water also enter roots through the epidermis. Some enter the apoplast along with water, but most ions important for plant nutrition tend to be much more concentrated in roots than in the surrounding soil, so they cannot follow a concentration gradient into root epidermal cells. Instead, the epidermal cells actively transport ions inward by means of membrane-bound protein transporters. Ions can enter the symplast immediately and travel to the xylem via the symplastic pathway, or they can move inward, following the apoplastic pathway until they reach the Casparian strip of the endodermis. In short, mechanisms that control which solutes will be absorbed by root cells ultimately determine which solutes will be distributed through the plant.

Once an ion reaches the stele, it diffuses from cell to cell until it is "loaded" into the xylem. Experiments to determine whether the loading is passive (by diffusion) or active have been inconclusive, so the details of this final step are not entirely clear. Because the xylem's conducting elements are not living, water and ions in effect reenter the apoplastic pathway when they reach the xylem. Once in the xylem, water and mineral ions can move laterally to and from tissues or travel upward in the conducting elements. Minerals are distributed to living cells and taken up by active transport. The following section examines how this long-distance transport occurs.

## STUDY BREAK QUESTIONS

1. Explain two key differences in how the apoplastic and symplastic pathways direct substances laterally in roots.
2. Where in a root is the Casparian strip, and what is its function?
3. How does an ion enter a root hair and then move to the xylem?

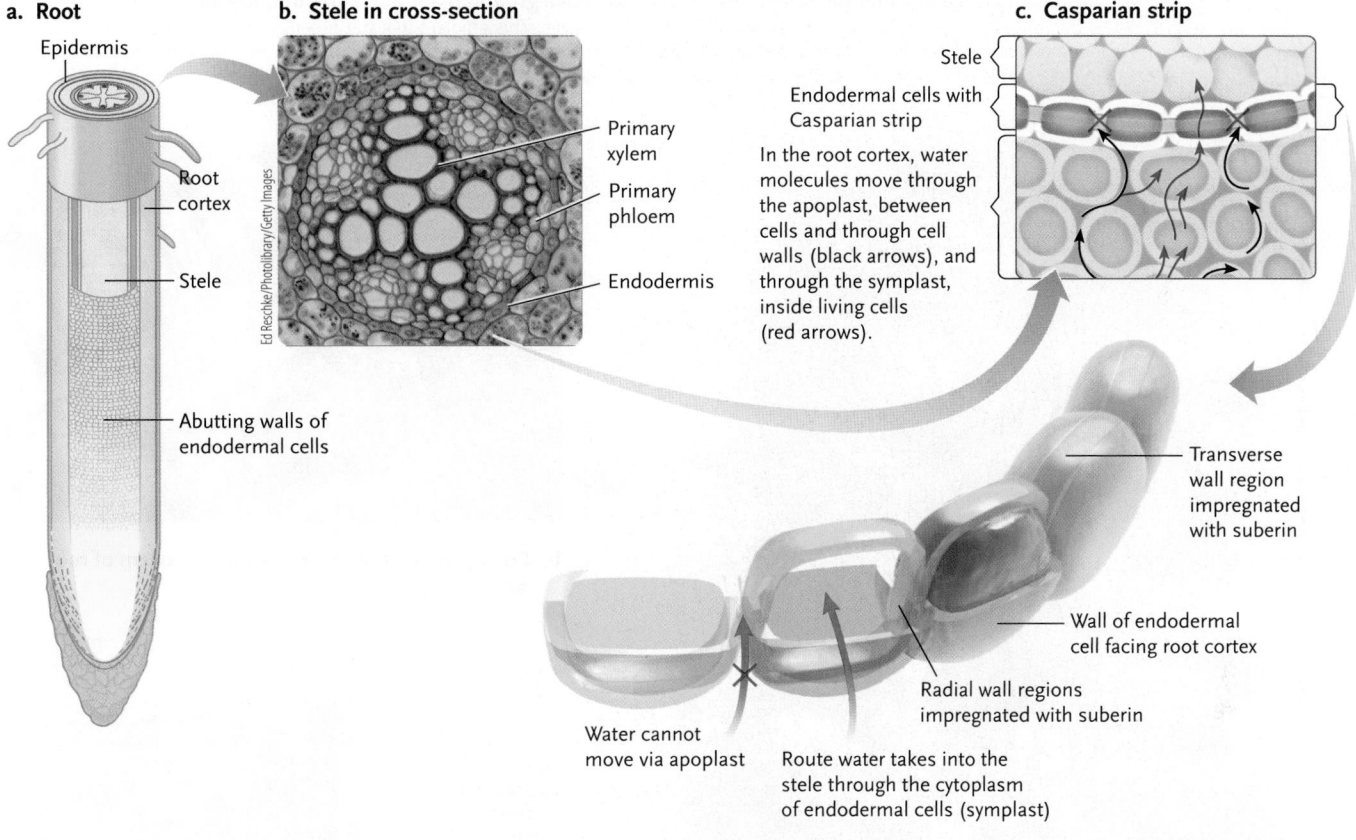

**a. Root**

Epidermis

Root cortex

Stele

Abutting walls of endodermal cells

**b. Stele in cross-section**

Primary xylem

Primary phloem

Endodermis

Ed Reschke/Photolibrary/Getty Images

**c. Casparian strip**

Stele

Endodermal cells with Casparian strip

In the root cortex, water molecules move through the apoplast, between cells and through cell walls (black arrows), and through the symplast, inside living cells (red arrows).

Transverse wall region impregnated with suberin

Wall of endodermal cell facing root cortex

Radial wall regions impregnated with suberin

Water cannot move via apoplast

Route water takes into the stele through the cytoplasm of endodermal cells (symplast)

**FIGURE 34.6 Location and function of Casparian strips in roots** Waxy, water-impervious Casparian strip (gold) in abutting walls of endodermal cells that control water and nutrient uptake.

## 34.3 Long-Distance Transport of Water and Minerals in the Xylem

We return now to the question that opened this chapter: How does the solution of water and minerals called *xylem sap* move—70 m or more in the tallest trees—from roots to stems and then into leaves? Inside a plant's tubelike vascular tissues, large amounts of water travel by **bulk flow**—the mass movement of molecules in response to a difference in pressure between two locations, like water in a closed plumbing system gushing from an open faucet. By the same principle, the dilute solution of water and ions that flows in the xylem, called **xylem sap**, moves by bulk flow from roots to shoots. However, because mature xylem cells are dead, they cannot expend energy to move water into and through the plant shoot. Instead, the driving force for the upward movement of xylem sap from root to shoot is the evaporation of water from leaves and other aboveground parts of land plants (**transpiration**). How is evaporation of water sufficiently powerful to pull water more than 70 m up through a tree? Transpiration is able to pull xylem sap upward through the plant body because of the cohesion of water molecules and the tension created by the evaporation of water from plant surfaces, as we will discuss in this section.

### 34.3a The Properties of Water Play a Key Role in Its Transport

*The Purple Pages* review several biologically important properties of water, two of which are important in understanding water movement in the xylem. First, water molecules are strongly *cohesive:* they tend to form hydrogen bonds with one another. Second, water molecules are *adhesive:* they form hydrogen bonds with molecules of other substances, including the carbohydrates in plant cell walls. Together, water's cohesive and adhesive forces pull water molecules into exceedingly small spaces, such as crevices in cell walls or narrow tubes such as those making up xylem in roots, stems, and leaves. In 1914, plant physiologist Henry Dixon explained the ascent of sap in terms of the relationship between transpiration and water's properties. His theory of xylem transport is now called the **cohesion–tension theory of water transport (Figure 34.7)**.

According to the cohesion–tension theory, water transport begins as water evaporates from the walls of mesophyll cells inside leaves and into the intercellular spaces. This water vapour escapes by transpiration through open stomata, the pores in the leaf surface. As water molecules exit the leaf, they are replaced by others from the cytoplasm of mesophyll cells. The water lost from mesophyll cells gradually reduces their water potential below the water potential in the leaf xylem.

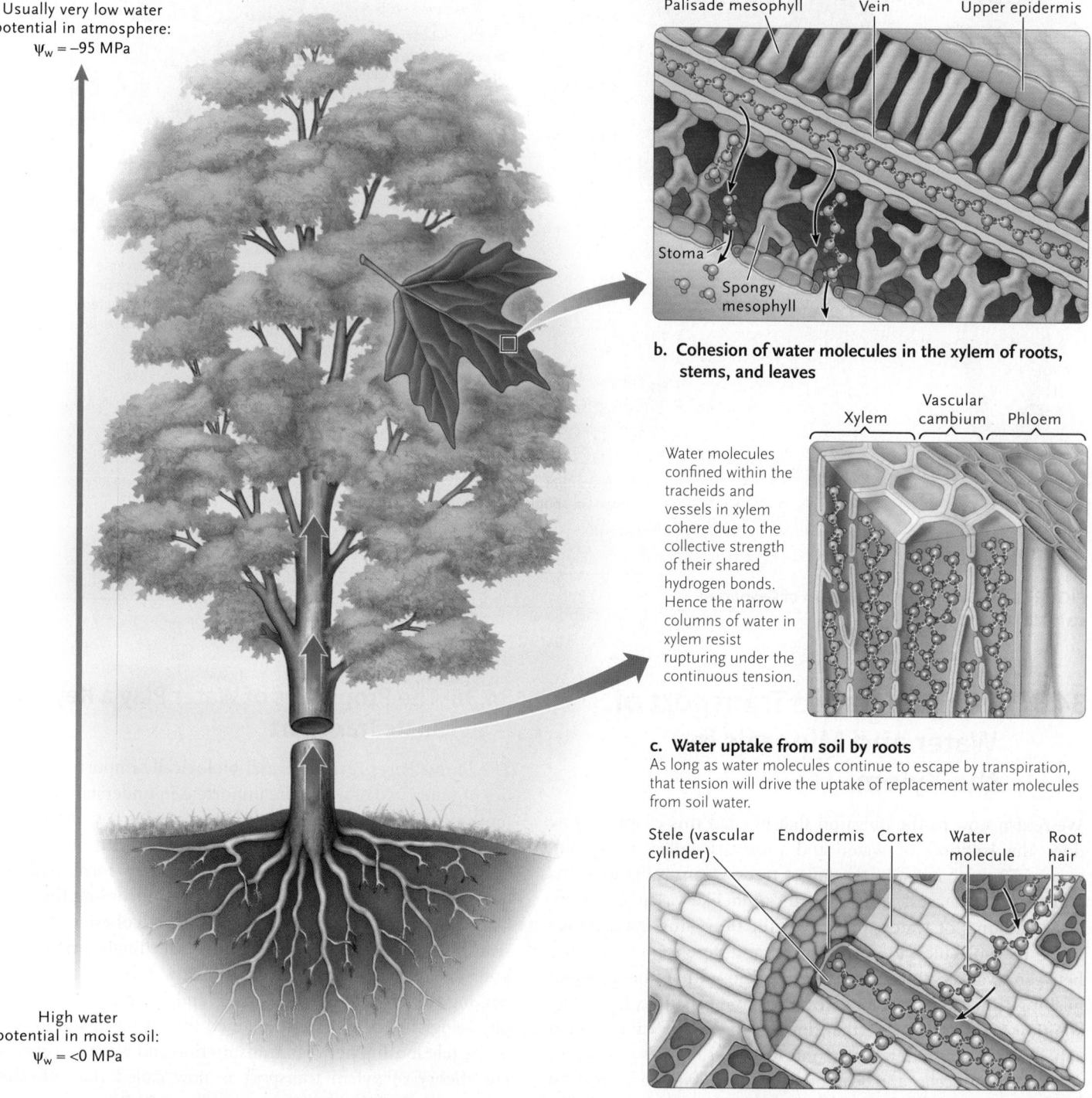

**a. The driving force of water movement from roots to above-ground plant parts and into dry air**
Water potential $\psi_w$ is generally lower in the atmosphere than in leaves. This gradient in water potential drives transpiration (evaporation) of water molecules from stomata in leaves and other above-ground plant parts. The process puts the water in the xylem sap in a state of tension that extends from roots to leaves, driving the upward bulk flow of xylem sap.

Usually very low water potential in atmosphere:
$\psi_w = -95$ MPa

Palisade mesophyll   Vein   Upper epidermis

Stoma   Spongy mesophyll

High water potential in moist soil:
$\psi_w = <0$ MPa

**b. Cohesion of water molecules in the xylem of roots, stems, and leaves**

Xylem   Vascular cambium   Phloem

Water molecules confined within the tracheids and vessels in xylem cohere due to the collective strength of their shared hydrogen bonds. Hence the narrow columns of water in xylem resist rupturing under the continuous tension.

**c. Water uptake from soil by roots**
As long as water molecules continue to escape by transpiration, that tension will drive the uptake of replacement water molecules from soil water.

Stele (vascular cylinder)   Endodermis   Cortex   Water molecule   Root hair

**FIGURE 34.7 Cohesion–tension mechanism of water transport.** Transpiration, the evaporation of water from shoot parts, creates tension on the water in xylem sap. This tension, which extends from root to leaf, pulls upward columns of water molecules that are hydrogen-bonded to one another.

Now, water from the xylem in the leaf veins follows the gradient into cells, replacing the water lost in transpiration.

In the xylem, water molecules are confined in narrow, tubular xylem cells. The water molecules form a long chain, like a string of weak magnets, which is held together by hydrogen bonds between individual molecules. When a water molecule moves out of a leaf vein into the mesophyll, its hydrogen bonds with the next molecule in line stretch but don't break. The stretching creates *tension*, a negative pressure gradient, in the column. Adhesion of the water column to xylem vessel walls adds to the tension. Under continuous tension from above, the entire column of water molecules in xylem is pulled upward, similar to how water is pulled up through a drinking straw. This tension in the xylem is transmitted distally in roots due to the presence of the Casparian strips in the root epidermis, thus forming a continuous water potential gradient from the soil, through the plant, to the air surrounding the plant's leaves.

Transpiration continues regardless of whether the water lost from leaves is replenished by water rapidly taken up from the soil. Wilting is visible evidence that the water potential gradient between soil and a plant's stem and leaves has shifted. As soil dries out, the remaining water molecules in the soil are held ever more tightly by the soil particles; this tension pulls the water molecules closer to the soil particles and reduces the water potential in the soil surrounding the roots, causing the roots to take up water more slowly. However, because the water that evaporates from the plant's leaves is no longer being fully replaced, the leaves wilt as turgor pressure drops. Reducing the water potential in soil by adding solutes such as those that make up fertilizers can cause the same wilting effect. When the water potential in the soil finally equals that in leaf cells, a gradient no longer exists and the movement of water from the soil into roots and up to the leaves comes to a halt.

### 34.3b Leaf Anatomy Contributes to Cohesion–Tension Forces

Leaf anatomy is key to the processes that move water upward in plants. To begin with, as much as two-thirds of a leaf's volume consists of air spaces, meaning that there is a large internal surface area for evaporation of water. Leaves may also have thousands to millions of stomata through which water vapour escapes. Both of these factors increase transpiration. Also, every square centimetre of a leaf contains thousands of tiny veins of xylem and phloem, so most leaf cells lie within half a millimetre of a vein. This close proximity supplies water to cells and the spaces between them, from which the water can readily evaporate.

As water evaporates from a leaf, the water film on the surface of mesophyll cells becomes thinner, meaning that the water molecules in the film are held more tightly to the surface of the cell walls. The decreased water potential on the surface of the cells results in increased tension, pulling water from the mesophyll cells and ultimately from the leaf veins **(Figure 34.8)**. This tension is multiplied many times over in all of the leaves and xylem veins of a plant. It increases further as the plant's metabolically active cells take up xylem sap.

### 34.3c In the Tallest Trees, the Cohesion–Tension Mechanism May Reach Its Physical Limit

Numerous experiments have tested the cohesion–tension theory and, thus far, all the data strongly support it. For example, the theory predicts that xylem sap will begin to move

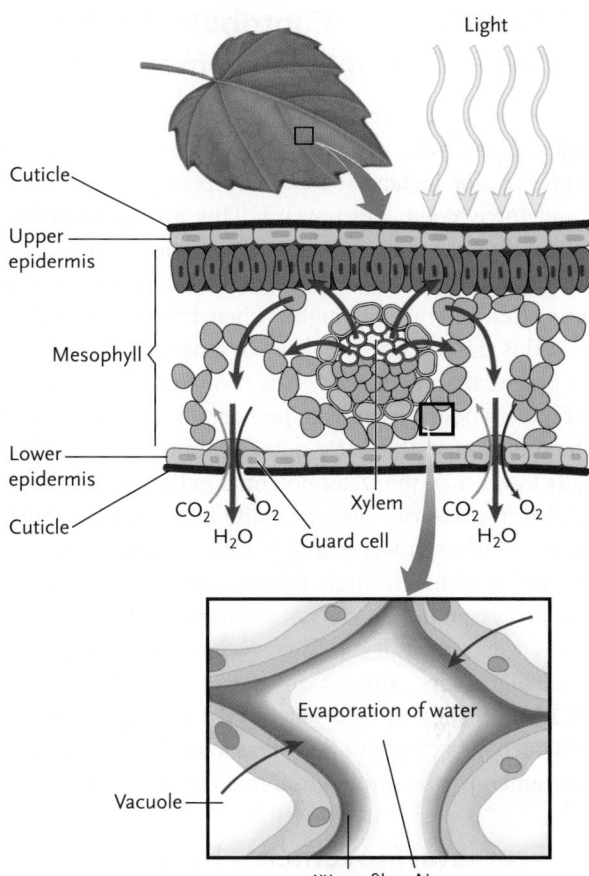

**FIGURE 34.8 Water evaporating from a leaf causes increasing tension on the remaining water inside the leaf, eventually pulling water up out of the xylem.** As water evaporates from the water lined air spaces in a leaf, the film of water on the mesophyll cells around the air space becomes thinner and thinner. The water molecules in this film are under increasing tension, causing a decrease in water potential in the film, which pulls water out of mesophyll cells and, ultimately, out of the xylem.

upward at the top of a tree early in the day when water starts to evaporate from leaves. Experiments with several different tree species have confirmed that this is the case. The experiments also showed that sap transport peaks at midday, when evaporation is greatest, and then tapers off in the evening, as transpiration slows down.

Other experiments have probed the relationship between xylem transport and tree height. One team of researchers studied eight of the tallest living redwoods, including one that towers nearly 113 m above the forest floor. When the scientists measured the maximum tension exerted in the xylem sap in twigs at the tops of the trees, they discovered that it approached the theoretical limit at which the bonds between water molecules in a column of water in a conifer's xylem will break. Based on this finding and other evidence, the team predicted that the maximum height for a healthy coast redwood tree is 122 to 130 m, so it is possible that the tallest redwood alive today may grow taller still!

## 34.3d Root Pressure Contributes to Upward Water Movement in Some Plants

The cohesion–tension mechanism accounts for upward water movement in tall trees. In some shorter non-woody plants, however—grasses, for instance—a positive pressure can develop in roots and force xylem sap upward. This **root pressure** occurs under conditions that reduce transpiration, such as high humidity or low light. In fact, the mechanism that produces root pressure often operates at night, when transpiration slows or stops. At this time, active transport of ions into the stele sets up a water potential gradient across the root. Because the Casparian strip of the endodermis tends to prevent ions from moving back into the root cortex, the water potential in the stele can be substantially lower than the water potential in the cortex. This water potential difference can become quite large and can cause the movement of enough water and dissolved solutes into the stele to produce a relatively high positive pressure in the xylem. Although this root pressure is not sufficient to force water to the top of a very tall plant, it can force water out of leaf openings in some smaller plant species in a process called **guttation** **(Figure 34.9)**. Pushed up and out of vein endings by root pressure, tiny droplets of xylem fluid that look like dew in the early morning emerge from modified stomata at the margins of leaves.

## 34.3e Stomatal Movements Regulate the Loss of Water by Transpiration

Three environmental conditions have major effects on the rate of transpiration: relative humidity, air temperature, and air movement. The most important is relative humidity, which is a measure of the amount of water vapour in air. The less water vapour in the air, the lower the water potential of the air and the more water that will evaporate from leaves. Increasing air temperatures at the leaf surface also increase the rate of transpiration: the amount of water lost can double with each 10°C rise in

air temperature. Air movement at the leaf surface carries water vapour away from the leaf surface and so makes a steeper water potential gradient. Together these factors explain why, on extremely hot, dry, windy days, the leaves of certain plants must completely replace their water each hour.

Even when conditions are not so extreme, more than 90% of the water moving into a leaf can be lost through transpiration. Of the remaining water, about 2% is used in photosynthesis and other metabolic activities. Obviously, it is crucial for plants to be able to control transpiration: if water loss from leaves exceeds water uptake by roots, the plant will not have enough water to carry out normal metabolic functions and may even wilt and die.

Plants have evolved strategies to limit and regulate water loss. The cuticle-covered epidermis of leaves and stems reduces the rate of water loss from above-ground plant parts, and plants can reduce transpiration by closing their stomata. Although both of these adaptations reduce water loss, they also limit the rate at which $CO_2$ for photosynthesis can diffuse into the leaf, so plants have to balance their need to conserve water against their need to fix carbon. This *transpiration–photosynthesis compromise* involves the regulation of transpiration and gas exchange by opening and closing stomata as environmental conditions change.

**OPENING AND CLOSING OF STOMATA** Two guard cells flank each stoma ("mouth"; plural, *stomata*) **(Figure 34.10)**. The inner cell walls of these guard cells are thicker and less elastic than the outer walls, and the cell walls are reinforced by cellulose microfibrils that wrap around the walls in a radial pattern, similar to the steel belts in an automobile's radial tires (Figure 34.10). These features play important roles in the regulation of stomatal opening by guard cells.

Stomata open when guard cells accumulate ions in their cytoplasm and water follows by osmosis; the resulting swelling of the guard cells causes the pair of cells to pull apart due to the radial arrangement of cellulose microfibrils in the walls (Figure 34.10c, d), thus increasing the aperture of the stoma. How do guard cells accumulate ions, and which ions are involved? The key ion is potassium ($K^+$): the $K^+$ concentration in turgid guard cells can be four to eight times that in flaccid (limp) guard cells **(Figure 34.11)**. Accumulation of $K^+$ ions inside guard cells is driven by proton pumps ($H^+$-ATPase pumps) in the plasma membrane of guard cells, which use the energy of ATP hydrolysis to pump protons out of the guard cell cytoplasm, thereby creating an electrochemical gradient across the guard cell membranes. Guard cells use this electrochemical gradient to drive the uptake of $K^+$ through ion channels into the cytoplasm. To maintain the charge difference across the plasma membrane, the accumulation of positively charged $K^+$ ions inside the cell is balanced by uptake of $Cl^-$ and other anions through anion channels in the plasma membrane. Most of these anions and the $K^+$ ions are transported

**FIGURE 34.9 Guttation caused by root pressure.** The drops of water appear at the endings of xylem veins along the leaf edges of a strawberry plant (*Fragaria*).

## a. Open stoma

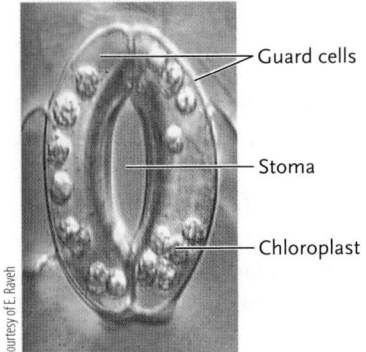

Guard cells

Stoma

Chloroplast

Courtesy of E. Raveh

## b. Closed stoma

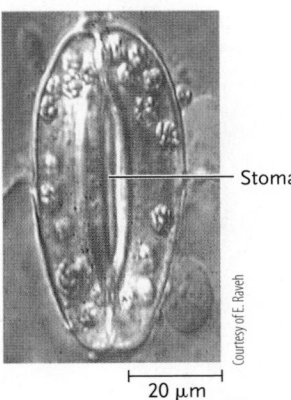

Stoma

Courtesy of E. Raveh

20 μm

## c. Cells turgid/stoma open

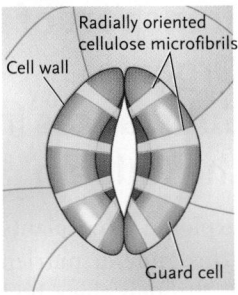

Radially oriented cellulose microfibrils

Cell wall

Guard cell

## d. Cells flaccid/stoma closed

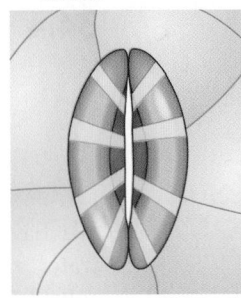

**FIGURE 34.10 Guard cells and stomatal action. (a)** An open stoma in the leaf of *Tradescantia*. The osmotic flow of water into the guard cells increases the turgor pressure inside the cells, causing them to move apart, thus opening the stoma. **(b)** A closed stoma. The osmotic flow of water out of guard cells reduces their turgor pressure, causing them to collapse against each other and close the stoma. **(c)** Arrangement of cellulose microfibrils in guard cells around open stoma. **(d)** Orientation of cellulose microfibrils in guard cells when stoma is closed.

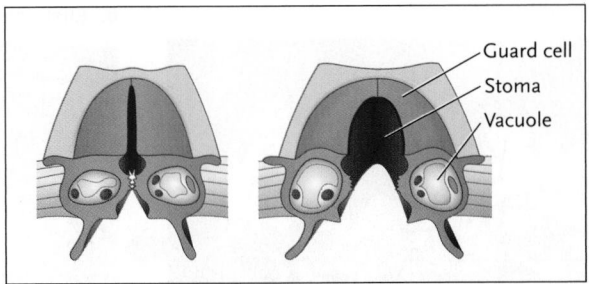

Guard cell

Stoma

Vacuole

|  | Closed stomata | Open stomata |
|---|---|---|
| Stomatal aperture | 0 μm | 8 μm |
| Guard cell turgor | 1.0 MPa | 4.5 MPa |
| K+ content | 0.3 pmol | 2.5 pmol |

**FIGURE 34.11 Evidence for potassium accumulation in stomatal guard cells undergoing expansion.** Strips from the leaf epidermis of a dayflower (*Commelina communis*) were immersed in a solution containing a stain that binds preferentially with potassium ions. In leaf samples with closed stomata, most of the potassium was concentrated in epidermal cells adjacent to the guard cells. In leaf samples with open stomata, most of the potassium was concentrated in the guard cells. Three-dimensional representation of guard cells when stoma is closed (left) and open (right). Data in the table indicate that changes in $K^+$ ion content of guard cells cause an influx of water into the cells, increasing their volume (primarily the vacuoles). The increased volume causes the guard cells to bend and change shape, opening the stoma.

Source: M. Rob G. Roelfsema, Rainer Hedrich, "In the light of stomatal opening: new insights into 'the Watergate'," *New Phytologist*, 167(3), September 2005, pp. 665–691. Copyright © 2005, John Wiley and Sons. *The New Phytologist* by Tansley, A. G. Reproduced with permission of BLACKWELL PUBLISHING LTD. in the format Book via Copyright Clearance Center.

These signals include humidity, $CO_2$ concentration in the air spaces inside leaves, the amount of water available to the plant, the time of day, and the presence of microbes.

### 34.3f In Dry Climates, Plants Exhibit Various Adaptations for Conserving Water

Many plants have evolutionary adaptations that conserve water, including modifications in leaf structure or physiology **(Figure 34.12)**. The stomata of oleanders, for example, lie at the bottom of pitlike invaginations (Figure 34.12a, b). These sunken stomata are less exposed to drying breezes, so that water evaporates from the leaf much more slowly.

The leaves of *xerophytes*—plants adapted to hot, dry environments in which water stress can be severe—often have a thickened cuticle that gives them a leathery feel and provides enhanced protection against evaporative water loss. In other xerophytes, such as cacti, leaves are reduced to thin spines, which reduces the surface area from which water is lost by transpiration; photosynthesis occurs in the stems, which are thickened, leaflike pads (see Figure 34.11c). These structural alterations reduce the surface area for transpiration.

One intriguing variation on water conservation mechanisms occurs in CAM plants, including cacti, orchids, and

into the vacuole rather than remaining in the cytoplasm, causing the water that flows into the guard cell by osmosis to move into the vacuole. Thus, the increase in the size of the guard cell is due mostly to increases in the volume of the vacuole (Figure 34.11).

During stomatal closure, anions are released from the guard cells by anion channels in the plasma membrane. This loss of anions reduces the charge difference across the guard cell plasma membrane, triggering the efflux of $K^+$ ions from the guard cells, and water follows by osmosis. When the water content of the guard cells drops, so does turgor pressure. The guard cells collapse against each other, closing the stoma (Figure 34.11).

In most plants, stomata are open in daylight and closed at night, indicating that guard cells clearly respond to light. But experiments have shown that guard cells can respond to a number of other environmental and internal signals, any of which can induce the ion flows that open and close stomata.

**a. Oleanders**

**b. Oleander leaf**

Cuticle
Multilayer epidermis

Recessed stoma

**c. Spines (modified leaves) on a cactus stem**

**d. CAM plant**

**FIGURE 34.12 Some adaptations that enable plants to survive water stress. (a)** Oleanders (*Nerium oleander*) are adapted to arid conditions. **(b)** As shown in the micrograph, oleander leaves have recessed stomata on their lower surface and a multilayer epidermis covered by a thick cuticle on the upper surface. **(c)** Like many other cacti, the leaves of the Graham dog cactus (*Opuntia grahamii*) are modified into spines that protrude from the underlying stem. Transpiration and photosynthesis occur in the green stems, such as the oval stem in this photograph. **(d)** *Sedum,* a CAM plant, in which the stomata open only at night.

most succulents. As discussed in Chapter 6, **Crassulacean acid metabolism** (CAM) is a biochemical variation of photosynthesis that was discovered in a member of the family Crassulaceae (the plant family to which a common houseplant, the jade plant, belongs). CAM plants generally have fewer stomata than other types of plants and, unlike most

plants, their stomata are closed during the day. At night, when temperatures are cooler and the relative humidity is higher, CAM plants open their stomata to take up carbon dioxide, which is converted to malate, an organic acid. In the daytime, the $CO_2$ is liberated from malate and diffuses into chloroplasts, so photosynthesis takes place even though a CAM plant's stomata are closed. This adaptation prevents heavy evaporative water losses during the heat of the day.

## 34.4 Transport of Organic Substances in the Phloem

We have explored how plants move water and the mineral nutrients dissolved in it through their bodies via their xylem. Plants have another long-distance transport system, the phloem, which carries huge amounts of carbohydrates; lesser but vital amounts of amino acids, fatty acids, and other organic compounds; and still other essential substances, such as hormones and signalling molecules. Unlike the xylem's unidirectional upward flow, the phloem transports substances throughout the plant to wherever they are used or stored. Organic compounds and water in the sieve tubes of phloem are under pressure and driven by concentration gradients.

### 34.4a Organic Compounds Are Stored and Transported in Different Forms

One problem in transporting the carbohydrates, proteins, and other organic compounds in the phloem is that most of these molecules are too large to cross the cell membranes and leave the cells in which they are made. They may also be too insoluble in water to be transported to other regions of the plant body. Consequently, in leaves and other plant parts, specific reactions convert organic compounds to transportable forms. For example, hydrolysis of starch liberates glucose units, which combine with fructose to form sucrose, the main

**STUDY BREAK QUESTIONS**

1. Explain the key steps in the cohesion–tension mechanism of water transport in a plant.
2. How and when do stomata open and close? In what ways is their functioning important to a plant's ability to manage water loss?

FIGURE 34.13 **Experimental Research**

## Translocation Pressure

**Question:** Is pressure responsible for the flow of phloem sap through sieve tubes from a source to a sink?

**Experiment:** In the late 1970s, John Wright and Donald Fisher of the University of Georgia devised an experiment to directly measure the turgor pressure in sieve tubes of weeping willow saplings (*Salix babylonica*) under non-destructive conditions, using aphids that feed on *S. babylonica* in the wild. Weeping willow saplings were grown in a greenhouse under natural conditions of light and moisture. Aphids were placed on the trees and allowed to begin feeding by inserting their stylets into sieve tubes in the normal fashion. After being anesthetized by exposure to high concentrations of carbon dioxide, the aphids' bodies were cut away and only their stylets were left embedded in the sieve tubes. A tiny pressure-measuring device called a *micromanometer* was then glued over the end of each stylet. The micromanometer registered the volume and pressure of phloem sap as it was exuded from the stylet over time periods ranging from 30 to 90 minutes.

**a. Aphid releasing honeydew**

**b. Micrograph of aphid stylet in sieve tube**

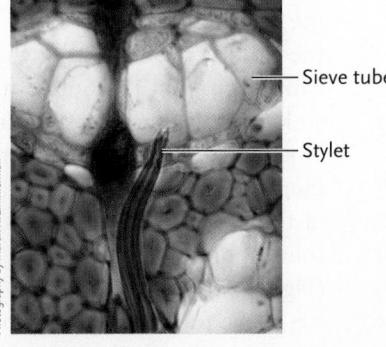

— Sieve tube

— Stylet

Harvard Forest Archives, Harvard Forest, Petersham, MA, USA. Photography by Martin H. Zimmerman

Harvard Forest Archives, Harvard Forest, Petersham, MA, USA. Photography by Martin H. Zimmerman

**Results:** In nearly all cases, a high volume of pressurized sap flowed through the severed stylets into the micromanometer during the test periods.

**Conclusion:** The evidence supports pressure flow as the mechanism that moves phloem sap through sieve tubes.

Other experiments have confirmed that both turgor pressure and the concentration of sucrose are highest in sieve tubes closest to the sap source. Phloem sap also moves most rapidly closest to the source, where pressure is highest.

Source: © Cengage Learning 2017. Based on J. P. Wright and D. B. Fisher. 1980. The direct measurement of sieve tube turgor pressure using severed aphid stylets. *Plant Physiology* 65:1133–1135.

form in which sugars are transported through the phloem of most plants. Proteins are broken down into amino acids, and lipids are converted into fatty acids. These forms are better able to cross cell membranes by passive or active mechanisms.

## 34.4b Organic Solutes Move by Translocation

In plants, the long-distance transport of substances such as sucrose is called **translocation**. We have the best understanding of how translocation occurs in flowering plants. In these plants, the phloem is composed of sieve tube member cells, which are joined together by their perforated end walls (sieve plates) to form interconnected sieve tubes (see Figure 34.10). Recall from Chapter 33 that, as sieve tube members mature, they lose many of their organelles, including nuclei. At maturity, like xylem cells, sieve tubes form a pipeline for transport but, unlike tracheids and vessels, sieve tube cells are alive and contain cytoplasm. The large pores of the perforated end walls allow water and organic compounds, collectively called **phloem sap**, to flow rapidly through the sieve tubes, another example of a structural adaptation that suits a particular function. But sieve tubes do not move phloem sap by themselves: the companion cells connected via plasmodesmata to sieve tubes and to surrounding parenchyma cells are also necessary for transport of phloem sap.

## 34.4c Phloem Sap Moves from Source to Sink Under Pressure

Over the decades, plant physiologists have proposed several mechanisms of translocation, but it was the tiny aphid, an insect that annoys gardeners, that helped demonstrate that organic compounds flow under high pressure in the phloem **(Figure 34.13)**—the pressure can be as high as five times the pressure in an automobile tire! An aphid attacks plant leaves and stems, forcing its needle-like stylet (a mouthpart) into sieve tubes—with incredible precision—to obtain the dissolved sugars and other nutrients inside. When an aphid feeds on phloem sap, this pressure forces the fluid through the aphid's gut and (minus nutrients absorbed) out its anus as "honeydew" (Figure 34.13). If you park your car under a tree being attacked by aphids, it might get spattered with sticky honeydew droplets, thanks to the high fluid pressure in the tree's phloem.

In flowering plants, sucrose-laden phloem sap flows from a starting location, called the *source,* to another site, the *sink,* along gradients of decreasing solute concentration and pressure. A **source** is any region of the plant where organic substances are being loaded into the phloem's sieve tube system; for example, actively photosynthesizing leaves are sources **(Figure 34.14)**. A **sink** is any region

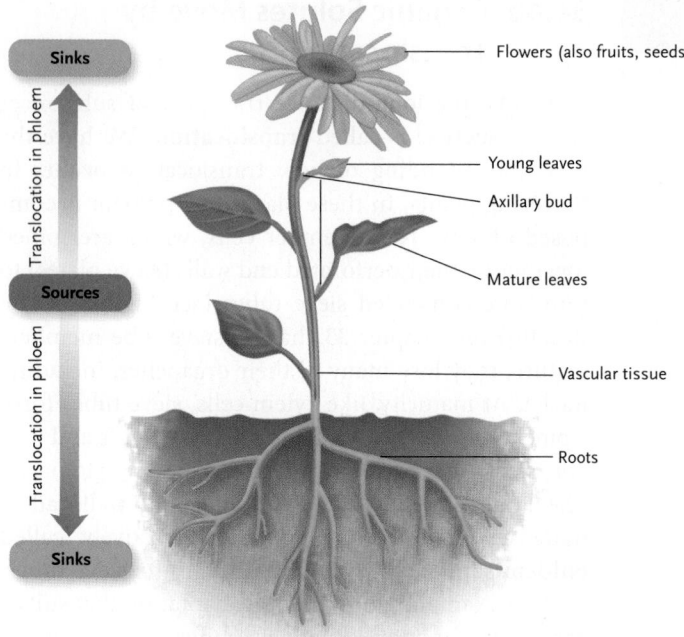

**Sinks**

Translocation in phloem

**Sources**

Translocation in phloem

**Sinks**

Flowers (also fruits, seeds)

Young leaves

Axillary bud

Mature leaves

Vascular tissue

Roots

**FIGURE 34.14 Sources and sinks in a plant.** Mature leaves of this plant act as sources for sugars and other organic substances that are transported via the phloem to sinks, regions of the plants that have a high demand for these substances.

where organic substances are being unloaded from the sieve tube system and used or stored; a developing fruit is a sink.

The same plant organ can act as a source or a sink at different times during development. For example, think about a tulip bulb: in spring, food stored in the bulb is mobilized for transport upward to growing plant parts, but after the plants bloom, the bulb becomes a sink, as sugars manufactured in the tulip plant's leaves are moved into it for storage. Leaves, roots, and fruits generally start out as sinks, only to become sources when the season changes or the plant enters a new developmental phase. In general, sinks receive organic compounds from sources closest to them. Hence, the lower leaves on a rose bush may supply sucrose to roots, whereas leaves farther up the shoot supply the rapidly growing shoot tip.

What causes sucrose and other solutes produced in leaf mesophyll to flow from a source to a sink? All the evidence to date indicates that solute movement through the sieve tubes is driven by a pressure gradient between a source and a sink: as sugars and other macromolecules are loaded into the phloem at a source, the resulting pressure pushes these solutes by bulk flow toward a sink, where they are unloaded, resulting in lower pressure. **Figure 34.15** summarizes this **pressure-flow mechanism**.

Most substances carried in phloem are loaded into sieve tube members by active transport (Figure 34.15a). For example, the sucrose formed in mesophyll cells of leaves is actively pumped into companion cells by $H^+$/sucrose symport, where $H^+$ ions move into the cell through the same carrier that takes up the sugar molecules. From the companion cells, most

sucrose crosses into the living sieve tube members through plasmodesmata.

In some plants, companion cells become modified into **transfer cells**, which facilitate the short-distance transport of organic solutes from one cell to another. Transfer cells generally form when large amounts of solutes must be loaded or unloaded into the phloem, and they shunt substances through plasmodesmata to sieve tube members. How do transfer cells facilitate solute transport? As a transfer cell is forming, parts of its cell wall grow inward like pleats **(Figure 34.16)**. The underlying plasma membrane, packed with transport proteins, enfolds each pleat in the cell wall, thus increasing the surface area across which solutes can be taken up. Xylem parenchyma transfer cells also enhance transport between living cells in the xylem, and they occur in glandlike tissues that secrete nectar. Transfer cells occur in species from every taxonomic group in the plant kingdom, as well as in fungi and algae.

When sucrose is loaded into sieve tubes of small leaf veins, its concentration rises inside the tubes. The increased solute concentration causes a decrease in water potential inside the sieve tube members, and water flows into the cells by osmosis. As water enters the sieve tubes, turgor pressure in the tubes increases, and the sucrose-rich fluid moves by bulk flow into the increasingly larger sieve tubes of larger veins. Eventually, the fluid is pushed out of the leaf into the stem and toward a sink (Figure 34.15). Solute unloading is mostly symplastic in sink cells. When sucrose is unloaded into the sink, the amount of solutes in the sieve tube member decreases, resulting in an increase in the water potential and the movement of water out of the sieve tube by osmosis. Some of this water "follows the solutes" into the sink cells, but most of it enters the xylem (Figure 34.15b, step 5).

Sieve tubes are mostly passive conduits for translocation. The system works because companion cells supply most of the energy that loads sucrose and other solutes at the source and because solutes are removed at their sinks. For example, as sucrose enters a sink, its concentration in the sieve tubes decreases and water moves out of the cell, causing the pressure potential to decrease. Thus, for sucrose and other solutes transported in the phloem, there is always a gradient of concentration from source to sink, and a pressure gradient that keeps the solute moving along.

As noted previously, phloem sap moving through a plant carries a wide variety of substances, including amino acids, organic acids, agricultural chemicals, and organic nitrogen compounds and mineral ions that are removed from dying leaves and stored for reuse in root tissue. The phloem also transports hormones and other signal molecules such as RNA from one part of a plant to another, and so plays a much greater role in the plant than just a pipeline to move sucrose: it acts as an "information superhighway."

The transport functions of xylem and phloem are closely integrated with plant reproduction, development of embryos, and the hormone-based regulation of plant growth. We will explore these topics in Chapter 37.

## a. Loading at a source

Photosynthetic cells in leaves are a common source of carbohydrates that must be distributed through a plant. Small, soluble forms of these compounds move from the cells into phloem (in a leaf vein).

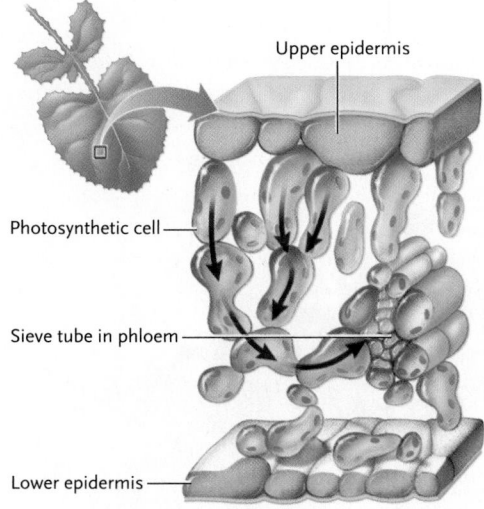

Upper epidermis

Photosynthetic cell

Sieve tube in phloem

Lower epidermis

## b. Bulk flow from source to sink

Organic solutes are loaded into sieve tubes at a source, such as a leaf, and move by bulk flow toward a sink, such as roots or rapidly growing stem parts.

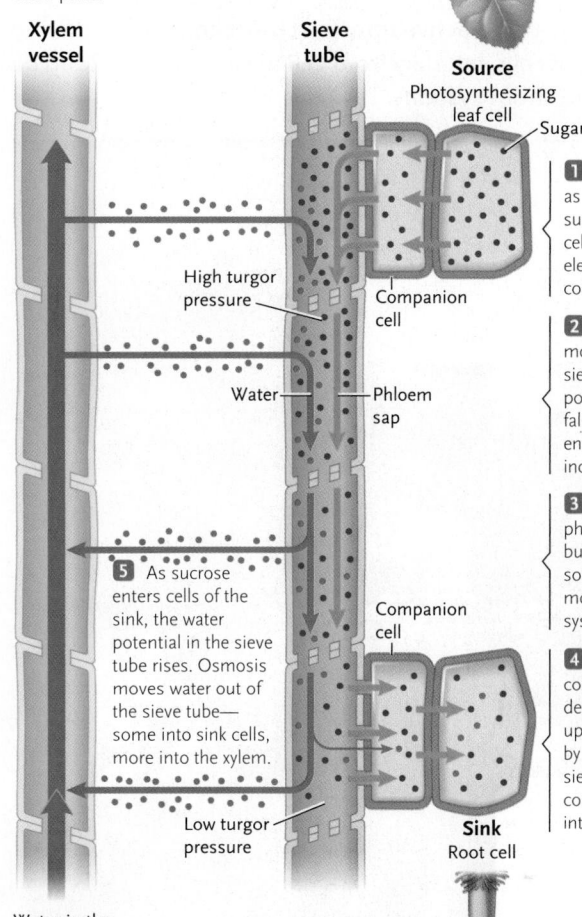

Xylem vessel

Sieve tube

**Source**
Photosynthesizing leaf cell

Sugar (sucrose)

High turgor pressure

Companion cell

Water

Phloem sap

**1** Phloem sap forms as active transport loads sucrose into companion cells and then into sieve elements, against concentration gradients.

**2** As sucrose becomes more concentrated in the sieve tube, the water potential in the sieve tube falls, so water from xylem enters the tube by osmosis, increasing turgor pressure.

**3** Under high pressure, phloem sap moves by bulk flow between a source and a sink. Water moves into and out of the system all along the way.

**5** As sucrose enters cells of the sink, the water potential in the sieve tube rises. Osmosis moves water out of the sieve tube— some into sink cells, more into the xylem.

Companion cell

**4** Pressure and sucrose concentration gradually decrease as the sink takes up sucrose from phloem by active transport from sieve-tube elements into companion cells and then into sink cells.

Low turgor pressure

**Sink**
Root cell

Water in the transpiration stream moves upward in xylem.

**FIGURE 34.15 Summary of the pressure-flow mechanism in the phloem of flowering plants.** Organic solutes are loaded into sieve tubes at a source **(a)**, such as a leaf, and move by bulk flow toward a sink **(b)**, such as roots or rapidly growing stem parts.
© Cengage Learning 2017.

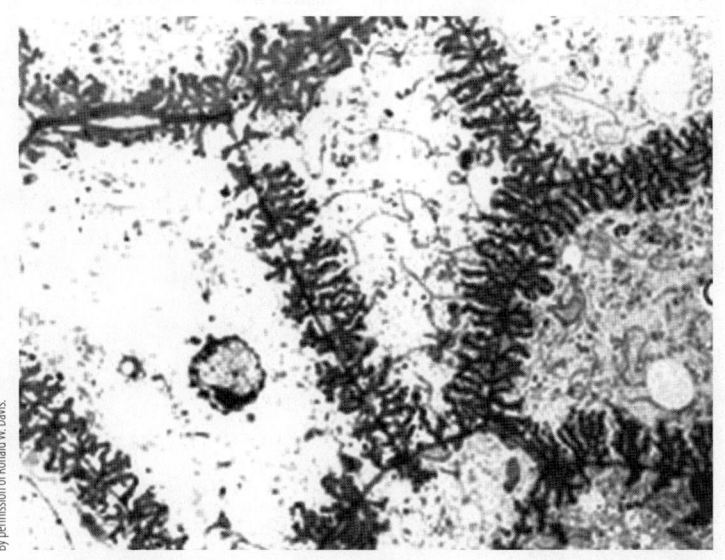

Davis et al., "Anatomy of the transfer cell region in corn." *Maize Genetics Cooperation Newsletter*, Volume 62, 1988. By permission of Ronald W. Davis.

**FIGURE 34.16 Transmission electron micrograph showing transfer cells in corn (*Zea mays*) in cross-section.** Both the cell wall and the underlying plasma membrane of these transfer cells are highly folded, increasing the surface area for solute transfer.

## STUDY BREAK QUESTIONS

1. What is the difference between translocation and transpiration?

2. Using sucrose as your example, summarize how a substance moves from a source into sieve tubes and is then unloaded at a sink. What is this mechanism called, and why?

# Summary Illustration

Plants have both passive and active transport mechanisms for moving water and solutes into and out of cells, laterally from cell to cell, and over long distances between the root and shoot systems.

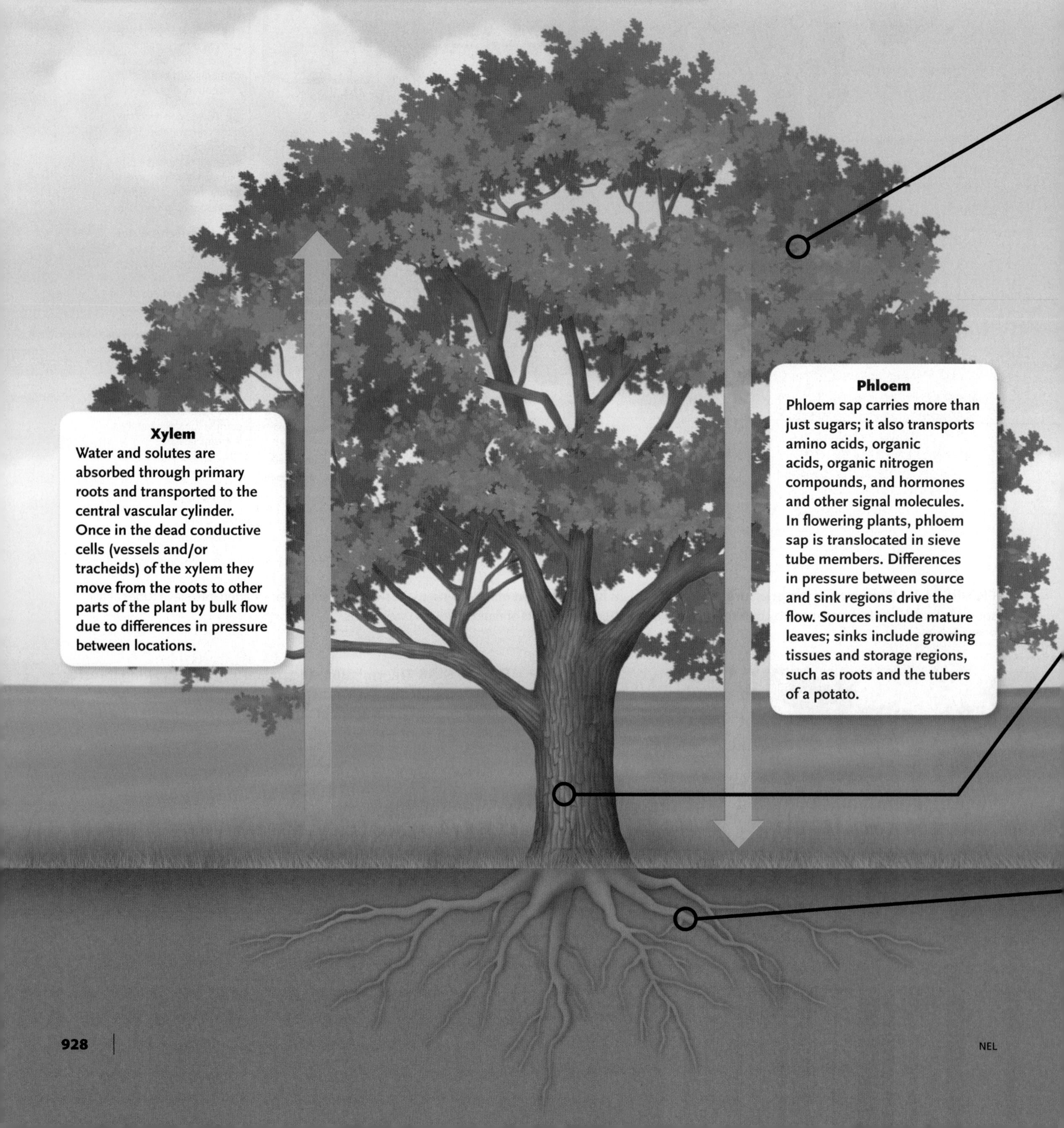

## Xylem

Water and solutes are absorbed through primary roots and transported to the central vascular cylinder. Once in the dead conductive cells (vessels and/or tracheids) of the xylem they move from the roots to other parts of the plant by bulk flow due to differences in pressure between locations.

## Phloem

Phloem sap carries more than just sugars; it also transports amino acids, organic acids, organic nitrogen compounds, and hormones and other signal molecules. In flowering plants, phloem sap is translocated in sieve tube members. Differences in pressure between source and sink regions drive the flow. Sources include mature leaves; sinks include growing tissues and storage regions, such as roots and the tubers of a potato.

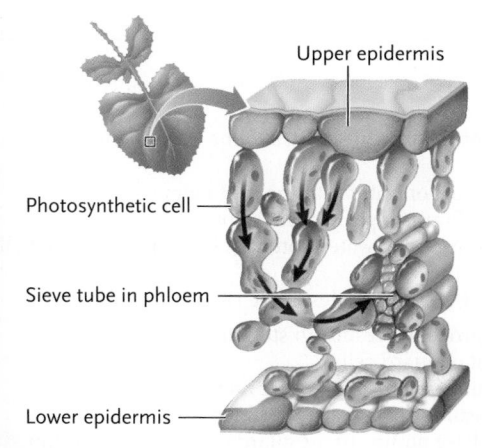

Upper epidermis

Photosynthetic cell

Sieve tube in phloem

Lower epidermis

© Cengage Learning 2017

Photosynthates and other macromolecules are transported from mesophyll cell to mesophyll cell until they reach a vascular bundle, where they are loaded into companion cells and then into sieve tubes.

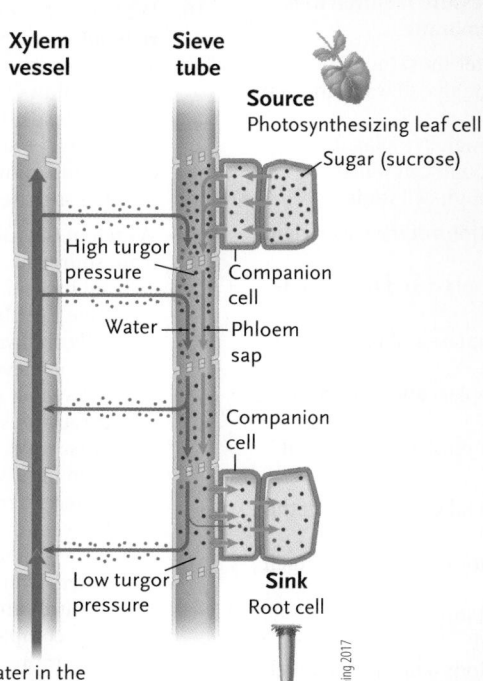

Xylem vessel

Sieve tube

Source
Photosynthesizing leaf cell

Sugar (sucrose)

High turgor pressure

Companion cell

Water

Phloem sap

Companion cell

Low turgor pressure

Sink
Root cell

Water in the transpiration stream moves upward in xylem.

© Cengage Learning 2017

### Xylem

Transpiration, the evaporation of water from leaves and shoots, creates tension (negative pressure) on the water in the xylem. Cohesion between water molecules creates a continuous column of water molecules that is pulled by the tension created as water exits a plant's leaves. Thus, the negative pressure generated in the shoot drives bulk flow of xylem sap.

### Phloem

In the photosynthetic parts of flowering plants, sucrose is actively transported into companion cells adjacent to sieve tube members, and then loaded into the sieve tubes through plasmodesmata. As the sucrose concentration increases in the sieve tubes, water potential decreases. The resulting influx of water causes pressure to build up inside the sieve tubes, so the sucrose-laden fluid flows in bulk toward the sink, where sucrose and water are unloaded and distributed among surrounding cells and tissues.

In the **apoplastic pathway** (red), water moves through nonliving regions—the continuous network of adjoining cell walls and tissue air spaces. However, when it reaches the endodermis, it passes through one layer of living cells.

In the **symplastic pathway** (green), water passes into and through living cells. After being taken up into root hairs, water diffuses through the cytoplasm and passes from one living cell to the next through

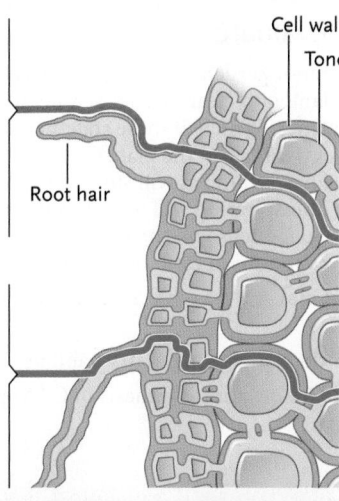

Cell wall

Tono

Root hair

There are two main ways in which water moves through the primary root to the xylem. In the **apoplastic pathway**, water diffuses into roots in the cell walls of root epidermal cells and moves across the cortex to the endodermis via cell walls and intercellular spaces. By contrast, in the **symplastic pathway**, water and solutes absorbed by roots can flow from the cytoplasm of one cortical cell to the next via plasmodesmata.

# SELF-TEST QUESTIONS

## Recall/Understand

1. Which of the following *best* describes turgor pressure?
   a. the force equivalent to water's potential pressure
   b. the pressure of the movement of water into a cell by osmosis
   c. the driving force for osmotic movement of water
   d. the pressure exerted by fluid inside a plant cell against the cell wall

2. Which of these statements *best* describes water potential?
   a. the driving force for the potential osmotic movement of water into plant cells
   b. a measure of the combined effects of a solution's pressure potential and its solute potential
   c. the force that is less negative in a solution that has more solute molecules relative to water molecules
   d. a measure of the potential physical pressure required to halt osmotic water movement across a membrane

3. Which match is correct with respect to water movement?
   a. symplastic pathway: water moves through cell walls and cell cytoplasm
   b. apoplastic pathway: water moves through cytoplasm
   c. symplastic pathway: water moves through cell walls
   d. apoplastic pathway: water moves through cell walls

4. Which of the following describes the functions of the Casparian strip in the root?
   a. to prevent water from moving via symplast and to promote backflow
   b. to prevent water from moving via apoplast and to promote backflow
   c. to prevent water from moving via apoplast and to prevent backflow
   d. to prevent water from moving via symplast and to prevent backflow

5. Which type of transport do roots utilize to take up ions from the soil? Why?
   a. active transport, because the needed ions concentrate much more in the root than in the soil
   b. passive transport, because the needed ions concentrate much more in the root than in the soil
   c. active transport, because the needed ions concentrate much more in the soil than in the roots
   d. passive transport, because the needed ions concentrate much more in the soil than in the roots

## Apply/Analyze

6. Which of the following will happen if you place a plant cell with $\psi_s$ of $-0.4$ MPa and $\psi_p$ of 0.2 MPa into a chamber filled with pure water that is pressurized at 0.5 MPa?
   a. Water will flow into the cell.
   b. Water will flow out of the cell.
   c. The cell will be crushed.
   d. The cell will explode.

7. A plant cell with a solute potential of $-0.65$ MPa maintains a constant volume when bathed in a solution in an open container that has a solute potential of $-0.3$ MPa. Which of these conclusions can you form from this information?
   a. This cell has a pressure potential of $+0.65$ MPa.
   b. This cell has a pressure potential of $+0.35$ MPa.
   c. This cell has a water potential of $-0.65$ MPa.
   d. This cell has a water potential of 0 MPa.

8. Which of these processes contributes to the movement of water up a plant stem?
   a. active transport of water into the root hairs
   b. absorption of raindrops on a leaf's epidermis
   c. higher (less negative) water potential in the leaf's mesophyll layer than in the xylem
   d. cohesion of water molecules in the stem and leaf xylem

9. Which of these processes results in stomata opening?
   a. $K^+$ flows out of guard cells.
   b. $CO_2$ concentration inside the leaf increases.
   c. Turgor pressure in the guard cells increases.
   d. The $H^+$-ATPase pumps in the guard cell membranes stop pumping.

10. Which of the following occurs during translocation of sucrose-rich phloem sap?
    a. Companion cells pump sucrose into sieve tube members.
    b. Sap flows toward a source as pressure builds up at a sink.
    c. Sucrose diffuses into companion cells, and $H^+$ simultaneously leaves the cells by a different route.
    d. Companion cells use energy to load solutes at a source, and the sucrose then follows the concentration gradients to sinks.

11. Which of the following is the order of events during bulk flow from source to sink?
    a. sucrose loaded into companion cells and then into sieve tube members; water potential in the sieve tube member falls and water enters by osmosis; turgor pressure increased within sieve tube member; phloem sap moved by bulk flow between a source and a sink; sink takes up sucrose
    b. turgor pressure increased within sieve tube member; sucrose loaded into companion cells and then into sieve tube members; water potential in the sieve tube member falls and water enters by osmosis; phloem sap moved by bulk flow between a source and a sink; sink takes up sucrose
    c. water potential in the sieve tube member falls and water enters by osmosis; phloem sap moved by bulk flow between a source and a sink; sink takes up sucrose; sucrose loaded into companion cells and then into sieve tube members; turgor pressure increased within sieve tube member
    d. sink takes up sucrose; phloem sap moved by bulk flow between a source and a sink; turgor pressure increased within sieve tube member; water potential in the sieve tube member falls and water enters by osmosis; sucrose loaded into companion cells and then into sieve tube members

## Create/Evaluate

12. An indoor gardener leaving for vacation completely wraps a potted plant with clear plastic. Temperature and light are left at low intensities. Which of these statements *best* describes how this strategy will affect the plant?
    a. Photosynthesis will stop.
    b. Transpiration will be reduced.
    c. Guard cells will shrink and stomata will open.
    d. Evaporation from leaf mesophyll cells will be increased.

13. What makes it possible for a very tall tree to transport water to its top?

14. How do plants living in dry habitats conserve water?

15. Explain how photosynthesis in CAM plants differs from other plants.

# Chapter Roadmap

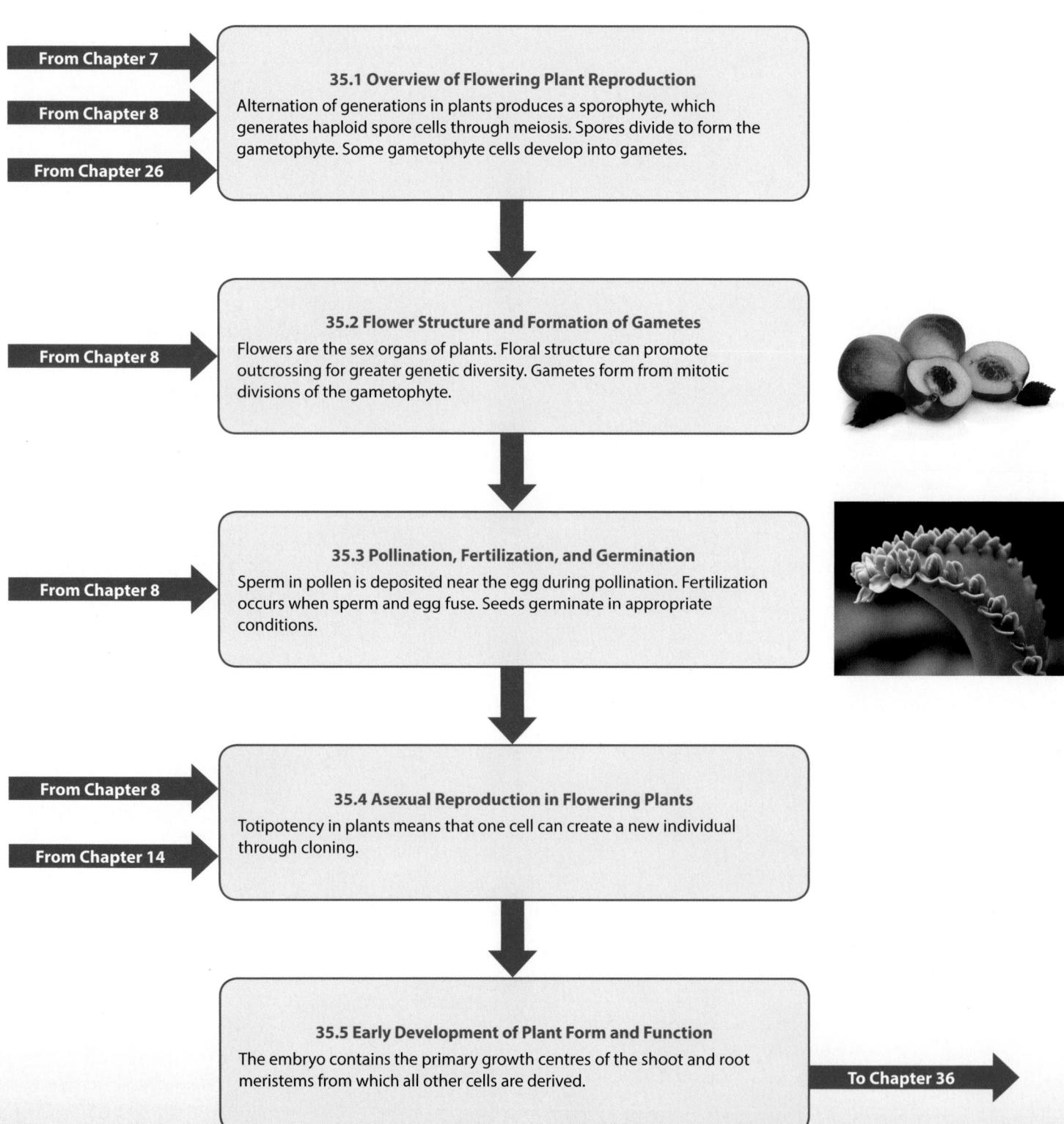

**Reproduction and Development in Flowering Plants**

**From Chapter 7**
**From Chapter 8**
**From Chapter 26**

### 35.1 Overview of Flowering Plant Reproduction
Alternation of generations in plants produces a sporophyte, which generates haploid spore cells through meiosis. Spores divide to form the gametophyte. Some gametophyte cells develop into gametes.

**From Chapter 8**

### 35.2 Flower Structure and Formation of Gametes
Flowers are the sex organs of plants. Floral structure can promote outcrossing for greater genetic diversity. Gametes form from mitotic divisions of the gametophyte.

**From Chapter 8**

### 35.3 Pollination, Fertilization, and Germination
Sperm in pollen is deposited near the egg during pollination. Fertilization occurs when sperm and egg fuse. Seeds germinate in appropriate conditions.

**From Chapter 8**
**From Chapter 14**

### 35.4 Asexual Reproduction in Flowering Plants
Totipotency in plants means that one cell can create a new individual through cloning.

### 35.5 Early Development of Plant Form and Function
The embryo contains the primary growth centres of the shoot and root meristems from which all other cells are derived.

**To Chapter 36**

Photos.com

Ed Reschke/Photolibrary/Getty Images

The reproductive structures of an ornamental poppy (*Papaver rhoeas*). Male reproductive structures, which produce pollen, surround the female reproductive structure, which produces eggs and is the site of fertilization and seed development.

# Reproduction and Development in Flowering Plants

# 35

**Why it matters . . .** Did your mother ever pack you a lunch for you when you went to school? The mother of the next generation of plants packs food for her offspring for when they leave! In angiosperms (the flowering plants), the female gametophyte provides food for the seed, which contains the embryo of a new individual. Think about how heavy a bagged lunch is. A thermos of soup weighs more than a simple sandwich. A bag of chips that were fried in oil is light, but Tupperware containing sugar-rich fruit weighs a lot. If you were young and had a long way to walk, the logistics of what to pack probably played a role in what you found in your lunch bag. Indeed, the composition of your meal also reflected your nutritional needs and cost in addition to the energy provided.

Energy is often obtained from the macromolecules polysaccharides, polypeptides, or lipids. Polysaccharides break down to simple sugars. They tend to be heavy because they hold onto water due to their charged hydroxyl groups (see *The Purple Pages*). As you know, starch has a lot of energy, and it's readily metabolized by mitochondria through glycolysis and the citric acid cycle, which you studied in Chapter 5. Polypeptides, another term for proteins, are hydrolyzed into amino acids. These also can provide energy. It is common knowledge that lipids such as fats and oils are very energy dense. Small masses contain a lot of energy: one gram of fat provides over twice the amount of energy that a gram of protein or carbohydrate does.

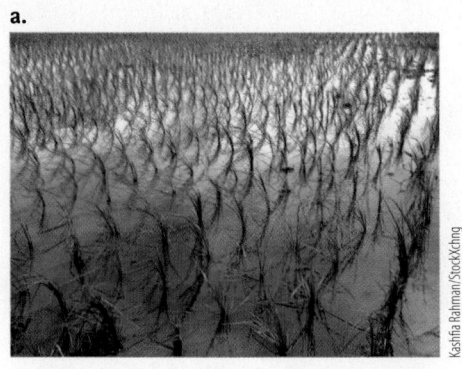

a.

b.

c.

Kashfia Rahman/StockXchng

Isa Fernandez Fernandez/Shutterstock.com

Photos.com

FIGURE 35.1 **The world's three most important crop plants (from a human perspective). (a)** Rice (*Oryza sativa*) plants in a rice paddy, **(b)** maize (*Zea mays*) plants, and **(c)** wheat (*Triticum aestivum*) plants.

Most seeds are provided with either starch, which accumulates rapidly in photosynthesizing creatures, or lipids, which are lightweight. These are, of course, specific to the plant type. Mom's choice of material is a factor of genetics and not a result of careful planning ahead! Although plants—and indeed all organisms—have protein, it is typically found in lower concentration in plants. With rare exceptions, only the seeds of some plants contain significant amounts of protein, and they do so in order to provide materials and energy for the seedling that emerges from the seed. It is for this reason that people who adopt a vegan diet typically include protein-rich legumes to get the essential amino acids (the ones that cannot be created in the human metabolism) that are in high quantity in animal products.

Worldwide, the top 10 crop plants are angiosperms. Consider the top three crop plants in the world: rice, maize, and wheat **(Figure 35.1)**. Millions of people rely either directly on the seeds and/or fruit of these plants or on products made from their parts (e.g., flour). As in other flowering plants, the fruits and seeds of rice, wheat, and corn result from sexual reproduction. The elaborate reproduction systems of angiosperms, which are housed in flowers, produce and protect gametes and developing embryos as they mature. The flowers of many species also serve as invitations to animal pollinators.

In this chapter, we first investigate how sexual reproduction occurs in flowering plants. We then compare sexual reproduction with asexual reproduction, which occurs in many angiosperms under certain circumstances to produce clones that are genetically identical to their parents. Using molecular biology, plant biologists are beginning to understand some of the mechanisms by which these developmental pathways unfold. We conclude the chapter by looking at some of these mechanisms.

## 35.1 Overview of Flowering Plant Reproduction

In plants, as in animals, sexual reproduction occurs when male and female haploid gametes unite to create a diploid zygote, which then embarks on a developmental course of mitotic cell divisions, cell enlargement, and **cell differentiation**. In flowering plants, subsequent steps result in distinctive haploid and diploid forms of an individual.

### 35.1a Diploid and Haploid Generations Arise in the Angiosperm Life Cycle

An angiosperm zygote develops into an embryo enclosed within a seed. In a seed, early versions of the basic plant tissue systems are already in place, so the embryo is already a **sporophyte**—a term that refers to the diploid, spore-producing body of a plant (see Chapter 26). What we see when we look at a flowering plant, such as a wild rose (*Rosa acicularis*), is the sporophyte **(Figure 35.2)**.

At some point during one or more seasons of an angiosperm sporophyte's growth and development, one or more of its vegetative shoots undergoes changes in structure and function and becomes a reproductive shoot that will give rise to a flower or an **inflorescence** (a group of flowers on the same floral shoot). Within the sexual organs of the flower, certain cells divide by meiosis. Unlike in most animals, meiosis in plants does not produce gametes. Instead, meiosis gives rise to haploid **spores**, walled cells that develop by mitosis into multicellular haploid **gametophytes**. The gametophytes produce haploid gametes, again by mitosis. Male gametophytes produce sperm, and female gametophytes produce eggs. This division of a life cycle into a diploid, spore-producing generation and a haploid, gamete-producing generation is called **alternation of generations** (a phenomenon described more fully in Chapter 26).

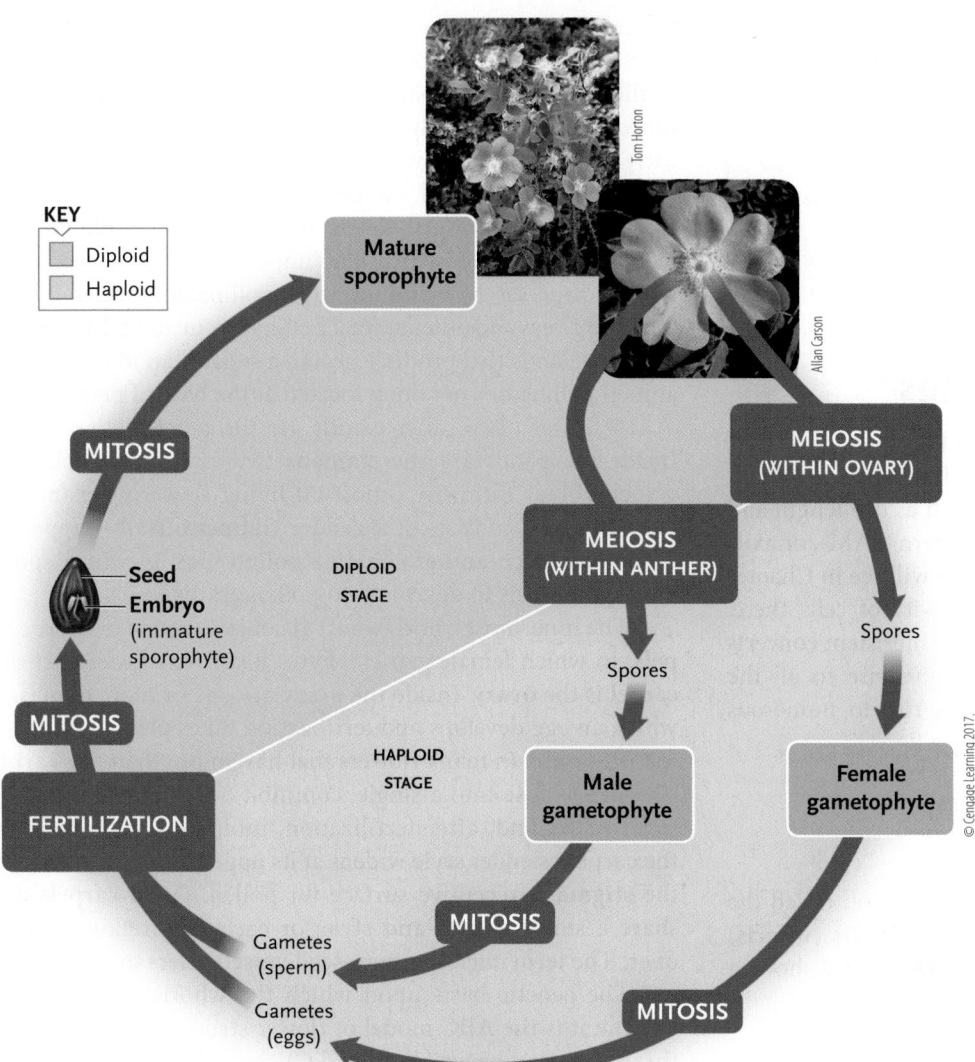

KEY

Diploid
Haploid

**Mature sporophyte**

**MITOSIS**

**MEIOSIS (WITHIN OVARY)**

**Seed**
**Embryo**
(immature sporophyte)

DIPLOID STAGE

**MEIOSIS (WITHIN ANTHER)**

Spores

**MITOSIS**

Spores

HAPLOID STAGE

**FERTILIZATION**

**Male gametophyte**

**Female gametophyte**

Gametes (sperm)

**MITOSIS**

Gametes (eggs)

**MITOSIS**

Tom Horton

Allan Carson

© Cengage Learning 2017.

**FIGURE 35.2 Overview of the flowering plant life cycle, using the wild rose (*Rosa acicularis*) as an example.** This type of reproductive cycle, alternation of generations, has a haploid phase in which multicellular but reduced gametophytes produce gametes, which fuse to form a zygote. This zygote develops into a multicellular embryo within the seed and then into a mature sporophyte. Meiotic divisions in the flower of the sporophyte produce spores, which give rise to new gametophytes.

In virtually all plants, the gametophyte and the sporophyte are strikingly different from one another in both function and structure. As you learned in Chapter 26, in mosses and other bryophytes, the gametophyte is longer lived than the sporophyte; the sporophyte grows out of the gametophyte and remains attached to and nourished by the gametophyte. In ferns, which are seedless vascular plants, the gametophyte is much smaller than the sporophyte and, while it is free living for much of its life and nourishes itself by photosynthesis, it does not live as long as the sporophyte generation. In angiosperms and other seed plants, gametophytes are so reduced in size that they are retained *inside* sporophyte tissue for all or part of their lives. Female gametophytes of a flowering plant usually consist of only seven cells, which are embedded in floral tissues, as you will read shortly. Male gametophytes are released into the environment as pollen grains and are so small that they are measured in micrometres (μm). The pollen grain matures when it reaches floral tissue, producing a pollen tube that grows through floral

tissue to the egg, carrying sperm with it. When the pollen tube enters the ovules inside the ovary, the sperm are released, resulting in fertilization and production of a new generation of seeds.

Although sexual reproduction is a major life phase of sporophytes, they may also reproduce asexually. For instance, strawberry (*Fragaria* species) plants send out horizontal stems, or stolons, and new roots and shoots develop at each node along the stems. Short underground stems of onions and lilies put out buds that grow into new plants. In summer and fall, quackgrass (*Elymus repens*) produces new plants at nodes along its subterranean rhizomes. Asexual reproduction can also be induced artificially. Whole orchards of genetically identical fruit trees are grown from the cuttings or buds of a single parent tree.

We will look at asexual reproduction and how it can be exploited for research and commercial purposes, but for now we will consider sexual reproduction in angiosperms, beginning with the crucial step in which flowers develop.

1. What are the two alternating generations of plants? How do these two life phases differ in structure and function?

2. How does meiosis in plants differ from meiosis in animals? How is it similar?

3. What are the advantages and costs of sexual versus asexual reproduction?

## 35.2 Flower Structure and Formation of Gametes

Flowering marks a developmental shift for an angiosperm. What triggers the formation of flowers? Biochemical signals, triggered in part by environmental cues such as day length and temperature, travel to the shoot apical meristem (SAM), or **axillary meristems** (found at the nodes), as you will see in Chapter 37, and set in motion changes in the activity of cells there. Instead of continuing **vegetative** growth, the meristem converts into an inflorescence meristem that will give rise to all the flowers. This inflorescence meristem gives rise to numerous **floral meristems**, each of which will create a flower.

### 35.2a A Flower Consists of Both Sterile and Fertile Parts

A flower develops from the end of the floral shoot, called the **receptacle.** Flowers consist of four concentric circles (**whorls**) of organs, all of which are modified leaves; **Figure 35.3** shows a

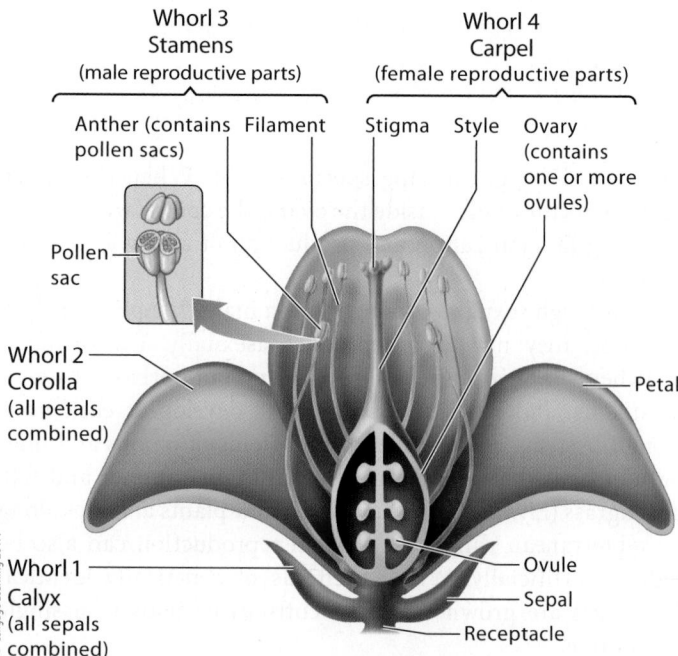

© Cengage Learning 2017.

**FIGURE 35.3 Structure of a generalized flower, with the four whorls indicated.** The anthers of the stamens produce haploid pollen. The stigma of the carpel receives pollen. Ovules inside the ovary contain haploid eggs.

typical flower. The two outer whorls consist of non-fertile, vegetative organs. The outermost whorl (whorl 1) is made up of leaflike **sepals**. The sepals of whorl 1 are collectively called the *calyx.* Sepals are usually green and enclose all the other parts early in the flower's development, as in an unopened rosebud. The next whorl, called the *corolla,* is made up of **petals**, the showy parts of flowers. Petals have distinctive colours, patterning, and shapes, which play important roles in promoting pollen dispersal by wind in wind-pollinated species and in attracting bees and other animal pollinators in animal-pollinated species. Glands that produce nectar, a sugary liquid that attracts animal pollinators, are often located at the base of petals.

A flower's two inner whorls are the reproductive organs. Inside the petals are the **stamens** (whorl 3), in which male gametophytes form. In almost all living flowering plant species, a stamen consists of a slender **filament** (stalk) capped by an **anther**. Each anther contains **pollen sacs**, in which spores undergo mitosis to develop into pollen grains.

The innermost whorl (whorl 4) consists of one or more **carpels**, in which female gametophytes form. The lower part of a carpel is the **ovary**. Inside the ovary are one or more **ovules**, in which an egg develops and fertilization takes place. A seed is a mature ovule. In many flowers that have more than one carpel, the carpels fuse into a single, common ovary containing multiple ovules and, after fertilization, multiple seeds. Typically, the carpel's slender **style** widens at its upper end, terminating in the **stigma**, a receptive surface for pollen. Fused carpels may share a single stigma and style, or each may retain separate ones. The term *angiosperm* (= seed vessel) refers to the carpel.

The genetic basis upon which the whorls are defined is elegant; it is the ABC model of flower structure. The action of three classes of genes (A, B, and C) controls the type of modified leaf that is formed. In **Figure 35.4** you can see that the proteins formed by three different genes determine whether sepals, petals, anthers, or carpels form. Sepals form when gene product "A" alone is expressed, just as product "C" by itself produces carpels. "B" protein can modify carpels to form stamens, and it can modify sepals to form petals. Mutant analysis done by knocking out specific genes has allowed prediction of the resulting flower phenotypes. For example, removing "B" gene expression leads to a plant that forms two carpel whorls in the centre, surrounded by two whorls of sepals. There are elaborations of this model involving other genes for specific tissue production within each organ, but this simple model is still generally supported.

Due to the simple genetic control of floral organ production, useful adaptations can form. For example, removing stamens from a flower means it will no longer self-fertilize. Plants that lack any one of the whorl types are called **imperfect flowers** and are further divided according to whether individual plants produce both sexual types of flowers or only one. In **monoecious** (*mon* = one; *oikos* = house) species, such as corn (*Zea mays*), each plant has some "male" flowers with only stamens and some "female" flowers with only carpels. In **dioecious** (*di* = two; *oikos* = house) species, such as willows (*Salix* species),

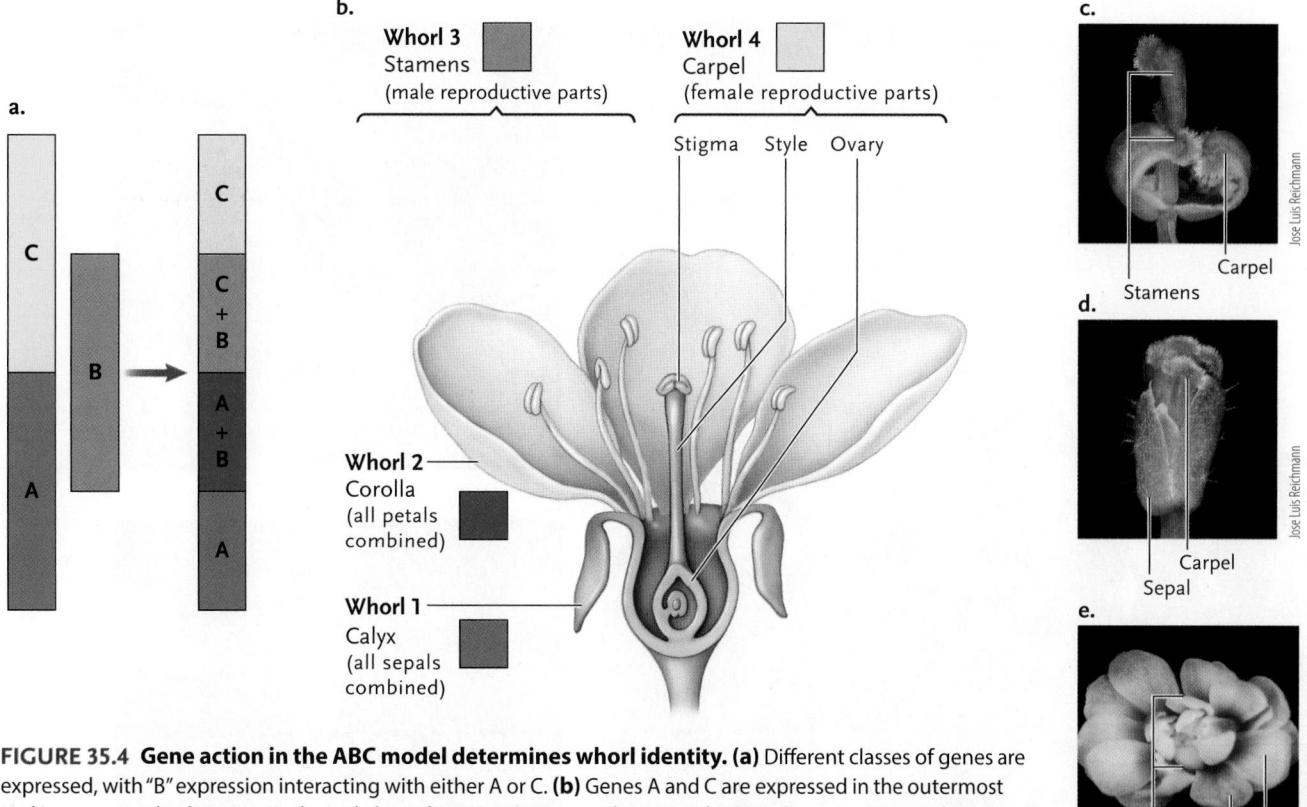

**FIGURE 35.4 Gene action in the ABC model determines whorl identity. (a)** Different classes of genes are expressed, with "B" expression interacting with either A or C. **(b)** Genes A and C are expressed in the outermost and innermost whorls respectively, and alone they give rise to sepals or carpels. Gene B expression overlaps A or C but not both. When "B" product is added to "A," petals result; when "B" interacts with "C," stamens form. **(c)** Mutants that do not express "A" genes have stamens and carpels only. **(d)** Mutants that do not express "B" genes form only sepals and carpels. **(e)** Mutants that do not express "C" form only sepals and petals.

a given plant produces flowers with only stamens or carpels **(Figure 35.5)**. In addition, some flowers lack the showy petals of the typical flower in Figure 35.4 or may have highly modified petals.

Let us now turn to the processes that produce male and female gametes.

## 35.2b Pollen Grains Arise from Microspores in Anthers

Most of a flowering plant's reproductive life cycle, from production of spores to production of a mature seed, takes place within its flowers. **Figure 35.6** shows this cycle as it unfolds in a flower with both stamens and carpels. The spores that give rise to male gametophytes are produced in anthers (see Figure 35.6, left). The pollen sacs inside each anther are microsporangia and contain diploid microsporocytes (also called *microspore mother cells*); each microsporocyte produces four small haploid **microspores** by meiosis. Inside the spore wall, each microspore divides again, this time by mitosis. The result is a haploid male gametophyte, a **pollen grain**. A pollen grain consists of two cells: a larger vegetative (or tube) cell that will later produce a pollen tube, and a smaller **generative cell** that will later divide to produce two gametes, or sperm.

When pollen lands on a stigma, it germinates, forming a pollen tube, which grows through the tissues of the carpel to carry the sperm to the ovule.

The walls of pollen grains are tough enough to protect the male gametophyte during the precarious journey from anther to stigma. These walls are so distinctive that the family to which a plant belongs can usually be identified from pollen alone based on the size and wall sculpturing of the grains as well as the number of pores in the wall **(Figure 35.7)**. Because they withstand decay, pollen grains fossilize well and provide revealing clues about the evolution of seed plants. These help biologists reconstruct ancient plant communities and determine how climates have changed over time.

## 35.2c Eggs and Other Cells of Female Gametophytes Arise from Megaspores in Ovaries

The ovary of a flower contains one or more ovules (see Figure 35.6, right), which develop into seeds after fertilization. Only one ovule forms in the carpel of some flowers, such as in the sunflower (note that the showy head of a sunflower is actually an inflorescence, a collection of individual flowers). Dozens, hundreds, or thousands of ovules may form in the

**FIGURE 35.5 Examples of monoecious and dioecious plants. (a)** Corn (*Zea mays*) has separate male (the tassels at the top of the plants) and female (the "ears" of the corn) flowers on the same plant. Willows (*Salix* species) have separate female **(b)** and male **(c)** plants.

carpels of other flowers, such as those of a bell pepper plant (*Capsicum annuum*). Each ovule consists of a stalk bearing a **nucellus** (the inner part of an ovule, in which the embryo sac develops; equivalent to a megasporangium) enveloped in additional layers of sporophyte tissue called **integuments**, with an opening (the **micropyle**) at one end.

Formation of the female gametophyte varies among plant species, but we will consider only the most commonly observed pattern of development. Inside the ovule, a diploid megasporocyte (also called a *megaspore mother cell*) divides by meiosis, forming four haploid **megaspores**. In most plants, three of these megaspores disintegrate. The remaining megaspore enlarges and develops into the female gametophyte (embryo sac) in a sequence of steps tracked in Figure 35.6, #3 on the right hand side.

First, three rounds of mitosis occur *without* cytoplasmic division; these divisions produce a single cell with eight nuclei, four at each pole of the cell. Next, one nucleus in each group

migrates to the centre of the cell; these two **polar nuclei** ("polar" because they migrate from opposite ends of the cell) may fuse or remain separate. Subsequent cell wall formation results in the formation of seven cells: three at each pole and one large *central cell* containing the two polar nuclei. Of the three cells that form a cluster near the micropyle, one is an **egg cell** that may eventually be fertilized; the other two are called *synergids*. Experiments suggest that synergids play a role in fertilization by providing chemicals that guide the pollen tube to the micropyle. At the other end of the embryo sac are three cells called *antipodals*; their function is unknown, although, in some plants they may play a role in nutrient transfer from maternal tissues to the endosperm. The eventual result of all these events is an **embryo sac** (female gametophyte) containing seven cells and eight nuclei.

As the male and female gametophytes complete their maturation, the stage is set for fertilization and the development of a new individual.

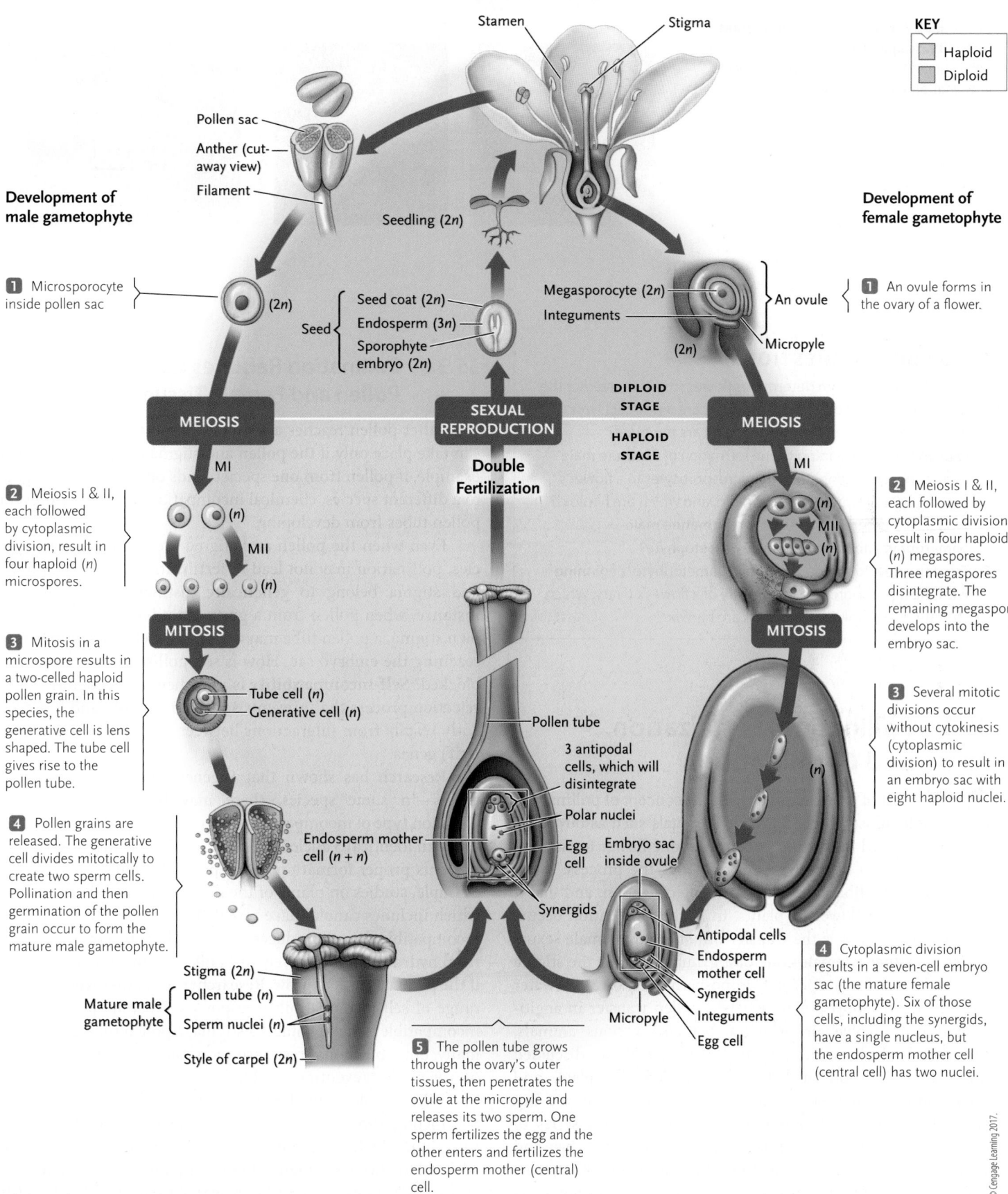

**Development of male gametophyte**

**KEY**
- Haploid
- Diploid

Stamen — Stigma

Pollen sac

Anther (cut-away view)

Filament

Seedling (2n)

**Development of female gametophyte**

**1** Microsporocyte inside pollen sac (2n)

**1** An ovule forms in the ovary of a flower.

Seed coat (2n)
Endosperm (3n)
Sporophyte embryo (2n)
Seed

Megasporocyte (2n)
Integuments
An ovule
Micropyle
(2n)

**MEIOSIS**

**SEXUAL REPRODUCTION**

**DIPLOID STAGE**
**HAPLOID STAGE**

**MEIOSIS**

MI

Double Fertilization

MI

**2** Meiosis I & II, each followed by cytoplasmic division, result in four haploid (n) microspores.

(n)

MII

(n) MII (n)

**2** Meiosis I & II, each followed by cytoplasmic division, result in four haploid (n) megaspores. Three megaspores disintegrate. The remaining megaspore develops into the embryo sac.

(n)

**MITOSIS**

**MITOSIS**

**3** Mitosis in a microspore results in a two-celled haploid pollen grain. In this species, the generative cell is lens shaped. The tube cell gives rise to the pollen tube.

Tube cell (n)
Generative cell (n)

(n)

**3** Several mitotic divisions occur without cytokinesis (cytoplasmic division) to result in an embryo sac with eight haploid nuclei.

Pollen tube

3 antipodal cells, which will disintegrate

Polar nuclei

**4** Pollen grains are released. The generative cell divides mitotically to create two sperm cells. Pollination and then germination of the pollen grain occur to form the mature male gametophyte.

Endosperm mother cell (n + n)

Egg cell

Embryo sac inside ovule

Synergids

Antipodal cells
Endosperm mother cell
Synergids
Integuments
Egg cell

**4** Cytoplasmic division results in a seven-cell embryo sac (the mature female gametophyte). Six of those cells, including the synergids, have a single nucleus, but the endosperm mother cell (central cell) has two nuclei.

Mature male gametophyte:
Stigma (2n)
Pollen tube (n)
Sperm nuclei (n)
Style of carpel (2n)

Micropyle

**5** The pollen tube grows through the ovary's outer tissues, then penetrates the ovule at the micropyle and releases its two sperm. One sperm fertilizes the egg and the other enters and fertilizes the endosperm mother (central) cell.

© Cengage Learning 2017.

**FIGURE 35.6 Sexual reproduction in a generalized angiosperm.** Pollen grains develop in pollen sacs (microsporangia) within the anthers. An embryo sac forms inside each ovule within an ovary, and an egg forms within the embryo sac. Pollen grains are released and deposited on the stigma and then germinate to produce a pollen tube that carries two sperm to an ovule within the ovary, where double fertilization occurs. An embryo sporophyte and nutritive endosperm develop and become encased in a seed coat.

**FIGURE 35.7 Examples of pollen grain diversity.** Scanning electron micrographs of pollen grains from **(a)** a grass, **(b)** chickweed (*Stellaria*), and **(c)** ragweed (*Ambrosia*) plants.

a.

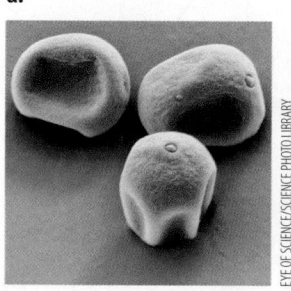

b.

c.

EYE OF SCIENCE/SCIENCE PHOTO LIBRARY

Dr. Jeremy Burgess/Science Source

daniel mathys/iStock/Thinkstock

## STUDY BREAK QUESTIONS

1. If the ABC mechanism determines flower structure, predict the phenotype if only the C gene products are produced. How about A alone? What if A or C products are removed?

2. Explain the steps leading to the formation of a mature male gametophyte, beginning with microsporocytes in a flower's anthers. Which structures are diploid, and which are haploid? What is the difference between an immature male gametophyte and a mature male gametophyte?

3. Trace the development of a female gametophyte, beginning with the megasporocyte in an ovule of a flower's ovary. Which structures are diploid, and which are haploid?

## 35.3 Pollination, Fertilization, and Germination

**CONCEPT FIX** Most of us are familiar with the concept of pollination; for example, most people know that animals such as birds and bees are involved in moving pollen from one flower to another. But there is also a lot of confusion about the process: many people think pollination is the same as fertilization, and that it only happens in flowering plants. In reality, pollination occurs in all seed plants: it is the transfer of pollen to a female sexual structure, either a female cone of a gymnosperm or the stigma of a flower in an angiosperm. Gymnosperms rely on air or water currents to transport pollen, whereas pollen transfer in angiosperms can involve air or wind, but also various animals, including birds, bats, and insects. In Chapter 26, we discussed the complex relationship between some flowering plants and their animal pollinators. Pollination and fertilization are not synonymous: pollination is only the first step in a series of events that can lead to *fertilization*, the fusion of an egg and sperm inside an ovule, but because there are many other steps before successful fertilization occurs, pollination does not guarantee that fertilization will happen. A fertilized ovule matures into a seed, and the zygote that results from fertilization matures into an embryo, a young sporophyte. ⬡

### 35.3a Pollination Requires Compatible Pollen and Female Tissues

Even after pollen reaches a stigma, pollination and fertilization can take place only if the pollen and stigma are compatible. For example, if pollen from one species lands on a stigma belonging to a different species, chemical incompatibilities usually prevent pollen tubes from developing.

Even when the pollen and stigma are from the same species, pollination may not lead to fertilization unless the pollen and stigma belong to genetically distinct individuals. For instance, when pollen from a given plant lands on that plant's own stigma, a pollen tube may begin to develop but stop before reaching the embryo sac. How is self-pollination detected and blocked? **Self-incompatibility** is a biochemical recognition and rejection process that prevents **self-fertilization**, and it apparently results from interactions between proteins encoded by *S* (self) genes.

Research has shown that *S* genes usually have multiple alleles—in some species, there may be hundreds—and a common type of incompatibility occurs when pollen and stigma carry an identical *S* allele. The result is a biochemical signal that prevents proper formation of the pollen tube **(Figure 35.8)**. For example, studies on plants of the mustard family (*Brassicaceae*, which includes canola) have revealed that pollen contacting an incompatible stigma produces a protein that prevents the stigma from hydrating the relatively dry pollen grain, an essential step if the pollen tube is to grow. Researchers have discovered a wide range of self-incompatibility responses. In some plants, when incompatible pollen contacts a stigma, a pollen tube grows normally, but a hormonal response soon causes the flower to drop off the plant, preventing fertilization.

Why is it desirable for plants not to pollinate themselves? Self-incompatibility prevents inbreeding and promotes genetic variation, which is the raw material for natural selection and adaptation. Even so, many flowering plants do self-pollinate, either partly or exclusively, because that mode, too, has benefits in some circumstances. (Mendel's peas are a classic example.) For instance, *selfing* may help preserve adaptive traits in a population. It also reduces or eliminates a plant's reliance on wind,

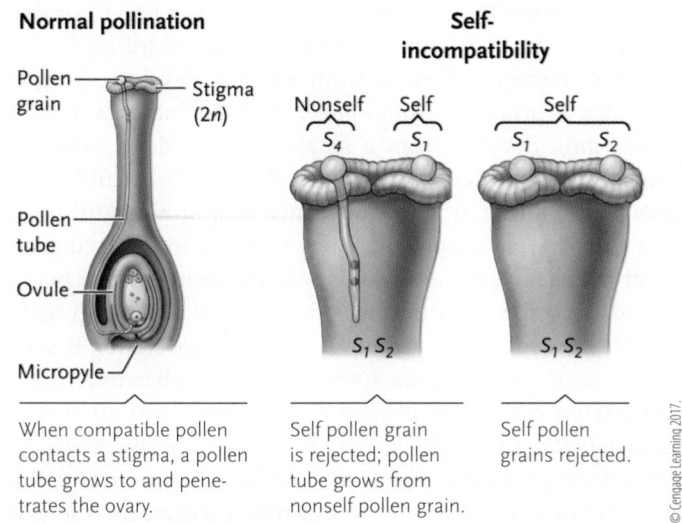

**Normal pollination**

Pollen grain — Stigma (2n)

Pollen tube

Ovule

Micropyle

When compatible pollen contacts a stigma, a pollen tube grows to and penetrates the ovary.

**Self-incompatibility**

Nonself $S_4$  Self $S_1$

Self $S_1$  $S_2$

$S_1 S_2$

$S_1 S_2$

Self pollen grain is rejected; pollen tube grows from nonself pollen grain.

Self pollen grains rejected.

© Cengage Learning 2017.

**FIGURE 35.8 Self-incompatibility.** When a pollen grain has an *S* allele that matches one in the stigma (which is diploid), the result is a biochemical response that prevents fertilization, in this illustration, by preventing the growth of a pollen tube.

water, or animals for pollination, and thus ensures that seeds will form when conditions for cross-pollination are unfavourable, as when pollinators or potential mates are scarce.

## 35.3b Double Fertilization Results in the Formation of Embryos and Endosperm

If a pollen grain lands on a compatible stigma, it absorbs moisture and produces a pollen tube, which digests its way through the stigma and style toward an ovule **(Figure 35.9a)**. The synergids secrete proteins that guide the pollen tube to the micropyle. The pollen grain's haploid generative cell

divides by mitosis to form two haploid sperm. When the pollen tube reaches the ovule, it enters through the micropyle. By this time, one synergid has begun to die (an example of programmed cell death), and the two sperm are released from the tube and into the disintegrating cell's cytoplasm (Figure 35.9b). Experiments suggest the synergid's cytoskeleton guides the sperm onward: one to the egg cell and the other to the central cell.

Next, a remarkable sequence of events occurs called **double fertilization**, which has been observed only in flowering plants and (in a somewhat different version) in the gnetophyte *Ephedra* (see Chapter 26). Typically, one sperm fuses with the egg to form a diploid (2n) zygote. The other sperm fuses with the central cell, forming a cell with a triploid (3n) nucleus. This 3n nucleus (the primary endosperm nucleus) divides repeatedly along with its surrounding cytoplasm to form a tissue called **endosperm** (= inside the seed). The endosperm nourishes the embryo, and in some plants the seedling, until vegetative leaves form and photosynthesis begins.

Embryo-nourishing endosperm forms only in flowering plants; its evolution coincided with a reduction in the size of the female gametophyte. In other land plants, such as gymnosperms and ferns, the gametophyte itself contains enough stored food to nourish the embryonic sporophytes. Endosperm offers an advantage over female gametophyte tissue as a nutrient source for embryos because its development is tied to that of the embryo: if no embryo forms, the plant does not commit resources to endosperm. In gymnosperms, resources are committed to female gametophyte tissue even if no embryo forms. And if an angiosperm embryo is aborted, which can happen if environmental conditions become unfavourable for embryo development (e.g., in the case of drought), endosperm development also ceases, saving the plant energy and resources.

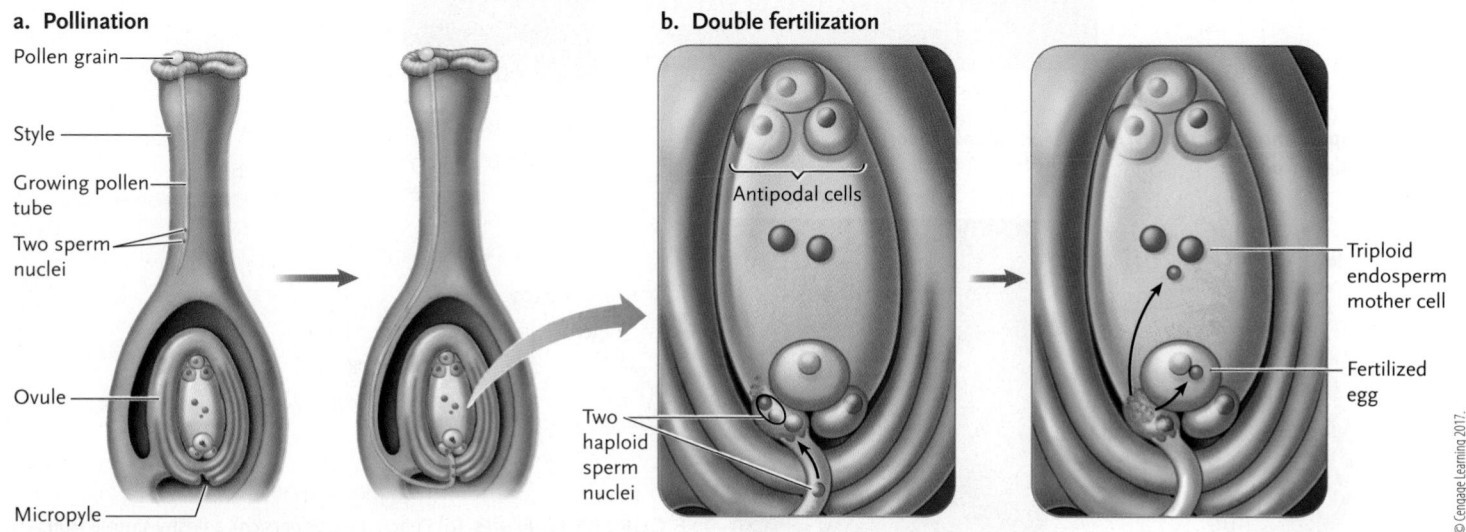

**a. Pollination**

Pollen grain

Style

Growing pollen tube

Two sperm nuclei

Ovule

Micropyle

Two haploid sperm nuclei

**b. Double fertilization**

Antipodal cells

Triploid endosperm mother cell

Fertilized egg

© Cengage Learning 2017.

**FIGURE 35.9 Double fertilization in angiosperms. (a)** Germination of a pollen grain creates a pollen tube that grows from the stigma through the style to the micropyle of the ovary. **(b)** One sperm joins the egg to form a zygote; the other joins the two nuclei in the central cell to form triploid endosperm.

## 35.3c After Fertilization, Ovaries Develop into Fruits That Protect Seeds and Aid Seed Dispersal

Most angiosperm seeds are housed inside fruits, which provide protection for the developing seeds and often aid in seed dispersal. Contrary to popular assumption, the fruit does not provide any nutrients to the developing seeds. A **fruit** is a mature or ripened ovary. Usually, fruits begin to develop after ovules are fertilized, but some plants can produce fruit without fertilization, via a process called *parthenocarpy*. Parthenocarpy occurs naturally in some plants, and can be induced in others, to produce seedless fruits such as bananas, pineapples, and watermelons. The fruit wall (**pericarp**) develops from the ovary wall and can have several layers. Hormones from pollen turn on the genetic machinery leading to fruit development; additional signals come from hormones produced by the developing seeds.

Fruits are extremely diverse, and biologists classify them into types based on combinations of structural features. A key feature is whether the pericarp is fleshy (as in a peach) or dry (as in a hazelnut). A fruit is also classified according to the number of ovaries or flowers from which it develops. **Simple fruits**, such as peaches (*Prunus persica*) and tomatoes (*Solanum lycopersicum*), develop from a single ovary and, in many of them, at least one layer of the pericarp is fleshy and juicy **(Figure 35.10)**. Other simple fruits, including grains and nuts, have a thin dry pericarp, which may be fused to the seed coat. The garden pea (*Pisum sativum*) is a simple fruit, the peas being the seeds and the surrounding pod the pericarp. **Aggregate fruits** are formed from several ovaries in a single flower. Examples are raspberries (*Rubus* species) and strawberries, which develop from clusters of ovaries. Strawberries also qualify as *accessory fruits*, in which floral parts in addition to the ovary become incorporated as the fruit develops. Anatomically, the fleshy part of a strawberry is an expanded receptacle (the end of the floral shoot) and the strawberry fruits are the tiny dry specks (called *achenes*) you see embedded in the fleshy tissue of each berry. **Multiple fruits** develop from several ovaries in

**a. Peach (*Prunus*), a simple fruit**

Fleshy pericarp

**b. Raspberry (*Rubus*), an aggregate fruit**

**c. Strawberry (*Fragaria*), an accessory fruit**

Fruit wall

**d. Pineapple (*Ananus comosus*), a multiple fruit**

One of many individual fruits

**e. Maple (*Acer*) fruit**

Wing

Seed (in carpel)

**FIGURE 35.10 Fruits. (a)** Peach (*Prunus persica*), a fleshy simple fruit. **(b)** Raspberry (*Rubus*), an aggregate fruit. **(c)** Strawberry (*Fragaria ananassa*), an accessory fruit that is also an aggregate fruit. **(d)** Pineapple (*Ananas comosus*), a multiple fruit. **(e)** Winged fruits of maple (*Acer*)

multiple flowers. For example, a pineapple (*Ananas* species) is a multiple fruit that develops from the enlarged ovaries of several flowers clustered together in an inflorescence. Figure 35.10 shows examples of some different types of fruits.

Fruits have two functions: they protect seeds and they aid seed dispersal in specific environments. For example, the shell of a sunflower "seed" is a pericarp that protects the seed within. A pea pod is a pericarp that, in nature, splits open to disperse the seeds (peas) inside. Maple fruits have winglike extensions for dispersal (see Figure 35.10e). When the fruit drops, the wings cause it to spin sideways to be carried away on a breeze. This aerodynamic property propels maple seeds to new locations, where they will not have to compete with the parent tree for water and minerals. Fruits may also have hooks, spines, hairs, or sticky surfaces that allow them to be carried to new locations when they adhere to the feathers or fur of animals or the clothing of people that brush against them. Fleshy fruits such as blueberries

and cherries are nutritious food for many animals; their seeds are adapted for surviving digestive enzymes in the animal gut. The seeds are distributed away from the parent plant in the animal's feces.

## 35.3d The Embryonic Sporophyte Develops inside a Seed

When the zygote first forms, it starts to develop and elongate even before mitosis begins. Most of the organelles in the zygote, including the nucleus, become situated in the top half of the cell, whereas a vacuole takes up most of the lower half. The first round of mitosis divides the zygote into an upper *apical cell* and a lower *basal cell* (**Figure 35.11**). The apical cell then gives rise to the multicellular embryo, although most descendants of the basal cell form a simple row of cells, the **suspensor**, which transfers nutrients from the parent sporophyte to the embryo (see Figure 35.11).

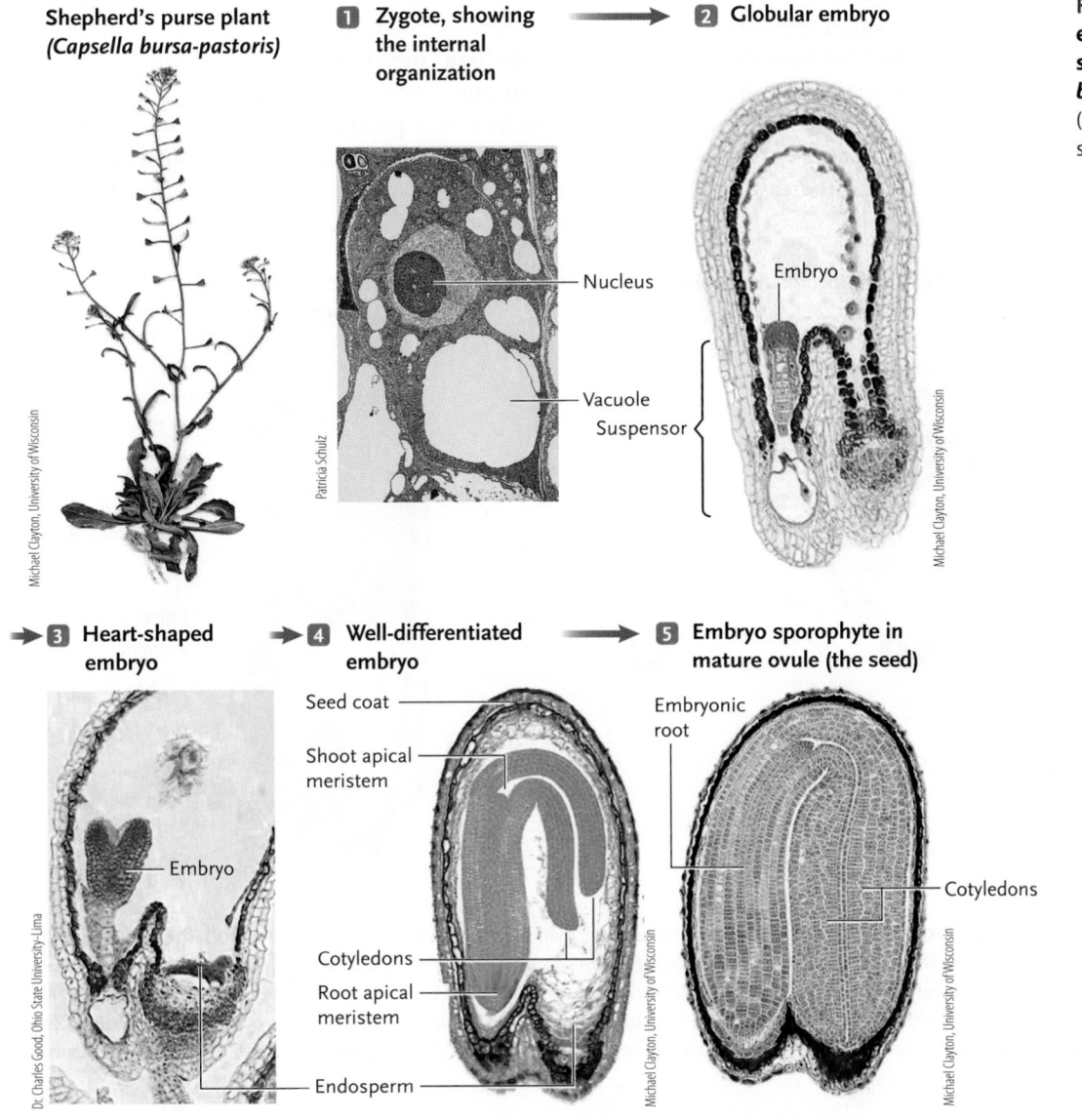

**FIGURE 35.11 Stages in the embryonic development of shepherd's purse (*Capsella bursa-pastoris*), a eudicot.** (The micrographs are not to the same scale.)

Shepherd's purse plant (*Capsella bursa-pastoris*)

Michael Clayton, University of Wisconsin

**1** Zygote, showing the internal organization

Nucleus

Vacuole
Suspensor

Patricia Schulz

**2** Globular embryo

Embryo

Michael Clayton, University of Wisconsin

**3** Heart-shaped embryo

Embryo

Dr. Charles Good, Ohio State University–Lima

**4** Well-differentiated embryo

Seed coat

Shoot apical meristem

Cotyledons

Root apical meristem

Endosperm

Michael Clayton, University of Wisconsin

**5** Embryo sporophyte in mature ovule (the seed)

Embryonic root

Cotyledons

Michael Clayton, University of Wisconsin

CHAPTER 35    REPRODUCTION AND DEVELOPMENT IN FLOWERING PLANTS

The first apical cell divisions produce a globe-shaped structure attached to the suspensor. As they continue to grow, eudicot embryos become heart-shaped (see Figure 35.11); each lobe of the "heart" is a developing **cotyledon** (embryonic leaf), which provides nutrients for growing tissues. These embryonic leaves can be genetically programmed differently than vegetative leaves, acting as nutrient delivery organs rather than wide plates that maximize light absorption for photosynthesis. By the time the ovule is mature (i.e., a fully developed seed), it has become encased by a protective **seed coat**. Inside the seed, the sheltered embryo has a lengthwise axis with a root apical meristem at one end and a shoot apical meristem at the other.

In seeds of some plants, such as castor bean, endosperm is maintained as a tissue outside the embryo. In these plants, the cotyledons form an interface between the rest of the embryo and the endosperm; they produce enzymes that digest the endosperm and transfer the liberated nutrients to the seedling. In other seeds, the cotyledons absorb much of the nutrient-storing endosperm and become plump and fleshy. For instance, the mature seeds of a sunflower (*Helianthus annuus*) have no endosperm at all. Monocots have one large cotyledon that acts like pea seed cotyledons; that is, it is an interface between the endosperm and the embryo, transferring nutrients to the embryo.

**Figure 35.12a, b** illustrates the structure of the seeds of two eudicots, the kidney bean (*Phaseolus vulgaris*) and the castor bean (*Ricinus communis*). The kidney bean has broad, fleshy cotyledons, whereas the castor bean has much thinner ones. In other ways, however, the embryos are quite similar. The **radicle**, or embryonic root, is located near the micropyle, where the pollen tube entered the ovule before fertilization. The cotyledons are attached to the stem. The portion of stem below the point of attachment is called the *hypocotyl* (= below the cotyledons); the stem above the point of attachment of the cotyledons is called the **epicotyl** (= above the cotyledons). The epicotyl has the shoot apical meristem at its tip and often bears a cluster of tiny foliage leaves. This small shoot is called the **plumule**. At germination, when the root and shoot first elongate and emerge from the seed, the cotyledons are positioned at the first stem node, with the epicotyl above them and the hypocotyl below them.

The embryos of monocots such as corn (Figure 35.12c) differ structurally from those of eudicots in several ways. In addition to having only one very large cotyledon, monocots also have protective tissues that shield the root and shoot apical meristems. The shoot apical meristem and first leaves are covered by a **coleoptile**, a sheath of cells that protects them during upward growth through the soil. A similar covering, the **coleorhiza**, sheathes the radicle until it breaks out of the seed coat and enters the soil as the primary root. The actual embryo of a corn plant is buried deep within the corn "kernel," which is technically called a *grain*. Most of the moist interior of a fresh corn grain is endosperm; the single

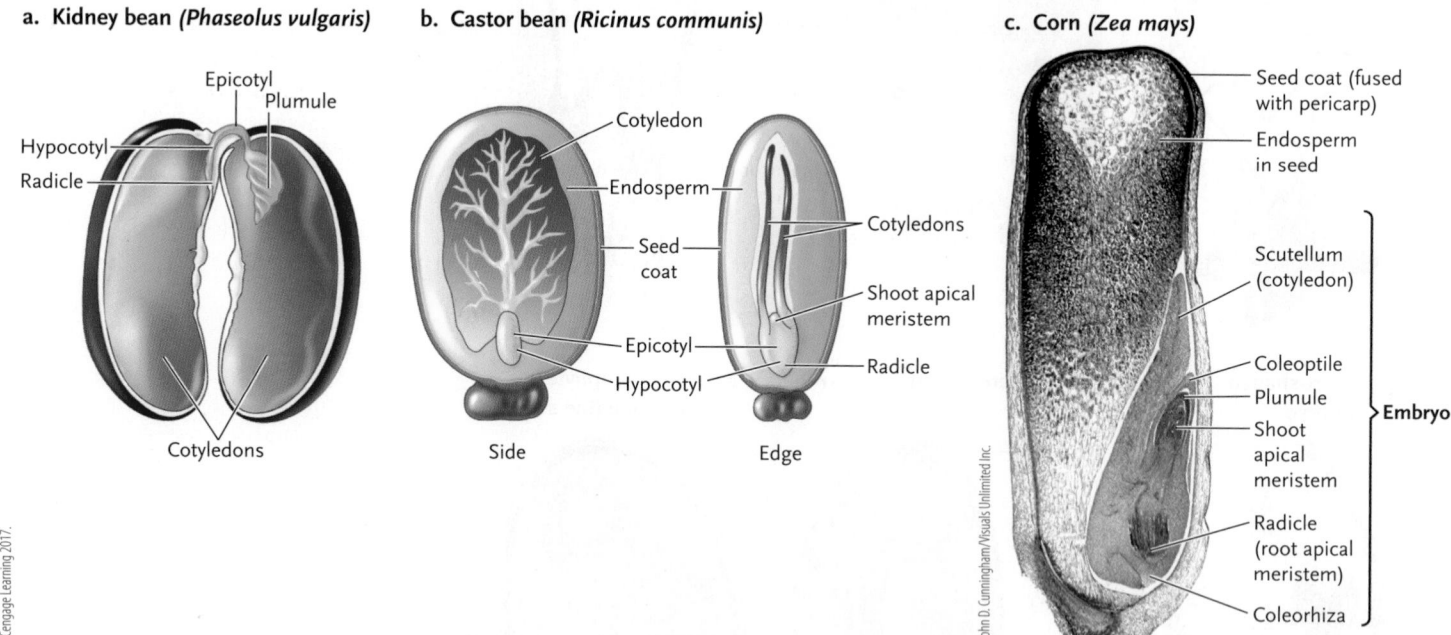

a. **Kidney bean (Phaseolus vulgaris)**    b. **Castor bean (Ricinus communis)**    c. **Corn (Zea mays)**

© Cengage Learning 2017.

Dr. John D. Cunningham/Visuals Unlimited Inc.

**FIGURE 35.12 The structure of eudicot and monocot seeds.** Eudicot seeds have two cotyledons, which store food absorbed from the endosperm; the timing of this function varies in different species. **(a)** The cotyledons of a kidney bean (*Phaseolus vulgaris*) take up nutrients from endosperm while the seed develops, becoming plump and fleshy. **(b)** In the castor bean (*Ricinus communis*), the endosperm is thick and the cotyledons are thin until the seed germinates, when the cotyledons begin to take up endosperm nutrients. The drawing on the right gives a side view of the embryo. **(c)** A kernel of corn (*Zea mays*), a representative monocot seed, is shown here in longitudinal section. Monocot seeds have a single cotyledon, which becomes shield-shaped and absorbs nutrients from endosperm.

cotyledon forms a plump mass that absorbs nutrients from the endosperm.

## 35.3e Seed Germination Continues the Life Cycle

A mature seed is essentially dehydrated. Why is being dehydrated important? It allows the seed to stay in a state of "suspended animation" and also allows it to travel further from the mother plant. On average, only about 10% of a seed's mass is water; too little for **cell expansion** or metabolism. After a seed is dispersed and germinates, the embryo inside it becomes hydrated and resumes growth. Ideally, a seed germinates when external conditions favour the survival of the embryo and growth of the new sporophyte. This timing is important because, once germination is underway, the embryo loses the protection of the seed coat and other structures that surround it. Soil moisture and oxygen, the temperature, day length, and other environmental factors influence when germination takes place.

In some species, the life cycle may include a period of seed **dormancy** (*dormire* = to sleep), in which biological activity is suspended. Plant biologists have described a striking array of variations in the conditions required for dormant seeds to germinate. For instance, seeds may require minimum periods of daylight or darkness, repeated soaking, mechanical abrasion, exposure to certain enzymes, the high heat of a fire, or a freeze–thaw cycle before they finally break dormancy. In some desert plants, hormones in the seed coat inhibit the growth of a seedling until heavy rains flush the hormones away. This prevents seeds from germinating unless there is enough water in the soil to support the growth and maturation of the plant. Harsh climates like the desert or alpine tundra can be accommodated by plants developing from seed to flowering within a few weeks, with longer seed dormancy taking up the rest of the year. Many seeds will not germinate until they have passed through the gut of an animal: their seed coats contain germination-inhibiting substances that are broken down by the acids and enzymes of an animal's digestive tract, allowing the seeds to germinate after they are deposited in the animal's feces.

How long can a seed remain viable? The seeds of some species appear to remain potent for amazing lengths of time; for example, 1000-year-old lotus seeds (*Nelumbo lutea*) discovered in a dry lakebed have germinated without difficulty. The record for the oldest seed to germinate is a 2000-year-old date palm seed that was germinated in 2005; as of 2010, the plant was about 2 m tall.

Germination begins with **imbibition**, in which water moves into the seed, attracted to hydrophilic proteins and ions in the seed and facilitated by cell wall and organ adaptations. As water enters, the seed swells to rupture the seed coat and the radicle begins its downward growth into the soil. As always, however, there are many variations among plants.

Once the seed coat splits, water and oxygen move more easily into the seed. Metabolism switches into high gear as cells divide and elongate to produce the seedling. Enzymes that were synthesized before dormancy become active; other enzymes are produced as the genes encoding them begin to be expressed. Among other roles, the increased gene activity and enzyme production mobilize the seed's food reserves in cotyledons or endosperm. Nutrients released by the enzymes sustain the rapidly developing seedling until its root and shoot systems are established.

The events of seed germination have been studied extensively in cereal grains, which are monocots. As a hydrating seed imbibes water, the embryo produces *gibberellin*, a hormone that stimulates the production of enzymes. Some of these enzymes digest components of endosperm cell walls; others digest the proteins, nucleic acids, and starch of the endosperm, releasing nutrient molecules for use by cells of the young root and shoot. Although it is clear that nutrient reserves are also mobilized by metabolic activity in eudicots and in gymnosperms, the details of the process are not well understood.

Inside a germinating seed, embryonic root cells are generally the first to divide and elongate, producing a radicle. When the radicle emerges from the seed coat as the primary root, germination is complete. **Figures 35.13** and **35.14** depict the stages of early development in a kidney bean (a eudicot) and in a corn plant (a monocot). As the young plant grows, its development continues to be influenced by interactions of hormones and environmental factors, as you will read in Chapter 37.

Many plants produce large numbers of seeds because, normally, only a tiny fraction of seeds survive, germinate, and eventually grow into another mature plant. Because flowers, seeds, and fruits represent major investments of plant resources, asexual reproduction, discussed next, is a more "economical" means of propagation.

### STUDY BREAK QUESTIONS

1. Explain the sequence of events in a flowering plant that begins with the formation of a pollen tube and culminates with the formation of a diploid zygote and the 3*n* cell that will give rise to endosperm in a seed.
2. Early angiosperm embryos undergo a series of general changes as a seed matures. Summarize this sequence, and then describe the structural differences that develop in the seeds of monocots and eudicots.

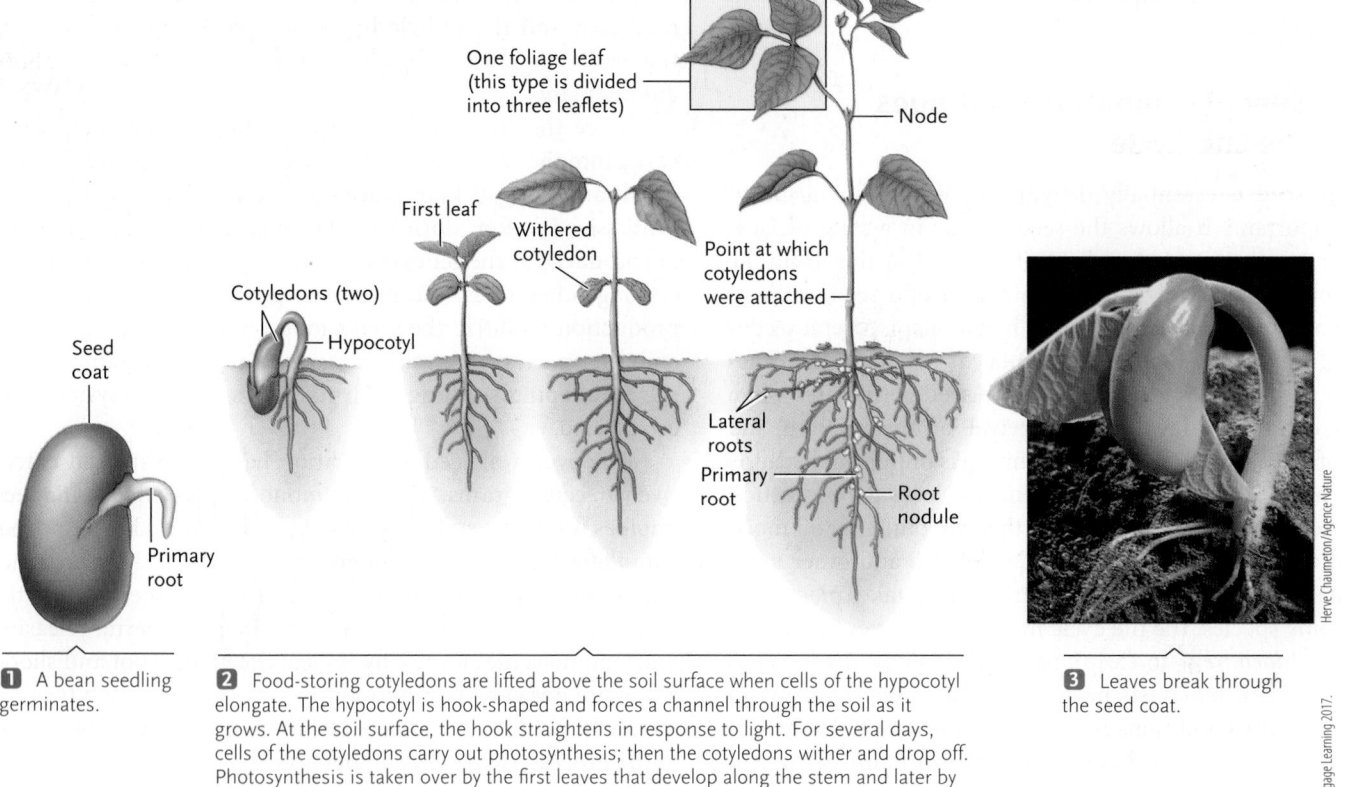

One foliage leaf (this type is divided into three leaflets)

Node

First leaf

Withered cotyledon

Point at which cotyledons were attached

Cotyledons (two)

Hypocotyl

Seed coat

Lateral roots

Primary root

Root nodule

Primary root

Hervé Chaumeton/Agence Nature

**1** A bean seedling germinates.

**2** Food-storing cotyledons are lifted above the soil surface when cells of the hypocotyl elongate. The hypocotyl is hook-shaped and forces a channel through the soil as it grows. At the soil surface, the hook straightens in response to light. For several days, cells of the cotyledons carry out photosynthesis; then the cotyledons wither and drop off. Photosynthesis is taken over by the first leaves that develop along the stem and later by foliage leaves.

**3** Leaves break through the seed coat.

© Cengage Learning 2017.

**FIGURE 35.13 Stages in the development of a representative eudicot, the kidney bean (*Phaseolus vulgaris*)**

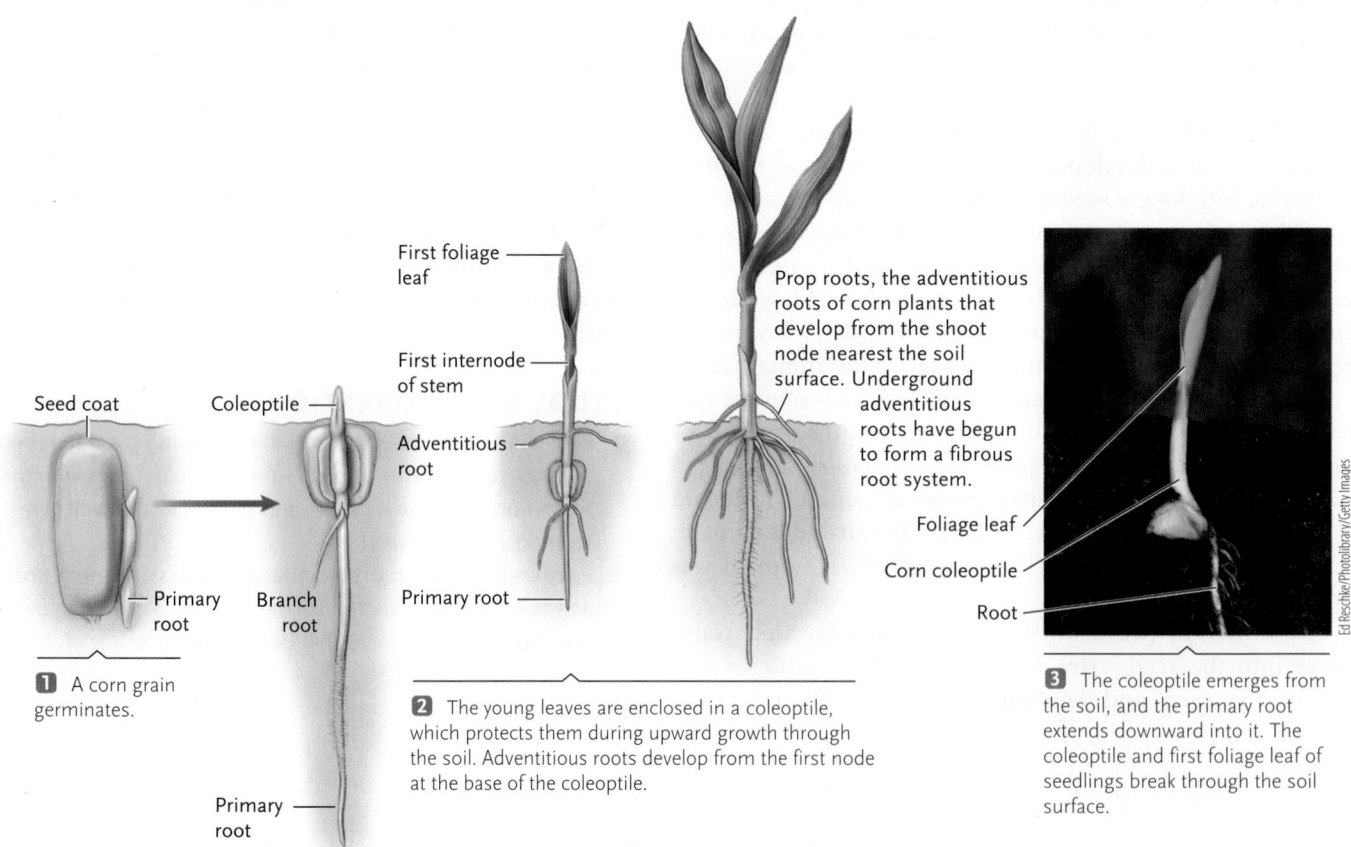

First foliage leaf

First internode of stem

Seed coat

Coleoptile

Adventitious root

Prop roots, the adventitious roots of corn plants that develop from the shoot node nearest the soil surface. Underground adventitious roots have begun to form a fibrous root system.

Foliage leaf

Corn coleoptile

Root

Primary root

Branch root

Primary root

Primary root

Ed Reschke/Photolibrary/Getty Images

**1** A corn grain germinates.

**2** The young leaves are enclosed in a coleoptile, which protects them during upward growth through the soil. Adventitious roots develop from the first node at the base of the coleoptile.

**3** The coleoptile emerges from the soil, and the primary root extends downward into it. The coleoptile and first foliage leaf of seedlings break through the soil surface.

© Cengage Learning 2017.

**FIGURE 35.14 Stages in the development of a representative monocot, the corn plant (*Zea mays*)**

## 35.4 Asexual Reproduction in Flowering Plants

As noted in Chapter 33, nodes in the stolons of strawberries and the rhizomes of quackgrass can each give rise to new individuals, as can *suckers* that sprout from the roots of raspberry bushes and *eyes* in the tubers of potatoes. All these examples involve asexual or **vegetative reproduction** from a non-reproductive plant part, usually a bit of meristematic tissue in a bud on the root or stem. All of them produce offspring that are clones of the parent. Vegetative reproduction relies on an intriguing property of plants, namely, that many fully differentiated plant cells are **totipotent** (= all powerful); that is, they have the genetic potential to develop into a whole, fully functional plant, as discussed in Chapter 33. Under appropriate conditions, a totipotent cell can *dedifferentiate*: it returns to an unspecialized embryonic state, and the genetic program that guides the development of a new individual is turned on.

### 35.4a Vegetative Reproduction Is Common in Nature

Various plant species have developed different mechanisms for reproducing asexually. In the type of vegetative reproduction called **fragmentation**, cells in a piece of the parent plant dedifferentiate and then regenerate missing plant parts. Many gardeners have discovered to their frustration that a piece of dandelion root left in the soil can rapidly grow into a new dandelion plant in this way.

Potatoes that we eat are modified stems. Axillary buds ("the eyes") can form new shoots **(Figure 35.15a)**. A sectioned potato can be used to generate multiple clones, a fact the hero of the movie *The Martian* used to stave off starvation.

When a leaf falls or is torn away from a jade plant (*Crassula* species), a new plant can develop from meristematic tissue in the detached leaf adjacent to the wound surface. In the mother of thousands plant, *Kalanchoe daigremontiana*, meristematic tissue in notches along the leaf margin gives rise to tiny plantlets (Figure 35.15b) that eventually fall to the ground, where they can sprout roots and grow to maturity.

Some flowering plants, including Kentucky bluegrass (*Poa pratensis*), a common lawn grass in Canada, can reproduce asexually through a mechanism called **apomixis** whereby a diploid embryo develops from an unfertilized egg—derived from a megaspore mother cell that does *not* complete meiosis—or from diploid cells in the ovule tissue around the embryo sac. The resulting seed is said to contain a **somatic embryo**, which is genetically identical to the parent.

In native plant species, most types of asexual reproduction result in offspring located near the parent. These clonal populations lack the variability provided by sexual reproduction, variation that enhances the odds for survival when environmental conditions change. Yet asexual reproduction offers an advantage in some situations. It usually requires less energy than producing complex reproductive structures such as seeds and showy flowers to attract pollinators. Moreover, clones are likely to be well-suited to the environment in which the parent grows.

For centuries, gardeners and farmers have used asexual plant propagation to grow particular crops and trees and some ornamental plants. They routinely use *cuttings,* pieces of stems or leaves, to generate new plants; placed in water or moist soil, a cutting may sprout roots within days or a few weeks. Vegetative propagation can also be used to grow plants from single cells. Rose bushes and fruit trees from nurseries, and

**a. Young potato plant**

Kim Fennema/Visuals Unlimited, Inc.

**b. Mother-of-thousands plant**

Ed Reschke/Photolibrary/Getty Images

**FIGURE 35.15 Examples of asexual reproduction in flowering plants.** **(a)** Young potato plant (*Solanum tuberosum*) growing from an "eye," an axial bud. **(b)** *Kalanchoe daigremontiana*, the mother-of-thousands plant. Each plantlet growing from the leaf margin can become an independent adult plant.

# FIGURE 35.16    Research Method

## Plant Tissue Culture Protocol

**Problem:** How can you rid a plant of a virus that has infected the majority of the sporophyte cells?

**Purpose:** Viruses are so small that they can easily move between cells that are connected by plasmodesmata, cytoplasmic bridges that pierce the cell wall between adjacent cells (see Chapter 2). If a valuable plant is identified but is also contaminated with viruses, they cannot be filtered away. Plants also do not have immune systems, so vaccination would not work. Seeds *could* be generated, but perhaps there's something special about the genetics of your plants that makes altering the genome through fertilization undesirable.

The meristems of plants have undifferentiated cells that are not connected to the plant through vasculature that facilitates virus transfer. The rapidly dividing cells of the meristems are therefore sources of virus-free material.

**Protocol:** In a sterile environment, a researcher soaks donor tissue in a mild bleach solution to remove surface contaminants, and removes a few cells from the shoot apical meristem **(a)**. These cells are placed on growth medium **(b)** and allowed to grow into a callus **(c)**. Media can be used to regenerate shoots and roots in culture **(d)** or artificial seeds through somatic embryogenesis **(e)**.

**Results:** Many genetically identical offspring are created as clones.

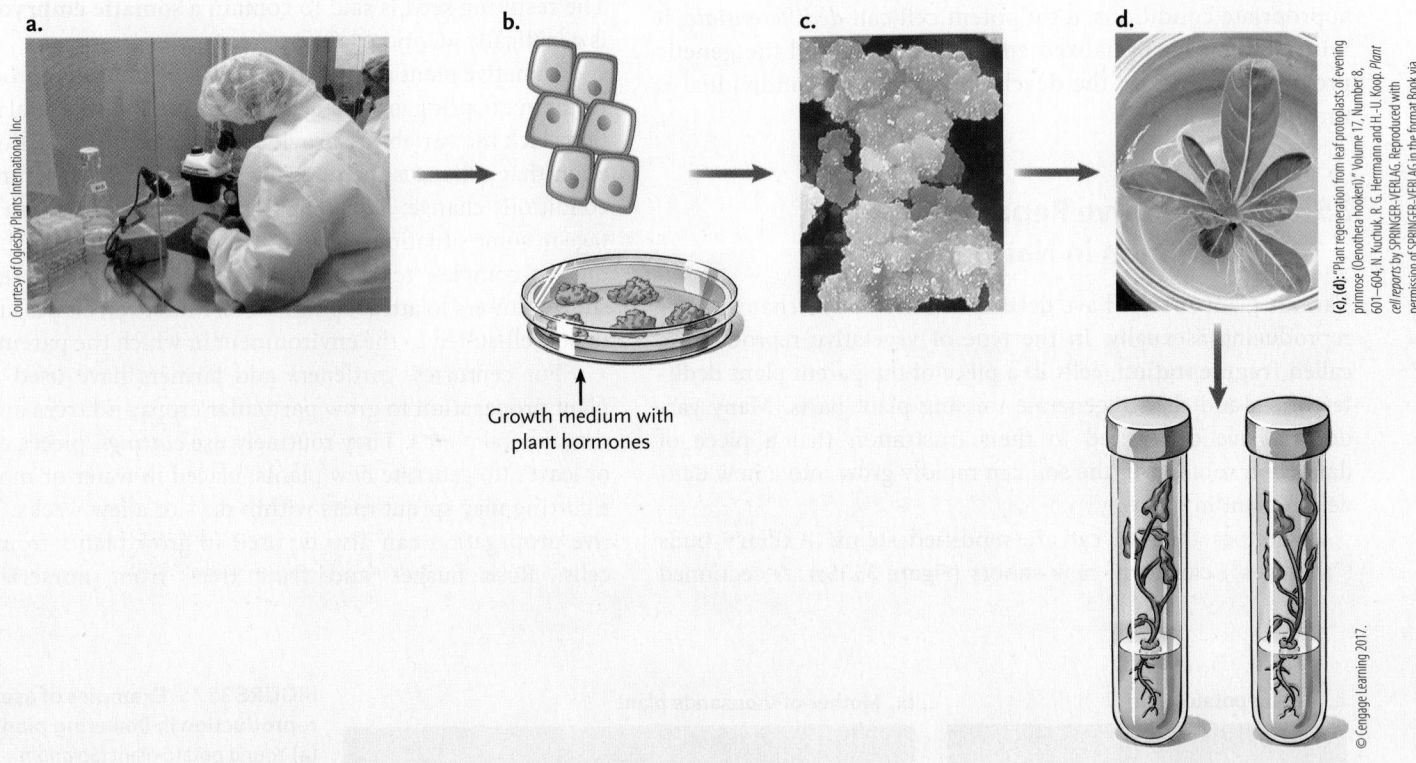

Growth medium with plant hormones

(c), (d): "Plant regeneration from leaf protoplasts of evening primrose (Oenothera hookeri)," Volume 17, Number 8, 601–604, N. Kuchuk, R. G. Herrmann and H.-U. Koop. *Plant cell reports* by SPRINGER-VERLAG. Reproduced with permission of SPRINGER-VERLAG in the format Book via Copyright Clearance Center.

© Cengage Learning 2017.

Courtesy of Oglesby Plants International, Inc.

Source: Based on D. Adilakshmi, Suresh M, Rajkumar N, Jayachandra K, & Bebi P. 2016. Evaluation of Tissue Culture Seedlings for Their Genetic Fidelity and Virus Indexing in Sugarcane. *IRA-International Journal of Applied Sciences* (ISSN 2455-4499), 3(2). doi: http://dx.doi.org/10.21013/jas.v3.n2.p3

commercially important crops such as Bartlett pears, McIntosh apples, Thompson seedless grapes, and asparagus come from plants produced vegetatively in tissue culture conditions that cause their cells to dedifferentiate to an embryonic stage.

## 35.4b    Plants Can Be Propagated Asexually Using Tissue Culture

Researchers have taken advantage of the totipotency of plant cells to develop plant tissue culture techniques. Entire plants can be generated from single cells that have desirable traits, such as genetic modification, or which are disease free. Plant tissue culture is generally simple **(Figure 35.16)**. Tissue is excised from a donor and grown in a nutrient medium. The procedure disrupts normal interactions between cells in the tissue, causing them to dedifferentiate into an unorganized mass called a **callus**. When cultured, some cells of the callus regain totipotency and develop into plantlets with roots and shoots.

Plant tissue culture is the foundation for the technique called *somatic embryogenesis*. Single cells from a callus are placed in a medium containing nutrients and hormones that promote cell differentiation. Totipotent cells in the sample eventually give rise to diploid somatic embryos that can be packaged with nutrients and hormones in artificial "seeds." Endowed with the same traits as their parent, crop plants grown from somatic embryos are genetically uniform.

Regardless of its origin, the young sporophyte changes significantly as it begins the developmental journey toward maturity, when it will be capable of reproducing. Next we explore what researchers are learning about these developmental changes.

**STUDY BREAK QUESTIONS**

1. What is the major disadvantage of asexual reproduction (relative to sexual reproduction)? Are there any advantages? If so, what are they?
2. How do methods of tissue culture exploit the totipotency of plant cells?

## 35.5 Early Development of Plant Form and Function

As you learned in Chapter 33, one difference between plants and animals is that plant organs, such as leaves and flowers, may arise from meristems throughout an individual's life, sometimes over a period of thousands of years. Accordingly, in plants, the biological role of embryonic development is not to generate the tissues and organs of the adult but to establish a basic body plan—the root–shoot axis and the radial, "outside-to-inside" organization of epidermal, ground, and vascular tissues (see Chapter 33)—and the precursors of the primary meristems. Although they may sound simple, these fundamentals and the stages beyond them all require an intricately orchestrated sequence of molecular events that plant scientists are defining through experimentation.

One of the most fruitful experimental approaches has been the study of plants with natural or induced gene mutations that block or otherwise affect steps in development, and thus lend insight into the developmental roles of the normal, wild-type versions of these abnormal genes. Although researchers work with various species to probe the genetic underpinnings of early plant development, thale cress (*Arabidopsis thaliana*) has become an important model organism for plant genetic research.

The entire *Arabidopsis* genome has been sequenced, providing a powerful molecular database for determining the genetic controls that shape the plant body. Experimenters' ability to trace the expression of specific genes has shed considerable light on how the root–shoot axis is set, and how the three basic plant tissue systems arise.

### 35.5a Within Hours, an Early Plant Embryo's Basic Body Plan Is Established

What determines which part of the embryo will be the root and which part will be the shoot? Studies on *Arabidopsis* reveal that the first, asymmetrical division of the zygote results in the two daughter cells receiving very different mixes of mRNAs. The asymmetry is due to the apical cell receiving the majority of the zygote's cytoplasm; the basal cell receives the zygote's large vacuole. This means that the apical and basal cells produce very different proteins; of particular interest are *transcription factors* (proteins that regulate transcription) that will be produced in the two daughter cells. Different transcription factors control particular genes in the apical and basal cells so that distinct biochemical pathways unfold in the two cells, differentiating root and shoot systems.

As development proceeds, cells at different sites become specialized in prescribed ways as a particular set of genes is expressed in each type of cell, a process known as *differentiation*. Differentiated cells, in turn, are the foundation of specialized tissues and organs. We are starting to unravel how plants regulate differentiation, but much of this topic is beyond the scope of this chapter.

In nature, genes that govern plant development switch on or off in response to changing environmental conditions. Their signals determine the course of a plant's vegetative growth throughout its life. In many perennials, new leaves begin to develop inside buds in autumn, and then become dormant until the following spring, when external conditions favour further growth. Environmental cues stimulate the gene-guided production of hormones that travel through the plant in xylem and phloem, triggering renewed leaf growth and expansion. Leaves and other shoot parts also age, wither, and fall away from the plant as hormonal signals change. The far-reaching effects of plant hormones on growth and development are the subject of Chapter 37.

The life-cycle strategy that plants use benefits the plant of course, but also is the reason that agriculture is so important to people. Plants create a large sporophyte capable of efficient growth for nutrient accumulation, which in turn allows the production of many gametophytes, each of which can contribute to a seed. These seeds are packed with food reserves to give a kick start to the next generation of gametophytes. The "lunch" packed by the seed's mother gives the embryo a head start, but is also an important resource for humans.

**STUDY BREAK QUESTIONS**

1. What does the term *differentiation* mean?
2. What event sets the stage for differentiation of a plant into root and shoot systems?

# Summary Illustration

Alternation of generations means the flowering plant life cycle switches between multicellular haploid and diploid stages. In the diploid phase, the zygote develops into a multicellular embryo in a seed and then into a mature sporophyte. Meiosis in sporophyte flowers produce spores, which give rise to new gametophytes. Environmental factors cue the transition of a vegetative meristem into a floral meristem, which gives rise to flowers.

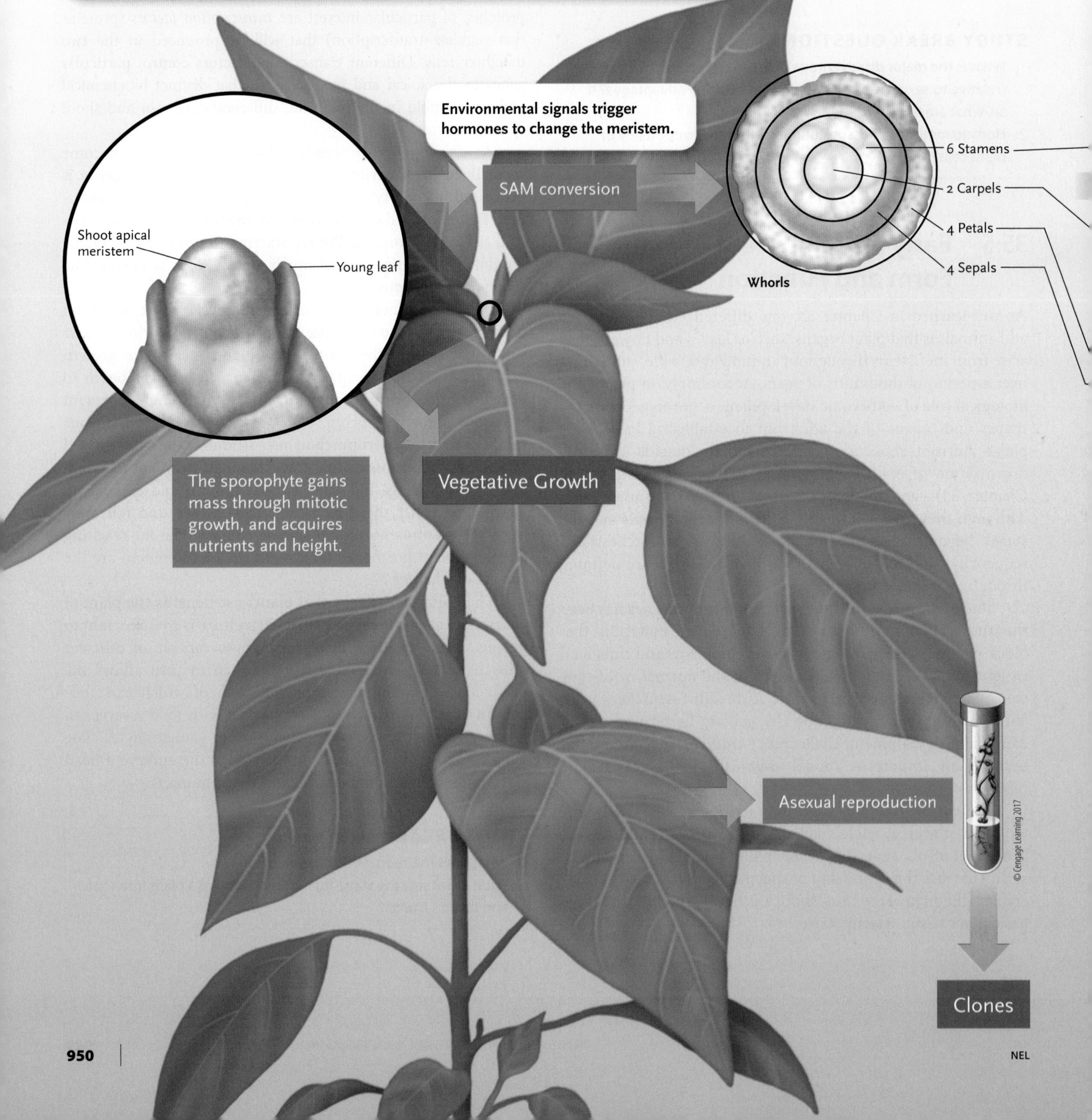

Shoot apical meristem

Young leaf

Environmental signals trigger hormones to change the meristem.

SAM conversion

6 Stamens

2 Carpels

4 Petals

4 Sepals

Whorls

Vegetative Growth

The sporophyte gains mass through mitotic growth, and acquires nutrients and height.

Asexual reproduction

Clones

© Cengage Learning 2017

Pollination happens when the pollen grain lands on the stigma. The pollen will germinate, forming a pollen tube that moves through the style to the micropyle of an ovule. There are two sperm nuclei in the pollen tube; one fertilizes the egg to make a zygote, and the other makes triploid endosperm when it fuses with the two nuclei in the central cell.

## Ovary and Stamens
- They are reproductive, "fertile" parts.
- Female gametophytes form within ovules that are enclosed in carpels. If several carpels are present, they may fuse into an ovary. Single carpels are one ovary.
- Eggs and other haploid cells develop in the ovule, which is where fertilization takes place.
- Pollen is the male gametophyte; it consists of only a few haploid cells, one of which is the sperm mother cell.

**Stamen** (male reproductive parts): filament, anther (with pollen sacs)

Anther (with pollen sacs)

Filament

## Flower Formation

**Carpel** (female reproductive parts): stigma, style, ovary (has one or more ovules)

Stigma

Style

Ovary

Ovules

Petal

Sepal

## Petals and Sepals
- They are non-reproductive, "sterile" parts.
- They assist pollination (e.g., by attracting pollinators).
- Sepals protect flowers by enclosing immature reproductive structures.

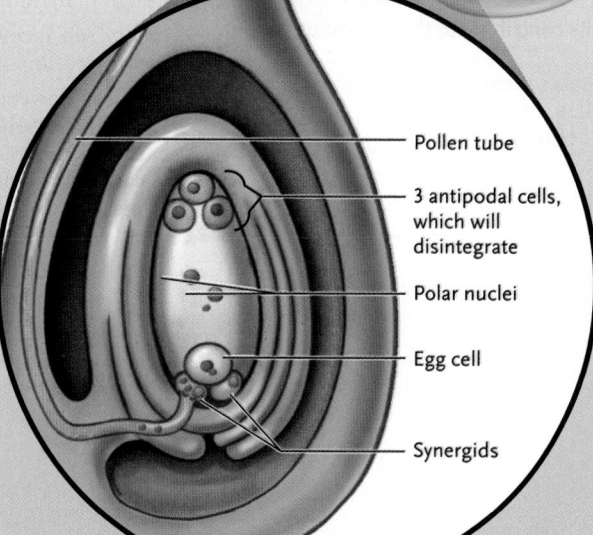

Pollen tube

3 antipodal cells, which will disintegrate

Polar nuclei

Egg cell

Synergids

In plants, meiosis creates haploid spores that can divide mitotically to create the gametophyte (which obviously must be haploid!). One or more of these haploid cells differentiate to form sperm or an egg cell. Evolutionarily, this reduction in the size of the gametophyte was gradual. Now, the male gametophyte (pollen) consists of only two or three cells!

# SELF-TEST QUESTIONS

## Recall/Understand

1. In angiosperms, an egg cell is produced in which structure and by which process?
   a. embryo sac, by meiosis
   b. embryo sac, by mitosis
   c. central cell, by mitosis
   d. female gametophyte, by meiosis

2. What cells are produced when the microspore of an angiosperm divides?
   a. two generative cells
   b. two tube cells
   c. a sperm cell, a generative cell, and a tube cell
   d. a generative cell and a tube cell

3. Which of these statements best describes double fertilization?
   a. Two sperm simultaneously fertilize two eggs in two separate ovules.
   b. One sperm fertilizes the egg, and a second sperm fertilizes the central cell.
   c. Two sperm simultaneously fertilize two antipodal cells.
   d. One sperm fertilizes the egg, and a second sperm fertilizes a synergid, forming endosperm.

4. Which of these events happens in angiosperm reproduction?
   a. Ovaries become fruit.
   b. Megaspores become eggs.
   c. The tube cell produces two sperm cells.
   d. Sperm is produced by meiosis.

5. What is the term for the transfer of a pollen grain from an anther to a stigma?
   a. fertilization
   b. pollination
   c. germination
   d. sexual reproduction

6. Which of these terms *best* describes a seed?
   a. an endosperm
   b. a mature ovary
   c. a mature ovule
   d. a mature megaspore

7. In which one of these ways do fruits contribute to the success of angiosperms?
   a. They nourish the plant that makes them.
   b. They attract insects to the pollen inside.
   c. They nourish the developing seedling.
   d. They facilitate seed dispersal.

8. What does a primary root develop from?
   a. a radicle
   b. an epicotyl
   c. a hypocotyl
   d. a coleoptile

## Apply/Analyze

9. Which of these statements describes why a seed coat ruptures?
   a. The cotyledons have emerged.
   b. Enzymes have been activated in the endosperm.
   c. Water has entered the seed by imbibition.
   d. Cell division has suddenly increased in the cotyledons.

10. Which of these statements describes the offspring produced by vegetative reproduction in angiosperms?
    a. They are haploid.
    b. They are genetically different than those produced by sexual reproduction.
    c. They are genetically inferior to those produced by sexual reproduction.
    d. They are genetically identical to the parent.

11. Which is the order of the following processes occurring in plant reproduction?
    a. seed dispersal; germination; fertilization; pollination
    b. fertilization; seed dispersal; pollination; germination;
    c. pollination; fertilization; seed dispersal; germination
    d. germination; seed dispersal; pollination; fertilization

12. In which of these processes are angiosperms unique among living organisms?
    a. flower production and double fertilization
    b. flower production and coevolution
    c. germination and double fertilization
    d. germination and coevolution

## Create/Evaluate

13. Describe the ABC model of flower development. What would the flower look like if, for example, the gene for protein A is disabled through mutation?

14. Evaluate self-incompatibility in plants. Explain how it happens and why it is important.

15. Sketch two flowers, one without stamens and one without carpels. After doing so, label all structures in your diagram and name the type of flowers you sketched. Describe advantages for flowers to have all parts of their whorl, and advantages to plants which have flowers such as those you diagrammed.

# Chapter Roadmap

**Plant Nutrition**

From Purple Pages →

From Chapter 30 →

From Chapter 31 →

From Chapter 35 →

**36.1 Plant Nutritional Requirements**

Plants can make all the macromolecules, including their subunits.
Plants supply macromolecules to other trophic levels.
Nitrogen acquisition often limits plant growth.
Symbiosis and predation on animals are adaptations to help plants thrive.

**To Chapter 42** →

From Purple Pages →

From Chapter 34 →

**36.2 Soil**

Plant health depends on soil for both texture and dissolved nutrients.
Humus provides nutrition and also stores water, both of which are absorbed by roots.
Soil acidity and ion content also affect availability of dissolved nutrients to the plant

From Chapter 25 →

From Chapter 34 →

**36.3 Root Adaptations for Obtaining and Absorbing Nutrients**

Symbiotic associations are involved in making nutrients from the soil more available to the plant.
Microorganisms such as bacteria and fungi contribute to nutrient cycling.
Special root adaptations encourage symbiotic interactions.
Xylem carries dissolved materials to the shoots from the roots.

Wasu Watcharadachaphong/Shutterstock.com

Science VU/R.Roncadori/Visuals Unlimited, Inc.

Lush azaleas (*Rhododendron*) and a stately Southern live oak (*Quercus virginiana*) draped with the unusual flowering plant called *Spanish moss* (*Tillandsia usneoides*). The roots of shrubs, trees, and most other plants take up water and minerals from soil, but Spanish moss is an epiphyte—it lives independently on other plants and obtains nutrients by way of absorptive hairs on its leaves and stems.

# Plant Nutrition

# 36

**Why it matters . . .** Tropical rainforests are among the most biologically diverse ecosystems on Earth. In addition to containing countless thousands of species of animals, fungi, protists, and prokaryotes, these lush domains are dense with broadleaved evergreen trees, sinuous vines, and other vegetation. With rain a near-daily event, it may not seem surprising that the trees' foliage is a deep, luxuriant green **(Figure 36.1)**.

Tropical rainforests are demanding places for plants to survive, in large part because the soil is chronically deficient in nutrients necessary for plant metabolism. This nutrient scarcity is a direct outcome of the incessant rain and the high acidity of tropical rainforest soil. There is ample moisture in the upper layer of soil, but in acidic soil, minerals vital to plant metabolism, such as potassium, calcium, magnesium, and phosphorus, are subject to **leaching**—being washed into deeper soil levels that are not as accessible to plant roots. In addition, in the warm, moist environment of a tropical rainforest, bacteria and fungi speedily decompose fallen leaves and other organic remains. Just as rapidly, established trees and vines take up any nutrients these decomposers have released, leaving few or none to enrich the soil. As falling rain dissolves some atmospheric $CO_2$, it creates carbonic acid—a type of "acid rain"—which exacerbates the leaching problem even more.

Such poor soil and the near perpetual twilight at the forest floor make it extremely difficult for small shrubs and herbaceous plants to survive. Nearly all such plants climb upward as vines, using the tree trunks for mechanical support, or they live attached to the upper branches of taller species, where they can absorb needed minerals from falling dust or from the surfaces of other

**FIGURE 36.1** **A lush tropical rainforest in Southeast Asia**

plants. These intricate adaptations allow the plants to secure energy and raw materials and to use both for growth and development.

Tropical rainforests are not unique in creating nutritional challenges for plants. In fact, plants rarely have ready access to a full complement of necessary resources. In a rainforest, the carbon, hydrogen, and oxygen that plants need for photosynthesis are relatively easy to come by: plants there usually get enough carbon from the $CO_2$ in air, and their roots can take up enough water to gain the necessary hydrogen and oxygen. But soils in other environments are frequently dry, making water a limited resource, and almost nowhere in nature do soils hold lavish amounts of dissolved minerals such as nitrogen, calcium, and others that are vital for a plant's survival. In response to the challenge of obtaining nutrients, plants have evolved the range of structural and physiological adaptations that we consider in this chapter.

As you read, you might ask how we can use science to optimize agriculture while still preserving local ecologies, and whether optimizing growing conditions for domesticated crops might invite disruptions to surrounding communities that are adapted for very different soil compositions.

# 36.1 Plant Nutritional Requirements

No organism grows normally when deprived of a chemical element essential for its metabolism. In the latter half of the nineteenth century, plant physiologists exploited rapid advances in chemistry to probe both the chemical composition of plants and the essential nutrients plants need to survive. In recent times, researchers have brought to bear sophisticated methods to expand our understanding of the range of plant nutrients, including those required only in trace amounts.

## 36.1a Plants Require Macronutrients and Micronutrients for Their Metabolism

By weight, the tissues of most plants are more than 90% water. Early researchers could obtain a rough idea of the composition of a plant's dry weight by burning the plant and then analyzing the ash. This method typically yielded a long list of elements, but the results were flawed. Chemical reactions during burning can dissipate quantities of some important elements, such as nitrogen. Also, plants take up a variety of ions that they do not use; depending on the minerals present in the soil where a plant grows, a plant's tissues can contain non-nutritive elements such as gold, lead, arsenic, and uranium.

**STUDYING PLANT NUTRITION USING HYDROPONICS** In 1860, German plant physiologist Julius von Sachs pioneered an experimental method for identifying the minerals absorbed into plant tissues that are essential for plant growth. Sachs carefully measured amounts of compounds containing specific minerals and mixed them in different combinations with pure water. He then grew plants in the solutions, a method now called **hydroponic culture** (*hydro* = water; *ponos* = work).

## FIGURE 36.2 Research Method

### Hydroponic Culture

**Purpose:** In studies of plant nutritional requirements, using hydroponic culture allows a researcher to manipulate and precisely define the types and amounts of specific nutrients that are available to the test plants.

**Protocol:** In a typical hydroponic apparatus, many plants are grown in a single solution containing pure water and a defined mix of mineral nutrients. The solution is replaced or refreshed as needed and is aerated with a bubbling system.

**a. Basic components of a hydroponic apparatus**

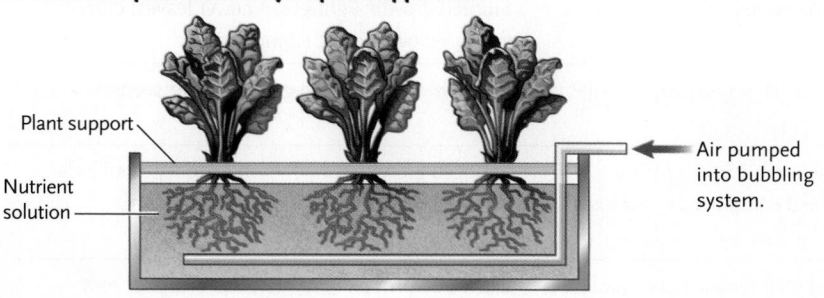

Plant support

Nutrient solution

Air pumped into bubbling system.

**b. Procedure for identifying elements essential for proper plant nutrition**

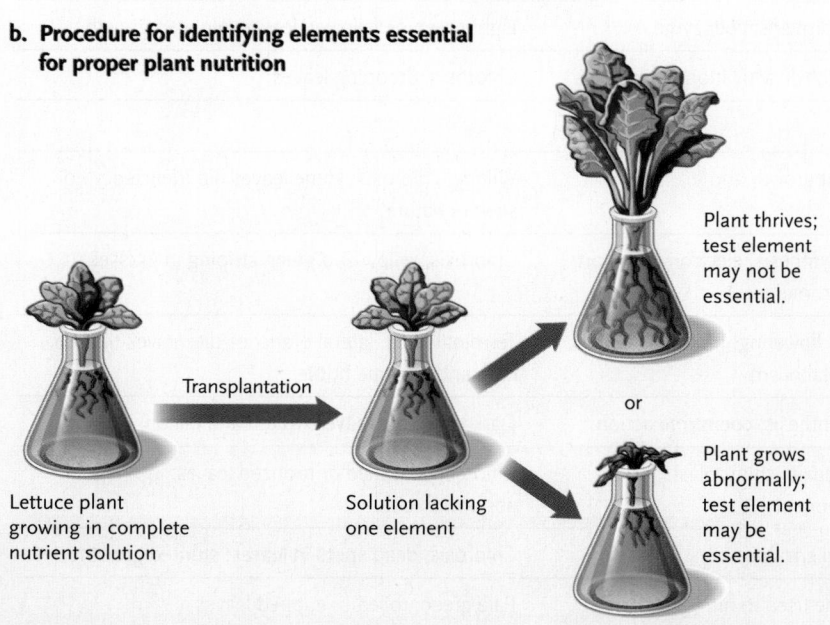

Lettuce plant growing in complete nutrient solution

Transplantation

Solution lacking one element

or

Plant thrives; test element may not be essential.

Plant grows abnormally; test element may be essential.

A "complete" solution contains all the known and suspected essential plant nutrients. An "incomplete" solution contains all but one of the same nutrients, in the same amounts. For experiments, researchers first grow plants in a complete solution, then transplant some of the plants to an incomplete solution.

**Interpreting the Results:** Normal growth of test plants suggests that the missing nutrient is not essential, whereas abnormal growth is evidence that the missing nutrient may be essential.

By eliminating one element at a time and observing the results, Sachs deduced a list of six essential plant nutrients, in descending order of the amount required: nitrogen, potassium, calcium, magnesium, phosphorus, and sulfur.

Sachs's innovative research paved the way for decades of increasingly sophisticated studies of plant nutrition, and the eventual identification of many more essential plant nutrients. In the spirit of his work, one basic experimental method involves growing a plant in a solution containing a complete spectrum of known and possible essential nutrients **(Figure 36.2a)**. The healthy plant is then transferred to a solution that is identical, except that it lacks one element having an unknown nutritional role (Figure 36.2b). Abnormal growth of the plant in this solution is evidence that the missing element is essential. If the plant grows normally, the missing element may not be essential; however, only further experimentation can confirm this hypothesis.

In a typical, modern, hydroponic apparatus, the nutrient solution is refreshed regularly, and air is bubbled into it to supply oxygen to the roots. Without sufficient oxygen for respiration, the plants' roots do not absorb nutrients efficiently. The same effect occurs in poorly aerated soil. Variations of this technique are used on a commercial scale to grow some vegetables, such as lettuce and tomatoes.

**ESSENTIAL MACRONUTRIENTS AND MICRO-NUTRIENTS** Hydroponics research has revealed that plants generally require 17 essential elements **(Table 36.1)**. By definition, an **essential element** is necessary for normal growth and reproduction, cannot be functionally replaced by a different element, and has one or more roles in plant metabolism. With enough sunlight and the 17 essential elements, plants can synthesize all the compounds they need for growth and maintenance.

Nine of the essential elements are **macronutrients**, meaning that plants incorporate relatively large amounts of them into their tissues. Three of these elements, carbon, hydrogen, and oxygen, account for about 96% of a plant's dry mass. Together, these three elements are the key components of lipids and of carbohydrates such as cellulose; with the addition of nitrogen, they form the basic building blocks of proteins and nucleic acids. Plants also use phosphorus in constructing nucleic acids, ATP, and phospholipids, and they use potassium for functions ranging from enzyme activation to mechanisms that control the opening and closing of stomata. Rounding out the list of macronutrients are calcium, sulfur, and magnesium. All macronutrients except carbon, hydrogen, and oxygen are classified as minerals, which chemists usually define as elements or compounds with a crystalline structure that are formed by geological processes. Minerals are available to plants

TABLE 36.1 | Essential Plant Nutrients and Their Functions

| Element | Commonly Absorbed Forms | Some Known Functions | Some Deficiency Symptoms |
|---|---|---|---|
| **Macronutrients** | | | |
| Carbon* | $CO_2$ | Raw materials for photosynthesis | Rarely deficient |
| Hydrogen* | $H_2O$ | | No symptoms; available from water |
| Oxygen* | $O_2$, $H_2O$, $CO_2$ | | No symptoms; available from water and $CO_2$ |
| Nitrogen | $NO_3^-$, $NH_4^+$ | Component of proteins, nucleic acids, coenzymes, chlorophylls | Stunted growth; light-green newer leaves; older leaves yellow and die (chlorosis) |
| Phosphorus | $H_2PO_4^-$, $HPO_4^{2-}$ | Component of nucleic acids, phospholipids, ATP, several coenzymes | Purplish veins; stunted growth; fewer seeds, fruits |
| Potassium | $K^+$ | Activation of enzymes; key role in maintaining water–solute balance and so influences osmosis (such as for stomatal function) | Reduced growth; curled, mottled, or spotted older leaves; burned leaf edges; weakened plant |
| Calcium | $Ca^{2+}$ | Roles in formation and maintenance of cell walls and in membrane permeability; enzyme cofactor | Leaves deformed; terminal buds die; poor root growth |
| Sulfur | $SO_4^{2-}$ | Component of most proteins, coenzyme A | Light green or yellowed leaves; reduced growth |
| Magnesium | $Mg^{2+}$ | Component of chlorophyll; activation of enzymes | Chlorosis; drooping leaves |
| **Micronutrients** | | | |
| Chlorine | $Cl^-$ | Role in root and shoot growth and in photosynthesis | Wilting; chlorosis; some leaves die (deficiency not seen in nature) |
| Iron | $Fe^{2+}$, $Fe^{3+}$ | Roles in chlorophyll synthesis, electron transport; component of cytochrome | Chlorosis; yellow and green striping in grasses |
| Boron | $H_3BO_3$ | Roles in germination, flowering, fruiting, cell division, nitrogen metabolism | Terminal buds, lateral branches die; leaves thicken, curl, and become brittle |
| Manganese | $Mn^{2+}$ | Role in chlorophyll synthesis; coenzyme action | Dark veins, but leaves whiten and fall off |
| Zinc | $Zn^{2+}$ | Role in formation of auxin, chloroplasts, and starch; enzyme component | Chlorosis; mottled or bronzed leaves; abnormal roots |
| Copper | $Cu^+$, $Cu^{2+}$ | Component of several enzymes | Chlorosis; dead spots in leaves; stunted growth |
| Molybdenum | $MoO_4^{2-}$ | Component of enzyme used in nitrogen metabolism | Pale green, rolled or cupped leaves |
| Nickel | $Ni^{2+}$ | Component of enzyme required to break down urea generated during nitrogen metabolism | Dead spots on leaf tips (deficiency not seen in nature) |

*Carbon, hydrogen, and oxygen are the nonmineral plant nutrients. All others are minerals.

through the soil as ions dissolved in water, and most minerals that serve as nutrients in plants are derived from the weathering of rocks and inorganic particles in Earth's crust.

The other elements essential to plants are also minerals, and are classed as **micronutrients** because plants require them only in trace amounts. Nevertheless, they are just as vital as macronutrients to a plant's health and survival. For example, it would take over one metric tonne of potatoes to extract the amount of copper for a single Canadian copper-plated penny; yet without copper, potato plants are sickly and do not produce normal tubers.

Chlorine, generally present in soil in its anionic form $Cl^-$ (chloride), was identified as a micronutrient nearly a century after Sachs's experiments. Chloride functions in some reactions of photosynthesis and (along with $K^+$) in the opening and closing of stomata, among other roles. The researchers who discovered its importance in plant nutrition performed hydroponic culture experiments in a California laboratory near the Pacific Ocean, where the air, like coastal air everywhere, contains sodium chloride. The investigators found that their test plants could obtain tiny but sufficient quantities of chloride from the air, as well as from sweat (which also contains NaCl) on the researchers' own hands. Great care had to be taken to exclude chlorine from the test plants' growing environment to prove that it was essential.

In some cases, plant seeds contain enough of certain trace minerals to sustain the adult plant. For example, nickel ($Ni^{2+}$) is a component of urease, the enzyme required to hydrolyze urea. Urea is a toxic by-product of the breakdown of nitrogenous compounds, and it will kill cells if it accumulates. In the late 1980s, investigators found that barley seeds contain enough nickel to sustain two complete generations of barley plants. Plants grown in the absence of nickel did not begin to show signs of nickel deficiency until the third generation.

In addition to the 17 essential elements, some species of plants may require additional micronutrients. Experiments suggest that many, perhaps most, plants adapted to hot, dry conditions require sodium; many plants that photosynthesize by the $C_4$ pathway (see Chapter 6) appear to be in this group. A few plant species require selenium, which is also an essential micronutrient for animals. Horsetails (*Equisetum*) require silicon, and some grasses, such as wheat, may also need it. Scientists continue to discover additional micronutrients for specific plant groups.

Both micronutrients and macronutrients play vital roles in plant metabolism. Many function as cofactors or coenzymes in protein synthesis, starch synthesis, photosynthesis, and aerobic respiration. Some also have a role in creating solute concentration gradients across plasma membranes, which are responsible for the osmotic movement of water.

## 36.1b Nutrient Deficiencies Cause Abnormalities in Plant Structure and Function

Plants differ in the quantity of each nutrient they require: the amount of an essential element that is adequate for one plant species may be insufficient for another. Lettuce and other leafy plants require more nitrogen and magnesium than do other plant types, for example, and alfalfa requires significantly more potassium than do lawn grasses. An adequate amount of an essential element for one plant may even be harmful to another. For example, the amount of boron required for normal growth of sugar beets is toxic for soybeans. For these reasons, the nutrient content of soils is an important factor in determining which plants will grow well in a given location. Carnivorous plants thrive in bogs and soils where nitrogen is scarce. They use protein-rich animals for the nitrogen in their amino acids. Plant diversity reflects the soils the plants are growing in.

Plants that are deficient in one or more of the essential elements develop characteristic symptoms. (Table 36.1 lists some observable symptoms of nutrient deficiencies.) The symptoms give some indication of the metabolic roles the missing elements play. Deficiency symptoms typically include stunted growth, abnormal leaf colour, dead spots on leaves, or abnormally formed stems **(Figure 36.3)**. For instance, iron is a component of the cytochromes on which the cellular electron transfer system depends, and it plays a role in reactions that synthesize chlorophyll. Iron deficiency causes **chlorosis**, a yellowing of plant tissues that results from a lack of chlorophyll (see Figure 36.3b). Because ionic iron ($Fe^{3+}$) is relatively insoluble in water, gardeners often fertilize plants with a soluble iron compound called *chelated iron* to stave off or cure chlorosis. Similarly, because magnesium is a necessary component of chlorophyll, a plant deficient in this element has fewer chloroplasts than normal in its leaves and other photosynthetic parts. It appears paler green than normal, and its growth is stunted because of reduced photosynthesis (see Figure 36.3c).

Plants that lack adequate nitrogen may also become chlorotic (see Figure 36.3d), with older leaves yellowing first because the nitrogen is preferentially shunted to younger, actively growing plant parts. This adaptation is not surprising given nitrogen's central role in the synthesis of amino acids, chlorophylls, and other compounds vital to plant metabolism. With some other mineral deficiencies, young leaves are the first to show symptoms. These kinds of observations underscore the point that plants use different nutrients in specific, often metabolically complex ways.

The Venus flytrap, the cobra lily, and various species of sundews are members of a curious group of plants that obtain nitrogen and other nutrients by trapping and digesting animals. A few species of tropical pitcher plants even capture and digest mice and small rats. Such carnivorous ("meat-eating") plants have become adapted to survive in nutrient-deficient—especially nitrogen-deficient—environments such as boggy and sandy areas through elaborate mechanisms for extracellular digestion and absorption. The cobra lily (*Darlingtonia californica*) is a good example. (It is shown among other plants using unorthodox methods of gathering nutrients in Figure 36.10a.) Its leaves form a "pitcher" that contains a pool of water with digestive enzymes. Insects lured in by attractive odours often wander deeper into the pitcher, encountering downward-pointing leaf hairs that have a slick, waxy coating and speed the insect's descent into the pool of enzymes. The plant then absorbs monomers released as the animal tissues are digested. Inside the leaf pitchers are complex ecosystems where living insect larvae and microorganisms such as bacteria and rotifers participate in breaking down organisms trapped in the leaf (see Chapter 31).

It's worth pointing out that nitrogen greatly influences both plants and animals, but in opposite ways. While plants have an abundant energy source (sunlight), they are often limited in their growing potential due to limited nitrogen availability; animals are energy-limited and must efficiently

**a. Plant grown using a complete growth solution**

**b. Iron deficiency**

**c. Magnesium deficiency**

**d. Nitrogen deficiency**

**e. Phosphorus deficiency**

**f. Potassium deficiency**

**g. Sulfur deficiency**

**h. Calcium deficiency**

**FIGURE 36.3 Leaves and stems of tomato plants showing visual symptoms of seven different mineral deficiencies.** The plants were grown in the laboratory, where the experimenter could control which nutrients were available.

eliminate excess nitrogen, often by detoxifying it into urea or uric acid. These challenges reinforce their ecological connections to each other (see Chapters 30, 31, and 42).

Soils are more likely to be deficient in nitrogen, phosphorus, potassium, or some other essential mineral than to contain too much, and farmers and gardeners typically add nutrients to suit the types of plants they wish to cultivate. They may observe the deficiency symptoms of plants grown in their locale or have soil tested in a laboratory and then choose a fertilizer with the appropriate balance of nutrients to compensate for the deficiencies. Packages of commercial fertilizers use a numerical shorthand (e.g., 15-30-15) to indicate the percentages of nitrogen, phosphorus, and potassium they contain. It's important to note that plants have diverse needs for nutrients. A field that has enough nitrogen for optimal corn production would cause grapes in a vineyard to experience burning of leaf margins and increased susceptibility to winter damage.

### STUDY BREAK QUESTIONS

1. What are the two main categories of the essential elements plants need? Give several examples of each.
2. Do all plants require the same basic nutrients in the same amounts? Explain.

## 36.2 Soil

Soil anchors plant roots and is the main source of the inorganic nutrients that plants require. It is also the source of water for most plants and of oxygen for respiration in root cells. The physical texture of soil is a factor in whether root systems have access to sufficient water and dissolved oxygen. Together, physical and chemical properties of soils have a major impact on the ability of plants to grow, survive, and reproduce in particular habitats.

### 36.2a The Components of Soil and the Size of the Particles Determine Its Properties

Soil is a complex mix of mineral particles, chemical compounds, ions, decomposing organic matter, air, water, and assorted living organisms. Most soils develop from the physical or chemical weathering of rock (which also liberates mineral ions). The different kinds of soil particles range in size from sand (2.0–0.02 mm) to silt (0.02–0.002 mm) and clay (diameter less than 0.002 mm). These mineral particles are usually mixed with various organic components, including **humus**—decomposing parts of plants and animals, animal droppings, and other organic matter. Dry humus has a loose, crumbly texture. It can absorb a great deal of water, contributing to the capacity of soil to hold water. Organic molecules in humus are reservoirs of nutrients, including nitrogen, phosphorus, and sulfur, that are vital to living plants.

The relative proportions of the different sizes of mineral particles give soil its basic texture: gritty if the soil is largely sand, smooth if silt predominates, and dense and heavy if clay is the major component. A soil's texture in turn helps determine the number and volume of pores—air spaces—that it contains. The relative amounts of sand, silt, and clay determine whether a soil is sticky when wet, with few air spaces (mostly clay), or dries quickly and may wash or blow away (mostly sand). Clay soils are more than 30% clay, whereas sandy soils contain less than 20% clay or silt.

The piles of bagged humus for sale at garden centres each spring reflect the fact that the amount of humus in a soil also affects plant growth. Its plentiful organic material feeds decomposers, whose metabolic activities in turn release minerals that plant roots can take up; but that is not its only value in soil. Humus helps retain soil water and, with its loose texture, helps aerate soil as well. Well-aerated soils containing roughly equal proportions of humus, sand, silt, and clay are **loams**, and they are the soils in which most plants do best.

## 36.2b Plants and Other Organisms Influence Soil Features

A square metre of fertile soil contains trillions of bacteria, hundreds of millions of fungi, and several million nematodes, plus an array of other worms and insects. It also contains dead plant roots, leaves, and other parts. Bacteria and fungi decompose this and other organic matter on and in the soil, and burrowing creatures such as earthworms aerate the soil. The roots and other tissues of plants may also play a key role in shaping the characteristics and composition of soil, including the abundance of soil-dwelling organisms.

Experiments document these soil-shaping activities. Edward Ayres and his colleagues at Colorado State University's Natural Resource Ecology Laboratory studied soil properties in Colorado's San Juan Mountains, where stands of trembling aspen (*Populus tremuloides*), lodgepole pine (*Pinus contorta*), or Engelmann spruce (*Picea engelmannii*) live in close proximity. *P. tremuloides* trees spread out more than pines and spruce trees do, all their leaves drop each year in autumn, and previous research had shown that *P. tremuloides* leaf litter has about twice the nitrogen content of the other two species. With these facts in mind, the Ayres team hypothesized that, in their four study areas, such species-specific characteristics would influence the physical, chemical, and biological properties of the soil. The data they gathered supported parts of their hypothesis and also raised questions. They found that, in all study areas, the soil in which the aspens grew was significantly warmer;

a difference that the team attributed to increased sunlight reaching the ground through the relatively open aspen canopies. The soil littered with aspen leaves also contained more nitrate—a form of nitrogen that plant roots can readily take up—than the nearby soil where the lignin-rich needlelike leaves of pines and spruces accumulated. The study was not designed to attempt a comprehensive analysis of the diversity of the soil's bacterial, fungal, and microscopic animal communities, but the researchers did document markedly different arrays of soil-dwelling organisms associated with the aspens, pines, and spruces in each study area. Clearly, we have a lot more to learn about the intricate interactions between plants, soils, and communities of soil organisms. The data we gather can let us understand more about the stability of communities or if different nutrients of the soil might promote growth of new species that are introduced.

As soils develop naturally, they tend to take on a characteristic vertical profile, with a series of layers, or **horizons** **(Figure 36.4)**. Each horizon has a distinct texture and composition that varies with soil type. The top layer of surface litter—organic matter such as twigs and leaves, animal dung, and fungi—is accordingly called the *O horizon*. **Topsoil**, the most fertile layer, occurs just below and forms the *A horizon*. This fairly loose layer may be less than a centimetre deep on steep slopes to more than a metre deep in grasslands. It consists of

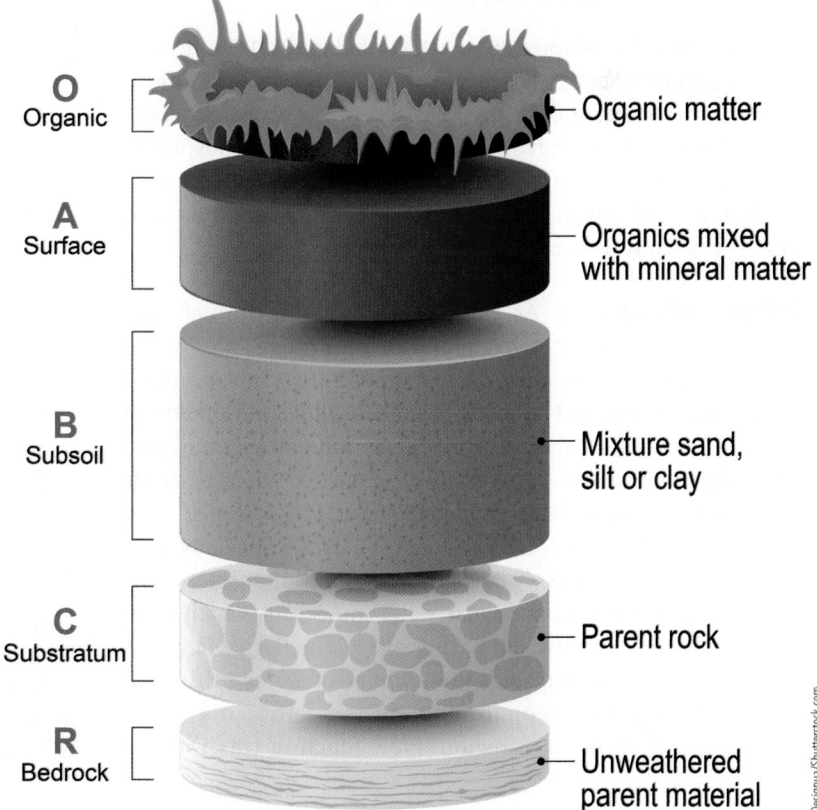

# SOIL LAYERS

**O**
Organic — Organic matter

**A**
Surface — Organics mixed with mineral matter

**B**
Subsoil — Mixture sand, silt or clay

**C**
Substratum — Parent rock

**R**
Bedrock — Unweathered parent material

Designua/Shutterstock.com

**FIGURE 36.4  Soil horizons in a grassland**

humus mixed with mineral particles and is where the roots of most herbaceous plants are located. Below the topsoil is the **subsoil**, or *B horizon*, a layer of larger soil particles containing relatively little organic matter. Mineral ions, including those that serve as nutrients in plants, tend to accumulate in the *B horizon*, and mature tree roots generally extend down into this layer. Under it is the *C horizon*, a layer of mineral particles and rock fragments that extends down to bedrock.

Regions where the topsoil is naturally deep and rich in humus are ideal for agriculture. Prime examples are the vast former grasslands of the North American Midwest and Ukraine now converted to fields of corn, wheat, soybeans, and other crops. Modern cultivation practices that sharply reduce erosion have helped maintain this soil resource. In arid regions, chronic, sparse rainfall generally correlates with low natural soil humus, and agriculture is only possible with intensive irrigation and soil management. Nor can agriculture flourish for long on land cleared of a tropical rainforest because of the soil leaching and lack of nutrients described in the chapter introduction. Using up nutrients in the soil can lead to crop failure such as the collapse of the cotton industry, which contributed to the Great Depression. When we consider only the crop we intend to harvest, is the local ecology being affected? Algal blooms occur along shorelines where fertilizer washes into the water, killing fish and altering the communities.

## 36.2c The Characteristics of Soil Affect Root–Soil Interactions

Roots are superbly adapted to penetrate soil and extract needed nutrients from it, but they are also quite sensitive to variations in the properties of soil. In the next section, we consider some adaptations plants have evolved in many otherwise inhospitable soil environments. First, however, we consider the general ways in which soil composition influences the ability of plant roots to obtain water and minerals.

**WATER AVAILABILITY** As water flows into and through soil, gravity pulls much of the water down through the spaces between soil particles into deeper soil layers. This available water is part of the **soil solution (Figure 36.5)**, a combination of water and dissolved substances that coats soil particles and partially fills pore spaces. The solution develops through ionic interactions between water molecules and soil particles. Clay particles and the organic components in soil (especially proteins) often bear negatively charged ions on their surfaces. The negative charges attract the polar water molecules, which form hydrogen bonds with the soil particles (see *The Purple Pages*).

Unless a soil is irrigated, the amount of water in the soil solution depends largely on the amount and pattern of precipitation (rain or snow) in a region. How much of this water is actually available to plants depends on the soil's composition: the size of the air spaces in which water can accumulate, and the proportions of water-attracting particles of clay and organic matter. By volume, soil is about one-half solid particles and one-half air space.

The type and size of the particles in a given soil have a major effect on how well plants will grow there. Sand particles are small, and sandy soil has relatively large air spaces, so water drains rapidly below the top two soil horizons, where most plant roots are located. Soils rich in clay or humus often hold quite a bit of water, but in the case of clay, ample water is not necessarily an advantage for plants. Whereas a humus-rich soil contains lots of air spaces, the closely layered particles in clay allow few air spaces, and what spaces there are tend to tightly hold the water that enters them. The lack of air spaces in clay soils also severely limits supplies of oxygen available to roots for cellular respiration, and the plant's metabolic activity suffers. Thus, few plants can flourish in clay soils, even when water content is high. (Overwatered houseplants die because their roots are similarly "smothered" by water.) Plants do not fare much better in drier clay-rich soils because roots cannot extract the existing water and cannot easily penetrate the densely packed clay. These characteristics explain why good agricultural soils tend to be sandy or silty loams, containing a mix of humus and coarse and fine particles.

As you learned in Chapter 33, root hairs are specialized extensions of root epidermal cells; they directly contact the soil solution and allow roots to absorb water (and dissolved ions). And as you saw in Section 34.2, differences in water potential govern the osmotic movement of water into plant roots.

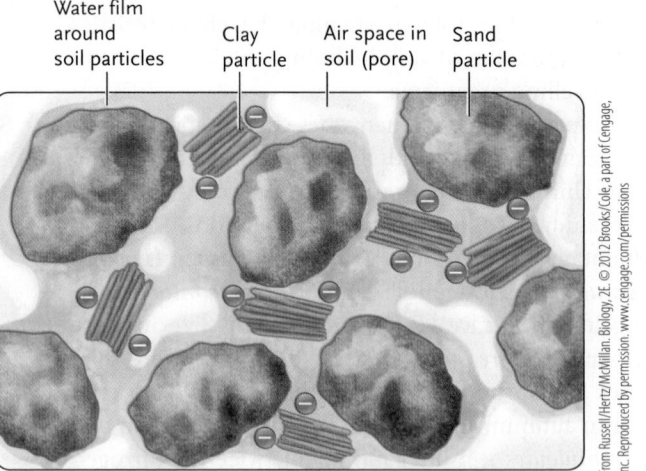

**FIGURE 36.5 Location of the soil solution.** Negatively charged ions on the surfaces of soil particles attract water molecules, which coat the particles and fill spaces between them (blue). Hydrogen bonds between water and soil components counteract the pull of gravity and help hold some water in the soil spaces.

**a. Adsorption of cations to a clay particle**

**b. Adding gypsum to the soil**

Negatively charged anions in soil solution

Negatively charged soil particle

Sand

Clay

$Mg^{2+}$

$K^+$

$K^+$

$Ca^{2+}$

$K^+$

$H^+$ $H^+$ $H^+$ $H^+$ $H^+$ $H^+$

Root hair

$Ca^{2+}$

$Mg^{2+}$

$Ca^{2+}$

$K^+$

Humus particle

© Cengage Learning 2017.

Wasu Watcharadachaphong/Shutterstock.com

**FIGURE 36.6** **(a)** Cation exchange on the surface of a clay particle. When cations come into contact with the negatively charged surface of the particle, they become adsorbed. As one type of cation, such as $H^+$, becomes adsorbed, other ions are liberated and can be taken up by plant roots. **(b)** A farmer in rural Thailand sprinkling gypsum on a plowed field. Gypsum, a complex compound of calcium, sulfur, and other elements, may alter the chemical characteristics of soil in various ways, including increasing the availability to plant roots of calcium and sulfur, reducing acidity, and counteracting excess sodium.

Remember that water moves from high water potential to low water potential, and that pure water in an open container at normal atmospheric pressure and temperature is $\psi_W = 0$ MPa. Adding solutes will reduce the water potential to a negative number. The soil solution usually contains fewer dissolved solutes than does the cytosol in plant roots. Accordingly, water tends to move from wet soil, where the water potential is higher, into roots, where the water potential is lower. The water potential in clay soils is significantly lower than in other soil types, even when clay is relatively wet. As roots extract water from clay soil, the water potential may fall below that in a plant's roots, making it impossible for water to diffuse into the roots. Water still continues to evaporate from leaves and to be used in photosynthesis, however, so the plant eventually wilts. Plants that survive in deserts or in salty soils have adaptations that permit their roots to absorb water even when osmotic conditions in soil do not favour water movement into the plant. *Salicornia europaea*, a plant known as "sea asparagus" in British Columbia, "samphire greens" on the East Coast, or "crow's foot greens," grows in salty water. When cooked, no salt is added; cells pump excess salt into their vacuoles.

**MINERAL AVAILABILITY** Some mineral nutrients enter plant roots as cations (positively charged ions) and some as anions (negatively charged ions). Although both cations and anions may be present in soil solutions, they are not equally available to plants.

Cations such as magnesium ($Mg^{2+}$), calcium ($Ca^{2+}$), and potassium ($K^+$) cannot easily enter roots because they are attracted by the net negative charges on the surfaces of soil particles. To varying degrees, they become reversibly bound to negative ions on the surfaces. Attraction in this form is called *adsorption*. Roots do acquire cations, however, through **cation exchange**. In this mechanism, one cation, usually $H^+$, replaces a soil cation **(Figure 36.6a)**. The protons ($H^+$) come from two main sources: Respiring root cells release carbon dioxide, which dissolves in the soil solution, yielding carbonic acid ($H_2CO_3$). Subsequent reactions ionize $H_2CO_3$ to produce bicarbonate ($HCO_3^-$) and $H^+$. Reactions involving organic acids inside roots also produce $H^+$, which is excreted. As $H^+$ enters the soil solution, it displaces adsorbed mineral cations attached to clay and humus, freeing them to move into roots. Other types of cations may also participate in this type of exchange, as shown in Figure 36.6a.

By contrast, anions in the soil solution, such as nitrate ($NO_3^-$), sulfate ($SO_4^{2-}$), and phosphate ($PO_4^{3-}$), are only weakly bound to soil particles and so they generally move fairly freely into root hairs. However, because they are so weakly bound compared with cations, anions are more subject to loss from soil by leaching.

The pH of soil affects the availability of some mineral ions. Soil pH is a function of the balance between cation exchange and other processes that raise or lower the concentration of $H^+$ in soil. As noted earlier, in areas that receive heavy rainfall, soils tend to become acidic (i.e., they have a pH of less than 7). This acidification occurs in part because moisture promotes the rapid decay of organic material in humus; as the material decomposes, it releases its organic acids. **Acid precipitation**, which results from the release of sulfur and nitrogen oxides into the air (in large measure from the burning of fossil fuels and industrial emissions), also contributes to soil acidification. By contrast, the soil in arid regions, where precipitation is low, is often alkaline (pH > 7). In fact, much of the effects caused by soil contamination work by changing the bioavailability of nutrients rather than affecting plant health directly, although both might play a role in reducing the plant's fitness.

Although most plants are not directly sensitive to soil pH, chemical reactions in very acid (pH < 5.5) or very alkaline (pH > 9.5) soils can have a major impact on whether plant roots take up various mineral cations. For example, experiments have shown that in the presence of $OH^-$ in alkaline soil, calcium and phosphate ions react to form insoluble calcium phosphates. The phosphate captured in these compounds is as unavailable to roots as if it were completely absent from the soil.

For a soil to sustain plant life over long periods, the mineral ions that plants take up must be replenished naturally or artificially (see Figure 36.6b). Over the long run, some mineral nutrients enter the soil from the ongoing weathering of rocks and smaller bits of minerals. In the shorter run, minerals, carbon, and some other nutrients are returned to the soil by the decomposition of organisms and their parts or wastes. Airborne compounds, such as sulfur in volcanic and industrial emissions, may enter soil when they dissolve in rain and fall to the ground. Minerals, including compounds of nitrogen and phosphorus, may also enter soil in fertilizers.

Although the use of commercial fertilizers maintains high crop yields, agricultural chemicals do not add humus to the soil. Their use can also cause serious pollution problems, as when nitrogen-rich runoff from agricultural fields promotes the severe overgrowth of algae in lakes and bays. In many parts of the world, industrial pollutants such as cadmium, lead, and mercury are increasingly grave soil contaminants.

**STUDY BREAK QUESTIONS**

1. Why is humus an important component of fertile soil?
2. How does the composition of a soil affect a plant's ability to take up water?
3. What factors affect a plant's ability to absorb minerals from the soil?

# 36.3  Root Adaptations for Obtaining and Absorbing Nutrients

Soil managed for agriculture can be plowed, precisely irrigated, and chemically adjusted to provide air, water, and nutrients in optimal quantities for a particular crop. In natural habitats, by contrast, wide variations in soil minerals, humus, pH, the presence of other organisms, and other factors influence the availability of essential elements. Although adequate carbon, hydrogen, and oxygen are typically available from the air and soil water, other essential elements that must be obtained from soil may not be as abundant. Nitrogen, phosphorus, and potassium are particularly scarce. Evolutionary solutions to these challenges include an array of adaptations in the structure and functioning of plant roots. As you will see, symbiosis with fungi and bacteria plays an enormous role in nutrient acquisition, particularly for phosphorus and nitrogen. Plants exude macromolecules that encourage the growth of these symbionts. In addition, root secretions can make soil nutrients more bioavailable for uptake.

## 36.3a  Root Systems Allow Plants to Locate and Absorb Essential Nutrients

Sessile organisms such as plants must locate nutrients in their immediate environment, and for plants the adaptive solution to this problem is an extensive root system. Roots make up 20%–50% of the dry weight of many plants, and even more in species growing where water or nutrients are especially scarce, such as Arctic tundra. As long as a plant lives, its root system continues to grow, branching out through the surrounding soil. Roots do not necessarily grow deeper as a root system branches out, however. In arid regions, a shallow-but-broad root system may be better positioned to take up water from occasional rains that may never penetrate below the first few inches of soil.

You may recall from Section 34.2 that roots take up ions in the regions just behind the root tips, where root hairs are present. These diminutive absorptive structures, shown in Figure 33.12c, are a major adaptation for the uptake of mineral ions and water. Over successive growing seasons, long-lived plants such as trees can develop millions, even billions, of root tips, each one a potential absorption site. In a plant such as a mature red oak (*Quercus rubra*), which has a vast root system, the total number of root hairs is astronomical. Even in young plants, root hairs greatly increase the root surface area available for absorbing water and ions. Recently, a team led by Chinese researcher Keke Yi uncovered a genetic "master switch" that regulates the growth of root hairs. Experiments with *Arabidopsis thaliana* plants, a weed that has become a key model organism for plant research, revealed that the activity of a transcription factor called *RSL4* activates downstream genes that promote the growth of long root hairs, while the absence of RSL4 stunts root hair growth. Apparently, expression of the *rsl4* gene is modulated by external cues, including soil phosphate levels and signals from the plant hormone auxin, which you will read more about in Chapter 37.

Chapter 34 also mentioned another plant adaptation for gaining access to mineral ions: ion-specific transport proteins in plant cell membranes by which the cells selectively absorb ions from soil. For example, from studies of plants such as *Arabidopsis thaliana*, we know that transport channels for potassium ions ($K^+$) are embedded in the cell membranes of root cortical cells. Such ion transporters absorb more or less of a particular ion, depending on chemical conditions in the surrounding soil.

## 36.3b Nutrients Move Into and Through the Plant Body by Several Routes

Plants obtain carbon, hydrogen, and oxygen from the air, but most mineral ions enter plant roots passively along with the water in which they are dissolved. Some enter root cells immediately. Others travel in solution *between* cells—in the apoplast—until they meet the endodermis sheathing the root's stele (see Figure 34.5). At the endodermis, the ions are actively transported into the endodermal cells and then into the xylem for transport throughout the plant. Inside cells, most mineral ions enter vacuoles or remain in the cytoplasm, where they are immediately available for metabolic reactions.

Some nutrients, such as nitrogen-containing ions, move in phloem from site to site in the plant, as dictated by growth and seasonal needs. In plants that shed their leaves in autumn, before the leaves age and fall, significant amounts of nitrogen, phosphorus, potassium, and magnesium move out of the leaves and into twigs and branches. This evolutionary adaptation conserves the nutrients, which will be used in new growth the next season. Likewise, in late summer, mineral ions move to the roots and lower stem tissues of perennial range grasses that typically die back during the winter. These activities are regulated by hormonal signals, which are the topic of Chapter 37.

Given the essential role of roots in a plant's nutritional survival, it is not surprising that research is uncovering an ever-growing list of root adaptations for exploiting and enhancing nutrient resources in soil. We now take a closer look at two of these adaptations: the associations called *mycorrhizae* and interactions with nitrogen-fixing microorganisms.

## 36.3c Symbiotic Interactions That Increase Plant Access to Scarce Nutrients

The course of plant evolution has resulted in vitally important symbioses that enhance access to nutrients. Phosphorus and nitrogen are critical to plant health (Section 36.1), but plants aren't often well-equipped to gather them from the air and soil. By encouraging growth of microorganisms, roots can use their symbionts to convert critical ions and molecules to forms that are easily absorbed.

**MYCORRHIZAL FUNGI ASSOCIATE WITH PLANT ROOTS TO SUPPLY NUTRIENTS AND WATER** Mycorrhizae are crucial symbiotic associations between a fungus and the roots of a plant (see Section 25.2b). They promote the uptake of water and nutritionally vital ions—especially phosphate—in most species of plants **(Figure 36.7)**. Although bacteria are often given the most credit for supplying nitrogen to plants, mycorrhizae are involved in this as well.

Some mycorrhizal fungi access sources of nutrients that are not available to plants; for example, some of them can penetrate directly into rocks and extract nutrients, which are then

**FIGURE 36.7 Effect of mycorrhizal fungi on plant growth.** These six-month-old juniper seedlings are in pots containing sterilized low-phosphorus soil. The middle and right-hand plants are inoculated with different species of mycorrhizal fungi.

transported to their plant hosts. Other associations involve carnivorous fungi that obtain nitrogen by trapping and killing soil invertebrates and then transferring it to their host plants. In exchange for soil nutrients, the plants provide the mycorrhizal fungi with sugars produced through photosynthesis. Mycorrhizas are generally mutualists, representing a win–win situation for the partners.

Fossil evidence suggests that fungi invaded cortical cells of plant roots, creating tree-like hyphal structures called "arbuscules" **(Figure 36.8a)**. For this reason, the association is called **arbuscular mycorrhiza** ("tree-like fungus," or sometimes "**endomycorrhiza**"; the term breaks down to "inside/fungus/root"). The branched hyphae increase surface area for better interaction. These are the oldest and most abundant type of mycorrhiza. Because of their ancient origins, some biologists speculate they might have been crucial for the colonization of land by plants; enhancing the transport of water and minerals to the plants.

Plant/fungal symbiosis also occurs as a network of hyphal filaments that surround the plant's roots. Because they don't penetrate root cells, they are called **ectomycorrhizae** (outside/fungus/root). Collectively, the hyphae provide a tremendous amount of extra surface area for absorbing water, phosphate, nitrogen, and ions from a large volume of soil. As with plant roots, transport proteins shepherd ions into hyphae. Some of the plant's sugars and nitrogenous compounds nourish the fungus and, as the root grows, it uses some of the minerals that the fungus has secured.

Ectomycorrhizae evolved more recently and involve basidiomycetes and some ascomycetes. In these mycorrhizae, fungal hyphae form a sheath or mantle around a root (see Figure 36.8b) and also grow between, but not inside, the root

### a. Ectomycorrhizae

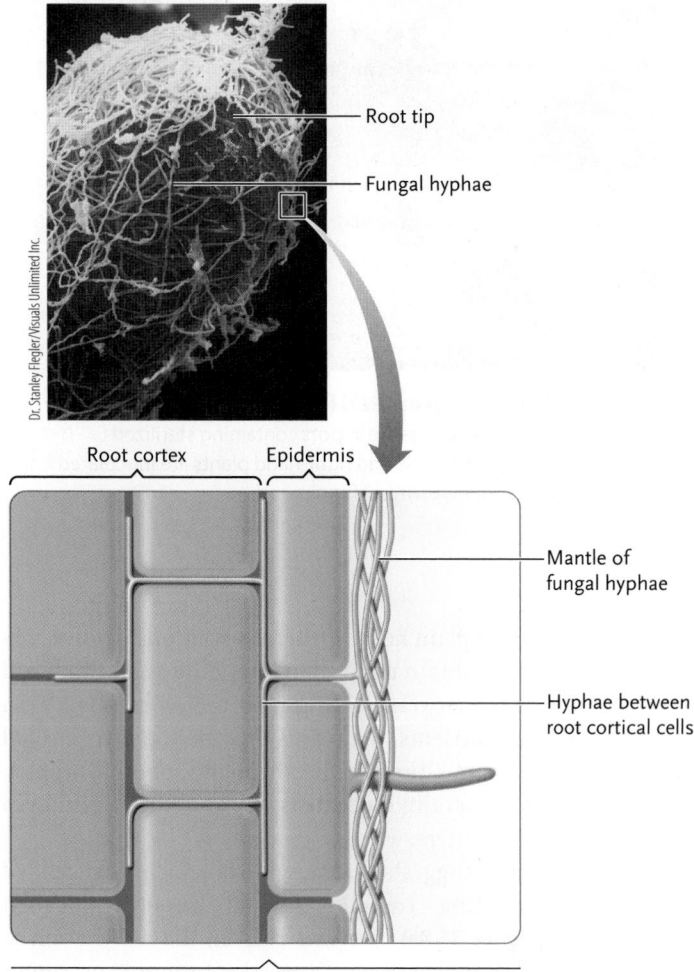

Root tip

Fungal hyphae

Dr. Stanley Flegler/Visuals Unlimited Inc.

Root cortex | Epidermis

Mantle of fungal hyphae

Hyphae between root cortical cells

In ectomycorrhizae, fungal hyphae form a sheathlike mantle around a plant root. The hyphae cross the root epidermis and infiltrate the spaces between root cortical cells (the apoplast). Carbohydrates from the plant's photosynthesis pass to the fungus, while water, phosphate, and other soil nutrients pass to the plant.

### b. Endomycorrhizae

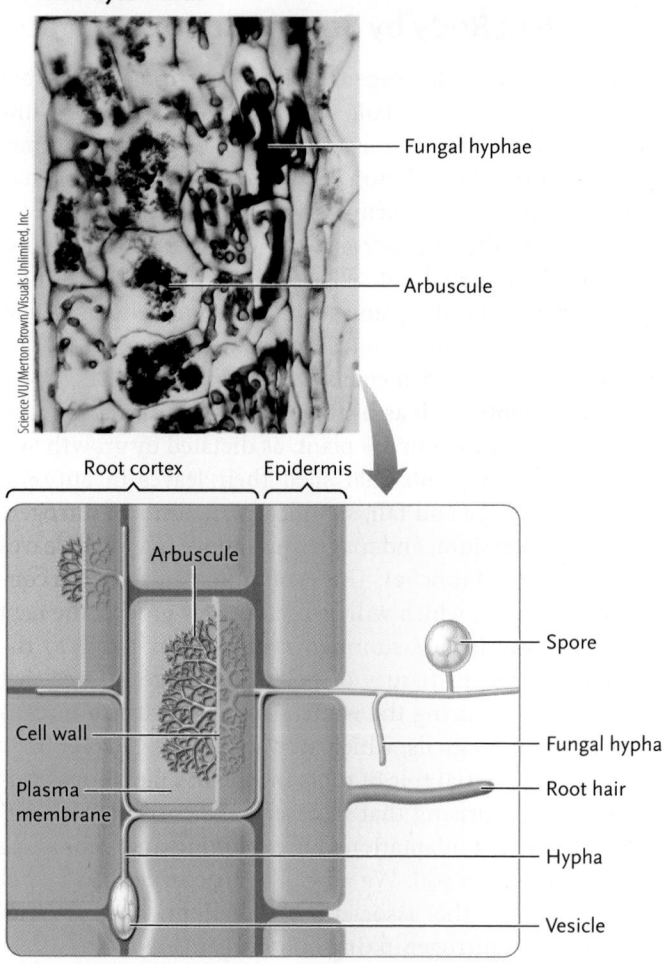

Fungal hyphae

Arbuscule

Science VU/Merton Brown/Visuals Unlimited, Inc.

Root cortex | Epidermis

Arbuscule

Cell wall

Plasma membrane

Spore

Fungal hypha

Root hair

Hypha

Vesicle

In endomycorrhizae, fungal hyphae penetrate root cortex cells. In the arbuscular type of endomycorrhizae shown here, hyphae are sandwiched between the root cell wall and the plasma membrane, where they branch repeatedly into treelike structures. Nutrient exchanges occur across the interface of an arbuscule and the root cell's plasma membrane.

© Cengage Learning 2017.

**FIGURE 36.8 Mycorrhizae**

cells of their plant hosts. Ectomycorrhizal associations are very common with trees, such as the conifers of Canada's **boreal forest** and coastal rainforests. The extensive root system of a single mature pine may be studded with ectomycorrhizae involving dozens of fungal species. The musky-flavoured truffles (*Tuber melanosporum*) prized by gourmets are ascomycetes that form ectomycorrhizal associations with oak trees (*Quercus* spp.).

**PLANTS DEPEND ON BACTERIA FOR AN ADEQUATE SUPPLY OF USABLE NITROGEN** It might seem that plants live surrounded by nitrogen: nitrogen steadily enters the soil in organic compounds released when dead organisms and animal wastes decompose, and air contains plenty of gaseous nitrogen—almost 80% by volume—but plants cannot extract it because they lack the enzyme necessary to break apart the three covalent bonds in each $N_2$ molecule ($N\equiv N$). Plants can absorb atmospheric nitrogen that reaches the soil in the form of nitrate ($NO_3^-$) and ammonium ion ($NH_4^+$), and experiments show that roots of at least some plant species take up amino acids directly. Even so, lack of nitrogen is the single most common limit to plant growth because there is usually not nearly enough nitrogen available in these forms to meet plants' ongoing needs.

Instead, the main natural processes that replenish soil nitrogen and convert it to an absorbable form are carried out by bacteria. These processes, which we'll now consider, are part of the *nitrogen cycle,* the global movement of nitrogen in its various chemical forms from the environment to organisms and back to the environment (described in Chapter 31).

## PRODUCTION AND ASSIMILATION OF AMMONIUM AND NITRATE
The incorporation of atmospheric nitrogen into compounds that plants can take up is called **nitrogen fixation**. Figure 36.9 summarizes the basic steps. Metabolic pathways of *nitrogen-fixing bacteria* living in the soil or in mutualistic association with plant roots add hydrogen to atmospheric $N_2$, producing two molecules of $NH_3$ (ammonia) and one $H_2$ for each $N_2$ molecule. The process requires a substantial input of ATP and is catalyzed by the enzyme nitrogenase. In a final step, $H_2O$ and $NH_3$ react, forming $NO_4^+$ (ammonium) and $OH^-$.

Another bacterial process, called **ammonification**, also produces $NH_4^+$ when soil bacteria known as *ammonifying bacteria* break down decaying organic matter. In this way, nitrogen already incorporated into plants and other organisms is recycled.

Although plants use $NH_4^+$ to synthesize organic compounds, most plants absorb nitrogen in the form of nitrate ($NO_3^-$). Nitrate is produced in soil by **nitrification**, in which $NH_4^+$ is oxidized to $NO_3^-$. Soils generally teem with *nitrifying bacteria*, which carry out this process. Because of ongoing nitrification, nitrate is far more abundant than ammonium in most soils. Usually, the only soils from which plant roots take up ammonium directly are highly acidic, such as in bogs, where the low pH is toxic to nitrifying bacteria.

## NITROGEN ASSIMILATION
Once inside root cells, absorbed $NO_3^-$ is converted by a multistep process back to $NH_4^+$. In this form, nitrogen is rapidly used to synthesize organic molecules, mainly amino acids. These molecules pass into the xylem, which transports them throughout the plant. In some plants, the nitrogen-rich precursors for needed substances travel in xylem to leaves, where different organic molecules are synthesized. These molecules travel to other plant cells in the phloem.

## NITROGEN FIXATION IN PLANT–BACTERIA ASSOCIATIONS
Although some nitrogen-fixing bacteria live free in the soil, by far the largest percentage of nitrogen is fixed by species of *Rhizobium* and *Bradyrhizobium*, which form mutualistic associations with the roots of plants in the legume family. The host

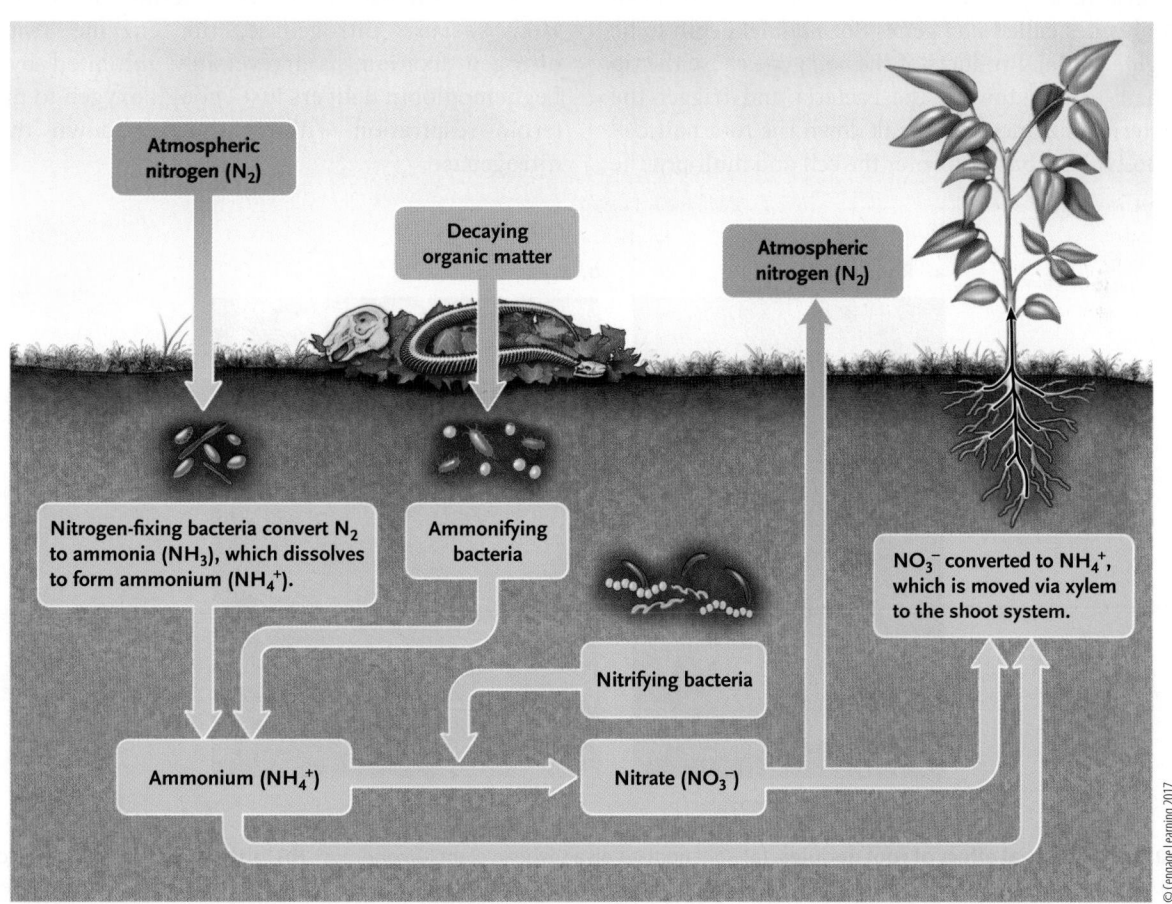

**FIGURE 36.9 How plants obtain nitrogen from soil.** Many commercial nitrogen fertilizers are in the chemical form of nitrate, which plant roots take up readily, or in the form of ammonium, which nitrifying bacteria convert to nitrate. Nitrate absorbed by root cells is converted to soluble forms that are transported to the shoot through the xylem.

plant supplies organic molecules that the bacteria use for cellular respiration, and the bacteria supply $NH_4^+$ that the plant uses to produce proteins and other nitrogenous molecules. In legumes—a large family that includes peas, beans, clover, alfalfa, and others—the nitrogen-fixing bacteria reside in **root nodules**, localized swellings on roots **(Figure 36.10)**. Even non-legumes such as alder make use of nitrogen-fixing bacteria. Farmers may exploit root nodules to increase soil nitrogen by rotating crops (e.g., planting soybeans and corn in alternating years). When the legume crop is harvested, the root nodules and other tissues remaining in the soil enrich its nitrogen content.

For a plant, an association with nitrogen-fixing bacteria offers the selective advantage of a steady source of absorbable nitrogen. Decades of research have revealed the details of how this remarkable relationship unfolds. Usually, a single species of nitrogen-fixing bacteria colonizes a single legume species, drawn to the plant's roots by chemical attractants—primarily compounds called *flavonoids*—that the roots secrete. Through a sequence of exchanged molecular signals, bacteria are able to penetrate a root hair and form a colony inside the root cortex.

An association between a soybean plant (*Glycine max*) and a bacterium (*Bradyrhizobium japonicum*) illustrates the process. In response to a specific flavonoid released by soybean roots, bacterial genes called *nod* genes (for *nodule*) begin to be expressed **(Figure 36.11a)**. Products of the *nod* gene cause the tip of the root hair to curl toward the bacteria and trigger the release of bacterial enzymes that break down the root hair cell wall (Figure 36.11b). As bacteria enter the cell and multiply, the

plasma membrane forms a tube called an **infection thread** that extends into the root cortex, allowing the bacteria to invade cortex cells (Figure 36.11c). The enclosed bacteria, now called **bacteroids**, enlarge and become immobile. Stimulated by still other *nod* gene products, cells of the root cortex begin to divide. This region of proliferating cortex cells forms the root nodule. Typically, each cell in a root nodule contains several thousand bacteroids; the plant takes up some of the nitrogen fixed by the bacteroids, and the bacteroids use some compounds produced by the plant.

Inside bacteroids, $N_2$ is reduced to $NH_4^+$ (ammonium) using ATP produced by cellular respiration. The process is catalyzed by nitrogenase. Ammonium is highly toxic to cells if it accumulates, however. Thus, $NH_4^+$ is moved out of bacteroids into the surrounding nodule cells and converted to other compounds, such as the amino acids glutamine and asparagine.

One factor encoded by the bacterial *nod* genes stimulates plant nodule cells to produce a protein called **leghemoglobin** ("legume hemoglobin"). Like the hemoglobin of animal red blood cells (Chapter 41), leghemoglobin contains a reddish, iron-containing heme group that binds oxygen. Its colour gives root nodules a pinkish cast (see Figure 36.10a). Leghemoglobin picks up oxygen at the cell surface and shuttles it inward to the bacteroids. This method of oxygen delivery is vital because nitrogenase, the enzyme responsible for nitrogen fixation, is irreversibly inhibited by excess $O_2$. Leghemoglobin delivers just enough oxygen to maintain bacteroid respiration without shutting down the action of nitrogenase.

**a. Root nodules**   **b. Bacteroids**

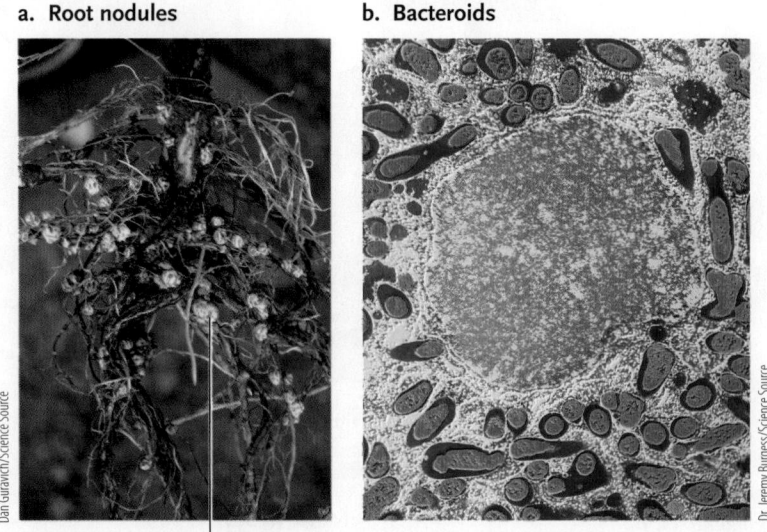

Root nodule

**FIGURE 36.10 The beneficial effect of root nodules. (a)** Root nodules on a soybean plant (*Glycine max*). **(b)** False-colour transmission electron micrograph showing membrane-bound bacteroids (red) in a root nodule cell. Membranes that enclose the bacteroids appear blue. The large yellow-green structure is the cell's nucleus.

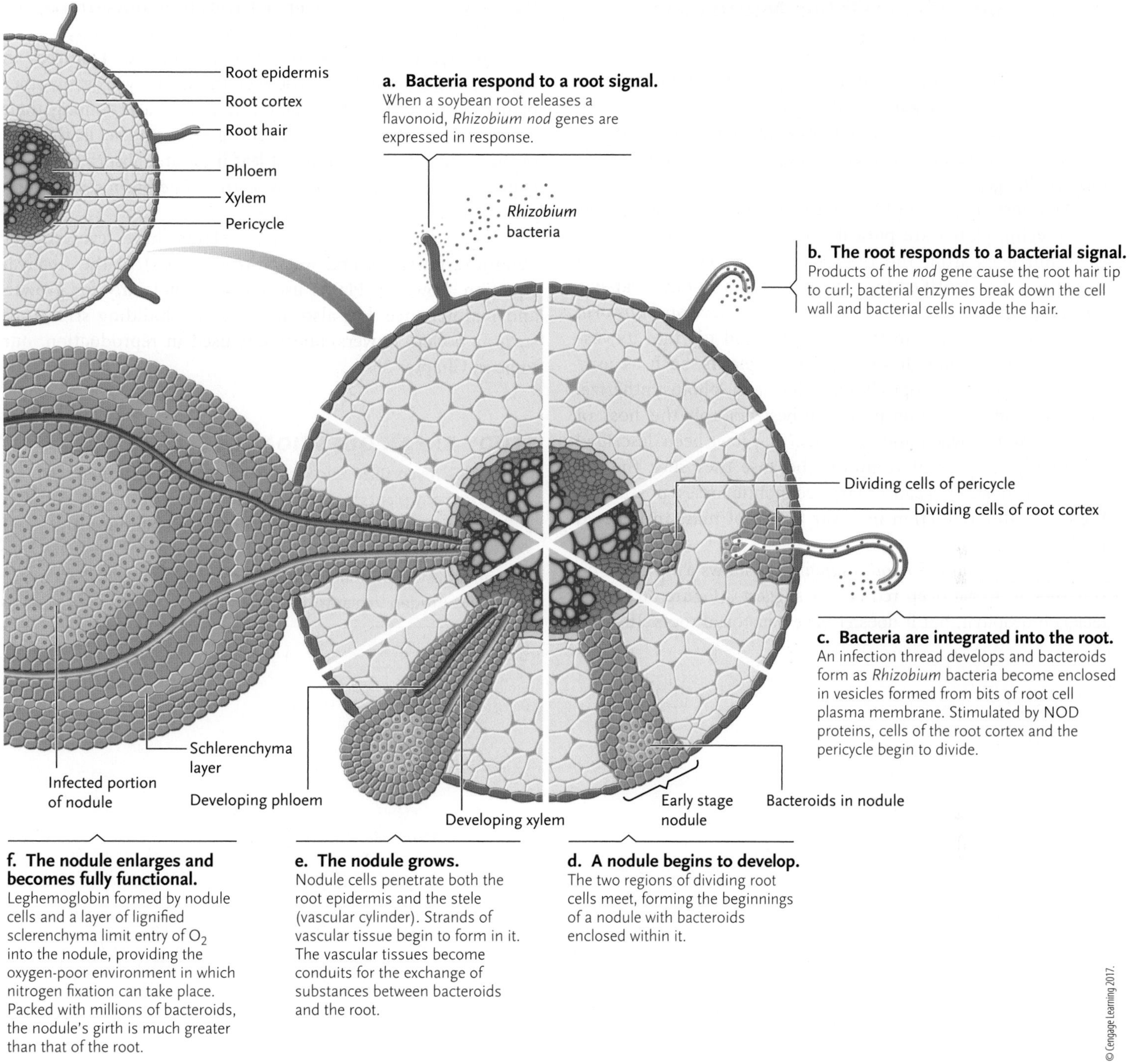

**Root epidermis**
**Root cortex**
**Root hair**
**Phloem**
**Xylem**
**Pericycle**

**a. Bacteria respond to a root signal.**
When a soybean root releases a flavonoid, *Rhizobium nod* genes are expressed in response.

*Rhizobium* bacteria

**b. The root responds to a bacterial signal.**
Products of the *nod* gene cause the root hair tip to curl; bacterial enzymes break down the cell wall and bacterial cells invade the hair.

Dividing cells of pericycle
Dividing cells of root cortex

**c. Bacteria are integrated into the root.**
An infection thread develops and bacteroids form as *Rhizobium* bacteria become enclosed in vesicles formed from bits of root cell plasma membrane. Stimulated by NOD proteins, cells of the root cortex and the pericycle begin to divide.

Schlerenchyma layer
Infected portion of nodule
Developing phloem
Developing xylem
Early stage nodule
Bacteroids in nodule

**f. The nodule enlarges and becomes fully functional.**
Leghemoglobin formed by nodule cells and a layer of lignified sclerenchyma limit entry of $O_2$ into the nodule, providing the oxygen-poor environment in which nitrogen fixation can take place. Packed with millions of bacteroids, the nodule's girth is much greater than that of the root.

**e. The nodule grows.**
Nodule cells penetrate both the root epidermis and the stele (vascular cylinder). Strands of vascular tissue begin to form in it. The vascular tissues become conduits for the exchange of substances between bacteroids and the root.

**d. A nodule begins to develop.**
The two regions of dividing root cells meet, forming the beginnings of a nodule with bacteroids enclosed within it.

© Cengage Learning 2017.

**FIGURE 36.11 Root nodule formation in legumes. (a)** Flavonoids attract bacteria, which express *nod* genes in response. **(b–e)** Symbiotic responses cause integration of bacteria into the root, resulting in the formation of a nodule **(f)**, a large mass specialized for efficient nitrogen fixation.

## 36.3d Some Plants Obtain Nutrients in Unusual Ways

Pitcher plants were described in Section 36.1b; you can see an example of one in **Figure 36.12a**. Their modified leaves help capture animals, which are rich in nitrogen and other nutrients. Other plants have evolved their root systems to deal with their food challenges.

Dodders (Figure 36.12b) and thousands of other species of flowering plants are parasites that obtain some of or all their nutrients from the tissues of other plants. They can sometimes be identified by their reductions in both leaf size and chlorophyll content. Parasitic species develop *haustoria* that penetrate deep into the host plant and tap into its vascular tissues. Although some parasitic plants, such as mistletoe, contain chlorophyll and thus can photosynthesize, dodders and other non-photosynthesizers rob the host of sugars as well as water and minerals. They have been described informally as "vegetal vampires" because they suck the sap from their host. This causes large economic losses, possibly as high as a 40% reduction in sugar beet root mass in infected fields.

The snow plant (*Sarcodes sanguinea*) shows a variation on this theme. As its deep red colour suggests (Figure 36.12c), it lacks chlorophyll, but it doesn't have haustorial roots. Instead, the snow plant's roots take up nutrients from mycorrhizae that they "share" with the roots of nearby conifers.

**Epiphytes**, such as the tropical orchid pictured in Figure 36.12d, are not parasitic even though they grow on other plants. Some trap falling debris and rainwater among their leaves, whereas their roots (including mycorrhizae, in the case of the orchid) invade the moist leaf litter and absorb nutrients from it as the litter decomposes. In temperate forests, many mosses and lichens are epiphytes.

These and other strategies plants have evolved for obtaining nutrients and water are only part of the survival equation, however. Plants use nutrients not only for growth and maintenance, but also of course for building structures such as pollen, flowers, and seeds used in reproduction, our topic in Chapter 35.

### STUDY BREAK QUESTIONS

1. What is a mycorrhiza, and why are mycorrhizal associations so vital to many plants?
2. Distinguish between nitrogen fixation, ammonification, and nitrification.
3. Summarize the mechanism by which associations with bacteria supply nitrogen to plants such as legumes.

**a. Cobra lily (*Darlingtonia californica*)**

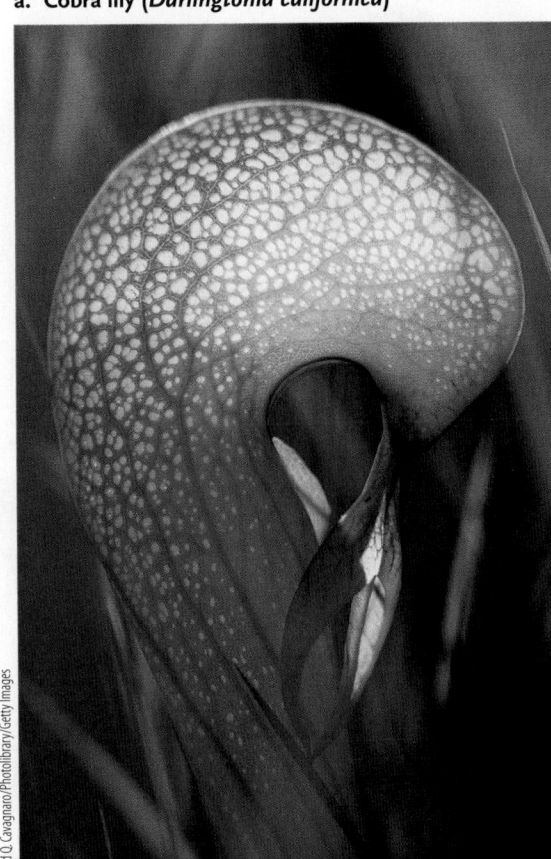

**b. Dodder (*Cuscuta*)**

**c. Snow plant (*Sarcodes sanguinea*)**

**d. Lady-of-the-night orchid (*Brassavola flagellaris*)**

**FIGURE 36.12 Some plants with unusual adaptations for obtaining nutrients. (a)** Cobra lily (*Darlingtonia californica*), a carnivorous plant. The patterns formed by light shining through the plant's pitcherlike leaves are thought to confuse insects that have entered the pitcher, making an exit more difficult. **(b)** A parasitic dodder, one of the more than 150 *Cuscuta* species. Dodders have slender yellow-orange stems that twine around the host plant before producing haustorial roots that absorb nutrients and water from the host's xylem and phloem. **(c)** Snow plant (*Sarcodes sanguinea*), which pops up in the deep humus of shady conifer forests after snow has melted in spring. This species lacks chlorophyll and does not photosynthesize. Instead, its roots intertwine with hyphae of soil fungi that also form associations with the roots of nearby conifers. Radiocarbon studies have shown that the fungi take up sugars and other nutrients from the trees and pass a portion of this food to the snow plant. **(d)** The lady-of-the-night orchid (*Brassavola nodosa*), a tropical epiphyte

# Summary Illustration

Being sessile (non-motile), plants must be able to accumulate the atoms required to manufacture all of the macromolecule classes. As the "producers" of the biosphere, plants enlist mechanisms to accumulate nitrogen, carbon, and in fact all the biologically significant atoms they need as their nutrients. Carbon fixation is done from an atmospheric source and is powered by photosynthesis, while other nutrients are picked up from the soil.

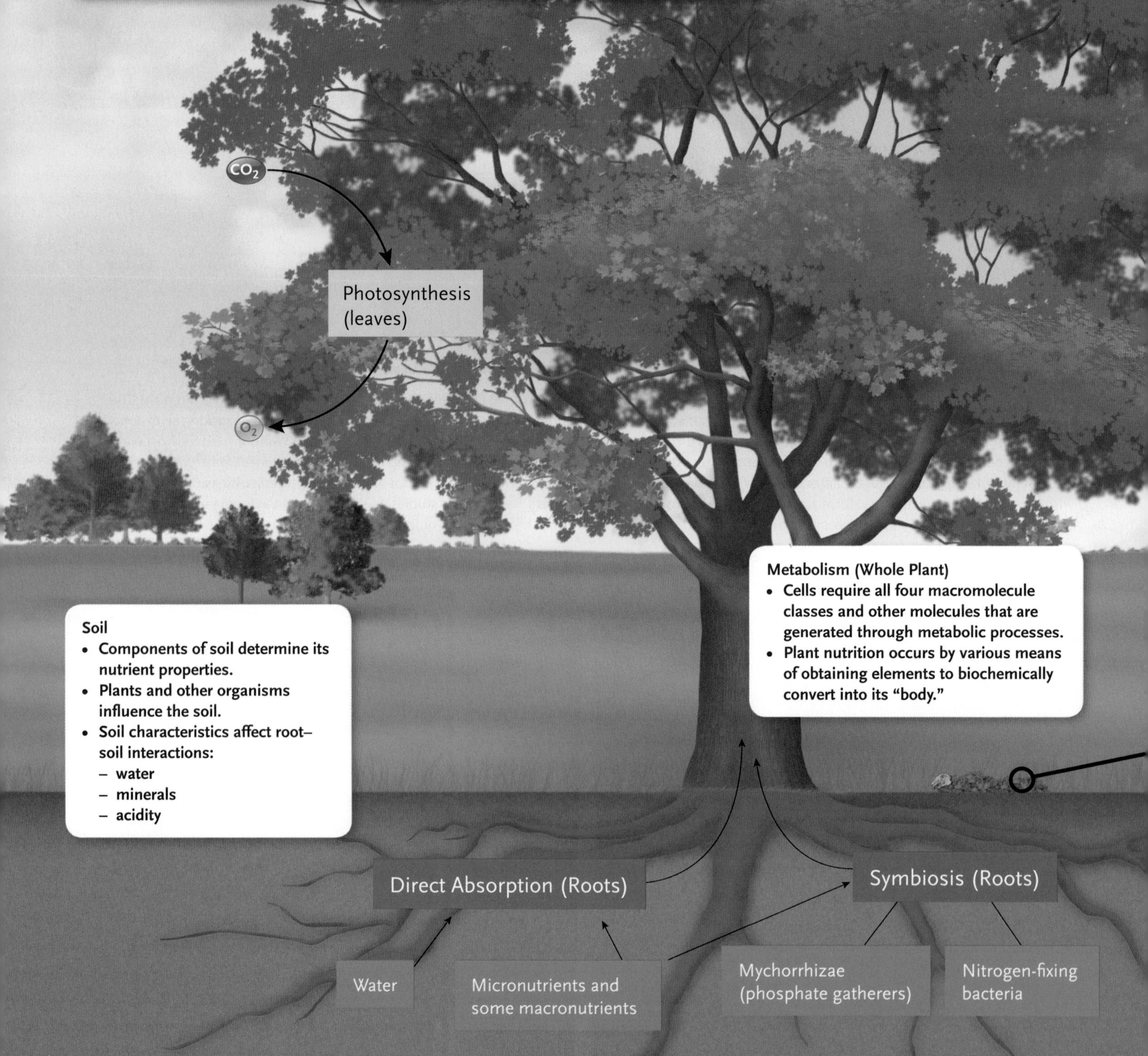

$CO_2$

Photosynthesis
(leaves)

$O_2$

**Soil**
- Components of soil determine its nutrient properties.
- Plants and other organisms influence the soil.
- Soil characteristics affect root–soil interactions:
  – water
  – minerals
  – acidity

**Metabolism (Whole Plant)**
- Cells require all four macromolecule classes and other molecules that are generated through metabolic processes.
- Plant nutrition occurs by various means of obtaining elements to biochemically convert into its "body."

Direct Absorption (Roots)

Symbiosis (Roots)

Water

Micronutrients and some macronutrients

Mychorrhizae (phosphate gatherers)

Nitrogen-fixing bacteria

Plants that do not receive sufficient amounts of one or more essential elements develop characteristic symptoms. The particular symptom often reflects the metabolic role that element plays.

**Plant grown using a complete growth solution** — Dianne Moule

**Iron deficiency** — Photos by E. Epstein, University of California, Davis

**Magnesium deficiency** — Photos by E. Epstein, University of California, Davis

**Nitrogen deficiency** — Photos by E. Epstein, University of California, Davis

**Phosphorus deficiency** — Photos by E. Epstein, University of California, Davis

**Potassium deficiency** — Photos by E. Epstein, University of California, Davis

**Sulfur deficiency** — Photos by E. Epstein, University of California, Davis

**Calcium deficiency** — Photos by E. Epstein, University of California, Davis

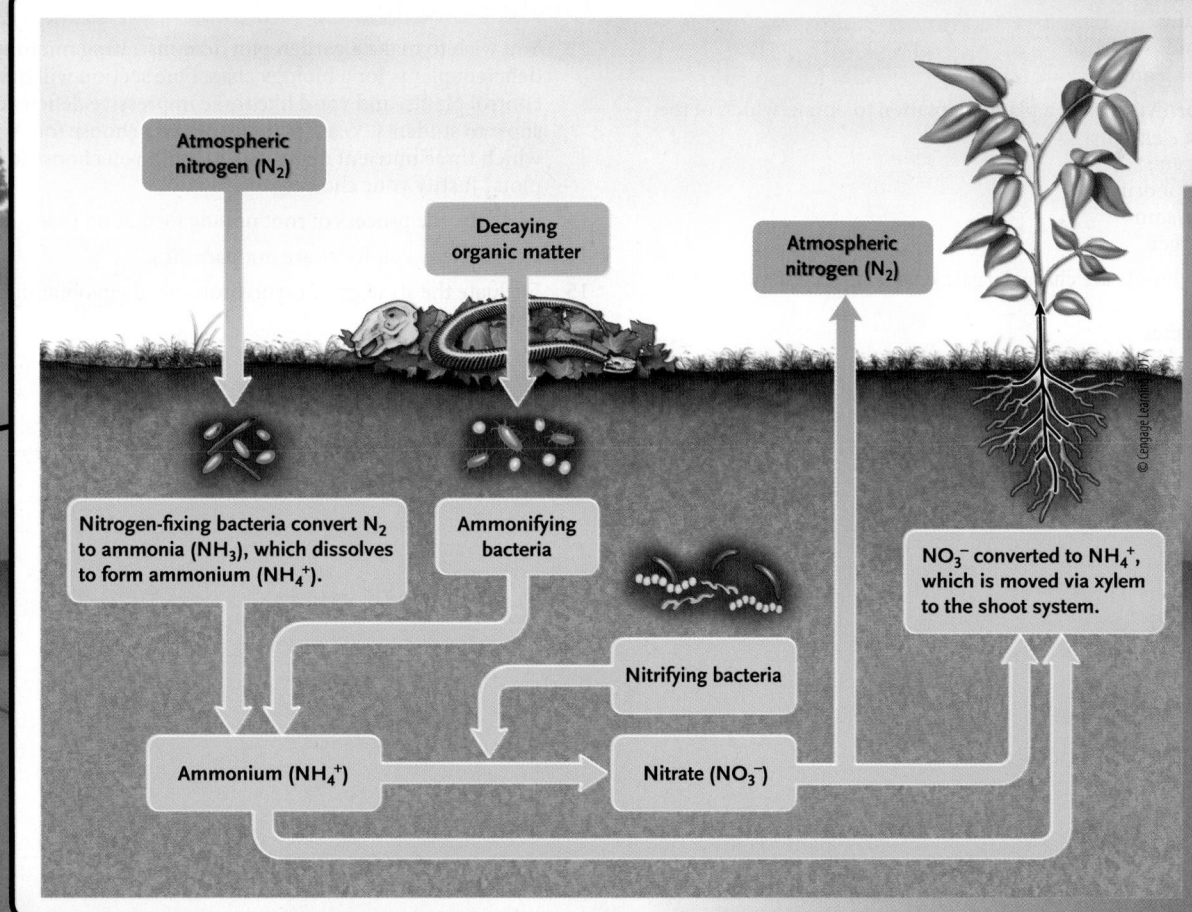

Atmospheric nitrogen ($N_2$)

Decaying organic matter

Atmospheric nitrogen ($N_2$)

Nitrogen-fixing bacteria convert $N_2$ to ammonia ($NH_3$), which dissolves to form ammonium ($NH_4^+$).

Ammonifying bacteria

$NO_3^-$ converted to $NH_4^+$, which is moved via xylem to the shoot system.

Nitrifying bacteria

Ammonium ($NH_4^+$)

Nitrate ($NO_3^-$)

© Cengage Learning 2017

# SELF-TEST QUESTIONS

## Recall/Understand

1. Which of these statements *best* applies to a micronutrient?
   a. It makes up 96% of the plant's dry mass.
   b. It cannot be replaced artificially.
   c. It is early on the periodic table compared with macronutrients.
   d. It is an essential element.

2. Which of these processes contributes to the uptake of calcium, magnesium, and potassium ions by plant roots?
   a. osmosis
   b. cation exchange
   c. anion leaching
   d. growth of root hairs

3. Which of the following was an experimental method used to identify the minerals absorbed into plant tissues that are essential for plant growth?
   a. rainfall
   b. hydroponic growth
   c. decomposition of organisms
   d. weathering of rock

4. Which of these processes is common for making usable nitrogen available to plants?
   a. nitrogen-fixing bacteria synthesizing nitrate from decaying organisms
   b. ammonifying bacteria using ammonium to produce nitrate
   c. nitrifying bacteria oxidizing $NH_4^+$ to $NO_3^-$
   d. direct absorption of $NH_4^+$ by root hairs

5. Which of these plants is a parasite?
   a. cobra lily
   b. dodder
   c. orchid
   d. snow plant

6. Being "carnivorous" is a plant adaptation to obtain which of the following elements?
   a. oxygen
   b. phosphorus
   c. potassium
   d. nitrogen

7. Haustorial roots are characteristic of which of these types of plants?
   a. parasites
   b. epiphytes
   c. nitrate fixers
   d. carnivorous

8. Describe the components of soil. Which part of soil is the humus? Why is humus important?

## Apply/Analyze

9. Rank the following atoms/nutrients in descending order of abundance in a plant, and for each explain why you picked it in its order.
   1. nitrogen
   2. sulfur
   3. oxygen
   4. iron
   5. phosphorus

10. Suppose that you bought a fertilizer labelled 15-30-15. What does it contain and in what proportions?
    a. 15% iron, 30% magnesium, 15% nitrogen
    b. 15% nitrogen, 30% phosphorus, 15% sulfur
    c. 15% nitrogen, 30% phosphorus, 15% potassium
    d. 15% selenium, 30% magnesium, 15% potassium

11. Suppose that you want to experiment using a method called *hydroponic culture*. Which of the following would you need to do?
    a. Grow plants in solutions containing different nutrients in carefully measured amounts, mixed in different combinations.
    b. Grow plants in carefully controlled light conditions, where some would be exposed to more light, and some to less.
    c. Grow plants in carefully controlled temperature conditions, where some would be exposed to higher temperatures, and others to lower.
    d. Grow plants in different soils containing carefully measured amounts of water.

## Create/Evaluate

12. You wish to make a garden plot demonstrating micronutrient-deficient plants for a biology class. One section will have healthy control plants, and you'd like three impressive deficiencies to show to students. What plant would you choose for all plots, and which three nutrient deficiencies would you choose for the other plots? Justify your choices.

13. Describe the process of root nodule formation in legumes.

14. Explain why epiphytes are not parasites.

15. Evaluate the strategy of carnivorous plants in obtaining nutrients.

# Chapter Roadmap

## Plant Signals and Responses to the Environment

From Purple Pages

From Chapter 4

### 37.1 Introduction to Plant Hormones

Phytohormones elicit a growth or metabolic response. Only a very small amount is needed for the response. They are typically *not* made of protein. Hormones bind to receptors on the cell surface, and signal transduction triggers a cellular response.

The most commonly discussed plant hormones are auxins, gibberellins, cytokinins, and ethylene.

From Purple Pages

From Chapter 3

From Chapter 25

From Chapter 28

### 37.2 Plant Chemical Defences

Some plant tissues release chemicals, such as enzymes, if stressed. Infected plant tissue is intentionally killed during the hypersensitive response.

Chitinases digest chitin, which provides some resistance to fungal or insect attack by breaking down their defensive barriers, while secondary metabolites can poison herbivores.

From Chapter 6

From Chapter 34

### 37.3 Plant Movements

Plants can grow differentially in order to reorient their organs.
The hormone auxin stimulates cell elongation.
Pigments absorb the light that the plant encounters and can encourage differential growth.
Gravity can also be sensed to orient shoots up and roots down.

Wally Eberhart/Visuals Unlimited, Inc.

From Chapter 5

From Chapter 6

From Chapter 8

### 37.4 Plant Biological Clocks

Plants exhibit circadian rhythms as well as seasonal changes in order to coordinate food gathering and food storage activities, and to allow for synchronized events such as gamete production and release.

Wally Eberhart/Visuals Unlimited, Inc.

Sunflower plants (*Helianthus*) with flower heads that orient toward the Sun's rays—an example of a plant response to shifting light levels in the environment

# Plant Signals and Responses to the Environment

# 37

**Why it matters . . .** What would you, a valuable collection of proteins, lipids, carbohydrates, and other prized nutrients, do if you found yourself stranded on an island with variable weather, scattered nutrients, and dangerous predators? The most likely answer is that you'd move to a safe area where there is food and shelter. But if you are a plant and rooted (literally!) in one place, you need other strategies.

Sunflowers are well known for **heliotropism**: rotation of leaves and flowers to stay perpendicular to the Sun as it travels the sky. The inflorescences are shown tracking the sun behind the photographer's back in the opening figure. Since more sunshine equals more energy, it makes sense for the leaves to rotate. But why move the flower, which is not a significant contributor to photosynthesis? Perhaps solar tracking heats the seeds to allow more efficient metabolism in developing embryos?

*Mimosa* seedlings collapse almost instantly when disturbed (**Figure 37.1a** and Figure 37.20). Wilted plants are less appealing to herbivores than nearby plants that are plump, giving these seedlings a slight edge of protection from being eaten.

In Chapter 36 (Section 36.3c) we noted that plants can secrete flavonoids to attract bacteria, then alter root hairs to provide a chamber for nitrogen fixation, a process called *nodulation* (Figure 37.1b). Other chemicals can be secreted to make materials in the soil more soluble, thereby facilitating absorption.

Ecologists have noted that individuals of single plant species may produce different protective chemicals despite having similar genomes. The guts of insects are sensitive to some defensive chemicals (e.g., Figure 37.12). The ability to produce hormones and chemicals that vary throughout a population of plants in a fixed area can help ensure that not all the plants get eaten. An additional trick plants can play is to release volatile chemicals that attract the natural predators of the herbivores that are feeding on them. The tansy, found in British Columbia and Eastern Canada (Figure 37.1c), releases camphor-based gases during aphid infestations, which attracts ladybugs, which dine on the aphids.

Plants that are found in windy, dry areas can be genetically selected for by being small and compact. However, some plants also take advantage of **thigmomorphogenesis**, where the plant body responds to mechanical stimulation by growing in girth, rather than length, or by grabbing onto supports (Figure 37.1d). This makes them more durable and able to handle wind gusts, but also with a developmental flexibility to grow large if the season is calm.

Plants can also tell time. Bean plants raise their leaves just prior to dawn; day length signals the best time to convert a shoot apical meristem into a floral meristem (Section 37.1d and Figure 37.25); and seasonal changes signal dormancy and even dropping of leaves in deciduous trees. Clearly, responding to these signals are important events!

**FIGURE 37.1** **(a)** Young plants of *Mimosa pudica* collapse when stimulated. **(b)** Root nodules form in soybeans in response to rhizobial bacteria. **(c)** The common tansy (*Tanacetum vulgare*) comes from Europe but is an invasive species. Gardeners in Canada use them for pest management: feeding aphids release a chemical that attracts predators like ladybugs. **(d)** Tendrils can sense when they touch a support and can use it to anchor the stem.

These and other adaptations are evolutionary solutions to the challenge of being sessile, allowing the vulnerable plant—rich sources of food for herbivores—to adapt to climatic and food challenges, avoid predation, and synchronize the production of flowers to help increase pollination. These elements are the focus of this chapter. By the end of the chapter, you should have an appreciation for the ways in which plants can respond to changes in their environment while being rooted in one place.

## 37.1 Introduction to Plant Hormones

A **hormone** (*hormon* = to stimulate) is a signalling molecule that regulates or helps coordinate some aspect of growth, metabolism, or development. Plant hormones may also be called *phytohormones*, especially in the scientific literature. Hormones are fundamental to the plant life cycle. They serve as triggers for seed germination and govern the development of a plant's body form, the shift from a vegetative growth phase to a reproductive phase, and the timed death of organs. Beyond their developmental roles, hormones mediate changes in the structure and functioning of plant parts in

response to external biotic factors such as predation, and abiotic factors such as the availability of light, moisture, and soil nutrients and effects of air currents, gravity, and physical contact with other objects. Some plant hormones exert their effects in the tissue where they are synthesized; others are transported from the tissue that produces them to another plant part. Hormonal effects may involve rapid responses to sudden environmental stimuli, or slower responses often involving changes in gene expression.

All plant hormones are rather small organic molecules that are active in extremely low concentrations. Hormones that have effects outside the tissue where they are produced typically diffuse to their target site(s) or travel to the site via vascular tissues. Plant hormones vary greatly in their effects, although each one affects a given tissue in a particular way. For instance, some stimulate one or more facets of growth or development, and others have an inhibiting influence. A given hormone can also have different effects in different plant tissues, and the effects can differ depending on a target tissue's stage of development. Adding to the complexity, many physiological responses result from the interaction of two or more hormones. Biologists recognize at least seven major classes of plant hormones **(Table 37.1)**: gibberellins,

**TABLE 37.1 | Major Plant Hormones and Signalling Molecules**

| Hormone/Signalling Compound | Where Synthesized | Tissues Affected | Effects |
|---|---|---|---|
| Auxins | Apical meristems, developing leaves and embryos | Growing tissues, buds, roots, leaves, fruits, vascular tissues | Promotion of growth and elongation of stems; promotion of formation of lateral roots and dormancy in lateral buds; promotion of fruit development; inhibition of leaf abscission; orientation of plants with respect to light, gravity |
| Gibberellins | Root and shoot tips, young leaves, developing embryos | Stems, developing seeds | Promotion of cell divisions and growth and elongation of stems; promotion of seed germination and bolting |
| Cytokinins | Mainly in root tips | Shoot apical meristems, leaves, buds | Promotion of cell division; inhibition of senescence of leaves; coordination of growth of roots and shoots (with auxin) |
| Ethylene | Shoot tips, roots, leaf nodes, flowers, fruits | Seeds, buds, seedlings, mature leaves, flowers, fruits | Regulation of elongation and division of cells in seedling stems, roots; in mature plants regulation of senescence and abscission of leaves, flowers, and fruits |
| Brassinosteroids | Young seeds; shoots and leaves | Mainly shoot tips, developing embryos | Stimulation of cell division and elongation, differentiation of vascular tissue |
| Abscisic acid | Leaves, chloroplasts, possibly roots in drying soils | Mainly shoot tips, developing embryos, leaves (stomata) | Stimulation of cell division and elongation, differentiation of vascular tissue, opening/closing of stomata |
| Jasmonates | Roots, seeds, probably other tissues | Various tissues, including damaged ones | In defence responses, promotion of transcription of genes encoding protease inhibitors; possible role in plant responses to nutrient deficiencies |
| Oligosaccharins | Cell walls | Damaged tissues; possibly active in most plant cells | Promotion of synthesis of phytoalexins in injured plants; may also have a role in regulating growth |
| Systemin | Damaged tissues | Damaged tissues | To date known only in tomato; roles in defence, including triggering jasmonate-induced chemical defences |
| Salicylic acid | Damaged tissues | Many plant parts | Triggering of synthesis of pathogenesis-related proteins, other general defences |

auxins, cytokinins, ethylene, brassinosteroids, abscisic acid (ABA), and jasmonates. Recent discoveries have added other hormonelike signalling agents to this list (see Table 37.1).

## 37.1a Plant Hormones Exert Their Effects via Signal Transduction Pathways

Target cells for a particular hormone generally have receptors that bind the hormone to activate cellular pathways. This mechanism unfolds in three basic steps as introduced in Chapter 4. We'll briefly review these steps here and consider current scientific understanding of the signal transduction pathways by which specific hormones exert their effects.

Recall from Chapter 4 that, in the first step of a signal transduction pathway, a target cell receptor receives the signal, which may be a molecule or an environmental cue such as sunlight. Next, the signal is transduced; that is, its "message" is changed into a form that can trigger the cellular response. In the third step, the transduced signal causes the cellular response **(Figure 37.2)**. Some transduced signals activate or turn off genes and so alter protein synthesis; others set in

motion events that modify existing cell proteins. Various plant hormones and growth factors bind to receptors at the target cell's plasma membrane. Others cross the plasma membrane and bind to receptors inside the cell. These receptors may be located on the endoplasmic reticulum (ER), in the cytoplasm, or in the nucleus. In many cases, hormone binding causes the receptor to change shape. Regardless, binding of a hormone triggers a complex pathway that leads to the cell's response: the opening of ion channels, activation of transport proteins, or some other event. Only cells with the appropriate receptor can respond to a particular hormone. For example, certain cells in developing seeds and maturing fruits have receptors for the "ripening hormone" ethylene, but cells in stems generally do not.

We can think of plant hormones as external "first messengers" that deliver the initial physiological signal to a target cell. Often, binding of these molecules triggers the synthesis of internal second messengers. These go-between molecules diffuse rapidly through the cytoplasm and provide the main chemical signal that alters cell functioning.

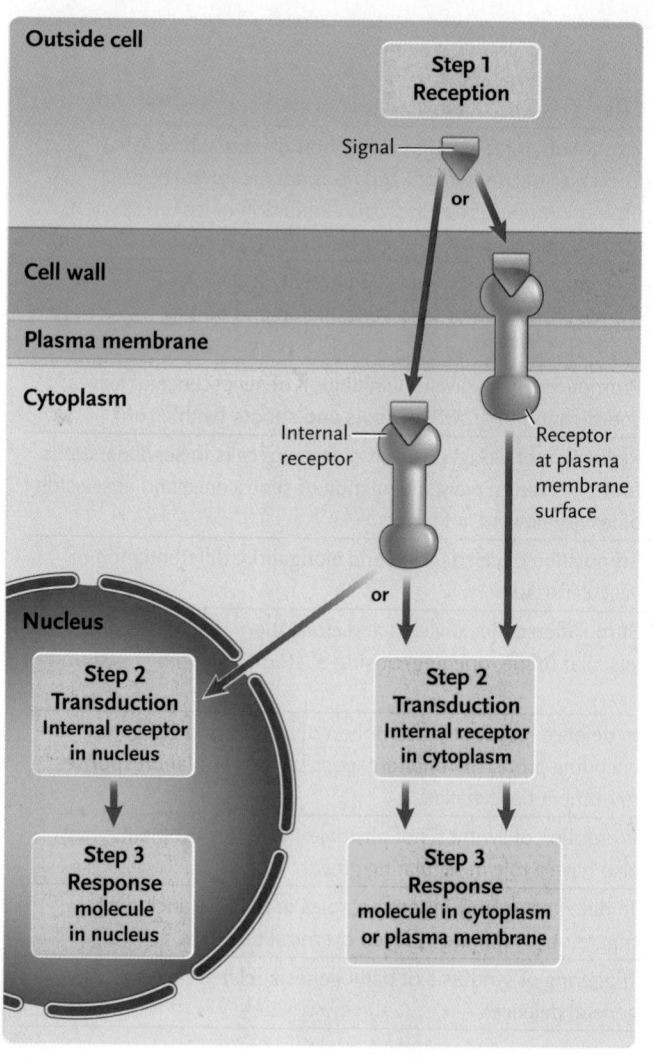

© Cengage Learning 2017

**1** An arriving signal binds and activates a receptor in the plasma membrane, cytoplasm, ER, or nucleus. In most cases, the receptor changes shape, which triggers the transduction pathway inside the cell.

**2** As the transduction pathway unfolds, receptor activation leads to activation of one or more proteins. This activation step may set in motion a cascade of protein phosphorylation, or it may mobilize second messenger molecules.

**3** Phosphorylated proteins or second messenger molecules trigger the cell response, such as a change in ion flow into or out of the cell, a shift in translation of mRNA, or altering gene transcription in the nucleus.

**FIGURE 37.2 Overview of signal transduction pathways in plant cells.** The three stages of a signal response pathway are shown. In step 1, the signal molecule binds to a receptor, changing its shape and eliciting a response. If the receptor spans the plasma membrane, binding of the hormone outside the cell causes the intracellular portion to change the chemistry on the inside of the cell, much like ringing a doorbell outside a house makes a sound inside the house. Some hormones enter the cell and bind a soluble protein in the cytoplasm. In step 2, the chemical changes induced by the membrane-bound receptor, or binding of the receptor/protein complex to other proteins in the nucleus, inform the cell of the presence of a signal. The cell's response (step 3) involves recognizing activated proteins or secondary messengers to perform the appropriate response, or in the case of a diffusible cytoplasmic protein, activation of signal-specific genes (compare to Figure 37.6).

## 37.1b Second Messenger Systems Enhance the Plant Cell's Response to a Hormone Signal

**Second messengers** are usually synthesized in the sequence of chemical reactions that convert an external signal into internal cell activity. For many years, the details of plant second messenger systems were sketchy and hotly debated. Fairly early on, calcium ions were found to play a second messenger role in some hormonal responses. Recent experimental evidence indicates that the hormonal signal from auxins is often conveyed by cAMP (cyclic adenosine monophosphate), a major second messenger in cells of animals and other organisms. **Inositol triphosphate (IP$_3$)**, a second messenger in plants, fungi, and animals, is involved in the reactions that close plant stomata in response to a signal from abscisic acid (ABA). Other research suggests that a molecule called *cGMP* (cyclic guanosine monophosphate) serves as a second messenger for auxins, ABA, and a few other plant hormones.

In addition to the basic signal transduction pathways described here, other routes may exist that are unique to plant cells. Light is the driving force for photosynthesis, and researchers are investigating the possibility that plants have evolved other unique light-related biochemical pathways as well. For instance, experiments are extending our knowledge of how plant cells respond to blue light, which, as you will read, triggers some photoperiod responses such as the opening and closing of stomata. Other exciting research suggests that it is probably common for signal response pathways in plant cells to include many steps in which different types of proteins and other molecules are mobilized, not unlike the steps in animal cells.

Auxins were the first plant hormones to be identified, and we start with them as we consider each major class of plant hormones and discuss some newly discovered signalling molecules as well.

## 37.1c Auxins Promote Growth

**Auxins** are synthesized mainly in the shoot apical meristem and young stems and leaves. They are crucial to plant growth. Among other effects, auxins are essential for the normal progression of the cell cycle, and they stimulate the elongation of cells in growing stems and coleoptiles. Auxins also mediate growth responses to light and gravity. Indoleacetic acid (IAA) is the most important natural auxin. Botanists often use the general term "auxin" to refer to IAA, a practice we follow here.

**EXPERIMENTS THAT LED TO THE DISCOVERY OF AUXINS** The path to the discovery of auxins began in the late nineteenth century in the library of Charles Darwin's home in the English countryside. Among his interests, Darwin was fascinated by plant **tropisms**—movements such as the bending of a houseplant toward light. This growth response, triggered by exposure to a directional light source, is an example of a **phototropism**.

Working with his son Francis, Darwin explored phototropisms by germinating seeds of two species of grasses, oats (*Avena sativa*) and canary grass (*Phalaris canariensis*), in pots on the sill of a sunny window. Recall from Chapter 33 that the shoot apical meristem and the plumule of grass seedlings are sheathed by a coleoptile—a protective structure that is extremely sensitive to light. Darwin did not know this detail, but he observed that, as the emerging shoots grew, within a few days they bent toward the light. He hypothesized that the tip of the shoot detected light and communicated that information to the coleoptile. Darwin and his son tested this idea in several ways **(Figure 37.3)** and concluded that, when seedlings are illuminated from the side, "some influence is transmitted from the upper to the lower part, causing them to bend."

The Darwins' observations spawned decades of studies that illustrate how scientific understanding typically advances step by step, as one set of experimental findings stimulates new research. First, scientists in Denmark and Poland showed that the bending of a shoot toward a light source was caused by something that could move through agar (a jellylike culture material derived from certain red algae) but not through a sheet of the mineral mica. This finding prompted experiments establishing that, indeed, the stimulus was a chemical produced in the shoot tip. Soon afterward, in 1926, experiments by the Dutch plant physiologist Frits Went confirmed that the growth-promoting chemical diffuses downward from the shoot tip to the stem below **(Figure 37.4)**. Using oat seeds, Went first sliced the tips from young shoots that had been grown under normal light conditions. He then placed the tips on agar blocks and left them there long enough for diffusible substances to move into the agar. Meanwhile, the decapitated stems stopped growing, but growth quickly resumed in seedlings that Went "capped" with the agar blocks (see Figure 37.4a). Clearly, a growth-promoting substance in the excised shoot tips had diffused into the agar, and from there into the seedling stems. Went also attached an agar block to one side of a decapitated shoot tip; when the shoot began growing again, it bent away from the agar (see Figure 37.4b). Importantly, Went performed his experiments in total darkness to avoid any "contamination" of his results by the possible effects of light.

Went did not determine the mechanism—differential elongation of cells on the shaded side of a shoot—by which the growth promoter controlled phototropism. However, he did develop a test that correlated specific amounts of the substance—later named auxin (*auxein* = to increase)—with particular growth effects. This careful groundwork culminated several years later when other researchers identified auxin as indoleacetic acid (IAA).

**EFFECTS OF AUXIN** Auxin is one of the first chemical signals to help shape the plant body. When the zygote first divides, forming an embryo that consists of a basal cell and an apical cell, auxin exported by the apical cell to the basal cell helps guide the development of the various features of the embryonic shoot.

CHAPTER 37 PLANT SIGNALS AND RESPONSES TO THE ENVIRONMENT |

FIGURE 37.3 **Experimental Research**

## The Darwins' Experiments on Phototropism

**Question:** Why does a plant stem bend toward the light?

**Experiment 1:** The Darwins observed that the first shoot of an emerging grass seedling, which is sheathed by a coleoptile, bends toward sunlight shining through a window. In their first experiment, they removed the shoot tip from a grass seedling and illuminated one side of the seedling.

**Result:** The seedling neither grew nor bent toward the light.

**Experiment 2:** The Darwins divided seedlings into three groups. They covered the shoot tips of one group with an opaque cap and the shoot tips of the another group with a translucent cap. In the third group, a light-blocking shield was placed around the shaft of the coleoptile so that only the shoot tip was exposed. All the seedlings were illuminated from the same side.

**Result:** The seedlings with opaque caps grew but did not bend. Those with translucent caps and the shielded shaft both grew *and* bent toward the light.

**Conclusion:** When seedlings are illuminated from one side, some factor was transmitted from a seedling's tip to the tissue below, causing it to bend toward the light.

© Cengage Learning 2017. Based on C. R. Darwin. 1880. *The Power of Movement in Plants.* London: John Murray.

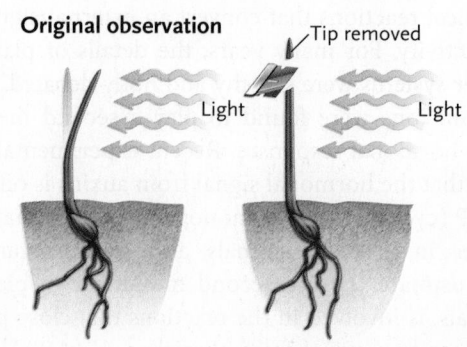

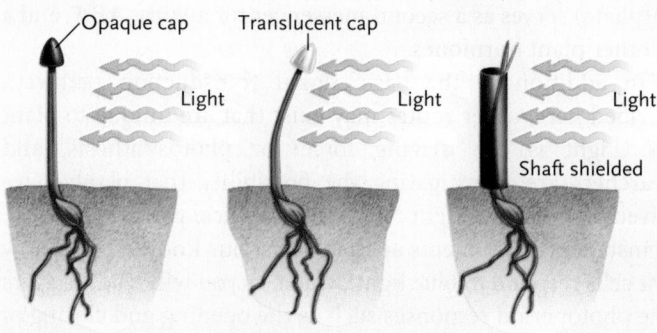

It plays a key role in when and where leaf primordia form in the apical meristem. As the embryo develops, the leaf primordium of the young shoot becomes the main source of IAA; a secondary signal stimulates the primary growth of the stem and root as long as the embryonic plant is underground. Once an elongating shoot breaks through the soil surface, its tip is exposed to sunlight, and the first leaves unfurl and begin photosynthesis. Shortly thereafter, the leaf tip stops producing IAA and that task is assumed first by cells at the leaf edges and then by cells at base of the young leaf. Even so, as described in Section 37.3, IAA continues to influence a plant's responses to light and plays a role in its growth responses to gravity as well. IAA also stimulates cell division in the vascular cambium and promotes the formation of secondary xylem, as well as the formation of new root apical meristems, including lateral meristems. Not all of auxin's effects promote growth, however. IAA also maintains apical dominance, which inhibits growth of lateral meristems on shoots and restricts the formation of branches. Hence, auxin is a signal that declares that the shoot apical meristem is present and active.

Commercial orchardists spray synthetic IAA on fruit trees because it promotes uniform flowering, helps set the fruit, and also helps prevent fruit from dropping off the plant prematurely. Various synthetic auxins are used as **herbicides** (generally, weed killers) that disrupt normal physiology, often causing the plants to blacken, twist, and die. The most widely used herbicide in the world is the synthetic auxin 2,4-D (2,4-dichlorophenoxyacetic acid). This chemical kills broadleaf eudicots but spares monocots such as grasses. It is used extensively to prevent broadleaf weeds from growing in fields of cereal crops such as corn and rice (which are monocots), and controls dandelions in grass found in peoples' yards.

**AUXIN TRANSPORT** To exert its far-reaching effects on plant tissues, auxin must travel away from its main synthesis sites in shoot meristems and young leaves. Although IAA moves through plant tissues slowly, roughly 1 cm/h, this rate is 10 times as fast as could be explained by simple diffusion. How, then, is auxin transported?

Researchers adapted the agar block method pioneered by Went to trace the direction and rate of auxin movements in different kinds of tissues. Careful measurements show that IAA accumulates in the shaded part of the stem. A thin slice of mica placed vertically in a shoot tip prevents lateral transport of auxin to the shaded side and the stem does not bend. If the mica barrier is shortened to allow the shaded and illuminated sides of the stem to touch, IAA moves toward the shade and the stem bends.

FIGURE 37.4 **Experimental Research**

## Two Experiments by Frits Went Demonstrating the Effect of Indoleacetic Acid (IAA) on an Oat Coleoptile

**Question:** Is a diffusible substance in shoot tips responsible for differential growth?

Frits Went knew that the shoot tip controlled elongation of the seedling because decapitated seedlings failed to grow.

**Experiment 1:** Went cut a tip from two oat seedlings (step 1), placing one on an agar block for a few hours so it would absorb the fluids from the tip (step 2). He placed the agar block on the cut end of one of the decapitated seedlings.

**Result:** The cut seedling without the agar block stopped growing, but for the seedling with the agar block containing fluids from the tip placed on its cut end, growth was comparable to an uncut control plant (step 3).

a. **The procedure showing that a diffusible substance promotes elongation of cells below the shoot tip**

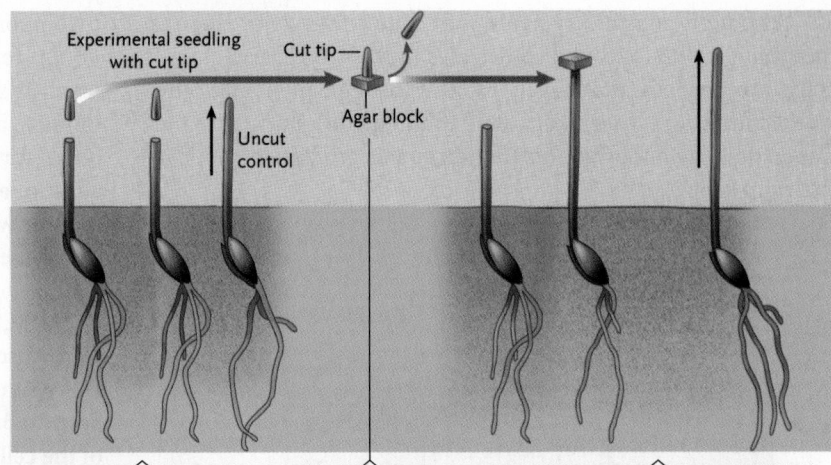

**1** After Went cut off the tip of an oat seedling, the shoot stopped elongating, while a control seedling with an intact tip continued to grow.

**2** He placed the excised tip on an agar block for 1–4 hours. During that time, something diffused into the agar block

**3** Went then placed the agar block on another detipped oat shoot, and the shoot resumed elongation, growing about as rapidly as in a control seedling with an intact shoot tip. The decapitated shoot does not grow.

**Experiment 2:** Went used a fluid-impregnated block (step 4) to show its effects on growing cells.

**Result:** Cells in contact with block grew faster (step 5), causing the seedling to curve in a direction opposite to the point of contact.

**Conclusion:** There is a substance that stimulates cell growth that is produced by the shoot tip and moves downward. Scientists later identified this substance as the plant hormone auxin, also known as *IAA*.

b. **The procedure showing that cells in contact with the agar block grow faster than those farther away**

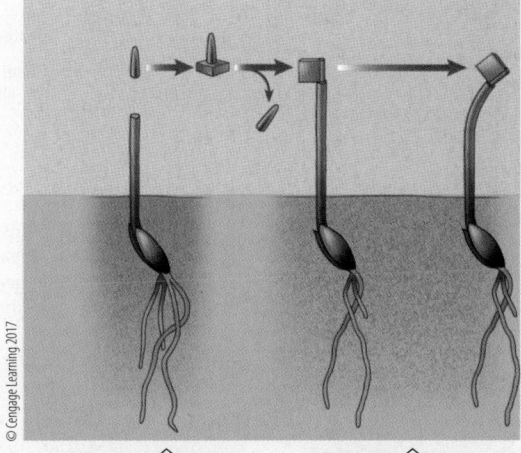

© Cengage Learning 2017

**4** Went removed the tip of a seedling and placed it on an agar block.

**5** He placed the agar block on one side of the shoot tip. something moved into the shoot tip on that side, causing it to bend away from the

In a stem, parenchyma cells next to vascular bundles apparently transport IAA. The hormone moves through and between cells, possibly travelling by **polar transport**, a path that moves auxin from its source toward the plant base, ending at the root tip. **Figure 37.5** diagrams one widely accepted model for this process. As you can see, IAA is cotransported with a proton through membrane channels, driven by concentration and electrochemical gradients produced by $H^+$ pumps in the plasma membrane. The hormone exits at the opposite end by active transport across the plasma membrane.

Although auxin is typically not found in xylem, there is increasing evidence that it sometimes moves from parenchyma cells into phloem and travels rapidly through plants. As this work continues, researchers will undoubtedly gain a clearer understanding of how plants distribute this crucial hormone to their growing parts.

**INSIGHTS INTO AUXIN SIGNAL TRANSDUCTION** Only in recent years have researchers begun to understand how target cells detect auxins and how subsequent transduction steps unfold. Experiments suggest that auxin binds different receptors, depending on the nature of the ensuing response.

Responses that require a change in gene expression rely on a family of proteins often called simply *TIR1*, after the original protein discovered. Research in several laboratories confirmed that, when IAA in a cell enters the nucleus and binds to TIR1, binding removes an existing inhibition of the transcription of particular genes. As a result, the previously repressed genes are turned on and the cell's activity changes in some way.

In responses that don't require a change in gene expression (such as swelling of the protoplast during cell expansion), auxin binds to a receptor called *ABP1* (auxin binding protein 1) at the outer surface of the plasma membrane. ABP1 binding triggers additional transduction steps within the cell, although the steps are not well understood. **Figure 37.6** sketches these pathways as researchers currently envision them.

**POSSIBLE MECHANISMS OF IAA ACTION** Ever since auxins were discovered, researchers have sought to understand how IAA stimulates plant cells to elongate. As you may recall from Section 35.5, in an elongating plant cell the cellulose meshwork of the cell wall is first loosened and then stretched by turgor pressure. Several hormones, and auxin especially, apparently increase the plasticity (stretching) of the cell wall. Two major hypotheses have sought to explain this effect; both may be correct.

Plant cell walls grow much faster in an acidic environment, that is, when the pH is less than 7. The **acid-growth hypothesis** proposes that auxin stimulates plasma membrane $H^+$ pumps to acidify the cell wall; this activates proteins called *expansins*, which disrupt bonds between cellulose microfibrils in the wall **(Figure 37.7)**. Activation of the plasma membrane $H^+$ pump also produces a membrane potential that pulls $K^+$ and other cations into the cell to make it hypertonic. This osmotic gradient draws water into the cell, increasing turgor pressure and helping to stretch the "loosened" cell walls. Experiments have shown that all these effects occur shortly after ABP1 binds auxin.

IAA triggers the expression of genes encoding enzymes that play roles in the synthesis of new wall components. Plant cells exposed to IAA do not show increased growth if they are treated with a chemical that inhibits protein synthesis. On the other hand, certain mRNAs rapidly increase in concentration within 10–20 minutes after stem sections are treated with auxin. It is not yet known exactly which proteins these mRNAs encode, although microRNAs (Chapter 13) may also be involved.

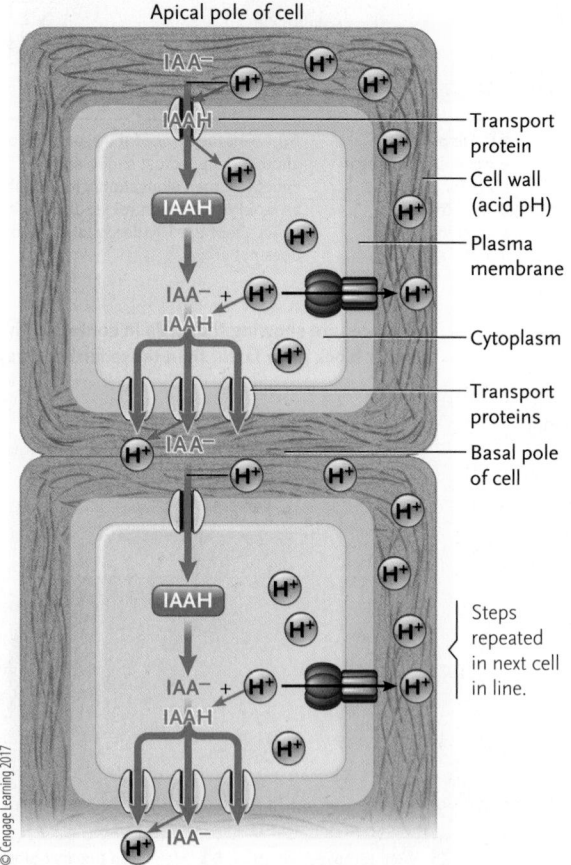

**FIGURE 37.5 The polar transport of auxin in plant shoots.** Studies of IAA transport in plants have demonstrated that the hormone moves in one direction only: from the shoot tip downward to plant parts below. This diagram shows one model for this polar auxin transport. In this model, a plasma membrane $H^+$ pump maintains gradients of pH and electrical charge across the membrane, moving $H^+$ out of the cell using energy from ATP hydrolysis. Following the gradients, at the basal pole of a cell IAA diffuses through the transport proteins into the cell wall, then (as IAAH) into the next cell in line.

### 37.1d Gibberellins Also Stimulate Growth, Including the Elongation of Stems

**Gibberellins** stimulate various aspects of plant growth. Collectively, they make up the largest class of plant hormones, with more than 130 recognized chemical variations. Gibberellins have been isolated from fungi and from flowering plants,

## a. Fast response to IAA

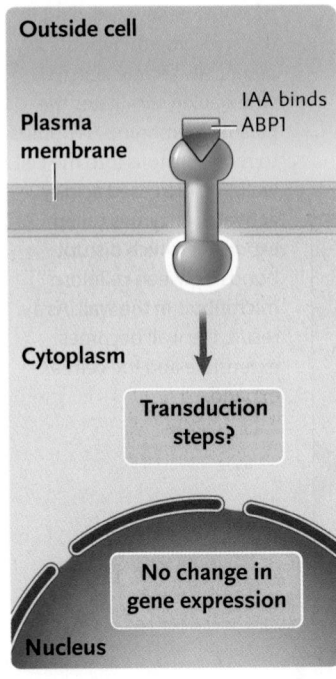

## b. IAA responses requiring change in gene expression

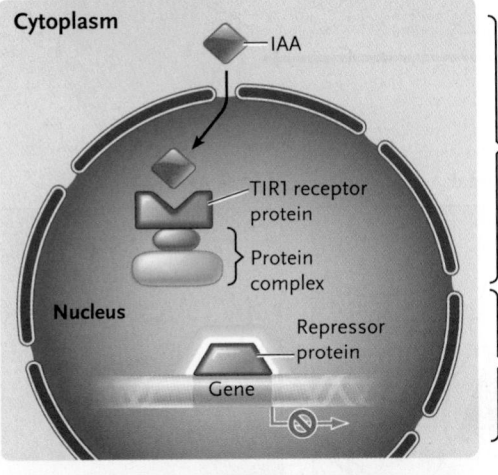

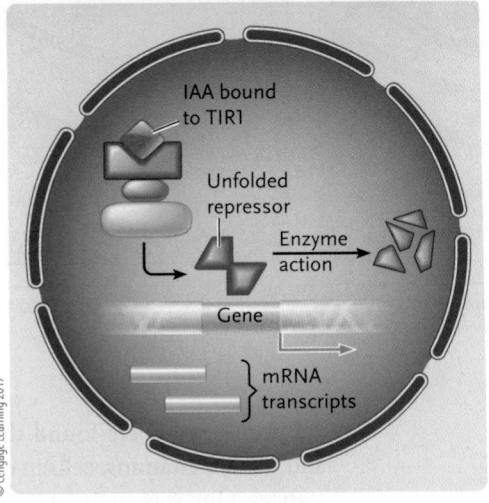

**FIGURE 37.6** Model for auxin signal transduction pathways

**1** IAA moves from the cytoplasm into the nucleus, where it can bind to TIR1 linked to a protein complex.

Until IAA binds TIR1, a repressor protein prevents transcription of the gene responsible for the cellular response to IAA.

**2** When IAA binds to TIR1, the protein complex is activated. It unfolds the repressor and the gene can be transcribed. Enzymes degrade the unfolded repressor and the released amino acids are recycled.

© Cengage Learning 2017

including eudicots and some monocots. They may also exist in other plant groups.

One of the most dramatic effects of gibberellins is to promote the lengthening of plant stems by stimulating both cell division and cell elongation. Synthesized in shoot and root tips and young leaves, gibberellins, like auxins, modify the cell walls to promote expansion. Although gibberellins do not acidify the cell wall, they may affect expansin activity, possible alone or with the activity of IAA. The general signal transduction pathway for gibberellins is similar to that for auxins: the target cell's activity is altered when a gene repressor in the cell nucleus is inactivated and the gene begins to be expressed (see Figure 37.6).

In most plant species analyzed to date, the hormone that controls stem elongation is the gibberellin called *GA1*. Normally, GA1 is synthesized in small amounts in young leaves and transported throughout the plant in the phloem. Disruption of GA1 synthesis can affect plant growth; for example, experiments with a dwarf variety of peas (*Pisum sativum*) and other species show that these plants and their taller relatives differ at a single gene locus. Dwarfism of plant lines can be traced to plants being homozygous for a defective allele of a gene involved in the GA1 synthetic pathway. Their internodes—

portions of stems between the sites where leaves attach—barely elongate at all because of insufficient GA1.

Another stark demonstration of the effect gibberellins can have on internode growth is **bolting**, growth of a floral stalk in plants that form vegetative rosettes such as cabbages (*Brassica* sp.), iceberg lettuce (*Lactuca* sp.), spinach (*Spinacia* sp.), and many agricultural and wild plants. By bolting, inflorescences are raised so that pollination can occur more efficiently and the resulting seeds can be dispersed more broadly. In a rosette plant, stem internodes are so short that the leaves appear to arise from a single node. When these plants flower, however, the internodes elongate rapidly and meristems switch from vegetative growth to making flowers (**Figure 37.8**; see also Section 35.2). In nature, external cues such as increasing day length or warming after a cold snap stimulate gibberellin synthesis, and bolting occurs soon afterward. This observation supports the hypothesis that, in rosette plants and possibly some others, gibberellins switch on internode lengthening when environmental conditions favour a shift from vegetative growth to reproductive growth.

Beyond the effects just mentioned, in monoecious species (having flowers of both sexual types on the same plant), applications of a gibberellin seem to encourage proportionately

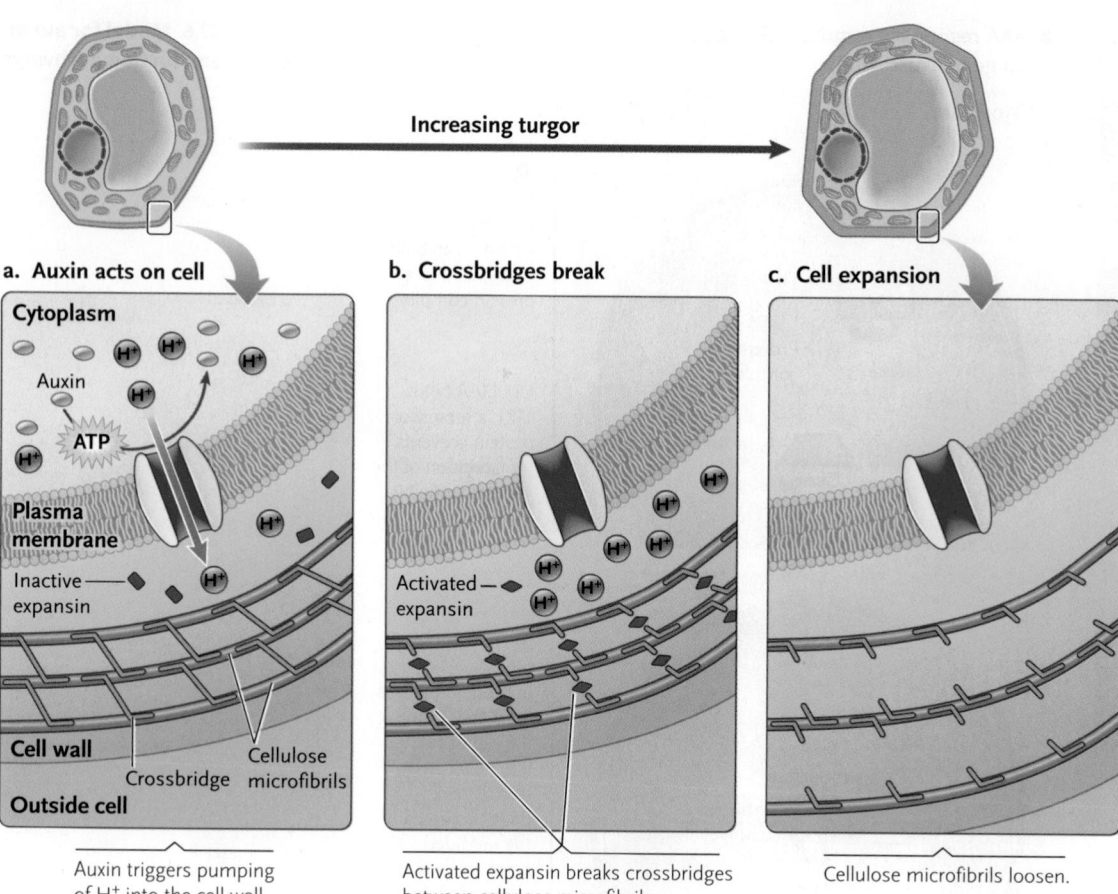

a. **Auxin acts on cell**

Cytoplasm

Auxin

ATP

Plasma membrane

Inactive expansin

Cell wall
Crossbridge | Cellulose microfibrils

Outside cell

Auxin triggers pumping of $H^+$ into the cell wall.

b. **Crossbridges break**

Activated expansin

Activated expansin breaks crossbridges between cellulose microfibrils.

c. **Cell expansion**

Cellulose microfibrils loosen.

Increasing turgor

**FIGURE 37.7 How auxin may regulate expansion of plant cells.** According to the acid-growth hypothesis, plant cells secrete acid ($H^+$) when auxin stimulates the plasma membrane $H^+$ pumps to move protons into the cell wall. The increased acidity activates enzymes called *expansins*, which disrupt bonds between cellulose microfibrils in the wall. As a result, the wall becomes extensible and the cell can expand.

© Cengage Learning 2017

Flowers

Jan Zeevaart

**FIGURE 37.8 Bolting in a spinach plant.** The plants grow in a compact rosette form until long day lengths stimulate bolting to produce a tall floral shoot, as shown here. After flowering, the plant dies.

more "male" flowers to develop. As a result, there may be more pollen available to pollinate "female" flowers and therefore more fruit produced.

## 37.1e Cytokinins Enhance Growth and Retard Aging

**Cytokinins** play a major role in stimulating cell division (hence the name, which refers to cytokinesis). Cytokinin action is often coupled to auxin activity. Cytokinins were first discovered during the development of nutrient media required for plant tissue

culture. Researchers found that, in addition to sugar, minerals, and certain vitamins, cells in culture also required two other substances. One was auxin, which promoted the elongation of plant cells but did not stimulate the cells to divide. Coconut milk, which is liquid endosperm, could promote cell division. Cytokinins in the endosperm were discovered to be the reason coconut milk stimulates plant tissue to grow in culture. Boiled DNA can degrade to a variety of products, including adenine, which also is effective in stimulating cell division. Adenine has a chemical structure similar to some types of cytokinins. When endosperm or boiled DNA was added to a culture medium along with an auxin, cultured cells would begin dividing and grow normally.

The most abundant natural cytokinin is zeatin, so-called because it was first isolated from the endosperm of young corn seeds (*Zea mays*). In endosperm, zeatin probably promotes the burst of cell division that takes place as a fruit matures. As you might expect, cytokinins are also abundant in the rapidly dividing meristem tissues of root and shoot tips. Cytokinins occur not only in flowering plants but also in many conifers, mosses, and ferns. They are also synthesized by many soil-dwelling bacteria and fungi and may be crucial to the growth of mycorrhizae, which help nourish thousands of plant species (see Section 36.3). *Agrobacterium*, a bacterial parasite of plants, stimulates tumour growth by injecting genes that produce cytokinins into the host plant: these tumours produce food specifically for the bacterium.

Cytokinins are synthesized mainly in root tips and apparently travel through the plant in xylem sap. In addition to promoting cell division generally, they stimulate the growth of lateral buds and have other developmental and metabolic effects. For example, cytokinins promote expansion of young leaves (as leaf cells expand), cause chloroplasts to mature, and retard leaf aging. In concert with auxin they also coordinate the growth of roots and shoots. Investigators culturing tobacco tissues found that the relative amounts of auxin and a cytokinin strongly influenced not only growth, but also development, as illustrated in **Figure 37.9**.

Natural cytokinins can prolong the life of stored vegetables. Similar synthetic compounds are already widely used to prolong the shelf life of lettuces and mushrooms, and to keep cut flowers fresh.

## 37.1f Ethylene Regulates Plant Aging and Some Other Responses

Most parts of a plant can produce **ethylene**, which is present in fruits, flowers, seeds, leaves, and roots and helps regulate a wide variety of plant physiological responses. Ethylene is also an unusual hormone, in part because it is structurally simple (see Table 37.1) and in part because it is a gas at normal temperature and pressure.

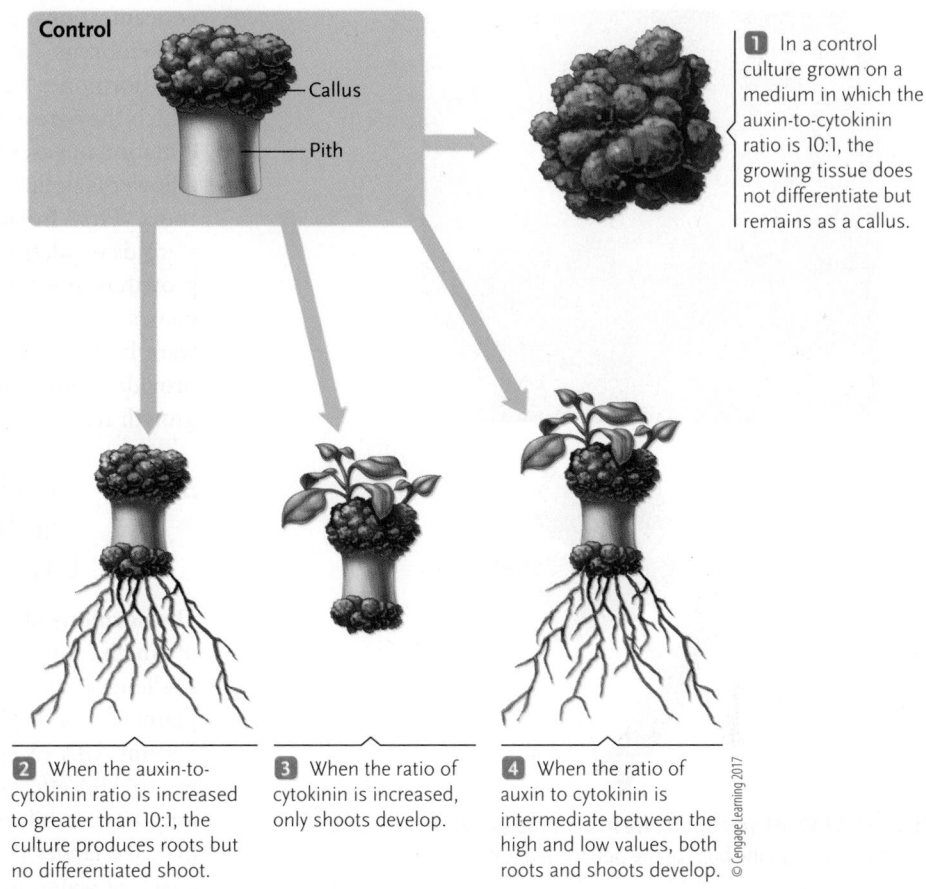

FIGURE 37.9 **Interaction of auxin and cytokinin in the development of plant roots and shoots.** Using callus tissue cultured from tobacco pith (spongy parenchyma from a stem), Folke Skoog and Carlos Miller demonstrated how normal development of tobacco plants requires the proportional interaction of auxin and cytokinin.

**ETHYLENE AND PLANT SENESCENCE** The aging of plant parts is termed **senescence**. Senescence is a controlled process of deterioration that leads to the death of plant cells. The leaves of deciduous trees senesce in autumn; many turn yellow or red as chlorophyll and proteins break down and new pigments are deposited. Ethylene triggers the expression of genes leading to the synthesis of chlorophyllases and proteases, enzymes that launch the breakdown process. In many plants, senescence is associated with **abscission**, the dropping of flowers, fruits, and leaves in response to environmental signals. In this process, ethylene apparently stimulates the activity of enzymes that digest cell walls in an abscission zone—a localized region at the base of the petiole. The petiole detaches from the stem at that point **(Figure 37.10)**.

Senescence appears to require a range of cues. For some species, the funnelling of nutrients into reproductive parts may help trigger senescence of leaves, stems, and roots. When the drain of nutrients is halted by removing each newly emerging flower or seed pod, a plant's leaves and stems stay green and vigorous much longer. Gardeners routinely remove flower buds from many plants to maintain vegetative growth. Evidence suggests that other cues are important, too. For instance, when a cocklebur is induced to flower under winter-like conditions, its leaves turn yellow regardless of whether the nutrient-demanding young flowers are left on or pinched off. It is as if a "death signal" forms that leads to flowering and senescence when there are fewer hours of daylight (typical of winter days). This observation underscores the general theme that many plant responses to the environment involve the interaction of multiple molecular signals.

**FRUIT RIPENING: A FORM OF SENESCENCE** Although the precise mechanisms are not completely understood, ripening begins when a fruit starts to synthesize ethylene. The ripening process may involve the conversion of starch or organic acids to sugars, the softening of cell walls, or the rupturing of the cell membrane and loss of cell fluid. The same kinds of events occur in wounded plant tissues, which also synthesize ethylene.

Ethylene from an outside source can stimulate senescence responses, including ripening of some (but not all) species of plants. Ethylene binds to specific protein receptors on plant cells. The ancient Chinese observed that they could induce picked fruit to ripen faster by burning incense; later, it was found that the incense smoke contains ethylene. Today ethylene gas is widely used to ripen tomatoes, pineapples, bananas,

Abscission zone at base of leaf where it joins the stem

**FIGURE 37.10 Abscission zone in a maple (*Acer*).** This longitudinal section is through the base of the petiole of a leaf.

honeydew melons, mangoes, papayas, and other fruit that have been picked and shipped while still green. Ripening fruit itself gives off ethylene, which is why placing a ripe banana in a closed sack of unripe peaches (or some other green fruit) can cause the fruit to ripen. Because sugars are added only when the fruit is attached to the plant, this kind of ripening affects texture and colour, but compromises sweetness. Note, however, that cherries and blueberries do not produce much ethylene, nor does ethylene influence how their fruit ripens. Oranges and other citrus fruits may be exposed to ethylene to brighten their rind. Conversely, limiting fruit exposure to ethylene can delay ripening. Apples will keep for months without rotting if they are exposed to a chemical that inhibits ethylene production or if they are stored in an environment that inhibits the hormone's effects, including low atmospheric pressure and a high concentration of $CO_2$, which may bind ethylene receptors through competitive inhibition (see Section 3.6b).

## 37.1g Brassinosteroids Regulate Plant Growth Responses

The dozens of steroid hormones classed as **brassinosteroids** all appear to be vital for normal growth in plants, for they stimulate cell division and elongation in a wide range of plant cell types. Confirmed as plant hormones in the 1980s, brassinosteroids are now the subject of intense research on their sources and effects. Although brassinosteroids have been detected in a wide variety of plant tissues and organs, the highest

concentrations are found in shoot tips and developing seeds and embryos—all examples of young, actively developing parts. The hormones have different effects depending on the tissue in which they are active. They can promote cell elongation, differentiation of vascular tissue, and elongation of a pollen tube after a flower is pollinated. By contrast, they inhibit the elongation of roots. First isolated from canola (*Brassica napus*), brassinosteroids regulate the expression of genes associated with a plant's growth responses to light. This role was underscored by the outcomes of experiments using mutant *Arabidopsis* plants that were homozygous for a defective gene called *bri1*. The results provide convincing evidence that brassinosteroids mediate growth responses to light.

## 37.1h Abscisic Acid Suppresses Growth and Influences Responses to Environmental Stress

The hormone **abscisic acid (ABA)** has a variety of effects, many of which represent **evolutionary adaptations** to environmental challenges. Plants apparently synthesize ABA from carotenoid pigments inside plastids in leaves and possibly other plant parts. Several ABA receptors have been identified. In general, we can group ABA effects into changes in gene expression that result in long-term inhibition of growth and rapid, short-term physiological changes that are responses to immediate stresses, such as a lack of water, in a plant's surroundings. As its name suggests, ABA was first thought to play a central role in abscission. We now know that ethylene (described in Section 37.1f) is the major abscission trigger.

**SUPPRESSING GROWTH IN BUDS AND SEEDS** Operating as a counterpoint to growth-stimulating hormones such as gibberellins, ABA inhibits growth in response to environmental cues, such as seasonal changes in temperature and light. This growth suppression can last for many months or even years. For example, one of ABA's major growth-inhibiting effects is apparent in perennial plants, in which the hormone promotes dormancy in leaf buds, an important adaptive advantage in places where the cold of winter can damage young leaves. If ABA is applied to a growing leaf bud, the bud's normal development stops and, instead, protective *bud scales*—modified, non-photosynthetic leaves that are small, dry, and tough—form around the apical meristem and insulate it from the elements **(Figure 37.11)**. After the scales develop, most cellular metabolic activity shuts down and the leaf bud becomes dormant.

In some plants that produce fleshy fruits, such as apples and cherries, ABA is associated with the dormancy of seeds as well. As the seed develops, ABA accumulates in the seed coat, and the embryo does not germinate even if it becomes hydrated. The build-up of ABA in developing seeds does more than simply inhibit development, however. As early development draws to a close, ABA stimulates the transcription of certain genes, and large amounts of their protein products are synthesized. These proteins are thought to store nitrogen and other nutrients that

**FIGURE 37.11  Bud scales on the bud of a perennial cornflower (*Centaurea montana*)**

the embryo will use when it eventually does germinate. Before such a seed can germinate, it will usually require a long period of cool, wet conditions, which stimulate the breakdown of ABA. Commercial growers often apply ABA and related growth inhibitors to plants slated to be shipped to plant nurseries. Dormant plants suffer less shipping damage, and the effects of the inhibitors can be reversed by applying a gibberellin.

**RESPONSES TO ENVIRONMENTAL STRESS**  ABA also triggers plant responses to various environmental stresses, including cold snaps, high soil salinity, and drought. A great deal of research has focused on how ABA influences plant responses to a lack of water. When a plant is water stressed, ABA helps prevent excessive water loss by stimulating stomata to close. As described in Chapter 34, flowering plants depend on the proper functioning of stomata. When affected by water stress, mesophyll cells in wilted leaves rapidly synthesize and secrete ABA. It diffuses to neighbouring guard cells, where it binds to its receptor. This binding stimulates the release of $K^+$ and water from the guard cells, and within minutes the stomata close.

ABA functions through signal transduction, just as do many of the other hormones. When ABA binds its receptor, G proteins activate specific lipases that create secondary messengers such as inositol triphosphate (IP3), which diffuses and binds various membrane and intracellular targets. The details are not the point of this section, but it's important to understand that hormones set into motion complex biochemical paths that result in numerous responses. As described in Section 4.7, the original hormone signal is amplified by a cascade of activated protein kinases, each of which can activate a large number of target proteins; a small quantity of hormone is capable of eliciting a substantial reaction.

## 37.1i  Jasmonates and Oligosaccharins Regulate Growth and Function in Defence

In recent years, studies of plant growth and development have helped define the roles—or revealed the existence—of several other hormonelike compounds in plants. Like the well-established plant hormones just described, these substances are organic molecules, and only tiny amounts are required to alter some aspect of a plant's functioning. Some have long been known to exist in plants, but the extent of their signalling roles has only recently become better understood. This group includes the **jasmonates** (JA), a family of about 20 compounds derived from fatty acids. Experiments have identified a number of genes that respond to JA, including genes that regulate root growth and seed germination. Jasmonate also appears to "manage" stresses caused by deficiencies of certain nutrients (such as $K^+$). The JA family is best known, however, as part of the plant arsenal to limit damage by pathogens and predators, the topic of the following section.

Some other substances are also drawing keen interest from plant scientists but, because their signalling roles are still poorly understood, they are not specifically accepted as plant hormones. For example, the complex carbohydrates that are structural elements in the cell walls of plants and some fungi can act as hormones. Experiments show that some of these **oligosaccharins** have a role in defending the plant from pathogens. In addition, oligosaccharins have been proposed as growth regulators that adjust the growth and differentiation of plant cells, possibly by modulating the influences of growth-promoting hormones such as auxin. Researchers are pursuing a deeper understanding of this curious subset of plant signalling molecules.

Like animals, plants use hormones to coordinate their cellular activities. It should be evident that coordinating growth and defence responses might be important in a variable environment. In the "stranded on an island" scenario at the beginning of this chapter, plants must be organized and strategic in how and where they grow; hormones are critical to coordinate this.

### STUDY BREAK QUESTIONS

1. Which plant hormones promote growth, and which inhibit it?
2. Give examples of how some hormones have both promoting and inhibiting effects on growth in different parts of the plant at different times of the life cycle.
3. Summarize the various ways that chemical signals reaching plant cells are converted to changes in cell functioning.

## 37.2  Plant Chemical Defences

Plants do not have immune systems like those that have evolved in animals, but higher plants have evolved an array of means for coping with biotic stressors in the environment. Over the millennia, exposure to predation by herbivores and the onslaught of pathogens have resulted in a striking array of chemical defences that ward off or reduce damage to plant tissues from infectious bacteria, fungi, worms, or plant-eating insects **(Table 37.2)**. You will discover in this section that plant defences include both general responses to any type of attack and specific responses to particular threats – just as we see in animal systems. Some get underway almost as soon as an attack begins, whereas others promote the plant's long-term survival. More often than not, multiple chemicals interact as the response unfolds.

**TABLE 37.2** | Summary of Plant Chemical Defences

| Type of Defence | Effects |
|---|---|
| **General Defences** | |
| Jasmonate (JA) responses to wounds/injury by pathogens; pathways often include other hormones, such as ethylene | Synthesis of defensive chemicals such as protease inhibitors |
| Hypersensitive response to infectious pathogens (e.g., fungi, bacteria) | Physically isolates infection site by surrounding it with dead cells |
| PR (pathogenesis-related) proteins | Enzymes, other proteins that degrade cell walls of pathogens |
| Salicylic acid (SA) | Mobilizes during other responses, and independently; induces the synthesis of PR proteins; operates in systemic acquired resistance |
| Systemin (in tomato) | Triggers JA response |
| **Secondary Metabolites** | |
| Phytoalexins | Antibiotic |
| Oligosaccharins | Trigger synthesis of phytoalexins |
| Systemic acquired resistance (SAR) | Long-lasting protection against some pathogens; components include SA and PR proteins that accumulate in healthy tissues |
| **Specific Defences** | |
| Gene-for-gene recognition of chemical features of specific pathogens (by binding with receptors coded by R genes) | Triggers defensive response (e.g., hypersensitive response, PR proteins) against pathogens |
| **Other** | |
| Heat-shock responses (encoded by heat-shock genes) | Synthesize chaperone proteins that reversibly bind other plant proteins and prevent denaturing caused by heat stress |
| "Antifreeze" proteins | In some species, stabilize cell proteins under freezing conditions |

© Cengage Learning 2017

## 37.2a Jasmonates and Other Compounds Interact in a General Response to Wounds

When an insect begins feeding on a leaf or some other plant part, the plant responds to the wound by launching a cascade of chemical responses. These signalling pathways often rely on interactions among jasmonates, ethylene, and other plant hormones that trigger the expression of genes leading to chemical and physical defences at the wound site. In some plants, jasmonate induces a response leading to the synthesis of protease inhibitors, which disrupt an insect's capacity to digest proteins in the plant tissue. The protein deficiency in turn hampers the insect's growth and functioning.

An unusual pathway that thus far is known only in tomato (*Solanum* spp.) and a few other species involves **systemin**, the first peptide hormone to be discovered in plants **(Figure 37.12)**. Because many animal hormones are peptides (Chapter 43), this is an interesting thing to find in plants. When a plant is wounded, it responds by releasing the protein hormone systemin.

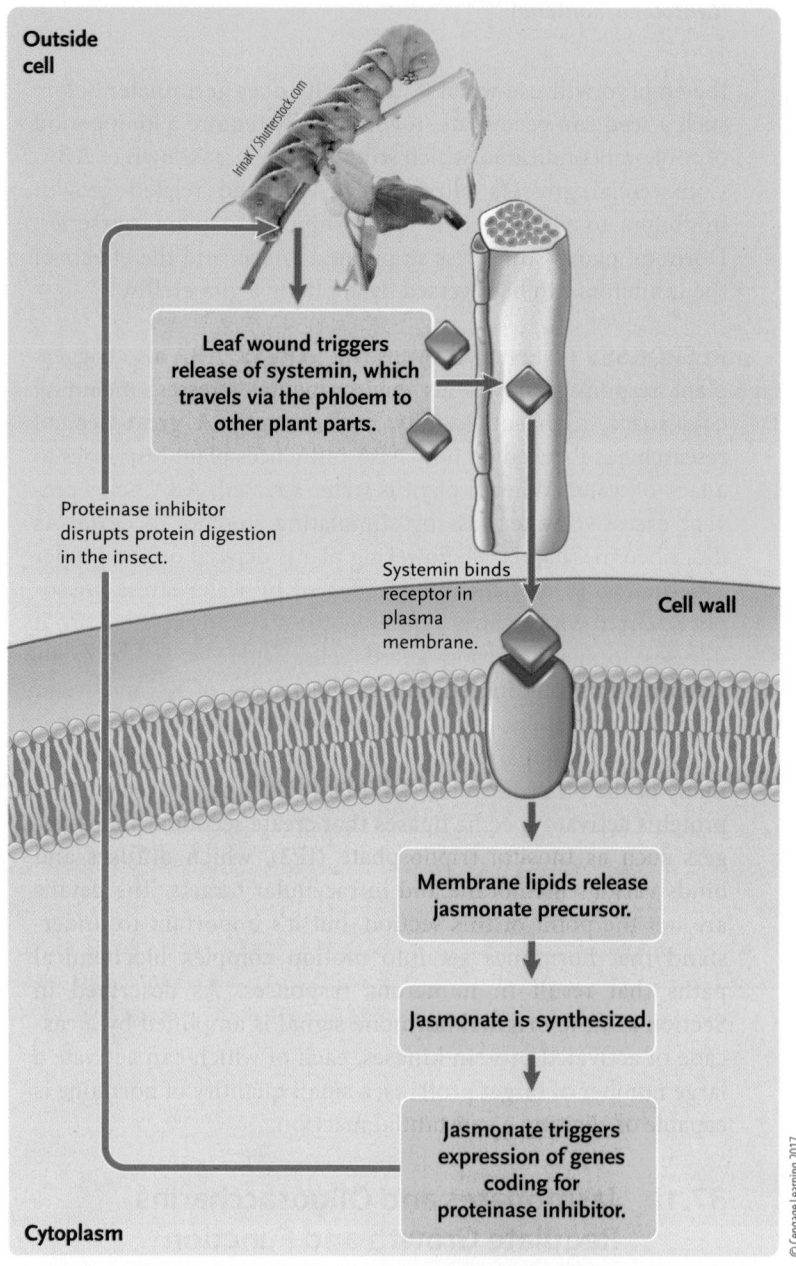

**FIGURE 37.12 The systemin response to wounding.** When a plant is wounded, it responds by releasing the protein hormone systemin. Transported through the phloem to other plant parts, in receptive cells systemin sets in motion a sequence of reactions that lead to the expression of genes encoding protease inhibitors, substances that can seriously disrupt an insect predator's capacity to digest protein.

Systemin enters the phloem and is transported throughout the plant. When receptors bind systemin, the plasma membranes of their cells release a lipid that is converted into jasmonate, which in turn causes the expression of genes that encode protease inhibitors that protect the plant against attack, even in parts remote from the original wound.

A plant's capacity to recognize and respond to the physical damage of a wound has also been subject to strong selection pressure during plant evolution. When a plant is wounded experimentally, numerous defensive chemicals can soon be detected in its tissues. One of these chemicals, **salicylic acid**, or **SA** (a compound similar to aspirin, which is acetylsalicylic acid), seems to have multiple roles in plant defences, including interacting with jasmonates.

## 37.2b The Hypersensitive Response and PR Proteins Are Other General Defences

Often, a plant that becomes infected by pathogenic bacteria or fungi counters the attack by way of a **hypersensitive response**, a defence that physically cordons off an infection site by surrounding it with dead cells. Initially, cells near the site respond by producing a burst of highly reactive oxygen-containing compounds (such as hydrogen peroxide, $H_2O_2$) that can break down nucleic acids, inactivate enzymes, or have other toxic effects on cells. The burst is catalyzed by enzymes in the plant cell's plasma membrane. It may begin the process of killing cells close to the attack site and, as the response advances, programmed cell death may also come into play. In short order, the "sacrificed" dead cells create a barrier that separates the infected area from the rest of the plant. The denial of nutrients causes the invading pathogen to die. A common sign of a successful hypersensitive response is a dead spot surrounded by healthy tissue **(Figure 37.13)**.

While the hypersensitive response is under way, salicylic acid triggers other defensive responses by an infected plant. One of its effects is to induce the synthesis of **pathogenesis-related proteins**, or **PR proteins**. Some PR proteins are hydrolytic enzymes that break down components of a pathogen's cell wall. Examples are chitinases, which dismantle the chitin in the cell walls of fungi as well as the exoskeleton of insects. In some cases, plant cell receptors also detect the presence of fragments of the disintegrating wall and set in motion additional defence responses.

## 37.2c Secondary Metabolites Defend against Pathogens and Herbivores

Many plants counter bacteria and fungi, and even viruses, by making **phytoalexins**, biochemicals of various types that function as antibiotics. When an infectious agent breaches a plant part, genes encoding phytoalexins are transcribed in the affected tissue. For instance, when a fungus invades plant tissues, the enzymes it secretes may trigger the release of oligosaccharins. In addition to their roles as growth regulators (described in Section 37.1i), these substances can also promote the production of phytoalexins, which have toxic effects on a variety of fungi.

Phytoalexins are among many *secondary metabolites* produced by plants. Such substances are termed "secondary" because they are not routinely synthesized in all plant cells as part of basic metabolism. A wide range of plant species deploy secondary metabolites as defences against feeding herbivores. Examples are alkaloids such as caffeine, cocaine, and the poison strychnine (found in seeds of *Strychnos nux-vomica*); tannins such as those in oak acorns; and various terpenes. The terpene family includes insect-repelling substances in cotton and the resins of conifers and the creosote bush, and essential oils produced by sage and basil plants. Because these terpenes are volatile—they easily diffuse out of the plant into the surrounding air—they can also provide indirect defence to a plant. Released from the wounds created by a munching insect, they attract other insects that prey on the herbivore.

## 37.2d Gene-for-Gene Recognition Allows Rapid Responses to Specific Threats

One of the most interesting questions with respect to plant defences is how plants first sense that an attack is under way. Some plants apparently detect an attack by a specific predator through a mechanism called **gene-for-gene recognition**. This term refers to a matchup between the products of dominant alleles of two types of genes: a so-called ***R* gene** (for "resistance") in a plant and an ***Avr* gene** (for "avirulence") in a particular pathogen. Thousands of *R* genes have been identified in a wide range of plant species. *R* alleles confer enhanced resistance to plant pathogens, including bacteria, fungi, and nematode worms that attack roots.

The basic mechanism of gene-for-gene recognition is simple: the *R* allele encodes a receptor in plant cell plasma membranes, and the pathogen *Avr* allele encodes a molecule that can bind the receptor. "Avirulence" implies that the

**FIGURE 37.13 Evidence of the hypersensitive response.** The dead region on this potato leaf (*Solanum tuberosum*) is the site where a pathogen (*Phytophthora infestans*) invaded, triggering the defensive destruction of the surrounding cells.

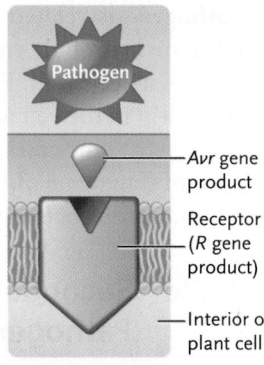

**Required precondition**
A plant has an *R* gene encoding a receptor that can bind the product of a specific pathogen *Avr* gene.

Avr gene product

Receptor (*R* gene product)

Interior of plant cell

**1** When the *R*-encoded receptor binds its matching *Avr* product, the binding triggers signalling pathways, leading to various defence responses in the plant.

**2** Fluxes of ions and enzyme activity at the plasma membrane contribute to the hypersensitive response. Soon PR proteins, phytoalexins, and salicyic acid (SA) are synthesized. The PR proteins and phytoalexins combat pathogens directly. SA promotes systemic acquired resistance.

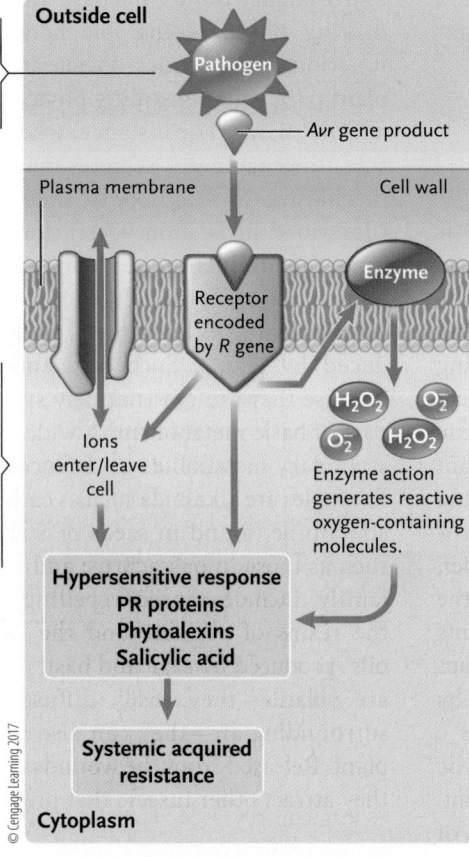

Outside cell

Pathogen

Avr gene product

Plasma membrane

Cell wall

Enzyme

Receptor encoded by *R* gene

$H_2O_2$ $O_2^-$

$O_2^-$ $H_2O_2$

Ions enter/leave cell

Enzyme action generates reactive oxygen-containing molecules.

**Hypersensitive response**
**PR proteins**
**Phytoalexins**
**Salicylic acid**

**Systemic acquired resistance**

Cytoplasm

© Cengage Learning 2017

**FIGURE 37.14 Model of how gene-for-gene resistance may operate.** For resistance to develop, the plant must have an *R* gene and the pathogen must have a corresponding *Avr* gene. Products of such "matching" genes can interact physically, rather like the lock-and-key mechanism of an enzyme and its substrate. Most *R* genes encode receptors at the plasma membranes of plant cells. As diagrammed in step 1, when one of these receptors binds an *Avr* gene's product, the initial result may be changes in the movements of specific ions into or out of the cell and the activation of membrane enzymes that catalyze the formation of highly reactive oxygen-containing molecules. Such events help launch other signalling pathways that lead to a variety of defensive responses, including the hypersensitive response (step 2).

pathogen becomes "not virulent" because binding of its *Avr* gene product triggers an immediate defence response in the plant. These *Avr* products run the gamut from proteins to lipids to carbohydrates that have been secreted by the pathogen or released from its surface as it infects the plant **(Figure 37.14).** Experiments have demonstrated a rapid-fire sequence of early

biochemical changes that follow binding of the *Avr*-encoded molecule, including changes in ion concentrations inside and outside plant cells and the production of biologically active oxygen compounds. Most instances of gene-for-gene recognition studied so far show that it triggers the hypersensitive response and the ensuing synthesis of PR proteins.

### 37.2e Systemic Acquired Resistance Can Provide Long-Term Protection

The defensive response to a microbial invasion may spread throughout a plant to make its healthy tissues less vulnerable to infection. This phenomenon is called **systemic acquired resistance**, and experiments using *Arabidopsis* plants have shed light on how it comes about **(Figure 37.15).** In a key early step, salicylic acid (SA) accumulates in affected tissues. By some route, probably through the phloem, the SA passes from the infected organ to newly forming organs such as leaves, which begin to synthesize PR proteins, again, providing the plant with a "home-grown" antimicrobial arsenal. How does the SA exert this effect? It seems that when enough SA accumulates in a plant cell's cytoplasm, a regulatory protein called *NPR-1* moves from the cytoplasm into the cell nucleus. There it interacts with factors that activate transcription of genes encoding PR proteins.

In addition to synthesizing SA that will be transported to other tissues by a plant's vascular system, the damaged leaf also synthesizes a chemically similar compound, methyl salicylate. This substance is volatile, and researchers speculate that it may serve as an airborne "harm" signal that promotes defence responses in the plant that synthesized it, and possibly in nearby plants as well.

### 37.2f Extremes of Heat and Cold Also Elicit Protective Chemical Responses

Plant cells also contain **heat-shock proteins (HSPs),** a type of chaperone protein (see *The Purple Pages*). These proteins were originally identified by their activation through heat stress, but other stressors such as toxins, hypoxia, or starvation also promote stress protein production. HSPs bind and stabilize other proteins, including enzymes, which might otherwise stop functioning if they were to become denatured. For example, experiments with cells and seedlings of soybean (*Glycine max*) showed that, when the temperature rose over 10°C higher than their normal optimum, in less than 5 minutes mRNA transcripts coding for as many as 50 different HSPs were present in cells. When the temperature returned to a normal range, HSPs released the proteins they bonded with,

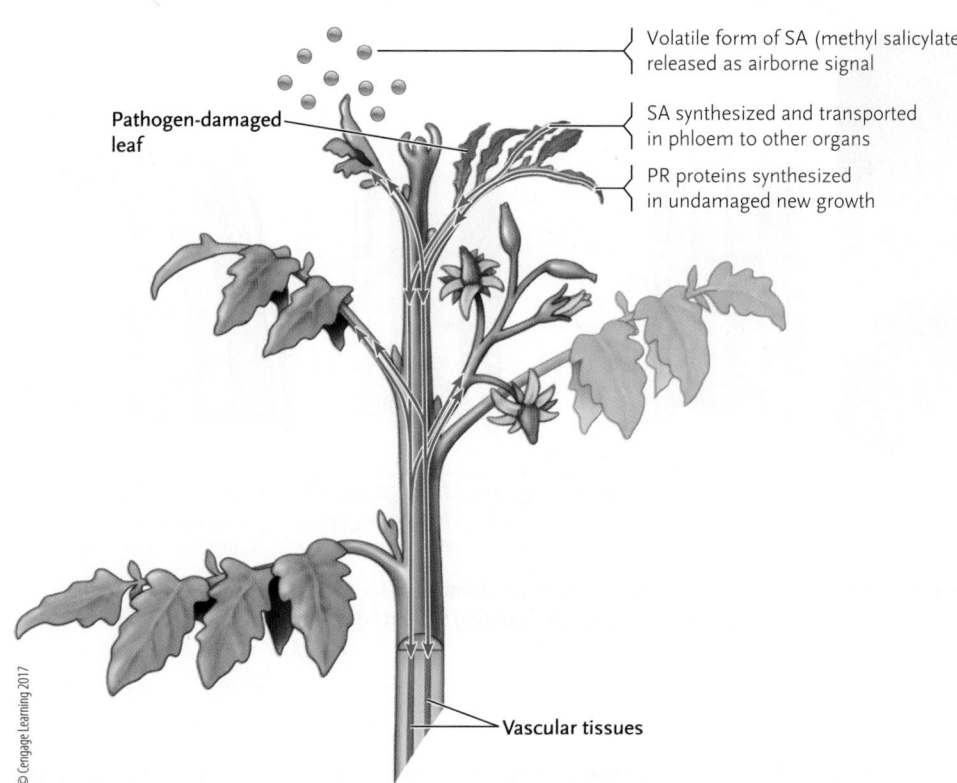

Pathogen-damaged leaf

Volatile form of SA (methyl salicylate) released as airborne signal

SA synthesized and transported in phloem to other organs

PR proteins synthesized in undamaged new growth

Vascular tissues

© Cengage Learning 2017

**FIGURE 37.15  A proposed mechanism for systemic acquired resistance.** When a plant successfully fends off a pathogen, the defensive chemical SA is transported in the phloem to other plant parts, where it may help protect against another attack by stimulating the synthesis of PR proteins. In addition, the plant synthesizes and releases a slightly different, more volatile form of SA called *methyl salicylate*. It may serve as an airborne signal to other parts of the plant as well as to neighbouring plants.

allowing them to resume their usual functions. Further studies have revealed that HSPs help protect plant cells subjected to other environmental stresses as well, including drought, salinity, and cold.

Like extreme heat, freezing can also be lethal to plants. If ice crystals form in cells, they can tear the cell membrane. In many cold-resistant species, dormancy (see Section 37.4) is the long-term strategy for dealing with cold, but in the short term, such as an unseasonable cold snap, some species also undergo a rapid shift in gene expression that equips cold-stressed cells with "antifreeze proteins." Like HSPs, these molecules are thought to protect the integrity of other cell proteins. For more information about antifreeze proteins see Table 37.2 and Section 42.6c.

Chemical defenses of plants are clearly advantageous to the plants that secrete them. They have also been used to advantage by us humans. The majority of medicines taken for such things as pain relief (like willow bark, which produces salicylate, which reduces pain) or malaria (extract of the Cinchona tree, which produces quinone) were first derived from secondary metabolites produced by plants.

### STUDY BREAK QUESTIONS

1. Which plant chemical defences are general responses to attack, and which are specific to a particular pathogen?
2. Why is salicylic acid considered to be a general systemic response to damage?
3. How is the hypersensitive response integrated with other chemical defences?

## 37.3  Plant Movements

Although a plant cannot move from place to place as external conditions change, plants can alter the orientation of their body parts in response to environmental stimuli. As noted earlier, growth toward or away from a unidirectional stimulus, such as light or gravity, is called a *tropism*. Tropic movement involves permanent changes in the plant body because certain cells are stimulated to elongate in response to the stimulus, permanently reorienting the plant's organs. This section will also touch on two other kinds of movements: developmental responses to physical contact, and changes in the position of plant parts that are not related to the location of the stimulus.

### 37.3a  Phototropisms Are Responses to Light

Light is a key abiotic stimulus for many kinds of organisms. Phototropisms, which we have already discussed in the section on auxins, are growth responses to a directional light source. As the Darwins discovered, if light is more intense on one side of a stem, the stem may curve toward the light **(Figure 37.16a)**. Phototropic movements are particularly adaptive for photosynthesizing organisms because they help maximize the exposure of photosynthetic tissues to sunlight.

How do auxins influence phototropic movements? In a coleoptile that is illuminated from one side, IAA moves by polar transport into the cells on the shaded side (Figure 37.16b–d). Phototropic bending occurs because cells on the shaded side elongate more rapidly than do cells on the illuminated side.

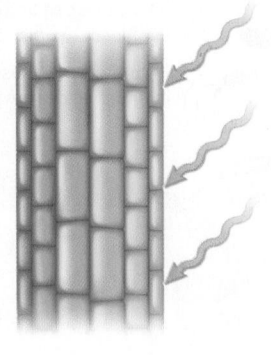

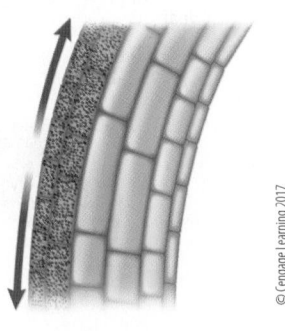

**a.** Seedlings bend toward light.

**b.** Rays from the Sun strike one side of a shoot tip.

**c.** Auxin (red) diffuses down from the shoot tip to cells on its shaded side.

**d.** The auxin-stimulated cells elongate more quickly, causing the seedling to bend.

**FIGURE 37.16 Phototropism in seedlings. (a)** Tomato seedling grown in darkness. Its right side was illuminated for a few hours before it was photographed. **(b–d)** Hormone-mediated differences in the rates of cell elongation bring about the bending toward light. (Auxin is shown in red.) Compare this result with Research Figure 37.3.

The main stimulus for phototropism is light of blue wavelengths. Experiments on corn coleoptiles have shown that a large, yellow pigment molecule called *phototropin* can absorb blue wavelengths, and it may play a role in stimulating the initial lateral transport of IAA to the dark side of a shoot tip. Studies with *Arabidopsis* suggest there is more than one blue light receptor, however. One is a light-absorbing protein called **cryptochrome**, which is sensitive to blue light and may also be an important early step in the various light-based growth responses. As you will read later, cryptochrome appears to have a role in other plant responses to light as well.

## 37.3b Gravitropism Orients Plant Parts to the Pull of Gravity

Plants show growth responses to Earth's gravitational pull, a phenomenon called **gravitropism**. After a seed germinates, the primary root curves down, toward the "pull" (positive gravitropism), and the shoot curves up (negative gravitropism).

Several hypotheses seek to explain how plants respond to gravity. The most widely accepted hypothesis proposes that plants detect gravity much as animals do; that is, particles called **statoliths** in certain cells move in the direction gravity pulls them. In the semicircular canals of human ears, calcium carbonate crystals serve as statoliths; in most plants the statoliths are amyloplasts, modified plastids that contain starch grains. In eudicot angiosperm stems, amyloplasts are often present in one or two layers of cells just outside the vascular bundles. In monocots such as cereal grasses, amyloplasts are located in a region of tissue near the base of the leaf sheath. In roots, amyloplasts occur in the root cap. If the spatial orientation of a plant cell is shifted experimentally, its amyloplasts sink through the cytoplasm until they come to rest at the bottom of the cell **(Figure 37.17)**.

How do amyloplast movements translate into an altered growth response? The full explanation appears to be complex, and there is evidence that somewhat different mechanisms operate in stems and in roots. In stems, the sinking of amyloplasts may provide a mechanical stimulus that triggers a gene-guided redistribution of IAA. For example, when a potted sunflower seedling is turned on its side in a dark room, within 15–20 minutes cell elongation decreases markedly on the upper side of the growing horizontal stem, but increases on the lower side. With the adjusted growth pattern, the stem curves upward, even in the absence of light. Using different types of tests, researchers have been able to document the shifting of IAA from the top to the bottom side of the stem. The changing auxin gradient correlates with the altered pattern of cell elongation.

In roots, a high concentration of auxin has the opposite effect: it inhibits cell elongation. If a root is placed on its side, amyloplasts in the root cap accumulate near the side wall that is now the bottom side of the cap. This shift stimulates cell elongation in the opposite wall, and within a few hours the root once again curves downward. In root tips of many plants, however, especially eudicots, researchers could not detect a change in IAA concentration that correlates with the changing position of amyloplasts. Experiments on gravitropism in soybean (*Glycine max*) root tips suggested that the IAA signal is transduced by way of a signal cascade. The hormone induces the accumulation of nitric oxide (NO) at the downward side of the root tip, where NO in turn appears to initiate cGMP production. This second messenger then delivers the original IAA signal. The sequence inhibits the elongation of cells on the tip's downward side, so the root curves downward.

**a. Root oriented vertically**

**b. Root oriented horizontally**

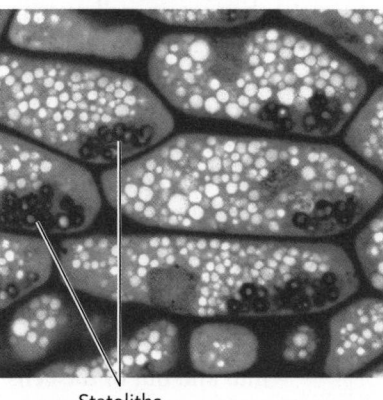

Micrographs courtesy of Randy Moore, from "How Roots Respond to Gravity," M. L. Evans, R. Moore, and K. Hasenstein, *Scientific American*, December 1986.

Statoliths

Statoliths

**FIGURE 37.17 Evidence that supports the statolith hypothesis.** When a corn root was laid on its side, amyloplasts—statoliths—in cells from the root cap settled to the bottom of the cells within 5 to 10 minutes. Statoliths may be part of a gravity-sensing mechanism that redistributes auxin through a root tip.

Andrew Ferguson/Shutterstock.com

**FIGURE 37.18 Thigmotropism in a passion flower (*Passiflora*) tendril, which is twisted around a support**

Calcium ions (Ca²⁺) appear to be involved in root and shoot gravitropism as well as IAA. Agar blocks impregnated with Ca²⁺ can stimulate a root to bend toward it when placed near a root cap. If roots are deprived of Ca²⁺, gravitropism abruptly stops. Negative gravitropism of shoots is inhibited by excess calcium. Ca²⁺ binds to a protein called *calmodulin*, activating it. Calmodulin is found in plants and animals and is implicated in many enzymatic pathways. Perhaps calmodulin activates membrane pumps involved in IAA transport.

Some of the most active research in plant biology focuses on the intricate mechanisms of gravitropism. For example, there is increasing evidence that, in many plants, cells in different regions of stem tissue differ in their sensitivity to IAA, and that gravitropism is linked in some fundamental way to these differences. In a few plants, including some cultivated varieties of corn and radish, the direction of the gravitropic response by a seedling's primary root is influenced by light. Clearly there is much more to be learned.

## 37.3c Thigmotropism and Thigmomorphogenesis Are Responses to Physical Contact

Varieties of peas, grapes, and some other plants demonstrate **thigmotropism** (*thigma* = touch), which is growth in response to contact with a solid object. Thigmotropic plants typically have long, slender stems and cannot grow upright without physical support. They often have *tendrils*, which are modified stems or leaves that can curl around a fencepost or the sturdier stem of a neighbouring plant. If one side of a grapevine stem grows against a trellis, for example, epidermal cells on that side of the stem tendril shorten, whereas cells on the other side of the tendril elongate. Within minutes, the tendril starts to curl around the trellis, forming tight coils that provide support for the vine stem. **Figure 37.18** shows thigmotropic twisting in the passion flower

(*Passiflora*). Auxin and ethylene may be involved in thigmotropism, but most details of the mechanism remain elusive.

The rubbing and bending of stems caused by frequent strong winds, rainstorms, grazing animals, and even farm machinery can inhibit the overall growth of plants and can alter their growth patterns. In this phenomenon, called *thigmomorphogenesis*, a stem stops elongating and instead adds girth when it is regularly subjected to mechanical stress. Merely shaking some plants daily for a brief period will inhibit their upward growth, but although such plants may be shorter, their thickened stems will be stronger. Thigmomorphogenesis helps explain why plants growing outdoors are often shorter, have somewhat thicker stems, and are not as easily blown over as plants of the same species grown indoors. Trees growing near the snowline of windswept mountains show an altered growth pattern that reflects this response to wind stress.

Research on the cellular mechanisms of thigmomorphogenesis has begun to yield tantalizing clues. In one study, investigators repeatedly sprayed *Arabidopsis* plants with water and imposed other mechanical stresses, and then sampled tissues from the stressed plants. The samples contained as much as double the usual amount of mRNA for at least four genes that had been activated by the stress. The mRNAs encoded calmodulin and several other proteins that may have roles in altering *Arabidopsis* growth responses. The test plants were also short, generally reaching only half the height of unstressed controls.

Stimuli other than touch can also trigger action potentials leading to nastic movements. Cotton, soybean, sunflower, and some other plants display solar tracking, nastic movements (see Section 37.3d) in which leaf blades are oriented toward the east in the morning and then steadily change their position during the day, following the Sun across the sky. Such movements maximize the amount of time that leaf blades are perpendicular to the Sun, which is the angle at which photosynthesis is most efficient, and which can warm the tissues to stimulate metabolism.

## 37.3d Nastic Movements Are Non-directional

Tropisms are responses to directional stimuli, such as light striking one side of a shoot tip, but many plants also exhibit **nastic movements** (*nastos* = pressed close together), reversible responses to non-directional stimuli, such as mechanical pressure or humidity. We see nastic movements in leaves, leaflets, and even flowers. For instance, certain plants exhibit nastic sleep movements, holding their leaves (or flower petals) in roughly horizontal positions during the day but folding them closer to the stem at night **(Figure 37.19)**. Tulip flowers "go to sleep" in this way.

**FIGURE 37.19 Nastic sleep movements in a bloodroot plant (*Sanguinaria canadensis*)**

Many nastic movements are temporary and result from changes in cell turgor. For example, the daily opening and closing of stomata in response to changing light levels are nastic movements, as is the traplike closing of the lobed leaves of the Venus flytrap when an insect brushes against hairlike sensory structures on the leaves. The leaves of *Mimosa pudica* ("the sensitive plant") also close in a nastic response to mechanical pressure. Each *Mimosa* leaf is divided into pairs of leaflets **(Figure 37.20a)**. Touching even one leaflet at the leaf tip triggers a chain reaction in which each pair of leaflets closes up within seconds (Figure 37.20b).

In many turgor-driven nastic movements, water moves into and out of the cells in **pulvini** (*pulvinus* = cushion), thickened pads of tissue at the base of a leaf or petiole. Stomatal movements depend on changing concentrations of ions within guard cells; pulvinar cells drive nastic leaf movements in *Mimosa* and numerous other plants by the same mechanism (Figure 37.20c).

How is the original stimulus transferred from cells in one part of a leaf to cells elsewhere? The answer lies in the polarity of charge across cell plasma membranes (see Section 4.5). Touching a *Mimosa* leaflet triggers an **action potential**—a brief reversal in the polarity of the membrane charge. When an action potential occurs at the plasma membrane of a pulvinar cell, the change in polarity causes potassium ion ($K^+$) channels to open and ions flow out of the cell, setting up an osmotic gradient that draws water out as well. As water leaves by osmosis, turgor pressure falls, pulvinar

**a. Undisturbed plant**

**b. Plant response to touch**

**FIGURE 37.20 Nastic movements in leaflets of *Mimosa pudica*, the sensitive plant. (a)** In an undisturbed plant, the leaflets are open. If a leaflet near the leaf tip is touched, changes in turgor pressure in pulvini at the base cause the leaf to fold closed **(b, c)**. The diagram sketches this folding movement in cross-section. Other leaflets close in sequence as action potentials transmit the stimulus along the leaf.

**c. Leaf folding mechanism**

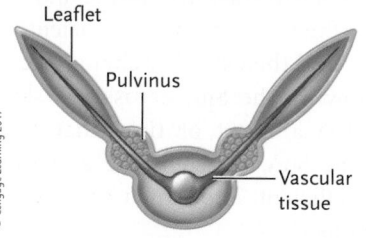

Leaflet

Pulvinus

Vascular tissue

Decrease of turgor in cells in pulvinus

cells become flaccid, and the leaflets move together. Later, when the process is reversed, the pulvinar cells regain turgor and the leaflets spread apart. Action potentials travel between parenchyma cells in the pulvini via plasmodesmata at the rate of about 2 cm/s. Animal nerves conduct similar changes in membrane polarity along their plasma membranes (see Chapter 43). These changes in polarity, which in animals are also called *action potentials*, occur much more rapidly, at velocities between 1 and 100 m/s.

The benefits of changing body shape in response to environmental stimulation should be clear, as would the advantage of gripping an existing support or appearing like a sick, wilted plant to an herbivore. Even the nocturnal behaviour of some flowers to synchronize pollen release with receptive female structures should make immediate sense. Certainly, if you were isolated on an island, you'd note and respond to the challenges and opportunities your environment presents you with.

**STUDY BREAK QUESTIONS**

1. What is the direct stimulus for phototropism? For gravitropism?
2. Explain how nastic movements differ from tropic movements.
3. In what ways do action potentials differ between nerve cells and pulvinus cells?
4. How might natural selection have influenced cellular differentiation differently between plants and animals?

## 37.4  Plant Biological Clocks

Like all eukaryotic organisms, plants have internal time-measuring mechanisms called **biological clocks** that adapt the organism to recurring environmental changes. In plants, biological clocks help adjust both daily and seasonal activities.

### 37.4a  Circadian Rhythms Are Based on 24-Hour Cycles

Some plant activities occur regularly in cycles of about 24 hours, even when environmental conditions remain constant. These are **circadian rhythms** (*circa* = around, *dies* = day). In Chapter 33, we noted that stomata open and close on a daily cycle, even when plants are kept in total darkness. Nastic sleep movements, described earlier, are another example of a circadian rhythm. Even when a plant that exhibits such movements is kept in constant light or darkness for a few days, it folds its leaves into the "sleep" position at roughly 24-hour intervals. In some way, the plant measures time without sunrise (light) and sunset (darkness). Such experiments demonstrate that internal controls, rather than external cues, largely govern circadian rhythms.

Circadian rhythms and other activities regulated by a biological clock help ensure that plants of a single species do the same thing, such as flowering, at the same time. For instance, flowers of the aptly named four-o'clock plant (*Mirabilis jalapa*) open predictably every 24 hours—in nature, in the late afternoon. Such coordination can be crucial for successful pollination. Although some circadian rhythms can proceed without direct stimulus from light, many biological clock mechanisms are influenced by the relative lengths of day and night.

### 37.4b  Photoperiodism Involves Seasonal Changes in the Relative Length of Night and Day

Obviously, environmental conditions in a 24-hour period are not the same in summer as they are in winter. In North America, for instance, winter temperatures are cooler and winter day length is shorter. Experimenting with tobacco and soybean plants in the early 1900s, two American botanists, Wightman Garner and Henry Allard, elucidated a phenomenon they called **photoperiodism**, in which plants respond to changes in the relative lengths of light and dark periods in their environment during each 24-hour period. Through photoperiodism, the biological clocks of plants (and animals) make seasonal adjustments in their patterns of growth, development, and reproduction.

In plants, we now know that a family of blue–green pigments collectively called **phytochrome** can serve as a switching mechanism in the photoperiodic response, signalling the plant to make seasonal changes. Plants synthesize phytochrome in an inactive form, $P_r$, which absorbs light of shorter wavelengths (about 660 nm) at the "red" end of the spectrum (see Figure 1.3). Sunlight contains relatively more red light than far-red light, which has a longer wavelength (about 730 nm). During daylight hours when red wavelengths dominate, $P_r$ absorbs red light. Absorption of red light triggers the conversion of phytochrome to an active form designated $P_{fr}$, which absorbs light of far-red wavelengths. At sunset, at night, or even in shade, where far-red wavelengths predominate, $P_{fr}$ reverts to $P_r$ **(Figure 37.21)**.

In nature, a high concentration of $P_{fr}$ "tells" a plant that it is exposed to sunlight. The plant's ability to sense sunlight is vital given that, over time, sunlight provides favourable conditions for leaf growth, photosynthesis, and flowering. Note in Figure 37.21c that lettuce seeds that have sufficient red light exposure tend to germinate. The seeds are small and lightweight, sacrificing having extra nutrients to allow them the ability to disperse farther. Therefore, they need to photosynthesize quickly and need to sense if there's enough sunlight for that to happen, which they do by detecting red light. Far-red light suggests to the seed that there's too much shade or that the seed is too deep in the soil. The **photoreversible** effect, where light absorption toggles between two molecular conformations, is shown in Figure 37.21.

Phytochrome activation may stimulate plant cells to take up $Ca^{2+}$ ions, or it may induce certain plant organelles to release them. Either way, when free calcium ions combine with calcium-binding proteins (such as calmodulin), they may initiate at least some response to light. Botanists suspect that $P_{fr}$ controls the types of enzymes being produced in particular cells,

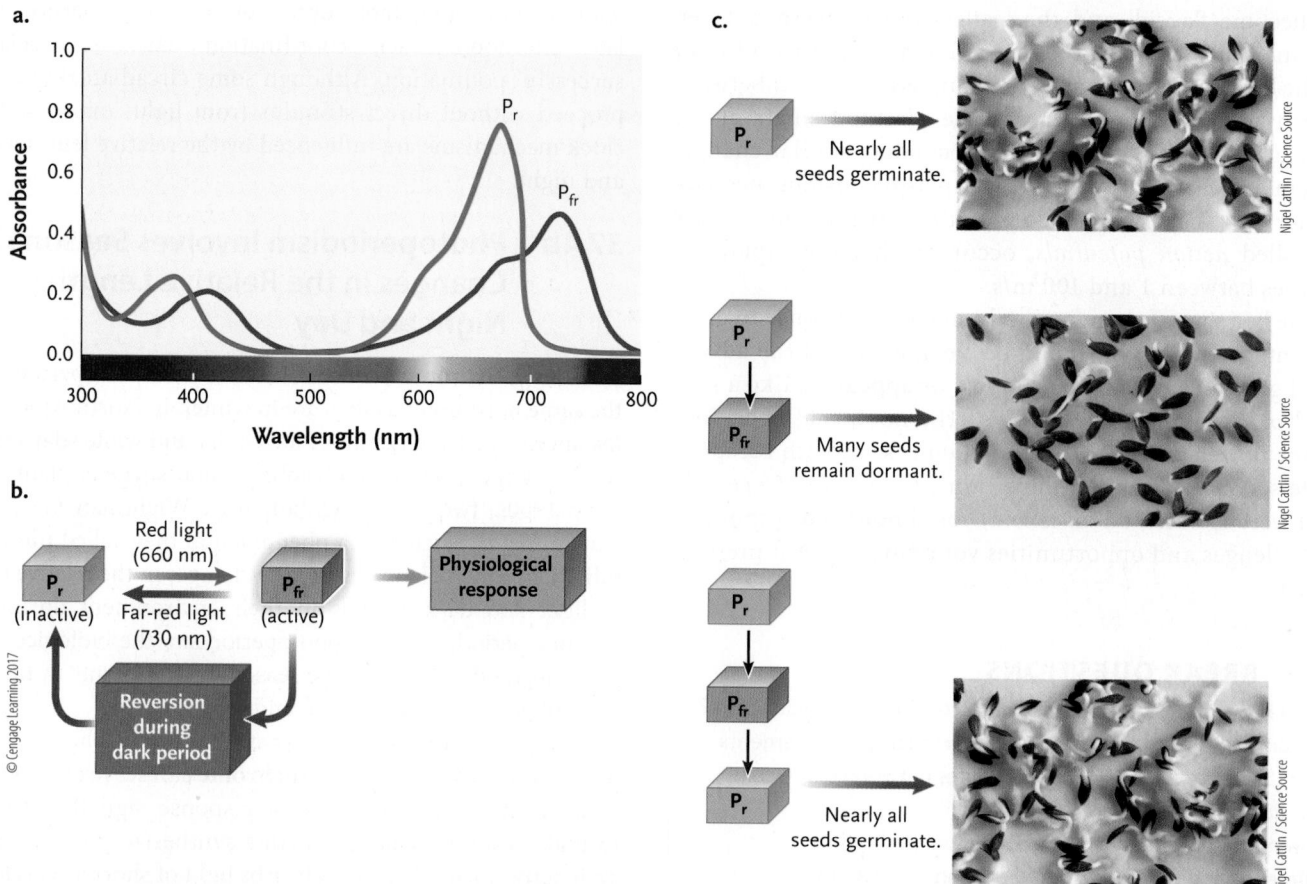

**FIGURE 37.21  The phytochrome switching mechanism, which can promote or inhibit growth of different plant parts. (a)** The absorption spectra associated with the interconversion of $P_r$ and $P_{fr}$. **(b)** Interconversion of phytochrome from the active form ($P_{fr}$) to the inactive form ($P_r$). **(c)** Effects of red or far-red light on germination of lettuce seeds. Note that the *last* form of light dictates whether they will germinate; red light stimulates germination, and far-red light reduces it.

and different enzymes are required for seed germination, stem elongation and branching, leaf expansion, and the formation of flowers, fruits, and seeds. When plants adapted to full sunlight are grown in darkness, they put more resources into stem elongation and less into leaf expansion or stem branching **(Figure 37.22)**. This can be beneficial to the seedling by allowing it to grow out from underneath a fallen tree trunk, or up past the canopy of plant leaves above it.

Cryptochrome, like phytochrome, is another light-sensitive pigment, but it responds to blue light and appears to influence different light-related growth responses. It also interacts with phytochromes in producing circadian responses. Researchers have recently discovered that cryptochrome occurs not only in plants but also in animals such as fruit flies and mice. Does it act as a circadian photoreceptor in both kingdoms? Only further study will provide the answer.

## 37.4c  Cycles of Light and Dark Often Influence Flowering

Photoperiodism is especially apparent in the flowering process. Like other plant responses, flowering is often keyed to changes in day length through the year and to the resulting changes in envi-

ronmental conditions. Corn, soybeans, peas, and other annual plants begin flowering after only a few months of growth. Roses and other perennials typically flower every year or after several years of vegetative growth. Carrots, cabbages, and other biennials typically produce roots, stems, and leaves during the first growing season, die back to soil level in autumn, then bolt, forming a specialized, elongated, flower-bearing stem the second season.

In the late 1930s, Karl Hamner and James Bonner grew cocklebur plants (*Xanthium strumarium*) in chambers in which the researchers could carefully control environmental conditions, including photoperiod. And they made an unexpected discovery: flowering occurred only when the test plants were exposed to a single night of 8.5 hours of uninterrupted darkness. The length of the "day" in the growth chamber did not matter, but if light interrupted the dark period for even a minute or two, the plant would not flower at all. Subsequent research confirmed that, for most angiosperms, it is the length of darkness, not light, that controls flowering.

**KINDS OF FLOWERING RESPONSES** The photoperiodic responses of flowering plants are so predictable that botanists have long used them to categorize plants **(Figure 37.23)**.

The categories, which refer to day length, reflect the fact that scientists recognized the phenomenon of photoperiodic flowering responses long before they understood that darkness, not light, was the cue. **Long-day plants**, such as irises, daffodils, and corn, usually flower in spring when dark periods become shorter and day length becomes longer than some critical value—usually 9–16 hours. **Short-day plants**,

**FIGURE 37.22 Effects of the absence of light on young bean plants (*Phaseolus* spp.).** The seedling on the left was grown in darkness for several days. Its leaves are yellow because, in darkness, it could form carotenoids but not chlorophyll. It also has a larger stem, smaller leaves, and a smaller root system than the seedling on the right, which was grown in the light.

**FIGURE 37.23 The poinsettia (*Euphorbia pulcherrima*) is a short-day plant that, in nature, blooms in autumn as nights become longer.** Commercial growers manipulate the lighting in greenhouses to delay flowering (and the development of the red, white, pink, or multicoloured bracts) until the Christmas holiday season, when poinsettias are in demand. The plant on the right was maintained in long-day conditions.

including cockleburs, chrysanthemums, and potatoes, flower in late summer or early autumn when dark periods become longer and day length becomes shorter than some critical value. **Intermediate-day plants**, such as sugarcane, flower only when day length falls between the values for long-day and short-day plants. **Day-neutral plants**, such as dandelions and roses, flower whenever they become mature enough to do so, regardless of photoperiod.

Experiments demonstrate what happens when plants are grown under the "wrong" photoperiod regimes. For instance, spinach, a long-day plant, flowers and produces seeds only if it is exposed to less than 10 hours of darkness each day for 2 weeks. **Figure 37.24** illustrates the results of an experiment to test the responses of short-day and long-day plants to night length. In this experiment, bearded iris plants, which are long-day plants, and chrysanthemums, which are short-day plants, were exposed to a range of light conditions. In each case, when the researchers interrupted a critical dark period with a pulse of red light, the light reset the plants' clocks. The experiment provided clear evidence that short-day plants flower only when nights are longer than a critical value, and long-day plants flower only when nights are shorter than a critical value.

Photoperiod behaviours in crop plants have been artificially selected for. Sorghum, an important grain crop that originated in the Sudan, has become diversified in variants with different photoperiods through artificial selection; plants have been selected to grow optimally at different latitudes because of cultivation. Nucleotide sequences of alleles of the *Prr37* gene have been used to track the path and history of sorghum introduction from its tropical origin 5000 years ago to temperate locations in Europe, Asia, and even North America after Benjamin Franklin brought it to the United States in the mid-1700s.

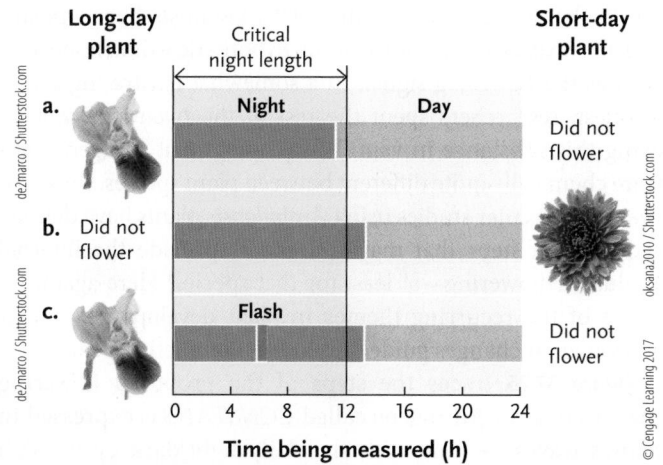

**FIGURE 37.24 Experiments showing that short-day and long-day plants flower by measuring night length.** Each horizontal bar signifies 24 hours. Blue bars represent night, and yellow bars day. **(a)** Long-day plants such as bearded irises flower when the night is shorter than a critical length, whereas **(b)** short-day plants such as chrysanthemums flower when the night is longer than a critical value. **(c)** When an intense red flash interrupts a long night, both kinds of plants respond as if it were a short night: the irises flowered but the chrysanthemums did not.

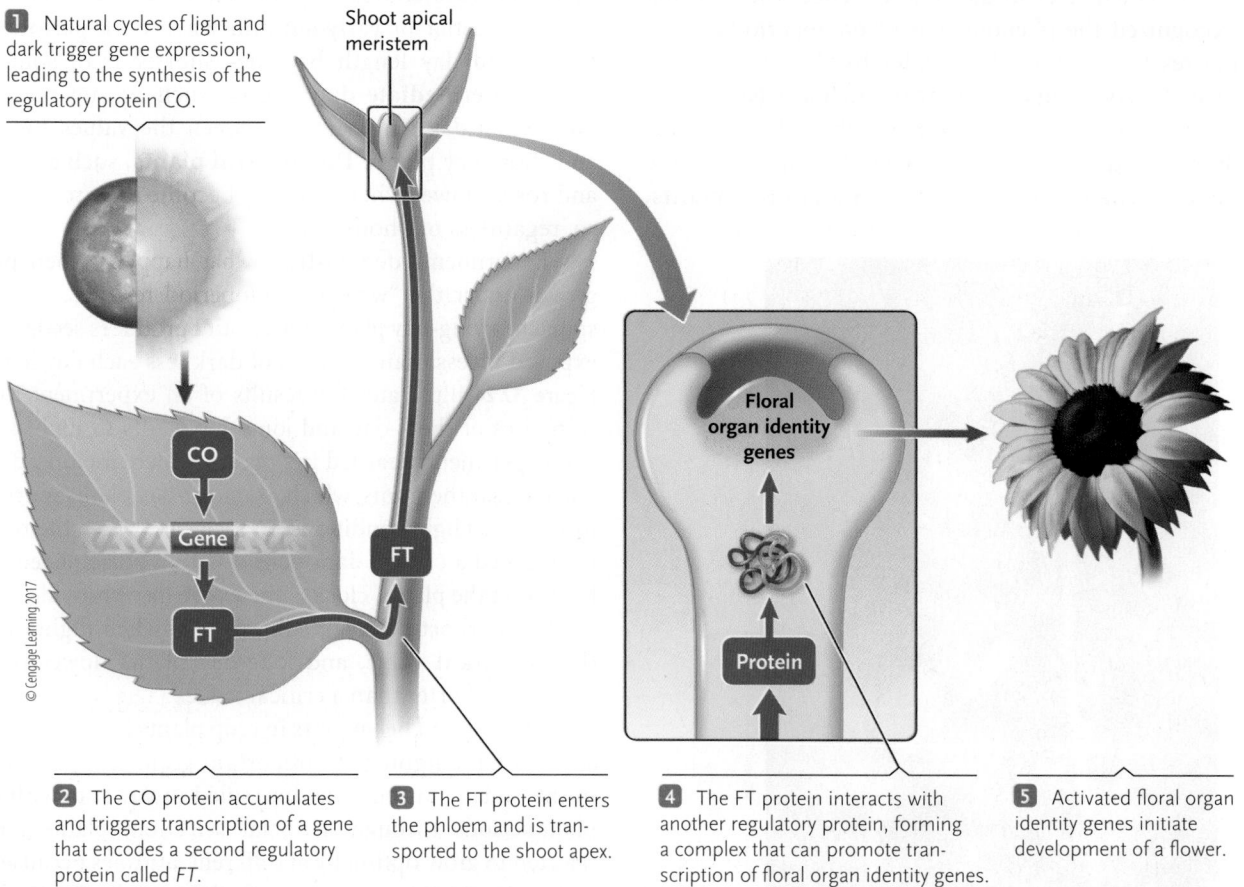

**1** Natural cycles of light and dark trigger gene expression, leading to the synthesis of the regulatory protein CO.

Shoot apical meristem

Floral organ identity genes

CO

Gene

FT

FT

Protein

© Cengage Learning 2017

**2** The CO protein accumulates and triggers transcription of a gene that encodes a second regulatory protein called *FT*.

**3** The FT protein enters the phloem and is transported to the shoot apex.

**4** The FT protein interacts with another regulatory protein, forming a complex that can promote transcription of floral organ identity genes.

**5** Activated floral organ identity genes initiate development of a flower.

**FIGURE 37.25 Proposed pathway for the flowering signal.** The pathway starts as shifting cycles of light and dark trigger expression of the *CONSTANS* gene. As described in the text, this step is the first in a sequence that leads to the activation of floral organ identity genes in the shoot apical meristem. When these genes are expressed, a flower develops.

**CHEMICAL SIGNALS FOR FLOWERING** When photoperiod conditions are right, what sort of chemical message stimulates a plant to develop flowers? In the 1930s botanists began postulating the existence of "florigen," a hypothetical hormone that served as the flowering signal. In a somewhat frustrating scientific quest, researchers spent the rest of the twentieth century seeking this substance in vain. It is possible that florigens exist but are chemically quite different between plant species. Recently, however, molecular studies using *Arabidopsis* plants have defined a sequence of steps that may collectively provide the internal stimulus for flowering—at least for that species! Here again, we see one of the recurring themes in plant development: major developmental changes guided by several interacting genes.

**Figure 37.25** traces the steps of the proposed flowering signal. To begin with, a gene called *CONSTANS* is expressed in a plant's leaves in tune with the daily light/dark cycle, with expression peaking at dusk (step 1). The gene encodes a regulatory protein called *CO* (not to be confused with carbon monoxide). As days lengthen in spring, the concentration of CO rises in leaves and, as a result, a second gene is activated (step 2). The product of this gene, a regulatory protein called *FT* (for flowering locus T), travels in the phloem to shoot tips (step 3). Once there, FT interacts with a second regulatory protein (step 4) that is synthesized only in shoot apical meristems

(step 5). The encounter apparently sparks the development of a flower by promoting the expression of floral organ identity genes in the meristem tissue (see Section 35.5).

**VERNALIZATION AND FLOWERING** Flowering is more than a response to changing night length. Temperatures also change with the seasons in most parts of the world, and they too influence flowering. For instance, unless buds of some biennials and perennials are exposed to low winter temperatures, flowers do not form on stems in spring. Low-temperature stimulation of flowering is called **vernalization** ("making springlike").

In 1915 the plant physiologist Gustav Gassner demonstrated that it was possible to influence the flowering of cereal plants by controlling the temperature of seeds while they were germinating. In one case, he maintained germinating seeds of winter rye (*Secale cereale*) at just above freezing (1°C) before planting them. In nature, winter rye seeds in soil germinate during the winter, giving rise to a plant that flowers months later, in summer. Plants grown from Gassner's test seeds, however, flowered the same summer even when the seeds were planted in the late spring. Home gardeners can induce flowering of daffodils and tulips by putting the bulbs (technically, *corms*) in a freezer for several weeks before early spring planting. Commercial growers use vernalization to induce millions of plants, such as Easter lilies, to flower just in time for seasonal sales.

## 37.4d Dormancy Is an Adaptation to Seasonal Changes or Stress

As autumn approaches and days grow shorter, growth slows or stops in many plants even if temperatures are still moderate, the sky is bright, and water is plentiful. When a perennial or biennial plant stops growing under conditions that seem (to us) quite suitable for growth, it has entered a state of **dormancy**. Ordinarily, its buds will not resume growth until early spring.

Short days and long nights—conditions typical of winter—are primary cues for dormancy. In one experiment, in which a short period of red light interrupted the long dark period for Douglas firs, the plants responded as if nights were shorter and days were longer; they continued to grow taller **(Figure 37.26)**. Conversion of $P_r$ to $P_{fr}$ by red light during the dark period prevented dormancy. In nature, buds may enter dormancy because less $P_{fr}$ can form when day length shortens in late summer. Other environmental cues are at work also. Cold nights, dry soil, and a deficiency of nitrogen apparently also promote dormancy.

The requirement for multiple dormancy cues has adaptive value. For example, if temperature were the only cue, plants might flower and seeds might germinate in warm autumn weather, only to be killed by winter frost.

A dormancy-breaking process is at work between fall and spring. Depending on the species, breaking dormancy probably involves gibberellins and abscisic acid, and it requires exposure to low winter temperatures for specific periods **(Figure 37.27)**. The temperature needed to break dormancy varies greatly among species. For example, the Delicious variety of apples grown in Utah requires 1230 hours near 6°C; apricots grown there require only 720 hours at that temperature. Generally,

Potted plant grown inside a greenhouse did not flower.

Branch exposed to cold outside air flowered.

**FIGURE 37.27 Effect of cold temperature on dormant buds of a lilac (*Syringa vulgaris*).** In this experiment, a lilac plant was grown in winter inside a warm greenhouse with one branch extending through a hole to the outdoors. Only the buds on the branch exposed to low outside temperatures resumed growth in spring. This experiment suggests that low-temperature effects are localized in plants.

trees growing in the southern United States or in Italy require less cold exposure than those growing in Canada or in Sweden.

If there are seasons in our "desert island" scenario, you would need to know when to gather and store food, and perhaps you would change your clothing. Some plants direct underground stems or roots to accumulate water and nutrients in preparation for tough weather, and some drop their precious leaves (after reabsorbing nitrogen and other recyclables) to reduce the damage that would occur when frost pulls water out of an organism. Solar tracking maximizes light and heat accumulation; closing flowers at night holds pollen in until receptive stigmas are presented with insect pollinators; and imposing dormancy on organs and seeds is vital for a species to thrive. Responding to time cues is an obvious benefit, and shows that complex decisions are possible for a plant that, at first glance, just sits there.

Let's think back on the desert island scenario that the chapter began with. What you've read in this chapter underscores ways that a plant, which at first glance is simply an immobile entity, can sense and respond to challenges. Through hormones, electrical conduction, and differential growth, plants are able to thrive in an astounding variety of conditions. Without the ability to adjust to changing climates, accommodate dispersed and diverse food sources, and to defend against pathogens and predators, plants might not be such an extraordinary part of all our ecosystems!

**FIGURE 37.26 Effect of the relative length of day and night on the growth of Douglas firs (*Pseudotsuga menziesii*).** The young tree at the left was exposed to alternating periods of 12 hours of light followed by 12 hours of darkness for a year; its buds became dormant because day length was too short. The tree at the right was exposed to a cycle of 20 hours of light and 4 hours of darkness; its buds remained active and growth continued. The middle plant was exposed each day to 12 hours of light and 11 hours of darkness, with a 1-hour light in the middle of the dark period. This light interruption of an otherwise long dark period also prevented buds from going dormant.

### STUDY BREAK QUESTIONS

1. Summarize the switching mechanism that operates in plant responses to changes in photoperiod.
2. Give some examples of how relative lengths of dark and light can influence flowering.
3. Explain why dormancy is an adaptive response to a plant's environment.

# Summary Illustration

Plants have many adaptations that are evolutionary solutions to being sessile and vulnerable to changes in the environment while rooted in one place. These adaptations help plants to combat weather and food challenges, avoid predation, and synchronize the production of flowers to help increase pollination.

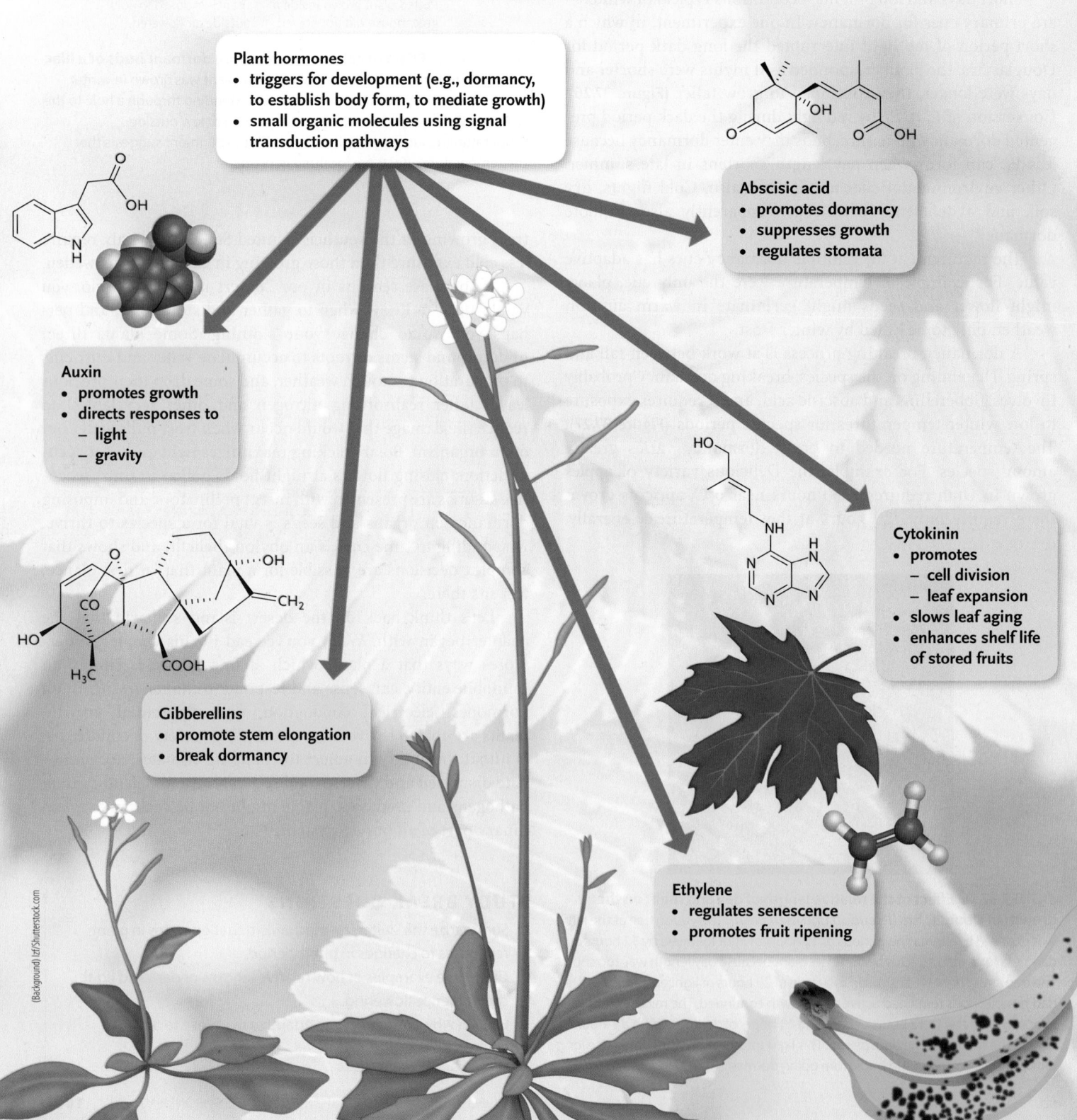

**Plant hormones**
- triggers for development (e.g., dormancy, to establish body form, to mediate growth)
- small organic molecules using signal transduction pathways

**Abscisic acid**
- promotes dormancy
- suppresses growth
- regulates stomata

**Auxin**
- promotes growth
- directs responses to
  - light
  - gravity

**Cytokinin**
- promotes
  - cell division
  - leaf expansion
- slows leaf aging
- enhances shelf life of stored fruits

**Gibberellins**
- promote stem elongation
- break dormancy

**Ethylene**
- regulates senescence
- promotes fruit ripening

(Background) lzf/Shutterstock.com

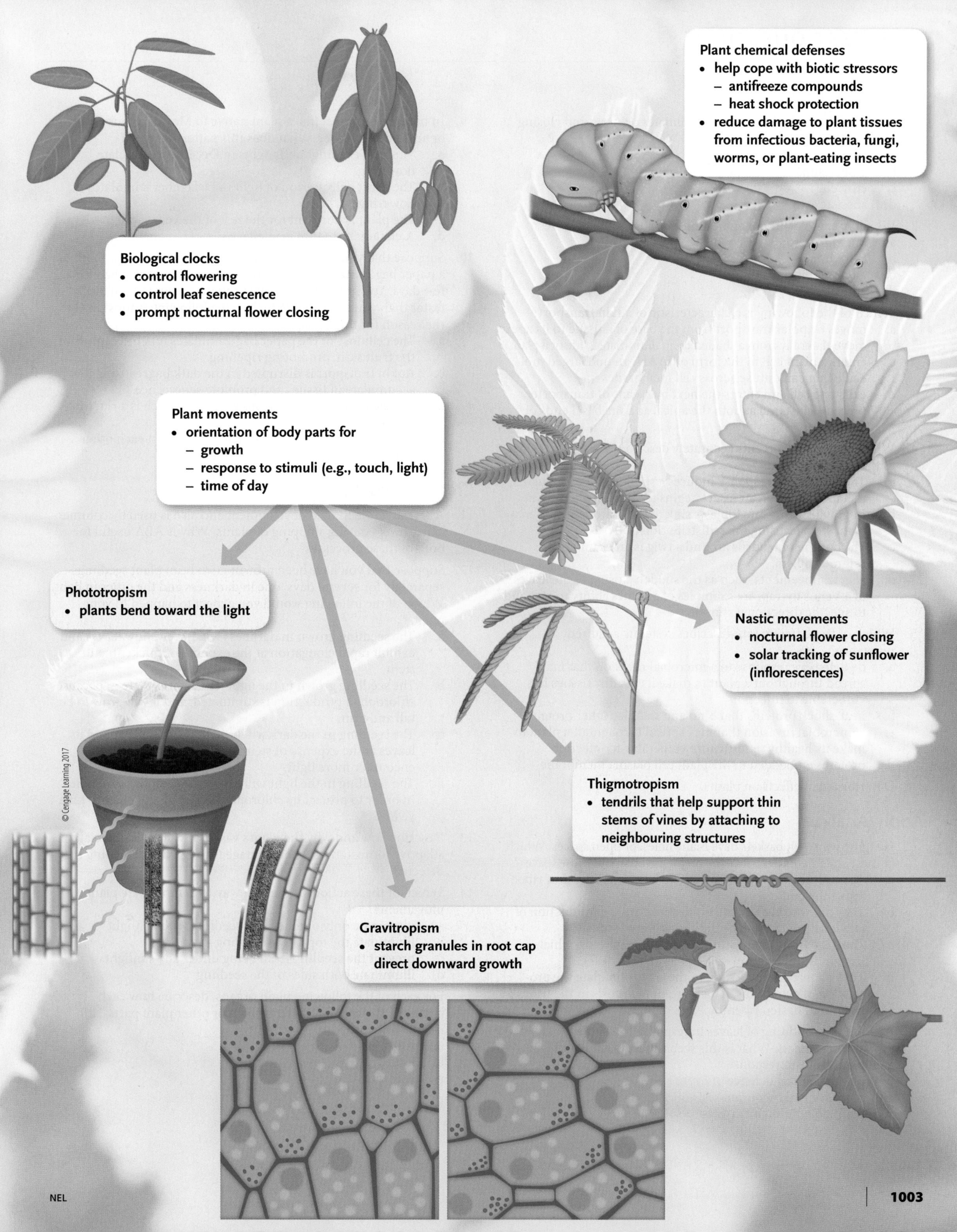

**Plant chemical defenses**
- help cope with biotic stressors
  - antifreeze compounds
  - heat shock protection
- reduce damage to plant tissues from infectious bacteria, fungi, worms, or plant-eating insects

**Biological clocks**
- control flowering
- control leaf senescence
- prompt nocturnal flower closing

**Plant movements**
- orientation of body parts for
  - growth
  - response to stimuli (e.g., touch, light)
  - time of day

**Phototropism**
- plants bend toward the light

**Nastic movements**
- nocturnal flower closing
- solar tracking of sunflower (inflorescences)

**Thigmotropism**
- tendrils that help support thin stems of vines by attaching to neighbouring structures

**Gravitropism**
- starch granules in root cap direct downward growth

© Cengage Learning 2017

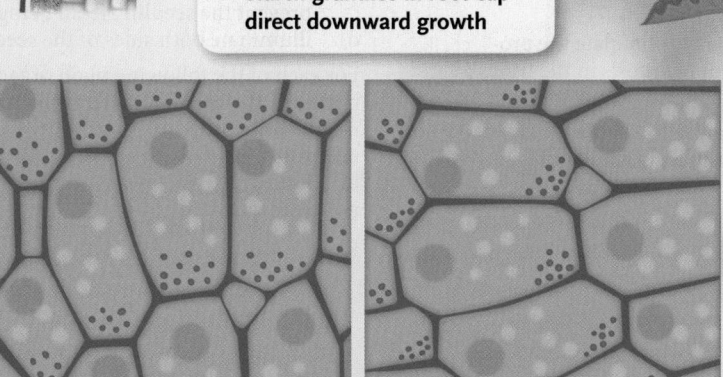

# SELF-TEST QUESTIONS

## Recall/Understand

1. Which of these plant hormones stimulates opening and closing of the stomata?
   a. auxin
   b. gibberellins
   c. ethylene
   d. abscisic acid

2. Which of these plant hormones inhibits abscission of leaves?
   a. brassinosteroids
   b. cytokinins
   c. gibberellins
   d. ethylene

3. Which of the following is a characteristic of auxin transport?
   a. moves by polar transport from the base of a tissue to its apex
   b. moves laterally from a shaded to an illuminated side of a plant
   c. enters a plant cell in the form of IAAH, an uncharged molecule that can diffuse across cell membranes
   d. exits one cell and enters the next by means of transporter proteins clustered at both the apical and the basal ends of the cells

4. Which of these statements accurately describes a plant's response to the environment?
   a. The heat-shock response induces a sudden halt to cellular metabolism when an insect begins feeding on plant tissue.
   b. In gravitropism, amyloplasts sink to the bottom of cells in a plant stem, causing the redistribution of IAA.
   c. The curling of tendrils around a twig is an example of thigmotropism.
   d. Nastic movements, such as the sudden closing of the leaves of a Venus flytrap, are examples of a plant's ability to respond to specific directional stimuli.

5. Which of these statements describes systemic acquired resistance?
   a. he defensive response to a microbial invasion that may spread throughout a plant to make its healthy tissues less vulnerable to infection
   b. heat-shock proteins that bind and stabilize other proteins
   c. a microbial invasion that may spread throughout a plant to make its healthy tissues more vulnerable to infection
   d. proteins embedded in the plant cell plasma membrane

6. Describe auxin effects on plants.

## Apply/Analyze

7. Hanging wire fruit baskets have many holes, or open spaces. Which of these statements describes the major advantage of these spaces?
   a. They allow the evaporation of ethylene, and thus slow ripening of the fruit.
   b. They allow oxygen in the air to stimulate the production of ethylene, which hastens the abscission of fruits.
   c. They allow oxygen to stimulate brassinosteroids, which hasten the maturation of seeds in/on the fruits.
   d. They allow carbon dioxide in the air to stimulate the production of cytokinins, which promote mitosis in the fruit tissue and hasten ripening.

8. ABA inhibits budding of leaves in response to attacks by sap-sucking insects. What is this scenario an example of?
   a. plant tropism response
   b. plant chemical defence
   c. plant systemic acquired resistance
   d. plant pollination by insects

9. In nature, the poinsettia, a plant native to Mexico, blooms only in or around December. What does this pattern suggest?
   a. The long evenings and nights in December stimulate flowering.
   b. The short daily period of light in December stimulates flowering.
   c. The plant is dormant for the rest of the year.
   d. A circadian rhythm is in effect.

10. Suppose that you buy some fresh bananas and you keep them in a paper bag containing older, mature ones that you've had for a few days. You notice that the new bananas seem to turn black faster than you expected. Which of the following is most likely the reason for this to happen?
    a. The cellulose of the paper bag stimulates touch receptors of the fruit skin, promoting ripening.
    b. Auxin transport is disrupted in the dark bag, causing it to accumulate in tissues and promote senescence.
    c. The closed bag traps gaseous ethylene, which is a ripening hormone.
    d. A stress reaction from fruits rubbing against each other releases jasmonic acid, which softens them.

## Create/Evaluate

11. ABA has a role in seed development and also is used by commercial growers during shipping of plants. Why is ABA useful for both of these processes?

12. Suppose that you have been growing two bean plant seedlings separately for several days: one in darkness and the other in light. Which of the following would you expect to happen to your plants?
    a. The seedling grown in darkness will have yellow leaves and exhibit rapid elongation at the expense of thickening its stem.
    b. The seedling grown in the light will be bright green because chlorophyll production is stimulated, and it will grow to be tall and thin.
    c. The seedling in the dark will be yellow but will expand its leaves at the expense of stem lengthening in order to encounter more light.
    d. The seedling in the light will accumulate more carotenoids in order to protect its chlorophyll, causing the plant to turn yellow.

13. Describe how and why the plant's vascular system is especially adaptive for instances when damage through insect feeding is detected.

14. Which of these actions is the best way to demonstrate plant movement?
    a. illuminate only one side of a seedling with sunlight
    b. illuminate the top of the seedling
    c. prevent the seedling from being under any sunlight
    d. illuminate both sides of the seedling

15. For each of the following plant organs, describe how each hormone they produce affects them or other plant parts.
    i. shoot
    ii. root
    iii. leaves
    iv. embryos

# Chapter Roadmap

## Introduction to Animal Organization and Physiology

Multicellular animals can maintain their own internal environment, distinct from the external environment surrounding them. This requires that groups of cells become specialized to perform specific functions.

### 38.1 Organization of the Animal Body

In most animals, cells are specialized and organized into tissues, tissues into organs, and organs into organ systems, each of which has specific functions.

### 38.2 Animal Tissues

Animal tissues are classified as epithelial, connective, muscle, or nervous. The properties of the cells of these tissues determine the structure and function of the tissue.

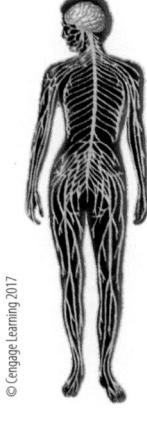

© Cengage Learning 2017

### 38.3 Coordination of Tissues in Organs and Organ Systems

Organs are composed of multiple tissues, and the organs in turn are organized into systems. In vertebrates, there are 12 systems that are coordinated to carry out vital tasks.

**To Chapters 39–46**

### 38.4 Homeostasis

Most animals maintain their internal environment constant using negative feedback control of the different systems to correct for any environmental (internal or external) perturbations.

Photos.com

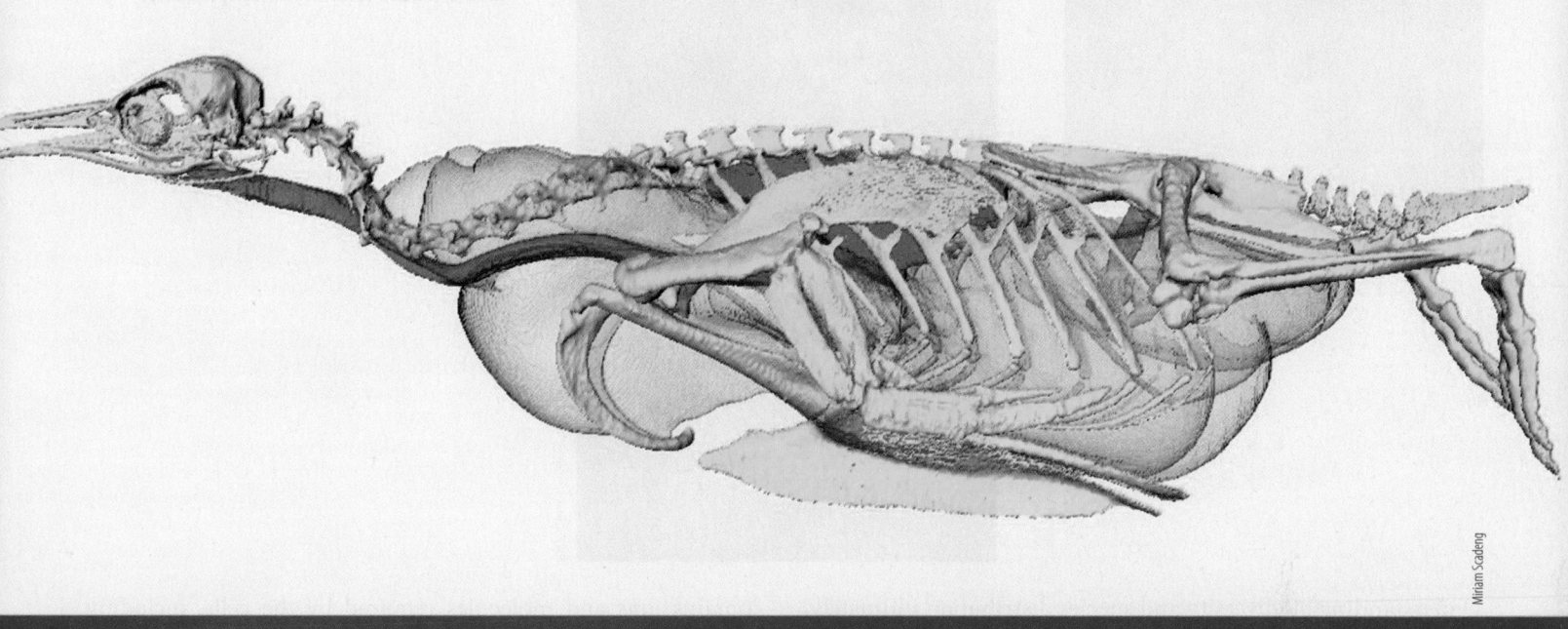

Miriam Scadeng

**A 3-D reconstruction of a penguin made from CT data.** Various organs can be seen in the image, including bones (yellow), trachea and lungs (red), and respiratory air sacs (blue). Can you name the tissues, organs, and organ systems found in all vertebrates, as well as their functions?

# Introduction to Animal Organization and Physiology

# 38

**Why it matters . . .** When winter sets in across Canada, different species of animals begin to prepare for the cold in different ways. Many species begin to slow body processes and prepare their cells to withstand freezing as a way of surviving until the spring. Others undergo changes that will allow them to remain fully active throughout the cold snowy months. Yet other species cannot tolerate the cold and migrate to warmer climates for the winter **(Figure 38.1)**. A full understanding of the factors that determine species tolerances and distributions requires detailed knowledge of how species are built and how their various parts work. What are the processes by which animals regulate their body temperatures, and why are some more proficient at this than others?

In multicellular organisms, cells differentiate to form different tissues. In animals, tissues combine in different ways to form organs and organ systems. Each organ system has a unique function. This specialization allows multicellular organisms to establish an internal environment around their cells that can be maintained relatively independent of the external environment through a process called **homeostasis** (*homeo* = the same; *stasis* = standing or stopping). The processes and activities responsible for homeostasis are called **homeostatic mechanisms**. Being able to maintain an internal environment relatively independent of changes in the external environment greatly broadens the geographic range over which animals can live actively.

a.

b.

c.

**FIGURE 38.1** (a) **Ways of surviving the winter include avoidance (migratory birds),** (b) **cold adaptation (small mammals),** and (c) **freeze tolerance (many insects)**

Understanding biodiversity and species distribution ultimately requires an understanding of the form and function of the organs and organ systems within each species, which in turn requires an understanding of the specialized cells and tissues that compose them. **Anatomy** is the study of the structures of organisms, and **physiology** is the study of the functions of the cells, tissues, organs, and organ systems.

In this chapter, we begin by examining the organization of individual cells into tissues, organs, and organ systems, the major body structures that carry out animal activities. Our discussion continues by examining the coordination of the processes and activities of organ systems that accomplish homeostasis. The other eight chapters in this unit discuss the individual organ systems that carry out major body functions such as digestion, movement, and reproduction. Although we emphasize vertebrates throughout the unit (including humans), we also make comparisons with invertebrates to keep the structural and functional diversity of the animal kingdom in perspective and to understand the evolution of the structures and processes involved.

## 38.1 Organization of the Animal Body

### 38.1a In Animals, Specialized Cells Are Organized Into Tissues, Tissues Into Organs, Organs Into Organ Systems, and Organ Systems Into Organisms

The individual cells of multicellular animals have the same requirements as cells of any kind, including single-celled organisms. They must be surrounded by an aqueous solution that contains ions and molecules required by the cells, including complex organic molecules that can be used as energy sources. The concentrations of these molecules and ions must be balanced to keep cells from shrinking or swelling excessively due to osmotic water movement (see Section 4.4d). Most animal cells also require oxygen to serve as the final acceptor for electrons removed in oxidative reactions (see Section 5.6b). Animal cells must be able to release waste molecules and other by-products of their activities, such as carbon dioxide and nitrogenous wastes, to their environment. Physical conditions of the cellular environment, such as temperature, must also remain within tolerable limits.

The evolution of multicellularity (see Section 21.5) made it possible for organisms to produce a protective external layer (cuticle, shell, skin, etc.) and create an internal fluid environment (the extracellular fluid) that supplies all the needs of individual cells, including nutrient supply, waste removal, and osmotic balance. By regulating this internal environment despite changes in the external environment, multicellular organisms can occupy diverse habitats, including dry terrestrial habitats that would be lethal to single cells. While multicellular organisms can become very large, their individual cells remain small enough to exchange ions and molecules easily with the internal fluid.

The evolution of multicellularity also allowed specialized groups of cells to differentiate and take on specific life functions, with each group of cells concentrating primarily on a single activity. Specialization greatly increases the efficiency by which animals carry out these functions. In most animals, these specialized groups of cells are organized into tissues, the tissues into organs, and the organs into organ systems **(Figure 38.2)**. A **tissue** is a group of cells with the same structure and function, working together as a unit to carry out one or

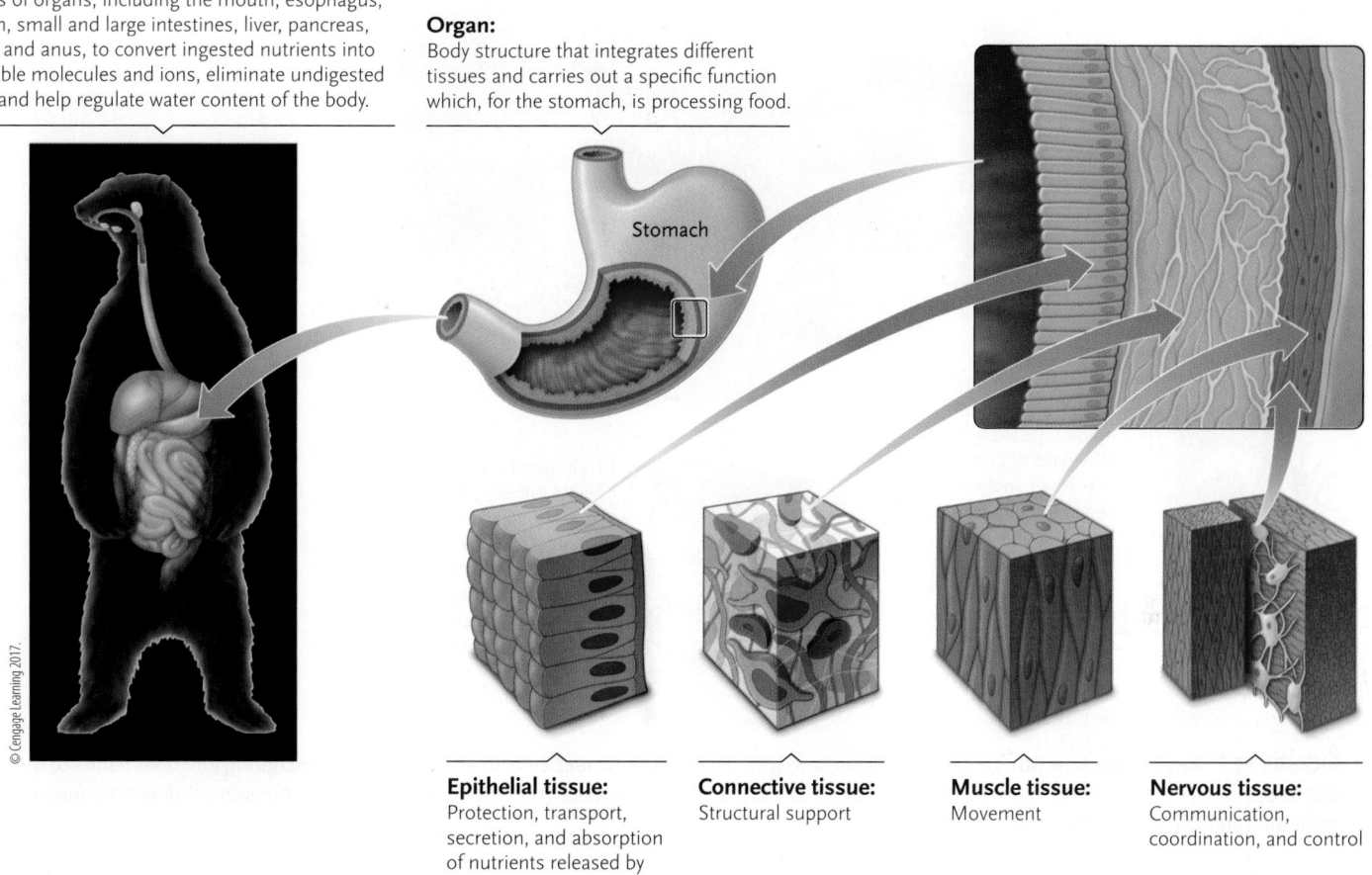

**Organ system:**
A set of organs that interact to carry out a major body function. The digestive system coordinates the activities of organs, including the mouth, esophagus, stomach, small and large intestines, liver, pancreas, rectum, and anus, to convert ingested nutrients into absorbable molecules and ions, eliminate undigested matter, and help regulate water content of the body.

**Organ:**
Body structure that integrates different tissues and carries out a specific function which, for the stomach, is processing food.

Stomach

© Cengage Learning 2017.

**Epithelial tissue:**
Protection, transport, secretion, and absorption of nutrients released by digestion of food

**Connective tissue:**
Structural support

**Muscle tissue:**
Movement

**Nervous tissue:**
Communication, coordination, and control

**FIGURE 38.2** Organization of animal cells into tissues, organs, and organ systems, as exemplified here by the digestive system

more activities. Four types of tissue are shown in Figure 38.2: epithelial, connective, muscle, and nervous tissue. An **organ** integrates two or more different tissues into a structure that carries out a specific function. The eye, liver, and stomach are examples of organs. An **organ system** coordinates the activities of two or more organs to carry out a major body function such as digestion, excretion, or reproduction. The organ system carrying out digestion, for example, coordinates the activities of its organs, which include the mouth, stomach, pancreas, liver, and small and large intestines. Some organs contribute functions to more than one organ system. For instance, the pancreas forms part of the endocrine system as well as the digestive system.

## STUDY BREAK QUESTIONS

1. What are the differences among tissues, organs, and organ systems?
2. Why do multicellular organisms have organs and organ systems? What is the benefit?

## 38.2  Animal Tissues

Although the most complex animals may contain hundreds of distinct cell types, all can be classified into one of only four basic tissue groups: epithelial, connective, muscle, and nervous (see Figure 38.2). Each tissue type is assembled from individual cells. The properties of these cells determine the structure and therefore the function of the tissue. More specifically, the structure and function of a tissue depends on the structure and organization of the cytoskeleton within the cell, the junctions holding the cells together, and the type and organization of the extracellular matrix surrounding the cell. The extracellular matrix (ECM) is a non-living material secreted by cells and consists of a variety of proteins and glycoproteins. The ECM provides support and shape for tissues and organs. The cell walls of plants and the cuticle of arthropods are examples of specialized ECM.

Junctions of various kinds link cells into tissues **(Figure 38.3)**:

- **Anchoring junctions** form buttonlike spots or belts that weld cells together. They are most abundant in tissues subject to stretching, such as skin and heart muscle.

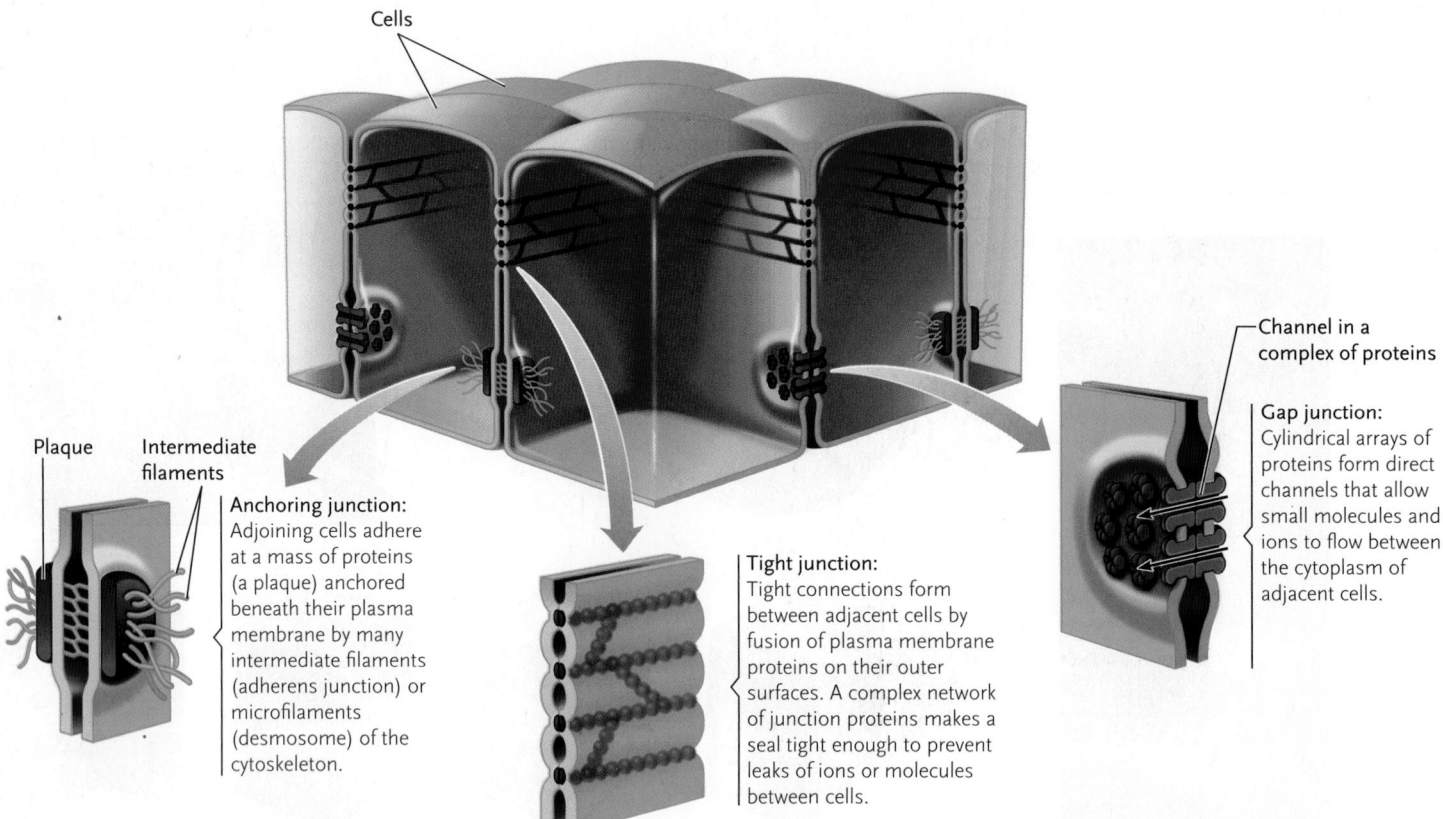

Cells

Plaque · Intermediate filaments

**Anchoring junction:** Adjoining cells adhere at a mass of proteins (a plaque) anchored beneath their plasma membrane by many intermediate filaments (adherens junction) or microfilaments (desmosome) of the cytoskeleton.

**Tight junction:** Tight connections form between adjacent cells by fusion of plasma membrane proteins on their outer surfaces. A complex network of junction proteins makes a seal tight enough to prevent leaks of ions or molecules between cells.

Channel in a complex of proteins

**Gap junction:** Cylindrical arrays of proteins form direct channels that allow small molecules and ions to flow between the cytoplasm of adjacent cells.

**FIGURE 38.3 Anchoring junctions, tight junctions, and gap junctions connect cells in animal tissues.** Anchoring junctions reinforce the cell-to-cell connections made by cell adhesion molecules; tight junctions seal the spaces between cells; and gap junctions create direct channels of communication between animal cells.

- **Tight junctions** seal the spaces between cells, keeping molecules and even ions from leaking between cells. For example, tight junctions in the tissue lining the urinary bladder prevent waste molecules and ions from leaking out of the bladder into other body tissues.
- **Gap junctions** are open channels between cells in the same tissue. They allow ions and small molecules to flow freely from one cell to another. For example, gap junctions between muscle cells help muscle tissue to function as a unit.

## 38.2a Epithelial Tissue Forms Protective, Secretory, and Absorptive Coverings and Linings of Body Structures

**Epithelial tissue** (*epi* = over; *thele* = covering) consists of sheet-like layers of cells that are usually joined tightly together, with little ECM material between them **(Figure 38.4)**. Also called *epithelia* (singular, *epithelium*), these tissues cover body surfaces and the surfaces of internal organs and line cavities and ducts within the body. They protect body surfaces from invasion by bacteria and viruses and secrete or absorb substances. They often have other roles. For example, the epithelium covering a fish's gill structures serves as a barrier to bacteria and viruses

while at the same time serving as an exchange site for oxygen, carbon dioxide, and ions with the aqueous environment. The epithelium of the external surface of arthropods secretes the tough cuticle that, in addition to acting as a barrier to the environment, functions as their skeleton. Some epithelial cells in the epidermis of vertebrates also contain a network of fibrous proteins (keratin) that form such protective structures as scales, nails, claws, hooves, and horns, as well as hair and feathers.

Some epithelia, such as those lining the capillaries of the circulatory system, act as filters, allowing ions and small molecules to leak from the blood into surrounding tissues while barring the passage of blood cells and large molecules such as proteins (see Section 41.4b).

Because epithelia form coverings and linings, they have a free (or outer) surface and an inner surface. The outer **apical surface** may be exposed to water, air, or fluids within the body. In internal cavities and ducts, the apical surface is often covered with cilia, which beat like oars to move fluids through the cavity or duct. The epithelium lining the oviducts in mammals, for example, is covered with cilia that generate fluid currents to move eggs from the ovaries to the uterus. In free-living flatworms, the ventral epithelium of the animal is frequently ciliated, allowing the worm to glide over surfaces. In some epithelia, including the lining of the small intestine,

### a. Simple squamous epithelium

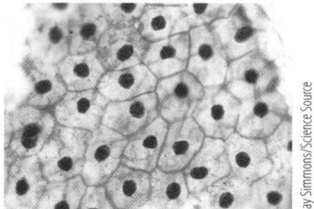

Ray Simmons/Science Source

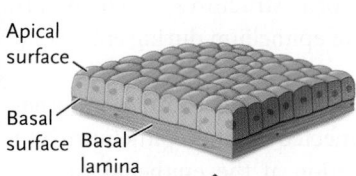

**Description:** Layer of flattened cells

**Common locations:** Blood vessel inner lining (called *endothelium*); air sacs of lungs

**Function:** Diffusion

### b. Stratified squamous epithelium

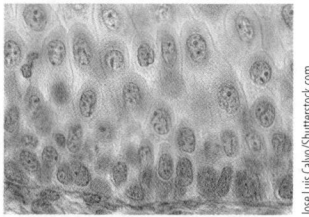

Jose Luis Calvo/Shutterstock.com

**Description:** Several layers of flattened cells

**Common locations:** Skin and other surfaces subject to abrasion, such as the mouth, esophagus, and vagina

**Function:** Protection against abrasion; typically not involved in secretion or absorption

### c. Cuboidal epithelium

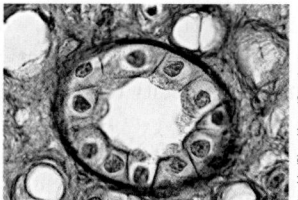

Ed Reschke/Photolibrary/Getty Images

**Description:** Layer of cubelike cells; free surface may have microvilli

**Common locations:** Glands and tubular parts of nephrons in kidneys

**Function:** Secretion, absorption

**FIGURE 38.4 Principle types of epithelia**

© Cengage Learning 2017.

### d. Simple columnar epithelium

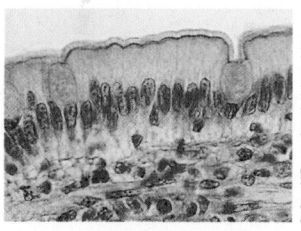

Dr. Donald Fawcett/Visuals Unlimited, Inc

**Description:** Layer of tall, slender cells with nuclei near base; free surface may have microvilli or cilia; may contain secretory vesicles

**Common locations:** Lining of gut, cervical canal, and gallbladder

**Function:** Secretion, absorption, such as secreting digestive enzymes and absorbing nutrients in the gut; protection; secreting mucus

### e. Simple pseudostratified columnar epithelium

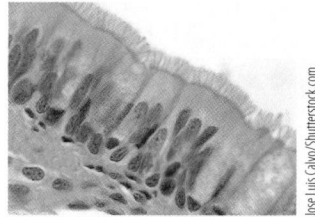

Jose Luis Calvo/Shutterstock.com

**Description:** Single layer of columnar cells of differing heights; some cells do not reach the apical surface. Due to the cell organization, the nuclei are staggered, giving the epithelium the false appearance of stratification. May be ciliated.

**Common locations:** Nasal cavities, trachea, and upper digestive tract; some parts of male reproductive system

**Function:** Protection; secretes mucus and moves it across surface

the free surface is crowded with microvilli, fingerlike extensions of the plasma membrane that increase the area available for secretion or absorption (see Figure 39.11).

The inner, **basal surface** of an epithelium adheres to a layer of ECM secreted by the epithelial cells called the **basal lamina** (see Figure 38.4). In many cases, such as the intestinal epithelium of vertebrates, a further layer of fibres is secreted by underlying connective tissue, but this is lacking in most invertebrate epithelia. The entire assemblage is the **basement membrane**.

**TYPES OF EPITHELIA** Epithelia are classified as simple—formed by a single layer of cells—or stratified—formed by multiple cell layers (see Figure 38.4). The shapes of cells within an epithelium may be squamous (mosaic, flattened, and spread out), cuboidal (shaped roughly like dice or cubes), or columnar (elongated, with the long axis perpendicular to the epithelial layer). Five principle types of epithelia are found in the body (see Figure 38.4).

The cells of some epithelia, such as those forming the skin and the lining of the intestine, divide constantly to replace worn and dying cells. New cells are produced through division of stem cells in the basal (lowest) layer of the skin. **Stem cells** are undifferentiated (unspecialized) cells in the tissue that divide to produce more stem cells as well as cells that differentiate (i.e., become specialized into one of the many cell types of the body). Stem cells are found in both adult organisms and embryos. In addition to the skin, adult stem cells are found in tissues of the brain, bone marrow, blood vessels, skeletal muscle, and liver. Stem cells are important for development in many invertebrates. In some cases, the stem cells may already be programmed for a specific cell type, as in the eye or the wing disks of insect pupae, whereas in others, the stem cells may be totipotent, as in flatworms (Chapter 27). A totipotent cell has the capacity to form an entire organism.

**GLANDS FORMED BY EPITHELIA** Epithelia typically contain or give rise to cells that are specialized for secretion. Some of these secretory cells are scattered among non-secretory cells within the epithelium. Others form structures called **glands**, which are derived from pockets of epithelium during embryonic development.

Some glands, called **exocrine glands** (*exo* = external; *crine* = secretion), remain connected to the epithelium by a duct, which empties their secretion at the epithelial surface. Exocrine secretions include mucus, saliva, digestive enzymes, sweat, earwax, oils, milk, and venom (**Figure 38.5a** shows an exocrine gland in the skin of a poisonous tree frog). Other glands, called **endocrine glands**, may not be composed of epithelial cells. They have no ducts but secrete their products, hormones, into the interstitial fluid to be picked up by the blood for circulation to the organs and tissues of the body (Figure 38.5b). The endocrine glands are considered in detail in Chapter 43.

Some glands contain both exocrine and endocrine elements. For example, some cells of the pancreas form an exocrine gland that secretes pancreatic juice through a duct into the small intestine, where it plays an important role in food digestion (see Chapter 39); different cells of the pancreas serve an endocrine function by secreting the hormones insulin and glucagon into the bloodstream to help regulate glucose levels in the blood (see Chapter 43).

Some epithelial cells, particularly in the epidermis of vertebrates, contain a network of fibres of keratin, a family of tough proteins. Keratin forms the scales of fish and reptiles (including the shells of turtles); the feathers of birds; and the hair, claws, hooves, horns, and fingernails of mammals.

## 38.2b Connective Tissue Supports Other Body Tissues

Most animal body structures contain one or more types of **connective tissue**. Connective tissues support other body tissues and transmit mechanical and other forces. They consist of cells that form networks or layers in and around body structures and that are separated by non-living material, specifically the **extracellular matrix (ECM)** secreted by the cells of the tissue. Many forms of connective tissue have more non-living ECM material (both by weight and by volume) than living cellular material.

The mechanical properties of a connective tissue depend on the type and quantity of its ECM. The consistency of the ECM ranges from fluid (as in blood and lymph), through soft and firm gels (as in tendons), to hard and crystalline (as in bone). In most connective tissues, the ECM consists primarily of the fibrous

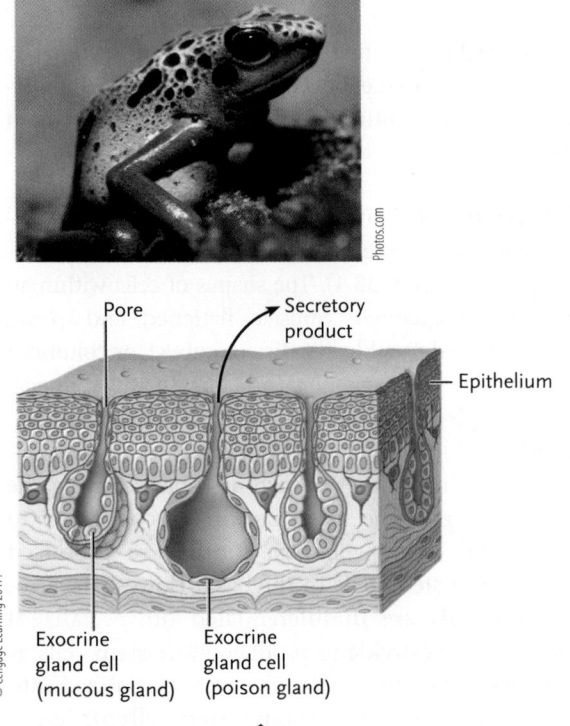

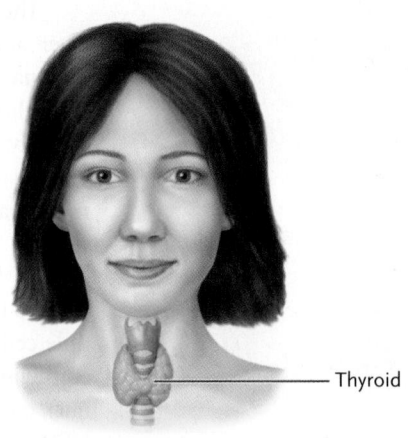

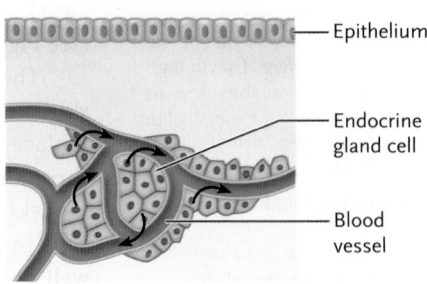

Pore — Secretory product

Epithelium

Exocrine gland cell (mucous gland)

Exocrine gland cell (poison gland)

© Cengage Learning 2017.

Photos.com

**a.** Examples of exocrine glands: The mucus- and poison-secreting glands in the skin of a blue poison frog

Thyroid

Epithelium

Endocrine gland cell

Blood vessel

**b.** Example of an endocrine gland: The thyroid gland, which secretes hormones that regulate the rate of metabolism and other body functions

**FIGURE 38.5 Exocrine and endocrine glands. (a)** The poison secreted by the blue poison frog (*Dendrobates azureus*) is one of the most lethal glandular secretions known. **(b)** The hormones secreted by the thyroid gland are vital for growth, development, maturation, and metabolism in all vertebrates.

glycoprotein **collagen** embedded in a network of proteoglycans—glycoproteins that are very rich in carbohydrates. Collagen is the most abundant family of proteins in animals. More than 25 different forms have been described, and some form of collagen occurs in all Metazoa, including Porifera (sponges). The collagen molecule is thus an ancient one that has been modified during evolution. In bone, the glycoprotein network surrounding the collagen is impregnated with mineral deposits that produce a hard, yet still somewhat elastic, structure. Another class of glycoproteins, **fibronectin**, aids in the attachment of cells to the ECM and helps hold the cells in position.

In some connective tissues, another rubbery protein, **elastin**, adds elasticity to the ECM. It is able to return to its original shape after being stretched, bent, or compressed. Elastin fibres, for example, help the skin return to its original shape when pulled or stretched and give the lungs the elasticity required for their alternating inflation and deflation. Resilin is a protein related to elastin that occurs only in insects and some Crustacea. It is the most elastic material known and is the basis for the jumping of fleas and locusts. Fleas are able to jump very large distances because muscle contractions store energy in pads of resilin in the hind legs. The sudden release of this energy, in less than a millisecond, propels the jump with an instantaneous acceleration greater than that of the space shuttle. It is also involved in the movements of the membrane that produce the song of cicadas that vibrate several thousand times per second. Like other elastic proteins, resilin is composed of coiled protein molecules cross-linked to one another, and their stretching involves uncoiling.

Vertebrates have six major types of connective tissue: loose connective tissue, fibrous connective tissue, cartilage, bone, adipose tissue, and blood. Each type has a characteristic function correlated with its structure **(Figure 38.6)**.

### LOOSE CONNECTIVE TISSUE **Loose connective tissue** consists of sparsely distributed cells surrounded by a more or less open network of collagen and other glycoprotein fibres (see Figure 38.6a). The cells, called *fibroblasts*, secrete most of the collagen and other proteins in this connective tissue.

In vertebrates, loose connective tissues support epithelia and form a corsetlike band around blood vessels, nerves, and some internal organs; they also reinforce deeper layers of the skin. Sheets of loose connective tissue, covered on both surfaces with epithelial cells, form the **mesenteries**, which hold the abdominal organs in place and provide lubricated, smooth surfaces that prevent chafing or abrasion between adjacent structures as the body moves. This is the reason that your lungs do not become abraded from rubbing against the chest wall every time they expand and contract. In insects, and perhaps some other invertebrates, the loose connective tissues suspending organs and providing support for epithelia are the products of specialized cells circulating in the blood.

### FIBROUS CONNECTIVE TISSUE In **fibrous connective tissue**, fibroblasts are sparsely distributed among dense masses of collagen and elastin fibres that are lined up in highly ordered, parallel bundles (see Figure 38.6b). The parallel arrangement produces maximum tensile strength and elasticity. Examples include **tendons**, which attach muscles to bones, and **ligaments**, which connect bones to each other at a joint. The cornea of the eye is a transparent fibrous connective tissue formed from highly ordered collagen molecules.

In some invertebrates, fibrous connective tissue provides shape to the animal, as in many sponges (see Chapter 27) and echinoderms. In sea cucumbers (see Chapter 27), the rigidity of the connective tissue can be changed quickly by the animal, resulting in a loss or change of shape. This acts as an escape response.

### CARTILAGE **Cartilage** consists of sparsely distributed cells called *chondrocytes* that are surrounded by networks of collagen fibres embedded in a tough but elastic matrix of the glycoprotein chondroitin sulfate (see Figure 38.6c). Elastin is also present in some forms of cartilage.

The elasticity of cartilage allows it to resist compression and stay resilient, like a piece of rubber. Bending your ear or pushing the tip of your nose, which are supported by cores of cartilage, will give you a good idea of the flexible nature of this tissue. Cartilage also supports the larynx, trachea, and smaller air passages in the lungs. It forms the disks cushioning the vertebrae in the spinal column and the smooth, slippery capsules around the ends of bones in joints, such as the hip and knee. Cartilage also serves as a precursor to bone during embryonic development; in sharks and rays and their relatives, almost the entire skeleton remains as cartilage in adults.

### BONE The densest form of connective tissue, **bone**, forms the skeleton in vertebrates, which supports the body, protects softer body structures such as the brain, and contributes to body movements by forming levers for muscles to pull on.

Mature bone consists primarily of cells called **osteocytes** (*osteon* = bone) embedded in an ECM containing collagen fibres and glycoproteins impregnated with calcium phosphate (see Figure 38.6d). The collagen fibres give bone tensile strength and elasticity; the hydroxyapatite resists compression and allows bones to support body weight. Cells called **osteoblasts** (*blast* = bud or sprout) produce the collagen and mineral of bone—as much as 85% of the weight of bone is mineral deposits. Osteocytes, in fact, are osteoblasts that have become trapped and surrounded by the bone materials they themselves produce. **Osteoclasts** (*clast* = break) remove the minerals and recycle them through the bloodstream. Bone is not a stable tissue: it is reshaped continuously by the bone-building osteoblasts and the bone-degrading osteoclasts.

Although bones appear superficially to be solid, they are actually porous structures consisting of a system of microscopic spaces and canals. The structural unit of bone is the **osteon**. It consists of a minute central canal surrounded by osteocytes embedded in concentric layers of mineral matter (see Figure 38.6d). A blood vessel and extensions of nerve cells

**a. Loose connective tissue**

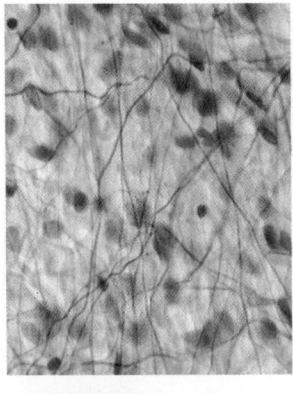

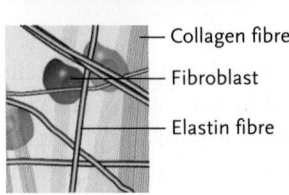

— Collagen fibre
— Fibroblast
— Elastin fibre

**Description:** Fibroblasts and other cells surrounded by collagen and elastin fibres forming a glycoprotein matrix

**Common locations:** Under the skin and most epithelia

**Function:** Support, elasticity, diffusion

**b. Fibrous connective tissue**

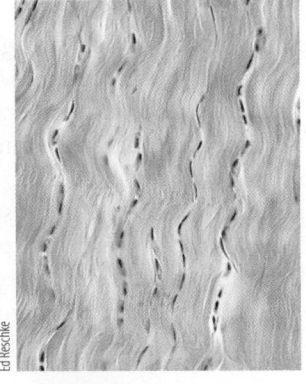

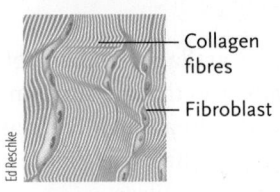

— Collagen fibres
— Fibroblast

**Description:** Long rows of fibroblasts surrounded by collagen and elastin fibres in parallel bundles with a dense ECM

**Common locations:** Tendons, ligaments

**Function:** Strength, elasticity

**c. Cartilage**

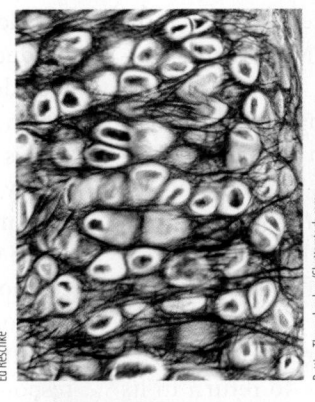

— Collagen fibres embedded in an elastic matrix
— Chondrocyte

**Description:** Chondrocytes embedded in a pliable, solid matrix of collagen and chondroitin sulfate

**Common locations:** Ends of long bones, nose, parts of airways, skeleton of vertebrate embryos

**Function:** Support, flexibility, low-friction surface for joint movement

**d. Bone tissue**

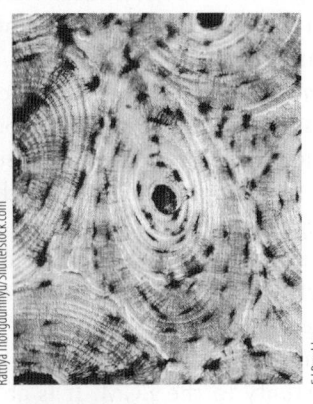

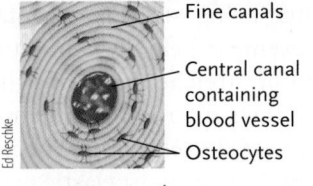

— Fine canals
— Central canal containing blood vessel
— Osteocytes

**Description:** Osteocytes in a matrix of collagen and glycoproteins hardened with hydroxyapatite

**Common locations:** Bones of vertebrate skeleton

**Function:** Movement, support, protection

**e. Adipose tissue**

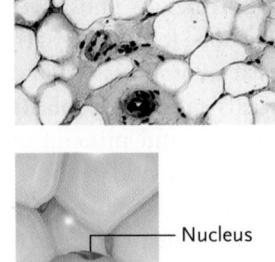

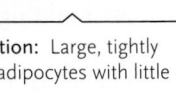

— Nucleus
— Fat deposit

**Description:** Large, tightly packed adipocytes with little ECM

**Common locations:** Under skin; around heart, kidneys

**Function:** Energy reserves, insulation, padding

**f. Blood**

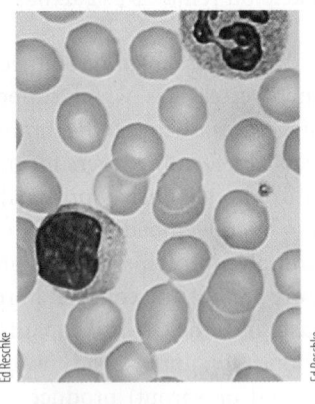

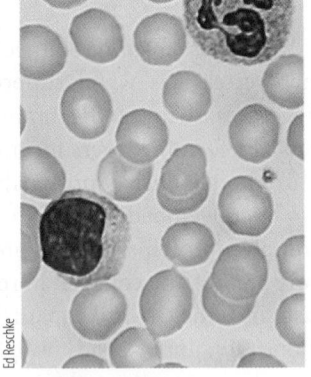

— Leukocyte
— Erythrocyte
— Platelet
— Plasma

**Description:** Leukocytes, erythrocytes, and platelets suspended in a plasma matrix

**Common locations:** Circulatory system

**Function:** Transport of substances

**FIGURE 38.6 The six major types of connective tissues in vertebrates**

run through the central canal, which is connected to the spaces containing cells by very fine, radiating canals filled with interstitial fluid. The blood vessels supply nutrients to the cells with which the bone is built, and the nerve cells innervate the blood vessels as well as the connective tissue (periosteum) surrounding the bone.

**ADIPOSE TISSUE** The connective tissue called **adipose tissue** contains mostly large, densely clustered cells called *adipocytes*, which are specialized for fat storage (see Figure 38.6e). It has little ECM. Adipose tissue also cushions the body and, in mammals, forms an especially important insulating layer under the skin.

The animal body stores limited amounts of carbohydrates, primarily in muscle and liver cells. Unlike plants, in animals excess carbohydrates are converted into the fats stored in adipocytes. The storage of chemical energy as fats offers animals a weight advantage. For example, the average human would weigh about 45 kg more if the same amount of chemical energy were stored as carbohydrates instead of fats. Adipose tissue is richly supplied with blood vessels, which move fats or their components to and from adipocytes.

© Cengage Learning 2017.

In invertebrates, fat storage may occur in a variety of tissues. Insects have a fat body, an organ that functions both as storage and as an important structure for metabolism, much like the vertebrate liver.

**BLOOD** Blood is considered to be a connective tissue because the fluid portion is essentially a fluid form of ECM. Blood functions as the principal transport vehicle to carry nutrients, oxygen (in most animals), and hormones to the tissues and to remove metabolic wastes for transport to the organs specialized for waste removal. It is also frequently involved in defence against disease and may be important in wound healing.

Vertebrates have two basic types of cells suspended in a straw-coloured fluid, the plasma (see Figure 38.6f). Erythrocytes (*erythros* = red), or red blood cells, contain hemoglobin, a protein to which $O_2$ binds; erythrocytes are specialized for $O_2$ transport. Several types of leukocytes (*leukos* = white), or white blood cells, protect the body against foreign elements such as viruses and bacteria. These are considered in Chapter 41. Vertebrate blood also contains platelets (often called *thrombocytes*), which are membrane-bound fragments of specialized, stem-cell derived megakaryocytes. They play an essential role in the formation of blood clots to heal wounds.

In invertebrates, oxygen-carrying pigments, such as hemoglobin, may be present either within special cells, as in some annelids, or free in the plasma. Blood cells in insects are also known to take part in wound healing and protection against foreign bodies.

## 38.2c  Muscle Tissue Produces Movement

**Muscle tissue** consists of cells that have the ability to contract (shorten). The contractions, which depend on the interaction of two proteins, actin and myosin, move body limbs and other structures, pump the blood, and produce a squeezing pressure in organs such as the intestine and the uterus. Three types of muscle tissue, skeletal, cardiac, and smooth, produce body movements in vertebrates **(Figure 38.7)**.

**SKELETAL MUSCLE** Skeletal muscle is so called because most muscles of this type are attached by tendons to the skeleton. Skeletal muscle cells are also called **muscle fibres** because each is an elongated cylinder (see Figure 38.7a). These cells contain many nuclei and are packed with actin and myosin molecules arranged in highly ordered, parallel units that give the tissue a banded, or striated, appearance when viewed under a microscope. Muscle fibres packed side by side into parallel bundles surrounded by sheaths of connective tissue form many body muscles.

Skeletal muscle contracts in response to signals carried by the nervous system. The contractions of skeletal muscles, which are characteristically rapid and powerful, move body parts and maintain posture. The contractions also release heat as a by-product of cellular metabolism. This heat helps mammals, birds, and some other vertebrates maintain their body temperatures, particularly through the process of shivering when environmental temperatures fall. (Skeletal muscle is discussed further in Chapter 46.)

**FIGURE 38.7  Structure of skeletal, cardiac, and smooth muscle**

### a. Skeletal muscle

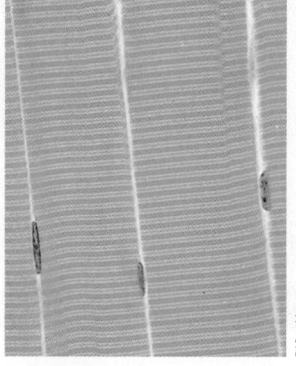

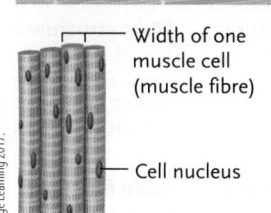

Width of one muscle cell (muscle fibre)

Cell nucleus

**Description:** Bundles of long, cylindrical, striated, contractile cells called *muscle fibres*

**Typical location:** Attached to bones of skeleton

**Function:** Locomotion, movement of body parts

### b. Cardiac muscle

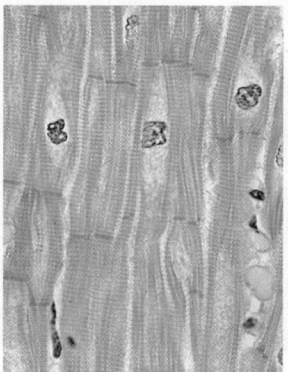

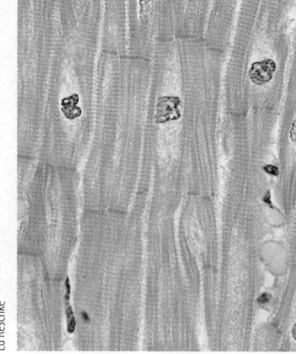

Cell nucleus

Intercalated disk

**Description:** Cylindrical, striated cells that have specialized end junctions

**Location:** Wall of heart

**Function:** Pumping of blood within circulatory system

### c. Smooth muscle

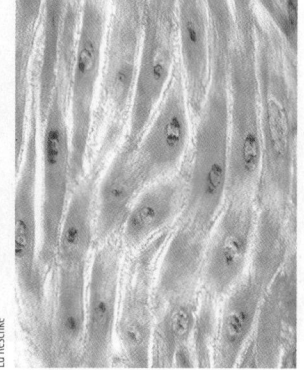

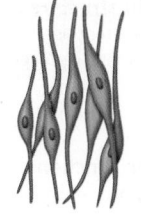

(cells separated for clarity)

**Description:** Contractile cells with tapered ends

**Typical location:** Wall of internal organs, such as stomach

**Function:** Movement of internal organs

**CARDIAC MUSCLE** **Cardiac muscle** is the contractile tissue of the heart (see Figure 38.7b). Cardiac muscle has a striated appearance because it contains actin and myosin molecules arranged like those in skeletal muscle. However, cardiac muscle cells are short and branched, with each cell connecting to several neighbouring cells; the joining point between two such cells is called an *intercalated disk*. Cardiac muscle cells thus form an interlinked network, which is stabilized by anchoring junctions and gap junctions. The gap junctions transmit electrical signals through the movement of ions that make cardiac muscles contract as a unit. Because of the gap junctions, when one cell contracts, all cells in the heart contract, and because each cell is connected tightly to many of its neighbours, heart muscle contracts in all directions. The cells pull on one another to produce a squeezing or pumping action rather than a lengthwise, unidirectional contraction as seen in skeletal muscle.

**SMOOTH MUSCLE** **Smooth muscle** is found in the walls of tubes and cavities in the body, including blood vessels, the stomach and intestine, the bladder, and the uterus. Smooth muscle cells are relatively small and spindle shaped (pointed at both ends), and their actin and myosin molecules are arranged in a loose network rather than in bundles (see Figure 38.7c). This loose network makes the cells appear smooth rather than striated when viewed under a microscope. Smooth muscle cells are connected by gap junctions and enclosed in a mesh of connective tissue. As in cardiac muscle, the gap junctions transmit signals that make smooth muscles contract as a unit, typically producing a squeezing motion. Although smooth muscle contracts more slowly than skeletal and cardiac muscles do, its contractions can be maintained at steady levels for a much longer time. These contractions move and mix the stomach and intestinal contents, constrict blood vessels, and push the infant out of the uterus during childbirth.

**INVERTEBRATE MUSCLE** In general, most invertebrates have striated muscles throughout, even muscles involved with structures such as the heart, intestine, and reproductive ducts. The striated muscle of invertebrates can't be subdivided into skeletal and cardiac, as in vertebrates, although different types of striation patterns do occur. In insects, the striated muscles that control the movements of some of the viscera, such as the ovaries

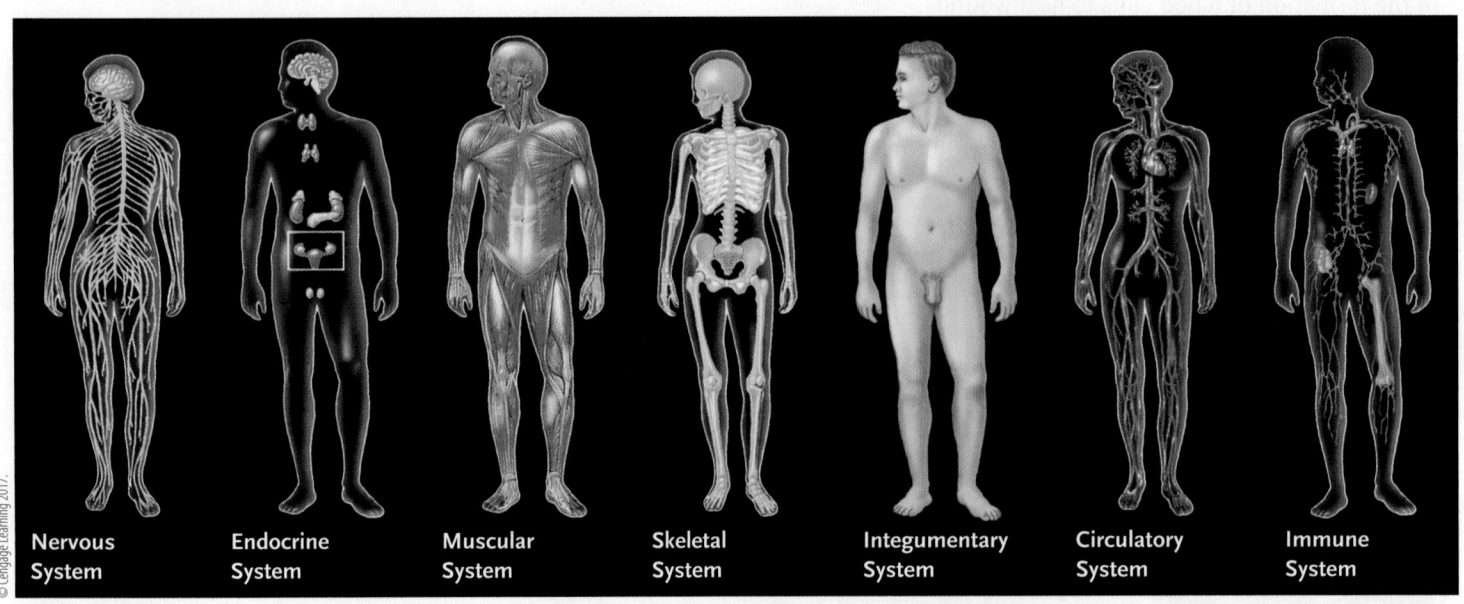

© Cengage Learning 2017.

| **Nervous System** | **Endocrine System** | **Muscular System** | **Skeletal System** | **Integumentary System** | **Circulatory System** | **Immune System** |
|---|---|---|---|---|---|---|
| **Main structures:** Brain, spinal cord, peripheral nerves, sensory organs | **Main structures:** Pituitary, hypothalamus, thyroid, adrenal, pancreas, and other hormone-secreting glands | **Main structures:** Skeletal, cardiac, and smooth muscle | **Main structures:** Bones, tendons, ligaments, cartilage | **Main structures:** Skin, sweat glands, hair, nails | **Main structures:** Heart, blood vessels, blood | **Main structures:** Lymph nodes, lymph ducts, spleen, thymus, bone marrow, and white blood cells |
| **Main functions:** Principal regulatory system; monitors changes in internal and external environments and formulates compensatory responses; coordinates body activities | **Main functions:** Regulates and coordinates body activities through secretion of hormones | **Main functions:** Moves body parts; helps run bodily functions; generates heat; moves intestinal lumen contents | **Main functions:** Supports and protects body parts; provides leverage for body movements; stores minerals | **Main functions:** Covers external body surfaces and protects against injury and infection; helps regulate water content and body temperature | **Main functions:** Distributes water, nutrients, oxygen, hormones, and other substances throughout body and carries away carbon dioxide and other metabolic wastes; helps stabilize internal temperature and pH | **Main functions:** Defends against disease-causing microorganisms and viruses (pathogens)

*(Cellular components of the immune system are not shown in the figure.)* |

and parts of the digestive system, are frequently branched and interconnected to form a lattice. Smooth muscle has been reported in some invertebrates only.

## 38.2d Nervous Tissue Receives, Integrates, and Transmits Information

**Nervous tissue** contains cells called **neurons** (also called *nerve cells*) that serve as lines of communication and control between body parts. Billions of neurons are packed into the human brain; others have extremely long processes that extend throughout the body. Nervous tissue also contains **glial cells** (*glia* = glue), which physically support and provide nutrients to neurons, provide electrical insulation between them, and scavenge cellular debris and foreign matter.

A neuron consists of a cell body, which houses the nucleus and organelles, and two types of cell extensions: dendrites and axons **(Figure 38.8)**. Dendrites receive chemical signals from other neurons or from body cells of other types and convert them into a graded electrical signal that is transmitted to the

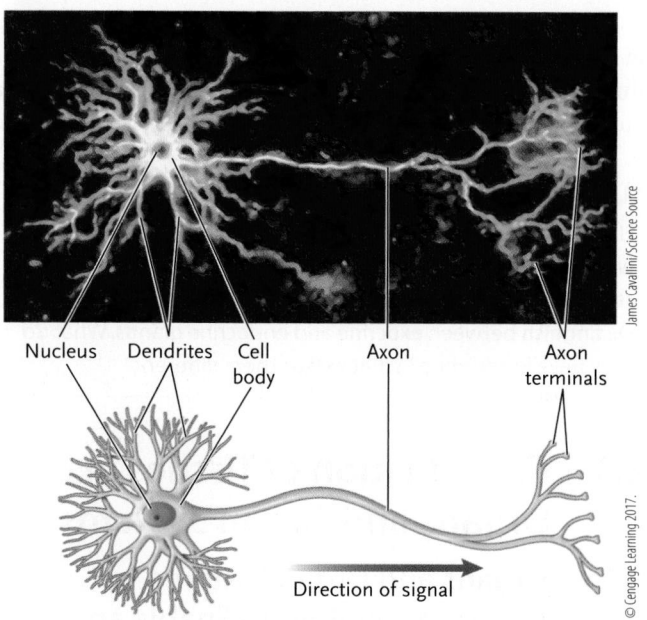

Nucleus   Dendrites   Cell body   Axon   Axon terminals

Direction of signal

James Cavallini/Science Source

© Cengage Learning 2017.

**FIGURE 38.8 Neurons and their structure.** The micrograph shows a motor neuron, which relays signals from the brain or spinal cord to muscles and glands.

cell body of the receiving neuron. Dendrites are usually highly branched. Axons conduct action potentials (large, non-graded electrical signals) away from the cell body to the axon terminals, or endings. At their terminals, most axons convert the electrical signal to a chemical signal that stimulates a response in nearby muscle cells, gland cells, or other neurons (direct electrical connections are discussed further in Chapter 41). Axons are usually unbranched, except at their terminals. Depending on the type of neuron and its location in the body, its axon may extend from a few micrometres or millimetres to more than a metre (the cell body of a neuron innervating the foot of a giraffe is in its spinal cord). (Neurons and their organization in body structures are discussed further in Chapter 45.)

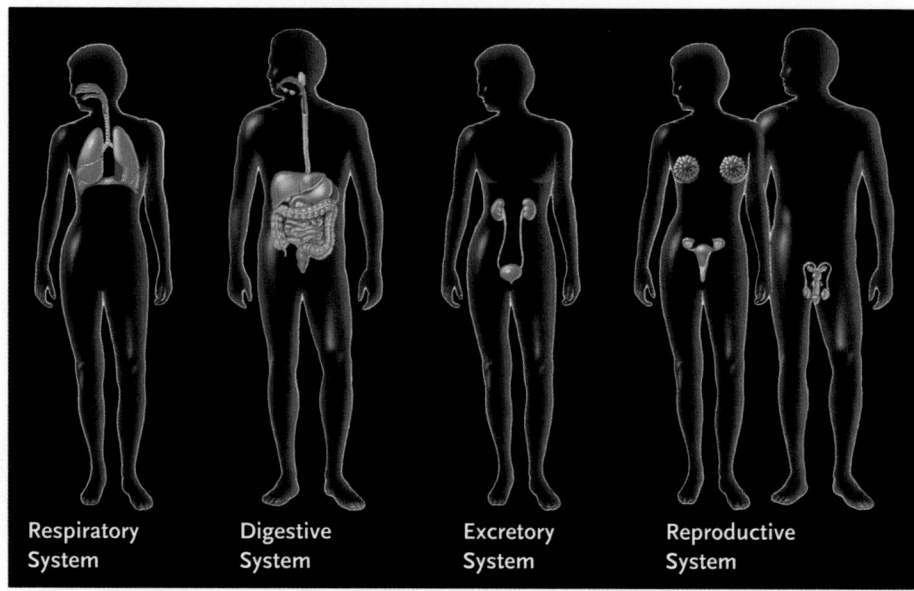

| Respiratory System | Digestive System | Excretory System | Reproductive System |
|---|---|---|---|
| **Main structures:** Lungs, diaphragm, trachea, and other airways | **Main structures:** Oral cavity, pharynx, esophagus, stomach, intestines, liver, pancreas, rectum, anus | **Main structures:** Kidneys, bladder, ureter, urethra | **Main structures:** *Female*: ovaries, oviducts, uterus, vagina, mammary glands<br>*Male*: testes, sperm ducts, accessory glands, penis |
| **Main functions:** Exchanges gases with the environment, including uptake of oxygen and release of carbon dioxide | **Main functions:** Converts ingested matter into molecules and ions that can be absorbed into body; eliminates undigested matter; helps regulate water content | **Main functions:** Removes and eliminates excess water, ions, and metabolic wastes from body; helps regulate internal osmotic balance and pH; helps regulate blood pressure | **Main functions:** Maintains the sexual characteristics and passes on genes to the next generation |

**FIGURE 38.9 Structures and functions of the organ systems of the human body**

All four major tissue types, epithelial, connective, muscle, and nervous, combine to form the organs and organ systems of animals. The next section depicts the major organs and organ systems of vertebrates and outlines their main tasks.

**STUDY BREAK QUESTIONS**

1. How many major tissue types are there in vertebrates, and what are the differences between them in terms of their structure and function?

2. Distinguish between exocrine and endocrine glands. What do they have in common? What makes them different?

## 38.3 Coordination of Tissues in Organs and Organ Systems

### 38.3a Organs and Organ Systems Function Together to Enable an Animal to Survive

In the tissues, organs, and organ systems of an animal, each cell engages in the basic metabolic activities that ensure its own survival and performs one or more functions of the system to which it belongs. All vertebrates have 11 major organ systems (see **Figure 38.9**). Most invertebrates have the same systems but do not have a separate system of lymphatic ducts.

The functions of all these organ systems are coordinated and integrated to collectively accomplish a series of tasks that are vital to all animals, whether a flatworm, a salmon, a moose, or a human. These tasks include

1. acquiring nutrients and other required substances, such as oxygen; coordinating their processing; distributing them throughout the body; and disposing of wastes;
2. synthesizing the protein, carbohydrate, lipid, and nucleic acid molecules required for body structure and function;
3. sensing and responding to changes in the environment, such as temperature, pH, and ion concentrations;
4. protecting the body against injury or attack from other animals and from viruses, bacteria, and other disease-causing agents; and
5. reproducing and, in many instances, nourishing and protecting offspring through their early growth and development.

Together these tasks maintain homeostasis, preserving the internal environment required for survival of the body. Homeostasis is the topic of the next section.

**CONCEPT FIX** While each organ system has a major role to perform for the body (e.g., the circulatory system moves essential materials around the body and removes wastes from tissues, and the integumentary system provides mechanical protection), it is not true that most organ systems serve only one role. Many have minor supporting roles in other functions, and none of these systems works in isolation. ⬡

**STUDY BREAK QUESTIONS**

1. What are the major functions of each of the 11 organ systems? What are the key organs in each?

2. What are the major organ systems in a duck? In a shark? In an insect? In an earthworm?

## 38.4 Homeostasis

To live, cells of all organisms must take in nutrients and $O_2$ from the external environment and eliminate wastes, such as $CO_2$ and nitrogenous wastes, to the external environment. A single-celled organism such as an amoeba is in direct contact with the external environment. Although most cells of a multicellular animal are isolated from direct contact with the external environment, these cells have the same needs for nutrient and $O_2$ input and waste elimination. These needs are met by the specialized tissues of the different organ systems that establish an internal environment in the form of the **extracellular fluid (ECF) (Figure 38.10)**. The ECF has two components:

- **plasma**, the fluid portion of the blood, and
- **interstitial fluid** (*inter* = between; *stitial* = that which stands), the fluid that surrounds the cells.

The ECF connects all cells to the external environment. Thus, no matter where a cell is within the body, it can make the exchanges essential to its life with the interstitial fluid. Particular organ systems enable these exchanges between the external and internal environments. The digestive system processes incoming food and transfers absorbed nutrients into the plasma of the blood. The nutrients reach all parts of the body by the action of the circulatory system, along with $O_2$ that enters the blood by the action of the respiratory system. The nutrients and $O_2$ in the plasma reach the interstitial fluid through the capillaries, and from there they enter the cells as needed. Waste

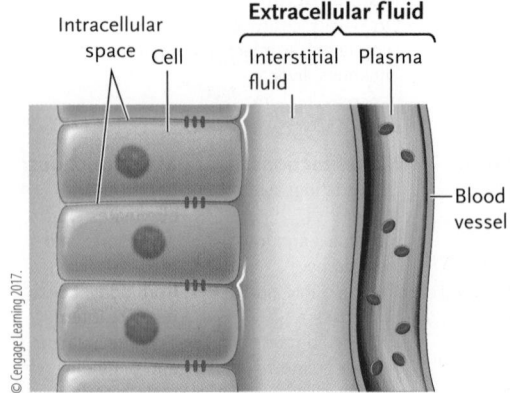

**FIGURE 38.10 Nature of the extracellular fluid (ECF)**

moves in the opposite direction: from the cells into the interstitial fluid and then into the plasma. The respiratory system handles the removal of $CO_2$, and the excretory system handles the metabolic wastes.

For optimal function of these systems, the composition and state of the ECF must be maintained within a narrow range so that cells have available to them the necessary nutrients and $O_2$, and so that $CO_2$ and wastes can be eliminated. Further, other aspects of the internal environment that are important for cellular (and therefore organismal) life, such as temperature, must also be regulated within a tolerable range.

Animals fall into two major categories in this respect: **regulators** maintain factors of the internal environment in a relatively constant state, and **conformers** have internal environments that change with changes in the external environment. Any given animal may regulate some factors and conform to others. For instance, animals such as fishes, reptiles, and insects are thermoconformers. Their body temperatures match that of their external environment. They are also osmoregulators, meaning that they maintain the ionic composition of their ECF relatively constant, regardless of the composition of their external environment. Homeostasis is the process by which animals regulate their internal environment to maintain a relatively stable state. Homeostasis is a dynamic process in which internal adjustments are made continuously to compensate for changes in the internal or external environment.

## 38.4a Many Factors of the Internal Environment Are Homeostatically Regulated

Factors of the internal environment that are regulated homeostatically include the following:

6. Nutrient concentration. Energy production by cells requires a constant supply of nutrient molecules. The energy generated by catabolizing the nutrients is used for basic cellular processes and any specialized activities of the cell.
7. Concentration of $O_2$. Cellular respiration (see Chapter 5), the process that generates energy from catabolic reactions, requires a constant supply of $O_2$ for optimal productivity.
8. Concentration of $CO_2$. The $CO_2$ produced by the catabolic reactions of cellular respiration must be removed as waste, or else the ECF will become increasingly acidic.
9. Concentration of waste chemicals. Particular biochemical reactions in the cell generate products that would be toxic to the cell if not removed as waste.
10. Concentration of water and NaCl. The relative concentrations of water and NaCl in the ECF affect how much water enters or leaves a cell and hence the cell's volume. These concentrations must be regulated to maintain a cell volume that is optimal for function; swollen or shrunken cells are typically functionally impaired.
11. pH. Changes in the pH of the ECF can adversely affect enzymatic activities within cells, as well as the functions of all other functional proteins (ion channels, receptors, etc.).
12. Volume and pressure of the plasma. Both the volume and the pressure in blood vessels must be maintained at adequate levels to distribute the fluid throughout the body. This circulation is vitally important for supplying cells with their needs and for removing wastes.
13. Temperature. Body cells function optimally within a specified temperature range. Outside that range, chemical reactions change their rates and may be completely inhibited. If cells become too cold, the rates of enzymatic reactions decrease too much, and if cells become too hot, structural and enzymatic proteins can be denatured and become inactive.

## 38.4b Homeostasis Is Accomplished by Negative Feedback Control Systems

Homeostatic control systems function primarily by using **negative feedback** to resist change. With negative feedback, a stimulus resulting from a change in the external or internal environment triggers a response that compensates for the environmental change **(Figure 38.11)**. The components of a negative feedback control system are as follows:

- A **stimulus** is an environmental change (external or internal) that triggers a response.
- A **sensor** is a tissue or organ that detects the environmental change (such as external temperature or the internal concentration of a molecule, such as glucose).
- An **integrator** is a control centre that compares the detected environmental change with a **set point**, the level at which the condition controlled by the pathway is to be maintained. In most animals, the integrator is part of the central nervous system or the endocrine system.
- An **effector** is a system that is activated by the integrator, and that returns the condition to the set point if it has strayed away. Effectors may include parts of any body tissue or organ.

**THE THERMOSTAT AS A NEGATIVE FEEDBACK MECHANISM**
The concept of negative feedback may be most familiar in systems designed by human engineers. The thermostat maintaining temperature at a chosen level in a house provides an example. The following are the components of the negative feedback system in a thermostat:

- The stimulus is a change in room temperature of a few degrees (up or down) from the temperature set on the thermostat.
- The sensor is the thermometer within the thermostat that measures the temperature.
- The integrator is the electrical circuit in the thermostat that activates the effectors.
- The effectors return the room temperature to the set point. If the temperature has fallen below the set point, the effector is

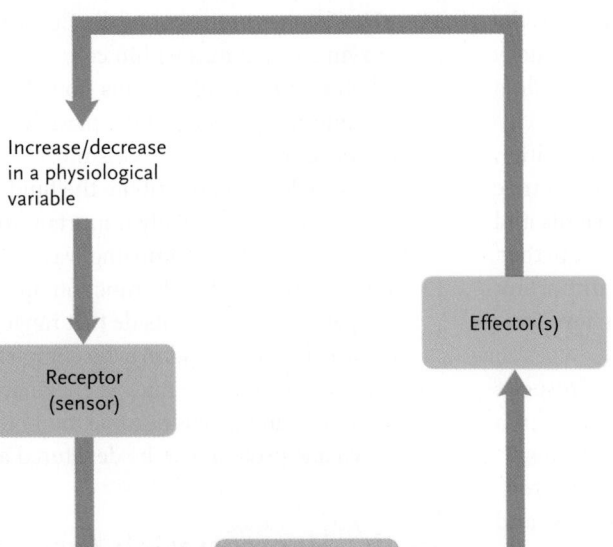

**1** A change in the internal or external environment produces a change in a physiological variable.

**2** The change is detected by specialized cells.

**3** The information is sent along an afferent (sensory) pathway.

Increase/decrease in a physiological variable

Receptor (sensor)

Integrator

**4** Specialized cells receive the sensory information and determine whether action is required.

Effector(s)

**7** Physiological actions of the effector(s) return conditions to desired levels.

**6** A system or systems produce compensatory changes in the physiological variable affected by the environmental change.

**5** The information is sent along an efferent (motor) pathway.

**FIGURE 38.11 Components of a negative feedback mechanism maintaining homeostasis.** The integrator coordinates a response by comparing the level of an environmental condition with a set point that indicates where the level should be.

From Russell/Hertz/McMillan. Biology, 2E. © 2012 Brooks/Cole, a part of Cengage, Inc. Reproduced by permission. www.cengage.com/permissions

the furnace, which adds heat to the house until the temperature rises to the set point. If the temperature has risen above the set point, the furnace is turned off and an air conditioner may be turned on to remove the heat more quickly from the room until the temperature falls to the set point.

**THERMOSTATS AND NEGATIVE FEEDBACK MECHANISMS IN ANIMALS** Mammals and birds also have a homeostatic mechanism that maintains body temperature within a relatively narrow range around a set point. The components of that negative feedback system are as follows:

- The stimulus is a change in body temperature beyond normal levels.
- The sensors are groups of neurons that detect changes in the temperature throughout the body.
- The integrator is the temperature control centre in a region of the brain called the *hypothalamus* that compares the changes in temperature of the brain and the rest of the body with the set point. For most mammals, including humans, the set point has a relatively narrow range centred at about 37°C.
- The effectors are physiological or behavioural responses that function to return the body temperature to desired levels (the set point).

All birds and mammals regulate their body temperature around a relatively narrow set point **(Figure 38.12)**. If the temperature falls below the lower limit, the hypothalamus activates

effectors that constrict the blood vessels in the skin. The reduction in blood flow means that less heat is conducted from the blood through the skin to the environment; in short, heat loss from the skin is reduced. Small muscles may be activated to cause the fur or feathers to stand up, increasing the thickness of the animal's insulation. Other effectors may induce shivering, a physical mechanism to generate body heat. Some animals are capable of nonshivering heat production using specialized fat cells (brown fat). Also, integrating neurons in the brain, stimulated by signals from the hypothalamus, initiate behavioural responses such as moving to a warmer area (see Chapter 42 for details).

Conversely, if the blood temperature rises above the set point, the hypothalamus triggers effectors that dilate the blood vessels in the skin, increasing blood flow to the skin and heat loss from it. Other effectors cause fur and feathers to flatten, reducing the insulation layer. Yet other effectors can induce sweating on bare patches of skin, which cools the skin and the blood flowing through it as the sweat evaporates. And again, through integrating neurons in the brain, animals may consciously sense being overheated, which may be counteracted by moving to a cooler location or taking a dip in a pool of water. **Figure 38.13**, illustrates how a dog responds to activity at high environmental temperatures. Temperature regulation is discussed in more detail in Chapter 42.

**CONCEPT FIX** It is commonly believed that all physiological variables that are homeostatically regulated are always held more or less constant. This is not always the case. For instance,

FIGURE 38.12   **Experimental Research**

## Demonstration of the Use of the Bill for Thermoregulation in Birds

**Question:** The structure of bird bills in large part reflects the diet of the bird. Is it also modified for use as a radiator for dissipating heat?

**Experiment:** Most birds release heat primarily by evaporative water loss through breathing (panting or gular fluttering). Releasing heat through the bill (dry heat) would reduce the amount of water lost in temperature regulation. If bird bills are used as a radiator to expel excess heat, birds from hot arid areas where water is limited should have larger bills than birds from habitats where thermal stress can be avoided.

Costal salt marshes and sand dune habitats are one environment where birds encounter heat along with a shortage of water. Russell Greenberg, from the Smithsonian Migratory Bird Center, and his colleagues from Brock University and the Virginia Polytechnic Institute, compared two subspecies of the song sparrow *Melospiza melodia*. One subspecies, the Atlantic song sparrow (*M. m. atlantica*), breeds in dune scrub and salt marsh edges along the mid-Atlantic coast, whereas the eastern song sparrow (*M. m. melodia*) is widespread in urban areas. They measured the surface temperature (using thermal imaging) of the body and the bill, along with body surface area and bill surface area, and then used physical modelling to estimate the contribution of each part of the body to heat loss. They made their measurements under temperature-controlled conditions while exposing the birds to temperatures between 15°C and 37°C.

**a. Eastern song sparrow**

**b. Atlantic song sparrow**

The eastern song sparrow **(a)** lives in areas where water is more abundant than in the Atlantic song sparrow's **(b)** area.

**Results:** The researchers found that the bills of Atlantic song sparrows had a 17% greater surface area than the eastern song sparrows' bills for similar body size, and that the bills of Atlantic song sparrows dissipated up to 33% more heat and 38% greater proportion of total heat than the bills of eastern song sparrows.

**Conclusion:** The 33% higher heat loss through the bill of the Atlantic song sparrow reduces the amount of heat lost through evaporative cooling by the respiratory system, and was estimated to potentially reduce water loss by roughly 8%. This demonstrates the role of the bill in heat and water balance as well as in feeding, and stresses the multifunctional role of most anatomical structures.

**Question to Ponder:** Would a bird always want to lose heat through its bill? Is heat loss through the bill a process that can be regulated? Can you design an experiment that would resolve these questions?

Source: Greenberg, R., Cadena, V., Danner, R.M. and Tattersall, G. 2012. Heat loss may explain bill size differences between birds occupying different habitats. *PLoSONE* 7(7):e40933.

sometimes the temperature set point changes, and the negative feedback mechanisms then operate to maintain body temperature at the new set point. Thus, when animals become infected by certain viruses and bacteria, the temperature set point increases to a higher level, producing a fever to help overcome the infection. Once the infection is combatted, the set point is readjusted down again to its normal level. Other examples of situations in which the set point of a process changes are the daily or circadian (*circa* = about or approximately; *dies* = day) changes in body temperature seen in many animals, and the

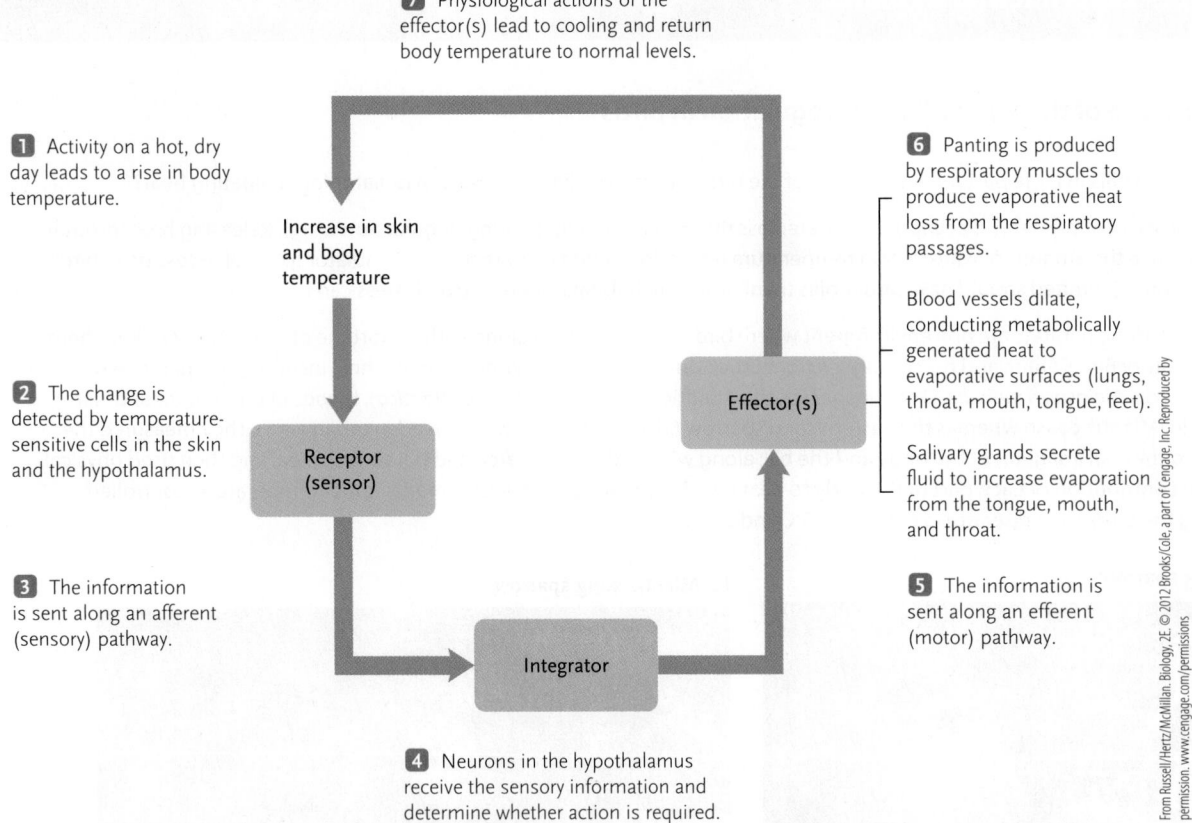

**1** Activity on a hot, dry day leads to a rise in body temperature.

**2** The change is detected by temperature-sensitive cells in the skin and the hypothalamus.

**3** The information is sent along an afferent (sensory) pathway.

**7** Physiological actions of the effector(s) lead to cooling and return body temperature to normal levels.

Increase in skin and body temperature

Receptor (sensor)

Integrator

Effector(s)

**4** Neurons in the hypothalamus receive the sensory information and determine whether action is required.

**6** Panting is produced by respiratory muscles to produce evaporative heat loss from the respiratory passages.

Blood vessels dilate, conducting metabolically generated heat to evaporative surfaces (lungs, throat, mouth, tongue, feet).

Salivary glands secrete fluid to increase evaporation from the tongue, mouth, and throat.

**5** The information is sent along an efferent (motor) pathway.

From Russell/Hertz/McMillan. Biology, 2E. © 2012 Brooks/Cole, a part of Cengage, Inc. Reproduced by permission. www.cengage.com/permissions

**FIGURE 38.13 Homeostatic mechanisms maintaining the body temperature of a husky when environmental temperatures are high**

Ermolaev Alexander/Shutterstock.com

seasonal or circannual changes in reproductive hormones seen in most animals. ⬡

Whereas mammals and birds regulate their internal body temperature within a narrow range around a set point, certain other vertebrates regulate over a broader range. These vertebrates use other negative feedback mechanisms for their temperature regulation. Snakes and lizards, for example, respond behaviourally to compensate for variations in environmental temperatures, using other, less precise negative feedback mechanisms for their temperature regulation. They may absorb heat by basking on sunny rocks in the cool early morning and move to cooler, shaded spots in the heat of the afternoon.

Many insects employ similar mechanisms to raise their body temperature. Some caterpillars group together, increasing their body temperatures by a degree or two and shortening the time of development by as much as three days. Flight requires energy, and the flight muscles operate best at higher temperatures. Some insects bask in the sunshine to warm the muscles. Many, such as dragonflies, bumblebees, butterflies, and moths, contract the flight muscles rapidly in a process similar to shivering in order to warm them. This is particularly important in moths that fly at night, when the environmental temperature is lower. Honeybees form masses in the winter and maintain their temperature by contracting the wing muscles. Once insects are in flight, however, the energy production is so high that they must dissipate the heat produced. In bees, the most important method is evaporative cooling by regurgitation of some of the intestinal contents onto the mouthparts, a process equivalent to panting in vertebrates.

## 38.4c Animals Also Have Positive Feedback Mechanisms That Do Not Result in Homeostasis

Under certain circumstances, animals respond to a change in an internal or external environmental condition by a **positive feedback** mechanism that intensifies or adds to the change. Such mechanisms, with some exceptions, do not result in homeostasis. They operate when the animal is responding to life-threatening conditions (an attack, for instance), or as part of reproductive processes, and produce sudden explosive events.

The birth process in mammals is a prime example. During human childbirth, initial contractions of the uterus push the head of the fetus against the **cervix**, the opening of the uterus into the vagina. The pushing causes the cervix to stretch. Sensors that detect the stretching signal the hypothalamus to release a hormone, oxytocin, from the pituitary gland. Oxytocin increases the uterine contractions, intensifying the squeezing pressure on the fetus and further stretching the cervix. That stretching results in more oxytocin being released and stronger uterine contractions, repeating the positive feedback circuit and increasing the squeezing pressure until the fetus is pushed entirely out of the uterus (see Chapter 44).

Because positive feedback mechanisms such as the one triggering childbirth do not result in homeostasis, most occur less commonly than negative feedback in animals. Others, such as the nerve action potential that will be discussed in Chapter 45, are very regular events.

### STUDY BREAK QUESTIONS

1. Describe how animals are able to maintain homeostasis despite changes in their external or internal environments. What are the elements of a homeostatic control system?

2. What is the difference between a positive and a negative feedback loop? Describe an example of each, listing the major components of each system.

# Summary Illustration

In most animals, individual cells are organized into tissues, which are classified as *epithelial*, *connective*, *muscle*, or *nervous*. Tissues are organized into organs, and organs into organ systems. The different physiological systems operate to homeostatically regulate body functions.

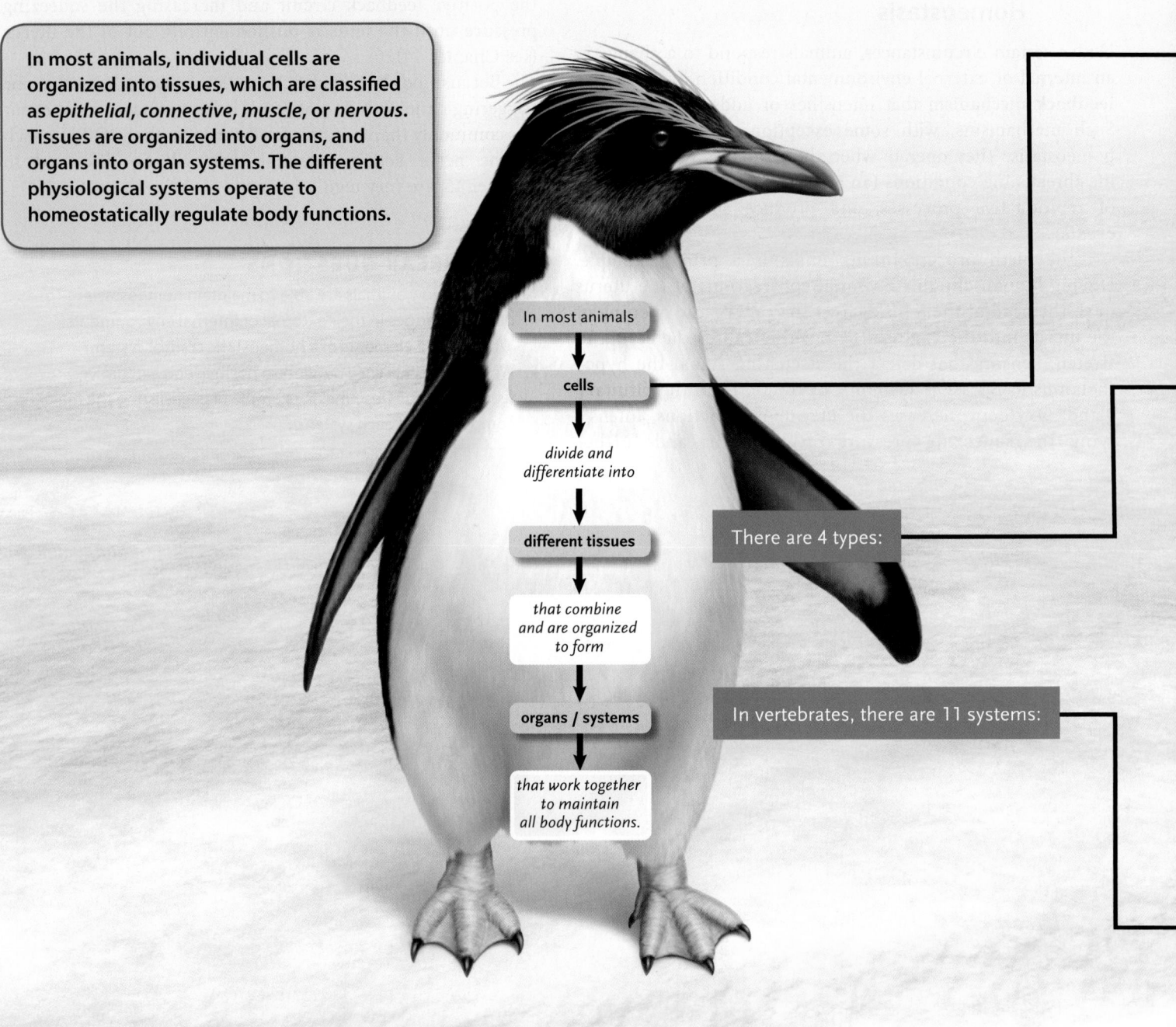

In most animals

↓

cells

↓

*divide and differentiate into*

↓

different tissues → There are 4 types:

↓

*that combine and are organized to form*

↓

organs / systems → In vertebrates, there are 11 systems:

↓

*that work together to maintain all body functions.*

**Homeostasis by negative feedback**

that send information to integrating sites

that activate effectors

are sensed by receptors

to produce changes that return things to normal

**Environmental changes** (internal or external)

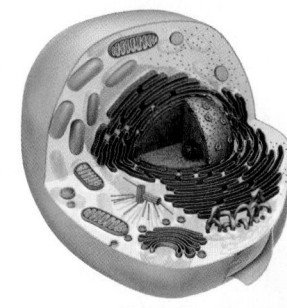

All animal cells contain the same basic organelles.

An animal cell contains a nucleus and cytoplasmic organelles, such as mitochondria, lysosomes, the endoplasmic reticulum, and the Golgi complex. It also has a highly developed cytoskeleton. Most animal cells secrete extracellular material and have structures at their surfaces that play vital roles in the support and organization of animal body structures.

Individual cells divide and differentiate into cells of 4 different tissues.

 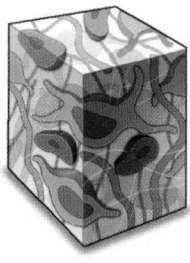  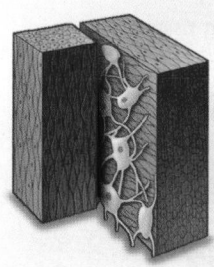

**Epithelial tissue:** Protection, transport, secretion, and absorption of nutrients released by digestion of food

**Connective tissue:** Structural support

**Muscle tissue:** Movement

**Nervous tissue:** Communication, coordination, and control

Different tissues combine and are organized to form up to 11 different organ systems.

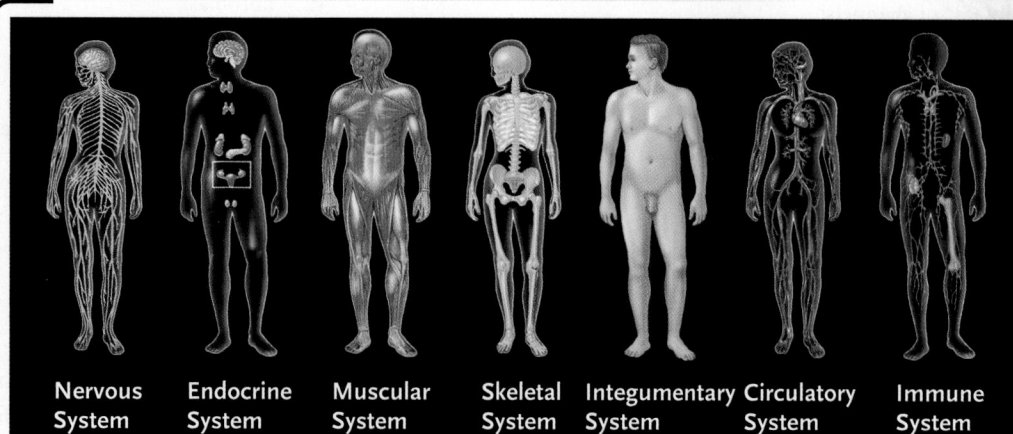

Nervous System | Endocrine System | Muscular System | Skeletal System | Integumentary System | Circulatory System | Immune System

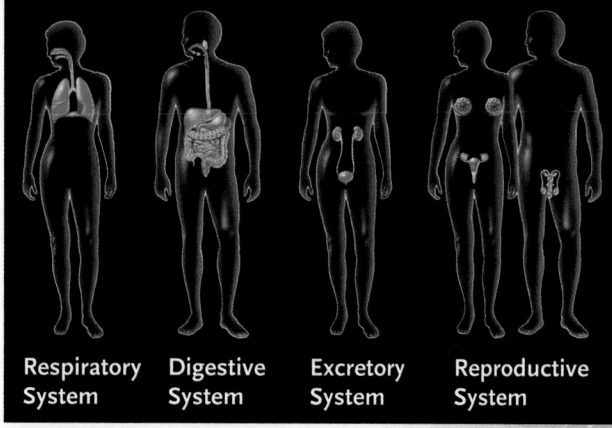

Respiratory System | Digestive System | Excretory System | Reproductive System

Organ systems work together to maintain homeostasis by negative feedback.

# SELF-TEST QUESTIONS

## Recall/Understand

1. Which of these structures has the highest level of organization (i.e., contains the other structures)?
   a. the liver
   b. the epithelium
   c. mitochondria
   d. the cell

2. Which of the following is a muscle, such as the biceps muscle, composed of?
   a. similar tissues
   b. different tissues
   c. different organs
   d. similar organs

3. Which tissue is a constant source of adult stem cells in a mammal?
   a. kidneys
   b. pancreas
   c. heart muscle
   d. bone marrow

4. Where is interstitial fluid found in organisms?
   a. in the cytoplasm
   b. in the cell membrane
   c. in the cell walls
   d. between cells

5. What type of junction allows ions and molecules to flow between cells by way of channels?
   a. tight junction
   b. gap junction
   c. anchoring junction
   d. plasmodesma junction

6. Which of these types of cells can a chemical signal be passed to after leaving a neuron?
   a. a gland cell, but not a muscle cell
   b. a muscle cell, but not a gland cell
   c. another neuron or a gland cell
   d. a gland cell, a neuron, or a muscle cell

7. The basketball players are dripping sweat at halftime. Which of the following is this an example of?
   a. thirst
   b. hunger
   c. homeostasis
   d. heat stroke

## Apply/Analyze

8. Which of these systems coordinates other organ systems?
   a. the skeletal system
   b. the muscular system
   c. the reproductive system
   d. the endocrine system

9. You are observing an unknown epithelium under the microscope, and you notice that it has several layers of flattened cells. Which of these tissue types is this epithelium *most* likely?
   a. cuboidal
   b. simple squamous
   c. stratified squamous
   d. columnar

10. You have injured your tendon. Which of these tissues have you injured?
    a. loose connective tissue
    b. fibrous connective tissue
    c. cartilaginous tissue
    d. adipose tissue

11. The bones of an elderly woman break more easily than those of a younger person. Which cell type would most likely diminish in activity with aging?
    a. osteocyte
    b. osteoblast
    c. osteoclast
    d. fibroblast

## Create/Evaluate

12. A decrease in body temperature causes the pituitary gland to release a hormone that stimulates the release of thyroxine from the thyroid gland. Thyroxine increases metabolism, generating heat. As the body temperature increases, the release of the pituitary hormone decreases, and less thyroxine is released. What is this an example of?
    a. integration
    b. osmolarity
    c. positive feedback
    d. negative feedback

13. Compare skeletal, cardiac, and smooth muscle.

14. Compare negative and positive feedback.

15. Considering characteristics of cartilage, explain why cartilage is found in the larger and smaller air passages in your body.

# Chapter Roadmap

## Animal Nutrition

All organisms require nutrients for reproduction, growth, and maintenance of life processes. Some nutrients are used to make or repair structures, but most are used as sources of energy.

### 39.1 Nutrients Are Essential Components of Any Diet

Some materials required for growth and maintenance are needed in large amounts (**macronutrients**), others are needed only in small amounts (**micronutrients**). Some are essential in the diet; most are not.

### 39.2 Feeding: Obtaining Nutrients

### 39.3 Digestive Processes

The chemical breakdown of food occurs at different sites and in different ways in different groups of animals.

**From Chapter 2**

**From Chapter 4**

### 39.4 Structure and Function of the Mammalian Digestive Tract

The structure and function of the digestive tract is examined in detail in humans.

### 39.5 Regulation of Digestive Processes

Digestion is regulated and coordinated by the nervous and endocrine systems.

**To Chapter 43**

**To Chapter 45**

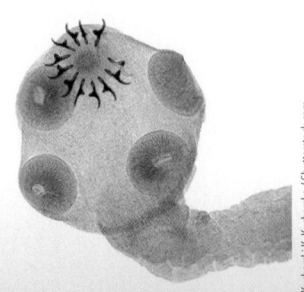

Birdiegal / Shutterstock.com

D. Kucharski K. Kucharska / Shutterstock.com

David Shale/npl/Minden Pictures

**Soil provides nutrients for plants, which provide nutrients for herbivores (such as deer), which provide nutrients for carnivores (such as the grey wolf).** Are the digestive systems and digestive processes different in herbivores and carnivores?

# Animal Nutrition

# 39

**Why it matters . . .** While many animal herbivores obtain nutrients directly from the plants they eat, two different groups of sea slugs have evolved ways of harnessing the ability of plants to convert the Sun's energy into sugars and other nutrients in very different ways. They use plants or plastids from plant cells in "solar panels" to obtain nutrients more directly. Some herbivorous nudibranchs (sacoglossans) have evolved branches of their gut (cerata) that ramify (branch out) throughout the body wall. These cerata greatly extend the surface area of the animals and contain plastids, the photosynthesizing "factories" extracted from the algae on which they feed. The cerata act as solar panels, rotating and exposing the plastids to sunlight for photosynthesis, and in return the plastids provide the sea slugs with valuable nutrients they need. In *Elysia chlorotica,* one of the solar-powered sea slugs found in Canadian waters **(Figure 39.1)**, the plastids are chloroplasts, but some sacoglossans feed on red and brown algae and keep the plastids from these algae alive as well.

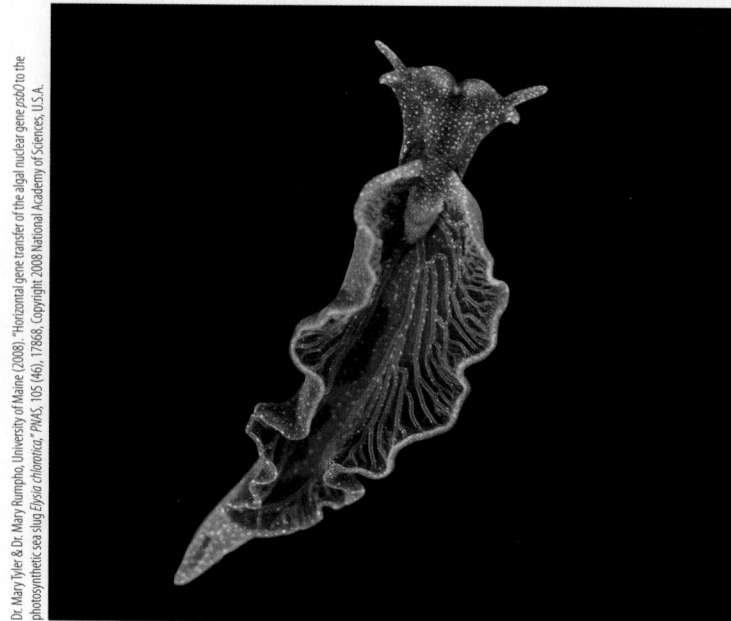

Dr. Mary Tyler & Dr. Mary Rumpho, University of Maine (2008). "Horizontal gene transfer of the algal nuclear gene *psbO* to the photosynthetic sea slug *Elysia chlorotica*," *PNAS*, 105 (46), 17868, Copyright 2008 National Academy of Sciences, U.S.A.

**FIGURE 39.1** *Elysia chlorotica,* **a solar-powered sea slug found in Canadian waters**

Other carnivorous nudibranchs have evolved ways of harvesting entire single-celled plants (zooxanthellae) living symbiotically in the animals that the nudibranchs ate. They then keep the zooxanthellae alive in their bodies as their own symbionts. Clearly, this form of symbiosis has evolved many times within the nudibranchs, with examples in many unrelated families and orders.

The subject of this chapter is animal **nutrition**, a topic that includes what nutrients are and the processes by which nutrients are obtained and absorbed into body cells and fluids. We begin with a discussion of the basic categories of nutrients. We then discuss **ingestion** in animals, the feeding methods used to take food into the digestive cavity, and the process of **digestion**, which is the splitting of carbohydrates, proteins, lipids, and nucleic acids in foods into chemical subunits small enough to be **absorbed** into an animal's body fluids and cells. The chapter also presents the main structural and functional features of digestive systems, with special emphasis on vertebrates. The adaptations animals use to obtain and digest food are among their most strongly defining anatomical and functional characteristics.

# 39.1 Nutrients Are Essential Components of Any Diet

Why do animals eat? What do they need to obtain and why? All organisms require nutrients to grow, maintain essential life functions, and reproduce. Some of these nutrients are used as building blocks to make structures, but most are used as sources of energy that is released and harnessed by carefully breaking chemical bonds (see Chapter 2). In the previous chapter we described how cells are organized to form tissues that, in turn, are organized to form organs and organ systems (Chapter 38). Organic and inorganic molecules are required to build these structures and to maintain them. Energy is also required for growth, development, and survival and this energy also comes from ingested organic material. The organic and inorganic molecules required for these two purposes are referred to as **nutrients**.

Some nutrients required for growth and maintenance are needed in relatively large amounts (**macronutrients**), while others are needed in only small or trace amounts (**micronutrients**). Some of these nutrients are essential in the food of animals but many can be either replaced with or converted from other substances. So what exactly are nutrients? We examine the nutrient requirements of animals in general, and humans in particular, in the next two sections.

## 39.1a Nutritional Requirements of Animals in General

Unlike plants that produce the organic materials they need through photosynthesis, animals must obtain all their nutrients by feeding. Animals can be classified according to what they feed on. **Primary consumers** (herbivores) eat plants, whereas **secondary consumers** (carnivores) eat primarily other animals. "Primarily" is an appropriate modifier because many herbivores sometimes eat animal matter (e.g., insects on the plants), and carnivores often eat plant material (e.g., grizzly bears, although primarily carnivorous, also eat berries). Animals that regularly take food from different trophic levels (see Chapter 30) are **omnivores**.

**FUEL** Animals must acquire enough fuel in their diets to cover their basic costs of operation. Carbohydrates, proteins, and fats are the primary organic fuel molecules used in cellular respiration (see Chapter 5). These molecules are broken down and the energy released when the chemical bonds are broken is stored as ATP. In animal nutrition, food energy is measured in kilocalories (1 kcal = 1000 calories). Carbohydrates can be broken down rapidly and are often the preferred source of energy. Fats are more difficult to process but provide about twice as much energy per gram as carbohydrates and proteins.

Animals store excess energy as glycogen and as fat. Glycogen provides a source of energy between meals; fat is utilized when energy is needed in greater supply. Since fat contains twice as many calories per gram as carbohydrates and proteins, this allows animals to be more compact and mobile than they would otherwise be. Thus, many species of birds that make long migratory flights without stopping to feed, as well as species of mammals that hibernate to survive the winter when food is not available, accumulate large stores of fat beforehand.

Undernourished animals suffer from inadequate intake of organic fuels or abnormal assimilation of these fuels. An undernourished animal can be starving for one or more essential nutrients (**malnutrition**) or can just be eating fewer calories than needed for daily activities (**undernutrition**). Animals with chronic undernutrition lose weight because they use molecules of their own bodies as fuels. Mammals use stored fat and glycogen first. Once those stores have been depleted, proteins are metabolized as fuel. The use of protein as fuel leads to muscle wasting and, eventually, to organ and brain damage, and then death.

**BUILDING BLOCKS** Organic molecules also serve as building blocks for carbohydrates, lipids, proteins, and nucleic acids. Animals can synthesize many of the organic molecules that they do not obtain directly in their diet by converting one type of building block into another. But there are some amino acids and fatty acids that most animals cannot synthesize and must obtain from organic molecules in their food. Lack of these **essential amino acids** and **essential fatty acids** can have serious consequences. Protein synthesis cannot continue unless all 20 amino acids are present.

**VITAMINS AND MINERALS** Animals must also ingest **vitamins**, organic molecules that are required in small quantities. Many animals cannot synthesize these for themselves. Many vitamins are coenzymes, nonprotein organic subunits associated with enzymes that assist in enzymatic catalysis (see Chapter 3). Various species also have different dietary requirements for inorganic minerals such as calcium, iron, and magnesium. Some minerals, such as potassium, are required in large amounts (macrominerals). Trace minerals, such as iodine and zinc, are required in only small amounts. All minerals are ingested by animals as compounds or as ions in solution.

The essential amino acids, essential fatty acids, vitamins, and minerals that an animal cannot synthesize itself but must obtain in its diet are known collectively as **essential nutrients**. The amount of each essential nutrient that a given animal requires is very species specific and explains the unique dietary needs of different animals (eucalyptus leaves for koala bears (*Phascolarctos cinereus*), for instance). As an example, we next explore the requirements in the diets of humans in a little more detail.

## 39.1b Nutritional Requirements of Humans

Adult humans require nine essential amino acids: lysine, histidine, tryptophan, phenylalanine, threonine, valine, methionine, leucine, and isoleucine. (Histidine originally was thought to be an essential amino acid only for infants and young children, but more recent studies have shown that it is also essential for adults.) Proteins in fish, meat, egg whites, milk, and cheese supply all the essential amino acids as long as they are eaten in adequate quantities. In contrast, the proteins of many plants are deficient in one or more of the amino acids essential to humans. Corn contains inadequate amounts of lysine, and beans contain little methionine. Vegetarians, especially vegans, whose diet includes no animal-derived nutrients, must choose their foods carefully to obtain all the essential amino acids.

Protein deficiency occurs when essential amino acids are not part of the diet. Consequently, many enzymes and other proteins cannot be synthesized in sufficient quantities. Protein deficiency is most damaging to the young because of their need for proteins for normal development and growth. Even mild protein starvation during pregnancy or for some months after birth can retard a child's growth and have negative effects on mental and physical development.

Two fatty acids, linoleic acid and linolenic acid, are essential because they are used in the synthesis of phospholipids that form parts of biological membranes and certain hormones. Because almost all foods contain these fatty acids, most people have no problem obtaining them. However, people on a low-fat diet deficient in linoleic acid and linolenic acid are at serious risk for developing coronary heart disease. Thus, ironically, Hindu vegetarians from India that eat mainly low-fat grains and legumes have a higher rate of coronary heart disease than rates in the United States and Europe, where dietary fat content is higher.

Humans require 13 known vitamins in their diet (**Table 39.1**). Many metabolic reactions depend on vitamins, and the absence of one vitamin can affect the functions of the others. Vitamins fall into two classes: **water-soluble vitamins** (which are hydrophilic) and **fat-soluble vitamins** (which are hydrophobic). The body stores excess fat-soluble vitamins in adipose tissues (fat), but any amount of water-soluble vitamins above daily nutritional requirements is passed in urine. Thus, meeting the daily minimum requirements of water-soluble vitamins is critical. The body can tap its stores of fat-soluble vitamins to meet daily requirements; however, these stores can be quickly depleted, and prolonged deficiencies of the fat-soluble vitamins may also become critical to health.

Humans can synthesize vitamin D (calciferol) through the action of ultraviolet light on lipids in the skin. People who are not exposed to enough sunlight to make sufficient quantities of the vitamin must rely on dietary sources. Although we cannot make vitamin K, much of what we require is supplied through the metabolic activity of bacteria living in our large intestine. Vitamin K deficiency is rare in healthy people. Vitamin K plays a role in blood clotting, so individuals with vitamin K deficiency will bruise easily and show increased blood-clotting times. Vitamin K deficiency can be caused in people on long-term antibiotic therapy because the antibiotics kill intestinal bacteria.

Other mammals have basically the same vitamin requirements as humans, with some differences. Most mammals can synthesize vitamin C; primates, guinea pigs, and fruit bats

| Vitamin | Common Sources | Main Functions | Selected Effects of Chronic Deficiency |
|---|---|---|---|
| **Fat-Soluble Vitamins** | | | |
| A (retinol) | Liver, fish oils, milk, eggs. (Beta-carotene, which is converted to vitamin A in the body, is in many plant foods such as sweet potato, spinach, and carrots.) | Component of visual pigments, bone metabolism, epithelial tissue maintenance | Night blindness, total blindness, skin disorders, decreased immunity |
| D | Fish liver oil, egg yolk, fortified milk; produced in skin exposed to sunshine | Calcium and phosphorus absorption from gut | Bone deformities (rickets) in children; bone softening in adults |
| E (tocopherol) | Nuts, seeds, vegetable oils | Antioxidant; maintenance of cell membranes | Neuromuscular problems |
| K | Intestinal bacteria, green vegetables | Promotes synthesis of blood-clotting protein by liver | Abnormal blood clotting, bleeding |
| **Water-Soluble Vitamins** | | | |
| $B_1$ (thiamine) | Yeast, cereal grains, beans, nuts, meat | Connective tissue formation; needed for folate utilization; coenzyme forming part of enzyme in oxidative reactions | Beriberi (a nervous system disorder that includes impaired sensory perception, limb weakness and pain, weight loss, cardiovascular malfunction) |
| $B_2$ (riboflavin) | Whole grains, poultry, fish, egg white, milk, lean meat | Coenzyme | Skin lesions |
| $B_6$ (pyridoxine) | Spinach, whole grains, tomatoes, potatoes, meat | Coenzyme in amino acid and fatty acid metabolism | Skin, muscle, and nerve damage |
| $B_{12}$ (cobalamin) | Eggs, meats, dairy products | Coenzyme in nucleic acid metabolism; red blood cell formation | Anemia; brain and nervous system damage |
| Biotin | Legumes, egg yolk; some synthesized by colon bacteria | Coenzyme in fat and glycogen formation and amino acid metabolism | Scaly skin (dermatitis), sore tongue, brittle hair, depression, weakness |
| C (ascorbic acid) | Fruits and vegetables, especially citrus, berries, cantaloupe, cabbage, broccoli, green pepper | Vital for collagen synthesis; antioxidant | Scurvy (weakness, anemia, gum disease, and skin problems), delayed wound healing, impaired immunity |
| Folic acid | Leafy vegetables, legumes, whole grains, yeast, liver, egg yolks | Coenzyme in nucleic acid and amino acid metabolism | Anemia diarrhea, impaired growth, birth defects |
| Niacin | Fruits and vegetables, nuts, grains, meats | Coenzyme of oxidative phosphorylation | Pellagra (diarrhea, dermatitis, dementia) |
| Pantothenic acid | In many foods (meat, yeast, egg yolk especially) | Coenzyme in carbohydrate and fat oxidation; fatty acid and steroid synthesis | Fatigue, tingling in hands, headaches, nausea |

cannot. To date, no mammals are known to synthesize B vitamins, but ruminants such as cattle and deer are supplied with these vitamins by microorganisms living in the digestive tract.

Several minerals are essential in the human diet **(Table 39.2)**. Potassium is a macromineral required in amounts ranging from 50 mg to more than 1 g per day; iodine and zinc are trace minerals required in only small amounts, less than 1 mg per day. Mineral and vitamin deficiencies have also been well characterized; chronic deficiencies lead to a host of debilitating conditions (Table 39.2; **Figure 39.2**).

A normal and varied diet supplies adequate amounts of essential nutrients. Supplements may be required for those on a strict vegetarian diet, the very young who are growing quickly and need to synthesize new compounds at a faster rate, the elderly, or those who have medical conditions or take medication that affects the body's uptake of nutrients. Vitamin or mineral deficiencies have adverse effects (see Tables 39.1 and 39.2).

| TABLE 39.2 | Minerals: Sources, Functions, and Effects of Deficiencies in Humans[a] | | |
|---|---|---|---|
| Mineral | Common Sources | Main Functions | Selected Effects of Deficiency |
| **Macrominerals** | | | |
| Calcium (Ca) | Leafy green vegetables, legumes, whole grains, nuts, dairy products, eggs | Bone and tooth formation; blood clotting; neural and muscle action | Stunted growth, loss of bone mass |
| Chlorine (Cl) | Table salt, vegetables, meat, dairy products, eggs | HCl formation in stomach; contributes to body's acid–base balance; necessary for neural function and water balance | Muscle cramps, impaired growth, poor appetite |
| Magnesium (Mg) | Green leafy vegetables, legumes, nuts, dairy products, meat | Required for many enzymes; in bones and teeth; ATP processing | Weak, sore muscles; nervous system problems |
| Phosphorus (P) | Whole grains, legumes, nuts, dairy products, eggs, meats | In bones and teeth; component of nucleic acids, ATP, and phospholipids; energy processing | Muscular weakness; loss of minerals from bone |
| Potassium (K) | Many vegetables and fruits, whole grains, dairy products | Muscle and neural function; water balance; acid–base balance; main positive ion in cell | Muscular weakness, cardiac abnormalities or failure |
| Sodium (Na) | Table salt, dairy products, eggs, meat | Acid–base balance; water balance; muscle and neural function; main positive ion in extracellular fluid | Muscle cramps |
| Sulfur (S) | Proteins from food sources, including legumes, nuts, dairy products, eggs, and meat | Component of body proteins | Same as protein deficiencies |
| **Trace Minerals[b]** | | | |
| Iodine (I) | Seafood, iodized salt | Thyroid hormone formation | Goiter (enlarged thyroid), with metabolic disorders |
| Iron (Fe) | Green leafy vegetables, legumes, whole grains, nuts, eggs, meats (particularly liver) | Component of hemoglobin, myoglobin, and electron carriers | Iron-deficiency anemia; weakness |
| Zinc (Zn) | Some vegetables, whole grains, legumes, nuts, fish, meats, many other foods | Component of many enzymes and some transcription factors; protein synthesis; DNA synthesis; cell division; immunity; wound healing | Impaired growth, loss of appetite, impaired immune function |

© Cengage Learning 2017.

[a] All the minerals in this table have harmful effects when excess amounts are consumed.

[b] Other trace minerals not listed in the table are chromium (Cr), cobalt (Co), copper (Cu), fluorine (F), manganese (Mn), molybdenum (Mo), and selenium (Se).

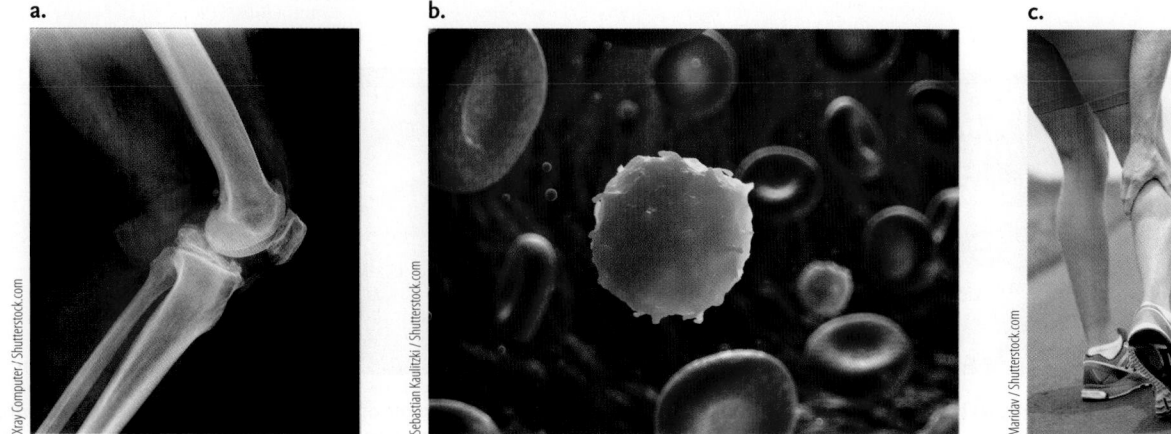

**a.**
Xray Computer / Shutterstock.com

**b.**
Sebastian Kaulitzki / Shutterstock.com

**c.**
Maridav / Shutterstock.com

**FIGURE 39.2 Results of mineral deficiencies. (a)** Calcium deficiency leads to osteoporosis. **(b)** Iron deficiency leads to anemia (low blood hemoglobin). **(c)** Potassium deficiency leads to muscular weakness and cramping.

For instance, ingesting excess sodium can lead to elevated blood pressure and excess water retention in tissues (see Chapter 42).

**CONCEPT FIX** It is a commonly held myth that eating fat makes you fat. The truth is that consuming more calories of anything (fat, carbohydrate, or protein) than you burn will lead to weight gain. It is also true that fat is a more concentrated form of calories than other substrates. Thus, gram for gram, you obtain more calories from fat than from other substrates. For humans, 20%–30% of daily caloric intake should come from fats. Remember that we do need the essential fatty acids. The opposite is also true: gram for gram, animals can store more energy in fat than in any other way. This is why, no matter how we obtain them, our excess calories will end up being deposited as fat. ⬡

### STUDY BREAK QUESTIONS

1. Why do animals eat? What must they obtain in their diets and why?
2. What do carnivores, herbivores, and omnivores eat?
3. What are essential nutrients, and are they the same for all animals?
4. What do vitamins do for animals? Why are they necessary in animals' diets?

## 39.2 Feeding: Obtaining Nutrients

### 39.2a Animals Eat to Acquire Nutrients

There are four basic feeding methods in animals, reflecting the physical states of the organic molecules they eat: fluid feeding, suspension feeding, deposit feeding, and bulk feeding (**Figure 39.3**).

**Fluid feeders** ingest liquids containing organic molecules in solution. Among invertebrates, aphids, mosquitoes, leeches, butterflies, and spiders are fluid feeders. Among vertebrates, lamprey eels, hummingbirds, nectar-feeding bats, and vampire bats are examples of fluid feeders (see Figure 39.3a). Many fluid feeders have mouthparts specialized for reaching the source of their nourishment. Mosquitoes, bedbugs, and aphids have needle-like mouthparts that pierce body surfaces. Nectar-feeding butterflies, birds, and bats have long tongues that can extend deep within flowers. Some fluid feeders use enzymes or other chemicals to liquefy their food or to keep it liquid during feeding. Spiders inject digestive enzymes that liquefy tissues inside their victim, providing a nutrient soup that they can ingest. The saliva of mosquitoes, leeches, and vampire bats includes chemicals that keep blood from clotting.

**a. Fluid feeder**

**b. Suspension feeder**

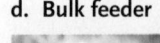
Baleen

**c. Deposit feeder**

**d. Bulk feeder**

**FIGURE 39.3 General feeding methods in animals. (a)** Hummingbirds, which eat nectar, are an example of a fluid feeder. **(b)** The northern right whale (*Balaena glacialis*), which gulps tonnes of water and filters out plankton, is an example of a suspension feeder. **(c)** The fiddler crab (*Uca* species), which sifts edible material from detritus, is an example of a deposit feeder. **(d)** This python, which can open its mouth very wide and take in large objects, such as a gazelle, is an example of a bulk feeder.

**Suspension feeders** ingest small organisms suspended in water, such as bacteria, protozoa, algae, and small crustaceans, or fragments of these organisms. Suspension feeders include aquatic invertebrates, such as clams, mussels, and barnacles, and vertebrates, such as many species of fishes, as well as some birds, pterosaurs, and whales (see Figure 39.3b). Suspension feeders strain (filter) food particles suspended in water through a body structure covered with sticky mucus, or through a filtering network of bristles, hairs, or other body parts. Trapped particles are funnelled into the animal's mouth, and the water is pushed out. Bits of organic matter are trapped by the gills of bivalves such as clams and oysters, and plankton is filtered from water by the sievelike fringes of horny fibre, called *baleen*, hanging in the mouths of baleen whales (see Figure 39.3b).

**Deposit feeders** pick up or scrape particles of organic matter from solid material that they live in or on. Earthworms are deposit feeders that eat their way through soil, taking the soil into their mouth and digesting and absorbing any organic material it contains. Some burrowing molluscs and tube-dwelling polychaete worms use body appendages to gather organic deposits from the sand or mud around them. Mucus on the appendages traps the organic material, and cilia move it to the mouth. The fiddler crab (*Uca* species) is a deposit feeder (see Figure 39.3c) with front claws differing dramatically in size. The small claw picks up sediment and moves it to the mouth,

where the contents are sifted (the large claw is used in signalling; see Section 32.7). The edible parts of the sediment are ingested, and the rest is put back on the sediment as a small ball. The feeding-related movement of the small claw over the larger claw looks as if the crab is playing the large claw like a fiddle, giving the crab its name.

**Bulk feeders** consume sizeable food items whole or in large chunks. Most mammals eat this way, as do reptiles, most birds and fishes, and adult amphibians. Depending on the animal, adaptations for bulk feeding include teeth for tearing or chewing, as well as claws and beaks for holding large food items. Some bulk feeders have flexible jaws, allowing them to ingest objects that are larger in diameter than their head (see Figure 39.3d).

While the four feeding methods just described apply in general to all animals, there are many intriguing variations on each theme. For instance, there are many forms of parasitic animals that obtain their nutrients across a permeable body wall by simply living in a host at a site where nutrients are readily available. Different species are adapted to living in the gastrointestinal tract, the blood, or the body tissues of their hosts **(Figure 39.4a)**.

In *Why It Matters* at the start of the chapter, we learned about *Elysia chlorotica*, the herbivorous sea slug (nudibranch) found in Canadian waters that has evolved branches of its gut (cerata) that extend out into their body wall, where they store

**a.**

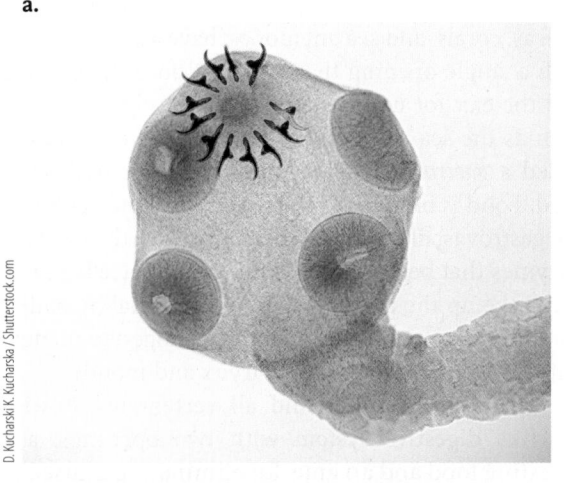

**c.**

**b.**

**d.**

**FIGURE 39.4 Alternate forms of feeding in animals: (a)** tapeworm (*Taenia solium*), **(b)** anglerfish (*Lophiiformes* sp.), **(c)** matamata (*Chelus fimbriata*), and **(d)** humpback whale (*Megaptera novaeangliae*)

plastids extracted from the algae they eat (Figure 39.1). It keeps the plastids alive and uses the cerata as solar panels, exposing them to sunlight and harvesting the products of photosynthesis directly (see *Why It Matters* for examples of other sea slugs that do similar things).

Anglerfish that live in the depths of the ocean where light does not penetrate have evolved a "lure" from a spine of the dorsal fin (Figure 39.4b). This lure dangles above their mouth. A symbiotic bacteria that lives within the lure is bioluminescent and causes it to glow. This attracts other fish that approach the lure and are engulfed as the anglerfish rapidly expands its buccal (mouth) cavity, sucking in the prey. Many other species use disguise to blend in with their surroundings and suck in prey that venture too close. Moray eels and the Amazonian freshwater turtle, the matamata (Figure 39.4c), use this strategy.

The opposite of suction feeding is lunge feeding, in which animals accelerate to high speeds and lunge toward their prey, engulfing them whole. Lunge feeding is seen in pelicans and humpback and blue whales. These whales accelerate to high speeds and lunge toward schools of fish, approaching from below and opening their mouths wide to engulf large numbers in a single lunge (Figure 39.4d).

**STUDY BREAK QUESTIONS**

1. Describe the four basic feeding types in animals. Give examples of species that use each.
2. Can a single species employ more than one feeding type?
3. How would you categorize yourself in terms of feeding type?

# 39.3 Digestive Processes

Digestive processes break food into its component parts, eventually breaking molecules into molecular subunits that can be absorbed into body fluids and transported to and moved into cells. Mechanical breakdown often involves grinding, sometimes with teeth and sometimes in a muscular **gizzard**. Chemical breakdown occurs by **enzymatic hydrolysis**, in which chemical bonds are broken by the addition of $H^+$ and $OH^-$, the components of water (see *The Purple Pages*). Specific enzymes speed these reactions: amylases catalyze the hydrolysis of starches, lipases break down fats and other lipids, proteases hydrolyze proteins, and nucleases digest nucleic acids. Enzymatic hydrolysis of food molecules may take place inside or outside the body cells, depending on the animal.

## 39.3a Intracellular Digestion

In intracellular digestion cells take in food particles by endocytosis (see Section 4.6). Inside the cell, endocytic vesicles containing food particles fuse with a lysosome, a vesicle containing hydrolytic enzymes. The molecular subunits produced by the hydrolysis pass from the vesicle to the cytosol. Any undigested material remaining in the vesicle is released to the outside of the

cell by exocytosis. Only a few animals (sponges and some cnidarians) break down food exclusively be intracellular digestion. In sponges, water-containing particles of organic matter and microorganisms enter the body through pores in the body wall **(Figure 39.5a)**. In the body cavity, individual choanocytes (collar cells) lining the body wall trap food particles, take them in by endocytosis, and transport them to amoeboid cells, where intracellular digestion takes place.

## 39.3b Extracellular Digestion

Extracellular digestion takes place in a pouch or tube enclosed within the body but outside the body cells, the digestive tract. Epithelial cells lining the pouch or tube secrete enzymes that digest the food. Processing food in this specialized compartment prevents self-digestion of the body tissues of the animal itself. Extracellular digestion, which occurs in most invertebrates and all vertebrates, greatly expands the range of available food sources by allowing animals to deal with much larger food items than those that can be engulfed by single cells. Extracellular digestion also allows animals to eat large batches of food that can be stored and digested while the animal continues other activities.

## 39.3c Gastrointestinal Cavities and Tracts

Some animals, including flatworms and cnidarians such as hydras, corals, and sea anemones, have a saclike digestive system with a single opening that serves as both the entrance for food and the exit for undigested material. In some of these animals, such as the sea anemone (Figure 39.5b), the digestive cavity is called a *gastrovascular cavity* because it circulates and digests food. Food is brought to the mouth by tentacles and then enters the gastrovascular cavity, where glands in the cavity wall secrete enzymes that begin the digestive process. Cells lining the cavity then take up the partially digested material by endocytosis and complete digestion intracellularly. Undigested matter is released to the outside through the pharynx and mouth.

Most invertebrates and all vertebrates, however, have a tubelike digestive system with two openings: a mouth for ingesting food and an anus for eliminating unused material. In these animals, contents move in one direction along the tube. The lumen of a digestive tube (also known as a *gut, alimentary canal, digestive tract*, or *gastrointestinal tract*) is external to all body tissues.

In most animals with a digestive tube, digestion occurs in five successive steps, each taking place in a specialized region of the tube. The tube is a biological disassembly line, with food entering at one end and leftovers leaving from the other. Five main processes occur, from the ingestion of food to the expulsion of wastes:

1. Mechanical processing. Chewing, grinding, and tearing food chunks into smaller pieces makes them easier to move through the tract and increases the surface area exposed to digestive enzymes.

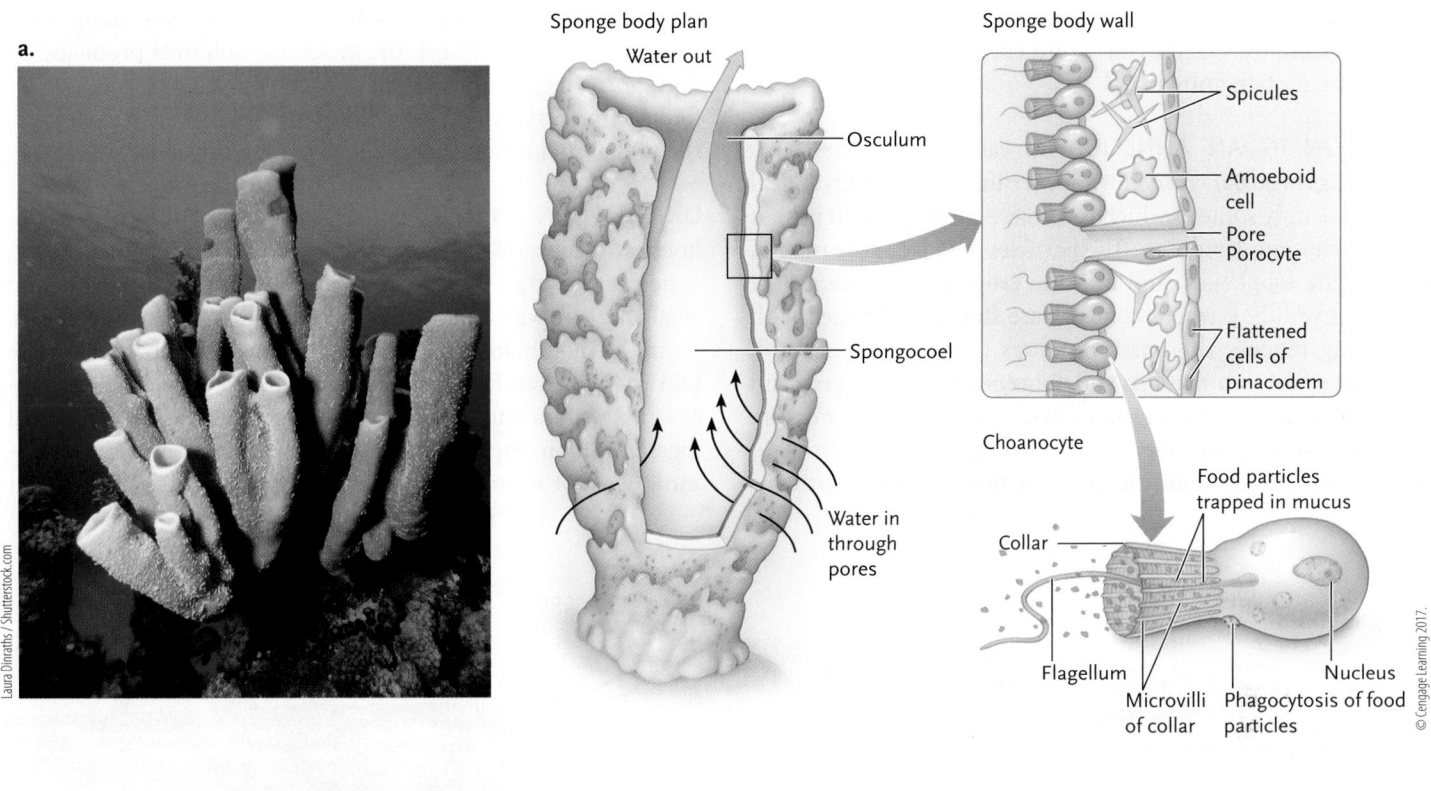

a.

Sponge body plan

Water out

Osculum

Spongocoel

Water in through pores

Sponge body wall

Spicules

Amoeboid cell

Pore
Porocyte

Flattened cells of pinacodem

Choanocyte

Collar

Flagellum

Microvilli of collar

Food particles trapped in mucus

Phagocytosis of food particles

Nucleus

© Cengage Learning 2017.

Laura Dinraths / Shutterstock.com

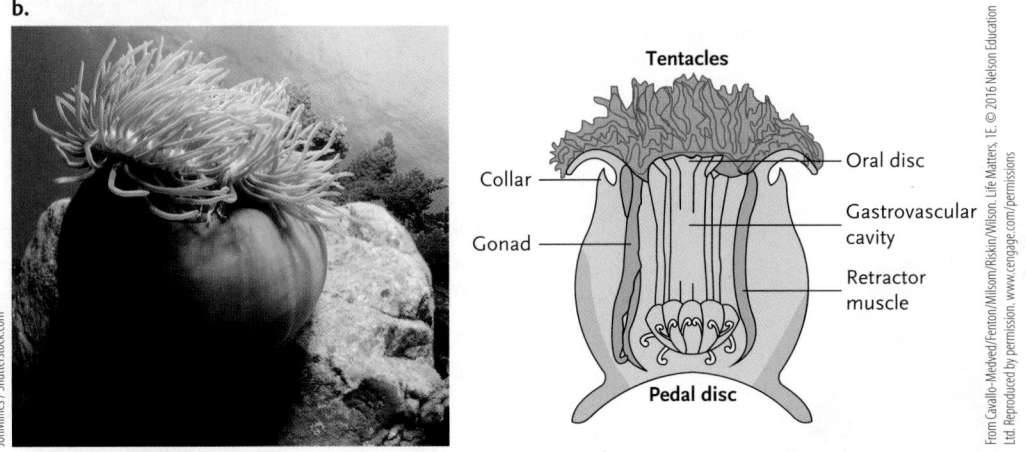

b.

JonMilnes / Shutterstock.com

Tentacles

Collar

Gonad

Oral disc

Gastrovascular cavity

Retractor muscle

Pedal disc

From Cavallo-Medved/Fenton/Milsom/Riskin/Wilson. Life Matters, 1E. © 2016 Nelson Education Ltd. Reproduced by permission. www.cengage.com/permissions

**FIGURE 39.5** **(a)** Digestion in the sponge is intracellular. **(b)** Digestion in the sea anemone is extracellular.

2.  Secretion of enzymes and other digestive aids. Enzymes and other substances that aid the process of digestion, such as acids, emulsifiers, and lubricating mucus, are released into the tube.

3.  Enzymatic hydrolysis. Food molecules are broken down through enzyme-catalyzed reactions into absorbable molecular subunits.

4.  Absorption. The molecular subunits are absorbed from the digestive contents into body fluids and cells.

5.  Elimination. Undigested materials are expelled through the anus.

Material being digested is pushed through the digestive tube by **peristalsis**, muscular contractions of its walls. During its progress through the tube, the digestive contents may be stored temporarily at one or more locations. Storage allows animals to take in larger quantities of food than they can process immediately, so feedings can be spaced over time rather than continuous.

CONCEPT FIX We tend to think that, once we have swallowed food, it is inside our body. And while there is no doubt that it is now within our body, it has yet to enter into the "internal milieu." Gastrointestinal tracts are epithelial lined and lead from an opening at one end of the animal to an exit at the other end. As such, substances passing through the tube have passed through the body without ever entering it. This is why glands entering into the gastrointestinal tract are considered exocrine glands. Only through digestion and ultimately absorption do materials leave the external environment and enter the internal environment of an animal. ⬡

**DIGESTION IN AN ANNELID** The earthworm (*Lumbricus* species; **Figure 39.6a**) is a deposit feeder that ingests a great deal of material, only some of which is edible. As it burrows, it pushes soil particles into its mouth. The particles pass from the mouth, through the esophagus, and into the **crop** (an enlargement of the digestive tube), where contents are stored and mixed with lubricating mucus. This mixture enters the muscular gizzard, where muscular contractions and abrasion by sand grains grind the food mixture into fine particles. The pulverized mixture then enters a long intestine, where organic matter is hydrolyzed by enzymes secreted into the digestive tube. As muscular con-

tractions of the intestinal wall move the mixture along, cells lining the intestine absorb the molecular subunits produced by digestion. The absorptive surface of the intestine is increased by folds of the wall, called *typhlosoles*. At the end of the intestine, the undigested residue is expelled through the anus.

**DIGESTION IN AN INSECT** Herbivorous insects such as grass-hoppers (Figure 39.6b) are more selective in what they ingest. When eating, grasshoppers tear leaves and other plant parts into small particles with their mandibles, the hard external mouthparts. From the mouth, food particles pass through the pharynx, where salivary secretions moisten the mixture before it enters the esophagus and passes into the crop and begins the process of chemical digestion. From the crop, the food mass enters the muscular giz-zard, where it is ground into smaller pieces. Food particles then

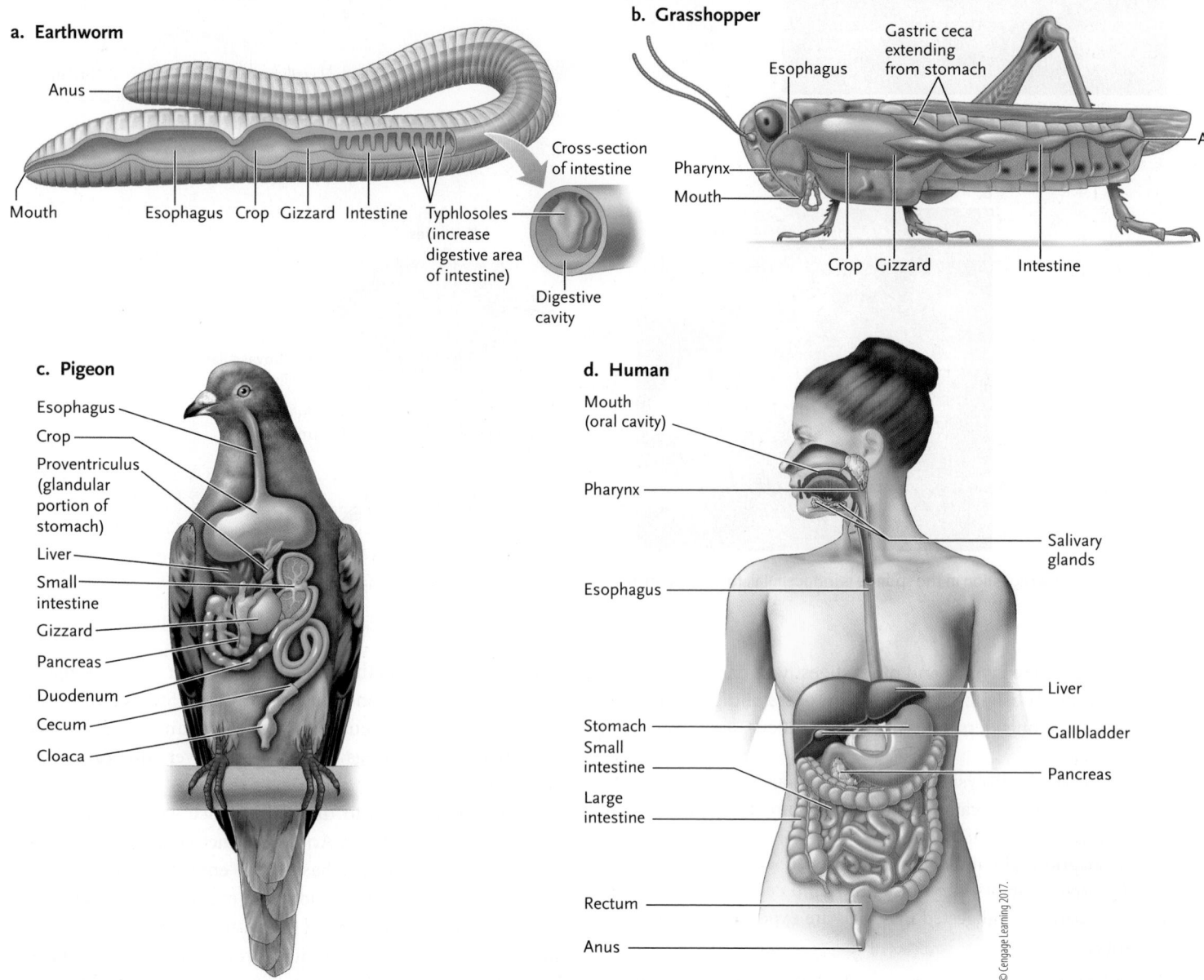

**FIGURE 39.6  The digestive systems of** (a) **an annelid (earthworm),** (b) **an insect (grasshopper),** (c) **a bird (pigeon), and** (d) **a mammal (human)**

enter the stomach, where food is stored and digestion continues. In gastric ceca (saclike outgrowths of the stomach; *cecum* = blind), enzymes hydrolyze food, and the products of digestion are absorbed through the walls of the ceca. Undigested food moves into the intestine for further digestion and absorption. At the end of the intestine, water is absorbed from undigested matter and the remnants (frass) are expelled through the anus. The digestive systems of other arthropods are similar to the insect system.

**DIGESTION IN A BIRD** A pigeon (Figure 39.6c) is also selective in what it ingests. A pigeon picks up seeds with its bill and uses its tongue to move them into its mouth, where they are moistened by mucus-filled saliva and swallowed whole. Seeds pass through the pharynx and into the esophagus. Birds such as parrots and cardinals use their bills to crack open seeds, but ingestion occurs as it does in pigeons. The anterior end of the esophagus is tubelike, but it opens into a crop, where food can be stored. The food moves to the proventriculus, the anterior glandular portion of the stomach that secretes digestive enzymes and acids. The food then passes to the gizzard, where muscular action grinds the seeds into fine particles. Ingested bits of sand and rock aid in the grinding process. Food particles then enter the intestine, where secretions from the liver (**bile**) and pancreas (digestive enzymes) are added. Molecular subunits produced by enzymatic digestion are absorbed as the mixture passes along the intestine, and the undigested residues are expelled through the anus, which opens to the cloaca (a common chamber that receives the contents from the digestive tract, the kidneys, and the reproductive tract). Structures such as the mouth, pharynx, esophagus, stomach, intestine, liver, and pancreas occur in almost all vertebrates.

**DIGESTION IN A MAMMAL** Humans (Figure 39.6d) are omnivores—different populations specialize in different diets. Humans are one of the many mammals capable of chewing their food. As a result, physical digestion begins in the mouth and is assisted by chemical digestion by salivary amylase. This enzyme begins the digestion of sugars and starches, making certain foods taste sweet. Food then passes into the stomach, where it mixes with acid and proteases (protein-digesting enzymes). The combination of mechanical churning and chemical digestion reduces the food to a liquid form. When sufficiently broken down, the partially digested food is slowly released into the small intestine. Here it is neutralized by bicarbonate, stopping the action of the proteases and preventing the acid from damaging the intestine. In the small intestine, carbohydrases, lipases, other proteases, and nucleases are secreted from the liver, the pancreas, and the epithelial cells lining the intestine itself. This finishes the digestion of the food and most absorption begins in the small intestine. The large intestine is also a site of absorption, primarily for water. Bacteria that thrive on the sugars and other nutrients remaining in the feces produce fatty acids as well as folic acid and biotin (vitamins $B_9$ and $B_7$), which are also absorbed across the intestinal wall. They also produce the gases that create flatulence. This along with undigested residues is expelled through the anus.

These examples give a brief overview of the structures involved in the digestion of food and the absorption of nutrients. In the next section we examine the structure and function of the different parts of the mammalian digestive system in more detail as a single example of the complexity of the process.

**STUDY BREAK QUESTIONS**

1. What is the difference between intracellular and extracellular digestion? Name a species where each is found.
2. Describe a general digestive tract. What are the five processes that occur in a digestive tract?
3. What is a gizzard? What does it do? Which animals have one? How do animals without a gizzard achieve the same results?

# 39.4 Structure and Function of the Mammalian Digestive Tract

The mammalian digestive system consists of a series of specialized regions that include the mouth, pharynx, esophagus, stomach, small and large intestines, rectum, and anus, which perform the five steps listed above (Figure 39.6). Each region is under the control of the nervous and endocrine systems. The system allows mammals to ingest, digest, and absorb fuel substances and the essential nutrients (the amino acids, fatty acids, vitamins, and minerals) that cannot be synthesized within our bodies.

## 39.4a Each of the Four Layers of the Digestive Tract Has a Specialized Function

The wall of the digestive tract in mammals and other vertebrates contains four major layers. Each has a specialized function, and the contribution of each layer to the wall varies in different parts of the digestive tract (**Figure 39.7**). From the inner surface outward the layers are as follows:

6. The **mucosa** contains epithelial and glandular cells and lines the inside of the gut. The epithelial cells form a barrier to contain the digestive contents; the glandular cells secrete enzymes, lubricating mucus, and substances that adjust the pH of the digestive contents. The epithelial cells also play a key role in absorbing digested nutrients in segments of the digestive tract.
7. The **submucosa** is a thick layer of elastic connective tissue containing neuron networks and blood and lymph vessels. Neuron networks control digestive activity and carry signals between the gut and the central nervous system. Lymph vessels carry absorbed lipids to other parts of the body.
8. In most regions of the gut, the **muscularis** is formed by two smooth muscle layers: a circular layer that constricts

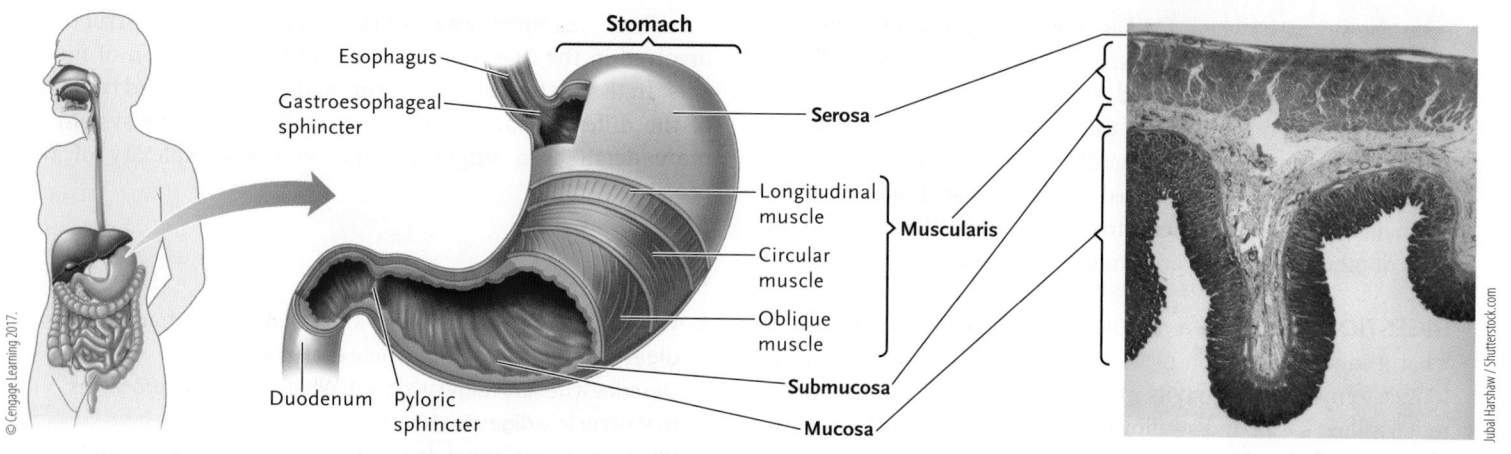

**FIGURE 39.7** Layers of the gut wall in vertebrates as seen in the stomach wall

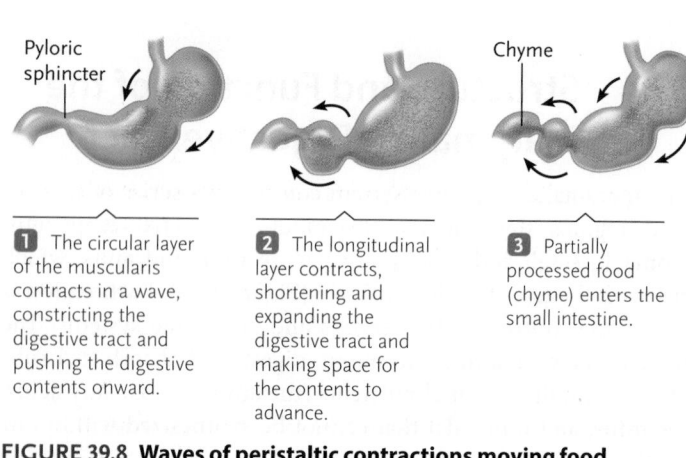

**1** The circular layer of the muscularis contracts in a wave, constricting the digestive tract and pushing the digestive contents onward.

**2** The longitudinal layer contracts, shortening and expanding the digestive tract and making space for the contents to advance.

**3** Partially processed food (chyme) enters the small intestine.

**FIGURE 39.8** Waves of peristaltic contractions moving food through the stomach

the diameter of the gut when it contracts and a longitudinal layer that shortens and widens the gut. The stomach also has an oblique layer running diagonally around its wall. The circular and longitudinal muscle layers work together to push the digestive contents through the gut by peristalsis **(Figure 39.8)**.

9. The **serosa** is the outermost gut layer. It consists of connective tissue that secretes an aqueous, slippery fluid that lubricates areas between the digestive organs and other organs. This allows the stomach and intestines to move freely, allowing them to slide past each other and reducing friction between them.

Mesenteries, thin tissues attached to the stomach and intestines, suspend the digestive system from the inner wall of the abdominal cavity.

**Sphincters** are powerful rings of smooth muscle that form valves between major regions of the digestive tract. By contracting and relaxing, the sphincters control the passage of the digestive contents from one region to another, and finally out through the anus. The adult human digestive tract in its normal living contracted state is about 4.5 m long. It is about twice as long when fully extended, as in a cadaver (all muscles relaxed).

## 39.4b Down the Tube: The Role of the Mouth, Pharynx, and Esophagus

Food begins its travel through the gastrointestinal tract in the mouth, where the teeth cut, tear, and crush food items. The number and shape of the teeth reflect the diet of the animal **(Figure 39.9)**. Typically, mammals have four types of teeth. **Incisors** are located at the front of the mouth and are designed to nip or cut food. As a result, they are flattened and chisel shaped. **Canines** are located at the sides of the incisors and are specialized for biting and piercing. The canines are very prominent in carnivores such as wolves where they are used to pierce and kill prey but are greatly reduced or absent in many herbivores. **Premolars** and **molars** are located along the sides of the jaw and are used for crushing, grinding, and shearing food. In herbivores such as deer, these are blocky teeth with bumps or ridges to help crush and grind fibrous material during chewing. In some carnivores, such as cats, they have sharp, shearing surfaces that can slice meat efficiently. All four types of teeth are typically well-developed in omnivores such as humans.

During chewing, **salivary glands** secrete saliva through ducts that open on the inside of the cheeks and under the tongue. Saliva, which is more than 99% water, moistens the food and begins digestion with **salivary amylase** and **lingual lipase**. Salivary amylase initiates digestion of starch during chewing and can break down significant amounts of starch even before the food is swallowed. Taste buds sense the levels of sugar and starch and give the animal an indication of the quality of the food it is eating. Lingual lipase starts the breakdown of saturated fatty acids. Saliva also contains mucus to lubricate the food mass, and bicarbonate ions ($HCO_3^-$) to neutralize acids in the food and keep the pH of the mouth between 6.5 and 7.5, the optimal range for salivary amylase to

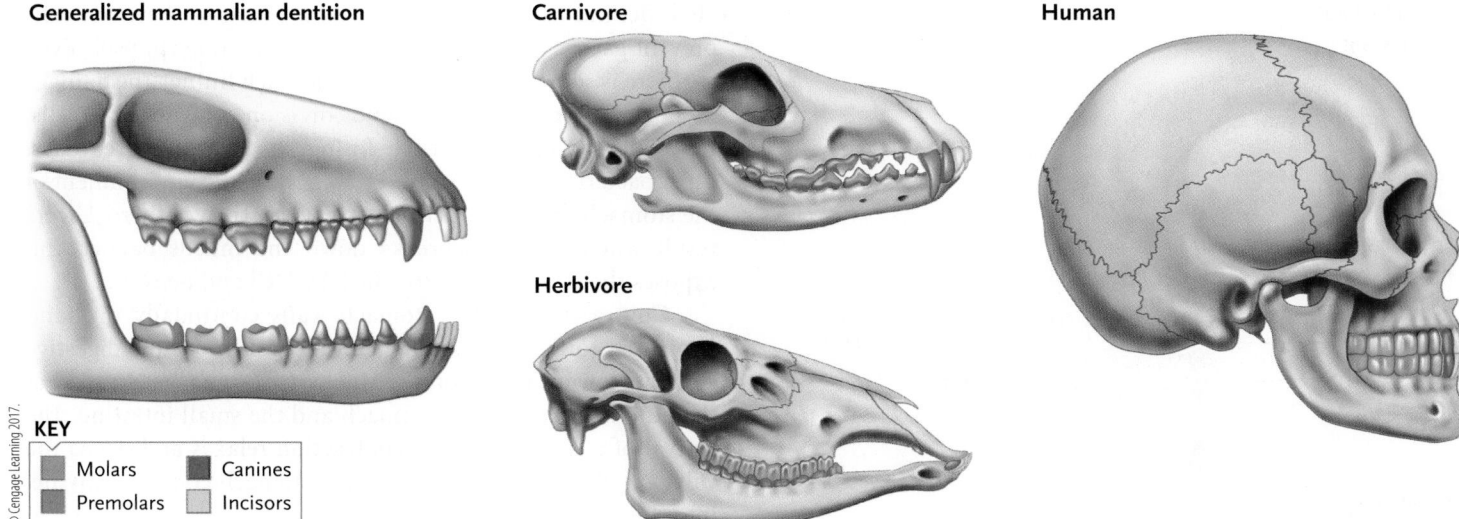

Generalized mammalian dentition    Carnivore    Human

Herbivore

KEY

- Molars
- Premolars
- Canines
- Incisors

© Cengage Learning 2017.

**FIGURE 39.9 Mammalian dentition**

function. Saliva also contains a lysozyme, an enzyme that kills bacteria by breaking open their cell walls.

After a suitable period of chewing, the food mass, called a **bolus**, is pushed by the tongue to the back of the mouth, where touch receptors detect the pressure and trigger the **swallowing reflex (Figure 39.10)**. This reflex is an involuntary action produced by contractions of muscles in the walls of the pharynx that direct food into the esophagus. Peristaltic contractions of the esophagus, aided by mucus secreted by the esophagus, propel the bolus toward the stomach. The passage down the esophagus stimulates the gastroesophageal sphincter at the junction between the esophagus and the stomach to open and admit the bolus into the stomach. After the bolus enters the stomach, the sphincter closes tightly. If the closure is imperfect, the acidic stomach contents can enter the esophagus, in humans causing **acid reflux**, or heartburn.

Mammals consciously initiate the swallowing reflex, but once it has begun, they cannot stop it because, whereas the muscles of the pharynx and upper esophagus are skeletal muscles under voluntary control, the muscles below are smooth muscles under involuntary control.

Involuntary movements of the tongue and soft palate at the back of the mouth prevent food from backing into the mouth or nasal cavities. The glottis (the space between vocal cords) and the **epiglottis**, a flaplike valve, prevent entry of food into the trachea.

## 39.4c The Stomach Stores Food and Continues Digestion

The stomach is a muscular, elastic sac that stores food and adds secretions, furthering digestion. The stomach lining, the mucosa, is covered with tiny **gastric pits**, entrances to millions of gastric glands. These glands extend deep into the stomach wall and contain cells that secrete some of the products needed to digest food. Entry of food into the stomach activates stretch receptors in its wall. Signals from stretch receptors stimulate the secretion of **gastric juice (Figure 39.11)**, which contains the digestive enzyme pepsin, hydrochloric acid (HCl), and lubricating mucus. The stomach secretes about 2 L of gastric juice each day.

Pepsin begins the digestion of proteins by creating breaks in polypeptide chains. Pepsin is secreted in the form of an inactive precursor molecule, pepsinogen, by cells called **chief cells**. Pepsinogen is converted to pepsin by the highly acidic conditions of the stomach. Once produced, pepsin itself can catalyze the reaction, converting more pepsinogen to pepsin. The activation of pepsin illustrates a common theme in digestion. Powerful hydrolytic enzymes such as pepsin would be dangerous to the cells that secrete them; however, enzymes are synthesized as inactive precursors and are not converted into an active form until exposed to the digestive contents.

Parietal cells in the gastric pits secrete $H^+$ and $Cl^-$, which combine to form HCl in the lumen of the stomach. The HCl lowers the pH of the digestive contents to pH ≤ 2, the level at which pepsin reaches optimal activity. To put this pH in perspective, lemon juice is pH 2.4, and sulfuric acid, or battery acid, is about pH 1. The acidity of the stomach helps break up food particles and causes proteins in the stomach contents to unfold, exposing their peptide linkages to hydrolysis by pepsin. The acid also kills most bacteria that reach the stomach, and stops the action of salivary amylase. Some nectar-feeding bats that digest pollen drink their own urine to make their stomach more acid.

A thick coating of alkaline mucus is secreted by mucus cells and protects the stomach lining from attack by pepsin and

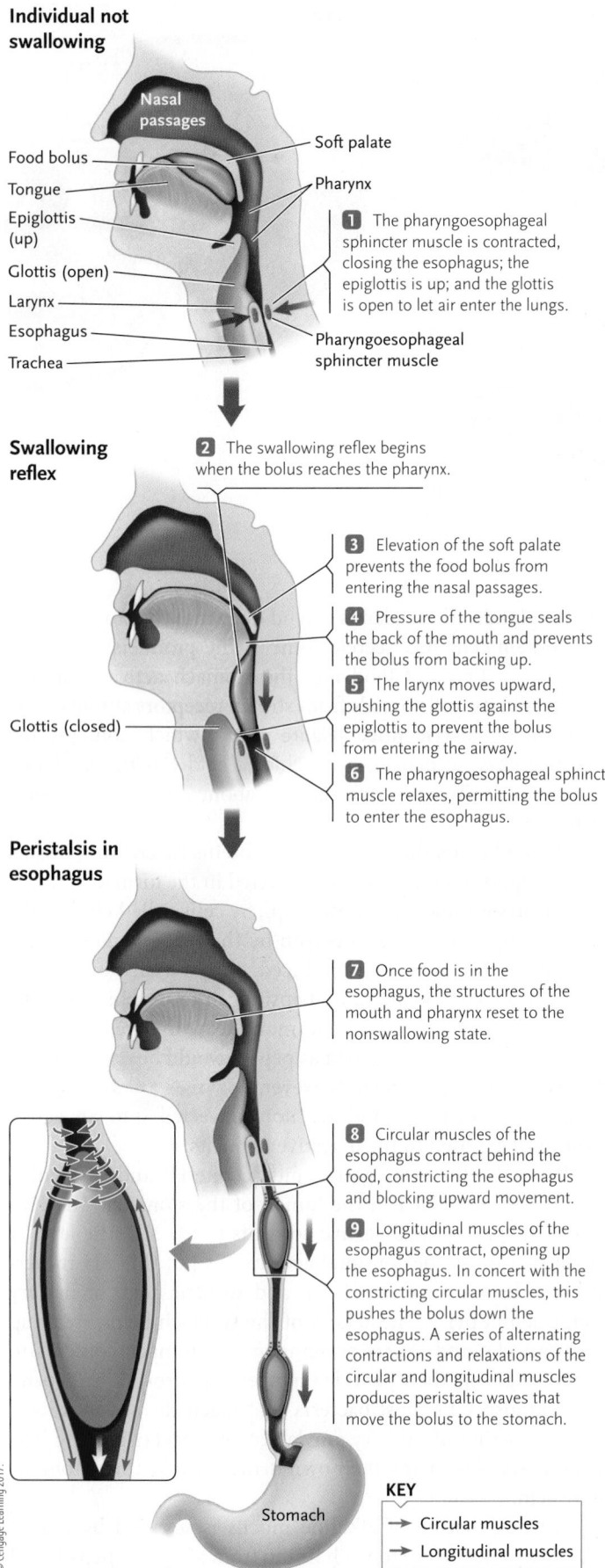

**Individual not swallowing**

Nasal passages
Food bolus
Tongue
Epiglottis (up)
Glottis (open)
Larynx
Esophagus
Trachea
Soft palate
Pharynx

**1** The pharyngoesophageal sphincter muscle is contracted, closing the esophagus; the epiglottis is up; and the glottis is open to let air enter the lungs.

Pharyngoesophageal sphincter muscle

**Swallowing reflex**

**2** The swallowing reflex begins when the bolus reaches the pharynx.

**3** Elevation of the soft palate prevents the food bolus from entering the nasal passages.

**4** Pressure of the tongue seals the back of the mouth and prevents the bolus from backing up.

Glottis (closed)

**5** The larynx moves upward, pushing the glottis against the epiglottis to prevent the bolus from entering the airway.

**6** The pharyngoesophageal sphincter muscle relaxes, permitting the bolus to enter the esophagus.

**Peristalsis in esophagus**

**7** Once food is in the esophagus, the structures of the mouth and pharynx reset to the nonswallowing state.

**8** Circular muscles of the esophagus contract behind the food, constricting the esophagus and blocking upward movement.

**9** Longitudinal muscles of the esophagus contract, opening up the esophagus. In concert with the constricting circular muscles, this pushes the bolus down the esophagus. A series of alternating contractions and relaxations of the circular and longitudinal muscles produces peristaltic waves that move the bolus to the stomach.

Stomach

**KEY**
→ Circular muscles
→ Longitudinal muscles

© Cengage Learning 2017.

**FIGURE 39.10 The swallowing reflex and peristalsis in the esophagus**

HCl. Behind the mucus barrier, tight junctions between cells prevent gastric juice from seeping into the stomach wall. Even so, there is some breakdown of the stomach lining. The damage is normally repaired by rapid division of mucosal cells, replacing the entire stomach lining about every three days. Most bacteria cannot survive the highly acidic environment of the stomach, but one, *Helicobacter pylori*, thrives there. Ulcers result when *H. pylori* breaks down the mucus barrier and exposes the stomach wall to attack by HCl and pepsin.

Contractions of the stomach walls continually mix and churn the contents. Peristaltic contractions move the digestive contents toward the pyloric sphincter (*pylorus* = gatekeeper) at the junction between the stomach and the small intestine. The arrival of a strong stomach contraction relaxes and opens the valve briefly, releasing a pulse of the stomach contents, **chyme**, into the small intestine.

Feedback controls regulate the rate of gastric emptying, matching it to the rate of digestion so that food is not moved along faster than it can be chemically processed. In particular, chyme with high fat content and high acidity stimulates the secretion of hormones by cells in the mucosal layer of the duodenum. These hormones slow the process of stomach emptying. Fat is digested in the lumen of the small intestine more slowly than other nutrients, so further emptying of the stomach is prevented until fat processing has been completed in the small intestine. A fatty meal, such as a greasy pizza, feels heavy in the stomach because it sits there so much longer than a less fatty meal. Highly acidic chyme must be neutralized by bicarbonate in the small intestine. Unneutralized stomach acid inactivates digestive enzymes secreted in the small intestine and inhibits further emptying of the stomach until it is neutralized.

## 39.4d Small Intestine: Completion of Digestion and Absorption of Nutrients

The small intestine completes digestion and begins the absorption of nutrients. Nutrients are not absorbed in the mouth, pharynx, or esophagus. Substances such as alcohol, aspirin, caffeine, and water are absorbed in the stomach, but most absorption occurs in the small intestine, where digestion is completed. The small intestine is smaller in diameter than the large intestine. The lining of the small intestine is folded into ridges densely covered by microscopic, fingerlike extensions, the intestinal villi (singular, villus). In addition, the epithelial cells covering the villi themselves have fingerlike extensions, the microvilli. The microvilli are so fine that the surface of each epithelial cell looks like a brush, and hence the fingerlike projections of the plasma membrane are referred to as a *brush border* (**Figure 39.12**). The intestinal villi and microvilli in humans increase the absorptive surface area of the small intestine to 300 m², about the size of a doubles tennis court.

**ENZYMATIC DIGESTION IN THE SMALL INTESTINE** Digestion in the small intestine depends on enzymes and other substances secreted by the intestine itself and by the pancreas and liver.

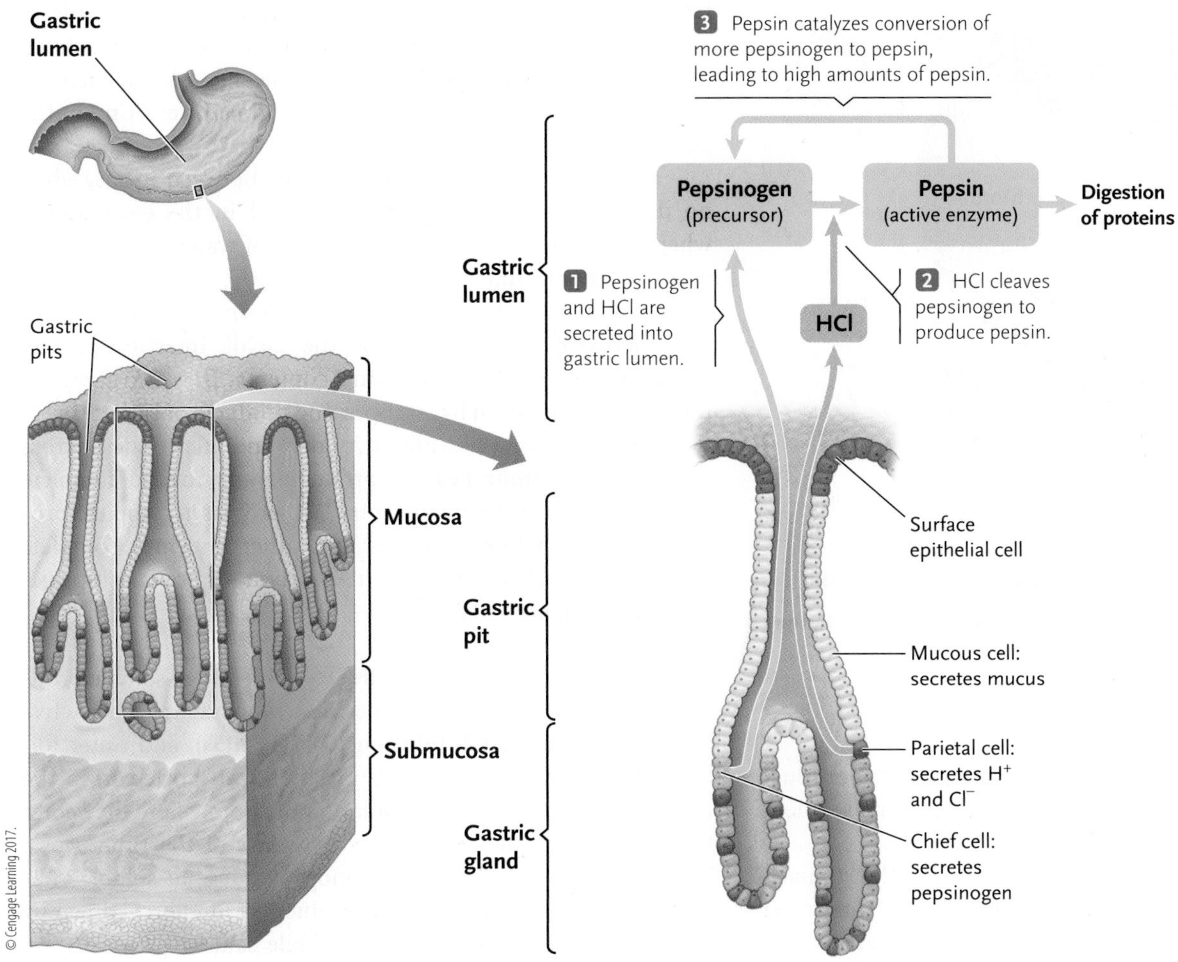
Gastric lumen
Gastric pits
Mucosa
Submucosa
Gastric lumen
Gastric pit
Gastric gland
3 Pepsin catalyzes conversion of more pepsinogen to pepsin, leading to high amounts of pepsin.
Pepsinogen (precursor)
Pepsin (active enzyme)
Digestion of proteins
1 Pepsinogen and HCl are secreted into gastric lumen.
HCl
2 HCl cleaves pepsinogen to produce pepsin.
Surface epithelial cell
Mucous cell: secretes mucus
Parietal cell: secretes H+ and Cl−
Chief cell: secretes pepsinogen
© Cengage Learning 2017.

**FIGURE 39.11 Cells that secrete mucus, pepsin, and HCl in the stomach lining**

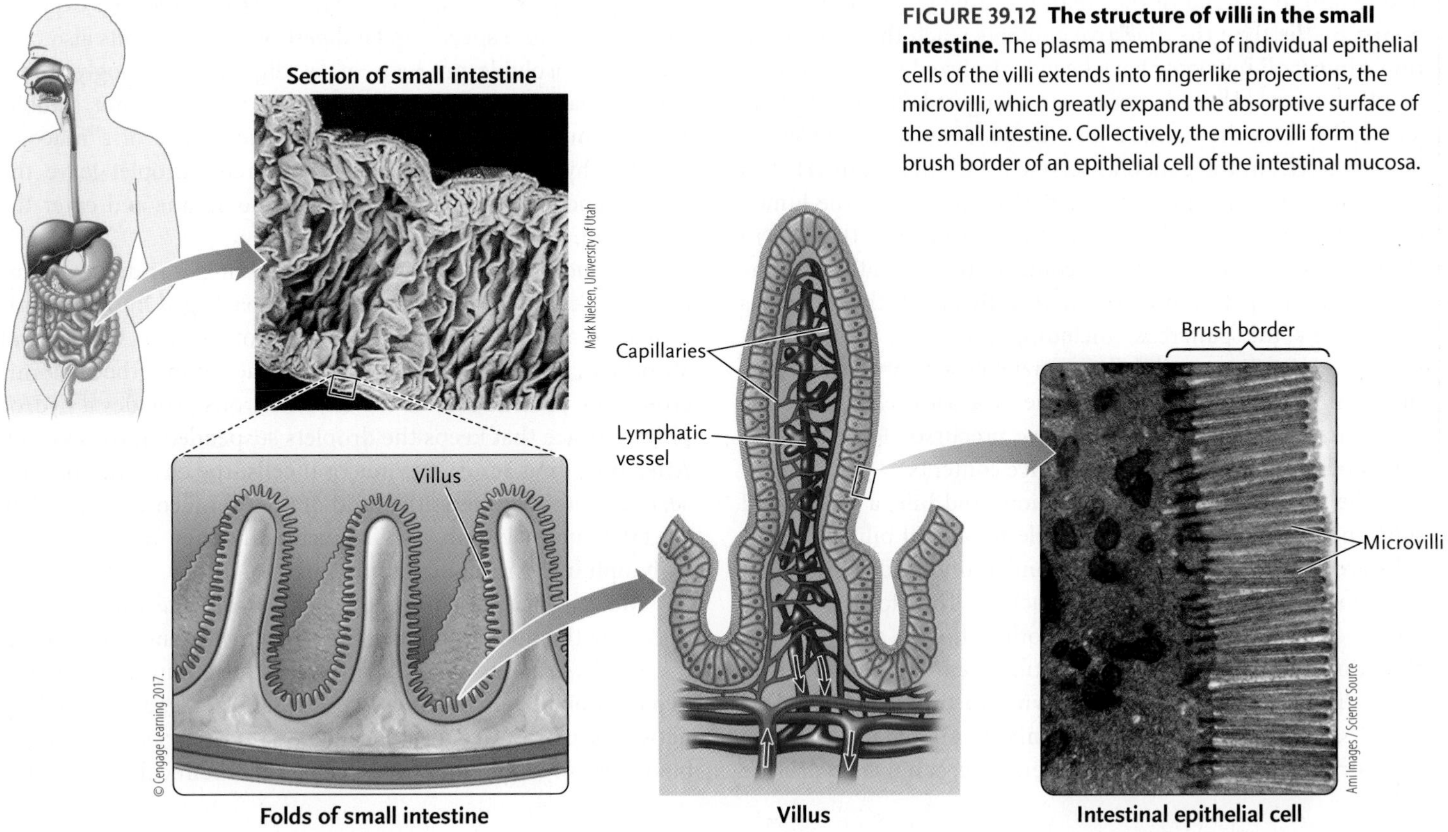
Section of small intestine
Mark Nielsen, University of Utah
Villus
Folds of small intestine
Capillaries
Lymphatic vessel
Villus
Brush border
Microvilli
Intestinal epithelial cell
© Cengage Learning 2017.
Ami Images / Science Source

**FIGURE 39.12 The structure of villi in the small intestine.** The plasma membrane of individual epithelial cells of the villi extends into fingerlike projections, the microvilli, which greatly expand the absorptive surface of the small intestine. Collectively, the microvilli form the brush border of an epithelial cell of the intestinal mucosa.

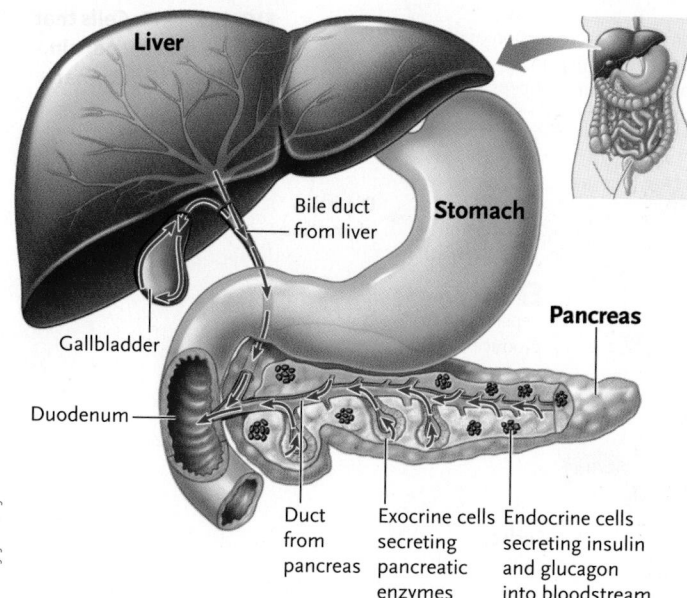

Liver

Bile duct
from liver

Stomach

Gallbladder

Pancreas

Duodenum

Duct
from
pancreas

Exocrine cells
secreting
pancreatic
enzymes

Endocrine cells
secreting insulin
and glucagon
into bloodstream

**FIGURE 39.13** **The ducts delivering bile and pancreatic juice to the duodenum of the small intestine**

Secretions from the pancreas and liver enter a common duct that empties into the lumen of the **duodenum**, the first segment of the small intestine **(Figure 39.13)**.

About 95% of the volume of material leaving the stomach is absorbed as water and nutrients as digestive contents travel along the small intestine through the next two segments, the **jejunum** and the **ileum**. Movement of the contents from the duodenum to the end of the small intestine takes three to five hours. By the time the digestive contents reach the large intestine, almost all nutrients have been hydrolyzed and absorbed.

In humans, the pancreas is an elongated, flattened gland located between the stomach and the duodenum (Figure 39.13). Exocrine cells in the pancreas secrete bicarbonate ions ($HCO_3^-$) and pancreatic enzymes into ducts that empty into the lumen of the duodenum. The bicarbonate ions neutralize the acid in chyme, bringing the digestive contents to a slightly alkaline pH. Alkaline pH allows optimal activity of the enzymes secreted by the pancreas, including proteases, an amylase, nucleases, and lipases. All these enzymes act in the lumen of the small intestine. Like pepsin, the proteases released by the pancreas are secreted in an inactive precursor form and are activated by contact with the digestive contents.

The **liver** secretes bicarbonate ions and bile, a mixture of substances including bile salts, cholesterol, and bilirubin. Bile salts are derivatives of cholesterol and amino acids that aid fat digestion through their detergent action. They form a hydrophilic coating around fats and other lipids, allowing the churning motions of the small intestine to emulsify fats. During emulsification, fats are broken down into tiny droplets called *micelles*, much the same effect as mixing oil and vinegar in a salad dressing. Lipase, a pancreatic enzyme, can then hydrolyze

fats in the micelles to produce monoglycerides and free fatty acids. Bilirubin, a waste product derived from worn-out red blood cells, is yellow and gives the bile its colour. Bacterial enzymes in the intestines modify the pigment, resulting in the characteristic brown colour of feces.

The liver secretes bile continuously. Between meals, when no digestion is occurring, bile is stored in the **gallbladder**, where it is concentrated by the removal of water. After a meal, entry of chyme into the small intestine stimulates the gallbladder to release the stored bile into the small intestine.

Microvilli on the villi of the small intestine secrete water and mucus into the intestinal contents. They also carry out intracellular digestion by transporting products of earlier digestion, including disaccharides, peptides, and nucleotides, across their plasma membranes and producing enzymes to complete the breakdown of these nutrients. Two proteases complete protein digestion while nucleases and other enzymes complete digestion of nucleic acids into five-carbon sugars and nitrogenous bases **(Figure 39.14)**.

**ABSORPTION IN THE SMALL INTESTINE** Water-soluble products of digestion enter the intestinal mucosal cells by active transport or facilitated diffusion **(Figure 39.15a)**, and water follows by osmosis. The nutrients are then transported from the mucosal cells into the extracellular fluids, from where they enter the bloodstream in the capillary networks of the submucosa. The absorption of fatty acids, monoglycerides, fat-soluble vitamins, and cholesterol and other products of lipid breakdown by lipase occurs with the assistance of bile salts (Figure 39.15b). Bile salts emulsify fat globules, dispersing them into fatty droplets. This increases the number of triglyceride molecules exposed to the lipases and speeds up fat digestion. The bile salts also coat the water-insoluble products of fat digestion (monoglycerides and free fatty acids), forming micelles that are water soluble. When a micelle contacts the plasma membrane of a mucosal cell, the hydrophobic molecules within the droplet leave the micelle and freely penetrate the lipid membrane and enter the cytoplasm.

In mucosal cells, fatty acids and monoglycerides are combined back into fats (triglycerides) and packaged into **chylomicrons**, small droplets covered by a protein coat. Cholesterol absorbed in the small intestine is also packed into the chylomicrons. The protein coat of the chylomicrons provides a hydrophilic surface that keeps the droplets suspended in the cytosol. After travelling across the mucosal cells, the chylomicrons are secreted into the interstitial fluid of the submucosa, where they are taken up by lymph vessels. Eventually, they are transferred by lymph into the blood circulation.

Many nutrients absorbed by the small intestine are processed by the liver. Capillaries absorbing nutrient molecules in the small intestine collect into veins that join to form the **hepatic portal vein**, a larger blood vessel that leads to capillary networks in the liver. In the liver, some nutrients leave the bloodstream and enter liver cells for chemical processing.

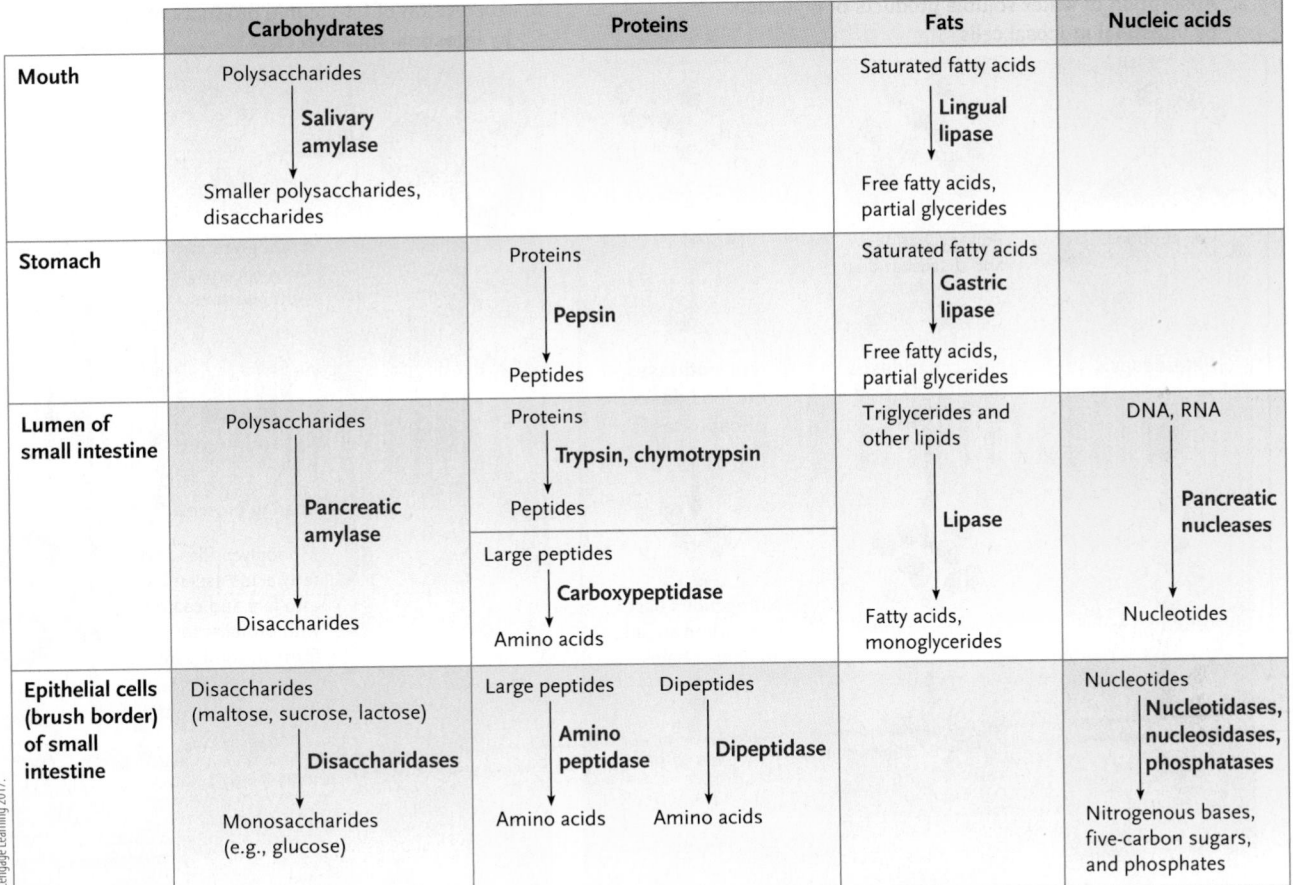

| | Carbohydrates | Proteins | Fats | Nucleic acids |
|---|---|---|---|---|
| **Mouth** | Polysaccharides<br>↓ **Salivary amylase**<br>Smaller polysaccharides, disaccharides | | Saturated fatty acids<br>↓ **Lingual lipase**<br>Free fatty acids, partial glycerides | |
| **Stomach** | | Proteins<br>↓ **Pepsin**<br>Peptides | Saturated fatty acids<br>↓ **Gastric lipase**<br>Free fatty acids, partial glycerides | |
| **Lumen of small intestine** | Polysaccharides<br>↓ **Pancreatic amylase**<br>Disaccharides | Proteins<br>↓ **Trypsin, chymotrypsin**<br>Peptides<br>Large peptides ↓ **Carboxypeptidase** Amino acids | Triglycerides and other lipids<br>↓ **Lipase**<br>Fatty acids, monoglycerides | DNA, RNA<br>↓ **Pancreatic nucleases**<br>Nucleotides |
| **Epithelial cells (brush border) of small intestine** | Disaccharides (maltose, sucrose, lactose)<br>↓ **Disaccharidases**<br>Monosaccharides (e.g., glucose) | Large peptides ↓ **Amino peptidase** Amino acids | Dipeptides ↓ **Dipeptidase** Amino acids | Nucleotides<br>↓ **Nucleotidases, nucleosidases, phosphatases**<br>Nitrogenous bases, five-carbon sugars, and phosphates |

© Cengage Learning 2017.

**FIGURE 39.14 Enzymatic digestion of carbohydrates, proteins, fats, and nucleic acids in the human digestive system**

Among the reactions taking place in the liver is the combination of excess glucose units into glycogen, which is stored in liver cells. This reaction reduces the glucose concentration in the blood exiting the liver to about 0.1%. If the glucose concentration in the blood entering the liver falls below 0.1% between meals, the reaction reverses. The reversal adds glucose to return the blood concentration to the 0.1% level before it exits the liver (see Chapter 43, Section 43.4f).

The liver also synthesizes lipoproteins that transport cholesterol and fats in the bloodstream, detoxifies ethyl alcohol and other toxic molecules, and inactivates steroid hormones and many types of drugs. As a result of the liver's activities, the blood leaving it has a markedly different concentration of nutrients than the blood carried into the liver by the hepatic portal vein. From the liver, blood goes to the heart and is then pumped to deliver nutrients to all parts of the body (see Chapter 41).

## 39.4e Large Intestine: Absorption of Water

From the small intestine, the contents move on to the large intestine, or **colon**. A sphincter at the junction between the small and large intestines controls the passage of material and prevents backward movement of contents. By this point, almost all nutrients have been digested and absorbed. The inner surface of the large intestine is relatively smooth and contains no villi.

The large intestine has several distinct regions (**Figure 39.16**). At the junction with the small intestine, a part of the large intestine forms the **cecum**, a blind pouch. A fingerlike sac, the **appendix**, extends from the cecum. The cecum merges with the colon, which forms an inverted U, finally connecting with the **rectum**, the terminal part of the large intestine.

The large intestine secretes mucus and bicarbonate ions and absorbs water and other ions, primarily $Na^+$ and $Cl^-$. The absorption of water condenses and compacts the digestive contents into solid masses, the **feces**. Normally, fecal matter reaching the rectum contains less than 200 mL of the fluid that enters the digestive tract each day. Animals suffering from diarrhea produce liquid fecal matter. Diarrhea is a higher-than-normal rate of movement of materials through the small intestine, which does not leave adequate time for absorption of water. Diarrhea can be caused by infection, emotional stress, or irritation of the small intestine wall.

Feces entering the rectum stretch its walls, at some point triggering a defecation reflex that opens the anal sphincter

## a. Absorption of water-soluble products of digestion by intestinal mucosal cells

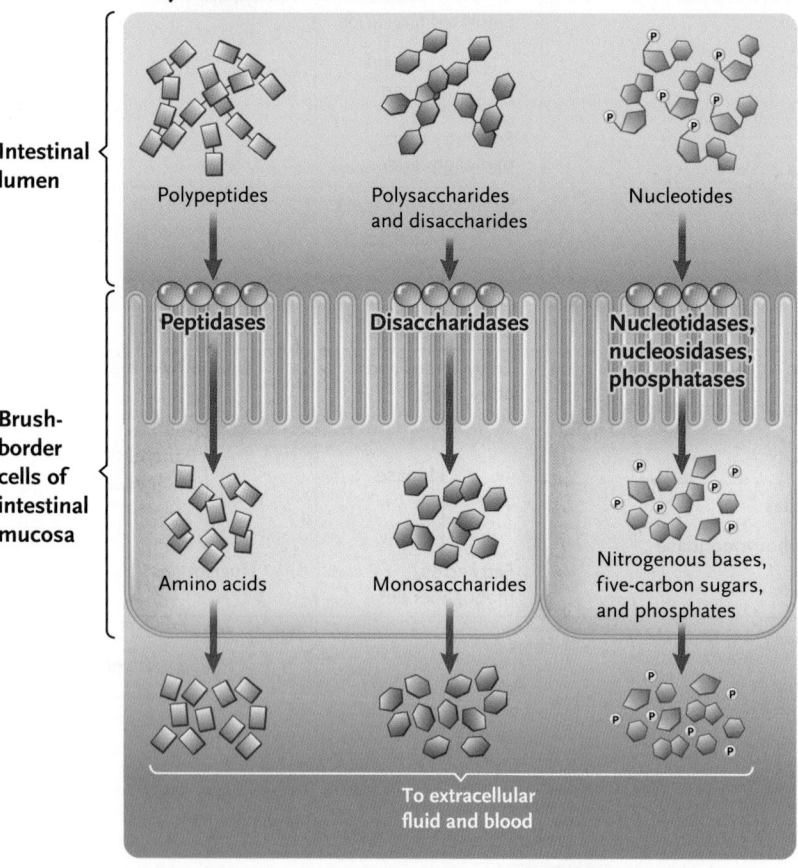

**Intestinal lumen**

Polypeptides

Polysaccharides and disaccharides

Nucleotides

**Brush-border cells of intestinal mucosa**

Peptidases

Disaccharidases

Nucleotidases, nucleosidases, phosphatases

Amino acids

Monosaccharides

Nitrogenous bases, five-carbon sugars, and phosphates

To extracellular fluid and blood

Water-soluble molecules are broken into absorbable subunits at brush borders of mucosal cells and transported inside; the subunits are transported on the other side to extracellular fluid and blood.

## b. Absorption of fat-soluble products of digestion by intestinal mucosal cells

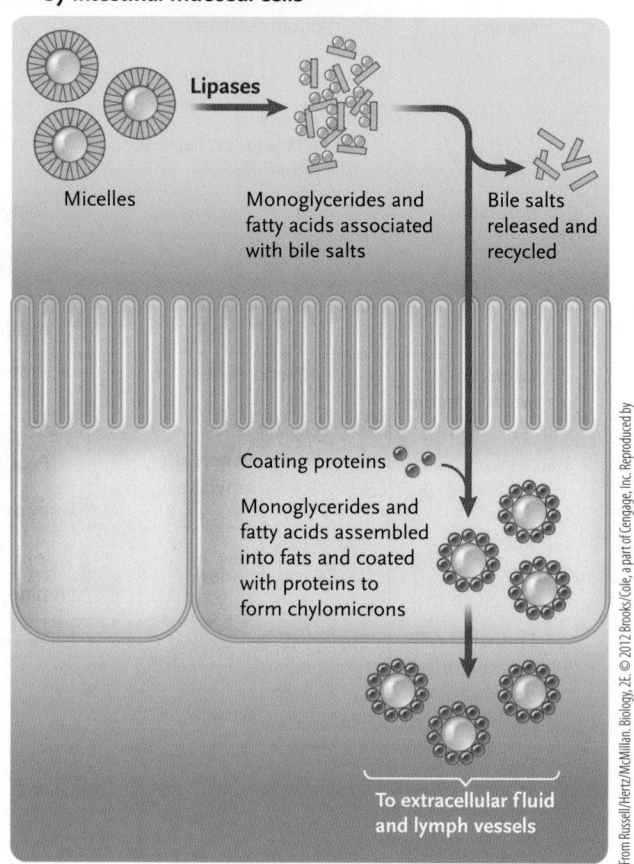

Micelles

**Lipases**

Monoglycerides and fatty acids associated with bile salts

Bile salts released and recycled

Coating proteins

Monoglycerides and fatty acids assembled into fats and coated with proteins to form chylomicrons

To extracellular fluid and lymph vessels

Micelles (fats coated with bile salts) are digested to monoglycerides and fatty acids, which penetrate into cells and are assembled into fats. The fats are coated with proteins to form chylomicrons, which are released by exocytosis to extracellular fluids, where they are picked up by lymph vessels.

From Russell/Hertz/McMillan. Biology, 2E. © 2012 Brooks/Cole, a part of Cengage, Inc. Reproduced by permission. www.cengage.com/permissions

**FIGURE 39.15 Absorption of digestive products by the epithelial cells of the intestinal mucosa**

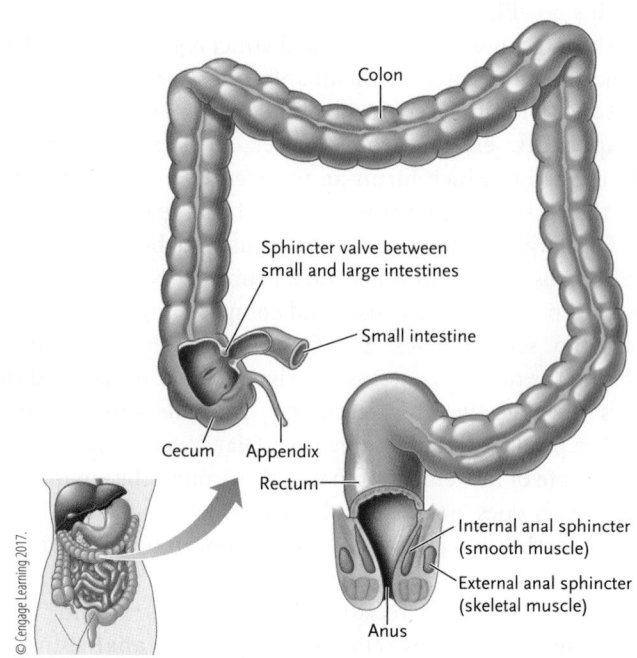

Colon

Sphincter valve between small and large intestines

Small intestine

Cecum    Appendix

Rectum

Internal anal sphincter (smooth muscle)

External anal sphincter (skeletal muscle)

Anus

© Cengage Learning 2017.

**FIGURE 39.16 The human large intestine**

and expels the feces through the anus. Because the anal sphincter contains rings of voluntary skeletal muscle as well as involuntary smooth muscle, animals can resist the defecation reflex by voluntarily tightening the striated muscle ring, but only for a short period before the involuntary reflex wins out.

## GUT MICROBIOMES AID DIGESTION IN MANY ORGANISMS

As many as 500 species of bacteria make up 30%–50% of the dry matter of feces in humans and other vertebrates. Most of these bacteria live as essentially permanent residents in the large intestine. The complete collection of microorganisms (bacteria, archaea, protists, yeasts, other fungi, and viruses) make up the gut **microbiome**. *Escherichia coli* is the most common bacterium in the guts of humans and other mammals. Intestinal bacteria metabolize sugars and other nutrients remaining in the digestive residue. They produce useful fatty acids and vitamins (such as vitamin K, the B vitamins, folic acid, and biotin), some of which are absorbed in the large intestine. Bacterial activity in the large intestines produces large quantities of gas (flatus), primarily $CO_2$, methane, and hydrogen sulfide. Most of the gas is absorbed through the intestinal mucosa, and the rest is expelled through the anus in the process of flatulence. The amount and composition of flatus depend on the type of food ingested and the particular population of bacteria present in the large intestine. Foods such as beans contain carbohydrates that humans cannot digest. These carbohydrates can be metabolized by gas-producing intestinal bacteria, however, explaining the connection between beans and flatulence.

In herbivorous animals, the gut microbiome takes on even more importance. Most animals cannot digest cellulose because they lack cellulase, which hydrolyzes cellulose into glucose subunits. Many herbivorous animals use the hydrolytic capabilities of microorganisms that do produce cellulase. In this way, bacteria, protists, and fungi help other animals to digest plant material.

Herbivores using microorganisms house these symbionts in specialized structures along the alimentary canal. These structures occur in the esophagus, stomach, or ceca, depending on the species. Ruminant mammals (Bovidae, Cervidae) and termites are well-known examples of animals that use symbionts to digest cellulose.

Ruminants use their teeth to crop and chew plant material. They swallow the masticated material, moving it to a complex, four-chambered rumen **(Figure 39.17)**. The first three chambers of the rumen are derived from the esophagus, whereas the fourth, the abomasum, is the stomach. Swallowed food material arrives in the reticulum and then moves to the rumen. Then ruminants chew their cuds, regurgitating material from the reticulum and rumen, rechewing it, and macerating it into smaller fragments before swallowing it again. This exposes more surface area to microbial enzymes, giving them more time to act.

Fermentation by the microorganisms occurs in the reticulum and in the rumen. Oxygen levels in the chambers are too low to support mitochondrial reactions (see Chapter 5). Matter digested and liquefied by microorganisms moves to the *omasum*, where water is absorbed from the mass. In the *abomasum* (the ruminant's true stomach), acids and pepsin are added to the food mass, killing the microorganisms and starting the process of "typical" vertebrate digestion. As the food mass moves to the small intestine, dead microorganisms, themselves a rich source of proteins, vitamins, and other nutrients, are digested and absorbed along with other hydrolyzable molecules.

Fermentation generates products such as alcohols and amino acids that are used as nutrients. It also produces volatile fatty acids that move from the rumen to the blood and are used as sources of carbon and energy. Microorganisms use 40%–60% of the food protein produced by fermentation, and in turn their bodies are protein for the host. Methane, another product, collects in the fermentation chambers, so ruminants belch the gas in huge quantities. One cow can release more than 400 L of methane per day. Cattle are estimated to contribute 20% of the methane polluting our atmosphere. A 500 kg cow with a 70 L rumen produces about 60 L of saliva per day and ingests 40 L of water. Fermentation takes time: the leaves eaten by a cow take about 55 hours to move through its digestive system.

Many other mammals have esophageal or gastric chambers that house plant-digesting, symbiotic microorganisms. Biologists had long thought that the weight of the fermentation chamber made digestion by fermentation inaccessible to birds. But at least one species of bird, the South American hoatzin, uses fermentation **(Figure 39.18)**. Freshly caught hoatzins smell like cattle dung, perhaps giving a clue to their use of fermentation. Hoatzins eat young leaves that are fermented in the enlarged forestomach. This fermentation centre takes up some space occupied by flight muscles in "normal" birds. Hoatzins are weak fliers, probably because of reduction in the mass of their flight muscles to accommodate the enlarged forestomach.

a.

Chewing, swallowing, regurgitation, rechewing, and reswallowing of food through esophagus

b.

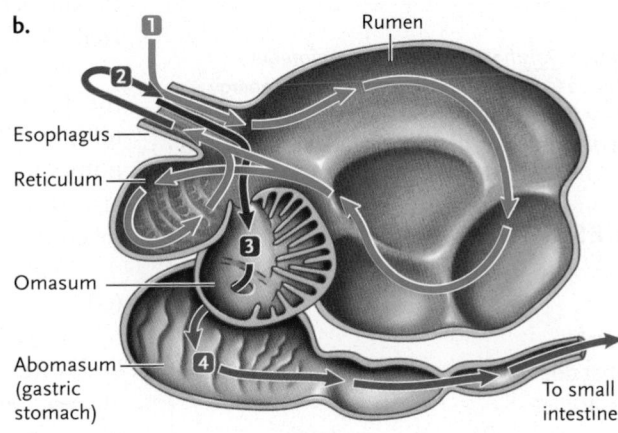

Esophagus
Reticulum
Omasum
Abomasum (gastric stomach)
Rumen
To small intestine

**1** Swallowed boluses go to rumen and reticulum, where fermentation reactions by symbiotic microorganisms begin digesting the plant matter.

**2** The animal chews its cud by regurgitating material, rechewing it, and swallowing it again.

**3** Reswallowed cud goes to the omasum, where water is absorbed.

**4** Matter then moves to the abomasum, where typical gastric digestion occurs.

© Cengage Learning 2017.

Michael S. Nolan/age fotostock/Getty Images

**FIGURE 39.17** (a) **A ruminant, the pronghorn antelope (*Antilocapra americana*), and** (b) **its four-chambered stomach, which digests plant material with the aid of mutualistic microorganisms**

CHAPTER 39 ANIMAL NUTRITION |

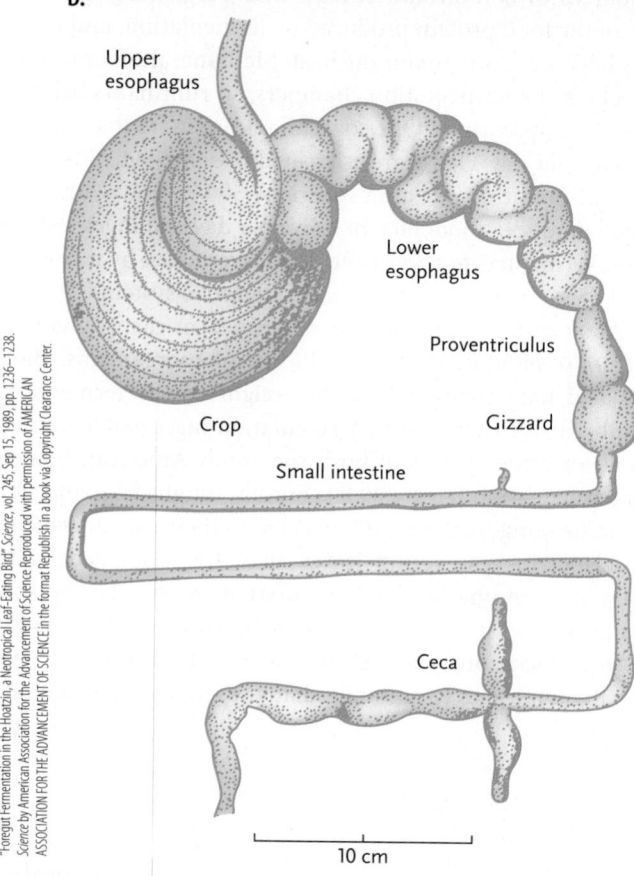

FIGURE 39.18 **(a)** The hoatzin (*Opisthocomus hoazin*) uses foregut fermentation to digest cellulose to meet a high percentage of its energy requirements. The contents of the crop and lower esophagus account for over 15% of adult mass. **(b)** Deep ridges in the lining of the crop increase its surface area.

From ALEJANDRO GRAJAL, STUART D. STRAHL, RODRIGO PARRA, MARIA GLORIA DOMINGUEZ, ALFREDO NEHER, "Foregut Fermentation in the Hoatzin, a Neotropical Leaf-Eating Bird", *Science*, vol. 245, Sep 15, 1989, pp. 1236–1238. *Science* by American Association for the Advancement of Science Reproduced with permission of AMERICAN ASSOCIATION FOR THE ADVANCEMENT OF SCIENCE in the format Republish in a book via Copyright Clearance Center.

**Labels on figure b:** Upper esophagus, Lower esophagus, Proventriculus, Crop, Gizzard, Small intestine, Ceca, 10 cm

## STUDY BREAK QUESTIONS

1. Describe the four layers of the digestive tract, and outline their distinctive features.
2. What is the role of saliva?
3. What is peristalsis? What does it do? Is it unique to mammals?
4. Why is the stomach so acidic?
5. What are the roles of the small and large intestine? Which comes first along the digestive tract?
6. Why are feces brown?

# 39.5 Regulation of Digestive Processes

The digestive processes are regulated and coordinated largely by automated controls, most of which originate in the neuron networks of the submucosa of the digestive tract itself. Other controls, particularly those regulating appetite and oxidative metabolism, originate in the brain, in control centres that form part of the hypothalamus (see Chapter 45).

Movement of food through the digestive system is controlled by receptors in and hormones secreted by various parts of the system **(Figure 39.19)**. Control starts with the mouth, where the presence of food activates receptors that increase the rate of salivary secretion by as much as 10-fold over the resting state.

Swallowed food expands the stomach and sets off signals from stretch receptors in the stomach walls. Chemoreceptors in the stomach respond to the presence of food molecules, particularly proteins. Signals from these receptors are integrated in neuron networks in the stomach and the autonomic nervous system to produce several reflex responses. One response is an increase in the rate and strength of stomach contractions. Another is secretion of a hormone, gastrin, into the blood leaving the stomach. After travelling through the circulatory system, gastrin returns to the stomach, where it stimulates the secretion of HCl and pepsinogen. These molecules are used in the digestion of the protein in the food that was responsible for their secretion. Gastrin also stimulates stomach and intestinal contractions, which serve to keep the digestive contents moving through the digestive system when a new meal arrives.

Three hormones secreted into the lumen of the duodenum participate in regulating digestive processes. When chyme is emptied into the duodenum, its acidic nature stimulates the release of the hormone secretin. Secretin inhibits further gastric emptying to prevent more acid from entering the duodenum until the newly arrived chyme is neutralized. Secretin also inhibits gastric secretion to reduce acid production in the stomach and stimulates secretion of ($HCO_3^-$) into the lumen of the duodenum to neutralize the acid. If the acid is not neutralized, the duodenal wall can be damaged.

Fat and, to a lesser extent, protein in the chyme entering the duodenum stimulate the release of the hormone cholecystokinin (CCK). CCK inhibits gastric activity, allowing time for nutrients in the duodenum to be digested and absorbed. CCK also stimulates the secretion of pancreatic enzymes to digest macromolecules in chyme.

The hormone glucose-dependent insulinotropic peptide (GIP) acts primarily to stimulate insulin release into the blood by the pancreas. Insulin changes the metabolic state of the body after a meal is ingested so that new nutrients, particularly glucose, are used and stored. Glucose in the duodenum increases GIP secretion, triggering the release of insulin.

Two interneuron centres in the hypothalamus work in opposition to control appetite and oxidative metabolism. One

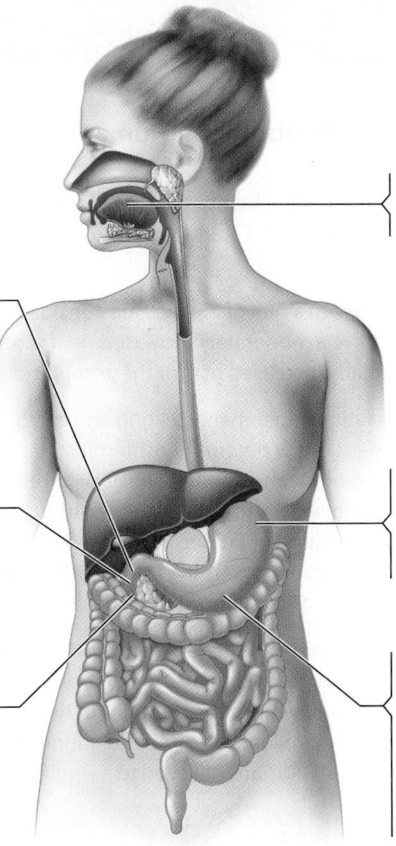

**Hormonal controls**

Acidic chyme stimulates release into the bloodstream of the hormone **secretin** from glandular cells in the small intestine. Secretin inhibits gastric emptying and gastric secretion and stimulates $HCO_3^-$ secretion into the duodenum.

Fat (mostly) in chyme stimulates release of the hormone **cholecystokinin (CCK).** CCK inhibits gastric activity and stimulates secretion of pancreatic enzymes.

A meal entering the digestive tract stimulates **GIP** (glucose-dependent insulinotropic peptide) secretion, which triggers **insulin** release. Insulin stimulates the uptake and storage of glucose from the digested food.

**Receptor controls**

Receptors in the mouth respond to food by increasing salivary secretion.

Stretch receptors in the stomach respond to food, signalling neuron networks to increase stomach contractions.

Chemoreceptors in the stomach respond to food, signalling neuron networks to stimulate the stomach to secrete the hormone **gastrin,** which in turn stimulates the stomach to secrete HCl and pepsinogen.

© Cengage Learning 2017.

centre stimulates appetite and reduces oxidative metabolism; the other stimulates the release of α-melanocyte-stimulating hormone (α-MSH), a peptide hormone that inhibits appetite. Leptin (*leptos* = thin), a peptide hormone, is a major link between these two pathways. Fat-storing cells secrete leptin when deposition of fat increases in the body. Leptin travels in the bloodstream and binds to receptors in both centres in the hypothalamus. Binding stimulates the centre that reduces appetite and inhibits the centre that stimulates appetite. Leptin also binds to receptors on body cells, triggering reactions that oxidize fatty acids rather than converting them to fats. When fat storage is reduced, leptin secretion drops off, and signals from other pathways activate the appetite-stimulating centre in the hypothalamus and turn off the appetite-inhibiting centre. These controls closely match the activity of the digestive system to the amount and types of foods ingested, and coordinate appetite and oxidative metabolism with the body's needs for stored fats **(Figure 39.20)**.

The caption to the opening figure to this chapter asked you, "Are the digestive systems and digestive processes different in herbivores and carnivores?" Now having read the chapter you should easily be able to begin to answer this question. The Chapter Roadmap shows how the sections in the chapter link to one another. All animals need to acquire nutrients for fuel and to grow and maintain all the tissues and organs in the body. Some nutrients can be converted from one form to another, but others cannot and it is essential that they are obtained in the diet. For most animals this means that food must be ingested and digested, and the nutrients released in this process must then be absorbed. The digestive systems of different animals reflect adaptations to accommodate different diets.

## STUDY BREAK QUESTIONS

1. What is the role of the stretch receptors in the stomach?
2. What are the roles of gastrin, secretin, and cholecystokinin?
3. What is leptin? What role does it play in digestion?

FIGURE 39.20    **Experimental Research**

## Association of Bacterial Populations in the Gut Microbiome with Obesity in Humans

Obesity can lead to elevated blood pressure, heart disease, stroke, diabetes, and other ailments. Obese humans are 20% or more heavier than an optimal body weight. The body mass index (BMI), a measure of an individual's body fat, is a standard way to estimate obesity: BMI = weight in kilograms ÷ (height in metres)$^2$.

People with a BMI between 18.5 and 24.9 have a normal weight, whereas those with a BMI of 25–29.9 are considered overweight. People with a BMI of 30.0 or more are considered obese. People with a BMI greater than 27 have a moderately increased risk for developing type 2 diabetes, high blood pressure, and heart disease. Those with a BMI greater than 30 have a greatly increased risk for these conditions.

Conventional wisdom asserts that eating less is the way to lose weight. The relationship between eating and excessive body weight, however, is much more complex. One complicating factor is the probable existence of a genetically determined, homeostatic set point for body weight. If our body weight varies from the set point, compensating mechanisms adjust metabolism and eating behaviour to return body weight to the set point. But, if a genetically determined set point governs human body weight, then why is the incidence of obesity increasing in the population? Some researchers speculate that our set points are changing toward greater deposition of fat because, on average, we are less physically active and have greater access to food, especially fatty foods and sugars. The search for factors governing the set point and the general concern over growing obesity have sparked intensive research into the genetic mechanisms that might control fat deposition and maintain body weight.

Leptin is a circulating hormone derived from adipocytes (fat cells). It informs the brain about energy stores. Mice with mutant forms of the genes encoding leptin or leptin receptors become morbidly fat. Studies have revealed, however, that the genetics of weight control are considerably more complex in humans than they are in mice. Inconclusive results of leptin trials have turned attention to the development of other drugs to control obesity. PYY (pancreatic polypeptide YY), a recently discovered hormone, stimulates the appetite-suppressive centre in the hypothalamus and inhibits the appetite-stimulating centre. Trial injections of PYY in mice, rats, and humans have led to a significant decrease in appetite and eating.

To add to the complex story, recent studies also indicate that the microorganisms that inhabit our guts may contribute to obesity. The human gut microbiome contains an estimated $10^{13}$–$10^{14}$ microorganisms. Gut microorganisms consist largely of bacteria, with two groups predominating: the Firmicutes (a phylum of Gram-positive bacteria) and the Bacteroidetes (a phylum of Gram-negative bacteria). Jeffrey Gordon and his group at Washington University School of Medicine, St. Louis, have shown that genetically obese mice (genotype *ob/ob*) have about 50% fewer Bacteroidetes, and correspondingly more Firmicutes, than do normal, lean siblings (genotype *ob*+/*ob*+), leading to the conclusion that particular distributions of bacteria in the gut microbiome correlate with obesity.

**Research Question:** Are particular populations of bacteria in the gut microbiome associated with obesity in humans?

**Experiment:** Gordon's group studied the relationship between intestinal populations of the two types of bacteria and body fat in humans. They worked with 12 people classified as being obese according to the standard criterion of having a body mass index (BMI) of ≥ 30. **Figure 1** shows the experimental design of Gordon's research.

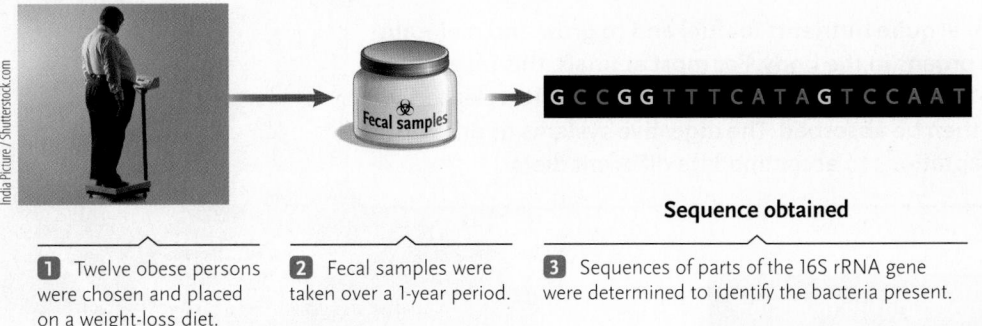

**Sequence obtained**

1️⃣ Twelve obese persons were chosen and placed on a weight-loss diet.

2️⃣ Fecal samples were taken over a 1-year period.

3️⃣ Sequences of parts of the 16S rRNA gene were determined to identify the bacteria present.

**Figure 1  Experimental design**

Sequencing specific regions of the 16S rRNA gene (which encodes an rRNA found only in the ribosome of prokaryotes) enabled the researchers to identify the bacteria in the fecal sample. The regions sequenced vary significantly among species, permitting the identification of species present in a mixed sample without having to culture the organisms. Analyzing these sequences is one of the methods used in molecular phylogenetics (see Section 19.7).

**Results:** Most of the bacteria present in the obese individuals and in two lean individuals (controls) were Firmicutes or Bacteroidetes. As shown in **Figure 2**, (1) before embarking on the diet, obese individuals had more Firmicutes and fewer Bacteroidetes than lean individuals; and (2) over the course of the diet, as weight loss occurred, the relative abundance of Firmicutes decreased, and the relative abundance of Bacteroidetes increased.

**Conclusion:** Obese and lean individuals showed significant differences in their intestinal content of Firmicutes and Bacteroidetes. Moreover, the data from the effects of the weight-loss diet indicate a dynamic relationship between the intestinal populations of the two groups of bacteria and body fat content. Taken with the results of the mouse study, this suggests that manipulation of intestinal microbial communities could be a potential way to treat obesity. However, we must be cautious. The results of this research must not be interpreted to mean that microbiome composition is the cause of obesity. That is, gut microbiome composition is only one factor contributing to obesity. Other factors include genetics, described above, as well as hormones, neurological effects, the environment, and lifestyle choices.

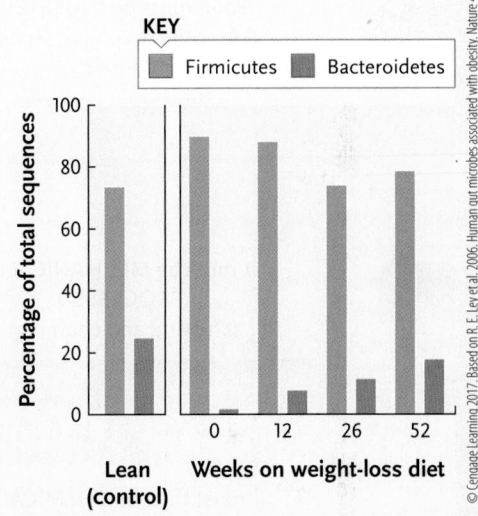

**Figure 2  Results**

© Cengage Learning 2017. Based on R. E. Ley et al. 2006. Human gut microbes associated with obesity. Nature 444:1022–1023; P. J. Turnbaugh et al. 2006. An obesity-associated gut microbiome with increased capacity for energy harvest. Nature 444:1027–1031.

# Summary Illustration

All animals need to acquire nutrients for fuel and to grow and maintain all the tissues and organs in the body. For most animals, this means that food must be ingested and digested, and the nutrients released in this process must then be absorbed. The digestive systems of different animals reflect adaptations to accommodate different diets.

**Five main processes occur from ingestion of food to expulsion of wastes**

Food must be INGESTED.
(There are four basic feeding methods.)

It must be MECHANICALLY PROCESSED
(chewing and churning).

**Stomach**

Food is typically processed by a muscular stomach in mammals.

It must then be CHEMICALLY DIGESTED.
(This involves secretion of enzymes and enzymatic hydrolysis.)
This occurs primarily in the stomach and the small intestine.

**Section of small intestine**

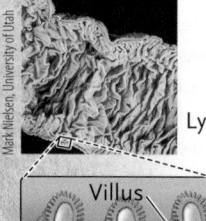

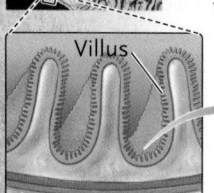

Folds of small intestine

**Capillaries**

**Lymphatic vessel**

**Villus**

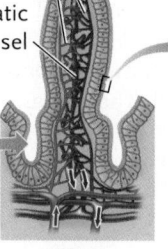

Villus

Chemical digestion and absorption primarily take place in the intestine in mammals.

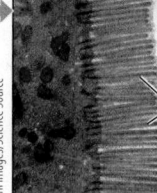

Microvilli

Intestinal epithelial cell

These small molecules are then ABSORBED, primarily in the small intestine.
(Some substances are absorbed in the stomach and some ions in the large intestine.)
Water remaining in the feces is ABSORBED in the large intestine.

Waste material is ELIMINATED.

**All steps are controlled.**

Colon

Small intestine

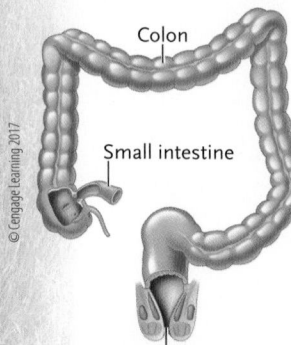

Anus

Waste material is eliminated through the anus.

Mark Nielsen, University of Utah

© Cengage Learning 2017

Ami Images/Science Source

© Cengage Learning 2017

© Cengage Learning 2017

It is essential that the food contain sufficient fuel to provide energy for the body, and all the molecules required to build, repair, and maintain tissues, organs, enzymes, hormones, receptor molecules, etc.

# SELF-TEST QUESTIONS

## Recall/Understand

1. Vitamins are which of these types of compound?
   a. coenzymes
   b. fatty acids
   c. amino acids
   d. carbohydrates

2. Which type of molecules do animals require but cannot synthesize?
   a. nonessential nutrients
   b. essential nutrients
   c. enzymes
   d. proteins

3. In which of these types of animals is the *crop* part of the digestive tract?
   a. birds and insects
   b. reptiles and birds
   c. humans and insects
   d. humans and reptiles

4. Which of these components are required for protein synthesis to continue?
   a. all macrominerals
   b. all vitamins
   c. all 20 amino acids
   d. essential amino acids only

5. Which of the following is the role of the liver in digestion?
   a. to synthesize lipase to form free fatty acids
   b. to secrete trypsin to break the bonds in polypeptides
   c. to secrete bile and bicarbonate ions to help emulsify fats
   d. to store bile between meals

6. Cellulose is digested by fermentation in which of these animals?
   a. humans
   b. ruminants
   c. birds
   d. amphibians

7. Which of these sets of animals includes those that eat blood and body fluids exclusively?
   a. earthworms, frogs, and aphids
   b. tapeworms, flukes, and butterflies
   c. blackflies, leeches, and vampire bats
   d. wolves, cats, and hummingbirds

8. Which of these statements *best* describes regulation of digestion?
   a. Gastrin stimulates pancreatic secretion of HCl and pepsinogen.
   b. Secretin stimulates gastric emptying into the duodenum.
   c. CCK stimulates gastric activity to activate the duodenum.
   d. Leptin binds different hypothalamic receptors to stimulate appetite.

## Apply/Analyze

9. Which of the following shows a correct order of successive steps in digestion?
   a. Absorption follows enzymatic hydrolysis.
   b. Secretion of enzymes follows absorption of digestive material.
   c. Mechanical processing follows enzyme secretion.
   d. Enzymatic hydrolysis precedes secretion of digestive aids.

10. Suppose you notice that your muscles are weak and sore. You suspect a lack of minerals. What should you be eating to alleviate these problems?
    a. shellfish and nuts
    b. lean meat and lots of fruits
    c. eggs and green leafy vegetables
    d. whole grains and legumes

## Create/Evaluate

11. Suppose a friend complains to you that she has muscle cramps and poor appetite. Which of these elements is she most likely lacking?
    a. chromium
    b. chlorine
    c. calcium
    d. cobalt

12. You want to remain healthy. Which of these vitamins would you most likely need to maintain your nervous system?
    a. A
    b. $B_{12}$
    c. C
    d. D

13. Suppose that your friend is diagnosed with malnutrition. She asks you to help her understand what this means. Which of these statements would you most likely use to explain it to her?
    a. She is eating too many calories per day.
    b. She is suffering from a malignant problem in her guts.
    c. She is starved for one or more essential nutrients.
    d. She is eating fewer calories than she needs for her daily activities.

14. Suppose that you wanted to create a nutritious meal that contains calcium, phosphorus, sulfur, and potassium. What should you include in your meal?

15. Suppose that you notice muscular weakness and cramps in your dog. What would you consider feeding more of to your dog to improve its condition?

# Chapter Roadmap

**Gas Exchange: The Respiratory System**
Oxygen must be delivered to mitochondria to produce ATP, and carbon dioxide must be removed from cells and excreted.

**From Chapter 4**

**From Chapter 6**

**40.1 General Principles**
$O_2$ and $CO_2$ are delivered to, and exchanged across, specialized surfaces.

**40.2 Gas Exchange Organs**
There are a wide variety of surfaces across which $O_2$ and $CO_2$ are exchanged.

**40.3 The Mammalian Respiratory System**
The human respiratory system is used as an example to explore the details of how gases are exchanged.

**40.4 Exchange of Gas with Blood**
There are three different ways gas exchange is achieved in different animals.

**40.5 Transport of Gases in Blood**
Oxygen and carbon dioxide are transported from gas exchange surfaces to tissues in the blood.

**To Chapter 41**

© Cengage Learning 2017.

THE CANADIAN PRESS/Chris Bolin

A CT scan of healthy human lungs

# Gas Exchange: The Respiratory System

# 40

**Why it matters . . .** Most animals with an active metabolism must breathe to survive. The mitochondria of their cells need a constant supply of $O_2$ to generate ATP. $O_2$ is required as the terminal electron acceptor of respiratory electron transport (see Chapter 5). In addition, respiration also produces $CO_2$, which needs to be rapidly removed from animal cells because high cellular $CO_2$ is a narcotic poison that damages nerve function. High cellular $CO_2$ also produces changes in cellular pH, which in turn alter the activity levels of all functional proteins (enzymes, receptors, transport proteins, etc.; see Chapter 3).

This is particularly challenging for animals that live in habitats where oxygen is limited (**hypoxic** environments), such as stagnant ponds, ice covered lakes, in underground burrows, or at altitude. Not surprisingly, animals that live under these conditions display adaptations that help to overcome this problem. Marine mammals, such as dolphins, must come to the water's surface to breathe and they exhibit adaptations that prolong breath holding during diving. Many species of fish living in oxygen-poor waters also have adaptations that allow them to breathe air at the water's surface **(Figure 40.1a)**. Species native to high altitude are well adapted to survive under conditions where few humans can go without supplemental oxygen (Figure. 40.1b, c). An understanding of the basic mechanisms underlying gas exchange and the suite of **respiratory** adaptations found in animals gives us insight into species' range distribution (who can live where), the consequences of climate change (how this affects who can live where), and steps that can be taken to alleviate respiratory distress in animals and humans.

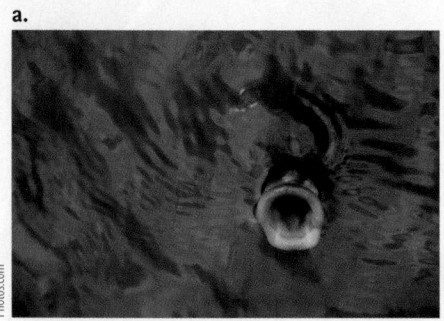

**FIGURE 40.1** **(a)** Carp air-breathing in hypoxic water. **(b)** Llama living at high altitude. **(c)** Human using supplemental oxygen to climb at high altitude

What are the adaptations that allow animals to live in oxygen-limited environments? In this chapter, we introduce the physical laws that are the basis for gas exchange and describe how evolution has produced a range of adaptations that maximize the rate of gas exchange both into and out of the tissues of animals living in different environments. For single-celled organisms, exchange is simply across the plasma membrane. For large, multicellular organisms, however, exchange generally entails a series of steps known as the **gas transport cascade**. These steps (shown for an air-breathing vertebrate in **Figure 40.2**) transport oxygen and carbon dioxide between the environment and mitochondria that are too far from the body surface to exchange gases by simple diffusion alone.

## 40.1 General Principles

Air normally contains about 78% nitrogen ($N_2$), 21% oxygen ($O_2$), and less than 1% carbon dioxide ($CO_2$) and other gases (**Table 40.1**). While this percentage composition of air remains constant from sea level up into the atmosphere, the number of molecules of $O_2$ (and any other gas) in air decreases. This is because air has weight! Thus, the more air above us, the greater the pressure of the air pushing down and the more compressed (thicker) the air is. The density (thickness or thinness) of the air in the atmosphere is measured as the **atmospheric pressure**, which is greater the closer you are to sea level and decreases with increasing altitude. The unit of measurement is often millibars or pounds per square inch; in the biomedical world it is usually expressed as millimetres of mercury (mm Hg) or kilopascals (kPa; 1 kPa = 7.501 mm Hg). At sea level, the atmospheric pressure is 760 mm Hg (or 101.3 kPa): the pressure generated by the weight of a column of air descending from the atmosphere to the surface of Earth is sufficient to support a vertical column of mercury 760 mm high. This pressure is the sum of the pressures of all the gases in a mixture.

The individual pressure exerted by each gas within a mixture of gases such as air is defined as its **partial pressure** (that part of the total pressure due to that gas). It is calculated by multiplying the fractional composition of that gas by the atmospheric pressure. Given that $O_2$ is 0.21 (i.e., 21%) of air, the partial pressure of $O_2$, abbreviated as $P_{O_2}$, at sea level is 0.21 × 760 mm Hg, or 160 mm Hg. Thus, the fractional composition of air at the top of Mount Everest is the same as that at sea level, but the partial pressures of each major gas in air are reduced to roughly one third those at sea level (the air is thinner and weighs less; Table 40.1). The atmospheric pressure in a burrow at sea level is the same as that of the air outside. However, animals living in the burrow consume oxygen and produce $CO_2$; thus, the composition will be different from the air outside due to the slow exchange of gases between the burrow and the environment (Table 40.1).

**CONCEPT FIX** It is a myth that dissolved gases in aqueous solutions always diffuse from areas of high to areas of low concentration. Gases are not equally soluble in different fluids or in the same fluid at different temperatures. For instance, oxygen is far more soluble in lipid or air than it is in water, and it is more soluble in cold fluids than in warm ones. Thus, when oxygen is in equilibrium between two different solutions, the concentrations in each may be very different if the solubility of the gas in each solution is different, but their partial pressures will be the same. Just as a solute will move by simple diffusion from an area of high concentration to an area of low concentration, a gas will move down a partial pressure gradient from a region of high partial pressure to an area of low partial pressure. ⬡

### 40.1a The Movement of Gases Is Due to Several Factors

While gases diffuse between two sites due to differences in partial pressure, the rate (amount per unit time) at which a gas will diffuse depends on a set of factors, only one of which is the difference in partial pressure between the two regions. The other factors include the area of the surface across which diffusion occurs, the thickness of the surface across which it occurs, the temperature, the size of the molecule, and the nature of the medium through which it is diffusing (gas, liquid, or solid).

a.

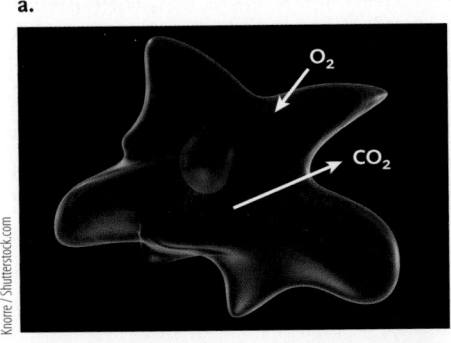

b.

c.

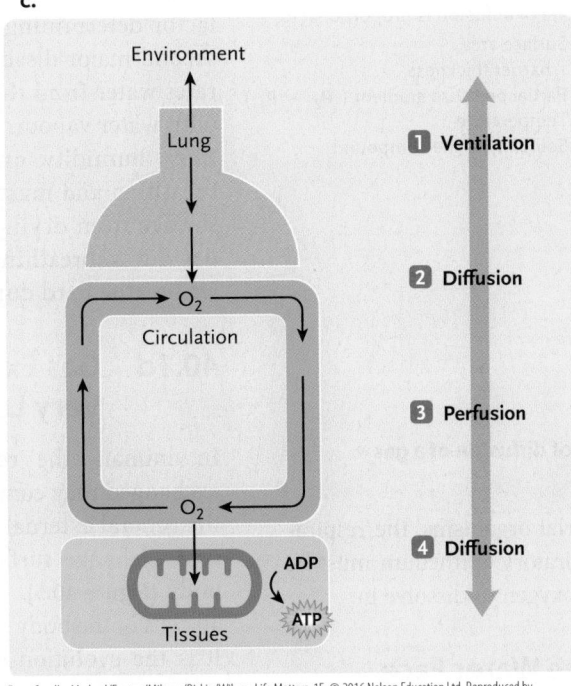

Environment

Lung

Ventilation

O₂

Circulation

Diffusion

Perfusion

O₂

ADP

Diffusion

ATP

Tissues

From Cavallo-Medved/Fenton/Milsom/Riskin/Wilson. Life Matters, 1E. © 2016 Nelson Education Ltd. Reproduced by permission. www.cengage.com/permissions

**FIGURE 40.2 (a)** In single-celled organisms, oxygen and carbon dioxide are exchanged with the external environment directly across the cell membrane. **(b)** For large multicellular organisms (e.g., polar bear, *Ursus maritimus*), this is not possible because most cells have no contact with the external environment. For these organisms, gas exchange involves multiple steps. **(c)** The steps in the cascade for the transport of oxygen between the environment and the mitochondria in an air-breathing vertebrate are shown here. There are four steps: (1) ventilation to move gas into and out of the lungs, (2) diffusion of oxygen into the blood, (3) perfusion or transport of blood by the heart to the tissues, and (4) diffusion of oxygen from the blood in the capillaries in the tissues into the mitochondria in the cells. The steps for the transport of $CO_2$ from the cells to the environment are the reverse of this.

| TABLE 40.1 | The Gas Composition of the Atmosphere at Two Different Elevations and in an Underground Burrow |
|---|---|

The composition of each gas is given both as a percentage of the total and, in brackets, as a partial pressure of total atmospheric pressure.

| Gas | Sea Level Atmosphere | Top of Mount Everest Atmosphere | Burrow Atmosphere |
|---|---|---|---|
| Nitrogen ($N_2$) | 78.09 (593) | 78.09 (196) | 78.09 (593) |
| Oxygen ($O_2$) | 20.95 (159) | 20.95 (53) | 12–18 (91–137) |
| Carbon dioxide ($CO_2$) | 0.03 (0.25) | 0.03 (0.08) | 3–9 (23–68) |
| Other gases | 0.93 (7.75) | 0.93 (1.92) | 0.93 (7.5) |
| Total | 100 (760) | 100 (251) | 100 (760) |

From Cavallo-Medved/Fenton/Milsom/Riskin/Wilson. Life Matters, 1E. © 2016 Nelson Education Ltd. Reproduced by permission. www.cengage.com/permissions

Anything that increases the diffusion coefficient, increases the surface area of the exchange surface, enhances the partial pressure gradient (P1 – P2), or reduces the thickness of the diffusion path will speed the rate of diffusion **(Figure 40.3)**. We will briefly discuss some of these factors next.

## 40.1b Gas Exchange Surfaces Must Be Moist

For gases to pass across an epithelium and enter the cells of animals, they must be dissolved and in solution; they cannot enter as a bubble of gas. For aquatic organisms, oxygen is already dissolved

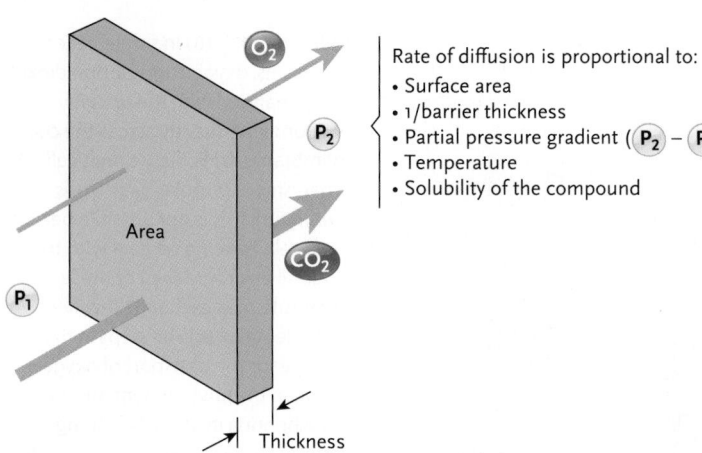

Rate of diffusion is proportional to:
- Surface area
- 1/barrier thickness
- Partial pressure gradient ($P_2 - P_1$)
- Temperature
- Solubility of the compound

**FIGURE 40.3 Factors affecting the rate of diffusion of a gas**

in the water they breathe. For terrestrial organisms, the respiratory medium is air, and thus the respiratory epithelium must be covered by a thin film of fluid for the oxygen to dissolve in.

## 40.1c Animals That Breathe Water Face Different Problems Than Those That Breathe Air

All gases diffuse slower in water than in air and the solubility of many gases is very different in water than in air. $O_2$ at 20°C diffuses approximately 10 000 times faster in air than in water. In addition, for the same volume, there is approximately 30 times the amount of $O_2$ in air as in water for the same partial pressure. These two factors require animals that live in water to breathe much more in order to obtain the same volume of $O_2$ as an animal that breathes air. Moreover, the **density** of water is about 1000 times that of air, and its **viscosity** is about 50 times that of air. Therefore, it takes significantly more energy to move water than air over a respiratory surface.

In addition, temperature and solutes affect the $O_2$ content of water. That is, as either the temperature or the amount of solute increases, the amount of gas that can dissolve in water decreases. Therefore, with respect to obtaining $O_2$, aquatic animals that live in warm water are at a disadvantage compared with those that live in cold water. And because solutes (such as sodium chloride) are higher in sea water than in freshwater, animals living in a marine environment are at a disadvantage compared to those living in a freshwater environment.

There are advantages to breathing water, however. Since $CO_2$ is roughly 20 times more soluble in water than $O_2$, $CO_2$ excretion is easily achieved as a result of the ventilation required to obtain oxygen in aquatic organisms. Thus, aquatic animals face challenges in obtaining $O_2$ from water compared with terrestrial animals (**Figure 40.4**) but have a much easier time eliminating $CO_2$. For air-breathing organisms, the relatively high $O_2$ content, low density, and low viscosity of air greatly reduce the energy required to breathe. There are disadvantages to breathing air, however. $CO_2$ is not eliminated as easily in

air-breathing organisms. Thus, excretion of $CO_2$ is the major factor determining the need of humans to breathe at rest. A second major disadvantage of air is that it constantly evaporates water from the respiratory surface unless it is saturated with water vapour. Therefore, except in an environment with 100% humidity, animals lose water by evaporation during breathing and must replace the water to keep the respiratory surface from drying. Humans loose roughly 1 L of water per day due to breathing at rest. We lose significantly more when we breathe hard during exercise or when we talk a lot.

## 40.1d Gas Exchange Surfaces Are Usually Very Large

In animals, the **respiratory surface** across which gas is exchanged may consist of the individual cells of the organism, the general external surface of the organism, or highly specialized exchange surfaces restricted to specialized areas of the body (**Figure 40.5**). The first two strategies are only effective if all cells of the body are close to the body surface (Figure 40.5a). It is the evolution of larger, specialized, respiratory surfaces

a.

b.

**FIGURE 40.4 (a)** Salmon extract $O_2$ from water. **(b)** Moose extract $O_2$ from air.

**a. Extended body surface: flatworm**

©iStock.com/Piero Malaer

**b. External gills: mudpuppy**

Jack Dermid/Visuals Unlimited, Inc.

**c. Lungs: human**

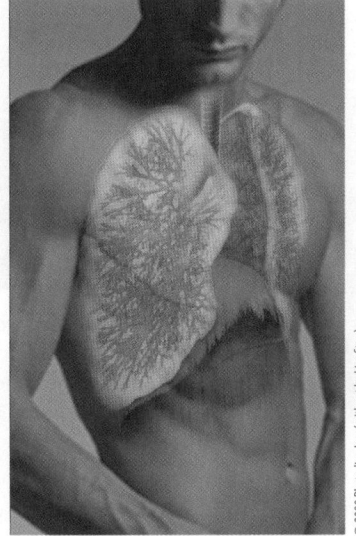

© 2000 Photodisc, Inc. (with art by Lisa Starr)

**FIGURE 40.5 Adaptations increasing the area of the respiratory surface.**
**(a)** The flattened and elongated body surface of a flatworm. **(b)** The highly branched, feathery structure of the external gills in an amphibian, the mudpuppy (*Necturus*). **(c)** The many branches and pockets expanding the respiratory surface in the human lung

and/or some means of transporting gases to and from the surfaces of cells within the organism that have permitted the development of larger and more complex animals. In aquatic animals, these specialized surfaces usually take the form of gills as outward extensions of the body surface (Figure 40.5b). In terrestrial animals, they take the form of inward, moist, protected surfaces such as lungs (Figure 40.5c). The specialized respiratory surfaces are often very large, increasing the surface area. The total area of the lungs in humans is about 100 m². In addition, the cells that make up the specialized respiratory layer are thin, squamous epithelium, decreasing the thickness of the barrier between the water or air outside and the blood.

### 40.1e Ventilation and Perfusion Increase Gas Exchange across Respiratory Surfaces

All gas exchange across respiratory surfaces occurs by diffusion. The primary driving force for diffusion is the partial pressure difference of each gas across the surface. Two adaptations help most animals maximize the difference in partial pressure between gases outside and gases inside the respiratory surface. One is **ventilation**, the flow of the respiratory medium (air or water, depending on the animal) over the respiratory surface. The second is **perfusion**, the flow of blood or other body fluids on the internal side of the respiratory surface (steps 1 and 3 in the gas transfer cascade in Figure 40.2). The evolution of muscular pumps to ventilate specialized gas exchange surfaces and hearts to transport gases between the environment and the tissues throughout the bodies of animals was essential for the evolution of large multicellular organisms.

**VENTILATION** As they respire, animals remove $O_2$ from the respiratory medium and replace it with $CO_2$. Without ventilation, the concentration of $O_2$ would fall in the respiratory medium close to the respiratory surface, and the concentration of $CO_2$ would rise, gradually reducing the partial pressure difference for both gases and reducing their rates of diffusion to below that necessary to sustain life. Examples of ventilation are the one-way flow of water over the gills in fishes and many other aquatic animals and the in-and-out flow of air in the lungs of most vertebrates and in the tracheal system of insects at rest.

**PERFUSION** The rate at which blood or other fluid is replaced on the internal side of the respiratory surface similarly helps maintain a large partial pressure difference for diffusion. The circulatory system in animals that have one brings blood to the internal side of the respiratory surface, transporting $CO_2$ (often in the form of bicarbonate) from all cells of the body. At the surface, $CO_2$ is released into the medium, and a fresh supply of $O_2$ is picked up. Insects, as we will see, do not use blood to transport these gases.

### STUDY BREAK QUESTIONS

1. The air at the top of Mt. Everest still contains 21% oxygen. Why then is it so difficult to breathe?
2. Explain why it is that, when water and air are in equilibrium, there is 30 times as much oxygen in each millilitre of air. Why doesn't oxygen keep diffusing into the water?
3. Why must gas exchange surfaces be moist?
4. How do muscular hearts and respiratory pumps contribute to gas exchange?

## 40.2 Gas Exchange Organs

### 40.2a Small Animals Exchange Gas by Simple Diffusion across the Body Surface

Relying on diffusion alone for gas exchange limits both the size and, to some degree, the shape of the organism. Animals that do so require a large surface area-to-volume ratio and no cell can be far from the body surface. Bacteria have a surface area-to-volume ratio of 6 000 000:1. They can clearly rely on diffusion alone for gas exchange because the surface area is large with respect to the volume, and the distance that the gases must diffuse is relatively small. The same is true of protists. Among multicellular organisms, however, an increase in size can be accommodated only if the distance over which diffusion must occur is minimized. Gas exchange by diffusion in multicellular

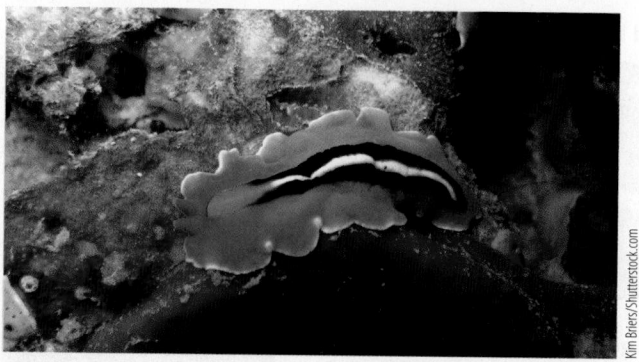

**FIGURE 40.6 Flatworms are an example of a multicellular organism that relies on simple diffusion for gas exchange.** Most free-living flatworms are small, but they may range up to 10 cm or more in length; parasitic forms such as tapeworms may be as long as 3 m or more (see Chapter 27).

organisms can only occur if the organisms are thin and flat (**Figure 40.6**).

## 40.2b Most Aquatic Animals Have Either External or Internal Gills

Gills are respiratory surfaces that are branched and folded evaginations (outward extensions) of the body. They increase the area over which diffusion can take place. **External gills** (Figure 40.5b, **Figure 40.7a**) extend out from the body and do not have protective coverings. They occur in some molluscs, some annelids, the larvae of some aquatic insects, the larvae of some fishes, and the larvae of amphibians. **Internal gills** (Figure 40.7b, c, d) are located within chambers of the body. This provides protection for delicate structures and also allows currents of water to be directed over the gills. Most crustaceans, molluscs, sharks, and bony fishes have internal gills. In adult bony fishes, the gills extend into a chamber covered by gill flaps, or *opercula* (singular, *operculum* = little lid), that serve as part of a one-way pumping system that ventilates the gills (Figure 40.7d).

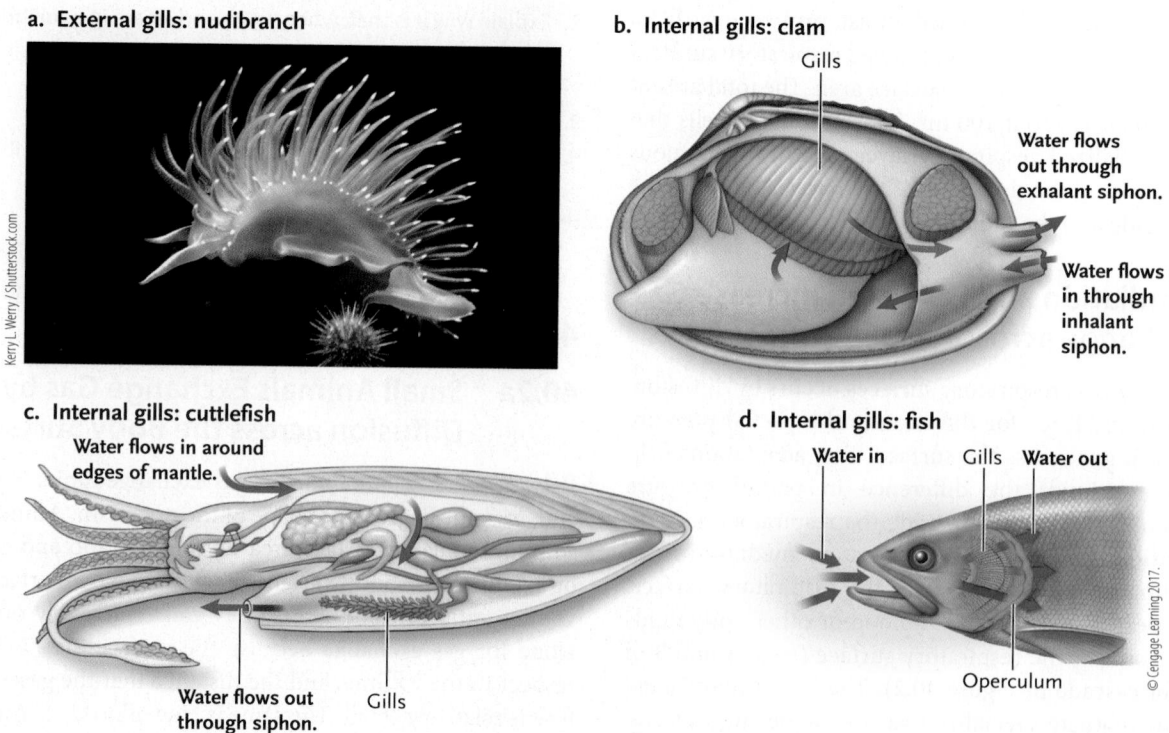

**a. External gills: nudibranch**

**b. Internal gills: clam**

Gills

Water flows out through exhalant siphon.

Water flows in through inhalant siphon.

**c. Internal gills: cuttlefish**

Water flows in around edges of mantle.

Water flows out through siphon.

Gills

**d. Internal gills: fish**

Water in    Gills    Water out

Operculum

**FIGURE 40.7 External and internal gills. (a)** The external gills of a nudibranch (*Flabellina iodinea*). **(b)** The internal gills in a clam. **(c)** The internal gills of a cuttlefish. **(d)** The internal gills of a bony fish. Water enters through the mouth and passes over the filaments of the gills before exiting through an opening at the edges of the flaplike protective covering, the operculum.

## 40.2c Insects Use a Tracheal System for Gas Exchange

Insects breathe air by a unique respiratory system consisting of air-conducting tubes called *tracheae* (*trachea* = windpipe; **Figure 40.8**). The tracheae are invaginations of the outer epidermis of the animal. They are lined with a thin layer of the same cuticle as the exoskeleton and are reinforced by rings of cuticle. They lead from the body surface and branch repeatedly. With each branching, the diameter of the tracheae is reduced, and the tracheae ultimately end as tracheoles less than 1 μm in diameter. Every cell in an insect's body makes contact with at least one tracheole. In the case of large, metabolically active cells, such as the flight muscles, tracheoles may penetrate individual cells via invaginations of the cell membrane. Tracheoles are dead-end tubes with very small tips filled with fluid. Air is transported by the tracheal system to those tips, and gas exchange occurs directly across the very thin cuticle and epithelium of the tracheoles and the plasma membranes of the body cells. At places within the body, the tracheae may expand into internal air sacs that act as reservoirs to increase the volume of air in the system.

Air enters and leaves the tracheal system at openings in the insect's chitinous exoskeleton called **spiracles** (*spiraculum* = air hole). The spiracles are located in a row on either side of the thorax and the abdomen, typically one pair per body segment. Each spiracle incorporates a muscle that allows the spiracles to open and close. $O_2$ is consumed by the tissues and $CO_2$ is taken up by the bicarbonate buffering system, resulting in a small negative pressure inside the tracheal system. The small inward current of air flowing through the reduced opening of the spiracle prevents water vapour from escaping. As the bicarbonate buffering system becomes saturated, free $CO_2$ builds up inside the insect, causing the spiracles to open briefly, allowing $CO_2$ (and water vapour) to escape. In periods of greater activity, as in flight, this mechanism is replaced by one in which alternating compression and expansion of the thorax by the flight muscles also pumps air through the tracheal system.

## 40.2d Most Air-Breathing Vertebrates Exchange Gases Using Lungs

**Lungs** are one of the primary adaptations that allowed vertebrates to fully invade terrestrial environments. Many researchers believe that the bony fish evolved from a freshwater ancestor that had both fins and lungs. The lungs arose as invaginations of the upper digestive tract. Two lines evolved from this ancestor. In one line, the lung lost its connection to the digestive system and became the swim bladder, which controls buoyancy in the modern teleost fishes. The other line (Sarcopterygii), represented by only a few living species, retained the lung, enabling them to survive in $O_2$-poor water or in periods when pools dried up. This line gave rise to the tetrapod vertebrates. In these fish, air is obtained by **positive pressure breathing**, a gulping or swallowing motion that generates a positive pressure that forces air into the lungs.

The lungs of mature amphibians such as frogs and salamanders are also thin-walled sacs with relatively little folding or pocketing. Amphibians also fill their lungs by positive pressure breathing.

In most adult amphibians, a breathing cycle begins with expansion of the buccal (mouth) cavity with the nostrils open and the entrance into the lungs constricted by the glottis (the space between the vocal cords) **(Figure 40.9)**. This draws fresh air into the mouth. Next, the glottis opens, and gas from the lungs enters the buccal cavity, where it mixes with the fresh air to varying degrees as it exits via the mouth and nares (nostrils), which remain open. The nares and mouth then close, and buccal compression forces buccal gas into the lungs. The glottis then closes, and any excess gas left in the buccal cavity is expelled through the nares or mouth at the end of the buccal compression phase. Rhythmic motions of the floor of the mouth with the nostrils open ensure that the buccal cavity contains fresh air for the beginning of the next cycle. Much of the $CO_2$ is lost through the skin, increasing the efficiency of the system.

In reptiles, birds, and mammals, the lungs become more folded, with many pockets, increasing the surface for gas exchange **(Figure 40.10)**. Mammalian lungs consist of millions of tiny air pockets, the **alveoli** (singular, *alveolus*), each surrounded by dense capillary networks. Reptiles, birds, and mammals fill their lungs by **negative pressure breathing** in which muscular contractions expand the chest and lungs, which generates a negative pressure in the air in the lungs, causing air to be pulled inward. The muscles involved in doing this are largely those of the ribcage, but can be assisted by other muscles. In crocodilians, for example, the contraction of a muscle connecting the liver to the pelvis pulls the liver back, causing the lungs to expand, while compression of the abdomen pushes the liver forward, forcing gases out of the lungs.

**FIGURE 40.8 The tracheal system of insects.** This photograph of a translucent caterpillar shows the spiracles opening into the branching network of tracheae. The tracheal system terminates in many tracheolar end cells that have branches with a diameter of less than 1 μm.

Brett Cole

**1** The frog lowers the floor of the mouth and inhales through its nostrils.

**2** Air in the lungs is exhaled when the glottis opens due to elastic recoil of the lungs and body wall.

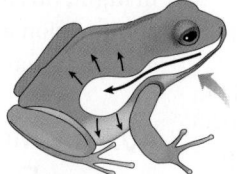

**3** The frog closes its nostrils and elevates the floor of the mouth, forcing air into the lungs.

**4** Rhythmic movements flush the mouth cavity with fresh air for the next cycle.

**FIGURE 40.9 Positive pressure breathing in an amphibian (frog)**

© Cengage Learning 2017.

a.

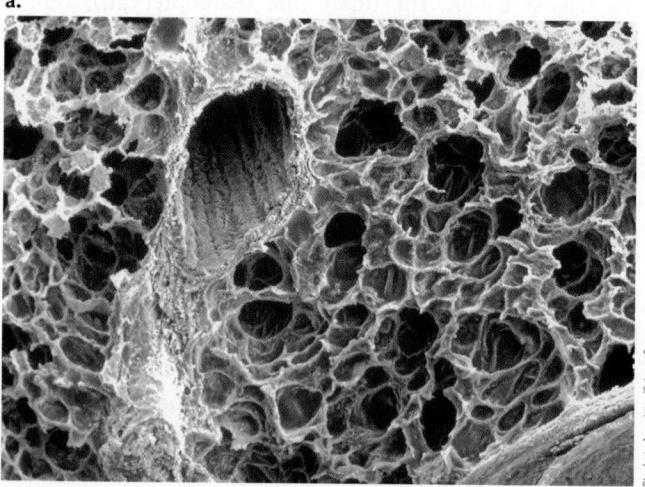

Biophoto Associates/Science Source

b.

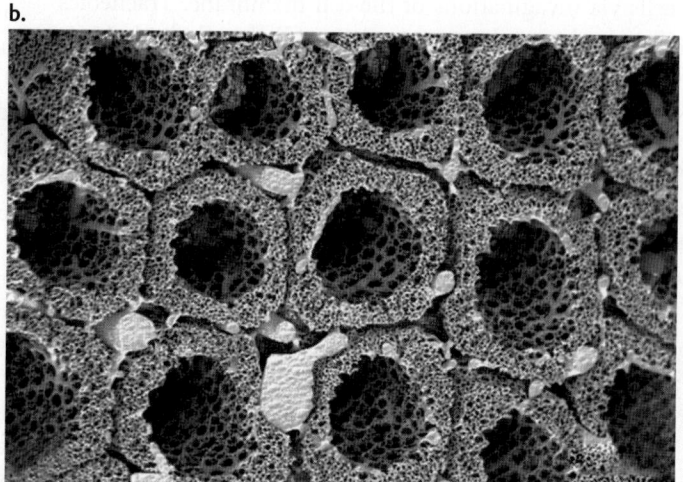

A. N. Makanya, V. Djonov. 2009. "Parabronchial angioarchitecture in developing and adult chickens." *J Appl Physiol* 106:1959–1969. Copyright © 2009, The American Physiological Society. *Journal of Applied Physiology* by AMERICAN PHYSIOLOGICAL SOCIETY. (1887– ) Reproduced with permission of AMERICAN PHYSIOLOGICAL SOCIETY, in the format Republish in a book via Copyright Clearance Center.

**FIGURE 40.10 Scanning electron micrographs of** (a) **the alveoli in a mammalian lung and** (b) **the parabronchial air channels in a bird lung**

The mechanism in mammals is described in detail in the next section.

In addition to paired lungs, birds have up to nine pairs of air sacs that branch off the respiratory tract **(Figure 40.11)**. The air sacs, which collectively contain several times as much air as the lungs, are not respiratory surfaces. Unlike other vertebrate lungs, bird lungs are rigid and do not expand or contract. The air sacs do, however, and they set up a pathway that allows air to flow in one direction through the lungs rather than in and out, as in other vertebrates. As illustrated in Figure 40.11, two cycles of inhalation and exhalation are needed to move a specific volume of air through the bird respiratory system. Within the lungs, air always flows from back to front through an array of fine, parallel tubes, the **parabronchi**. The parabronchi give

rise to blind-ended air capillaries that are surrounded by a blood capillary network. The blood flows in a direction across that of the airflow, setting up a **crosscurrent** exchange (see Section 40.4).

## STUDY BREAK QUESTIONS

1. What is the difference between positive pressure breathing and negative pressure breathing?
2. Describe the similarities and differences in the gas exchange systems of birds and mammals.
3. Why do insects not depend on the circulatory system to deliver $O_2$ to their tissues?

### a. Lungs and air sacs of a bird

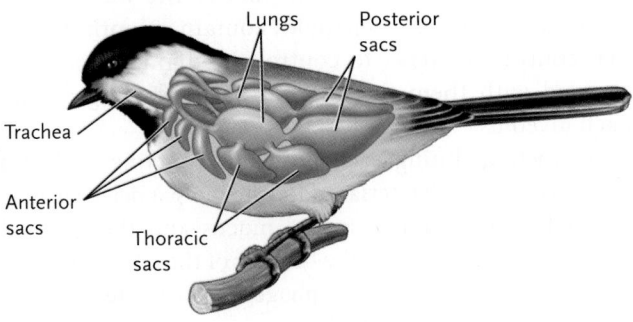

### b. Crosscurrent exchange

**Cycle 1**

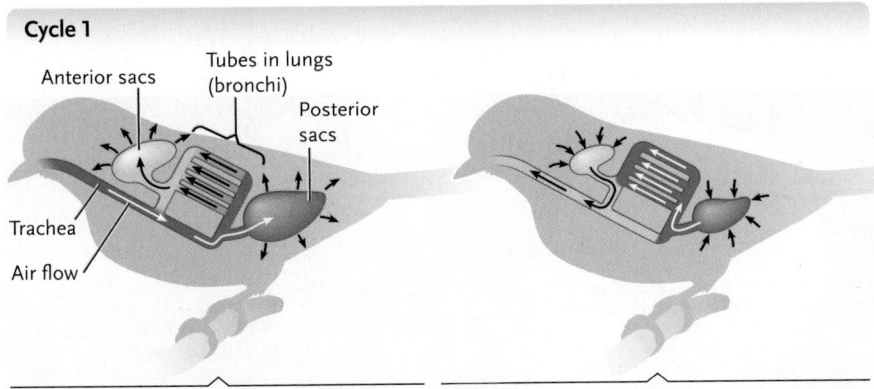

**1** During the first inhalation, most of the oxygen flows directly to the posterior air sacs. The anterior air sacs also expand but do not receive any of the newly inhaled oxygen.

**2** During the following exhalation, both anterior and posterior air sacs contract. Oxygen from the posterior sacs flows into the gas-exchanging tubes (bronchi) of the lungs.

**Cycle 2**

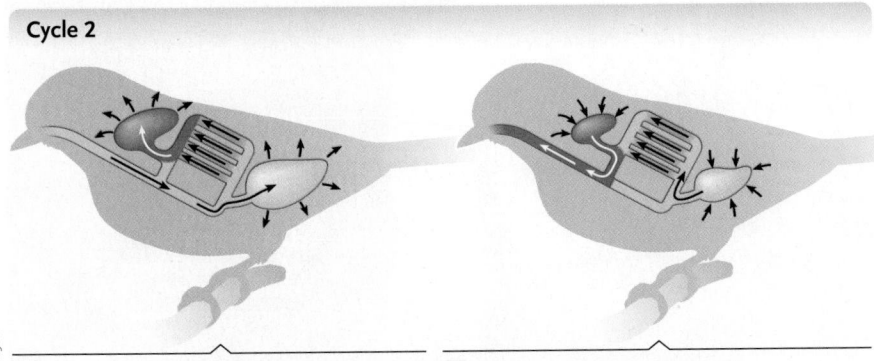

**1** During the next inhalation, air from the lung (now deoxygenated) moves into the anterior air sacs.

**2** In the second exhalation, air from anterior sacs is expelled to the outside through the trachea.

**FIGURE 40.11 Crosscurrent exchange in bird lungs. (a)** Unlike mammalian lungs, bird lungs do not expand and contract. Changes in pressure in the expandable air sacs move air in and out. **(b)** Air flows in one direction through the tubes of the lungs; blood flows across this direction in the surrounding capillary network. Two cycles of inhalation and exhalation are needed to move a specific volume of air through the bird respiratory system.

© Cengage Learning 2017.

## 40.3 The Mammalian Respiratory System

All mammals have a pair of lungs. A diaphragm in the chest cavity acts as the pump that produces the negative pressure required for breathing. Ventilation, pumping air in and out of the lungs, and perfusion by the heart pumping blood through the dense capillary networks in the lungs maximize gas exchange. We will use humans as an example to explore the details of these processes, illustrating how gases are exchanged between the atmospheric air and the blood that transports gases between the lungs and the mitochondria in the tissues.

### 40.3a The Airways Leading to the Lungs Filter, Moisten, and Warm the Entering Air

The human respiratory system is typical for a terrestrial mammal **(Figure 40.12)**. Air enters and leaves the respiratory system through the nostrils and the mouth. Hairs in the nostrils and mucus covering the surface of the airways filter out and trap dust and other large particles. Inhaled air is moistened and warmed as it moves through the mouth and nasal passages.

Next, air moves into the throat, or **pharynx**, which forms a common pathway for air entering the **larynx**, or voice box, and food entering the esophagus, which leads to the stomach. The airway through the larynx is open except during swallowing.

From the larynx, air moves into the **trachea**, which branches into two airways, the **bronchi** (singular, *bronchus*). The bronchi lead to the two elastic, cone-shaped lungs, one on each side of the chest cavity. Inside the lungs, the bronchi narrow and branch repeatedly, becoming progressively narrower and more numerous. The terminal airways, the **bronchioles**, lead into cup-shaped pockets, the **alveoli** (shown in Figure 40.12 insets).

Each of the 150 million alveoli in each lung is surrounded by a dense network of capillaries. By the time inhaled air reaches the alveoli, it has been moistened and brought to body temperature. The many alveoli provide an enormous area for gas exchange. The epithelium of the alveoli is composed of very thin squamous cells.

The trachea and larger bronchi are nonmuscular tubes encircled by rings of cartilage that prevent the tubes from compressing. The largest of the rings, which reinforces the larynx, stands out at the front of the throat as the Adam's apple, which is more prominent in males. The walls of the smaller bronchi and the bronchioles contain smooth muscle cells that contract or relax to control the diameter of these passages and with them the amount of air flowing to and from each alveolus.

The epithelium lining each bronchus contains cilia and mucus-secreting cells. Bacteria and airborne particles such as dust and pollen are trapped in the mucus and then moved upward and into the throat by the beating of the cilia lining the airways. Infection-fighting macrophages (see Chapter 41) also patrol the respiratory epithelium.

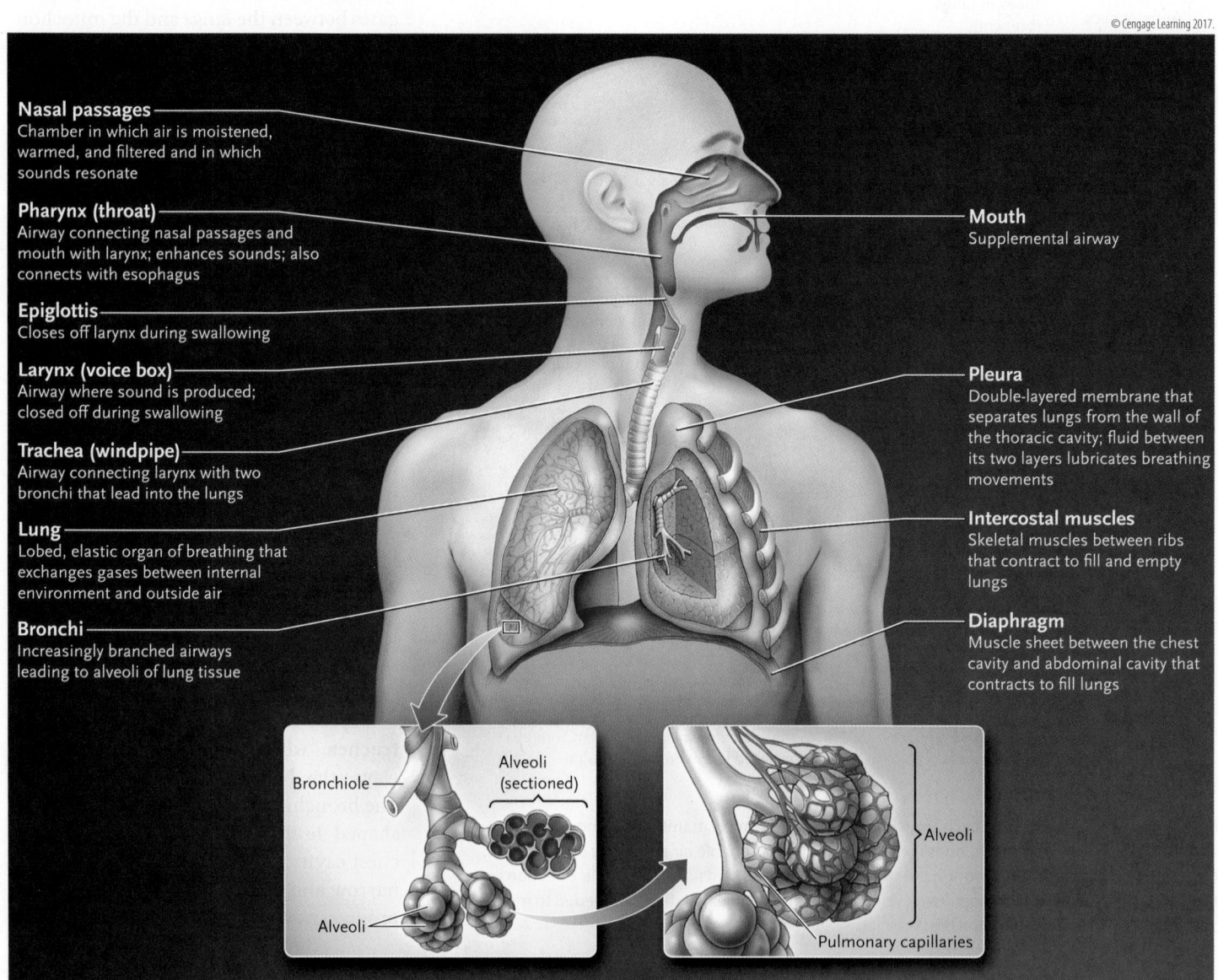

**Nasal passages**
Chamber in which air is moistened, warmed, and filtered and in which sounds resonate

**Pharynx (throat)**
Airway connecting nasal passages and mouth with larynx; enhances sounds; also connects with esophagus

**Epiglottis**
Closes off larynx during swallowing

**Larynx (voice box)**
Airway where sound is produced; closed off during swallowing

**Trachea (windpipe)**
Airway connecting larynx with two bronchi that lead into the lungs

**Lung**
Lobed, elastic organ of breathing that exchanges gases between internal environment and outside air

**Bronchi**
Increasingly branched airways leading to alveoli of lung tissue

**Mouth**
Supplemental airway

**Pleura**
Double-layered membrane that separates lungs from the wall of the thoracic cavity; fluid between its two layers lubricates breathing movements

**Intercostal muscles**
Skeletal muscles between ribs that contract to fill and empty lungs

**Diaphragm**
Muscle sheet between the chest cavity and abdominal cavity that contracts to fill lungs

Bronchiole

Alveoli (sectioned)

Alveoli

Alveoli

Pulmonary capillaries

**FIGURE 40.12** **The human respiratory system, which is typical for a terrestrial mammal**

## 40.3b Contractions of the Diaphragm and Muscles between the Ribs Produce Airflow

The lungs are located inside the ribcage above the **diaphragm**, a dome-shaped sheet of skeletal muscle separating the chest cavity from the abdominal cavity. The lungs are covered by a double layer of epithelial tissue called the **pleura**. The inner pleural layer is attached to the surface of the lungs, and the outer layer is attached to the surface of the chest cavity. A narrow space between the inner and outer layers is filled with slippery fluid, which allows the lungs to move within the chest cavity without rubbing or abrasion as they expand and contract. This fluid also creates a surface tension between the chest wall and the outer covering of the lung. As a result, the lungs cling to the chest wall (like any two wet surfaces) and expand and contract passively as the volume of the chest cavity changes. If air is introduced into this space, due to either rupture of the lung or a penetrating injury to the chest wall (pneumothorax), the lung on that side will collapse.

Contraction of the diaphragm and the intercostal muscles between the ribs brings air into the lungs by a negative pressure mechanism. As an inhalation begins, the diaphragm contracts and flattens, and one set of muscles between the ribs, the external intercostal muscles, contracts, pulling the ribs upward and outward **(Figure 40.13)**. These movements expand the chest cavity and lungs, lowering the air pressure in the lungs below that of the atmosphere. As a result, air is drawn into the lungs, expanding and filling them.

The expansion of the lungs is much like filling two rubber balloons. Like balloons, the lungs are elastic and resist stretching as they are filled. Also like balloons, the stretching stores energy that can expel air from the lungs. During an exhalation by a person at rest, the diaphragm and muscles between the ribs relax, and the elastic recoil of the lungs expels the air.

When physical activity increases the body's demand for $O_2$, contractions of other muscles help expel the air by forcefully reducing the volume of the chest cavity. That is, the abdominal wall muscles contract, which increases abdominal pressure. That pressure exerts an upward-directed force on the relaxed diaphragm, which is pushed upward. In addition, internal intercostal muscles contract, pulling the chest wall inward and downward, causing it to flatten. As a result, the dimensions of the chest cavity decrease.

## 40.3c The Volume of a Breath Can Vary Widely

The volume of air entering and leaving the lungs during inhalation and exhalation is called the **tidal volume**. In a human at rest, the tidal volume amounts to about 500 mL. As physical activity increases, the tidal volume increases to match the body's demands for $O_2$; at maximal levels, the tidal volume reaches about 3400 mL in females and 4800 mL in males. This maximum tidal volume is called the **vital capacity** of an individual.

Even after the most forceful exhalation, about 1200 mL of air remains in the lungs in males and about 1000 mL in females; this is the **residual volume** of the lungs. The lungs cannot be deflated completely because small airways collapse during forced exhalation, blocking further outflow of air. Because air cannot be removed from the lungs completely, some gas exchange can always occur between blood flowing through the lungs and the air in the alveoli.

## 40.3d Ventilation Is Initiated and Controlled by Centres in the Brain

The respiratory movements are controlled by centres in the medulla and pons, parts of the brain stem (see Chapter 45 and **Figure 40.14**). Nerve signals from these centres to the muscles involved in breathing

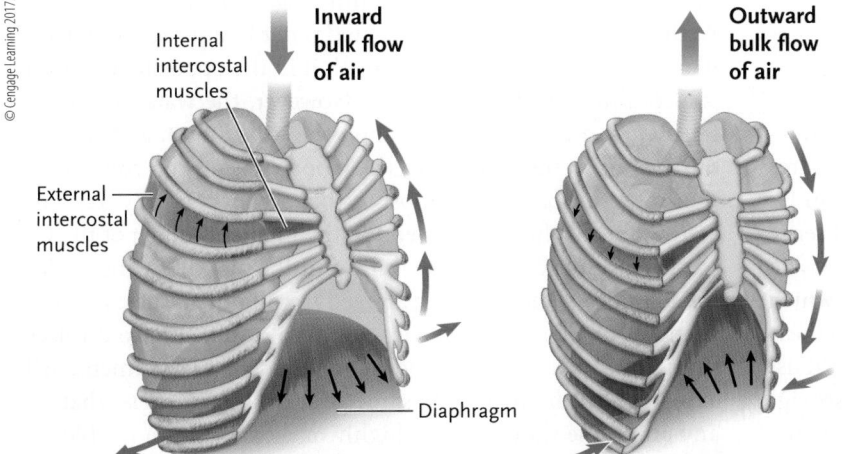

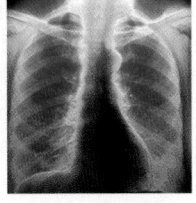

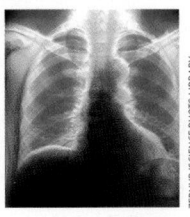

**Inhalation.**
The diaphragm contracts and moves down. The external intercostal muscles contract and lift the rib cage upward and outward. The lung volume expands.

**Exhalation during breathing or rest.**
The diaphragm and the external intercostal muscles return to the resting positions. The rib cage moves down. The lungs recoil passively.

**FIGURE 40.13 The respiratory movements of humans during breathing at rest.** The movements of the ribcage and diaphragm fill and empty the lungs. Inhalation is powered by contractions of the external intercostal muscles and diaphragm, and exhalation is passive. During exercise or other activities characterized by deeper and more rapid breathing, contractions of the internal intercostal muscles and the abdominal muscles add force to exhalation.

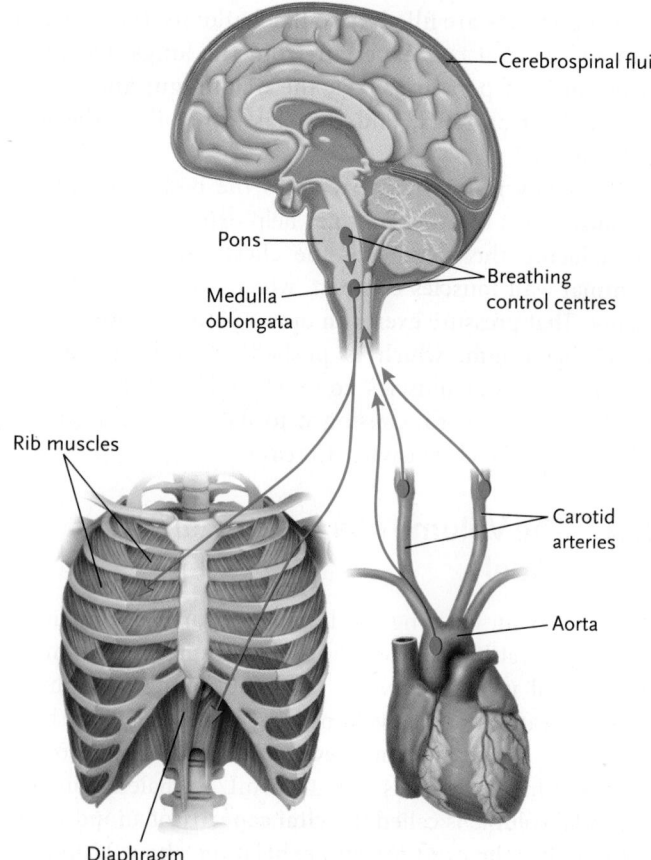

Cerebrospinal fluid

Pons

Medulla oblongata

Breathing control centres

Rib muscles

Carotid arteries

Aorta

Diaphragm

**FIGURE 40.14 Respiratory control centres in the medulla spontaneously produce neural output to the respiratory muscles (the diaphragm and muscles of the rib cage).** The activity of these centres is modulated by neural input from chemoreceptors on the carotid arteries and the aorta, as well as from $CO_2$-sensitive chemoreceptors in the medulla itself.

can vary the intake of air from as little as 5–6 L per minute to as much as 150 L per minute (for very brief periods). These centres integrate information about $O_2$ and $CO_2$ in the blood from $O_2$ and $CO_2$ receptors. These receptors are located in special sense organs (the **carotid bodies**) in the **carotid arteries**, which supply the brain, and in the aorta (the **aortic bodies**), which supplies blood to the rest of the body (Figure 40.14). These receptors are more sensitive to changes in $CO_2$: the $P_{O_2}$ must drop below about 100 mm Hg before their activity increases significantly. The medulla integrates this information with information coming from its own receptors, which monitor the pH of the cerebrospinal fluid. The pH of this fluid is determined mostly by the $CO_2$ concentration in the blood. (Remember that the pH decreases as $CO_2$ levels increase.) In general, the $CO_2$ level is most closely monitored. The $O_2$ receptors act as a backup system, which comes into play only when blood $O_2$ concentration falls to critically low levels. This reflects the fact that air-breathing vertebrates have far more trouble eliminating $CO_2$

than obtaining $O_2$ under normal conditions (see Section 40.1), along with the fact that small changes in pH due to changes in the levels of $CO_2$ throughout the body profoundly affect the activity of all functional proteins, such as enzymes.

## STUDY BREAK QUESTIONS

1. How is breathing in mammals produced? Describe the events associated with inspiration and expiration.
2. How do the upper airways "condition" the air entering the lungs?
3. Explain, based on Figure 40.14, how the fall in $O_2$ at altitude leads to increased breathing.

## 40.4 Exchange of Gas with Blood

Ventilation moves water or air over the respiratory surface. Here oxygen and $CO_2$ are exchanged between the water or air and the blood flowing through the capillaries of the gills or lungs ($O_2$ in; $CO_2$ out). This takes place by simple diffusion, but the efficiency of this exchange is affected by the way in which the water/air and blood come into contact.

Sharks, fishes, and some Crustacea take advantage of one-way flow of water over the gills to maximize the amounts of $O_2$ and $CO_2$ exchanged with water through a mechanism called *countercurrent exchange*. The water flowing over the gills moves in a direction opposite to the flow of blood under the respiratory surface. **Figure 40.15** illustrates countercurrent exchange in the uptake of $O_2$. Because oxygen-rich water and oxygen-deficient blood flow in opposite directions, oxygen diffusion is continuous along the full length of the gill filament. At the point where fully oxygenated water first passes over a gill filament, the blood flowing beneath it in the opposite direction is also almost fully oxygenated. However, the water still contains $O_2$ at a higher concentration than the blood, and the gas diffuses from the water into the blood, raising the concentration of $O_2$ in the blood almost to the level of the fully oxygenated water. At the opposite end of the filament, much of the $O_2$ has been removed from the water, but the blood flowing under the filament, which has just arrived from body tissues, is deoxygenated and contains even less $O_2$. As a result, $O_2$ also diffuses from the water to the blood at this end of the filament. All along the gill filament, the same relationship exists so that, at any point, the water is more highly oxygenated than the blood. With countercurrent exchange, 80%–90% of the $O_2$ in the water may be removed as it flows over the gills. Efficient removal of $O_2$ from water is important because of the much lower $O_2$ content of water compared with air (see Section 40.1c).

In comparison, by breathing in and out and constantly reversing the direction of airflow (uniform and mixed pool flow), mammals manage to remove only about 25% of the $O_2$ content of air (Figure 40.15). The fresh air arriving with each

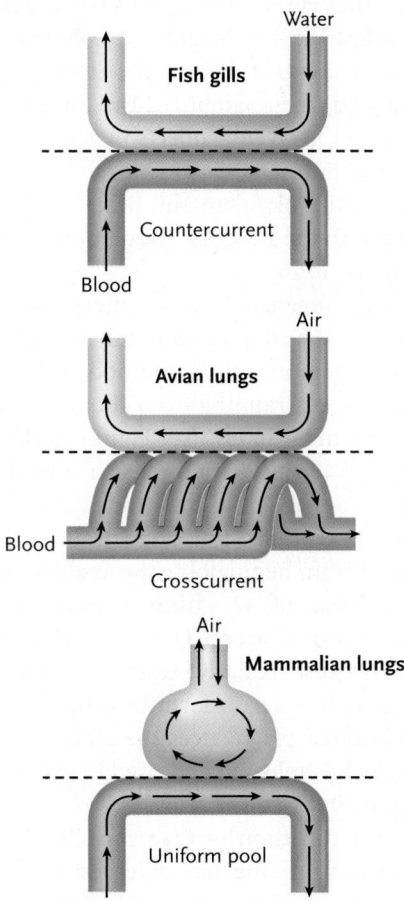

**FIGURE 40.15** The three patterns of gas transfer encountered in vertebrate gas exchange organs are countercurrent, crosscurrent, and uniform (mixed) pool

breath mixes with the residual air remaining in the lungs, diluting it and lowering the concentration of $O_2$ (and increasing the concentration of $CO_2$). The blood comes into equilibrium with this diluted mixture.

In birds, the crosscurrent exchange system makes their lungs the most efficient vertebrate lungs (Figure 40.15). The crosscurrent exchange allows bird lungs to extract more of the $O_2$ from the air than the lungs of mammals do, but less than with the countercurrent exchange system seen in fish.

## STUDY BREAK QUESTIONS

1. Explain how a countercurrent exchange system works.
2. Compare and contrast the way in which air and blood come into contact in a bird lung versus a mammalian lung.
3. What features do fish gills, bird lungs, and mammalian lungs have in common?

## 40.5 Transport of Gases in Blood

In this section, we consider the means by which gases are transported between the respiratory exchange surfaces and other body tissues. Recall that $O_2$ is not very soluble in fluids, and so transport within the body is aided in most animals by pigment molecules that can bind and transport larger quantities of $O_2$. Hemoglobin is the vertebrate respiratory pigment (there are others in invertebrates).

At both the respiratory exchange surface and body tissues, gas exchange occurs when the gas diffuses from an area of higher partial pressure to an area of lower partial pressure. At the sites of gas exchange with the environment, the $P_{O_2}$ in the environment is higher than the $P_{O_2}$ in deoxygenated blood entering the network of capillaries in the gills or lungs (**Figure 40.16**). As a result, $O_2$ readily diffuses into the plasma solution in the capillaries.

### 40.5a Hemoglobin Greatly Increases the Capacity of the Blood to Transport $O_2$

In vertebrates, after $O_2$ enters the plasma, it diffuses into **erythrocytes** (red blood cells), where it combines with hemoglobin. The combination with hemoglobin removes $O_2$ from the plasma, lowering the $P_{O_2}$ of the plasma and increasing $\Delta P_{O_2}$ between alveolar air and the blood. This increases the rate of diffusion of $O_2$ across the alveoli and into the plasma.

Hemoglobin consists of four polypeptides, each linked to a nonprotein heme group that contains an iron atom in its centre (**Figure 40.17**). It is the iron atom that binds $O_2$ molecules, and it is the oxygenation of the iron that gives arterial blood its bright red colour (and red blood cells their name), just as the oxygenation of iron in nature gives rust its colour. Because each hemoglobin molecule has four heme groups, a hemoglobin molecule can potentially bind a total of four molecules of $O_2$ (Figure 40.17).

The number of hemoglobin molecules circulating in the blood is large. In humans there are on average 20 pg of hemoglobin in each red blood cell, and 4–6 million red blood cells in each microlitre of blood. As a result, the combination of $O_2$ with hemoglobin allows blood to carry about 60 times as much $O_2$ (about 200 mL per L) as it could if the $O_2$ simply dissolved in the plasma (about 3 mL per L). About 98.5% of the $O_2$ in blood is carried by hemoglobin, and about 1.5% is carried in solution in the blood plasma.

The reversible combination of hemoglobin with $O_2$ is related to the $P_{O_2}$ in a pattern shown by the hemoglobin–$O_2$ equilibrium curve in **Figure 40.18**. (The curve is generated by measuring the percent of heme groups on each hemoglobin bound to $O_2$ at a given $P_{O_2}$. When all heme groups are bound to an $O_2$, it is fully (100%) saturated.) In air-breathing vertebrates, the curve is not linear but S-shaped, with a plateau region. As the $P_{O_2}$ of the plasma increases, hemoglobin binds to the $O_2$ until every hemoglobin molecule is bound to four molecules of

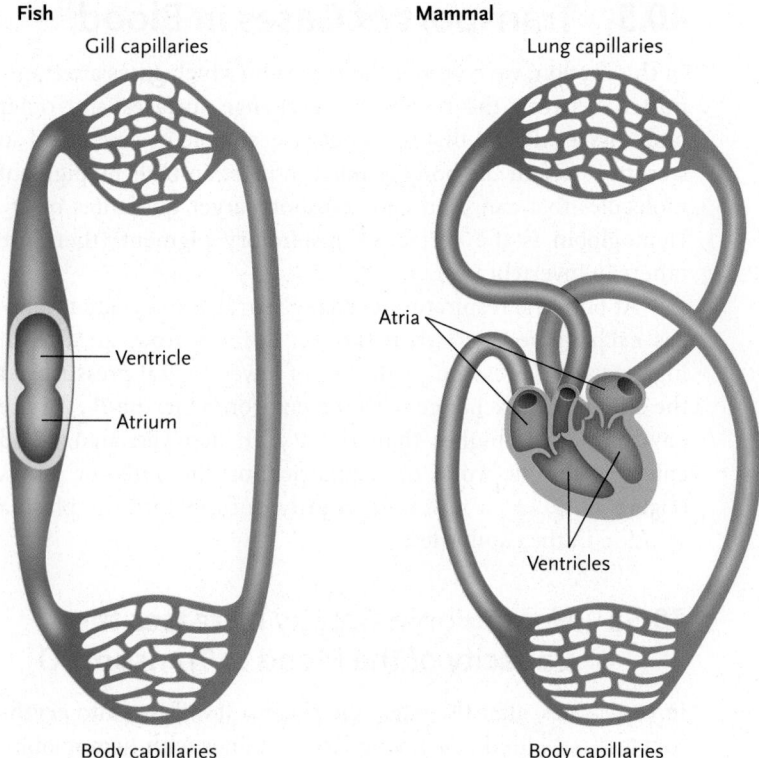

**Fish** — Gill capillaries, Ventricle, Atrium, Body capillaries

**Mammal** — Lung capillaries, Atria, Ventricles, Body capillaries

**FIGURE 40.16 Circulatory systems of a fish and a mammal.** Vessels high in $O_2$ and low in $CO_2$ are coloured red; those high in $CO_2$ and low in $O_2$ are coloured blue

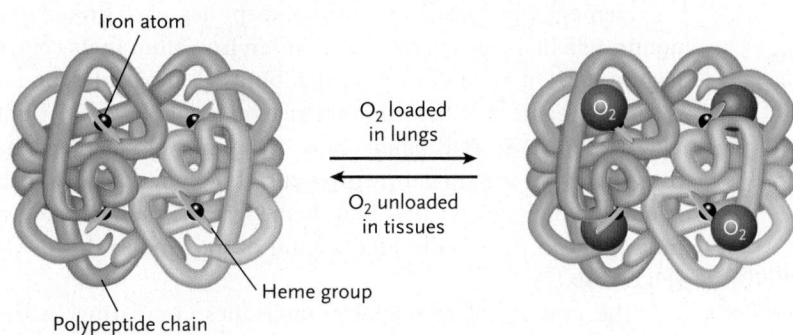

Iron atom, Heme group, Polypeptide chain

$O_2$ loaded in lungs

$O_2$ unloaded in tissues

**FIGURE 40.17 Oxygen binding to hemoglobin**

$O_2$. Once the hemoglobin is fully saturated, further increases in $P_{O_2}$ lead to only a small extra amount of $O_2$ going into solution—the hemoglobin can hold no more. Note that, over the steep part of the curve between 0 and 60 mm Hg (the range found in the capillaries throughout the bodies of most vertebrates), small changes in $P_{O_2}$ result in large changes in the amount of $O_2$ bound to hemoglobin.

Because the $P_{O_2}$ in alveolar air is about 100 mm Hg (13.3 kPa), most of the hemoglobin molecules in the blood leaving the alveolar networks are fully saturated, meaning that most of the hemoglobin molecules have bound four $O_2$ molecules (see Figure 40.18a). The $P_{O_2}$ of the $O_2$ in solution in the blood plasma has risen to approximately the same level as in the alveolar air,

about 100 mm Hg (13.3 kPa). This blood will also change colour, reflecting the bright red colour of oxygenated hemoglobin compared with the darker red colour of deoxygenated hemoglobin. The oxygenated blood exiting from the alveoli collects in venules, which merge to form the pulmonary veins leaving the lungs. These veins carry the blood to the heart, which pumps the blood through the systemic circulation to all parts of the body (Figure 40.16).

As the oxygenated blood enters the capillary networks of body tissues, it encounters regions in which the $P_{O_2}$ in the interstitial fluid and body cells is lower than that in the blood, ranging from about 40 mm Hg downward to 20 mm Hg or less (see Figure 40.18b). As a result, $O_2$ diffuses from the blood plasma into the interstitial fluid, and from the fluid into body cells. As $O_2$ diffuses from the blood plasma into body tissues, it is replaced by $O_2$ released from hemoglobin. Several factors contribute to the release of $O_2$ from hemoglobin, including increased acidity (lower pH) in active tissues. The acidity increases because oxidative reactions release $CO_2$, which combines with water to form bicarbonate ($HCO_3^-$) and $H^+$. The lowered pH reduces the affinity of hemoglobin for $O_2$, which is released and used in cellular respiration (see Figure 40.18b).

The net diffusion of $O_2$ from blood to body cells continues until the blood leaves the capillary networks in the body tissues, at which point roughly 40% of the $O_2$ has been removed from hemoglobin. The blood, now with a $P_{O_2}$ of 40 mm Hg or less, returns in veins to the heart, which pumps it through the pulmonary arteries to the lungs for oxygenation.

Because red blood cells (RBCs) greatly increase the ability of blood to transport oxygen, enhancing the number of RBCs in the bloodstream can enhance athletic performance. Initially, blood doping was achieved by the transfusion of blood, either from other individuals (homologous transfusion) or withdrawn earlier from the athlete and stored until just before a competition (autologous transfusion). Both types of transfusion can be dangerous for a host of reasons, including improperly stored blood, risks of communication of infectious diseases, possibility of a transfusion reaction, and risk of infection. More recently, blood doping has been achieved by the use of the hormone **erythropoietin (EPO)**. EPO is a naturally occurring growth factor that stimulates the formation of new RBCs. Injections of EPO can increase RBC counts for more than six months, and its use has become widespread in endurance sports. Again, it is not without risk. If the RBC count becomes too high, the blood becomes more viscous (thicker, heavier), increasing the work that must be done by the heart.

Becky Scott, now a retired Canadian cross-country skier, was originally awarded a bronze medal at the 2002 Salt Lake

## a. Hemoglobin saturation level in lungs

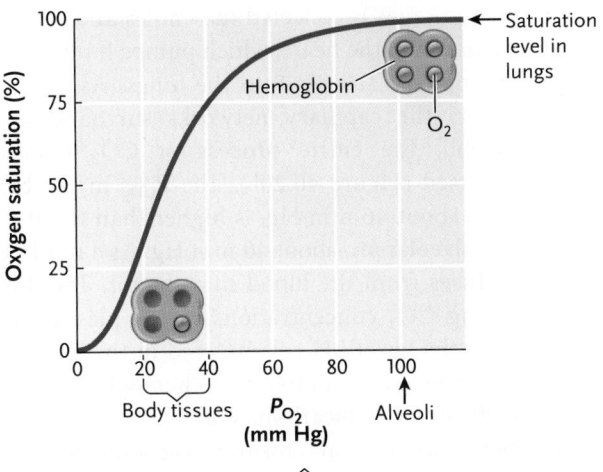

In the alveoli, in which the $P_{O_2}$ is about 100 mm Hg and the pH is 7.4, most hemoglobin molecules are 100% saturated, meaning that almost all have bound four $O_2$ molecules.

## b. Hemoglobin saturation range in body tissues

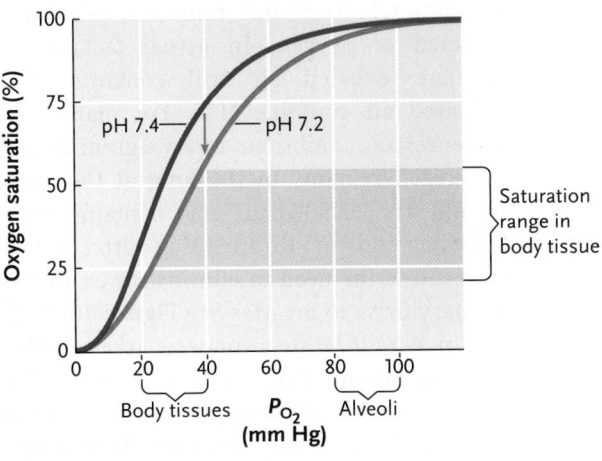

In the capillaries of body tissues, where the $P_{O_2}$ varies between about 20 and 40 mm Hg, depending on the level of metabolic activity, and the pH is about 7.2, hemoglobin can hold less $O_2$. As a result, most hemoglobin molecules release two or three of their $O_2$ molecules to become between 25% and 50% saturated. Note that the drop in pH to 7.2 (red line) in active body tissues reduces the amount of $O_2$ hemoglobin can hold as compared with pH 7.4. The reduction in binding affinity at lower pH increases the amount of $O_2$ released in active tissues.

© Cengage Learning 2017.

**FIGURE 40.18 Hemoglobin–$O_2$ equilibrium curves, which show the degree to which hemoglobin is saturated with $O_2$ at increasing $P_{O_2}$**

City Olympic Games for the 5 km pursuit. Scott's performance was all the more impressive given the nature of her competition. Her medal was later upgraded to a silver and then gold after both of the other medallists tested positive for darbepoetin,

THE CANADIAN PRESS/Chris Bolin

**FIGURE 40.19 Becky Scott with her gold medal**

a pharmacological version of EPO that stimulates erythropoiesis (**Figure 40.19**).

## 40.5b Carbon Dioxide Is Transported Primarily in the Blood as Bicarbonate in Plasma

The $CO_2$ produced by cellular oxidation diffuses from active cells into the interstitial fluid, where it reaches a partial pressure of about 46 mm Hg. Because this is higher than the 40 mm Hg in the blood entering the capillary networks of body tissues, $CO_2$ diffuses from the interstitial fluid into the blood plasma (**Figure 40.20a**).

Some of the $CO_2$ remains in solution as a gas in the plasma. In many organisms, however, significant amounts combine with water to produce carbonic acid ($H_2CO_3$), which dissociates into bicarbonate and $H^+$ ions. In the erythrocyte, the enzyme carbonic anhydrase accelerates the reaction. This reaction maintains a maximal concentration gradient of $CO_2$ between the cells and the blood, and is a means of temporarily storing the gas in a harmless form until it can be transported to the respiratory surface of the animal for release once more as a gas.

Most of the $H^+$ ions produced by the **dissociation** of carbonic acid combine with hemoglobin or with proteins in the blood. This combination, by removing excess $H^+$ from the blood solution, buffers the pH of the blood, helping to maintain it at the set point appropriate for the species, usually about 7.4.

Most of the $H^+$ ions produced by the dissociation of carbonic acid combine with hemoglobin or with proteins in the plasma, so that the pH is maintained. Note, however, that if $CO_2$ levels are high, pH will fall, resulting in changes in breathing. The combination of solution in the plasma, conversion to bicarbonate, and combination with hemoglobin operate to maximize the $\Delta P$ of the gaseous $CO_2$ so that the rate of diffusion from the interstitial fluid into the blood is optimal.

## a. Body tissues

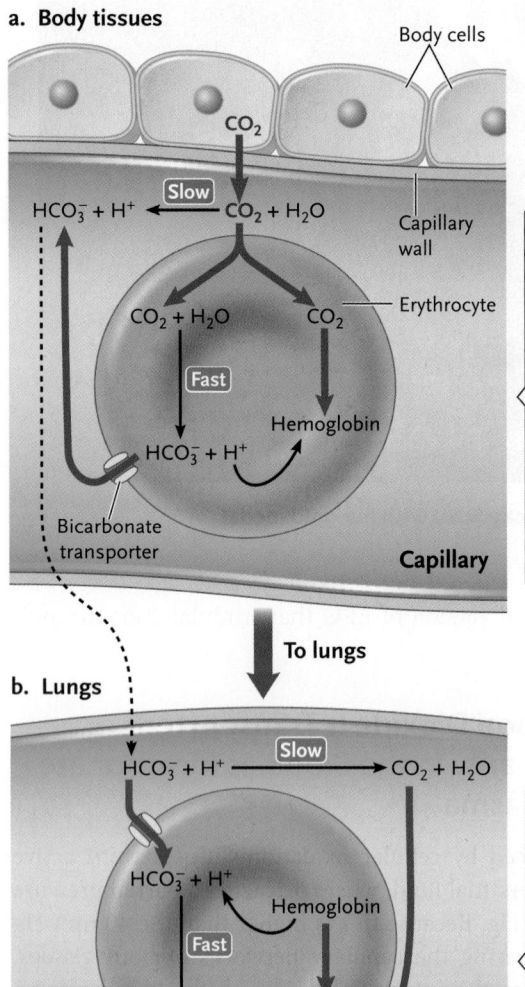

In body tissues, some of the $CO_2$ released into the blood combines with water in the blood plasma to form $HCO_3^-$ and $H^+$. However, most of the $CO_2$ diffuses into erythrocytes, where some combines directly with hemoglobin and some combines with water to form $HCO_3^-$ and $H^+$. The $H^+$ formed by this reaction combines with hemoglobin; the $HCO_3^-$ is transported out of erythrocytes to add to the $HCO_3^-$ in the blood plasma.

**To lungs**

## b. Lungs

In the lungs, the reactions are reversed. Some of the $HCO_3^-$ in the blood plasma combines with $H^+$ to form $CO_2$ and water. However, most of the $HCO_3^-$ is transported into erythrocytes, where it combines with $H^+$ released from hemoglobin to form $CO_2$ and water. $CO_2$ is released from hemoglobin. The $CO_2$ diffuses from the erythrocytes and, with the $CO_2$ in the blood plasma, diffuses from the blood into the alveolar air.

© Cengage Learning 2017.

**FIGURE 40.20 The reactions occurring during the transfer of $CO_2$ from body tissues to alveolar air**

## STUDY BREAK QUESTIONS

1. Why is hemoglobin so important for $O_2$ transport in the blood?
2. Why is the pH of the blood different in tissues and lungs? What is the effect of the change in pH between these two sites for $O_2$ binding to hemoglobin?
3. How is $CO_2$ transported in the blood? Why is hemoglobin not as important for $CO_2$?

The blood leaving the capillary networks of body tissues is collected in venules and veins and returned to the heart, which pumps it through the pulmonary arteries into the lungs. As the blood enters the capillary networks surrounding the alveoli, the entire process of $CO_2$ uptake is reversed (Figure 40.20b). The $P_{CO_2}$ in the blood, now about 46 mm Hg, is higher than the $P_{CO_2}$ in the alveolar air, about 40 mm Hg. As a result, $CO_2$ diffuses from the blood into the air. The diminishing $CO_2$ concentrations in the plasma, along with the lower pH encountered in the lungs, promote the release of $CO_2$ from hemoglobin. As $CO_2$ diffuses away, bicarbonate ions in the blood combine with $H^+$ ions, forming carbonic acid molecules that break down into water and additional $CO_2$. This $CO_2$ adds to the quantities diffusing from the blood into the alveolar air. By the time the blood leaves the capillary networks in the lungs, its $P_{CO_2}$ has been reduced to the same level as that of the alveolar air, about 40 mm Hg.

**CONCEPT FIX** It is a common misconception that, in mammals (including humans), exhaled air is depleted of oxygen. In actual fact, for most humans, exhaled air still contains 16% $O_2$ (inspired air contains 21%). For many animals under resting conditions, a very significant reserve of oxygen remains in the lung at the end of a breath. The exhaled air also contains 4% $CO_2$, however, and for air-breathing terrestrial vertebrates, it is the need to eliminate $CO_2$ that is the primary drive to breathe. See **Figure 40.21**.

In *Why It Matters* you were asked, "What are the adaptations that allow animals to live in oxygen-limited environments?" Having read the chapter, examine the summary illustration that describes the pathway that oxygen takes to reach the mitochondria from the atmosphere. Reflect on the adaptations that have been described that enhance the flow of $O_2$ along this pathway. Those adaptations associated with the heart, blood circulation, and tissue capillary exchange will be described in detail in the next chapter.

FIGURE 40.21  **Experimental Research**

## Demonstration of a Molecular Basis for High-Altitude Adaptation in Deer Mice

**Question:** Do the mutations seen in hemoglobin genes underlie high-altitude adaptation in deer mice?

**Experiment:** Hemoglobin of adult mammals consists of two α-globin and two β-globin polypeptides. As already discussed (Section 40.5a), hemoglobin binds oxygen and transports it in the blood. There are multiple forms of hemoglobin, many of which have arisen from point mutations in the polypeptide globin molecules. Some hemoglobins bind to oxygen more readily than others, and this would be an advantage for species living where there is less oxygen.

Deer mice (*Peromyscus maniculatus*) live and thrive in a wide variety of environments, including at high altitude. Deer mice have two gene loci each for the α-globin and β-globin polypeptides. Jay Storz and his colleagues at the University of Nebraska–Lincoln, and collaborators at the University of Kansas, the University of Porto in Portugal, and the University of Aarhus in Denmark, tested the hypothesis that, compared with their lowland relatives, deer mice living at high altitude have mutations in their α-globin and β-globin genes that lead to hemoglobin molecules adapted to carrying oxygen in low-oxygen environments.

The experimenters isolated DNA from deer mice living at high altitude and at low altitude and compared the sequences of the two α-globin and two β-globin genes.

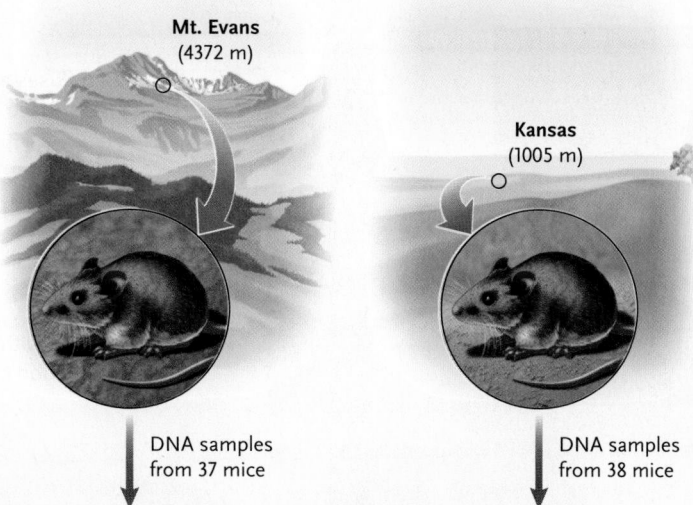

Mt. Evans
(4372 m)

Kansas
(1005 m)

DNA samples
from 37 mice

DNA samples
from 38 mice

The two α-globin and two β-globin genes from each mouse
were cloned, sequenced, and compared.

**Results:** The investigators identified a number of mutations in the four genes of the high-altitude mice. The researchers determined that the mutations increase the oxygen-binding affinity of hemoglobin compared with the low-altitude hemoglobin. This increased binding affinity in turn increased the $O_2$ concentration in arterial blood, thereby enabling the mice to tolerate chronic hypoxia.

**Conclusion:** The research identified specific mutations that correlate with the evolutionary adaptation of deer mice to high altitude.

**Question to Ponder:** The alpine regions in which the high-altitude mice now live were covered with glaciers in the last Ice Age and were not free of ice until about 10 000 years ago. What does that information say about the adaptation of deer mice to high altitude? Also, is there a cost associated with this adaptation? Why is it not also seen in the low altitude mice?

Source: © Cengage Learning 2017. Based on J. Storz et al. 2009. Evolutionary and functional insights intos the mechanism underlying high-altitude adaptation of deer mouse hemo-globin. Proceedings of the National Academy of Sciences USA 106:14450–14455.

# Summary Illustration

For species that use lungs and species that use gills, oxygen takes a particular pathway to reach the mitochondria from the atmosphere to produce ATP. There are also important adaptations that enhance the flow of $O_2$ along this pathway.

$O_2$

Breathing requires a muscular pump (respiratory muscles) to produce breathing.

Breathing transports $O_2$ to the gas exchange surfaces (gills and lungs).

Requires a large, thin, moist, protected surface with a rich blood supply.

$O_2$ then diffuses across the exchange surface into the blood.

Blood must contain special pigments to transport $O_2$.

$O_2$ combines with hemoglobin inside red blood cells.

Requires a muscular pump (heart) to circulate the blood.

The red blood cells are pumped to the tissues by the heart.

Must be large, thin, moist and protected.

$O_2$ diffuses from the tissue capillaries to the mitochondria inside cells where it is used to make ATP.

All steps are controlled.

ATP

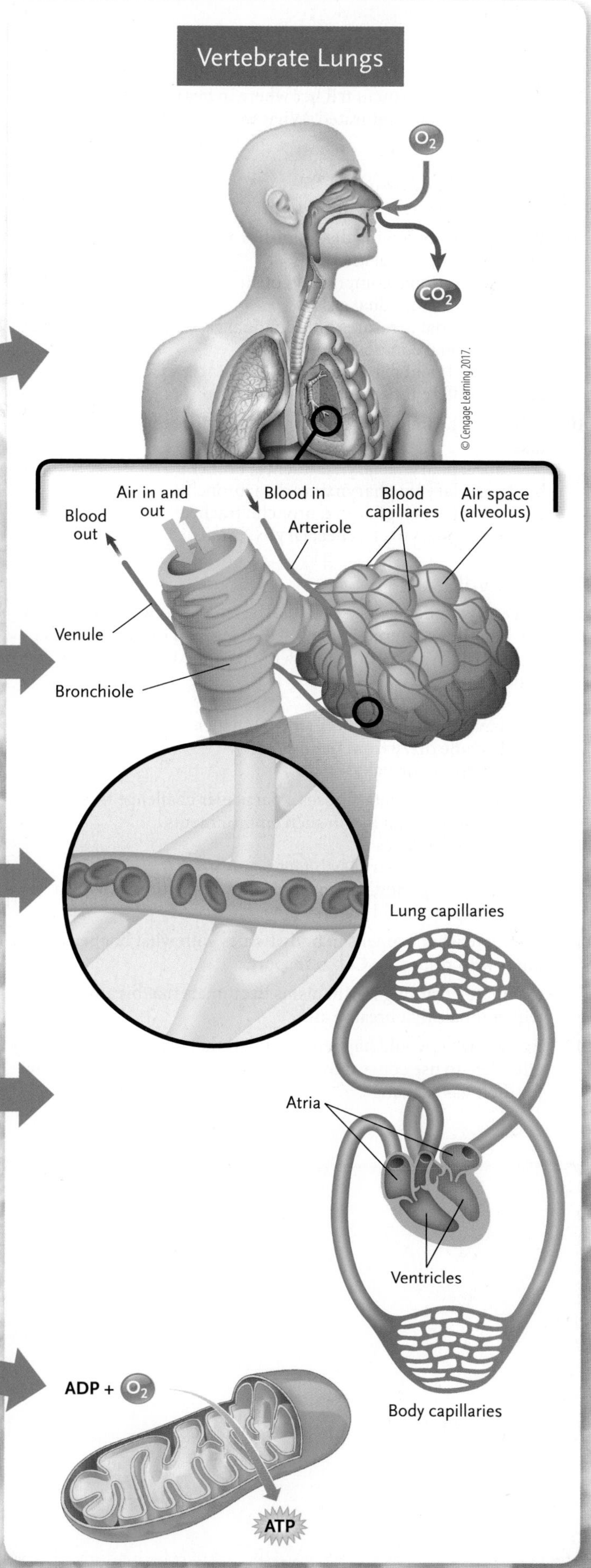

Vertebrate Lungs

$O_2$

$CO_2$

© Cengage Learning 2017.

Air in and out
Blood out
Blood in
Blood capillaries
Air space (alveolus)
Arteriole
Venule
Bronchiole

Lung capillaries

Atria

Ventricles

Body capillaries

ADP + $O_2$

ATP

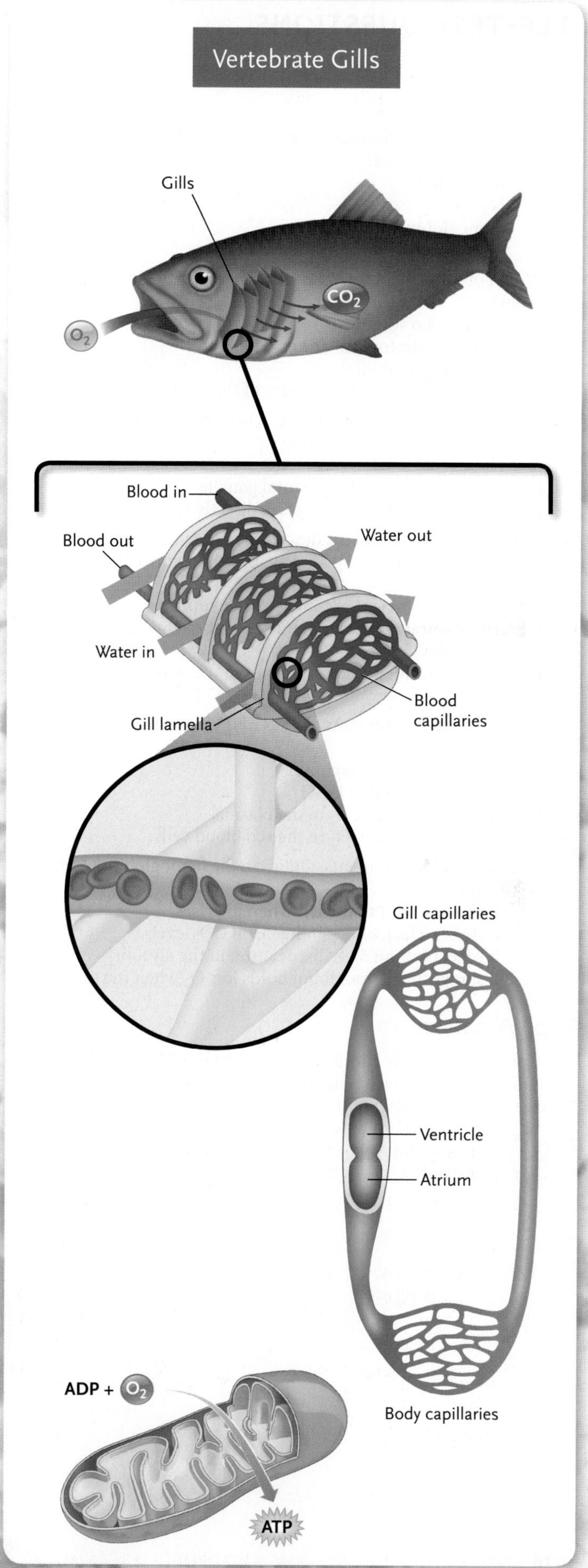

Vertebrate Gills

Gills

$O_2$

$CO_2$

Blood in
Blood out
Water out
Water in
Gill lamella
Blood capillaries

Gill capillaries

Ventricle

Atrium

Body capillaries

ADP + $O_2$

ATP

# SELF-TEST QUESTIONS

## Recall/Understand

1. Which of these molecules greatly increases the $O_2$-carrying capacity of the blood?
   a. myoglobin
   b. $N_2$
   c. hemoglobin
   d. $CO_2$

2. Which of these factors is an advantage associated with breathing water?
   a. low oxygen solubility
   b. dense respiratory medium
   c. high $CO_2$ solubility
   d. can breathe a greater amount of the medium

3. Which of the following is characteristic of tracheal systems?
   a. positive pressure breathing
   b. closed tubes that circulate gases
   c. $CO_2$ sensors in the segmental ganglia
   d. transport of respiratory gases directly to every cell

4. Which of these statements describes countercurrent exchange?
   a. It is an exchange of gasses against their concentration gradient.
   b. It is a less efficient exchange than a uniform pool exchange.
   c. The respiratory medium moves in the same direction as the blood flow.
   d. The respiratory medium moves in the opposite direction to the blood flow.

5. Which of these statements applies to the majority of $CO_2$ in the blood?
   a. It is bound to hemoglobin.
   b. It is transported as $HCO_3^-$.
   c. It is dissolved as $CO_2$ in the plasma.
   d. It is dissolved as $CO_2$ in the red blood cells.

6. Which of these statements applies to the hemoglobin–$O_2$ equilibrium curve?
   a. It shows a shift to the left when pH rises.
   b. It shows a lack of dependence on $CO_2$ levels.
   c. It reflects about 50% dissociation in the alveoli.
   d. It shows that hemoglobin holds less $O_2$ when the pH rises.

## Apply/Analyze

7. Canadian Olympic speed skating champion Christine Nesbitt is finishing her last lap. Which of the following occurs at this time?
   a. Her peak tidal volume is at vital capacity.
   b. Her residual volume momentarily reaches zero.
   c. Her lungs undergo elastic recoil when she inhales.
   d. Her diaphragm contracts when she exhales.

8. Your friend asks you to tell her where in her body most of her hemoglobin is 100% saturated. What would you tell her?
   a. in her heart
   b. in her alveoli
   c. in her body tissues
   d. in her central nervous system

9. Which of the following distinguishes air at the top of a high mountain from air at sea level?
   a. the fractional composition of air, but not the partial pressures of individual gasses
   b. the partial pressures of individual gasses only, and not the fractional composition of air
   c. the different percentage of $CO_2$
   d. the different percentage of $O_2$

10. Which of the following orders of organs does the air pathway take?
    a. nose; pharynx; larynx; trachea; bronchi
    b. nose; larynx; pharynx; trachea; bronchi
    c. nose; larynx; pharynx; bronchi; trachea
    d. nose; pharynx; trachea; larynx; bronchi

## Create/Evaluate

11. You and your dog live at sea level. The atmospheric $P_{O_2}$ is 150 mm Hg. Your dog's arterial $P_{O_2}$ is 100 mm Hg, and his tissue $P_{O_2}$ is 10 mm Hg. Which of the following would you expect your dog to do?
    a. accumulate $CO_2$
    b. have a serious but nonlethal $O_2$ deficit
    c. become dizzy from too much $O_2$
    d. function normally

12. Which of these habitats poses a particular challenge to respiration in animals that live in such environments?
    a. rivers and lakes
    b. sea level terrestrial habitats
    c. stagnant ponds, ice-covered lakes, and altitudes
    d. oceans and cold waters

13. Compare what happens in body tissues with what happens in the lungs with respect to $CO_2$ transport.

14. Compare breathing mechanisms in animals that breathe water with animals that breathe air.

15. Explain what would happen if animals that breathe with internal gills were to use concurrent flow instead of countercurrent flow for their gas exchange.

# Chapter Roadmap

## Internal Transport: The Circulatory System

In animals, most cells lie too deep within the body to exchange substances directly with the environment via diffusion. These animals have a circulatory system that conducts $O_2$, $CO_2$, and nutrients among the cells and tissues.

### 41.1 Animal Circulatory Systems: An Introduction

All animal circulatory systems share certain basic features: a specialized fluid, a pump, and conducting vessels.

### 41.2 Blood and Its Components

From Chapter 39

From Chapter 40

Plasma
Ions/Proteins
Cells

$O_2$, $CO_2$
Nutrients
Wastes
Hormones

To Chapter 42

To Chapter 43

### 41.3 The Heart

The structure and function of the heart are examined in detail in mammals.

### 41.4 Blood Vessels of the Circulatory System

The structure and function of the different blood vessels of the circulatory system are described in detail.

### 41.5 Maintaining Blood Flow and Pressure

Controlling blood pressure regulates the delivery of substances to tissues.

To Chapter 44

To Chapter 46

### 41.6 The Lymphatic System

The lymphatic system helps maintain blood volume and also fights disease.

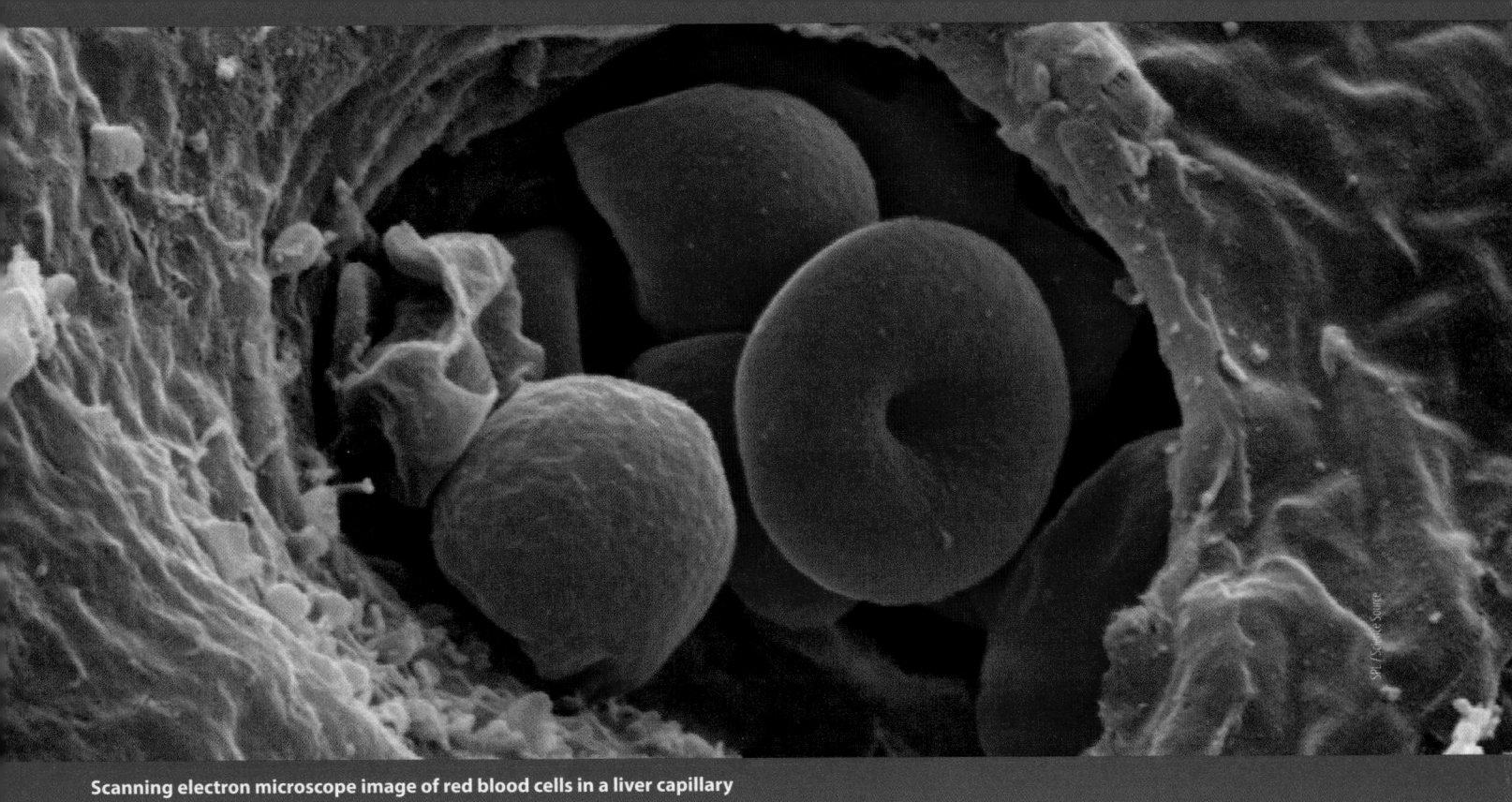

# Internal Transport: The Circulatory System

# 41

**Why it matters . . .** While small animals have low rates of oxygen consumption relative to large animals in absolute terms, their mass-specific metabolic rates (the rate of oxygen consumption of each gram of tissue) is higher; mass-specific metabolic rate increases as body mass decreases. As a result, each gram of a shrew or a hummingbird, two of the smallest endotherms on Earth, consumes approximately 50 times as much oxygen per minute as each gram of a human. When these animals go from rest to maximum levels of activity, their metabolic rates increase by 7–10 times! To deliver the amount of oxygen to the tissues required to sustain activity, these animals must increase their heart rates. The resting heart rate of the Etruscan shrew, the smallest mammal (mean adult body mass 2 g), is around 800 beats per minute, and the maximum heart rate recorded in these animals is just over 1500 beats per minute. Similar maximum heart rates of 1200 beats per minute have been recorded in hummingbirds and small bats (Kitti's hog-nosed bat also weighs only 2 g). The hearts of these animals must contract and relax 20–25 times each second when they are exercising! For comparison, humans have resting heart rates in the range of 50 to 80 beats per minute and maximum heart rates of just over 200.

It has long been known that larger animals with lower mass-specific metabolic rates and heart rates live longer. This gave rise to the hypothesis that all endotherms have a limited number of heartbeats (and breaths) in their lifetime. This was an intriguing idea and was supported by estimates of resting heart rates and lifespans in many birds and mammals. This hypothesis, however, failed to recognize that animals do not spend all their time resting. Thus, the hypothesis fails in most instances. This demonstrates the weakness of basing scientific hypotheses on correlation rather than causation. By the time you finish reading this chapter you should be able to identify other ways, apart from beating faster, that the heart can increase the delivery of blood to tissues.

In the examples just described, the beating of the heart provides the pumping mechanism for moving blood carrying oxygen and nutrients to the tissues. The heart is part of the **circulatory system**, an **organ system** consisting of a fluid and a pump (usually a heart) and vessels for moving important molecules, and often cells, from one tissue to another. Examples of transported molecules are nutrients (Chapter 39), oxygen and carbon dioxide (Chapter 40), waste products (Chapter 42), and hormones (Chapter 43). The system also includes the specialized vessels across which substances are exchanged (the capillaries) and an accessory circulatory system, the **lymphatic system**, which consists of its own vessels and organs. The lymphatic system balances the distribution of fluid between the blood in the vessels and the extracellular fluid (ECF) surrounding the tissues. It also participates in the body's defences against invading disease organisms.

## 41.1 Animal Circulatory Systems: An Introduction

Protostomes with simple body plans, including sponges, flatworms, and nematodes, function with no specialized circulatory system. Nearly all these animals are aquatic or, like parasitic flatworms, live surrounded by the body fluids or intestinal contents of a host animal. Their bodies are structured as thin sheets of cells that lie close to the fluids of the surrounding environment. Nutrients, $O_2$, and $CO_2$ are exchanged with the medium through the surface of the animal, and the products of digestion diffuse among the cells via the interstitial fluids.

In sponges, water carrying nutrients and $O_2$ is pumped by surface cells with beating flagella through hundreds of pores in the body wall, into a central cavity. It then passes through the cavity and leaves through a large exit pore carrying $CO_2$ and wastes **(Figure 41.2a)**. Hydras, jellyfish, sea anemones, and other cnidarians have a central gastrovascular cavity with a mouth that opens to the environment. Water enters and leaves through the mouth, and the gastrovascular cavity serves for both digestion (gastro) and circulation (vascular; Figure 41.2a).

### 41.1a Animal Circulatory Systems Share Basic Elements

In larger and more complex animals, most cells lie in cell layers too deep within the body to exchange substances directly with the environment via diffusion. Instead, the animals have a circulatory system, composed of tissues and organs, that distributes $O_2$, $CO_2$, nutrients, and the products of metabolism among the cells and tissues. The circulatory system connects all tissues to the specialized regions of the animal, where substances are exchanged with the external environment. For example, oxygen is absorbed from the environment in the gills or lungs of many animals and is carried by the blood to all parts of the body; $CO_2$ released from body cells is carried by the blood to the lungs or gills, where it is released to the environment. Soluble wastes are conducted from body cells to the kidneys or other excretory organs, which remove wastes from circulation and excrete them into the environment.

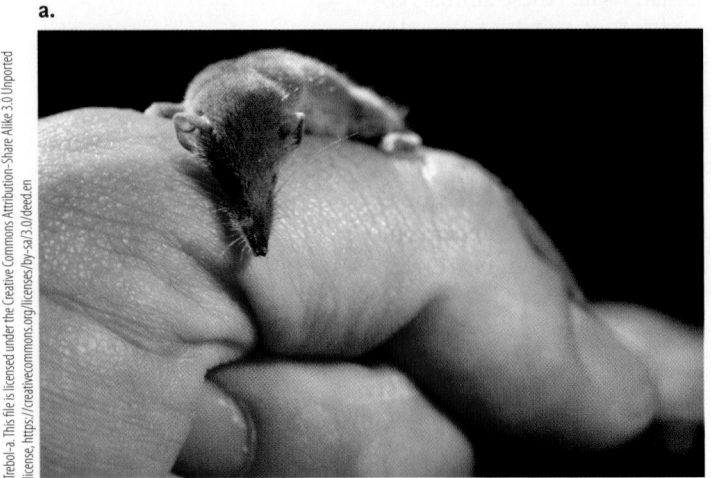

a.

b.

**FIGURE 41.1 (a)** The Etruscan shrew, *Suncus etruscus*. **(b)** A ruby-throated hummingbird (*Archilochus colubris*)

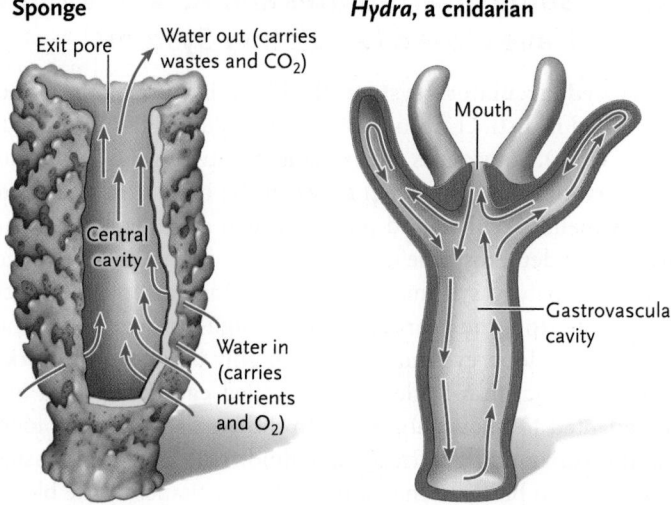

**Sponge**

Exit pore

Water out (carries wastes and $CO_2$)

Central cavity

Water in (carries nutrients and $O_2$)

**Hydra, a cnidarian**

Mouth

Gastrovascular cavity

**a.** Circulation of external fluid through an open body cavity

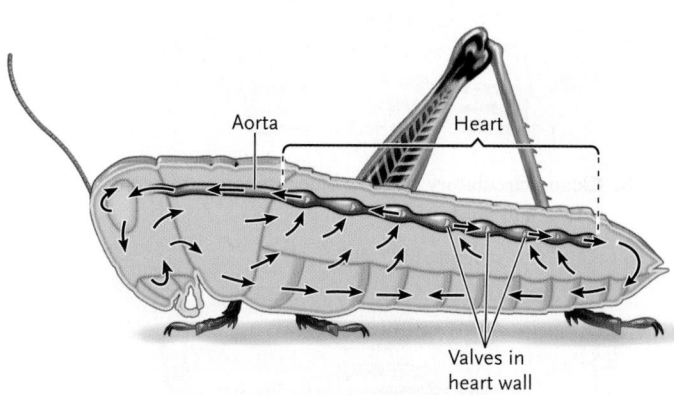

Aorta

Heart

Valves in heart wall

**b.** Circulation of internal fluid through an open body cavity

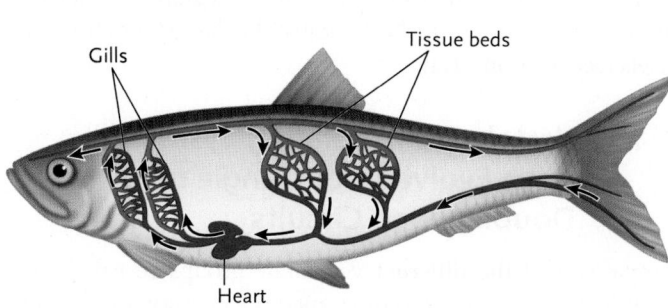

Gills

Tissue beds

Heart

**c.** Circulation of internal fluid through a closed body cavity

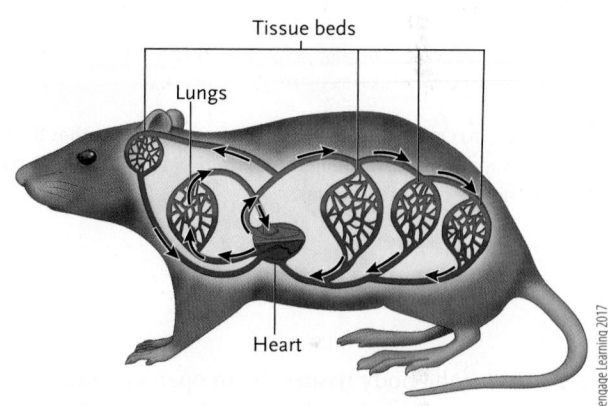

Tissue beds

Lungs

Heart

**d.** Circulation of internal fluid through a closed circulatory system with a double circuit

**FIGURE 41.2 The general plan of the circulatory system in different animals. (a)** Multicellular organisms such as sponges and cnidarians use the external medium to transport molecules between cells. **(b)** Most invertebrates circulate an internal fluid through an open circulatory system. **(c)** Some invertebrates and all vertebrates move an internal fluid through a closed circulatory system in which blood is separated from the interstitial fluid. **(d)** In birds and mammals, two separate circuits serve the lungs and all other tissues of the body.

Animal circulatory systems carrying out these roles share certain basic features:

- **Fluid.** A specialized fluid medium, usually containing at least some cells, carries nutrients from the digestive system, the products of metabolism, and soluble wastes. With the conspicuous exception of the insects, this specialized fluid also transports $O_2$ and $CO_2$ (see Chapter 40).
- **Heart.** A muscular heart pumps the fluid through the circulatory system. Words associated with the heart often include *cardio*, from *kardia*, Greek for "heart."
- **Vessels.** The fluid is usually contained in tubular vessels that distribute it to the various organs. Vessels conducting blood

away from the heart are called **arteries**, and vessels returning blood to the heart are called **veins**.

## 41.1b Most Invertebrates Have Open Circulatory Systems

Animal circulatory systems take one of two forms, either open or closed. In an **open circulatory system,** vessels leaving the heart release fluid, usually termed **hemolymph**, directly into body spaces or into sinuses surrounding organs (Figure 41.2b; **Figure 41.3a**). The blood is not conveyed directly to all cells by tubes but is ejected from the open ends of the blood vessels and

**a. Open circulatory system: no distinction between hemolymph and interstitial fluid**

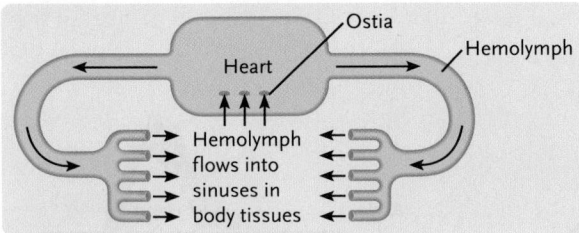

**b. Closed circulatory system: blood separated from interstitial fluid**

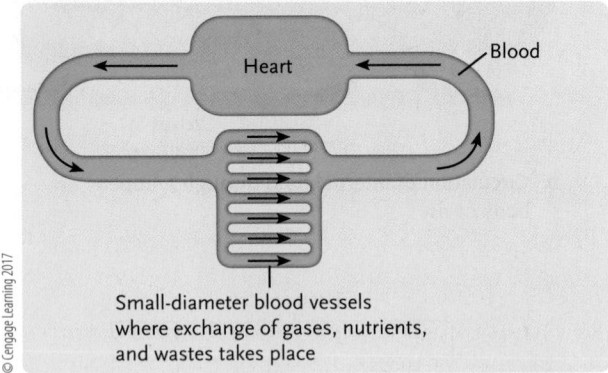

FIGURE 41.3 **(a)** Open circulatory system: hemolymph bathes the organs and body tissues. **(b)** Closed circulatory system: blood is confined in tubes that lie among the cells of all tissues.

directly bathes the body tissues. In an open system, most of the fluid pressure generated by the heart dissipates when the blood is released from vessels into body spaces. The hemolymph re-enters the heart through valves in the heart wall that close each time the heart pumps, thereby maintaining a unidirectional flow. Because of one-way valves in the heart and vessels, the beating heart draws hemolymph in from the tissue spaces as they expand and pushes it out through the vessels as the heart contracts (Figure 41.3a). Although the pressure remains low, the rate at which the blood circulates can be increased by an increase in the rate of beating of the heart. In highly active invertebrates, such as flying insects, the heart rate may rise to three or more times the resting rate, increasing the circulation of the hemolymph among the tissues. In addition, most insects have accessory hearts associated with the wings and each leg, which experience the same increases in rate during periods of high metabolic activity.

Among the protostomes, arthropods and most molluscs have open circulatory systems with one or more muscular hearts. In insects and molluscs, heart rate is controlled in some cases by nerves but largely by a variety of amine and peptide hormones (see Chapter 43).

### 41.1c Some Invertebrates and All Vertebrates Have Closed Circulatory Systems

In a **closed circulatory system**, the blood is confined to blood vessels and is distinct from the interstitial fluid (Figure 41.2c, d; Figure 41.3b). Substances are exchanged between the blood and the interstitial fluid, and then between the interstitial fluid and cells. Annelids, cephalopod molluscs such as squids and octopuses, most deuterostome invertebrates, and all vertebrates have closed circulatory systems. In these systems, arteries conduct blood away from the heart at relatively high pressure. From the arteries, the blood eventually enters highly branched networks of microscopic, thin-walled vessels called **capillaries** that are well adapted to allow substances to diffuse between the blood and the surrounding extracellular fluid. Nutrients and wastes are exchanged between the blood and body tissues as the blood moves through the capillaries. The blood then flows at relatively low pressure from the capillaries to larger vessels, the veins, which carry the blood back to the heart. Typically, the blood is maintained at a higher pressure and moves more rapidly through the body in closed systems than in open systems. In many animals, closed systems allow precise control of the distribution and rate of blood flow to different body regions by means of muscles that contract or relax to adjust the diameter of the blood vessels (see Section 41.4).

### 41.1d Vertebrate Circulatory Systems Have Evolved from Single to Double Blood Circuits

Comparison of the different vertebrate groups reveals several evolutionary trends that accompanied the invasion of terrestrial habitats. Among the most striking are the changes that occurred in the major vessels of the body and the heart. These changes converted the single-circuit system of sharks and bony fish, in which the gills are in the same circuit as the rest of the blood vessels, to a double-circuit system in which the circulation to the lungs parallels the circulation to the rest of the body (Figure 41.2 and **Figure 41.4**).

There were two major developments. In one, the blood vessels supplying the gills were reorganized to accommodate the appearance of lungs. There is an evolutionary progression to an increasing separation of blood flow to the gas exchange organs (**pulmonary circuit**) and to the rest of the body (**systemic circuit**; Figure 41.4).

The second involved developments in the structure of the heart. In a shark or bony fish (Figure 41.4a), venous deoxygenated blood from the tissues enters the first chamber, the atrium. The atrium contracts, forcing open flaplike valves leading into the ventricle and closing valves that prevent backflow into the veins. Contraction of the ventricle propels the blood forward into the ventral aorta leading to the blood vessels going to the gills (the aortic arches), the gill capillaries, and then the dorsal

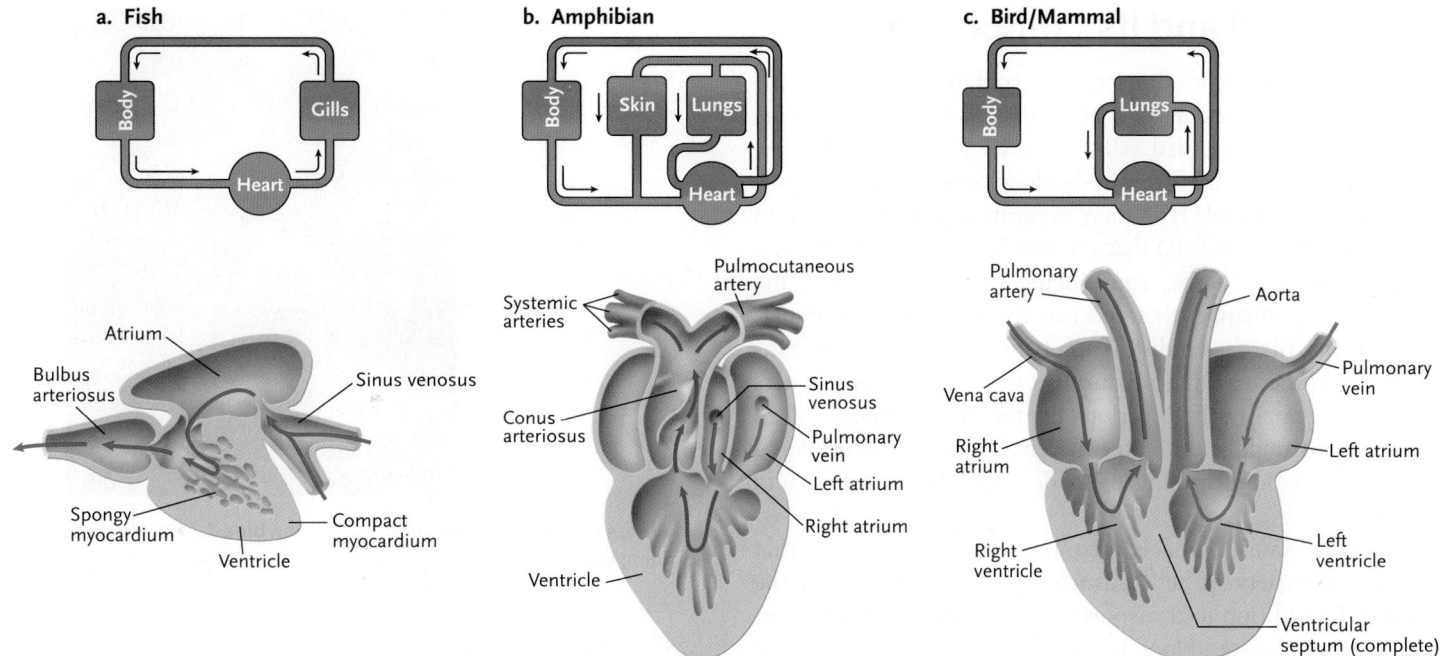

**FIGURE 41.4 Major steps in the evolution of the circulation. (a)** The single circulation of most fishes is powered by a two-chambered heart (one atrium and one ventricle). This gives rise to **(b)** a double circulation in amphibians powered by a three-chambered heart (two atria and one ventricle) that eventually gives rise to **(c)** a double circulation powered by a four-chambered heart (two atria and two ventricles) that provides separate circulations to the lungs and body.

aorta, which carries blood to the tissues. In amphibians, the atrium is divided, with one side (left atrium) receiving oxygenated blood from the lungs and the other side (right atrium) receiving deoxygenated blood from the body and partially oxygenated blood from the skin (Figure 41.4b). In the single ventricle, some separation of the two streams is achieved by the spongy nature of the ventricle, which prevents open mixing, and by a flaplike structure in the vessel leaving the heart that can direct blood into the arteries going to the skin and lungs, or into the arteries going to the rest of the body (Figure 41.4b).

In modern reptiles such as lizards and snakes, the ventricle is partially divided. Full separation of the blood supply to the lungs occurs in mammals, birds, and crocodilians (alligators and crocodiles share ancestry with birds) by complete division of the ventricle (Figure 41.4c). There are thus two separate circuits. One circuit delivers oxygenated blood from the lungs into the left atrium, which then propels it into the left ventricle. The contraction of the left ventricle sends blood to the body circulation via the carotid arteries to the head and the dorsal aorta, which supplies the remainder of the body. In the other circuit, deoxygenated blood from the body and head enters the right atrium and is propelled via the right ventricle to the lungs via the pulmonary artery.

This progressive separation of the body and lung circulation and the accompanying changes in the architecture of the heart (illustrated in Figure 41.4) demonstrate that, although evolution happens by changes in existing structures, changes in one set of structures are correlated with changes in other structures. In this case, changes in the aortic arches are associated with changes in the heart.

*CONCEPT* The partially divided ventricle of most reptiles is often referred to as *incompletely divided*, with the inference that this is a phylogenetic artifact and less than ideal. The cardiovascular systems of reptiles, however, are extraordinarily flexible and no less adaptive for their lifestyles than the systems found in birds and mammals. Evolution of the cardiovascular system does not represent a progressive improvement in design, but rather different adaptive alternatives for meeting the different demands that different lifestyles place on the circulatory system. In the case of the reptiles, the amount of mixing of blood returning from the two atria that occurs in the ventricles can be carefully regulated. ⬡

## STUDY BREAK QUESTIONS

1. What are the differences between open and closed circulatory systems? Has the closed system evolved only once? What are the advantages of a closed system over an open one?
2. Which vertebrates have a separate pulmonary circulation? Compare and contrast the circulatory systems of a fish, a frog, and a beaver, and describe the changes in the structure of the heart that accompany them.

CHAPTER 41   INTERNAL TRANSPORT: THE CIRCULATORY SYSTEM

## 41.2 Blood and Its Components

Although the blood of all vertebrates contains blood cells, the blood of some invertebrates may consist exclusively of plasma with few or no suspended cells, as in the Nematoda. In other invertebrates such as the arthropods, blood cells—or hemocytes—of various recognizable types may occur in large numbers (up to 275 000 per µL in crickets) that can vary with activity and developmental stage. Whereas some hemocytes circulate with the hemolymph (remember that, in invertebrates with open circulatory systems, there is no distinction between blood and interstitial fluid, so the resulting mixture is called *hemolymph*), others may attach temporarily to various tissues. These hemocytes can be mobilized rapidly and enter the circulation, for example, to take part in wound healing or in defence against disease and parasites.

In vertebrates, blood is a complex connective tissue that contains a variety of cells suspended in a liquid called the **plasma**. In addition to transporting nutrients, dissolved gases, and metabolic wastes, blood helps stabilize the internal pH and salt composition of body fluids and serves as a highway for cells of the immune system and the antibodies produced by some of these cells. It also helps regulate body temperature by transferring heat between warmer and cooler body regions and between the body and the external environment (see Chapter 42). The total blood volume of most vertebrates is 5%–8% of body mass (about 4–5 L in an average-sized adult human). The plasma, a clear, straw-coloured fluid, is about 45%–55% of the volume of blood in most vertebrates (55% in human males and 58% in human females). In humans, blood cells develop in red bone marrow, primarily in the vertebrae, sternum (breastbone), ribs, and pelvis. Blood cells originate from cells called *pluripotent* (*plura* = multiple; *potens* = power) stem cells that retain the embryonic capacity to divide (see Chapter 38). Suspended in the plasma are two main types of blood cells, **erythrocytes** and **leukocytes,** which account for the remainder of the blood volume. Vertebrate blood also contains platelets (often called *thrombocytes*), which are membrane-bound fragments of specialized stem-cell–derived megakaryocytes. They play an essential role in the formation of blood clots to heal wounds. These three major blood components are shown in **Figure 41.5**, and the typical components of human blood are given in **Table 41.1**.

### 41.2a Plasma Is an Aqueous Solution of Proteins, Ions, Nutrient Molecules, and Gases

Plasma is complex, and its composition varies depending on many factors (Table 41.1). The plasma proteins of vertebrates fall into three classes: the albumins, the globulins, and fibrinogen. The **albumins**, the most abundant proteins of the plasma, are important for osmotic balance and pH buffering. They also transport a wide variety of substances through the circulatory

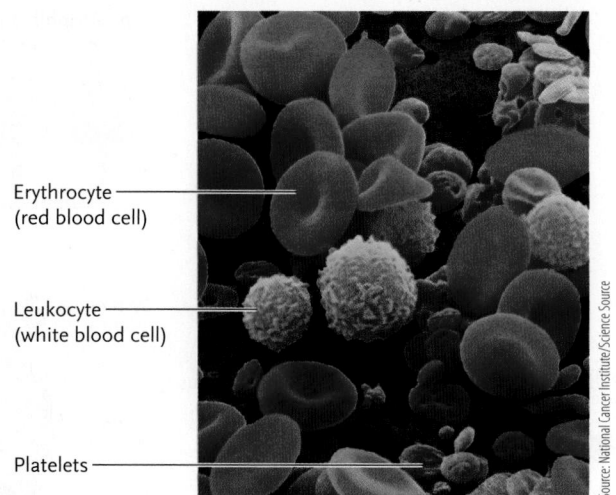

**FIGURE 41.5 Typical components of human blood.** This colourized scanning electron micrograph shows the three major blood components.

system, including hormones and metabolic wastes. Because of their similar chemical composition to hormones, many therapeutic drugs are designed to be transported this way. The **globulins** transport lipids (including cholesterol) and fat-soluble vitamins; a specialized subgroup of globulins, the **immunoglobulins**, includes antibodies and other molecules that contribute to the immune response. Some globulins are also enzymes. **Fibrinogen** plays a central role in the clotting mechanism of blood.

The ions of the plasma include $Na^+$, $K^+$, $Ca^{2+}$, $Cl^-$, and $HCO_3^-$ (bicarbonate). The $Na^+$ and $Cl^-$ ions are the most abundant and are present in concentrations similar to those of sea water, reflecting evolutionary ancestry. Some of the ions, particularly the bicarbonate ion, help maintain arterial blood at its characteristic pH (see Chapter 42).

### 41.2b Erythrocytes Are the Oxygen Carriers of Vertebrate Blood

Erythrocytes, or red blood cells, carry $O_2$ from the lungs to body tissues. Each microlitre of human blood normally contains about 5 million erythrocytes, which are small, flattened, and disclike. They measure about 7 µm in diameter and 2 µm in thickness. Microtubules of the cytoskeleton (see Chapter 2) are arranged beneath the surface of the cell so that they are *biconcave*—thinner in the middle than at the edges (see Figure 41.5). The proteins of the cytoskeleton that determine their shape also give them the flexibility to squeeze through narrow capillaries.

Like all blood cells, erythrocytes arise from stem cells (see Chapter 38) in the red bone marrow. As they mature, mammalian erythrocytes lose their nucleus, cytoplasmic organelles, and ribosomes. Because they are no longer capable of synthesizing new proteins, this limits their metabolic capabilities and their lifespan (as short as 35 days in a chicken, but 120 days in a human). The remaining cytoplasm contains enzymes, which

TABLE 41.1 | The Composition of Human Blood

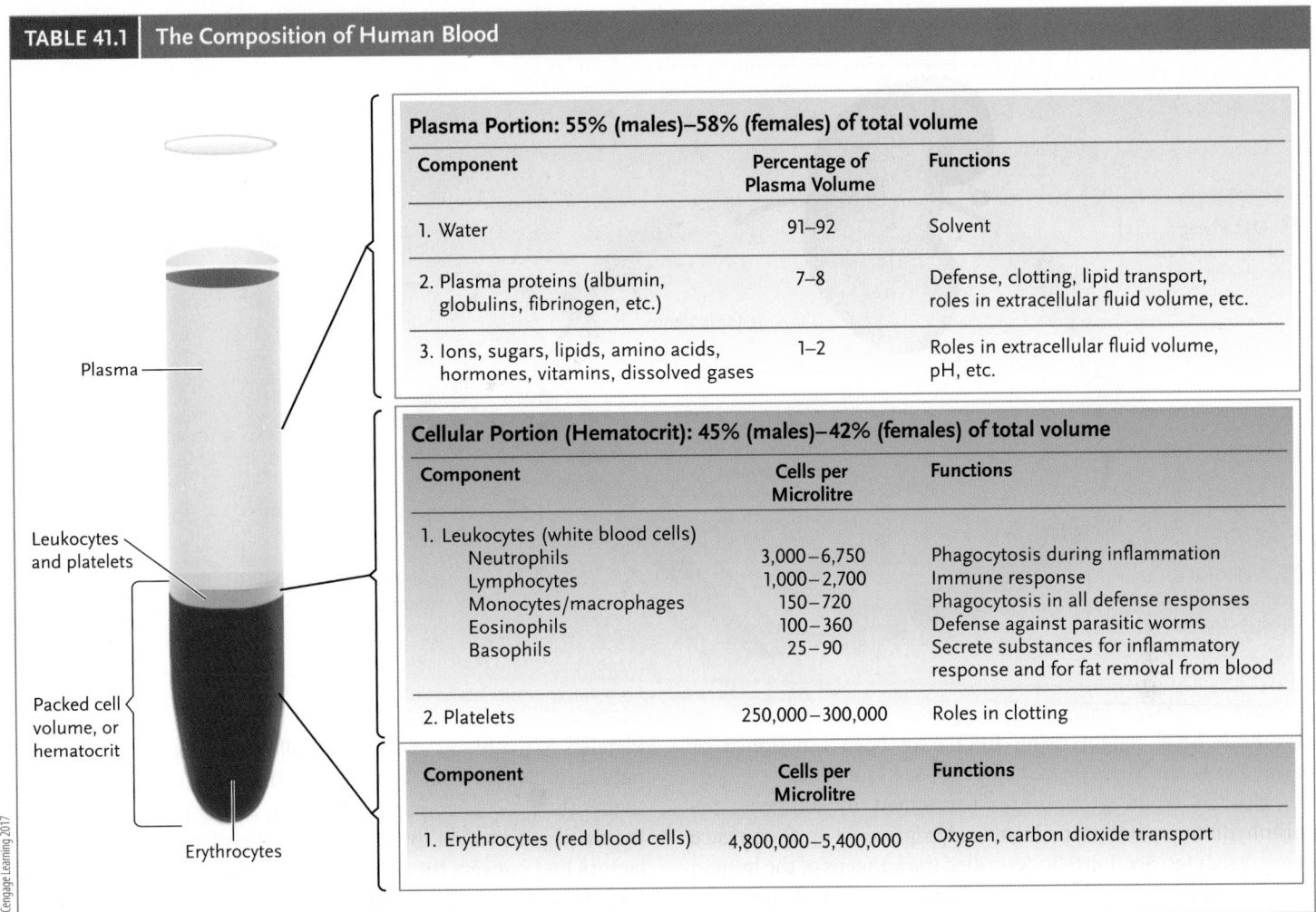

**Plasma Portion: 55% (males)–58% (females) of total volume**

| Component | Percentage of Plasma Volume | Functions |
|---|---|---|
| 1. Water | 91–92 | Solvent |
| 2. Plasma proteins (albumin, globulins, fibrinogen, etc.) | 7–8 | Defense, clotting, lipid transport, roles in extracellular fluid volume, etc. |
| 3. Ions, sugars, lipids, amino acids, hormones, vitamins, dissolved gases | 1–2 | Roles in extracellular fluid volume, pH, etc. |

**Cellular Portion (Hematocrit): 45% (males)–42% (females) of total volume**

| Component | Cells per Microlitre | Functions |
|---|---|---|
| 1. Leukocytes (white blood cells) | | |
|     Neutrophils | 3,000–6,750 | Phagocytosis during inflammation |
|     Lymphocytes | 1,000–2,700 | Immune response |
|     Monocytes/macrophages | 150–720 | Phagocytosis in all defense responses |
|     Eosinophils | 100–360 | Defense against parasitic worms |
|     Basophils | 25–90 | Secrete substances for inflammatory response and for fat removal from blood |
| 2. Platelets | 250,000–300,000 | Roles in clotting |

| Component | Cells per Microlitre | Functions |
|---|---|---|
| 1. Erythrocytes (red blood cells) | 4,800,000–5,400,000 | Oxygen, carbon dioxide transport |

Plasma

Leukocytes and platelets

Packed cell volume, or hematocrit

Erythrocytes

carry out glycolysis, and large quantities of **hemoglobin**, the $O_2$-carrying protein of the blood. The erythrocytes of nearly all other vertebrates retain a nucleus.

Hemoglobin, the molecule that gives erythrocytes, and thus blood, their red colour, consists of four polypeptides, each linked to a nonprotein heme group that contains an iron atom in its centre. The iron atom binds $O_2$ molecules as the blood circulates through the lungs, and releases the $O_2$ as the blood flows through other body tissues. This is described in detail in Chapter 40. It is the oxygenation of the iron that gives arterial blood its bright red colour (and red blood cells their name; *eruthros* = red), just as the oxygenation of iron in nature gives rust its colour. When hemoglobin releases its oxygen, the venous blood changes to a much darker colour.

Some 2 to 3 million erythrocytes are produced in the average human each second. As mentioned earlier, the lifespan of an erythrocyte in the human circulatory system is about 120 days. At the end of their useful life, erythrocytes are engulfed and destroyed by macrophages (*macro* = big; *phagein* = to eat), a type of large leukocyte, in the spleen, liver, and bone marrow.

A negative feedback mechanism keyed to the blood's $O_2$ content stabilizes the number of erythrocytes in blood (**Figure 41.6**). If the $O_2$ content drops below the normal level, the kidneys synthesize **erythropoietin (EPO)**, a peptide hormone that stimulates stem cells in bone marrow to increase erythrocyte production. Erythropoietin is also secreted after blood loss and when mammals move to higher altitudes. As new red blood cells enter the bloodstream, the $O_2$-carrying capacity of the blood rises. If the $O_2$ content of the blood rises above normal levels, erythropoietin production falls and red blood cell production drops (see Chapter 40).

The gene encoding human EPO has been cloned, allowing researchers to produce this protein in large quantities. It can be injected into the body to stimulate erythrocyte production in, for example, patients with anemia (lower than normal hemoglobin levels) caused by kidney failure or chemotherapy. It can also supplement or even replace blood transfusions. Some endurance athletes, such as triathletes, bicycle racers, marathon runners, and cross-country skiers, have used EPO to increase their erythrocyte levels to enhance performance. The use of EPO (a type of blood doping) is considered illegal and, as a result, many athletes

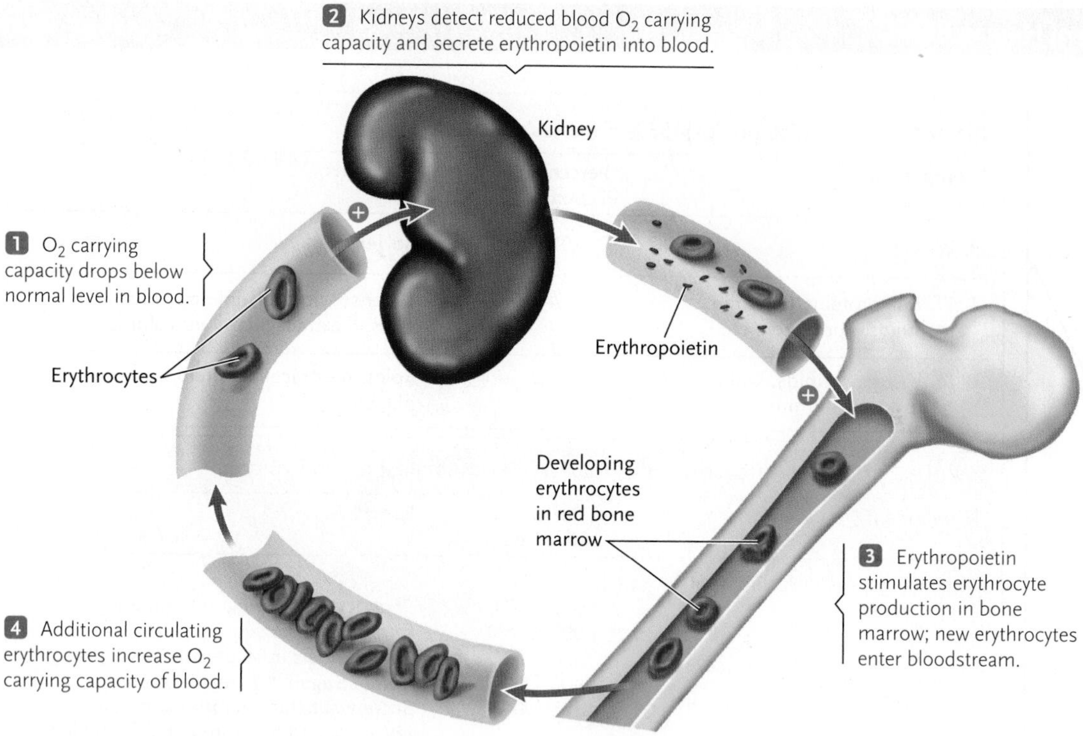

## FIGURE 41.6 Control of red blood cell production

**2** Kidneys detect reduced blood $O_2$ carrying capacity and secrete erythropoietin into blood.

Kidney

**1** $O_2$ carrying capacity drops below normal level in blood.

Erythrocytes

Erythropoietin

Developing erythrocytes in red bone marrow

**3** Erythropoietin stimulates erythrocyte production in bone marrow; new erythrocytes enter bloodstream.

**4** Additional circulating erythrocytes increase $O_2$ carrying capacity of blood.

© Cengage Learning 2017

that have been caught using EPO have been sanctioned or banned in recent years (see Chapter 40, Section 40.5a).

Human blood groups are determined by antigens, the carbohydrate portion of particular glycoproteins on the surface of erythrocytes. Section 9.2c described the antigens of the human ABO blood group and how they are important in transfusions.

### 41.2c Leukocytes Provide the Body's Front Line of Defence against Disease

Leukocytes eliminate dead and dying cells from the body, remove cellular debris, and provide the body's first line of defence against invading organisms. They are called *white blood cells* because they are colourless, in contrast to the red blood cells. Because leukocytes retain their nuclei, cytoplasmic organelles, and ribosomes, they are fully functional cells.

Like red blood cells, leukocytes arise from the division of stem cells in red bone marrow. As they mature, they are released into the bloodstream, from which they enter body tissues in large numbers. Some types of leukocytes are capable of continued division in the blood and body tissues.

### 41.2d Platelets Induce Blood Clots That Seal Breaks in the Circulatory System

Blood **platelets** are oval or rounded cell fragments, 2–4 μm in diameter, each enclosed in its own plasma membrane. They are produced in red bone marrow by the division of stem cells. Platelets contain enzymes and other factors that take part in blood clotting. When blood vessels are damaged, collagen fibres in the extracellular matrix are exposed to the leaking blood.

Platelets in the blood stick to the collagen fibres and release signalling molecules that induce additional platelets to stick to them. The process continues, forming a plug that helps seal off the damaged site. As the plug forms, the platelets release other factors that convert the soluble plasma protein, fibrinogen, into long, insoluble threads of **fibrin**. Cross-links between the fibrin threads form a meshlike network that traps blood cells and platelets and further seals the damaged area **(Figure 41.7)**. The entire mass is a blood clot. Animals that feed on blood, such as mosquitos and vampire bats, secrete anticoagulants to prevent blood from clotting while they are feeding.

### STUDY BREAK QUESTIONS

1. Why is blood considered a tissue? What are the three main cellular components of blood, and what are their functions?
2. How does EPO work to increase the hematocrit?

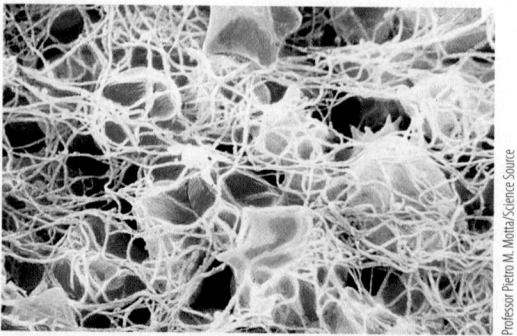

Professor Pietro M. Motta/Science Source

**FIGURE 41.7 Red blood cells caught in a meshlike network of fibrin threads during formation of a blood clot**

**1086** | UNIT EIGHT SYSTEMS AND PROCESSES: ANIMALS

NEL

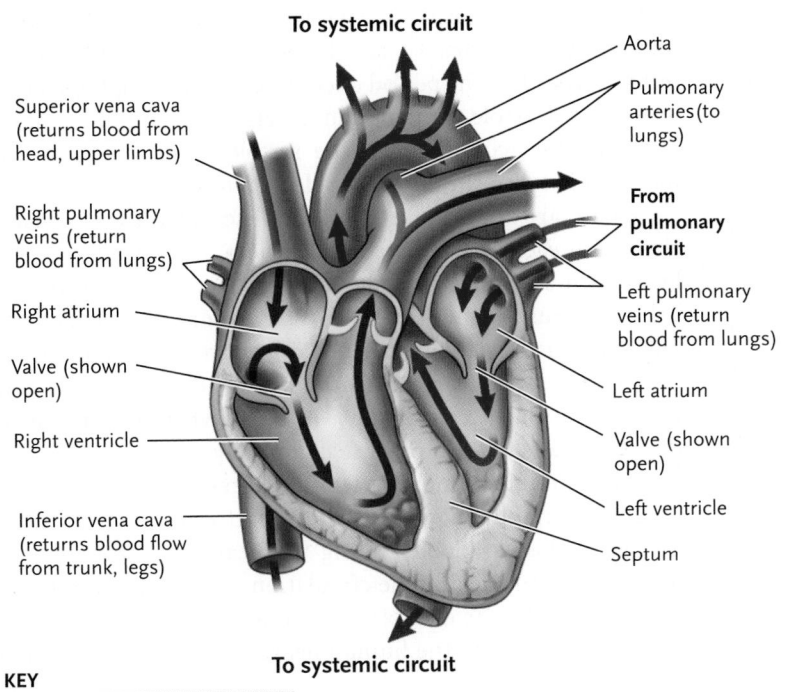

To systemic circuit

Superior vena cava
(returns blood from
head, upper limbs)

Right pulmonary
veins (return
blood from lungs)

Right atrium

Valve (shown
open)

Right ventricle

Inferior vena cava
(returns blood flow
from trunk, legs)

Aorta

Pulmonary
arteries (to
lungs)

From
pulmonary
circuit

Left pulmonary
veins (return
blood from lungs)

Left atrium

Valve (shown
open)

Left ventricle

Septum

To systemic circuit

**KEY**

☐ Semilunar (SL) valves

☐ Atrioventricular (AV) valves

© Cengage Learning 2017

**FIGURE 41.8 Cutaway view of a mammalian heart showing its internal organization**

## 41.3 The Heart

The vertebrate heart is composed of cardiac muscle cells (see Chapters 38 and 46). In mammals, we have seen that the heart is a four-chambered pump with two atria (singular, atrium) and two ventricles (**Figure 41.8**). The atria pump blood into the ventricles, and then powerful contractions of the ventricles push the blood at relatively high pressure into arteries leaving the heart. This arterial pressure is responsible for blood circulation. Valves between the atria and the ventricles—the **atrioventricular (AV) valves**—and between the ventricles and the arteries leaving the heart—the **semilunar (SL) valves**—keep the blood from flowing backward.

The mammalian heart pumps the blood through two completely separate circuits of blood vessels: the systemic circuit and the pulmonary circuit (**Figure 41.9**).

1.  The right atrium (toward the right side of the body) receives blood returning from the entire body, except for the lungs. The superior vena cava conveys blood returning from the head and forelimbs, and the inferior vena cava conveys blood returning from the abdominal organs and hind limbs. This blood is depleted of $O_2$ and has a high $CO_2$ content.

2.  The right atrium pumps the blood into the right ventricle, which contracts to push the blood into the pulmonary arteries leading to the lungs. In the capillaries of the lungs, the blood releases $CO_2$ and picks up $O_2$. The oxygenated blood completes this pulmonary circuit by returning to the heart in pulmonary veins.

3.  Blood returning from the pulmonary circuit enters the left atrium, which pumps it into the left ventricle.

4.  This ventricle, the most thick-walled and powerful chamber, contracts to send the oxygenated blood into a large artery, the **aorta**, which branches into arteries leading to all body regions except the lungs.

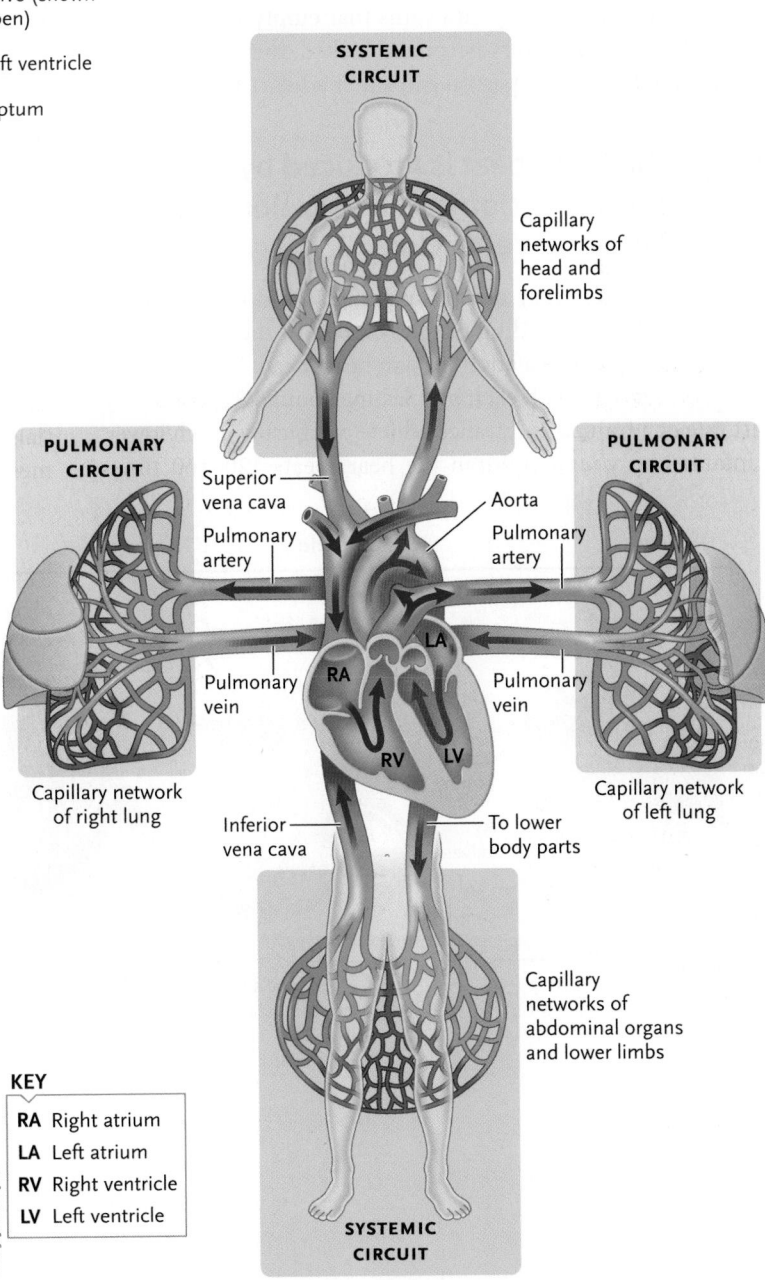

**KEY**

**RA** Right atrium
**LA** Left atrium
**RV** Right ventricle
**LV** Left ventricle

© Cengage Learning 2017

**FIGURE 41.9 The pulmonary and systemic circuits of a typical mammal (a human).** The right half of the heart pumps blood into the pulmonary circuit, and the left half of the heart pumps blood into the systemic circuit.

The arteries divide into smaller and smaller arteries (arterioles) and then into capillary networks, in which the blood releases $O_2$ and picks up $CO_2$. The $O_2$-depleted blood collects in venules that merge to form veins, which complete the systemic circuit. The blood from the veins enters the right atrium (step 1 above).

The amount of blood pumped by the two halves of the heart is normally balanced so that neither side pumps more than the other.

The heart also has its own circulation, called the *coronary circulation*. Two small coronary arteries branch off the aorta and then branch extensively over the heart, leading to dense capillary beds that serve the cardiac muscle cells. The blood from the capillary networks collects into veins that empty into the right atrium. If a coronary artery becomes blocked, the muscle cells it supplies can die and the person can suffer a heart attack.

## 41.3a The Heartbeat Is Produced by a Cycle of Contraction and Relaxation of the Atria and Ventricles

Average heart rates vary among mammals (and among vertebrates generally), depending on body size and the overall level of metabolic activity. An adult human heart beats 72 times each minute, on average, with each beat lasting about 0.8 second. The heart rate of a trained endurance athlete is typically much lower. In infants and young children the heart beats 120–160 times

each minute. The heart of a flying bat may beat 1200 times a minute, whereas that of an elephant beats only 30 times a minute. **Systole** is the period of contraction and emptying of the heart, and **diastole** is the period of relaxation and filling of the heart between contractions. The systole–diastole sequence of the heart is called the **cardiac cycle (Figure 41.10)**.

The heart valves make a "lub-dub" sound as they open and close with each heart beat; you can hear it by listening to the heart with a stethoscope. The lub sound occurs when the AV valves are pushed shut by the contraction of the ventricles; the dub sound is made when the SL valves are forced shut as the ventricles relax. Heart murmurs are abnormal sounds produced by turbulence created by the blood when one or more of the valves fails to open or close completely.

Each minute in most vertebrates at rest, a ventricle pumps roughly an amount equivalent to the entire volume of blood in the body; that is, blood leaving the heart takes roughly one minute to complete a single circulation. At maximum rate and strength, the hearts of most vertebrates pump about 10 times the resting amount. The human heart is capable of only about half this increase.

## 41.3b The Cardiac Cycle Is Initiated within the Heart

Contraction of cardiac muscle cells is triggered by action potentials (see Chapter 45) that spread across the muscle cell membranes. Recall that cardiac muscle cells are connected to

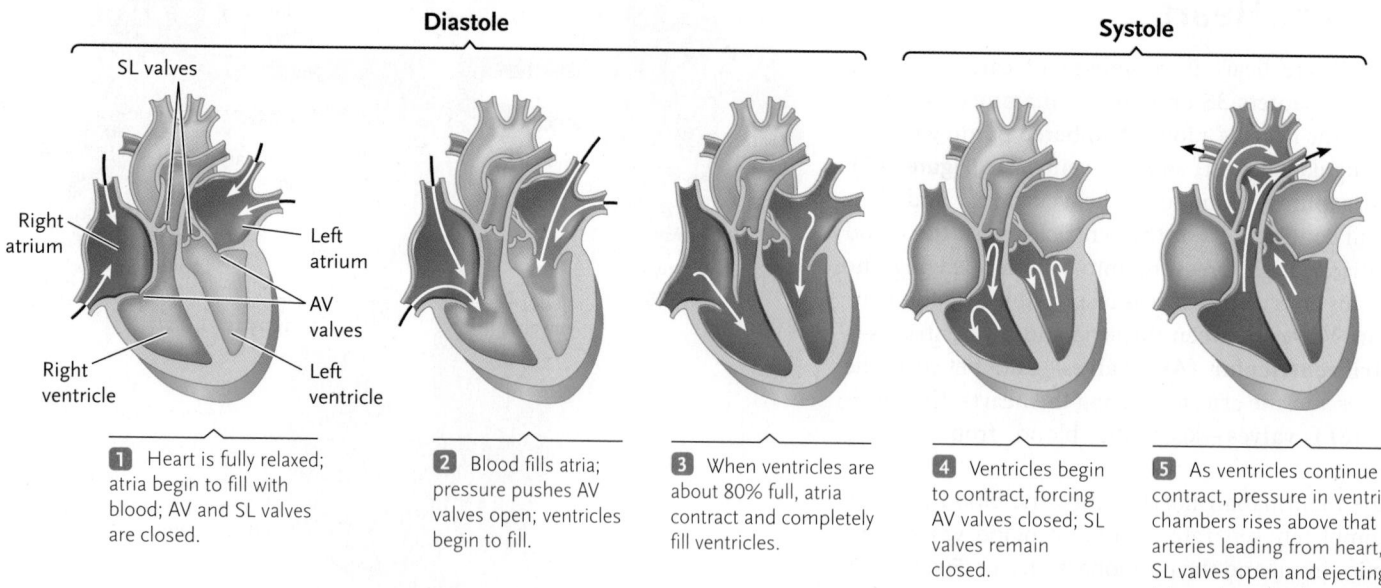

| Diastole | | | Systole | |

SL valves
Right atrium
Left atrium
AV valves
Right ventricle
Left ventricle

**1** Heart is fully relaxed; atria begin to fill with blood; AV and SL valves are closed.

**2** Blood fills atria; pressure pushes AV valves open; ventricles begin to fill.

**3** When ventricles are about 80% full, atria contract and completely fill ventricles.

**4** Ventricles begin to contract, forcing AV valves closed; SL valves remain closed.

**5** As ventricles continue to contract, pressure in ventricle chambers rises above that in arteries leading from heart, forcing SL valves open and ejecting blood into aorta and pulmonary arteries. About two-thirds of blood in ventricles enters arteries. Ventricles now relax, lowering pressure in ventricle chambers below that in arteries. Blood pressure in ventricles now closes SL valves. The cycle begins again.

© Cengage Learning 2017

**FIGURE 41.10 The cardiac cycle.** This figure shows one full cardiac cycle beginning at the start of diastole.

one another by gap junctions (see Chapters 38 and 46). As a result, electrical activity can pass rapidly from one cell to its neighbours. Crustaceans, such as crabs and lobsters, have **neurogenic hearts**, that is, hearts that beat under the control of signals from the nervous system. Each contraction is initiated by signals from a nerve ganglion (the cardiac ganglion) located in the heart, and the heart will continue to beat and respond to some environmental signals in isolation from the central nervous system, as long as the ganglion is intact. Other animals, including all insects and all vertebrates, have **myogenic hearts**, which maintain their contraction rhythm with no requirement for signals from the nervous system. Isolated cardiac myocytes contract rhythmically when grown in a suitable medium. Both neurogenic and myogenic hearts can also be influenced by signals from the central nervous system and by hormones.

The rate and timing of the contraction of individual cardiac muscle cells in a mammalian myogenic heart are coordinated by a region of the heart called the **sinoatrial (SA) node**.

The SA node consists of **pacemaker cells**, which are specialized cardiac muscle cells in the upper wall of the right atrium (**Figure 40.11**, step 1). Ion channels in these cells open in a cyclic, self-sustaining pattern that alternately depolarizes and repolarizes their plasma membranes (see Chapter 45). The regularly timed depolarizations spread to neighbouring cells, causing them to contract and initiating waves of contraction that travel over the entire heart.

A layer of connective tissue separates the atria from the ventricles, acting as a layer of electrical insulation between the two sets of chambers of the heart. The insulating layer keeps a contraction signal from the SA node from spreading directly from the atria to the ventricles (Figure 41.11, step 2). Instead, the atrial wave of contraction excites cells of the **atrioventricular (AV) node**, located in the heart wall between the right atrium and the right ventricle, just above the insulating layer of connective tissue. The signal produced travels from the AV node to the bottom of the heart via Purkinje fibres (step 3). These fibres follow a path downward, through the insulating layer, to the bottom of the heart, where they branch through the walls of the ventricles. The signal carried by the Purkinje fibres induces a wave of contraction that begins at the bottom of the heart and spreads from cell to cell upward, squeezing the blood from the ventricles into the aorta and pulmonary arteries (step 4). The transmission of a signal from the AV node to the ventricles takes about 0.1 second; this delay gives the atria time to finish their contraction before the ventricles contract.

The electrical signals passing through the heart can be detected by attaching electrodes to different points on the surface of the body. The signals change in a regular pattern corresponding to the electrical signals that trigger the cardiac cycle, producing what is known as an **electrocardiogram** (**ECG**; also *EKG*, from the German *Elektrokardiogramm*). The highlighted region of the ECG above each stage of the cardiac cycle in Figure 41.11 indicates the electrical activity measured in those stages. Many malfunctions of the heart alter the ECG pattern in characteristic ways, providing clues to the location and type of heart disease.

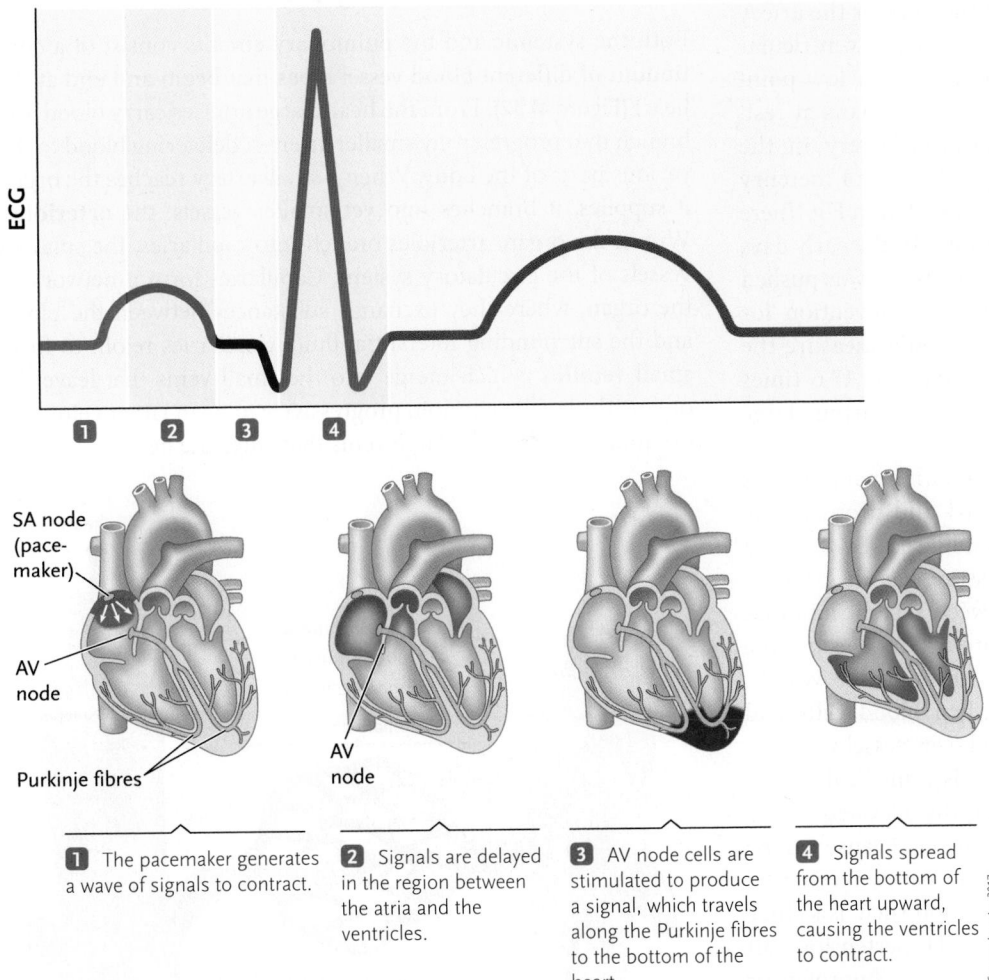

**1** The pacemaker generates a wave of signals to contract.

**2** Signals are delayed in the region between the atria and the ventricles.

**3** AV node cells are stimulated to produce a signal, which travels along the Purkinje fibres to the bottom of the heart.

**4** Signals spread from the bottom of the heart upward, causing the ventricles to contract.

© Cengage Learning 2017

**FIGURE 41.11  The electrical control of the cardiac cycle.** The bottom part of the figure shows how a signal originating at the SA node leads to ventricular contraction. The top part of the figure shows the electrical activity for each of the stages as seen in an ECG. The colours in the hearts show the location of the signal at each step and correspond to the colours in the ECG.

### 41.3c Arterial Blood Pressure Cycles between a High Systolic and a Low Diastolic Pressure

The pressure exerted by a fluid in a confined space is called *hydrostatic pressure*; that is, fluid in a container exerts some pressure on the wall of the container. Blood vessels are essentially tubular containers that are part of a closed system filled with fluid. Hence, the blood in vessels exerts hydrostatic pressure against the walls of the vessels. Blood pressure is the measurement of that hydrostatic pressure on the walls of the arteries as the heart pumps blood through the body. Blood pressure is determined by the force and amount of blood pumped by the heart and the size and stiffness of the arteries. In any animal, blood pressure changes in response to activity, temperature, body position, behaviour, time of day, and diet.

As the ventricles contract, a surge of high-pressure blood moves outward through the arteries leading from the heart. This peak of high pressure, called the *systolic blood pressure*, can be felt as a pulse by pressing a finger against an artery that lies near the skin, such as the arteries of the neck or the artery that runs along the inside of the wrist. Between ventricular contractions, the arterial blood pressure reaches a low point called the *diastolic blood pressure*. In healthy humans at rest, the systolic pressure, measured in the large artery in the forearm, is equivalent to between 90 and 120 mm of mercury (mm Hg), and the diastolic to between 60 and 80 mm Hg. There are several units used for measuring pressure. In the early days it was measured by determining how high mercury was pushed in a glass tube, and this has remained the convention for recording blood pressure to this day. One could measure the height to which water was pushed but mercury is 13.6 times heavier, making it more practical for measuring large pressures.

The blood pressure in the systemic and pulmonary circuits is highest in the arteries leaving the heart and drops as the blood passes from the arteries into the capillaries. By the time the blood returns to the heart, its pressure has dropped to 2–5 mm Hg, with no differentiation between systolic and diastolic pressures. The reduction in pressure occurs because the blood encounters resistance as it moves through the vessels, due primarily to the friction created when blood cells and plasma proteins move over each other and over vessel walls.

Hypertension or high blood pressure is a medical condition in which blood pressure is chronically elevated above normal values. In some cases no specific medical cause can be found to explain the hypertension. In other cases, the hypertension results from another medical condition such as kidney disease or disorders of the adrenal glands. Hypertension can also be caused by certain medications, such as ibuprofen or steroids. Age is also a contributor to hypertension because the walls of blood vessels become stiffer over time as more collagen fibres are added, decreasing the elasticity of the arteries. During systole, the arteries cannot expand as much, and this results in a higher arterial blood pressure. Hypertension also occurs for short periods during sustained contraction of a muscle group or groups. In elite weight lifters, for instance, blood pressure during lifts can reach 300/150 mm Hg (systolic pressure/diastolic pressure). Similar high pressures can be reached during strained defecation.

### STUDY BREAK QUESTIONS

1. What is the role of each of the four chambers of the mammalian heart in blood circulation?
2. Distinguish between systolic and diastolic blood pressure. Why are these two values different?
3. How do neurogenic and myogenic hearts differ?
4. Describe the electrical events that occur during the cardiac cycle in a mammalian heart.

## 41.4 Blood Vessels of the Circulatory System

Both the systemic and the pulmonary circuits consist of a continuum of different blood vessel types that begin and end at the heart (**Figure 41.12**). From the heart, large arteries carry blood and branch into progressively smaller arteries, delivering blood to the various parts of the body. When a small artery reaches the organ it supplies, it branches into yet smaller vessels, the **arterioles**. Within the organ, arterioles branch into capillaries, the smallest vessels of the circulatory system. Capillaries form a network in the organ, where they exchange substances between the blood and the surrounding interstitial fluid. Capillaries rejoin to form small **venules**, which merge into the small veins that leave the organ. The small veins join progressively to form larger veins that eventually become the large veins that enter the heart.

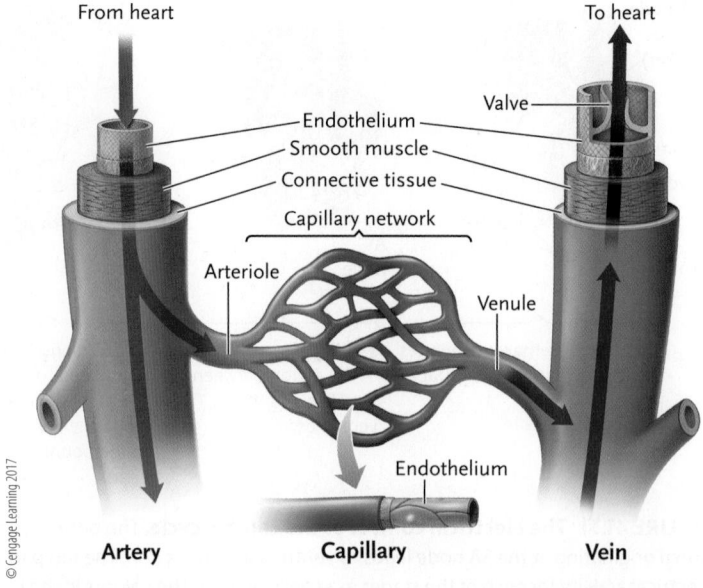

**FIGURE 41.12 The structures of arteries, capillaries, and veins, and their relationships in blood circuits**

## 41.4a Arteries Transport Blood Rapidly to the Tissues and Serve as a Pressure Reservoir

Arteries have relatively large diameters and therefore provide little resistance to blood flow. They are structurally adapted to the relatively high pressure of the blood passing through them. The walls of arteries consist of three major tissue layers (see Figure 41.12):

- an outer layer of connective tissue containing collagen fibres mixed with fibres of the protein elastin, making the vessel elastic and giving it the ability to recoil;
- a relatively thick middle layer of vascular smooth muscle cells also mixed with elastin fibres; and
- an inner layer of flattened cells only one cell in thickness, forming an endothelium.

In addition to being conduits for blood travelling to the tissues, arteries also act as a pressure reservoir for blood movement when the heart is relaxing. When contraction of the ventricles pumps blood into the arteries, a greater volume of blood enters the arteries than leaves them to flow into the smaller vessels downstream because of the higher resistance to blood flow in these smaller vessels. Arteries accommodate the excess volume of blood because of their elastic walls, which allow the arteries to expand in diameter. When the heart relaxes and blood is no longer being pumped into the arteries, the arterial walls recoil passively back to their original state and the pressure in them falls from systolic to diastolic levels. The longer the interval between heartbeats, the more the diastolic pressure falls. The recoil pushes the excess blood from the arteries into the smaller downstream vessels. As a result, blood flow to tissues is continuous during systole and diastole, even though the heart is relaxing and not contracting during diastole.

## 41.4b Capillaries Are the Sites of Exchange between the Blood and the Interstitial Fluid

Capillaries thread through nearly every tissue in the body and are arranged in networks that bring them within 0.01 mm of most body cells. In humans, capillaries are estimated to have a surface area of about 2600 km$^2$ for the exchange of gases, nutrients, and wastes with the interstitial fluid. Capillary walls consist of a single layer of endothelial cells contained by a thin basement membrane (Figure 41.12). They do not contain smooth muscle (see Chapter 38).

**CONTROL OF BLOOD FLOW THROUGH CAPILLARIES** Blood flow through capillary networks is controlled by contraction of smooth muscle in the arterioles that feed them **(Figure 41.13)**. In addition to the normal layer of smooth muscle, some arterioles have circular rings of smooth muscle, called *precapillary sphincter muscles*, at the entrance to the capillary bed. When the arteriole and sphincter smooth muscles are relaxed, blood

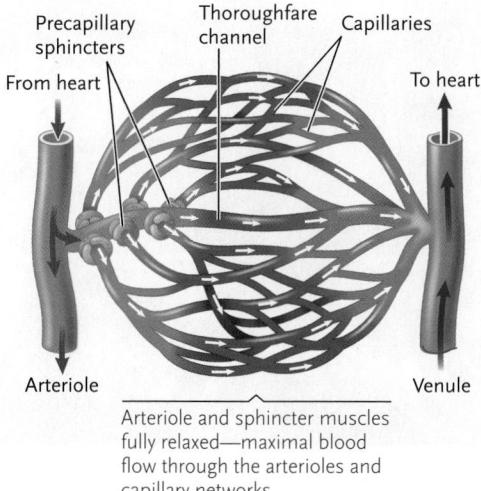

**a. Fully relaxed**

Arteriole and sphincter muscles fully relaxed—maximal blood flow through the arterioles and capillary networks.

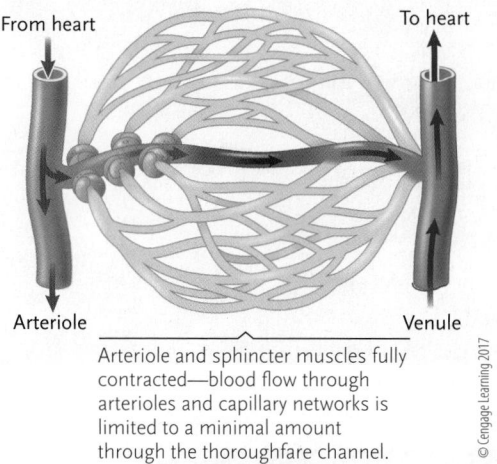

**b. Fully contracted**

Arteriole and sphincter muscles fully contracted—blood flow through arterioles and capillary networks is limited to a minimal amount through the thoroughfare channel.

© Cengage Learning 2017

**FIGURE 41.13 Control of blood flow through capillary networks.** **(a)** Maximal blood flow when arteriole and sphincter muscles are fully relaxed. **(b)** Minimal blood flow when the arteriole and sphincter muscles are fully contracted

flows readily through the arterioles and capillary networks. When they are contracted, blood flow through the arterioles and capillary networks is limited. By varying the contraction of the arteriole and sphincter smooth muscles, the rate of flow through the capillary networks of individual organs can be adjusted. For example, during exercise, the flow of blood through the capillary networks of the intestines is decreased, and that through the muscles of the legs is increased.

**THE VELOCITY OF BLOOD FLOW THROUGH CAPILLARIES** Although their total surface area is astoundingly large, the diameter of individual capillaries is so small that red blood cells must squeeze through most of them in single file **(Figure 41.14)**. As a result, each capillary presents a high resistance to blood flow. In addition, there are so many billions of capillaries in the networks that their combined diameter is about 1300 times the cross-sectional area of the aorta. As a result of the resistance and

a.

*Eye of Science/Science Source*

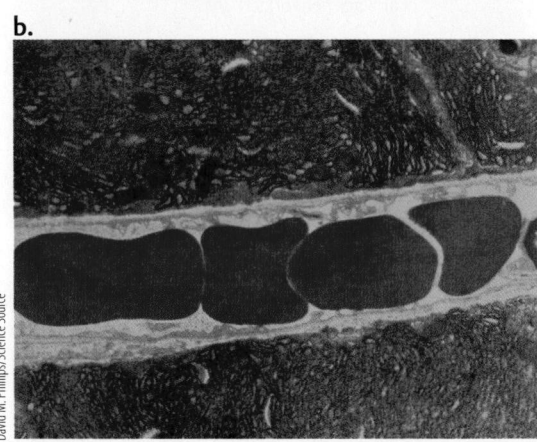

b.

*David M. Phillips/Science Source*

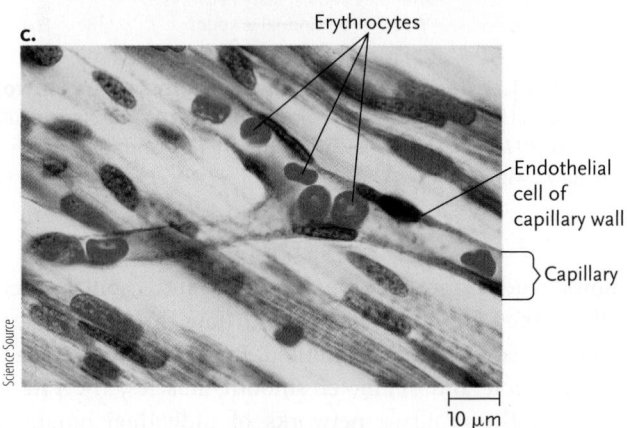

c.

Erythrocytes

Endothelial
cell of
capillary wall

Capillary

*Science Source*

10 μm

**FIGURE 41.14 Erythrocytes moving through a capillary.** The capillary is just wide enough to admit the cells in single file, as seen by **(a)** scanning electron microscopy, **(b)** cross-section and staining using light microscopy, and **(c)** sagittal section through muscle fibres.

the vastly increased diameter of the combined tubes, blood slows considerably as it moves through capillaries, maximizing opportunities for exchange between the blood and the interstitial fluids **(Figure 41.15)**. As they leave the tissues, capillaries rejoin to

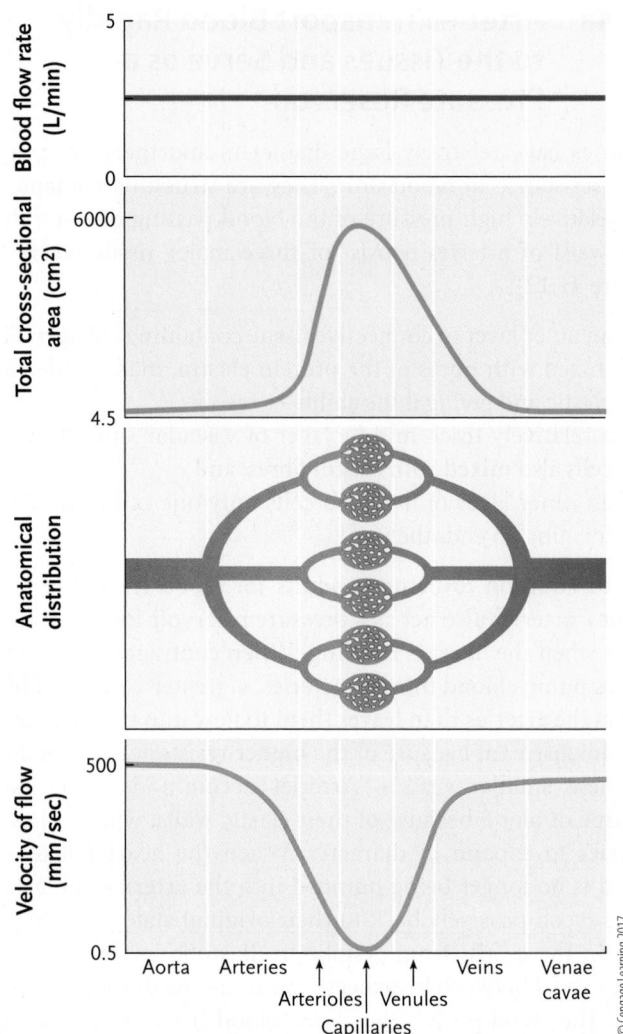

Blood flow rate (L/min)

5

0

Total cross-sectional area (cm²)

6000

4.5

Anatomical distribution

Velocity of flow (mm/sec)

500

0.5

Aorta  Arteries  Arterioles | Venules  Veins  Venae cavae

Capillaries

© Cengage Learning 2017

**FIGURE 41.15 Blood flow rate and velocity of flow in relation to total cross-sectional area of the blood vessels.** The blood flow rate is identical throughout the circulatory system and is equal to the cardiac output. The velocity of flow in the different types of blood vessels is inversely related to the total cross-sectional area of all the vessels of a particular type; for example, the velocity is highest in the aorta, which has the smallest cross-sectional area, and lowest in the capillaries, which collectively have the largest cross-sectional area.

form venules and veins. Veins have a total cross-sectional area that is smaller than the total cross-sectional area of the capillaries, so the velocity of flow increases as blood returns to the heart.

**THE EXCHANGE OF SUBSTANCES ACROSS CAPILLARY WALLS** In most body tissues, narrow spaces between the capillary endothelial cells allow water, ions, and small molecules such as glucose to pass freely between blood and interstitial fluid. Erythrocytes, platelets, and most plasma proteins are too large to pass between the cells and are retained inside capillaries, except for molecules that are transported through epithelial cells by specific carriers. Leukocytes, however, can squeeze actively between the cells and pass from the blood to the interstitial fluid.

There are exceptions to these general properties. In the brain, endothelial cells are tightly sealed together, preventing all molecules and ions from passing between them. The tight seals set up the blood–brain barrier (Chapter 45). This limits the exchange between capillaries and brain tissues to molecules and ions that are specifically transported through the capillary endothelial cells. At the other extreme are capillaries in the liver, in which the spaces between endothelial cells are wide enough to admit most plasma proteins (most plasma proteins are synthesized in the liver), and in the small intestines, where wide spaces between capillary endothelial cells allow many nutrient molecules to pass into the bloodstream. In bone marrow and other sites of erythrocyte production, spaces are large enough to admit red blood cells.

## 41.4c Venules and Veins Serve as Blood Reservoirs in Addition to Conduits to the Heart

Because of the high resistance in the capillaries, the pressure remaining in the blood is low as it enters the venules and veins. Accordingly, the walls of venules and veins are thinner than those of arteries and contain little elastin. Many veins have flaps of connective tissue that extend inward from their walls. These flaps form one-way valves that keep blood flowing toward the heart **(Figure 41.16)**.

Because of the differences in their structure, the relatively thin walls of venules and veins can expand over a relatively wide range without developing much recoil. This allows them to act as blood reservoirs as well as conduits. At times, venules and

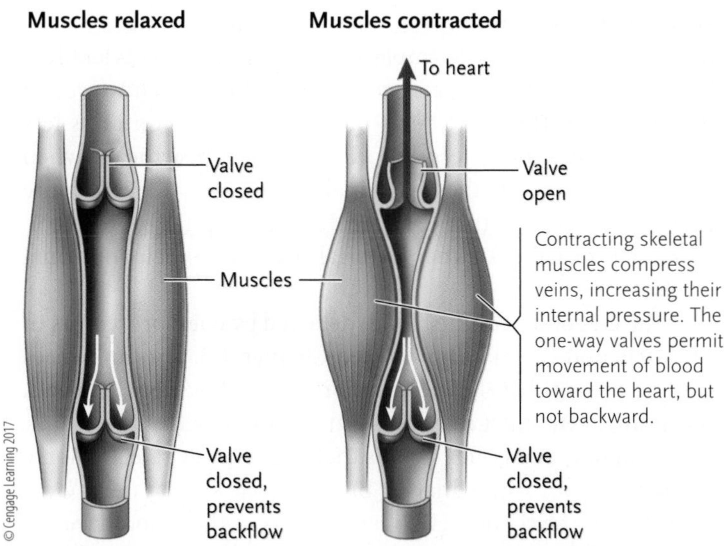

**FIGURE 41.16  How skeletal muscle contraction and the valves inside veins help move blood toward the heart**

veins may contain from 60% to 80% of the total blood volume of the body. The stored volume is adjusted by skeletal muscle contraction and valves in response to metabolic conditions and signals carried by hormones and neurotransmitters.

Although blood pressure in the venous system is relatively low, several mechanisms assist the movement of blood back to the heart. The contraction of skeletal muscles compresses nearby veins, increasing their internal pressure (Figure 41.16). The one-way valves in the veins, especially numerous in the larger veins of the limbs, keep the blood from flowing backward when the muscles relax. Respiratory movements also force blood from the abdomen toward the chest cavity.

### STUDY BREAK QUESTIONS

1. Why must arterial walls be thick and elastic?
2. During strenuous exercise, more capillary beds open up to receive blood flow. Where does the extra blood that it takes to fill them come from?
3. How do skeletal muscles assist in the circulation of blood?

## 41.5 Maintaining Blood Flow and Pressure

Arterial blood pressure is the principal force moving blood to the tissues. Blood pressure must be regulated carefully so that the brain and other tissues receive adequate blood flow, but it must not be so high that the heart is overburdened, risking damage to blood vessels (see Section 41.3c). The three main regulators of blood pressure are

- cardiac output, the amount of blood pumped by the left and right ventricles combined, which is a product of the rate at which the heart beats (heart rate) and the amount of blood pumped with each beat (stroke volume);
- the degree of constriction of the blood vessels (primarily the arterioles); and
- the total blood volume.

The autonomic nervous system and the endocrine system interact to coordinate the mechanisms controlling these factors. The system counteracts the effects of constantly changing internal and external conditions, such as movement from rest to physical activity or ending a period of fasting by eating a large meal. In humans, for example, moderate physical activity results in an increase in blood flow to the heart itself by 360%, to the muscles of the skin by 370% (increases loss of heat), and to the skeletal muscles by 1060%. Flow is decreased to the digestive tract and liver by 60%, to the kidneys by 40%, and to the bone and most other tissues by 30%. Only the blood flow to the brain remains unchanged. These changes are the result of changes in cardiac output together with adjustments to the muscles in the

FIGURE 41.17 **Experimental Research**

## Demonstration of a Vasodilatory Signalling Molecule

**Research Question:** What causes arteries to vasodilate?

**Experiment:** In mammals, the neurotransmitter acetylcholine (see Chapter 45) is a potent vasodilator. Experiments conducted by R.H. Furchgott and J.V. Zawadzki using strips of rabbit aorta were designed to determine how acetylcholine caused vasodilation. They attached the strips of aorta to an apparatus that recorded the tension in the muscle due to stretch. Contraction shortens the muscle and increases tension, whereas relaxation (which would be equivalent to vasodilation in the intact blood vessel) decreases tension. They first applied norepinephrine to the strips to make them contract, and then added acetylcholine. They did this on two different preparations. In the first they used aorta strips that had been handled gently and were completely intact. In the second they used aortic strips from which the endothelial cells had been removed by rubbing.

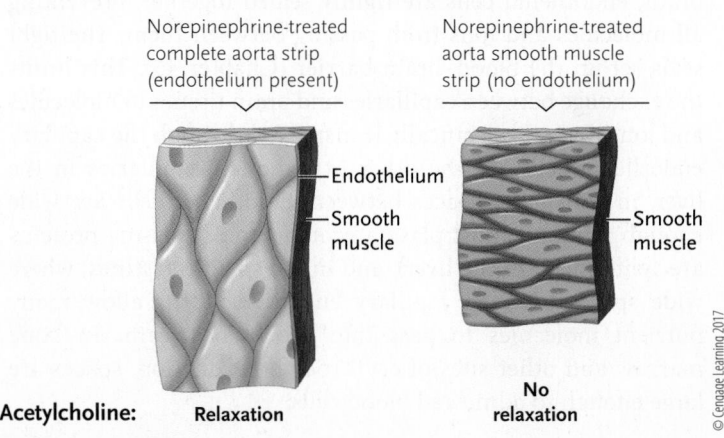

**Figure 1 Experimental results**

**Results:** The results are shown in **Figure 1**. The strips that had been handled gently and that had an intact endothelium relaxed when the acetylcholine was applied. The strips that had been rubbed and were devoid of endothelium did not. They repeated these experiments with a number of other rabbit arteries and with arteries from a variety of other animal species. They hypothesized that the endothelial cells produced a vasodilatory signalling molecule, which they named endothelium-derived relaxing factor (EDRF).

**Conclusion:** Vasodilation of arteries occurs as a result of release of a signalling molecule from the endothelial cells of the arteries. Subsequently, EDRF was determined to be nitric oxide (NO) (see Section 41.5c). NO released from endothelial cells is also the signalling molecule responsible for vasodilation of arterioles.

Nitroglycerin is routinely prescribed by doctors to help alleviate angina, a condition where the heart does not receive sufficient oxygen. Nitroglycerin acts by releasing nitric oxide, which relaxes narrowed blood vessels, increasing oxygen and blood flow. Viagra also works by influencing enzymes in the nitric oxide pathway. One cause of impotence is unhealthy and aged arteries that feed blood to the sexual organs. Viagra enhances nitric oxide release, causing more blood flow and better erections.

arterioles supplying the various organs as described above in Section 41.4b.

## 41.5a Cardiac Output Is Controlled by Regulating the Rate and Strength of the Heartbeat

Regulation of the strength and rate of the heartbeat starts at **stretch receptors** called *baroreceptors* (a type of mechanoreceptor; see Chapter 45), located in the walls of blood vessels. The baroreceptors in the cardiac muscle, aorta, and carotid arteries (which supply blood to the brain) are the most crucial. By detecting the amount of stretch of the vessel walls, baroreceptors constantly provide information about blood pressure, sending signals to the medulla within the brain stem. In response, the brain stem sends signals to the heart (primarily the SA node) and muscles of the blood vessels via the autonomic nervous system (see Chapter 45). The

sympathetic system, using norepinephrine, stimulates the heart, whereas the parasympathetic system uses acetylcholine to slow heart rate. These signals adjust the rate and force of the heartbeat: the heart beats more slowly and contracts less forcefully (pumping less blood with each heartbeat) when arterial pressure is above normal levels, and it beats more rapidly and contracts more forcefully (pumping more blood with each heartbeat) when arterial pressure is below normal levels.

The $O_2$ content of the blood, detected by chemoreceptors in the aorta and carotid arteries (see Chapter 45), also influences cardiac output. If $O_2$ concentration falls below normal levels, the brain stem integrates this information with the baroreceptor signals and issues signals that increase the rate and force of the heartbeat while dilating blood vessels so that more $O_2$ is delivered to the tissues. High levels of $O_2$ in the blood have the opposite effect, reducing cardiac output and constricting blood vessels (see Section 41.5c).

## 41.5b Hormones Regulate Both Cardiac Output and Arteriole Diameter

Hormones secreted by several glands contribute to the regulation of blood pressure and flow. For example, as part of the stress response, the adrenal medulla reinforces the action of the sympathetic nervous system by secreting epinephrine and norepinephrine into the bloodstream (see Chapter 43). Epinephrine in particular raises cardiac output by increasing the strength and rate of the heartbeat. It also stimulates vasoconstriction (decrease in diameter) of arterioles in some parts of the body, including the skin, gut, and kidneys, and induces vasodilation (increase in diameter) of arterioles that deliver blood to the heart, skeletal muscles, and lungs. Thus, epinephrine increases blood flow to the structures essential for dealing with stress and reduces blood flow to those structures that are not necessary at that time.

Blood can also serve as a hydraulic fluid strengthening and elongating structures under hormonal control. Nectar-feeding bats pump blood into the tongue to extend it to allow penetration into the nectaries of flowers. Similarly, erectile tissue, such as the penis and clitoris in mammals, become erect when engorged with blood during sexual arousal.

## 41.5c Local Controls Also Regulate Arteriole Diameter

Several automated mechanisms also operate locally to increase the flow of blood to body regions engaged in increased metabolic activity. Repeated contraction of the muscles of the legs during the escape response of an antelope produces low $O_2$ and high $CO_2$ concentrations in the legs because of the increased oxidation of glucose and other fuels. This increases vasodilation of the arterioles and hence the blood supply serving the muscles. At least part of the vasodilation is caused by nitric oxide (NO) produced by arterial endothelial cells. NO is broken down quickly after its release, ensuring that its effects are local **(Figure 41.17)**.

**CONCEPT FIX** The interaction between blood pressure, cardiac output, and blood vessel resistance is complex. People often believe that heart rate is the key regulated variable in the circulatory system. This is because heart rate changes, but the changes maintain constant blood pressure, which is the true controlled variable. The reason that a constant blood pressure is so important is that each capillary bed is capable of controlling its own blood flow (as just described). The job of the heart is to ensure that the total blood flow, that is, the cardiac output, is equal to the local demands of all the tissues. The way this occurs is by monitoring blood pressure and altering cardiac output to keep it constant (increasing cardiac output when blood pressure falls, and dropping cardiac output when it increases). Since the local tissues alter their flow by constricting and dilating blood vessels, which alters resistance and hence blood pressure, if the heart can maintain blood pressure constant, then the total flow will equal all the local demands. ⬣

# 41.6 The Lymphatic System

Under normal conditions, a little more fluid from the blood plasma in the capillaries enters the interstitial fluid than is reabsorbed into the plasma. The **lymphatic system** is an extensive network of vessels that collects excess interstitial fluid and returns it to the venous blood **(Figure 41.18a)**. Interstitial fluid picked up by the lymphatic system is called **lymph**. This system also collects fats that have been absorbed from the small intestine and delivers them to the blood circulation. The lymphatic system is also a key component of the immune system.

## 41.6a Vessels of the Lymphatic System Extend Throughout Most of the Body

Vessels of the lymphatic system collect lymph and transport it to lymph ducts, which empty into the veins of the circulatory system. Lymph capillaries, the smallest vessels of the system, are distributed throughout the body, intermixed intimately with the capillaries of the circulatory system. Although they are several times as large in diameter as the blood capillaries, the walls of lymph capillaries also consist of a single layer of endothelial cells resting on a basement membrane. Interstitial fluid becomes lymph when it enters the lymph capillaries at sites in their walls where the endothelial cells overlap, forming a flap that is forced open by the higher pressure of the interstitial fluid. The openings are wide enough to admit all components of the interstitial fluid, including bacteria, damaged cells, cellular debris, and **lymphocytes**.

Lymph capillaries merge into lymph vessels, which contain one-way valves that prevent the lymph from flowing backward. Lymph vessels lead to the thoracic duct and the right lymphatic duct (see Figure 41.18b), which empty the lymph into a vein beneath the clavicles (collarbones).

Breathing movements and movements of skeletal muscles adjacent to lymph vessels help move lymph through the vessels, just as they help move the blood through veins. Over a day, the human lymphatic system returns about 3–4 L of fluid to the bloodstream. In fishes, amphibians, and reptiles, the lymphatic vessels have lymphatic hearts, regions of the ducts equipped with striated muscle, that propel the lymph through the vessels.

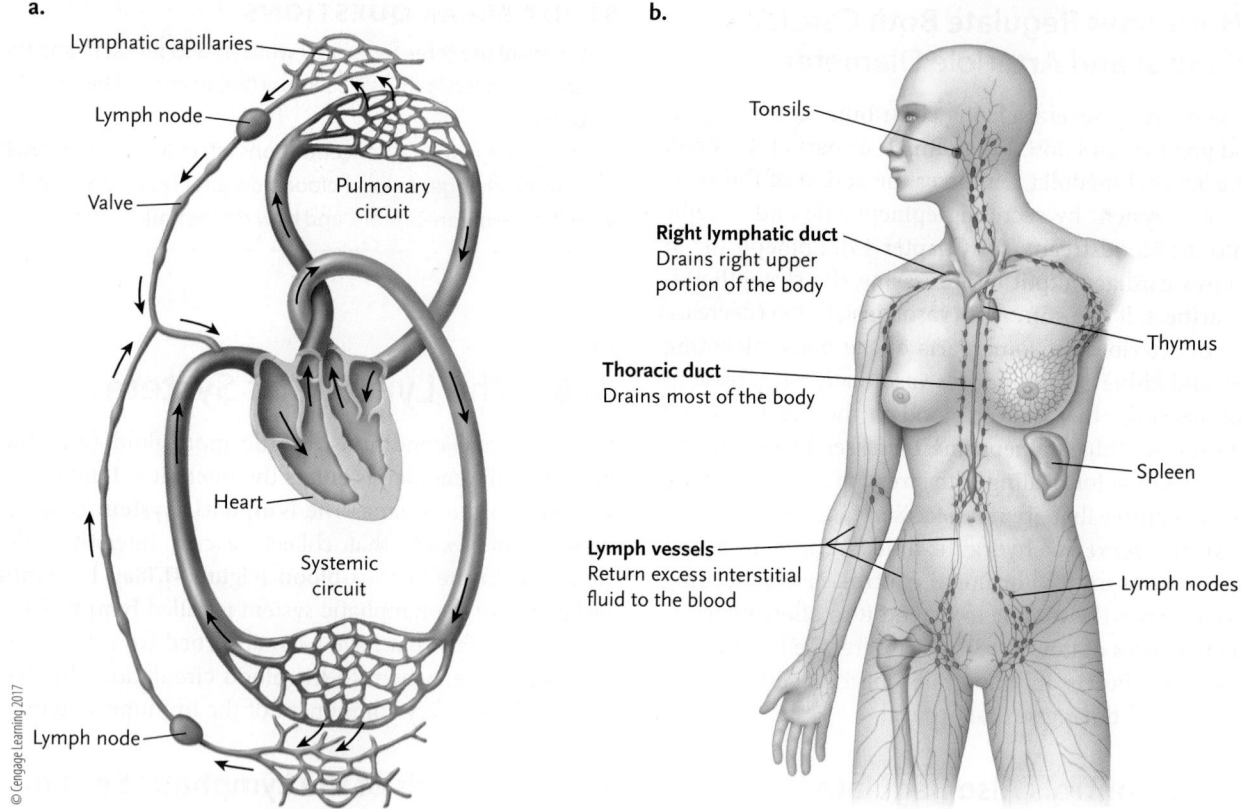

**a.**

Lymphatic capillaries

Lymph node

Valve

Pulmonary circuit

Heart

Systemic circuit

Lymph node

© Cengage Learning 2017

**b.**

Tonsils

**Right lymphatic duct**
Drains right upper portion of the body

Thymus

**Thoracic duct**
Drains most of the body

Spleen

**Lymph vessels**
Return excess interstitial fluid to the blood

Lymph nodes

**FIGURE 41.18  The human lymphatic system. (a)** The lymphatic system is an extensive network of vessels that collect excess interstitial fluid from the tissues and return it to the lowest-pressure component of the systemic circulation, the venous system outside the heart. **(b)** The tissues and organs of the lymphatic system include the lymph nodes, patches in the small intestine, the spleen, the thymus, the tonsils, and the appendix.

## 41.6b Lymphoid Tissues and Organs Act as Filters and Participate in the Immune Response

Tissues and organs of the lymphatic system include the lymph nodes, the spleen, the **thymus**, and the tonsils. They play primary roles in filtering viruses, bacteria, damaged cells, and cellular debris from the lymph and bloodstream and in defending the body against infection and cancer. Lymphoid tissue also occurs in other regions of the body, particularly the digestive tract, where patches of lymph cells can be found beneath the epithelium of the intestine, in the colon, and in the appendix.

**Lymph nodes** are small, bean-shaped organs spaced along the lymph vessels and clustered along the sides of the neck, in the armpits and groin, and in the centre of the abdomen and chest cavity (see Figure 41.18b). Spaces in nodes contain macrophages, a type of leukocyte that engulfs and destroys cellular debris and infecting bacteria and viruses in the lymph. The lymph nodes also contain other leukocytes, which produce antibodies that aid in the destruction of invading pathogens.

In most multicellular animals, most cells lie too deep within the body to exchange substances directly with the environment via diffusion. These animals have evolved circulatory systems that deliver $O_2$, $CO_2$, and nutrients to the cells and remove metabolic wastes and deliver them to excretion sites. The system has also evolved to take on other functions, such as pH regulation, temperature regulation, hormone delivery, and various aspects of the body's defence against disease. In *Why It Matters*, you were asked to consider, apart from beating faster, how else the heart could increase the delivery of blood to tissues. Based on your understanding of the chapter and the summary figure provided here, you should now be able to answer that question. Test your understanding further by considering how this summary figure would change for an insect with an open circulatory system and hemolymph.

### STUDY BREAK QUESTIONS

1. Why do we need a lymphatic system? What are its three functions?
2. If this is a system, what are its main organs?

# Summary Illustration

In most multicellular animals, most cells lie too deep within the body to exchange substances directly with the environment via diffusion. These animals have evolved circulatory systems that deliver $O_2$, $CO_2$, and nutrients to the cells and remove metabolic wastes and deliver them to excretion sites. These systems have also evolved to take on other functions, such as pH regulation, temperature regulation, hormone delivery, and various aspects of the body's defense against disease.

The lymphatic system helps maintain blood volume and also fights disease.

By adjusting the cardiac output to keep blood pressure constant, all tissues are supported.

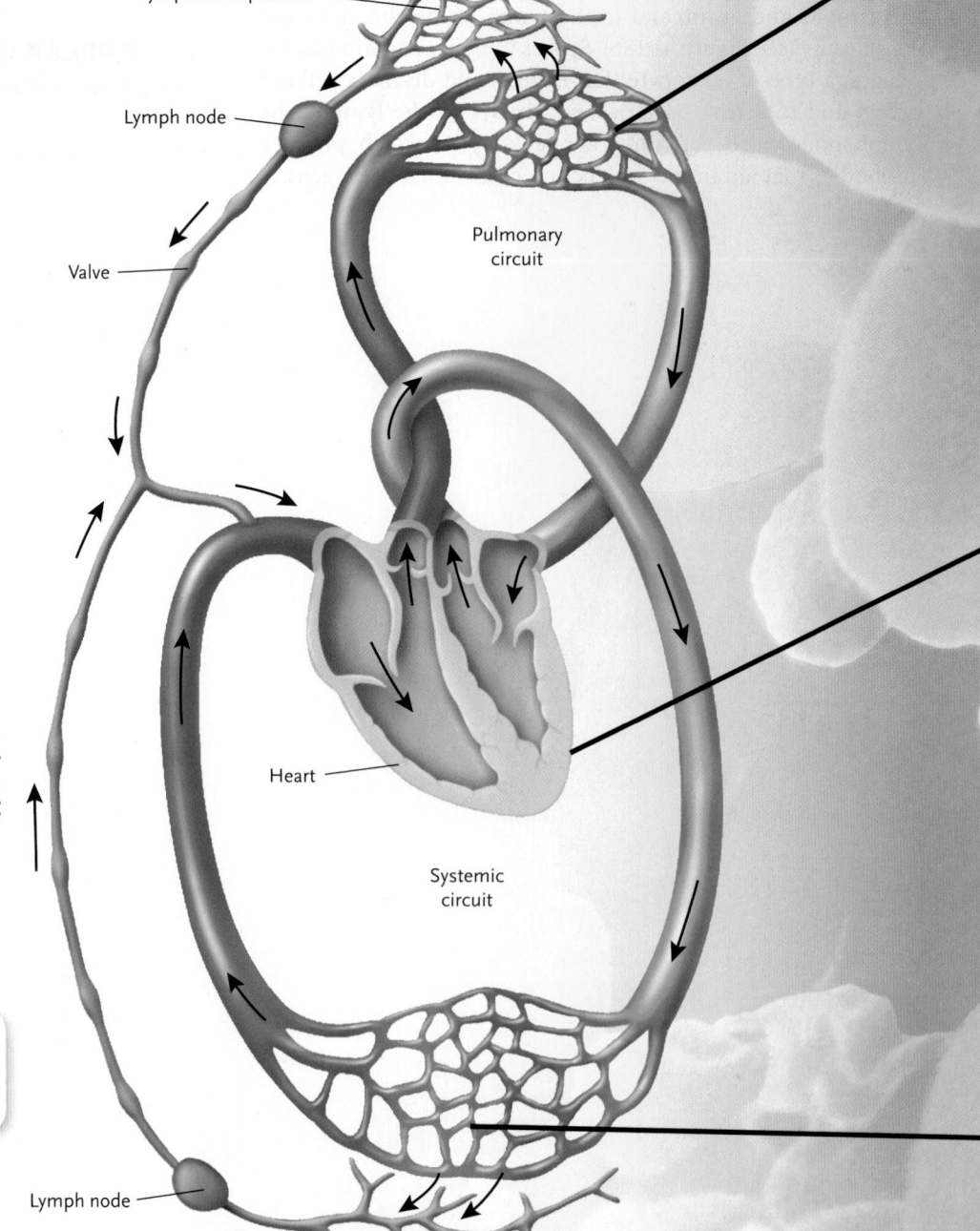

Lymphatic capillaries

Lymph node

Valve

Pulmonary circuit

Heart

Systemic circuit

Lymph node

© Cengage Learning 2017

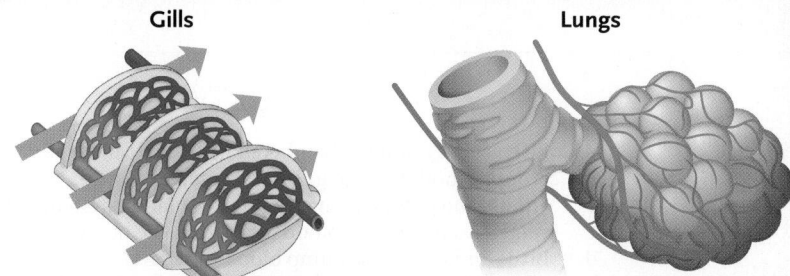

Gills

Lungs

$O_2$ and $CO_2$ are exchanged at the capillaries in the gills or lungs.

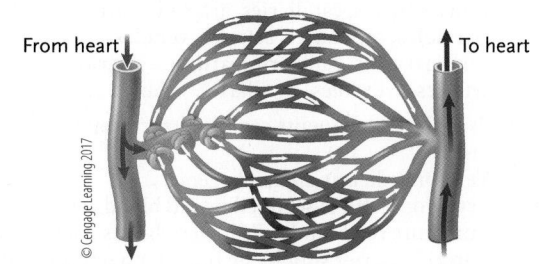

From heart

To heart

© Cengage Learning 2017

In animals with a closed circulatory system, the circuit consists of an aorta giving rise to arteries that give rise to arterioles that terminate in capillaries. The capillaries give rise to venules that coalesce into veins that join to form the vena cavae returning blood to the heart.

Fish

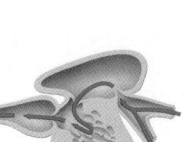

Amphibian

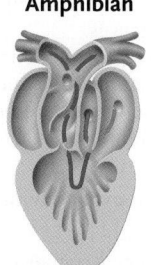

Bird/Mammal

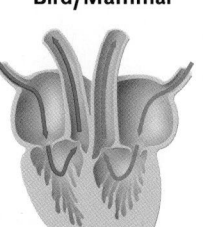

The heart is the pump that powers the system. It can increase blood flow by either increasing the rate at which it beats or the volume of blood pumped with each beat.

National Cancer Institute/Science Source

The blood that transports materials in the circulatory system consists of plasma, a variety of proteins and ions, and a variety of different cells. The red blood cells transport $O_2$ and $CO_2$, the white blood cells play roles in the body's immune system, and the platelets help preserve the integrity of the blood vessels. Most substances being transported are carried dissolved in the plasma.

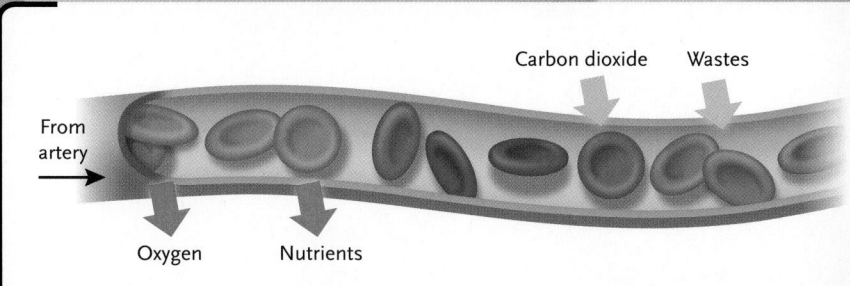

Carbon dioxide

Wastes

From artery

Oxygen

Nutrients

There are capillary beds throughout the body. In most tissues, these are the sites where nutrients and $O_2$ are exchanged for waste products and $CO_2$. Nutrients are taken up across the capillaries in the digestive system. Wastes are eliminated across the capillaries in the kidney.

# SELF-TEST QUESTIONS

## Recall/Understand

1. All circulatory systems must have which of these features?
   a. a pump, fluid, and vessels
   b. a pump and fluid, but not vessels
   c. fluid and vessels, but not a pump
   d. vessels and a pump, but not fluid

2. Which of the following is a characteristic of blood circulation through or to the mammalian heart?
   a. The superior vena cava conveys blood to the head.
   b. The inferior vena cava conveys blood to the right atrium.
   c. The pulmonary veins convey blood into the left ventricle.
   d. The pulmonary arteries convey blood from the lungs to the left atrium.

3. Pulmonary arteries carry blood that is which of the following?
   a. low in $O_2$ and high in $CO_2$
   b. low in both $O_2$ and $CO_2$
   c. high in both $O_2$ and $CO_2$
   d. high in $O_2$ and low in $CO_2$

4. Which of these features is a characteristic of veins and venules?
   a. thick walls
   b. large muscle mass in walls
   c. a large quantity of elastin in the walls
   d. have one-way valves to prevent backflow of blood

5. The blood plays roles in which of the following?
   a. transporting gas and buffering pH, but not clotting or defence
   b. defence, transporting gas, clotting, and buffering pH
   c. clotting and buffering pH, but not transporting gas or defence
   d. defence and buffering pH, but not transporting gas or clotting

6. Which of these characteristics is associated with systolic pressure?
   a. occurs during the relaxation phase of the heart cycle
   b. generated by the atrium
   c. generated by the ventricle
   d. measured in the pulmonary veins

## Apply/Analyze

7. Which circulatory system best matches the given animal or animals?
   a. Amphibians and reptiles use a two-chambered heart to separate oxygenated and deoxygenated blood.
   b. Fishes have a single-chambered heart with an atrium that pumps blood through gills for oxygen exchange.
   c. Squids and octopuses have open circulatory systems with ventricles that pump blood away from the heart.
   d. Birds and mammals pump blood to separate pulmonary and systemic systems from two separate ventricles in a four-chambered heart.

8. In general, the path of blood in the systemic circulation in a vertebrate occurs in the order of which of these series?
   a. veins, venules, capillaries, arterioles, arteries
   b. arterioles, capillaries, arteries, venules, veins
   c. venules, veins, capillaries, arteries, arterioles
   d. arteries, arterioles, capillaries, venules, veins

9. Which of these statements can be correctly applied to circulatory systems?
   a. Vertebrate hearts are neurogenic.
   b. Erythropoietin is secreted by red blood cells.
   c. Immature red blood cells in vertebrates contain no nuclei.
   d. Carotid arteries supply the brain with oxygenated blood.

## Create/Evaluate

10. Which of these actions would increase cardiac output?
    a. Baroreceptors signal high pressure to the brain via the sympathetic nerves.
    b. Chemoreceptors are stimulated by excessive blood oxygen.
    c. The adrenal medulla and sympathetic nervous system secrete epinephrine and norepinephrine.
    d. The autonomic nervous system decreases the force of the heartbeat.

11. Trace an erythrocyte arriving from your leg through your heart to the lungs.

12. Trace another erythrocyte arriving to the heart from the lungs and going to the systemic circulation.

13. We see that, as rivers narrow, the velocity of the water increases. How then is it possible to have efficient gas exchange in the smallest of all blood vessels, the capillaries. Why isn't blood flow too fast?

14. Explain the evolutionary trend in animal circulatory systems.

15. Explain what a diving reflex is, and why it is defensive.

# Chapter Roadmap

## Regulation of the Internal Environment: Water, Solutes, and Temperature

Organisms living in different biomes face different challenges for maintaining the integrity of their internal ions, water, and temperature in the face of changes in their external environment.

From Chapter 32

### 42.1 Introduction to Osmoregulation and Excretion

Maintaining solute and water balance takes place across tubules using a four step process: filtration, reabsorption, secretion, and excretion.

### 42.2 Osmoregulation and Excretion in Invertebrates

Invertebrates can be osmoconformers or osmoregulators. Osmoregulators use a variety of specialized tubules to achieve solute and water balance.

### 42.3 Osmoregulation and Excretion in Non-Mammalian Vertebrates

Animals living in fresh water, salt water, and on land face different problems and excrete nitrogenous wastes in different forms.

### 42.4 Osmoregulation and Excretion in Mammals

The mammalian kidney is unique in its ability to produce a hyperosmotic (concentrated) urine.

### 42.5 Introduction to Thermoregulation

Animals exchange heat with their environment by conduction, convection, radiation, and evaporation to achieve optimal physiological performance.

### 42.6 Ectothermy

Ectotherms obtain most of their heat from the environment and regulate their temperatures primarily by behavioural means.

### 42.7 Endothermy

Endotherms generate most of their heat internally and regulate their temperatures primarily by physiological means.

From Chapter 39

John L. Absher / Shutterstock.com

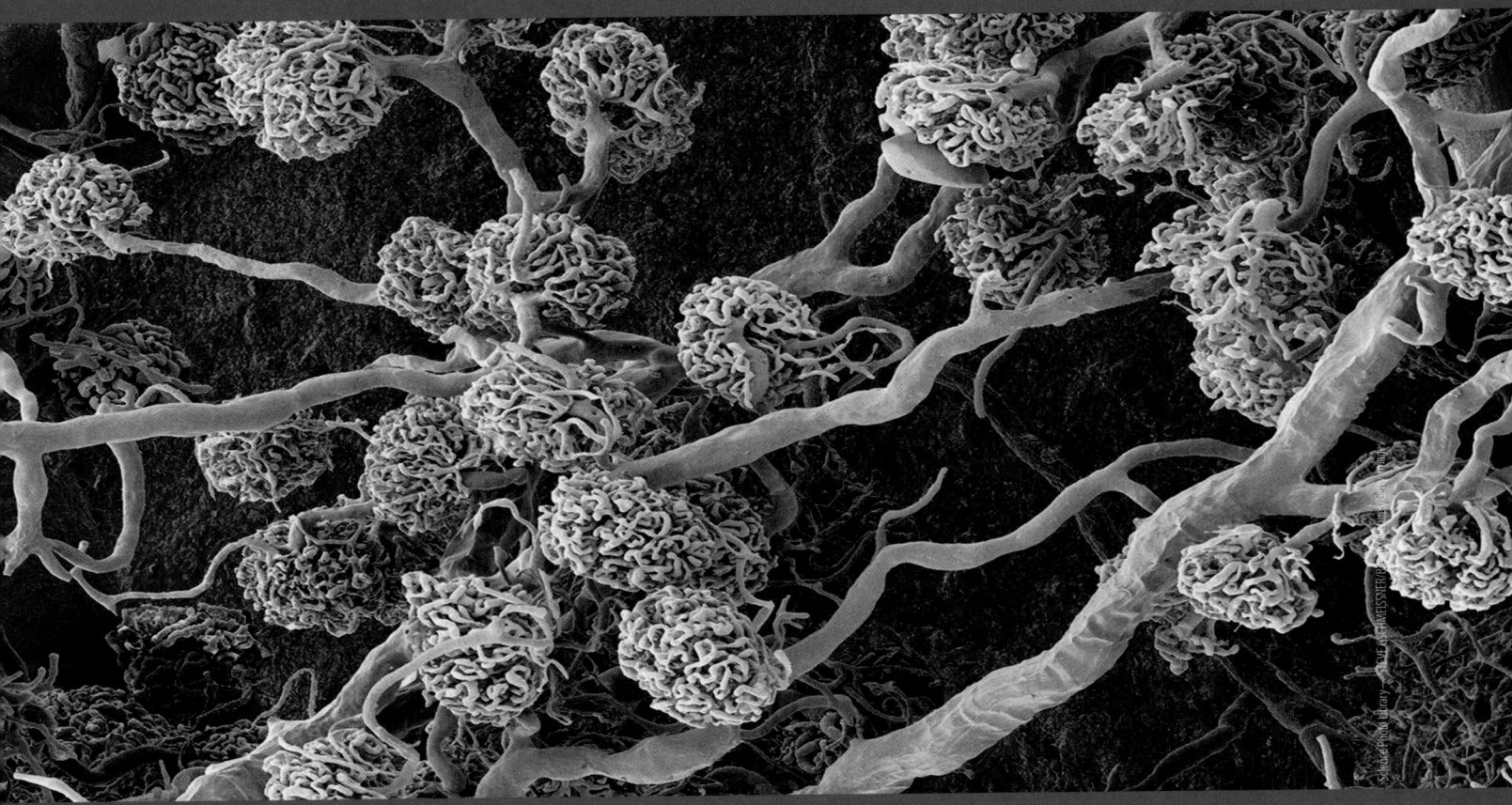

**Nephrons in a human kidney (colourized scanning electron micrograph).** Nephrons are the specialized tubules in kidneys that filter the blood to conserve nutrients and water, balance salts in the body, and concentrate wastes for excretion from the body.

# Regulation of the Internal Environment: Water, Solutes, and Temperature

# 42

**Why it matters . . .** In the Miramichi River of New Brunswick, Atlantic salmon (*Salmo salar*) spend two or three years growing from an egg to a fish about 10–25 cm in length. In the spring, as day length increases and the water temperature begins to rise, they undergo a number of physiological, morphological, and behavioural changes. They lose some of their mottled coloration, becoming silvery in appearance, and begin to migrate downstream. They may pause at the estuary of the river for a day or two, but then they abandon their freshwater environment and enter the sea, where they will remain for two or more years, feeding and growing to maturity. Eventually, they will return to the Miramichi to spawn **(Figure 42.1)**.

When the salmon leave the fresh water of the river and enter the salt water of the North Atlantic Ocean, they move from an environment in which the total concentration of solutes is about 0.1% to another with a concentration of about 3.5%. Their own body fluids contain about 1% solutes. Since water and many salts move freely across the gills of fish, which have a large surface area for gas exchange (see Chapter 40), the salmon move, over the course of a few days, from a situation where they are constantly losing salts and taking up water from the environment to one in which the opposite occurs; they constantly take up salts and lose water to their environment.

a.

b.

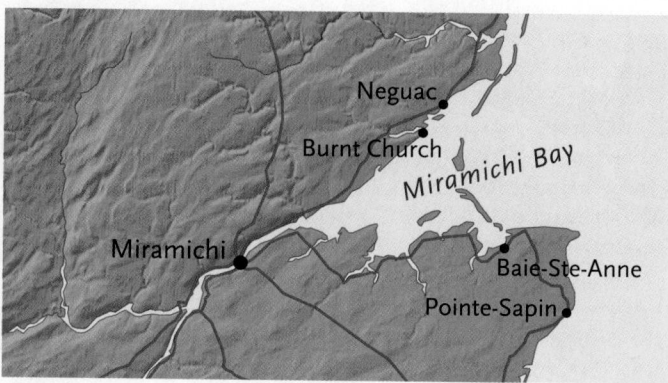

**FIGURE 42.1 (a)** Adult Atlantic salmon, ready to return to the river of their birth. **(b)** A photo and map show the estuary of the Miramichi River in New Brunswick.

Neguac

Burnt Church

Miramichi Bay

Miramichi

Baie-Ste-Anne

Pointe-Sapin

Since all the cells of the body need to retain a relatively constant level of ions and water (neither shrinking nor swelling), dramatic changes must occur in the physiological processes that correct for these effects and maintain ion and water balance in body fluids. These physiological changes accompany their morphological changes and allow them to prosper in both environments.

All organisms may be subject to short-term fluctuations in their external environment that present challenges for them to maintain not only the integrity of their internal ions and fluids, but also the functioning of all the systems that sustain life. Many are subject to seasonal changes that can also be challenging. The maintenance of a steady internal environment is called **homeostasis** (introduced in Chapter 38). In previous chapters, we discussed why and how blood pressure (Chapter 41), blood glucose levels (Chapter 43), and blood oxygen levels (Chapter 40) are maintained relatively constant. In this chapter, we will discuss the ways in which animals regulate water and ion balance as well as their body temperatures.

Consider the vast variety of habitats found on Earth, from deserts to lush rain forests, from the frozen poles to the tropics, from shallow streams to the depths of the oceans. What are the different challenges that organisms face living in each of these habitats? An understanding of the adaptations that allow some organisms but not others to live in different habitats not only gives us insight into the function of basic mechanisms, it also gives us insights into what the consequences will be of such things as climate change and habitat disruption.

# 42.1 Introduction to Osmoregulation and Excretion

Through evolution, a variety of physiological and behavioural mechanisms have arisen that permit organisms to exploit environments with varying challenges for maintaining water and solute balance. Significant among them are those mechanisms that accompanied the emergence from living in water to living on land. There are several important differences among marine, freshwater, and terrestrial environments. Organisms living in marine and terrestrial environments require mechanisms to obtain and conserve water; those in freshwater environments do not. On the other hand, obtaining salts and ions is relatively easy in marine environments, but more difficult in freshwater and terrestrial environments.

In this section, we review the mechanisms cells use to exchange water and solutes with their surrounding fluid through osmosis. We also look at how animals harness osmosis to regulate their internal water balance, the equilibrium between the inward and outward flow of water.

## 42.1a Osmosis Is Passive Diffusion

In osmosis (see Chapter 4), water molecules move across a selectively permeable membrane (one that lets water through but excludes most solutes) from a region of lesser solute concentration to a region of greater solute concentration. Selective permeability is a key factor in osmosis because it helps maintain differences in solute concentration on either side of biological membranes. Proteins are among the most important solutes in establishing the conditions producing osmosis. The passive transport of water occurs constantly in living cells; any net transport of ions or other solutes across a membrane will cause water to follow, developing forces that lead to cell swelling or shrinking.

The total solute concentration of a solution may be measured in one of two ways. **Osmolarity** is measured in osmoles—the number of solute molecules and ions (in moles)—per *litre of solution*. **Osmolality** is measured in osmoles *per kilogram of solution*. Osmolality is used more frequently to measure the osmotic concentration of a solution. This is because a kilogram of water will change volume if it is heated or cooled, but neither the weight nor the number of solute particles will change (i.e., osmolarity will change; osmolality will not).

Because the total solute concentration in the body fluids of most animals is less than 1 osmole, osmolality is usually expressed in thousandths of an osmole, or milliosmoles (mOsm) per kilogram. As shown in **Figure 42.2**, the osmolality of body fluids in terrestrial vertebrates (including humans) is about 300 mOsm/kg. It is similar in freshwater organisms; in a goldfish, a freshwater teleost, it is about 290 mOsm/kg; marine invertebrates, such as lobsters, have osmolalities close to that of sea water, about 1000 mOsm/kg. Interestingly, the osmolality in marine teleosts (bony fish such as the flounder) is only about 330 mOsm/kg. The relatively low osmotic concentration in marine teleosts reflects their evolutionary history. Early marine teleosts invaded fresh water and prospered there. During the extensive radiation of the group in fresh water, many reinvaded the marine habitat.

A solution of higher osmolality on one side of a selectively permeable membrane is said to be hyperosmotic to a solution of lower osmolality on the other side, and a solution of lower osmolality is said to be hypoosmotic to a solution of higher osmolality. If the solutions on either side of a membrane have the same osmotic concentrations, they are isoosmotic. Water moves across the membrane between solutions that differ in osmolality, whereas when two solutions are isoosmotic, no *net* water movement occurs, although water exchanges from one side to the other. (Compare this to the discussion of hypotonic, hypertonic, and isotonic in Section 4.4d and Figure 4.16, in Chapter 4.)

The principles that determine osmotic concentration also determine the freezing point and boiling point of a solution. Increasing solute concentration (increasing osmolality) reduces the freezing point and increases the boiling point of a solution.

**CONCEPT FIX** It is a misconception that, once a cell is killed, diffusion and osmosis stop. Diffusion and osmosis are passive processes and will occur as long as the cell membrane is intact, providing a selectively permeable barrier. Since ion transporters are no longer working, the ability of the cell to correct for passive movement will be gone, and, of course, with time, the cell membrane will break down. ⬡

## 42.1b  Animals Use Different Approaches to Regulate Osmosis

Because even small differences in osmotic concentration can cause cells to swell or shrink, animals must keep their cellular and extracellular fluids isoosmotic. In some animals, called **osmoconformers**, the osmotic concentrations of the cellular and extracellular solutions simply match that of the environment.

Many marine invertebrates are osmoconformers: when placed in dilute sea water, the osmotic concentration of their body fluids decreases and their weight increases as a result of the osmotic influx of water. Other animals, called **osmoregulators**, use control mechanisms to keep the osmolality of cellular and extracellular fluids constant (i.e., homeostatically controlled) but at levels that may differ from the osmolality of the surroundings. Most freshwater and terrestrial invertebrates, and almost all vertebrates, are osmoregulators. It is important to recognize that the various solutes contributing to the osmotic concentration may be at different concentrations inside the cell, in the extracellular fluids, and in the environment. Organisms can regulate different ions to reach the appropriate osmolality.

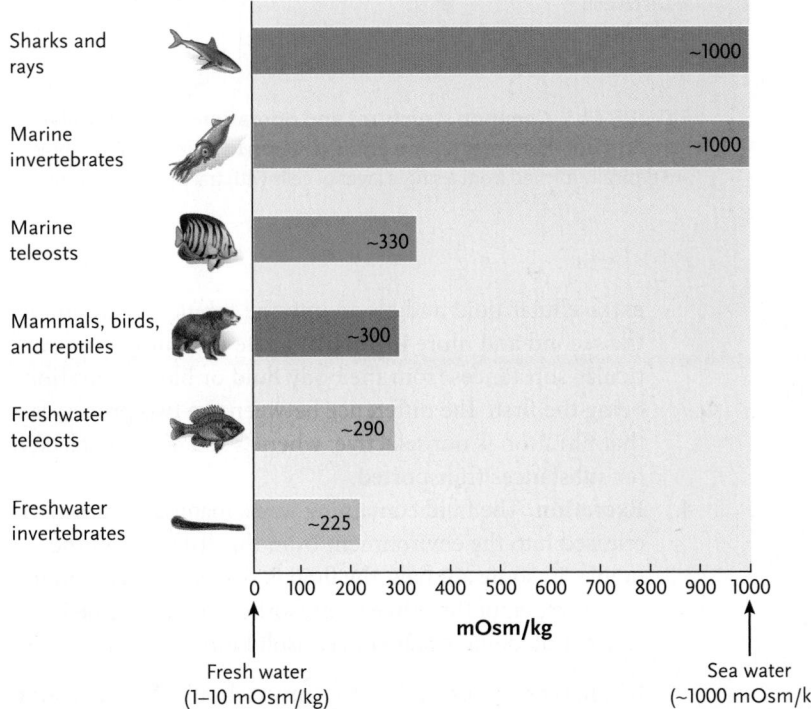

FIGURE 42.2  **Osmolality of body fluids in some animal groups**

## 42.1c Excretion Is Closely Tied to Osmoregulation

Cells must control their ionic and pH balance as well as their osmotic concentration. This may require the removal of certain ions from cells and body fluids and their release into the environment. Animals excrete excess $H^+$ ions to keep the pH of body fluids near the neutral levels required by cells for survival. Animals also excrete toxic products of metabolism, such as nitrogenous (nitrogen-containing) compounds resulting from the breakdown of proteins and nucleic acids, and breakdown products of poisons and toxins. Excretion of ions and metabolic products is accompanied by water excretion because water serves as a solvent for those molecules. Animals that take in large amounts of water may also excrete water to maintain osmolality.

## 42.1d Microscopic Tubules Form the Basis of Excretion in Most Animals

Except in the simplest animals, minute tubular structures carry out osmoregulation and excretion **(Figure 42.3)**. The tubules are immersed in body fluids at one end (called the proximal end of the tubules) and open directly or indirectly to the body exterior at the other end (called the distal end of the tubules). The tubules are formed from a **transport epithelium**, a layer of cells with specialized transport proteins in their plasma membranes. The transport proteins move specific molecules and ions into and out of the tubule by either active or passive transport, depending on the particular substance and its concentration gradient.

Typically, the tubules function in a four-step process:

1. **Filtration.** Filtration is the nonselective movement of water and a number of solutes—ions and small molecules, but not large molecules such as proteins—into the proximal end of the tubules through spaces between cells. In animals with an open circulatory system, the water and solutes come from body fluids. Movement into the tubules is driven by the higher pressure of the body fluids compared with the fluid inside the tubule. In animals with a closed circulatory system, such as humans, the water and solutes come from the blood in capillaries that surround the tubules. Movement into the tubules is similarly driven by hydrostatic pressure. (Open and closed circulatory systems are described in Section 41.1, Chapter 41.)

2. **Reabsorption.** In reabsorption, some molecules (e.g., glucose and amino acids) and ions are transported by the transport epithelium back into the extracellular fluid and eventually into the blood as the filtered solution moves through the excretory tubule; that is, the system takes back the solutes it wants to keep.

3. **Secretion.** Secretion is a selective process in which specific small molecules and ions are transported from the

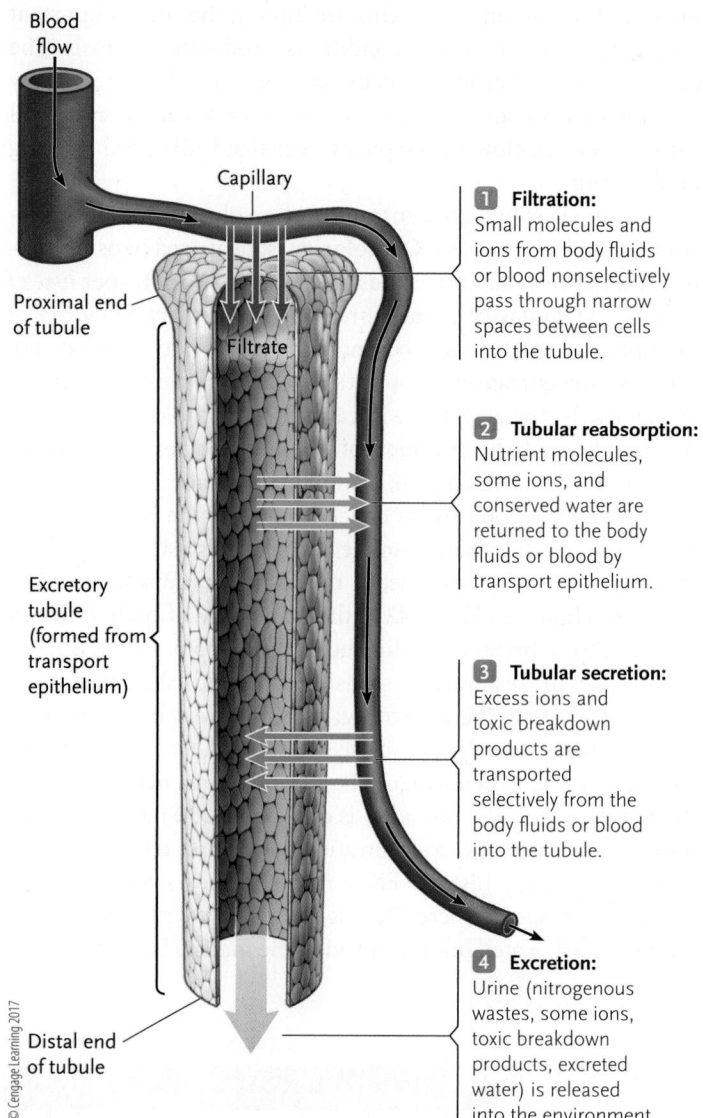

**1 Filtration:** Small molecules and ions from body fluids or blood nonselectively pass through narrow spaces between cells into the tubule.

**2 Tubular reabsorption:** Nutrient molecules, some ions, and conserved water are returned to the body fluids or blood by transport epithelium.

**3 Tubular secretion:** Excess ions and toxic breakdown products are transported selectively from the body fluids or blood into the tubule.

**4 Excretion:** Urine (nitrogenous wastes, some ions, toxic breakdown products, excreted water) is released into the environment.

© Cengage Learning 2017

**FIGURE 42.3 Common structures and operations of the tubules carrying out osmoregulation and excretion in animals.** The tubules are typically formed from a single layer of cells with transport functions.

extracellular fluid and blood into the tubules. Secretion is the second and more important route for eliminating particular substances from the body fluid or blood, filtration being the first. The difference between the two processes is that filtration is nonselective, whereas secretion is selective for substances transported.

4. **Excretion.** The fluid containing waste materials—urine—is released into the environment from the distal end of the tubule. In some animals, the fluid is stored in a bladder; in others, much of the water is reabsorbed and the urine is concentrated into a solid or semisolid form.

In all vertebrates and many invertebrates, the excretory tubules are concentrated in specialized organs, the kidneys, which are discussed in later sections.

## 42.1e Animals Excrete Nitrogen Compounds as Metabolic Wastes

The metabolism of ingested food is a source of both energy and molecules for the biosynthetic activities of an animal. Importantly, metabolism of ingested food produces metabolic water, which is used in chemical reactions as well as being involved in physiological processes such as the excretion of wastes. As we will discuss later in the chapter, some animals can survive on the production of metabolic water alone and never need to drink.

The proteins, amino acids, and nucleic acids in food are continually broken down as part of digestion (see Chapter 39) and by the constant turnover and replacement of these molecules in body cells. The nitrogenous products of this breakdown are excreted by most animals as ammonia, urea, or uric acid or a combination of these substances (**Figure 42.4**). The particular molecule or combination of molecules depends on a balance among toxicity, water conservation, and energy requirements.

**AMMONIA** Ammonia ($NH_3$) results from the metabolism of amino acids and proteins and is highly toxic: it can be safely transported and excreted from the body only in dilute solutions. Those animals with a plentiful supply of water, such as freshwater or marine invertebrates, teleost fish, and larval amphibians, excrete ammonia as their primary nitrogenous waste. Other animals detoxify ammonia by converting it to urea or uric acid.

**UREA** All mammals, most amphibians, some reptiles, some marine fishes, and some terrestrial invertebrates combine ammonia

with $HCO_3^-$ and convert the product in a series of steps to urea, a soluble substance that is less toxic than ammonia. Although producing urea requires more energy than forming ammonia, excreting urea instead of ammonia requires much less water.

**URIC ACID** Water is conserved further in some animals, including many terrestrial invertebrates, reptiles, and birds, by the formation of uric acid instead of ammonia or urea. Uric acid is nontoxic, but its great advantage is its low solubility. During the concentration of the urine in the final stages of its formation, the uric acid precipitates as crystals that can be expelled with minimal water. (The white substance in bird droppings is uric acid.) The embryos of reptiles and birds, which develop within leathery or hard-shelled eggs that are impermeable to liquids, also conserve water by forming uric acid, which is stored as a waste product inside the shell. Similarly, the pupae of insects store uric acid in the rectum.

Many animals have the capacity to form all three products of nitrogen metabolism. Mammalian urine, for example, contains small amounts of uric acid, although urea predominates. Some tree frogs, such as *Phyllomedusa sauvagii* (see Figure 42.9), have uric acid as their principal excretory product. This has enabled them to exploit the woodlands of South America, where the dry season is extremely arid. Conversely, the American cockroach, *Periplaneta americana*, an insect that normally lives in damp environments, uses ammonia as its primary excretory product and stores uric acid in special cells during periods when water is less available.

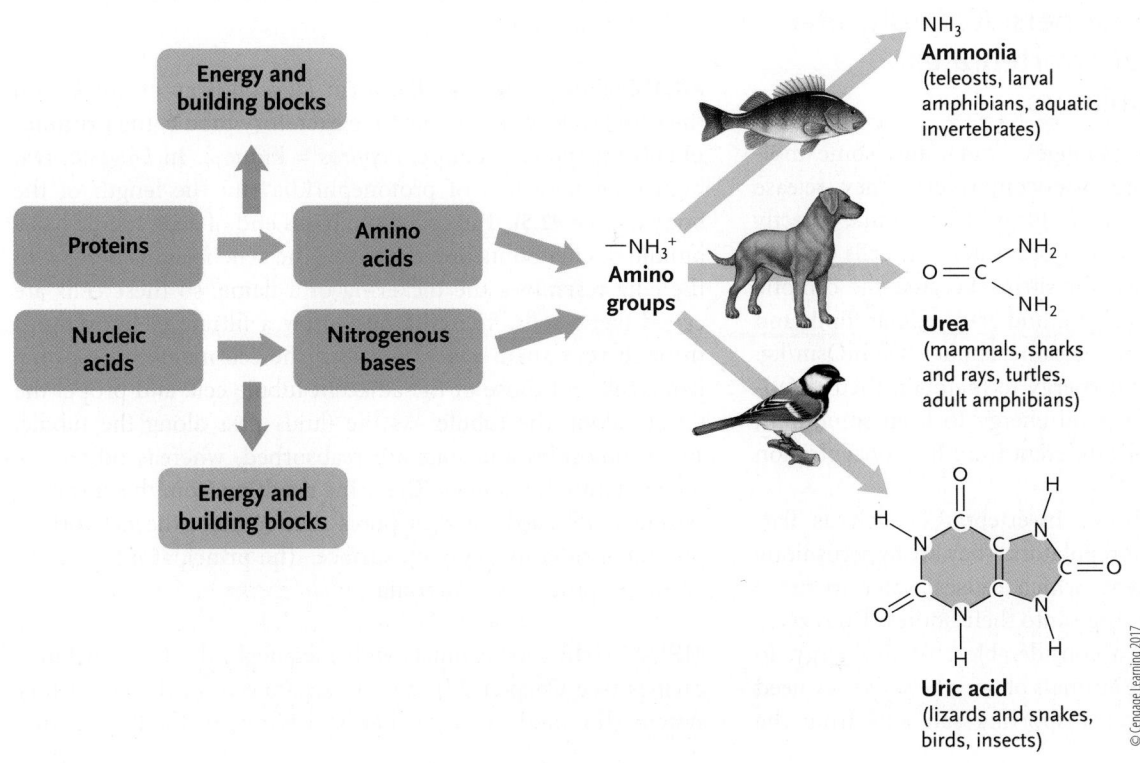

**FIGURE 42.4 Nitrogenous wastes excreted by different animal groups.** Although humans and other mammals excrete primarily urea, they also excrete small amounts of ammonia and uric acid.

© Cengage Learning 2017

Sharks and rays maintain their osmotic concentration near that of their marine environment by retaining urea in their tissues and blood. (This is why shark and ray meat cut with a cookie cutter and falsely sold as scallops has a faint taste of urine.)

In the following sections, we look at the specifics of osmoregulation and excretion in different animal groups, beginning with the invertebrates.

## STUDY BREAK QUESTIONS

1. Define *osmolality*. How does it differ from osmolarity? Why is osmolality used more frequently to measure the osmotic concentration of a solution? What problems for a fish are associated with living in a high- or low-osmolar environment?
2. What are the sources of ammonia, urea, and uric acid in excretory products? Why do different species produce these different compounds? What are the advantages and disadvantages of each strategy?
3. Why do mammals convert ammonia to urea and not simply excrete it as ammonia as fish do?

# 42.2 Osmoregulation and Excretion in Invertebrates

Both osmoconformers and osmoregulators occur among the invertebrates, and most carry out excretion by specialized excretory structures.

## 42.2a Most Marine Invertebrates Are Osmoconformers; All Freshwater and Terrestrial Invertebrates Are Osmoregulators

Many marine invertebrates (sponges, cnidarians, some molluscs, and echinoderms) are osmoconformers. They release nitrogenous wastes, usually in the form of ammonia, directly from body cells to the surrounding sea water. The cells of these animals do not normally swell or shrink because the osmotic concentrations of their intracellular and extracellular fluids and the surrounding sea water are the same, about 1000 mOsm/kg. Although they do not expend energy to maintain their osmolality, osmoconformers do expend energy to keep some ions, such as Na+, at concentrations different from the concentration in sea water.

By contrast, all freshwater invertebrates, such as flatworms and mussels, are osmoregulators. They are hyperosmotic relative to their environment, which causes water to move constantly from the surroundings into their bodies. This excess water must be excreted, at a considerable cost in energy, to maintain homeostasis. These animals obtain the salts they need from foods and by actively transporting salt ions from the water into their bodies (even fresh water contains some dissolved salts). This active ion transport occurs through the body surface or the gills. Although osmoregulation is energetically expensive and comes at a cost, these invertebrates can live in more varied habitats than osmoconformers can.

Terrestrial osmoregulators include annelids (earthworms), arthropods (insects, spiders and mites, millipedes, and centipedes), and molluscs (land snails and slugs). Although they do not have to excrete water entering by osmosis, they must constantly replace water lost from their bodies by evaporation and excretion. Most obtain water from their food, and some drink water. Like their freshwater relatives, these invertebrates must obtain salts from their surroundings, usually in their foods.

## 42.2b Specialized Excretory Tubules Participate in Osmoregulation

Most invertebrates (except marine osmoconformers) use specialized tubular structures to carry out excretion. These include protonephridia in flatworms and larval molluscs, metanephridia in annelids and most adult molluscs, and Malpighian tubules in insects and other arthropods. What are the differences? In protonephridia, the excretory tubules are open only at one end. Body fluids do not enter protonephridia directly. An ultrafiltrate enters the tubule through narrow extracellular spaces that permit only small molecules to enter, and exclude larger molecules such as proteins. Metanephridia, by contrast, are open at both ends. They are characteristic of animals with coeloms, and the coelomic fluid is already an ultrafiltrate of the blood in the closed circulatory system. Malpighian tubules have a closed proximal end that is immersed in the hemolymph, and the distal ends of the tubules empty into the gut. We take a closer look at each of these next.

PROTONEPHRIDIA The flatworm *Dugesia* is an example with the simplest form of invertebrate excretory tubule, the **protonephridium** (*proto* = before; *nephros* = kidney). In *Dugesia*, two branching networks of protonephridia run the length of the body **(Figure 42.5)**. The cell at the blind end of each tubule has a bundle of cilia on its inner surface. The synchronous beating of the cilia resembles the flickering of a flame, so these cells are called flame cells. The cilia help draw a filtrate of body fluids through very small spaces between the cell membranes of the flame cell and those of the adjacent tubule cell, and propel the filtrate along the tubule. As the fluids pass along the tubule, some molecules and ions are reabsorbed, whereas others are secreted into the tubules. The urine resulting from this filtration system is released through pores that connect the network of protonephridia to the body surface. The principal nitrogenous excretory product is ammonia.

METANEPHRIDIA Animals with metanephridia have coelomic cavities (see Chapter 27) that are separate from the circulatory system. The fluid in the coelom is a filtrate of the hemolymph

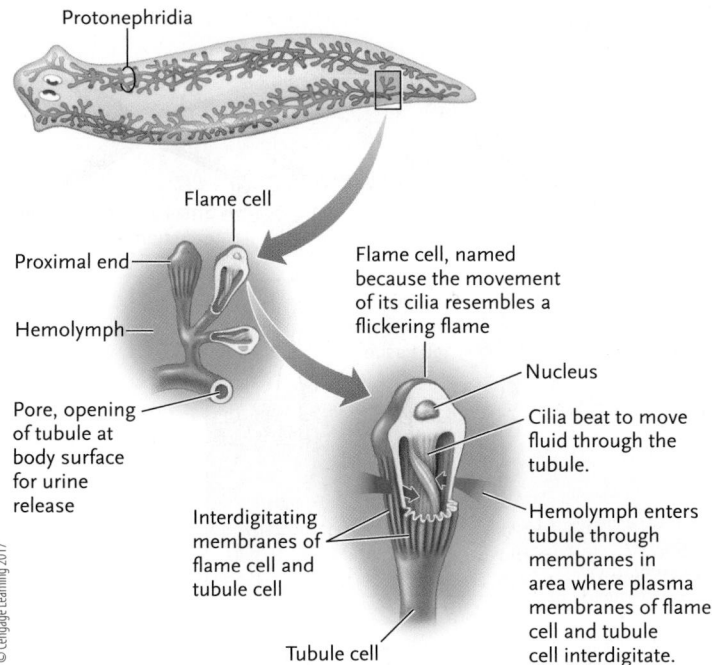

FIGURE 42.5 **The protonephridia of the planarian *Dugesia*, showing the flame cells**

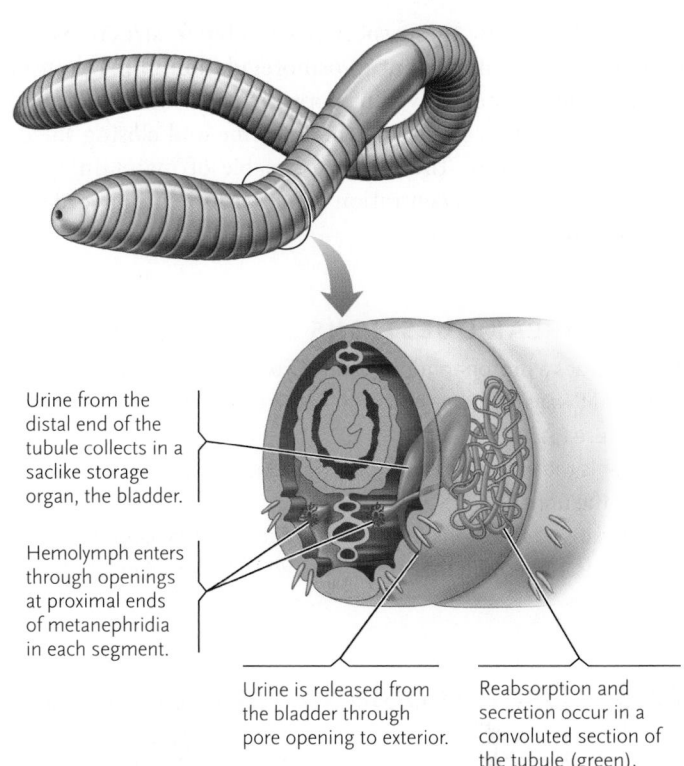

FIGURE 42.6 **A metanephridium of an earthworm**

or blood. Coelomic fluid enters the proximal end of the excretory tubule, and ions and other solutes are reabsorbed or secreted as the fluid moves along the tubule. In annelids, the **metanephridium (Figure 42.6)** is a segmental structure. The proximal ends of a pair of metanephridia are located in each body segment, one on each side of the animal. A funnel-like opening surrounded by cilia admits coelomic fluid. Each tubule of the pair extends into the following segment, where it bends and folds into a convoluted arrangement surrounded by a network of blood vessels. Reabsorption and secretion of specific molecules and ions take place in the convoluted section. Urine from the distal end of the tubule collects in a saclike storage organ, the bladder, from where it is released through a pore on the surface of the segment.

**MALPIGHIAN TUBULES** The excretory tubules of insects, the **Malpighian tubules**, have a closed proximal end that is immersed in the hemolymph **(Figure 42.7)**. The distal ends of the tubules empty into the gut. The fluid in the tubules results primarily from secretion, although in some insects an ultrafiltrate of the hemolymph may enter the upper part of the tubule through extracellular spaces. In particular, uric acid and several ions, including $Na^+$ and $K^+$, are actively secreted into the tubules. As the concentration of these substances rises, water moves osmotically from the hemolymph into the tubule. The fluid then passes into the hindgut (intestine and rectum) of the insect as dilute urine. Cells in the hindgut wall actively reabsorb most of the $Na^+$ and $K^+$ back into the hemolymph, and water follows by osmosis. The uric acid left in the gut precipitates into crystals, which mix with the undigested matter in the rectum and are released with the feces. This arrangement is important in conserving water.

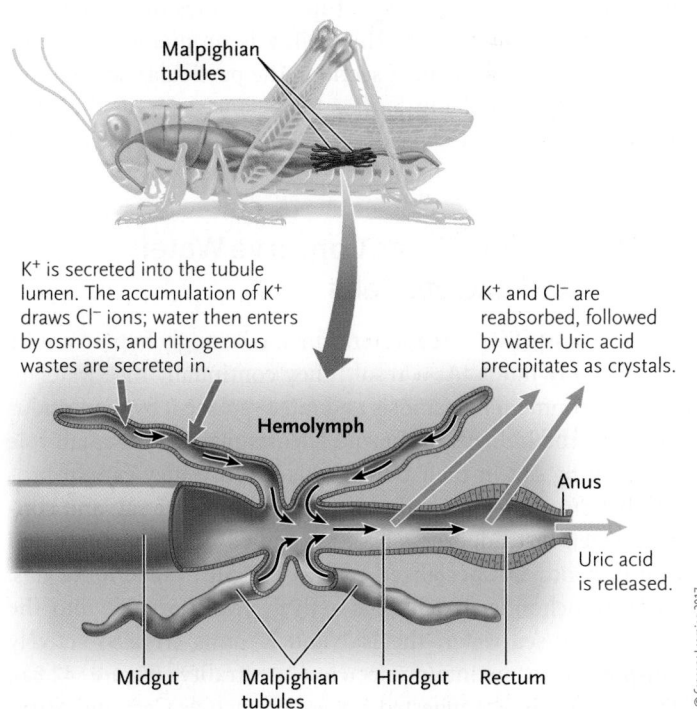

FIGURE 42.7 **Excretion through Malpighian tubules in a grasshopper**

In addition to these specialized tubular structures, the body wall is also important in osmoregulation in many invertebrates. Researchers have cut parasitic cod worms and made sausagelike sacs by removing the intestine and closing the cut ends with ligatures. The sacs are capable of maintaining the internal osmotic concentration in environments of different osmotic concentrations.

## STUDY BREAK QUESTIONS

1. How does a protonephridium differ from a metanephridium? In what ways are they similar? In which animal groups are each of these found?

2. What is the excretory product of most insects? How does it get into the urine?

3. Some insects feed on plants, such as tobacco, that contain poisons. How could they be eliminated by Malpighian tubules?

# 42.3 Osmoregulation and Excretion in Non-mammalian Vertebrates

In all vertebrates, the specialized excretory tubules that contribute to osmoregulation and excretion are called **nephrons**, and are located in a specialized organ, the kidney. In all non-mammalian vertebrates, the kidneys produce a urine that is either hypoosmotic (dilute) or isoosmotic to body fluids, with the exception of some birds, which can produce urine that is weakly hyperosmotic. Mammals, on the other hand, can produce a very concentrated urine (up to 25 times the solute concentration of body fluids). This ability is unique to mammals and is discussed in the next section. The particular adaptations that maintain osmolality and water balance among the non-mammalian vertebrates vary depending on whether retention of water or of salts is the major issue.

## 42.3a Marine Fishes Conserve Water and Excrete Salts

Marine teleosts live in sea water, which is strongly hyperosmotic to their body fluids. As a result, they continually lose water to their environment by osmosis and must replace it by continuous drinking. The kidneys of marine teleosts play only a small role in regulating salt in their body fluids because they cannot produce hyperosmotic urine that would both remove salt and conserve water. Instead, excess $Na^+$, $K^+$, and $Cl^-$ ions are eliminated from the body by specialized cells in the gills, called ionocytes. These mitochondrial rich cells actively transport $Cl^-$ into the surrounding sea water; the $Na^+$ and $K^+$ ions are also actively transported to maintain electrical neutrality **(Figure 42.8a)**. Divalent ions in the ingested sea water, such as $Ca^{2+}$ and $Mg^{2+}$, are removed by the kidneys in an isoosmotic urine. On balance, a marine teleost is able to retain most of the water it drinks and

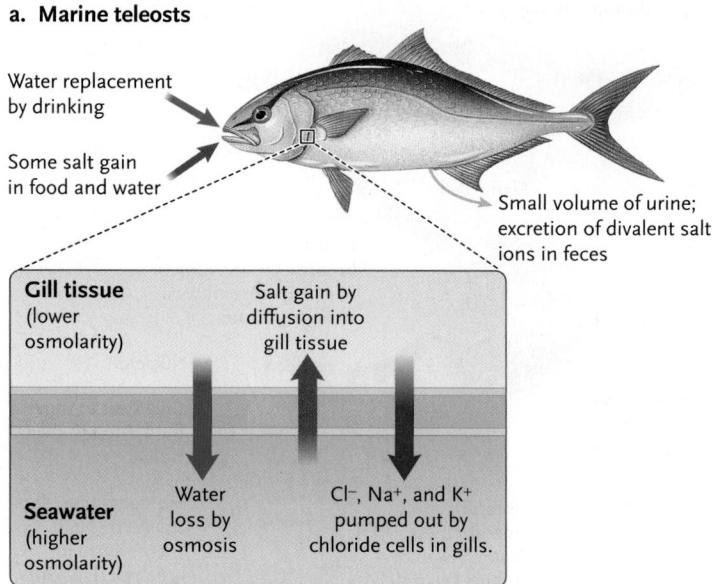

**a. Marine teleosts**

Water replacement by drinking

Some salt gain in food and water

Small volume of urine; excretion of divalent salt ions in feces

**Gill tissue** (lower osmolarity)

Salt gain by diffusion into gill tissue

**Seawater** (higher osmolarity)

Water loss by osmosis

$Cl^-$, $Na^+$, and $K^+$ pumped out by chloride cells in gills.

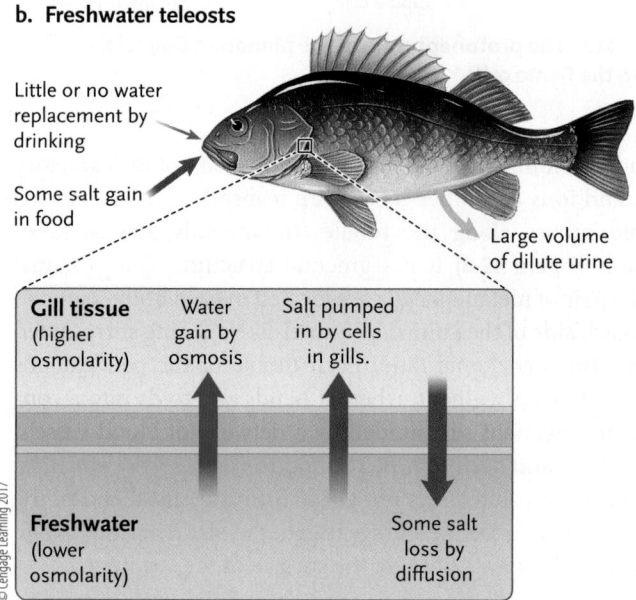

**b. Freshwater teleosts**

Little or no water replacement by drinking

Some salt gain in food

Large volume of dilute urine

**Gill tissue** (higher osmolarity)

Water gain by osmosis

Salt pumped in by cells in gills.

**Freshwater** (lower osmolarity)

Some salt loss by diffusion

© Cengage Learning 2017

**FIGURE 42.8  The mechanisms balancing the water and salt content of** (a) **marine teleosts and** (b) **freshwater teleosts**

eliminate most of the salt, allowing its tissue fluids to remain hypoosmotic to the surrounding water without producing hyperosmotic urine. The kidneys play a small role in the removal of nitrogenous wastes; these are also released from the gills, primarily as ammonia, by simple diffusion.

Sharks and rays have a different adaptation to sea water: the osmolality of their body fluids is maintained close to that of sea water by retaining high levels of urea in body fluids, along with another nitrogenous waste, trimethylamine oxide (TMAO). Elasmobranchs (see Chapter 27) may have concentrations of urea as high as 1300 mg per 100 mL of blood. The match in osmolality keeps sharks and rays from losing water to the surrounding sea by osmosis, and they do not have to drink sea water continuously to maintain their water balance. Excess salts ingested with food are excreted in the kidney and by specialized secretory cells in a rectal salt gland located near the anal opening. The importance of urea as an osmolyte is illustrated by those species of stingrays that inhabit fresh water. In such species, the concentration of urea is reduced to about 2–3 mg per 100 mL of blood.

## 42.3b Freshwater Fishes and Amphibians Excrete Water and Conserve Salts

The body fluids of freshwater fishes and aquatic amphibians (no amphibians live in sea water, although the crab-eating frog (*Fejervarya cancrivora*) lives in mangrove swamps in Southeast Asia and can tolerate saltwater conditions) are hyperosmotic to the surrounding water, which usually ranges from about 1 to 10 mOsm/kg. Water therefore moves osmotically into their tissues. Such animals rarely drink, and they excrete large volumes of dilute urine to get rid of excess water (Figure 42.8b). In freshwater fishes, salt ions lost with the urine are replaced by salt in foods and by active transport of Na$^+$, K$^+$, and Cl$^-$ into the body by the gills. Aquatic amphibians obtain salt in the diet and by active transport across the skin from the surrounding water. Nitrogenous wastes are excreted from the gills as ammonia in both freshwater fishes and aquatic amphibians.

Terrestrial amphibians must conserve both water and salt, which are obtained primarily in foods. In these animals, the kidneys secrete salt into the urine, causing water to enter the urine by osmosis. In the bladder, the salt is reclaimed by active transport and returned to body fluids. The water remains in the bladder, making the urine very dilute; during times of drought, the water can be reabsorbed. Terrestrial amphibians also have behavioural adaptations that help minimize water loss, such as seeking shaded, moist environments and remaining inactive during the day.

Most adult amphibians excrete nitrogenous wastes through their kidneys as urea. The leaf frog, *Phyllomedusa sauvagii* **(Figure 42.9)**, however, produces uric acid as the principal nitrogenous waste. In addition, it secretes a waxy substance from glands in its skin and uses its legs to smear this over its entire body surface, thereby minimizing water loss.

## 42.3c Reptiles and Birds Excrete Uric Acid to Conserve Water

Terrestrial reptiles and most birds conserve water by excreting nitrogenous wastes in the form of an almost water-free paste of uric acid crystals. Further water conservation occurs as the epithelial cells of the cloaca, the common exit for the digestive and excretory systems, absorb water from feces and urine before those wastes are eliminated. This arrangement is similar to the strategy used by insects, described earlier. In reptiles, the scales covering the skin allow almost no water to escape through the body surface.

**FIGURE 42.9** *Phyllomedusa sauvagii* **is a tree frog that prospers in the dry woodlands of South America.** Among its many adaptations to a dry environment are the production of uric acid and the secretion from skin glands of a waterproofing waxy material.

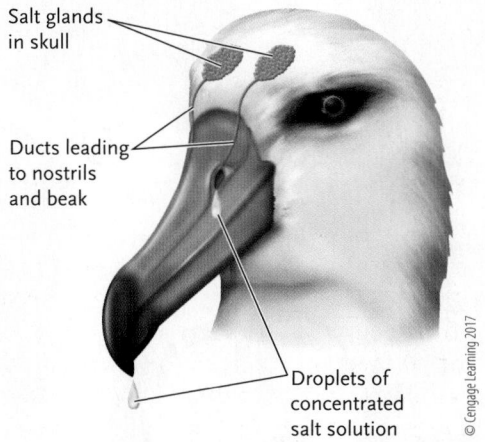

Salt glands in skull

Ducts leading to nostrils and beak

Droplets of concentrated salt solution

**FIGURE 42.10** **Salt glands in a bird living on a seacoast**

Reptiles, such as crocodilians, sea snakes, and sea turtles, and birds, such as seagulls, penguins, and pelicans, that live in or around sea water take in large quantities of salt with their food and rarely or never drink fresh water. These animals typically excrete excess salt through specialized salt glands located in the head **(Figure 42.10)** that remove salts from the blood by active transport. The salts are secreted to the environment as a water solution in which salts are two to three times as concentrated as in body fluids. The secretion exits through the nostrils of birds and lizards, through the mouth of marine snakes, and as salty tears from the eye sockets of sea turtles and crocodilians.

### STUDY BREAK QUESTIONS

1. What are the osmoregulatory problems faced by marine and freshwater teleosts, and how are they solved?
2. What excretory strategy is used by birds and reptiles to conserve water?
3. How do marine birds and reptiles excrete excess salts?

## 42.4 Osmoregulation and Excretion in Mammals

Since water moves by osmosis from areas of low solute concentration to areas of high solute concentration, it would seem impossible to produce a hyperosmotic urine, one in which water is reabsorbed into the body, leaving high concentrations of salt behind in the urine. We next describe the structure and function of the mammalian kidney and the unique way in which "the impossible" has been achieved.

## 42.4a The Kidneys, Ureters, Bladder, and Urethra Constitute the Urinary System

Mammals have a pair of kidneys, one located on each side of the vertebral column on the dorsal side of the abdominal cavity (i.e., low in the abdomen against the backbone) **(Figure 42.11)**. Internally, the mammalian kidney is divided into an outer region, the **renal cortex,** surrounding a central region, the **renal medulla (Figure 42.12)**.

A **renal artery** carries blood to each kidney, where metabolic wastes and excess water and ions are excreted in the urine

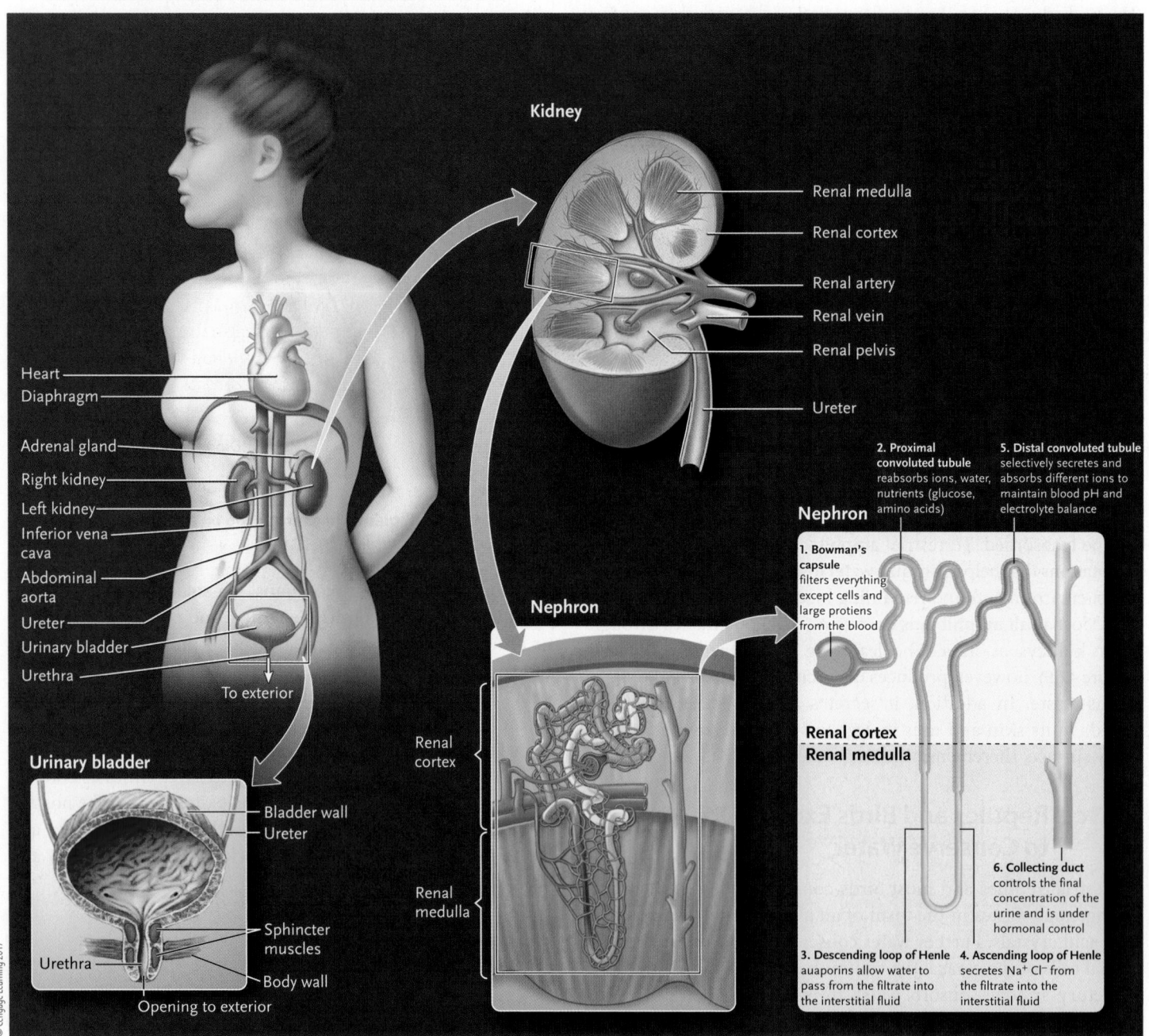

**FIGURE 42.11  Human kidneys and urinary system in a female**

## a.
**Nephron**

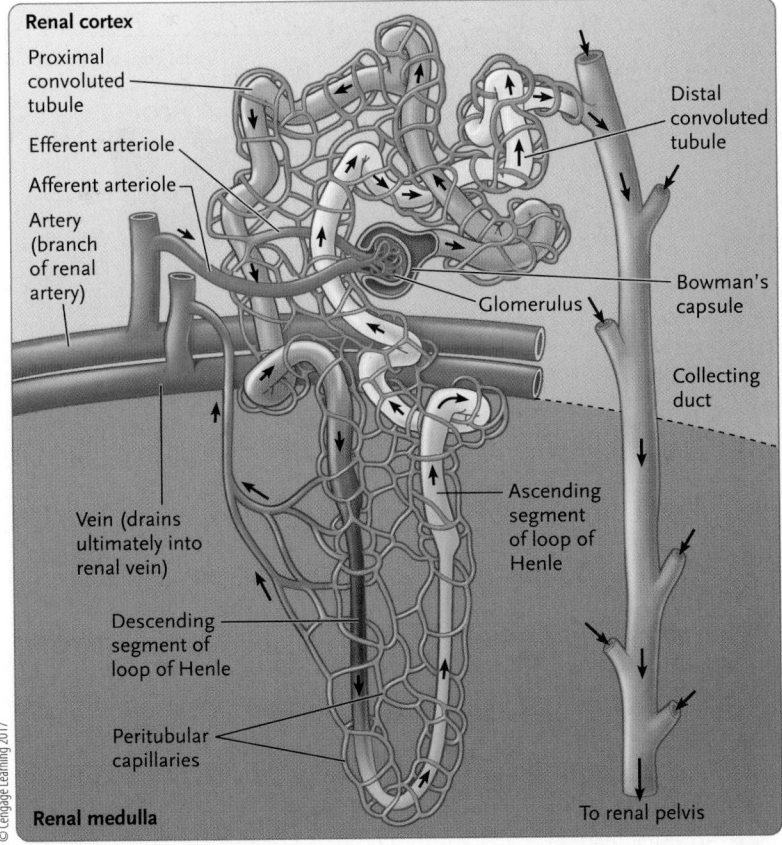

Renal cortex

Proximal convoluted tubule

Efferent arteriole

Afferent arteriole

Artery (branch of renal artery)

Distal convoluted tubule

Glomerulus

Bowman's capsule

Collecting duct

Vein (drains ultimately into renal vein)

Ascending segment of loop of Henle

Descending segment of loop of Henle

Peritubular capillaries

Renal medulla

To renal pelvis

© Cengage Learning 2017

## b.

Science Photo Library—STEVE GSCHMEISSNER/Brand X Pictures/Getty Images

**FIGURE 42.12 (a)** A nephron and its blood circulation. For a detailed description of the blood flow, see text. **(b)** Glomeruli, ball-like tufts of capillaries in the nephrons of a kidney (colourized scanning electron micrograph)

by the action of the nephrons. Blood returns from the kidney by the **renal vein**. The urine is produced in individual nephrons and is then processed further in **collecting ducts** that drain into a central cavity in the kidney called the **renal pelvis**.

From the renal pelvis, the urine flows through a tube called the **ureter** to the **urinary bladder**, a storage sac located outside the kidneys. Urine leaves the bladder through another tube, the **urethra**, which opens to the outside. Two sphincter muscles control the flow of urine from the bladder to the urethra. In human females, the opening of the urethra is just in front of the vagina; in males, the urethra opens at the tip of the penis. The two kidneys and two ureters, the urinary bladder, and the urethra constitute the mammalian urinary system.

### 42.4b Regions of Nephrons Have Specialized Functions

Mammalian nephrons are differentiated into regions that perform successive steps in excretion. The steps are those previously described in Section 42.1d and Figure 42.3 (filtration, reabsorption, secretion, and excretion). At its proximal end, a nephron forms **Bowman's capsule**, an infolded region that cups around a ball of blood capillaries called the **glomerulus** (Figure 42.12). The capsule and glomerulus are located in the renal cortex, the outer portion of the kidney. Filtration takes place as fluids are forced into Bowman's capsule from the capillaries of the glomerulus by the blood pressure.

Bowman's capsule gives rise to a **proximal convoluted tubule** in the renal cortex (Figure 42.12). This is where the reabsorption of nutrients, amino acids, and many ions takes place. The proximal tubule then descends into the medulla in a U-shaped bend, called the **loop of Henle**, that creates a concentration gradient in the interstitial fluid, increasing in concentration from the cortex to the centre of the medulla. The loop of Henle gives rise to the **distal convoluted tubule**, where additional wastes are secreted (Figure 42.12). The distal tubule drains the urine into a branching system of collecting ducts that lead down through the concentration gradient in the interstitial fluid of the medulla to the renal pelvis (Figure 42.12). Regulatory mechanisms act on secretory processes in both the distal convoluted tubule and the collecting ducts to regulate water and ion balance. As many as eight nephrons may drain into a single branch of a collecting duct. The combined activities of the proximal convoluted tubule, the loop of Henle, the distal convoluted tubule, and the collecting duct convert the filtrate that enters the nephron at the Bowman's capsule into the urine that is excreted.

Unlike most capillaries in the body, the capillaries in the glomerulus do not lead directly to venules. Instead, they form another arteriole that branches into a second network of capillaries, the **peritubular capillaries**. These capillaries thread around the proximal and distal convoluted tubules and the loop of Henle (Figure 42.12). As will be described in a moment, molecules or ions leave the tubules by passing through the one-cell-thick endothelial wall, then diffuse through the interstitial fluid and pass into the peritubular capillaries through their endothelial walls.

Each human kidney has more than a million nephrons. Of these, about 20% (the juxtamedullary nephrons) have long loops that descend deeply into the medulla of the kidney. The remaining 80% (the cortical nephrons) have shorter loops, most of which are located entirely in the cortex, and the remainder of which extend only partway into the medulla.

## 42.4c Nephrons and Other Kidney Structures Produce Hyperosmotic Urine

In mammals, urine is hyperosmotic to body fluids. Except for a few aquatic bird species, all other vertebrates produce urine that is hypoosmotic to body fluids, or is at best isoosmotic. Production of hyperosmotic urine, a water-conserving adaptation, arises due to both structural (anatomical) and functional (physiological) features. Three features interact to conserve nutrients and water, balance salts, and concentrate wastes for excretion from the body:

- the structural arrangement of the loop of Henle, which descends into the medulla and returns to the cortex;
- differences in the permeability of successive regions of the nephron to water and ions, as established by a specific group of membrane transport proteins in each region; and
- a gradient in the concentration of molecules and ions in the interstitial fluid of the kidney, as established by these structural and functional processes. The concentration of molecules in the interstitial fluid increases gradually, from the renal cortex to the deepest levels of the renal medulla.

Researchers determined the transport activities of specific regions of nephrons by dissecting them out of an animal and experimentally manipulating them *in vitro*. They placed segments in different buffered solutions and passed solutions containing various components of filtrates through the segment. By radioactively labelling specific molecules or ions, the scientists followed the movements of molecules in the solution surrounding the nephron segment or in the filtrate. The following three sections describe what they found.

## 42.4d Filtration in Bowman's Capsule Begins the Process of Excretion

The mechanisms of excretion (**Figure 42.13** and summarized in **Table 42.1**) begin in Bowman's capsule. The cells forming the walls of the capillaries of the glomerulus within Bowman's

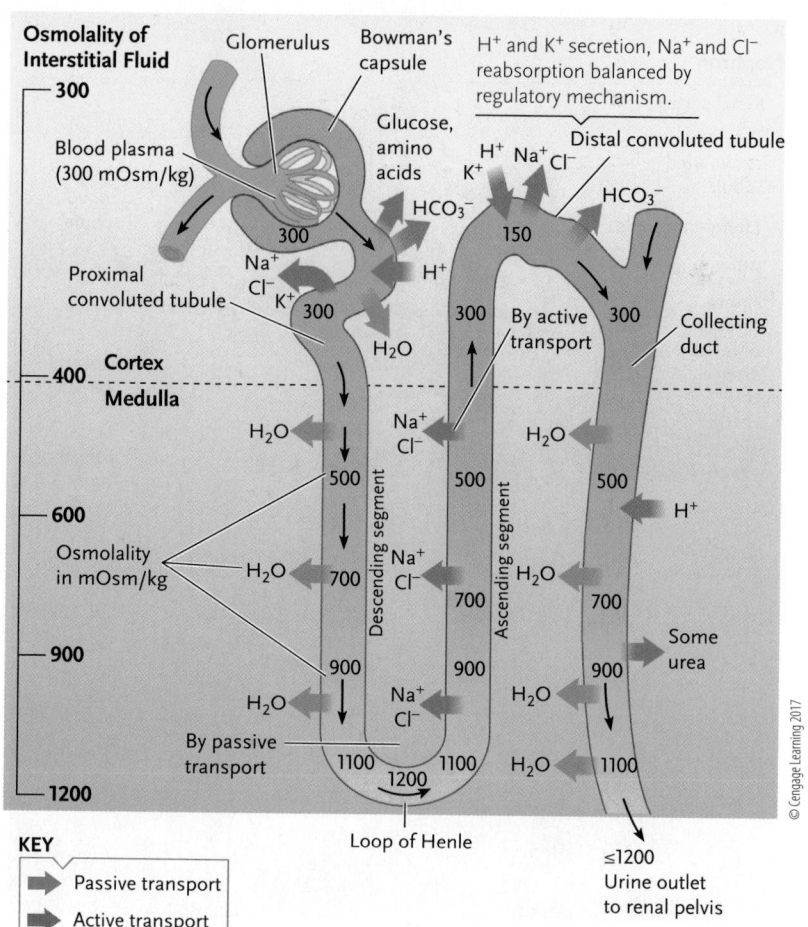

**FIGURE 42.13  The movement of ions, water, and other molecules to and from nephrons and collecting tubules in the mammalian kidney.** Nephrons in birds work in a similar fashion.

capsule, and the cells of the capsule itself, are loosely connected, leaving spaces just wide enough to allow water; ions; small nutrient molecules, such as glucose and amino acids; and nitrogenous waste molecules, primarily urea, to pass into the lumen of the capsule. The higher pressure of the blood drives fluid containing these molecules and ions from the capillaries of the glomerulus into the capsule. A thin net of connective tissue between the capillary and Bowman's capsule epithelia contributes to the filtering process. Blood cells and plasma proteins are too large to pass and are retained inside the capillaries.

This filtrate contains many molecules (nutrients and ions) that the body does not want to lose. The fundamental process that occurs in the nephron consists of eliminating all small molecules and then taking back what is important, rather than actively secreting waste molecules and toxic substances. The advantage of producing urine in this manner is that animals have not had to evolve transport proteins for foreign and unwanted substances. They pass directly into the filtrate and are not reabsorbed.

In humans, Bowman's capsules collectively filter about 180 L of fluid each day from a daily total of 1400 L of blood that passes through the kidneys. The human body contains only

| Segment | Location | Permeability and Movement | Osmolality of Filtrate and Urine | Result of Passage |
|---|---|---|---|---|
| Bowman's capsule | Cortex | Water, ions, small nutrients, and nitrogenous wastes move through spaces between epithelia. | 300 mOsm/kg, same as surrounding interstitial fluid | Water and small substances, but not proteins, forced into nephron. |
| Proximal convoluted tubule | Cortex | $Na^+$ and $K^+$ actively reabsorbed, $Cl^-$ follows; water leaves through aquaporins; $H^+$ actively secreted; $HCO_3^-$ actively reabsorbed into plasma of peritubular capillaries; glucose, amino acids, and other nutrients actively reabsorbed. | 300 mOsm/kg | 67% of ions, 65% of water, 50% of urea, and all nutrients return to interstitial fluid; pH maintained. |
| Descending segment of loop of Henle | Cortex into medulla | Water leaves through aquaporins; no movement of ions or urea | From 300 mOsm/kg at top to 1200 mOsm/kg at bottom of loop | Water drawn into interstitial fluid |
| Ascending segment of loop of Henle | Medulla into cortex | $Na^+$ and $Cl^-$ actively transported out; no movement of water; no movement of urea | From 1200 mOsm/kg at bottom to 150 mOsm/kg at top of loop | Ions pumped into interstitial fluid, creating osmotic gradient |
| Distal convoluted tubule | Cortex | $K^+$ and $Na^+$ secreted via active transport into urine; $Na^+$ and $Cl^-$ actively reabsorbed; water moves out of urine through aquaporins; $HCO_3^-$ actively reabsorbed into plasma of peritubular capillaries | From 150 mOsm/kg at beginning to 300 mOsm/kg at junction with collecting duct | Ions balanced; pH balanced |
| Collecting ducts | Cortex through medulla, empties into renal pelvis | Water moves out via aquaporins; some active secretion of ions; some urea leaves at bottom of duct | From 300 to 1200 mOsm/kg at junction with renal pelvis | More water and some urea moves to interstitial fluid; some $H^+$ added to urine. |

about 2.75 L of blood plasma, meaning that the kidneys filter a fluid volume equivalent to 65 times the volume of the blood plasma each day. On average, more than 99% of the filtrate, mostly water, is reabsorbed in the nephrons, leaving about 1.5 L to be excreted daily as urine.

## 42.4e Reabsorption and Secretion Occur in the Nephron

The fluid filtered into Bowman's capsule contains water, glucose, amino acids, other small molecules, and ions at the same concentrations as the blood plasma. By the time the fluid reaches the ureters, essential ions and molecules must be reabsorbed along with water to produce a concentrated urine.

**THE PROXIMAL CONVOLUTED TUBULE REABSORBS NUTRIENTS AND SOLUTES** This is the segment of the nephron where the valuable nutrients and ions that the body needs to retain are reabsorbed. $Na^+/K^+$ pumps in the epithelium of the proximal convoluted tubule actively move $Na^+$ and $K^+$ from the filtrate into the interstitial fluid surrounding the tubule (see Figure 42.13), and $Cl^-$ ions follow passively. Active transport

proteins also move essentially all the glucose, amino acids, and other nutrient molecules out of the filtrate into the interstitial fluid. This makes the filtrate hypoosmotic to the interstitial fluid surrounding the tubule and, as a result, water moves from the tubule into the interstitial fluid by osmosis. The osmotic movement is aided by aquaporins, proteins that form passages for water molecules in the transport epithelium of the tubule cells. In all, the proximal convoluted tubule reabsorbs about 67% of the $Na^+$, $K^+$, and $Cl^-$ ions; 65% of the water; and essentially all the glucose, amino acids, and other nutrient molecules from the filtrate. The ions, nutrients, and water reabsorbed by the tubule are transported into the interstitial fluid and then into capillaries of the peritubular network where they are returned to the circulation. The proximal convoluted tubule has structural specializations that fit its function. The epithelial cells that make up its walls are carpeted on their inner surface by a brush border of microvilli. These microvilli greatly increase the surface area available for reabsorption and secretion in a similar fashion to the microvilli in the small intestine.

By the time the filtrate enters the descending segment of the loop of Henle, most of the ions and molecules that the body wants to retain have already been taken back. The rest of the tubule is involved primarily in recovering water and concentrating the urine, as well as in balancing a few essential ions, H$^+$ and HCO$_3^-$ being two key essential ions.

### THE LOOP OF HENLE CREATES A CONCENTRATION GRADIENT FROM THE CORTEX TO THE CENTRE OF THE MEDULLA

As the filtrate flows from the proximal convoluted tubule into the descending segment of the loop of Henle, it passes through regions of increasingly high solute concentrations in the interstitial fluid of the medulla (shown in Figure 42.13). (The generation of this concentration gradient is described later.) As a result, water moves out of the tubule by osmosis as the fluid travels through the descending segment. The descending segment has aquaporins, which allow the rapid transport of water, but it has no other transport proteins. The outward movement of water concentrates the molecules and ions inside the tubule, gradually increasing the osmolality of the fluid to a peak of about 1200 mOsm/kg at the bottom of the loop. This is the same as the osmolality of the interstitial fluid at the bottom of the medulla. Since water is moving into the interstitial fluid, how is the concentration gradient retained? That is the role of the ascending loop of Henle.

As the fluid moves into the ascending segment of the loop of Henle, Na$^+$ and Cl$^-$ are actively transported into the interstitial fluid. The ascending segment has membrane proteins that transport salt ions, but it lacks aquaporins. Because water is trapped in the ascending segment, the osmolality of the urine is progressively reduced moving up this segment as salt ions, primarily Na$^+$ and Cl$^-$, are pumped out of the tubule.

The active transport of salt ions from the tubule into the interstitial fluid establishes the concentration gradient of the medulla: high near the renal pelvis and low near the renal cortex. The energy required to transport NaCl from the ascending segment makes the kidneys one of the major ATP-consuming organs of the body. By the time the fluid reaches the cortex at the top of the ascending loop, its osmolality has dropped to about 150 mOsm/kg.

What was achieved by transport through the loop of Henle? During the travel of fluid around the loop of Henle, first water was reabsorbed from the filtrate and then ions were transported out of the filtrate. As a result, the total volume of the filtrate in the nephron was greatly reduced. Urea and other nitrogenous wastes remain, however, and have been concentrated in the filtrate. In the process, the concentration gradient from the cortex to the bottom of the medulla was established. This gradient plays an important role for water reabsorption from the collecting ducts (see below).

### THE DISTAL CONVOLUTED TUBULE SELECTIVELY SECRETES AND ABSORBS DIFFERENT IONS TO MAINTAIN BLOOD pH AND ELECTROLYTE BALANCE

The transport epithelium of the distal convoluted tubule works to balance the salt and bicarbonate concentrations of the filtrate against body fluids. In response to hormones triggered by changes in the body's salt concentrations, varying amounts of K$^+$ and H$^+$ ions are secreted into the filtrate, and varying amounts of Na$^+$ and Cl$^-$ ions are reabsorbed. Bicarbonate ions may also be reabsorbed from the filtrate.

In total, more ions move outward than inward in the distal tubule and, as a consequence, water moves out of the tubule by osmosis through aquaporins. The amounts of urea and other nitrogenous wastes remain the same. By the time the filtrate, now urine, enters the collecting ducts at the end of the nephron, its osmolality is about 300 mOsm/kg.

### THE COLLECTING DUCTS CONTROL THE FINAL CONCENTRATION OF THE URINE AND ARE UNDER HORMONAL CONTROL

The collecting ducts concentrate the urine. These ducts, which are permeable to water but not to salt ions, descend downward from the cortex through the medulla of the kidney. As the ducts descend, they travel through the gradient of increasing solute concentration in the medulla. This increase makes water move osmotically out of the ducts and greatly increases the concentration of the urine, which can become as high as 1200 mOsm/kg at the bottom of the medulla.

In addition to these mechanisms, H$^+$ ions are actively secreted into the fluid. The balance of the H$^+$ and bicarbonate ions established in the urine, interstitial fluid, and blood, achieved by secretion of H$^+$ into the urine by the nephrons and collecting ducts, is important for regulating the pH of blood and body fluids. The kidneys thus provide a safety valve if the acidity of body fluids rises beyond levels that can be controlled by the blood's buffer system (see Chapter 41).

Urine flows from the end of the collecting ducts into the renal pelvis and then through the ureters into the urinary bladder, where it is stored. From the bladder, urine exits through the urethra to the outside.

## 42.4f Regulation of Mammalian Kidney Function

The final concentration of the urine leaving the collecting ducts is under hormonal control and can be adjusted depending on what is required to homeostatically maintain water and ion balance. The concentration gradient in the interstitial fluid of the kidney from the cortex to the medulla established by the loop of Henle will draw water out of the urine by osmosis as it passes through the collecting ducts, but only if the collecting ducts are permeable to water. The water permeability of the collecting ducts is under hormonal control. Antidiuretic hormone (ADH; sometimes called vasopressin) is a peptide hormone secreted by the posterior pituitary gland (Chapter 43) that controls the water permeability of the collecting ducts. Receptors in the hypothalamus monitor the concentration of solutes in the blood. If solute concentrations are too high, they stimulate the posterior pituitary to release ADH, which in turn acts on the cells in the walls of the collecting ducts. Aquaporins are inserted into the membranes of the cells in response, and the collecting duct walls become permeable to water **(Figure 42.14)**. The net result is that the urine becomes very concentrated and water is conserved.

If the cells of the hypothalamus sense that solute concentrations are too low, no ADH is released and the walls of the collecting ducts remain impermeable to water. When mammals are well hydrated they will produce a more dilute urine. Diuretic substances, such as alcohol and caffeine, interfere with ADH production and therefore reduce the water permeability of the collecting ducts and produce a dilute urine. This leads to water loss and dehydration.

Major changes in body fluid balance leading to changes in blood volume and pressure also occur when the body loses or gains $Na^+$ in excessive amounts. Excessive $Na^+$ loss may result from prolonged and heavy sweating, repeated vomiting, severe diarrhea, or insufficient $Na^+$ uptake in the diet. The $Na^+$ loss reduces the osmolarity of body fluids, which causes less water to be reabsorbed in the kidneys. The water loss reduces the volume of blood and interstitial fluid and causes the blood pressure to drop. Excessive $Na^+$ intake in salty foods may have the opposite effects.

The renin–angiotensin–aldosterone system (RAAS) is the most important hormonal system involved in regulating $Na^+$.

At normal body salt concentrations, the RAAS allows about 10 g of salt to be excreted in the urine each day. If excessive $Na^+$ is excreted, blood pressure and body fluid volume drop. In response to this condition, cells in the juxtaglomerular apparatus (a specialized group of cells in the kidney, located at a point where the distal convoluted tubule contacts the **afferent arteriole** carrying blood to the glomerulus, that monitor the salt level of the fluid flowing past them in the tubule) secrete the enzyme renin into the bloodstream. (The RAAS also is activated to secrete renin when blood pressure or blood volume decreases independently of $Na^+$ levels, as in the case of a hemorrhage.)

Renin cleaves a protein normally present in the plasma called angiotensinogen to produce angiotensin I. Angiotensin-converting enzyme (ACE), an enzyme normally present in the plasma, converts angiotensin I to angiotensin II.

Angiotensin II has three effects: (1) it raises blood pressure quickly by constricting arterioles in most parts of the body; (2) it stimulates synthesis of the steroid hormone aldosterone and its secretion from the adrenal cortex; and (3) it stimulates thirst so that more water is brought into the body. The aldosterone increases Na+ reabsorption in the kidneys, which raises the osmolarity of body fluids. As a result, water moves from the tubules into the interstitial fluid, which conserves water. Angiotensin II may also stimulate secretion of ADH by the posterior pituitary. ADH increases water absorption in the kidneys **(Figure 42.15)**. Overall, the combined effects of angiotensin II act to return the blood pressure to normal.

In the opposite situation, when salt intake is too high, both body fluid volume and blood pressure rise above normal. Under these conditions, renin secretion is inhibited and, as a result, angiotensin II production and aldosterone synthesis are not stimulated. The reduction in angiotensin II lowers blood pressure by allowing arterioles to dilate; the reduction in aldosterone increases $Na^+$ loss in the urine by retarding the reabsorption of $Na^+$ and $Cl^-$ from the kidney tubules.

## 42.4g Terrestrial Mammals Have Water-Conserving Adaptations

Terrestrial mammals have other adaptations that complement the water-conserving activities of the kidneys. One is the location of the lungs deep inside the body, which reduces water loss by evaporation during breathing (see Chapter 40). Another is a body covering of keratinized skin. Skin is so impermeable that it almost eliminates water loss by evaporation, except for the controlled loss through evaporation of sweat in mammals with sweat glands.

Among mammals, water-conserving adaptations reach their greatest efficiency in desert rodents such as the kangaroo rat **(Figure 42.16)**. The proportion of nephrons with long loops extending deep into the kidney medulla of kangaroo rats is very high, allowing them to excrete urine that is 20 times as concentrated as body fluids. Further, most of the water in the

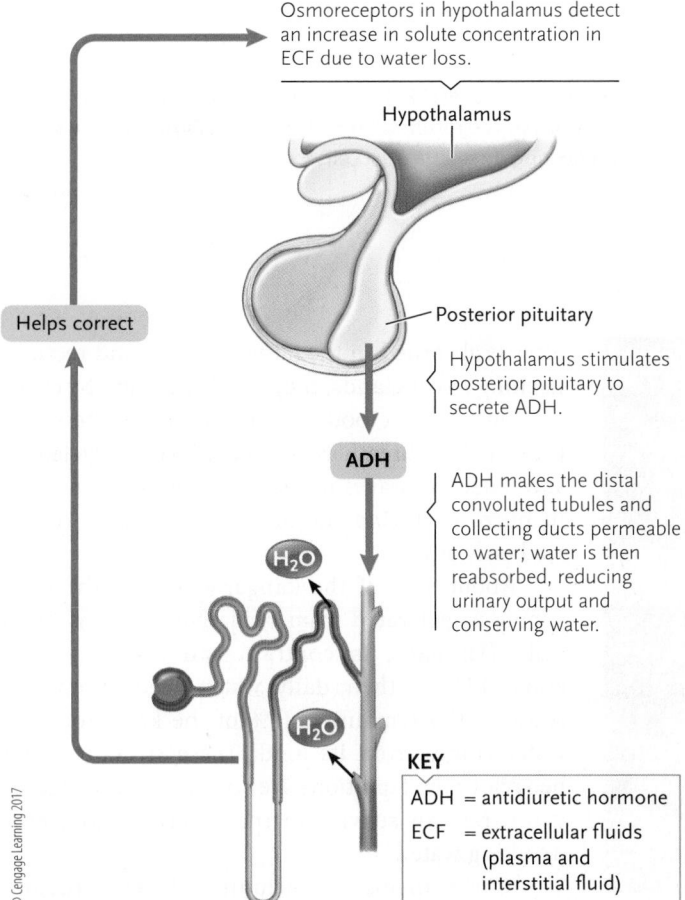

**FIGURE 42.14 The ADH regulatory system, which stimulates water reabsorption to compensate for a loss in the fluid volume of the extracellular fluids because of excess water loss from the body**

Osmoreceptors in hypothalamus detect an increase in solute concentration in ECF due to water loss.

Hypothalamus

Posterior pituitary

Hypothalamus stimulates posterior pituitary to secrete ADH.

ADH

ADH makes the distal convoluted tubules and collecting ducts permeable to water; water is then reabsorbed, reducing urinary output and conserving water.

$H_2O$

$H_2O$

Helps correct

**KEY**

ADH = antidiuretic hormone

ECF = extracellular fluids (plasma and interstitial fluid)

© Cengage Learning 2017

FIGURE 42.15 **Experimental Research**

## ADH-Stimulated Water Reabsorption in the Kidney Collecting Duct

**Research Question:** How does ADH cause water reabsorption in the kidney collecting ducts?

**Experiment:** The peptide hormone ADH causes the reabsorption of water in the kidney by increasing the number of aquaporin2 (AQP2) water channels in the plasma membrane of the collecting duct cells, as described in Section 42.4f. AQP2 is the only aquaporin expressed exclusively in the collecting duct. Mark Knepper and his colleagues at the National Institutes of Health, Bethesda, Maryland, and the University of Aarhus, Denmark, investigated the mechanism by which ADH causes AQP2 to appear in the plasma membrane. They tested the "shuttle" hypothesis, which states that ADH induces the movement of AQP2 from intracellular vesicles (IVs) to the plasma membrane of cells on the lumen side of the collecting duct. The researchers first attached sections of collecting duct from rat kidneys to a pipette and passed an ADH solution through the duct **(Figure 1)**. They then counted the AQP2 in the IVs and in the plasma membrane of the lumen cells. To do this, they cut treated ducts into thin sections and added an antibody that specifically recognizes AQP2. The antibody had gold particles attached to it; the electron-dense gold is easily visualized under an electron microscope. Counting the gold particles therefore quantified the AQP2.

Pipette

Solutions passed through duct

Buffer

Section of collecting duct

© Cengage Learning 2017

**Figure 1**

**Results:** The researchers measured the distribution of AQP2 in the absence of ADH, in the presence of ADH, and then after ADH had been washed away. Their results are expressed as the ratio of AQP2 in the plasma membrane of lumen cells to AQP2 in IVs:

1. Before ADH treatment: 0.32 ± 0.03

2. In the presence of ADH: 0.38 ± 0.14

3. After ADH removal: 0.35 ± 0.04

**Conclusion:** ADH induces a change in distribution of AQP2, consistent with the shuttle hypothesis of AQP2 channels moving from IVs to the plasma membrane of lumen cells. The redistribution of AQP2 channels is reversible, as shown by the results after ADH removal. **Figure 2** shows the current molecular model for the ADH-induced redistribution of AQP2 channels in collecting duct epithelial cells.

*(Continued)*

| | Kangaroo Rat | Human |
|---|---|---|
| **Water gain (millilitres)** | | |
| From ingesting food | 6.0 | 850 |
| From drinking liquids | 0.0 | 1400 |
| By metabolism | 54.0 | 350 |
| | 60.0 | 2600 |
| **Water loss (millilitres)** | | |
| In urine | 13.5 | 1500 |
| In feces | 2.6 | 200 |
| By evaporation | 43.9 | 900 |
| | 60.0 | 2600 |

© Rick & Nora Bowers/Alamy

**FIGURE 42.16 A comparison of the sources of water for a human and a kangaroo rat (*Dipodomys species*).** Water conservation in the kangaroo rat is so efficient that the animal never has to drink water.

feces is absorbed in the large intestine and rectum. Lacking sweat glands, they lose little water by evaporation from the body surface. Much of the moisture in their breath is condensed and recycled by specialized passages in the nasal cavities. They stay in burrows during the daytime and come out to feed only at night.

About 90% of the kangaroo rat's daily water supply is generated from oxidative reactions in its cells. (Humans, in contrast, can make up only about 12% of their daily water needs from this source.) The remaining 10% of the kangaroo rat's water comes from its food. These structural and behavioural adaptations are so effective that a kangaroo rat can survive in the desert without ever drinking water.

Marine mammals, including whales, seals, and manatees, eat foods that are high in salt content. They are able to survive the high salt intake because they produce urine that is more concentrated than

FIGURE 42.15 **Experimental Research** (*Continued*)

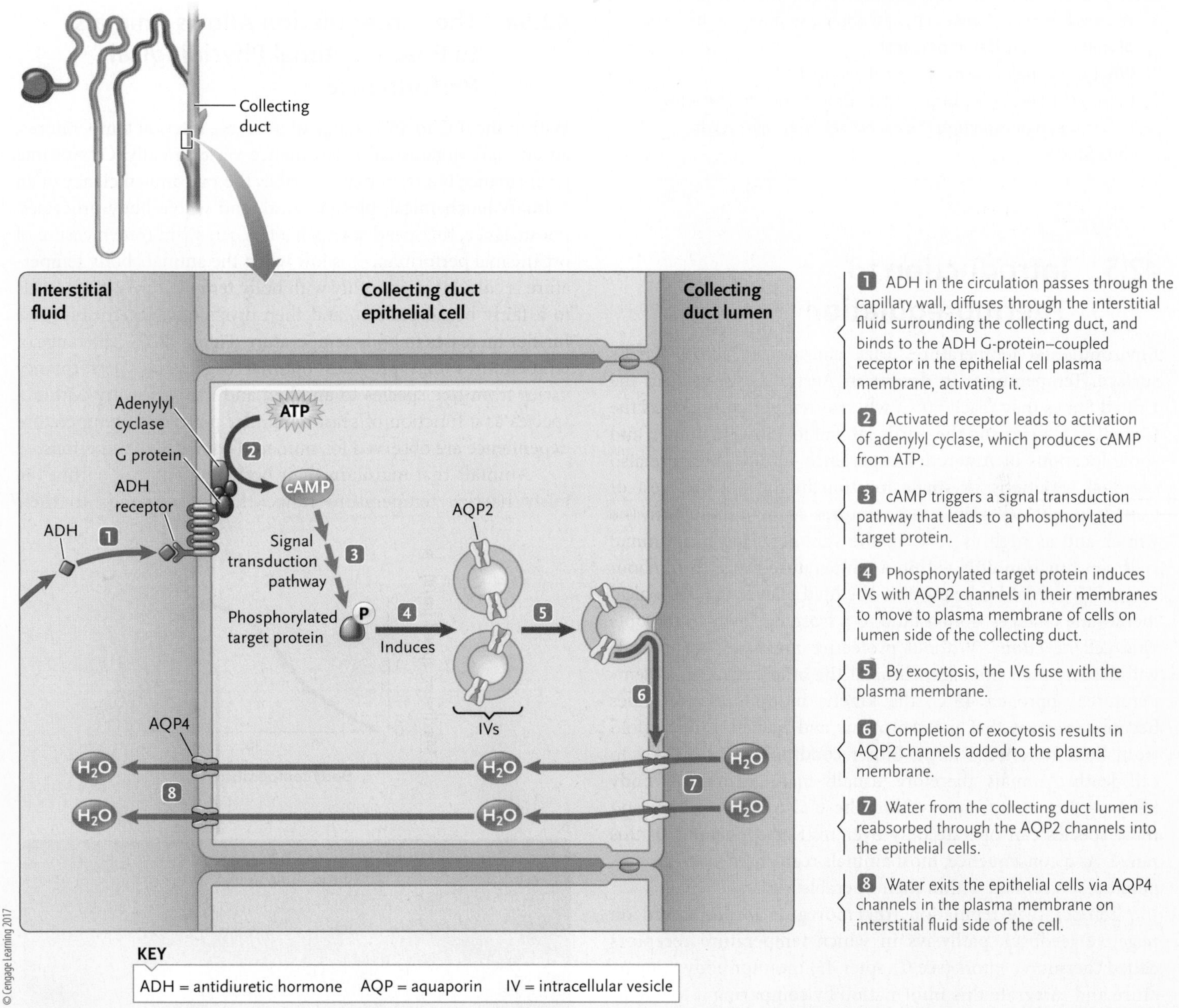

Collecting
duct

Interstitial
fluid

**Collecting duct
epithelial cell**

**Collecting
duct lumen**

Adenylyl
cyclase

ATP

G protein

cAMP

ADH
receptor

ADH

AQP2

Signal
transduction
pathway

Phosphorylated
target protein

Induces

IVs

AQP4

$H_2O$

$H_2O$

$H_2O$

$H_2O$

$H_2O$

$H_2O$

**1** ADH in the circulation passes through the capillary wall, diffuses through the interstitial fluid surrounding the collecting duct, and binds to the ADH G-protein–coupled receptor in the epithelial cell plasma membrane, activating it.

**2** Activated receptor leads to activation of adenylyl cyclase, which produces cAMP from ATP.

**3** cAMP triggers a signal transduction pathway that leads to a phosphorylated target protein.

**4** Phosphorylated target protein induces IVs with AQP2 channels in their membranes to move to plasma membrane of cells on lumen side of the collecting duct.

**5** By exocytosis, the IVs fuse with the plasma membrane.

**6** Completion of exocytosis results in AQP2 channels added to the plasma membrane.

**7** Water from the collecting duct lumen is reabsorbed through the AQP2 channels into the epithelial cells.

**8** Water exits the epithelial cells via AQP4 channels in the plasma membrane on interstitial fluid side of the cell.

**KEY**

ADH = antidiuretic hormone    AQP = aquaporin    IV = intracellular vesicle

© Cengage Learning 2017

**Figure 2**

sea water. As a result, they are easily able to excrete all the excess salt they ingest in their diet.

The adaptations described in this section allow animals to maintain the concentration of body fluids at levels that keep cells from swelling or shrinking, and permit excretion of toxic wastes. An equally important challenge is maintaining an internal temperature that allows the organ systems to function with maximum efficiency. We look at these processes in the next section.

## STUDY BREAK QUESTIONS

1. What can mammalian kidneys do that the kidneys of other vertebrates cannot?

2. Where does active transport of ions occur in the nephron?

3. What is the major event in the ascending segment of the loop of Henle? Why is this important?

4. What is the major event in the collecting duct?

5. Compare how marine birds and marine mammals deal with the problem of excreting the excess salt they take in with their food.

# 42.5 Introduction to Thermoregulation

Environmental temperatures vary enormously across Earth's surface. Temperatures in deserts in Australia, Africa, and the United States may reach 50°C, whereas temperatures across the Canadian prairies and the north can fall to –50°C in winter, and some locations in Antarctica experience –80°C. There are also seasonal variations. A single location in the boreal forest of Canada might experience temperatures as low as –40°C in the winter and as high as 35°C in the summer. However, animal cells can function only within a temperature range from about 0°C to 45°C. Not far below 0°C, the lipid bilayer of a biological membrane changes from a fluid to a frozen gel, which disrupts vital cell functions. Without protective measures, ice crystals will destroy the cell's organelles. At the other extreme, as temperatures approach 45°C, the kinetic motions of molecules become so great that most proteins and nucleic acids unfold from their functional form. Either condition leads quickly to cell death. Animals, therefore, usually maintain internal body temperatures somewhere within the 0°C to 45°C limits, and most species can operate only over restricted portions of this range. As a consequence, most animals regulate their body temperatures to remain within their operable limits.

Temperature regulation (**thermoregulation**) is based on negative feedback pathways in which temperature receptors called thermoreceptors (see Chapter 45) monitor body temperature and integrate this information by comparing it to a temperature set point (see Section 38.4b for a description of the set point). Differences from the set point trigger physiological and behavioural responses that return the temperature to the set point. The responses triggered by negative feedback mechanisms involve adjustments in the rate of heat-generating oxidative reactions within the body, coupled with adjustments in the rate of heat gain or loss at the body surface. The particular adaptations that accomplish these responses vary widely among species, however. And although body temperature is closely regulated around a set point in all endotherms, the set point itself may vary over the course of a day and between seasons (see Chapter 38).

In this section, we describe the structures, mechanisms, and behavioural adaptations that enable animals to regulate their body temperature.

## 42.5a Thermoregulation Allows Animals to Reach Optimal Physiological Performance

Within the 0°C to 45°C range of tolerable internal temperatures, an animal's organismal performance varies greatly. Organismal performance is a term that describes the rate and efficiency of an animal's biochemical, physiological, and whole-body processes. For instance, the speed at which a fish can swim (one measure of organismal performance) is low when the animal's body temperature is cold, rises smoothly with body temperature until it levels to a fairly broad plateau, and then drops off dramatically with further increases in body temperature **(Figure 42.17)**. The range of temperatures that provides optimal organismal performance varies from one species to another, and may also vary within a species as a function of season. Similar patterns of temperature dependence are observed for numerous other body functions.

Animals that maintain their body temperature within the fairly narrow temperature range that corresponds to their

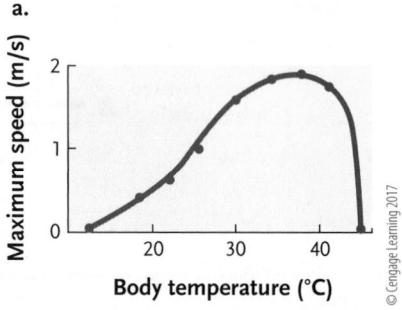

**FIGURE 42.17 Body temperature and organismal performance.** **(a)** The maximum swimming speed of a fish changes dramatically with body temperature. **(b)** Rising water temperatures in many rivers in British Columbia are influencing the ability of migrating salmon to return to their native streams.

optimal temperature can move quickly, digest food efficiently, and carry out necessary activities and processes rapidly and effectively. Thus, in addition to keeping body temperatures within tolerable limits, thermoregulation allows animals to maintain an optimal level of organismal performance.

## 42.5b Animals Exchange Heat with Their Environment by Conduction, Convection, Radiation, and Evaporation

As part of thermoregulation, animals exchange heat with their environment. Virtually all heat exchange occurs at surfaces where the body meets the external environment. As with all physical bodies, heat flows into animals if they are cooler than their surroundings and flows outward if they are warmer. This heat exchange occurs by four mechanisms: conduction, convection, radiation, and evaporation **(Figure 42.18)**.

**Conduction** is the flow of heat between atoms or molecules in direct contact. An animal loses heat by conduction when it contacts a cooler object, and gains heat when it contacts an object that is warmer. **Convection** is the transfer of heat from a body to a fluid (air or water) that passes over its surface. The movement maximizes heat transfer by replacing fluid that has absorbed or released heat with fluid at the original temperature. **Radiation** is the transfer of heat energy as electromagnetic radiation. Any object warmer than absolute zero (–273°C) radiates heat; as the object's temperature rises, the amount of heat it loses as radiation increases as well. Animals also gain heat through radiation, particularly by absorbing radiation from the Sun. **Evaporation** is heat transfer through the energy required to change a liquid to a gas.

Animals do not lose heat directly by sweating. Evaporation of water from a surface, however, is an efficient way to transfer heat; when the water in sweat evaporates from the body surface, the body cools down because heat is being transferred to the evaporated water in the surrounding air. In hot, humid regions where the air is saturated with water vapour, sweat does not evaporate and no heat can be lost in this manner. Thus, it is not the sweating that dissipates heat but the evaporation of the sweat. ⬢

All animals gain or lose heat by a combination of these four mechanisms. A moose struggling with the heat on a sunny summer day (Figure 42.18) loses heat by the evaporation of sweat from the skin and from the surface of the lungs, by convection as air flows over the skin, by conduction from the legs to the pond it is standing in, and by outward infrared radiation. It gains heat from internal biochemical reactions and by absorbing infrared and solar radiation. To maintain a constant body temperature, the heat gained and lost through these pathways must balance.

## 42.5c Ectothermic and Endothermic Animals Rely on Different Heat Sources to Maintain Body Temperature

Different animals use one of two major strategies to balance heat gain and loss. Animals that obtain heat primarily from the external environment are known as ectotherms (*ecto* = outside); those obtaining most of their heat from internal physiological sources are called **endotherms** (*endo* = inside). All ectotherms generate at least some heat from internal reactions, however, and endotherms can obtain heat from the environment under some circumstances.

Most invertebrates, fishes, amphibians, and reptiles are **ectotherms**. Although these animals are popularly described as cold-blooded, the body temperature of some, such as an active lizard on a sunny day, may be as high as or higher than ours. Ectotherms regulate body temperature by controlling the rate of heat exchange with the environment. Through behavioural and physiological mechanisms, they adjust body temperature toward a level that allows optimal physiological performance. However, most ectotherms are unable to maintain optimal body temperature when the temperature of their surroundings departs too far from that optimum, particularly when environmental temperatures fall. As a result, the body temperatures of ectotherms fluctuate with environmental temperatures, and ectotherms are typically less active when it is cold.

The endotherms—birds and mammals—keep their bodies at an optimal temperature by regulating two processes: (1) the amount of heat generated by internal oxidative reactions, and (2) the amount of heat exchanged with the environment.

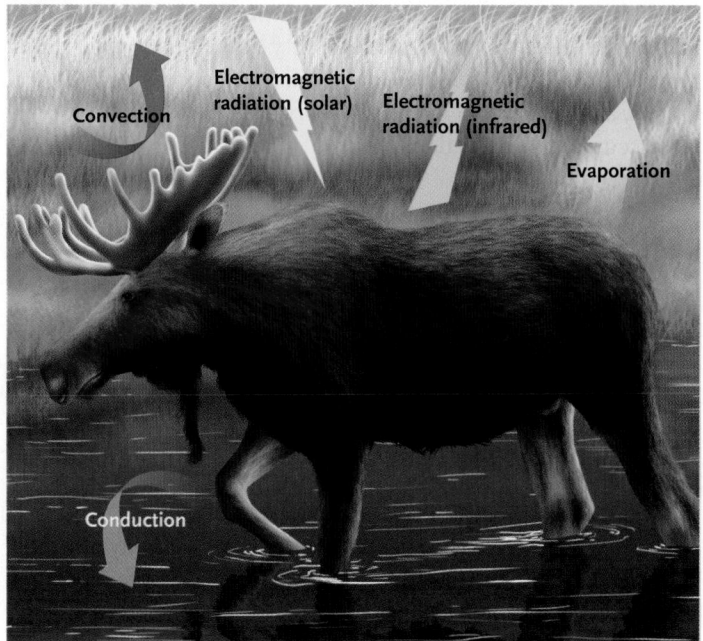

**FIGURE 42.18 Heat flows into and out of a moose on a hot, sunny day.** Unlike conduction, convection, and evaporation, which take place through the kinetic movement of molecules, electromagnetic radiation (infrared) is transmitted through space as waves of energy.

Because endotherms use internal heat sources to maintain body temperature at optimal levels, they can remain active over a broader range of environmental temperatures than ectotherms. However, endotherms require a nearly constant supply of energy to maintain their body temperatures. And because that energy is provided by food, endotherms must typically consume much more food than ectotherms of equivalent size. Some fishes, sea turtles, and invertebrates are also capable of generating significant amounts of internal heat.

The difference between ectotherms and endotherms is reflected in their metabolic responses to environmental temperature **(Figure 42.19)**. The metabolic rate of a resting mouse *increases* steadily as the environmental temperature falls from 25°C to 10°C. This increase reflects the fact that, to maintain a constant body temperature in a colder environment, endotherms must process progressively more food and generate more heat to compensate for their increased rate of heat loss.

By contrast, the metabolic rate of a resting lizard typically *decreases* steadily over the same temperature range. Because ectotherms do not maintain a constant body temperature, their biochemical and physiological functions, including oxidative reactions, slow down as environmental and body temperatures decrease. Thus, an ectotherm consumes less food and requires less energy when it is cold than when it is warm.

Ectothermy and endothermy represent different strategies for coping with the variations in environmental temperature that all animals encounter; neither strategy is inherently superior to the other. Endotherms can remain fully active over a wide temperature range. Cold weather does not prevent them

from foraging, mating, or escaping from predators, but it does increase their energy and food needs. To satisfy their need for food, they may not have the option of staying curled up safely in a warm burrow. Ectotherms do not have the capacity to be active when environmental temperatures drop too low; they move sluggishly and are unable to capture food or escape from predators. However, because their metabolic rates are lower under such circumstances, so are their food needs, and they do not have to actively look for food and expose themselves to danger to the extent that endotherms do.

Having laid the ground rules of heat transfer and weighed the relative advantages and disadvantages of ectothermy and endothermy, we now begin a more detailed examination of how individual animals actually regulate their body temperatures within these overall strategies.

**STUDY BREAK QUESTION**

1. What are the advantages and disadvantages of ectothermy and endothermy? Would these be different in tropical versus temperate regions?

## 42.6  Ectothermy

Because ectotherms obtain most of their body heat from their environment, they generally have body temperatures very similar to the ambient temperature that surrounds them. To change body temperature to improve performance, these species live in or seek warm or temperate environments, where temperatures fall within the range that produces optimal physiological performance. Ectotherms have some ability to regulate their body temperature by physiological means, but use mainly behavioural means, and those with a greater ability to thermoregulate generally occupy more varied habitats.

### 42.6a  Ectotherms Are Found in All Invertebrate Groups

Aquatic invertebrates are limited thermoregulators. Their body temperature closely follows the temperature of their surroundings. Intertidal marine invertebrates, however, that are routinely exposed to air use behavioural responses to regulate body temperature. For example, a South American intertidal mollusc, *Echinolittorina peruviana*, is longer than it is wide. Researchers in Chile have shown that this animal orients itself as a means of thermoregulation. To prevent overheating on sunny summer days, it faces the Sun, offering a smaller surface area for the Sun's rays. On overcast summer days, or during the winter, it orients itself with its side, which has the larger surface area, toward the Sun's rays to increase its body temperature.

Invertebrates living in terrestrial habitats regulate their body temperatures more closely. Many also use behavioural responses, such as moving between shaded and sunny regions, to regulate body temperature. Some winged arthropods,

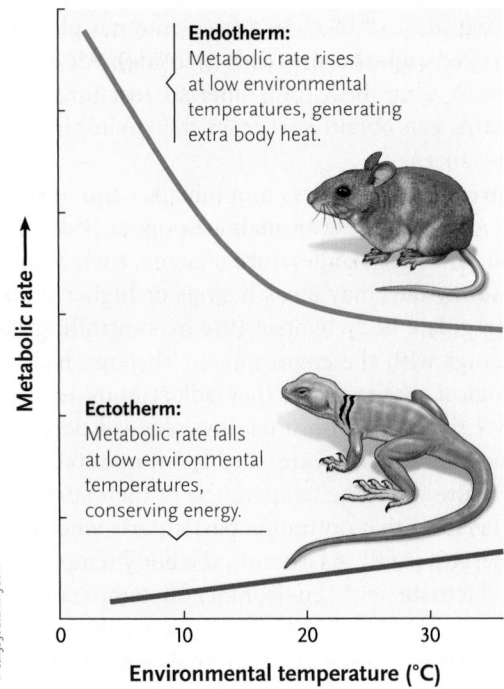

**FIGURE 42.19  Metabolic responses of ectotherms and endotherms to cooling environmental temperatures.** At any temperature, the metabolic rates of endotherms are always higher than those of ectotherms of comparable size.

including bees, moths, butterflies, and dragonflies, use a combination of behavioural and heat-generating physiological mechanisms for thermoregulation. In cool weather, these animals warm up before taking flight by rapidly vibrating the large flight muscles in the thorax in a mechanism similar to shivering in humans. The tobacco hawkmoth (*Manduca sexta*) vibrates its flight muscles until its thoracic temperature reaches about 36°C before flying. During flight, metabolic heat generated by the flight muscles sustains the elevated thoracic temperature, so much so that a flying sphinx moth produces more heat per gram of body weight than many mammals **(Figure 42.20)**. Honeybees (*Apis mellifera*) form masses in the hive in winter and use the heat generated by vibrating their flight muscles to maintain the temperature inside the hive. Even in a Manitoba winter, with external temperatures below –20°C, the temperature in the mass of bees is normally about 30°C, and the bees may continue to raise offspring, using food stored in the hive.

## 42.6b Most Fishes, Amphibians, and Reptiles Are Ectotherms

Vertebrate ectotherms (most fishes, amphibians, and reptiles) also vary widely in their ability to thermoregulate. Most aquatic species have a more limited thermoregulatory capacity than that found among terrestrial species, particularly the reptiles. Some fishes, however, are highly capable thermoregulators.

**FISHES** The body temperatures of most fishes remain within one or two degrees of their aquatic environment. However, many fishes use behavioural mechanisms to keep body temperatures at levels that allow good physiological performance. Many freshwater species perform better at lower temperatures and may use opportunities provided by the thermal stratification of lakes and ponds to sustain optimal performance in the summer. They remain in deep, cool water during hot summer days, moving to the shallows to feed only during early morning and late evening when air and water temperatures are lower.

Some cold-water marine teleosts (such as tunas and mackerels) and some sharks (such as the great white), on the other hand, use endothermy in their aerobic swimming muscles to maintain muscle temperature as much as 10°C–12°C warmer than their surroundings to improve performance. These animals have in common the fact that they move over long distances, swimming continuously. The action of the muscles generates heat that permits the muscles and other organs to operate more efficiently. Much of this heat generated in other fish is lost at the gill–water interface. However, a countercurrent heat exchanger between the arteries and the veins in the swimming muscles of these specialized fishes minimizes this loss (see Chapter 40 for a description of countercurrent exchange). The anatomical details of the heat exchanger vary. In principle, however, the venules containing warm blood from the muscles form a network with arterioles containing cold blood coming from the gills. The heat from the venules is transferred to the arterioles and returned to the muscles. This transfer not only increases the temperature of the exercising muscle, it also reduces the temperature of the blood from the muscles returning to the heart on its way to the gills, thus heat loss to the environment is minimized.

**AMPHIBIANS AND REPTILES** The body temperature of most amphibians also closely matches the environmental temperature. The tadpoles of foothill yellow-legged frogs (*Rana boylii*) regulate their body temperature to some degree by changing their location in ponds and lakes to take advantage of temperature differences between deep and shallow water or between sunny and shaded regions. Some terrestrial amphibians bask in sunlight to raise their body temperature, and seek shade to lower their body temperature. However, basking can be dangerous to amphibians because they lose water rapidly through their permeable skin. We have already noted that the leaf frog *Phyllomedusa sauvagii* (Figure 42.9), which often basks in sunlight, avoids this problem by coating itself with waterproofing lipids secreted by glands in its skin.

Thermoregulation is more pronounced among terrestrial reptiles. Some lizard species can maintain temperatures that are nearly as constant as those of endotherms **(Figure 42.21)**. For small lizards, the most common behavioural thermoregulatory mechanism is moving between sunny (warmer) and shady (cooler) regions. In the desert, lizards and other reptiles retreat into burrows during the hottest part of summer days. Some, such as the desert iguana (*Dipsosaurus dorsalis*), lose excess heat by panting—rapidly moving air in and out of the airways. The air movement increases heat loss by evaporation of water from the respiratory tract.

Lizards also frequently adjust their posture to foster heat exchange with the environment, and control the angle of their body relative to the rays of the Sun. Horned lizards (genus *Phrynosoma*) often warm up by flattening themselves against warm, sunlit rocks to maximize their rate of heat gain by conduction from the rock and radiation from the Sun. Snakes and lizards can often be found on large rocks and roads on chilly nights, taking advantage of the heat retained by the stone or concrete. *Trapelus savignii* (Savigny's agama), a lizard that lives

**FIGURE 42.20 During flight, the metabolic heat generated by the flight muscles of a flying sphinx moth produces more heat per gram of body weight than many mammals.**

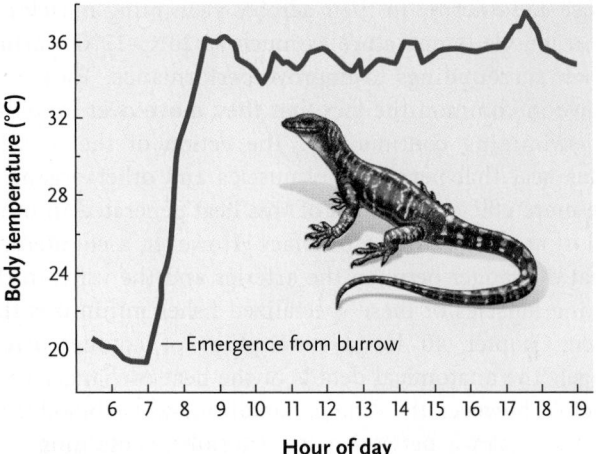

**FIGURE 42.21 An example of excellent thermoregulation in ectotherms.** The body temperature of the Australian lizard *Varanus varius* rises quickly after the animal emerges from its burrow, and remains relatively stable throughout the day as the lizard shuttles between sunshine and shade.

in the Negev Desert in Israel, cools off at midday by climbing into shady bushes, moving away from the hot sand, and catching a cooling breeze.

Researchers have demonstrated experimentally that several lizard species couple physiological responses to behavioural mechanisms of thermoregulation. When a Galápagos marine iguana (*Amblyrhynchus cristatus*) is exposed to heat from infrared radiation, blood flow increases in the heated regions of the skin. The blood absorbs heat rapidly and carries it to critical organs in the core of the body. Conversely, when an area of skin is experimentally cooled, blood flow to it is restricted, thereby preventing the loss of heat to the external environment.

## 42.6c Ectotherms Can Compensate for Seasonal Variations in Environmental Temperature

Many ectotherms undergo seasonal physiological changes called **thermal acclimatization**. These changes allow the animals to attain good physiological performance at both winter and summer temperatures.

For example, in the summer, bullhead catfish (*Ameiurus* species) can survive water temperatures as high as 36°C but cannot tolerate temperatures below 8°C. In the winter, however, the bullhead cannot survive water temperatures above 28°C but can tolerate temperatures near 0°C. Scientists have hypothesized that the production of different versions of some enzymes (perhaps encoded by different genes or produced as a result of alternative splicing) having optimal activity at cooler or warmer temperatures underlies such acclimatization.

Another acclimatizing change involves the phospholipids of biological membranes. Membrane phospholipids have higher proportions of double bonds in carp living in colder environments than in carp living in warmer environments. The higher proportion of double bonds makes it harder for the membrane

to freeze. A higher proportion of cholesterol also protects membranes from freezing.

For birds and mammals, freezing temperatures lead to the formation of ice crystals that disrupt cell membranes and kill cells. Many ectotherms, however, encounter temperatures in winter that are well below the freezing point of their body fluids and yet their cells do not die. The tiny second-stage caterpillar of the spruce budworm (*Choristoneura fumiferana*) spends the winter at the tips of spruce trees in Canada, where temperatures may reach –40°C **(Figure 42.22a, b)**. Their ability to survive

**FIGURE 42.22 Surviving freezing. (a)** The effects of spruce budworm on stands of western Douglas fir. **(b)** Spruce budworm (*Choristoneura fumiferana*). **(c)** The icefish *Trematomus bernacchii*. **(d)** Frozen specimens of the wood frog *Rana sylvatica*

depends on the production of an antifreeze protein. Antifreeze proteins also occur in marine fishes that occupy habitats where the water temperature may be below the freezing point of their body fluids (Figure 42.22c); they also occur in some amphibians (Figure 42.22d), such as the wood frog (*Rana sylvatica*). These proteins bond with forming ice crystals, limiting their growth, so although the water freezes, the crystals remain small enough that cell structure is not disrupted.

## STUDY BREAK QUESTIONS

1. Describe mechanisms an ectothermic animal can use to regulate its temperature.
2. What is thermal acclimatization? Why is it important?

## 42.7 Endothermy

Endotherms (mostly birds and mammals) have the most elaborate and extensive thermoregulatory adaptations of all animals. Set points (the core body temperatures that endotherms maintain homeostatically) vary with species and lie between about 39°C and 42°C in birds, and between 32°C and 39°C in mammals.

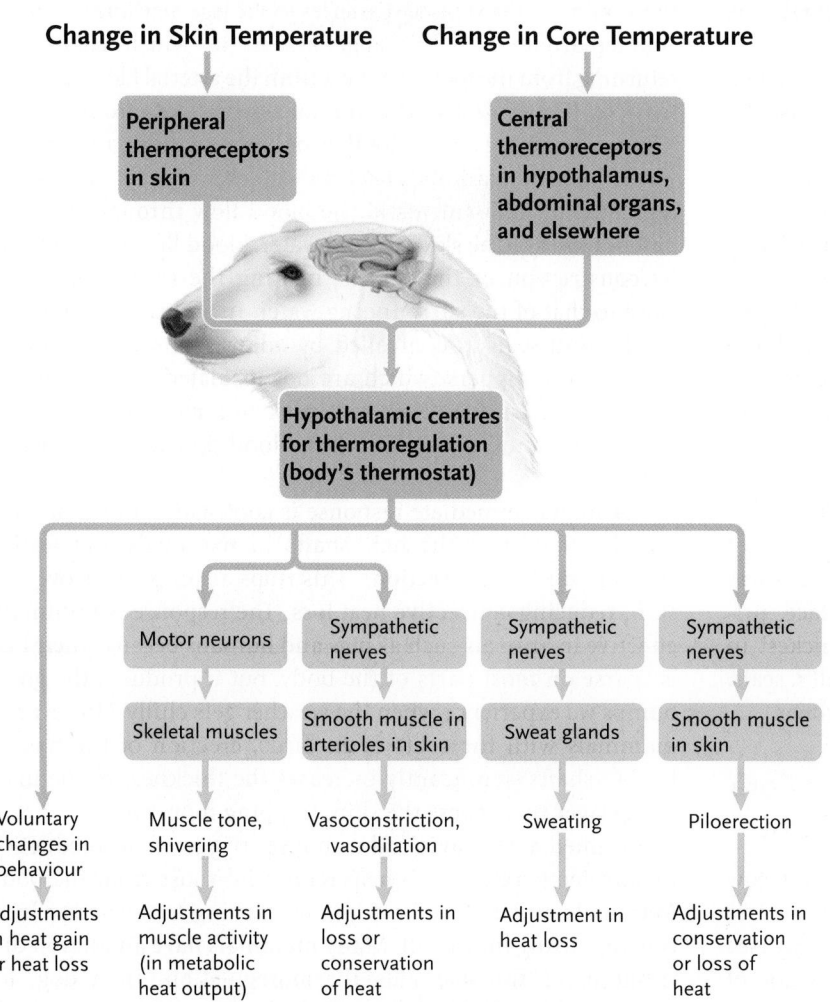

**Change in Skin Temperature** | **Change in Core Temperature**

Peripheral thermoreceptors in skin

Central thermoreceptors in hypothalamus, abdominal organs, and elsewhere

Hypothalamic centres for thermoregulation (body's thermostat)

| Motor neurons | Sympathetic nerves | Sympathetic nerves | Sympathetic nerves |

| Skeletal muscles | Smooth muscle in arterioles in skin | Sweat glands | Smooth muscle in skin |

Voluntary changes in behaviour | Muscle tone, shivering | Vasoconstriction, vasodilation | Sweating | Piloerection

Adjustments in heat gain or heat loss | Adjustments in muscle activity (in metabolic heat output) | Adjustments in loss or conservation of heat | Adjustment in heat loss | Adjustments in conservation or loss of heat

**FIGURE 42.23 The physiological and behavioural responses of birds and mammals to changes in skin and core temperature (see also Figure 38.12)**

We have already noted that the range of environmental temperatures that different organisms encounter is very great. A single species may encounter seasonal variations in environmental temperatures ranging over 70°C or more between winter and summer, yet their body temperatures do not vary.

We begin by describing the basic feedback mechanisms that maintain body temperature in this group.

### 42.7a The Hypothalamus Integrates Information from Thermoreceptors

Thermoreceptors are found in various locations in the bodies of endotherms, including the integument (skin), spinal cord, and hypothalamus. Two types of thermoreceptors occur in skin (see Chapter 45). In mammals, warm receptors send signals to the hypothalamus as the skin temperature rises above 30°C and reach maximum activity when the temperature rises above 40°C. Another type, the cold receptor, sends signals when skin temperature falls below about 35°C and reaches maximum activity at 25°C. By contrast, the highly sensitive thermoreceptors in the hypothalamus itself produce signals when the blood temperature shifts from the set point by as little as 0.01°C.

Signals from the thermoreceptors are integrated in the hypothalamus and other regions of the brain to bring about compensating physiological and behavioural responses (**Figure 42.23**; see also Figure 38.12, Chapter 38). The responses keep body temperature close to the set point, which, in most mammals, varies normally between 35°C and 39°C for the head and trunk. The appendages may vary more widely in temperature. In very cold weather, for example, the legs, the feet, and especially the ears and nose are typically lower in temperature than the body core.

The hypothalamus was identified as a major thermoreceptor and response integrator in mammals by experiments on animals in which various regions of the brain were heated or cooled with a temperature probe. Within the brain, cooling and warming only the hypothalamus produced thermoregulatory responses such as shivering and panting. Later experiments revealed a similar response if regions of the spinal cord were cooled, indicating that thermoreceptors also occur in this location. The hypothalamus is also a major thermoreceptor and response integrator in fishes and reptiles. In birds, thermoreceptors in the spinal cord appear to be more significant in thermoregulation.

### 42.7b The Skin Controls Heat Transfer with the Environment

In addition to its defensive role against infection, the skin of birds and mammals is an organ of heat transfer. It is a very large surface, in direct contact

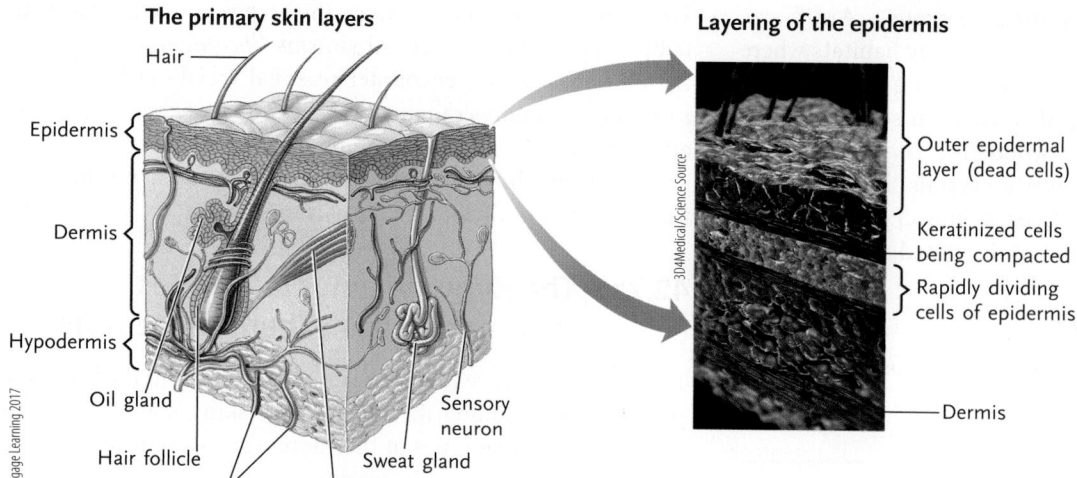

**The primary skin layers**

Hair

Epidermis

Dermis

Hypodermis

Oil gland

Hair follicle

Blood vessels

Sensory neuron

Sweat gland

Smooth muscle

© Cengage Learning 2017

**Layering of the epidermis**

3D4Medical/Science Source

Outer epidermal layer (dead cells)

Keratinized cells being compacted

Rapidly dividing cells of epidermis

Dermis

**FIGURE 42.24  The structure of human skin**

with the environment, across which heat can be transferred readily.

The outermost living tissue of human skin, the **epidermis**, consists of cells that divide and grow rapidly **(Figure 42.24)**, becoming packed with fibres of a highly insoluble protein, keratin (see Chapter 38). When fully formed, the epidermal cells die and become compacted into a tough, impermeable layer.

Below the epidermis lies the **dermis**, a tissue layer packed with connective tissue fibres, such as collagen, that resist the compression, tearing, or puncture of the skin.

The dermis also contains thermoreceptors and a dense network of arterioles, capillaries, and venules. The arterioles delivering blood to the capillary networks of the skin constrict or dilate to control blood flow and, with it, the amount of heat transferred from the body core to the surface. This is why our skin flushes pink on hot days, when the vessels dilate to dump heat, and turns white on cold days, when they constrict to prevent heat loss. Sweat glands and hair and feather follicles are also embedded in the dermis.

The innermost layer of the skin, the **hypodermis,** contains larger blood vessels and additional reinforcing connective tissue. The hypodermis also contains an insulating layer of fatty tissue below the dermal capillary network, which ensures that heat flows between the body core and the surface, primarily through the blood. The insulating layer is thickest in mammals that live in cold environments, such as whales, seals, walruses, and polar bears, in which it is known as blubber.

## 42.7c  The Body Reduces Heat Loss When Core Temperature Falls Below the Set Point

When thermoreceptors signal a fall in core temperature below the set point, the hypothalamus triggers compensating responses by sending signals through the autonomic nervous system (see Chapter 45). Among the immediate responses is constriction of the arterioles in the skin (vasoconstriction), which reduces the flow of blood to the skin's capillary networks. The reduced flow

cuts down the amount of heat that is delivered to the skin and therefore lost from the body surface. The reduction in flow is most pronounced in the skin covering the extremities, where blood flow may be reduced by as much as 99% when core temperature falls. This is particularly important for animals in polar regions. In these animals, the veins and arteries to the legs may form a simple, countercurrent, heat exchange system in which cold blood returning from the foot takes heat from the arterial blood entering the foot **(Figure 42.25)**. This minimizes heat loss from the foot while maintaining a nutritive flow of blood to the extremity.

In marine mammals such as whales and seals, heat loss is regulated by adjustments in the blood flow through the thick blubber layer to the skin. In cold water, blood flow is minimized by constriction of the vessels, making the skin temperature close to that of the surrounding water. In addition, heat loss in whales and seals is controlled by adjustments of the flow of blood to the flippers, which are not insulated by blubber and act as heat radiators. When heat must be conserved to maintain core temperature at the set point, blood flow to the flippers is reduced.

Another immediate response is contraction of the smooth muscles that erect the hair shafts in mammals and feather shafts in birds (piloerection). This traps air in pockets over the skin, reducing convective heat loss. The response is minimally effective in animals such as pigs and humans because their hair is sparse on most parts of the body, but it produces the goose bumps we experience when the weather gets chilly. However, in mammals with fur coats or in birds, erection of the hair or feather shafts significantly increases the thickness of the insulating layer that covers the skin, trapping more air.

Immediate behavioural responses triggered by a reduction in skin temperature also help reduce heat loss from the body. Mammals may reduce heat loss by moving to a warmer location or curling into a ball. Many mammals have an uneven distribution of fur that aids thermoregulation. In a dog, for example, the fur is thickest over the back and sides of the body and the tail, and thinnest under the legs and over the belly.

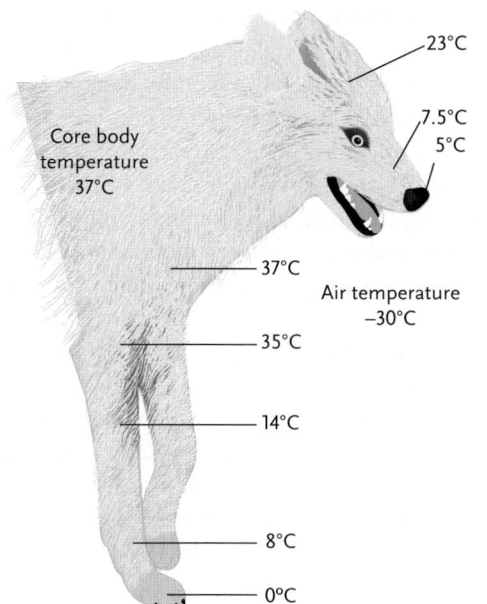

Core body temperature 37°C

23°C

7.5°C
5°C

Air temperature −30°C

37°C

35°C

14°C

8°C

0°C

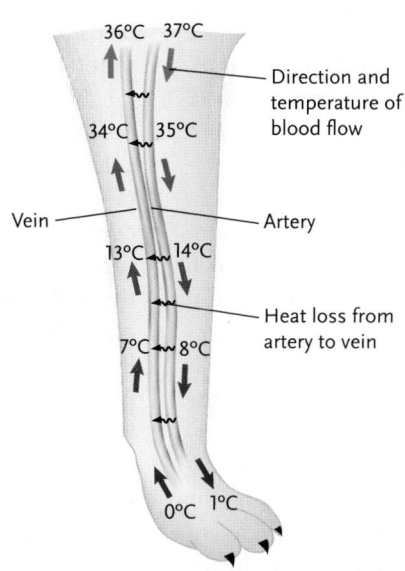

36°C  37°C

Direction and temperature of blood flow

34°C  35°C

Vein

Artery

13°C  14°C

Heat loss from artery to vein

7°C  8°C

0°C  1°C

**FIGURE 42.25 Countercurrent circulation in the leg of an Arctic wolf.** The vein and artery are parallel and close together so that heat from the warm blood in the artery is transferred to the cold blood returning from the foot, minimizing heat loss through the foot.

a.

Jens Ottoson/Shutterstock.com

b.

© david tipling/Alamy

c.

Photos.com

d.

Sumikophoto/Shutterstock.com

**FIGURE 42.26 Structural and behavioural adaptations controlling heat transfer at the body surface.** **(a)** A husky (*Canis lupus familiaris*) conserving heat by curling up with the limbs under the body and the tail around the nose. **(b)** Penguins huddle together to conserve heat. **(c)** An elephant cools off by spraying itself with water. **(d)** A jackrabbit (*Lepus californicus*) dissipating heat from its ears on a hot summer day. Notice the dilated blood vessels in its large ears. Both the large surface area of the ears and the extensive network of blood vessels promote the dissipation of heat by convection and radiation.

In cold weather, a dog will curl up, pull in its limbs, wrap its tail around its body, and bury its nose in its tail so that only body surfaces insulated by thick fur are exposed to the air **(Figure 42.26a)**. Many birds and mammals also huddle together to conserve heat. Many of us have seen puppies huddled together to keep warm; birds such as penguins also keep warm by huddling (Figure 42.26b).

If these immediate responses do not return body temperature to the set point, the hypothalamus triggers further responses, most notably the rhythmic tremors of skeletal muscle we know as shivering. The heat released by the muscle contractions and the oxidative reactions powering them can raise the total heat production of the body substantially. At the same time, the hypothalamus triggers secretion of epinephrine (from the adrenal medulla) and thyroid hormone (see Chapter 43), both of which increase heat production by stimulating the oxidation of fats and other fuels. The generation of heat by oxidative mechanisms in nonmuscle tissue throughout the body is termed **nonshivering thermogenesis**.

In the young of many mammals (including newborn human infants), the most intense heat generation is by nonshivering thermogenesis that takes place in a specialized **brown adipose tissue** (also called *brown fat*), which can produce heat rapidly. Heat is generated by a mechanism that uncouples electron transport from ATP production in mitochondria (see Chapter 5); the heat is transferred throughout the body by the blood. Animals that hibernate or are active in cold regions contain larger amounts of brown adipose tissue. In most mammals, brown adipose tissue is concentrated between the shoulders in the back and around the neck where it preferentially warms the heart and the blood leaving the heart in the arteries. In human newborns, this tissue accounts for about 5% of body weight. The tissue normally shrinks during late childhood and is absent or nearly so in most adults. However, if exposure to cold is ongoing, the tissue remains. Some Japanese and Korean divers who harvest shellfish in frigid waters, and Finns who work outside during the winter, have significant amounts of brown adipose tissue.

If none of these responses succeed in raising body temperature to the set point, the result is **hypothermia**, a condition in which the core temperature falls below normal for a prolonged period. In humans, a drop in core temperature of only a few degrees affects brain function and leads to confusion; progressive or continued hypothermia can lead to coma and death.

## 42.7d The Body Increases Heat Loss When Core Temperature Rises above the Set Point

When the core temperature rises above the set point, the hypothalamus sends signals through the autonomic system that trigger responses that lower body temperature. As an immediate response, the signals relax smooth muscles of arterioles in the skin (vasodilation), increasing blood flow and, with it, the heat lost from the body surface. In marine mammals in warmer water, blood flow to the skin above the blubber increases, allowing excess heat to be lost from the body surface. In addition, when a whale generates excessive internal heat through the muscular activity of swimming, the flow of blood from the body core to the flippers increases.

The smooth muscles to feathers and fur in birds and mammals in hot climates also relax, and these layers are flattened, removing trapped air and decreasing their insulating capability. In addition, in mammals with sweat glands, such as antelopes, cows, humans, and horses, signals from the hypothalamus trigger the secretion of sweat, which absorbs heat as it evaporates from the surface of the skin. Some endotherms, including dogs (which have sweat glands only on their feet) and many

birds (which have no sweat glands), use panting as a major way to release heat.

These physiological changes are reinforced by behavioural responses such as seeking shade or a cool burrow, plunging into cold water, wallowing in mud, or taking a cold drink. Elephants take up water in their trunks and spray it over their bodies to cool off in hot weather (Figure 42.26c); dogs spread their limbs, turn on their side or back, and expose the relatively bare skin of the belly, which acts as a heat radiator. In hot weather, many birds fly with their legs extended so that heat flows from their legs into the passing air. Similarly, penguins expose featherless patches of skin under their wings to cool off on days when the weather is too warm. Jackrabbits (Figure 42.26d) and elephants dissipate heat from their large ears, which are richly supplied with blood vessels. In times of significant heat stress, kangaroos and rats spread saliva on their fur to increase heat loss by evaporation; some bats coat their fur with both saliva and urine.

When the heat gain of the body is too great to be counteracted by these responses, **hyperthermia** results. An increase of only a few degrees above normal for a prolonged period is enough to disrupt vital biochemical reactions and damage brain cells. Most adult humans become unconscious if their body temperature reaches 41°C and die if it goes above 43°C for more than a few minutes.

As with ectotherms, many mammals also undergo thermal acclimatization with seasonal temperature changes. Although in many cases a change in day length appears to be the actual trigger, the development of a thick fur coat in winter that is shed in summer enables them to adapt to seasonal temperatures. Some Arctic and sub-Arctic mammals develop a thicker layer of insulating fat in winter.

## 42.7e Birds and Mammals Have Daily and Seasonal Rhythms

The temperature set point in many birds and mammals varies in a regular cycle during the day. In some, the daily variations are relatively small. In others, larger variations are correlated with daily or seasonal temperature changes. These rhythms are a response to day length rather than temperature change.

Humans are among the endotherms for which daily variations in the temperature set point are small. Normally, human core temperature varies from a minimum of about 35.5°C in the morning to a maximum of about 37.7°C in the evening. Women also show a monthly variation keyed to the menstrual cycle, with temperatures rising about 0.5°C from the time of ovulation until menstruation begins. The physiological significance of these variations is unknown.

Camels undergo a daily variation of as much as 7°C in set point temperature. During the day, a camel's set point gradually resets upward, an adaptation that allows its body to absorb a large amount of heat. The heat absorption conserves water that would otherwise be lost by evaporation to keep the body at a lower set point. At night, when the desert is cooler, the thermostat resets again, allowing the body temperature to cool several degrees, releasing the excess heat absorbed during the day.

When the environmental temperature is cool, having a lowered temperature set point greatly reduces the energy required to maintain body temperature. In many animals, the lowered set point is accompanied by reductions in metabolic, nervous, and physical activity (including slower respiration and heartbeat), producing a sleeplike state known as **torpor**.

Entry into **daily torpor**, a period of inactivity keyed to variations in daily temperature, is typical of many small mammals and birds. These animals expend more energy per unit of body weight to keep warm than larger animals because the ratio of body surface area to volume increases as body size decreases; that is, the ratio of surface area across which animals lose heat increases while the volume of cells producing heat decreases. Hummingbirds feed actively during the daytime, when their set point is close to 40°C. During the cool of night, however, the set point drops to as low as 13°C. This allows the birds to conserve enough energy to survive overnight when they are unable to feed and would otherwise be unable to obtain enough fuel to produce heat; they would literally starve to death. Some nocturnal animals, including bats and small rodents such as the deer mouse, become torpid in cool locations during daylight hours when they do not actively feed. At night, their temperature set point rises and they become fully active **(Figure 42.27)**.

Many animals enter a prolonged state of torpor tied to the seasons, triggered in most cases by the change in day length that signals the transition between summer and winter. The importance of day length has been demonstrated by laboratory experiments in which animals have been induced to enter seasonal torpor by changing the period of artificial light to match the winter or summer day length.

During winter, many mammals enter a more extreme state of metabolic suppression called **hibernation** (*hiberna* = winter), greatly reducing metabolic expenditures when food is unobtainable. Hibernators must store large quantities of fat to serve as energy reserves. The drop in body temperature during hibernation varies with the mammal. In some, such as hedgehogs,

groundhogs, and ground squirrels, body temperature falls to within 1°C of environmental temperatures, down to just above freezing. In some species of hedgehogs, body temperature falls from about 38°C in the summer to as low as 5°C–6°C during winter hibernation. The Arctic ground squirrel's body supercools (goes to a below-freezing, unfrozen state) during hibernation, with its body temperature dropping to about –3°C. Most hibernating mammals rouse for brief periods during the course of the winter.

In larger mammals such as bears, the degree of metabolic suppression and the fall in body temperature are less pronounced. The core temperature of bears drops only 5°C–10°C. Although sluggish, hibernating bears will waken readily if disturbed. They also waken normally from time to time, as when females wake to give birth during the winter season.

Some ectotherms, including amphibians and reptiles living in northern latitudes, also become torpid during winter. The Antarctic codfish, *Notothenia coriiceps*, spends the summer feeding on phytoplankton. In the winter, however, phytoplankton are reduced as a result of the low levels of light. The fish enter a state similar to hibernation. They remain relatively immobile in refuges, and their metabolic rate drops by about one-third. Because the temperature of the water remains constant over the seasons, the fish clearly have the capacity to control their metabolic rate independent of temperature.

Some mammals enter seasonal torpor during summer, called **estivation** (*aestivalis* = of summer), when environmental temperatures are high and water is scarce. Some ground squirrels remain inactive in the cooler temperatures of their burrows during extreme summer heat. Many ectotherms, among them land snails, lungfishes, many toads and frogs, and some desert-living lizards, weather such climates by digging into the soil and entering a state of estivation that lasts throughout the hot dry season.

In *Why It Matters*, you were asked to consider the vast variety of habitats found on Earth, from deserts to lush rain forests, from the frozen poles to the tropics, from shallow streams to the depths of the oceans, and to answer the question, "What are the different challenges that organisms face living in each of these habitats?" In the course of this chapter we have discussed the problems associated with maintaining water and solute balance and of regulating body temperature while living in salt water, fresh water, and terrestrial environments ranging from deserts to the frozen North. Based on your understanding of the chapter, and the summary figure provided here, you should now be able to answer this question.

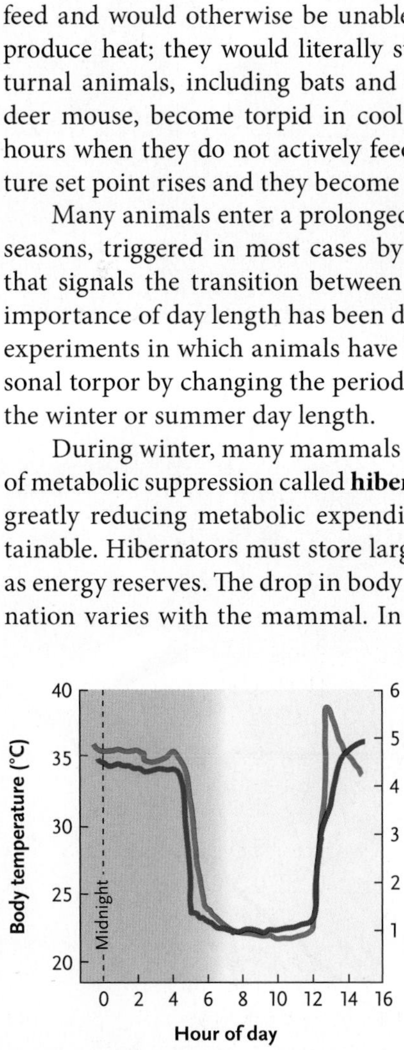

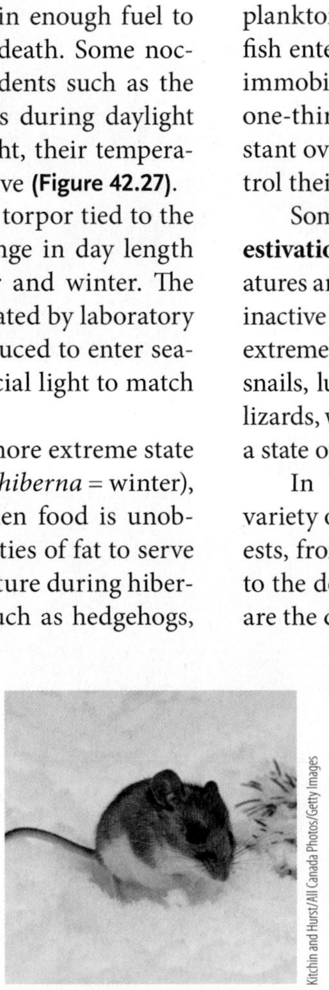

FIGURE 42.27 **Cycle of daily torpor in a deer mouse (*Peromyscus maniculatus*)**

Kitchin and Hurst/All Canada Photos/Getty Images

## STUDY BREAK QUESTIONS

1. What can birds and mammals do to dissipate heat on very hot days? How would this be affected by high humidity?

2. Mammals that live in the desert are often nocturnal. What advantages are there in terms of thermoregulation?

# Summary Illustration

An understanding of the adaptations that allow some organisms but not others to live in different habitats gives us insight into physiological mechanisms and the consequences of such things as climate change on organismal performance. Two of the major abiotic factors that are affected by climate change are temperature and water availability. Animals can only live with body temperatures within a restricted range. They exchange heat with their environment by conduction, convection, radiation, and evaporation.

Evaporation

Electromagnetic radiation (solar)

Electromagnetic radiation (infrared)

Convection

Ectotherms obtain most of their body heat from their environment. They generally have body temperatures similar to ambient temperature.

Conduction

Ectothermy and endothermy represent different strategies for coping with the variations in environmental temperature that all animals encounter; each has its advantages and disadvantages.

Temperature regulation (thermoregulation) is based on negative feedback pathways that maintain body temperatures within ranges that produce optimal physiological performance.

Endotherms obtain most of their body heat from their own metabolism. They generally maintain body temperatures between 30°C and 42°C.

Electromagnetic radiation (solar)

Convection

Evaporation

Electromagnetic radiation (infrared)

Conduction

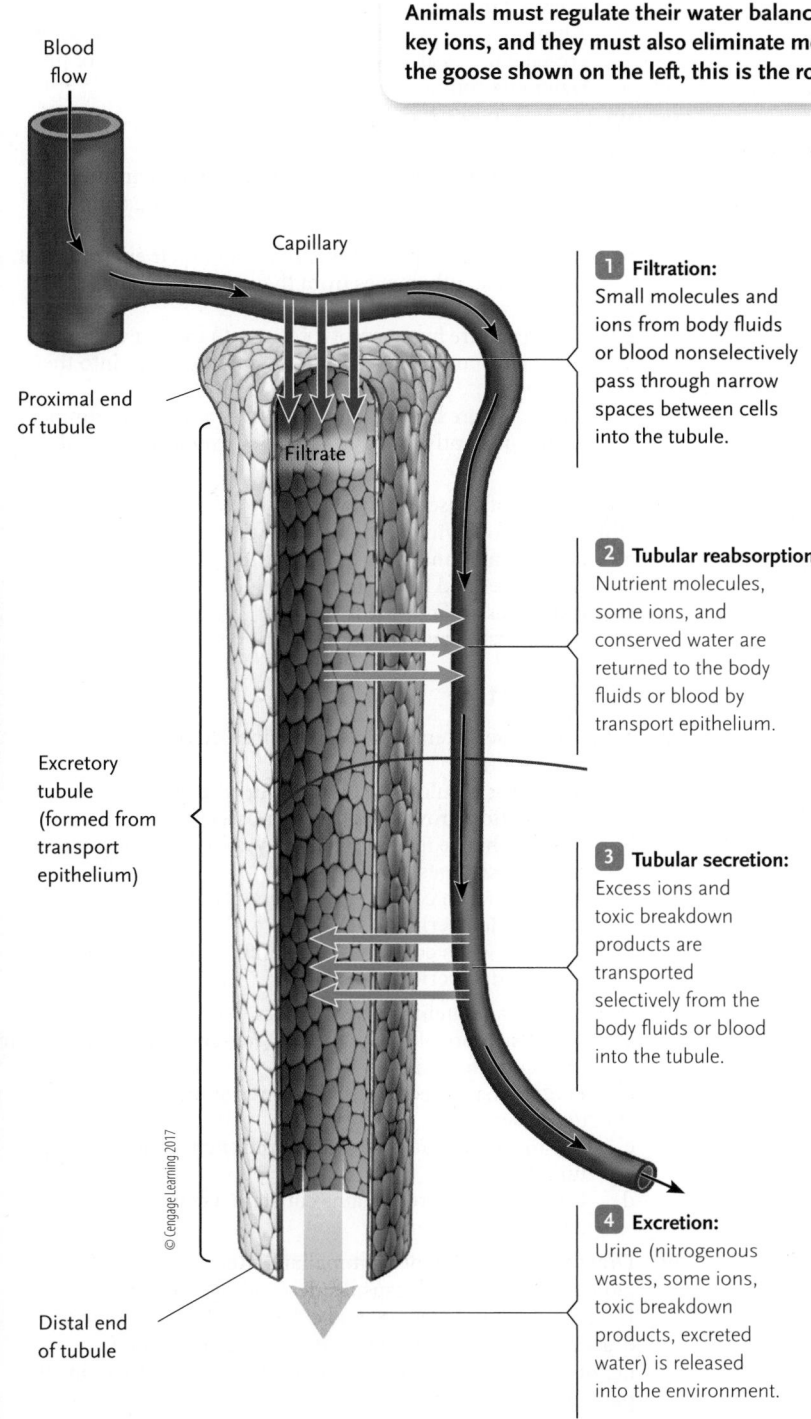

Animals must regulate their water balance, their pH, and concentrations of key ions, and they must also eliminate metabolic wastes. In the lizard and the goose shown on the left, this is the role of tubules within the kidneys.

Blood flow

Capillary

Proximal end of tubule

Filtrate

**1 Filtration:** Small molecules and ions from body fluids or blood nonselectively pass through narrow spaces between cells into the tubule.

Excretory tubule (formed from transport epithelium)

**2 Tubular reabsorption:** Nutrient molecules, some ions, and conserved water are returned to the body fluids or blood by transport epithelium.

**3 Tubular secretion:** Excess ions and toxic breakdown products are transported selectively from the body fluids or blood into the tubule.

© Cengage Learning 2017

Distal end of tubule

**4 Excretion:** Urine (nitrogenous wastes, some ions, toxic breakdown products, excreted water) is released into the environment.

While the structure of the tubules may vary in different animals (invertebrates to mammals), the process is always the same and consists of the four steps shown on the left.

The nitrogenous products of digestion are excreted by most animals as ammonia, urea, or uric acid; the particular molecule depends on the need to conserve water.

There are some important differences among marine, freshwater, and terrestrial animals. Animals living in marine and terrestrial environments require mechanisms to obtain and conserve water; those in freshwater environments do not. On the other hand, obtaining salts and ions is relatively easy in marine environments but more difficult in freshwater and terrestrial ones.

In many aquatic animals, exchange of water and solutes also takes place across the skin and the gills.

Maintaining homeostatic levels of water and solutes under changing conditions requires that animals be able to sense the osmotic concentration of body fluids and adjust rates of reabsorption and secretion.

# SELF-TEST QUESTIONS

## Recall/Understand

1. In which way are most sharks like freshwater fish?
   a. They are osmoregulators.
   b. They are osmoconformers.
   c. The salt in the animals is more concentrated than in the water in which they live.
   d. The salt in the animals is less concentrated than in the water in which they live.

2. Which of these structures can carry out filtration and/or excretion?
   a. ciliated metanephridia in insects
   b. a nephron and a bladder in insects
   c. the hindgut of earthworms
   d. protonephridia containing flame cells in flatworms

3. Which of these statements describes what happens in the kidneys?
   a. In the descending loop of Henle, water leaves the tubule.
   b. In the collecting duct, water enters the tubule via aquaporins.
   c. The fluid that enters Bowman's capsule is identical to the blood.
   d. In the descending loop of Henle, $Na^+$ and $K^+$ enter the tubule by simple diffusion.

4. Which substances end up excreted in urine from the body?
   a. those that leave the kidney through the renal vein
   b. those that remain in the ascending loop of Henle
   c. those that are not reabsorbed
   d. those that return to the glomerulus

5. Which of the following is unique to endotherms?
   a. torpor
   b. thermal acclimatization
   c. thermoregulation by the hypothalamus
   d. body temperature regulated by endogenous heat production

6. Boa constrictors wrap themselves around their eggs and shiver. Which term refers to this warming mechanism?
   a. evaporation
   b. conduction
   c. convection
   d. radiation

7. If the set point for temperature regulation were increased, which of these would you expect to occur?
   a. decrease in epinephrine
   b. shivering
   c. vasodilation
   d. increase in brown adipose tissue

## Apply/Analyze

8. If an animal secretes uric acid crystals, in which environment could you conclude that the animal most likely lives?
   a. fresh water
   b. marine
   c. terrestrial and very dry
   d. terrestrial and very wet

9. What is the reason that ammonia is found mostly as a waste chemical in animals that can produce large quantities of dilute urine?
   a. Ammonia is very toxic, and a large amount of water dilutes it, so that animals are not affected by their own toxic waste.
   b. Ammonia is not toxic, and this is just a coincidence.
   c. Ammonia readily absorbs moisture, and as such is easily excreted in water environments.
   d. Ammonia is a gas, and as such it easily dissolves in water, creating the weak base needed for proper balance of pH in water environments.

10. Which of the following occurs in flatworms and freshwater mussels?
    a. Since they are isoosmotic relative to their environment, water constantly moves from the surroundings into their bodies.
    b. Since they are hyperosmotic relative to their environment, water constantly moves from their bodies into their surroundings.
    c. Since they are hypoosmotic relative to their environment, water constantly moves from the surroundings into their bodies.
    d. Since they are hyperosmotic relative to their environment, water constantly moves from the surroundings into their bodies.

11. The strategy of conserving water and excreting salts is utilized by which of the following?
    a. land animals and river fishes
    b. river fishes and lake fishes
    c. lake fishes and marine fishes
    d. marine fishes and land animals

## Create/Evaluate

12. Which of these statements best describes thermal acclimatization?
    a. It involves regulation of body temperature in response to information provided by a thermoreceptor.
    b. It is the change in an animal's physiology that accompanies seasonal changes.
    c. It occurs when core body temperature is below normal for an extended period of time.
    d. It occurs when core body temperature is above normal for an extended period of time.

13. Which of these statements best applies to ectotherms?
    a. They use more of their energy to maintain body temperature than endotherms use.
    b. Food demand decreases when environmental temperature decreases.
    c. The metabolic rate increases as the environmental temperature decreases.
    d. Body temperature remains constant when environmental temperatures change.

14. Draw a cross-section of mammalian kidney, showing glomerulus, Bowman's capsule, descending segment, loop of Henle, ascending segment, and collecting duct. Label on your drawing the movement of water and salts throughout the nephron, showing passive and active transport of these in all parts of the nephron.

15. On the same drawing of the nephron, label changes in the osmolarity of interstitial fluid, as well of the filtrate/urine.

# Chapter Roadmap

## Control of Animal Processes: Endocrine Control

Along with the central nervous system (CNS), hormones of the endocrine system provide the communication that coordinates the activities of multicellular life. In general, they control activities that involve slower, longer-acting responses of multiple tissues or organs.

### 43.1 Hormones and Their Secretion

Hormones produce responses to environmental stimuli, regulate growth and development, and homeostatically regulate many processes.

### 43.2 Mechanisms of Hormone Action

Hormones control cell functions by first binding to receptor molecules on or in their target cells. This either alters functional proteins already present in the cell or leads to the production of new functional proteins.

**From Chapter 42**

### 43.3 The Hypothalamus and Pituitary

Some sensory signals are processed in the brain and communicate with the endocrine system through the hypothalamus and the pituitary gland.

**To Chapter 44**

**From Chapter 40**

**From Chapter 41**

### 43.4 Other Major Endocrine Glands of Vertebrates

Some sensory signals communicate directly with various endocrine glands.

**To Chapter 45**

### 43.5 Endocrine Systems in Invertebrates

Many of the same hormones and hormone receptors are found in invertebrates and vertebrates; others are unique to invertebrates.

Stubblefield Photography / Shutterstock.com

Photos.com

**Two North American bull elks contesting for cows.** The shorter days of autumn trigger hormone production, battling, and reproductive behaviour.

# Control of Animal Processes: Endocrine Control

# 43

**Why it matters . . .** Every September, as the days grow shorter, bull elks (*Cervus canadensis*) begin to strut their stuff. Although they have grazed peacefully together at high mountain elevations, they now become testy with each other. Soon, they descend to lower elevations, where the cow elks have been feeding in large nursery groups with their calves and yearlings. The bulls chase away the male yearlings. As part of the mating ritual, the bulls bugle, square off, strut, and circle. Then they clash their antlers together, attempting to drive each other from the cows. The winning males claim harems of about 10 females each. After the mating season ends, tranquillity returns. The cows again graze in herds. The males form now-friendly bachelor groups that also feed quietly in the meadows. The young will be born eight to nine months later, when summer returns. The transition to mating behaviour is triggered by the shortening days of late summer and fall. Detected by the eyes and registered in the brain, reduced day length initiates changes in the secretion of long-distance signalling molecules called **hormones** (*horme* = to excite). By the time you finish reading this chapter you should be able to construct the pathway that produces the mating behaviour just described.

Hormones are secreted by cells of the **endocrine system** (*endo* = within; *krinein* = separate). Along with the central nervous system (CNS), hormones of the endocrine system provide the communication that coordinates the activities of multicellular life. These two systems are structurally, chemically, and functionally related, but they control different types of activities.

The nervous system (Chapter 45) acts through high-speed electrical signals to enable an organism to react rapidly to changes in its internal or external environment. The nervous system also activates or inhibits highly specific localized targets.

In general, the endocrine system controls activities that involve slower, longer-acting responses of multiple tissues or organs. Some of these responses may be relatively quick (less than a minute) and directed, as in the stimulation of milk secretion by the suckling of an infant (see discussion of oxytocin, Section 43.3b). Many also involve transcription and translation of DNA, leading to sustained long-lasting responses (hours, weeks, months, or even years), incorporating the activities of many tissues and organs, such as the regulation of metabolism and growth by thyroxine (see discussion of the thyroid hormones in Section 43.4a). For more complex animals

such as insects and mammals, a large variety of hormones regulate a host of functions, from the concentration of salt and glucose in body fluids to body growth and sexual maturation. The mechanisms and functions of the endocrine system are the subjects of this chapter.

## 43.1 Hormones and Their Secretion

Cells signal other cells in several ways. Local regulators are used to communicate between neighbouring cells, while hormones and nerves are used to communicate with distant organs.

### 43.1a The Endocrine System Includes Four Major Types of Cell Signalling

Four types of cell signalling occur in the endocrine system. In **autocrine regulation**, a local regulator acts on the same cells that release it **(Figure 43.1a)**. This is a common mechanism used by cells to either reduce or increase their sensitivity to other stimuli. In **paracrine regulation**, a cell releases signalling molecules that diffuse through the extracellular fluid and act on nearby cells (Figure 43.1b). In both these instances, regulation is local rather than at a distance. Many of the growth factors that regulate cell division and differentiation act in both an autocrine

**a. Autocrine regulation**

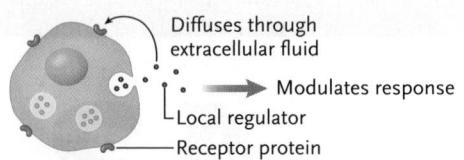

**b. Paracrine regulation**

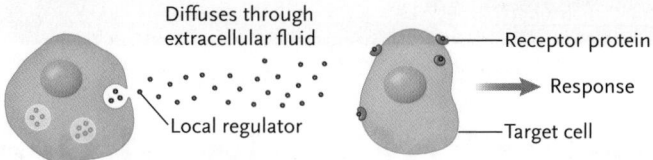

**c. Endocrine regulation**

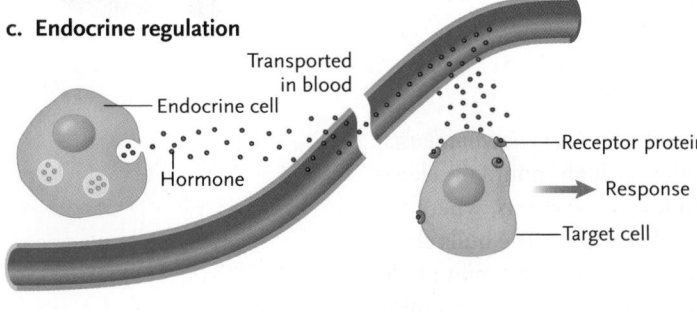

**d. Neuroendocrine regulation**

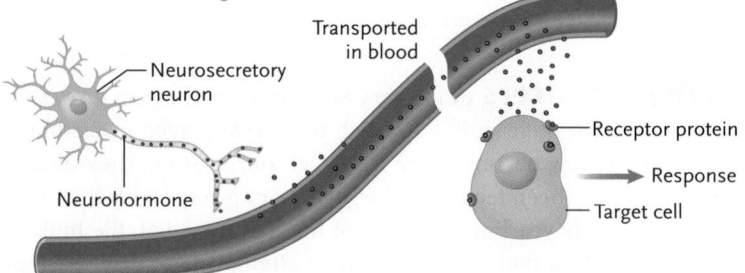

**e. Neural regulation**

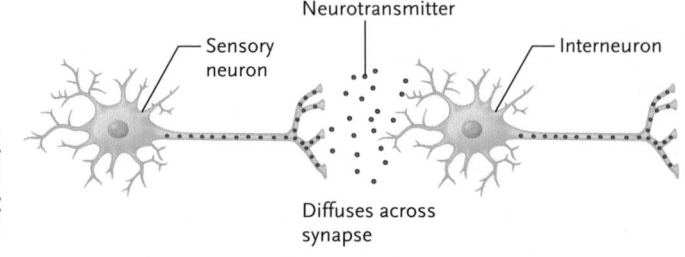

© Cengage Learning 2017

**FIGURE 43.1  The major types of cell signalling in the endocrine and nervous systems**

and a paracrine fashion. In **endocrine regulation**, hormones are secreted into the blood or extracellular fluid by the cells of duct-less secretory organs called **endocrine glands** (Figure 43.1c and **Figure 43.2b**). Hormones are circulated throughout the body in the blood or other body fluids and, as a result, most body cells are constantly exposed to a wide variety of hormones. Only the **target cells** of a hormone, those with receptor proteins (Chapter 4) recognizing and binding that hormone, respond to it. Hormones are cleared from the body at a steady rate by enzymatic breakdown in their target cells or blood or organs such as the liver or kidneys, and the breakdown products are excreted.

In **neuroendocrine regulation**, specialized **neurosecretory neurons** respond to and conduct electrical signals, but rather than synapsing with target cells, they release a neurohormone into the circulation when appropriately stimulated (Figure 43.1d). The hormone is produced in the cell body and packaged in membrane-bound vesicles that are transported along the axon to the release sites. The neurohormone is usually distributed in blood or other body fluids and elicits a response in target cells some distance away that have receptors for the neurohormone. In contrast, in **neural regulation**, **neurons** synapse directly with target cells, releasing neurotransmitters into a synapse (Figure 43.1e) or neuromuscular junction (see Chapters 45 and 46 respectively for details). Note that both neurohormones and neurotransmitters are secreted by neurons. Neurohormones are distinguished from neurotransmitters in that neurohormones affect distant target cells, whereas neurotransmitters affect adjacent cells.

Both neurohormones and neurotransmitters function in the same way: they cause cellular responses by interacting with specific receptors on target cells.

**CONCEPT** Exocrine glands, such as the sweat and salivary glands, release their secretions into ducts that lead outside the body or into the cavities of the digestive tract (see Chapter 39) (Figure 43.2a). Secretions from the stomach, liver, pancreas, gall bladder, intestine, and so on, that are released into the digestive tract are not endocrine secretions (Figure 43.2b) but, rather, are exocrine, since the lumen of the digestive tract is technically outside the body. The digestive tract extends from the mouth to the anus, and unless substances are absorbed across cell membranes along the digestive tract, they pass through the body without ever entering it. As a result, secretions that enter the digestive tract via ducts from glands along its length are exocrine in nature. ⬡

## 43.1b Hormones and Their Receptors Are Evolutionarily Conserved

It may be surprising to know that many of the same hormones, and hormone receptors, are found in invertebrates and vertebrates. This suggests that they evolved before the vertebrates diverged from their invertebrate ancestors over 800 million years ago. The same hormone may serve similar roles in different groups. For instance, fruit flies, molluscs, and humans have insulin-like hormones and receptors. The same hormone may also have different roles in different groups, not just different roles in invertebrates and vertebrates, but different roles in different groups of vertebrates. For instance, the thyroid hormones that are essential for growth, development, maturation, and metabolism in all vertebrates, also control the metamorphosis of amphibian tadpoles into frogs and toads, and seasonal moulting leading to changes in plumage in birds, and coat colour in some mammals (see Section 43.4a).

Research indicates that the receptors for many hormones evolved before the hormones that interact with them. And while the structure of the hormone and its receptor is conserved in very different groups, the example of the thyroid hormone just given indicates that the hormones and their receptors can evolve to take on new roles as organisms encounter new environments and stresses. Melatonin is important in regulating daily and annual cycles in most animals. However, it also plays a role in regulating the salt gland of marine birds. The same hormone may have different functions at different stages in the life of an animal. The juvenile hormone of insects acts to maintain insects in a larval state but also controls reproduction in the adult.

As described in the previous section, the distinction between hormones, neurohormones, and neurotransmitters is based on the cells that secrete them, the distance they travel before having their effect, and the speed and duration of the response. It should not be surprising to learn that the same chemical compound can play more than one of these roles. Norepinephrine is a classic example, playing a role as a neurotransmitter in the sympathetic nervous system where it is activated under stressful situations, but also being released as a hormone from the adrenal gland acting to reinforce the action of the sympathetic nervous system and prolong the response (see Section 43.4c).

In general, all hormones are involved in one or more of three basic functions, as described in the next sections.

**a. Exocrine gland**

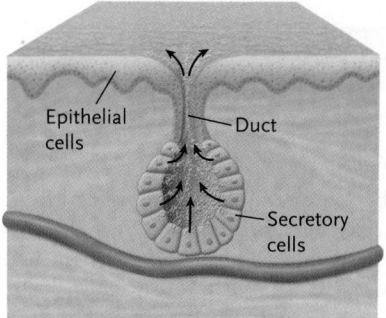

**b. Endocrine gland**

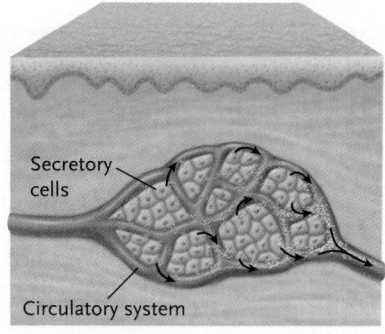

**FIGURE 43.2 The structure of exocrine and endocrine glands. (a)** Exocrine glands secrete chemicals into ducts that lead to the surface of the body or the digestive tract. **(b)** Endocrine glands secrete hormones directly into body fluids, especially into the circulatory system.

## 43.1c Hormones Produce Responses to Environmental Stimuli

The example described in *Why It Matters* demonstrates the manner in which environmental change (in this case the shortening days of late summer) can lead to profound physiological responses (such as mating behaviour). There are many environmental stimuli, such as changes in temperature, day length, or the sight of a predator or potential mate, that lead to hormonal responses. The environmental stimuli are usually detected by the nervous system and transmitted to the endocrine system. The endocrine system then produces slow, sustained responses involving multiple tissues or organs that adjust the functional state of the body.

Another example of such a response is the so-called *fight-or-flight response*. This response requires careful communication between cells in all parts of the body. The nervous system of a mammal, for instance, sensing the presence of a predator, produces immediate changes in blood flow to muscles, lungs, and heart that prepare an animal to either flee or defend itself. The hormonal system produces slower but longer-lasting changes in such things as glucose and fat metabolism to sustain the elevated activities of these other systems. It is important that all these changes be coordinated. The glucose must be released from the liver and the fat from body lipid stores, both to fuel increased activity. The tissues involved will need more oxygen to metabolize these compounds. This will require an increase in breathing to obtain more oxygen, an increase in heart rate to transport it, and changes in blood flow to muscles and other organs to ensure that the extra oxygen is delivered to the right destination. This is a well-orchestrated series of events, one that requires perfectly timed interactions and excellent intercellular communication.

These are only two examples of the way in which the activities of different organs and organ systems in animals must be coordinated.

## 43.1d Hormones Are Involved in Growth and Development

The endocrine system, acting through a variety of hormones, is instrumental in regulating the growth and development of animals. It plays key roles in regulating moulting and metamorphosis in insects as well as growth and sexual maturation in vertebrates. This will be discussed in more detail in Section 43.5 and in the following chapter (Chapter 44).

## 43.1e Hormones Are Involved in Homeostatic Regulation

Many hormones are involved in the homeostatic regulation of various physiological functions. The secretion of many hormones is regulated by feedback pathways, some of which operate partially or completely independent of neuronal controls. Most pathways are controlled by negative feedback, in which a product of the

pathway inhibits an earlier step in the pathway. For instance, in vertebrates, secretion by the thyroid gland is regulated by a negative feedback loop **(Figure 43.3)**. Neurosecretory neurons in the hypothalamus secrete thyroid-releasing hormone (TRH) into a vein connecting the hypothalamus to the pituitary gland (neuroendocrine regulation). In response, the pituitary releases thyroid-stimulating hormone (TSH) into the blood, which stimulates the thyroid gland to release thyroid hormones (endocrine regulation). As the thyroid hormone concentration in the blood increases, it begins to inhibit TRH secretion by the hypothalamus and TSH secretion by the pituitary gland. In turn, TSH and secretion of the thyroid hormones are reduced. This feedback control can be exclusively hormonal (Figure 43.3, yellow boxes) but may also involve neurosecretory pathways coordinating hormone levels to environmental factors (Figure 43.3, blue boxes).

Although much less common, some hormones are involved in positive feedback cycles. With positive feedback, a product of the pathway excites an earlier step in the pathway, leading to progressive excitation and generally resulting in an explosive response. For instance, during the birthing process in many mammals, the onset of uterine contractions stimulates the

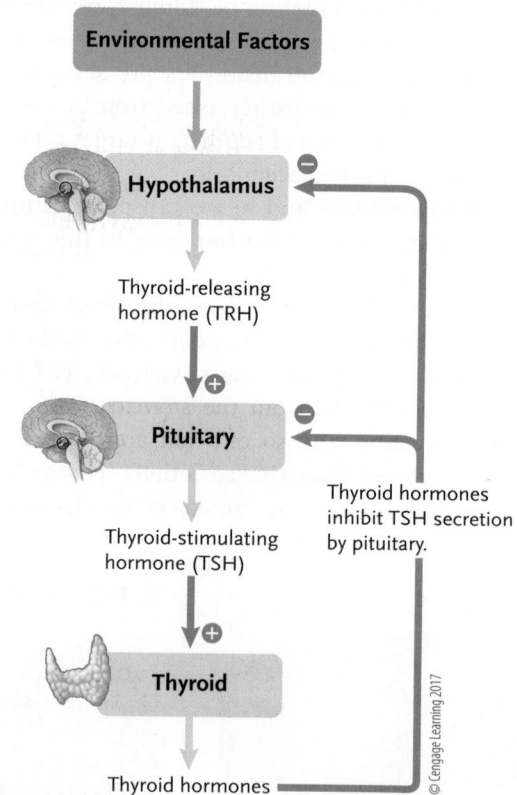

**FIGURE 43.3 A negative feedback loop regulating secretion of thyroid hormones.** In this case, when the concentration of thyroid hormones in the blood increases, the hormones inhibit earlier steps in the pathway (indicated by the red arrows and negative sign) to maintain their levels more or less constant. This feedback control can be exclusively hormonal (yellow boxes) but may also involve neurosecretory pathways coordinating hormone levels to environmental factors (light blue box = neuroendocrine; dark blue box = neural). Green arrows produce stimulation; red arrows produce inhibition.

pituitary gland to release oxytocin. Oxytocin stimulates the uterine muscles to contract more forcefully. This results in an increasing stimulus to release more oxytocin, resulting in more frequent and forceful contractions that ultimately culminate in the birth of the young.

## 43.1f Body Processes Are Regulated by Coordinated Hormone Secretion

Although we discuss mostly individual hormones in the remainder of the chapter, most body processes are affected by more than one hormone. The blood concentrations of glucose, fatty acids, and ions such as $Ca^{2+}$, $K^+$, and $Na^+$ are regulated by the coordinated activities of several hormones secreted by different glands. Similarly, body processes such as oxidative metabolism, digestion, growth, sexual development, and reactions to stress are all controlled by multiple hormones.

In many of these systems, negative feedback loops adjust the levels of secretion of hormones that act in antagonistic (opposing) ways, creating a balance in their effects that maintains body homeostasis (see Chapters 38 and 42). Consider the regulation of fuel molecules such as glucose, fatty acids, and amino acids in the blood. We usually eat three meals per day and fast to some extent between meals. During these periods of eating and fasting, five hormone systems act in a coordinated fashion to keep fuel levels in balance: (1) gastrin and ghrelin secreted by the stomach, and secretin from the intestine; (2) insulin and glucagon, secreted by the pancreas; (3) growth hormone, secreted by the anterior pituitary; (4) epinephrine and norepinephrine, released by the sympathetic nervous system and the adrenal medulla; and (5) glucocorticoid hormones, released by the adrenal cortex.

The entire system of hormones regulating fuel metabolism resembles the fail-safe mechanisms designed by engineers in which redundancy, overlapping controls, feedback loops, and multiple safety valves ensure that vital functions are maintained at appropriate levels in the face of changing and even extreme circumstances.

### STUDY BREAK QUESTIONS

1. What are the functions of the endocrine and nervous systems? How are they the same, and how do they differ? What is the significance of this?
2. What are the major types of cell signalling that occur in the endocrine system? How do they work?
3. Do individual hormones act in isolation?

# 43.2 Mechanisms of Hormone Action

Hormones control cell functions by first binding to receptor molecules on or in their target cells. This initiates a signalling cascade within the cell that ultimately leads to the desired effect.

Hormones may be charged compounds, in which case they are water soluble (hydrophilic) but not lipid soluble and do not cross cell membranes easily. Their receptors are found in the cell membrane exposed to the interstitial fluid. Other hormones are neutral compounds, in which case they are lipid soluble but not water soluble (hydrophobic) and do cross cell membranes easily. Their receptors are found within the cell.

## 43.2a Hydrophilic Hormones Bind to Surface Receptors, Altering the Activity of Ion Channels, Transport Proteins, or Enzymes Inside Cells

Water soluble hormones include the amine and peptide hormones. The peptide hormones are amino acid based and range in length from as few as 3 amino acids to more than 200 amino acids. These hormones bind to receptor molecules in the plasma membrane and produce their responses by altering functional proteins already present in the cell, such as ion channels, transport proteins, and enzymes. In the first two cases, this can alter the flow of ions or other molecules across the cell membrane. In the latter case, it activates an intracellular signal transduction cascade that ultimately causes a cellular response (**Figure 43.4a**; and see Chapter 4). Typically, these signal transduction pathways involve enzymes that add phosphate groups to proteins (protein kinases). Adding a phosphate group to a protein may activate or inhibit it, depending on the protein (see Figures 4.22, 4.23, and 4.24). For instance, the peptide hormone glucagon binds to surface receptors on liver cells and triggers a series of steps leading to the phosphorylation and activation of the enzyme governing the breakdown of glycogen stored in those cells into glucose.

## 43.2b Hydrophobic Hormones Bind to Receptors Inside Cells, Activating or Inhibiting Genetic Regulatory Proteins

Lipid soluble hormones include the steroid and fatty acid hormones. These hormones must bind to water-soluble carrier proteins for transport in the blood or other fluids since they are not soluble in plasma. Once they contact their target cell they are released from their carrier protein and diffuse rapidly through the lipid bilayer of the plasma membrane. After passing through the plasma membrane, they bind to internal receptors in the nucleus or cytoplasm (Figure 43.4b). Binding of the hormone activates the receptor, which then binds to a control sequence of specific genes. Depending on the gene, binding the control sequence either activates or inhibits its transcription, leading to changes in protein synthesis that accomplishes the cellular response. The characteristics of the response depend on the specific genes controlled by the activated receptors and on the presence of other proteins that modify the activity of the receptor.

For instance, if blood pressure falls below optimal levels, the steroid hormone aldosterone is secreted by the adrenal glands. It circulates throughout the body in the blood but affects only cells

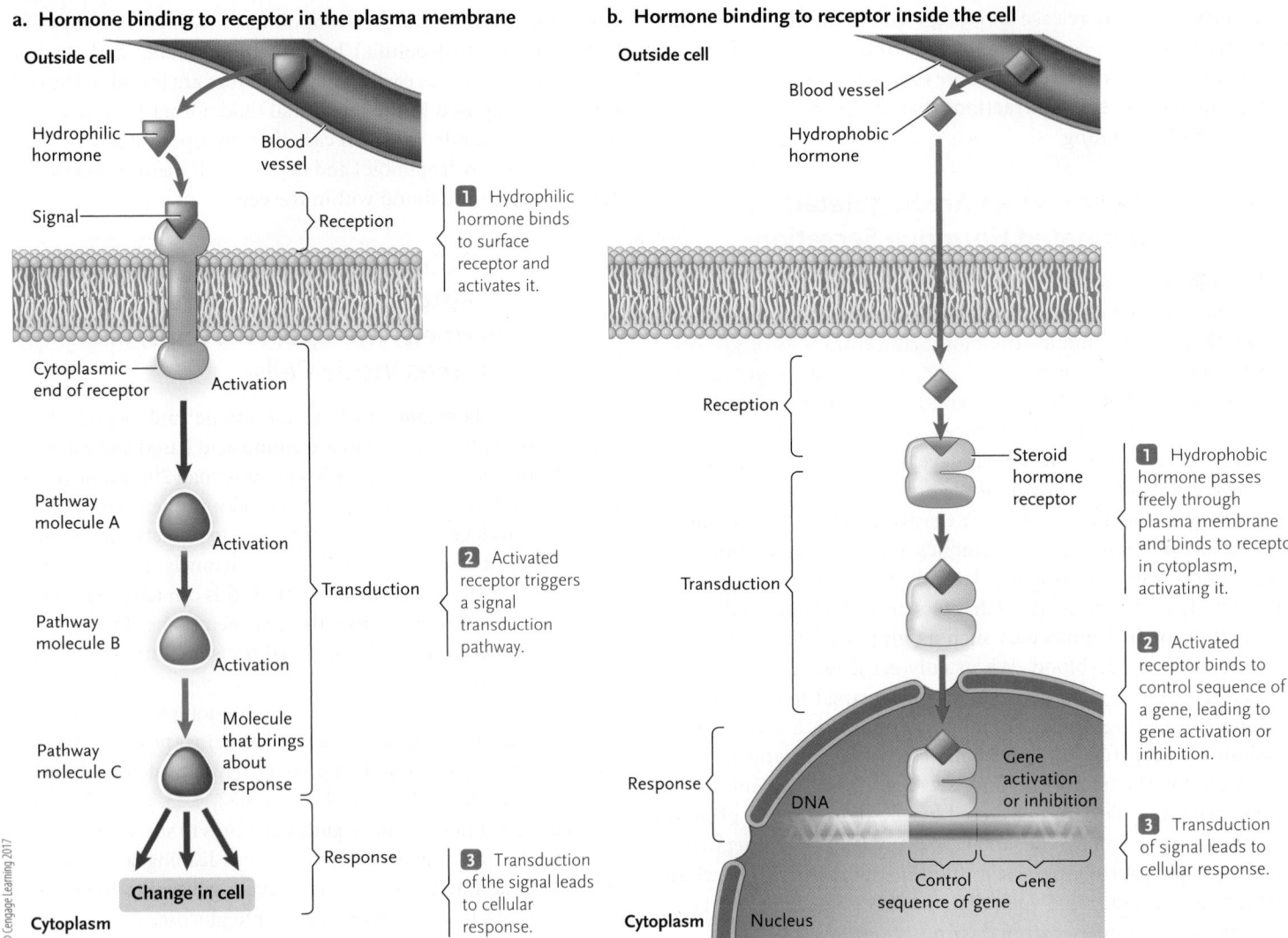

**a. Hormone binding to receptor in the plasma membrane**

Outside cell

Hydrophilic hormone

Blood vessel

Signal

Reception

**1** Hydrophilic hormone binds to surface receptor and activates it.

Cytoplasmic end of receptor — Activation

Pathway molecule A

Activation

Pathway molecule B

Transduction

**2** Activated receptor triggers a signal transduction pathway.

Activation

Pathway molecule C

Molecule that brings about response

Response

Change in cell

Response

**3** Transduction of the signal leads to cellular response.

Cytoplasm

© Cengage Learning 2017

**b. Hormone binding to receptor inside the cell**

Outside cell

Blood vessel

Hydrophobic hormone

Reception

Steroid hormone receptor

**1** Hydrophobic hormone passes freely through plasma membrane and binds to receptor in cytoplasm, activating it.

Transduction

**2** Activated receptor binds to control sequence of a gene, leading to gene activation or inhibition.

Response

DNA

Gene activation or inhibition

**3** Transduction of signal leads to cellular response.

Control sequence of gene

Gene

Cytoplasm    Nucleus

**FIGURE 43.4 The reaction pathways activated by hormones that bind to receptor proteins (a) in plasma membranes or (b) inside cells.** In both mechanisms, the signal—the binding of the hormone to its receptor—is transduced to produce the cellular response.

(mostly in the kidney) that contain the aldosterone receptor in their cytoplasm (step 1 in Figure 43.4b). When activated by aldosterone, the receptor binds to the control sequence of a gene (step 2 in Figure 43.4b), leading to the synthesis of membrane transport proteins that increase reabsorption of $Na^+$ by the kidney cells (step 3 in Figure 43.4b) (see also Chapter 42). The resulting increase in $Na^+$ concentration in body fluids increases water retention and, with it, blood volume. The increase in blood volume returns (increases) blood pressure back to normal, removing the stimulus for aldosterone secretion from the adrenal glands.

### 43.2c    Hormone Signals Are Amplified in Both Pathways

Small quantities of hormones can typically produce profound effects in cells and body functions due to **amplification**. In amplification, an activated receptor activates many proteins. Each of these in turn activates an even larger number of proteins

for the next step in the cellular pathway, and so on in each subsequent step (see Chapter 4, Figure 4.25). It has been estimated that, by amplification, a single molecule of epinephrine acting on a liver cell will liberate over 100 molecules of glucose from stored glycogen.

### 43.2d    Target Cells May Respond to More Than One Hormone, and Different Target Cells May Respond Differently to the Same Hormone

A single target cell may have receptors for several hormones and respond differently to each hormone. Vertebrate liver cells have receptors for the pancreatic hormones insulin and glucagon. Insulin increases glucose uptake and conversion to glycogen, which decreases blood glucose levels, whereas glucagon stimulates the breakdown of glycogen into glucose, which increases blood glucose levels **(Figure 43.5)**.

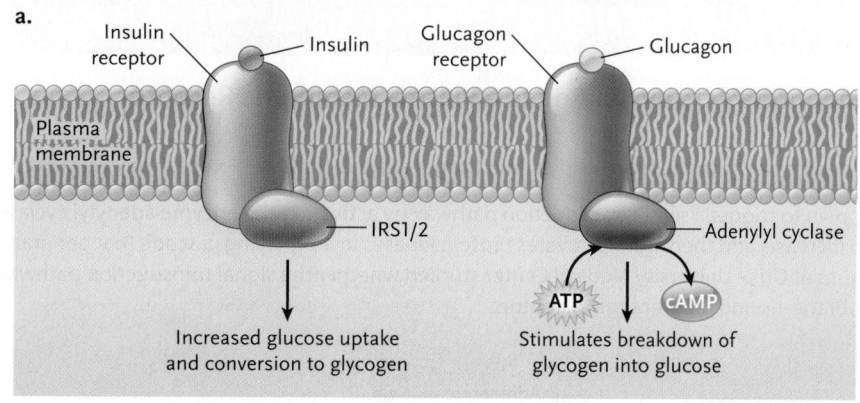

**a.**

Insulin receptor — Insulin

Glucagon receptor — Glucagon

Plasma membrane

IRS1/2

Adenylyl cyclase

ATP

cAMP

Increased glucose uptake and conversion to glycogen

Stimulates breakdown of glycogen into glucose

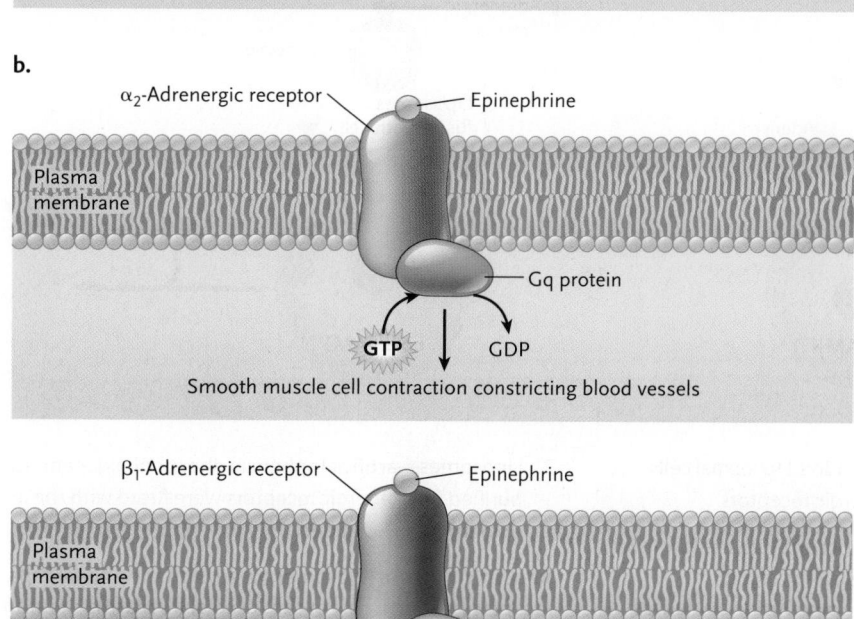

**b.**

α2-Adrenergic receptor — Epinephrine

Plasma membrane

Gq protein

GTP — GDP

Smooth muscle cell contraction constricting blood vessels

β1-Adrenergic receptor — Epinephrine

Plasma membrane

Gs protein

GTP — GDP

Cardiac cell contraction increasing heart rate

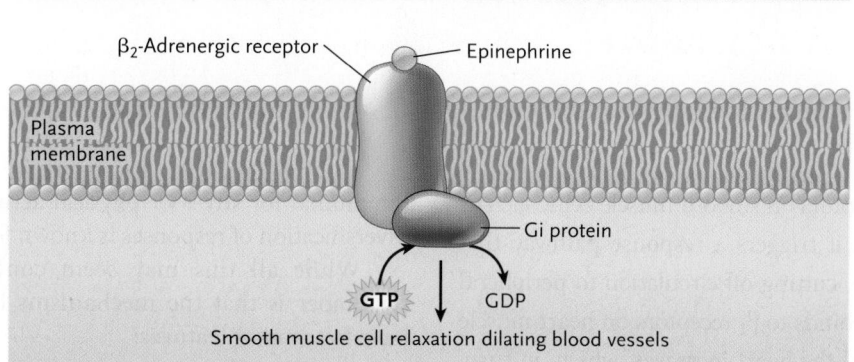

β2-Adrenergic receptor — Epinephrine

Plasma membrane

Gi protein

GTP — GDP

Smooth muscle cell relaxation dilating blood vessels

**FIGURE 43.5 (a)** Target cells may respond to more than one hormone, and **(b)** different target cells may respond differently to the same hormone.

Conversely, particular hormones interact with different types of receptors in or on a range of target cells. Different responses are then triggered in each target cell type because the receptors trigger different transduction pathways. For example, the amine hormone epinephrine prepares the body for handling stress (including dangerous situations) and physical activity. In mammals, epinephrine can bind to three different plasma membrane–embedded receptors: α, β1, and β2 receptors **(Figure 43.6)**. When

FIGURE 43.6    **Experimental Research**

## Demonstration That Epinephrine Acts by Binding to a Plasma Membrane Receptor

**Research Question:** How does epinephrine in the extracellular fluid trigger a signal transduction pathway within cells?

**Experiment:** Epinephrine is known to trigger a signal transduction pathway by activating the enzyme adenylyl cyclase. This causes the level of the second messenger cAMP to increase, and then cAMP activates protein kinases in a signalling cascade that generates a cellular response. Richard Cerione and his colleagues at Duke University Medical Center studied whether the signal transduction pathway was activated by the binding of epinephrine to membrane-bound β-adrenergic receptors.

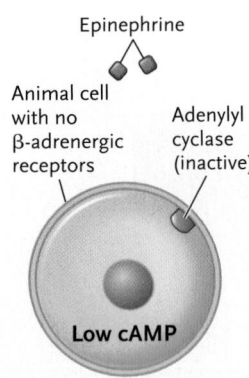

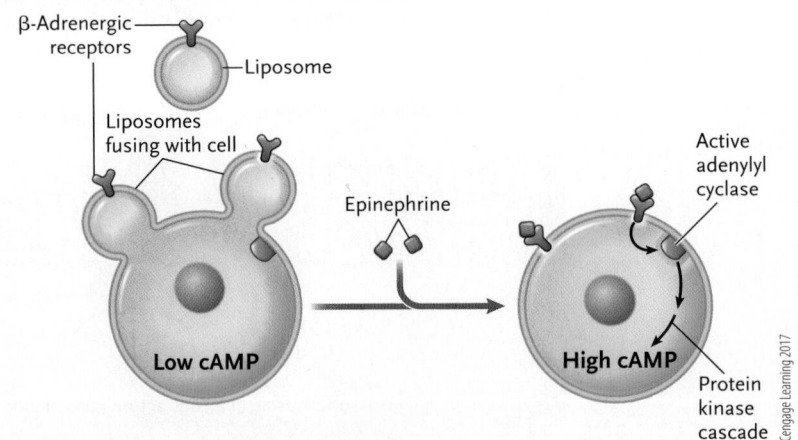

© Cengage Learning 2017

1.  Epinephrine was added to animal cells lacking β-adrenergic receptors.

    **Result:** No change occurred to the low level of cAMP in those cells. This result demonstrated that epinephrine alone was not able to trigger an increase in cAMP.

2.  Liposomes—artificial spherical phospholipid membranes—containing purified β-adrenergic receptors were fused with the animal cells, and then epinephrine was added.

    **Result:** When the liposomes fused with the animal cells, β-adrenergic receptors became part of the fused cell's plasma membrane. Then, adding epinephrine triggered synthesis of cAMP, resulting in high levels of cAMP in the cells. This result demonstrated that β-adrenergic receptors must be present in the membrane for epinephrine to activate adenylyl cyclase within the cell.

**Conclusion:** The cellular response depended on binding of the hydrophilic hormone to a specific plasma membrane-embedded receptor.

epinephrine binds to α receptors on smooth muscle cells, such as those of the blood vessels, it triggers a response pathway that causes the cells to constrict, cutting off circulation to peripheral organs. When epinephrine binds to $\beta_1$ receptors on heart muscle cells, the contraction rate of the heart increases, which, in turn, enhances blood supply. When epinephrine binds to $\beta_2$ receptors on liver cells, it stimulates the breakdown of glycogen to glucose, which is released from the cell. The overall effect of these and a number of other responses to epinephrine secretion is to supply energy to the major muscles responsible for locomotion, preparing

the animal for stress or physical activity. Similar tissue-specific diversification of responses is known for many hormones.

While all this may seem confusing, the key thing to remember is that the mechanisms by which hormones work have four major features:

1.  Only cells that contain surface or internal receptors for a particular hormone (target cells) respond to that hormone.
2.  Once bound by their receptors, hormones produce a wide variety of responses. These may involve stimulation or inhibition of cellular processes, depending on the specific types of internal molecules activated by the hormone.

3. Because of the amplification that occurs through both the surface and the internal receptor mechanisms, hormones are effective in very small concentrations.
4. The response to any hormone may differ among target cells.

In the next two sections, we discuss the major endocrine cells and glands of vertebrates. The locations of these cells and glands in mammals (including humans) and their functions are summarized in **Figure 43.7** and **Table 43.1**. The sections that follow provide more specific details.

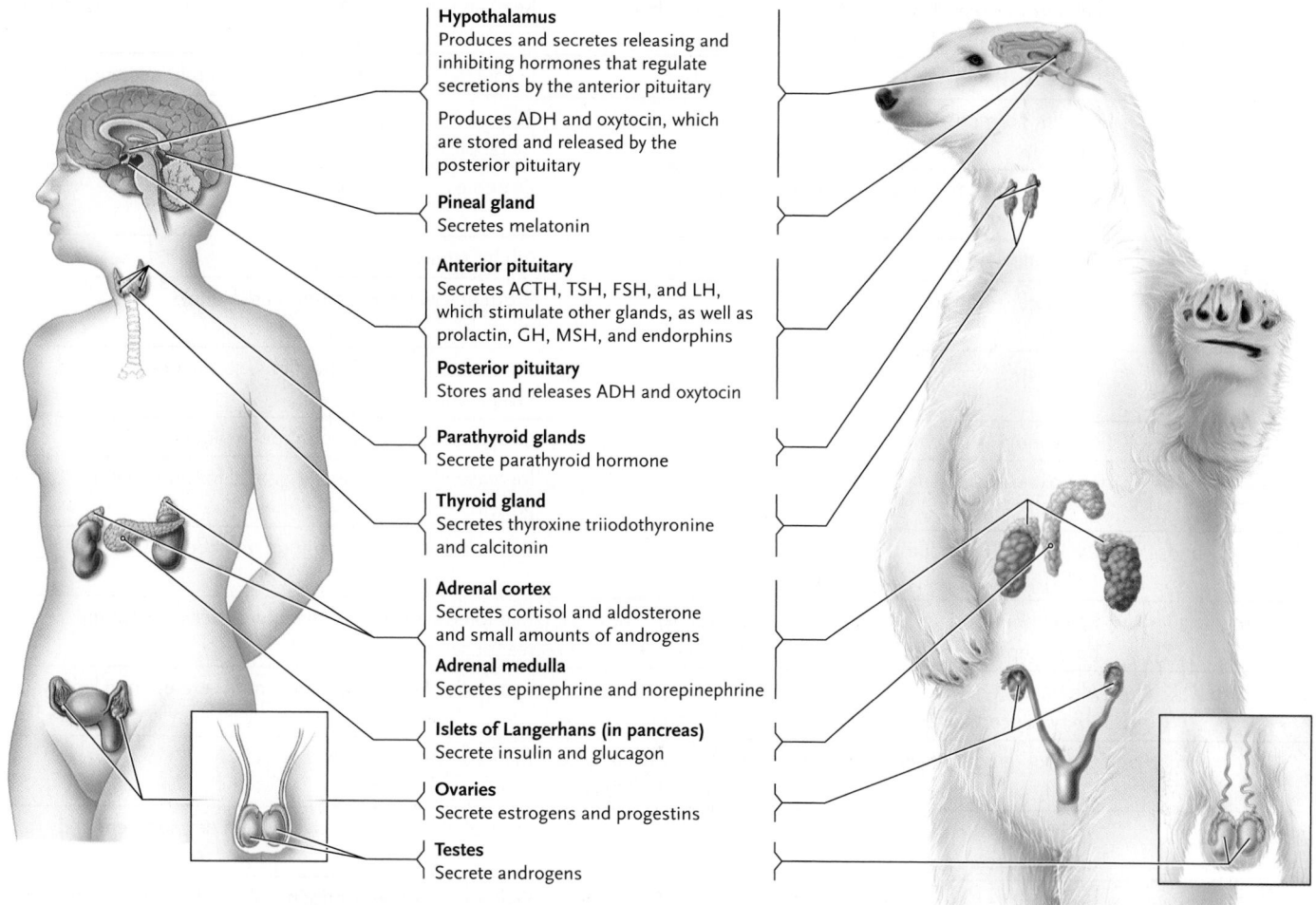

**Hypothalamus**
Produces and secretes releasing and inhibiting hormones that regulate secretions by the anterior pituitary

Produces ADH and oxytocin, which are stored and released by the posterior pituitary

**Pineal gland**
Secretes melatonin

**Anterior pituitary**
Secretes ACTH, TSH, FSH, and LH, which stimulate other glands, as well as prolactin, GH, MSH, and endorphins

**Posterior pituitary**
Stores and releases ADH and oxytocin

**Parathyroid glands**
Secrete parathyroid hormone

**Thyroid gland**
Secretes thyroxine triiodothyronine and calcitonin

**Adrenal cortex**
Secretes cortisol and aldosterone and small amounts of androgens

**Adrenal medulla**
Secretes epinephrine and norepinephrine

**Islets of Langerhans (in pancreas)**
Secrete insulin and glucagon

**Ovaries**
Secrete estrogens and progestins

**Testes**
Secrete androgens

© Cengage Learning 2017

**FIGURE 43.7** **This diagram shows the major endocrine glands in a mammal's body, using a human and a bear as models.**

| TABLE 43.1 | The Major Human Endocrine Glands and Hormones | | |
|---|---|---|---|
| Secretory Tissue or Gland | Hormones | Target Tissue | Principal Actions |
| Hypothalamus | Releasing and inhibiting hormones | Anterior pituitary | Regulate secretion of anterior pituitary hormones |
| Anterior pituitary | Thyroid-stimulating hormone (TSH) | Thyroid gland | Stimulates secretion of thyroid hormones |
| | Adrenocorticotropic hormone (ACTH) | Adrenal cortex | Stimulates secretion of glucocorticoids by adrenal cortex |

*(Continued)*

**TABLE 43.1** | **The Major Human Endocrine Glands and Hormones (*Continued*)**

| Secretory Tissue or Gland | Hormones | Target Tissue | Principal Actions |
|---|---|---|---|
| | Follicle-stimulating hormone (FSH) | Ovaries in females, testes in males | Stimulates egg growth, secretion of female sex hormones, sperm production |
| | Luteinizing hormone (LH) | Ovaries in females, testes in males | Regulates ovulation and secretion of male sex hormones |
| | Prolactin (PRL) | Mammary glands | Stimulates breast development and milk secretion |
| | Growth hormone (GH) | Bone, soft tissue | Stimulates bone growth; helps control metabolism |
| | Melanocyte-stimulating hormone (MSH) | Melanocytes in skin of some vertebrates | Promotes darkening of the skin |
| | Endorphins | Pain pathways of PNS | Inhibit perception of pain |
| Posterior pituitary | Antidiuretic hormone (ADH) | Kidneys | Promotes water reabsorption in kidneys |
| | Oxytocin | Uterus, mammary glands | Promotes uterine contractions; stimulates milk production and secretion |
| Thyroid gland | Calcitonin | Bone | Lowers calcium concentration in blood |
| | Thyroxine and triiodothyronine | Most cells | Increase metabolic rate; essential for normal body growth |
| Parathyroid glands | Parathyroid hormone (PTH) | Bone, kidneys, intestine | Raises calcium concentration in blood |
| Adrenal medulla | Epinephrine and norepinephrine | Sympathetic receptor sites throughout body | Reinforce sympathetic nervous system; contribute to responses to stress |
| Adrenal cortex | Aldosterone (mineralocorticoid) | Kidney tubules | Increases Na$^+$ reabsorption and K$^+$ excretion in kidneys |
| | Cortisol (glucocorticoid) | Most body cells, particularly muscle, liver, and adipose cells | Increases blood glucose levels |
| Testes | Androgens, such as testosterone[a] | Various tissues | Control male reproductive system development and maintenance |
| | Oxytocin | Uterus | Promotes uterine contractions |
| Ovaries | Estrogens, such as estradiol[b] | Breast, uterus, other tissues | Stimulate maturation of sex organs at puberty, and development of secondary sexual characteristics |
| | Prolactins, such as progesterone[b] | Uterus | Prepare and maintain uterine lining |
| Pancreas (islets of Langerhans) | Glucagon (alpha cells) | Liver cells | Raises glucose concentration in blood |
| | Insulin (beta cells) | Most cells | Lowers glucose concentration in blood |
| Pineal gland | Melatonin | Brain, anterior pituitary, reproductive organs, immune system, possibly others | Helps synchronize body's biological clock with day length |
| Many cell types | Growth factors | Most cells | Regulate cell division and differentiation |
| | Prostaglandins | Various tissues | Have many diverse roles |

[a] Small amounts also secreted by ovaries and adrenal cortex.
[b] Small amounts also secreted by testes.
In addition to these major endocrine organs, important hormones are also secreted by organs that have other primary functions, including the kidney, heart, liver, and intestine. In particular, the digestive system is the source of several peptide hormones, many of which are also produced elsewhere. The gut is increasingly recognized as an important endocrine organ in many animals. Among vertebrates, it is a more important source for circulating levels of melatonin than the pineal body with which that hormone is traditionally associated.

## STUDY BREAK QUESTIONS

1. What are the four major features of the mechanism by which hormones work?
2. Explain how one type of target cell could respond to different hormones, and how the same hormone could produce different effects in different cells.
3. Explain how a small amount of hormone can produce very large responses.

# 43.3 The Hypothalamus and Pituitary

Hormones of vertebrates are released in response to sensory information about both the external and the internal environment. Some sensory signals communicate directly with various endocrine glands, but many are processed in the brain and communicate with the endocrine system through the hypothalamus and pituitary gland.

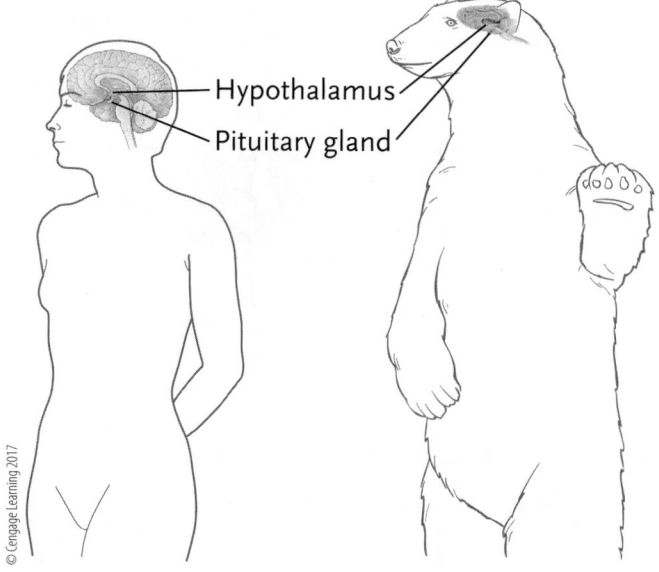

The hypothalamus is a region of the brain located in the floor of the cerebrum (see Chapter 45). The **pituitary** is suspended just below the hypothalamus by a slender stalk of tissue that contains both neurons and blood vessels **(Figure 43.8)**. The pituitary consists of two lobes that have different embryonic origins and different functions. The **anterior pituitary** develops from epithelial cells from the roof of the mouth. It does not contain neurons and its connection to the hypothalamus is via the circulation. The **posterior pituitary** develops from neural tissue at the base of the brain. As a result, it contains axons and endings of neurosecretory neurons that originate in the hypothalamus.

## 43.3a The Anterior Pituitary Secretes Eight Hormones

The secretions of the anterior pituitary are under the control of peptide neurohormones, called **releasing hormones (RHs)** and **inhibiting hormones (IHs)**, produced by the hypothalamus. These neurohormones are carried in the blood to the anterior pituitary in a **portal vein**, a special vein that connects the capillaries of the two structures. The portal vein ensures that the blood flow to the anterior pituitary comes directly from the hypothalamus (Figure 43.8). The RHs and IHs regulate the anterior pituitary's secretion of eight hormones.

Four of the major hormones secreted by the anterior pituitary control endocrine glands elsewhere in the body. **Thyroid-stimulating hormone (TSH)** stimulates the thyroid gland to grow in size and secrete thyroid hormones (see Section 43.4a). **Adrenocorticotropic hormone (ACTH)** triggers hormone secretion by cells in the adrenal cortex (see Section 43.4d). **Follicle-stimulating hormone (FSH)** controls egg development and the secretion of sex hormones in female mammals, and sperm production in males. **Luteinizing hormone (LH)** regulates part of the menstrual cycle in human females and the secretion of sex hormones in males. FSH and LH are grouped together as **gonadotropins** because they regulate the activity of the gonads (ovaries and testes). The roles of the gonadotropins and sex hormones in the reproductive cycle are described in Chapter 44.

Two other major hormones secreted by the anterior pituitary are prolactin and growth hormone. **Prolactin (PRL)** influences reproductive activities and parental care in vertebrates. In mammals, PRL stimulates development of the secretory cells of mammary glands during late pregnancy, and stimulates milk synthesis after a female mammal gives birth. Stimulation of the mammary glands and the nipples, as occurs during suckling, leads to PRL release. PRL occurs in non-mammalian vertebrates, where it has a variety of functions. In fish, for example, it is among the hormones controlling water balance. In all vertebrates, it has a role in promoting both maternal and paternal behaviour.

**Growth hormone (GH)** stimulates cell division, protein synthesis, and bone growth in children and adolescents, thereby causing body growth. GH also stimulates protein synthesis and cell division in adults. For these actions, GH binds to target tissues, mostly liver cells, causing them to release **insulin-like growth factor (IGF)**, a peptide that directly stimulates growth processes. GH also controls a number of major metabolic processes in mammals of all ages, including the conversion of glycogen to glucose and fats to fatty acids as a means of regulating their levels in the blood. In addition, GH stimulates body cells to take up fatty acids and amino acids and limits the rate at which muscle cells take up glucose. These actions help maintain the availability of glucose and fatty acids to tissues and organs between feedings; this is

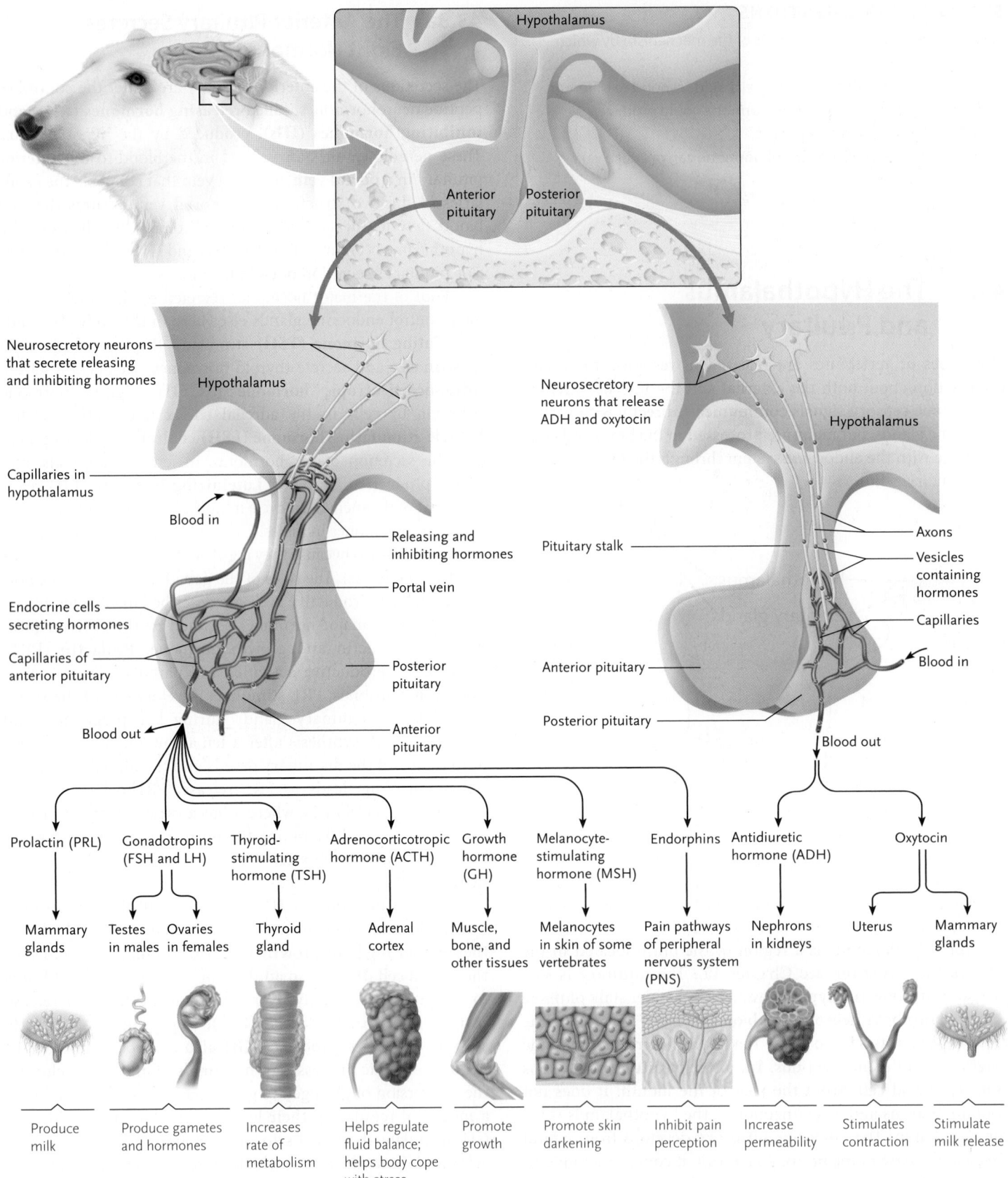

**FIGURE 43.8 The hypothalamus and pituitary.** Hormones secreted by the anterior and posterior pituitary are controlled by neurohormones released in the hypothalamus.

**FIGURE 43.9 The results of overproduction and underproduction of growth hormone by the anterior pituitary.** The man on the left is of normal height. The man in the centre is a pituitary giant whose pituitary produced excess GH during childhood and adolescence. The man on the right is a pituitary dwarf whose pituitary produced too little GH.

particularly important for the brain. In humans, deficiencies in GH secretion during childhood produce pituitary dwarfs, who remain small in stature through childhood and into adulthood **(Figure 43.9)**. Overproduction of GH during childhood or adolescence, often due to a tumour of the anterior pituitary, produces pituitary giants, who may grow above 2.4 m in height.

**Melanocyte-stimulating hormone (MSH)** and **endorphins** are also secreted by the anterior pituitary. MSH is named because of its effect in some vertebrates on melanocytes, skin cells that contain the black pigment melanin. An increase in secretion of MSH produces a marked darkening of the skin of fishes, amphibians, and reptiles. The darkening is produced by a dispersal of melanin in melanocytes so that it covers a greater area. In humans, an increase in MSH secretion also causes skin darkening, although the effect is by no means as obvious as in the other vertebrates mentioned.

Endorphins are another peptide hormone produced by the anterior pituitary. In the peripheral nervous system (PNS), endorphins act as neurotransmitters in pathways that control pain, thereby inhibiting the perception of pain. Hence, endorphins are often called *natural painkillers*.

## 43.3b The Posterior Pituitary Secretes Two Hormones

The neurosecretory neurons in the posterior pituitary secrete two peptide hormones, antidiuretic hormone and oxytocin, directly into the body circulation (see Figure 43.8). These hormones are produced in the hypothalamus and released from the terminals of the neurosecretory neurons in the posterior pituitary.

**Antidiuretic hormone** (**ADH**; also known as *vasopressin*) stimulates kidney cells to absorb more water from urine, thereby increasing the volume of the blood. The hormone is released when sensory receptor cells of the hypothalamus detect an increase in the blood's $Na^+$ concentration during periods of dehydration or after a salty meal. Ethyl alcohol and caffeine inhibit ADH secretion, explaining in part why alcoholic drinks and coffee increase the volume of urine excreted. Nicotine and emotional stress, in contrast, stimulate ADH secretion and water retention. After severe stress is relieved, the return to normal ADH secretion often makes a trip to the bathroom among our most pressing needs. The hypothalamus also releases a flood of ADH when an injury results in heavy blood loss, or when some other event triggers a severe drop in blood pressure. ADH helps maintain blood pressure by reducing water loss and by causing small blood vessels in some tissues to constrict.

Hormones with structure and action similar to those of ADH are also secreted in fishes, amphibians, reptiles, and birds. In amphibians, these ADH-like hormones increase the amount of water entering the body through the skin and from the urinary bladder.

**Oxytocin** stimulates the ejection of milk from the mammary glands of a nursing mother. Stimulation of the nipples in suckling sends neuronal signals to the hypothalamus and leads to the release of oxytocin from the posterior pituitary. The released oxytocin stimulates more oxytocin secretion by a positive feedback mechanism. Oxytocin causes the smooth muscle cells surrounding the mammary glands to contract, forcibly expelling the milk through the nipples. The entire cycle, from the onset of suckling to milk ejection, takes less than a minute in mammals. Oxytocin also plays a key role in childbirth (see Chapter 44).

In males, oxytocin is secreted into the seminal fluid by the testes. When the seminal fluid is ejaculated into the vagina during sexual intercourse, the hormone stimulates contractions of the uterus that aid movement of sperm through the female reproductive tract.

### STUDY BREAK QUESTIONS

1. Distinguish between the anterior and the posterior pituitary. How is the release of hormones from each of these controlled?
2. Which hormones released by the anterior pituitary act on other endocrine glands, and which ones act on tissues directly?

# 43.4 Other Major Endocrine Glands of Vertebrates

In addition to the hypothalamus and pituitary, the body has seven major endocrine glands or tissues, many of them regulated by the hypothalamus–pituitary connection. Included are the thyroid gland, parathyroid glands, adrenal medulla, adrenal cortex, gonads, pancreas, and pineal gland (shown in Figure 43.7, and summarized in Table 43.1).

## 43.4a The Thyroid Hormones Stimulate Metabolism, Development, and Maturation

The **thyroid gland,** located in the front of the throat in all terrestrial vertebrates, including humans, secretes hormones with an extraordinarily wide range of effects. The primary thyroid hormone, **thyroxine,** is known as $T_4$ because it contains four iodine atoms. The thyroid also secretes smaller amounts of a closely related hormone, **triiodothyronine ($T_3$),** which contains three iodine atoms. Normally, their concentrations are kept at finely balanced levels in the blood by negative feedback loops such as the loop described in Figure 43.3.

These hormones are hydrophobic and thus most of the circulating hormone is bound to a transport protein, thyroglobulin, and only the free hormone is available to enter cells. Once inside a cell, the $T_4$ is deiodinated, forming $T_3$, the form that combines with internal receptors in the nucleus, altering gene expression, which brings about many of the hormone's effects.

Thyroid hormones are vital to growth, development, maturation, and metabolism in all vertebrates. They interact with GH for their effects on growth and development. The release of too much thyroid hormone (hyperthyroidism) elevates metabolic rate, leading to increased appetite and weight loss. Too little thyroid hormone (hypothyroidism) produces a reduced metabolic state, creating fatigue and sluggishness.

Insufficient iodine in the diet can cause goitre, enlargement of the thyroid. Without iodine, the thyroid cannot make $T_3$ and $T_4$ in response to stimulation by TSH. Because the thyroid hormone concentration remains low in the blood, TSH continues to be secreted, and the thyroid grows in size. Dietary iodine deficiency has been eliminated in developed regions of the world by the addition of iodine to table salt.

In amphibians, rising concentrations of thyroid hormones trigger **metamorphosis,** or a change in body form from tadpole to adult **(Figure 43.10).** Teleost fish undergo a form of metamorphosis during their early development, and the transformation from a hatchling larval form to a juvenile form is also triggered by rising concentrations of thyroid hormones. Thyroid hormones also contribute to seasonal moulting, leading to changes in the plumage of birds and coat colour in mammals.

The thyroid also has specialized cells that secrete **calcitonin,** a peptide originally discovered in fish by Harold Copp, working at the University of British Columbia. The hormone lowers the level of $Ca^{2+}$ in the blood by inhibiting the ongoing dissolution of calcium from bone. Calcitonin secretion is stimulated when $Ca^{2+}$ levels in blood rise above the normal range, and inhibited when $Ca^{2+}$ levels fall below the normal range. Calcitonin is also synthesized in the lung and intestine. In non-mammalian vertebrates, a separate gland, the ultimobranchial gland, produces calcitonin.

Thyroid gland

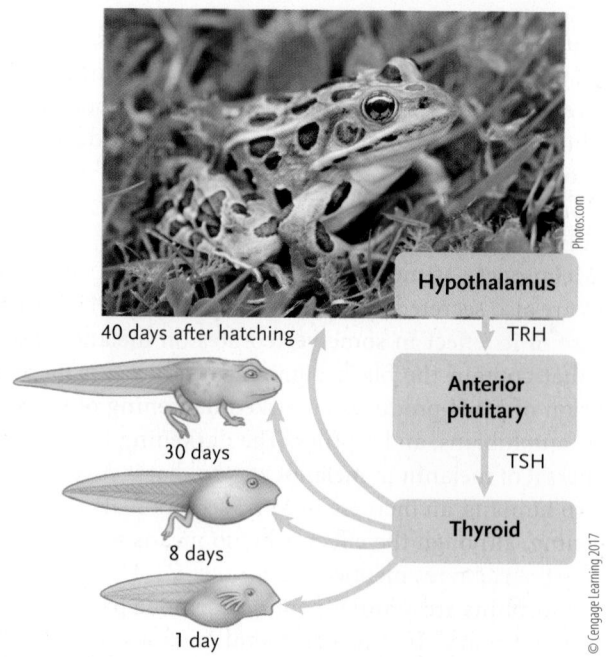

**FIGURE 43.10 Metamorphosis of a tadpole into an adult frog, under the control of thyroid hormones.** As part of the metamorphosis, changes in gene activity lead to a change from an aquatic to a terrestrial habitat. TRH = thyroid-releasing hormone; TSH = thyroid-stimulating hormone.

## 43.4b The Parathyroid Glands Regulate Ca²⁺ Levels in the Blood

The **parathyroid glands** occur only in tetrapod vertebrates (amphibians, reptiles, birds, and mammals). Each is a spherical structure about the size of a pea. Mammals have four parathyroids located on the posterior surface of the thyroid gland, two on each side. The **parathyroid hormone (PTH),** is secreted in response to a fall in blood Ca²⁺ levels. PTH stimulates bone cells to dissolve the mineral matter of bone tissues, releasing both calcium and phosphate ions into the blood. The released Ca²⁺ is available for enzyme activation, conduction of nerve signals across synapses, muscle contraction, blood clotting, and other uses. How blood Ca²⁺ levels control PTH and calcitonin secretion is shown in **Figure 43.11.**

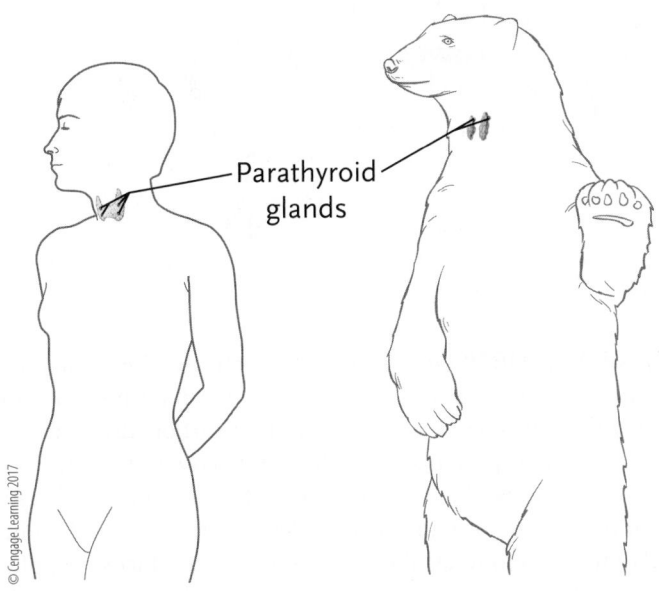

PTH also stimulates enzymes in the kidneys that convert **vitamin D,** a steroidlike molecule, into its fully active form in the body. The activated vitamin D increases the absorption of Ca²⁺ and phosphates from ingested food by promoting the synthesis of a calcium-binding protein in the intestine. It also increases the release of Ca²⁺ from bone in response to PTH.

PTH underproduction causes Ca²⁺ concentration to fall steadily in the blood, disturbing nerve and muscle function—the muscles twitch and contract uncontrollably, and convulsions and cramps occur. Without treatment, the condition is usually fatal because the severe muscular contractions, particularly of the muscles of the abdomen and thorax, interfere with breathing. Overproduction of PTH results in the loss of so much calcium from the bones that they become thin and fragile. At the same time, the elevated Ca²⁺ concentration in the blood causes calcium deposits to form in soft tissues, especially in the lungs, arteries, and kidneys (where the deposits form kidney stones).

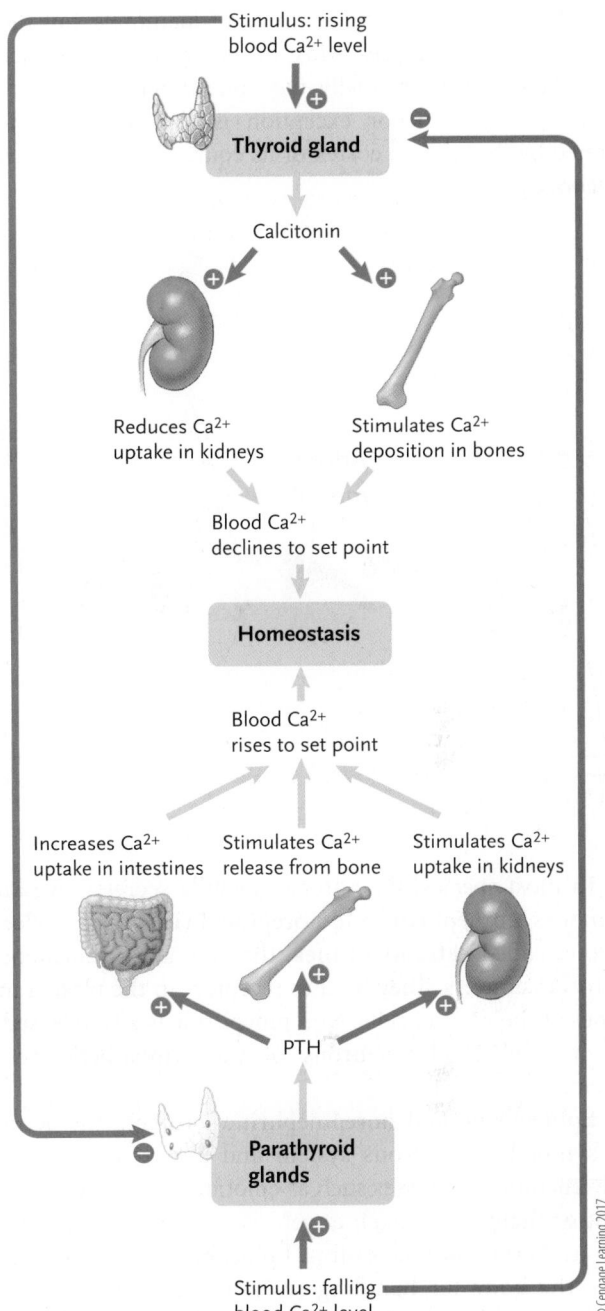

**FIGURE 43.11 Negative feedback control of PTH and calcitonin secretion by blood Ca²⁺ levels**

## 43.4c The Adrenal Medulla Releases Two Fight-or-Flight Hormones

The adrenal glands (*ad* = next to; *renes* = kidneys) of mammals have two distinct regions. The central region, the **adrenal medulla,** contains highly modified neurosecretory neurons that have lost their axons and dendrites. The tissue surrounding it, the **adrenal cortex,** contains non-neural endocrine cells. The two regions secrete hormones with entirely different functions. Non-mammalian vertebrates have glands equivalent to the adrenal medulla and adrenal cortex of mammals, but the two parts are separate entities. Most of the hormones produced by these glands have essentially the same functions in all vertebrates. The only major exception is aldosterone, which is secreted by the adrenal cortex or its equivalent only in tetrapod vertebrates.

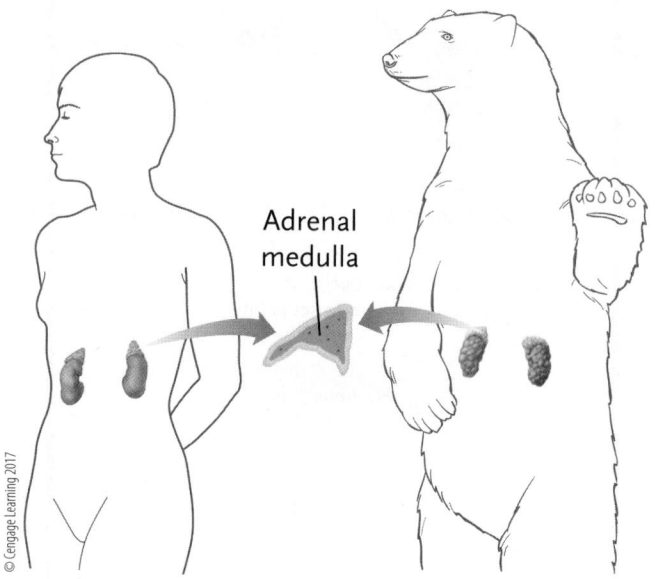

In most species, the adrenal medulla secretes two amine hormones, **epinephrine** and **norepinephrine,** which belong to a group called **catecholamines,** that can act as hormones or neurotransmitters. They bind to receptors in the plasma membranes of their target cells. Norepinephrine is also released as a neurotransmitter by neurons of the sympathetic nervous system.

Epinephrine and norepinephrine reinforce the action of the sympathetic nervous system and are secreted when the body encounters stresses such as emotional excitement, danger (fight-or-flight situations), anger, fear, infections, injury, and even midterm and final exams. Epinephrine in particular prepares the body for handling stress or physical activity. The heart rate increases. Glycogen and fats break down, releasing glucose and fatty acids into the blood as fuel molecules. In the heart, skeletal muscles, and lungs, the blood vessels dilate to increase blood flow. Elsewhere in the body, the blood vessels constrict, reducing blood flow to the intestine and kidneys and inhibiting smooth muscle contractions, which reduces water loss and slows down the digestive system. Airways in the lungs also dilate, helping to increase the flow of air.

The effects of norepinephrine on heart rate, blood pressure, and blood flow to the heart muscle are similar to those of epinephrine. However, in contrast to epinephrine, norepinephrine causes blood vessels in skeletal muscles to constrict. This contrary effect is largely cancelled out because epinephrine is secreted in much greater quantities.

## 43.4d The Adrenal Cortex Secretes Two Groups of Steroid Hormones

The adrenal cortex of mammals secretes two major classes of steroid hormones: **glucocorticoids** help maintain the blood concentration of glucose and other fuel molecules, and **mineralocorticoids** regulate the levels of Na$^+$ and K$^+$ ions in the blood and extracellular fluid.

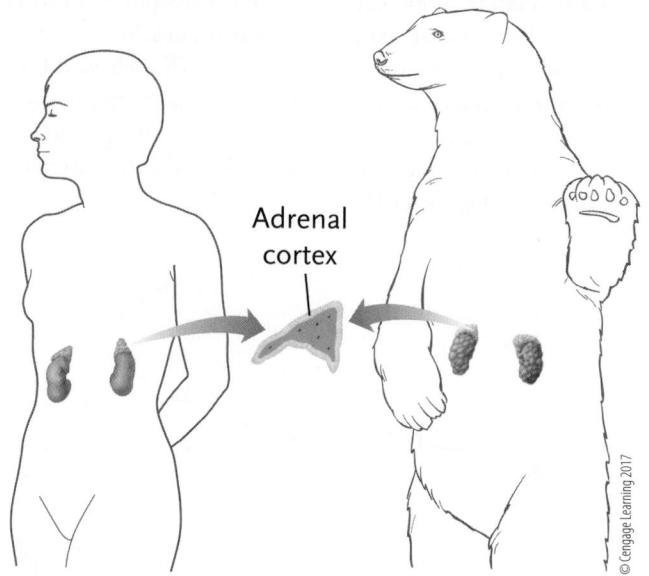

**THE GLUCOCORTICOIDS** The glucocorticoids help maintain glucose levels in the blood by three major mechanisms: (1) stimulating the synthesis of glucose from non-carbohydrate sources such as fats and proteins; (2) reducing glucose uptake by body cells, except those in the CNS; and (3) promoting the breakdown of fats and proteins, which releases fatty acids and amino acids into the blood as alternative fuels when glucose supplies are low. The favouring of glucose uptake in the CNS keeps the brain well supplied with glucose between meals and during periods of extended fasting. **Cortisol** is the major glucocorticoid secreted by the adrenal cortex.

Secretion of glucocorticoids is ultimately under the control of the hypothalamus **(Figure 43.12)**. Low glucose concentrations in the blood, or elevated levels of epinephrine secreted by the adrenal medulla in response to stress, are detected in the hypothalamus, leading to secretion of the hormone ACTH by the anterior pituitary. ACTH promotes the secretion of glucocorticoids by the adrenal cortex.

Glucocorticoids also have anti-inflammatory properties; consequently, they are used to treat conditions such as arthritis and dermatitis. They also suppress the immune system and are used in the treatment of autoimmune diseases such as rheumatoid arthritis.

**THE MINERALOCORTICOIDS** In tetrapods, the mineralocorticoids, primarily **aldosterone,** increase the amount of Na$^+$

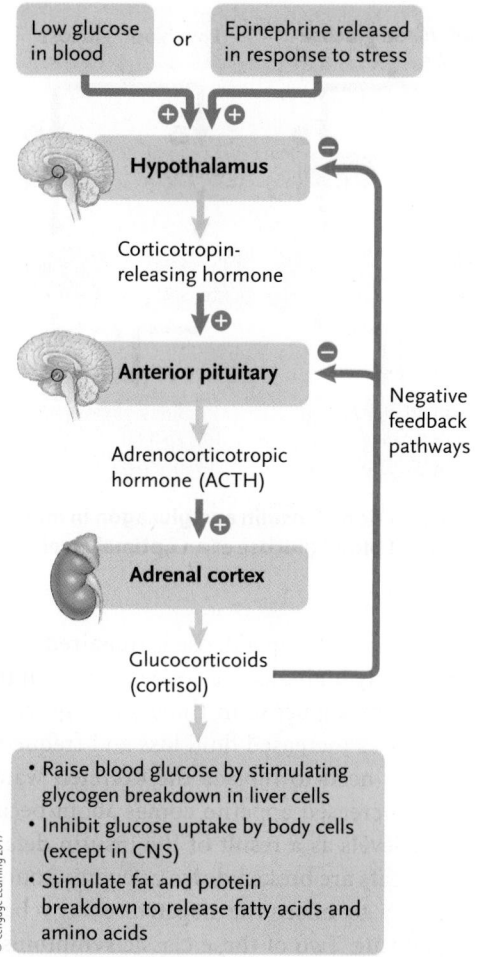

FIGURE 43.12 **Pathways linking secretion of glucocorticoids to low blood sugar and epinephrine secretion in response to stress**

reabsorbed from the urine in the kidneys and absorbed from foods in the intestine. They also reduce the amount of Na⁺ secreted by salivary and sweat glands and increase the rate of K⁺ excretion by the kidneys. The net effect is to keep Na⁺ and K⁺ balanced at the levels required for normal cellular functions, including those of the nervous system. Secretion of aldosterone is linked tightly to blood volume and indirectly to blood pressure.

## 43.4e The Gonadal Sex Hormones Regulate the Development of Reproductive Systems, Sexual Characteristics, and Mating Behaviour

The **gonads,** the testes and ovaries, are the primary source of sex hormones in vertebrates. The steroid hormones they produce, the **androgens, estrogens,** and **progestins,** have similar functions in regulating the development of male and female reproductive systems, sexual characteristics, and mating behaviour. Both males and females produce all three types of hormones, but in different proportions. Androgen production is predominant in males, whereas estrogen and progestin production is predominant in females. An outline of the actions of these hormones is presented here; a more complete picture is given in Chapter 44.

The **testes** (singular, testis) of male vertebrates secrete androgens, steroid hormones that stimulate and control the development and maintenance of male reproductive systems. The principal androgen is testosterone, the male sex hormone. In young adult males, a jump in **testosterone** levels stimulates puberty and the development of secondary sexual characteristics, including the growth of facial and body hair, muscle development, changes in vocal cord morphology, and development of normal sex drive. The synthesis and secretion of testosterone by cells in the testes are controlled by the release of LH from the anterior pituitary, which in turn is controlled by **gonadotropin-releasing hormone (GnRH),** a hormone secreted by the hypothalamus.

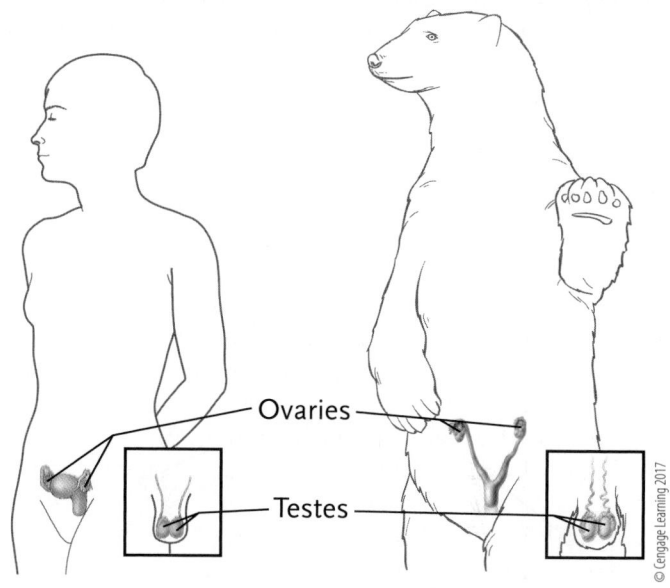

Androgens are natural types of **anabolic steroids,** hormones that stimulate muscle development. Natural and synthetic anabolic steroids have been in the news over the years because of their use by bodybuilders and other athletes from sports in which muscular strength is important.

The **ovaries** of females produce estrogens, steroid hormones that stimulate and control the development and maintenance of female reproductive systems. The principal estrogen is **estradiol,** which stimulates maturation of sex organs at puberty and the development of secondary sexual characteristics. Ovaries also produce progestins, principally **progesterone,** the steroid hormone that prepares and maintains the uterus for implantation of a fertilized egg and the subsequent growth and development of an embryo. The synthesis and secretion of progesterone by cells in the ovaries are controlled by the release of FSH from the anterior pituitary, which in turn is controlled by the same GnRH as in males.

## 43.4f   The Pancreatic Islets of Langerhans Hormones Regulate Glucose Metabolism

Most of the **pancreas,** a relatively large gland located just behind the stomach, forms an exocrine gland that secretes digestive enzymes into the small intestine (see Chapter 39). About 2% of the cells in the pancreas are endocrine cells that form the **islets of Langerhans.** Found in all vertebrates, the islets secrete the peptide hormones insulin and glucagon into the bloodstream.

Insulin and glucagon regulate the metabolism of fuel substances in the body. **Insulin** is secreted by beta cells in the islets. It acts mainly on nonworking skeletal muscles, liver cells, and adipose tissue (fat). Brain cells do not require insulin for glucose uptake. Insulin lowers blood glucose, fatty acid, and amino acid levels and promotes their storage. The actions of insulin include stimulation of glucose transport into cells, glycogen synthesis from glucose, uptake of fatty acids by adipose tissue cells, fat synthesis from fatty acids, and protein synthesis from amino acids. Insulin inhibits glycogen degradation to glucose, fat degradation to fatty acids, and protein degradation to amino acids.

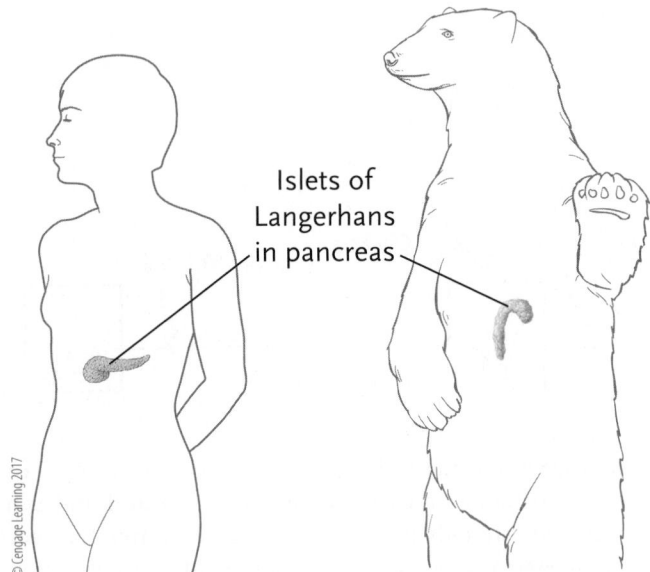

Islets of Langerhans in pancreas

**Glucagon,** secreted by alpha cells in the islets, has effects opposite to those of insulin: it stimulates glycogen, fat, and protein degradation. Glucagon also results in amino acids and other non-carbohydrates being used for glucose synthesis; this aspect of glucagon function operates during fasting. Negative feedback mechanisms keyed to the concentration of glucose in the blood control secretion of both insulin and glucagon to maintain glucose homeostasis **(Figure 43.13).**

**Diabetes mellitus,** a disease that afflicts more than 2 million people in Canada and at least 200 million worldwide, results from problems with insulin production or action. The three classic diabetes symptoms are frequent urination, increased thirst (and consequently increased fluid intake), and increased appetite. Frequent urination occurs because the

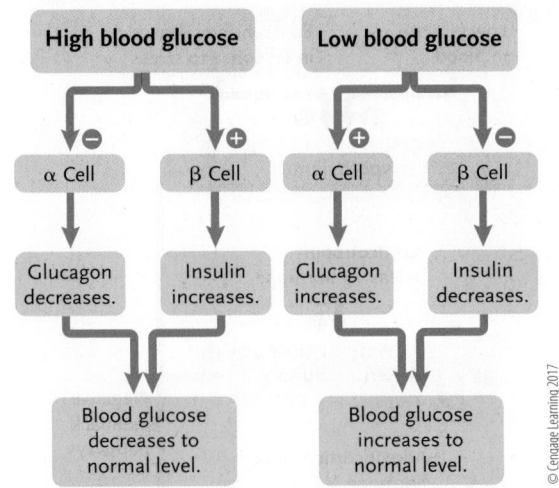

**FIGURE 43.13  The action of insulin and glucagon in maintaining the concentration of blood glucose at an optimal level**

ability of body cells to take up glucose is impaired in diabetics, leading to abnormally high glucose concentration in the blood. Excretion of the excess glucose in the urine requires water to carry it, which causes increased fluid loss and frequent trips to the bathroom. The need to replace the excreted water causes increased thirst. Increased appetite comes about because cells have low glucose levels as a result of the insulin defect; therefore, proteins and fats are broken down as energy sources. Food intake is necessary to offset the negative energy balance, or weight loss will occur. Two of these classic symptoms gave the disease its name: diabetes is derived from a Greek word meaning "siphon," referring to the frequent urination, and mellitus, a Latin word meaning "sweetened with honey," refers to the sweet taste of a diabetic's urine. (Before modern blood or urine tests were developed, physicians tasted a patient's urine to detect the disease.)

The disease occurs in two major forms, called *type 1* and *type 2.* Type 1 diabetes, which occurs in about 10% of diabetics, results from insufficient insulin secretion by the pancreas. This type of diabetes is usually caused by an autoimmune reaction that destroys pancreatic beta cells. To survive, type 1 diabetics must receive regular insulin injections (typically, a genetically engineered human insulin called *Humulin*); careful dieting and exercise also have beneficial effects, because active skeletal muscles do not require insulin to take up and utilize glucose.

In type 2 diabetes, insulin is usually secreted at or above normal levels, but the target cells of affected people have significantly reduced responsiveness to the hormone compared with the cells of normal people. About 90% of patients in the developed world with type 2 diabetes are obese. A genetic predisposition can also be a factor. Most affected people can lead a normal life by controlling their diet and weight, exercising, and taking drugs that enhance insulin action or secretion.

Diabetes has long-term effects on the body. The body's cells, unable to utilize glucose as an energy source, start breaking down proteins and fats to generate energy. The protein breakdown weakens blood vessels throughout the body, particularly in the arms and legs and in critical regions such as the kidneys and retina of the eye. The circulation becomes so poor that tissues degenerate in the arms, legs, and feet. At advanced stages of the disease, bleeding in the retina causes blindness. The breakdown of circulation in the kidneys can lead to kidney failure. In addition, in type 1 diabetes, acidic products of fat breakdown (**ketones**) are produced in abnormally high quantities and accumulate in the blood. The resulting lowering of blood pH can disrupt heart and brain function, leading to coma and death if the disease is untreated.

## 43.4g The Pineal Gland Regulates Some Biological Rhythms

The earliest vertebrates had a third, light-sensitive eye at the top of the head, and *Sphenodon* and some lizards have an eyelike structure in this location. In most vertebrates, the third eye became modified into a **pineal gland,** which in many groups retains some degree of photosensitivity. For the most part in birds and mammals, the gland is exclusively endocrine and no longer involved in photoreception. In mammals, it is too deeply buried in the brain to be affected directly by light; nonetheless, specialized photoreceptors in the eyes make connections to the pineal gland.

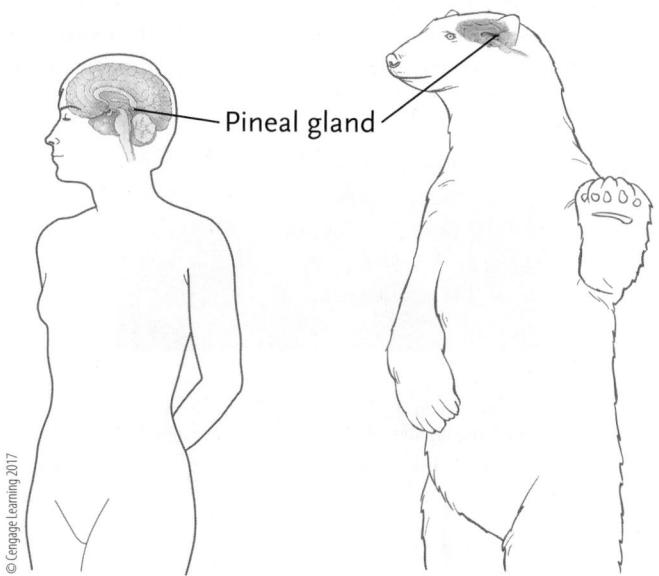

Pineal gland

© Cengage Learning 2017

The pineal gland regulates some biological rhythms. It secretes the amine hormone **melatonin,** which helps maintain daily biorhythms. Secretion of melatonin is regulated by an inhibitory pathway: light hitting the eyes generates signals that inhibit melatonin secretion; consequently, the hormone is secreted most actively during periods of darkness. Melatonin targets a part of the hypothalamus called the *suprachiasmatic nucleus,* which is the primary structure coordinating body activity to a daily cycle. The nightly release of melatonin may help synchronize the biological clock with daily cycles of light and darkness. The physical and mental discomfort associated with jet lag may reflect the time required for melatonin

secretion to reset a traveller's daily biological clock to match the period of daylight in a new time zone.

Melatonin occurs throughout the animal kingdom, as well as in many plants and fungi. In some fishes, amphibians, and reptiles, melatonin and other hormones produce changes in skin colour through their effects on melanophores, the pigment-containing cells of the skin. Skin colour may vary with the season, the animal's breeding status, or the colour of the background. In invertebrates, it is known to be important in the control of diurnal (daily) rhythms.

### STUDY BREAK QUESTIONS

1. What are the hormones controlling $Ca^{2+}$ levels in the blood of vertebrates, and how do they control $Ca^{2+}$ levels? Why is it important to control $Ca^{2+}$ levels?
2. Distinguish between the adrenal medulla and the adrenal cortex. What hormones do they secrete, and what are their functions?
3. How are levels of glucose in the blood maintained? Which tissues do not require insulin to regulate glucose uptake? Why is this important?
4. How do you explain the fact that both epinephrine and norepinephrine produce the same effect in some cells, but different effects in other cells?

## 43.5 Endocrine Systems in Invertebrates

In even the simplest animals, such as the cnidarian *Hydra,* hormones produced by neurosecretory neurons control the reproduction, growth, and development of some body features. In annelids, arthropods, and molluscs, endocrine cells and glands produce hormones that regulate development, reproduction, water balance, heart rate, sugar levels, and behaviour, just as they do in vertebrates.

Many of the hormones found in invertebrates are similar or almost identical to those found in vertebrates although their functions may be different, as described in Section 43.1b. Insulin-like hormones can be found in most invertebrates, and receptors are known from insects and nematodes. The protist *Tetrahymena* binds and exhibits responses to insulin and $T_4$. Some peptides controlling diuresis in insects are structural homologues of vertebrate corticotropin-releasing factor. Other diuretic peptides in insects are related to calcitonin. The larva of the tapeworm *Spirometra mansonoides* has developed the capacity to secrete vertebrate growth hormone so that its host rat grows larger. Other hormones, such as the peptide proctolin and the insect juvenile hormones, do not occur in vertebrates.

The endocrinology of the more complex invertebrates, formerly thought to be relatively simple, is emerging as very complex: about 200 bioactive peptides have thus far been described in insects, which are probably more closely governed by hormones than any other animals. The development of the eggs and the egg-laying behaviour of insects are controlled by more than a dozen hormones.

Among the best known invertebrate hormonal systems is the one governing growth and development in insects **(Figure 43.14).** As insects grow, they undergo a series of moults during which a new cuticle is laid down beneath the old cuticle, and the old cuticle is shed (see Chapter 27). The signal to the epidermal cells to begin the process is provided by a steroid hormone, ecdysone, from the prothoracic glands. The prothoracic glands are stimulated to secrete ecdysone by a peptide, prothoracicotropic hormone (PTTH), a **brain hormone** produced in neuroendocrine cells in the brain and released from the corpus cardiacum.

The corpus allatum is an endocrine gland that secretes **juvenile hormone,** a fatty acid derivative. Juvenile hormone controls metamorphosis: when it is present, the insect remains larval. In its absence, the next moult is metamorphic, producing a pupa and then an adult in those insects with a pupal stage, or proceeding directly to the adult in those lacking a pupal stage. In the adult of most insects, the corpus allatum becomes active once more, secreting juvenile hormone and stimulating a number of reproductive processes, especially egg development. The secretion of juvenile hormone by the corpus allatum is controlled by both inhibitory and stimulatory peptides from the brain.

The intricate process of shedding the old cuticle involves complex behaviours that are controlled by the interaction of up to five neurohormones; the hardening of the new cuticle requires a sixth.

Hormones that control moulting have also been detected in crustaceans, including lobsters, crabs, and crayfish. During the period between moults, **moult-inhibiting hormone (MIH),** a peptide neurohormone secreted by cells in the eyestalks (extensions of the brain leading to the eyes), inhibits ecdysone secretion **(Figure 43.15).** The first step in the moulting process is the inhibition of MIH secretion. Ecdysone secretion increases, and the processes leading to the replacement of the exoskeleton are initiated. As in insects, metamorphosis and reproduction

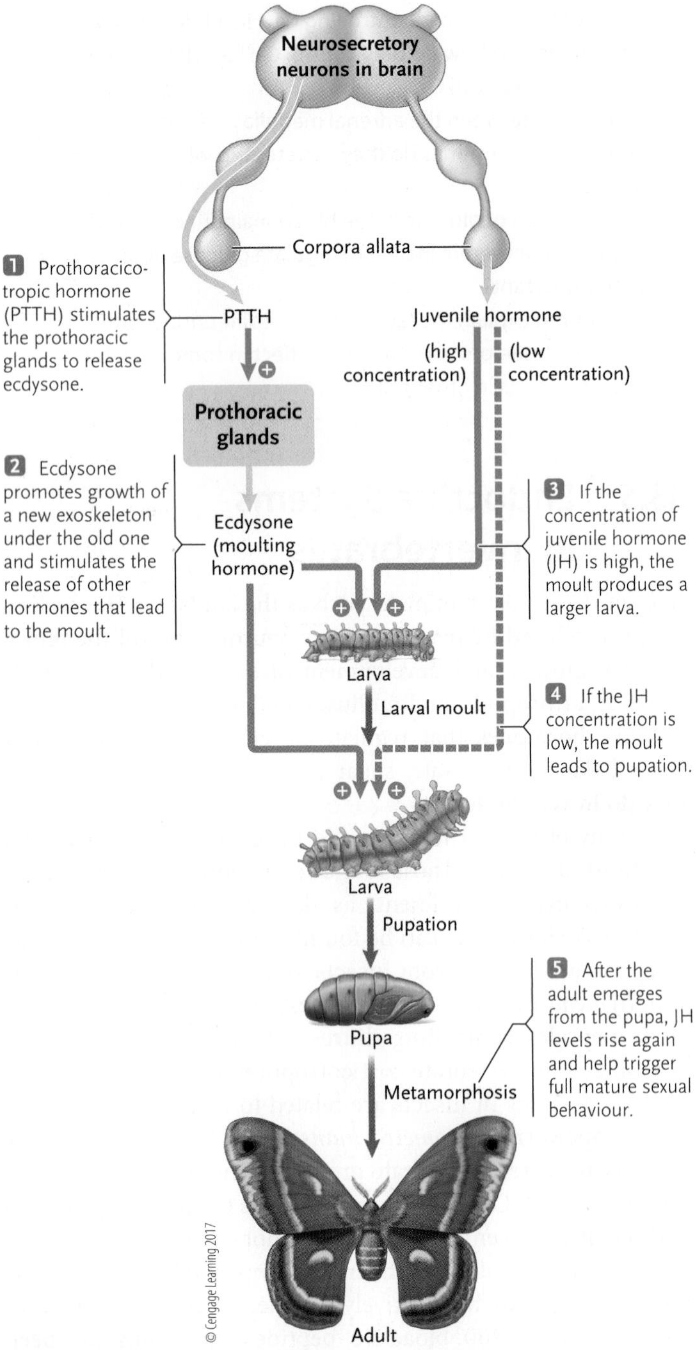

**1** Prothoracicotropic hormone (PTTH) stimulates the prothoracic glands to release ecdysone.

**2** Ecdysone promotes growth of a new exoskeleton under the old one and stimulates the release of other hormones that lead to the moult.

**3** If the concentration of juvenile hormone (JH) is high, the moult produces a larger larva.

**4** If the JH concentration is low, the moult leads to pupation.

**5** After the adult emerges from the pupa, JH levels rise again and help trigger full mature sexual behaviour.

**FIGURE 43.14 The roles of prothoracicotropic hormone, ecdysone, and juvenile hormone in the development of a silkworm moth**

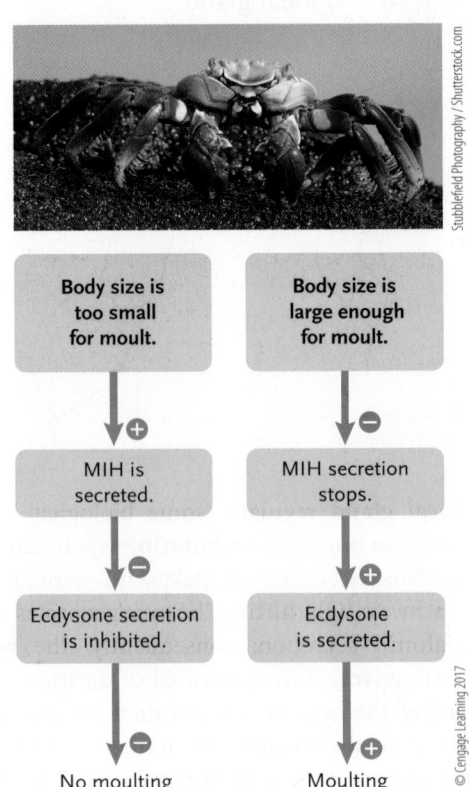

**FIGURE 43.15 Control of moulting by moult-inhibiting hormone (MIH), which is secreted by a gland in the eye stalks of crustaceans such as the crab**

FIGURE 43.16    **Experimental Research**

## Demonstration That Growth and Moulting in Insects Is Hormonally Controlled

**Research Question:** The blood sucking insect *Rhodnius prolixus* grows through five successive larval stages (nymphs) before metamorphosing into its adult form **(Figure 1)**. If unfed, the nymph remains in a state of suspended development. It must take a blood meal before it develops into the next stage. The British comparative physiologist, V.B. Wigglesworth, at Cambridge University, hypothesized that a hormone, released from the brain of the insect, diffuses throughout the body and causes moulting.

**Experiment:** Juvenile *Rhodnius* can be decapitated without killing the larva. Wigglesworth fed nymphs a blood meal and then decapitated them after different periods of time **(Figure 2)**.

**Results:** Nymphs that were decapitated within hours of a blood meal failed to moult. Those decapitated days after a blood meal did moult. This established the fact that a hormone that caused moulting was slowly released from the head. To confirm this, Wigglesworth performed a second experiment. He took two nymphs, one that had been decapitated one hour after a blood meal and one that had been decapitated one week after a blood meal, and he joined them together (a procedure called *parabiosis*) at the neck. They both subsequently began to form a new cuticle.

**Conclusion:** Growth and moulting are regulated by a hormone released from the head after a blood meal. This process requires a period of several days.

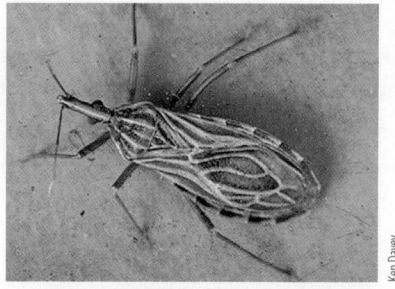

**Figure 1   The adult female of *Rhodnius prolixus***

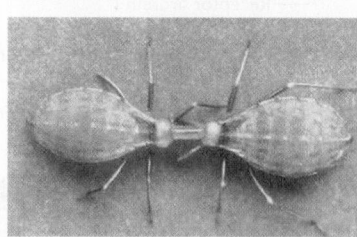

**Figure 2   The nymph on the right was decapitated within a day of feeding, before the hormones from the head governing moulting were secreted; therefore, it should not develop.** The nymph on the left was decapitated after the hormones were released and would develop normally. The two were joined so that their hemocoels were connected. As a result, they both initiated moulting driven by hormones from the nymph on the left that diffused into the nymph on the right.

---

are governed by a hormone different from but structurally related to juvenile hormone **(Figure 43.16)**.

Although we are accustomed to thinking of stress as a human or mammalian phenomenon, it has emerged as a response in a wide range of animals. Any unaccustomed sensory input (whether from external or internal events) leads to release of many hormones, and if the input continues, this can result in pathology or death. Stress, with the release of corticosteroid hormones, is well studied in most vertebrates. Even in cockroaches, forced activity or forced inactivity will cause the release of many neurohormones, and the insect will die. ⬢

In *Why It Matters*, you were told that, by the time you finished reading this chapter, you should be able to construct the pathway that produced the mating behaviour of the male elk. The stimulus was shortening day length in the fall, an external stimulus perceived by the eyes and transmitted to the pineal gland and the hypothalamus. The pineal gland releases melatonin, which also acts on the hypothalamus.

The hypothalamus releases GnRh, which travels in the blood to the anterior pituitary, causing it to release LH, which in turn leads to the release of testosterone from the gonads. Thus, less daylight triggers an increase in a buck's testosterone, which causes antler maturation/growth and changes in behaviour.

## STUDY BREAK QUESTIONS

1. How can an invertebrate surrounded by a rigid exoskeleton grow? Describe the process of moulting and growth in insects, and describe how it is regulated.

2. How are the pituitary of vertebrates and the corpus cardiacum of invertebrates similar? How do they differ?

3. The occurrence in many invertebrates of peptide hormones that closely resemble those in vertebrates is striking. What are the possible explanations for this in evolutionary terms?

# Summary Illustration

Hormones produce responses to environmental stimuli as well as regulate growth and development and many homeostatic processes. Along with the central nervous system (CNS), hormones of the endocrine system provide the communication that coordinates the activities of multicellular life. In general, they control activities that involve slower, longer-acting responses of multiple tissues or organs.

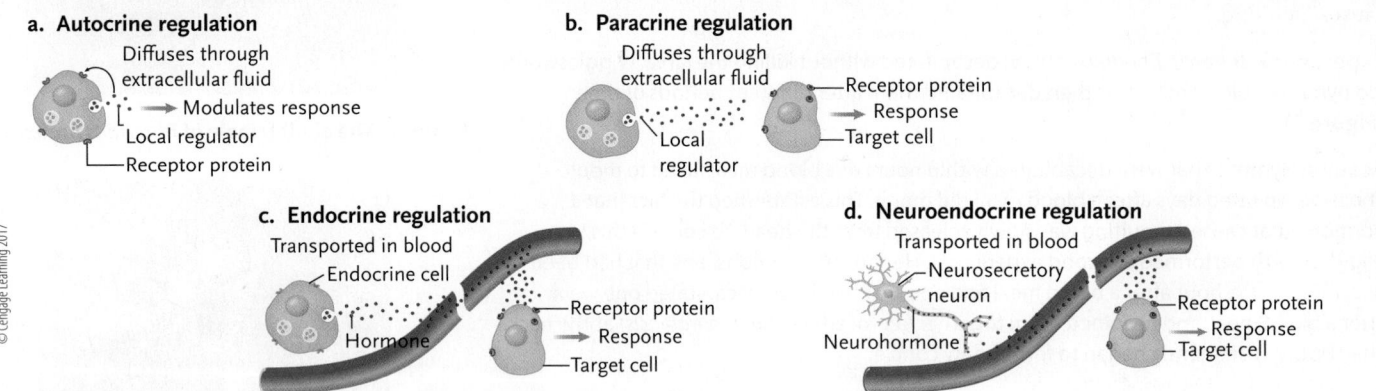

**a. Autocrine regulation**
Diffuses through extracellular fluid
→ Modulates response
Local regulator
Receptor protein

**b. Paracrine regulation**
Diffuses through extracellular fluid
Receptor protein
→ Response
Target cell
Local regulator

**c. Endocrine regulation**
Transported in blood
Endocrine cell
Receptor protein
→ Response
Target cell
Hormone

**d. Neuroendocrine regulation**
Transported in blood
Neurosecretory neuron
Receptor protein
→ Response
Target cell
Neurohormone

© Cengage Learning 2017

**Hypothalamus**
Produces and secretes releasing and inhibiting hormones that regulate secretions by the anterior pituitary

Produces ADH and oxytocin, which are stored and released by the posterior pituitary

**Pineal gland**
Secretes melatonin

**Anterior pituitary**
Secretes ACTH, TSH, FSH, and LH, which stimulate other glands, as well as prolactin, GH, MSH, and endorphins

**Posterior pituitary**
Stores and releases ADH and oxytocin

**Parathyroid glands**
Secrete parathyroid hormone

**Thyroid gland**
Secretes thyroxine triiodothyronine and calcitonin

**Adrenal cortex**
Secretes cortisol and aldosterone and small amounts of androgens

**Adrenal medulla**
Secretes epinephrine and norepinephrine

**Islets of Langerhans (in pancreas)**
Secrete insulin and glucagon

**Ovaries**
Secrete estrogens and progestins

**Testes**
Secrete androgens

Many of the same hormones, and hormone receptors, are found in invertebrates and vertebrates (shown above). The same hormone may serve similar or different roles in different groups.

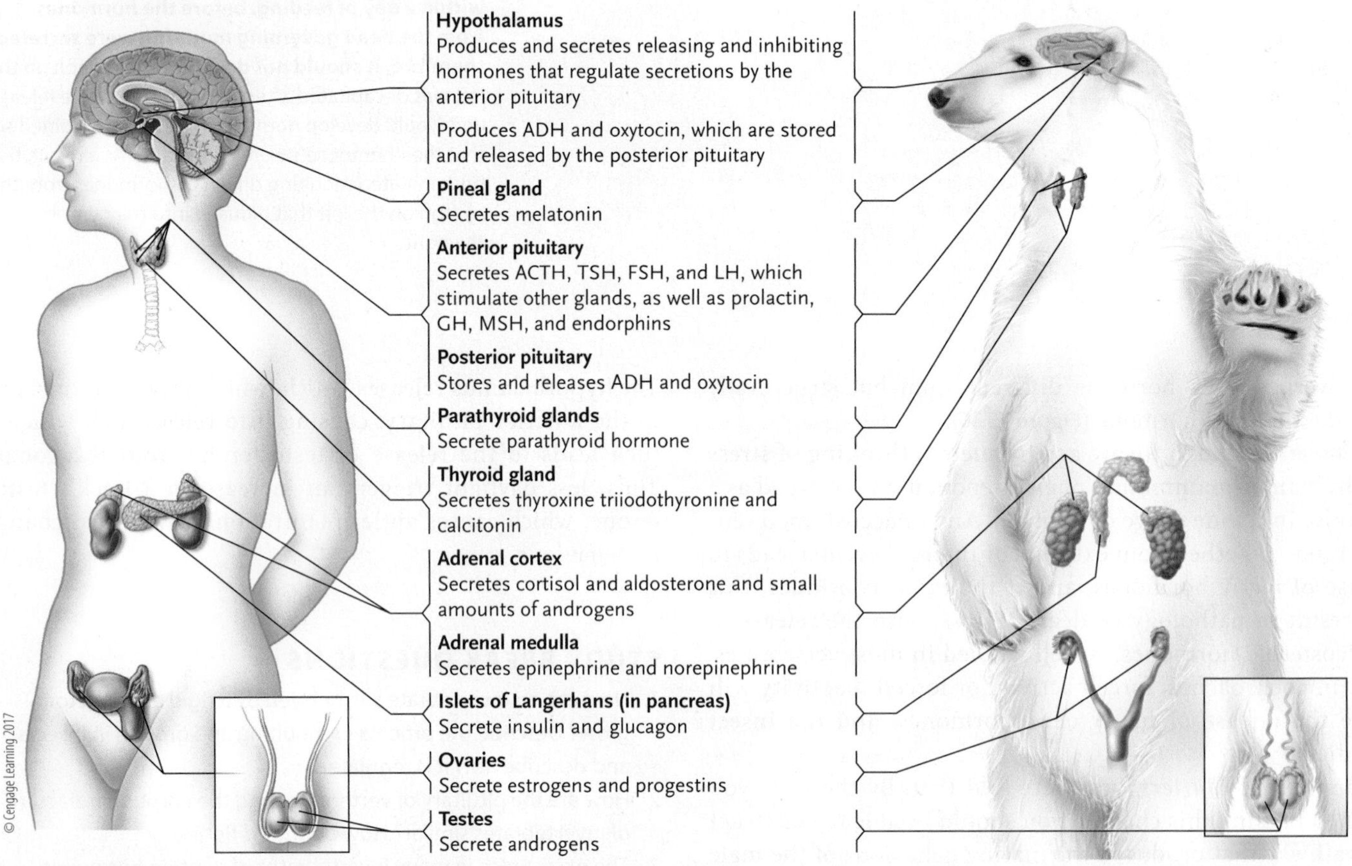

© Cengage Learning 2017

(Background) Pan Xunbin/Shutterstock.com

## Hormone binding to receptor in the plasma membrane

Outside cell

Hydrophilic hormone

Blood vessel

Signal

**Reception** { ❶ Hydrophilic hormone binds to surface receptor and activates it.

Cytoplasmic end of receptor

Activation

Pathway molecule A

Activation

**Transduction** { ❷ Activated receptor triggers a signal transduction pathway.

Pathway molecule B

Activation

Pathway molecule C

Molecule that brings about response

**Response** { ❸ Transduction of the signal leads to cellular response.

Change in cell

Cytoplasm

Hormones control cell functions by first binding to receptor molecules on or in their target cells. This either alters functional proteins already present in the cell or leads to the production of new functional proteins.

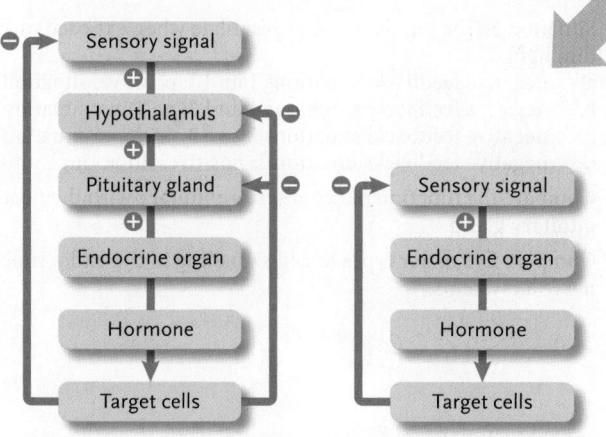

Sensory signal

Hypothalamus

Pituitary gland

Endocrine organ

Hormone

Target cells

Sensory signal

Endocrine organ

Hormone

Target cells

Some sensory signals are processed in the brain and communicate with the endocrine system through the hypothalamus and pituitary gland; others communicate directly with various endocrine glands.

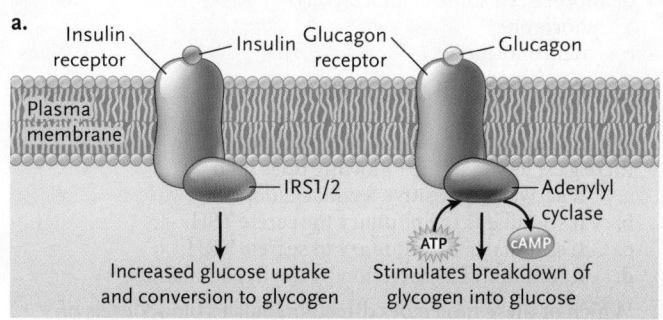

a. Insulin receptor — Insulin    Glucagon receptor — Glucagon

Plasma membrane

IRS1/2    Adenylyl cyclase

ATP    cAMP

Increased glucose uptake and conversion to glycogen

Stimulates breakdown of glycogen into glucose

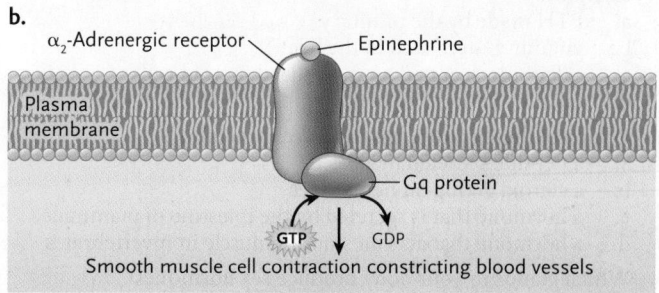

b. $\alpha_2$-Adrenergic receptor — Epinephrine

Plasma membrane

Gq protein

GTP    GDP

Smooth muscle cell contraction constricting blood vessels

$\beta_1$-Adrenergic receptor — Epinephrine

Plasma membrane

Gs protein

GTP    GDP

Cardiac cell contraction increasing heart rate

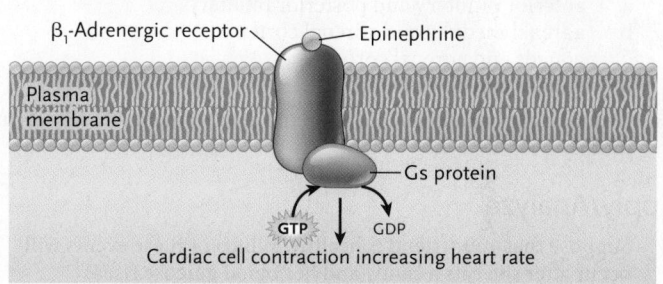

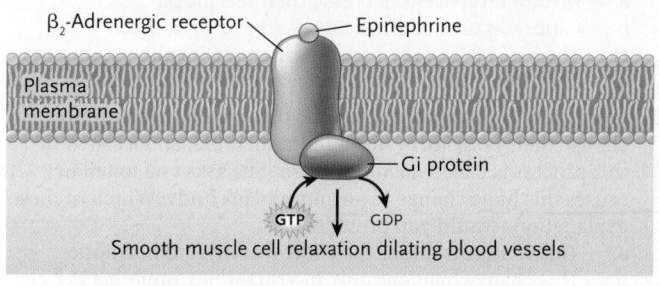

$\beta_2$-Adrenergic receptor — Epinephrine

Plasma membrane

Gi protein

GTP    GDP

Smooth muscle cell relaxation dilating blood vessels

1. Only cells that contain surface or internal receptors for a particular hormone respond to that hormone.
2. Once bound by their receptors, hormones produce a wide variety of responses.
3. Due to amplification, hormones are effective in very small concentrations.
4. The response to any hormone may differ among target cells.
5. Target cells may respond to more than one hormone, and different target cells may respond differently to the same hormone.

© Cengage Learning 2017

# SELF-TEST QUESTIONS

## Recall/Understand

1. Which of the following is a chemical that is released from an epithelial cell in a gland and enters the blood to affect the activity of another cell some distance away?
   a. hormone
   b. neurohormone
   c. pheromone
   d. bile

2. When the concentration of thyroid hormone in the blood increases, which of the following does it do?
   a. It activates a positive feedback loop.
   b. It stimulates the pituitary to secrete TSH.
   c. It stimulates the pituitary to secrete TRH.
   d. It inhibits TRH secretion by the hypothalamus.

3. Which of these molecules directly regulates blood levels of calcium?
   a. PTH made by the pituitary
   b. vitamin D activated in the liver
   c. calcitonin secreted by specialized thyroid cells
   d. insulin synthesized by the alpha cells of the pancreas

4. Which of these statements describes proctolin?
   a. a peptide secreted by insects
   b. a steroid acting on nematodes
   c. a hormone that is secreted by the intestine of mammals
   d. a hormone that acts on smooth muscle in invertebrates

5. Which glands in your body produce sex hormones?
   a. anterior pituitary and posterior pituitary
   b. adrenal medulla and adrenal cortex
   c. gonads and adrenal cortex
   d. gonads and adrenal medulla

6. Describe the hormonal control in the development of a silkworm moth.

## Apply/Analyze

7. Suppose that your friend is healthy. Which of these events will occur after she eats a candy and her blood glucose rises?
   a. Insulin target cells decrease their receptors.
   b. Glucagon uses amino acids as an energy source.
   c. The beta cells of the pancreas increase insulin production.
   d. The alpha cells of the pancreas increase glucagon secretion.

8. Your friend was amazed when she discovered that amphibians change their body form throughout their life, and learned that this process is called *metamorphosis*. She asks you to tell her what causes this huge change in an amphibian's body. Which of these explanations would you provide?
   a. This change is under the control of thyroid hormones.
   b. This change happens only in years when amphibians lack food.
   c. This is an amphibian's defence mechanism against extreme weather.
   d. This happens under the control of reproductive hormones.

9. Recently, your friend became a mom, and she wants to breastfeed her newborn baby. However, she is experiencing problems with milk production and secretion, and she wonders which hormones she might be lacking. Which of these hormones would you suggest might be lacking in her body?
   a. estrogen and oxytocin
   b. oxytocin and prolactin
   c. progestins and oxytocin
   d. prolactin and estrogen

## Create/Evaluate

10. Negative feedback mechanisms often control hormone secretion in the body. Which of the following does such control include?
    a. no change in hormone secretion
    b. a decrease in hormone secretion
    c. a change that maintains homeostasis
    d. an increase in hormone secretion

11. Which of these statements describes endocrine glands?
    a. They secrete hormones indirectly into the blood.
    b. They secrete hormones directly into the blood.
    c. They secrete digestive enzymes directly into the small intestine.
    d. They secrete hormones directly into ducts.

12. The thyroid gland is important for homeostatic regulation. Which of these thyroid gland functions plays a crucial role in vertebrates?
    a. regulation of calcium levels in the blood
    b. maintenance of muscle tone
    c. maintenance of blood pressure
    d. regulation of development and maturity

13. You are presented with these three situations. Each is an example of either negative or positive feedback. Evaluate the situations and select which are examples of negative and which are examples of positive feedback control mechanisms.

    Situation 1: During the summer, your body maintains normal body temperature by dissipating heat to the environment.

    Situation 2: You cut yourself, and this leads to the formation of a blood clot.

    Situation 3: The pupils of your eyes dilate when exposed to dim light.
    a. negative feedback: situations 1 and 3; positive: situation 2
    b. negative feedback: situations 1 and 2; positive: situation 3
    c. negative feedback: situations 2 and 3; positive: situation 1
    d. negative feedback: situation 1; positive: situations 2 and 3

14. Compare the function of the anterior pituitary with the posterior pituitary gland.

15. Compare five major types of cell signalling in the endocrine and nervous systems.

# Chapter Roadmap

**Animal Reproduction**

From Chapter 33

### 44.1 The Drive to Reproduce

The success of any species is contingent on its reproductive success. All energy that does not go into growth, development, and maintenance goes into reproduction.

### 44.2 Asexual and Sexual Reproduction

**Asexual reproduction**, reproduction by a single individual with no genetic input from another individual, is advantageous in stable environments. **Sexual reproduction** between a male and a female through the union of egg and sperm is advantageous in changing environments.

### 44.3 Mechanisms of Sexual Reproduction

The cellular mechanisms of sexual reproduction include **gametogenesis**, the formation of male and female gametes, and **fertilization**, the union of gametes, which initiates development of a new individual.

From Chapter 43

### 44.4 Sexual Reproduction in Mammals

Male sexual organs function in sperm production and delivery. Female sexual organs function in oocyte production, fertilization, and embryonic development.

From Chapter 43

### 44.5 Development

The process of development takes an animal from the zygote (fertilized egg) to the complete adult stage of the life cycle. These processes include mitosis, cell migration, selective cell adhesion, induction, determination, differentiation, and apoptosis.

Catchlight Lens/Shutterstock.com

A dolphin on a coral reef

# Animal Reproduction

# 44

**Why it matters . . .** Over a few nights each year along the Great Barrier Reef off the east coast of Australia, many species of reef-building corals synchronously spawn, releasing eggs and sperm into the water. Timing is important for the corals because they rely on external fertilization. Male and female gametes must be released at the same time to maximize the chances of meeting. The circadian clocks of the corals control the reproductive event, which is synchronized to the lunar cycle. The mass spawning occurs over several nights after the full moon. Spawning is triggered by changes in lunar irradiance intensity. Many species of corals release eggs and sperm at the same time, but chemicals in the egg coatings and in the sperm head interact to ensure fertilization of eggs only by sperm of the same species.

Bottle-nosed dolphins, on the other hand, have a breeding season during which males compete for females. Mating involves copulation that ensures that sperm and eggs from the same species meet in a protected site inside the body of the female. The fertilized egg is nourished inside the uterus of the female for 12 months on average, and then the newborn is nursed by the female for a further 18–20 months. These are two very different strategies for allocating resources for reproduction: mass spawning with no parental care, and selective reproduction with a large investment in parental care.

As in plants, bacteria, fungi, and all other life, reproduction ensures the transfer of genes (as allowed by natural selection). There is a strong drive to reproduce, and considerable time and resources are devoted to reproductive processes. For animals that reproduce by eggs and sperm, the adaptations are as diverse as the number of species on Earth. This diversity allows individuals of the same species to find each other and unite eggs and sperm. Within the diversity, however, are underlying patterns that are shared by all animals. Both the underlying patterns and the diversity of animal reproduction are the subjects of this chapter.

We also discuss the formation of eggs and sperm, their union, which begins the development of a new individual, and the events of development that lead from the fertilized egg to the adult animal. Think about this now and make a list of the steps. Then, after reading the chapter, do it again and see how well it matches the summary illustration at the end of the chapter.

## 44.1   The Drive to Reproduce

The success of any species is contingent on its reproductive success. Accordingly, organisms have a strong drive to reproduce, and they go to considerable lengths to ensure that their genes are represented in future generations. All energy that does not go into growth, development, and maintenance goes into reproduction. This chapter outlines various strategies taken by different species to ensure that this energy is spent wisely. The strategies employed are diverse, reflecting differences in habitat and lifestyle, but all are designed to ensure that the species survives. As we go through the chapter, keep in mind that energy spent on any one activity is energy not available for other purposes, and imagine the selection pressures that have led to the diversity we see.

## 44.2   Asexual and Sexual Reproduction

**Reproduction** is the means of passing on an individual's genes to a new generation, making it the most vital function of living organisms. In **asexual reproduction**, a single individual gives rise to offspring with no genetic input from another individual. In **sexual reproduction**, male and female parents produce zygotes (fertilized eggs) through the union of egg and sperm.

**CONCEPT FIX**   A common misconception is that sexual reproduction is always a better **reproductive strategy** than asexual reproduction. As you will see in the next sections, asexual reproduction gives rise to genetically uniform offspring, which can be advantageous in stable, uniform environments. Sexual reproduction, on the other hand, gives rise to genetically diverse offspring, which is advantageous in unstable, changing environments. Thus, each may be a superior strategy depending on environmental conditions. ⬡

### 44.2a   Asexual Reproduction: Reproduction without Recombination Is Advantageous in Stable Environments

Many aquatic invertebrates and some terrestrial annelids and insects reproduce asexually. This mode of reproduction is much less common among vertebrates. In asexual reproduction, anywhere from one to many cells of a parent's body develop directly into a new individual. Cells involved in asexual reproduction in animals are usually produced by mitosis (see Chapter 8) and sometimes by meiosis (see Chapters 8 and 9). When cells involved in asexual reproduction are produced by mitosis, the resulting offspring are genetically identical to one another and to the parent (clonal reproduction).

Genetic uniformity of offspring can be advantageous in stable, uniform environments. In these cases, successful individuals with the "best" combinations of genes perpetuate the most competitive genotypes through asexual reproduction. Individuals do not have to expend energy to produce gametes or find a mate. Asexual reproduction is also advantageous to individuals living in sparsely settled populations or to sessile (immobile) animals.

In animals, asexual reproduction involving mitosis occurs by three basic mechanisms: fission, budding, and fragmentation. In **fission**, the parent splits into two or more offspring of approximately equal size. Some species of planarians (Platyhelminthes) reproduce asexually by fission, dividing transversely or longitudinally **(Figure 44.1a)**. In **budding**, a new individual grows and develops while attached to the parent. Sponges, tunicates, and some cnidarians reproduce asexually by budding, and offspring may break free from the parent or remain attached to form a colony. In the cnidarian *Hydra*, an offspring buds and grows from one side of the parent's body and then detaches to become a separate individual (Figure 44.1b). In corals, buds often remain attached when their growth is complete, forming colonies of thousands of interconnected individuals. In **fragmentation**, pieces separate from a parent's body and develop (regenerate) into new individuals. Many species of cnidarians, flatworms, annelids, and some echinoderms can reproduce by fragmentation (Figure 44.1c).

Some animals produce offspring by **parthenogenesis** (*parthenos* = virgin; *genesis* = birth), which is the growth and development of an unfertilized egg. Offspring produced by parthenogenesis may be haploid or diploid (see Section 8.3), depending on the species. Because the egg from which a parthenogenetic offspring is produced derives from meiosis in the female parent, the offspring are not genetically identical to the parent or to each other. (We describe below how chromosome segregation and genetic recombination during meiosis produce gametes with gene combinations different from the parent.) In some species, the offspring are all female; in other species, they are all males. All whiptail lizard species (*Cnemidophorus* spp.; Figure 44.1d) consist of females produced by parthenogenesis. These females still go through the motions of mating with each other (see Section 18.1 on species concepts).

Parthenogenesis occurs in some invertebrates, including certain aphids, water fleas, bees, and crustaceans. In bees, haploid drones (males) are produced parthenogenetically from unfertilized eggs produced by reproductive females (queens). New queens and sterile workers develop from fertilized eggs. Parthenogenesis also occurs in some vertebrates (e.g., certain fishes, salamanders, amphibians, lizards, and turkeys).

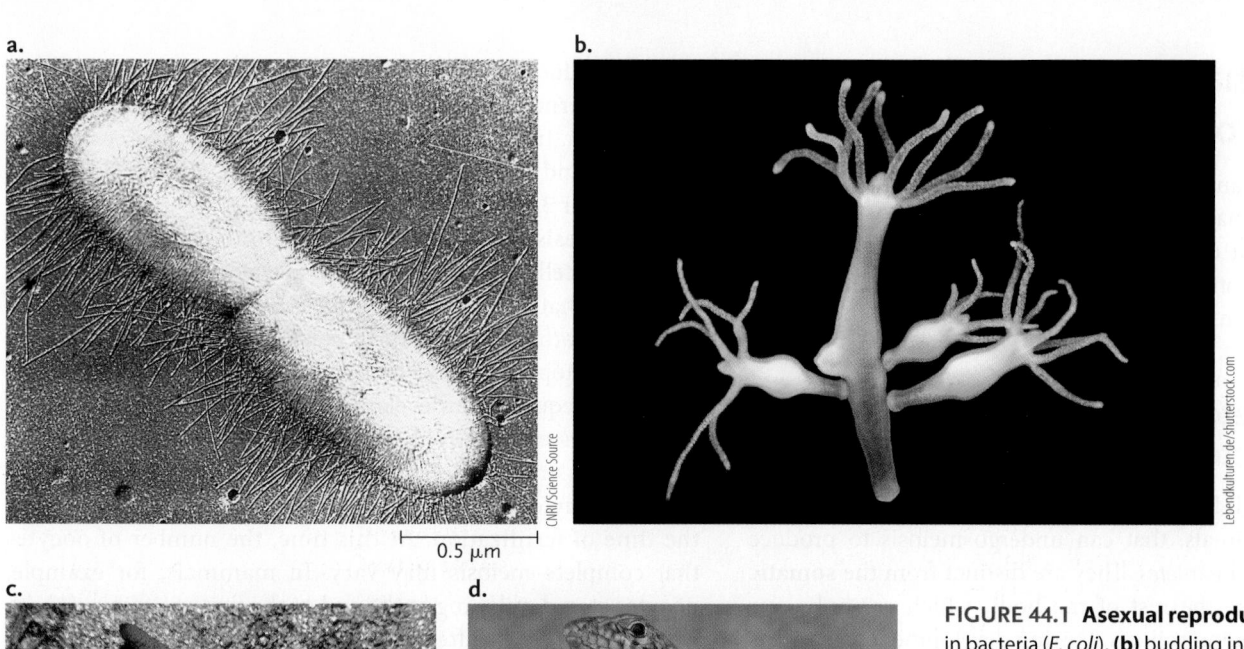

**FIGURE 44.1  Asexual reproduction. (a)** Fission in bacteria (*E. coli*), **(b)** budding in *Hydra* species, **(c)** fragmentation in *Echinoderm* species, and **(d)** a whiptail lizard (*Cnemidophorus deppei*) that reproduces by parthenogenesis and in which all individuals are female

## 44.2b  Sexual Reproduction: Reproduction with Recombination Is Advantageous in Changing Environments

Animals reproduce sexually through the union of **sperm** and **eggs**. The overriding advantage of sexual reproduction is the generation of genetic diversity among offspring. Genetic diversity of offspring is advantageous in unstable, changing environments. Genetic diversity increases the chances that at least some offspring will be better adapted to altered conditions and be more likely to survive and reproduce. Genetic recombination and independent assortment of chromosomes are two mechanisms of meiosis that give rise to genetic diversity in eggs and sperm (see Chapter 8). Genetic recombination mixes the alleles of parents into new combinations within chromosomes. Independent assortment randomly combines maternal and paternal chromosomes in the gamete nuclei. Additional variability is generated at fertilization when eggs and sperm from genetically different individuals fuse together at random to initiate the development of new individuals. Adding to the effects of genetic recombination and independent assortment, random mutations in DNA are the ultimate source of variability for both sexual and asexual reproduction.

Sexual reproduction can be a disadvantage because of the costs in energy and raw materials associated with producing gametes and finding mates. Finding mates can expose animals to predation and may conflict with the need to find food and shelter and care for existing offspring. It also opens routes for infection, and the strategies employed to mitigate against this are metabolically costly.

## 44.2c  Some Species Reproduce Both Asexually and Sexually

Many organisms reproduce both asexually and sexually. Indeed, most organisms that reproduce asexually also reproduce sexually at some time. As a rule, in these groups asexual reproduction occurs when the environment is stable, but can change to sexual reproduction when environmental conditions are less favourable.

### STUDY BREAK QUESTIONS

1.  What are the advantages of sexual reproduction over asexual reproduction?
2.  Which would be the better strategy (asexual versus sexual reproduction) for an organism to use if it were living in a stable versus an unstable environment? Explain your answer in detail.

# 44.3 Mechanisms of Sexual Reproduction

The cellular mechanisms of sexual reproduction include **gametogenesis**, the formation of male and female gametes, and **fertilization**, the union of gametes that initiates development of a new individual. Mating is the pairing of a male and a female for sexual reproduction.

## 44.3a Gametogenesis: Production of Gametes

**Germ cells** are cell lines, set aside early in embryonic development in most animals, that can undergo meiosis to produce haploid cells called *gametes*. They are distinct from the **somatic cells** that compose the rest of the body, which are only ever capable of undergoing mitosis. During development, germ cells collect in gonads, the specialized gamete-producing organs: **testes** (singular, *testis*) in males and **ovaries** in females. Germ cells initially undergo mitotic division to produce large numbers of **spermatogonia** (singular, *spermatogonium*) in males and **oogonia** (singular, *oogonium*) in females. It is these cells that then undergo meiosis to produce gametes **(Figure 44.2)**. In some animals, germ cells also give rise to families of cells that assist gamete development.

Meiosis reduces the number of chromosomes from diploid to haploid. Thus, while somatic cells have two copies of each chromosome, gametes have one. Fertilization, the fusion of a haploid sperm and a haploid egg, restores the diploid condition and produces a **zygote**, or fertilized egg, the first cell of a new individual. The zygote will then divide by mitosis to produce a new adult within which only one cell line will retain the ability to undergo meiosis: the germ cells that produce gametes.

**Spermatogenesis** produces haploid cells specialized to deliver their nuclei to eggs produced by members of the same species. Two meiotic divisions produce four haploid spermatids (see Figure 44.2a), each of which develops into a mature sperm (*spermatozoon* = sperm; plural, **spermatozoa**; see **Figure 44.3**). Sperm are specialized to move toward, contact, and penetrate eggs. During sperm maturation, they lose most of their cytoplasm. Mitochondria are concentrated in the cytoplasm around the base of the flagellum. These mitochondria produce ATP, the energy source for beating of the flagellum. The **acrosome**, a specialized secretory vesicle, forms a cap over the nucleus at the other end of the sperm. The acrosome contains enzymes and other proteins that help the sperm attach to and penetrate the surface coatings of an egg of the same species.

Although sperm are usually smaller than eggs, they show considerable range in size, even in related species; for example, they range from 4.5 to 16.5 μm long among *Drosophila* species. The size of individual sperm influences the speed at which they swim (longer sperm move more quickly than shorter sperm). But producing longer sperm may reduce total sperm production and limit a male's reproductive success because sperm must be numerous to maximize the chances of fertilization. In mammals, variations in sperm size, volume of ejaculate, and sperm density often reflect mating behaviour (see Chapter 32).

**Oogenesis** produces an **ovum** (plural, *ova*), or egg. Only one of the cell products of meiosis develops into a functional egg, with that cell retaining almost all the cytoplasm of the parent; the other products form polar bodies (see Figure 44.2b). Unequal cytoplasmic divisions concentrate nutrients and other molecules required for development in the egg. In most species, polar bodies eventually disintegrate and do not contribute to fertilization or embryonic development.

The oocytes of most animals do not complete meiosis until the time of fertilization. At this time, the number of oocytes that complete meiosis may vary. In mammals, for example, oocytes stop developing at the end of the first meiotic prophase within a few weeks after a female is born. The oocytes remain in the ovary at this stage of development until the female is sexually mature. Then, one to several oocytes advance to the metaphase of the second meiotic division and are released from the ovary at intervals ranging from days to months, or at certain seasons, depending on the species. In humans, some oocytes may remain in prophase of the first meiotic division for 50 years. In other animals, such as the corals described in *Why It Matters*, thousands of eggs are released simultaneously once a year.

The egg **(Figure 44.4)** typically has specialized features, including stored nutrients required for at least the early stages of embryonic development, as well as one or more kinds of coatings that protect the egg from mechanical injury and infection. In some species, egg coats protect the embryo immediately after fertilization and prevent penetration by more than one sperm (see Section 44.3c).

Egg coats are surface layers added during oocyte development or fertilization. The **vitelline coat** (the **zona pellucida** in mammals; see Figure 44.4) is a gel-like matrix of proteins, glycoproteins, and/or polysaccharides lying immediately outside the plasma membrane of the egg cell. Eggs that are laid or deposited outside the body of the female usually have extra layers to protect them and prevent desiccation. Insect eggs have additional outer protein coats forming a hard, water-impermeable layer that prevents desiccation. In amphibians and some echinoderms, egg jelly forms the outer coat protecting the egg from desiccation. In birds, reptiles, and monotremes (see Chapter 27), egg white, a thick solution of proteins, surrounds the vitelline coat. Outside the white is the shell of the egg, which is flexible and leathery in reptiles and mineralized and brittle in birds. Both egg white and shell are added while the egg moves along the **oviduct**, the tube connecting the ovary to the outside of the body. For the egg to be fertilized, it must encounter sperm before these layers are added to the egg. If it does not encounter sperm before this stage, the egg will be laid unfertilized.

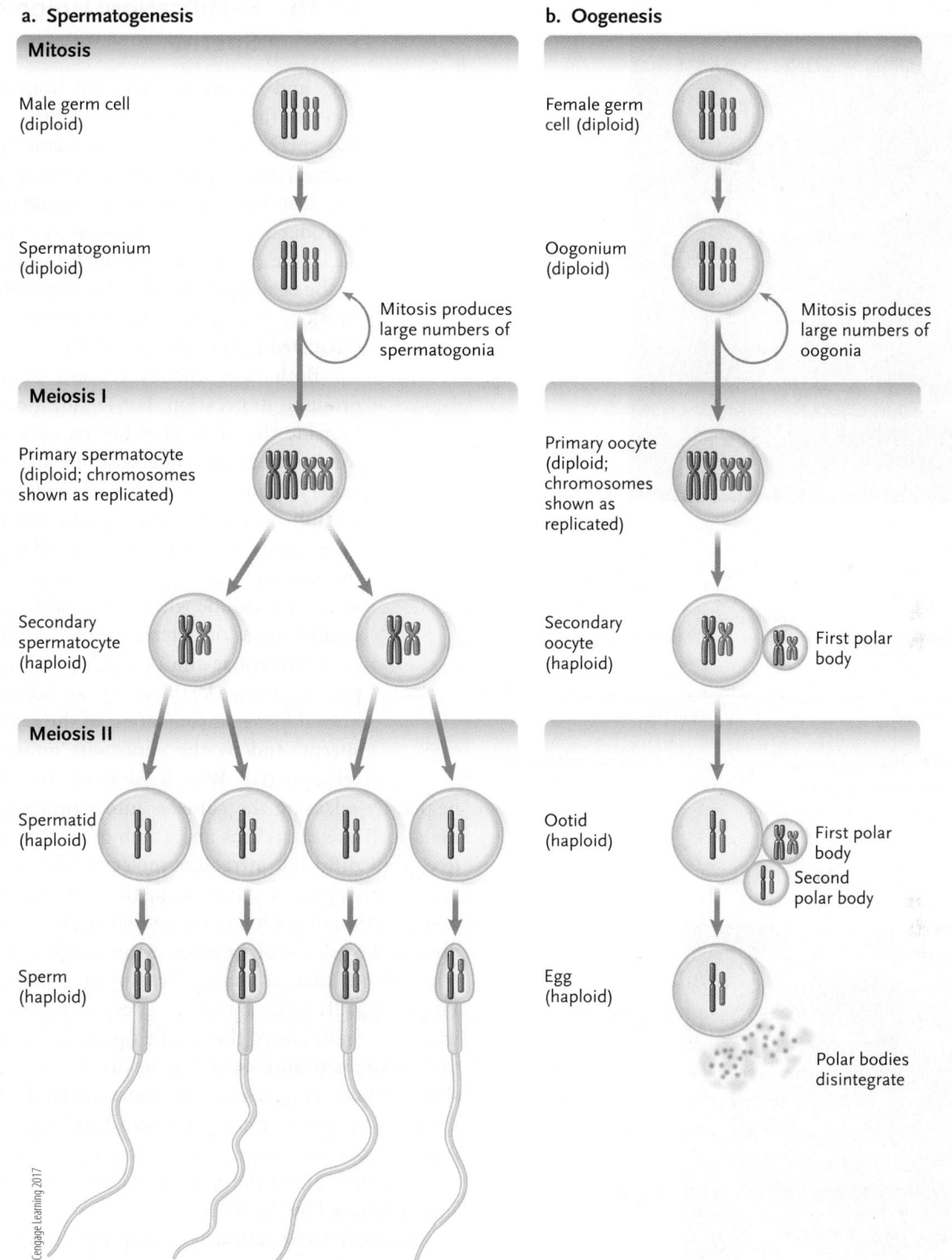

**a. Spermatogenesis**

**Mitosis**

Male germ cell (diploid)

Spermatogonium (diploid)

Mitosis produces large numbers of spermatogonia

**Meiosis I**

Primary spermatocyte (diploid; chromosomes shown as replicated)

Secondary spermatocyte (haploid)

**Meiosis II**

Spermatid (haploid)

Sperm (haploid)

**b. Oogenesis**

**Mitosis**

Female germ cell (diploid)

Oogonium (diploid)

Mitosis produces large numbers of oogonia

**Meiosis I**

Primary oocyte (diploid; chromosomes shown as replicated)

Secondary oocyte (haploid)

First polar body

**Meiosis II**

Ootid (haploid)

First polar body

Second polar body

Egg (haploid)

Polar bodies disintegrate

© Cengage Learning 2017

**FIGURE 44.2  The mitotic and meiotic divisions that produce eggs and sperm from germ cells. (a)** Spermatogenesis. **(b)** Oogenesis. The first **polar body** may or may not divide, depending on the species, so that either two or three polar bodies may be present at the end of meiosis. Two are shown in this diagram.

In the mammalian ovary, the egg is surrounded by **follicle cells** during its development. Follicle cells grow from ovarian tissue and nourish the developing egg. They also make up part of the zona pellucida while the egg is in the ovary and they remain as a protective layer after it is released.

Mature eggs can be the largest cells in an animal (see Figure 27.113, Chapter 27). Mammalian eggs are microscopic, with few stored nutrients, because the embryo develops inside the mother and is supplied with nutrients by her body. The eggs of birds are huge because they contain all the nutrients required for

## a. Human sperm

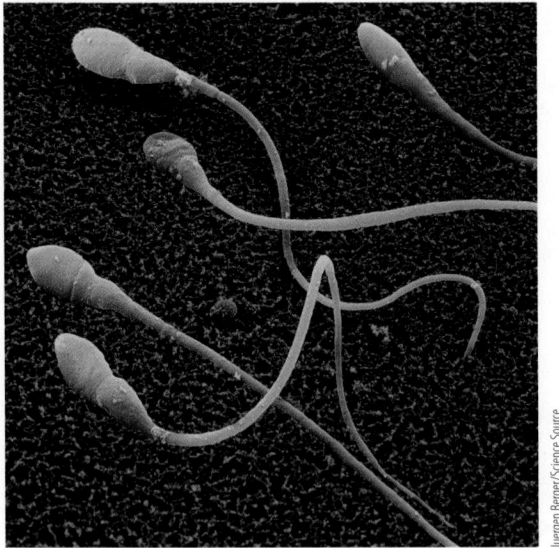

Juergen Berger/Science Source

## b. Sperm structure

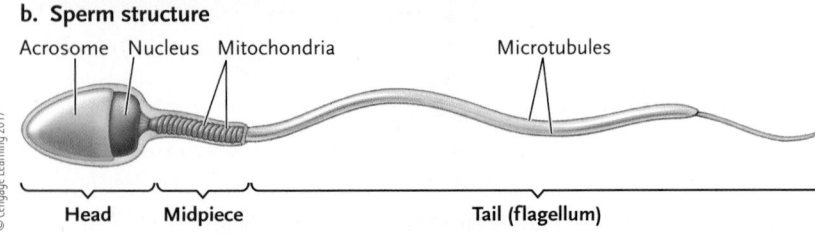

Acrosome  Nucleus  Mitochondria          Microtubules

Head    Midpiece              Tail (flagellum)

© Cengage Learning 2017

**FIGURE 44.3 Spermatozoa. (a)** Scanning electron microscopy of human sperm and **(b)** the structure of a sperm

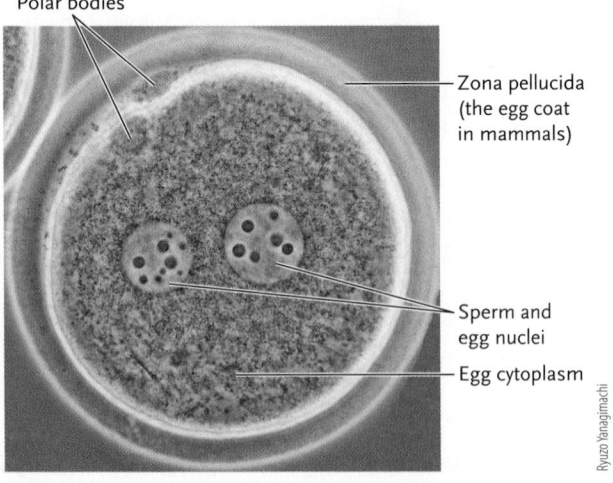

Polar bodies

Zona pellucida (the egg coat in mammals)

Sperm and egg nuclei

Egg cytoplasm

Ryuzo Yanagimachi

**FIGURE 44.4  A mature hamster egg that has been fertilized.**
The sperm and egg nuclei are about to fuse together.

complete embryonic development. The bird egg includes the *yolk*, which contains the nutrients for the developing egg; the ovum, or egg cell; and the white. Regardless of size, cytoplasm makes up most of the volume of an animal egg, and the nucleus of the egg is usually microscopic.

## 44.3b  Fertilization: Union of Egg and Sperm

Eggs and sperm are delivered from the ovaries and testes to the site of fertilization by oviducts (females) and sperm ducts (males). In many species, external accessory sex organs participate in the delivery of gametes. The basic design of vertebrate and invertebrate reproductive systems **(Figure 44.5)** is similar. Nonmotile eggs move through oviducts on currents generated by the beating of cilia that line the oviducts, or by contractions of the oviducts or the body wall. Sperm are ejaculated but are motile and then swim on their own.

Both eggs and sperm are small, fragile, and prone to desiccation. For fertilization to be external (outside the body of either parent), it must be in a watery medium. Otherwise it must be internal in a watery fluid inside a female's body. **External fertilization** occurs in most aquatic invertebrates, bony fishes, and amphibians. Sperm and eggs are shed into the surrounding water, and then the sperm swim until they collide with an egg of the same species. A disadvantage of external fertilization in an aquatic environment is the possibility of dispersion of the gametes before fertilization can occur. The process is helped by synchronization of the release of eggs and sperm, and by the enormous numbers of gametes released (see *Why It Matters*). In other cases, it is helped by releasing the gametes into a protected nest. In animals such as sea urchins and amphibians, sperm are attracted to eggs by diffusible attractant molecules released by the egg.

Another means of increasing the odds of fertilization is the juxtaposition of genital openings between the male and female during the release of gametes. Most amphibians, even terrestrial species such as toads, mate in an aquatic environment. Frogs typically mate by a reflex response called *amplexus*, in which the male clasps the female tightly around the body with his forelimbs **(Figure 44.6)**. Amplexus stimulates the female to shed a mass of eggs into the water through the cloaca. The cloaca is the cavity into which intestinal, urinary, and genital tracts empty in reptiles, birds, amphibians, and many fishes (see Chapter 32). As the eggs are released, they are fertilized by sperm released by the male.

**Internal fertilization** is widespread in terrestrial animals. Internal fertilization occurs in invertebrates such as annelids, some arthropods, and some molluscs and in vertebrates, from fishes and salamanders to reptiles, birds, and mammals. With internal fertilization, the male releases sperm close to or inside the entrance to the female's reproductive tract. The sperm swim through fluids in the reproductive tract until one reaches and fertilizes an egg. In some species, molecules released by the egg attract the sperm. Internal fertilization involves copulation, which occurs when a male's accessory sex organ (e.g., a penis) is inserted into a female's accessory sex organ (e.g., a vagina). Internal fertilization makes terrestrial life possible because the female's body

### a. Insect (fruit fly)

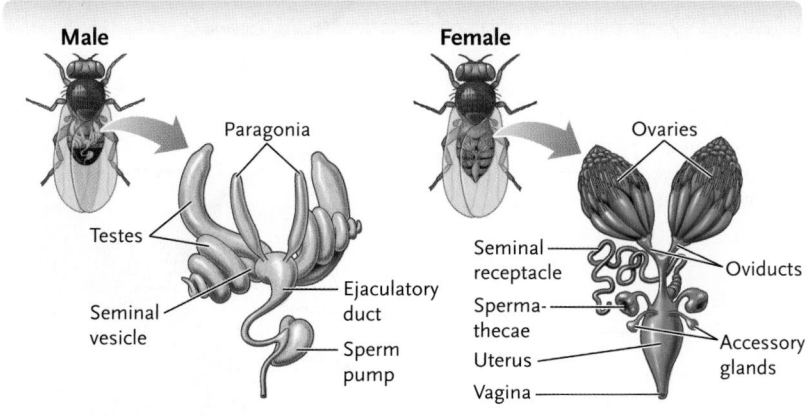

**Male**

Paragonia
Testes
Seminal vesicle
Ejaculatory duct
Sperm pump

**Female**

Ovaries
Seminal receptacle
Sperma-thecae
Uterus
Vagina
Oviducts
Accessory glands

### b. Amphibian (frog)

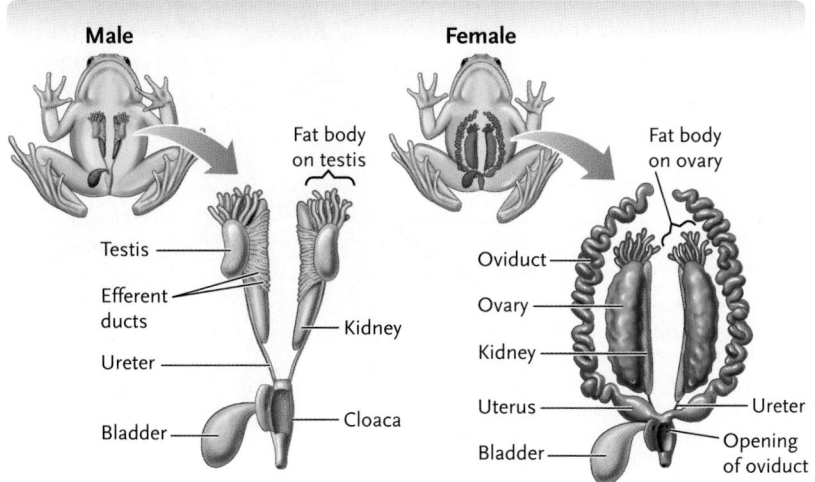

**Male**

Fat body on testis
Testis
Efferent ducts
Ureter
Bladder
Kidney
Cloaca

**Female**

Fat body on ovary
Oviduct
Ovary
Kidney
Uterus
Bladder
Ureter
Opening of oviduct

### c. Mammal (cat)

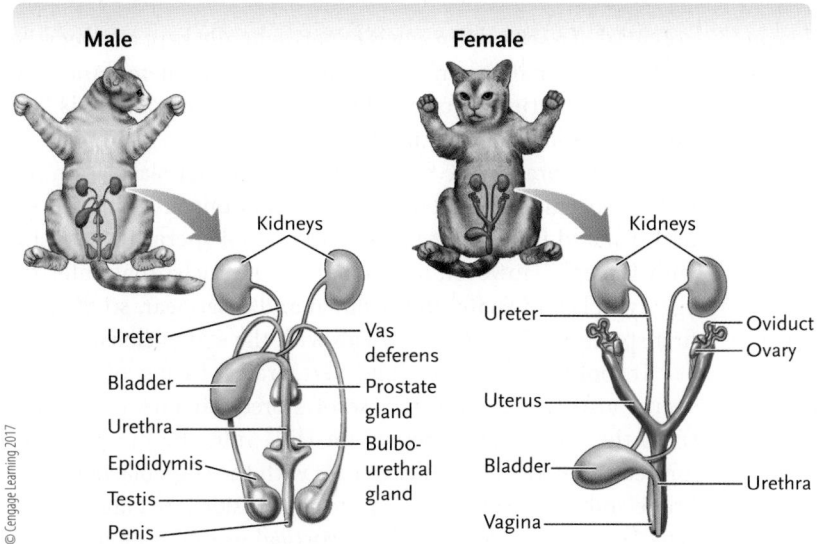

**Male**

Kidneys
Ureter
Bladder
Urethra
Epididymis
Testis
Penis
Vas deferens
Prostate gland
Bulbo-urethral gland

**Female**

Kidneys
Ureter
Uterus
Bladder
Vagina
Oviduct
Ovary
Urethra

© Cengage Learning 2017

**FIGURE 44.5 Some reproductive systems. (a)** An insect, *Drosophila* (fruit fly). **(b)** An amphibian, a frog. **(c)** A mammal, a cat. Female systems are shown in blue and male systems in yellow.

provides the aquatic medium required for fertilization without the danger of gametes drying when exposed to the air. Effecting internal fertilization means close contact between individuals.

Hans Pfletschinger

Eggs

**FIGURE 44.6 A male leopard frog (*Rana pipiens*) clasping a female during a mating embrace known as *amplexus*.** The tight squeeze by the male frog stimulates the female to release her eggs, which stream from her body embedded in a mass of egg jelly. Sperm released by the male fertilize the eggs as they pass from the female.

Male sharks and rays use a pair of modified pelvic fins as accessory sex organs that channel sperm directly into the female's cloaca. Male reptiles, birds, and mammals also use accessory sex organs to place sperm directly inside the reproductive tract of females, where fertilization takes place. In reptiles and birds that lay their eggs, sperm must fertilize eggs as they are released from the ovary and travel through the oviducts, before the shell is added. In mammals, the penis delivers sperm into the female's vagina, which is a specialized structure for reproduction. Fertilization takes place when a sperm meets an egg in the oviducts.

Once a sperm touches the outer surface of an egg of the same species **(Figure 44.7a)**, receptor proteins in the sperm plasma membrane bind the sperm to the vitelline coat, or zona pellucida (Figure 44.7b, step 4). In most animals, only a conspecific (same species) sperm is recognized and binds to the egg surface. Species recognition between sperm and eggs is particularly important in animals using external fertilization because water surrounding the egg may contain sperm from many different species. This aspect is less important in species using internal fertilization, where structural adaptations and behavioural patterns usually limit sperm transfer from males to females of the same species.

After initial attachment of sperm to egg, the events of fertilization proceed in rapid succession (see Figure 44.7b). The acrosome of the sperm releases its contents, including enzymes that dissolve a path through the egg coats. The sperm, with its tail still beating, follows the path until its plasma membrane touches

**a. Sperm adhering to egg**

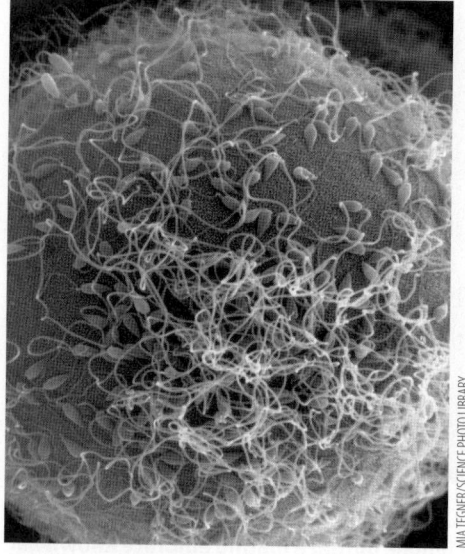

MIA TEGNER/SCIENCE PHOTO LIBRARY

**b. Steps in fertilization**

**1** A sperm contacts the jelly layer of the egg.

**2** The acrosomal reaction begins: Enzymes contained in the acrosome are released and dissolve a path through the jelly layer.

**3** Proteins in its plasma membrane bind the sperm to the vitelline coat.

**4** The sperm lyses a hole in the vitelline coat. The sperm and egg plasma membranes fuse.

**5** Membrane depolarization produces the fast block to polyspermy.

**6** The sperm nucleus and centriole enter the egg. The sperm nucleus then fuses with the egg nucleus.

**7** The fusion of egg and sperm triggers the release of $Ca^{2+}$ ions, which trigger the cortical reaction, the fusion of secretory **cortical granules** with the egg's plasma membrane. The enzymes of the granules released to the outside alter the egg coats, producing the slow block to polyspermy.

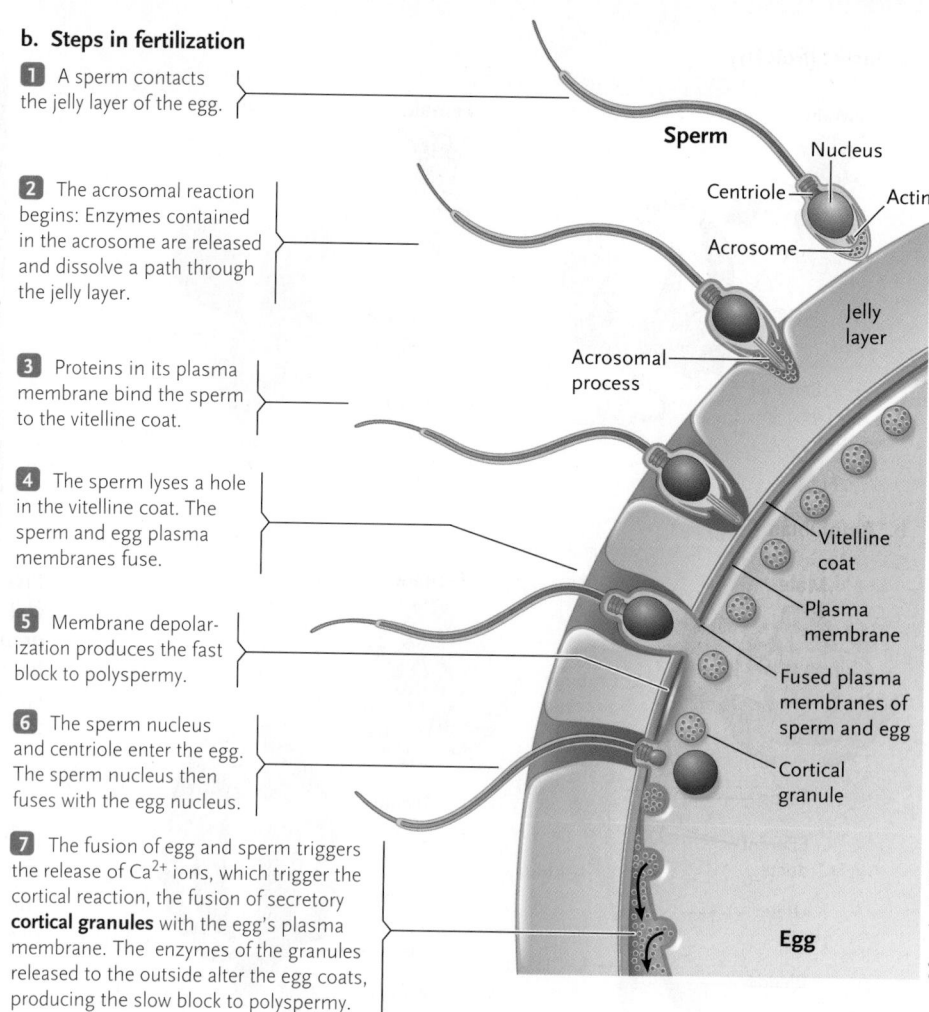

© Cengage Learning 2017

**FIGURE 44.7 Fertilization. (a)** Sperm adhering to the surface coat of a sea urchin egg. Of the many sperm that may initially adhere to the outer surface of the egg, usually only one accomplishes fertilization. **(b)** Steps of fertilization in a sea urchin

and fuses with the egg's plasma membrane (step 5). Fusion introduces the sperm nucleus into the egg cytoplasm and activates the egg to complete meiosis and begin development.

### 44.3c Polyspermy: Keeping Sperm Out of the Fertilized Egg

Protection against polyspermy (more than one sperm fertilizing an egg) is widespread in the animal kingdom. Two mechanisms help prevent polyspermy: a **fast block** that works within seconds of fertilization, and a **slow block** that works in minutes. In invertebrate species such as the sea urchin, fusion of egg and sperm opens ion channels in the egg's plasma membrane, spreading a wave of electrical depolarization over the egg surface (much like a nerve impulse travelling along a neuron). Depolarization alters the egg plasma membrane so that it cannot fuse with any additional sperm, eliminating the possibility of more than one set of paternal chromosomes entering the egg. This fast block occurs within a few seconds of fertilization.

The fast block depends on a change in the egg's membrane potential from negative to positive. When the membrane

potential of a sea urchin egg is experimentally kept at a negative value, additional sperm fuse with the plasma membrane. Fertilization is entirely blocked, however, if the membrane is kept positive before sperm contact.

In vertebrates, the wave of membrane depolarization following sperm–egg fusion is not as pronounced as it is in sea urchins, and it does not prevent additional sperm from fusing with the egg. However, additional sperm nuclei that enter the egg cytoplasm usually break down and disappear, so only the first sperm nucleus to enter fuses with the egg nucleus.

In both invertebrates and vertebrates, fusion of egg and sperm also triggers the release of stored calcium ($Ca^{2+}$) ions from the endoplasmic reticulum (ER) into the cytosol. $Ca^{2+}$ ions cause cortical granules to fuse with the egg's plasma membrane and release their contents to the outside (see Figure 44.7b, step 7). Enzymes released from cortical granules alter the egg coats within minutes of fertilization, so no further sperm can attach to or penetrate the egg. This process is the slow block to polyspermy.

The importance of $Ca^{2+}$ to cortical granule release has been demonstrated experimentally. Granules are released in unfertilized eggs if $Ca^{2+}$ is added experimentally to the cytoplasm. Conversely, if chemicals that bind $Ca^{2+}$ are added to the cytoplasm of unfertilized eggs, the concentration of $Ca^{2+}$ cannot rise and cortical granule release does not occur after fertilization.

After the sperm nucleus enters the egg cytoplasm, microtubules move the sperm and egg nuclei together in the egg cytoplasm until they fuse. The chromosomes of egg and sperm nuclei then assemble and enter mitosis. The subsequent, highly programmed events of embryonic development convert the fertilized egg into an individual capable of independent existence (see Section 44.5).

The paternal chromosomes, the microtubule organizing centre, and one or two centrioles (see Chapter 7) are the only components of sperm to survive in the egg. Therefore, almost all cytoplasmic structures of the embryo and of the new individual are maternal in origin. The centrioles of the new individual are normally of paternal origin.

### 44.3d Reproductive Systems May Be Oviparous, Ovoviviparous, or Viviparous in Animals with Internal Fertilization

In animals with internal fertilization, three major types of support for embryonic development have evolved: oviparity, meaning egg laying; viviparity, meaning giving birth to live offspring; and ovoviviparity, meaning giving birth to live offspring that first hatch internally from eggs.

- **Oviparous** animals (*ovum* = egg; *parere* = to bring forth, to bear) lay eggs that contain the nutrients needed for development of the embryo outside the mother's body. Examples are insects, spiders, most reptiles, and birds **(Figure 44.8a)**. The only oviparous mammals are the monotremes: the echidnas and the duck-billed platypus (*Ornithorhynchus anatinus*), both of which are native to Australasia and Papua New Guinea.

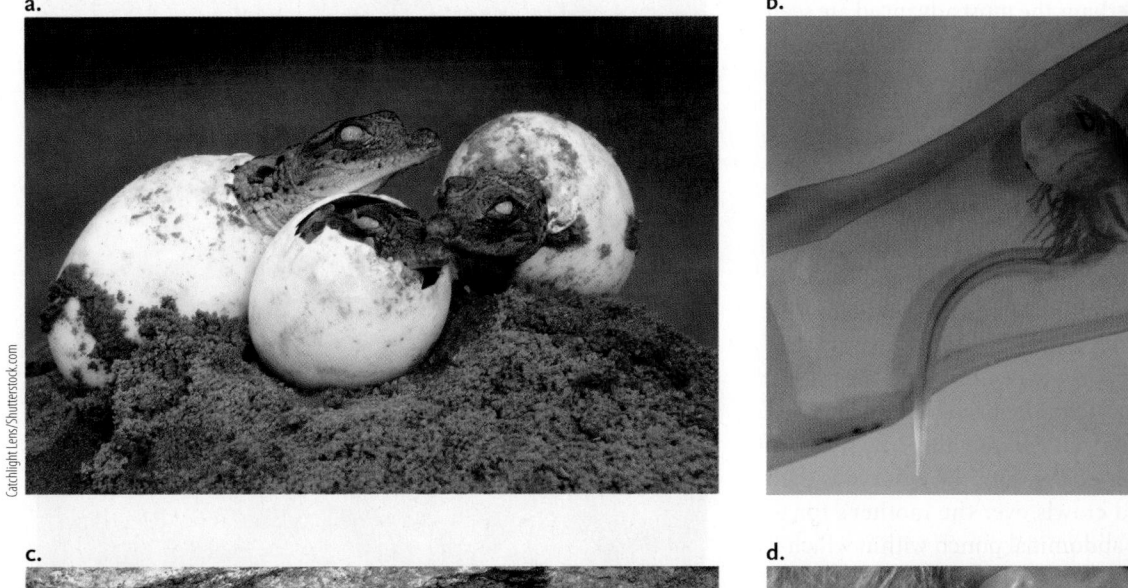

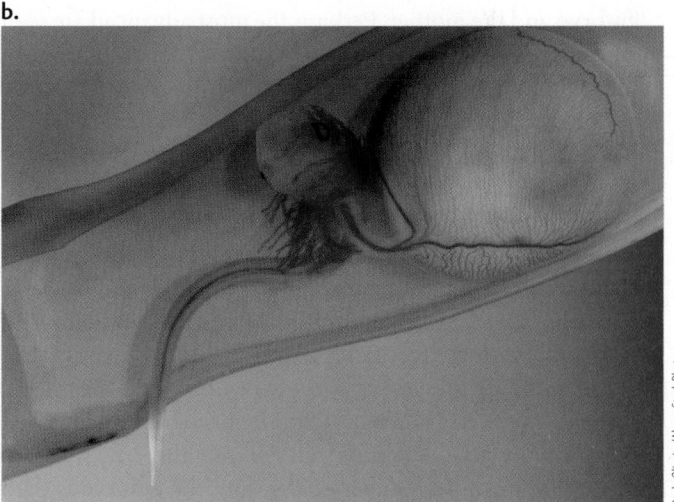

**FIGURE 44.8** **(a)** Oviparous alligators hatching directly from external eggs. **(b)** The ovoviviparous embryo of a shark developing within an egg within the reproductive tract of its mother. **(c)** An ovoviviparous snake giving birth to young that developed from eggs within her reproductive tract. **(d)** Developing offspring of a marsupial mammal, an opossum (*Didelphis virginiana*), attached to a nipple in the marsupium (pouch) of its mother

- **Ovoviviparous** animals retain fertilized eggs within the body, and the embryo develops using the nutrients provided by the egg. When development is complete, the eggs hatch inside the mother and the offspring are released to the exterior. Ovoviviparity is seen in some fishes, lizards, and amphibians; many snakes; and many invertebrates (Figure 44.8b, c). There are also examples where it is the male that hosts the developing eggs, as seen in some species of mouth brooding fish.

- **Viviparous** animals (*vivus* = alive) retain the embryo within the mother's body and nourish it during at least early embryo development. All mammals except the monotremes are viviparous. Viviparity is also seen in all other vertebrate groups except for crocodilians, turtles, and birds. An exceptionally well preserved Devonian fossil placoderm (*Materpiscis attenboroughi*) reveals that viviparity is an ancient trait in vertebrates. In viviparous animals, development of the embryo takes place in a specialized portion of the female reproductive tract, the **uterus** (womb). Various structural adaptations are present in different species to enhance nutrient, waste, and gas exchange between the developing embryo and the mother. Perhaps the most advanced are seen among the mammals. One group, called the *placental mammals*, or *eutherians*, has a specialized temporary structure, the **placenta**, which connects the embryo to the uterus. The placenta facilitates the transfer of nutrients from the blood of the mother to the embryo, and the movement of wastes in the opposite direction. Humans are placental mammals. Another group of mammals, the marsupials, or metatherians, were originally called *non-placental mammals* because of a belief that they lacked a placenta. In fact, they do have a placenta, but it derives from a different tissue than that of eutherians and does not connect the embryo and the uterus. Instead, it provides nutrients to the embryo from an attached membranous sac containing yolk for only the early stages of its development. In many metatherians, the embryo is then born at an early stage and crawls over the mother's fur to reach the **marsupium**, an abdominal pouch within which it attaches to nipples and continues its development (Figure 44.8d). Kangaroos, koalas, wombats, and opossums are marsupials.

## 44.3e  Hermaphroditism: Producing Eggs and Sperm in One Individual

Hermaphroditic (from Hermes + Aphrodite, a Greek god and goddess) individuals can produce both eggs and sperm. **Hermaphroditism** is more common among sponges (Porifera), Cnidaria, flatworms (Platyhelminthes), earthworms, land snails, and some other invertebrates than it is in vertebrates.

Simultaneous hermaphrodites are individuals that develop functional ovaries and testes at the same time. Earthworms, as shown in **Figure 44.9**, are a good example of **simultaneous hermaphroditism**. The only known vertebrate simultaneous hermaphrodites are hamlets (genus *Hypoplectrus*), a group of predatory sea basses (Figure 44.9). Most simultaneous hermaphroditic individuals do not fertilize themselves.

**FIGURE 44.9 (a)** Simultaneous hermaphroditism in the earthworm. Copulation by a mating pair of earthworms, in which each individual releases sperm that fertilizes the eggs in its partner. **(b)** *Hypoplectrus gummigutta,* a predatory sea bass that is a simultaneous hermaphrodite. **(c)** Sequential hermaphrodism in the clown fish (*Amphiprion* sp.), in which individuals begin life as males but then become females

Self-fertilization is prevented by anatomical barriers that preclude introduction of sperm into the hermaphrodite's own body, or by mechanisms that cause eggs and sperm to mature at different times. The prevention of self-fertilization maintains the genetic variability of sexual reproduction.

Sequential hermaphrodites are individuals that change from one sex to the other. **Sequential hermaphroditism** occurs in many invertebrates (e.g., some crustaceans) and some ectothermic vertebrates. Well-known examples are the genus *Amphiprion*, in which, in some species, the initial sex is male (as in clownfish), whereas in others, it is female. In still other species, individuals may waver between sexes with no discernible order, the sex of any individual being determined by the ratio of sexes in its immediate community (many species of gobies).

## STUDY BREAK QUESTIONS

1. What are egg coats and what is their function? What egg coats do mammalian and bird eggs have?
2. Why do the eggs of animals differ so much in size? What are the implications for development?
3. What are the costs and benefits of internal fertilization? What are the costs and benefits of external fertilization?

# 44.4 Sexual Reproduction in Mammals

Reproductively, humans are typical eutherian (placental) mammals. Males and females each have a pair of gonads (testes or ovaries). As in other vertebrates, gonads serve a dual function, producing gametes and secreting hormones responsible for sexual development and mating behaviour.

## 44.4a Female Sexual Organ Function in Oocyte Production, Fertilization, and Embryonic Development

Human females have a pair of ovaries suspended in the abdominal cavity (**Figure 44.10**). An oviduct leads from each ovary to the uterus, which is hollow and has walls that contain smooth muscle. The uterus is lined by the endometrium, which is formed by layers of connective tissue with embedded glands and richly supplied with blood vessels. If an egg is fertilized and begins development, it must implant in the endometrium to continue developing. The lower end of the uterus, the cervix, opens into a muscular canal, the **vagina**, which leads to the exterior. Sperm enter the female reproductive tract via the vagina, and at birth the baby passes from the uterus through the vagina to the outside.

The **vulva**, the external female sex organs (genitalia), surround the opening of the vagina (Figure 44.10). Two folds of tissue, the **labia minora**, run from front to rear on either side of the opening. Labia minora are partially covered by **labia majora**, a pair of fleshy, fat-padded folds that also run from front to rear on either side of the vagina. At the anterior end of the vulva, the labia minora join to partly cover the **clitoris**, a bulblike erectile organ with the same embryonic origins as the male penis. Two **greater vestibular glands** open near the entrance to the vagina and secrete a mucus-rich fluid that lubricates the vulva. The urethra conducts urine from the bladder to the outside and opens between the clitoris and the vaginal opening. Most nerve endings associated with erotic sensations are concentrated in the clitoris and the labia minora and around the opening of the vagina. When a human female is born, a thin flap of tissue, the **hymen**, partially covers the opening of the vagina. This membrane, if it has not already been ruptured by physical exercise or other disturbances, is broken during the first sexual intercourse.

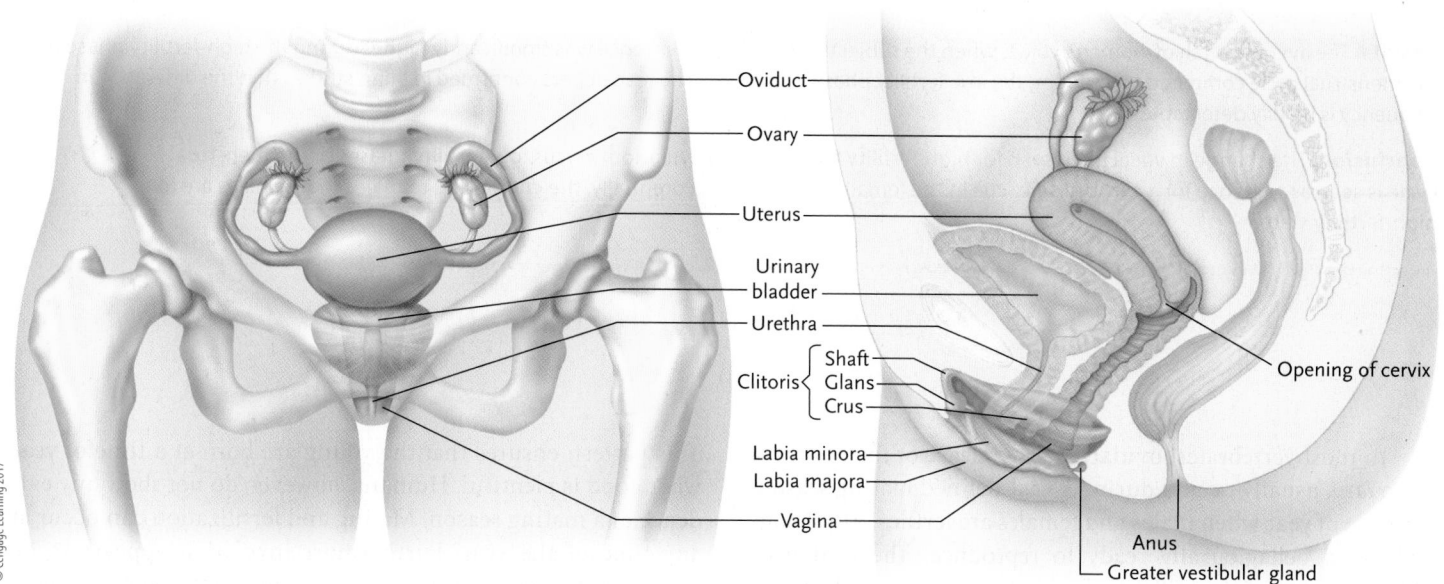

© Cengage Learning 2017

**FIGURE 44.10 The reproductive organs of a human female**

FIGURE 44.11   **Experimental Research**

## Vocal Cues to Ovulation in Human Females

**Question:** Are there cues to ovulation in human females?

**Experiment:** Primate females other than humans display well-characterized visual or olfactory cues that signal their reproductive state **(Figure 1a)**. Some research has documented particular cues associated with ovulation in humans; those cues relate to femininity and female attractiveness. Based on those observations, Gregory Bryant and Martie Haselton, of the University of California, Los Angeles, hypothesized that vocal cues associated with female attractiveness would increase in frequency (pitch) over the menstrual cycle. A higher voice pitch is a signal associated with higher levels of female sex hormones and correlates with being younger, both of which correlate with high fertility. To test their hypothesis, the researchers recruited 69 women with normal menstrual cycles and collected two sets of vocal samples from them saying "Hi, I'm a student at UCLA." One set was taken during a high-fertility phase of the cycle (at a time near ovulation) and the other set was taken during a low-fertility phase (at the luteal phase). The phase of the menstrual cycle at the time of vocal sampling was confirmed directly by hormonal tests. The samples were analyzed for the pitches of the voices. Significant differences were determined using statistical methods.

**a. Ovulating female baboons**

**b. Human female voice pitch during ovulation**

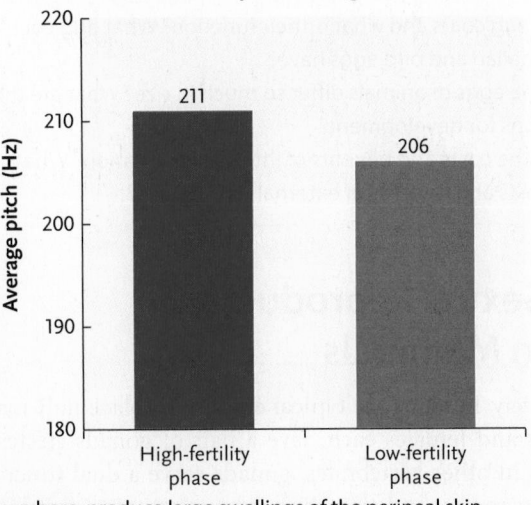

**Figure 1**  **(a)** Females of some primate species, such as the baboons shown here, produce large swellings of the perineal skin, often with bright coloration, around the time of ovulation. Male baboons fight more aggressively and spend more time grooming females with larger swellings. **(b)** Human females change the pitch of their voice around the time of ovulation, a subtle but detectable difference in frequency.

**Results:** The average pitch of women's voices when the subjects said a simple sentence was significantly higher during the high-fertility phase of the menstrual cycle compared with during the low-fertility phase (Figure 1b). The researchers confirmed in blind studies that the difference in frequency is readily detectable.

**Conclusion:** The change in vocal pitch seen for high-fertility (approaching ovulation) versus low-fertility phases of the menstrual cycle is seen as evidence for a cyclic fertility cue in the female human voice. Potentially, the cue signals to males that females are in a high-fertility state.

© Cengage Learning 2017. Based on G. A. Bryant and M. G. Haselton. 2009. Vocal cues of ovulation in human females. Biology Letters 5:12–15; L. G. Domb and M. Pagel. 2000. Sexual swellings advertise female quality in wild baboons. Nature 410:204–206.

In most vertebrates, **ovulation**, the release of the egg from the ovary, usually occurs during a well-defined mating season, the time of year when males and females are fertile—physiologically and behaviourally ready to reproduce. The timing of mating seasons is usually under the general control of day length (photoperiod), with some adjustment for local weather. This pattern ensures that the young are born at a time of year when food is plentiful. Humans, however, do not show any evidence of a mating season. Mating and fertilization can occur at any time of the year. Furthermore, ovulation appears to be cryptic in humans, meaning that many women do not know when they are ovulating, nor do their partners **(Figure 44.11)**.

Reproduction in human females is under neuroendocrine control, involving complex interactions between the hypothalamus, pituitary, ovaries, and uterus. The **ovarian cycle** occurs from puberty to menopause and involves the events in the ovaries leading to the release of a mature egg approximately every 28 days. In human females, at birth, each ovary contains about 1 million oocytes whose development is arrested at the end of the first meiotic prophase. Although 200 thousand to 380 thousand oocytes survive until a female reaches sexual maturity, only about 380 are actually ever ovulated. These are released as immature eggs, usually one per cycle, into the abdominal cavity and pulled into the nearby oviduct by the current produced by the beating of the cilia that line the oviduct. The cilia propel the egg along the oviduct and into the uterus. Fertilization usually occurs in the oviduct. The ovarian cycle is coordinated with the **uterine cycle**, or **menstrual cycle** (*menses* = month), events in the uterus that prepare it for implantation of the egg if fertilization occurs.

The beginning of the ovarian cycle **(Figure 44.12)** is stimulated by the release of gonadotropin-releasing hormone (GnRH) by the hypothalamus. GnRH stimulates the pituitary to release follicle-stimulating hormone (FSH) and luteinizing hormone (LH) into the bloodstream **(Figure 44.13a)**.

FSH stimulates 6–20 oocytes in the ovaries to begin meiosis. As oocytes develop, they become surrounded by cells that form a **follicle** (the ovum and follicle cells; see Figure 44.12, step 1 and Figure 44.13a, day 2). During this phase, the follicle grows and develops, and at its largest size becomes filled with fluid and may be 12–15 mm in diameter. Usually, only one follicle develops to maturity with release of the egg (secondary oocyte) by ovulation. Multiple births can result if two or more follicles develop and their eggs ovulate in one cycle.

As the follicle enlarges, FSH and LH interact to stimulate estrogen (female sex hormone, primarily estradiol) secretion by follicular cells. Initially, estrogens are secreted in low amounts and have a negative feedback effect on the pituitary, inhibiting secretion of FSH. As a result, FSH secretion declines briefly. But estrogen secretion increases steadily, and its level peaks about 12 days after the beginning of follicle development (Figure 44.13c, day 12). High estrogen level has a positive feedback effect on the hypothalamus and pituitary, increasing secretion of GnRH and stimulating the pituitary to release a burst of FSH and LH. Increased estrogen levels convert the mucus secreted by the uterus to a thin and watery consistency, making it easier for sperm to swim through the uterus.

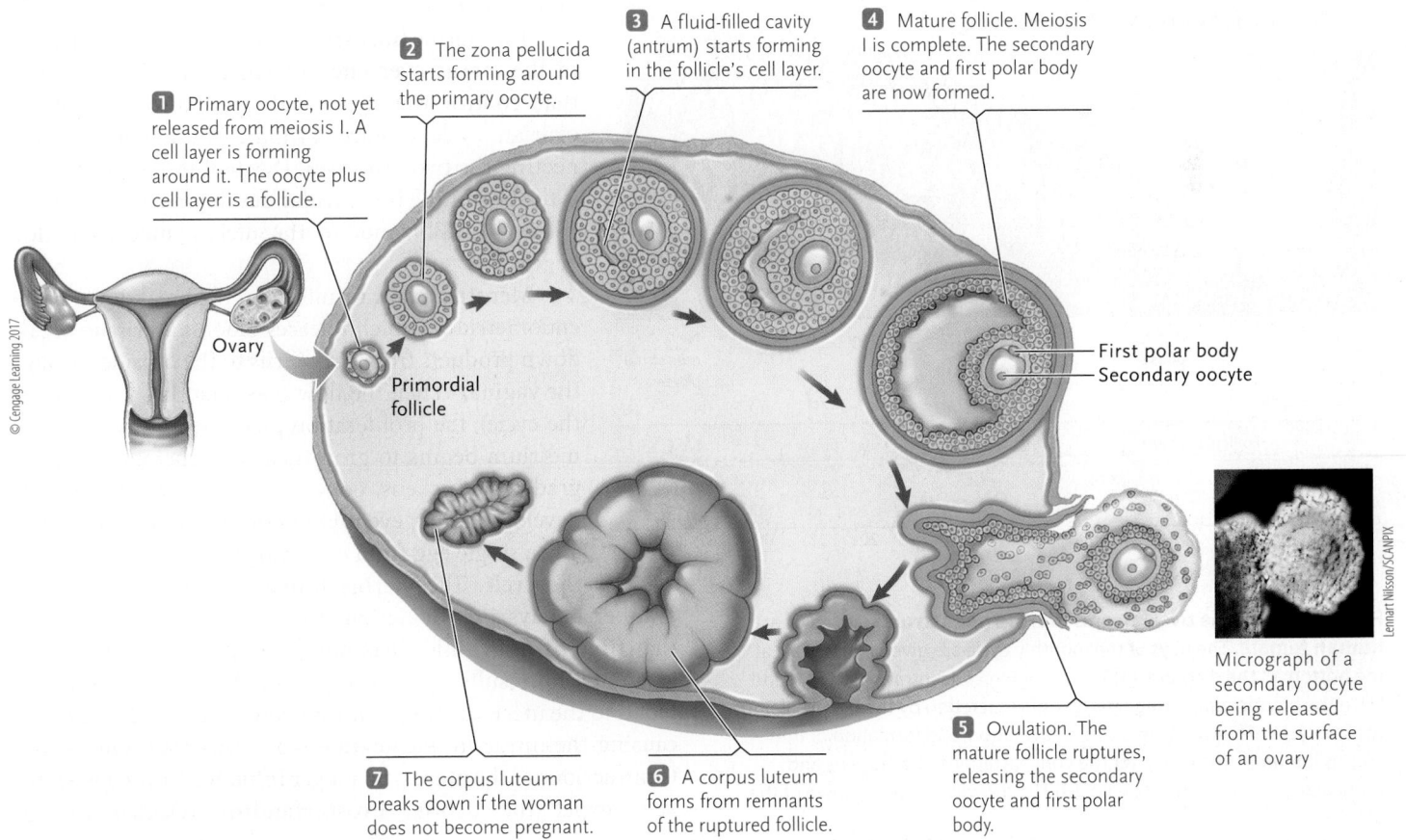

**1** Primary oocyte, not yet released from meiosis I. A cell layer is forming around it. The oocyte plus cell layer is a follicle.

**2** The zona pellucida starts forming around the primary oocyte.

**3** A fluid-filled cavity (antrum) starts forming in the follicle's cell layer.

**4** Mature follicle. Meiosis I is complete. The secondary oocyte and first polar body are now formed.

Ovary

Primordial follicle

First polar body
Secondary oocyte

**7** The corpus luteum breaks down if the woman does not become pregnant.

**6** A corpus luteum forms from remnants of the ruptured follicle.

**5** Ovulation. The mature follicle ruptures, releasing the secondary oocyte and first polar body.

Micrograph of a secondary oocyte being released from the surface of an ovary

© Cengage Learning 2017

Lennart Nilsson/SCANPIX

**FIGURE 44.12 The growth of a follicle, ovulation, and the formation of the corpus luteum in a human ovary**

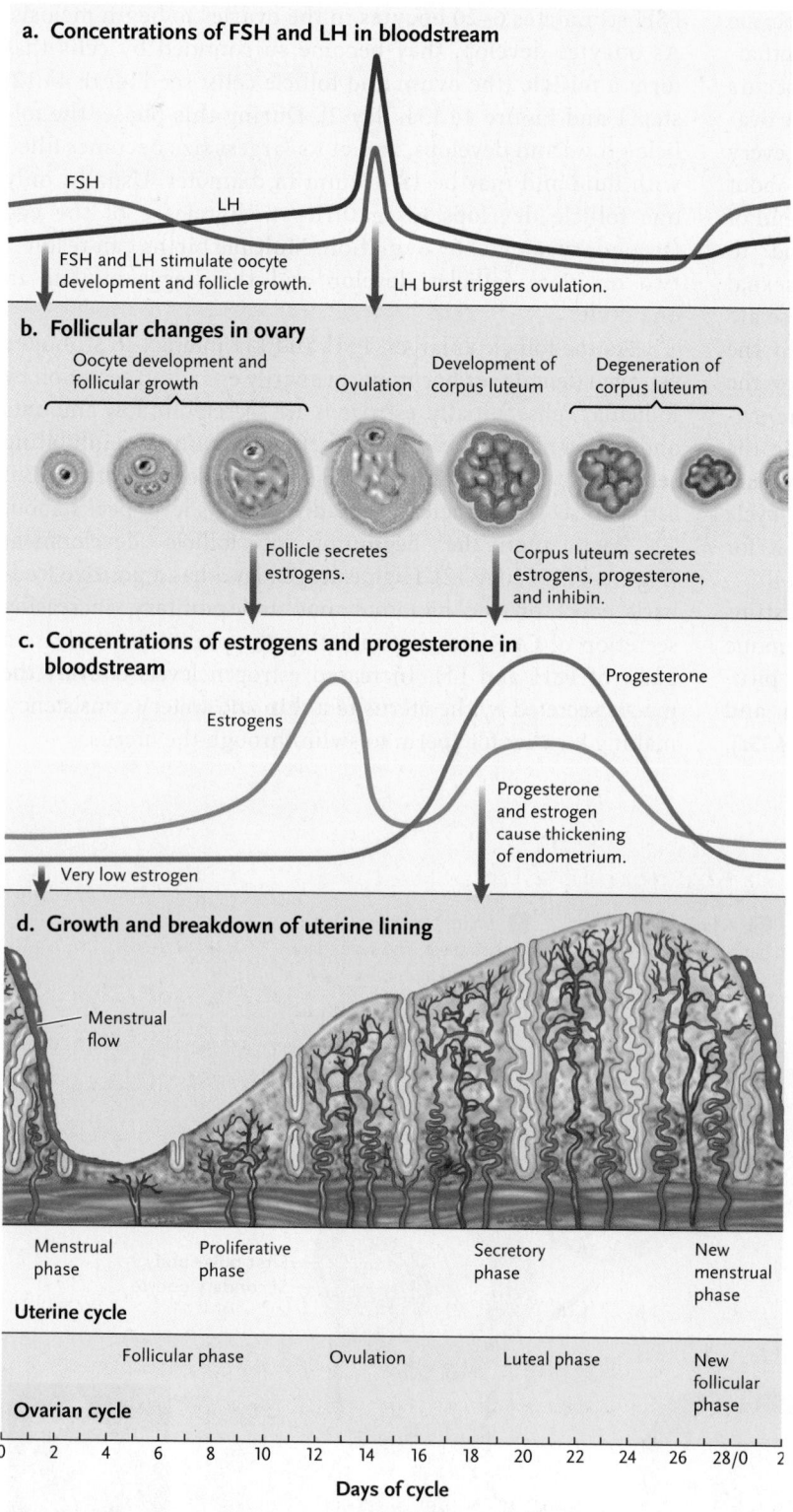

**a. Concentrations of FSH and LH in bloodstream**

FSH

LH

FSH and LH stimulate oocyte development and follicle growth.

LH burst triggers ovulation.

**b. Follicular changes in ovary**

Oocyte development and follicular growth

Ovulation

Development of corpus luteum

Degeneration of corpus luteum

Follicle secretes estrogens.

Corpus luteum secretes estrogens, progesterone, and inhibin.

**c. Concentrations of estrogens and progesterone in bloodstream**

Progesterone

Estrogens

Progesterone and estrogen cause thickening of endometrium.

Very low estrogen

**d. Growth and breakdown of uterine lining**

Menstrual flow

Menstrual phase

Proliferative phase

Secretory phase

New menstrual phase

**Uterine cycle**

Follicular phase

Ovulation

Luteal phase

New follicular phase

**Ovarian cycle**

0  2  4  6  8  10  12  14  16  18  20  22  24  26  28/0  2

**Days of cycle**

© Cengage Learning 2017

**FIGURE 44.13 The ovarian and uterine (menstrual) cycles of a human female.** The days of the monthly cycle are given in the scale at the bottom of the diagram. **(a)** The changing concentrations of FSH and LH in the bloodstream, triggered by GnRH secretion by the hypothalamus. **(b)** The cycle of follicle development, ovulation, and formation of the corpus luteum in the ovary. **(c)** The concentrations of estrogens and progesterone in the bloodstream. **(d)** The growth and breakdown of the uterine lining

Ovulation occurs after the burst in LH secretion stimulates the follicle cells to release enzymes that digest away the wall of the follicle, causing it to rupture and release the egg (see Figure 44.12, step 5). LH also causes the follicle cells remaining at the surface of the ovary to grow into the **corpus luteum**, an enlarged, yellowish structure (*corpus* = body; *luteum* = yellow), initiating the luteal phase. The corpus luteum (see Figure 44.12, step 6) acts as an endocrine gland that secretes estrogens, as well as large quantities of progesterone, a second female sex hormone, and **inhibin**, another hormone. Progesterone stimulates growth of the uterine lining and inhibits contractions of the uterus. Progesterone and inhibin have a negative feedback effect on the hypothalamus and pituitary. Progesterone inhibits secretion of GnRH and, in turn, secretion of FSH and LH by the pituitary. Inhibin specifically inhibits FSH secretion. The fall in FSH and LH levels diminishes the signal for follicular growth, and no new follicles begin to grow in the ovary.

If fertilization does not occur, the corpus luteum gradually shrinks, perhaps because of the low levels of LH. About 10 days after ovulation, the shrinkage has inhibited secretion of estrogen, progesterone, and inhibin. In the absence of progesterone, menstruation begins. As progesterone and inhibin levels decrease, FSH and LH secretion is no longer inhibited and a new monthly cycle begins.

The uterine (menstrual) cycle includes the changes in the uterus over one ovarian cycle. The hormones that control the menstrual cycle also control the ovarian cycle (Figure 44.13d), physiologically connecting the two processes. Day 0 of the monthly cycle is the beginning of follicular development in the ovary (Figure 44.13b) and, in the uterus, menstrual flow begins.

Menstrual flow results from the breakdown of the endometrium, which releases blood and tissue breakdown products from the uterus to the outside through the vagina. When the flow ceases (at day 4 to day 5 of the cycle), the proliferation phase begins as the endometrium begins to grow again. As the endometrium gradually thickens, oocytes in both ovaries begin to develop further, eventually leading to ovulation (usually a single egg from one ovary) at about 14 days into the cycle. The uterine lining continues to grow for another 14 days after ovulation. This is the secretory phase. At that time, if fertilization has not taken place, the absence of progesterone results in contraction of the arteries supplying blood to the uterine lining, shutting down the blood supply and causing the lining to disintegrate. The menstrual flow begins. Contractions of the uterus, no longer inhibited by progesterone, help expel the debris. **Prostaglandins** released by the degenerating endometrium add to uterine contractions, making them severe enough to be felt as the pain of cramps and sometimes producing other effects, such as nausea, vomiting, and headaches.

Menstruation occurs only in human females and our closest primate relatives, gorillas and chimpanzees. In other mammals, the uterine lining is completely reabsorbed if a fertilized egg does not implant during the period of reproductive activity. The uterine cycle in these mammals is called the *estrous cycle*, and females are said to be in estrus when fertile.

**DELAYING REPRODUCTION** Unlike humans, many mammals have a distinct reproductive season. Its timing is often triggered by changes in photoperiod that herald the changing seasons of the year or by lunar events (e.g., in corals). Other animals are more opportunistic. For instance, many species of seals disassociate the act of mating from birth (also known as *parturition*; **Figure 44.14**). Males defend territories on beaches where females haul out to give birth. Females undergo a postpartum estrus, so they are ready to mate (fertile) immediately after giving birth. The seals mate, the egg is fertilized, and the zygote is formed, but implantation is delayed for several months and the young are born a year later. The time between mating and birth is considerably longer than the gestation period (the time needed for the growth and development of the fetus). This approach to reproduction maximizes the chances of males and females finding mates, yet still giving birth at opportune times.

Bats in the families Rhinolophidae and Vespertilionidae separate the acts of copulation and ovulation. The gestation period in these species is about 60 days. In temperate regions, species in both families mate in late summer and early autumn (**Figure 44.15**). Females store the sperm in their uteri and then enter hibernation. Ovulation and fertilization occur when

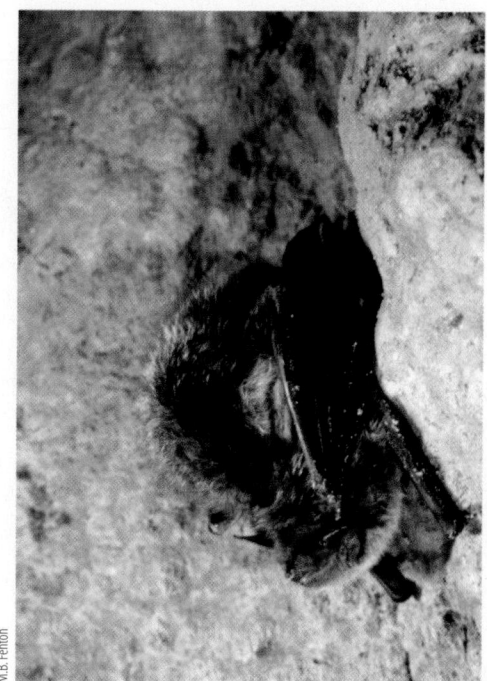
M.B. Fenton

**FIGURE 44.15 A pair of little brown bats *(Myotis lucifugus)* mating.** The male is on the female's back.

females leave hibernation in the spring, and the young are born when spring is well advanced.

Fertilization followed by delays in development or implantation can allow males and females more control over mate choice through interactions among sperm or between sperm and the females' reproductive tract. Delays achieved by sperm storage and postponement of ovulation raise possibilities of competition between sperm or other mechanisms for selecting the sperm that fertilizes the egg.

## 44.4b Male Sexual Organs Function in Sperm Production and Delivery

Organs that produce and deliver sperm make up the male reproductive system (**Figure 44.16**). Human males have a pair of testes (singular, *testis*), suspended in a baglike **scrotum**. Keeping the testes at cooler temperatures than the body core provides an optimal environment for sperm development. Some land mammals, such as elephants and monotremes, with relatively low body temperatures have internal (cryptic) testes carried within the body. Marine mammals such as whales and dolphins also have internal testes despite relatively high body temperatures. In these animals, countercurrent exchange between cool blood flowing from the tail flukes to the testis cools them enough to allow the production of fertile sperm. In many mammals (e.g., grey squirrels, *Sciurus carolinensis*), the testes descend into the scrotum only during the mating season. Otherwise, they are

Christopher Boswell/Shutterstock.com

**FIGURE 44.14 A pair of northern elephant seals *(Mirounga angustirostris)* mating**

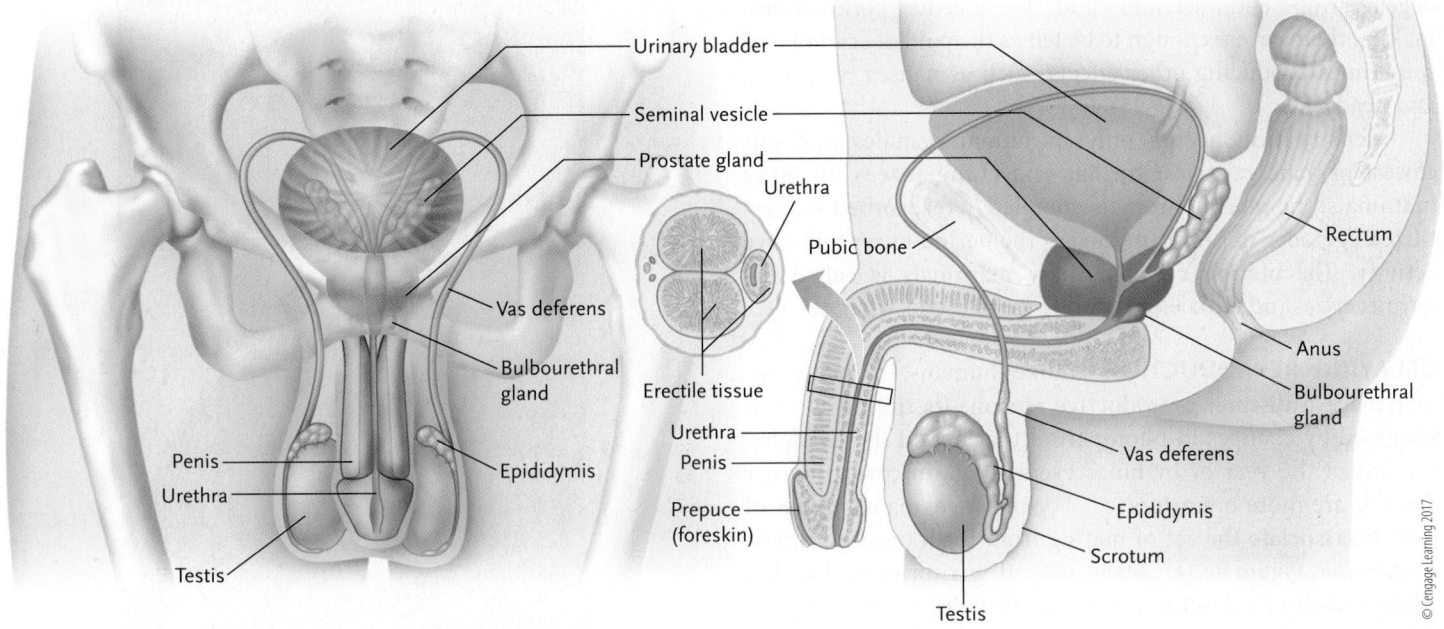

**FIGURE 44.16 The reproductive organs of a human male**

© Cengage Learning 2017

cryptic—kept in the body captivity—where temperatures are too warm to produce fertile sperm.

In human males, each testicle is packed with about 125 m of **seminiferous tubules** in which sperm proceed through all stages of spermatogenesis **(Figure 44.17)**. The entire process, from spermatogonium to sperm, takes 9–10 weeks, and the testes produce about 130 million fertile sperm each day.

**Sertoli cells** are supportive cells that completely surround the developing spermatocytes in the seminiferous tubules. Sertoli cells supply nutrients to the spermatocytes and seal them off from the body's blood supply. **Leydig cells**, located in the tissue surrounding the developing spermatocytes, produce the male sex hormones (**androgens**), most notably, **testosterone**.

Mature sperm flow from seminiferous tubules into the **epididymis**, a coiled storage tubule attached to the surface of each testis. Rhythmic muscular contractions of the epididymis move sperm into a thick-walled, muscular tube, the **vas deferens** (plural, vasa deferentia), which extends through the abdominal cavity. Just below the bladder, the vasa deferentia join the urethra. During ejaculation, muscular contractions force the sperm into the urethra and out of the penis. At this time, the sperm are activated and become motile when they come into contact with alkaline secretions added to the ejaculated fluid by accessory glands.

About 150–350 million sperm are released in a single ejaculation. **Semen**, the ejaculate, is a mixture of sperm and the secretions of several accessory glands. In humans, about two-thirds of the volume is produced by a pair of **seminal vesicles** that secrete seminal fluid, a thick, viscous liquid, into the vasa deferentia near the point where they join with the urethra. Seminal fluid contains prostaglandins that, when ejaculated into the female, trigger contractions of the female reproductive tract that help move the sperm into and through the uterus.

The **prostate gland**, which surrounds the region where the vasa deferentia empty into the urethra, adds a thin, milky fluid to the semen. The alkaline prostate secretion makes up about one-third of the volume of semen, raising its pH (and that of the vagina) to about pH 6, the level of acidity best tolerated by sperm. This pH level also fosters sperm motility. As part of the prostate secretion, a fast-acting enzyme converts the semen to a thick gel at ejaculation. The thickened consistency helps keep the semen from draining from the vagina when the penis is withdrawn. A second, slower-acting enzyme in the prostate secretion gradually breaks down the semen clot and releases the sperm to swim freely in the female reproductive tract.

Finally, a pair of **bulbourethral glands** secrete a clear, mucus-rich fluid into the urethra before and during ejaculation. This fluid lubricates the tip of the penis and neutralizes the acidity of any residual urine in the urethra. In total, the secretions of the accessory glands make up more than 95% of the volume of semen; less than 5% is sperm.

Most of the interior of the penis is filled with three cylinders of spongelike tissue (corpora cavernosa) that become filled with blood and cause erection during sexual arousal. Although the human penis depends solely on engorgement of spongy

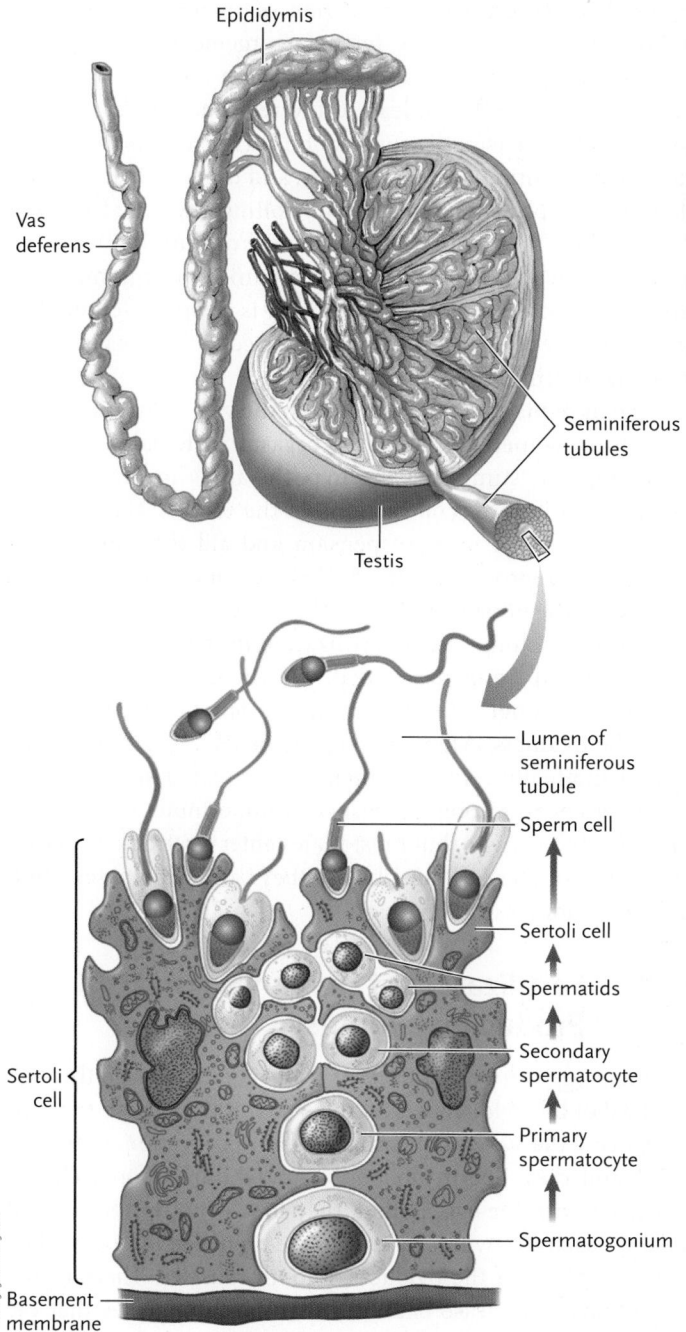

Epididymis

Vas
deferens

Seminiferous
tubules

Testis

Lumen of
seminiferous
tubule

Sperm cell

Sertoli cell

Spermatids

Secondary
spermatocyte

Sertoli
cell

Primary
spermatocyte

Spermatogonium

Basement
membrane

© Cengage Learning 2017

**FIGURE 44.17 The structure of seminiferous tubules and the stages of spermatogenesis.** Spermatogonia are located nearest the outer wall and mature sperm cells nearest the tubule lumen. Sertoli cells completely surround the developing spermatocytes and protect them from attack by the immune system.

tissue for erection, the males of many mammals, including bats, rodents, carnivores, and most other primates, have a baculum, or penis bone **(Figure 44.18)**, that helps maintain the penis in an erect state. The presence of bacula in a species usually coincides with the presence of a baubellum (clitoris bone) in females.

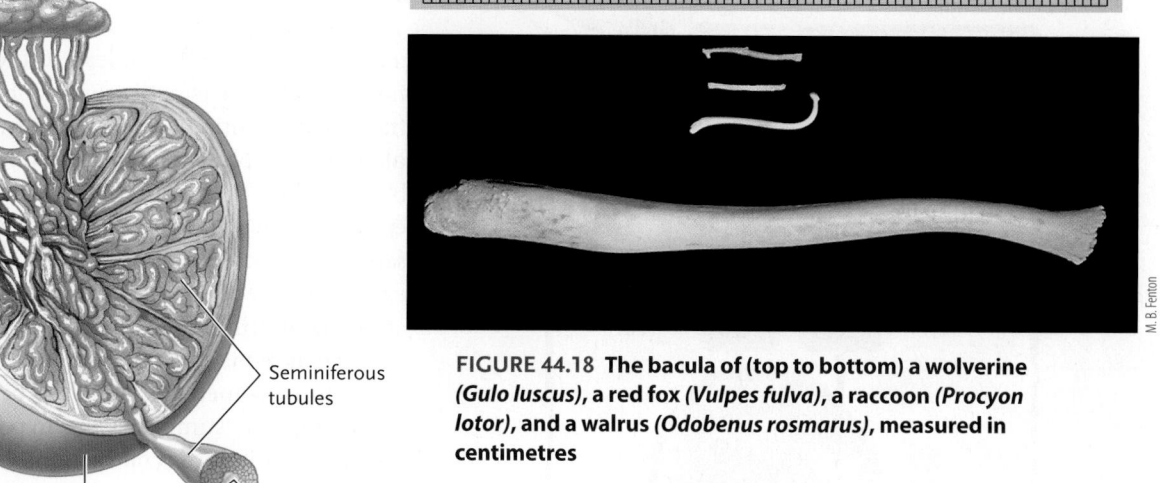

M. B. Fenton

**FIGURE 44.18 The bacula of (top to bottom) a wolverine (*Gulo luscus*), a red fox (*Vulpes fulva*), a raccoon (*Procyon lotor*), and a walrus (*Odobenus rosmarus*), measured in centimetres**

The penis ends in the **glans**, a soft, caplike structure. Most nerve endings producing erotic sensations are crowded into the glans and the region of the penile shaft just behind the glans. The **prepuce**, or **foreskin**, is a loose fold of skin that covers the glans (see Figure 44.16). In many human cultures, the foreskin is removed for hygienic, religious, or other ritualistic reasons by **circumcision** (= around cut). In 2007, the World Health Organization stated that male circumcision is an important strategy to prevent heterosexually acquired HIV infection in males. Female circumcision, the removal of the labia minora and the clitoris, is often called *female genital mutilation* (FGM). FGM is practised in various countries in western, eastern, and north-eastern Africa and in parts of Asia and the Middle East. The World Health Organization estimates that 100–140 million women and girls around the world have experienced the procedure. It is now considered a human rights violation carried out to reduce libido and control women's sexuality. The United Nations holds an International Day of Zero Tolerance to Female Genital Mutilation each February 6.

Many of the hormones regulating the menstrual cycle, including GnRH, FSH, LH, and inhibin, also regulate male reproductive functions. Testosterone, secreted by the Leydig cells in the testes, also plays a key role **(Figure 44.19)**. In sexually mature males, the hypothalamus secretes GnRH in brief pulses every 1 to 2 hours. GnRH stimulates the pituitary to secrete LH and FSH. LH stimulates the Leydig cells to secrete testosterone, which stimulates sperm production and controls the growth and function of male reproductive structures. FSH stimulates Sertoli cells to secrete a protein and other molecules required for spermatogenesis.

Concentrations of male reproductive hormones are maintained by negative feedback mechanisms. If the concentration of testosterone falls in the bloodstream, the hypothalamus

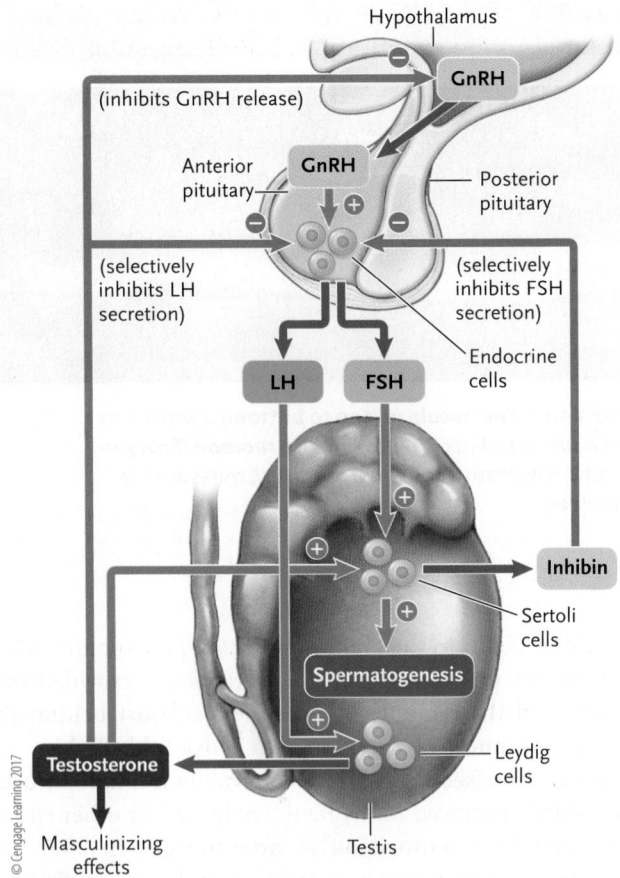

Hypothalamus

GnRH

(inhibits GnRH release)

GnRH

Anterior pituitary

Posterior pituitary

(selectively inhibits LH secretion)

(selectively inhibits FSH secretion)

Endocrine cells

LH    FSH

Inhibin

Sertoli cells

Spermatogenesis

Testosterone

Leydig cells

© Cengage Learning 2017

Masculinizing effects

Testis

**FIGURE 44.19 Hormonal regulation of reproduction in the male and the negative feedback systems controlling hormone levels**

responds by increasing GnRH secretion. If testosterone levels rise too high, the overabundance inhibits LH secretion. An overabundance of testosterone also stimulates Sertoli cells to secrete inhibin, which inhibits FSH secretion by the pituitary. As a result, testosterone secretion by the Leydig cells drops off, returning the concentration to optimal levels in the bloodstream.

When the male is sexually aroused, sphincter muscles controlling the flow of blood to the spongy erectile tissue of the penis relax, allowing the tissue to become engorged with blood (the penis is a hydrostatic skeleton structure; see Chapter 46). As the spongy tissue swells, it maintains the pressure by compressing and almost shutting off the veins draining blood from the penis. The engorgement produces an erection in which the penis lengthens, stiffens, and enlarges. During continued sexual arousal, lubricating fluid secreted by the bulbourethral glands may be released from the tip of the penis.

Female sexual arousal results in enlargement and erection of the clitoris in a process analogous to erection of the penis. The labia minora become engorged with blood and swell in size, and lubricating fluid is secreted onto the surfaces of the vulva by the vestibular glands. In addition to these changes, the

nipples become erect by contraction of smooth muscle cells, and the breasts swell in size due to engorgement with blood.

Insertion of the penis into the vagina and the thrusting movements of copulation lead to the reflex actions of ejaculation, including spasmodic contractions of muscles surrounding the vasa deferentia, accessory glands, and urethra. During ejaculation, the sphincter muscles controlling the exit from the bladder close tightly, preventing urine from mixing with the ejaculate. Ejaculation is usually accompanied by orgasm, a sensation of intense physical pleasure that is the peak (climax) of excitement for sexual intercourse, followed by feelings of relaxation and gratification.

The motions of copulation stretch the vagina and stimulate the clitoris, sometimes inducing orgasm in females. Vaginal stretching also stimulates the hypothalamus to secrete oxytocin, which induces contractions of the uterus. The contractions keep the sperm in suspension and aid their movement through the reproductive tract. Uterine contractions are also induced by the prostaglandins in the semen.

Sperm reach the site of fertilization in the oviducts within 30 minutes of being ejaculated. Of the millions of sperm released in a single ejaculation, only a few hundred actually reach the oviducts. After orgasm, the penis, clitoris, and labia minora gradually return to their unstimulated size. Females can experience additional orgasms within minutes or even seconds of a first orgasm, but most males enter a refractory period lasting 15 minutes or longer before they can regain an erection and have another orgasm.

## 44.4c Fertilization of Human Eggs: Producing Zygotes

A human egg can be fertilized only during its passage through the third of the oviduct nearest the ovary. If the egg is not fertilized during the 12–24 hours that it is in this location, it disintegrates and dies. Sperm do not swim randomly for a chance encounter with the egg. Rather, they first swim up the cervical canal to reach the oviduct and then are propelled up the oviduct by contractions of the oviduct's smooth muscles. There is evidence that eggs release chemical attractant molecules that the sperm recognize, causing them to swim directly toward the egg.

**CONCEPT FIX** Although 150–350 million sperm are released in a single ejaculation by a human male, an ovum can only be fertilized by one sperm. It is a misconception that several sperm can fertilize a single ovum. ⬡

Sperm must first penetrate the layer of follicle cells surrounding the egg, aided by enzymes in the sperm plasma membrane **(Figure 44.20)**. Then the sperm adhere to receptor molecules on the surface of the zona pellucida. This contact triggers the **acrosome reaction** in which enzymes contained in the acrosome are released from the sperm onto the zona pellucida, where they digest a path to the plasma membrane of the egg. This is the same process described earlier in the chapter (Figure 44.7). As soon as the first sperm cell reaches the egg, sperm and egg plasma membranes fuse, and the sperm cell is

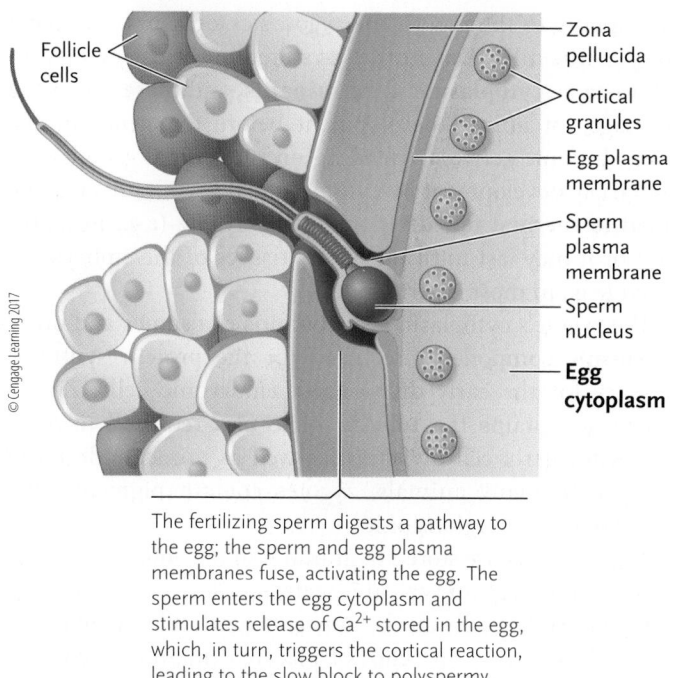

Follicle cells

Zona pellucida

Cortical granules

Egg plasma membrane

Sperm plasma membrane

Sperm nucleus

**Egg cytoplasm**

© Cengage Learning 2017

The fertilizing sperm digests a pathway to the egg; the sperm and egg plasma membranes fuse, activating the egg. The sperm enters the egg cytoplasm and stimulates release of Ca²⁺ stored in the egg, which, in turn, triggers the cortical reaction, leading to the slow block to polyspermy.

**FIGURE 44.20 Fertilization in mammals**

engulfed by the cytoplasm of the egg. Although only one sperm fertilizes the egg, the combined release of acrosomal enzymes from many sperm greatly increases the chance that a complete channel will be opened through the zona pellucida. This is, in part, why a low sperm count is often a source of male infertility. Low sperm counts can be caused by infection, heat, frequent ejaculation, smoking, and excessive alcohol consumption.

Membrane fusion activates the egg. The sperm that enters the egg releases nitric oxide that stimulates the release of stored Ca²⁺ in the egg. Ca²⁺ triggers cortical granule release to the outside of the egg. Enzymes from the cortical granules cross-link molecules in the zona pellucida, hardening it and sealing the channels opened by acrosomal enzymes. The enzymes also destroy receptors that bind sperm to the surface of the zona pellucida. As a result, no further sperm can bind to the zona pellucida or reach the plasma membrane of the egg. The Ca²⁺ also triggers the completion of meiosis of the egg. The sperm and egg nuclei then fuse, and the cell is now considered a zygote. Mitotic divisions of the zygote soon initiate embryonic development.

The first cell divisions of embryonic development take place while the fertilized egg is still in the oviduct. About seven days after ovulation, the embryo passes from the oviduct and implants in the uterine lining. During and after implantation, cells associated with the embryo secrete **human chorionic gonadotropin (hCG)**, a hormone that keeps the corpus luteum in the ovary from breaking down. Excess hCG is excreted in the urine; its presence in urine or blood provides the basis of pregnancy tests.

Continued activity of the corpus luteum keeps estrogen and progesterone secretion at high levels, maintaining the uterine lining and preventing menstruation. The high progesterone level also thickens the mucus secreted by the uterus, forming a plug that seals the opening of the cervix from the vagina. The plug keeps bacteria, viruses, and sperm cells from further copulations from entering the uterus.

About 10 weeks after implantation, the placenta takes over the secretion of progesterone, hCG secretion drops off, and the corpus luteum regresses. However, the corpus luteum continues to secrete the hormone relaxin, which inhibits contraction of the uterus until near the time of birth.

## 44.4d Controlling Reproduction: Contraception

Knowledge about the details of reproduction can allow us to control fertility. In some cases, this means increasing the chances of reproducing, whereas in other cases, it means minimizing them. In human society, pregnancy can be a blessing or a disaster, depending on the situation. Statistics describing the effectiveness of different means of limiting human reproductive output **(Table 44.1)** illustrate our progress in the area of family planning. Knowledge about the timing of ovulation, for example (see Figure 44.13), can provide the means to maximize or minimize the chances of pregnancy.

Biologists working to conserve biodiversity often attempt to control reproduction. When a species is on the brink of extinction, the goal is to maximize reproductive output. Techniques

| TABLE 44.1 | Pregnancy Rates for Birth Control Methods | |
|---|---|---|
| Method | Lowest Expected Rate of Pregnancy[a] | Typical-Use Rate of Pregnancy[b] |
| Rhythm method | 1–9% | 25% |
| Withdrawal | 4% | 19% |
| Condom (male) | 3% | 14% |
| Condom (female) | 5% | 21% |
| Diaphragm and spermicidal jelly | 6% | 20% |
| Vasectomy (male sterilization) | 0.1% | 0.15% |
| Tubal ligation (female sterilization) | 0.5% | 0.5% |
| Contraceptive pill (combination estrogen–progestin) | 0.1% | 5% |
| Contraceptive pill (progestin only) | 0.5% | 5% |
| Implant (progestin) | 0.09% | 0.09% |
| Intrauterine device (IUD) (copper T) | 0.6% | 0.8% |

[a] Rate of pregnancy when the birth control method was used correctly every time.

[b] Rate of pregnancy when the method was used typically, meaning that it may not have always been used correctly every time.

Source: U.S. Food and Drug Administration. Data reported in 1997 for effectiveness of methods in a one-year period.

can range from the use of foster parents to raise young to using reproductive technologies such as *in vitro* fertilization and implantation of embryos. For example, biologists working with black-footed ferrets, which are highly endangered, strive to maximize reproductive output to increase the population.

Similarly, when an increasing population of one species threatens to overwhelm other species or an ecosystem, the goal is to prevent reproduction. Biologists faced with growing populations of African elephants try to reduce reproductive output using techniques ranging from the application of contraceptives to females to culling (killing) individuals in the population. Culling usually targets females because they produce young (see Chapter 29). The same principles of controlling reproductive output have been central to humans' domestication of other organisms.

## STUDY BREAK QUESTIONS

1. How does the reproductive pattern of human females differ from that of other mammals? What is the significance of this? (See also Chapters 27, 29, and 32.)
2. Given all the changes in hormones associated with the ovarian and uterine cycles, which hormones can be used as good predictors of ovulation?
3. How can biologists control reproduction? Why is access to control of reproduction important?

## 44.5 Development

The process of development takes an animal from the zygote (fertilized egg) to the complete adult stage of the life cycle. The surroundings of the developing animal (embryo or larva) can influence the process, although the mechanisms and the major patterns of development are common among multicellular animals. Genetic controls underlie the cellular and molecular processes involved in animal development and include apoptosis, the programmed death of cells. Exploration of the development processes in a range of animals illustrates both diversity and underlying principles.

### 44.5a Mechanisms of Embryonic Development

When a sperm fertilizes an egg, a zygote is produced. At this point, embryonic development begins, ultimately producing a free-living individual from the single fertilized cell! All the instructions required for the production of all the different structures of the animal are packed into the zygote; all are produced by mitotic divisions of the zygote (see Chapter 7).

The early cell divisions are directed by information stored in two locations in the zygote. The nucleus houses the DNA derived from egg and sperm nuclei. This DNA directs development as individual genes are turned on and off in a regulated and ordered manner. The balance of the information is stored in the zygote's cytoplasm. Because sperm contribute essentially

no cytoplasm to the zygote, the zygote's cytoplasm is maternal in origin. The mRNA and proteins stored in the egg cytoplasm are known as **cytoplasmic determinants**, and these direct the first stages of animal development before the genes in the nucleus become active. Depending on the animal group, control of early development by cytoplasmic determinants may be limited to the first few divisions of the zygote (e.g., in mammals), or it may last until the actual tissues of the embryo are formed (e.g., in most invertebrates).

The zygote's cytoplasm also contains ribosomes and other cytoplasmic components required for the protein synthesis necessary for the early divisions of embryonic cells. Zygote cytoplasm contains the tubulin molecules required to form spindles for early cell divisions, as well as mitochondria and nutrients. In many animals, zygotes contain pigments that colour the egg, or regions of it.

The nutrients are stored in granules in the **yolk** and in lipid droplets. In the eggs of typical insects, reptiles, and birds, large amounts of yolk supply all the nutrients for development of the embryo. In contrast, the eggs of placental mammals contain very little yolk, which is used only to support the earliest stages of development.

Depending on the species, yolk may be concentrated at one end of the egg, in the centre of the egg, or distributed evenly throughout the egg. Unequal distribution of yolk and other components in the egg is termed **polarity**. In most species, the egg's nucleus is located toward one end, called the **animal pole**. The animal pole typically gives rise to surface structures and the anterior end of the embryo. The opposite end of the egg, the **vegetal pole**, typically gives rise to internal structures such as the gut, along with the posterior end of the embryo. When yolk is unequally distributed in the egg cytoplasm, it is usually concentrated in the vegetal half of the egg. Egg polarity plays a role in setting the three body axes of bilaterally symmetrical animals, namely the anterior–posterior axis, the dorsal–ventral (back–front) axis, and the left–right axis **(Figure 44.21)**.

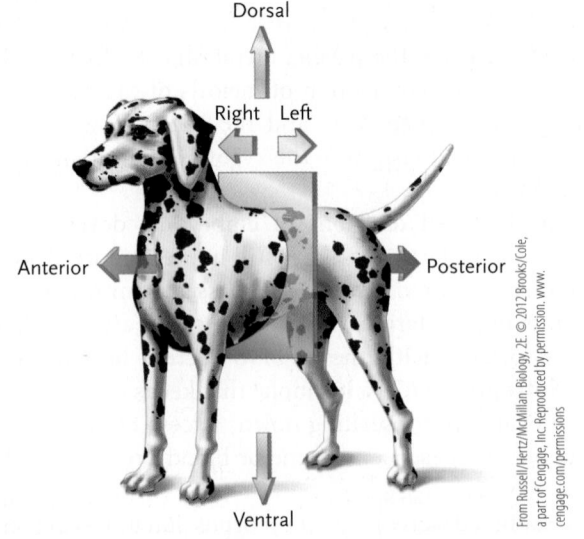

**FIGURE 44.21 Body axes: anterior–posterior, dorsal–ventral, and left–right**

From Russell/Hertz/McMillan. Biology, 2E. © 2012 Brooks/Cole, a part of Cengage, Inc. Reproduced by permission. www.cengage.com/permissions

**CLEAVAGE AND GASTRULATION: ZYGOTE TO MULTICELLULAR EMBRYO** Soon after fertilization, the zygote begins a series of mitotic divisions in which cycles of DNA replication and division occur without the production of new cytoplasm. Thus, the cytoplasm of the zygote is partitioned into successively smaller cells without increasing the size or mass of the embryo **(Figure 44.22)**. These are referred to as *cleavage divisions*. In the frog *Xenopus laevis*, 12 cleavage divisions produce an embryo of about 4000 cells that collectively occupy about the same volume and mass as the original zygote.

**Cleavage** is the first of three major developmental stages that, with modifications, are common to the early development of most animals. It leads to the formation of a ball of cells. **Gastrulation**, the stage following cleavage, produces an early embryo in which three distinct primary tissue layers appear. **Organogenesis** follows gastrulation and gives rise to the development of the major organ systems. At the end of organogenesis, the embryo has the body organization characteristic of its species. Cell division, cell movements, and cell rearrangements occur during gastrulation and organogenesis. **Figure 44.23** shows these stages as part of the life cycle of a frog.

In frogs, further cleavage divisions (divisions that cleave a cell in two) form two different structures in succession **(Figure 44.24)**. As more cells are produced, they form a solid ball or layer of cells, the **morula** (= mulberry). As cleavage divisions continue, the ball or the layer hollows out to form the **blastula** (*blast* = bud or offshoot; *ula* = small), the second structure, in

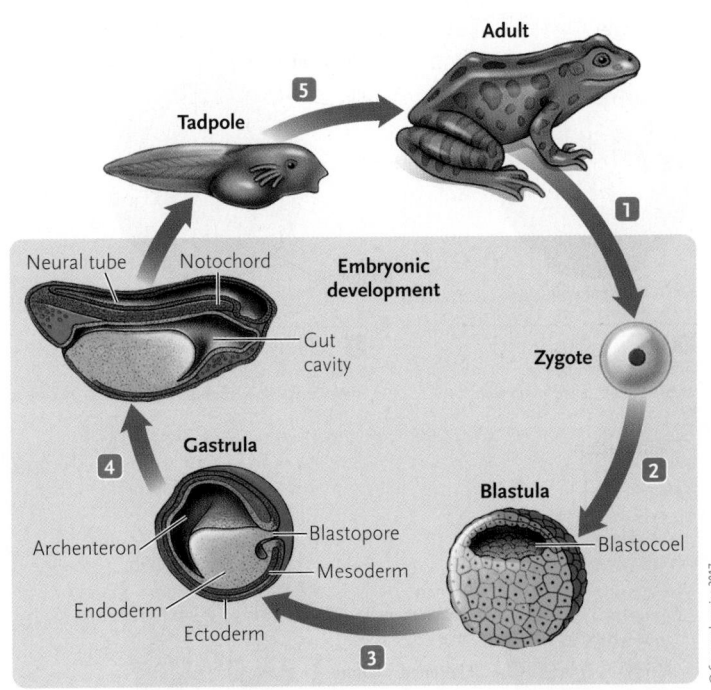

**1** **Fertilization:** A sperm penetrates an egg and their nuclei fuse, producing a zygote.

**2** **Cleavage:** Mitotic cell divisions produce a morula, a solid ball of blastomeres. Further divisions produce a blastula, a hollowed ball of blastomeres.

**3** **Gastrulation:** Cell divisions, cell migrations, and rearrangements produce a gastrula, an early embryo that has primary tissue layers.

**4** **Organogenesis:** Cell divisions, cell movements, and other cellular mechanisms produce the major tissues and organ systems, and a body organization characteristic of the species.

**5** **Metamorphosis:** The animal develops into the adult, with characteristic adult appearance and all tissues and organs carrying out their specialized functions.

**FIGURE 44.23** **Stages of animal development shown in a frog**

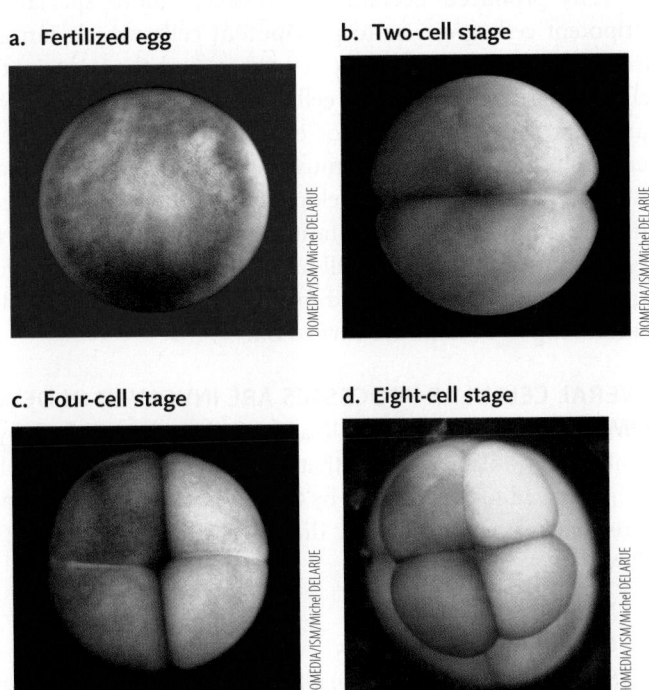

**a. Fertilized egg**

**b. Two-cell stage**

**c. Four-cell stage**

**d. Eight-cell stage**

**FIGURE 44.22** **The first three cleavage divisions of a frog embryo, which convert the fertilized egg into a two-, then a four-, then an eight-cell mass.** Note that no new cytoplasm is produced and so the volume of the single fertilized egg is repackaged into successively smaller cells.

which cells, now called **blastomeres** (*mere* = part or division), enclose a fluid-filled cavity, the **blastocoel** (*coel* = hollow).

Gastrulation occurs once cleavage is complete. Cells of the blastula migrate and divide to produce the **gastrula** (*gaster* = gut or belly). As the blastula develops into the gastrula, embryonic cells begin to differentiate, becoming recognizably different in biochemistry, structure, and function. This process dramatically rearranges the cells of the blastula into the three **primary cell layers** of the embryo: **ectoderm**, the outer layer (*ecto* = outside; *derm* = skin); **endoderm**, the inner layer (*endo* = inside); and **mesoderm** (*meso* = middle), the middle layer between ectoderm and endoderm. In the process, gastrulation establishes the body pattern. Each tissue and organ of the adult animal originates from one of the three primary cell layers of the gastrula **(Table 44.2)**. Cell movements also contribute to the formation of the **archenteron** (*arch* = beginning; *enteron* = intestine or gut), a new cavity within the embryo that is lined with endoderm (Figure 44.24).

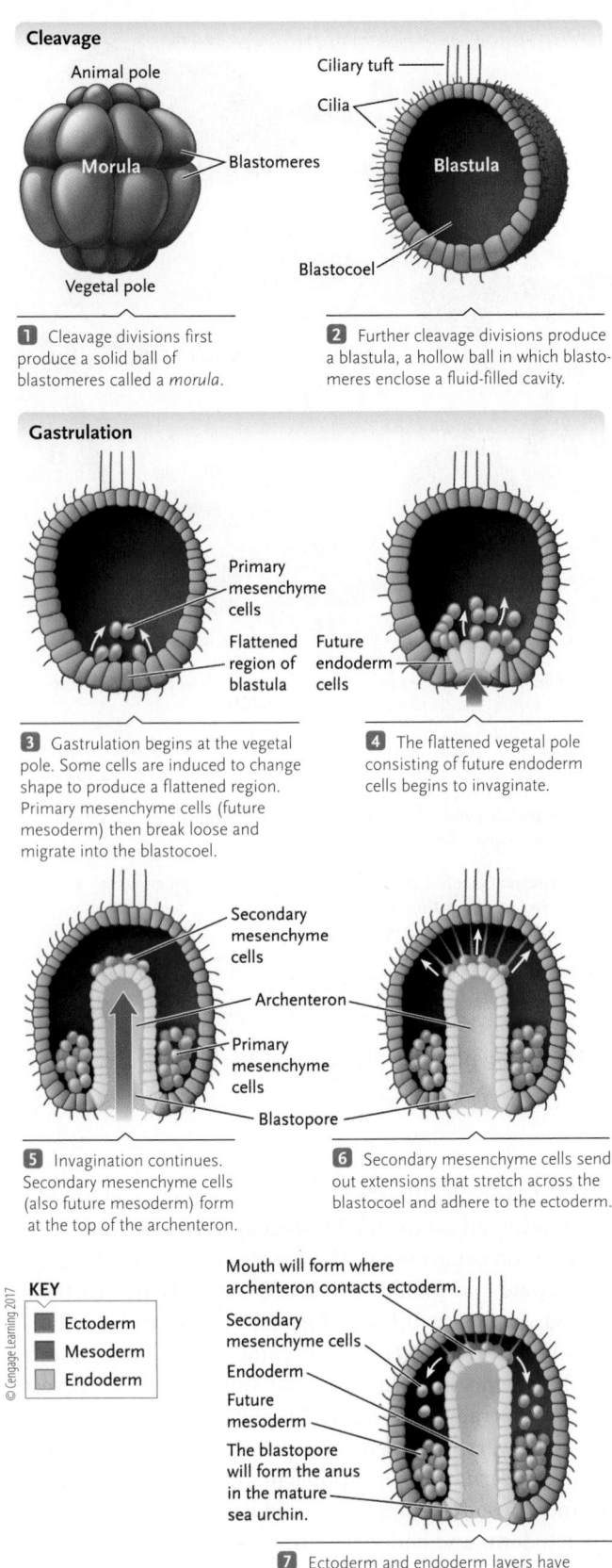

**Cleavage**

Animal pole

Morula

Blastomeres

Vegetal pole

1 Cleavage divisions first produce a solid ball of blastomeres called a *morula*.

Ciliary tuft

Cilia

Blastula

Blastocoel

2 Further cleavage divisions produce a blastula, a hollow ball in which blastomeres enclose a fluid-filled cavity.

**Gastrulation**

Primary mesenchyme cells

Flattened region of blastula

Future endoderm cells

3 Gastrulation begins at the vegetal pole. Some cells are induced to change shape to produce a flattened region. Primary mesenchyme cells (future mesoderm) then break loose and migrate into the blastocoel.

4 The flattened vegetal pole consisting of future endoderm cells begins to invaginate.

Secondary mesenchyme cells

Archenteron

Primary mesenchyme cells

Blastopore

5 Invagination continues. Secondary mesenchyme cells (also future mesoderm) form at the top of the archenteron.

6 Secondary mesenchyme cells send out extensions that stretch across the blastocoel and adhere to the ectoderm.

**KEY**

- Ectoderm
- Mesoderm
- Endoderm

Mouth will form where archenteron contacts ectoderm.

Secondary mesenchyme cells

Endoderm

Future mesoderm

The blastopore will form the anus in the mature sea urchin.

7 Ectoderm and endoderm layers have formed; mesoderm cells are between them, some derived from primary mescenchyme cells and others from secondary mesenchyme cells.

**FIGURE 44.24 Cleavage and gastrulation in the sea urchin**

| TABLE 44.2 | Origins of Adult Tissues and Organs in the Three Primary Tissue Layers |
| --- | --- |
| **Primary Tissue Layer** | **Adult Tissues and Organs** |
| Ectoderm | Skin and its elaborations, including hair, feathers, scales, and nails; nervous system, including brain, spinal cord, and peripheral nerves; lens, retina, and cornea of eye; lining of mouth and anus; sweat glands, mammary glands, adrenal medulla, and tooth enamel |
| Mesoderm | Muscles; most of skeletal system, including bones and cartilage; circulatory system, including heart, blood vessels, and blood cells; internal reproductive organs; kidneys and outer walls of digestive tract |
| Endoderm | Lining of digestive tract, liver, pancreas, lining of respiratory tract, thyroid gland, lining of urethra, and urinary bladder |

As the three primary cell layers form, the developmental potential of the cells becomes more limited than that of the fertilized egg from which they originated. In other words, although a fertilized egg is **totipotent**, meaning that it is capable of producing all the various types of cells of the adult, the cells produced become progressively more specialized. Totipotent cells give rise to **pluripotent** cells, which can give rise to most but not all adult cell types, and then pluripotent cells give rise to **multipotent** cells, which give rise to cells with particular functions. Thus, for example, a multipotent mesoderm cell may develop into muscle or bone but not normally into skin or brain, which develop from ectodermal cells. These differentiating cells each contain the complete genome of the organism, but each type of cell has a different program of gene expression; genes not required for the functions that the cell is specializing to become are turned off.

**SEVERAL CELLULAR PROCESSES ARE INVOLVED IN DEVELOPMENT** Development in all animals is accomplished by a number of cellular processes that are under genetic control but are influenced to some extent by the environment (e.g., temperature affects the rate of cell division). The processes are as follows:

- **Mitotic cell division**
- **Cell migration**
- **Selective cell adhesion**, in which cells make and break specific connections to other cells or to the extracellular matrix
- **Induction**, in which one group of cells (the inducer cells) causes or influences another nearby groups of cells (the

© Cengage Learning 2017

responder cells) to follow a particular developmental pathway

- **Determination**, in which the developmental fate of a cell is set and it is committed to becoming a particular cell type. Typically, determination is the result of induction.
- **Differentiation**, which follows determination, establishes a cell-specific developmental program in cells. Differentiation results in cell types with clearly defined structures and functions.
- **Apoptosis**, programmed cell death, in which tissues no longer required for continued development of the organism are removed

## STUDY BREAK QUESTIONS

1. What is yolk? What role does it play?
2. How do cleavage divisions differ from cell division in an adult organism?
3. What are the primary cell layers of the embryo, and what process is responsible for producing them?
4. What mechanisms are involved in animal development from the zygote?

## 44.5b Major Patterns of Cleavage and Gastrulation

With the principles of early embryonic development established, we describe cleavage and gastrulation in three animal groups that have been models in **embryology** (the study of embryos and their development): sea urchins, amphibians, and birds. Later in the chapter, we describe cleavage and gastrulation in mammals, including humans, which resemble the patterns in birds.

**SEA URCHIN** Cleavage divisions proceed at approximately the same rate in all regions of a sea urchin embryo (Figure 44.24, step 1), reflecting uniform distribution of yolk in the egg. These divisions continue until a blastula containing about a thousand cells is formed (step 2).

Gastrulation begins at the vegetal pole of the blastula. Through induction, some cells in the middle of the vegetal pole become elongated and cylindrical, causing the region to flatten and thicken. Then some cells (primary mesenchyme; *mesen* = middle; *chyme* = juice) break loose and migrate into the blastocoel (step 3), making and breaking adhesions until eventually they attach along the ventral sides of the blastocoel. These cells form the future mesoderm (see Figure 44.24, step 7), which give rise to skeletal elements of the embryo. Next, the flattened vegetal pole of the blastula invaginates, pushing gradually into the interior (steps 4 and 5). The cells that invaginate will become endoderm cells. The inward movement, much like pushing in the side of a hollow rubber ball, generates the archenteron, a new cavity that opens through the blastopore.

As the archenteron forms, extensions of cells of the invaginated layer stretch across the blastocoel and contact the inside of the ectoderm (Figure 44.24, step 6). These extensions make tight adhesions and then contract, pulling the invaginated cell layer inward with them, eliminating most of the blastocoel.

Now the embryo has two complete cell layers. The outer layer—the original blastula surface—forms embryonic ectoderm. Cells of the second, inner layer are derived from the archenteron and become endoderm. Mesodermal cells, which begin to form a third layer, are derived from the primary mesenchyme cells and from secondary mesenchyme cells that migrated into the space between the ectoderm and endoderm (step 7). After the formation of the three primary cell layers, cells begin to differentiate based on the activation of different genes and the synthesis of different proteins in each layer.

As ectoderm, mesoderm, and endoderm layers develop, the embryo lengthens into an ellipsoidal shape, with the blastopore marking the posterior end of the embryo. From here on, further cell divisions, combined with cell movements, selective cell adhesions, induction, and differentiation, lead to differentiation of organ systems. In sea urchins and other deuterostomes (see Chapter 27), the blastopore forms the anus, and the mouth will form at the opposite, anterior end of the gut.

**AMPHIBIANS** In the eggs of amphibians such as frogs, yolk is concentrated in the vegetal half, giving it a pale colour. The animal half is darkly coloured because of a layer of pigment granules just below the surface. A sperm normally fertilizes the egg in the animal half (**Figure 44.25**, step 1). After fertilization, the pigmented layer of cytoplasm rotates toward the site of sperm entry, exposing a crescent-shaped region of underlying cytoplasm at the side opposite the point of sperm entry (step 2). This region, the **grey crescent**, establishes the dorsal–ventral axis of the embryo and marks the future dorsal side of the animal.

Normally, the first cleavage division runs perpendicular to the long axis of the grey crescent and divides the crescent equally between resulting cells (step 3). If the first two blastomeres are experimentally divided so that one does not receive grey crescent material, and the two cells are separated, the blastomere without grey crescent material divides but ends up in a disordered mass that stops developing. The blastomere receiving grey crescent material produces a normal embryo. Cytoplasmic material localized in the grey crescent is essential to normal development in frog embryos.

As cleavage of the frog embryo continues, cell divisions proceed more rapidly in the animal half, producing smaller and more numerous cells there than in the yolky vegetal half. By the time cleavage has produced an embryo with 15 000 cells, the animal half has hollowed out, forming the blastula (**Figure 44.26**, step 1).

Gastrulation begins when cells from the animal pole begin to migrate across the embryo surface to reach the region derived from the grey crescent. This site is marked by a crescent-shaped

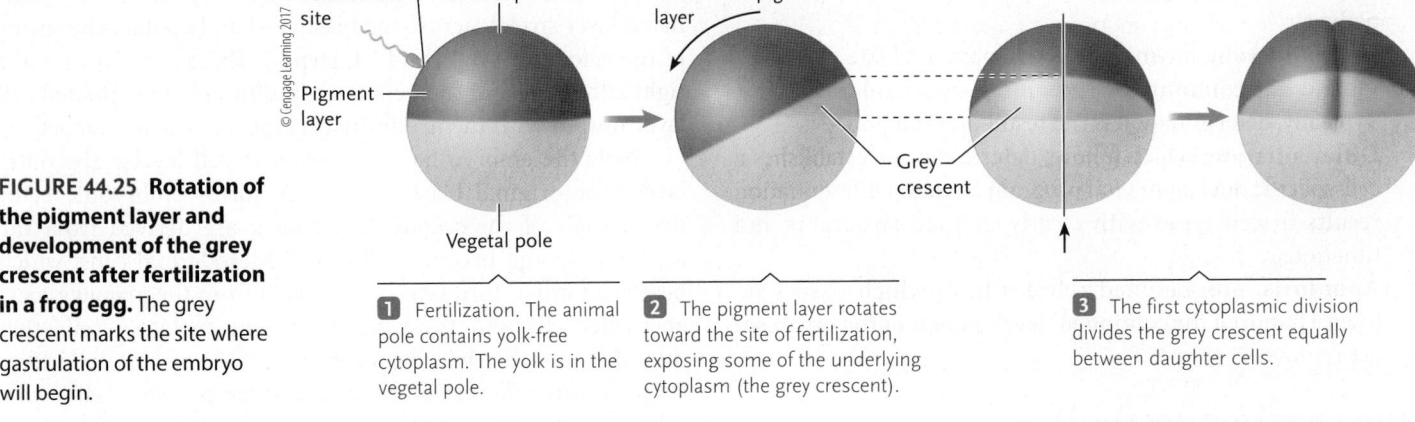

**FIGURE 44.25 Rotation of the pigment layer and development of the grey crescent after fertilization in a frog egg.** The grey crescent marks the site where gastrulation of the embryo will begin.

1 Fertilization. The animal pole contains yolk-free cytoplasm. The yolk is in the vegetal pole.

2 The pigment layer rotates toward the site of fertilization, exposing some of the underlying cytoplasm (the grey crescent).

3 The first cytoplasmic division divides the grey crescent equally between daughter cells.

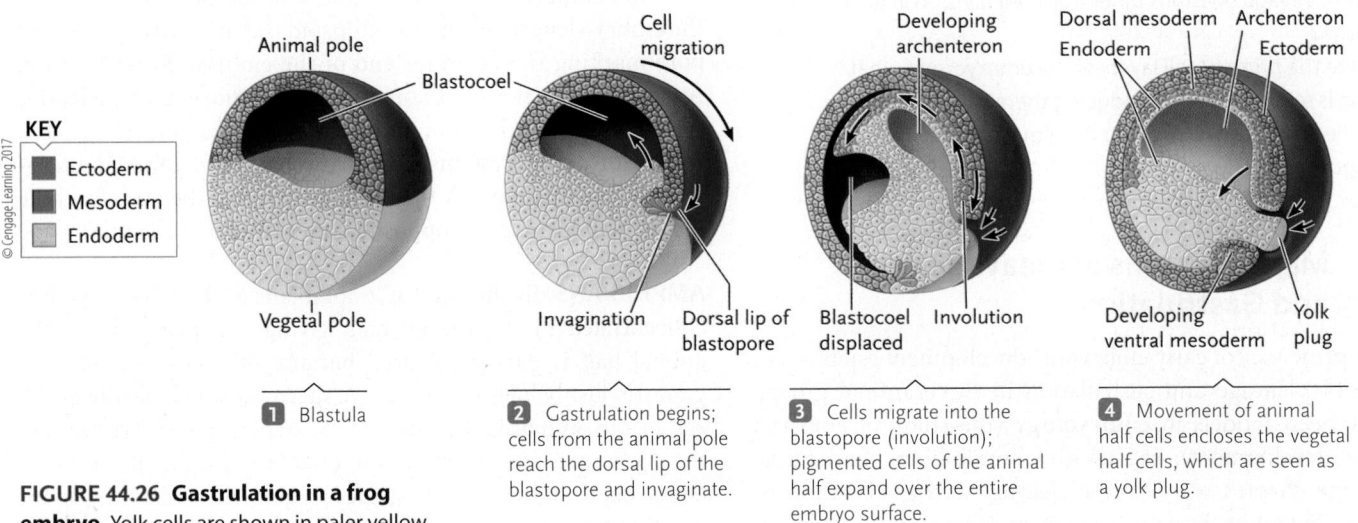

**KEY**
- Ectoderm
- Mesoderm
- Endoderm

1 Blastula

2 Gastrulation begins; cells from the animal pole reach the dorsal lip of the blastopore and invaginate.

3 Cells migrate into the blastopore (involution); pigmented cells of the animal half expand over the entire embryo surface.

4 Movement of animal half cells encloses the vegetal half cells, which are seen as a yolk plug.

**FIGURE 44.26 Gastrulation in a frog embryo.** Yolk cells are shown in paler yellow.

depression rotated 90° clockwise and called the **dorsal lip of the blastopore** (see Figure 44.26, step 2). These cells invaginate, changing shape and pushing inward from the surface to produce the depression. The depression eventually forms a complete circle (the blastopore) after further inward movement of additional cells (see Figure 44.26, step 3).

Cells migrate into the blastopore by **involution**, and the pigmented cell layer of the animal half expands to cover the entire embryo surface (see Figure 44.25, step 4). Cells of the vegetal half are enclosed by this cell migration, becoming visible on the outside as a yolk plug in the blastopore. The blastopore gives rise to the anus.

Continuing involution moves cells into the interior and upward (see Figure 44.26, steps 3 and 4), forming two layers that line the inside top half of the embryo. Dorsal mesoderm (shown in red) is the uppermost of these induced layers. Beneath it is the endoderm (shown in yellow), containing cells originating from both the outer surface of the embryo and the yolky interior. Ectoderm (shown in blue) forms from pigmented cells remaining at the surface of the embryo. Induction of the ventral mesoderm begins near the vegetal pole.

As mesoderm and endoderm form, the depression created by inward cell movements gradually deepens and extends inward as the archenteron (Figure 44.26, steps 3 and 4), displacing the blastocoel. Cells of the three primary cell layers continue to increase in number by further migrations and divisions as development proceeds.

The major induction centre during frog gastrulation is the dorsal lip of the blastopore. If cells are removed from the dorsal lip and transplanted elsewhere in the egg, they form a second blastopore (and a second embryo).

The events of gastrulation in frogs thus include the same developmental processes as in sea urchins—cell division, cell migration, selective adhesion, induction, and differentiation—although the details are different.

**BIRDS** Gastrulation in amniotes (see Chapter 27) such as birds and reptiles is modified by the distribution of the yolk, which occupies almost the entire volume of the egg. A thin layer of cytoplasm at the egg's surface gives rise to primary tissues of the embryo. Although mammalian eggs have relatively little yolk, gastrulation in them follows a similar pattern.

Early cleavage divisions in birds produce the **blastodisc**, a thin layer of cells at the yolk's surface (**Figure 44.27**, step 1). The complete blastodisc is a layer with about 20 000 cells. Cells of the blastodisc then separate into two layers, the **epiblast** (top layer) and the **hypoblast** (bottom layer). The blastocoel is the flattened cavity between them (step 2).

Gastrulation begins as cells in the epiblast stream toward the midline of the blastodisc, thickening it in this region. The thickened layer (or **primitive streak**) is first evident in the posterior end of the embryo and extends toward the anterior end as more cells of the epiblast move into it (Figure 44.27, step 3). A thickening at the anterior end of the primitive streak (the primitive knot) is the functional equivalent of the amphibian dorsal lip of the blastopore. The primitive streak initially marks the future posterior end of the embryo, and by the time it has elongated fully it has established the left and right sides of the embryo. The streak forms on what will become the dorsal side of the embryo, with the ventral side below.

As the primitive streak forms, its midline sinks, forming the **primitive groove**. The primitive groove is a conduit for migrating cells to move into the blastocoel. The first cells to migrate through the primitive groove are epiblast cells (Figure 44.27, step 4), which will form the endoderm. Cells migrating laterally between the epiblast and the endoderm form the mesoderm. The epiblast cells left at the surface of the blastodisc form the ectoderm (see step 4). Thus, all three primary tissue layers of the chick embryo arise from the epiblast.

Initially, ectoderm, mesoderm, and endoderm are located in three more or less horizontal layers in the chick embryo. During gastrulation, the endoderm pushes upward along its midline, and its left and right sides fold downward, forming a tube that is oriented parallel to the primitive streak (Figure 44.27, step 5). The archenteron is the central cavity of the tube, the primitive gut. Mesoderm separates into two layers, forming the coelom, a fluid-filled body cavity lined with mesoderm. These movements complete the formation of the gastrula.

## STUDY BREAK QUESTIONS

1. What are important differences between typical patterns of development in sea urchins, amphibians, birds, and mammals?
2. What evidence indicates that cells of the dorsal lip of the blastopore act as inducer cells?

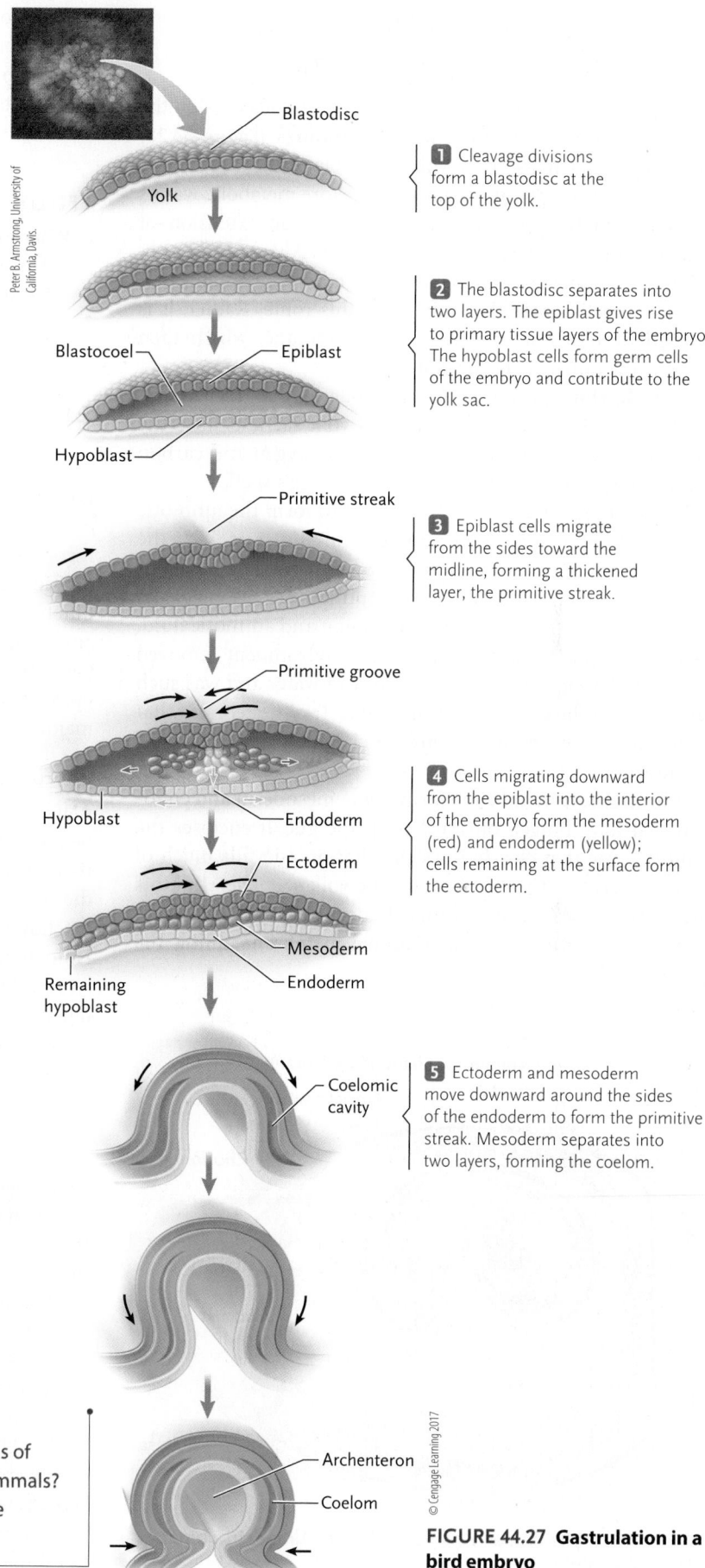

Peter B. Armstrong, University of California, Davis.

**1** Cleavage divisions form a blastodisc at the top of the yolk.

**2** The blastodisc separates into two layers. The epiblast gives rise to primary tissue layers of the embryo. The hypoblast cells form germ cells of the embryo and contribute to the yolk sac.

**3** Epiblast cells migrate from the sides toward the midline, forming a thickened layer, the primitive streak.

**4** Cells migrating downward from the epiblast into the interior of the embryo form the mesoderm (red) and endoderm (yellow); cells remaining at the surface form the ectoderm.

**5** Ectoderm and mesoderm move downward around the sides of the endoderm to form the primitive streak. Mesoderm separates into two layers, forming the coelom.

© Cengage Learning 2017

**FIGURE 44.27 Gastrulation in a bird embryo**

## 44.5c Extra-embryonic Membranes: Amnion, Chorion, Allantois

Each primary tissue layer of a bird embryo extends outside the embryo to form **extra-embryonic membranes (Figure 44.28)** that conduct nutrients from yolk to embryo, exchange gases with the environment outside the egg, or store metabolic wastes removed from the embryo. The **yolk sac** is an extension of mesoderm and endoderm enclosing the yolk. Although the yolk sac remains connected to the gut of the embryo by a stalk, yolk does not directly enter the embryo by this route. Rather, it is absorbed by blood in vessels in the membrane, which then transport the nutrients to the embryo.

The **chorion**, produced from ectoderm and mesoderm, completely surrounds the embryo and yolk sac and lines the inside of the shell. The chorion exchanges oxygen and carbon dioxide with the environment through the egg's shell.

The **amnion** closes over the embryo to form the amniotic cavity. Cells of the amnion secrete amniotic fluid into the cavity, which bathes the embryo and provides an aquatic environment in which it can develop. Reptilian and mammalian embryos are also surrounded by an amnion and amniotic fluid. Providing the embryo with an aquatic environment removed the need to lay eggs in an external body of water and was such a key factor in the evolution of fully terrestrial vertebrates that reptiles, birds, and mammals are all classified as members of the **Amniota**.

The **allantoic membrane** forms from mesoderm and endoderm that have bulged outward from the gut. It encloses the allantois, a sac that closely lines the chorion and fills much of the space between the chorion and the yolk sac. The **allantois** stores nitrogenous wastes (primarily uric acid) removed from the embryo. The part of the allantoic membrane lining the chorion forms a rich bed of capillaries connected to the embryo by arteries and veins. This circulatory system delivers carbon dioxide to the chorion and picks up the oxygen that is absorbed through the shell and chorion. At hatching, part of the allantoic membrane becomes the lining of the bladder.

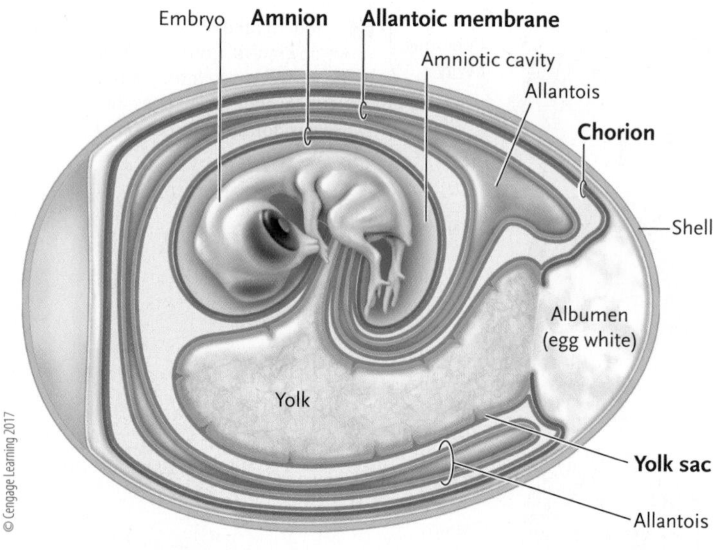

### STUDY BREAK QUESTIONS

1. What are the extra-embryonic membranes in birds, and what are their functions?
2. What are the features of an amniote egg? What is its evolutionary significance?

## 44.5d Organogenesis: Gastrulation to Adult Body Structures

Following gastrulation, organogenesis gives rise to the body organization characteristic of the species. Organogenesis involves the same mechanisms used in gastrulation, namely, cell division, cell movement, selective cell adhesion, induction, and differentiation. Organogenesis also involves an additional mechanism, **apoptosis**, in which certain cells are programmed to die (see Chapter 7). To illustrate how cellular mechanisms of development interact in organogenesis, we follow the formation of major organ systems in the bird embryo.

**ECTODERM AND THE NERVOUS SYSTEM: NEURAL TUBE AND NEURAL CREST CELLS** In vertebrates, organogenesis begins with **neurulation**, which is the development of nervous tissue from ectoderm. As a preliminary to neurulation, cells of the mesoderm form the notochord, a solid rod of tissue extending the length of the embryo under the dorsal ectoderm. Notochord cells carry out a major induction, causing the overlying ectoderm to form the **neural plate**, a thickened and flattened longitudinal band of cells (**Figure 44.29**, steps 1 and 2). The neural plate does not form if the notochord is removed.

Once induced, the neural plate sinks downward along its midline (Figure 44.29, steps 2 and 3), creating a deep longitudinal groove and ridges (neural crests) that rise along the sides of the neural plate. The neural tube forms when the neural crests move together and close over the centre of the groove along the length of the developing embryo (steps 4 and 5). The neural tube then pinches off from the overlying ectoderm, which closes over the tube (step 6). The central nervous system, including the brain and spinal cord, develops directly from the neural tube.

During formation of the neural tube, **neural crest** cells (see Figure 44.29) migrate into the mesoderm and follow specific routes to reach distant points in the developing embryo, where they contribute to the formation of a variety of organ systems. Some cells develop into cranial nerves in the head, whereas others contribute to the bones of the inner ear and skull, cartilage of facial structures, and teeth. Still others form ganglia of the autonomic nervous system, peripheral nerves leading from the spinal cord to body structures, and nerves of the developing

FIGURE 44.28 **The four extra-embryonic membranes in a bird embryo (in bold)**

Labels: Embryo, **Amnion**, **Allantoic membrane**, Amniotic cavity, Allantois, **Chorion**, Shell, Albumen (egg white), Yolk, **Yolk sac**, Allantois

© Cengage Learning 2017

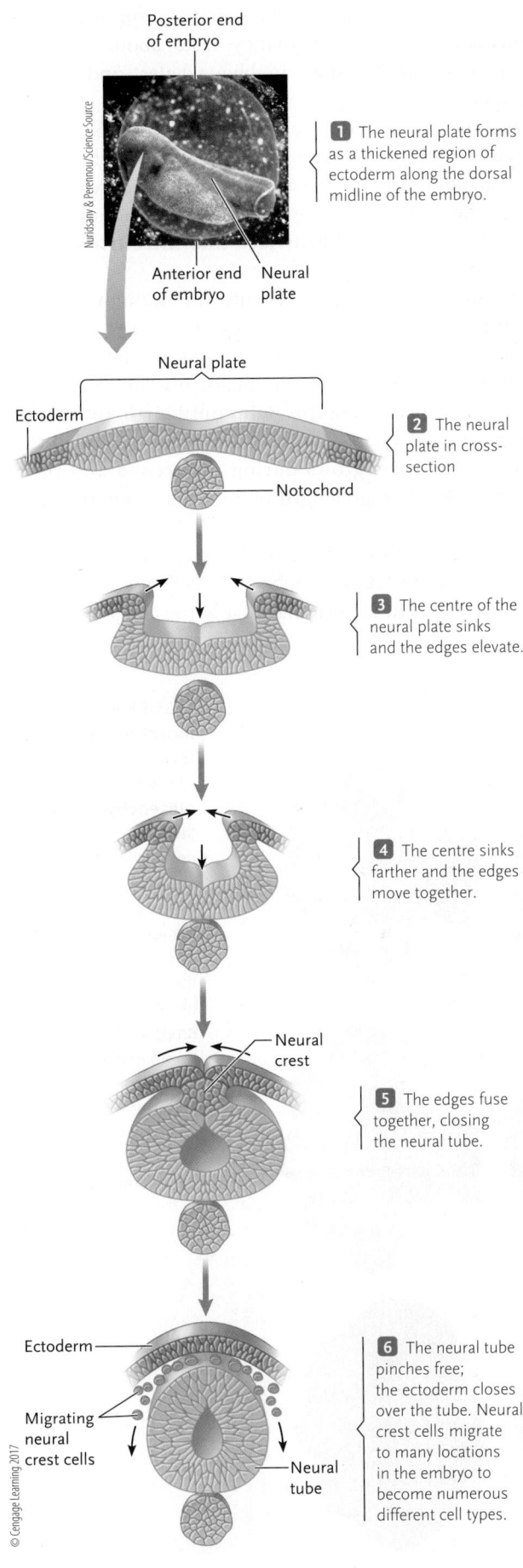

Posterior end
of embryo

Anterior end
of embryo

Neural
plate

Nuridsany & Perennou/Science Source

**1** The neural plate forms
as a thickened region of
ectoderm along the dorsal
midline of the embryo.

Neural plate

Ectoderm

Notochord

**2** The neural
plate in cross-
section

**3** The centre of the
neural plate sinks
and the edges elevate.

**4** The centre sinks
farther and the edges
move together.

Neural
crest

**5** The edges fuse
together, closing
the neural tube.

Ectoderm

Migrating
neural
crest cells

Neural
tube

**6** The neural tube
pinches free;
the ectoderm closes
over the tube. Neural
crest cells migrate
to many locations
in the embryo to
become numerous
different cell types.

© Cengage Learning 2017

**FIGURE 44.29 Development of the neural tube and neural crest cells in vertebrates.** Photo is of an embryo; drawings show steps in a bird embryo

gut. Neural crest cells also move to the skin, where they form pigment cells, and to the adrenal glands, where they form the medulla of the kidney. The migration of neural crest cells contributes to development in all vertebrates.

**MESODERM AND THE FORMATION OF MUSCLE AND BODY ORGANS** Other structures differentiate in the embryo while the neural tube is forming. On each side of the notochord, mesoderm separates into **somites**, blocks of cells spaced one after the other **(Figure 44.30)**. Somites give rise to the vertebral column, ribs, repeating sets of muscles associated with the ribs and vertebral column, and limb muscles. Mesoderm outside the somites extends around the primitive gut (lateral mesoderm in Figure 44.30) and splits into two layers, one covering the surface of the gut and the other lining the body wall. The space between the layers is the adult coelom. The lateral mesoderm also gives rise to other structures, such as the heart and blood vessels.

**APOPTOSIS: PROGRAMMED CELL DEATH** Induction and differentiation build complex, specialized organs from three fundamental tissue types. Apoptosis (see Chapter 7), programmed cell death, complements these processes by removing tissues

**KEY**

Ectoderm

Mesoderm

**a. Somites, derived from mesoderm**

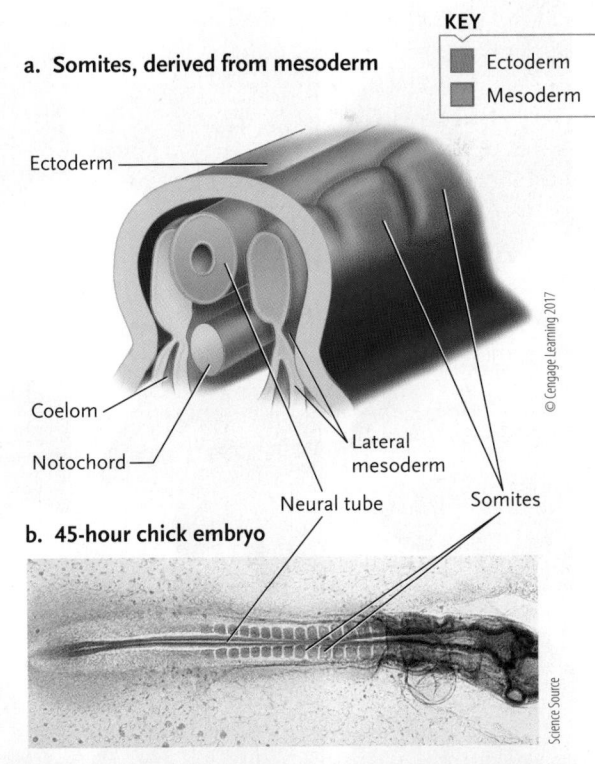

Ectoderm

Coelom

Notochord

Lateral
mesoderm

Neural tube

Somites

© Cengage Learning 2017

**b. 45-hour chick embryo**

Science Source

**FIGURE 44.30 Later development of the mesoderm. (a)** Somites develop into segmented structures such as the vertebrae, the ribs, and the musculature between the ribs. The lateral mesoderm gives rise to other structures, such as the heart and blood vessels and the linings of internal body cavities. **(b)** The somites in a 45-hour chick embryo

CHAPTER 44 ANIMAL REPRODUCTION |

needed during development but not present in the fully formed organ. Apoptosis plays an important role in the development of both invertebrates and vertebrates. The development of wings and hind feet in short-tailed fruit bats (*Carollia perspicillata*; **Figure 44.31**) demonstrates how apoptosis in the hind limbs leads to "normal" mammalian feet, but wings on the forelimbs.

### STUDY BREAK QUESTIONS

1. How does the neural tube develop?
2. How does the coelom develop?
3. What embryonic tissue gives rise to the heart?

## 44.5e Embryonic Development of Humans and Other Mammals

The embryonic development of humans is representative of placental mammals. In the uterus, the embryo is nourished by the placenta, which supplies oxygen and nutrients to the embryo and carries carbon dioxide and nitrogenous wastes away from it.

**Pregnancy**, or gestation, the period of mammalian *in utero* development, varies among species. Larger mammals bearing larger young tend to have longer gestation periods. From fertilization to birth, pregnancy lasts about 600 days in elephants, about 365 days in blue whales, and 21 days in hamsters.

In humans, gestation takes an average of 266 days, about 38 weeks. Because the date of fertilization can be difficult to establish, human gestation is usually calculated from the beginning of the menstrual cycle in which fertilization took place. The nine-month period is divided into three **trimesters**, each three months long.

Major developmental events in human gestation—cleavage, gastrulation, and organogenesis—take place during the first trimester. By week 4, the embryo's heart is beating, and by the end of week 8, the major organs and organ systems have formed. From this point until birth, the developing human is called a **fetus**. Only 5 cm long by the end of the first trimester, the fetus grows during the second and third trimesters to an average length of 50 cm and an average mass of 3.5 kg.

Cleavage occurs during the passage of the developing embryo down the fallopian tube and while it is still enclosed in the zona pellucida, the original coat of the egg **(Figure 44.32)**.

**Forelimbs**    **Hindlimbs**

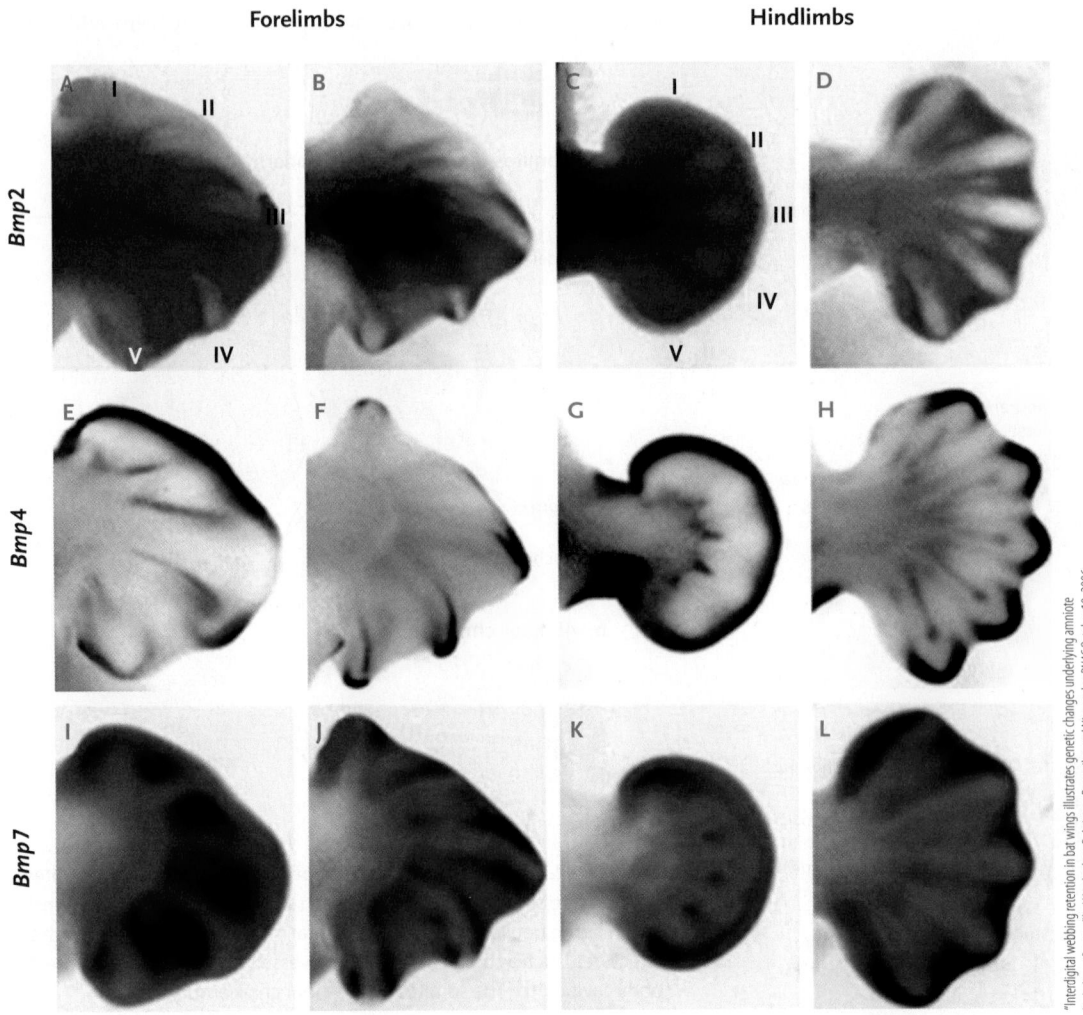

**FIGURE 44.31 Bone morphogenetic proteins (Bmps) trigger apoptosis of interdigital mesenchyme.** In short-tailed fruit bats (*Carollia perspicillata*), apoptosis occurs in the hind feet, where there are no antagonists to Bmps. Apoptosis does not occur in the forelimbs of the bats because antagonists to Bmps inhibit apoptosis. Compared here are expressions of Bmps inhibitors in the forelimbs and hind feet of the bats. Roman numerals indicate digit numbers.

"Interdigital webbing retention in bat wings illustrates genetic changes underlying amniote limb diversification," by Weatherbee, Behringer, Rasweiler, and Niswander. *PNAS* October 10, 2006 vol. 103 no. 41, 15103–15107. Copyright 2006 National Academy of Sciences, U.S.A.

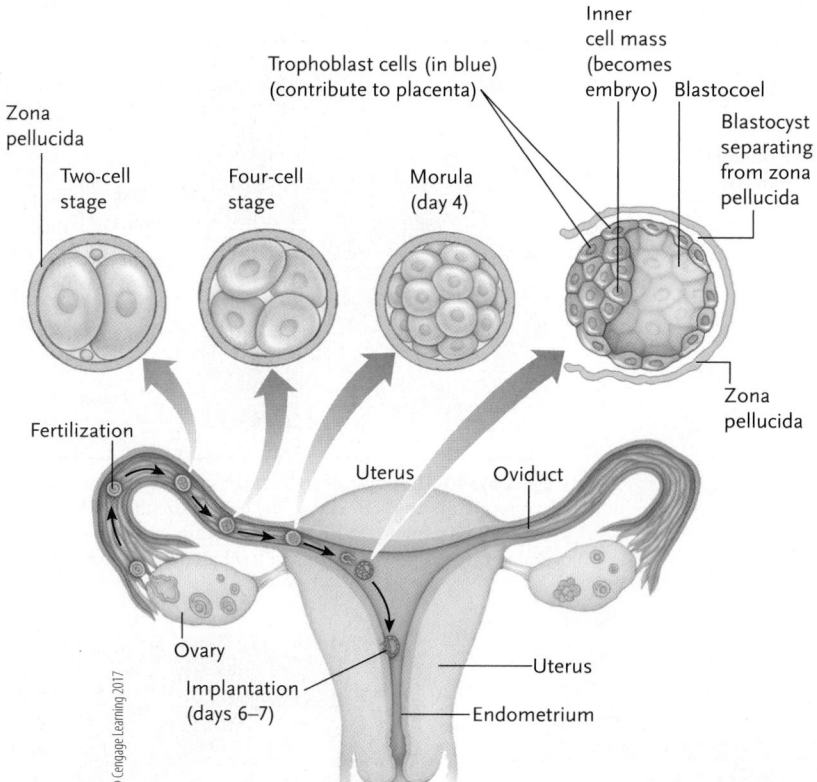

Zona pellucida

Two-cell stage

Four-cell stage

Trophoblast cells (in blue) (contribute to placenta)

Morula (day 4)

Inner cell mass (becomes embryo)

Blastocoel

Blastocyst separating from zona pellucida

Zona pellucida

Fertilization

Uterus

Oviduct

Ovary

Implantation (days 6–7)

Uterus

Endometrium

© Cengage Learning 2017

**FIGURE 44.32  Early stages in the development of the human embryo**

By day 4, the morula, a ball of 16–32 cells, has been produced. By the time the endometrium (uterine lining) is ready for implantation (about 7 days after ovulation), the morula has reached the uterus and through further cell divisions and differentiation has become a blastocyst. The **blastocyst** is a hollow ball of about 120 cells in a single layer, with a fluid-filled cavity, the blastocoel, which has a dense mass of cells localized on one side. This **inner cell mass** will become the embryo itself, whereas the outer, single layer of cells of the blastocyst, the **trophoblast**, will become tissues that support development of the embryo in the uterus.

When ready to implant, the blastocyst breaks out of the zona pellucida and sticks to the endometrium on its inner cell mass side (**Figure 44.33**, step 1). Implantation begins when the trophoblast cells that overlie the inner cell mass secrete proteases that digest pathways between endometrial cells. Dividing trophoblast cells fill in the digested spaces, appearing as fingerlike projections into the endometrium. These cells continue to digest nutrient-rich endometrial cells, producing a hole in the endometrium for the blastocyst and releasing nutrients for the developing embryo after it has consumed the small amount of yolk contained in egg cytoplasm. While the blastocyst burrows into the endometrium, the inner cell mass separates into the embryonic disc, which consists of two distinct cell layers (see Figure 44.33, step 1). The epiblast, the layer farther from the blastocoel, gives rise to the embryo proper. The hypoblast, the

layer nearer the blastocoel, generates part of the extra-embryonic membranes. When implantation is complete, the blastocyst has completely burrowed into the endometrium and is covered by a layer of endometrial cells (Figure 44.33, step 2).

Gastrulation proceeds as in birds (see Figure 44.27), with the formation of a primitive streak in the epiblast. Soon after the inner cell mass separates into epiblast and hypoblast, a layer of cells separates from the epiblast along its top margin (Figure 44.33, step 2). The amniotic cavity is the fluid-filled space created by the separation. The layer of cells forming its roof becomes the amnion, which expands until it completely surrounds the embryo, suspending it in amniotic fluid.

Also as in birds, the hypoblast develops into the yolk sac. In mammals, the mesoderm of the yolk sac gives rise to the blood vessels in the embryonic portion of the placenta. The allantois stores nitrogenous wastes in birds, but it is a small, vestigial sac in human embryos because most nitrogenous wastes are transferred across the placenta to the mother via blood vessels in the placenta and the umbilical cord.

While the amnion is expanding around the embryo, blood-filled spaces form in maternal tissue, and trophoblast cells grow rapidly around both the embryo and the amnion to form the chorion (Figure 44.33, step 3), the membrane that forms most of the embryonic portion of the placenta. Next, a connecting stalk forms between the embryonic disc and the chorion, which begins to grow into the endometrium as fingerlike extensions called **chorionic villi** (singular, *villus*; Figure 44.33, step 4). Chorionic villi increase the surface area of the chorion. The placenta forms in the area where these villi grow into the endometrium. As the chorion develops, mesodermal cells of the yolk sac grow into it and form a rich network of blood vessels, the embryonic circulation of the placenta. At the same time, the expanding chorion stimulates the blood vessels of the endometrium to grow into the maternal circulation of the placenta (Figure 44.33, step 5).

Within the placenta of humans, apes, monkeys, and rodents, the maternal circulation opens into spaces where maternal blood directly bathes capillaries coming to the placenta from the embryo (Figure 44.33, step 6). (Other mammals have different types of placentas.) The embryonic circulation remains closed so that the embryonic blood and the maternal blood do not mix directly. This isolation prevents the mother from developing an immune reaction against cells of the embryo, which may be recognized as foreign. Eventually, the placenta and its blood circulation grow to cover about a quarter of the inner surface of the enlarged uterus and reach the size of a dinner plate.

When the amnion forms (Figure 44.33, step 5), the embryo remains connected to the developing placenta through the **umbilicus**, a cord of tissue. Blood vessels in the umbilical cord conduct

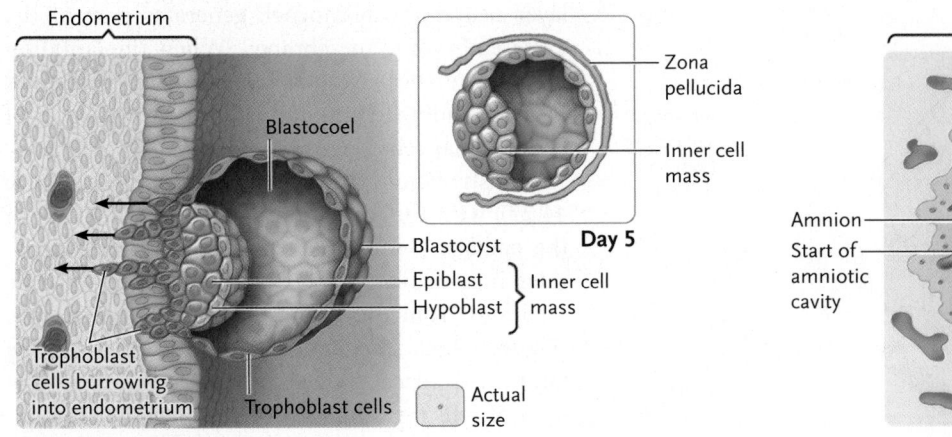

**1** **Days 6–7:** Surface cells of the blastocyst attach to the endometrium and start to burrow into it. Implantation is under way.

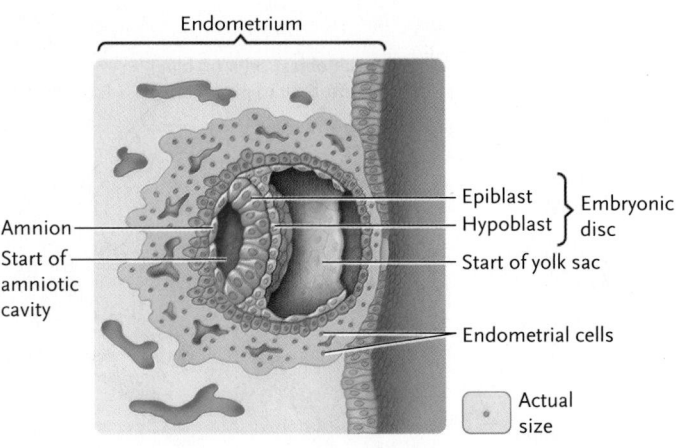

**2** **Days 10–11:** A layer of epiblast cells separates, producing the amniotic cavity. The cells above the cavity become the amnion, which eventually surrounds the embryo. The hypoblast begins to form around the yolk sac.

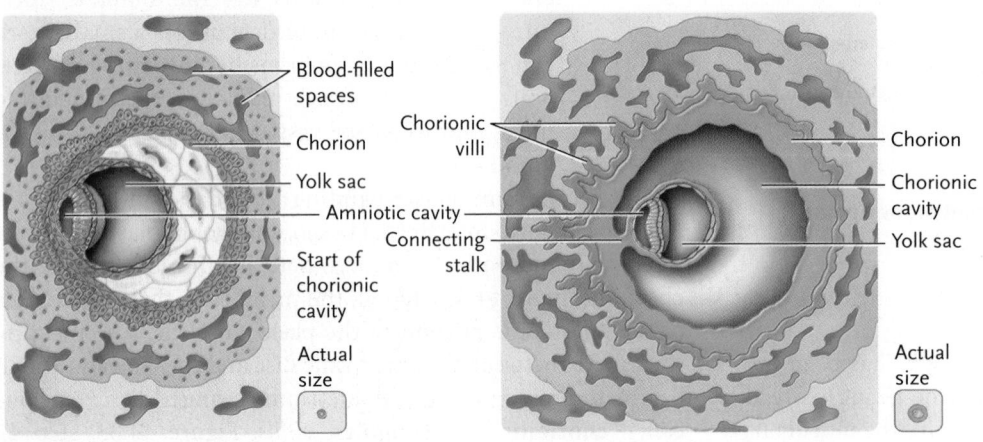

**3** **Day 12:** Blood-filled spaces form in maternal tissue. The chorion forms, derived from trophoblast cells, and encloses the chorionic cavity.

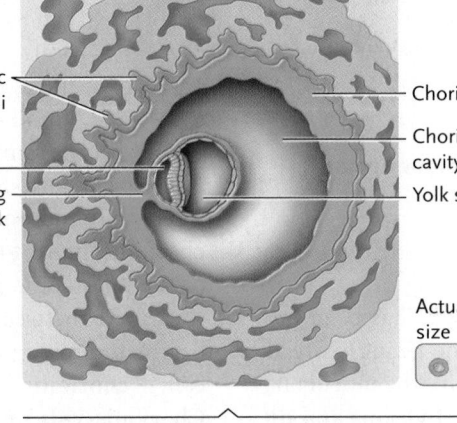

**4** **Day 14:** A connecting stalk has formed between the embryonic disc and chorion. Chorionic villi, which will be features of a placenta, start to form.

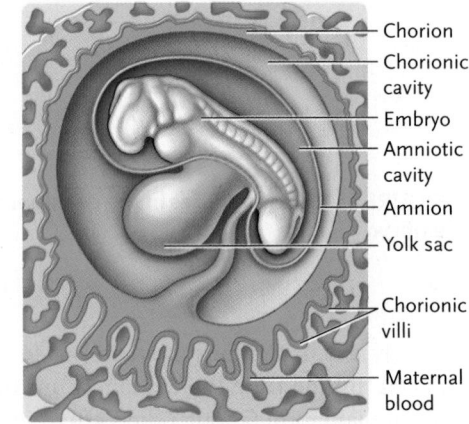

**5** **Day 25:** The chorion continues to grow into the endometrium, producing the chorionic villi. The chorion growth stimulates blood vessels of the endometrium to grow into the maternal circulation of the placenta.

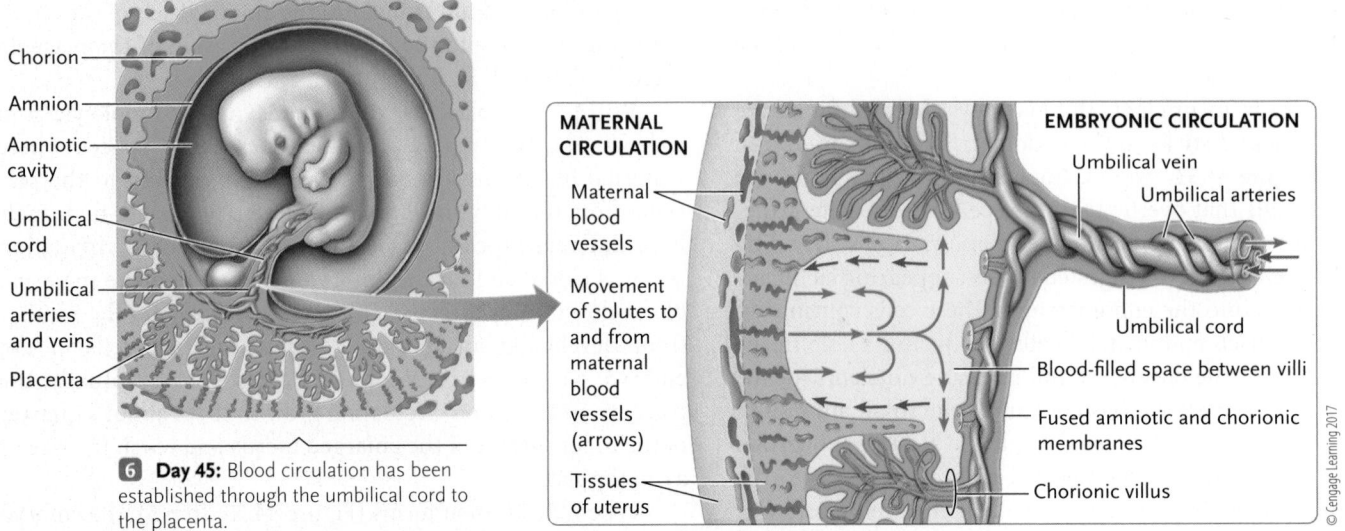

**6** **Day 45:** Blood circulation has been established through the umbilical cord to the placenta.

© Cengage Learning 2017

**FIGURE 44.33** **Implantation of a human blastocyst in the endometrium of the uterus and the establishment of the placenta**

blood between the embryo and the placenta (Figure 44.33, step 6, inset). Within the placenta, nutrients and oxygen pass from the mother's circulation into the circulation of the embryo. Carbon dioxide and nitrogenous wastes pass from the embryo to the mother and are disposed of by the mother's lungs and kidneys.

Cells from the embryonic portion of the placenta or from the amniotic fluid are derived from the embryo. To test for the presence of genetic diseases such as cystic fibrosis or Down syndrome, these cells can be obtained by chorionic villus sampling or by amniocentesis (*centesis* = puncture; referring to the use of a needle, which is pushed through the abdominal wall to obtain fluid from the amniotic cavity). Chorionic villus sampling can be carried out as early as the eighth week of pregnancy, compared with 14 weeks for amniocentesis.

**BIRTH: THE FETUS LEAVES THE MOTHER** By the end of its fourth week, a human embryo is 3–5 mm long, 250–500 times the size of the zygote **(Figure 44.34a)**. It has a tail and gill arches, embryonic features of all vertebrates (see Chapter 27). Gill arches contribute to the formation of the face, neck, mouth, nasal cavities, larynx, and pharynx. After five to six weeks, most of the tail has disappeared, and the embryo begins to be a recognizable human form (Figure 44.34b). At eight weeks, the embryo, now a fetus, is about 2.5 cm long (Figure 44.34c). Its organ systems have formed, and its limbs, with fingers or toes at their ends, have developed.

After about 38 weeks, fetal growth comes to a close, the cervix of the uterus softens, and the fetus typically turns so that its head is downward, pressed against the cervix. At this time, a steep rise in levels of estrogen secreted by the placenta cause uterine cells to express the gene for the receptor of the hormone oxytocin (secreted by the pituitary; see Chapter 43). Receptors become inserted into the plasma membranes of uterine cells. Oxytocin binds to its receptors, triggering contractions of smooth muscle cells of the uterine wall, beginning the rhythmic contractions of labour. These contractions mark the beginning of the three steps culminating in birth, or **parturition** (*parturire* = to be in labour).

Contractions push the fetus against the cervix and stretch its walls (**Figure 44.35**, step 1). In response, stretch receptors in the walls send nerve signals to the hypothalamus, which responds by stimulating the pituitary to secrete more oxytocin. Oxytocin stimulates more forceful contractions of the uterus, pressing the fetus more strongly against the cervix and further stretching its walls. The positive feedback cycle continues, steadily increasing the strength of the uterine contractions.

As the contractions force the head of the fetus through the cervix (Figure 44.35, step 2), the amniotic membrane bursts, releasing the amniotic fluid. Usually after 12–15 hours from the onset of uterine contractions, the head passes entirely through the cervix. Once the head is through, the rest of the body follows quickly and the entire fetus is forced out through the vagina, still connected to the placenta by the umbilical cord (Figure 44.35, step 3).

After the baby takes its first breath, the umbilical cord is cut and tied off by the birth attendant. Uterine contractions continue expelling the placenta and any remnants of the umbilical cord and embryonic membranes as the afterbirth, usually within 15–60 minutes after the infant's birth. The short length of umbilical cord still attached to the infant dries and shrivels within a few days. Eventually, it separates entirely and leaves a scar, the umbilicus or navel, to mark its former site of attachment during embryonic development. Immediately after birth, some

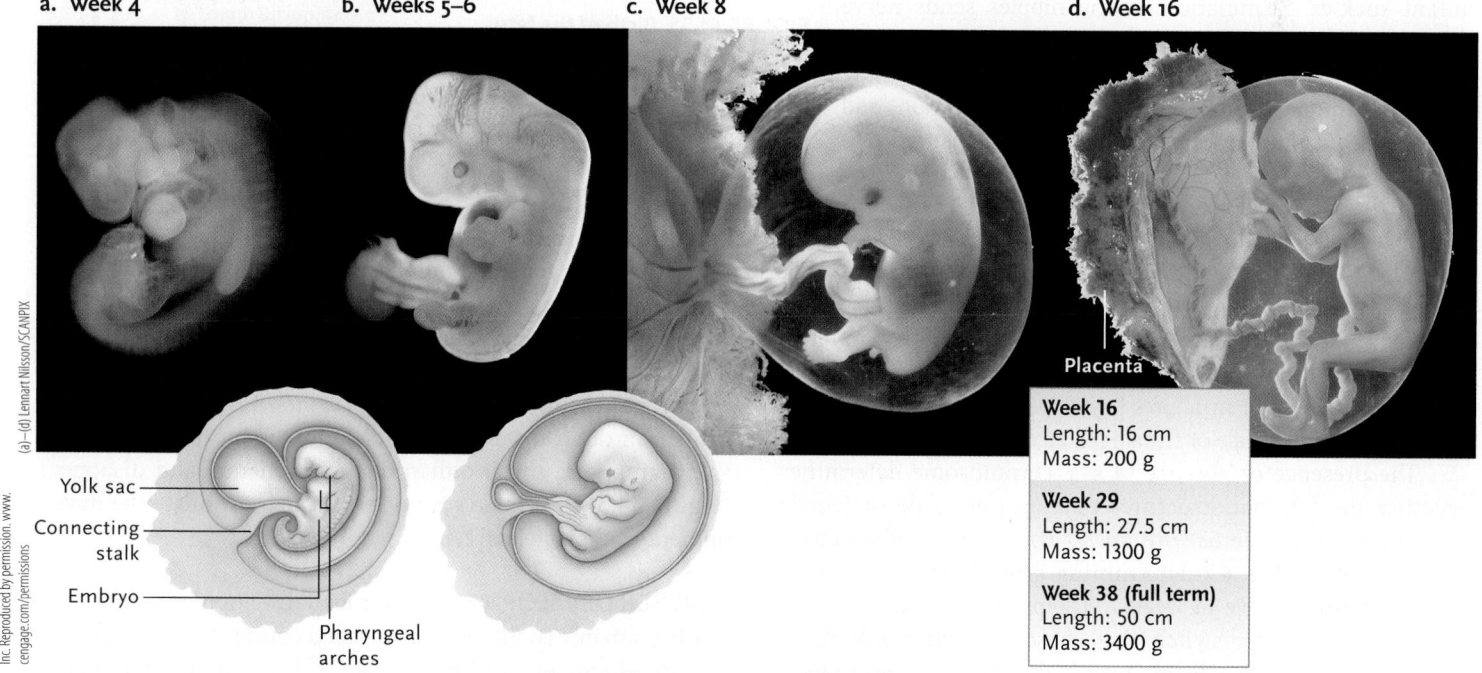

**a. Week 4**  **b. Weeks 5–6**  **c. Week 8**  **d. Week 16**

Yolk sac

Connecting stalk

Embryo

Pharyngeal arches

Placenta

**Week 16**
Length: 16 cm
Mass: 200 g

**Week 29**
Length: 27.5 cm
Mass: 1300 g

**Week 38 (full term)**
Length: 50 cm
Mass: 3400 g

(a)–(d) Lennart Nilsson/SCANPIX

**FIGURE 44.34 The human embryo at various stages of development, beginning at week 4.** The chorion has been moved aside to reveal the embryo in the amnion at week 8 and week 16. By week 16, movements begin as nerves make functional connections with the forming muscles.

CHAPTER 44  ANIMAL REPRODUCTION

mammals (e.g., *Gazella* species) can stand and are soon able to run. The newborns of these **precocial** species contrast with those of **altricial** species, which are immobile and helpless for some considerable time after birth. The same terms, *precocial* and *altricial*, also apply to other animals.

Many people believe that all mammals give birth to live young. In reality, mammals such as the duck-billed platypus and spiny anteater lay eggs. These mammals are the living representatives of an ancient group of mammals, the monotremes. Although they lay eggs, female platypuses and spiny anteaters feed their young milk like other mammals do.

**MILK: FOOD FOR THE YOUNG** Before birth, estrogen and progesterone secreted by the placenta stimulate the growth of the mammary glands in the mother's breasts. But high levels of these hormones prevent mammary glands from responding to **prolactin**, the hormone secreted by the pituitary that stimulates the glands to produce milk. After birth and the release of the placenta, levels of estrogen and progesterone in the mother's bloodstream fall steeply, and the breasts begin to produce milk (stimulated by prolactin) and secrete it (stimulated by oxytocin; see Chapter 43).

Continued milk secretion depends on whether the infant suckles. Stimulation of the nipples sends nerve impulses to the hypothalamus, which responds by signalling the pituitary to release a burst of prolactin and oxytocin. Hormonal stimulation of milk production and secretion continues as long as the infant is breast-fed.

**GONADAL DEVELOPMENT: THE SEX OF THE FETUS** Gonads and their ducts begin to develop in the fetus during week 4 of gestation. Until week 7, male and female embryos have the same set of internal structures derived from mesoderm, including a pair of gonads **(Figure 44.36a)**. Each gonad is associated with two primitive ducts, the **Wolffian duct** and the **Müllerian duct**, that lead to a cloaca. These internal structures have bipotential because they can develop into either male or female sexual organs.

The presence or absence of a Y chromosome determines whether the internal structures develop into male or female sexual organs. In a fetus with an XY combination of sex chromosomes, *SRY* (the sex-determining gene on the Y chromosome) becomes active in week 7. The protein encoded by *SRY* induces a molecular switch that causes primitive gonads to develop into testes. Fetal testes secrete two hormones, testosterone and the **anti-Müllerian hormone** (AMH). Testosterone stimulates development of the Wolffian ducts into a

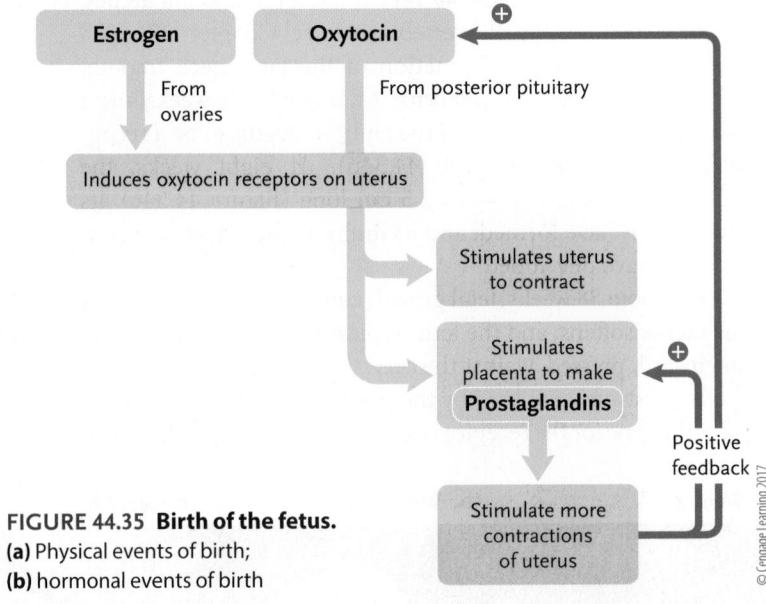

**a. Physical events of birth**

Umbilical cord · Vagina · Uterus · Partially dilated cervix

**1** Contractions of the uterus press the head against the cervix, stretching the cervical opening.

**2** The baby's head pushes through the cervix, into the vagina. Continued contractions push the baby through the birth canal to the exterior.

**3** The placenta and umbilical cord will be forced out of the uterus as the "afterbirth."

Placenta · Uterus · Umbilical cord

**b. Hormonal events of birth**

Estrogen — From ovaries
Oxytocin — From posterior pituitary
Induces oxytocin receptors on uterus
Stimulates uterus to contract
Stimulates placenta to make **Prostaglandins**
Stimulate more contractions of uterus
Positive feedback

© Cengage Learning 2017

**FIGURE 44.35  Birth of the fetus.**
**(a)** Physical events of birth;
**(b)** hormonal events of birth

male reproductive tract, including the epididymis, vas deferens, and seminal vesicles (Figure 44.36b). AMH causes the Müllerian ducts to degenerate and disappear. Testosterone also stimulates development of male genitalia.

In a fetus with XX chromosomes, no *SRY* protein is produced. The primitive gonads, under the influence of estrogens and progesterone secreted by the placenta, develop into ovaries. Müllerian ducts develop into oviducts, the uterus, and part of the vagina, and the Wolffian ducts degenerate and disappear (Figure 44.36c). Female sex hormones also stimulate the development of the external female genitalia.

**FURTHER DEVELOPMENT** Once fetal development is over, the newborn mammal follows a prescribed course of further growth and development, leading to the mature adult. In humans, internal and external sexual organs mature and secondary sexual characteristics appear at puberty. Similar changes occur

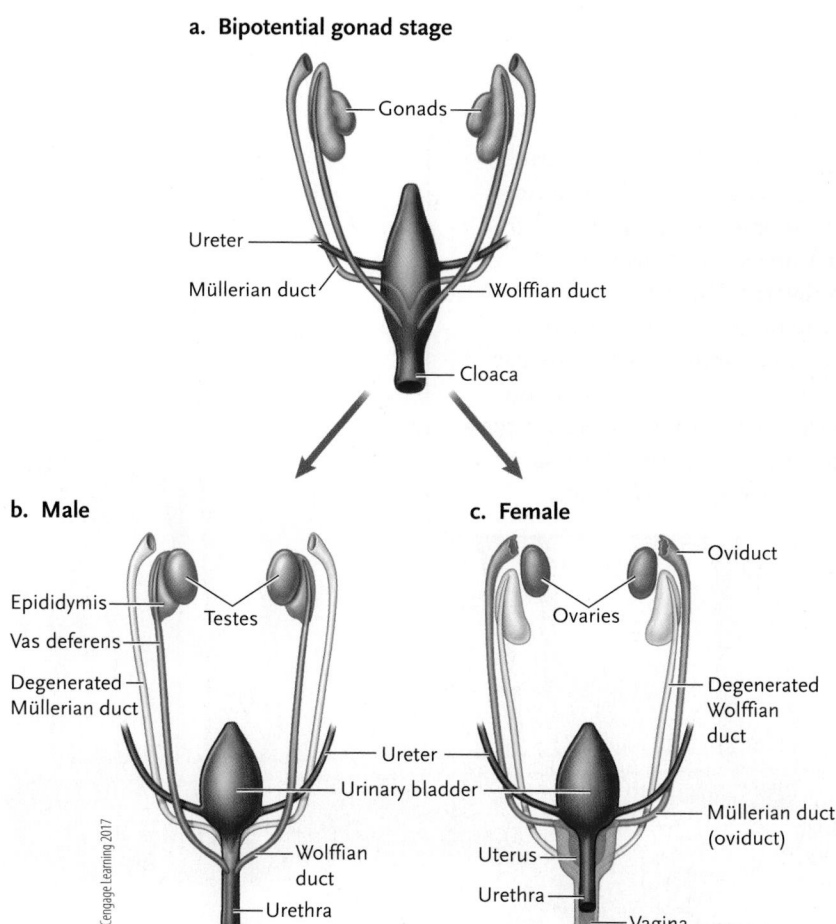

**a. Bipotential gonad stage**

Gonads

Ureter

Müllerian duct — Wolffian duct

Cloaca

**b. Male**

Epididymis
Vas deferens — Testes
Degenerated Müllerian duct
Ureter
Urinary bladder
Wolffian duct
Urethra

**c. Female**

Oviduct
Ovaries
Degenerated Wolffian duct
Müllerian duct (oviduct)
Uterus
Urethra
Vagina

© Cengage Learning 2017

**FIGURE 44.36 Development of the internal sexual organs of males and females from common bipotential origins**

in most mammals. There are many other examples among different animal groups of developmental changes that take place after hatching or birth.

During this period, many animal parents invest significant energy in protecting and feeding their developing young. This is one aspect of the genetically selfish drive to ensure that their genes are represented in future generations. There is a recurring tendency across phyla for parents to put eggs and developing young in situations that minimize their exposure to predators and parasites while maximizing favourable conditions for growth and development. Many species of birds use nests to house their eggs and unfledged young. Parents of other species, such as some species of scorpions, frogs, and insects, carry their young with them, often on their backs. This allows the parent (or parents) to avoid or actively deter would-be predators.

An escalation in **parental investment** is moving eggs and young inside the parent's body (vivipary and ovoviviparity; see Section 44.3d). Although we associate vivipary with mammals, many species of fish are mouth-breeders, keeping eggs and, for a time, developing young in their mouths. Other fish, such as sea horses and pipefish (family Syngnathidae, order Gasterosteiformes; **Figure 44.37**), keep eggs and developing young in specialized incubation areas, called *brood pouches*, located on the

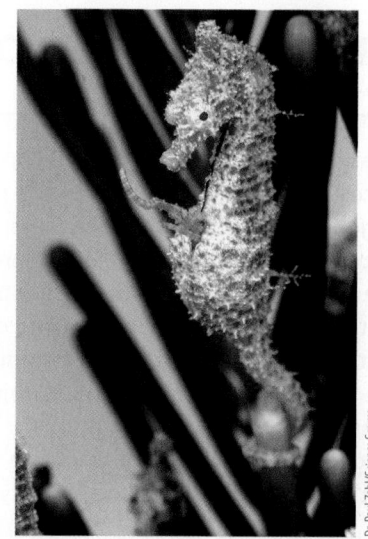

Dr. Paul Zahl/Science Source

**FIGURE 44.37 A male sea horse gives birth**

tail or trunk of the male. "Pregnancy" in male sea horses represents an increase in parental investment. It also allows males to be confident about the paternity of the young they raise.

Some amphibians also show high levels of parental care. In Australia, female frogs, *Rheobatrachus silus*, use their stomachs as brood pouches. While the young are developing, they secrete prostaglandin $E_2$, which inhibits the secretion of gastric acid in the stomach and saves the developing young from being digested. On Mount Nimba in West Africa, female toads (*Nimbaphrynoides occidentalis*) harbour developing young in their uterus, where the young feed on uterine secretions in the absence of a placenta. The gestation period for these toads is 9 months, and newborns are 7–8 mm long and weigh 30–60 mg. Retention of developing embryos in the oviducts has evolved independently in each of the three living groups of Amphibia: Anura, Urodela, and Gymnophiona (see Chapter 27).

**STUDY BREAK QUESTIONS**

1. Define the terms *blastocyst*, *chorionic villi*, and *parturition*.
2. What is a placenta? Name some animals with placentas.
3. What is SRY? What role does it play?
4. Where can embryos develop in a parent?

For all animals, there is a strong drive to reproduce, and considerable time and resources are devoted to reproductive processes. For animals that reproduce by eggs and sperm, the adaptations are diverse. This diversity allows individuals of the same species to find each other and unite eggs and sperm. The fertilized egg develops from a single cell into an adult animal. There are also diverse ways in which this occurs. Within the diversity, however, are underlying patterns that are shared by all animals. This summary illustration uses the life cycle of a frog to outline the major steps in a sexually reproducing species. Compare this to the human life cycle and identify shared versus divergent processes.

# Summary Illustration

For all animals there is a strong drive to reproduce, and considerable time and resources are devoted to reproductive processes. The success of any species is contingent on its reproductive success. All energy that does not go into growth, development, and maintenance goes into reproduction. For animals that reproduce by eggs and sperm, the adaptations are diverse. This diversity allows individuals of the same species to find each other and unite eggs and sperm. The fertilized egg develops from a single cell into an adult animal. There are also diverse ways in which this occurs. Within the diversity, however, are underlying patterns that are shared by all animals. This summary illustration uses the life cycle of a frog to outline the major steps in a sexually reproducing species. Compare this to the human life cycle and identify shared versus divergent processes.

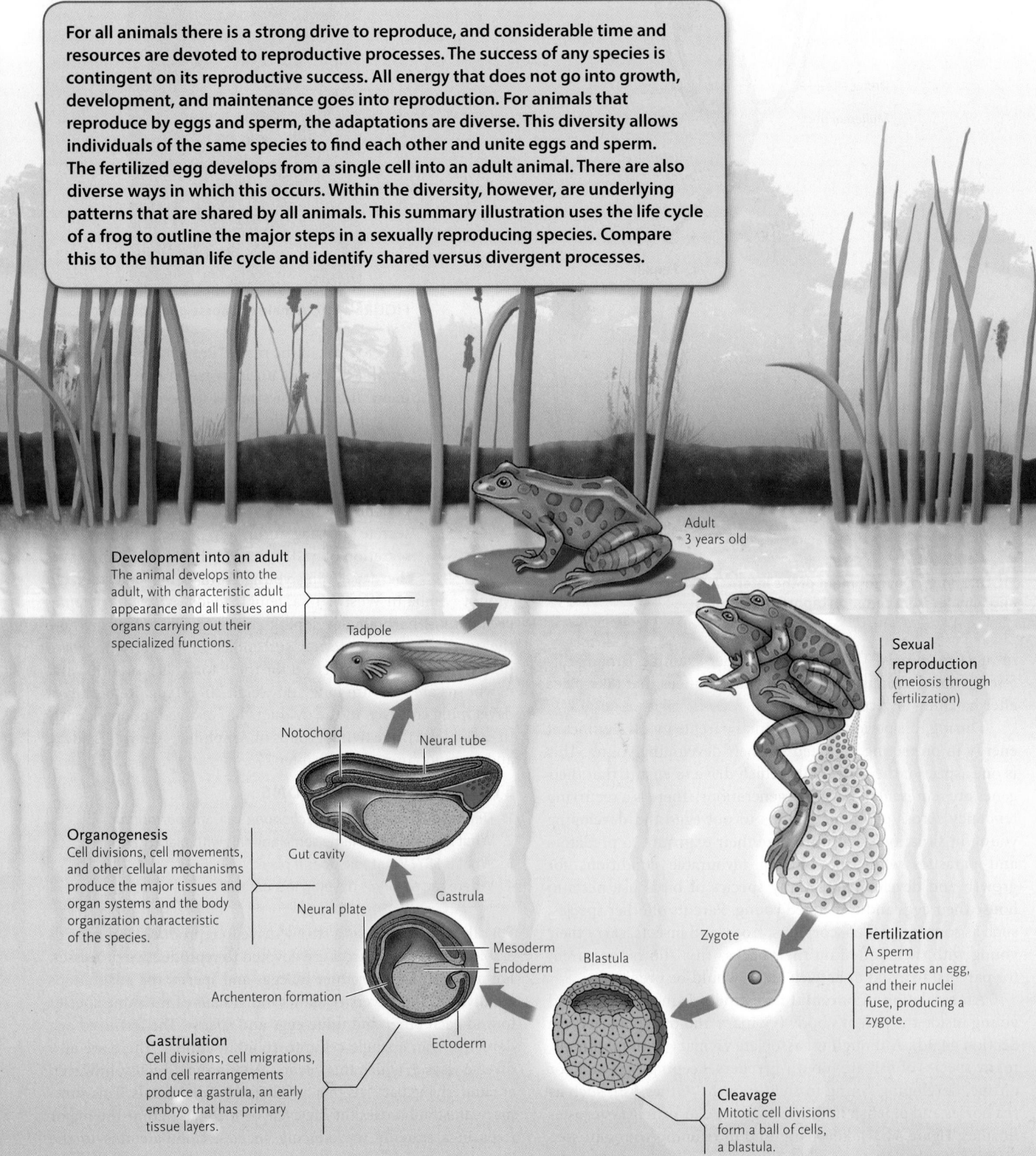

**Adult**
3 years old

**Development into an adult**
The animal develops into the adult, with characteristic adult appearance and all tissues and organs carrying out their specialized functions.

Tadpole

**Sexual reproduction**
(meiosis through fertilization)

Notochord

Neural tube

**Organogenesis**
Cell divisions, cell movements, and other cellular mechanisms produce the major tissues and organ systems and the body organization characteristic of the species.

Gut cavity

Gastrula

Neural plate

Zygote

**Fertilization**
A sperm penetrates an egg, and their nuclei fuse, producing a zygote.

Mesoderm

Endoderm

Blastula

Archenteron formation

**Gastrulation**
Cell divisions, cell migrations, and cell rearrangements produce a gastrula, an early embryo that has primary tissue layers.

Ectoderm

**Cleavage**
Mitotic cell divisions form a ball of cells, a blastula.

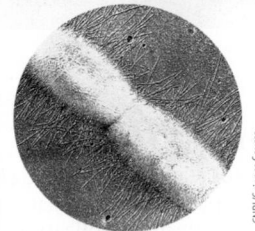

**Fission**

CNRI/Science Source

**Budding**

Lebendkulturen.de/Shutterstock.com

**Fragmentation**

Wolfgang Pölzer/Alamy Stock Photo

**Parthenogenesis**

reptiles4all/Shutterstock.com

**Sexual reproduction** between a male and female through the union of egg and sperm is advantageous in changing environments.

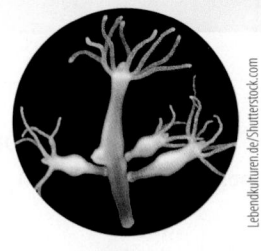

**Simultaneous hermaphrodite**

Pakhnyushcha/Shutterstock.com

**Sequential hermaphrodite**

Hans Gert Broeder/Shutterstock.com

**External fertilization**

harsh.barala/Shutterstock.com

**Internal fertilization**

Christopher Boswell/Shutterstock.com

## Reproduction and development from egg and sperm to adult animal

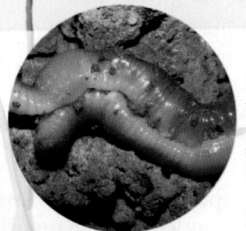

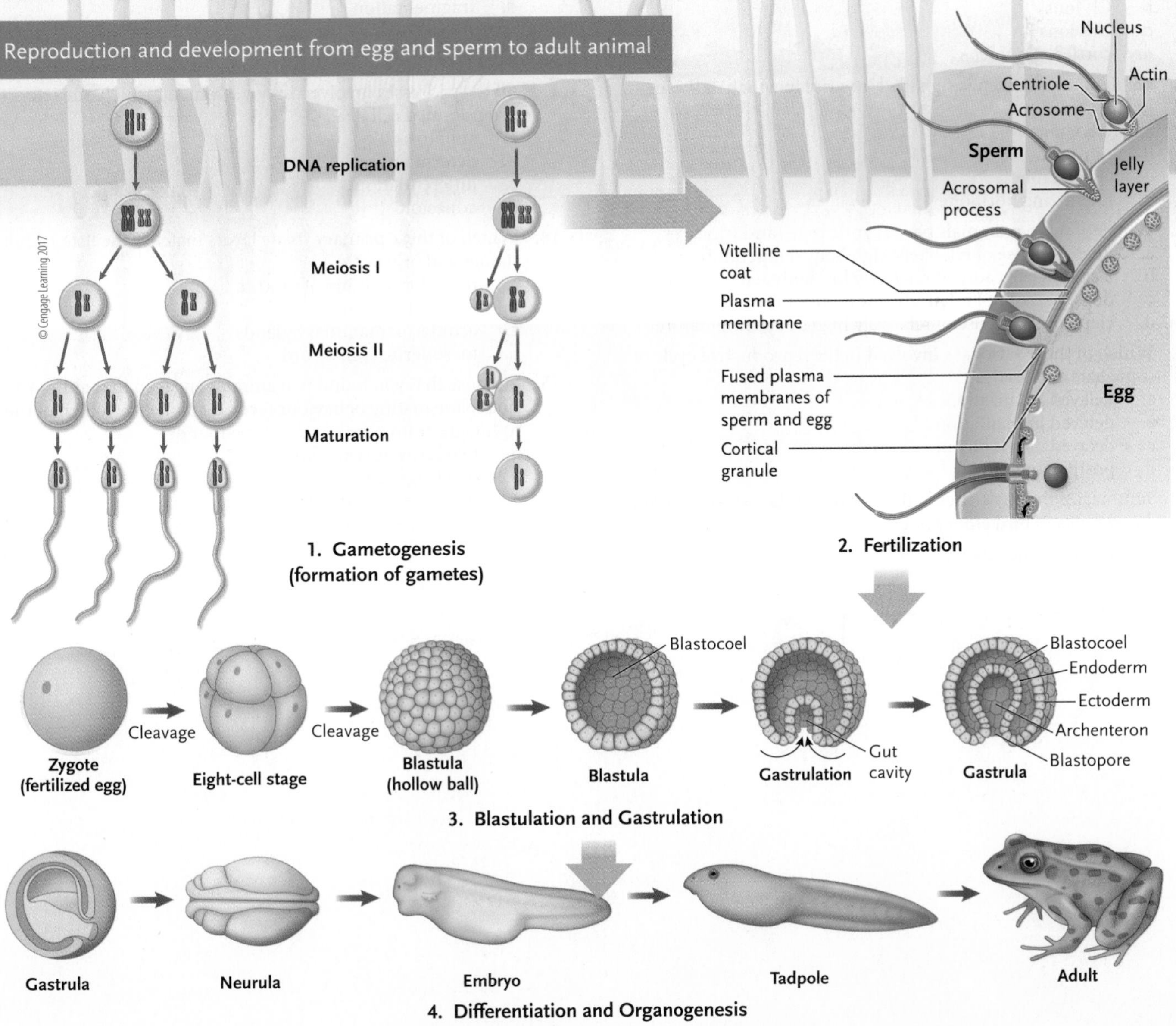

DNA replication

Meiosis I

Meiosis II

Maturation

© Cengage Learning 2017

**1. Gametogenesis (formation of gametes)**

Nucleus

Centriole — Actin

Acrosome

**Sperm**

Jelly layer

Acrosomal process

Vitelline coat

Plasma membrane

Fused plasma membranes of sperm and egg

Cortical granule

**Egg**

© Cengage Learning 2017

**2. Fertilization**

Blastocoel

**Zygote (fertilized egg)** — Cleavage — **Eight-cell stage** — Cleavage — **Blastula (hollow ball)** — **Blastula** — **Gastrulation** — Gut cavity — **Gastrula**

Blastocoel
Endoderm
Ectoderm
Archenteron
Blastopore

**3. Blastulation and Gastrulation**

**Gastrula** — **Neurula** — **Embryo** — **Tadpole** — **Adult**

**4. Differentiation and Organogenesis**

# SELF-TEST QUESTIONS

## Recall/Understand

1. In vertebrates, the blastopore becomes which of these structures?
   a. the mouth
   b. the nostrils
   c. the anus
   d. the auditory meatus

2. Germ cells give rise to which of the following?
   a. haploid gametes
   b. diploid somatic cells
   c. diploid gametes
   d. haploid somatic cells

3. In which of these groups does internal fertilization rarely occur?
   a. Platyhelminthes
   b. bedbugs
   c. mammals
   d. frogs

4. In slow blocks, fertilization of an egg by more than one sperm is prevented by changes in which of the following?
   a. $Ca^{2+}$ ions
   b. $Cl^-$ ions
   c. $Na^+$ ions
   d. cortical granules

5. Ovulation in women is signalled by a rise in which of these hormones?
   a. relaxin
   b. estrogen
   c. testosterone
   d. luteinizing hormone

6. Which of these mammals have cryptic testes and why?
   a. dogs, because of relatively high body temperature
   b. elephants, because of relatively low body temperature
   c. dogs, because of relatively low body temperature
   d. elephants, because of relatively high body temperature

7. Which of these actions is involved in the reproductive cycle of some bats and turtles?
   a. delayed fertilization
   b. delayed implantation
   c. delayed development
   d. postpartum estrus

8. Summarize the structures and functions of the extra-embryonic membranes in bird embryos.

9. Explain spermatogenesis.

## Apply/Analyze

10. A sea star is cut into two separate pieces and each develops into a complete sea star. What is this an example of?
    a. external fertilization
    b. fission
    c. budding
    d. fragmentation

11. Suppose that you found an egg with large amount of yolk. Which animal does such an egg most likely belong to?
    a. a mammal
    b. a bird
    c. a bony fish
    d. an amphibian

12. Suppose that you work in an In Vitro Fertilization Clinic, and you noticed that an unfertilized human egg divided. What is this most likely a result of?
    a. meiosis
    b. budding
    c. parthenogenesis
    d. fragmentation

## Create/Evaluate

13. Of the processes involved in development, which one refers to programmed cell death?
    a. apoptosis
    b. determination
    c. differentiation
    d. adhesion

14. Which of these primary tissue layers matches the listed adult tissues and organs?
    a. mesoderm: lining of urethra
    b. endoderm: skin
    c. ectoderm: mammary glands
    d. mesoderm: spinal cord

15. Suppose that you found two animals engaged in mating. You notice the mating behaviour termed amplexus. Which of the following animals might you have found?
    a. two birds or two rabbits
    b. two frogs or two toads
    c. two salmon or two trout
    d. two hamsters or two mice

# Chapter Roadmap

**Control of Animal Processes: Neural Control**

The cells that make up the nervous system are responsible for receiving, analyzing, and transmitting information.

**45.1 The Basis of Information Flow in Nervous Systems: An Overview**

Messages are carried in the form of action potentials; the rate of conduction and the strength of each message are affected by various physical and chemical factors.

**45.2 Sensory Inputs: Reception**

Sensory systems begin with **sensory receptors (transducers)** that detect sensory information, convert it to neural activity, and pass the information along neurons to the central nervous system.

**45.3 The Central Nervous System: Integration**

Neurons in the CNS receive stimulatory and inhibitory signals and integrate them to produce a response.

**45.4 The Peripheral Nervous System: Transmission and Response**

The PNS includes all neurons that transmit sensory information to the CNS and the neurons that carry signals to muscles and glands to produce responses.

**From Chapter 43** →

**To Chapter 46** →

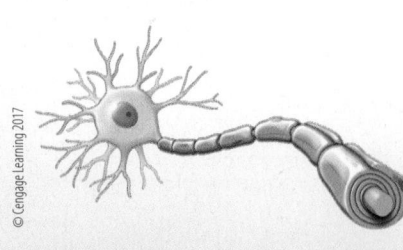

reptiles4all/Shutterstock.com

© Cengage Learning 2017

**Female firefly (*Photinus* species) with abdomen flashing**

# Control of Animal Processes: Neural Control

# 45

**Why it matters . . .** On a warm evening in early summer, the twilight in a garden in Montreal is punctuated by brief bursts of light from the abdomen of a flying male of the beetle *Photuris versicolor*, the firefly. The flashes of light have a specific duration and come at specific intervals, constituting a code unique to that species. These visible mating calls are answered by a female perched on the vegetation below that emits flashes with the same code. The male flies toward her. This photonic conversation continues until the male lands on the vegetation and mates with the female, which then ceases flashing. A day or two later, the mated female has begun to make eggs and again responds to flashes from males flying overhead. But now she responds to and mimics codes of flashing from males of other species of firefly. A male, lured to her by her mimicry of the flashing code for his species, lands and expects to mate but becomes prey, is eaten, and provides nutrition, enabling her to enhance egg production.

This behaviour requires the complex interaction of cells within the nervous systems of the flies. The brain or **central nervous system (CNS)** of the male sends the appropriate rhythmic signals (the code) to the light-producing organ in his abdomen. It also sends signals to the muscles controlling the wings so that he can fly toward the female. The female's eyes detect the light flashes, and her nervous system processes the information, causing her brain to send the appropriate signals to her own light-producing organ so that she responds with the appropriate code. Amazingly, all of this can happen in under a second! Mating is a complex behaviour involving coordinated movements not only of the genital apparatus but also of the other appendages. This act of mating turns off the flashing response of the female and signals the endocrine system of the female to release the hormones involved in egg production. A chemical transferred by the male in his semen acts on the brain of the female so that it no longer responds to the code for her species and causes her to mimic the codes of other species. Sensing of the environment leading to rapid, specific communication between cells in multicellular organisms is the domain of the nervous system and the topic of this chapter. By the time you finish this chapter, you should be able to trace the information flow required to produce the response of the male firefly in the example through the four components of neural signalling.

## 45.1 The Basis of Information Flow in Nervous Systems: An Overview

One of the consequences of multicellularity and tissue differentiation, discussed in Chapter 38, is that cells must communicate over long distances. There are several ways this can occur, but the fastest is via transmission by neurons. Most multicellular animals have a nervous system that may be composed of hundreds to billions of neurons (depending on the animal) that work together carrying the electrical messages that control every aspect of bodily function. Messages are carried in the form of action potentials, and the rate of conduction and the strength of each message are affected by various physical and chemical factors. Neurons are connected to one another and other body tissues via chemical or electrical synapses. The detection and flow of information from the environment and between the individuals, and the instantaneous analysis and processing of that information to produce specific behaviour, are astounding, even in relatively simple animals. In this chapter, we first examine the properties of the cells that make up the nervous system and that are responsible for receiving, analyzing, and transmitting information. These functions result from the activities of only two major cell types: **neurons** and glial cells. In most animals, these cells are organized into complex networks called **nervous systems**. In the **peripheral nervous system (PNS)**, the long slender projections of neurons (**axons**) are bundled into cablelike projections called **nerves** that provide a common pathway between different structures and the CNS. In the CNS, networks are organized into **ganglia** and **brains**.

### 45.1a Neurons and Their Organization in Nervous Systems

Communication between cells in an animal by **neural signalling** involves the flow of information at two levels: within a single neuronal cell, or **neuron**, and between neurons within networks or circuits. In most animals, the four components of neural signalling are reception, integration, transmission, and response, and all four components are found in both individual neurons and neuronal networks.

- **Reception** is the detection of a stimulus.
- **Integration** is the sorting and interpretation of sensory inputs, or neural messages, and determination of the appropriate response(s).
- **Transmission** is the sending of a message along a neuron to another neuron or to a muscle or gland.
- **Response** is the output or action resulting from the integration of neural messages.

**NEURONS ARE SPECIALIZED FOR THE RECEPTION, INTEGRATION, AND TRANSMISSION OF INFORMATION LEADING TO A VARIETY OF RESPONSES** Neurons vary widely in shape and size. All have an enlarged cell body and two types of extensions, or processes: dendrites and axons (**Figure 45.1**).

- **Reception:** The **dendrites**, and often the **cell body**, receive signals that they integrate and transmit toward a specialized part of the neuron called the *spike initiation zone*. The dendrites are generally highly branched, forming a treelike outgrowth at one end of the neuron (*dendros* = tree). Dendrites and cell bodies conduct graded electrical signals produced by ions flowing down electrochemical gradients through channels in the plasma membrane.
- **Integration:** The spike initiation zone is the first site along the neuron capable of generating an action potential. If the magnitude of the signal arriving from the dendrites and cell body is large enough, an action potential is initiated.
- **Transmission:** Axons (*axon* = axis) conduct signals away from the spike initiation zone to another neuron or an effector. Neurons typically have a single axon that arises from a junction with the cell body called an **axon hillock**, and in many but not all neurons this is the spike initiation zone (compare the motor and sensory neurons in Figure 45.1). The axon has branches at its tip that end as small, buttonlike swellings called **axon terminals**. The more terminals contacting a neuron, the greater its capacity to integrate incoming information.
- **Response:** This is the output or action resulting from the generation of the action potential. It could be the stimulation

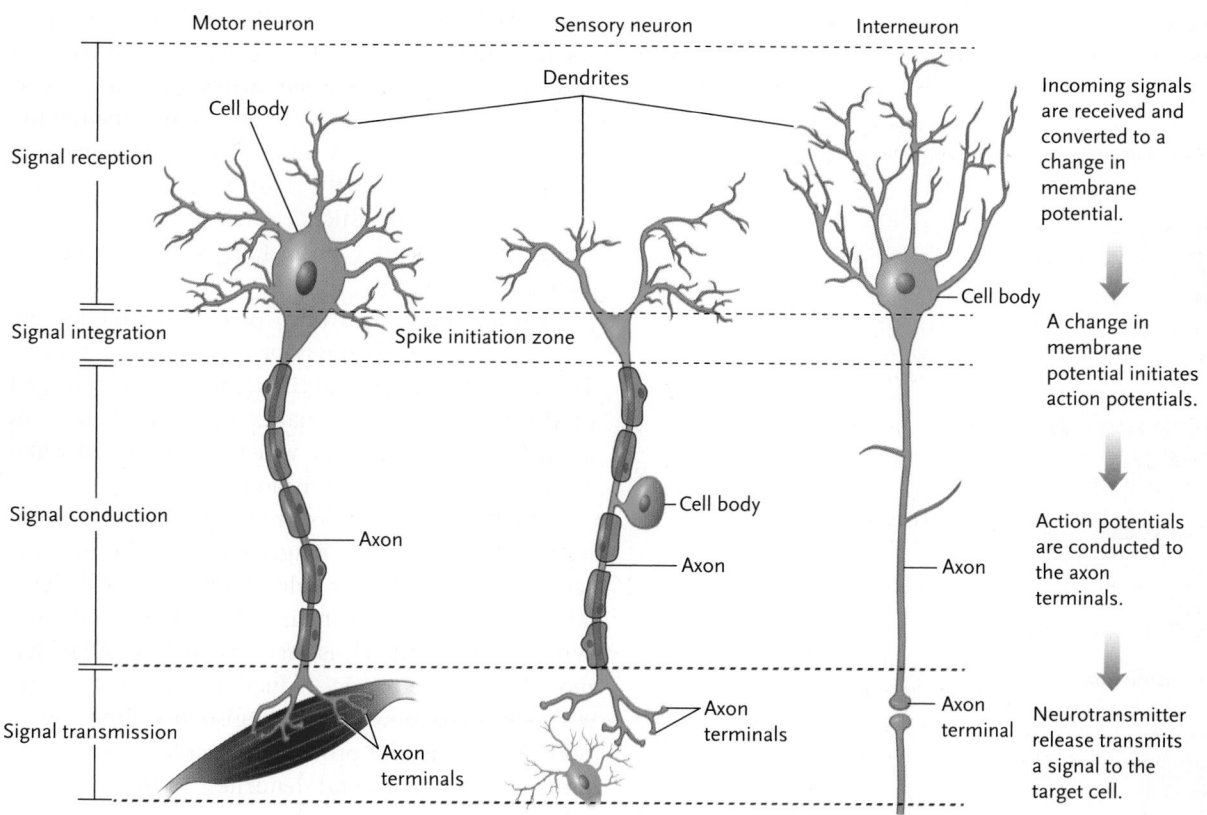

**FIGURE 45.1 Neural signals: steps in processing of information in single neurons.** There is considerable variation in the size and shape of neurons, but most of them are divided into distinct regions that serve in receiving signals, integrating them, conducting them, and transmitting them to other cells.

Labels within figure:

Motor neuron Sensory neuron Interneuron

Dendrites

Cell body

Signal reception — Incoming signals are received and converted to a change in membrane potential.

Cell body

Signal integration — Spike initiation zone — A change in membrane potential initiates action potentials.

Signal conduction — Axon — Cell body — Axon — Axon — Action potentials are conducted to the axon terminals.

Signal transmission — Axon terminals — Axon terminals — Axon terminal — Neurotransmitter release transmits a signal to the target cell.

---

of another neuron, the release of a hormone from a gland, or the contraction of a muscle.

The cell body, which contains the nucleus and the majority of cell organelles, synthesizes most of the proteins, carbohydrates, and lipids of the neuron.

**NEURAL CIRCUITS ARE ALSO SPECIALIZED FOR THE RECEPTION, INTEGRATION, AND TRANSMISSION OF INFORMATION** Connections between the axon terminals of one neuron and the dendrites or cell body of a second neuron link neurons into **neuronal circuits**. These circuits involve the same four components of neural signalling but at a higher level **(Figure 45.2)**.

- **Reception:** Afferent neurons (also called **sensory neurons**) transmit stimuli collected by sensory receptors on those neurons to interneurons.
- **Integration: Interneurons** integrate the information to formulate an appropriate response. In humans and some other primates, 99% of all neurons are interneurons. Interneurons may receive input from several axons and may, in turn, connect to other interneurons and several efferent neurons. In this way, circuits combine into networks that interconnect the parts of the nervous system.
- **Transmission: Efferent neurons** carry the signals initiating a response away from the interneuron networks to the **effectors**.

- **Response:** This is carried out by muscles and glands. Efferent neurons that carry signals to skeletal muscle are called **motor neurons**.

In vertebrates, the afferent (sensory) neurons and efferent neurons collectively form the PNS. The interneurons that form the brain and spinal cord make up the CNS. As depicted in Figure 45.2, afferent (carrying toward) information is ultimately transmitted to the CNS, where efferent (carrying away) information is initiated. The nervous systems of most invertebrates are also composed of central and peripheral divisions.

**NEURONS ARE SUPPORTED STRUCTURALLY AND FUNCTIONALLY BY GLIAL CELLS** Glial cells are non-neuronal cells that provide nutrition and support to neurons. One type, called **astrocytes** because they are star-shaped **(Figure 45.3)**, were formerly thought to play only a supporting role in the CNS by maintaining ion concentrations in the interstitial fluid surrounding the neurons. More recently, however, scientists have realized that, in vertebrates and some invertebrates, astrocytes communicate with neurons and may influence their activity (see next Concept Fix).

Two other types of glial cells, **oligodendrocytes** in the CNS and **Schwann cells** in the PNS, form tightly wrapped layers of plasma membrane, called *myelin sheaths*, around

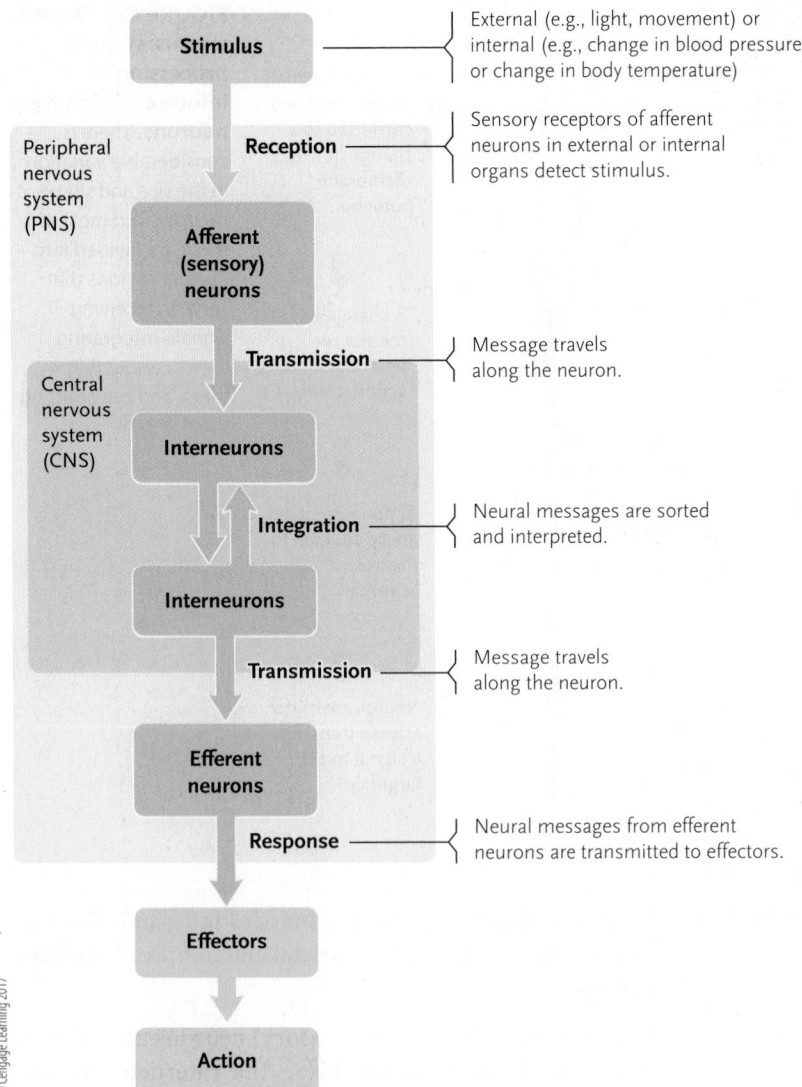

External (e.g., light, movement) or internal (e.g., change in blood pressure or change in body temperature)

Sensory receptors of afferent neurons in external or internal organs detect stimulus.

Message travels along the neuron.

Neural messages are sorted and interpreted.

Message travels along the neuron.

Neural messages from efferent neurons are transmitted to effectors.

© Cengage Learning 2017

**FIGURE 45.2 Neural signalling: the information-processing steps in neural circuits**

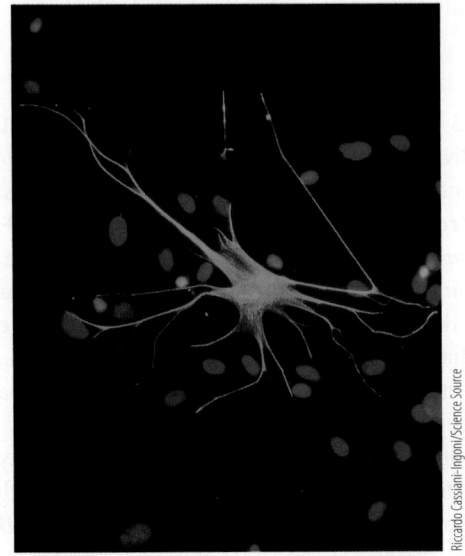

Riccardo Cassiani-Ingoni/Science Source

**FIGURE 45.3 An astrocyte**

axons **(Figure 45.4)**. These myelin sheaths act as electrical insulators due to the membrane's high lipid content. The gaps between Schwann cells, called **nodes of Ranvier**, expose the axon membrane directly to extracellular fluids. This arrangement of insulated stretches of the axon punctuated by gaps speeds the rate at which electrical impulses move along the axons they protect, as will be discussed later in this chapter.

Unlike most neurons, glial cells retain the capacity to divide throughout the life of the animal. This capacity allows glial tissues to replace damaged or dead cells but also makes them the source of almost all brain tumours, which are produced when regulation of glial cell division is lost.

CONCEPT FIX That glial cells only support and provide nutrition to neurons no longer appears to be an accurate assessment of their roles. Some glial cells regulate the clearance of neurotransmitters from the synaptic cleft and release factors such as ATP that modulate presynaptic function. During early embryogenesis, other glial cells also direct the migration of neurons and produce molecules that modify the growth of axons and dendrites. In the past, glial cells were not believed to have chemical synapses or to release neurotransmitters. They were regarded as a "glue" in the nervous system, as their name implies. More recently it has been shown that the only notable differences between neurons and glial cells are that the latter lack axons and dendrites and they lack the ability to generate action potentials. Attention is now being paid to their roles in the formation and modulation of synapses and in the repair of neurons after injury. ⬡

CONCEPT FIX Neurons are sometimes called *nerve cells*, but this is technically incorrect. Many neurons, such as those within the CNS, do not form nerves, and nerves usually contain non-neuronal cells, such as Schwann cells, that coat the axons in myelin. ⬡

### STUDY BREAK QUESTIONS

1. Describe reception, integration, transmission, and response at the level of a single neuron as well as in a complex neural circuit.
2. What are the different roles of glial cells and neurons?

## 45.1b Action Potentials: A Unique Feature of Excitable Cells

**ALL CELLS HAVE A RESTING MEMBRANE POTENTIAL** As you learned in Chapter 4, plasma membranes are selectively permeable in that they allow some molecules but not others to move across the membrane through protein channels embedded

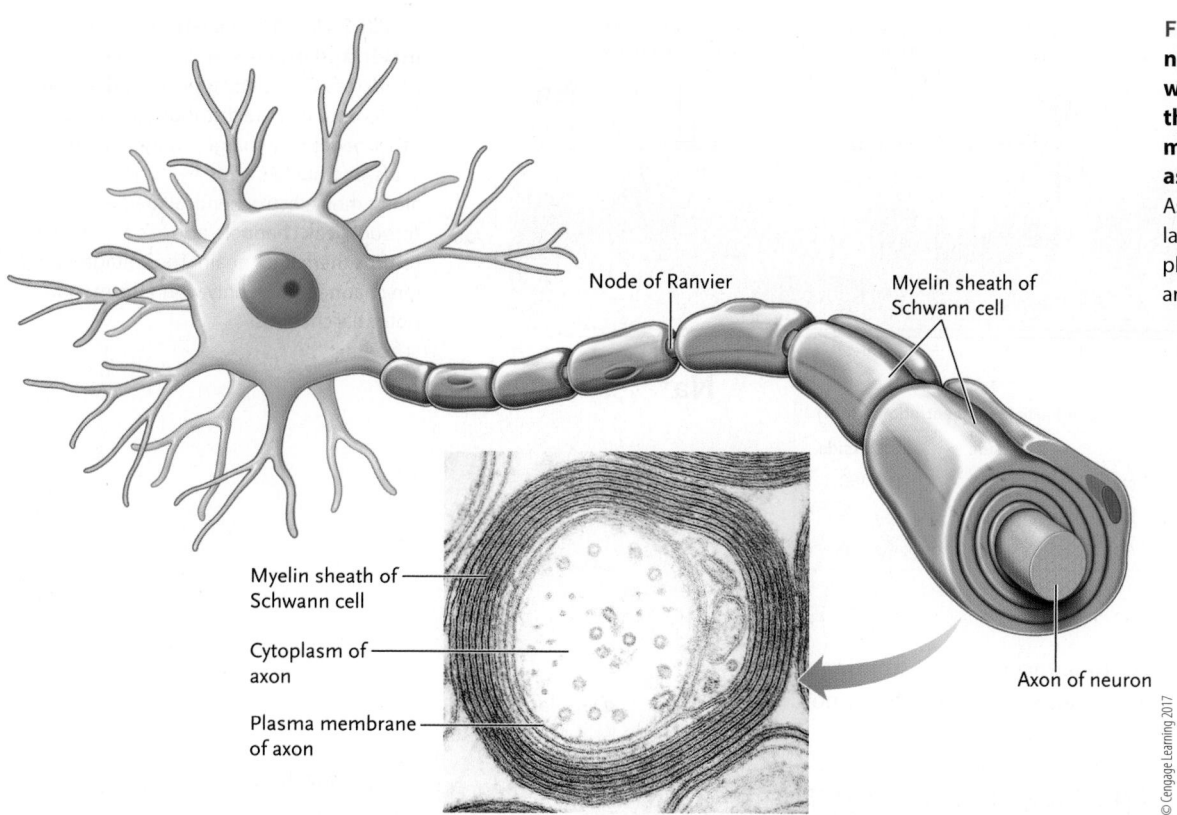

FIGURE 45.4 **Myelinated neurons have axons wrapped in Schwann cells that coat the axon in a myelin sheath, which acts as an electrical insulator.** As many as 300 overlapping layers of the Schwann cell plasma membrane wind around an axon like a jelly roll.

Node of Ranvier

Myelin sheath of Schwann cell

Myelin sheath of Schwann cell

Cytoplasm of axon

Plasma membrane of axon

Axon of neuron

Science VU/C. Raines/Visuals Unlimited, Inc.

© Cengage Learning 2017

in the phospholipid bilayer. Many of these molecules are charged (remember that **anions** are ions that carry a negative charge, and **cations** are ions that carry a positive charge; see *The Purple Pages*). All animal cells have more negatively charged molecules (anions, amino acids, nucleic acids, etc.) inside the cell than outside the cell. The separation of positive and negative charges across the plasma membrane produces an electrical gradient, or potential difference, across the plasma membrane called the **membrane potential**. All cells exhibit a membrane potential and are said to be polarized. The membrane potential of a cell under normal conditions is often called the **resting potential**.

In all cells at rest, there are more K$^+$ ions inside the cell, with a net tendency to diffuse out due to their concentration gradient, but a net tendency to remain inside the cell due to their electrical charge (like charges repel and unlike charges attract). These don't quite balance out, and thus there is a small net tendency (i.e., a small net **electrochemical gradient**) for K$^+$ to diffuse out of the cell through various channels. There are more Na$^+$ ions outside the cell than inside, and both electrical and concentration gradients (i.e., electrochemical gradient) favour movement into the cell. The plasma membrane, however, is not normally very permeable to Na$^+$, and so only a small amount leaks in. Na$^+$/K$^+$ transport pumps embedded in the plasma membrane use energy from ATP to actively pump three Na$^+$ out of the cell for every two K$^+$ pumped in, maintaining a steady state and a steady resting membrane potential. For most cells, this membrane potential is very stable. The distribution of

ions inside and outside an axon that produces the membrane potential is shown in **Figure 45.5**.

Like all cells, neurons also have a voltage difference between the inside and the outside of the cell. However, neurons and muscle cells are excitable. In response to electrical, chemical, mechanical, and certain other types of stimuli, their membrane potential changes rapidly and transiently. Excitability, produced by a sudden flow of ions across the plasma membrane, is the basis for nerve impulse generation. It also gives neurons the ability to store, recall, and distribute information.

The membrane of a neuron that is not conducting an impulse exhibits a steady negative membrane potential called the *resting potential* because the neuron is at rest. The resting potential has been measured at about –70 mV in isolated neurons. The change in membrane potential that occurs when a neuron is excited is the **action potential**, which will be discussed shortly. As we will see in the following discussion, the action potential results from the opening and closing of voltage-gated ion channels for Na$^+$ and K$^+$.

**CONCEPT FIX** The statement that the diffusion of ions is due to differences in concentration between two sites is not always true. While ions diffuse along concentration gradients, this is not the only factor that determines the direction of the net diffusion of ions. Ions really diffuse along energy gradients, and the energy gradient for any specific ion is also determined by electrical charge (for charged molecules), temperature, and

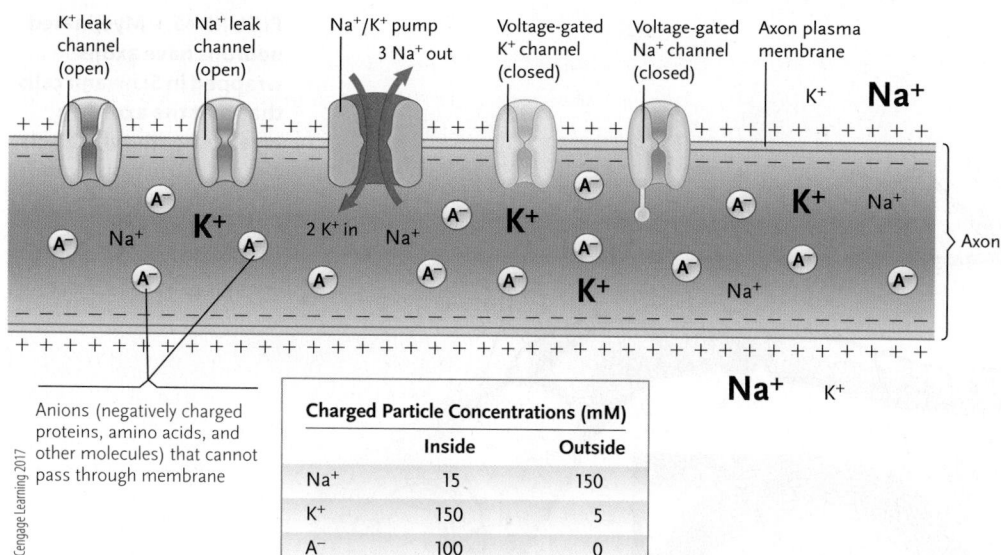

Anions (negatively charged proteins, amino acids, and other molecules) that cannot pass through membrane

© Cengage Learning 2017

| Charged Particle Concentrations (mM) | | |
|---|---|---|
| | Inside | Outside |
| Na⁺ | 15 | 150 |
| K⁺ | 150 | 5 |
| A⁻ | 100 | 0 |

**FIGURE 45.5 The distribution of ions inside and outside an axon that produces the resting potential, −70 mV.** A⁻ incorporates the distribution of Cl⁻ and other negatively charged anions, amino acids, and nucleic acids. Na⁺ and K⁺ diffuse along their electrochemical gradients through leak channels, and the Na⁺/K⁺ pump returns them back again. The voltage-gated ion channels open only when the membrane potential changes.

pressure. Diffusion is due to concentration gradients alone if all other factors are equal, something that is not common in living cells. ⬡

## GRADED POTENTIALS CAN OCCUR IN ALL CELLS DUE TO CHANGES IN MEMBRANE PERMEABILITY TO IONS AND CAN VARY IN MAGNITUDE

The permeability of most membranes to ions is not constant but changes as various channels in the membrane open and close. If, as a result of such events, positively charged ions (such as Na⁺) enter the cell, or negatively charged ions leave the cell, the charge across the membrane will become less negative and the membrane will be less polarized, or **depolarized** (**Figure 45.6**). If, on the other hand, positively charged ions (such as K⁺) leave the cell, or negatively charged ions (such as Cl⁻) enter, the membrane will become more polarized, or **hyperpolarized**. The more ions that cross the membrane, the greater the depolarization or hyperpolarization; that is, these events are graded. As the ions are restored to their initial levels, the membrane is **repolarized** and the cell membrane returns to its resting membrane potential. These changes in membrane potential due to changes in membrane permeability to ions are called **graded potentials**. Because the ions that enter through any channel will disperse within the cell, graded potentials will radiate over the cell membrane, decreasing in magnitude as they move farther away from the open ion channel. They can occur in any cell and are not confined to nerve cells. In neurons, graded potentials are part of the integration that takes place in dendrites and cell bodies (see Section 45.3a).

## AN ACTION POTENTIAL IS NOT GRADED BUT IS A RAPID, REVERSIBLE EVENT

Although graded potentials cannot be transmitted over long distances, action potentials can. Only certain parts of a neuron can generate action potentials (as a rule, dendrites and cell bodies cannot), and, as mentioned ear-

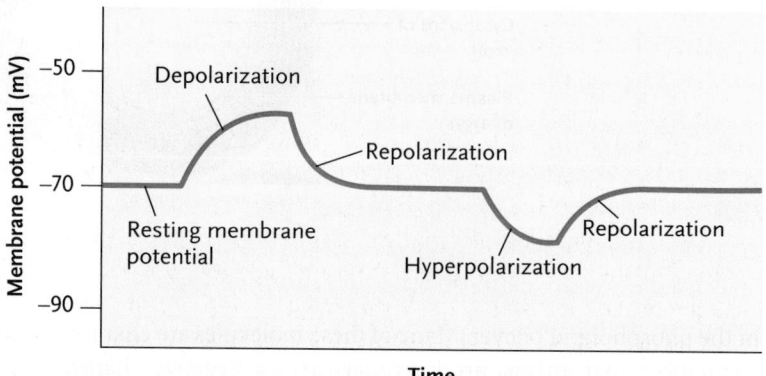

**FIGURE 45.6 Changes in membrane potential in a cell due to changes in ion permeability.** The resting membrane potential in this cell is −70 mV. During depolarization, the membrane potential becomes less negative. During hyperpolarization, the membrane potential becomes more negative. During repolarization, the membrane potential returns to its resting level.

lier, the site where action potentials are initiated in the neuron is referred to as the *spike initiation zone* (or trigger zone; see Figure 45.1). If graded potentials spreading over the dendrites and cell body are sufficient to depolarize the membrane at the site of the spike initiation zone to a level known as the **threshold potential**, about −50 to −55 mV in isolated neurons, an action potential occurs at this site. In less than 1 ms (millisecond), the inside of the plasma membrane at this site becomes positive because of an influx of positive ions across the cell membrane, momentarily reaching a value of +30 mV or more (**Figure 45.7**). The membrane potential at this site then falls, in many cases becoming hyperpolarized and dropping to about −80 mV before rising again to the resting potential. The entire change, from initiation of the action potential to the return to the resting potential, takes less than 5 ms in the fastest neurons. Action potentials take the same basic form in neurons of all types, although there may be differences in the values of the resting potential and the

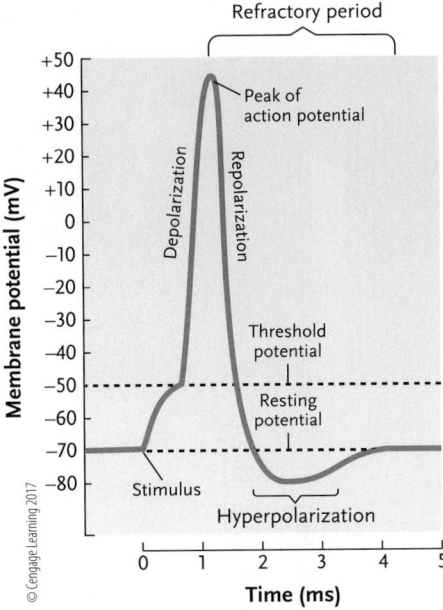

FIGURE 45.7 **Changes in membrane potential during an action potential**

peak of the action potential and in the time required to return to the resting potential.

An action potential is produced only if the depolarization arriving at the spike initiation zone is strong enough to cause the membrane potential to reach threshold. Furthermore, once triggered, the changes in membrane potential take place independently of the strength of the stimulus. No matter how strong the stimulus, once threshold is reached, the action potential will always be the same size. This is referred to as the **all-or-nothing principle**.

Beginning at the peak of an action potential, the membrane enters a **refractory period** of a few milliseconds that lasts until the membrane has stabilized at the resting potential. As we will see, the refractory period keeps impulses travelling in a one-way direction in neurons.

**THE ACTION POTENTIAL IS PRODUCED BY ION MOVEMENTS THROUGH THE PLASMA MEMBRANE** The action potential is produced by movements of $Na^+$ and $K^+$ through the plasma membrane that are controlled by specific **voltage-gated ion channels**, membrane-embedded proteins that open and close as the membrane potential changes **(Figure 45.8)**. Voltage-gated $Na^+$ channels have two gates, an activation gate and an inactivation gate; voltage-gated $K^+$ channels have one gate, an activation gate.

Figure 45.8 shows how the two voltage-gated ion channels operate when generating an action potential. When the membrane is at its resting potential, the activation gates of both the $Na^+$ and the $K^+$ channel are closed. A depolarizing stimulus, such as a neurotransmitter substance, produces a graded depolarization that spreads to the spike initiation zone and

depolarizes (raises) the membrane potential to the threshold. This change in membrane charge attracts and pulls the activation gate of the voltage-gated $Na^+$ channels open, allowing $Na^+$ ions to flow into the axon along their electrochemical gradient. Once above the threshold, the more the membrane depolarizes, the more the voltage-gated $Na^+$ channels open, causing a rapid inward flow of positive charges that raises the membrane potential to the peak of the action potential. As the action potential peaks, the change in charge at the plasma membrane causes the inactivation gates of the $Na^+$ channels to close (resembling putting a stopper in a sink), which stops the inward flow of $Na^+$. The refractory period now begins; $Na^+$ can no longer enter the cell, and so another action potential cannot be initiated until these gates return to normal.

At the same time, the activation gates of the $K^+$ channels begin to open, allowing $K^+$ ions to flow rapidly outward in response to their electrochemical gradient (the cell is now positive on the inside and negative on the outside so that both concentration and electrical gradients favour the movement of $K^+$ out of the cell). The movement of $K^+$ ions contributes to the refractory period and compensates for the inward movement of $Na^+$ ions, returning the membrane to the resting potential. As the resting potential is reestablished, the activation gates of the $K^+$ channels close, as do those of the $Na^+$ channels, and the inactivation gates of the $Na^+$ channels open. The opening of the inactivation gates and the resetting of the activation gates on the $Na^+$ and $K^+$ channels end the refractory period. Another action potential can now be generated. The opening and closing of the gates are the result of interactions between charge on the plasma membrane and charge on the gates themselves, either pulling the gates toward the membrane and opening them, or pushing the gates away and closing them; this is the basis of the operation of all voltage-gated channels.

In some neurons, closure of the voltage-gated $K^+$ channels is slow, and $K^+$ continues to flow outward for a brief time after the membrane returns to the resting potential. This excess outward flow causes the hyperpolarization shown in Figure 45.7 and Figure 45.8 (step 6), in which the membrane potential dips briefly below the resting potential.

At the end of an action potential, the membrane potential has returned to its resting state, but the ion distribution has been changed slightly. That is, some $Na^+$ has entered the cell and some $K^+$ has left the cell. Actually, relatively few of the total number of $Na^+$ and $K^+$ ions change locations during an action potential (ions flow for only 5 ms). Hence, additional action potentials can occur without the need to completely correct the altered ion distribution. In the long term, the $Na^+/K^+$ active transport pumps restore the $Na^+$ and $K^+$ to their original locations.

⬢ CONCEPT Not all channels in membranes work the same way. Leak channels are proteins whose structure leaves gaps large enough for some molecules to pass through passively. Ligand-gated channels are proteins whose structure is altered when a specific molecule (the ligand) binds to it. This change in shape

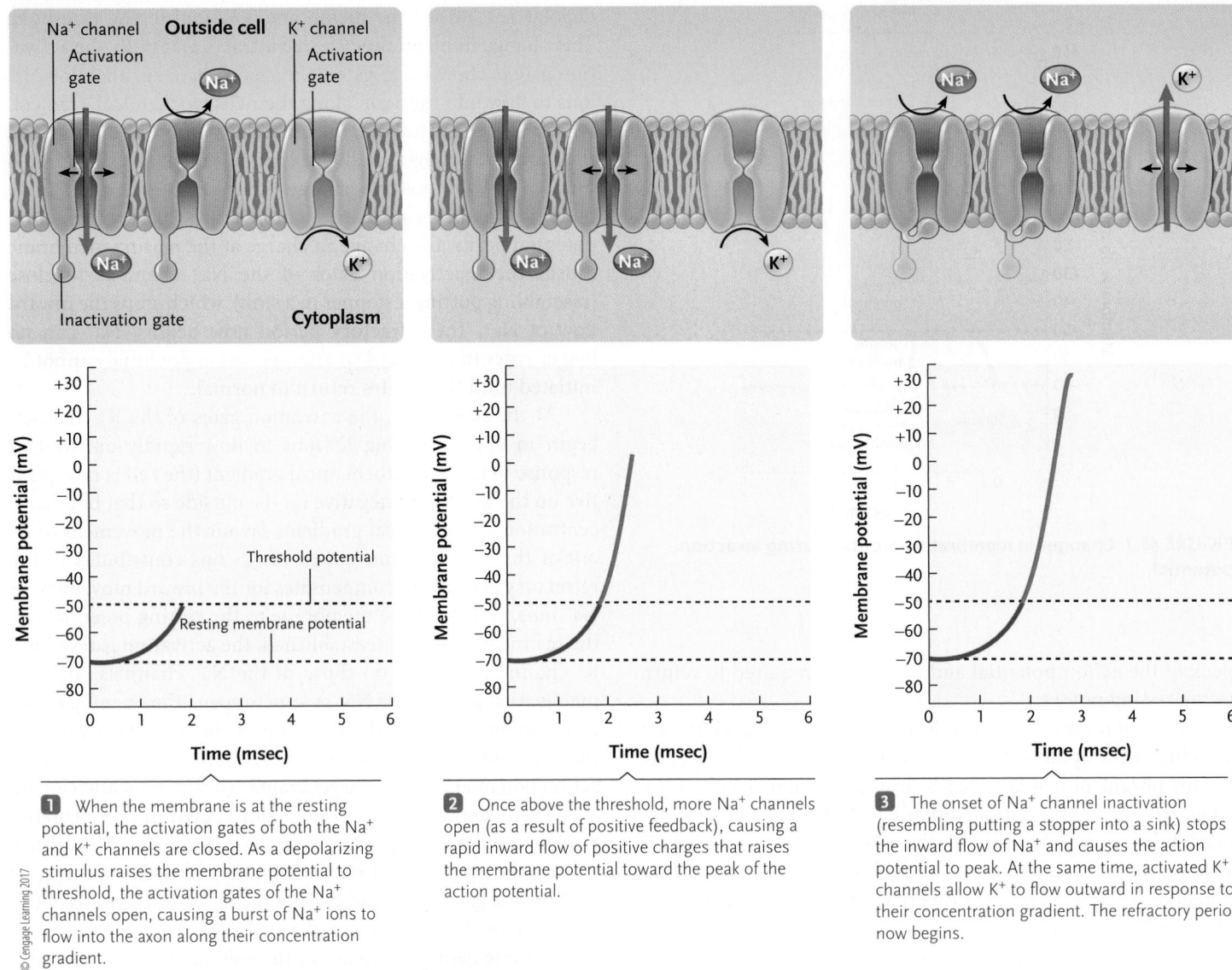

**1** When the membrane is at the resting potential, the activation gates of both the Na⁺ and K⁺ channels are closed. As a depolarizing stimulus raises the membrane potential to threshold, the activation gates of the Na⁺ channels open, causing a burst of Na⁺ ions to flow into the axon along their concentration gradient.

**2** Once above the threshold, more Na⁺ channels open (as a result of positive feedback), causing a rapid inward flow of positive charges that raises the membrane potential toward the peak of the action potential.

**3** The onset of Na⁺ channel inactivation (resembling putting a stopper into a sink) stops the inward flow of Na⁺ and causes the action potential to peak. At the same time, activated K⁺ channels allow K⁺ to flow outward in response to their concentration gradient. The refractory period now begins.

© Cengage Learning 2017

**FIGURE 45.8  Changes in voltage-gated Na⁺ and K⁺ channels that produce the action potential**

either opens or closes the channel. Voltage-gated channels are proteins with a flexible portion (the gate) that carries a charge. If the charge on the membrane changes, it can either attract or repel the charge on the protein (opposite charges attract; like charges repel), moving the flexible gate such that it opens or closes a channel. ⬡

## STUDY BREAK QUESTIONS

1. What is the difference between an excitable cell, such as a neuron, and other cells, such as liver or blood cells?

2. Can all parts of a neuron generate an action potential? Why or why not?

3. Describe all the steps involved in the production of an action potential.

### 45.1c  Conduction of Action Potentials along Neurons

**ACTION POTENTIALS ARE PROPAGATED ALONG AXONS** Once an action potential is initiated at the spike initiation zone, it passes along the surface of a neuron as an automatic wave of depolarization. It travels away from the stimulation point without requiring further triggering events **(Figure 45.9)**. This is called **propagation**, or **conduction**, of the action potential.

In a segment of an axon generating an action potential, the outside of the membrane becomes temporarily negative and the inside positive. Because opposites attract, as the membrane potential reverses in the region of the spike initiation zone, local current flow occurs between the area undergoing an action potential and the adjacent downstream inactive area, both inside and outside the membrane (see arrows in

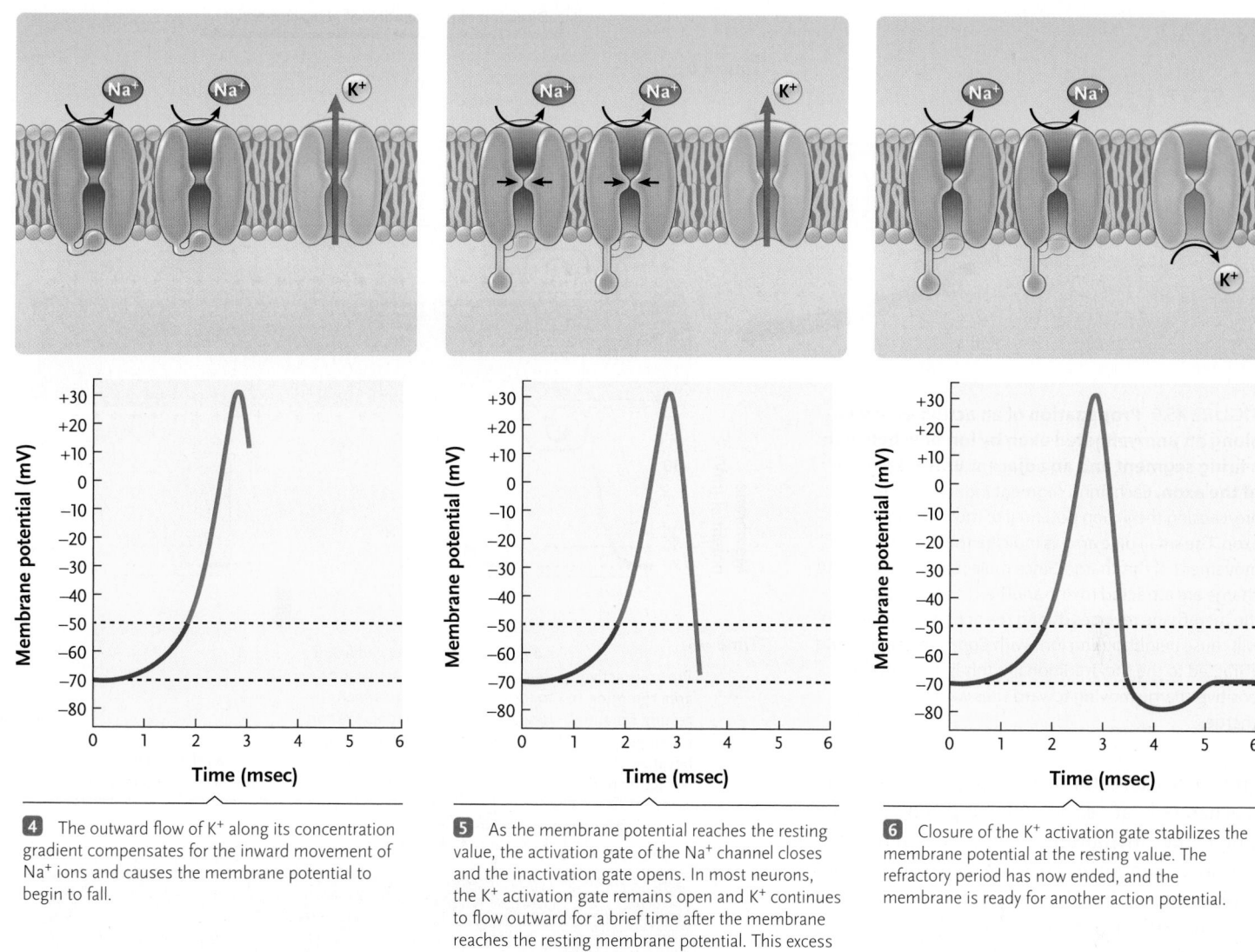

4 The outward flow of K⁺ along its concentration gradient compensates for the inward movement of Na⁺ ions and causes the membrane potential to begin to fall.

5 As the membrane potential reaches the resting value, the activation gate of the Na⁺ channel closes and the inactivation gate opens. In most neurons, the K⁺ activation gate remains open and K⁺ continues to flow outward for a brief time after the membrane reaches the resting membrane potential. This excess outward flow causes hyperpolarization, in which the membrane potential dips briefly below the resting membrane potential (the dip is seen in step 6).

6 Closure of the K⁺ activation gate stabilizes the membrane potential at the resting value. The refractory period has now ended, and the membrane is ready for another action potential.

Figure 45.9). This current flow (flow of charge, like the flow of electrical current in a wire) makes nearby regions of the axon membrane less positive on the outside and more positive on the inside; in other words, the membrane of these adjacent regions depolarizes.

In regions of the neuron capable of propagating action potentials, voltage-gated channels occur throughout the membrane. The local depolarization spreading from the spike initiation zone is large enough to push the membrane potential of the neighbouring voltage-gated Na⁺ and K⁺ channels past their threshold, starting an action potential in the adjacent downstream region. In this way, each segment of the axon stimulates the next segment to fire, and the action potential moves rapidly along the axon as a nerve impulse.

The refractory period keeps an action potential from reversing direction. Because of the refractory period, only the region in front of the action potential can fire, and not the region behind it. When the inactivation gate closes on a voltage-gated Na⁺ channel, this site on the membrane is not capable of generating another action potential until this gate reopens and the activation gates on the Na⁺ and K⁺ channels are reset. The upstream voltage-gated ion channels need time to reset to their original positions before they can open again. Therefore, only downstream voltage-gated ion channels are able to open, ensuring the one-way movement of the action potential along the axon toward the axon terminals. By the time the refractory period ends in a membrane segment that has just fired an action potential, the action potential has moved too far away to cause a second action potential to develop in the same segment.

The magnitude of an action potential stays the same as it travels along an axon, even where the axon branches at its tips.

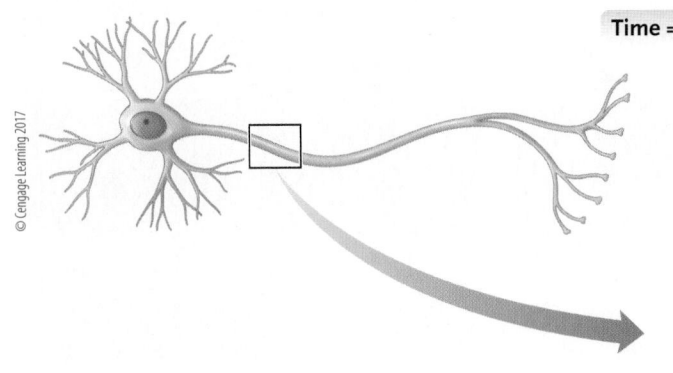

Direction of propagation of action potential
Time = 0
Active area at peak of action potential
Adjacent inactive area into which depolarization is spreading; will soon reach threshold
Remainder of axon still at resting potential
Na+
Na+
Membrane potential (mV)
+30
0
–50
–70
Time = 1
Previous active area returning to resting potential; no longer active because of refractory period
Adjacent area that was brought to threshold by local current flow; now active at peak of action potential
New adjacent inactive area into which depolarization is spreading; will soon reach threshold
Remainder of axon still at resting potential
K+
Na+
K+
Na+
Membrane potential (mV)
+30
0
–50
–70
Time = 2
At resting potential
K+
Na+
K+
Na+
Membrane potential (mV)
+30
0
–50
–70

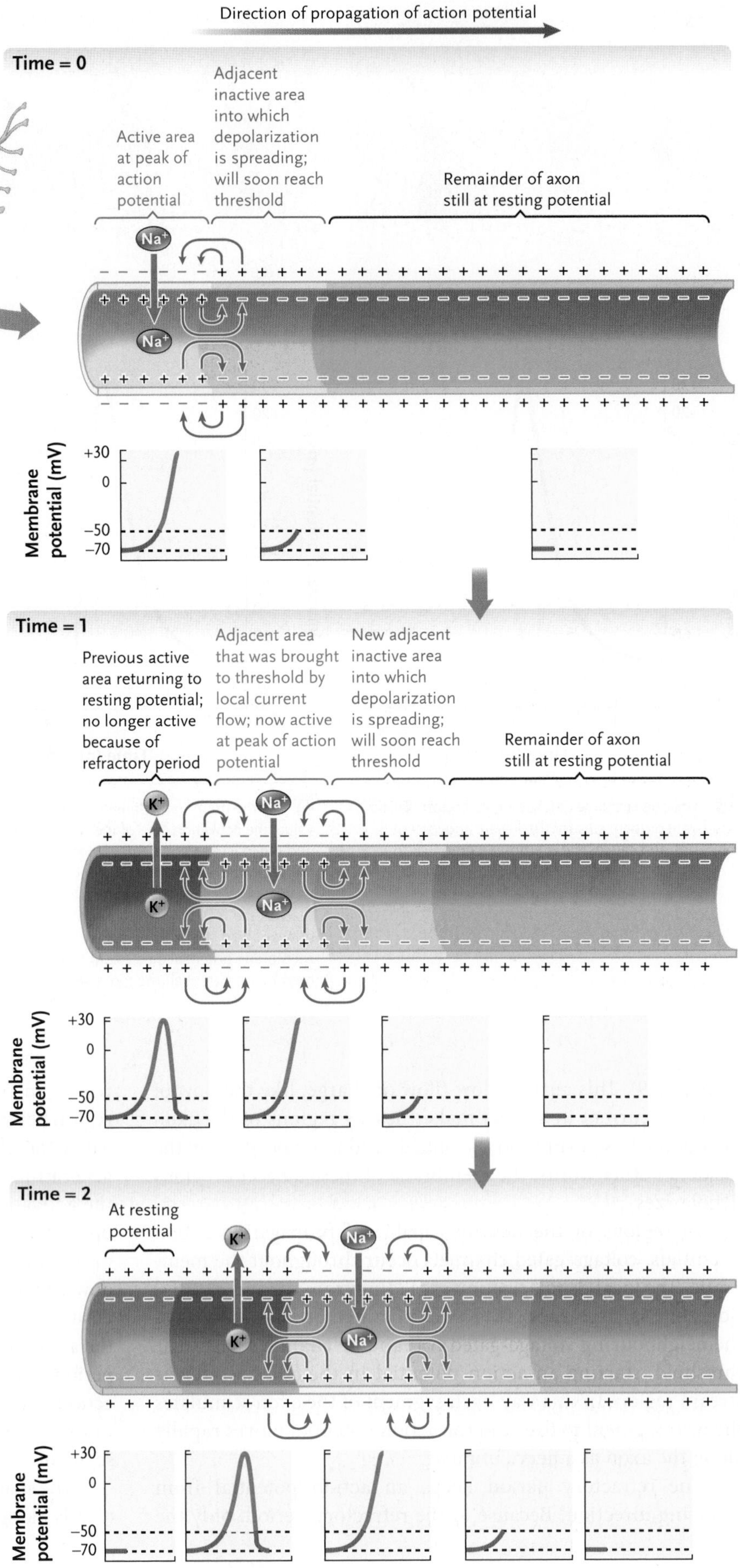

**FIGURE 45.9 Propagation of an action potential along an unmyelinated axon by ion flow between a firing segment and an adjacent unfired region of the axon.** Each firing segment induces the next to fire, causing the action potential to move along the axon. The small blue arrows indicate the direction of movement of the charge. Since molecules with opposite charge are attracted to one another, as the charge on the membrane reverses during the action potential, this will cause neighbouring ions with opposite charge to be attracted to the site. Traditionally, this is illustrated as positive charge moving toward sites with negative charge.

This is because the action potential is being regenerated at each voltage-gated channel along the membrane. Once the refractory period is complete, an axon can fire another action potential of the same intensity.

The all-or-nothing principle of action potential generation means that the intensity of a stimulus is reflected in the frequency of action potentials rather than the size of the action potential. The greater the stimulus, the more action potentials per second are generated, up to a limit that depends on the axon type. For most neuron types, the limit lies between 10 and 100 action potentials per second.

**SALTATORY CONDUCTION INCREASES PROPAGATION RATES** In the propagation pattern shown in Figure 45.9, an action potential is regenerated at every voltage-gated channel along the length of the axon. The rate of conduction increases with the rate of local current flow, which increases with the diameter of the axon. Some specialized axons with very large diameters occur in invertebrates such as lobsters, earthworms, and squids, as well as a few marine fishes. Giant axons typically carry signals that produce an escape or withdrawal response, such as the sudden flexing of the tail (abdomen) in lobsters that propels the animal

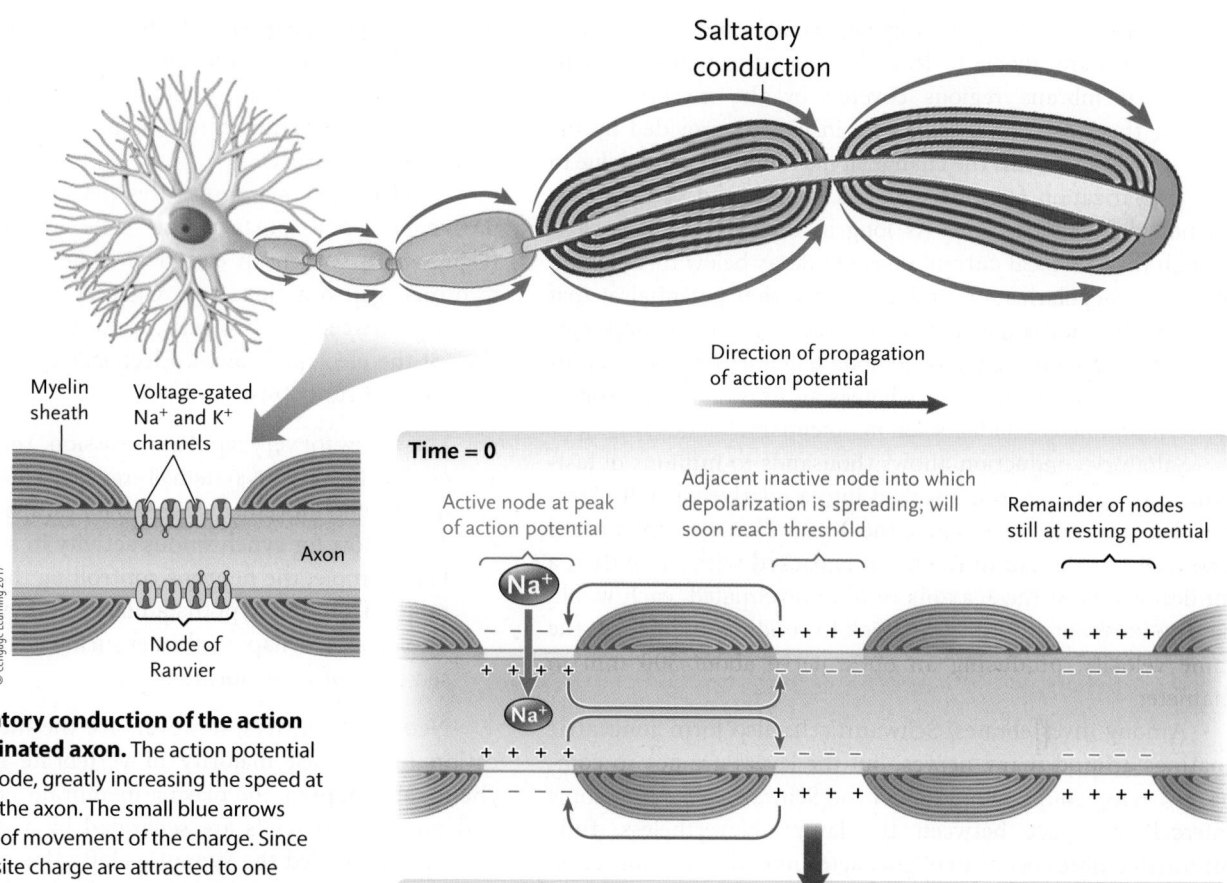

Saltatory
conduction

Direction of propagation
of action potential

**Myelin sheath** **Voltage-gated Na⁺ and K⁺ channels**

© Cengage Learning 2017

Axon

**Node of Ranvier**

**FIGURE 45.10 Saltatory conduction of the action potential by a myelinated axon.** The action potential jumps from node to node, greatly increasing the speed at which it travels along the axon. The small blue arrows indicate the direction of movement of the charge. Since molecules with opposite charge are attracted to one another, as the charge on the membrane reverses during the action potential, this will cause neighbouring ions with opposite charge to be attracted to the site. Traditionally, this is illustrated as positive charge moving toward sites with negative charge.

**Time = 0**

Active node at peak of action potential | Adjacent inactive node into which depolarization is spreading; will soon reach threshold | Remainder of nodes still at resting potential

**Time = 1**

Previous active node returning to resting potential; no longer active because of refractory period | Adjacent node that was brought to threshold by local current flow now active at peak of action potential | New adjacent inactive node into which depolarization is spreading; will soon reach threshold

**Time = 2**

At resting potential | Previous active node returning to resting potential; no longer active because of refractory period | Adjacent node that was brought to threshold by local current flow now active at peak of action potential

backward. The largest known axons, 1.7 mm in diameter, occur in fanworms (Phylum Annelida, Class Polychaeta; fanworms are a group of which the feather duster worm is a member). The signals they carry contract a muscle that retracts the fanworm's body into a protective tube when the animal is threatened. (See the video *Fan worms (Sabellastarte sp.) retracting underwater in Australia*, clip ID 2199481, on Shutterstock.com/video/.)

Although large-diameter axons can conduct impulses as rapidly as 25 m/s, they take up a great deal of space. In the jawed vertebrates, insulating axons with myelin sheaths (Figure 45.4) produce **saltatory conduction** (*saltare* = to leap), allowing action potentials to "leap" rapidly along axons.

Saltatory conduction depends on the gaps in the insulating myelin sheath that surrounds many axons. These gaps, known as *nodes of Ranvier*, expose the axon membrane to extracellular fluids. Voltage-gated Na⁺ and K⁺ channels crowded into the nodes allow action potentials to develop at these positions **(Figure 45.10)**. The inward movement of Na⁺ ions produces depolarization, but the excess positive ions are unable to leave the axon through the neighbouring membrane regions covered by the myelin sheath. Because the ions cannot leave, the insulation provided by the myelin sheath prevents the change in membrane potential due to the depolarization from decaying as rapidly, and so it spreads further along the neuron. As long as the next node is close enough that the local current does not decay below threshold, it will cause depolarization, inducing an action potential at that node. As this mechanism repeats, the action potential jumps rapidly along the axon from node to node. Saltatory conduction proceeds at rates up to 130 m/s, whereas an unmyelinated axon of the same diameter conducts action potentials at about 1 m/s.

Saltatory conduction allows thousands to millions of fast-transmitting axons to be packed into a relatively small diameter. For example, in humans, the 3-mm-diameter optic nerve leading from the eye to the brain is packed with more than a million axons. If those axons were unmyelinated, each would have to be about 100 times as thick to conduct impulses at the same velocity, producing an optic nerve about 300 mm in diameter.

Among invertebrates, Schwann cells also form concentric coatings around many nerves, but the layers are not so compact, leaving some cytoplasm in the Schwann cells and some intercellular space between the layers. Nevertheless, fully myelinated fibres occur in oligochaete annelids and some crustaceans, complete with gaps to permit saltatory transmission. The occurrence of myelin in some protostome invertebrates and its absence from the lower vertebrates suggests that this important mechanism has evolved more than once, presenting another example of convergent evolution. The embryonic origin of Schwann cells is also different in vertebrates and invertebrates, confirming the independent evolution of myelination in both groups.

The disease multiple sclerosis (*sclero* = hard) underscores the importance of myelin sheaths to the operation of the vertebrate nervous system. In this disease, myelin is attacked by the immune system and is progressively lost from axons and replaced by hardened scar tissue. The changes block or slow the transmission of action potentials, producing numbness, muscular weakness, faulty coordination of movements, and paralysis that worsens as the disease progresses. Although genetic factors are involved, the environment also plays a role: the incidence of the disease increases with the distance from the equator. The incidence in Canada, 2.4 people per 1000 population, is one of the highest in the world.

## 45.1d  Neurons Communicate via Synapses

A **synapse** (*synapsis* = juncture) is a site where a neuron makes a communicating connection with either another neuron or an effector, such as a muscle fibre or gland. On one side of the synapse is the axon terminal of a **presynaptic cell**, the neuron that transmits the signal. On the other side is the dendrite, or cell body, of a **postsynaptic cell**, the neuron or the surface of an effector that receives the signal. Communication across a synapse may occur by the direct flow of an electrical signal or by means of a **neurotransmitter**, a chemical released by an axon terminal at a synapse.

In **electrical synapses**, the plasma membranes of the presynaptic and postsynaptic cells are in direct contact (**Figure 45.11**). When an electrical impulse arrives at the axon terminal, gap junctions (see Chapter 38) allow ions to flow directly between the two cells, leading to unbroken transmission of the electrical signal. Electrical synapses are useful for two types of functions:

- They allow for very rapid transmission. They were first discovered in the nervous system of crayfish, where they are involved in the rapid movements needed for escape from predators.
- They allow for synchronous activity in a group of neurons. For example, the neurons controlling the secretion of hormones from the hypothalamus of mammals are connected by electrical synapses, thus ensuring a coordinated burst of secretion of some hormones.

Neurotransmitters, however, are the means of communication in the vast majority of vertebrate neurons. In these **chemical synapses**, the plasma membranes of the presynaptic and postsynaptic cells are separated by a narrow gap, about 25 nm wide, called the **synaptic cleft**. The arrival of an action potential causes neurotransmitter molecules synthesized in the cell body of the neuron to be released across the plasma membrane of the axon terminal, called the **presynaptic membrane (Figure 45.12)**. The neurotransmitter diffuses across

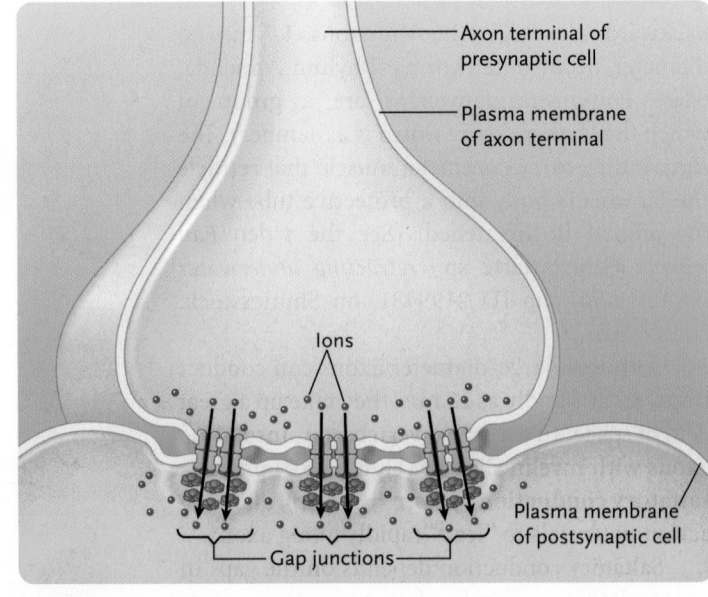

In an electrical synapse, the plasma membranes of the presynaptic and postsynaptic cells make direct contact. Ions flow through gap junctions that connect the two membranes, allowing impulses to pass directly to the postsynaptic cell.

**FIGURE 45.11  Function of electrical synapses**

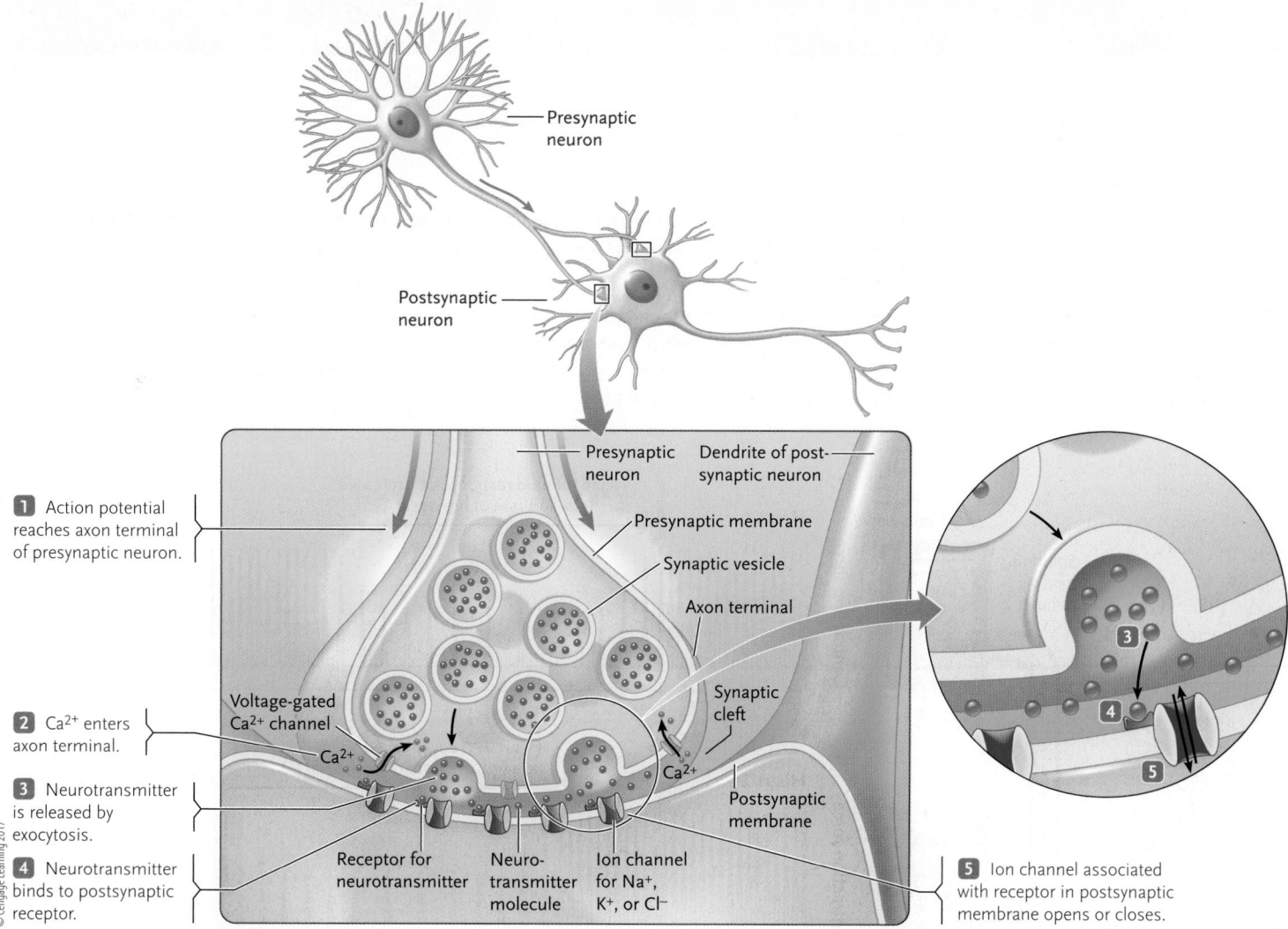

**1** Action potential reaches axon terminal of presynaptic neuron.

**2** Ca²⁺ enters axon terminal.

**3** Neurotransmitter is released by exocytosis.

**4** Neurotransmitter binds to postsynaptic receptor.

Presynaptic neuron

Postsynaptic neuron

Presynaptic neuron

Dendrite of post-synaptic neuron

Presynaptic membrane

Synaptic vesicle

Axon terminal

Synaptic cleft

Postsynaptic membrane

Voltage-gated Ca²⁺ channel

Ca²⁺

Ca²⁺

Receptor for neurotransmitter

Neuro-transmitter molecule

Ion channel for Na⁺, K⁺, or Cl⁻

**5** Ion channel associated with receptor in postsynaptic membrane opens or closes.

© Cengage Learning 2017

**FIGURE 45.12 Function of chemical synapses**

the cleft and alters ion conduction by activating ligand-gated ion channels in the **postsynaptic membrane**, the plasma membrane of the postsynaptic cell. **Ligand-gated ion channels** are channels that open or close when a specific chemical, the ligand, binds to the channel, altering its shape.

**Neurotransmitters work in one of two ways.** Some bind directly to a ligand-gated ion channel in the postsynaptic membrane (ionotropic receptors; Figure 45.12), which opens or closes the channel gate and alters the flow of a specific ion or ions in the postsynaptic cell. The time between arrival of an action potential at an axon terminal and alteration of the membrane potential in the postsynaptic cell may be as little as 0.2 ms. Others work more slowly (on the order of hundreds of milliseconds). They act as first messengers, binding to G-protein–coupled receptors (metabotropic receptors) in the postsynaptic membrane, activating a second messenger, such as cyclic AMP, or other processes. The cascade of second-messenger reactions opens or closes ion-conducting channels in the post-

synaptic membrane. Metabotropic neurotransmitters typically have effects that may last for minutes or hours.

Some neurotransmitters bind to only one type of receptor, whereas others bind to both types of receptor, bringing about different responses depending on which type of receptor they bind to in the receiving cell.

Not all the chemicals released at nerve terminals directly stimulate the postsynaptic neuron to fire. Some may inhibit the neuron from firing; others may enhance the action of other transmitters. These transmitters are sometimes called **neuromodulators**.

The time required for the release, diffusion, and binding of neurotransmitters across chemical synapses delays transmission compared with the almost instantaneous transmission of impulses across electrical synapses. (Also see **Figure 45.13**.) However, communication through chemical synapses allows postsynaptic neurons to integrate inputs from many presynaptic axons at the same time. Some neurotransmitters have stimulatory effects; others have inhibitory effects. All the

FIGURE 45.13    **Experimental Research**

## Demonstration of Chemical Transmission of Nerve Impulses at Synapses

**Question:** How do neurons transmit signals across synapses?

**Experiment:** In the first part of the twentieth century, many scientists thought the signal transmitted across synapses was electrical, like the nerve signal itself; others thought that chemicals were involved. In 1921, Otto Loewi, of Graz University, Austria, performed an experiment demonstrating that chemicals can transmit a signal across the synapse.

**Results:** Loewi isolated the hearts from two frogs, putting each into a separate container filled with a warm solution that kept the hearts alive. The two containers were linked to allow interchange of solutions. In this setup, the hearts could continue to beat for several hours. Loewi stimulated the vagus nerve of heart 1, which resulted in a rapid decrease in the strength and rate of its beating. Loewi observed that, after a short delay, the strength and rate of beating of heart 2 in the connected container also decreased.

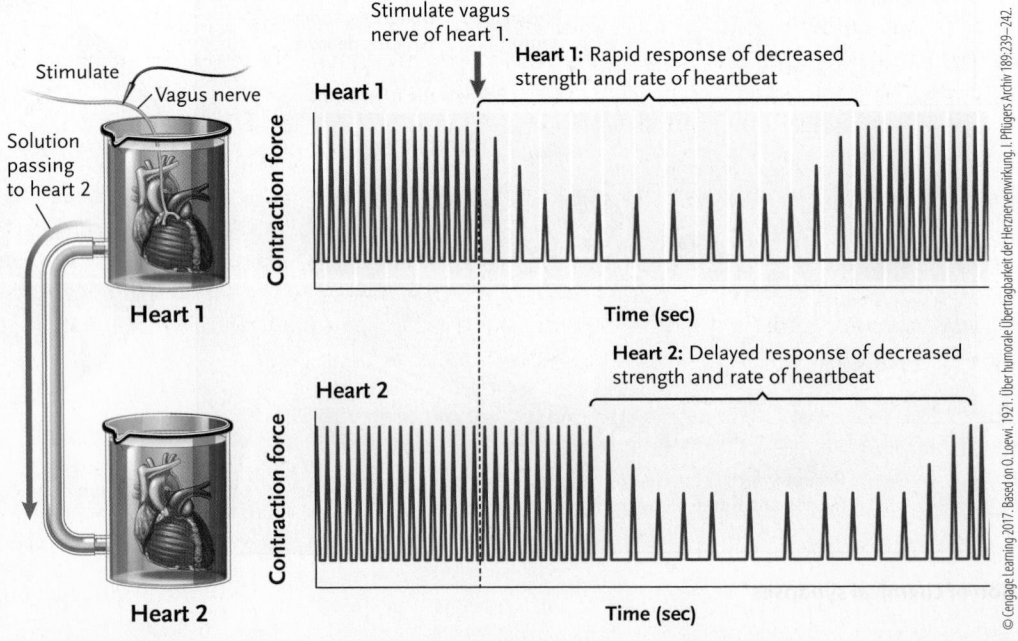

© Cengage Learning 2017. Based on O. Loewi. 1921. Über humorale Übertragbarkeit der Herznervenwirkung. I. Pflügers Archiv 189:239–242.

**Conclusion:** Loewi concluded that, when the vagus nerve was stimulated, some chemical substance was produced at the synapses of heart 1 that could diffuse through the solution and cause the same physiological effect in heart 2. The delayed response of heart 2 was the result of the time it took for the chemical to diffuse through the solution. Loewi called the chemical *Vagusstoff* ("vagal substance"), to relate it to the vagus nerve stimulation. Subsequently, Vagusstoff was shown to be acetylcholine.

---

information received at a postsynaptic membrane is integrated to produce a response that consists of the receptor neuron firing with a particular frequency (see Section 45.3a).

### NEUROTRANSMITTERS ARE RELEASED BY EXOCYTOSIS

Neurotransmitters are stored in secretory vesicles, called *synaptic vesicles*, in the cytoplasm of an axon terminal. The arrival of an action potential at the terminal releases the neurotransmitters by exocytosis: the vesicles fuse with the presynaptic membrane and release the neurotransmitter molecules into the synaptic cleft (Figure 45.12).

The release of synaptic vesicles depends on voltage-gated $Ca^{2+}$ channels in the plasma membrane of an axon terminal (see Figure 45.12). $Ca^{2+}$ ions are constantly pumped out of all animal cells by an active transport protein in the plasma membrane, keeping their concentration higher outside than inside. As an action potential arrives, the change in membrane potential opens the $Ca^{2+}$ channel gates in the axon terminal, allowing $Ca^{2+}$ to flow back into the cytoplasm. The rise in $Ca^{2+}$ concentration triggers a protein in the membrane of the synaptic vesicle that allows the vesicle to fuse with the plasma membrane, releasing neurotransmitter molecules into the synaptic cleft.

Each action potential arriving at a synapse typically causes approximately the same number of synaptic vesicles to release their neurotransmitter molecules. For example, arrival of an action potential at one type of synapse causes about 300 synaptic vesicles to release a neurotransmitter called *acetylcholine*. Each vesicle contains about 10 000 molecules of the neurotransmitter, giving a total of some 3 million acetylcholine molecules released into the synaptic cleft by each arriving action potential.

When a stimulus is no longer present, action potentials are no longer generated. When action potentials stop arriving at the axon terminal, the voltage-gated $Ca^{2+}$ channels in the axon terminal close, and the $Ca^{2+}$ in the axon cytoplasm is quickly pumped to the outside. The drop in cytoplasmic $Ca^{2+}$ stops vesicles from fusing with the presynaptic membrane, and no further neurotransmitter molecules are released. Any free neurotransmitter molecules remaining in the cleft are broken down by enzymes in the cleft or else reuptake occurs, meaning that the neurotransmitter molecules are pumped back into the axon terminals or into glial cells by active transport. Transmission of impulses across the synaptic cleft ceases within milliseconds after action potentials stop arriving at the axon terminal.

### MOST NEUROTRANSMITTERS ALTER FLOW THROUGH Na⁺, K⁺, OR Cl⁻ CHANNELS

Most neurotransmitters work by opening or closing membrane-embedded, ligand-gated, ion channels that conduct $Na^+$ or $K^+$ across the postsynaptic membrane, although some regulate chloride ions ($Cl^-$). The resulting ion flow may stimulate or inhibit the generation of action potentials by the postsynaptic cell. If $Na^+$ channels are opened, the inward $Na^+$ flow brings the membrane potential of the postsynaptic cell toward the threshold (the membrane becomes depolarized). If $K^+$ or $Cl^-$ channels are opened, the outward flow of $K^+$, or inward flow of $Cl^-$, has the opposite effect (the membrane becomes hyperpolarized). The combined effects of the various stimulatory and inhibitory neurotransmitters at all the chemical synapses of a postsynaptic neuron or muscle cell determine whether the postsynaptic cell triggers an action potential (see Section 45.3a).

### MANY DIFFERENT MOLECULES ACT AS NEUROTRANSMITTERS

Nearly 100 different substances are known or suspected to be neurotransmitters. Most of them are relatively small molecules that diffuse rapidly across the synaptic cleft. Some axon terminals release only one type of neurotransmitter; others release several types. Depending on the type of receptor to which it binds, the same neurotransmitter may stimulate or inhibit the generation of action potentials in the postsynaptic cell. **Table 45.1** lists some examples of neurotransmitters, the types of molecules they represent, their sites and type of action, and some drugs and other molecules that affect neurotransmission. (Note that this list is not complete, listing only the most common transmitter substances.)

---

**TABLE 45.1** | **Examples of Neurotransmitters and Drugs and Chemicals That Affect Neurotransmission**

| Neurotransmitter | Site(s) of Action | Action | Examples of Drugs and Other Molecules That Affect Neurotransmission |
|---|---|---|---|
| **Acetylcholine** | | | |
| Acetylcholine | Between some neurons of CNS and at neuromuscular junctions in PNS | Mostly excitatory; inhibitory at some sites | • Curare: blocks release<br>• Atropine: blocks receptors<br>Nicotine: activates receptors |
| **Monoamines (Biogenic Amines)** | | | |
| Norepinephrine | CNS interneurons involved in diverse brain and body functions, such as memory, mood, sensory perception, muscle movements, maintenance of blood pressure, and sleep | Excitatory or inhibitory | • Amphetamines: stimulate release of norepinephrine and dopamine and block their reuptake<br>• Methylphenidate (Ritalin): increases release<br>• Certain antidepressants: prevent reuptake |
| Dopamine | CNS interneurons involved in many pathways similar to norepinephrine | Mostly excitatory | • Amphetamines: stimulate release of norepinephrine and dopamine and block their reuptake<br>• Cocaine: stimulates release of norepinephrine and dopamine and blocks dopamine reuptake |
| Serotonin | CNS interneurons in a number of pathways, including those regulating appetite, reproductive behaviour, muscular movement, sleep, and some emotional states | Inhibitory or modulatory | • Fluoxetine (Prozac), sertraline (Zoloft), paroxetine (Paxil): block serotonin reuptake |

*(Continued)*

| Neurotransmitter | Site(s) of Action | Action | Examples of Drugs and Other Molecules That Affect Neurotransmission |
|---|---|---|---|
| **Amino Acids** | | | |
| Glutamate | Many CNS pathways, including those involved in vital brain functions such as memory and learning | Excitatory | • Phencyclidine (PCP or angel dust): blocks receptor |
| Gamma-aminobutyric acid (GABA) | Many CNS pathways; often acts in same circuits as glutamate | Inhibitory (main inhibitory neurotransmitter in mammalian CNS) | • Alcohol (ethanol): stimulates GABA neurotransmission, increases dopamine neurotransmission, and inhibits glutamate neurotransmission<br>• Some antianxiety/sedative drugs such as diazepam (Valium) and flunitrazepam (Rohypnol, the "date rape" drug): increase GABA neurotransmission<br>• Tetanus toxin: blocks GABA release in synapses that control muscle contraction |
| **Neuropeptides** | | | |
| Endorphins ("endogenous morphines") | Most act on CNS and PNS, as well as on effectors such as muscle, reducing pain and, in some cases, also inducing euphoria. | Inhibitory: modulate pain response | |
| Enkephalins (subclass of endorphins) | CNS | Inhibitory: modulate pain response | |
| Substance P | Released by special, unmyelinated sensory neurons in spinal cord | Excitatory: pain perception | |
| **Gaseous Neurotransmitters** | | | |
| Nitrous oxide (NO) | Diffuses across cell membranes in PNS rather than being released at synapses | Modulatory: relaxes smooth muscles in walls of blood vessels | • Sildenafil citrate (Viagra, an impotency drug): aids erection by inhibiting enzyme that normally reduces effects of NO in vascular beds of penis |

## STUDY BREAK QUESTIONS

1. How does the presence of a myelin sheath affect the conduction of impulses in neurons? What type of cell forms the myelin sheath?

2. What mechanism ensures that an electrical impulse in a neuron is conducted in only one direction down the axon? Why is this important?

3. Describe the steps from the arrival of an action potential at an axon terminal to the release of a neurotransmitter.

4. Describe how a neurotransmitter in a presynaptic neuron controls ion flow in a postsynaptic neuron via a ligand-gated ion channel.

5. Why aren't synaptic vesicles being released all the time? Why are they released only when an action potential arrives? How is this controlled?

# 45.2 Sensory Inputs: Reception

## 45.2a Sensory Receptors Are the First Step in Transmitting Information to the Nervous System

Sensory systems begin with **sensory receptors (transducers)** that detect sensory information, convert it to neural activity, and pass the information along neurons to the CNS. Sensory receptors are formed by the dendrites of afferent neurons or by specialized receptor cells **(Figure 45.14)**. Receptors collect information about the internal and external environments of organisms. In organisms with a developed head region (cephalized), many receptors for external stimuli are located there so that the organism can collect information about where it is going. Receptors associated with eyes, ears, skin, and other surface organs detect stimuli from the external environment. Sensory receptors associated with internal organs detect stimuli arising in the body interior.

### a. Sensory receptor consisting of free nerve endings—dendrites of an afferent neuron

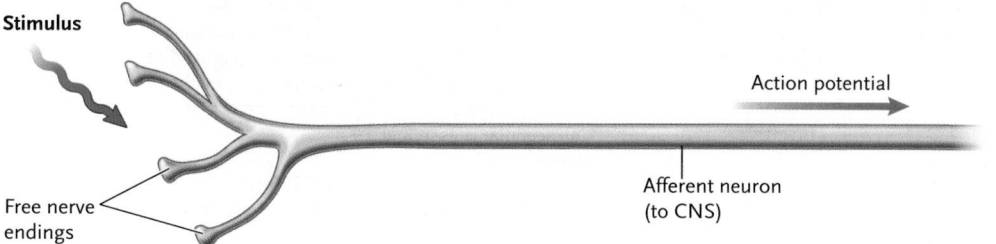

**Stimulus**

Action potential

Free nerve endings

Afferent neuron (to CNS)

In sensory receptors consisting of the dendrites of afferent neurons, a stimulus causes a change in membrane potential that generates action potentials in the axon of the neuron. Examples are pain receptors and some mechanoreceptors.

### b. Sense organ—sensory receptor involving nerve endings of an afferent neuron enclosed in a specialized structure

**Stimulus**

Action potential

Nerve ending

In sensory receptors involving nerve endings enclosed in a specialized structure, a stimulus affecting the structure triggers an action potential in the afferent neuron. Some mechanoreceptors are of this type.

### c. Sensory receptor formed by a cell that synapses with an afferent neuron

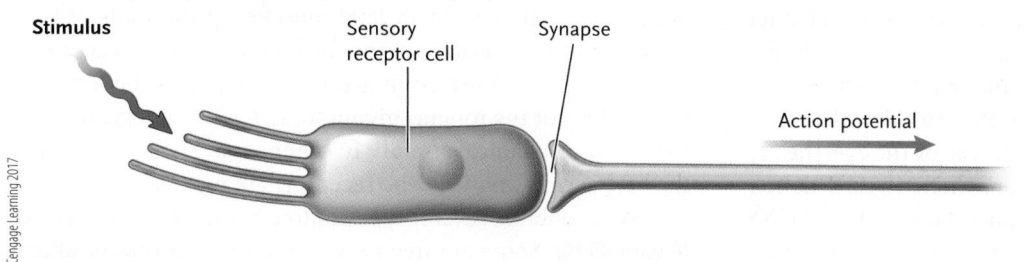

**Stimulus**

Sensory receptor cell

Synapse

Action potential

In sensory receptors consisting of separate cells, a stimulus causes a change in membrane potential that releases a neurotransmitter from the cell. The neurotransmitter triggers an action potential in the axon of an afferent neuron to which the sensory receptor cell is synapsed. Examples are photoreceptors, chemoreceptors, and some mechanoreceptors.

© Cengage Learning 2017

**FIGURE 45.14 Sensory receptors, formed (a) by the dendrites of an afferent neuron, (b) by nerve endings enclosed in specialized structures, or (c) by a separate cell or structure that communicates with an afferent neuron via a neurotransmitter**

**Sensory transduction** occurs when stimuli cause changes in membrane potentials in the sensory receptors. This is usually achieved by changes in rates at which channels conduct positive ions ($Na^+$, $K^+$, or $Ca^{2+}$) across the plasma membrane. Stimuli may be in the form of light, heat, sound waves, mechanical stress, or chemicals **(Figure 45.15)**. The change in membrane potential may generate one or more action potentials that travel along the axon of an afferent neuron to reach interneuron networks of the CNS. These interneurons integrate the action potentials, and the brain formulates a compensating response appropriate for the stimulus. In animals with complex nervous systems, interneuron networks may produce an awareness of a stimulus in the form of a conscious sensation or perception.

### BASIC TYPES OF RECEPTORS: WHAT CAN ANIMALS SENSE?

Sensory receptors are classified into five major types, based on the type of stimulus that each detects (Figure 45.15):

- **Mechanoreceptors** detect mechanical energy when it deforms membranes. Changes in pressure, body position, or acceleration, for instance, are detected by mechanoreceptors.

The auditory receptors in the ears are examples of mechanoreceptors.

- **Photoreceptors** detect the energy of light. In vertebrates, photoreceptors are located mostly in the retina of the eye.

- **Chemoreceptors** detect specific molecules or chemical conditions such as acidity. Taste buds on the tongue are examples of chemoreceptors.

- **Thermoreceptors** detect the flow of heat energy. Receptors of this type are located in the skin, where they detect changes in the temperature of the body surface.

- **Nociceptors** detect tissue damage or noxious chemicals; their activity registers as pain. Pain receptors are located in the skin and in some internal organs.

Some animals also have receptors that detect electrical or magnetic fields. Traditionally, humans are said to have five senses: vision, hearing, taste, smell, and touch. In reality, we can detect many more types of environmental stimuli. The traditional list should also include external heat; internal temperature; gravity; acceleration; the positions of muscles and joints; body balance; internal pH; and the internal concentrations of substances such as oxygen,

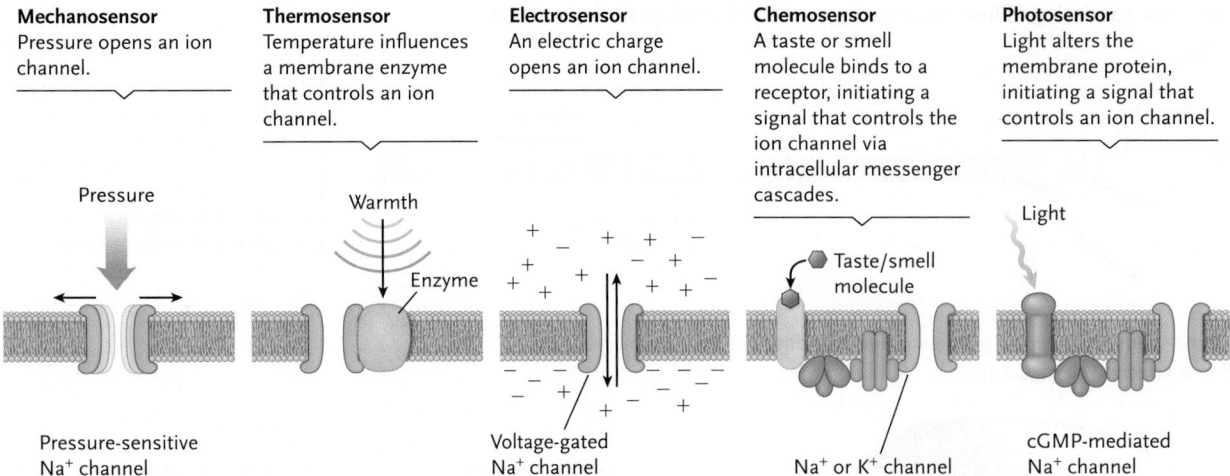

**Mechanosensor**
Pressure opens an ion channel.

**Thermosensor**
Temperature influences a membrane enzyme that controls an ion channel.

**Electrosensor**
An electric charge opens an ion channel.

**Chemosensor**
A taste or smell molecule binds to a receptor, initiating a signal that controls the ion channel via intracellular messenger cascades.

**Photosensor**
Light alters the membrane protein, initiating a signal that controls an ion channel.

Pressure

Warmth

Enzyme

Light

Taste/smell molecule

Pressure-sensitive Na⁺ channel

Voltage-gated Na⁺ channel

Na⁺ or K⁺ channel

cGMP-mediated Na⁺ channel

**FIGURE 45.15 Sensory cell membrane proteins respond to stimuli.** Sensory stimuli modify receptor proteins in the membranes of sensors, which in turn modify ion channels. The receptors in mechanoreceptors, thermosensors, and electrosensors are themselves ion channels. In chemosensors and photosensors, activated receptor proteins initiate biochemical cascades that eventually open or close ion channels.

carbon dioxide, salts, and glucose. Note, however, that these are all detected by one of the five classes of receptors listed above.

Sensory receptors are involved in neural signalling via the same four basic components described earlier in this chapter: reception, integration, transduction, and response. In highly specialized sensory organs, different anatomical features have evolved to amplify, filter, or modulate the stimulus. These are secondary sensory structures such as the ear or the eye; the primary structures are the sensory neurons themselves. This sensory information is conducted by peripheral nerves to the CNS, where complex neural processing occurs, integrating information from many sources to produce memory and appropriate responses. This is described for the vertebrate CNS (and, in particular, for the human nervous system, for which the most is known) in the third part of this chapter.

## 45.2b Mechanoreceptors and the Tactile and Spatial Senses

Mechanoreceptors detect mechanical stimuli such as touch and pressure. The mechanical force of a stimulus creates tension in the plasma membrane of a receptor cell, which causes ion channels to open. Ion flow changes the membrane potential of the receptors and generates action potentials in afferent neurons leading from the receptors to the CNS. Sensory information from these receptors informs the brain of the body's contact with objects in the environment, providing information on the movement, position, and balance of body parts, and underlies the sense of hearing. Mechanoreceptors are involved in sensing the external environment (touch and pressure), the internal environment (position and movement of the limbs, blood pressure, lung inflation), and the relationship between the two environments (balance and equilibrium related to position in space). As we will see, while the mechanism of transduction remains constant at the level of the receptor cell, there are a variety of ways in which the mechanical event leads to the deformation of the receptor cell.

**RECEPTORS FOR TOUCH AND PRESSURE OCCUR THROUGHOUT THE BODY** In vertebrates, mechanoreceptors that detect touch and pressure are embedded in the skin and other surface tissues, in skeletal muscles, in the walls of blood vessels, and in internal organs. In humans, touch receptors in the skin are concentrated in greatest numbers in the fingertips, lips, and tip of the tongue, giving these regions the greatest sensitivity to mechanical stimuli. In other areas, such as the skin of the back, arms, and legs, the receptors are more widely spaced.

Skin contains several types of touch and pressure receptors **(Figure 45.16)**. Some are free nerve endings, dendrites of afferent neurons with no specialized structures surrounding them. Free nerve endings wrapped around hair follicles respond when the hair is bent, making you instantly aware of a spider exploring your arm or leg as it brushes against the hairs. Other mechanoreceptors, such as Pacinian corpuscles, have structures surrounding the nerve endings that contribute to reception of stimuli.

**PROPRIOCEPTORS PROVIDE INFORMATION ABOUT MOVE-MENTS AND THE POSITION OF THE BODY** Proprioceptors (*proprius* = one's own) are mechanoreceptors that detect stimuli that are used by the CNS to maintain body balance and equilibrium and to monitor changes in the position of the head and limbs. The activity of proprioceptors allows you to touch the tip of your nose with your eyes closed or to precisely reach and scratch an itch on your back.

**Statocysts** (*statos* = standing; *kystis* = bag) are proprioceptors in aquatic invertebrates such as jellyfishes, some gastropods, and some arthropods. Most statocysts are fluid-filled chambers enclosing one or more movable, stonelike bodies called **statoliths**. The chamber walls contain **sensory hair cells (Figure 45.17)**. In lobsters (*Homarus americanus*), statoliths are sand grains stuck together by mucus. When the animal moves, the statoliths lag behind the movement, bending the sensory hairs and triggering action potentials in afferent neurons. Thus, statocysts signal the brain about the body's position and orientation with

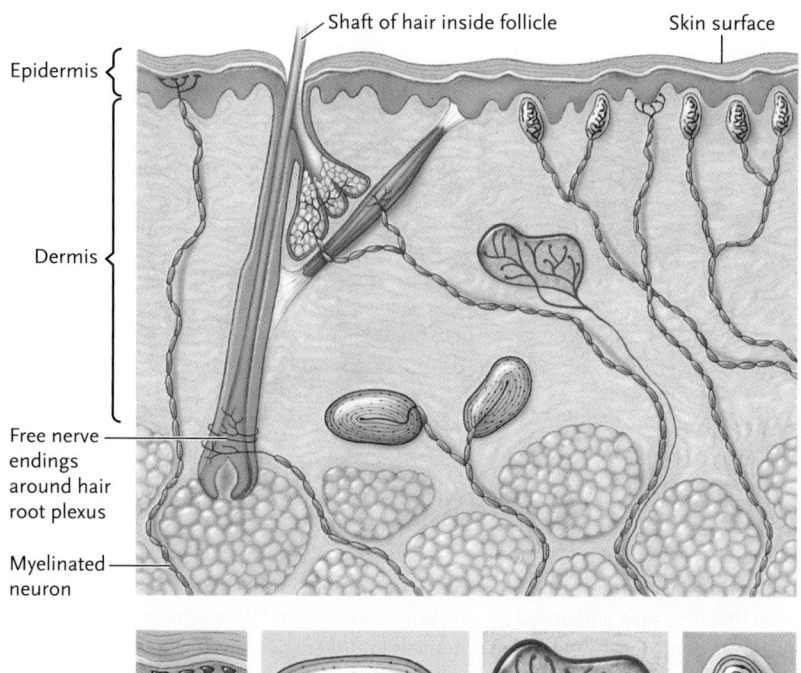

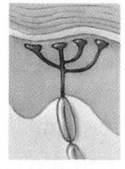

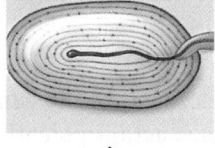
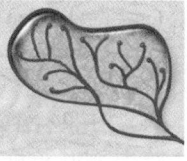
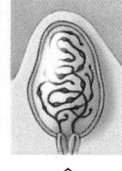

**Free nerve endings:** light touch

**Pacinian corpuscle:** deep pressure and vibrations

**Ruffini endings:** deep pressure

**Meissner's corpuscle:** light touch, surface vibrations

© Cengage Learning 2017

**FIGURE 45.16 Four types of mechanoreceptors detect tactile stimulation in human skin**

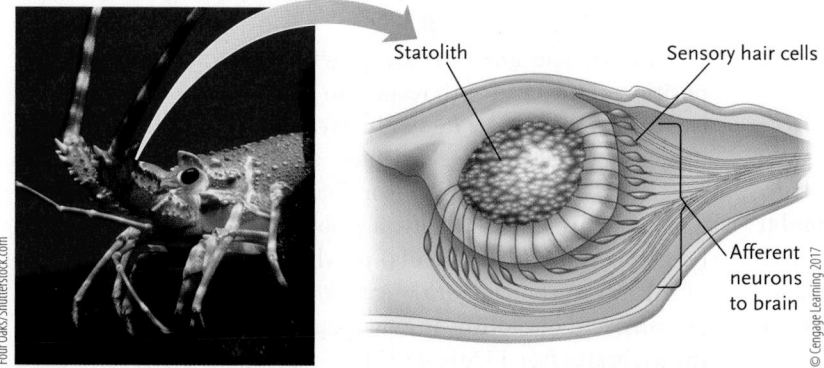

Four Oaks/Shutterstock.com

© Cengage Learning 2017

Statolith

Sensory hair cells

Afferent neurons to brain

**FIGURE 45.17 A statocyst, an organ of equilibrium in invertebrates, is located at the base of the antenna of a lobster.** In lobsters, the statoliths inside are usually formed from fused grains of sand (calcium carbonate).

respect to gravity. If you replace the sand grain statoliths with iron filings, you can use a magnet and emulate the lobster's response to the pull of gravity. In plants, statoliths control the direction of growth (see Chapter 37).

Information about self-motion is particularly important for flying animals and must be quickly (instantaneously) available. Typical insects have two pairs of wings, but species in the order Diptera (flies) have one. The second pair are reduced and

Claude Nuridsany & Marie Perennou/Science Source

**FIGURE 45.18 Halteres, vestigial hind wings of flies, transduce information about pitch, roll, and yaw during flight.** The fly shown here is a crane fly. Note the normal wings in the photo and the small vestigial wings below them. The head of the fly is at the top of the photo and the tail extends out of the photo at the bottom.

persist as halteres **(Figure 45.18)**. Halteres are club-shaped and oscillate at the wing-beat frequency. They transduce information about pitch (oscillation around a horizontal axis perpendicular to the direction of movement), roll (sway on the axis parallel to the direction of movement), and yaw (oscillation about a vertical axis) movements to the CNS. Hawk moths, with two pairs of wings, use mechanosensors on their antennae to mediate flight control. Mechanical input is essential for flight stability in moths. In bats, small hairs on the ventral surfaces of the wings are important for complex flight manoeuvres. Birds must also have mechanoreceptors associated with wings and flight, and, presumably, pterosaurs did as well. Clearly, the variety of ways in which animals detect motion are highly varied, demonstrating the importance of this sense and the divergent ways in which natural selection has found a mechanism to monitor it.

The **lateral line system** in fishes and some aquatic amphibians uses mechanoreceptors to detect vibrations and currents in the water **(Figure 45.19)**. Fishes have neuromasts, mechanoreceptors that provide information about the fish's orientation with respect to gravity, as well as its swimming velocity. In some fishes, neuromasts are exposed on the body surface; in others, they are recessed in water-filled canals with porelike openings to the outside (see Figure 45.19). Sensory hairs are clustered at the base of each dome-shaped neuromast hair cell. One surface of the hair cell is covered with **stereocilia**, microvilli or cell processes reinforced by bundles of microfilaments. Stereocilia extend into a gelatinous structure, the **cupula** (*cupule* = little cup), which moves with pressure changes in the surrounding water. Movement of the cupula bends the stereocilia, causing depolarization of the hair cell's plasma membrane and release of neurotransmitter

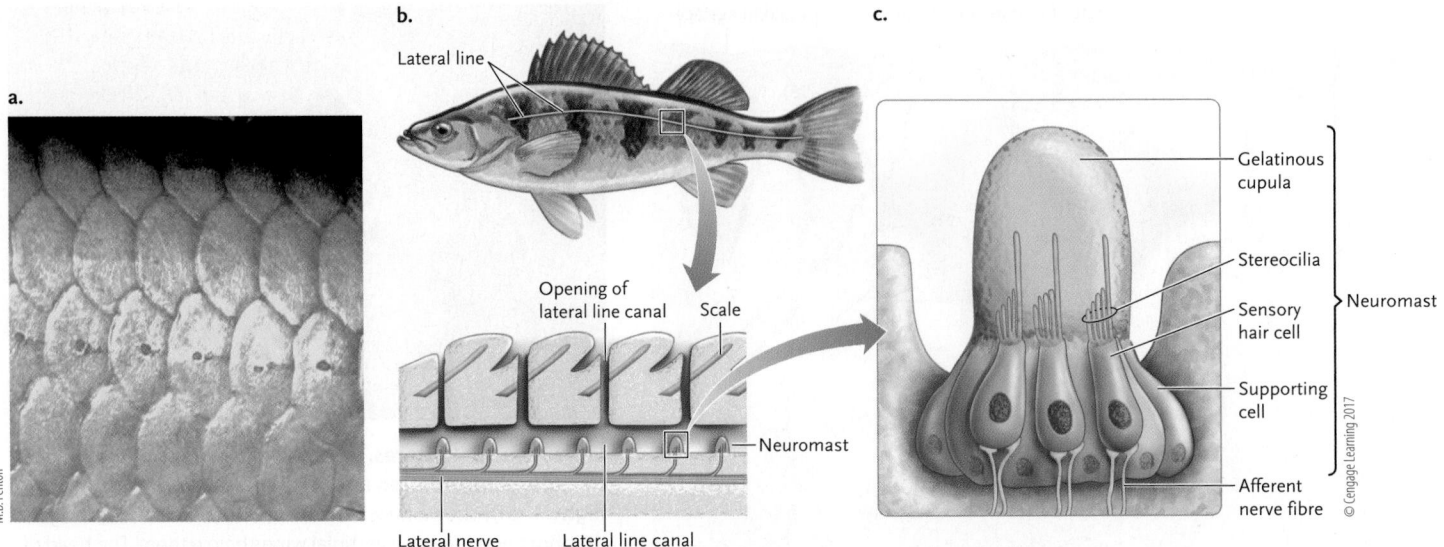

**FIGURE 45.19 The lateral line system of fishes. (a)** Pores along the lateral line of an arowana (*Scleropages* species). **(b)** Neuromasts are the sensory receptors in the lateral line system. **(c)** Neuromasts have a gelatinous cupula that is pushed and pulled by vibrations and currents transmitted through the lateral line canal. As the cupula moves, the stereocilia of the sensory hair cells are bent, generating action potentials in afferent neurons that lead to the brain.

molecules that generate action potentials in associated afferent neurons.

Vibrations detected by the lateral line enable fishes to avoid obstacles, orient in a current, and monitor the presence of other moving objects in the water. The system is also responsible for the ability of schools of fish to move in unison, turning and diving in what appears to be a perfectly synchronized aquatic ballet. In actuality, the movement of each fish creates a pressure wave in the water that is detected by the lateral line systems of other fishes in the school. Schooling fishes can still swim in unison even if blinded, but if the nerves leading from the lateral line system to the brain are severed, the ability to school is lost.

**THE VESTIBULAR APPARATUS OF VERTEBRATES PROVIDES A SENSE OF BALANCE AND ORIENTATION** The inner ear of most terrestrial vertebrates has two specialized sensory structures, the vestibular apparatus and the cochlea. The **vestibular apparatus** is responsible for perceiving the position and motion of the head and is essential for maintaining equilibrium and for coordinating head and body movements. The cochlea is used in hearing (see Section 45.2c).

The vestibular apparatus **(Figure 45.20)** consists of three **semicircular canals** and two chambers, the **utricle** and the **saccule**, filled with a fluid called *endolymph*. The semicircular canals are positioned at angles corresponding to the three planes of space. They detect rotational (spinning) motions. Each canal has an ampulla, a swelling at its base that is topped with sensory hair cells embedded in a cupula similar to that found in lateral line systems. Cupulas protrude into the endolymph of the canals. When the body or head rotates horizontally, vertically, or diagonally, endolymph in the semicircular canal corresponding to that direction lags behind, pulling the

cupula with it. Displacement of the cupula bends the sensory hair cells and generates action potentials in afferent neurons that make synapses with the hair cells.

CONCEPT FIX It is commonly thought that the semicircular canals are responsible for maintaining body balance. In fact, the semicircular canals only detect body movement and send this information to the CNS, including to the cerebellum. It is the job of the CNS to interpret this information and produce the responses that maintain balance. Clearly, receiving this information is essential for maintenance of balance, but it is only the first step in the process.

The utricle and saccule provide information about the position of the head with respect to gravity (up versus down), as well as changes in the rate of linear movement of the body. The utricle and saccule are oriented approximately 30° to each other, and each contains sensory hair cells with stereocilia. The hair cells are covered with a gelatinous otolithic membrane (which is similar to a cupula) in which **otoliths**, small crystals of calcium carbonate (*oto* = ear; *lithos* = stone), are embedded; the function of otoliths is analogous to that of the statoliths of invertebrates (see Figure 45.17).

When a tetrapod is standing in its normal posture, the sensory hairs in the utricle are oriented vertically, and those in the saccule are oriented horizontally. When the head is tilted in any other direction or when there is a change in the linear motion of the body, the otolithic membrane of the utricle moves and bends the sensory hairs. Depending on the direction of movement, the hair cells release more or less neurotransmitter, and the brain integrates the signals it receives and generates a perception of the movement. In humans, the saccule responds to the tilting of the head away from the horizontal (such as in diving) and to a change in movement up and down

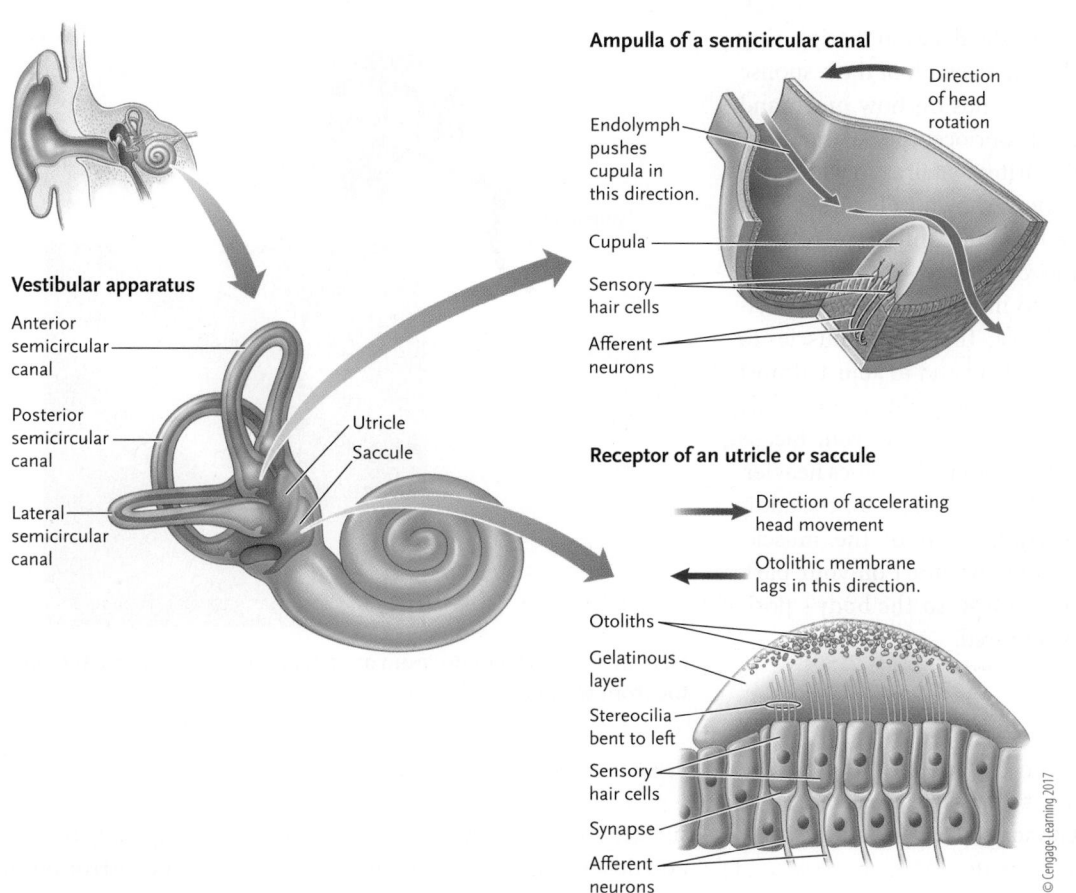

Ampulla of a semicircular canal

Direction of head rotation

Endolymph pushes cupula in this direction.

Cupula

Sensory hair cells

Afferent neurons

**FIGURE 45.20 The vestibular apparatus (and bony labyrinth) of the human ear.** The ampulla at the base of each semicircular canal detects rotational movement of the head and body. The otolith-containing receptors in the utricle and saccule detect accelerating and decelerating movements and the position of the head relative to gravity.

Vestibular apparatus

Anterior semicircular canal

Posterior semicircular canal

Lateral semicircular canal

Utricle

Saccule

Receptor of an utricle or saccule

Direction of accelerating head movement

Otolithic membrane lags in this direction.

Otoliths

Gelatinous layer

Stereocilia bent to left

Sensory hair cells

Synapse

Afferent neurons

© Cengage Learning 2017

(such as in jumping). The utricle and saccule adapt quickly to the body's motion, decreasing their response when there is no change in the rate or direction of movement.

Senses of up and down vary among animals, suggesting differences in how data from the utricle and saccule are interpreted. The "normal" posture of upside-down catfish (*Synodontis nigriventris*), many bats (Chiroptera), and sloths (genera *Choloepus* and *Bradypus*) differs from what is "normal" in other animals, so interpretation of information from the labyrinth must differ as well. As bipeds, the normal posture of humans is also aberrant, so interpretation of postural information must differ here too.

**STRETCH RECEPTORS IN VERTEBRATES KEEP TRACK OF TENSION ON MUSCLES** Stretch receptors are proprioceptors in the muscles and tendons of vertebrates that detect position and movement, for example, of the limbs. Stretch receptors in muscles are **muscle spindles**, bundles of small, specialized, muscle cells wrapped with the dendrites of afferent neurons and enclosed in connective tissue **(Figure 45.21)**. When the muscle stretches, the

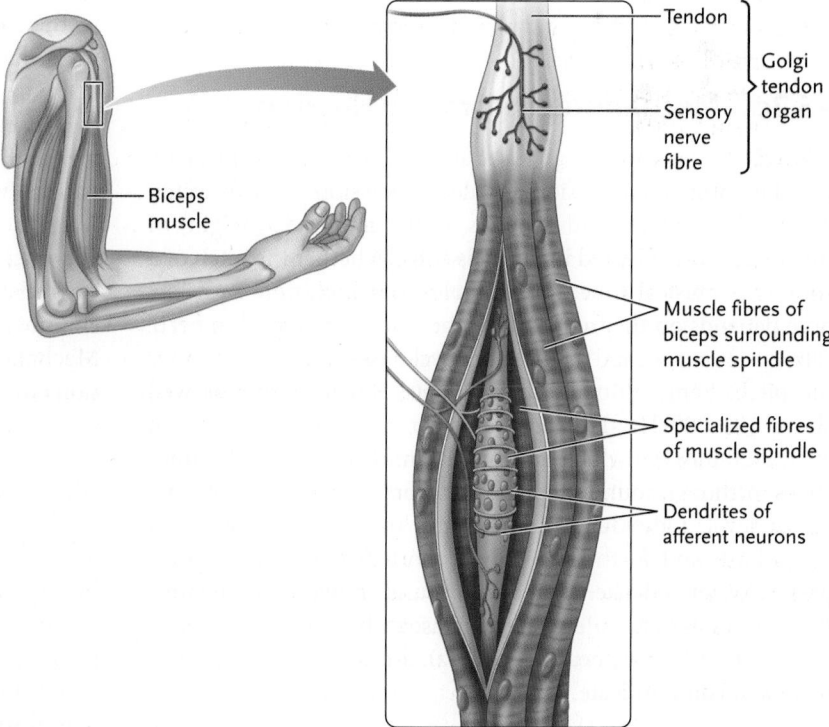

Tendon

Golgi tendon organ

Sensory nerve fibre

Biceps muscle

Muscle fibres of biceps surrounding muscle spindle

Specialized fibres of muscle spindle

Dendrites of afferent neurons

**FIGURE 45.21 Muscle spindles, which detect the stretch and tension of muscles, and Golgi tendon organs, which detect the stretch of tendons**

spindle stretches too, stimulating the dendrites and triggering the production of action potentials. The strength of the response of stretch receptors to stimulation depends on how much and how fast the muscle is stretched. Proprioceptors of tendons, called **Golgi tendon organs**, are dendrites that branch within the fibrous connective tissue of the tendon (shown in Figure 45.21). These nerve endings measure stretch and compression of the tendon as muscles contract and move limbs.

Proprioceptors allow the CNS to monitor the body's position and help keep the body in balance. They allow muscles to apply constant force under a constant load and to adjust almost instantly as the load changes. When you hold a cup while someone fills it with coffee, the muscle spindles in your biceps muscle detect the additional stretch as the cup becomes heavier. Signals from the spindles allow you to compensate for the additional weight by increasing the contraction of the muscle, keeping your arm level with no conscious effort on your part. Proprioceptors are typically slow to adapt, so the body's position and balance are constantly monitored.

## STUDY BREAK QUESTIONS

1. If two fruit flies landed on you, one on your face and the other on your leg, at which site would you be most likely to detect that there were two flies and not just one by touch receptors? Why?

2. What is the purpose of the vestibular apparatus in the inner ear of most vertebrates?

3. On what does the strength of the response of stretch receptors depend?

## 45.2c Mechanoreceptors and Hearing

**SOUND** Sounds are vibrations that travel as waves produced by the alternating compression and decompression of air or water. The loudness of a sound depends on the amplitude (height) of the wave. It is measured in decibels (dB). Whether the pitch of a sound—a musical tone, for example—is a high note or a low note depends on the frequency of the waves (measured in hertz (Hz; cycles per second)). The more cycles per second, the higher the pitch. Some animals, such as bats, can hear sounds well above 100 000 Hz. Humans can hear sounds between about 20 and 20 000 Hz, which is why we cannot hear the bat's sonar clicks. Although sound waves travel through air at about 340 m/s at sea level, individual air molecules transmitting the waves move back and forth over only a short distance as the wave passes. Water is denser than air, so sounds move approximately three times as fast under water. Infrasounds, frequencies below the range of human hearing (20 Hz), are used by African elephants to communicate.

### HEARING IN INVERTEBRATES INVOLVES MECHANORECEPTORS AND EARS Most invertebrates detect sound and other vibrations through mechanoreceptors in their skin or on other

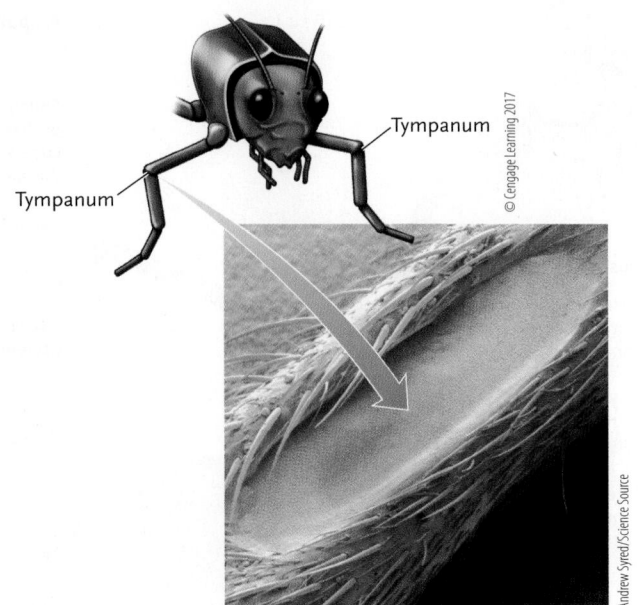

FIGURE 45.22 **The tympanum or eardrum of a cricket, located on the front walking legs**

surface structures. An earthworm, for example, quickly retracts into its burrow at the smallest vibration of the surrounding earth, even though it has no specialized structures serving as ears. Cephalopods (squids and octopuses) have a system of mechanoreceptors on their head and tentacles, similar to the lateral line of fishes. These mechanoreceptors detect vibrations in the surrounding water. In many insects and other arthropods, hairs or bristles act as sensory receptors, vibrating in response to sound waves, often at particular frequencies.

Insects such as grasshoppers and crickets have ears, complex auditory organs on each side of the abdomen or on the first pair of walking legs **(Figure 45.22)**, whereas in moths, these "ears" have been found on the head (mouthpart), thorax, and abdomen. These "ears" consist of a thinned region of the insect's exoskeleton forming a **tympanum** (drum) over a hollow chamber. Sounds reaching the tympanum cause it to vibrate. Mechanoreceptors connected to the tympanum translate vibrations into nerve impulses. Some insect ears respond to sounds only at certain frequencies, such as the pitch of a cricket's song.

### HEARING IN VERTEBRATES INVOLVES AUDITORY SYSTEMS The auditory structures of terrestrial vertebrates transduce vibrations in air (sound) to sensory hair cells that respond by triggering action potentials. The auditory system of humans is typical for mammals **(Figure 45.23)**. The **pinna** (or **outer ear;** *pinna* = wing or leaf) concentrates and focuses sound waves. Some animals have pinnae; others lack them **(Figure 45.24)**. Sound waves enter the auditory canal and strike a thin sheet of tissue (tympanic membrane or eardrum) and start it vibrating.

Vibrations in the tympanic membrane generate vibrations in the auditory ossicles located in the **middle ear**, which is an

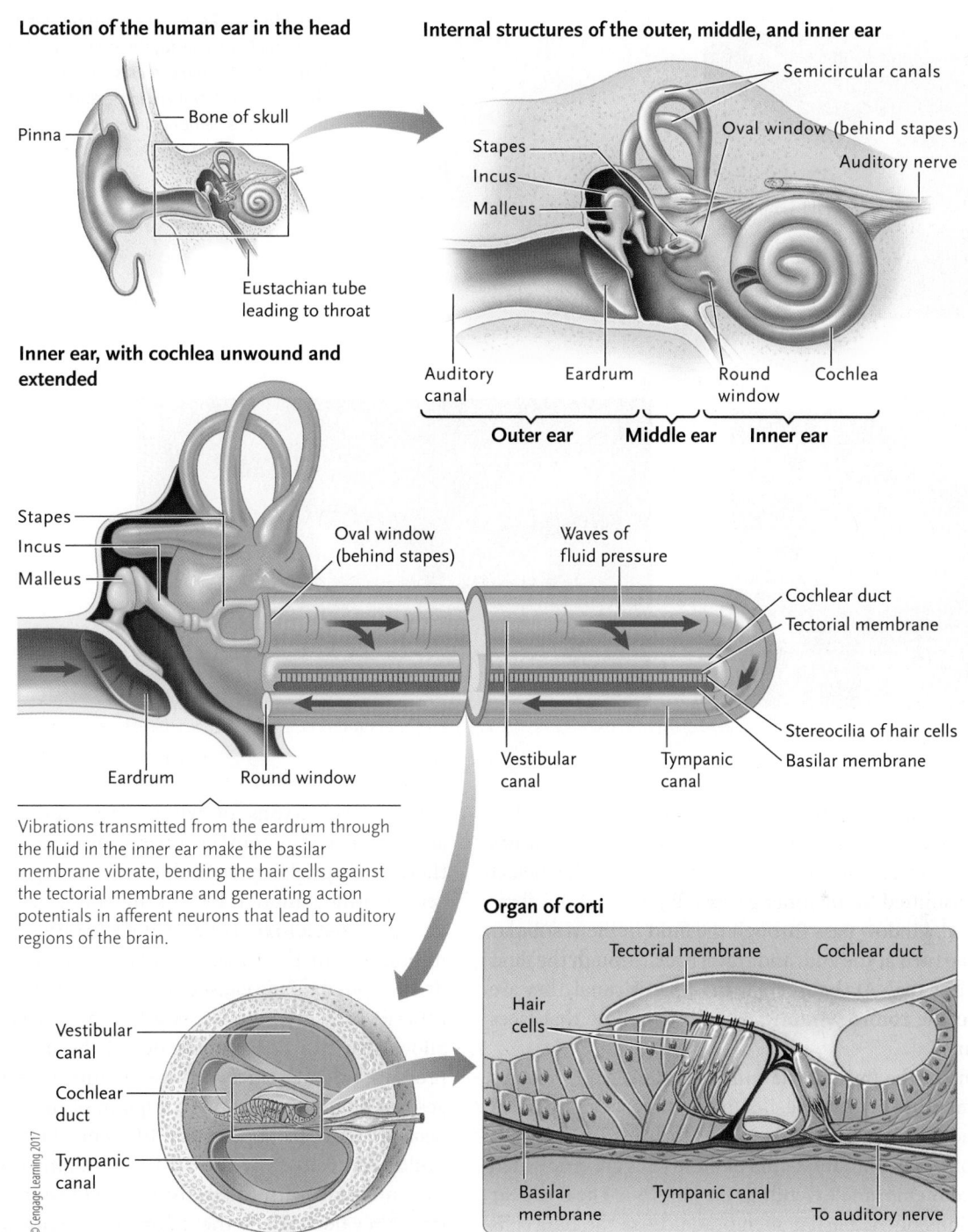

Location of the human ear in the head

Pinna
Bone of skull
Eustachian tube leading to throat

Internal structures of the outer, middle, and inner ear

Semicircular canals
Oval window (behind stapes)
Auditory nerve
Stapes
Incus
Malleus
Auditory canal
Eardrum
Round window
Cochlea

Outer ear | Middle ear | Inner ear

Inner ear, with cochlea unwound and extended

Stapes
Incus
Malleus
Oval window (behind stapes)
Waves of fluid pressure
Cochlear duct
Tectorial membrane
Stereocilia of hair cells
Basilar membrane
Eardrum
Round window
Vestibular canal
Tympanic canal

Vibrations transmitted from the eardrum through the fluid in the inner ear make the basilar membrane vibrate, bending the hair cells against the tectorial membrane and generating action potentials in afferent neurons that lead to auditory regions of the brain.

Organ of corti

Vestibular canal
Cochlear duct
Tympanic canal

Tectorial membrane
Cochlear duct
Hair cells
Basilar membrane
Tympanic canal
To auditory nerve

© Cengage Learning 2017

**FIGURE 45.23 Structures of the human ear**

air-filled cavity. Mammals have three auditory ossicles, the **malleus** (hammer), **incus** (anvil), and **stapes** (stirrup). The manubrium of the malleus sits immediately behind the eardrum, and the eardrum's vibrations are conducted from the malleus to the incus and the stapes. The stapes abuts the inner ear at the **oval window**, an elastic membrane where vibrations in bone are converted to vibrations in the fluid in the vestibular canal. Between the eardrum and the oval window, sounds are amplified at least 20 times.

The **inner ear** contains several fluid-filled compartments, the vestibular apparatus (see Section 45.2b), and the **cochlea**, a spiral tube (*kochlias* = snail). In humans, the cochlea twists through about 2.5 turns (if straightened, it would be about 3.5 cm long in an adult). The spiralling of the cochlea appears to make it more sensitive to lower-frequency sounds. Thin membranes divide the cochlea into three longitudinal chambers, the vestibular canal at the top, the cochlear duct in the middle, and the tympanic canal at the bottom (see Figure 45.23). The vestibular

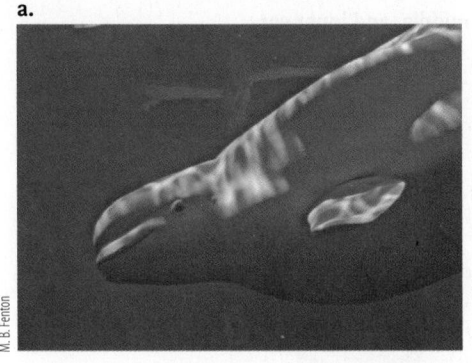
**a.**

**b.**

**c.**

**d.**

**FIGURE 45.24** Pinnae (external ears) are lacking in mammals such as **(a)** the beluga (*Delphinapterus leucas*), **(b)** birds (*Struthio camelus*), and **(c)** reptiles (*Varanus komodoensis*), but are large and conspicuous in **(d)** a bat (*Otonycteris hemprichii*).

canal and the tympanic canal join at the outer tip of the cochlea, so the fluid they contain is continuous. The **organ of Corti** lies within the cochlear duct. It contains sensory hair cells that detect vibrations transmitted to the inner ear (see Figure 45.23). Vibrations of the oval window pass through the fluid in the vestibular canal, make the turn at the end, and travel back through the fluid in the tympanic canal. At the end of the tympanic canal, they are transmitted to the **round window**, a thin membrane that faces the middle ear.

Vibrations in the fluid of the inner ear cause vibrations in the **basilar membrane**. The basilar membrane forms part of the floor of the cochlear duct and anchors the sensory hair cells in the organ of Corti. The stereocilia of these cells are embedded in the tectorial membrane extending the length of the cochlear canal. Vibrations of the basilar membrane cause the hair cells to bend, stimulating them to release a neurotransmitter that triggers action potentials in afferent neurons leading from the inner ear.

The basilar membrane is narrowest near the oval window and gradually widens toward the outer end of the cochlear duct. High-frequency vibrations produced by high-pitched sounds vibrate the basilar membrane most strongly near its narrow end, whereas vibrations of lower frequency vibrate the membrane nearer the outer end. Thus, each frequency of sound waves causes hair cells in a different segment of the basilar membrane to initiate action potentials. More than 15 000 hair cells are distributed in small groups along the basilar membrane. Each group of hairs is connected by synapses to afferent neurons, the axons of which are bundled together in the auditory nerve, a cranial nerve leading to the thalamus. From there, the signals are routed to specific regions in the auditory centre of the temporal lobe of the brain.

The **eustachian tube**, a duct leading from the air-filled middle ear to the throat (see Figure 45.23), protects the eardrum from damage caused by changes in environmental atmospheric pressure. As we swallow or yawn, the tube opens, allowing air to flow into or out of the middle ear, equalizing pressure on both sides of the eardrum. When swelling or congestion plugs the tube, we complain of having stopped-up ears because we sense a pressure difference between the outer and middle ear caused by the eardrum bulging inward or outward; this interferes with the transmission of sounds. This is particularly prevalent when the cabins of aircraft are depressurized during flight and repressurized during descent.

## STUDY BREAK QUESTIONS

1. How do most invertebrates detect sound? Give an example.
2. Explain in detail how a human detects sound. Is this fundamentally different from the way an invertebrate hears?
3. Why are the echolocation calls of many bats inaudible to humans despite their high intensity? If humans can't hear bats, how did they discover that bats could emit calls and hear in this frequency range?

FIGURE 45.25   **Experimental Research**

## How Do Sea Urchins Detect Light?

**Background:** It is one thing to demonstrate that an animal responds behaviourally to external stimuli, but it can be very challenging to determine how the stimuli were detected. For example, there is evidence of animals, such as garden toads (*Bufo bufo*), changing their behaviour in advance of an earthquake, but we do not know what cues trigger the response.

For some time, it was clear that echinoderms such as sea urchins respond to changing light conditions, but nobody had found photoreceptors in these animals (see Chapter 1 for a discussion of the significance of light and light sensing). The publication of the genome of purple urchins (*Strongylocentrotus purpuratus*; **Figure 1**) provided biologists with a means of investigating photoreception in these animals.

a.

b.

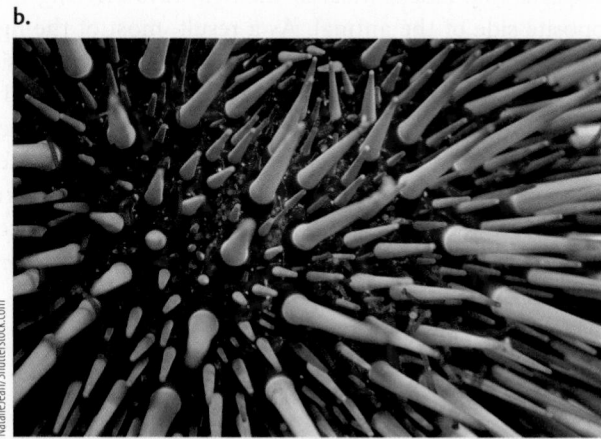

**Figure 1  (a)** The purple sea urchin *Strongylocentrotus purpuratus*. **(b)** Close-up showing the tube feet between the spines. The photoreceptors are located at the tips of the tube feet.

**Experiment:** Data in the genome showed that sea urchins possess several genes that code for a widely occurring eye protein, opsin. Discovering this, the researchers designed antibodies against different opsin proteins and performed *in situ* hybridization (see Chapters 14 and 15 for discussions of DNA technologies and genomics).

**Results:** They found that the urchins possess *Sp-opsin4* and *Sp-pax6,* two proteins that regulate phototaxis. This approach also allowed them to visualize where the photoreceptor cells were located: in the urchin's tube feet. The sea urchin photoreceptive cells are microvillar r-opsin, previously known only from protostomes.

**Conclusion:** Since tube feet are found all over the body of the sea urchin, it appears that the entire adult sea urchin acts as a huge compound eye!

## 45.2d   Photoreceptors and Vision

The great majority of animals have receptors that can detect and respond to light. As animals evolved and became more complex, the complexity of their visual sensory receptors increased, leading to the highly developed eyes of cephalopods and vertebrates.

**VISION INVOLVES DETECTION AND PERCEPTION OF RADIANT ENERGY** Photoreceptors detect light at particular wavelengths, and centres in a brain or central ganglion integrate signals arriving from the receptors into a perception of light. All animals use forms of a single lipidlike pigment, retinal (synthesized from vitamin A), in photoreceptors to absorb light energy. The simplest eyes are capable only of distinguishing light from

dark; the most complex eyes distinguish shapes and colours and focus an accurate image of objects being viewed onto a layer of photoreceptors.

**INVERTEBRATE EYES TAKE MANY FORMS** Some invertebrates, such as earthworms, do not have visual organs; instead, photoreceptors in their skin allow them to sense and respond to light. Earthworms respond negatively to light, as you can easily discover by shining a flashlight on an earthworm outside its burrow at night.

The eyes of other invertebrates are diverse, ranging from collections of photoreceptors with no lens and no image-forming capability to eyes remarkably like those of vertebrates (see **Figure 45.25**). The photoreceptors of invertebrates are depolarized when they absorb light, and they generate action potentials or increase their release of neurotransmitter molecules when they are stimulated. Vertebrate photoreceptors function differently, as we will see.

The simplest eye is the **ocellus** (plural, ocelli; also called an *eyespot* or *eyecup*). An ocellus, which detects light but does not form an image, consists of fewer than 100 photoreceptor cells lining a cup, or pit. In planarians, for example, photoreceptor cells in a cuplike depression below the epidermis are connected to the dendrites of afferent neurons, which are bundled into nerves that travel from the ocelli to the cerebral ganglion (**Figure 45.26**). Each ocellus is covered on one side by a layer of pigment cells that blocks most of the light rays arriving from the opposite side of the animal. As a result, most of the light received by the pigment cells enters the ocellus from the side that it faces. Through integration of information transmitted to the cerebral ganglion from the eyecups, planarians orient themselves so that the amount of light falling on the two ocelli is equal and diminishes as they swim. This reaction carries them directly away from the source of the light. Similar ocelli are found in a variety of animals, including insects, arthropods, and molluscs.

Two main types of image-forming eyes have evolved in invertebrates: compound eyes and single-lens eyes. The **compound eye** of insects, crustaceans, and a few annelids and molluscs contains hundreds to thousands of faceted visual units called **ommatidia** (*omma* = eye) fitted closely together (**Figure 45.27**). Each ommatidium samples a small part of the visual field. In insects, light entering an ommatidium is focused by a transparent **cornea** and a crystalline cone (just below the cornea) onto a bundle of photoreceptor cells. Microvilli of these cells interdigitate like the fingers of clasped hands, forming a central axis rich in rhodopsin, a retinal-containing **photopigment** (light-absorbing pigment). Absorption of light by rhodopsin causes action potentials to be generated in afferent neurons connected to the base of the ommatidium. From these signals, the brain receives a mosaic image of the world. Because even the slightest motion is detected simultaneously by many ommatidia, compound eyes are extraordinarily adept at detecting movement—a lesson soon learned by fly-swatting humans.

The **single-lens eye** of cephalopods (**Figure 45.28**) resembles a vertebrate eye in that both types operate like a camera. In the cephalopod eye, light enters through the transparent cornea; a **lens** concentrates the light; and a layer of photoreceptors at the back of the eye, the **retina**, records the image. Behind the cornea is the **iris**, which surrounds the **pupil**, the opening through which light enters the eye. Muscles in the iris adjust the size of the pupil to vary the

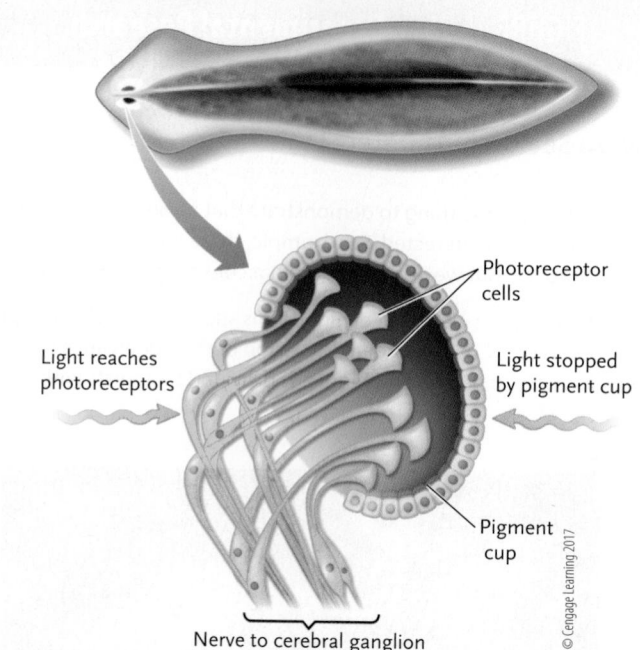

**FIGURE 45.26 The ocellus of a planarian flatworm, and the arrangement of pigment cells on which its orientation response is based**

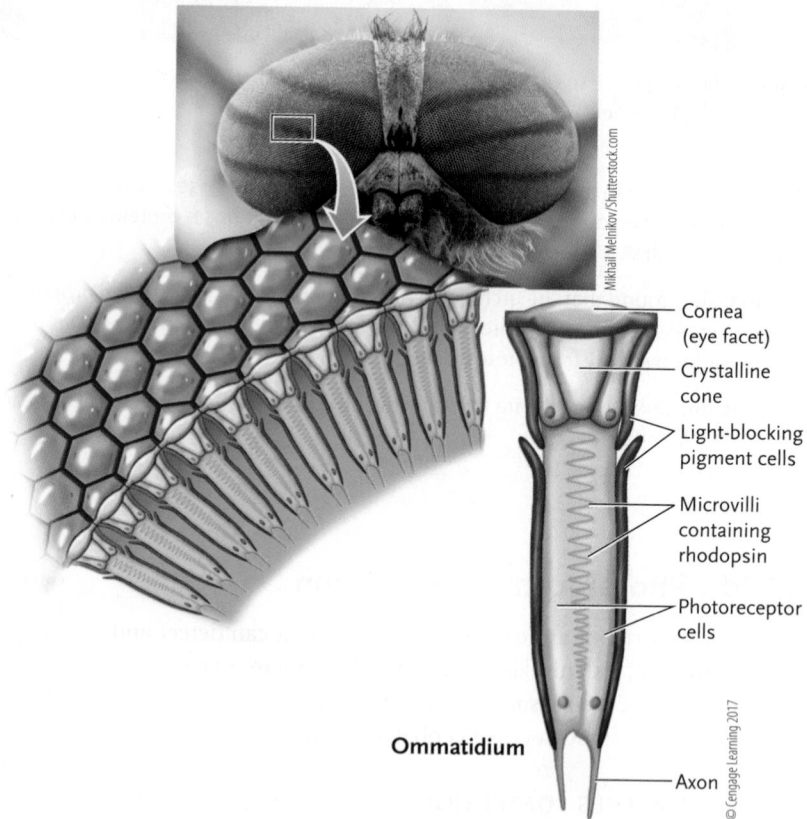

**FIGURE 45.27 The compound eye of a deer fly (*Chrysops* species).** Each ommatidium has a cornea that directs light into the crystalline cone; in turn, the cone focuses light on the photoreceptor cells. A light-blocking pigment layer at the sides of the ommatidium prevents light from scattering laterally in the compound eye.

FIGURE 45.28  **The eye of a squid, a cephalopod mollusc**

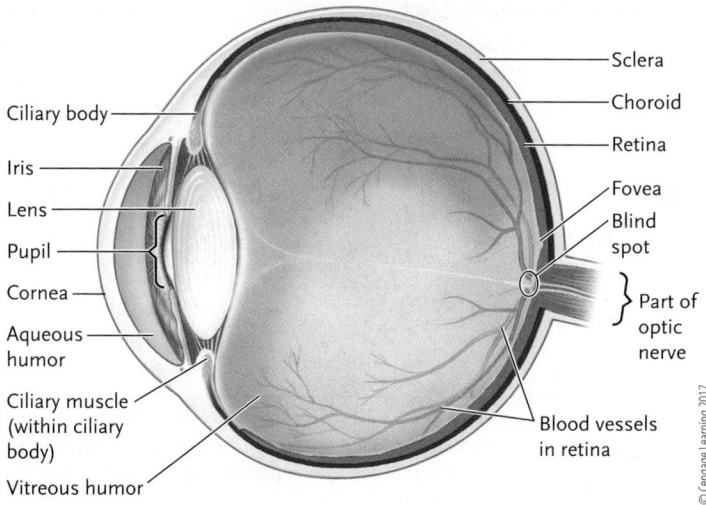

FIGURE 45.29  **Structures of the human eye**

amount of light entering the eye. When the light is bright, circular muscles in the iris contract, shrinking the size of the pupil and reducing the amount of light that enters. In dim light, radial muscles contract and enlarge the pupil, increasing the amount of light that enters the eye. Muscles move the lens forward and back with respect to the retina to focus the image. This is an example of **accommodation**, a process by which the lens changes to enable the eye to focus on objects at different distances. A neural network lies under the retina, meaning that light rays do not have to pass through the neurons to reach the photoreceptors. The vertebrate eye has the opposite arrangement. This and other differences in structure and function indicate that cephalopod and vertebrate eyes evolved independently but are remarkably similar.

**VERTEBRATE EYES HAVE A COMPLEX STRUCTURE** The human eye **(Figure 45.29)** has similar structures—cornea, iris, pupil, lens, and retina—to those of the cephalopod eye just described. Light entering the eye through the cornea passes through the pupil in the iris and then the lens. The lens focuses an image on the retina, and the axons of afferent neurons originating in the retina converge to form the optic nerve leading from the eye to the brain. A clear fluid called the **aqueous humour** fills the space between the cornea and the lens. This fluid carries nutrients to the lens and cornea, which do not contain any blood vessels. The main chamber of the eye, located between the lens and the retina, is filled with the jellylike **vitreous humour** (*vitrum* = glass). The outer wall of the eye contains a tough layer of connective tissue (the sclera). Inside it is a darkly pigmented layer (the choroid) that prevents light from entering except through the pupil. It also contains the blood vessels nourishing the retina.

Two types of photoreceptors, rods and cones, occur in the retina along with layers of neurons that carry out an initial integration of visual information before it is sent to the brain. The **rods** are specialized for detection of light at low intensities; the **cones** are specialized for detection of different wavelengths (colours). Accommodation does not occur by forward and backward movement of the lens, as described for cephalopods.

Rather, the lens of most terrestrial vertebrates is focused by changing its shape. The lens is held in place by fine ligaments that anchor it to a surrounding layer of connective tissue and muscle, the **ciliary body**. These ligaments keep the lens under tension when the ciliary muscle is relaxed. The tension flattens the lens, which is soft and flexible, and focuses light from distant objects on the retina **(Figure 45.30a)**. When the ciliary muscles contract, the lens assumes a more spherical shape, focusing light from nearby objects on the retina (Figure 45.30b).

**THE RETINA OF MAMMALS AND BIRDS CONTAINS RODS AND CONES AND A COMPLEX NETWORK OF NEURONS** The retina of a human eye contains about 120 million rods and 6 million cones organized into a densely packed single layer. Neural networks of the retina are layered on top of the photoreceptor cells, so that light rays focused by the lens on the retina must pass through the neurons before reaching the photoreceptors. The light must also pass through a layer of fine blood vessels covering the surface of the retina.

In mammals and birds with eyes specialized for daytime vision, cones are concentrated in and around a small region of the retina, the **fovea** (see Figure 45.29). The image focused by the lens is centred on the fovea, which is circular and less than a millimetre in diameter in humans. The rods are spread over the remainder of the retina. We can see distinctly only the image focused on the fovea; the surrounding image is what we term peripheral vision. Mammals and birds with eyes specialized for night vision have retinas containing mostly rods and lacking a defined fovea. Some fishes and many reptiles have cones generally distributed throughout their retina and very few rods.

The rods of mammals are much more sensitive than the cones to low-intensity light; in fact, they can respond to a single photon of light. This is why, in dim light, we can detect objects better by looking slightly to the side of the object. This action

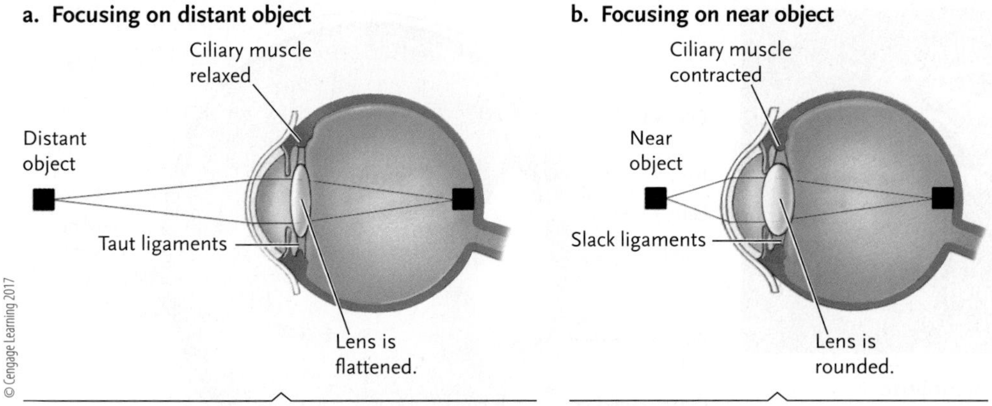

**a. Focusing on distant object**

Ciliary muscle relaxed

Distant object

Taut ligaments

Lens is flattened.

When the eye focuses on a distant object, the ciliary muscles relax, allowing the ligaments that support the lens to tighten. The tightened ligaments flatten the lens, bringing the distant object into focus on the retina.

**b. Focusing on near object**

Ciliary muscle contracted

Near object

Slack ligaments

Lens is rounded.

When the eye focuses on a near object, the ciliary muscles contract, loosening the ligaments and allowing the lens to become rounder. The rounded lens focuses a near object on the retina.

**FIGURE 45.30 Accommodation in terrestrial vertebrates occurs when the lens changes shape to focus on distant (a) and near (b) objects**

© Cengage Learning 2017

directs the image away from the cones in the fovea to the highly light-sensitive rods in surrounding regions of the retina.

**SENSORY TRANSDUCTION BY RODS AND CONES: CONVERTING SIGNALS TO ELECTRICAL IMPULSES** A photoreceptor cell has three parts:

- an outer segment, consisting of stacked, flattened, membranous discs;
- an inner segment, where the cell's metabolic activities occur; and
- the synaptic terminal, where neurotransmitter molecules are stored and released **(Figure 45.31a)**.

The light-absorbing pigment of rods and cones, retinal, is bound to **opsins** to produce photopigments. The photopigments are embedded in the membranous discs of the photoreceptors' outer segments (Figure 45.31b). The retinal–opsin photopigment in rods is **rhodopsin**. There are multiple forms of retinal-opsin photopigments in cones that are described below.

In the dark, the retinal segment of rhodopsin is inactive (*cis*-retinal; see Figure 45.31b) and rods steadily release the neurotransmitter glutamate. When rhodopsin absorbs a photon of light, retinal changes shape, becoming active (*trans*-retinal), and the rods decrease the amount of glutamate they release. Photoreceptors do not fire action potentials but rather the neurotransmitters they release act on neurons in the retina of the eye.

**VISUAL PROCESSING IN THE RETINA: EVENTS AT THE BACK OF THE EYE** In the vertebrate retina, the two types of photoreceptors are linked to a network of neurons that carry out initial integration and processing of visual information. There is a layer of **bipolar cells** just in front of the rods and cones **(Figure 45.32)**. In the dark, the steady release of glutamate from rods and cones depolarizes some postsynaptic bipolar cells and hyperpolarizes others. In the light, the decrease in neurotransmitter release from rods and cones results in the depolarized bipolar cells becoming hyperpolarized, and the hyperpolarized bipolar cells

becoming depolarized. These neurons synapse with **ganglion cells** at their other end. The axons of ganglion cells extend over the retina and collect at the back of the eyeball to form the optic nerve, which transmits action potentials to the brain. The point where the optic nerve exits the eye lacks photoreceptors. This **blind spot** can be several millimetres in diameter in humans. Because the photoreceptors in octopuses and squids are at the front of the retina and not at the back, these animals do not have a blind spot.

Whereas the human retina has over 120 million photoreceptors, it has only about 1 million ganglion cells. This disparity is explained by the fact that each ganglion cell receives signals from a clearly defined set of photoreceptors constituting the **receptive field** for that cell. Receptive fields are typically circular and are of different sizes. Smaller receptive fields result in sharper images because they send more precise information to the brain about the location in the retina where the light was received.

**Horizontal cells** connect neighbouring photoreceptor cells laterally to one another. Lateral movement of signals between rods or cones enhances contrast. To understand this, consider a spot of light falling on the retina. Photoreceptors detect the light and send a signal to bipolar cells and horizontal cells. Horizontal cells inhibit more-distant neighbouring bipolar cells that are outside the spot of light, causing the light spot to appear lighter and its surrounding dark area to appear darker. This type of visual processing is called **lateral inhibition** and serves both to sharpen the edges of objects and to enhance contrast in an image.

**Amacrine cells** connect neighbouring bipolar and ganglion cells. Their function is less well understood but appears to be to enhance motion detection and reinforce the role of the horizontal cells in adjusting light sensitivity.

**THREE KINDS OF OPSIN PIGMENTS UNDERLIE COLOUR VISION** Many invertebrates and some species in each class of vertebrates have colour vision, which depends on cones in the

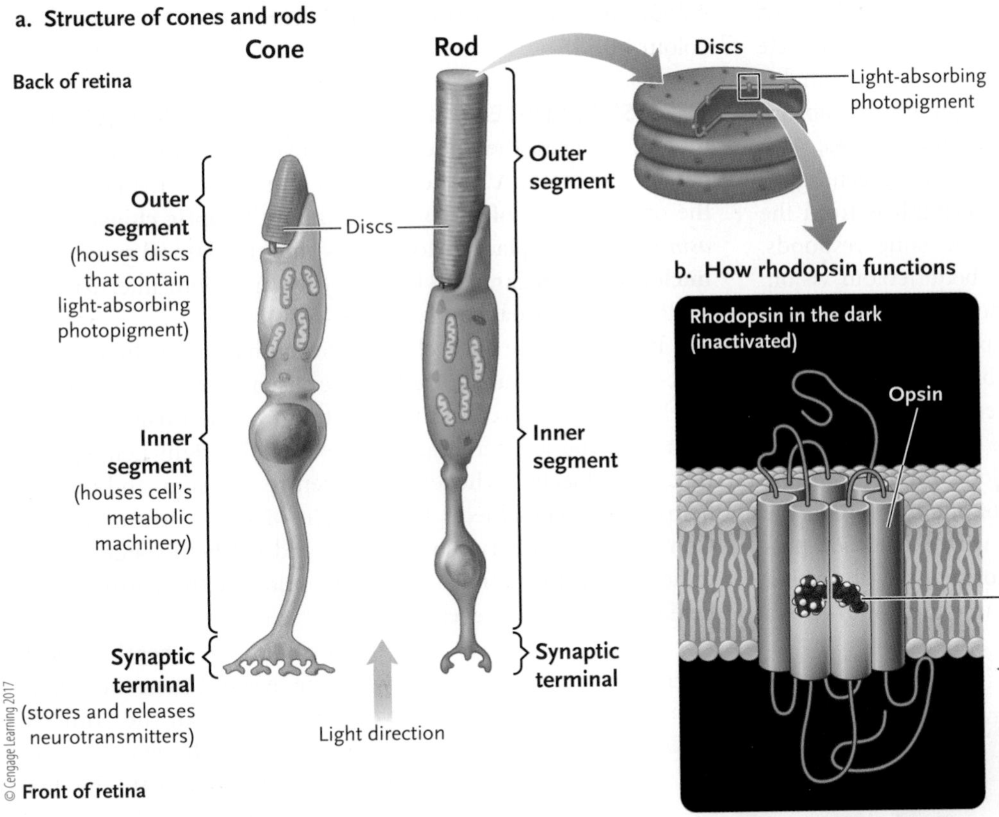

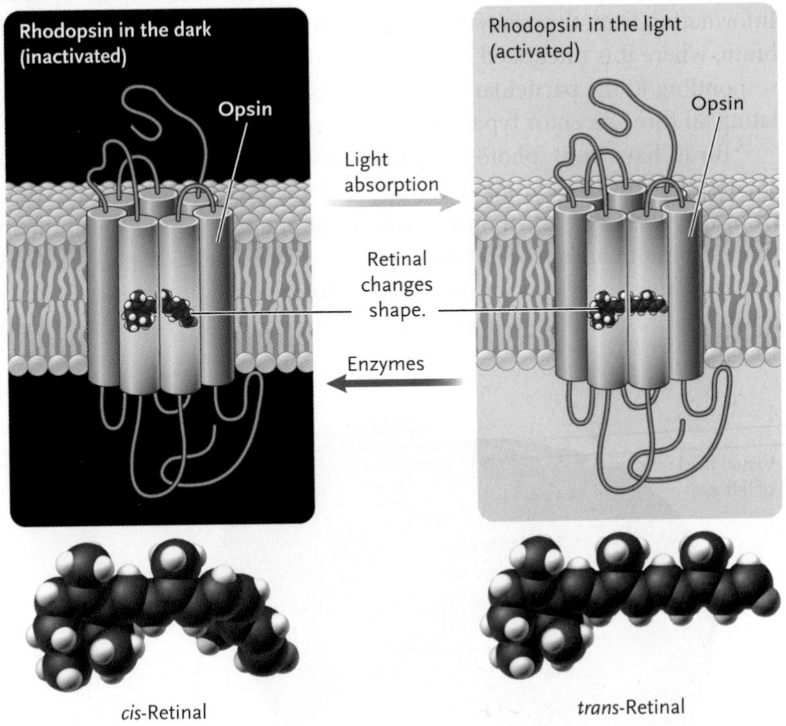

## a. Structure of cones and rods

**Back of retina**

**Cone**

**Rod**

**Discs**

Light-absorbing photopigment

**Outer segment**
(houses discs that contain light-absorbing photopigment)

Discs

**Outer segment**

**Inner segment**
(houses cell's metabolic machinery)

**Inner segment**

**Synaptic terminal**
(stores and releases neurotransmitters)

**Synaptic terminal**

Light direction

© Cengage Learning 2017

**Front of retina**

**FIGURE 45.31 Photoreceptors.**
**(a)** Structure of cones and rods, the photoreceptors of all mammals, and the location of photopigments in stacked, membranous discs. **(b)** The photopigment rhodopsin (found in rods), which consists of the opsin protein retinal. In response to light, the retinal changes from a bent to a straight structure.

## b. How rhodopsin functions

**Rhodopsin in the dark (inactivated)**

Opsin

Light absorption

Retinal changes shape.

Enzymes

**Rhodopsin in the light (activated)**

Opsin

*cis*-Retinal

*trans*-Retinal

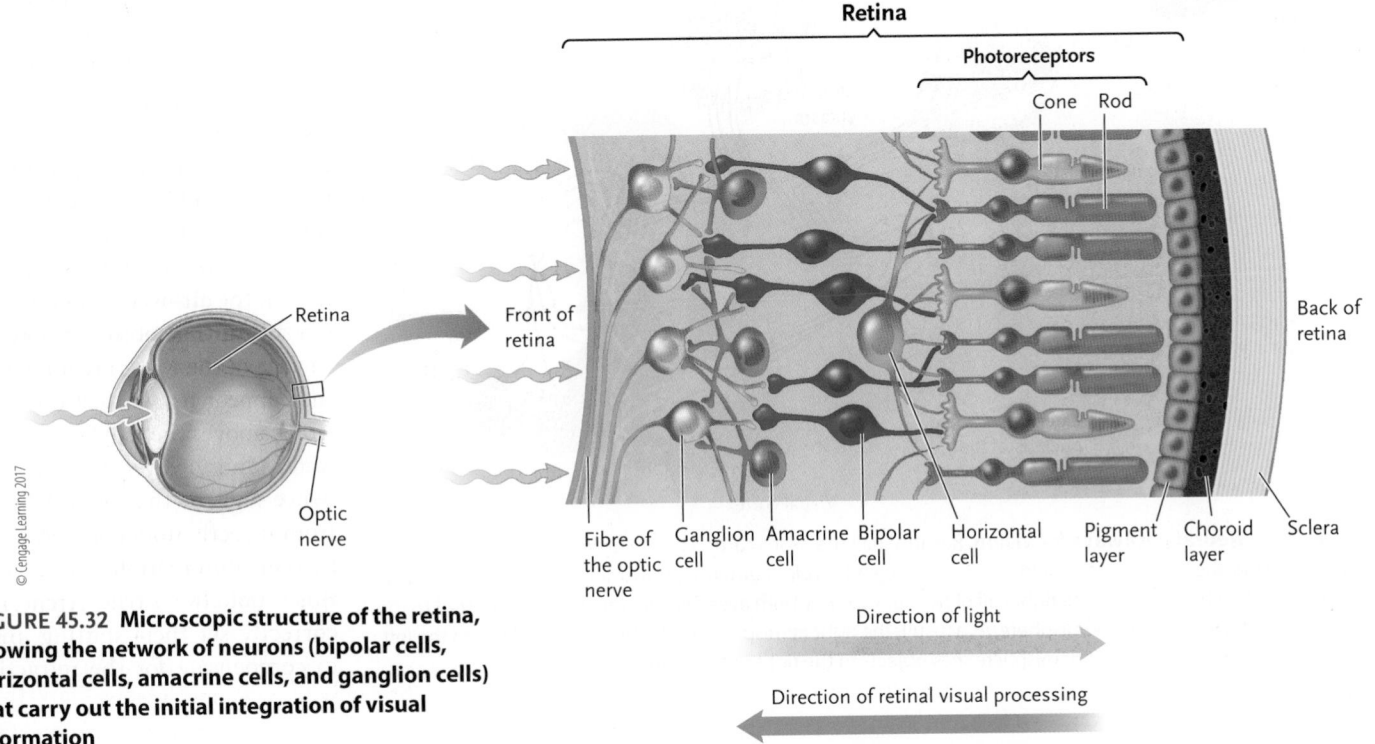

© Cengage Learning 2017

**Retina**

**Photoreceptors**

Cone   Rod

Retina

Front of retina

Back of retina

Optic nerve

Fibre of the optic nerve

Ganglion cell

Amacrine cell

Bipolar cell

Horizontal cell

Pigment layer

Choroid layer

Sclera

Direction of light

Direction of retinal visual processing

**FIGURE 45.32 Microscopic structure of the retina, showing the network of neurons (bipolar cells, horizontal cells, amacrine cells, and ganglion cells) that carry out the initial integration of visual information**

retina. Most mammals have two types of cones, whereas humans and other primates have three types. Each human or primate cone cell contains one of three **photopsins** in which retinal is combined with different opsins. The three photopsins absorb light over different, but overlapping, wavelength ranges, with peak absorptions at 445 nm (blue light), 534 nm (green light), and 570 nm (red light). The farther a wavelength is from the peak colour absorbed, the less strongly the cone responds. Having more types of cones translates into better colour vision. Information from the cones is relayed to the visual centres of the brain, where it is integrated into the perception of a colour corresponding to the particular wavelength absorbed. Light stimulating all three receptor types equally is seen as white.

Birds have four photopsins and are able to distinguish shades of colour that humans cannot. Colour-blindness results from inherited defects in opsin proteins of one or more of the three types of cones. For example, people with a mutation preventing cones from making a functional form of red-absorbing opsin see orange, yellow, and red as the same grey or greenish colour (unable to distinguish red from green, or red–green colour blind).

**THE VISUAL CORTEX GENERATES IMAGES IN THE BRAIN** Just behind the eyes, the optic nerves converge before entering the base of the brain. A portion of each optic nerve crosses over to the opposite side of the brain, forming the **optic chiasm** (*chiasma* = crossing place). Most axons enter the **lateral geniculate nuclei** in the thalamus, where they synapse with interneurons leading to the visual cortex **(Figure 45.33)**.

Because of the optic chiasm, the left half of the image seen by both eyes is transmitted to the visual cortex in the right cerebral hemisphere, and the right half of the image is transmitted to the left cerebral hemisphere. The right hemisphere thus sees objects to the left of the centre of vision, and the left hemisphere sees objects to the right of the centre of vision. Communication between the right and left hemispheres integrates this information into a perception of the entire visual field seen by the two eyes.

If you look at a nearby object with one eye and then the other, you will notice that the point of view is slightly different. Integration of the visual field by the brain creates a single picture with a sense of distance and depth. The greater the difference between the images seen by the two eyes, the closer the object appears to the viewer.

Archerfish **(Figure 45.34)** live in fresh water and knock flying or resting insects onto the water's surface with spit droplets. The fish then catch and eat the insects. During the spitting attacks, the fishes' eyes are below the surface of the water, posing a potentially serious problem because of refraction. Refraction is the deflection or bending of rays of light at the air–water interface. As a result of this, objects below the surface of the water are not where they appear to be when observed from above the surface of the water (and vice versa). Some evidence suggests that archerfish spit from directly under the prey, but further observations show that this is not always true. Archerfish correctly set their spitting angle to compensate for the refraction

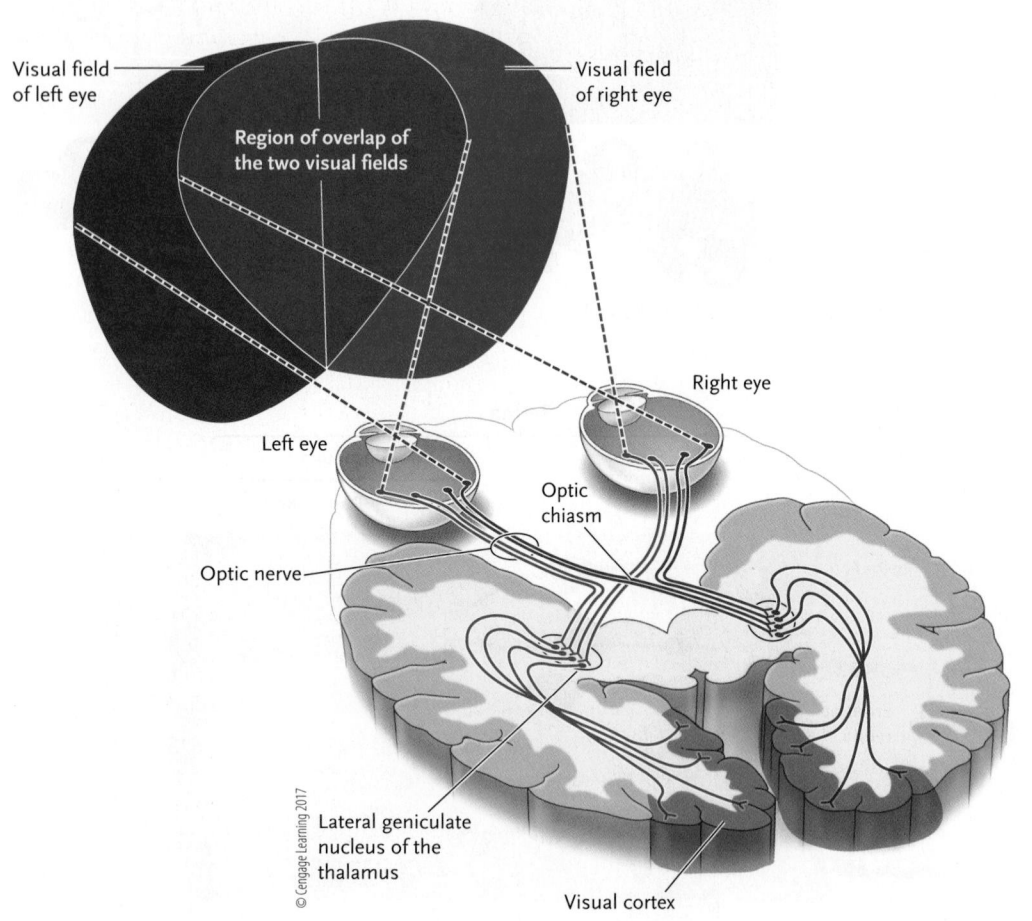

**FIGURE 45.33 Neural pathways for vision.** Because half the axons carried by the optic nerves cross over in the optic chiasma, the left half of the field seen by both eyes (purple segment) is transmitted to the visual cortex in the right cerebral hemisphere. The right half of the field seen by both eyes (blue segment) is transmitted to the visual cortex in the left cerebral hemisphere. As a result, the right hemisphere of the brain sees objects to the left of the centre of vision, and the left hemisphere sees objects to the right of the centre of vision.

a.

b.

**FIGURE 45.34** **(a)** An archerfish, *Toxotes chatareus*, projecting spit at an insect prey. **(b)** Pelicans, *Pelecanus occidentalis*, diving for fish

they experience at different positions. They also correct for curvature of the water droplet's trajectory. Other fish also spit at aerial prey, and some birds hunt fish from above the water's surface; both deal with the problems of refraction from a different standpoint.

In humans, the two optic nerves together contain more than a million axons, more than all other afferent neurons of the body put together. Almost one-third of the grey matter of the cerebral cortex is devoted to visual information. These numbers give some idea of the complexity of the information integrated into the visual image formed by the brain and the importance of visual information for everyday activity.

### STUDY BREAK QUESTIONS

1. What is the "simplest" eye? Why is it an eye, and how does it differ from image-forming eyes?
2. What causes colour-blindness?
3. Why are compound eyes so adept at detecting motion?
4. What is accommodation?

## 45.2e Chemoreceptors

Chemoreceptors provide information about taste (gustation) and smell (olfaction), as well as measures of intrinsic levels of molecules such as oxygen, carbon dioxide, and hydrogen ions. All chemoreceptors probably work through membrane receptor proteins that are stimulated when they bind with specific molecules in their environment (internal or external) and generate action potentials in afferent nerves leading to the CNS. In this section, we discuss sensing of external stimuli only through taste and smell.

**INVERTEBRATE ANIMALS EXPERIENCE A RICH WORLD OF ODOURS** In many invertebrates, the same receptors serve for sensing smell and taste. These receptors may be concentrated around the mouth or distributed over the body surface. The cnidarian *Hydra* has chemoreceptors around its mouth that respond to glutathione, a chemical released from prey organisms ensnared in the cnidarian's tentacles. Stimulation of chemoreceptors by glutathione causes the tentacles to retract, resulting in ingestion of the prey. In contrast, earthworms have taste and smell receptors distributed over the entire body surface.

Some terrestrial invertebrates have clearly differentiated receptors for taste and smell. In insects, taste receptors occur inside hollow sensory bristles called *sensilla* (singular, *sensillum*), usually located on the antennae, mouthparts, or feet **(Figure 45.35)**. Pores in the sensilla admit molecules from potential food to the chemoreceptors, which are specialized to detect sugars, salts, amino acids, or other chemicals. Many female

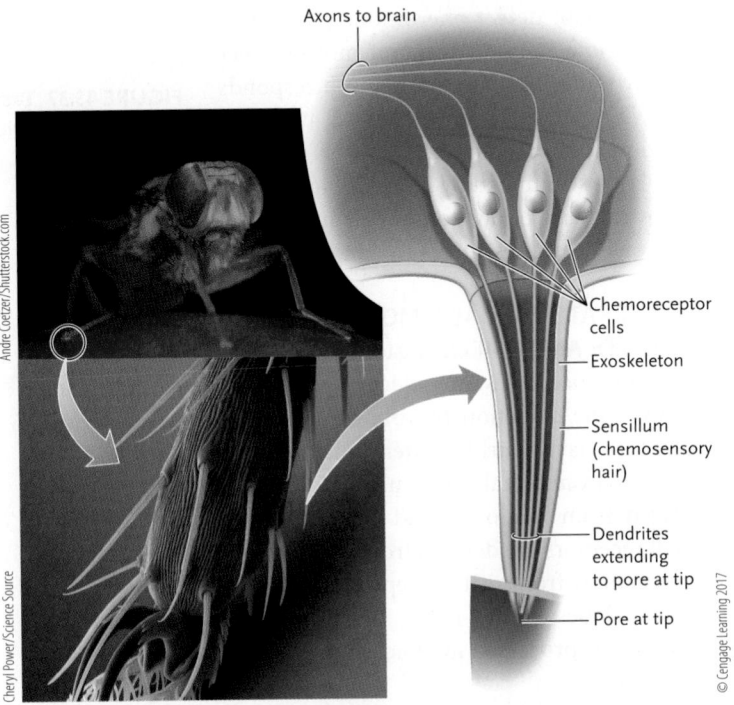

Axons to brain

Chemoreceptor cells

Exoskeleton

Sensillum (chemosensory hair)

Dendrites extending to pore at tip

Pore at tip

**FIGURE 45.35** **Taste receptors on the foot of a fruit fly (*Drosophila*)**

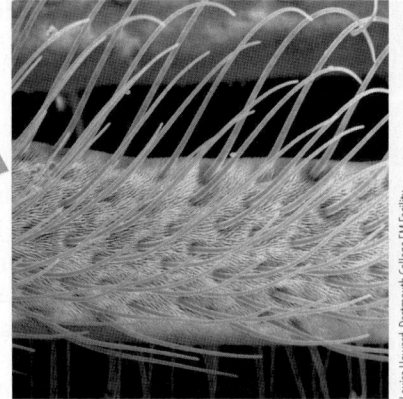

A. Shay/Oxford Scientific/Getty Images

Louisa Howard, Dartmouth College EM Facility

**FIGURE 45.36 The brushlike antennae of a male silkworm moth.** Fine sensory bristles containing olfactory receptor cells cover the filaments of the antennae.

25 µm

insects have chemoreceptors on their ovipositors, allowing them to lay their eggs on food appropriate for the larvae when they hatch.

Olfactory receptors detect airborne molecules such as pheromones, the chemicals used in communication by both animals and plants (see Chapter 32). Insects are excellent examples of animals that make extensive use of pheromones. Female insects use pheromones to attract males, and vice versa. Olfactory receptors in the bristles on the antennae of male silkworm moths (*Bombyx mori*; **Figure 45.36**) bind a pheromone released by females. Their olfactory receptors can detect pheromone concentrations as low as one attractant molecule per $10^{17}$ air molecules! The male moth responds by flying rapidly when as few as 40 of the 20 thousand receptor cells on an antenna have been stimulated by pheromone molecules. Ants, bees, and wasps may use odour to identify members of the same hive or nest, or to alert nestmates to danger.

### VERTEBRATE ANIMALS: MORE VARIATIONS ON THE SENSE OF TASTE AND SMELL

Taste involves the detection of potential food molecules in objects touched by a receptor. Smell involves the detection of airborne molecules. Taste and smell receptors have hairlike extensions that contain proteins that bind environmental molecules. Hairs of taste receptors are derived from microvilli and contain microfilaments. Hairs of smell receptors are derived from cilia and contain microtubules. Information from taste receptors is typically processed in the parietal lobes of the brain, whereas information from smell receptors is processed in olfactory bulbs and the temporal lobes of the brain.

**TASTE** Taste receptors of most vertebrates form part of a structure called a *taste bud*, a small, pear-shaped capsule with a pore

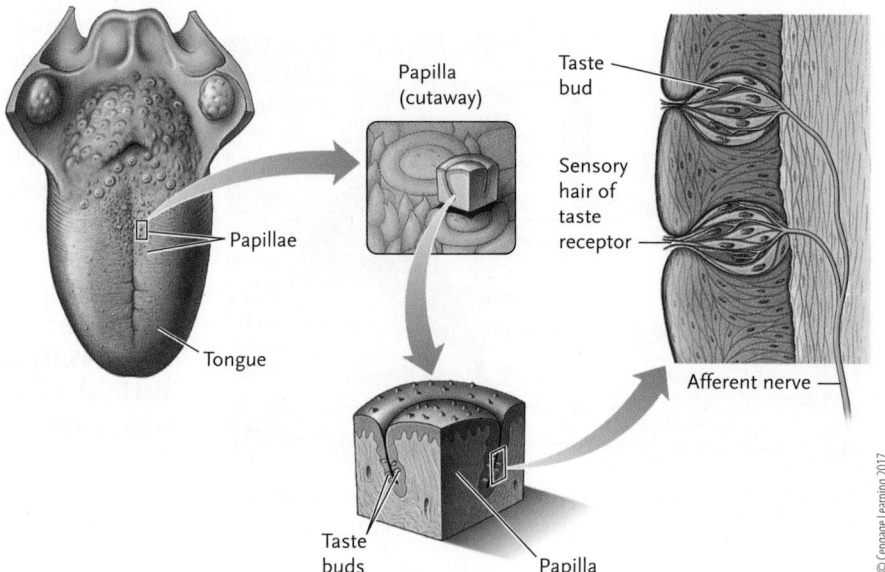

**FIGURE 45.37 Taste receptors in the human tongue.** The receptors occur in microscopic taste buds that line the sides of the furry papillae.

© Cengage Learning 2017

at the top opening to the exterior **(Figure 45.37)**. Sensory hairs of taste receptors pass through the pore of a taste bud and project to the exterior. The opposite end of the receptor cells synapses with dendrites of an afferent neuron.

Taste receptors of aquatic vertebrates (e.g., fishes and amphibian tadpoles) are generally found throughout the oral cavity but in some species may be found distributed all over the body surface. In terrestrial vertebrates, they are concentrated in the mouth. Humans have about 10 thousand taste buds, each 30 to 40 µm in diameter, scattered over the tongue, roof of the mouth, and throat. Those on the tongue are embedded in outgrowths called *papillae* (*papula* = pimple), which give the surface of the tongue its rough or furry texture. Taste receptors on the human tongue respond to five basic tastes: sweet, sour, salty, bitter, and umami (savoury). Some receptors for umami respond to the amino acid glutamate (familiar as monosodium glutamate or MSG).

Signals from taste receptors are relayed to the thalamus in the brain. From there, some signals lead to gustatory centres in the cerebral cortex, which integrate them into the perception of taste. Others lead to the brain stem and limbic system, which link tastes to involuntary visceral and emotional responses. Through brain stem and limbic connections, a pleasant taste may lead to salivation, secretion of digestive juices, sensations of pleasure, and sexual arousal, whereas an unpleasant taste may produce revulsion, nausea, and vomiting.

**SMELL** For water-dwelling vertebrates (e.g., fishes and amphibian tadpoles), the olfactory system detects chemicals present in the surrounding water. These receptors are found inside nasal sacs that open to the water through nares but that are blind ending and not used for breathing. For air-breathing vertebrates, the olfactory system primarily detects volatile (airborne) chemicals by receptors located in the nasal cavities. Bloodhounds have more than 200 million olfactory receptors in patches of olfactory epithelium in the upper nasal passages; humans have about 5 million olfactory receptors. On one end, each olfactory receptor cell has 10–20 sensory hairs projecting into a layer of mucus covering the olfactory area in the nose. To be detected, airborne molecules must dissolve in the watery mucus solution. At the other end, the olfactory receptor cells synapse with interneurons in the olfactory bulbs. Olfactory receptors are the only receptor cells that make direct connections with brain interneurons rather than via afferent neurons. It has commonly been believed that, at least in mammals, the olfactory epithelium does not detect odorants in water. However, star-nosed moles (*Condylura cristata*) and water shrews (*Sorex palustris*) exhale bubbles while diving. They re-inhale the bubbles that equilibrate with the water around them and in this way obtain airborne olfactory cues from the water **(Figure 45.38)**.

Nerves conduct signals directly from the olfactory bulbs to the olfactory centres of the cerebral cortex (see Section 45.3c). (This is the only sense that is not relayed through the thalamus in the brain.) Here they are integrated into the perception of tantalizing or unpleasant odours from a rose to a rotten egg. Most odour perceptions arise from combinations of different olfactory receptors. About 1000 different human genes give rise to an equivalent number of olfactory receptor types, each specific for a different class of chemicals. Recent experiments demonstrate that rats smell in stereo, accurately localizing odours in one or two sniffs. They could do so only with bilateral sampling. Some neurons in the olfactory bulb respond differently to stimuli from the left than from the right. Furthermore, some receptors in the olfactory cortex of mammals fire only upon stimulation by combinations of odorants, perhaps explaining why mixes of odours are perceived as novel by humans.

As in taste, other connections from the olfactory bulbs lead to the limbic system and brain stem, where the signals elicit emotional and visceral responses similar to those caused by pleasant and unpleasant tastes. Olfaction contributes to the sense of taste because vaporized molecules from foods are conducted from the throat to the olfactory receptors in the nasal cavities. This is the reason why anything that dulls your sense of smell, such as a head cold or holding your nose, diminishes the apparent flavour of food.

Many mammals use odours as a means of communication. Individuals of the same family or colony are identified by their odour; odours are also used to attract mates and to mark territories and trails. Dogs, for example, use their urine to mark home territories with identifying odours. Humans use the fragrances of perfumes and colognes as artificial sexual attractants.

## STUDY BREAK QUESTIONS

1. What is the difference between taste and smell? What are the similarities?
2. Distinguish among receptor proteins, receptor cells, and receptor organs.
3. For terrestrial vertebrates, describe the pathway by which a signal generated by taste receptors leads to a response.

**FIGURE 45.38 Star-nosed moles (*Condylura cristata*) have papillae around their noses.** Shown here, the papillae capture bubbles of air, allowing the submerged mole to smell airborne odours.

Ken Catania/Visuals Unlimited, Inc.

## 45.2f Thermoreceptors and Nociceptors

Thermoreceptors detect changes in the surrounding temperature. Nociceptors respond to stimuli that may potentially damage the surrounding tissues and produce pain. Both types of receptors consist of free nerve endings (Figure 45.14) formed by the dendrites of afferent neurons, with no specialized receptor structures surrounding them.

**THERMORECEPTION IS HEAT DETECTION** Most animals have thermoreceptors. Invertebrates such as mosquitoes and ticks use thermoreceptors to locate warm-blooded prey.

Some vertebrates, notably snakes such as rattlesnakes and pythons, also use thermoreceptors to detect the body heat of warm-blooded prey animals. These receptors are located in the pits of some pit vipers **(Figure 45.39)**, whereas those of pythons and boas may not have an opening to the surface. Vampire bats have infrared receptors on their noseleafs **(Figure 45.40)**, allowing them to detect places where blood (their food) flows close to the skin.

In vertebrates, distinct thermoreceptors respond to heat and cold. Researchers have shown that three members of the transient receptor potential (TRP)-gated $Ca^{2+}$-channel family act as heat receptors. One responds when the temperature reaches 33°C and another responds above 43°C, at which point heat starts to be painful. Both receptors are believed to be involved in thermoregulation. The third receptor responds at 52°C and above, in this case producing a pain response rather than being involved in thermoregulation.

Two cold receptors are known in mammals. One responds between 8°C and 28°C and is thought to be involved in thermoregulation. The second responds to temperatures below 8°C and appears to be associated with pain rather than thermoregulation. The molecular mechanisms controlling the opening and closing of heat and cold receptor chemical channels are not currently known.

Some neurons in the hypothalamus of mammals function as thermoreceptors, sensing changes in brain temperature and receiving afferent thermal information. They are highly sensitive to shifts from the normal body temperature and trigger involuntary responses such as sweating, panting, or shivering, which restore normal body temperature.

**NOCICEPTORS DETECT PAIN** Signals from nociceptors in mammals and possibly other vertebrates detect damaging stimuli that are interpreted by the brain as pain. Pain is a protective mechanism. In humans, pain prompts us to do something immediately to remove or decrease the damaging stimulus. Pain often elicits a reflex response, such as withdrawing the hand from a hot stove, that proceeds before we are consciously aware of the sensation.

Mechanical damage, such as a cut, pin prick, or blow to the body, and temperature extremes can cause pain. Some nociceptors are specific for a particular type of damaging stimulus; others respond to more than one kind. Axons that transmit pain are part of the somatic system of the peripheral nervous system (PNS; see Section 45.4). They synapse with interneurons in the grey matter of the spinal cord and activate neural pathways to the CNS by releasing the neurotransmitter glutamate or substance P. Glutamate-releasing axons produce sharp, prickling sensations that can be localized to a specific body part, such as the pain of stepping on a tack. Substance P–releasing axons produce dull, burning, or aching sensations that are not easily localized, such as the pain of tissue damage when you stub your toe.

As part of their protective function, pain receptors adapt very little, if at all (see Section 45.2h). Some pain receptors gradually intensify the rate at which they send out action potentials if the stimulus continues at a constant level. The CNS also has a pain-suppressing system. In response to stimuli, such as exercise, hypnosis, and stress, the brain releases **endorphins** (see Table 45.1), natural painkillers that bind to membrane receptors on substance P neurons, reducing the amount of neurotransmitter released.

Pit organs

**FIGURE 45.39 The pit organs of an albino Western diamondback rattlesnake (*Crotalus atrox*) are located in depressions on both sides of the head below the eyes.** These thermoreceptors detect infrared radiation emitted by warm-blooded prey such as mice and kangaroo rats.

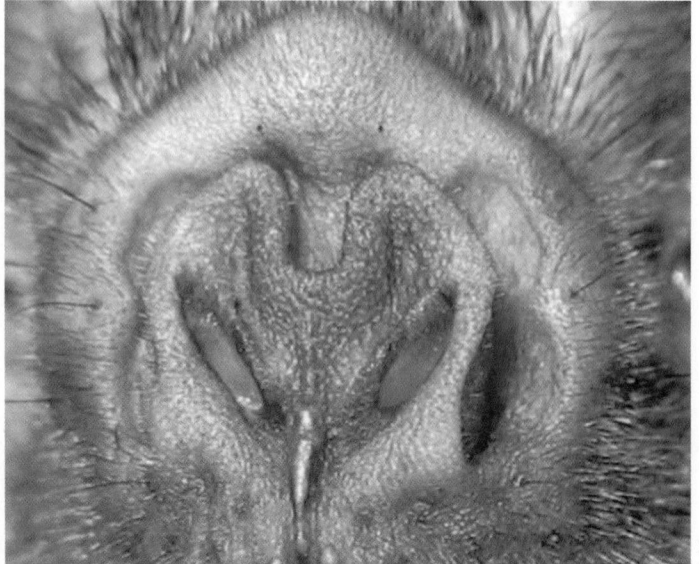

**FIGURE 45.40 The noseleaf on the face of a vampire bat (*Desmodus rotundus*) houses an infrared detector, allowing the bat to find places where blood flows close to the skin.** The bat then uses razor-sharp teeth to remove a divot of skin, and anticlotting chemicals in its saliva allow it to get a blood meal.

Nociceptors contribute to the taste of some spicy foods, particularly those containing capsaicin, the active ingredient in hot peppers. Researchers who study pain use capsaicin to identify nociceptors. To some, the burning sensation from capsaicin is addictive because, in its presence, nociceptors in the mouth, nose, and throat immediately transmit pain messages to the brain. The brain responds by releasing endorphins that act as a painkiller and create temporary euphoria.

**STUDY BREAK QUESTIONS**

1. What do thermoreceptors and nociceptors have in common?
2. Why is it important that pain receptors not adapt?

## 45.2g Electroreceptors and Magnetoreceptors

Some animals gain information about their environment by sensing electrical or magnetic fields. In so doing, they directly sense stimuli that humans can detect only with scientific instruments.

**ELECTRORECEPTION** Electroreception is an ancient trait in vertebrates. Although it was lost in ancestral bony fishes, it persists today in many sharks and has reappeared in some bony fishes and some amphibians. Mammals such as the star-nosed mole and duck-billed platypus detect electric fields with specialized **electroreceptors**.

Electroreceptors depolarize in an electric field, and the plasma membrane of an electroreceptor cell generates action potentials. The electrical stimuli detected by the receptors are used in different ways. Electrical information can be used to locate prey; to negotiate a way around obstacles in muddy water; or, by some fishes, to communicate. Some electroreception systems are passive, detecting electric fields in the environment, not the animal's own electric currents. Passive systems are used mainly to find prey. Sharks and rays use electroreceptors to locate prey buried under sand by detecting electrical currents generated by the prey's heartbeat or by the muscle contractions moving water over the gills.

Fishes in the orders Mormyriformes (elephant fish from Africa) and Osteoglossiformes (knifefish, also from Africa; **Figure 45.41a**) emit and receive low-voltage electrical signals, using them in prey location (electrolocation) and intraspecific communication. Some electric fishes can produce discharges of several hundred volts (e.g., *Electrophorus electricus*, the electric eel, Figure 45.41b, and *Malapterurus electricus*, the electric catfish) that stun or kill prey. The voltage discharged by an electric eel is high enough to stun, but not kill, a human.

**MAGNETORECEPTION AND NAVIGATION** Just as humans can use a magnetic compass to navigate, some animals use magnetic compasses in long-distance navigation. **Magnetoreceptors** allow animals to detect and use Earth's magnetic field as a source of directional information. The list includes butterflies,

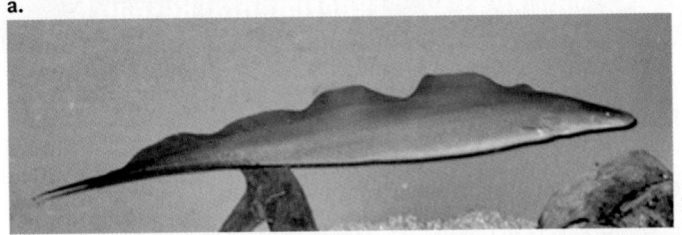

**FIGURE 45.41 Two electric fishes, one from Africa and one from South America. (a)** *Gymnarchus niloticus*, also known as *Gymnarchus electricus*, is a weakly electric fish that uses electrolocation. **(b)** *Electrophorus electricus*, the electric eel, stuns prey with an electric discharge.

beluga whales, sea turtles **(Figure 45.42)**, homing pigeons, and foraging honeybees (*Apis mellifera*).

The pattern of Earth's magnetic field differs from region to region yet remains almost constant over time, largely unaffected by changing weather or day and night. Animals with magnetic receptors can reliably monitor their location. Although little is known about the receptors that detect magnetic fields, they may depend on the fact that moving a conductor, such as an electroreceptor cell, through a magnetic field generates an electric current. Some magnetoreceptors may depend on the effect of Earth's magnetic field on the mineral magnetite, which is found in the bones or teeth of many vertebrates, including humans, and in insects, such as in the abdomen of the honeybee and the heads and abdomens of certain ants.

Animals such as homing pigeons (*Columba livia*), famous for their ability to find their way back to their nests even when released far from home, navigate by detecting their position with reference to both Earth's magnetic field and the Sun. Magnetite is located in the beaks of these birds, which is where magnetoreception likely occurs. Big brown bats (*Eptesicus fuscus*) also have a magnetic sense that influences their navigational abilities.

FIGURE 45.42 **Experimental Research**

## Magnetic Sense in Sea Turtles

**Question:** Can sea turtles sense magnetic fields?

**Experiment:** To determine whether loggerhead sea turtles (*Caretta caretta*) use a magnetoreceptor system for orientation, Kenneth Lohmann and colleagues at the University of North Carolina tested the responses of hatchling turtles to magnetic fields. They placed each turtle hatchling they tested in a harness and tethered it to a swivelling electronic system in the centre of a circular pool of water **(Figure 1a)**. The pool was surrounded by a large coil system, allowing the researchers to reverse the direction of the magnetic field (Figure 1b). The direction the turtle swam was recorded by the tracking system and relayed to a computer.

The turtles swam under two experimental conditions: half of them in Earth's magnetic field and the other half in a reversed magnetic field.

**Results:** Turtle hatchlings tested in Earth's magnetic field swam, on average, in an east-to-northeast direction, mimicking the direction they follow normally when migrating at sea. The hatchlings tested in the reversed magnetic field swam, on average, in a direction 180° opposite that of the hatchlings swimming in Earth's magnetic field.

**Conclusions:** The results indicate that loggerhead sea turtle hatchlings can detect Earth's magnetic field and that they use it to help them orient their migration. Their direction of migration, east to northeast, matches the inclination of Earth's magnetic field in the Atlantic Ocean where they migrate (see Figure 1c).

a.

Kenneth Lohmann/University of North Carolina

b.

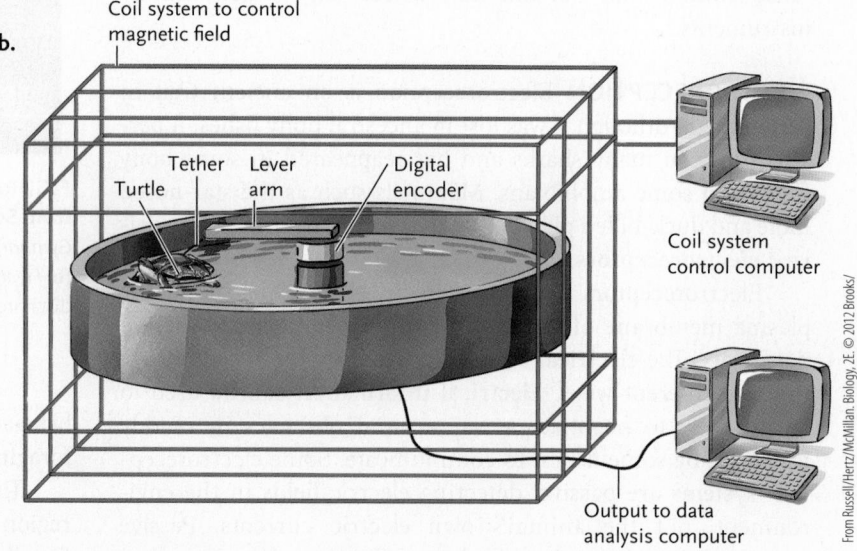

Coil system to control magnetic field

Tether Lever arm

Turtle    Digital encoder

Coil system control computer

Output to data analysis computer

From Russell/Hertz/McMillan. Biology, 2E. © 2012 Brooks/ Cole, a part of Cengage, Inc. Reproduced by permission. www.cengage.com/permissions

c.

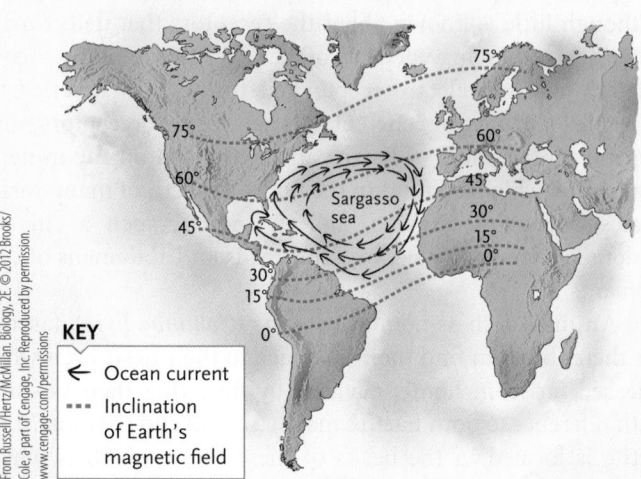

Sargasso sea

**KEY**
← Ocean current
- - - Inclination of Earth's magnetic field

From Russell/Hertz/McMillan. Biology, 2E. © 2012 Brooks/ Cole, a part of Cengage, Inc. Reproduced by permission. www.cengage.com/permissions

**Figure 1** Harnessed hatchling loggerhead sea turtles **(a)** were tested in a circular pool in which the magnetic field could be altered **(b)**. **(c)** Hatchlings swimming in the normal magnetic field of Earth swam in the directions they would travel at sea on migration.

STUDY BREAK QUESTIONS

1. How do animals use electrical information?
2. What are the advantages of a magnetic navigational system?

## 45.2h  Sensory Coding

**THE STRENGTH OF A STIMULUS IS ENCODED IN SEVERAL WAYS** Sensory pathways begin at a sensory receptor and proceed by afferent neurons to the CNS. Each type of receptor conveys information to a specific part of the CNS. Action potentials arising in the retina of the eye, for instance, travel along the optic nerves to the visual cortex, where they are interpreted by the brain as differences in pattern, colour, and intensity of light.

The frequency of action potentials that the stimulus generates in the afferent neuron (number per unit time) can indicate the intensity and extent of the stimulus. Stronger stimuli cause more action potentials than weaker ones. A light touch to the hand, for example, causes action potentials to flow at low frequencies along the axons leading to the primary somatosensory area of the cerebral cortex. As the pressure increases, the number of action potentials per second rises in proportion. In the brain, the increase is interpreted as greater pressure on the hand.

The number of afferent neurons sending action potentials in response to a stimulus can also convey information about the intensity and extent of a stimulus. The more sensory receptors that are activated, the more axons carry information to the brain. A light touch activates a relatively small number of receptors in a small area near the surface of the finger. But as the pressure increases, the resulting indentation of the finger's surface increases in area and depth, activating more receptors. In the appropriate somatosensory area of the brain, the larger number of axons carrying action potentials is interpreted as an increase in pressure spread over a greater area of the finger.

**MANY RECEPTORS ADAPT WHEN STIMULI REMAIN CONSTANT** In many sensory systems, the effect of a stimulus is reduced if it continues at a constant level. This reduction is called **sensory adaptation** (do not confuse this with adaptation used in the context of evolution). Some receptors adapt quickly and broadly; other receptors adapt only slightly. For example, when you walk outside on a pleasantly sunny day, it may seem exceptionally bright for a minute or two but the sensation passes and normal vision returns. In contrast, receptors detecting painful stimuli show little or no adaptation. Pain signals a danger to some part of the body, and the signal is maintained until a response by the animal compensates for the stimulus causing the pain. Being able to adapt to light intensity, on the other hand, allows the visual system to retain its sensitivity, whether on a moonlit night or in the middle of a sunny afternoon (remember that a neuron can only increase its action potential frequency so much).

Sensory adaptation also increases the sensitivity of receptor systems to changes in environmental stimuli. For some stimuli, these can be more important to survival than keeping track of constant environmental factors. For example, when something touches your skin you are initially aware of the touch and pressure. Within a few minutes, however, the sensation lessens or is lost, even though the pressure remains the same. The loss reflects adaptation of mechanoreceptors in your skin. If the intensity of the stimulus changes, the mechanoreceptors again become active. There are some sensations that organisms must always be aware of and others where receiving constant reminders are of less value than being able to perceive changes in the level of a stimulus.

**PERCEPTION OF A STIMULUS RESULTS FROM INTERPRETATION OF SENSORY INPUT** The conscious awareness of our external and internal environments is derived from the processing of sensory input. That is, the action potentials from sensory receptors are the signals the brain uses to generate an interpretation—the **perception**—of the external and internal environments. There are multiple aspects of this. In the first instance, an organism's perception of the world depends on the types of receptors it possesses. Our human perception of the world is significantly different from the perceptions of other organisms. For instance, many animals can detect much higher sound frequencies, and many insects can "see" ultraviolet light, making their perception of the same environment different than ours (see Figure 1.28, Chapter 1). Then, during processing, different forms of sensory input are given unique characteristics. Action potentials arriving in the sensory cortex from different receptors on the tongue may create a sweet or a tart sensation. These are a result of the processing. All taste receptors generate action potentials, but the action potentials arriving from different receptors give rise to different sensations. Finally, input is further processed by the cerebral cortex, including comparison of the particular input with other incoming sensory input and with memories of similar situations. Every individual (perhaps with the exception of identical twins) has slightly different perceptions of the world. The central processing and integration of information is considered in the next section.

CONCEPT FIX It is commonly thought that our perception of the environment arises from the sensory cells themselves. Perception, however, is the consequence of the processing of sensory information by the CNS. All taste receptors generate action potentials. It is the central processing of action potentials arriving in the sensory cortex from different receptors on the tongue that creates a sweet or tart sensation. ⬡

STUDY BREAK QUESTIONS

1. What are the different roles of primary and secondary sensory structures? What do the secondary structures contribute?
2. How is the strength of a sensory stimulus conveyed to the brain?
3. Why is it important that some receptors allow the effect of a stimulus to be reduced, whereas other receptors do not?

## 45.3 The Central Nervous System: Integration

The sensory pathways just described conduct information by afferent neurons to the CNS. Each type of receptor conveys information to a specific part of the CNS. Action potentials arising in the retina of the eye, for instance, travel along the optic nerves to the visual cortex, where they are interpreted by the brain as differences in pattern, colour, and intensity of light. In the next part of the chapter, we describe how integration occurs and then we discuss the roles of the major areas of the CNS where complex neural processing occurs.

### 45.3a Integration of Incoming Signals by Neurons

Most neurons receive a multitude of stimulatory and inhibitory signals carried by both ionotropic and metabotropic neurotransmitters. These signals are integrated by the postsynaptic neuron into a response that reflects their combined effects. The integration depends primarily on the patterns, number, types, and activity of the synapses that the postsynaptic neuron receives from presynaptic neurons. Inputs from other sources, such as indirect neurotransmitters and other signal molecules, can modify the integration. The response of the postsynaptic neuron is determined by the frequency of action potentials it generates.

**CONCEPT FIX** Not all parts of neurons can generate action potentials. In most, the dendrites and cell bodies can only generate graded potentials. As a result, some integration takes place at every synapse in a neural circuit. Higher-level integration takes place in the CNS, where interneurons are recruited specifically to integrate information coming in from many different sites in the body. ⬡

**INTEGRATION AT CHEMICAL SYNAPSES OCCURS BY SUMMATION** As mentioned earlier, depending on the type of receptor to which it binds, a neurotransmitter may stimulate or inhibit the generation of action potentials in the postsynaptic neuron. If a neurotransmitter opens a ligand-gated Na$^+$ channel, Na$^+$ enters the cell, causing a depolarization. This change in membrane potential pushes the neuron closer to threshold; that is, it is excitatory and is called an **excitatory postsynaptic potential (EPSP)**. On the other hand, if a neurotransmitter opens a ligand-gated ion channel that allows Cl$^-$ to flow into the cell or K$^+$ to flow out, hyperpolarization occurs. This change in membrane potential pushes the neuron farther from threshold; that is, it is inhibitory and is called an **inhibitory postsynaptic potential (IPSP)**. EPSPs and IPSPs are graded potentials, in which the membrane moves up or down in potential without necessarily triggering an action potential. There are no refractory periods for EPSPs and IPSPs.

A neuron typically has hundreds to thousands of chemical synapses formed by axon terminals of presynaptic neurons contacting its dendrites and cell body **(Figure 45.43)**. The events

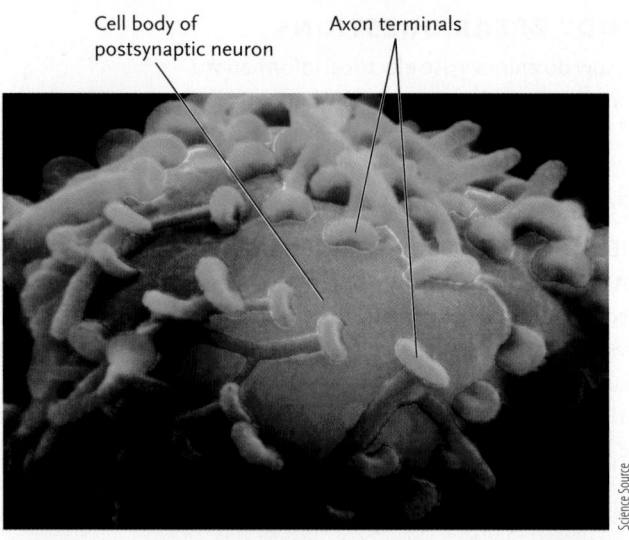

**FIGURE 45.43 The multiple chemical synapses relaying signals to a neuron.** The drying process used to prepare the neuron for electron microscopy has toppled the axon terminals and pulled them away from the neuron's surface.

that occur at each synapse produce either an EPSP or an IPSP in that postsynaptic neuron. But how is an action potential produced if a single EPSP is not sufficient to push the postsynaptic neuron to threshold? The answer involves the summation of all the inputs received through all the chemical synapses formed by presynaptic neurons. At any given time, some or many of the presynaptic neurons may be firing, producing EPSPs and/or IPSPs in the postsynaptic neuron. The sum of all the EPSPs and IPSPs at a given time determines the membrane potential in the postsynaptic neuron and, therefore, how that neuron responds. **Figure 45.44** shows, in a greatly simplified way, the effects of EPSPs and IPSPs on membrane potential and how the summation of inputs brings a postsynaptic neuron to threshold.

The postsynaptic neuron in Figure 45.44 has three neurons, Ex1, Ex2, and In1, forming synapses with it. Suppose that the axon of Ex1 releases a neurotransmitter that produces an EPSP in the postsynaptic cell (see Figure 45.44a). The membrane depolarizes, but not enough to reach threshold. If Ex1 input causes a new EPSP after the first EPSP has died down, it will be of the same magnitude as the first EPSP, so no progression toward threshold happens because no summation has occurred. If, instead, Ex1 input causes a new EPSP before the first EPSP has died down, the second EPSP will sum with the first, leading to a greater depolarization (see Figure 45.44b). The summation of several EPSPs at a common site produced by successive firing of a single presynaptic neuron over a short period of time is called **temporal summation**. If the total depolarization achieved in this way spreads to the axon hillock or spike initiation zone and brings it to threshold, an action potential will be produced in the postsynaptic neuron.

The postsynaptic cell may also be brought to threshold by **spatial summation**, the summation of EPSPs produced by the firing of different presynaptic neurons at different sites on the

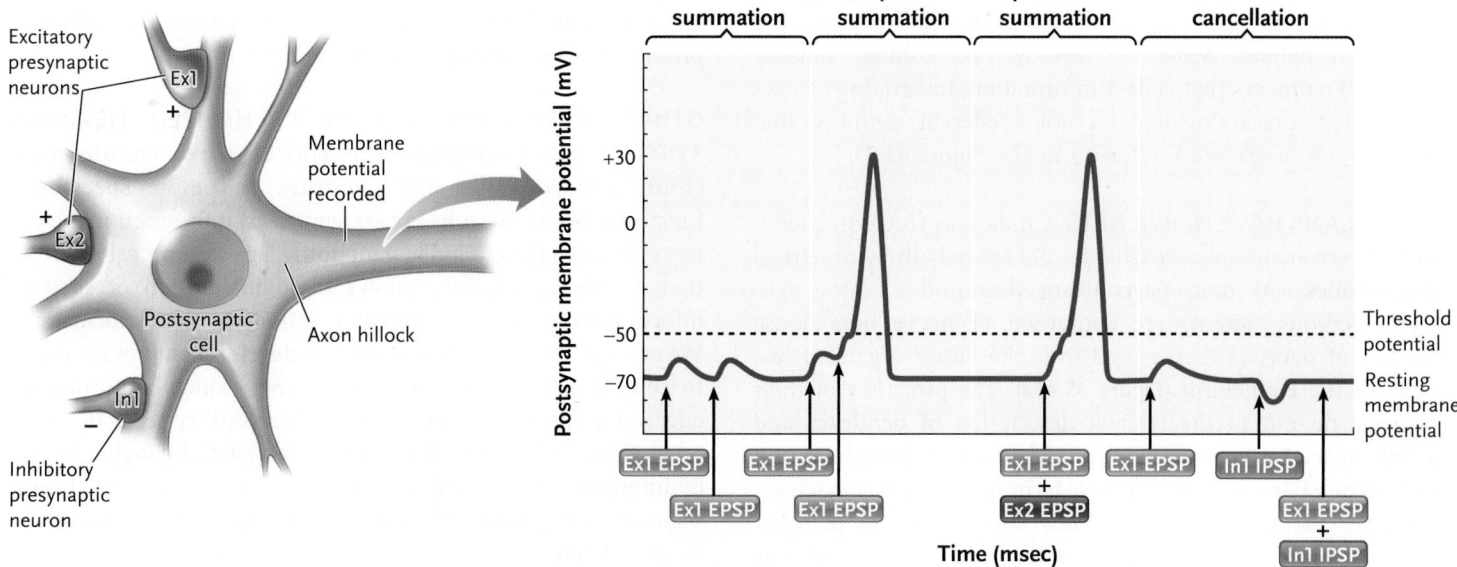

**a. No summation:** The axon of Ex1 releases a neurotransmitter, which produces an EPSP in the postsynaptic cell. The membrane depolarizes, but not enough to reach threshold. If Ex1 input causes a new EPSP after the first EPSP has died down, it will be of the same magnitude as the first EPSP and no progression toward threshold has taken place—no summation has occurred.

**b. Temporal summation:** If instead, Ex1 input causes a new EPSP before the first EPSP has died down, the second EPSP will sum with the first and a greater depolarization will have taken place. This summation of two (or more) EPSPs produced by successive firing of a single presynaptic neuron over a short period of time is **temporal summation**. If the total depolarization achieved in this way reaches threshold, an action potential is produced in the postsynaptic neuron.

**c. Spatial summation:** The postsynaptic neuron may be brought to threshold by **spatial summation**, the summation of EPSPs produced by the simultaneous firing of two different excitatory presynaptic neurons, such as Ex1 and Ex2.

**d. Summation resulting in cancellation:** EPSPs and IPSPs can sum to cancel each other out. In the example, firing of the excitatory presynaptic neuron Ex1 alone produces an EPSP, firing of presynaptic inhibitory neuron In1 alone produces an IPSP, while firing of Ex1 and In1 simultaneously produces no change in the membrane potential.

**FIGURE 45.44 Summation of EPSPs and IPSPs by a postsynaptic neuron**

postsynaptic cell, such as Ex1 and Ex2 (see Figure 45.44c). Lastly, EPSPs and IPSPs can cancel each other out. In the example shown in Figure 45.44d, firing of Ex1 alone produces an EPSP, and firing of In1 alone produces an IPSP, and the simultaneous firing of Ex1 and In1 produces no change in the membrane potential.

The key summation point for EPSPs and IPSPs is the axon hillock, or spike initiation zone, of the postsynaptic neuron. EPSPs and IPSPs spread over the membrane of the dendrites and cell body as graded potentials summing or cancelling each other as they meet. If the net change in membrane potential is sufficient to bring the spike initiation zone (the first site along the neuron where voltage-gated Na+ and K+ channels occur) to threshold, an action potential will result. This action potential will then be conducted or propagated along the neuron.

**THE PATTERNS OF SYNAPTIC CONNECTIONS CONTRIBUTE TO INTEGRATION** The total number of connections made by a neuron may be very large. Some single interneurons in the human brain, for example, form as many as 100 000 synapses with other neurons. The synapses are not absolutely fixed: they can change through modification, addition, or removal of synaptic connections, or even entire

neurons, as animals mature and experience changes in their environments. The combined activities of all the neurons in an animal provide the flow of information on which the integrated functioning of increasingly complex organisms depends. In the remainder of this chapter, we explore the ways that neurons are organized into nervous systems in the various major groups of animals.

**STUDY BREAK QUESTIONS**

1. Differentiate between spatial and temporal summation.
2. Describe the steps from the repeated release of an excitatory neurotransmitter at a synapse to the initiation of an action potential at an axon hillock.

## 45.3b Evolutionary Trends in Neural Integration: Networks, Ganglia, and Brains

The nervous systems of all animals are designed to effectively sense environmental changes (internal and external), integrate this information, and produce appropriate responses. The organization of the nervous systems of the different groups of invertebrate and vertebrate animals reflects differences in lifestyle and habitat. Most nervous systems contain sensory (afferent) pathways that collect information, integrating centres (where decisions are made), and motor (efferent) pathways that produce responses (see Section 45.1a and Figure 45.2).

**CNIDARIANS HAVE NERVE NETS** Cnidarians (including jellyfish and sea anemones; see Chapter 27) are radially symmetrical protostomes with body parts arranged around a central axis. Their nervous systems are composed of **nerve nets**, loose meshes of neurons that extend over the entire organism just beneath the epithelium **(Figure 45.45a)**. The processes of their neurons do not fit the normal description of dendrites and axons. Instead, all processes can conduct action potentials, and instead of having synapses at their terminals, there are synapses wherever the processes of neurons cross processes of other neurons. Moreover, both processes involved in a synapse may produce transmitters and have receptors for transmitters. When part of the animal is stimulated, impulses are conducted through the nerve net in all directions from the point of stimulation. Although there is no cluster of neurons that plays the coordinating role of a brain, nerve cells may be more concentrated in some regions. In the cnidarian hydra, they are more concentrated around the oral opening, allowing better coordination of tentacles for feeding. In the cnidarian jellyfish, which swim by rhythmic contraction of their bells, neurons are denser in a ring around the bell, in the same area as the contractile cells that produce the swimming movements.

**OTHER INVERTEBRATES HAVE CEPHALIZED NERVOUS SYSTEMS** More complex invertebrates have neurons with clearly defined axons and dendrites and more specialized functions. Some neurons are concentrated into functional clusters called *ganglia* (singular, ganglion). This anatomical localization of interconnections allows rapid integration of sensory information and more complex reactions to that information. We saw in Chapter 27 that segmental development has occurred twice in the evolution of the protostomes, which had profound effects on the development of the nervous system. In these organisms, each segment has a separate pair of ganglia, joined by interconnections, both between members of a pair within a segment and between the pairs of ganglia in the segments in front and behind.

Another key evolutionary development in invertebrates is a trend toward cephalization, the formation of a distinct head region. This head region usually contains major sensory structures, reflecting the tendency for the head of the animal, as it moves through its environment, to encounter new stimuli first. The formation of a distinct head is the result of the fusion of anterior segments and the paired ganglia associated with these segments to form a brain. This concentration of neurons at a

**a. Cnidarian (sea anemone)**

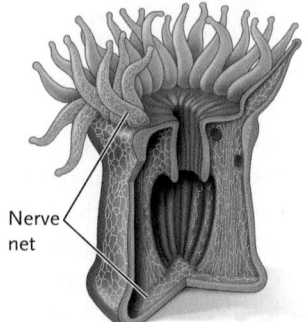

**b. Echinoderm (sea star)**

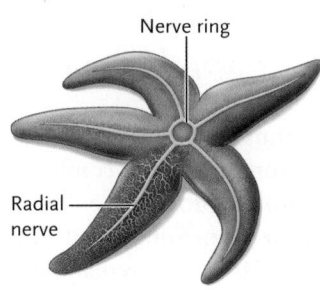

**c. Planarian (flatworm)**

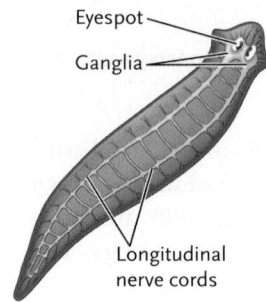

**d. Arthropod (grasshopper)**

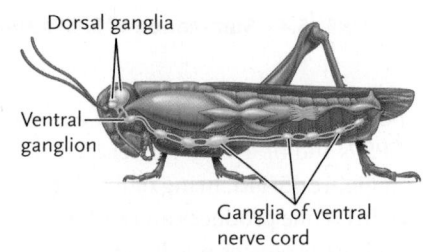

**e. Mollusc (octopus)**

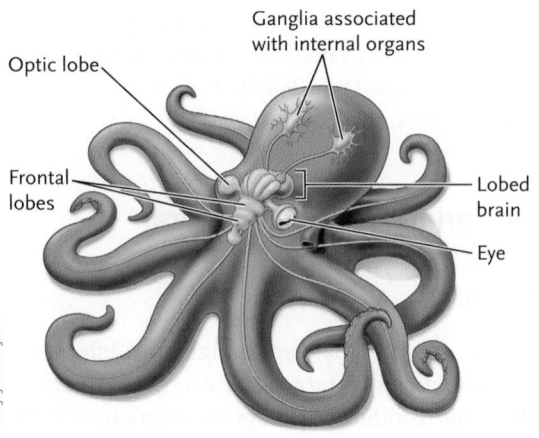

**f. Vertebrate (salamander)**

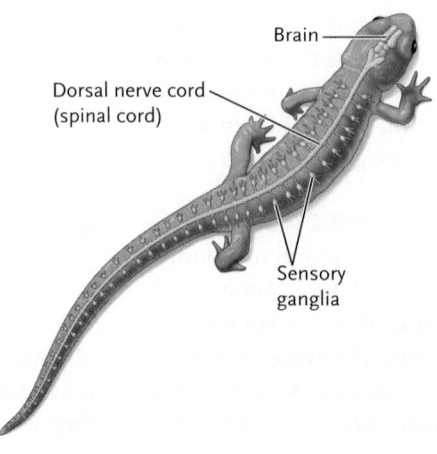

**FIGURE 45.45 Invertebrate and vertebrate nervous systems compared, showing increasing cephalization.** The exception to the trend is the echinoderms. The diagrams are not drawn to the same scale.

site close to the sensory structures reduces the transmission times for processing incoming signals and for integrating signals to produce appropriate responses. One or more solid **nerve cords**—bundles of nerves—extend from the central ganglia to the rest of the body; they are connected to smaller nerves. Another evolutionary trend is toward bilateral symmetry of the body and the nervous system, in which body parts are mirror images on left and right sides. These trends toward cephalization and bilateral symmetry are well illustrated in flatworms, arthropods, and molluscs (see Chapter 27).

In flatworms, a small brain consisting of a pair of ganglia at the anterior end is connected by two or more longitudinal nerve cords to nerve nets in the rest of the body (Figure 45.45b). The brain integrates inputs from sensory receptors, including a pair of anterior eyespots with receptors that respond to light. The brain and longitudinal nerve cords constitute the flatworm's CNS—the simplest one known—while the nerves from the CNS to the rest of the body constitute the PNS (see Section 45.4).

Arthropods, such as insects, have a head region that contains a brain, consisting of dorsal and ventral pairs of ganglia, and major sensory structures, usually eyes and **antennae** (Figure 45.45c). The brain exerts centralized control over the remainder of the animal. A ventral nerve enlarges into a pair of ganglia in each body segment. In arthropods with fused body segments, as in the thorax of insects, the ganglia are also fused into masses, forming secondary control centres.

Although different in basic plan from the arthropod system, the nervous systems of molluscs (such as clams, snails, and octopuses) also rely on neurons clustered into paired ganglia connected by major nerves. Different molluscs have varying degrees of cephalization, with cephalopods having the most pronounced cephalization of any invertebrate group. In the head of an octopus, for example, a cluster of ganglia fuse into a complex, lobed brain with clearly defined sensory and motor regions. Paired nerves link different lobes with muscles and sensory receptors, including prominent optic lobes linked by nerves to large, complex eyes (Figure 45.45d). Octopuses are capable of rapid movement to hunt prey and to escape from predators, behaviours that rely on rapid, sophisticated processing of sensory information. Indeed, the cephalopod brain is sufficiently advanced that the Canadian Council on Animal Care requires that this group receive special treatment.

The echinoderms, including sea stars, are an exception to this trend. Like cnidarians, this group is also radially symmetrical. These animals lack a cephalized brain and have instead a series of ganglia connected by a nerve ring that surrounds the centrally located mouth. Neurons are organized into radial nerves (Figure 45.45e). If the nerve serving an arm is cut, the arm can still move in response to stimuli, but not in coordination with the other arms (in fact the separated arm can grow into a complete new animal (see Chapter 44)). Echinoderms are descended from bilaterally symmetrical ancestors, and in many species the larvae are bilaterally symmetrical and develop radial symmetry during metamorphosis into adults.

**VERTEBRATES HAVE COMPLEX NERVOUS SYSTEMS** In vertebrates, the CNS consists of the brain and spinal cord, and the PNS consists of all the nerves and ganglia that connect the brain and spinal cord to the rest of the body (Figure 45.45f). All vertebrate nervous systems are highly cephalized, with major concentrations of neurons in a brain located in the head. In contrast to invertebrate nervous systems, which have solid nerve cords located ventrally, the brain and the nerve cord of vertebrates are hollow, fluid-filled structures located dorsally. The head contains specialized sensory organs that are connected directly to the brain by nerves. Compared with those in invertebrates, the ganglia are greatly reduced in mass and functional activity (except in the gut, which contains extensive interneuron networks), and the brains are greatly enlarged.

The structure of the vertebrate nervous system reflects its pattern of development. The nervous system of a vertebrate embryo begins as a hollow **neural tube** (discussed more in Chapter 44), the anterior end of which develops into the brain, and the rest into the **spinal cord**. The cavity of the neural tube becomes the fluid-filled **ventricles** of the brain and the **central canal** through the spinal cord. Adjacent tissues give rise to nerves that connect the brain and spinal cord with all the body regions. Just as in the invertebrates, the brain and longitudinal nerve cord (now the spinal cord) constitute the CNS, while the nerves connecting the CNS to the rest of the body constitute the PNS.

## 45.3c The Vertebrate Central Nervous System and Its Functions

Early in development, the anterior part of the neural tube enlarges into three distinct regions: forebrain, midbrain, and hindbrain **(Figure 45.46)**. A little later, the embryonic hindbrain subdivides into the metencephalon and myelencephalon, the midbrain develops into the mesencephalon, and the forebrain subdivides into the telencephalon and diencephalon.

The hindbrain of vertebrates develops into the medulla oblongata (commonly shortened to medulla; Figure 45.46), which controls many vital involuntary tasks, such as respiration and blood circulation. The metencephalon is associated with the developing ear (when present) and balance organs and gives rise to the cerebellum, which integrates sensory signals from the eyes, ears, and muscle spindles. The midbrain, or mesencephalon, receives input from the ears and from the eyes and coordinates reflex responses (involuntary reactions) to visual and auditory (hearing) input. In many vertebrates, a mass of fibres connecting the cerebellum to higher centres in the brain is so prominent that it is identified as the pons (bridge). The medulla and pons, along with the midbrain, form a stalk-like structure known as the **brain stem**, which connects the forebrain with the spinal cord. All but 2 of the 12 pairs of cranial nerves also originate from the brain stem. The cerebellum, with its deeply folded surface, is an outgrowth of the pons.

The forebrain, which makes up most of the mass of the brain in mammals, forms the diencephalon, which gives rise to the

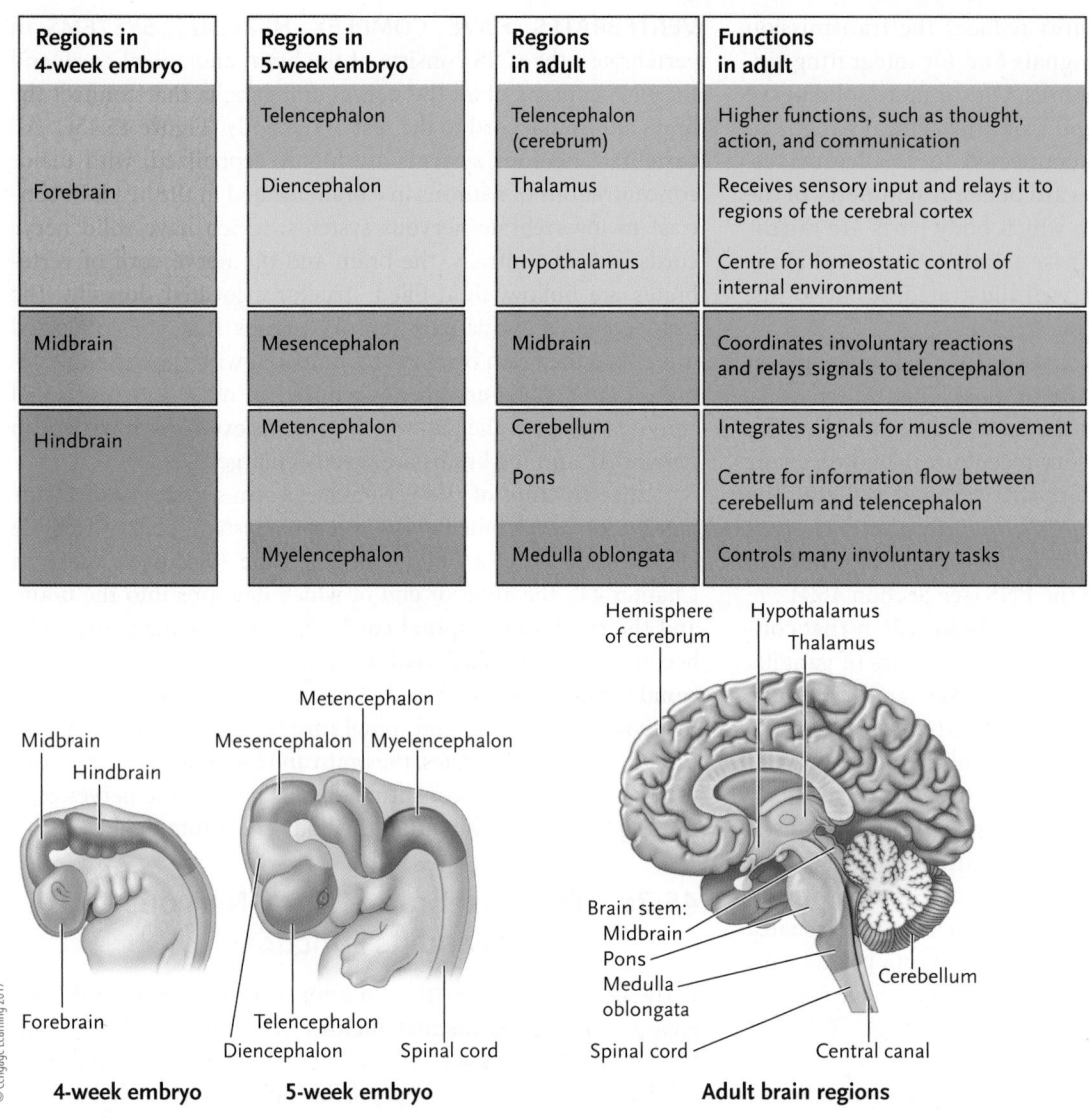

| Regions in 4-week embryo | Regions in 5-week embryo | Regions in adult | Functions in adult |
|---|---|---|---|
| Forebrain | Telencephalon | Telencephalon (cerebrum) | Higher functions, such as thought, action, and communication |
| | Diencephalon | Thalamus | Receives sensory input and relays it to regions of the cerebral cortex |
| | | Hypothalamus | Centre for homeostatic control of internal environment |
| Midbrain | Mesencephalon | Midbrain | Coordinates involuntary reactions and relays signals to telencephalon |
| Hindbrain | Metencephalon | Cerebellum | Integrates signals for muscle movement |
| | | Pons | Centre for information flow between cerebellum and telencephalon |
| | Myelencephalon | Medulla oblongata | Controls many involuntary tasks |

© Cengage Learning 2017

**4-week embryo**

Midbrain
Hindbrain
Forebrain

**5-week embryo**

Metencephalon
Mesencephalon  Myelencephalon
Telencephalon
Diencephalon  Spinal cord

**Adult brain regions**

Hemisphere of cerebrum  Hypothalamus
Thalamus

Brain stem:
Midbrain
Pons
Medulla oblongata
Spinal cord
Cerebellum
Central canal

**FIGURE 45.46 Development of the human brain from the anterior end of an embryo's neural tube**

mesencephalon are prominent, whereas the olfactory bulbs are less so. Birds also rely on vision for feeding and navigation, and their optic lobes reflect that.

One of the major trends in the evolution of the brain, however, is the increasing prominence of the cerebrum. Beginning with reptiles, it increased in size relative to the rest of the brain. In mammals, convolutions or folds appeared, increasing the amount of brain material in a particular volume. As well, the total mass of the brain relative to the size of the animal increased, permitting animals to undertake more complex tasks. The mass of bird and mammal brains is about 15 times that of other taxa when corrected for the size of the animal. With their advanced locomotor and navigational skills, birds and mammals also exhibit an increase in the cerebellum, a major coordinating centre for automatic activities.

thalamus and the hypothalamus, the primary centre for homeostatic control over the internal environment. It also forms the telencephalon (cerebrum). Its surface layer, the **cerebral cortex**, is a thin layer of grey matter in which numerous unmyelinated neurons are found. The cerebrum, which is divided into right and left cerebral hemispheres, is corrugated by fissures and folds that increase the surface area of the cerebral cortex (see **Figure 45.47**). This structure reflects two of the evolutionary tendencies in the brain of mammals: the corrugation of the hemispheres and the development of a layer of grey matter on the periphery. The basal nuclei, consisting of several regions of grey matter (cell bodies), are located deep within the white matter.

The general pattern of brain development underwent major modification in the evolution of various groups of animals **(Figure 45.48)**. In sharks, the cerebrum is relatively small, but the olfactory bulbs are prominent, testifying to the importance of olfaction in these very successful predators. Frogs are hunters that rely on vision, so the optic lobes of the

**THE CENTRAL NERVOUS SYSTEM IS PROTECTED BY THE MENINGES AND BY CEREBROSPINAL FLUID** The brain and the spinal cord are surrounded and protected by three layers of connective tissue, the **meninges** (*meninga* = membrane), and by the **cerebrospinal fluid**, which circulates through the central canal of the spinal cord, through the ventricles of the brain, and between two of the meninges. The fluid cushions the brain and the spinal cord from jarring movements and impacts, nourishes the CNS, and protects the CNS from toxic substances.

**THE BLOOD–BRAIN BARRIER REGULATES EXCHANGE BETWEEN THE BLOOD AND THE BRAIN** Unlike the epithelial cells that form capillary walls elsewhere in the body, which allow small molecules and ions to pass freely from the blood to surrounding fluids, those forming capillaries in the brain are sealed together by tight junctions (Chapter 38). The tight junctions set up a **blood–brain barrier** that prevents most substances dissolved in the blood from entering the cerebrospinal fluid, protecting the brain and the spinal cord from viruses, bacteria,

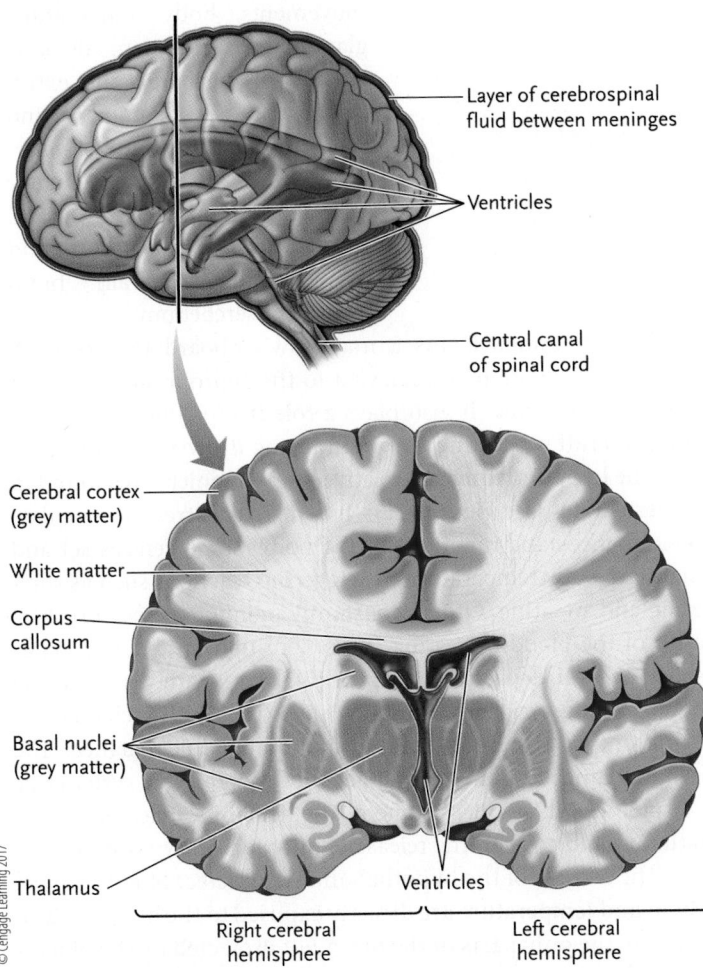

Layer of cerebrospinal fluid between meninges

Ventricles

Central canal of spinal cord

Cerebral cortex (grey matter)

White matter

Corpus callosum

Basal nuclei (grey matter)

Thalamus

Ventricles

Right cerebral hemisphere

Left cerebral hemisphere

© Cengage Learning 2017

**FIGURE 45.47** **The mammalian brain, illustrating the distribution of grey matter and the locations of the ventricles (in blue) with their connection to the central canal of the spinal cord. The spinal cord and brain contain both grey matter and white matter.** White matter is composed of axons (the myelination of the axons gives white matter its colour); grey matter is composed primarily of cell bodies. The brain is surrounded by meninges and circulating cerebrospinal fluid.

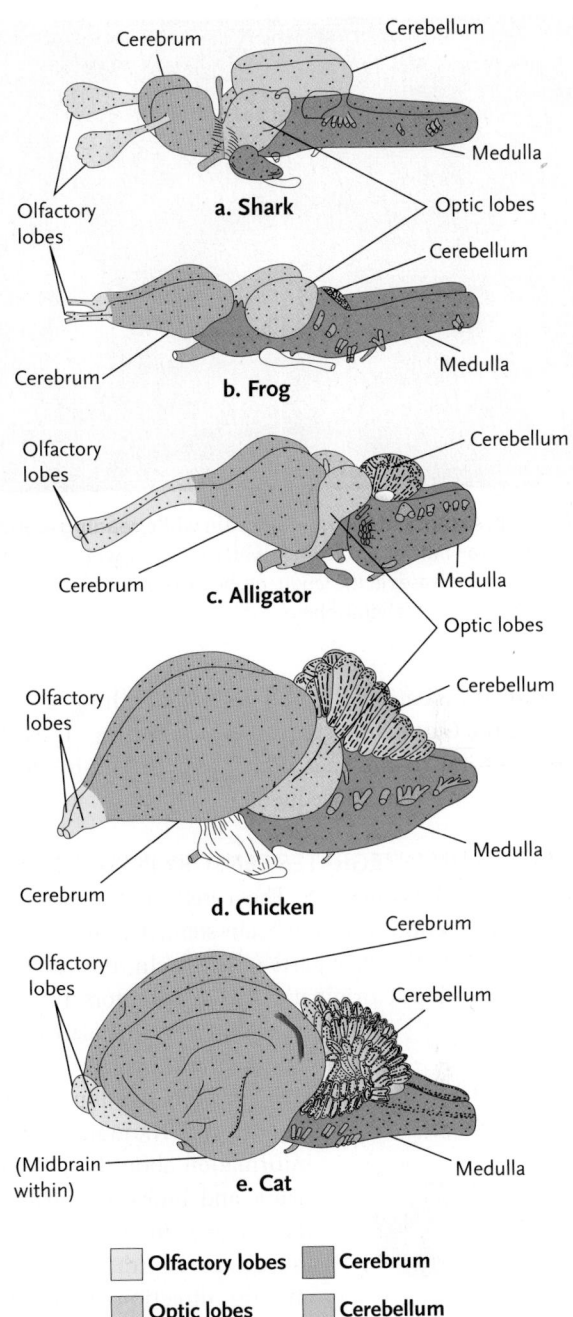

Cerebrum

Cerebellum

Olfactory lobes

**a. Shark**

Medulla

Optic lobes

Cerebellum

Cerebrum

Medulla

**b. Frog**

Olfactory lobes

Cerebellum

Cerebrum

**c. Alligator**

Medulla

Optic lobes

Olfactory lobes

Cerebellum

Cerebrum

**d. Chicken**

Medulla

Cerebrum

Olfactory lobes

Cerebellum

(Midbrain within)

**e. Cat**

Medulla

| | Olfactory lobes | | Cerebrum |
| --- | --- | --- | --- |
| | Optic lobes | | Cerebellum |

**FIGURE 45.48** **A comparison of brain structures in five different groups of vertebrates, illustrating the evolutionary trends described in the text**

and toxic substances that may circulate in the blood. A few types of non-polar molecules and ions, such as oxygen, carbon dioxide, alcohol, and anesthetics, can move directly across the lipid bilayer of the epithelial cell membranes by diffusion. A few other substances are moved across the plasma membrane by highly selective transport proteins. The most significant of these transported molecules is glucose, an important source of metabolic energy for the cells of the brain.

## THE BRAIN STEM REGULATES MANY VITAL HOUSEKEEPING FUNCTIONS OF THE BODY

Physicians and scientists have learned much about the functions of various brain regions by studying animals as well as patients with brain damage from strokes, infections, tumours, and mechanical

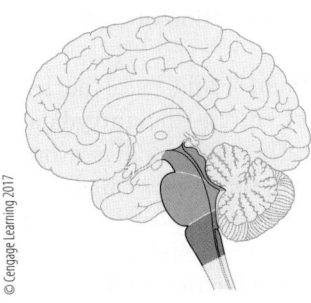

© Cengage Learning 2017

disturbances. Techniques such as functional magnetic resonance imaging (fMRI) and positron emission tomography (PET) allow researchers to identify the normal functions of specific brain regions in non-invasive ways. The instruments record a subject's brain activity during various mental and physical tasks by detecting increases in blood flow or metabolic activity in specific regions **(Figure 45.49)**.

From such analyses, we know that grey-matter centres in the brain stem control many vital body functions without conscious involvement or control by the cerebrum. Among these functions are the heart and respiration rates, blood pressure,

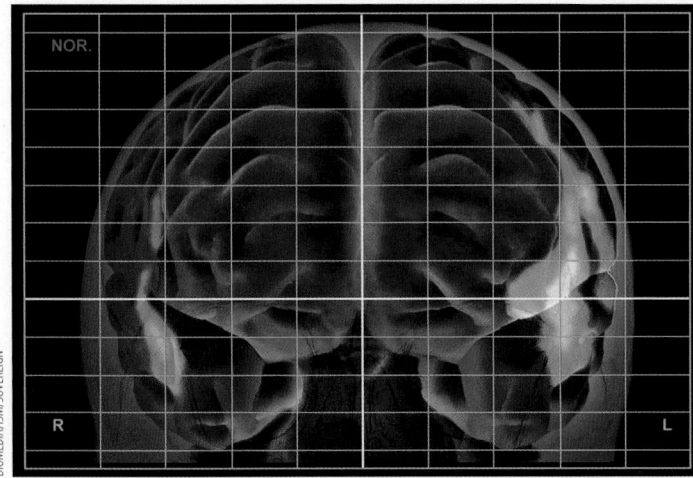

FIGURE 45.49 **Activity in the human brain while reading aloud.** The image combines an fMRI of a male brain with a PET scan, which shows that blood circulation increases in the language, hearing, and vision areas of the brain, especially in the left hemisphere.

constriction and dilation of blood vessels, coughing, and reflex activities of the digestive system such as vomiting. These functions are so vital to life that damage to the brain stem has serious and often lethal consequences.

**THE CEREBELLUM INTEGRATES SENSORY INPUTS TO COORDINATE BODY MOVEMENTS** The cerebellum is separate in structure and function from the brain stem. Through its extensive connections with other parts of the brain, the **cerebellum** receives sensory input originating from receptors in muscles

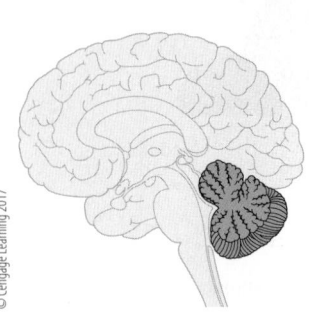

and joints; from balance receptors in the inner ear; and from the receptors of touch, vision, and hearing. These signals convey information about how the body trunk and limbs are positioned, the degree to which different muscles are contracted or relaxed, and the direction in which the body or limbs are moving. The cerebellum integrates these sensory signals and compares them with signals from the cerebrum that control voluntary body movements. Outputs from the cerebellum to the cerebrum, brain stem, and spinal cord modify and fine-tune the movements to keep the body in balance and directed toward targeted positions in space. The cerebellum is particularly important in flying birds, which make greater use of three-dimensional space, and, like the mammalian cerebellum, it has a folded structure, increasing its relative size.

**THE BASAL NUCLEI, THE THALAMUS, AND THE HYPOTHALAMUS CONTROL A VARIETY OF FUNCTIONS** Grey-matter centres derived from the embryonic telencephalon include the thalamus, hypothalamus, basal nuclei, and limbic system. They contribute to the control and integration of voluntary

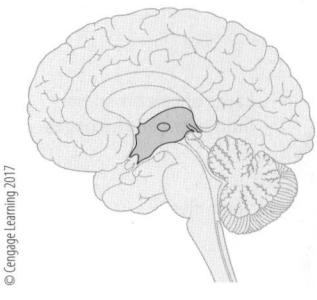

movements, body temperature, glandular secretions, osmotic balance of the blood and extracellular fluids, wakefulness, and the emotions, among other functions. Some of the grey-matter centres route information to and from the cerebral cortex and between the forebrain, brain stem, and cerebellum.

The **thalamus** forms a major switchboard that receives sensory information and relays it to the appropriate regions of the cerebral cortex. It also plays a role in alerting the cerebral cortex to full wakefulness or in inducing drowsiness or sleep.

The **hypothalamus** is a relatively small conical area found in all vertebrates (see Figure 43.8). It contains centres that regulate basic homeostatic functions of the body. Some centres set and maintain body temperature by triggering reactions such as shivering and sweating. Others constantly monitor the osmotic balance of the blood by testing its composition of ions and other substances. If departures from normal levels are detected, the hypothalamus triggers responses such as thirst or changes in urine output that restore the osmotic and fluid balance. The hypothalamus is an important part of the endocrine system (see Chapter 43). It produces some of the hormones released by the pituitary and governs the release of other pituitary hormones.

The centres of the hypothalamus that detect blood composition and temperature are directly exposed to the bloodstream: they are the only parts of the brain not protected by the blood–brain barrier. Parts of the hypothalamus also coordinate responses triggered by the autonomic system (see Section 45.3), making it an important link in such activities as control of the heartbeat, contraction of smooth muscle cells in the digestive system, and glandular secretion. Some regions of the hypothalamus establish a biological clock that sets up daily metabolic rhythms, such as the regular changes in body temperature, metabolic rate, and sleep state that occur on a daily cycle.

The **basal nuclei** are grey-matter centres that surround the thalamus on both sides of the brain. They moderate voluntary movements directed by motor centres in the cerebrum and can be recognized in all amniotes. Damage to the basal nuclei can affect the planning and fine-tuning of movements, leading to stiff, rigid motions of the limbs and unwanted or misdirected motor activity, such as tremors of the hands and inability to start or stop intended movements at the intended place and time. Parkinson's disease, in which affected individuals exhibit all of these symptoms, results from degeneration of centres in and near the basal nuclei.

Parts of the thalamus, hypothalamus, and basal nuclei, along with other nearby grey-matter centres—the **amygdala**, **hippocampus**, and olfactory bulbs—form a functional network called the **limbic system** (*limbus* = belt), sometimes called our *emotional brain*. The amygdala works as a switchboard, routing information about experiences that have an emotional component through the limbic system. The **olfactory bulbs** relay inputs from odour receptors to both the cerebral cortex and the limbic system. The olfactory connection to the limbic system may explain why certain odours can evoke particular, sometimes startlingly powerful, emotional responses.

The limbic system controls emotional behaviour and influences the basic body functions regulated by the hypothalamus and brain stem. Stimulation of different parts of the limbic system produces anger, anxiety, fear, satisfaction, pleasure, or sexual arousal. Connections between the limbic system and other brain regions bring about emotional responses such as smiling, blushing, or laughing.

### THE CEREBRAL CORTEX CARRIES OUT ALL HIGHER BRAIN FUNCTIONS

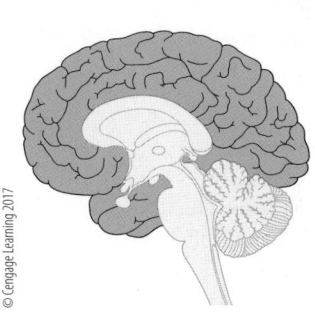

Over the course of evolution, the surface area of the cerebral cortex increased by continuously folding in on itself, thereby expanding the structure into sophisticated information-encoding and processing centres. Primates have cerebral cortices with the largest number of convolutions. In humans, each cerebral hemisphere is divided by surface folds into frontal, parietal, temporal, and occipital lobes (Figure 45.50). Uniquely in mammals, the top layer of the cerebral hemispheres is organized into six layers of neurons, called the *neocortex* (*neo* = new; these layers are the newest part of the cerebral cortex in an evolutionary sense).

The two cerebral hemispheres can function separately, and each has its own communication lines internally and with the rest of the CNS and the body. The left cerebral hemisphere responds primarily to sensory signals from, and controls movements in, the right side of the body. The right hemisphere has the same relationships to the left side of the body. The opposite connection and control reflect the fact that the nerves carrying afferent and efferent signals cross from left to right within the spinal cord or brain stem. Thick axon bundles, forming a structure called the **corpus callosum**, connect the two cerebral hemispheres and coordinate their functions.

**SENSORY REGIONS OF THE CEREBRAL CORTEX** Areas that receive and integrate sensory information are distributed over the cerebral cortex. In each hemisphere, the **primary somatosensory area**, which registers information on touch, pain, temperature, and pressure, runs in a band across the parietal lobes of the brain (see Figure 45.50). Experimental stimulation of this band in one hemisphere causes prickling or tingling sensations in specific parts on the opposite side of the body, beginning with the toes at the top of each hemisphere and running through the legs, trunk, arms, and hands, to the head **(Figure 45.51)**.

Other sensory regions of the cerebral cortex have been identified with hearing, vision, smell, and taste (see Figure 45.51). Regions of the temporal lobes on both sides of the brain receive auditory inputs from the ears, whereas inputs from the eyes are processed in the primary visual cortex in both occipital lobes. Olfactory input from the nose is processed in the olfactory lobes, located on the ventral side of the temporal lobes. Regions in the parietal lobes receive inputs from taste receptors on the tongue and other locations in the mouth.

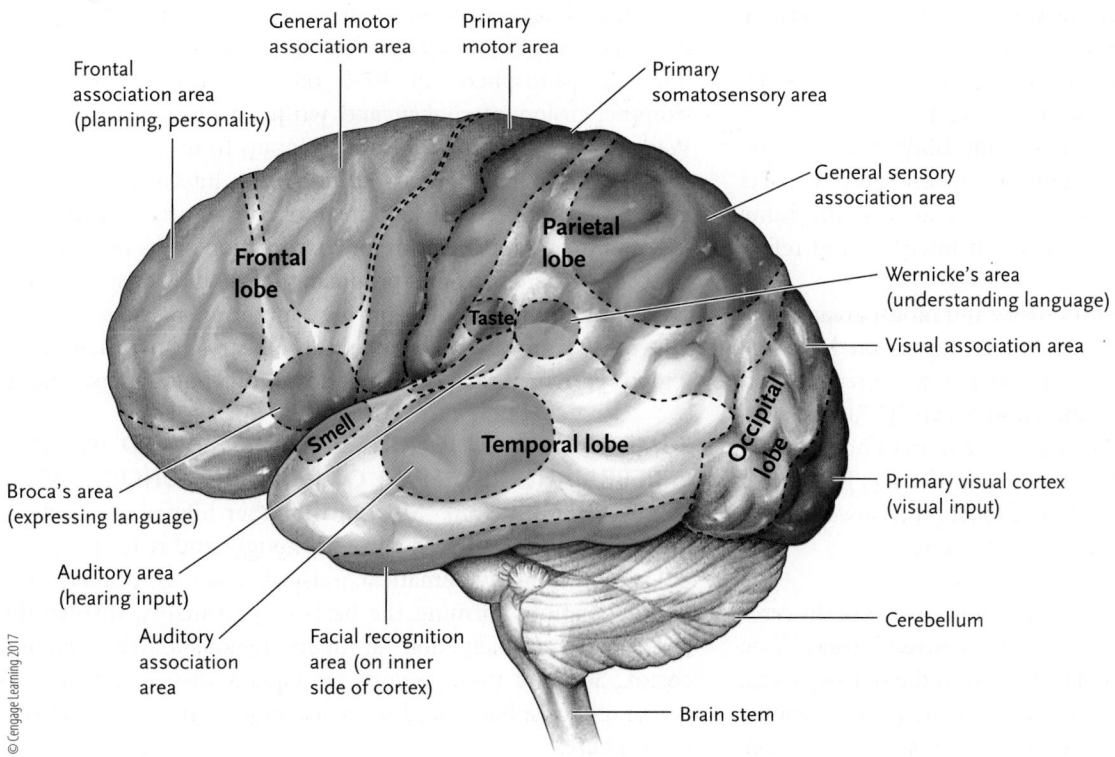

**FIGURE 45.50 The lobes of the cerebrum of the human brain, showing major regions and association areas of the cerebral cortex**

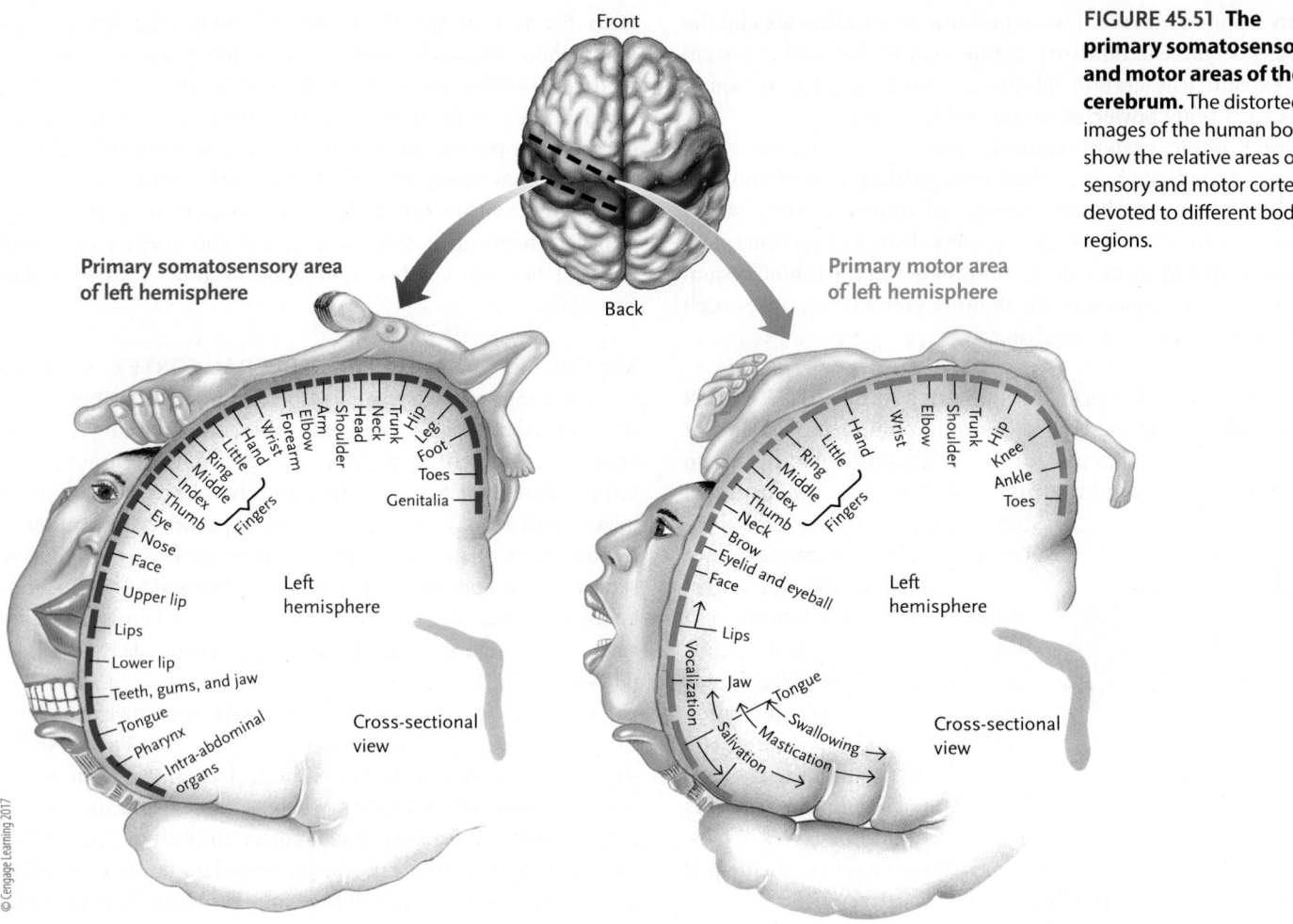

**FIGURE 45.51 The primary somatosensory and motor areas of the cerebrum.** The distorted images of the human body show the relative areas of the sensory and motor cortex devoted to different body regions.

Primary somatosensory area of left hemisphere

Front

Back

Primary motor area of left hemisphere

Little, Ring, Middle, Index, Thumb — Fingers, Hand, Wrist, Forearm, Elbow, Arm, Shoulder, Head, Neck, Trunk, Hip, Leg, Foot, Toes, Genitalia

Eye, Nose, Face, Upper lip, Lips, Lower lip, Teeth, gums, and jaw, Tongue, Pharynx, Intra-abdominal organs

Left hemisphere

Cross-sectional view

Little, Ring, Middle, Index, Thumb — Fingers, Hand, Wrist, Elbow, Shoulder, Trunk, Hip, Knee, Ankle, Toes

Neck, Brow, Eyelid and eyeball, Face, Lips, Vocalization, Jaw, Tongue, Swallowing, Mastication, Salivation

Left hemisphere

Cross-sectional view

© Cengage Learning 2017

**MOTOR REGIONS OF THE CEREBRAL CORTEX** The **primary motor area** of the cerebral cortex runs in a band just in front of the primary somatosensory area (see Figure 45.51). Experimental stimulation of points along this band in one hemisphere causes movement of specific body parts on the opposite side of the body, corresponding generally to the parts registering in the primary somatosensory area at the same level (see Figure 45.51). Other areas that integrate and refine motor control are located nearby.

In both the primary somatosensory and motor areas, some body parts, such as the lips and fingers, are represented by large regions, and others, such as the arms and legs, are represented by relatively small regions. As shown in Figure 45.51, the relative sizes produce a distorted image of the human body that is quite different from the actual body proportions. The differences are reflected in the precision of touch and movement in structures such as the lips, tongue, and fingers.

**ASSOCIATION AREAS** The sensory and motor areas of the cerebral cortex are surrounded by **association areas** (see Figure 45.50) that integrate information from the sensory areas, formulate responses, and pass them on to the primary motor area. Two of the most important association areas are Wernicke's

area and Broca's area, which function in spoken and written language. They are usually present on only one side of the brain, the left hemisphere in 97% of the human population. Comprehension of spoken and written language depends on Wernicke's area, which coordinates inputs from the visual, auditory, and general sensory association areas. Interneuron connections lead from Wernicke's area to Broca's area, which puts together the motor program for coordination of the lips, tongue, jaws, and other structures producing the sounds of speech, and passes the program to the primary motor area. The brain scan images in Figure 45.49 dramatically illustrate how these brain regions participate as a person performs different linguistic tasks.

**SOME HIGHER FUNCTIONS ARE DISTRIBUTED IN BOTH CEREBRAL HEMISPHERES; OTHERS ARE CONCENTRATED IN ONE HEMISPHERE** Most of the other higher functions of the human brain, such as abstract thought and reasoning; spatial recognition; mathematical, musical, and artistic ability; and the associations forming the basis of personality, involve the coordinated participation of many regions of the cerebral cortex. Some of these regions are equally distributed in both cerebral hemispheres, and some are more concentrated in one hemisphere.

Among the functions more or less equally distributed between the two hemispheres is the ability to recognize faces. Consciousness, the sense of time, and recognizing emotions also seem to be distributed in both hemispheres.

Typically, some brain functions are more localized in one of the two hemispheres, a phenomenon called **lateralization**. Studies of people with split hemispheres and surveys of brain activity by PET and fMRI have confirmed that, for the vast majority of people, the left hemisphere specializes in spoken and written language, abstract reasoning, and precise mathematical calculations. The right hemisphere specializes in nonverbal conceptualizing; intuitive thinking; musical and artistic abilities; and spatial recognition functions, such as fitting pieces into a puzzle. The right hemisphere also handles mathematical estimates and approximations that can be made by visual or spatial representations of numbers. Thus, the left hemisphere in most people is verbal and mathematical, and the right hemisphere is intuitive, spatial, artistic, and musical.

### STUDY BREAK QUESTIONS

1. What is the blood–brain barrier and what is its function?
2. What is the difference between white matter and grey matter?
3. What is the function of the brain stem?
4. Distinguish the functions of the cerebellum from those of the cerebral cortex.

## 45.3d  Memory, Learning, and Consciousness

We set memory, learning, and consciousness apart from the other CNS functions because they appear to involve coordination of structures from the brain stem to the cerebral cortex. **Memory** is the storage and retrieval of a thought or a sensory or motor experience. **Learning** involves a change in the response to a stimulus, based on information or experiences stored in memory. **Consciousness** is not easily defined. In a narrow sense, it involves awareness, a state of alertness to our surroundings. But there is a broader and deeper meaning that involves awareness of ourselves, our identity, and an understanding of the significance and likely consequences of events that we experience. Later in this section, we deal with sleep as a decrease in awareness.

**MEMORY TAKES TWO FORMS: SHORT TERM AND LONG TERM** Psychology research and our everyday experience indicate that humans have at least two types of memory. **Short-term memory** stores information for seconds, minutes, or at most an hour or so. **Long-term memory** stores information from days to years or even for life. Short-term memory, but not long-term memory, is usually erased if a person experiences a disruption such as a sudden fright, a blow, a surprise, or an electrical shock. For example, a person knocked unconscious by an accident typically cannot recall the accident itself or the events just before it, but long-standing memories are not usually disturbed.

To explain these differences, investigators propose that short-term memories depend on transient changes in neurons that can be erased relatively easily, such as changes in the membrane potential of interneurons caused by excitatory and inhibitory postsynaptic potentials (EPSPs and IPSPs) and the action of indirect neurotransmitters that lead to reversible changes in ion transport. By contrast, storage of long-term memory is considered to involve more or less permanent molecular, biochemical, or structural changes in interneurons, which establish signal pathways that cannot be switched off easily.

All memories probably register initially in short-term form. They are then either erased and lost or committed to long-term form. The intensity or vividness of an experience, the attention focused on an event, emotional involvement, and the degree of repetition may all contribute to the conversion from short-term to long-term memory.

The storage pathway typically starts with an input at the somatosensory cortex that then flows to the amygdala, which relays information to the limbic system, and to the hippocampus, which sends information to the frontal lobes, a major site of long-term memory storage. People with injuries to the hippocampus cannot remember information for more than a few minutes; long-term memory is limited to information stored before the injury occurred. Squirrels hoard food for the winter in a number of caches and can locate these by remembering the location from landmarks rather than by tracking a smell. Each autumn, the hippocampus of a squirrel increases in size by about 15%.

How are neurons and neuron pathways permanently altered to create long-term memory? One change that has been much studied is **long-term potentiation**: a long-lasting increase in the strength of synaptic connections in activated neural pathways following brief periods of repeated stimulation. The synapses become increasingly sensitive over time, so that a constant level of presynaptic stimulation is converted into a larger postsynaptic output that can last hours, weeks, months, or years. Other changes consistently noted as part of long-term memory include more or less permanent alterations in the number and the area of synaptic connections between neurons, in the number and branches of dendrites, and in gene transcription and protein synthesis in interneurons. Experiments on both vertebrates and invertebrates demonstrate that long-term memory depends on protein synthesis. For example, goldfish were trained to avoid an electrical shock by swimming to one end of an aquarium when a light was turned on. The fish could remember the training for about a month under normal conditions, but if they were exposed to a protein synthesis inhibitor while being trained, they forgot the training within a day.

**LEARNING INVOLVES COMBINING PAST AND PRESENT EXPERIENCES TO MODIFY RESPONSES** As with memory, most animals appear to be capable of learning to some degree. Learning involves three sequential mechanisms: (1) storing memories, (2) scanning memories when a stimulus is encountered, and (3) modifying the response to the stimulus in accordance with the information stored as memory.

One of the simplest forms of learning is an increased responsiveness to mild stimuli after experiencing a strong stimulus, often called **sensitization**. The process was nicely illustrated by Eric Kandel of Columbia University and his associates in experiments with a shell-less marine snail, the Pacific sea hare, *Aplysia californica*. The first time the researchers administered a single sharp tap to the siphon (the structure that admits water to the gills), the slug retracted its gills by a reflex movement. However, at the next touch, whether hard or gentle, the siphon retracted much more quickly and vigorously. Sensitization in *Aplysia* has been shown to involve changes in synapses. The synapses become more reactive because more of the neurotransmitter serotonin is released by each action potential. The cephalopod molluscs, such as octopuses, are capable of much more complex learning: they can distinguish and remember shapes and textures using only their tentacles.

**CONSCIOUSNESS INVOLVES DIFFERENT STATES OF AWARENESS** Most animals that have been investigated, including some invertebrates, experience a daily rhythm of activity and inactivity. The inactive period, sleep, is essential to normal functioning. Sleep deprivation leads to disruption of a number of functions, including memory and learning, and, if prolonged, can be fatal. During sleep, there is some degree of awareness since external stimuli such as sound, or internal stimuli such as a full bladder, can interrupt sleep.

In humans and other mammals, sleep is accompanied by changes in the electrical activity of the cerebrum as detected by electrodes applied to the scalp, producing an electroencephalogram. The waking state is characterized by rapid, irregular beta waves **(Figure 45.52)**. As the eyes close and you become fully relaxed, these give way to slower, more regular alpha waves. As you become drowsier, these are replaced by slower theta waves. Full sleep is characterized by even slower delta waves. The heart rate falls, and the muscles are relaxed.

During full sleep, the brain returns at intervals to periods of beta waves, during which the heart rate increases, the muscles may twitch, and the eyes move rapidly behind the closed lids,

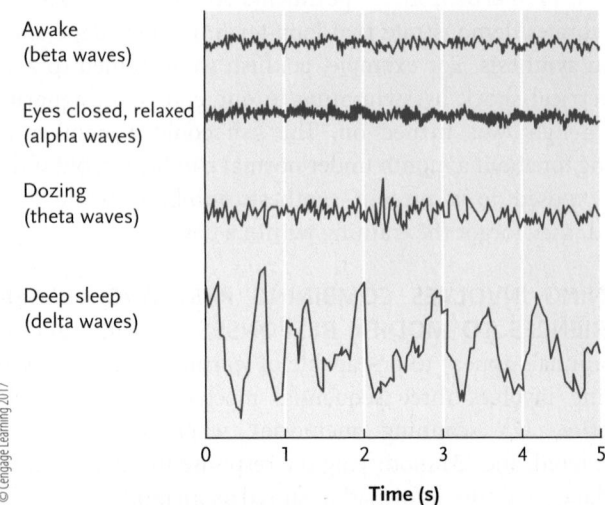

© Cengage Learning 2017

**FIGURE 45.52 Brain waves characteristic of various states of consciousness**

giving these periods the name **rapid eye movement (REM) sleep**. This brief period of about 10–15 minutes occurs every 90 minutes or so in healthy adults. Sleepers do most of their dreaming during REM sleep, and most individuals awakened from REM sleep report they were experiencing vivid dreams.

This pattern of alternating periods of greater or lesser cerebral activity is also characteristic of bird sleep, although birds may sleep on one side of the brain while the other remains fully alert as protection against predators. This is also true of some marine mammals. Reptiles, with their less-developed cerebrum, experience alternating patterns of activity in the amygdala.

Although we know that sleep is essential, we do not understand the physiological basis for these effects. What do these patterns of neural activity in the brain reflect, and why are they necessary? The fruit fly *Drosophila melanogaster* exhibits cycles of sleep. At night, it feeds and then seeks out an isolated place and becomes inactive for about eight hours. Interrupting the sleep interferes with memory and learning in the flies. Many labs are now using flies as models to identify genes involved in the sleep process.

**THE SPINAL CORD RELAYS SIGNALS BETWEEN THE PERIPHERAL NERVOUS SYSTEM AND THE BRAIN AND CONTROLS REFLEXES** The spinal cord, which extends dorsally from the base of the brain, carries impulses between the brain and the PNS and also contains interneuron circuits that control motor reflexes. In cross-section, the spinal cord has a butterfly-shaped core of **grey matter**, consisting of nerve cell bodies and dendrites. This is surrounded by **white matter**, consisting of axons, many of them surrounded by myelin sheaths (**Figure 45.53**, step 3). Pairs of **spinal nerves** connect with the spinal cord at spaces between the vertebrae.

The afferent (incoming) axons entering the spinal cord synapse with interneurons in the grey matter, which send axons upward through the white matter of the spinal cord to the brain. Conversely, axons from interneurons of the brain pass downward through the white matter of the cord and synapse with the dendrites and cell bodies of efferent neurons in the grey matter of the cord. The axons of these efferent (outgoing) neurons exit the spinal cord through the spinal nerves.

The grey matter of the spinal cord also contains interneurons of the pathways involved in **reflexes**, programmed movements that take place without conscious effort, such as the sudden withdrawal of a hand from a hot surface (shown in Figure 45.53). When your hand touches a hot surface, the heat stimulates an afferent neuron, which makes connections with at least two interneurons in the spinal cord. One of these interneurons stimulates an efferent neuron, causing the flexor muscle of the arm to contract. This bends the arm and withdraws the hand almost instantly from the hot surface. The other interneuron synapses with an efferent neuron connected to an extensor muscle, relaxing it so that the flexor can move more quickly. Interneurons connected to the reflex

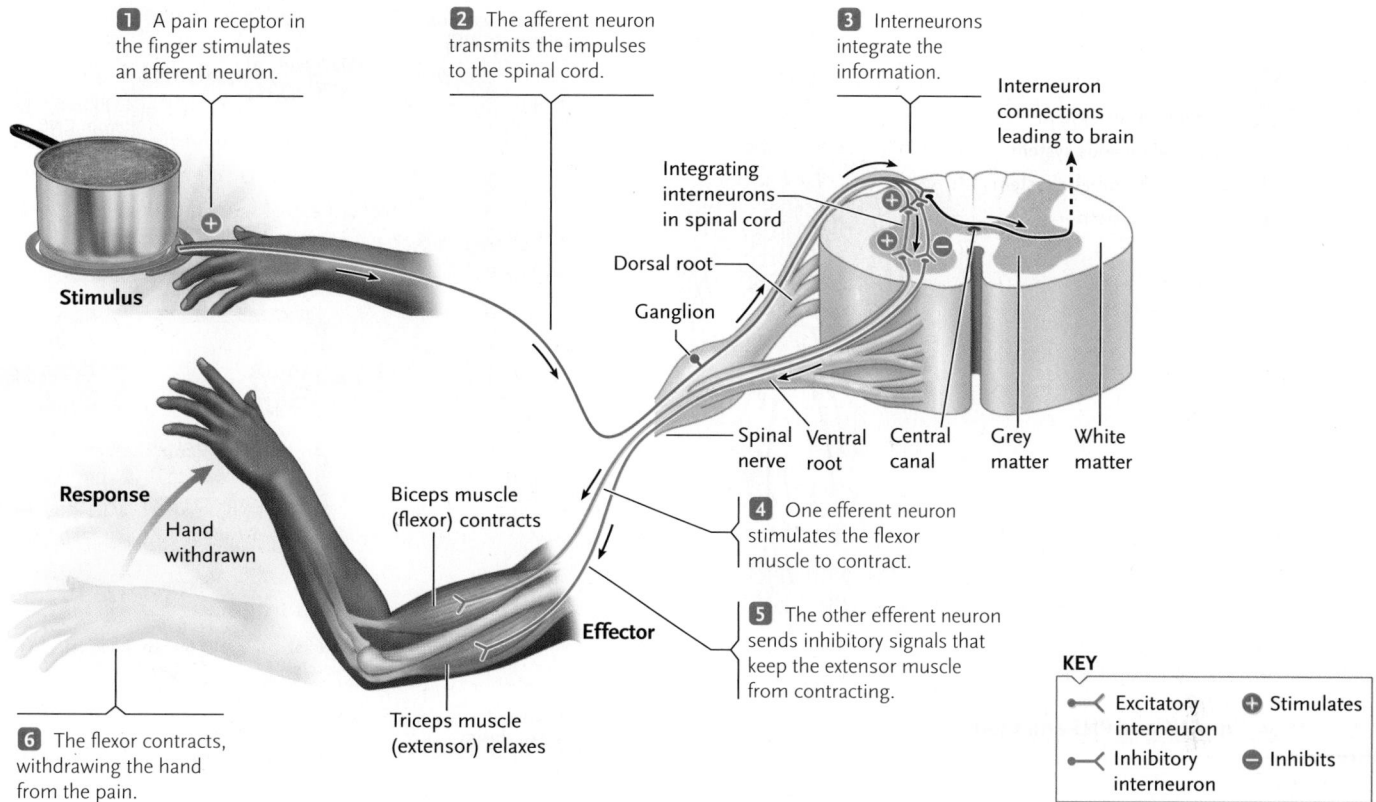

① A pain receptor in the finger stimulates an afferent neuron.

② The afferent neuron transmits the impulses to the spinal cord.

③ Interneurons integrate the information.

Interneuron connections leading to brain

Integrating interneurons in spinal cord

Dorsal root

Ganglion

Stimulus

Spinal nerve  Ventral root  Central canal  Grey matter  White matter

Response

Hand withdrawn

Biceps muscle (flexor) contracts

④ One efferent neuron stimulates the flexor muscle to contract.

⑤ The other efferent neuron sends inhibitory signals that keep the extensor muscle from contracting.

Effector

⑥ The flexor contracts, withdrawing the hand from the pain.

Triceps muscle (extensor) relaxes

KEY

⊣ Excitatory interneuron    ⊕ Stimulates

⊣ Inhibitory interneuron    ⊖ Inhibits

**FIGURE 45.53 Organization of the spinal cord and the withdrawal reflex.** The withdrawal reflex is an example of a relatively simple neuron circuit that integrates incoming information to produce an appropriate response. The reflex movement produced by this circuit is so rapid that the hand is withdrawn before the brain recognizes the sensation of pain.

circuits also send signals to the brain, making you aware of the stimulus causing the reflex. You know from experience that, when a reflex movement withdraws your hand from a hot surface or other damaging stimulus, you feel the pain shortly after the hand is withdrawn. This is the extra time required for impulses to travel from the neurons of the reflex to the brain.

**STUDY BREAK QUESTION**

1. Using long-term potentiation as an example, describe how neurons and neuron pathways can be altered to create memory.

# 45.4 The Peripheral Nervous System: Transmission and Response

The PNS can be divided into two main systems. The afferent system of the PNS includes all the neurons that transmit sensory information from receptors to the CNS. These were described in detail in Section 45.2. The efferent system consists of the axons of neurons that carry signals to the muscles and glands acting as effectors. The efferent system is further divided into somatic and autonomic systems **(Figure 45.54)**.

## 45.4a The Autonomic System Is Divided into Sympathetic and Parasympathetic Pathways

The **autonomic nervous system** controls largely involuntary processes such as digestion, secretion by sweat glands, circulation of the blood, many functions of the reproductive and excretory systems, and contraction of smooth muscles in all parts of the body. It is organized into sympathetic and parasympathetic divisions, which are always active and have opposing effects on the organs that they affect, thereby enabling precise control **(Figure 45.55)**. For example, in the circulatory system, sympathetic neurons stimulate the force and rate of the heartbeat, and parasympathetic neurons inhibit these activities. In the digestive system, sympathetic neurons inhibit the smooth muscle contractions that move materials through the small intestine, and parasympathetic neurons stimulate those same activities. These opposing effects control involuntary body functions precisely.

The pathways of the autonomic nervous system include two neurons **(Figure 45.56)**. The first neuron has its dendrites and cell body in the CNS, and its axon extends to a ganglion outside the CNS. There it synapses with the dendrites and cell body of the second neuron in the pathway. The axon of the second neuron extends from the ganglion to the effector carrying out the response.

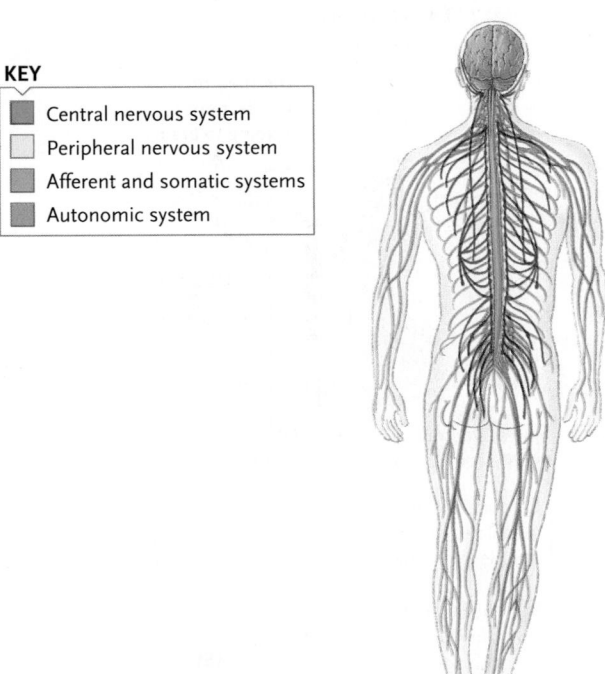

**KEY**

- Central nervous system
- Peripheral nervous system
- Afferent and somatic systems
- Autonomic system

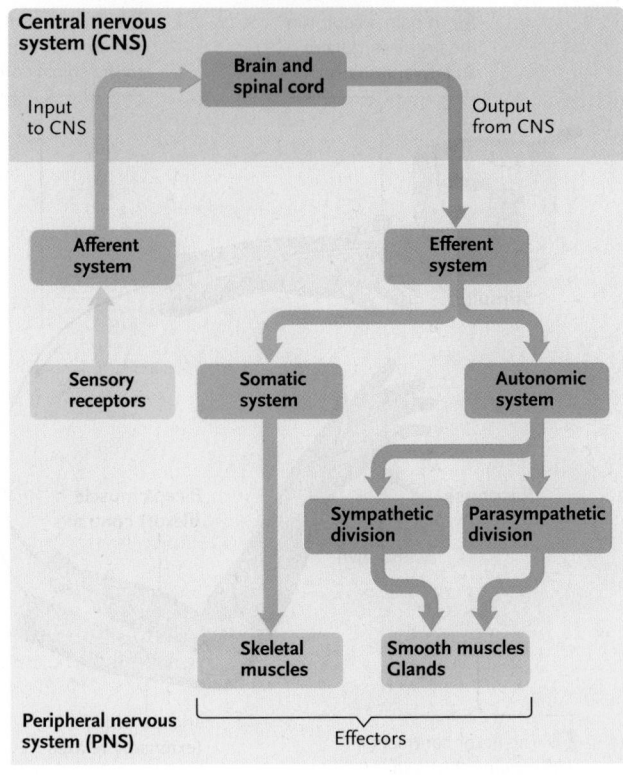

© Cengage Learning 2017

**FIGURE 45.54 The CNS and PNS and their subsystems**

The **sympathetic division** predominates in situations involving stress, danger, excitement, or strenuous physical activity. Signals from the sympathetic division increase the force and rate of the heartbeat, raise the blood pressure by constricting selected blood vessels, dilate air passages in the lungs, induce sweating, and open the pupils wide. Activities that are less important in an emergency, such as digestion, are suppressed by the sympathetic system. The ganglia between the first and second neurons in each sympathetic pathway occur as a chain of segmental ganglia just outside (ventral to) the vertebral column in the thoracic and abdominal regions (see Figure 45.55).

The **parasympathetic division**, in contrast, predominates during quiet, low-stress situations, such as relaxation. Under its influence, the effects of the sympathetic division, such as rapid heartbeat and elevated blood pressure, are reduced, and maintenance activities such as digestion predominate. The parasympathetic pathways originate either directly from the brain or from the sacral region of the spinal cord. The ganglia between the first and second neurons in the parasympathetic pathways are associated with the target organs (see Figure 45.55).

## 45.4b The Somatic System Controls the Contraction of Skeletal Muscles

The **somatic nervous system** controls body movements that are primarily conscious and voluntary. Its efferent neurons, called *motor neurons*, carry signals from the CNS to the skeletal muscles. The dendrites and cell bodies of motor neurons are located in the spinal cord. Their axons extend from the spinal cord, emanating from between the vertebrae, to the skeletal muscles they control. The cell bodies for the sensory nerves (the afferent neurons) are located outside the spinal cord, within the dorsal root, forming the dorsal root ganglion.

Although the somatic system is primarily under conscious, voluntary control, some contractions of skeletal muscles are unconscious and involuntary. These include reflexes, shivering, and the constant muscle contractions that maintain body posture and balance.

The next chapter describes the other excitable tissue, muscle, which is the target for the efferent neurons of the somatic nervous system.

In *Why It Matters*, we said, "By the time you finish this chapter, you should be able to trace the information flow required to produce the response of the male firefly in the example through the four components of neural signalling." See whether you can do so now, using the summary illustration.

### STUDY BREAK QUESTIONS

1. What two systems make up the PNS, and what do they generally control?
2. When an elk attempts to evade an attacking pack of wolves, what division of its autonomic nervous system dominates? What effects might result?

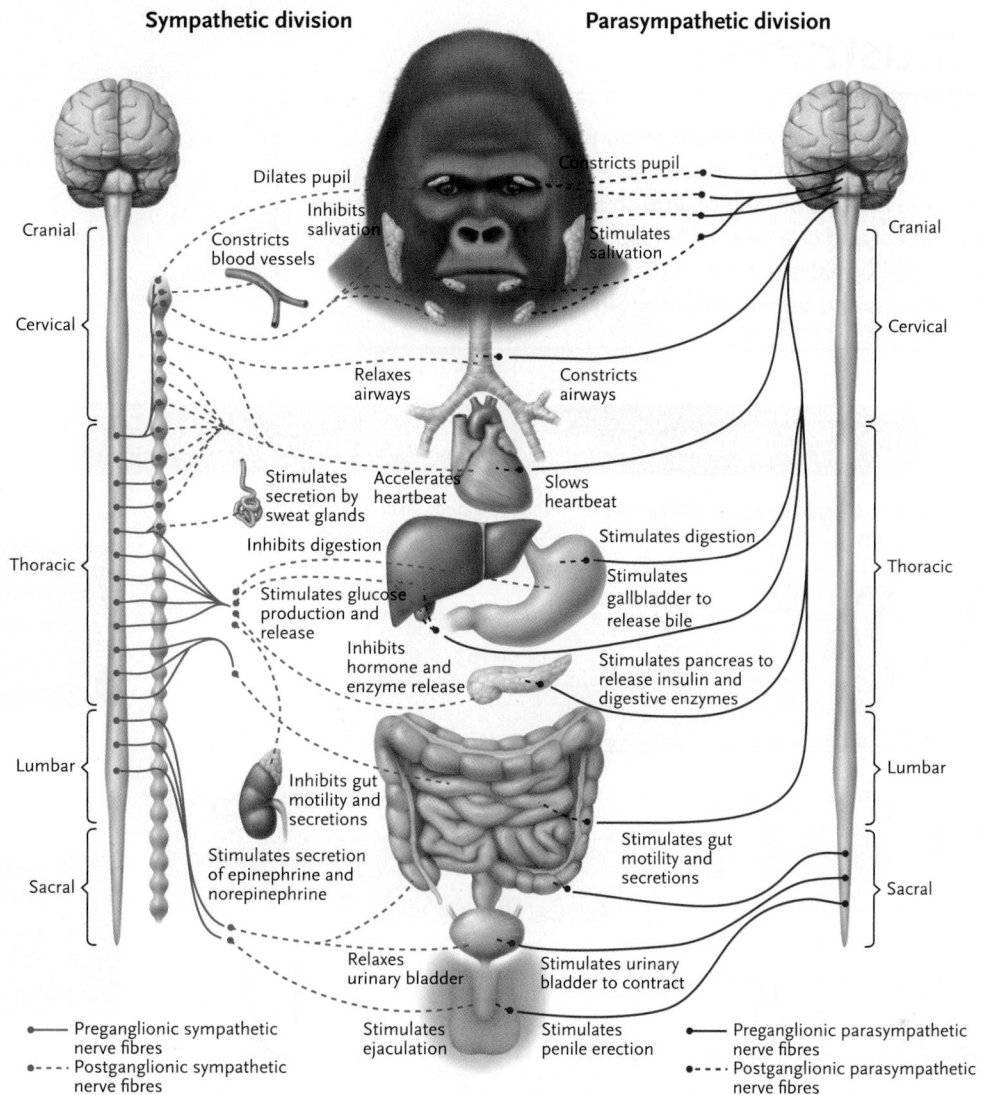

Sympathetic division       Parasympathetic division

Dilates pupil — Constricts pupil

Inhibits salivation — Stimulates salivation

Constricts blood vessels

Cranial / Cervical / Thoracic / Lumbar / Sacral

Relaxes airways — Constricts airways

Stimulates secretion by sweat glands

Accelerates heartbeat — Slows heartbeat

Inhibits digestion — Stimulates digestion

Stimulates glucose production and release — Stimulates gallbladder to release bile

Inhibits hormone and enzyme release — Stimulates pancreas to release insulin and digestive enzymes

Inhibits gut motility and secretions

Stimulates secretion of epinephrine and norepinephrine — Stimulates gut motility and secretions

Relaxes urinary bladder — Stimulates urinary bladder to contract

Stimulates ejaculation — Stimulates penile erection

•— Preganglionic sympathetic nerve fibres
•---- Postganglionic sympathetic nerve fibres

•— Preganglionic parasympathetic nerve fibres
•---- Postganglionic parasympathetic nerve fibres

**FIGURE 45.55 Effects of sympathetic and parasympathetic divisions on organ and gland function.** Only one side of each division is shown; both are duplicated on the left and right sides of the body.

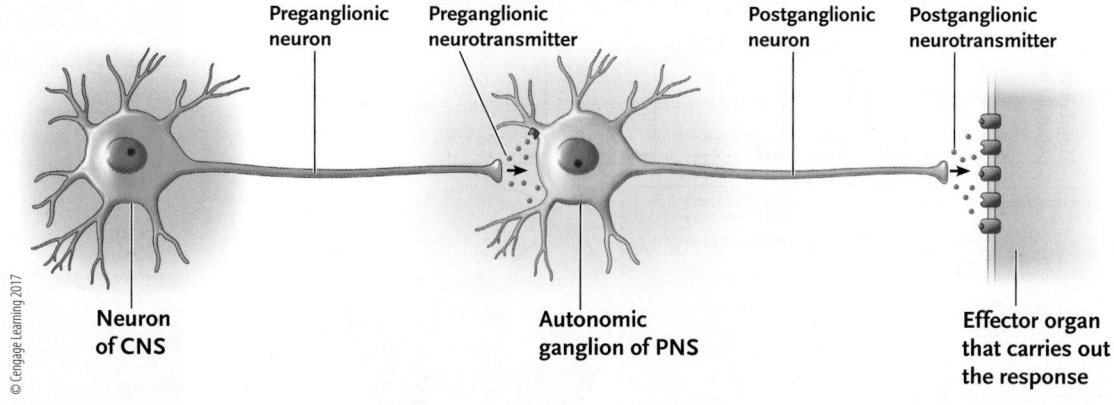

Preganglionic neuron    Preganglionic neurotransmitter    Postganglionic neuron    Postganglionic neurotransmitter

**Neuron of CNS**      **Autonomic ganglion of PNS**      **Effector organ that carries out the response**

© Cengage Learning 2017

**FIGURE 45.56 An autonomic nervous system pathway**

# Summary Illustration

The cells that make up the nervous system are responsible for receiving, analyzing, and transmitting information. Messages are carried in the form of action potentials, and the rate of conduction and strength of each message are affected by various physical and chemical factors. Communication between cells in an animal by neural signalling involves the flow of information at two levels: within single neurons and between neurons in networks.

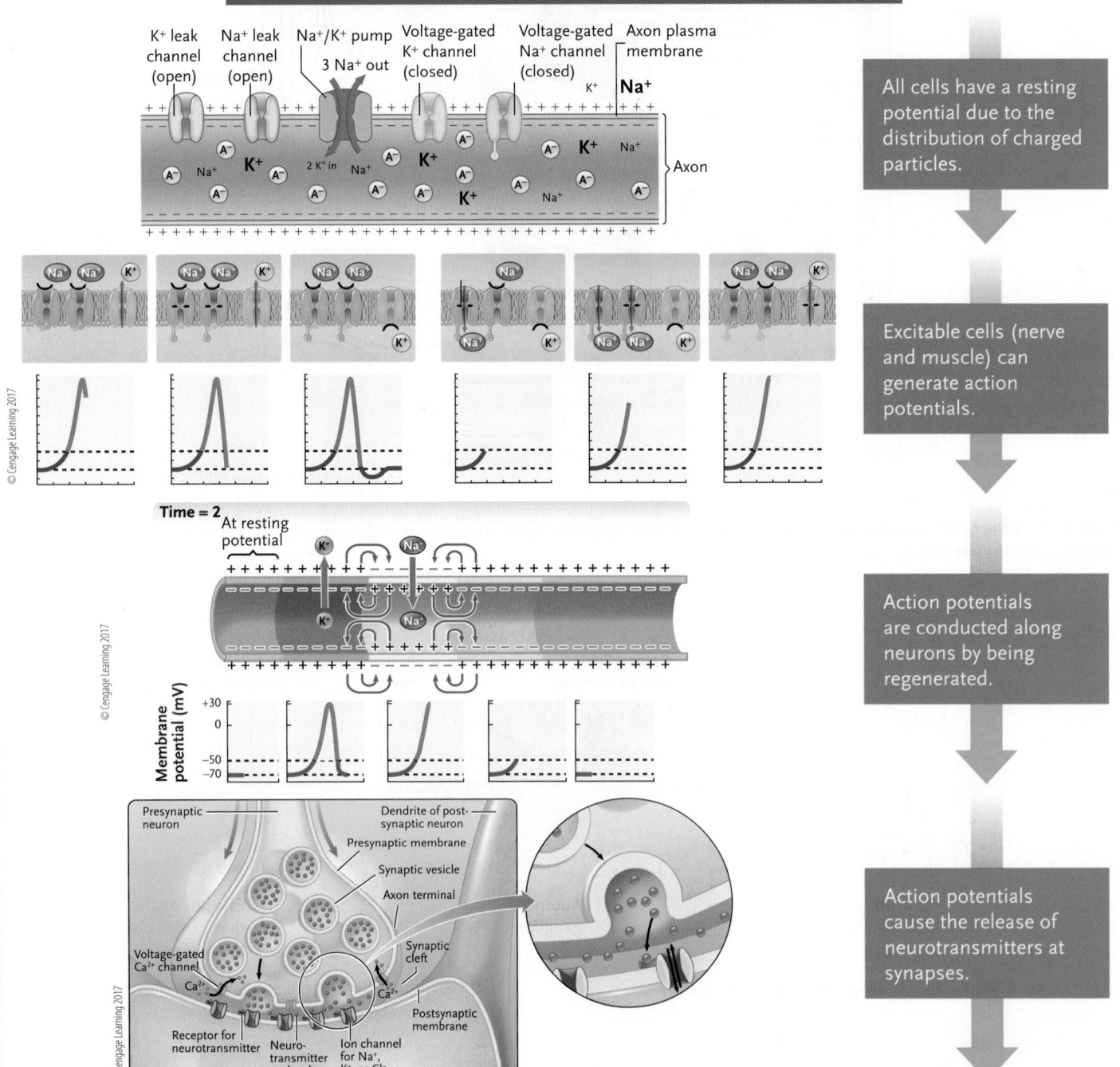

## Flow of Information Within a Single Neuronal Cell or Neuron

All cells have a resting potential due to the distribution of charged particles.

Excitable cells (nerve and muscle) can generate action potentials.

Action potentials are conducted along neurons by being regenerated.

Action potentials cause the release of neurotransmitters at synapses.

# Flow of Information Between Neurons within Networks or Circuits

In most animals, the four components of neural signalling are *reception*, *integration*, *transmission*, and *response*.

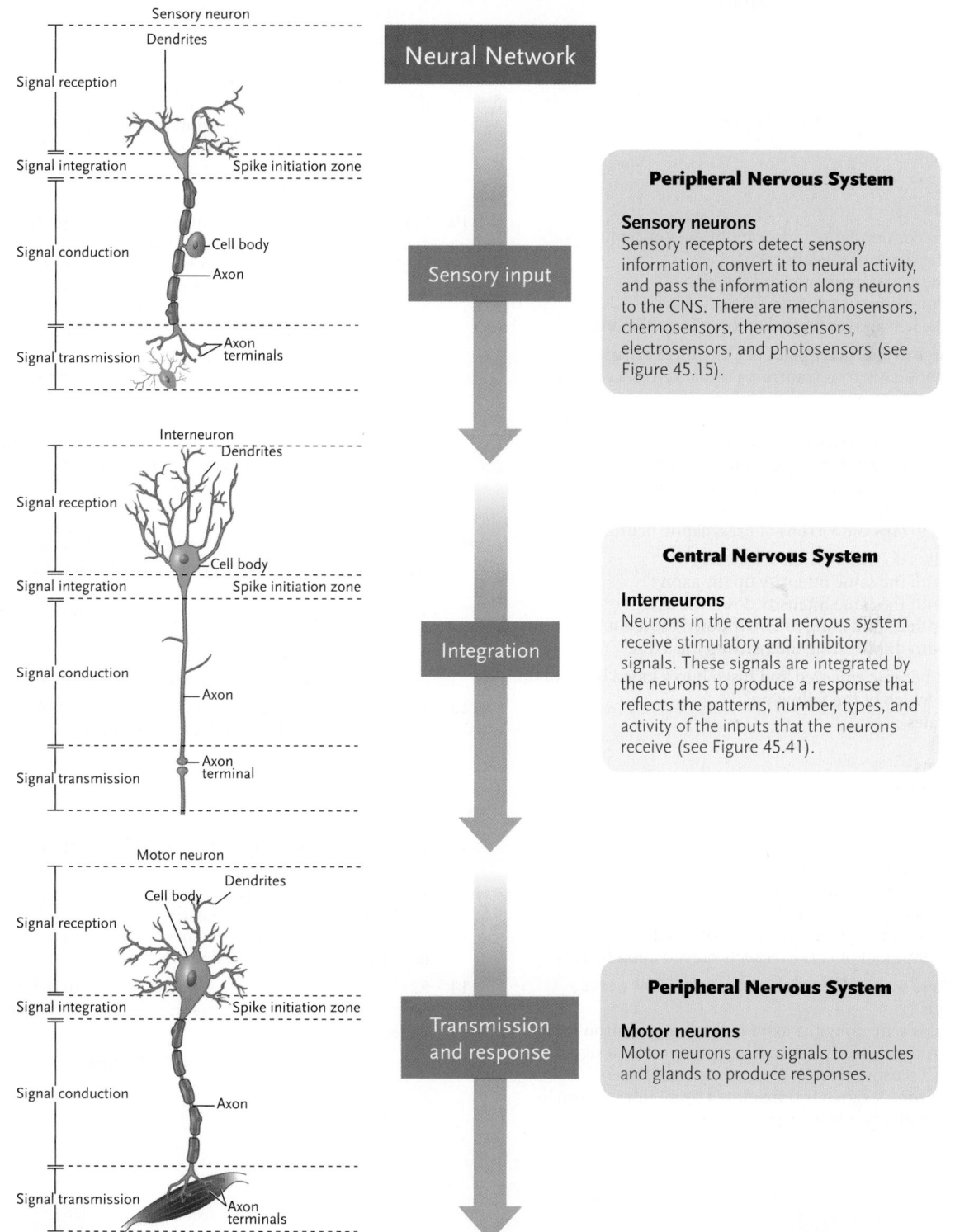

**Neural Network**

**Sensory input**

**Integration**

**Transmission and response**

Sensory neuron — Dendrites
- Signal reception
- Signal integration — Spike initiation zone
- Signal conduction — Cell body — Axon
- Signal transmission — Axon terminals

Interneuron — Dendrites
- Signal reception
- Signal integration — Spike initiation zone
- Signal conduction — Axon
- Signal transmission — Axon terminal

Motor neuron — Dendrites — Cell body
- Signal reception
- Signal integration — Spike initiation zone
- Signal conduction — Axon
- Signal transmission — Axon terminals

### Peripheral Nervous System

**Sensory neurons**
Sensory receptors detect sensory information, convert it to neural activity, and pass the information along neurons to the CNS. There are mechanosensors, chemosensors, thermosensors, electrosensors, and photosensors (see Figure 45.15).

### Central Nervous System

**Interneurons**
Neurons in the central nervous system receive stimulatory and inhibitory signals. These signals are integrated by the neurons to produce a response that reflects the patterns, number, types, and activity of the inputs that the neurons receive (see Figure 45.41).

### Peripheral Nervous System

**Motor neurons**
Motor neurons carry signals to muscles and glands to produce responses.

# SELF-TEST QUESTIONS

## Recall/Understand

1. Which of these substances is vital to the development of vision?
   a. vitamin E
   b. rhodopsin
   c. vitamin A
   d. fatty acid

2. Which of these organs is proprioceptive?
   a. eyes
   b. halteres
   c. statocysts
   d. ears

3. Which of these sensations are nociceptors sensitive to?
   a. pain
   b. touch
   c. light
   d. vibration

4. When does accommodation occur in the eyes of cephalopods?
   a. when the shape of the lens is changed
   b. when the retina moves toward the lens
   c. when the retina moves away from the lens
   d. when the lens moves toward or away from the retina

5. Which of these events takes place at a chemical synapse?
   a. Postsynaptic neurons transmit a signal across a cleft to a presynaptic neuron.
   b. The axons of a presynaptic neuron directly contact the dendrites of a postsynaptic neuron.
   c. The neurotransmitters released by an axon travel across a gap and are picked up by receptors on a muscle cell.
   d. An electrical impulse arrives at the end of a dendrite, causing ions to flow onto axons of presynaptic neurons.

6. Nerve impulses do which of the following?
   a. travel with the same intensity up the axon
   b. travel with the same intensity down the axon
   c. travel with diminishing intensity down the axon
   d. travel with diminishing intensity up the axon

7. Ganglia first became enlarged and fused into a lobed brain in the evolution of which of the following?
   a. vertebrates
   b. annelids
   c. flatworms
   d. cephalopods

## Apply/Analyze

8. Which of these changes can be involved in sensory adaptation?
   a. a reduction in the effect of stimuli
   b. the loss of eyes in cave-dwelling fish
   c. the development of an acute sense of smell
   d. the development of ears in insects preyed upon by bats

9. Which of these series of events best describes how nerve signals travel?
   a. A signal is sent along the axon of the motor neuron to the target. A dendrite of a sensory neuron receives a signal. The axon of a sensory neuron transmits a signal to an interneuron. A signal is transmitted by an interneuron to dendrites of a motor neuron.

   b. A dendrite of a sensory neuron receives a signal. The axon of a sensory neuron transmits a signal to an interneuron. A signal is sent along the axon of the motor neuron to the target. A signal is transmitted by an interneuron to dendrites of a motor neuron.
   c. A dendrite of a sensory neuron receives a signal. A signal is sent along the axon of the motor neuron to the target. The axon of a sensory neuron transmits a signal to an interneuron. A signal is transmitted by an interneuron to dendrites of a motor neuron.
   d. A dendrite of a sensory neuron receives a signal. The axon of a sensory neuron transmits a signal to an interneuron. A signal is transmitted by an interneuron to dendrites of a motor neuron. A signal is sent along the axon of the motor neuron to the target.

10. Suppose that you are analyzing events of bringing the postsynaptic neuron to threshold during spatial summation. Which of the following would you find evidence of?
    a. The postsynaptic neuron receives excitatory signals from two different presynaptic neurons.
    b. The postsynaptic neuron receives inhibitory signals from two different presynaptic neurons.
    c. The postsynaptic neuron receives an excitatory signal from one presynaptic neuron and an inhibitory signal from another.
    d. The postsynaptic neuron receives excitatory signals from one presynaptic neuron, but at different times.

## Create/Evaluate

11. Suppose that you are dissecting a neuron. Which of the following would be a consequence of you damaging the neuron's axon hillock?
    a. It would not be able to receive signals at its dendrites.
    b. It would not be able to receive signals at its axon.
    c. It would not be able to maintain its myelin sheath.
    d. It would not be able to generate its action potential.

12. Suppose that you suddenly suffer from vertigo. Which of these structures is most likely to have a problem?
    a. cochlea
    b. semilunar canals
    c. eardrum
    d. malleus

13. Which of the following is the advantage of action potentials being non-graded?
    a. They can be very fast.
    b. They can diminish along the way.
    c. They can be transmitted over long distances.
    d. They can regenerate along the way.

14. Explain why echinoderms are an exception to the increased cephalization trend in invertebrate and vertebrate nervous systems.

15. Compare electrical and chemical synapses.

**Muscles, Skeletons, and Body Movements**

The ability of animals to move is the consequence of muscles pulling against skeletal elements.

### 46.1 Vertebrate Skeletal Muscle Structure and Function

The way in which the operative proteins in skeletal muscle produce movement is controlled by a three-step filtration mechanism with each contraction. The speed and force to which muscle contraction can be matched and is scaled to work done by metabolism.

### 46.2 Skeletal Systems

Skeletons of which there are several provide firm attachment for the body and protection for the soft tissues.

### 46.3 Vertebrate Movement: The Interaction between Muscles and Bones

The skeletal system serves as a framework, along with muscles, working to produce the overall activity of organisms.

# Chapter Roadmap

**Muscles, Skeletons, and Body Movements**

The ability of animals to move is the consequence of muscles pulling against skeletal elements.

From Chapter 38

From Chapter 45

### 46.1 Vertebrate Skeletal Muscle Structure and Function

The way in which the specialized proteins in skeletal muscle produce movement is described by the *sliding filament mechanism* of muscle contraction. The speed and strength of muscle contraction can be regulated and is subject to evolutionary selection.

### 46.2 Skeletal Systems

Skeletons (of which there are three kinds) provide physical support for the body and protection for the soft tissues.

### 46.3 Vertebrate Movement: The Interactions between Muscles and Bones

The skeletal system also acts as a framework against which muscles work to move parts of the body or the entire organism.

Photos.com

Photos.com

**Movement of vertebrates such as this bald eagle occurs as a result of contractions and relaxations of skeletal muscles.** When stimulated by the nervous system, actin filaments in the muscles slide over myosin filaments to cause muscle contractions.

# Muscles, Skeletons, and Body Movements

# 46

**Why it matters . . .** On an early summer morning throughout the lakes of much of Canada, one can hear the haunting calls of loons (**Figure 46.1**). These charismatic birds are excellent divers, specialized for catching fish. They may dive as deep as 60 m while foraging. They are also excellent fliers, capable of long-distance migrations. During diving, they "fly" underwater using their feet for propulsion. To aid in this, their legs are positioned near the rear of their bodies. While ideal for diving, this is not ideal for walking. As a result, these birds are clumsy on land. All these activities—vocalization, diving, and flying—require the coordinated activity of skeletal muscles. In the case of vocalization, the muscles act on the lungs to force air over the vocal cords at the entrance to the respiratory system, and for locomotion they act on the bones of the limbs to produce movement of feet and wings. Not visible but also involved in all these activities are the actions of the heart and blood vessels, which deliver oxygen to the skeletal muscles to support their work. These too depend on muscles: cardiac muscle in the case of the heart, and smooth muscle in the case of the blood vessels. These muscles act to produce the forces needed to propel the nutrient-containing blood throughout the body.

Muscle tissue is another excitable tissue. Like the cells of the nervous system, cells of the muscular system, called **muscle fibres**, can generate and propagate action potentials. These cells, however, also contain a special group of proteins, contractile proteins, which are capable of shortening when excited. Thus, action potentials generated by muscle fibres lead to muscle contraction. The speed and strength of contraction vary as a result of the manner in which individual cells are constructed and excited. The action produced by the contraction, from the churning of the stomach to the flapping of wings, are a function of the structures to which the muscles are attached. In this chapter, we describe the structure and function of skeletal muscles, the skeletal systems found

FIGURE 46.1  **A successful catch by a loon (*Gavia* sp.)**

in invertebrates and vertebrates, and the methods by which skeletal muscles bring about movement. What do you think are the fastest muscles found in animals, and what functions do they perform? We will return to this at the end of the chapter.

# 46.1  Vertebrate Skeletal Muscle: Structure and Function

Most skeletal muscles in vertebrates are attached at both ends, across a joint, to bones of the skeleton. Some, such as those that move the lips, are attached to other muscles or connective tissues under the skin. Skeletal muscles are attached to bones by cords of connective tissue called *tendons* (see Chapter 38 and **Figure 46.2a**). Tendons vary in length from a few millimetres to over a metre long (such as those in the forelimbs of a giraffe). Depending on its points of attachment, contraction of a single skeletal muscle may extend or bend body parts, or may rotate one body part with respect to another. Most vertebrates (humans included) have more than 600 skeletal muscles, ranging in size from the small muscles that move the eyelids to the large muscles that move the legs. Skeletal muscles are controlled by the somatic nervous system (see Chapter 45).

## 46.1a  The Striated Appearance of Skeletal Muscle Fibres Results from a Highly Organized Internal Structure

A skeletal muscle consists of bundles of elongated, cylindrical cells called **muscle fibres**, which are 10–100 μm in diameter and run the

entire length of the muscle (Figure 46.2b). These fibres are formed by the fusion of cells, called *myoblasts*, generated during embryonic development in response to the appropriate signalling mechanisms. Reflecting this multicellular developmental origin, a single muscle fibre contains multiple nuclei. Some very small muscles, such as some of the muscles of the face, contain only a few hundred muscle fibres; others, such as the larger, leg muscles, contain hundreds of thousands. In both cases, the muscle fibres are held in parallel bundles by sheaths of connective tissue that surround them in the muscle (Figure 46.2c) and merge with the tendons that connect muscles to bones or other structures. Muscle fibres are richly supplied with nutrients and oxygen by an extensive network of blood vessels that penetrate the muscle tissue.

Muscle fibres are packed with **myofibrils**, cylindrical bundles of contractile proteins about 1 mm in diameter that run lengthwise inside the cells (Figure 46.2d). Each myofibril **(Figure 46.3a)** consists of a regular arrangement of **thick filaments** (13–18 nm in diameter) and **thin filaments** (5–8 nm in diameter; see Figure 46.3b and c). The thick and thin filaments alternate with one another in a stacked set.

The arrangement of thick and thin filaments forms a pattern of alternating dark bands and light bands, giving skeletal muscle a striated (banded) appearance under the microscope (see Figure 46.2c). As a result, skeletal muscle is often called

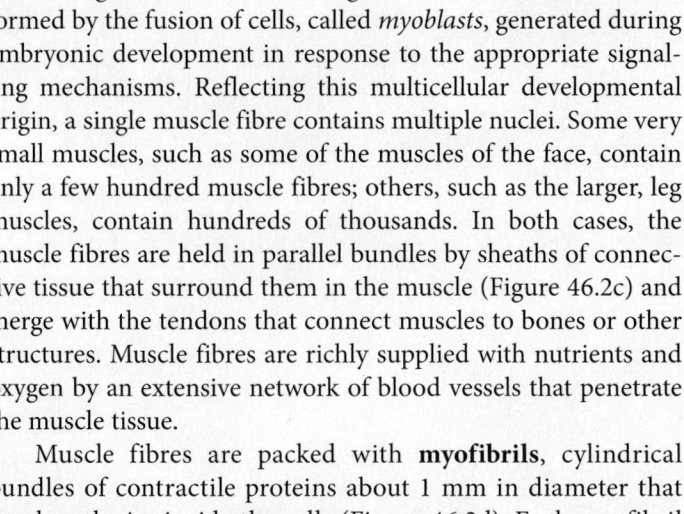
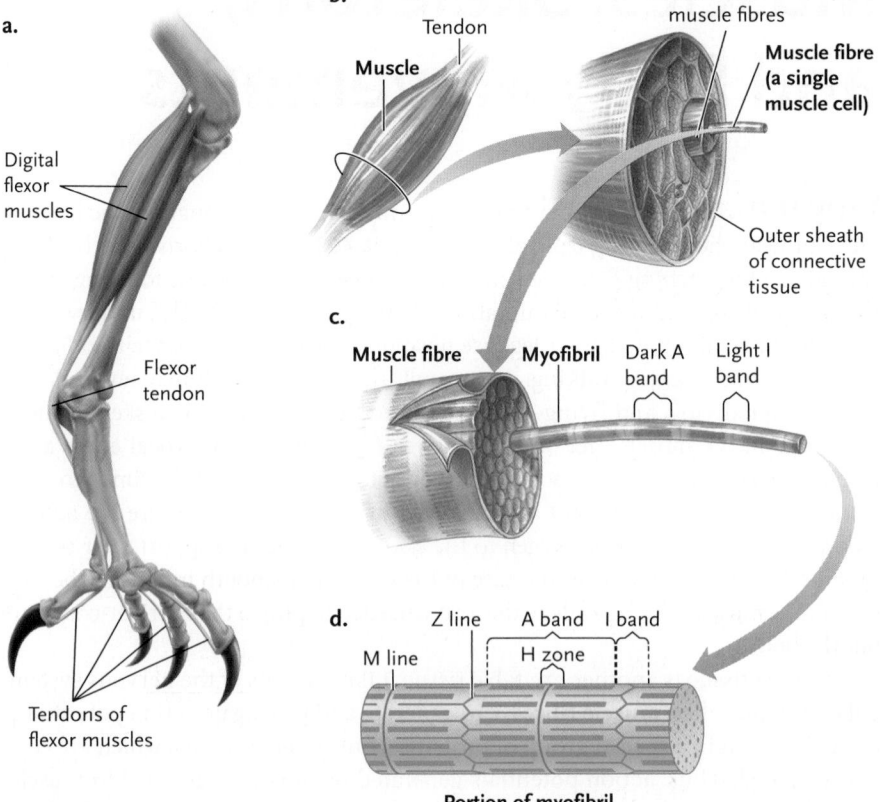

FIGURE 46.2  **Skeletal muscle structure.** Skeletal muscles are attached only at their ends to bones by tendons. Muscles are composed of bundles of cells called *muscle fibres;* within each muscle fibre are longitudinal bundles of contractile proteins called *myofibrils.*

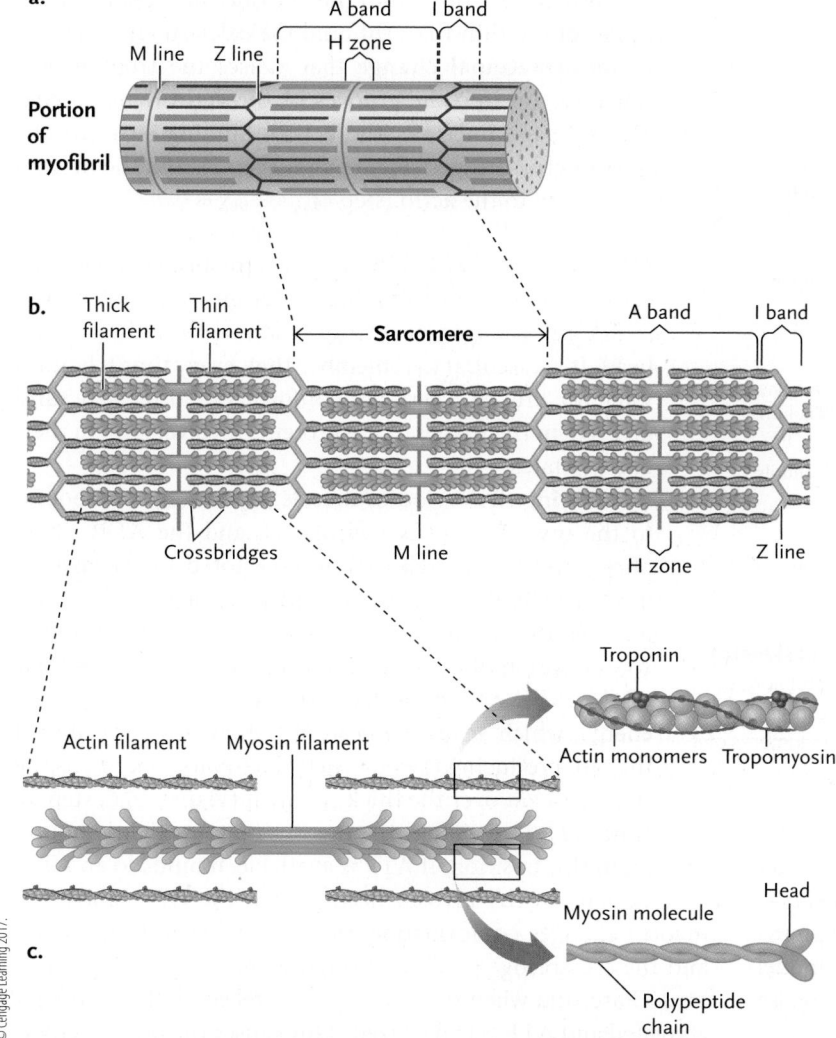

**a.**

Portion of myofibril

M line  Z line  H zone  A band  I band

**b.**

Thick filament  Thin filament  Sarcomere  A band  I band

Crossbridges  M line  H zone  Z line

Actin filament  Myosin filament

Troponin

Actin monomers  Tropomyosin

Myosin molecule  Head

Polypeptide chain

**c.**

© Cengage Learning 2017.

**FIGURE 46.3** **The unit of contraction within a myofibril, the sarcomere, consists of overlapping myosin thick filaments and actin thin filaments.** Each myosin molecule in the thick filaments consists of two subunits organized into a head and a tail wound in a double helix. The actin subunits in the thin filaments form twisted, double helices, with tropomyosin molecules arranged head to tail in the groove of the helix, and troponin bound to the tropomyosin at intervals along the thin filaments.

forming a tail (Figure 46.3). The head is bent toward the adjacent thin filament to form a crossbridge. In vertebrates, each thick filament contains some 200–300 myosin molecules and forms as many crossbridges. The thin filaments consist mostly of two linear chains of actin molecules twisted into a double helix, which creates a groove running the length of the molecule. Bound to the actin are tropomyosin and troponin proteins. Tropomyosin molecules are elongated fibrous proteins that are organized end to end next to the groove of the actin double helix. Troponin is a three-subunit globular protein that binds to tropomyosin at intervals along the thin filaments. While these proteins are not involved directly in muscle shortening, they play key roles in regulating muscle shortening (as described below).

At each junction of an A band and an I band, the plasma membrane folds in to form a **T (transverse) tubule (Figure 46.4)**, which extends deep within the muscle fibre and contains extracellular fluid vital for conducting electrical signals. The tubules come into close proximity to the intracellular endoplasmic reticulum, which in muscle cells takes a specialized form that wraps around the myofibrils and is referred to as the *sarcoplasmic reticulum*. The association between the T tubules and the sarcoplasmic reticulum is critical for coordinating the contraction of all the individual myofibrils in a muscle fibre.

An axon of an efferent neuron leads to each muscle fibre. The axon terminal makes a single, broad synapse with a muscle fibre called a **neuromuscular junction** (see Figure 46.4). The neuromuscular junction, T tubules, and sarcoplasmic reticulum are key components in the pathway for stimulating skeletal muscle contraction by neural signals, which starts with action potentials travelling down the efferent neuron, as described next.

### 46.1b During Muscle Contraction, Thin Filaments on Sarcomeres Slide Over Thick Filaments

The precise control of body motions depends on signalling pathways that carry information from nerves to muscle fibres. An action potential arriving at the neuromuscular junction leads to an increase in the concentration of $Ca^{2+}$ in the cytosol of the muscle fibre. The increase in $Ca^{2+}$ triggers a process in which the thin filaments on each side of a sarcomere slide over the thick filaments, toward the centre of the A band, which brings the Z lines closer together, shortening the sarcomeres and contracting the muscle **(Figure 46.5)**. This sliding filament mechanism of muscle contraction depends on dynamic interactions between actin and myosin proteins in the two filament

*striated muscle.* The dark bands, called *A bands,* consist of stacked thick filaments along with the parts of thin filaments that overlap both ends (see Figure 46.3). The lighter-appearing middle region of an A band, which contains only thick filaments, is the H zone. In the centre of the H zone is a disk of proteins called the *M line,* which holds the stack of thick filaments together. The light bands, called *I bands,* consist of the parts of the thin filaments not in the A band. In the centre of each I band is a thin Z line, a disk to which the thin filaments are anchored. The region between two adjacent Z lines is a **sarcomere** (*sarco* = flesh; *meros* = segment). Sarcomeres are the basic units of contraction in a myofibril and are repeated along the entire length of each myofibril.

The thick filaments are parallel bundles of myosin molecules; each myosin molecule consists of two protein subunits that together form a head connected to a long double helix

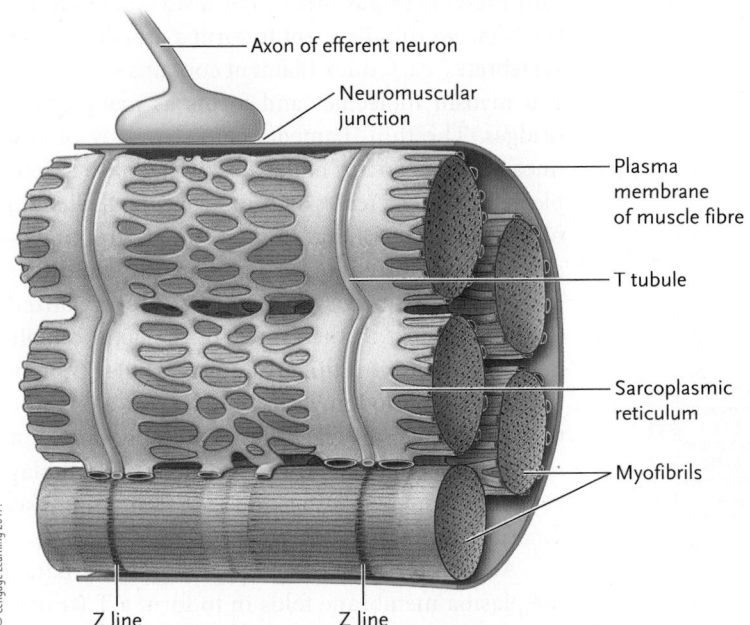

Axon of efferent neuron

Neuromuscular junction

Plasma membrane of muscle fibre

T tubule

Sarcoplasmic reticulum

Myofibrils

Z line          Z line

© Cengage Learning 2017.

**FIGURE 46.4 Components in the pathway for the stimulation of skeletal muscle contraction by neural signals.** T (transverse) tubules are infoldings of the plasma membrane into the muscle fibre, originating at each Z line in a sarcomere. The sarcoplasmic reticulum encircles the sarcomeres, and segments of it end in close proximity to the T tubules.

types. That is, the myosin crossbridges make and break contact with actin and pull the thin filaments over the thick filaments—the action is similar to the walking, rowing, or ratcheting process described for kinesin in Chapter 2 (Figure 2.22). A model for muscle contraction is shown in Figure 46.5. The precise details of this process are described below.

### CONDUCTION OF AN ACTION POTENTIAL INTO A MUSCLE FIBRE

Like neurons, skeletal muscle fibres are excitable, meaning that the electrical potential of their plasma membrane can change in response to a stimulus. When an action potential arrives at the neuromuscular junction, the axon terminal releases a neurotransmitter, acetylcholine, which triggers an action potential in the muscle fibre (**Figure 46.6a**, step 1). The action potential travels in all directions over the muscle fibre's surface membrane and penetrates into the interior of the fibre along the walls of the T tubules, which are extensions of the plasma membrane.

### RELEASE OF CALCIUM INTO THE CYTOSOL OF THE MUSCLE FIBRE

In the absence of a stimulus, $Ca^{2+}$ concentration is kept low in the cytosol by active transport proteins that continuously pump $Ca^{2+}$ out of the cytosol and into the sarcoplasmic reticulum. When an action potential reaches the end of a T tubule, it opens ion channels (ryanodine receptors are proteins that serve as both a receptor and a channel) in the sarcoplasmic reticulum that allow $Ca^{2+}$ to flow out, into the cytosol (Figure 46.6a, step 2).

When $Ca^{2+}$ flows into the cytosol, the troponin molecules of the thin filament bind the calcium and undergo a **conformational change** that causes the tropomyosin fibres to slip into the grooves of the actin double helix. The slippage uncovers the actin's binding sites for the myosin crossbridges (Figure 46.6, step 3), and the myosin heads bind to the actin (step 4).

### THE CROSSBRIDGE CYCLE

The crossbridge cycle that causes sarcomere shortening is driven by chemical and structural changes occurring solely within the myosin head. It is essential to remember that, every time a bond is made or broken, there are conformational or structural changes in the shapes of the proteins involved and in their energy states.

During the period of muscle relaxation, ATP bound to the myosin head is hydrolyzed, and the ADP, phosphate, and energy released are all stored in the myosin head. The binding of myosin to actin creates a crossbridge between the two molecules and results in a change in the conformation of the myosin head that triggers the release of the ADP and phosphate. It also releases the stored energy, which snaps the head of the myosin back toward the tail, producing the power stroke (motor) that pulls the thin filament over the thick filament (Figure 46.6, step 5). If no ATP is available, the myosin remains tightly bound to actin in this position. If ATP is available, it binds to an ATP-binding site on the myosin head. When the ATP binds, the myosin changes conformation and loses its affinity for actin, and the crossbridge is released (Figure 46.6, step 6). Myosin is an ATPase, and when the crossbridge is released, the ATPase is activated and ATP is hydrolyzed. This causes the myosin crossbridge to bend away from the tail (Figure 46.6, step 7) and bind to a newly exposed, myosin crossbridge binding site further along the actin molecule, and the cycle repeats (starting at step 4). Crossbridge cycles based on actin and myosin power movements in all living organisms, from cytoplasmic streaming in plant cells and amoebas to muscle contractions in animals. (Go to www.biologyedl2e.nelson.com to access animations illustrating crossbridge cycling.)

**CONCEPT FIX** For a long time, scientists believed that ATP remained bound to the myosin head in relaxed muscle. It is now believed that, while the binding of ATP to the myosin head causes the bond between myosin and actin to break, the ATP is quickly hydrolyzed to ADP and phosphate. This causes a change in the shape of the myosin, returning the head to its initial position (the position found in a relaxed muscle). The ADP, phosphate, and energy, however, are all stored in the myosin head. At the start of the next contraction, the binding of the myosin head to an actin molecule causes a conformational change in the myosin head, releasing the ADP, phosphate, and energy. The energy is then used to create the working stroke of the crossbridge cycle. ⬡

Although we have focused on the events taking place between a single myosin head and an actin filament in this

FIGURE 46.5  **Experimental Research**

## The Sliding Filament Model of Muscle Contraction

**Question:** What is the mechanism of muscle contraction?

**Experiment:** By 1954, researchers had established the locations and arrangements of actin and myosin in striated muscle. During that year, two independent teams, Andrew Huxley and Rolf Niedergerke of the University of Cambridge, United Kingdom, and Hugh Huxley and Jean Hanson of the Massachusetts Institute of Technology, used high-resolution light microscopy techniques to study how actin and myosin arrangements changed during muscle contraction.

**a. Relaxed muscle**

**b. Contracting muscle**

**c. Fully contracted muscle**

**Figure 1**  Shortening of sarcomeres by the sliding filament mechanism, in which the thin filaments are pulled over the thick filaments toward the M line in the middle of the A band

**Results:** Their micrographs provided important evidence for the sliding of filaments as the muscle went from being relaxed to fully contracted **(Figure 1)**. The key observations were that, (1) the I band and the H zone each decrease in length in proportion to the shortening of the sarcomere, and (2) the A band remains constant in length.

**Conclusion:** The light microscopy evidence supported a model—the sliding filament model—in which muscle shortening (sarcomere shortening) results from increased overlap of thick and thin filaments, and not from any change in length of those filaments. This model was revolutionary in the field of muscle physiology, as all models for muscle contraction at the time proposed folding or coiling of the protein molecules in the filaments.

Source: Based on A. F. Huxley and R. Niedergerke. 1954. Structural changes in muscle during contraction. *Nature* 173:971–973; H. Huxley and J. Hanson. 1954. Changes in the cross-striations of muscle during contraction and stretch and their structural interpretation. *Nature* 173:973–976.

discussion, within a sarcomere, each thick filament is surrounded by six thin filaments, and each thin filament is surrounded by three thick filaments **(Figure 46.7)**. While the force produced by a single myosin crossbridge is comparatively small, it is multiplied by the hundreds of crossbridges formed between a single thick filament and the thin filaments that surround it, and by the billions of thin filaments sliding in a contracting sarcomere. The force, multiplied further by the many sarcomeres and myofibrils in a muscle fibre, is transmitted to the plasma membrane of a muscle fibre by the attachment of myofibrils to elements of the cytoskeleton. From the plasma membrane, it is transmitted to bones and other body parts by the connective tissue sheaths surrounding the muscle fibres and by the tendons.

a.

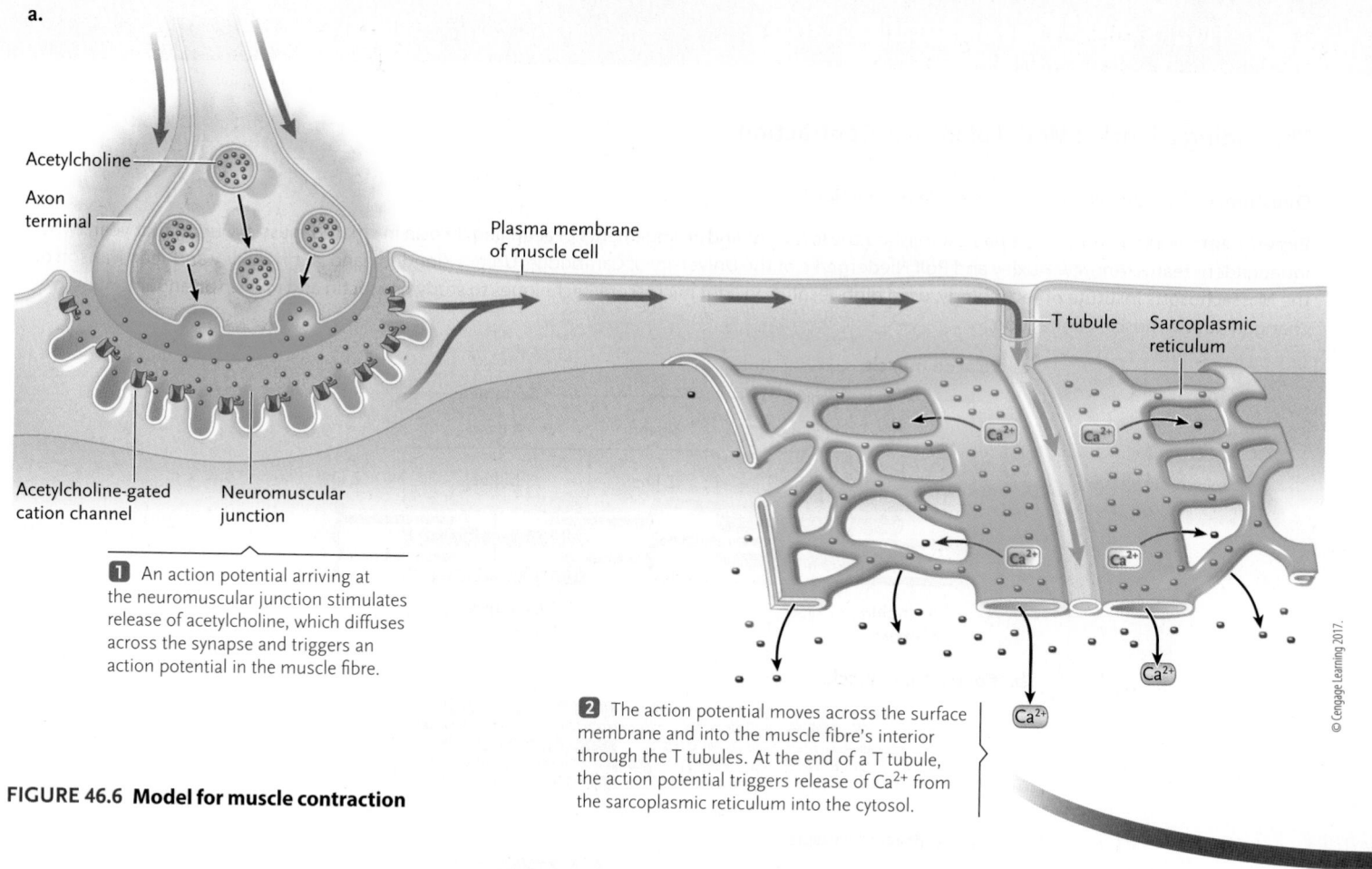

Acetylcholine

Axon terminal

Plasma membrane of muscle cell

T tubule

Sarcoplasmic reticulum

Acetylcholine-gated cation channel

Neuromuscular junction

**1** An action potential arriving at the neuromuscular junction stimulates release of acetylcholine, which diffuses across the synapse and triggers an action potential in the muscle fibre.

$Ca^{2+}$

**2** The action potential moves across the surface membrane and into the muscle fibre's interior through the T tubules. At the end of a T tubule, the action potential triggers release of $Ca^{2+}$ from the sarcoplasmic reticulum into the cytosol.

**FIGURE 46.6  Model for muscle contraction**

© Cengage Learning 2017.

**FROM CONTRACTION TO RELAXATION** As long as action potentials continue to arrive at the neuromuscular junction, $Ca^{2+}$ is released and remains in high concentration in the cytosol. As long as ATP is available, the crossbridge cycle continues to run, shortening the sarcomeres and contracting the muscle fibres. When action potentials stop, excitation of the T tubules ceases, and the $Ca^{2+}$ release channels in the sarcoplasmic reticulum close. The active transport pumps quickly remove the remaining $Ca^{2+}$ from the cytosol. In response, troponin releases its $Ca^{2+}$ and the tropomyosin fibres are pulled back to cover the myosin-binding sites in the thin filaments. The crossbridge cycle stops, and contraction of the muscle fibre ceases.

When an animal dies, its ATP levels decline. As a result, $Ca^{2+}$ is no longer actively sequestered in the sarcoplasmic reticulum but enters the cytosol. This allows the myosin to bind actin but, with no ATP available, these bonds remain firmly attached, and muscles become locked in *rigor mortis*.

**CONCEPT FIX** When muscles contract they shorten, but they do not get smaller. Mass must be conserved and therefore the contracted muscle gets fatter. This is why biceps and other muscles bulge when contracted. It is also why most skeletal muscles are only attached at both ends: they need to be able to shorten as they contract, and lengthen again as they relax. ⬣

## 46.1c  The Response of a Muscle Fibre to Action Potentials Ranges from Twitches to Tetanus

A single action potential arriving at a neuromuscular junction usually causes a single, weak contraction of a muscle fibre, called a **muscle twitch (Figure 46.8a)**. After a muscle twitch begins, the tension of the muscle fibre increases in magnitude for about 30–40 ms, and then peaks as the action potential runs its course through the T tubules and the $Ca^{2+}$ channels begin to close. Tension then decreases as the $Ca^{2+}$ ions are pumped back into the sarcoplasmic reticulum, falling to zero about 50 ms after the peak.

If a muscle fibre is restimulated after it has relaxed completely, a new twitch identical to the first is generated (see Figure 46.8a). However, if a muscle fibre is restimulated before it has relaxed completely, the second twitch is added to the first, producing what is called *twitch summation*, or **temporal summation**, which is basically a summed, stronger contraction (Figure 46.8b. And if action potentials arrive so rapidly (about 25 ms apart) that the fibre cannot relax between stimuli, the $Ca^{2+}$ channels remain open continuously and twitch summation produces a peak level of continuous contraction called

**tetanus** (Figure 46.8c). Contractile activity will then decrease if either the stimuli cease or the muscle fatigues.

Tetanus is an essential part of muscle fibre function. Even body movements that require relatively little effort, such as standing still but in balance, involve tetanic contractions of some muscle fibres.

### 46.1d Skeletal Muscle Control Is Divided among Motor Units

The control of muscle contraction extends beyond the simple ability to turn the crossbridge cycle on and off. We can adjust a handshake from a gentle squeeze to a strong grasp, or balance a feather or a heavy brick in our hand. How are entire muscles controlled in this way? The answer lies in activation of the muscle fibres in blocks called **motor units**.

The muscle fibres in each motor unit are controlled by branches of the axon of a single efferent neuron (**Figure 46.9**). As a result, all those fibres contract each time the neuron fires an action potential. When a motor unit contracts, its force is distributed throughout the entire muscle because the fibres are dispersed throughout the muscle rather than being concentrated in one segment, as shown in the figure.

For a delicate movement, only a few efferent neurons carry action potentials to a muscle, and only a few motor units contract. For more powerful movements, more efferent neurons carry action potentials, and more motor units contract. This is called **spatial summation**, the summing together of the activities of many motor units.

Muscles that can be precisely and delicately controlled, such as those moving the fingers in monkeys and humans, have many motor units in a small area, with only a few muscle

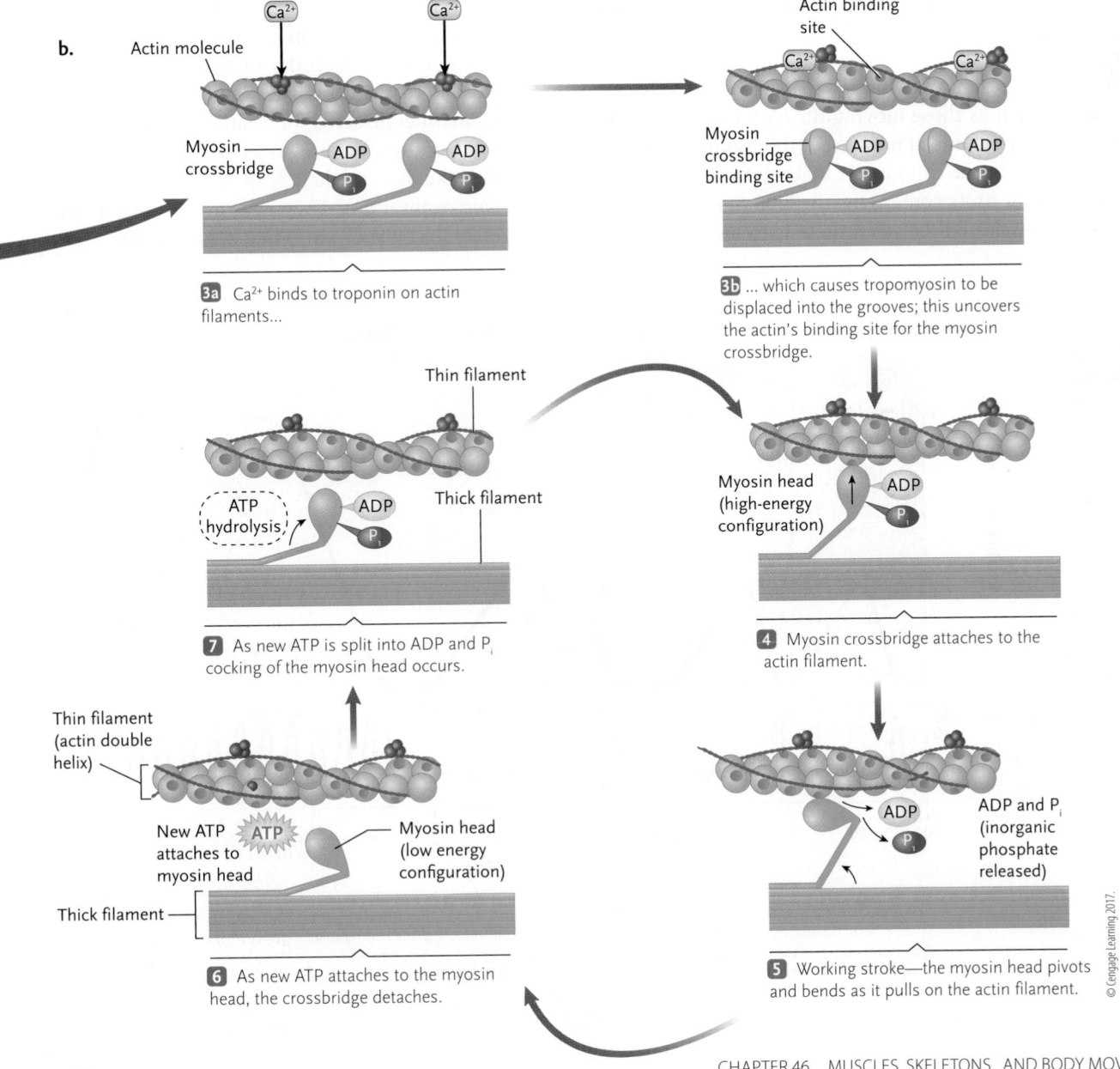

**b.**

Actin molecule
Ca²⁺    Ca²⁺
Myosin crossbridge
ADP    ADP
P_i    P_i

**3a** Ca²⁺ binds to troponin on actin filaments...

Actin binding site
Ca²⁺    Ca²⁺
Myosin crossbridge binding site
ADP    ADP
P_i    P_i

**3b** ... which causes tropomyosin to be displaced into the grooves; this uncovers the actin's binding site for the myosin crossbridge.

Thin filament
ATP hydrolysis
ADP
P_i
Thick filament

**7** As new ATP is split into ADP and P_i, cocking of the myosin head occurs.

Myosin head (high-energy configuration)
ADP
P_i

**4** Myosin crossbridge attaches to the actin filament.

Thin filament (actin double helix)
New ATP attaches to myosin head
ATP
Myosin head (low energy configuration)
Thick filament

**6** As new ATP attaches to the myosin head, the crossbridge detaches.

ADP
P_i
ADP and P_i (inorganic phosphate released)

**5** Working stroke—the myosin head pivots and bends as it pulls on the actin filament.

© Cengage Learning 2017.

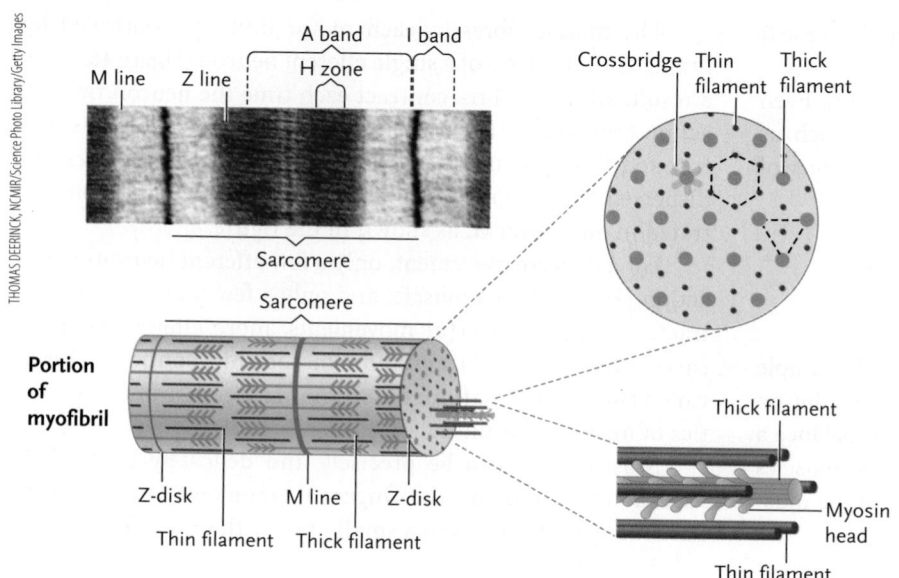

FIGURE 46.7 **Three-dimensional arrangement of thick and thin filaments within a sarcomere**

fibres—about 10 or so—in each unit. Muscles that produce grosser body movements, such as those moving the legs, have fewer motor units in the same volume of muscle but thousands of muscle fibres in each unit. In the calf muscle that raises the heel, for example, most motor units contain nearly 2000 muscle fibres. Other skeletal muscles fall between these extremes,

with an average of about 200 muscle fibres per motor unit.

The maximum force any muscle can produce comes when there is maximal temporal and spatial summation; all motor units are tetanically stimulated.

### 46.1e Muscle Fibres Differ in Their Rate of Contraction and Susceptibility to Fatigue

Muscle fibres differ in their rate of contraction and resistance to fatigue and thus can be classified as slow, fast aerobic, and fast anaerobic muscle fibres. Their properties are summarized in **Table 46.1**. The proportions of the three types of muscle fibres tailor the contractile characteristics of each muscle to suit its function within the body.

**Slow muscle fibres** contract relatively slowly, and the intensity of contraction is low because their myosin crossbridges hydrolyze ATP relatively slowly. They can remain contracted for relatively long periods without fatiguing. Slow muscle fibres typically contain many mitochondria and make most of their ATP by oxidative phosphorylation (aerobic respiration). They have a low capacity to make ATP by anaerobic glycolysis. They also contain high

FIGURE 46.8 **The relationship of the tension produced in a muscle fibre to the frequency of action potentials. (a)** Single twitches. **(b)** Summed twitches. **(c)** Tetanus.

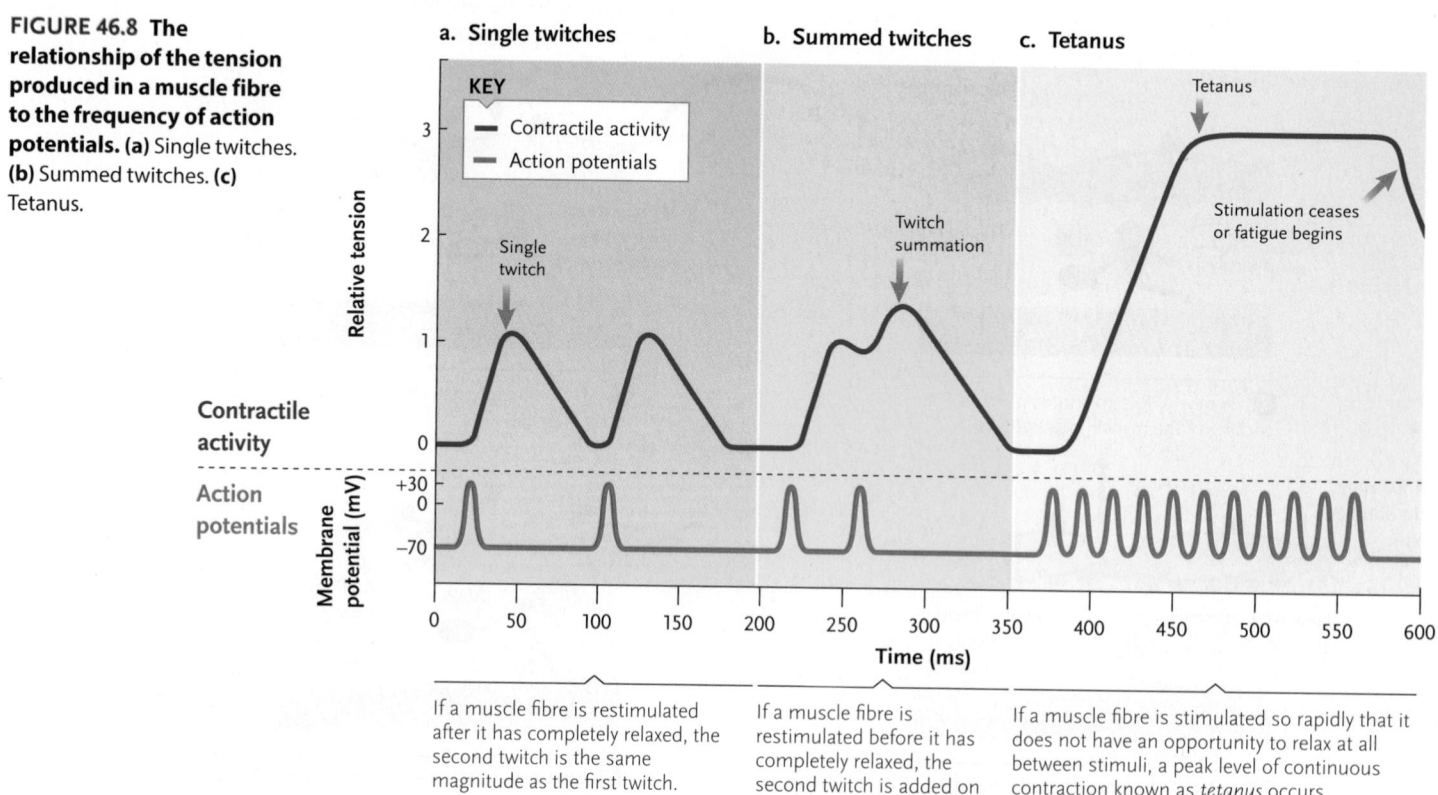

If a muscle fibre is restimulated after it has completely relaxed, the second twitch is the same magnitude as the first twitch.

If a muscle fibre is restimulated before it has completely relaxed, the second twitch is added on to the first twitch, resulting in summation.

If a muscle fibre is stimulated so rapidly that it does not have an opportunity to relax at all between stimuli, a peak level of continuous contraction known as *tetanus* occurs.

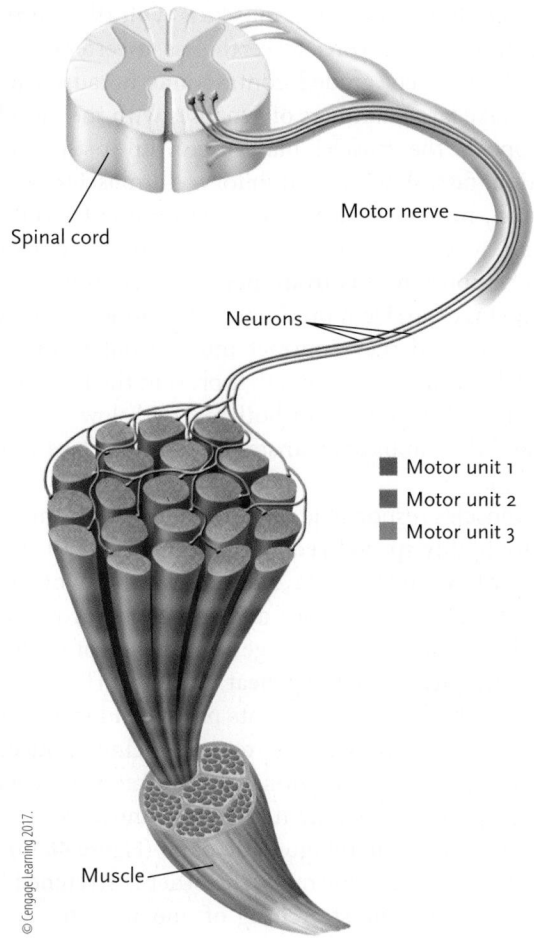

**FIGURE 46.9 Motor units in vertebrate skeletal muscles.** Each motor unit consists of groups of muscle fibres activated by branches of a single efferent (motor) neuron.

Spinal cord

Motor nerve

Neurons

Muscle

■ Motor unit 1
■ Motor unit 2
■ Motor unit 3

© Cengage Learning 2017.

| TABLE 46.1 | Characteristics of Slow and Fast Muscle Fibres in Skeletal Muscle | | |
|---|---|---|---|

| Property | Fibre Type | | |
| | Slow | Fast Aerobic | Fast Anaerobic |
|---|---|---|---|
| Contraction speed | Slow | Fast | Fast |
| Contraction intensity | Low | Intermediate | High |
| Fatigue resistance | High | Intermediate | Low |
| Myosin–ATPase activity | Low | High | High |
| Oxidative phosphorylation capacity | High | High | Low |
| Enzymes for anaerobic glycolysis | Low | Intermediate | High |
| Mitochondria | Many | Many | Few |
| Myoglobin content | High | High | Low |
| Fibre colour | Red | Red | White |
| Glycogen content | Low | Intermediate | High |

concentrations of the oxygen-storing protein **myoglobin**, which greatly enhances their oxygen supplies. Myoglobin is closely related to hemoglobin, the oxygen-carrying protein of red blood cells (see Chapter 41). Myoglobin gives slow muscle fibres, such as those in the legs of ground birds such as quail, chickens, and ostriches, a deep red colour. In sharks and bony fishes, strips of slow muscles concentrated in a band on either side of the body are used for slow, continuous swimming and maintaining body position. Our postural muscles are made up predominantly of slow muscle fibres that can be continuously active for prolonged periods but that do not need to generate much power.

**Fast muscle fibres** contract relatively quickly and powerfully because their myosin crossbridges hydrolyze ATP faster than those of slow muscle fibres. Fast aerobic fibres have abundant mitochondria, a rich blood supply, and a high concentration of myoglobin, which makes them red in colour. They have a high capacity for making ATP by oxidative phosphorylation, and an intermediate capacity for making ATP by anaerobic glycolysis. They fatigue more quickly than slow fibres, but not as quickly as fast anaerobic fibres. Fast aerobic

muscle fibres are abundant in the flight muscles of migrating birds such as ducks and geese. Most of the muscles in the human body used in locomotion also contain an abundance of fast aerobic fibres.

Fast anaerobic fibres typically contain high concentrations of glycogen, relatively few mitochondria, and a more limited blood supply than fast aerobic fibres. They generate ATP mostly by anaerobic respiration (glycolysis) and have a low capacity to produce ATP by oxidative respiration. Fast anaerobic fibres produce especially rapid and powerful contractions but are most susceptible to fatigue. Because their myoglobin supply is limited and they contain few mitochondria, they are pale in colour. Some ground birds have flight muscles consisting almost entirely of fast anaerobic muscle fibres. These muscles can produce a short burst of intensive contractions, allowing the bird to escape a predator, but they cannot produce sustained flight. Most muscles of lampreys, sharks, fishes, amphibians, and reptiles also contain fast anaerobic muscle fibres, allowing the animals to move quickly to capture prey and to avoid danger.

The muscles of most animals are mixed and contain different proportions of slow and fast muscle fibres, depending on their functions. Muscles specialized for prolonged slow contractions, such as the postural muscles of the back, have a high proportion of slow fibres and are a deep red colour. The muscles of the forearm that move the fingers have a higher proportion of fast fibres and are a paler red than the back muscles. These muscles can contract rapidly and powerfully, but they fatigue much more rapidly than the back muscles. The soleus muscle in our calves contain roughly 80% slow twitch fibres; the gastrocnemius and vastus lateralis muscles of the calf contain only roughly 60% slow twitch fibres. It is worth noting that all muscle fibres in a single motor unit are of the same fibre type.

**CONCEPT FIX** It is commonly believed that lactic acid is produced only by muscles under anaerobic conditions and is the source of muscle fatigue. There are several myths associated with this.

To begin with, muscles do not produce lactic acid; they produce lactate. As a result, lactate production does not cause the acidosis associated with strenuous exercise. The hydrogen ions that cause the acidosis are produced from the breakdown of ATP to ADP + phosphate. Under aerobic conditions, when there is no acidosis, the protons produced by the breakdown of ATP are consumed by the mitochondria during ATP production. Under anaerobic conditions, however, the mitochondria are incapable of consuming all the hydrogen ions produced from ATP breakdown, so hydrogen ions accumulate and acidosis ensues.

Next, some muscle cells produce lactate even under resting conditions, when there is ample oxygen available. The lactate can remain in the cell for energy or leave the cell and travel to the heart and to active and inactive muscles to be used as a fuel (many cells prefer lactate as a fuel source over glucose). It will also travel to the liver, where it is converted back into glucose.

Finally, it has been shown recently that the accumulation of hydrogen ions (acidosis) may actually counteract the effects of muscle fatigue. Strenuous muscle contraction also precipitates a variety of other disturbances to cell homeostasis, including perturbations to energy charge and ion balances (particularly $K^+$) that lead to loss of tetanic force. Whether $K^+$ imbalance always, sometimes, or hardly ever leads to fatigue during exercise is uncertain. In muscles studied in isolation, however, hydrogen ion accumulation offered a degree of protection against fatigue produced by extracellular $K^+$ accumulation.

Thus, increased lactate production coincides with cellular acidosis but is not the cause of the metabolic acidosis. If muscle did not produce lactate and acidosis, muscle fatigue would occur more quickly, and exercise performance would be severely impaired. ⬢

## 46.1f Invertebrates Move Using a Variety of Striated Muscles

Invertebrates also have muscle cells in which actin-based thin filaments and myosin-based thick filaments produce movements by the same sliding mechanism as in vertebrates. In most invertebrates (annelids, molluscs, echinoderms, nematodes, and arthropods), the actin and myosin fibrils are arranged in sarcomeres, forming striated muscle. In general, this is the dominant muscle type for these invertebrates and it functions not only in locomotion but also in movements of the viscera, such as the gut and heart. In some invertebrates, such as Cnidaria and flatworms, muscle cells lacking striations may occur. In the muscles that close the shells of clams and other bivalves (see Chapter 27), smooth muscle cells are present among the striated muscle cells.

In invertebrates, an entire muscle is typically controlled by one or a few motor neurons. Nevertheless, invertebrate muscles are capable of finely graded contractions because individual neurons make large numbers of synapses with the muscle cells. In arthropods, the muscles may receive up to three types of innervation: fast, slow, and inhibitory. All muscles receive fast innervation, in which release of a neuromuscular transmitter produces a twitch. Some also receive slow innervation, in which a graded response results from increased action potentials. As action potentials arrive more frequently, more $Ca^{2+}$ is released into the cells, and they contract more strongly. In addition, there may be inhibitory nerves that prevent the release of $Ca^{2+}$. The excitatory transmitter for both fast and slow nerves is glutamate, and the inhibitory transmitter is GABA (see Table 45.1, Chapter 45).

The muscles responsible for the movement of the wings in insects are highly specialized, striated muscles called *fibrillar muscles*. They possess a large number of gigantic mitochondria—in some cases about the size of a vertebrate red blood cell—so that the energetic demands of flight can be met. The frequency of wing beat of many flies, bees, and wasps is very high, up to 600 beats per second in mosquitoes. How is this achieved without tetanus being induced? The answer is that each contraction does not require new activation by another action potential. Flight muscles are stretch activated and occur in antagonistic pairs (**Figure 46.10**). When one muscle of the pair contracts, the other is stretched back to its relaxed length. The stretching of one activates the other, and vice versa. Nerve impulses arrive only about three times per second, keeping the muscles activated. The frequency with which they contract is determined by the elastic properties of the whole system.

### STUDY BREAK QUESTIONS

1. Compare thick and thin muscle filaments. How does their structure determine their function?
2. What is the role of the sarcoplasmic reticulum in muscle contraction?
3. What are the three types of muscle fibres, and how do they differ?
4. Greyhounds have muscles specialized for extreme speed over short distances. Sled dogs have muscles specialized for endurance over long distances. What kinds of muscle characteristics would each have?

## 46.2 Skeletal Systems

Animal skeletal systems provide physical support for the body and protection for the soft tissues. They also act as a framework against which muscles work to move parts of the body or the entire organism. Three main types of skeletons are found in both invertebrates and vertebrates: hydrostatic skeletons, exoskeletons, and endoskeletons.

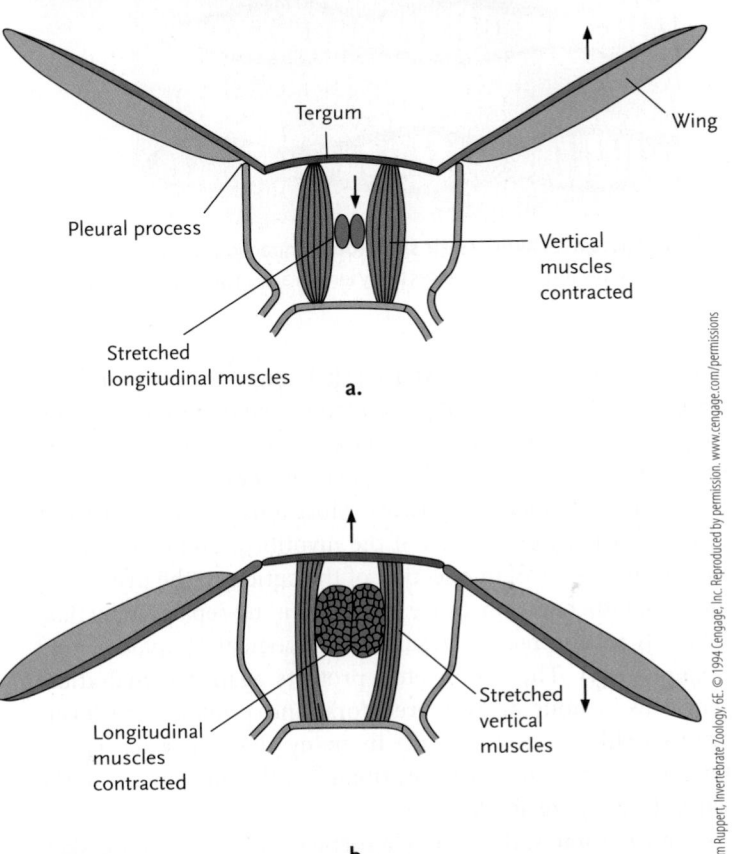

a.

b.

**FIGURE 46.10 The muscles in a flying insect.** When the vertical flight muscles contract, they pull on the cuticle forming the top of the segment, elevating the wings. The segment is constructed so that this action also elongates the cuticle of the thorax from front to rear (at right angles to the plane of the page), extending the longitudinal muscles. This stimulates the activated longitudinal muscles to contract, pushing up the tergum, elevating the wings, and elongating the vertical muscles. Because the cuticle is elastic, the whole system vibrates, producing very rapid wing beats.

*Labels in figure 46.10a:* Tergum; Wing; Pleural process; Vertical muscles contracted; Stretched longitudinal muscles

*Labels in figure 46.10b:* Longitudinal muscles contracted; Stretched vertical muscles

*From Ruppert, Invertebrate Zoology, 6E. © 1994 Cengage, Inc. Reproduced by permission. www.cengage.com/permissions*

*Dave Massey / Shutterstock.com*

## 46.2a A Hydrostatic Skeleton Consists of Muscles and Fluid

A **hydrostatic skeleton** (*hydro* = water; *statikos* = causing to stand) is a structure consisting of muscles and fluid that, by themselves, provide support for the animal or part of the animal; no rigid support such as bone is involved. A hydrostatic skeleton consists of a body compartment or compartments filled with water or body fluids. These are incompressible liquids.

When the muscular walls of the compartment contract, they pressurize the contained fluid. If muscles in one part of the compartment are contracted while muscles in another part are relaxed, the pressurized fluid will move to the relaxed part of the compartment, distending it. In short, the contractions and relaxations of the muscles surrounding the compartments change the shape of the animal.

Hydrostatic skeletons are the primary support systems of cnidarians, flatworms, roundworms, and annelids. In all these animals, compartments containing fluids under pressure make the body semi-rigid and provide a mechanical support on which muscles act. For example, sea anemones have a hydrostatic skeleton consisting of a fluid-filled body cavity surrounded by longitudinal and circular muscles within the body wall. Between meals, longitudinal muscles are contracted (shortened), whereas the circular ones are relaxed, and the animal looks short and squat (**Figure 46.11a**). The sea anemone lengthens into its upright feeding position by contracting the circular muscles and relaxing the longitudinal ones (**Figure 46.11b**). In flatworms, roundworms, and annelids, striated muscles in the body wall act on the hydrostatic skeleton to produce creeping, burrowing, or swimming movements. Among these animals, annelids have the most highly developed musculoskeletal systems, with an outer layer of circular muscles surrounding the body, and an inner layer of longitudinal muscles (**Figure 46.12**). Contractions of the circular muscles reduce the diameter of the body and increase the length; contractions of the longitudinal muscles shorten the body and increase its diameter. Because the coelom and musculature are divided into segments, expansion and contraction can be localized to individual segments. Annelids move along a surface or burrow by means of alternating waves of contraction of the two muscle layers that pass along the body,

a. Resting position   b. Feeding position

**FIGURE 46.11 Sea anemones in (a) the resting and (b) the feeding positions.** In (a), longitudinal muscles in the body wall are contracted, and circular muscles are relaxed. In (b), the longitudinal muscles are relaxed, and the circular muscles are contracted. Both sets of muscles work against a hydrostatic skeleton.

*Linda Pitkin*

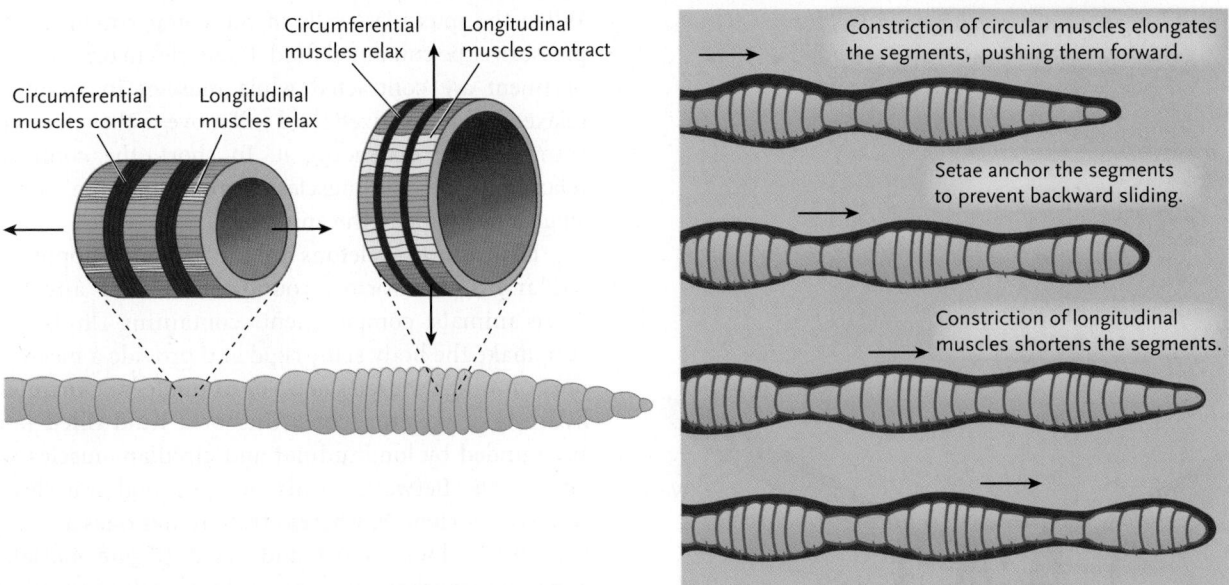

**FIGURE 46.12 Movement of an earthworm, showing how muscles in the body wall act on its hydrostatic skeleton.** Contraction of the circular muscles reduces body diameter and increases body length, whereas contraction of the longitudinal muscles decreases body length and increases body diameter.

working against the fluid-filled body compartments of the hydrostatic skeleton.

Some structures of echinoderms are supported by hydrostatic skeletons. The tube feet of sea stars and sea urchins, for example, have muscular walls enclosing the fluid of the water vascular system (see Chapter 27).

In vertebrates, the erectile tissue of the penis is a fluid-filled hydrostatic skeletal structure, although many mammals other than humans also possess a penis bone, the *os penis*, or baculum (see Figure 46.15d and Figure 44.18).

Hydrostatic movement may not involve a fluid but may simply depend on the incompressibility of muscles themselves. Although the muscles in the structure may contract, the total body of muscles remains at a constant volume. Our tongues and lips are capable of a range of movements, but no skeletal element supports the movement. The elephant's trunk can lift a large log but can also pick up small objects. How is this achieved? The trunk is basically an extension of the nose and upper lip. It has no skeleton but consists of an enormous number of muscle units attached to the skin or to one another. The muscle mass remains at a constant volume, and contractions of local muscle groups result in movement.

## 46.2b An Exoskeleton Is a Rigid External Body Covering

An **exoskeleton** (*exo* = outside) is a rigid, external, body covering, such as a shell that provides support. In an exoskeleton, the force of muscle contraction is applied against that covering. An exoskeleton also protects delicate internal tissues.

Many molluscs, such as clams and oysters, have an exoskeleton consisting of a hard calcium carbonate shell secreted by glands in the mantle. Arthropods, such as insects, spiders,

and crustaceans, have an external skeleton in the form of a chitinous cuticle (**Figure 46.13**), secreted by the underlying epidermis, that covers the outside surfaces of the animal. Like a suit of armour, the arthropod exoskeleton has movable joints, flexed and extended by muscles. Most muscles attach directly to the cuticle by extensions of the myofibrils and extend from the inside surface of one section of the cuticle to the inside surface of another section. Since the sections are separated by flexible cuticle, contraction results in movement about the joint (**Figure 46.14**). The exoskeleton protects against dehydration, serves as armour against predators, and provides the levers against which muscles work. In many flying insects, elastic flexing of the exoskeleton contributes to the movements of the wings (see Figure 46.10).

In vertebrates, the shell of a turtle or tortoise is an exoskeletal structure.

## 46.2c An Endoskeleton Consists of Supportive Internal Body Structures, Such as Bones

An **endoskeleton** (*endon* = within) consists of internal body structures, such as bones, that provide support. In an endoskeleton, the force of contraction is applied against those structures. The endoskeleton is the primary skeletal system of vertebrates. Most vertebrates have an endoskeleton arranged in two structural groups (**Figure 46.15**). The **axial skeleton**, which includes the skull, vertebral column, sternum, and ribcage, forms the central part of the structure (shaded in red in Figure 46.15a), defines the long axis of the vertebrate body, provides sites for muscle attachment, and supports most of the weight. The **appendicular skeleton** (shaded in green) includes the shoulder, hip, leg, and arm bones and provides the levers that are used to

**FIGURE 46.13** Arthropods, such as insects, spiders, and crustaceans, have an external skeleton in the form of a chitinous cuticle

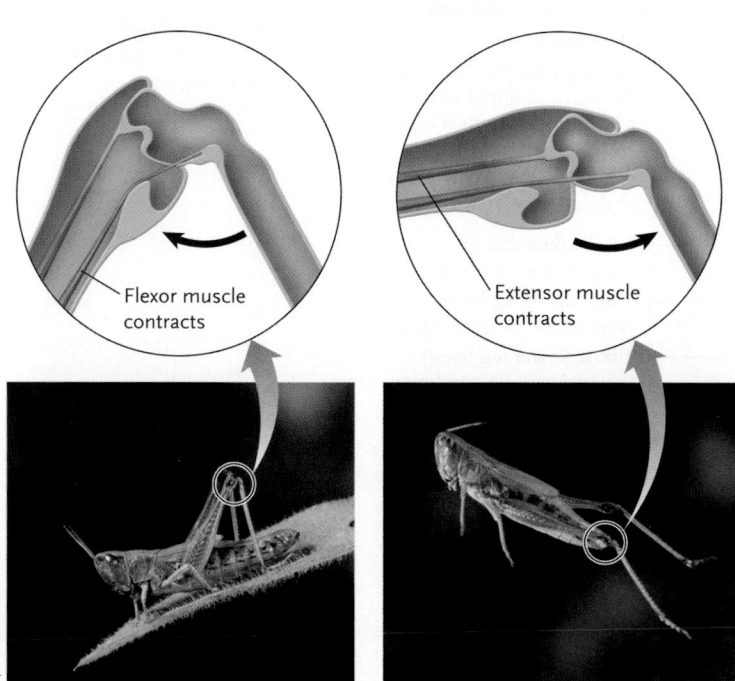

Flexor muscle contracts

Extensor muscle contracts

**FIGURE 46.14** Muscles are attached to the inside surfaces of the exoskeleton in a typical insect leg, such as those of the grasshopper shown here

## 46.2d Bones of the Vertebrate Endoskeleton Are Organs with Several Functions

The vertebrate endoskeleton supports and maintains the overall shape of the body and protects internal organs. Bones are complex organs built up from multiple tissues, including bone tissue, with cells of several kinds; blood vessels; nerves; and, in some, stores of adipose tissue. Bone tissue is distributed between dense, compact bone regions, which have essentially no spaces other than the microscopic canals of the osteons (see Chapter 38), and spongy bone regions, which may open into larger spaces (see Figure 46.15). Compact bone tissue generally forms the outer surfaces of bones, and spongy bone tissue forms the interior. The interior of some flat bones, such as the hip bones and the ribs, are filled with red marrow, a tissue that is the primary source of new red blood cells in mammals and birds. The shaft of long bones such as the femur contains large central canals filled with adipose tissue called *yellow marrow*, which is a source of some white blood cells.

Throughout the life of a vertebrate, calcium and phosphate ions are constantly deposited and withdrawn from bones. Hormonal controls maintain the concentration of $Ca^{2+}$ ions at optimal levels in the blood and extracellular fluids (see Chapter 43), ensuring that calcium is available for proper functioning of the nervous system, muscular system, and other physiological processes.

### STUDY BREAK QUESTIONS

1. Describe the similarities and differences between hydrostatic skeletons, exoskeletons, and endoskeletons. Give examples of each and describe which animal groups each can be found in.
2. Explain how the endoskeleton differs in humans compared with monkeys, lemurs, and raccoons (Figure 46.15), and, as best as you can, explain why these differences occur.
3. Describe how an animal with a hydrostatic skeleton can move.

## 46.3 Vertebrate Movement: The Interactions between Muscles and Bones

The skeletal system acts as a framework against which muscles work to move parts of the body or the entire organism. In this section, the muscle–bone interactions that are responsible for the movement of vertebrates are described.

produce locomotion. Four mammalian skeletons are included in Figure 46.15, illustrating how skeletons are adapted for particular lifestyles. The human skeleton reflects our upright movement, using only our hind feet, while those of the monkey, lemur, and raccoon reflect arboreal (tree-living), gliding, and terrestrial lifestyles. Like exoskeletons, endoskeletons also protect delicate internal tissues such as the brain and respiratory organs.

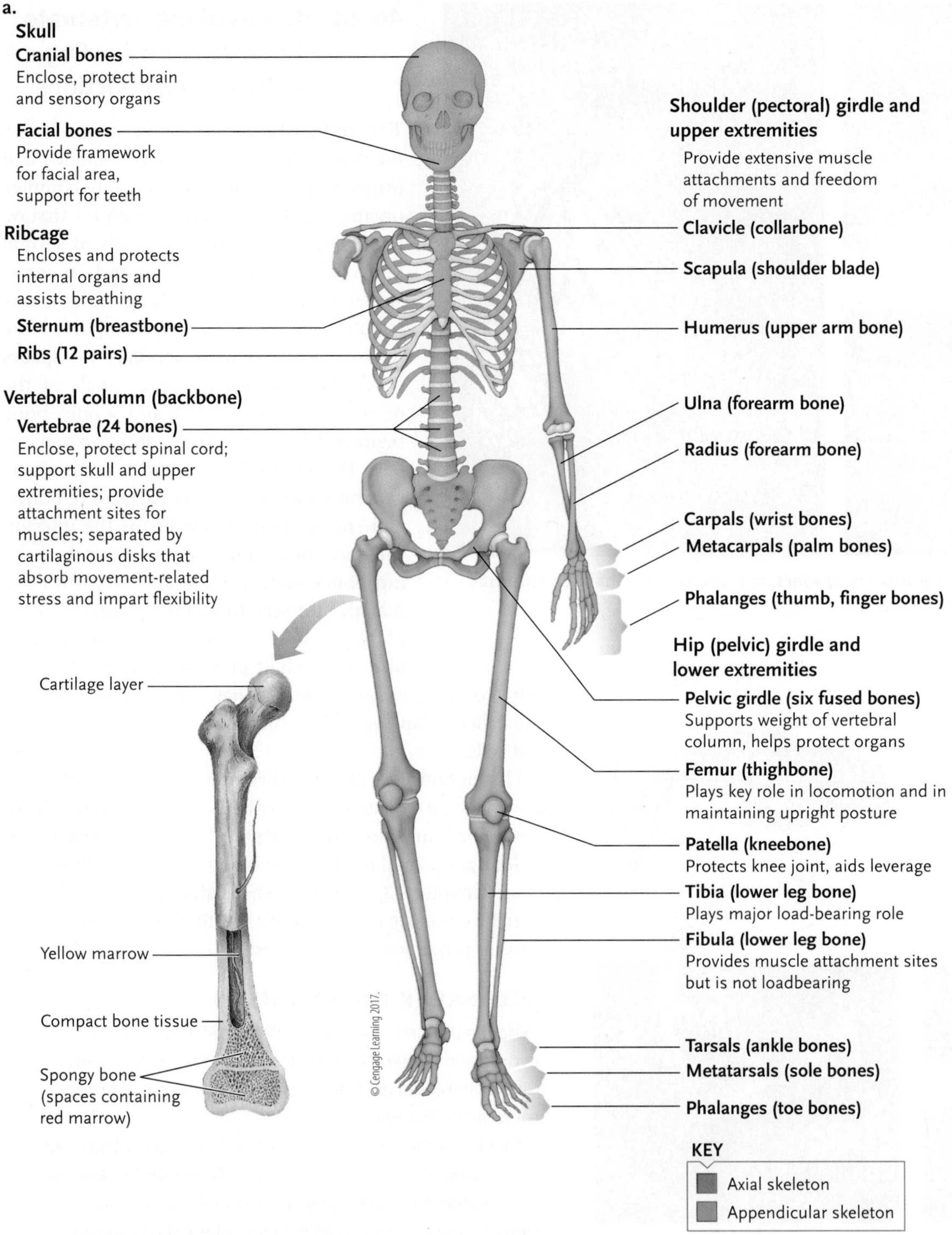

## a.

### Skull

**Cranial bones** — Enclose, protect brain and sensory organs

**Facial bones** — Provide framework for facial area, support for teeth

### Ribcage
Encloses and protects internal organs and assists breathing

**Sternum (breastbone)**

**Ribs (12 pairs)**

### Vertebral column (backbone)

**Vertebrae (24 bones)** — Enclose, protect spinal cord; support skull and upper extremities; provide attachment sites for muscles; separated by cartilaginous disks that absorb movement-related stress and impart flexibility

Cartilage layer

Yellow marrow

Compact bone tissue

Spongy bone (spaces containing red marrow)

© Cengage Learning 2017.

### Shoulder (pectoral) girdle and upper extremities
Provide extensive muscle attachments and freedom of movement

**Clavicle (collarbone)**

**Scapula (shoulder blade)**

**Humerus (upper arm bone)**

**Ulna (forearm bone)**

**Radius (forearm bone)**

**Carpals (wrist bones)**

**Metacarpals (palm bones)**

**Phalanges (thumb, finger bones)**

### Hip (pelvic) girdle and lower extremities

**Pelvic girdle (six fused bones)** — Supports weight of vertebral column, helps protect organs

**Femur (thighbone)** — Plays key role in locomotion and in maintaining upright posture

**Patella (kneebone)** — Protects knee joint, aids leverage

**Tibia (lower leg bone)** — Plays major load-bearing role

**Fibula (lower leg bone)** — Provides muscle attachment sites but is not loadbearing

**Tarsals (ankle bones)**

**Metatarsals (sole bones)**

**Phalanges (toe bones)**

**KEY**

| | |
|---|---|
| ■ | Axial skeleton |
| ■ | Appendicular skeleton |

**FIGURE 46.15 Mammalian skeletons. (a)** Major bones in the human. Inset shows the structure of the femur (thigh bone), with the location of red and yellow marrow. Internal spaces lighten the bone's density. At the joints, a cartilage layer forms a smooth slippery cushion between bones. Compare the general features of this skeleton with those shown in (b), (c), and (d). Note general and specific resemblances among the skeletons of the four mammals. **(b)** The new world monkey (family Cebidae) lives in trees. **(c)** The gliding lemur (family Cynocephalidae) is also arboreal, but a glider. **(d)** The raccoon (family Procyonidae) is terrestrial. Note the differences in skull shape, limb lengths, and feet. The raccoon is a male, reflected in the conspicuous baculum or penis bone (see also Figure 44.18, Chapter 44).

## b.

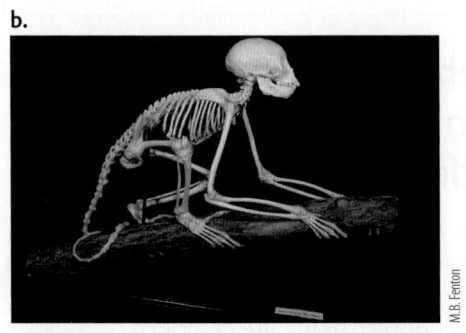

M.B. Fenton

## c.

M.B. Fenton

## d.

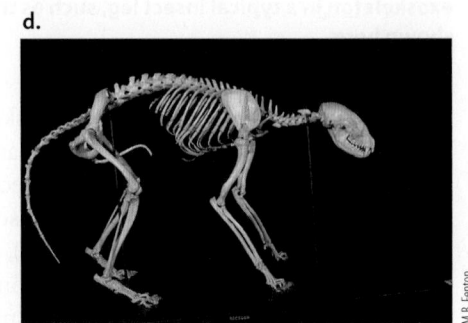

M.B. Fenton

## 46.3a Joints of the Vertebrate Endoskeleton Allow Bones to Move and Rotate

The bones of the vertebrate skeleton are connected by joints, many of them movable. The most movable joints, including those of the shoulders, elbows, wrists, fingers, knees, ankles, and toes, are synovial joints, consisting of the ends of two bones enclosed by a fluid-filled capsule of connective tissue (**Figure 46.16a**). Within the joint, the ends of the bones are covered by a smooth layer of cartilage and lubricated by synovial fluid, which makes the bones slide easily as the joint moves. Synovial joints are held together by straps of connective tissue called *ligaments,* which extend across the joints outside the capsule (Figure 46.16b). The ligaments restrict the motion of the joint and help prevent it from buckling or twisting under heavy loads.

In other, less movable joints, called *cartilaginous joints,* the ends of bones are covered with layers of cartilage but have no fluid-filled capsule surrounding them. Fibrous connective tissue covers and connects the bones of these joints, which occur between the vertebrae and some rib bones.

In still other joints, called *fibrous joints,* stiff fibres of connective tissue join the bones and allow little or no movement. Fibrous joints occur between the bones of the skull and hold the teeth in their sockets.

The bones connected by movable joints work like levers. A lever is a rigid structure that can move around a pivot point known as a *fulcrum* (**Figure 46.17a**). The most common type of lever system in the body—exemplified by the elbow joint—has the fulcrum at one end, the load at the opposite end, and the force applied at a point between the ends. Levers differ with respect to where the muscle is attached along the lever and therefore where the force is applied (Figure 46.17b). If the muscle is inserted (attached) near the fulcrum, the muscle favours speed, as a short contraction will move the lever a large distance in a short period of time (Figure 46.17c, left). If the muscle is inserted more distally to the fulcrum, it favours strength. The same amount of contraction will move the forearm a shorter distance in the same period of time (i.e., it moves more

slowly), but it will lift more weight (Figure 46.17c, right). Levers also differ with respect to where the fulcrum is located along the lever. In this case, if the fulcrum is located more distally, it favours speed, and if it is located more proximally, it favours strength (Figure 46.17d). A good example of the difference in design for speed versus strength is seen by comparing the forelimbs of burrowing and running species. Burrowing mammals have short, very stout forelimbs with muscles arranged so that contraction provides relatively little movement but great force (**Figure 46.18a**). Running species, on the other hand, have long, slender forelimbs with muscles arranged so that contraction provides rapid motion but less force (Figure 46.18b).

Most bones of vertebrate skeletons are moved by muscles arranged in **antagonistic pairs**: extensor muscles extend the joint, meaning increasing the angle between the two bones, and flexor muscles do the opposite. (Antagonistic muscles are also used in invertebrates for movement of body parts; e.g., the limbs of insects and arthropods.) In humans, one such pair is formed by the biceps brachii muscle at the front of the upper arm and the triceps brachii muscle at the back of the upper arm (**Figure 46.19**). When the biceps muscle contracts, the bone of the lower arm is bent (flexed) around the elbow joint, and the triceps muscle is passively stretched (see Figure 46.19a); when the triceps muscle contracts, the lower arm is straightened (extended), and the biceps muscle is passively stretched (see Figure 46.19b).

## 46.3b Vertebrates Have Muscle–Bone Interactions Optimized for Specific Movements

Vertebrates differ widely in the relative size and shapes of individual bones, the patterns by which muscles connect to the bones, the sites of the joints along the bones, and the length and mechanical advantage of the levers produced by these connections. All these differences reflect the lifestyles of the animals as reflected in the need for strength and speed of movement.

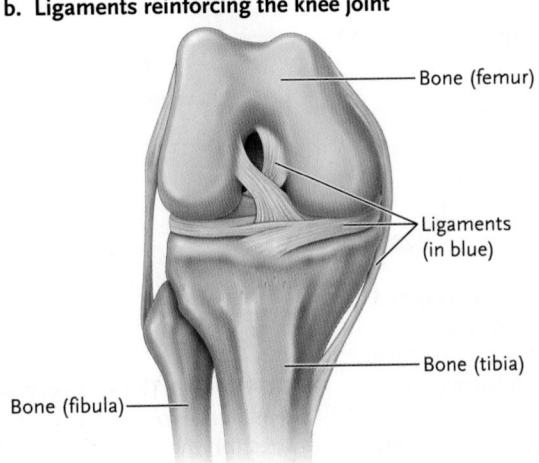

**a. Synovial joint cross-section**

Bone (femur)
Cartilage layer
Synovial fluid
Cartilage layer
Connective tissue capsule
Bone (tibia)

**b. Ligaments reinforcing the knee joint**

Bone (femur)
Ligaments (in blue)
Bone (tibia)
Bone (fibula)

**FIGURE 46.16 A synovial joint. (a)** Cross-section of a typical synovial joint. **(b)** Ligaments reinforcing the knee joint.

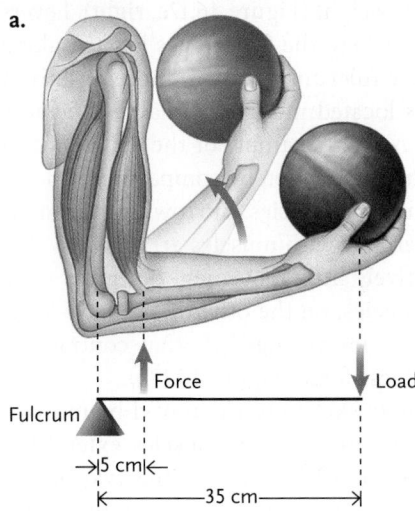

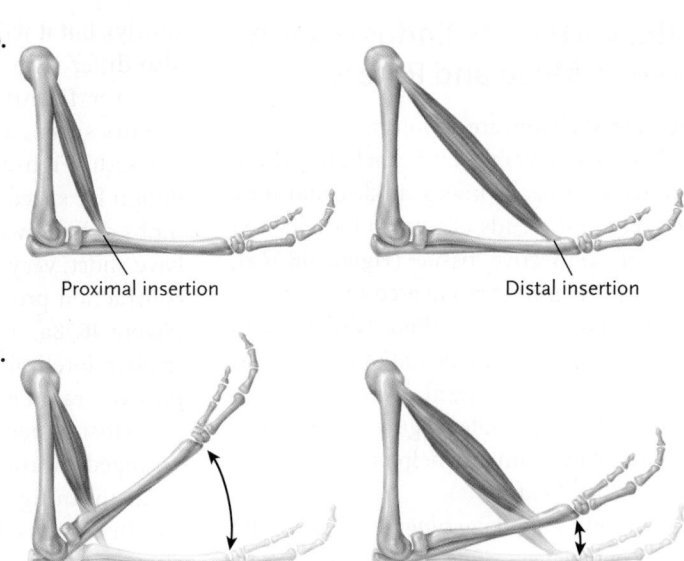

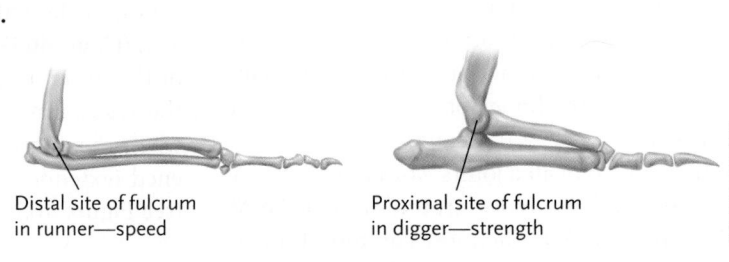

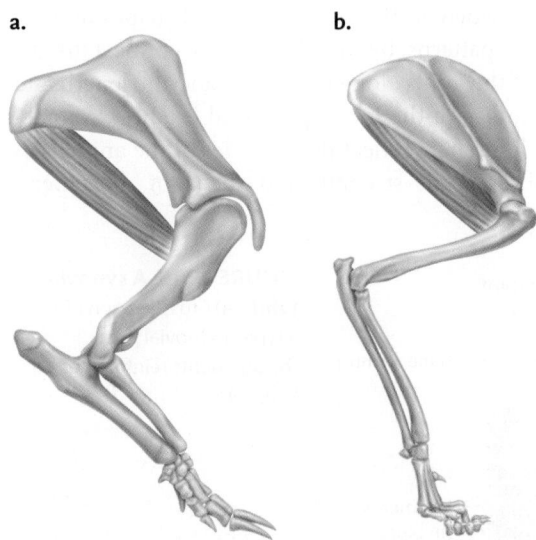

**FIGURE 46.17 A body lever. (a)** The lever formed by the bones of the forearm. The fulcrum (the hinge or joint) is at one end of the lever, the load is placed on the opposite end, and the force is exerted at a point on the lever between the fulcrum and the load. **(b)** Muscles can be attached proximal or distal to the fulcrum. **(c)** Proximal insertion favours speed; distal insertion favours strength. **(d)** The fulcrum can also vary in position, favouring either speed or strength.

Labels in figure (a): Force, Load, Fulcrum, 5 cm, 35 cm

Labels in figure (b): Proximal insertion, Distal insertion

Labels in figure (c): Proximal insertion of muscle—speed, Distal insertion of muscle—strength

Labels in figure (d): Distal site of fulcrum in runner—speed, Proximal site of fulcrum in digger—strength

© Cengage Learning 2017.

**FIGURE 46.18 Design for strength versus speed in forelimbs can be seen by comparing** (a) **an armadillo with** (b) **a cat.** Both forelimbs are drawn to be the same overall length. Note the differences in the size and mass of each of the bones, the points of insertion of the muscles, and the position of the joints along the bones.

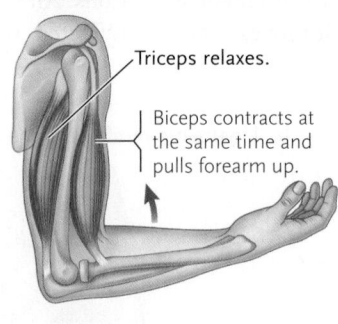

a. **Flexion:** When the biceps muscle (the flexor muscle) contracts and raises the forearm, its antagonistic partner, the triceps muscle (the extensor muscle), relaxes.

Triceps relaxes.

Biceps contracts at the same time and pulls forearm up.

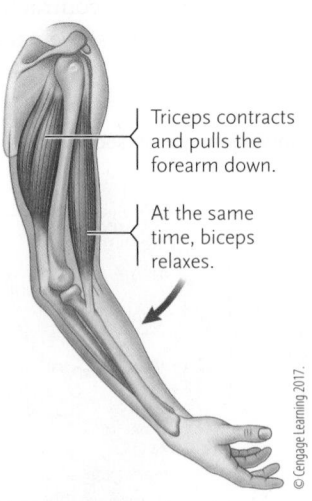

b. **Extension:** When the triceps muscle contracts and extends the forearm, the biceps muscle relaxes.

Triceps contracts and pulls the forearm down.

At the same time, biceps relaxes.

**FIGURE 46.19 The arrangement of skeletal muscles in antagonistic pairs. (a)** When the biceps muscle contracts and raises the forearm, its antagonistic partner, the triceps muscle, relaxes. **(b)** When the triceps muscle contracts and extends the forearm, the biceps muscle relaxes.

© Cengage Learning 2017.

**FIGURE 46.20 Examples of convergent evolution. (a)** A sea turtle. Note that the forelegs are winglike paddles that enhance swimming. **(b)** A penguin swimming using modified forelimbs (wings). **(c)** A sea lion swimming using modified forelimbs for manoeuvring. Note the resemblance in shape of the forelimbs in all three species.

Through evolutionary pressures to produce optimal interactions for specific movements, we see many examples of both conserved traits and convergent evolution.

There are many examples of convergent evolution. Sea turtles, for instance, have paddlelike forelimbs that they use in swimming, very much like those of penguins and sea lions (**Figure 46.20**).

The development of flight, represented by birds and, among the mammals, bats, is accompanied by some common modifications (**Figure 46.21**). In both groups, but particularly in birds, the sternum is greatly enlarged to provide attachment for the powerful pectoral muscles. The bones of the forelimbs are greatly modified to produce wings. While this is another example of convergent evolution, note that the way in which each wing has formed is different. In bats, the bones of the hand are extended to provide a framework for the sheets of skin that form the wing. In birds, the bones of the hand are fused and

support the feathers that make up the wing. The bones generally contain many cavities or spaces, making the body lighter.

Also note that, in both examples of convergent evolution presented here, the structures (wings in bats and birds; forelimb paddles in turtles, penguins, and sea lions) of the forelimb have diverged from that of other members of their classes. The bodies of animals are full of many similar examples, and these are the topic of comparative, functional anatomy.

## STUDY BREAK QUESTIONS

1. Distinguish synovial joints, cartilaginous joints, and fibrous joints.
2. Distinguish between ligaments and tendons.
3. What differences are there in the design of musculoskeletal systems for speed versus strength?
4. What are antagonistic muscle pairs? Give an example describing how they differ in the bone movements they produce.

In *Why It Matters* you were asked, "What do you think are the fastest muscles found in animals, and what functions do they perform?" While all skeletal muscles have the same basic structure, all do not have the same complement of enzymes and organelles. Table 46.1 lists the characteristics of slow and fast muscles. The fastest twitch fibres can be very rapid. The fastest human muscle is our oculomotor muscle, which generates the eye blink. It can contract 30 times each second. This is in the same range as finch and hummingbird flight muscles that can contract at 25–45 times per second. The fastest muscles found in vertebrates, however, are involved with moving air, and these are the bat cricothyroid muscle involved in echolocation and the toadfish sonicator muscle that is involved in sound production. These muscles are capable of contracting at an amazing 200–300 times per second. Vertebrates differ widely in the relative size and shapes of individual bones, the patterns by which muscles connect to the bones, the sites of the joints along the bones, and the length and mechanical advantage of the levers produced by these connections. All these differences reflect the lifestyles of the animals as reflected in their need for strength and speed of movement.

**a. Bird**

**b. Bat**

**c. Pterosaur**

■ Humerus
■ Radius
■ Ulna
■ Carpals
■ Metacarpals
■ Phalanges

**FIGURE 46.21 The bones of the wing of** (a) **a bird,** (b) **a bat, and** (c) **a pterosaur.** Note the convergent evolution presented here in the structures.

CHAPTER 46 MUSCLES, SKELETONS, AND BODY MOVEMENTS | **1271**

# Summary Illustration

Vertebrates differ widely in the relative sizes and shapes of individual bones, the patterns by which muscles connect to the bones, the sites of the joints along the bones, and the length and mechanical advantage of the levers produced by these connections. These differences reflect the lifestyle of each animal, including the need for strength and speed of movement. Animal skeletal systems provide physical support for the body and protection for the soft tissues. They also act as a framework against which muscles work to move parts of the body or the entire organism.

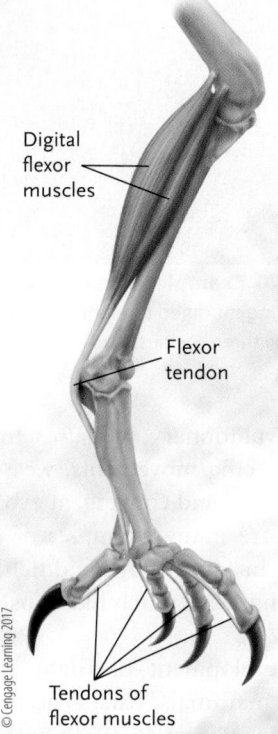

Digital flexor muscles

Flexor tendon

Tendons of flexor muscles

© Cengage Learning 2017

**a. Synovial joint cross section**

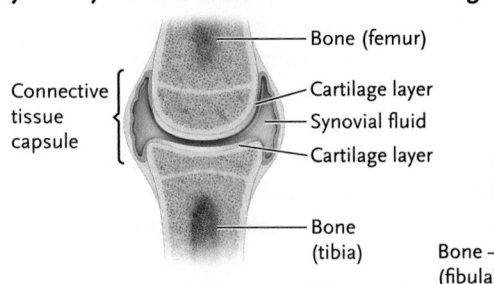

Bone (femur)

Connective tissue capsule

Cartilage layer
Synovial fluid
Cartilage layer

Bone (tibia)

© Cengage Learning 2017

**b. Ligaments reinforcing the knee joint**

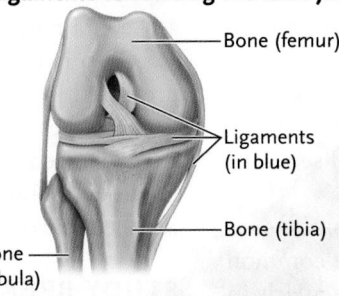

Bone (femur)

Ligaments (in blue)

Bone (fibula)

Bone (tibia)

The bones of the vertebrate skeleton are connected by joints, many of them movable. Ligaments restrict the motion of a joint and help prevent it from buckling or twisting under heavy loads. Most bones of vertebrate skeletons are moved by muscles arranged in antagonistic pairs.

Most skeletal muscles in vertebrates are attached at both ends, across a joint, to bones of the skeleton by cords of connective tissue called *tendons.*

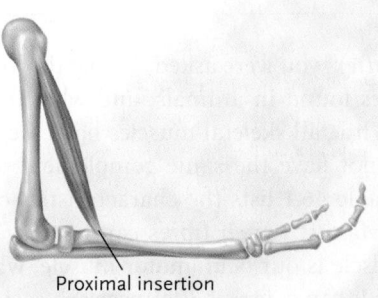

Proximal insertion

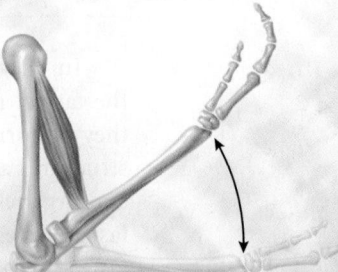

Proximal insertion of muscle—speed

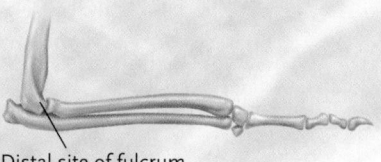

Distal site of fulcrum in runner—speed

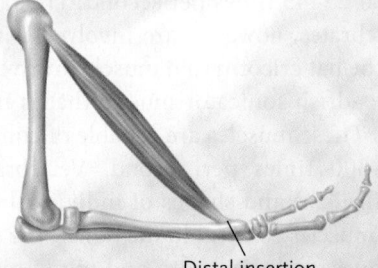

Distal insertion

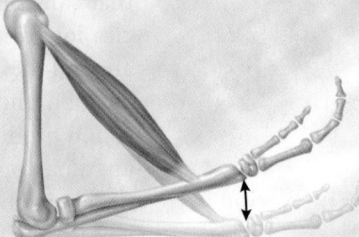

Distal insertion of muscle—strength

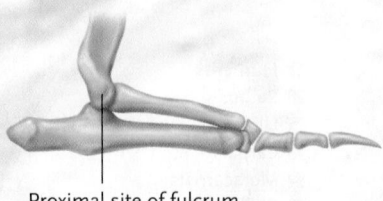

Proximal site of fulcrum in digger—strength

© Cengage Learning 2017

Bones connected by movable joints work like levers. The point of attachment of the muscle relative to the fulcrum and the position of the fulcrum along the lever determine speed versus strength.

# What Muscle Is Made Of

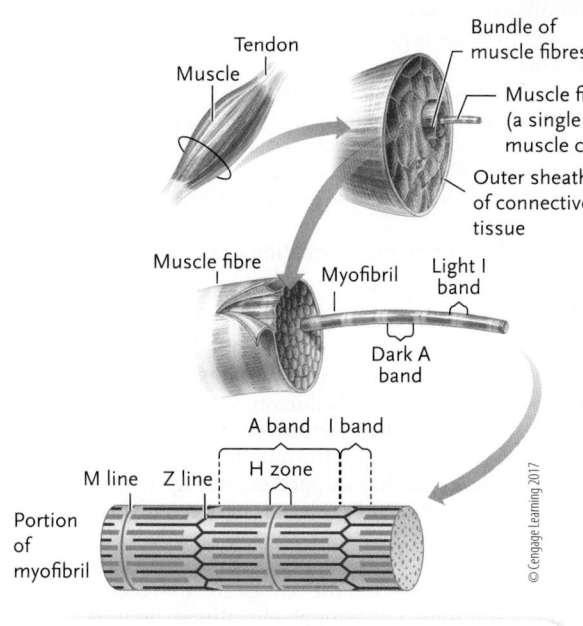

Skeletal muscle consists of muscle fibres, which contain myofibrils.

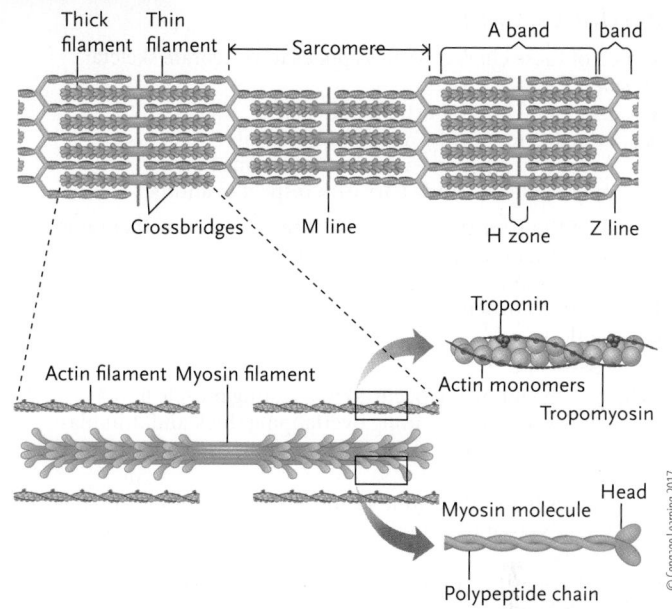

Myofibrils are arranged in sarcomeres, which consist of myosin thick filaments and actin thin filaments.

# How Muscle Contracts

1 and 2 An action potential at a neuromuscular junction stimulates release of acetylcholine. This triggers an action potential in the muscle fibre, which causes the release of $Ca^{2+}$.

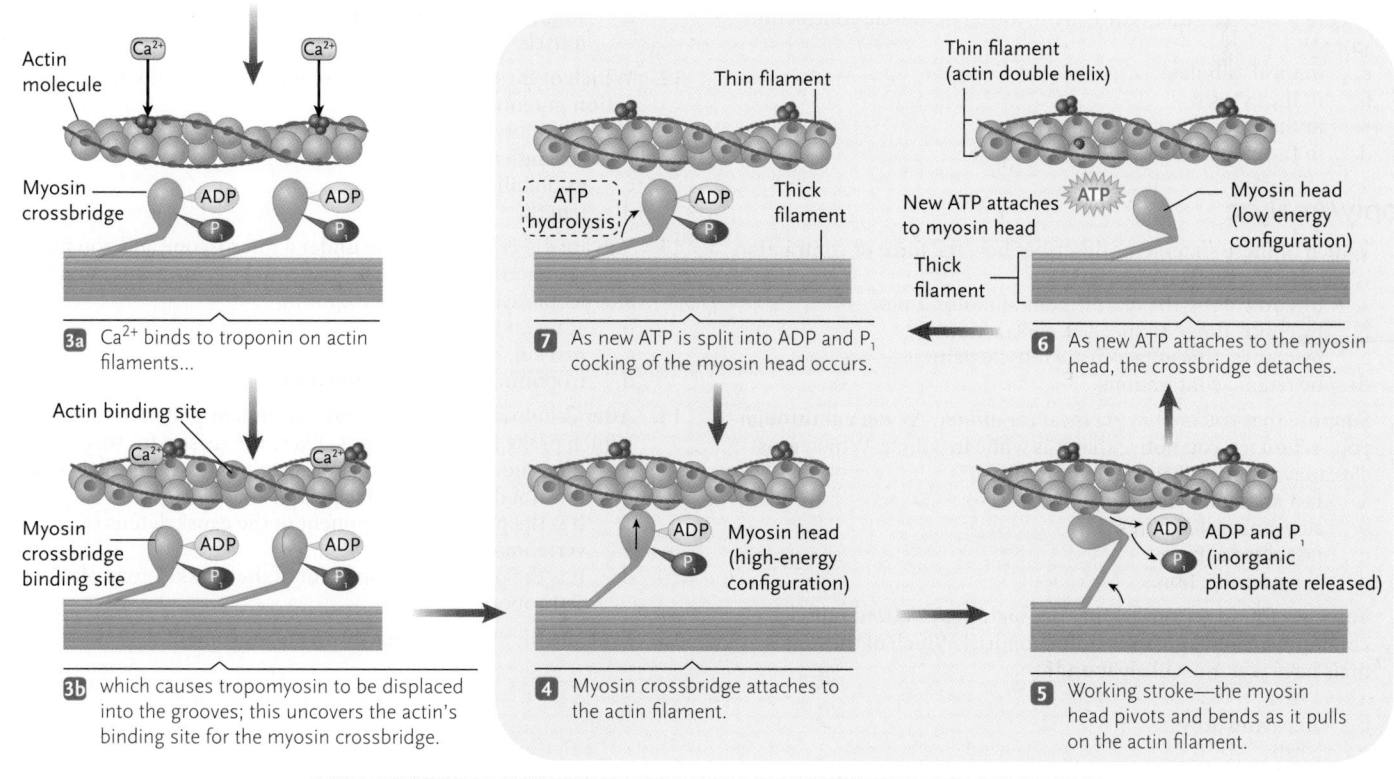

3a $Ca^{2+}$ binds to troponin on actin filaments...

3b which causes tropomyosin to be displaced into the grooves; this uncovers the actin's binding site for the myosin crossbridge.

7 As new ATP is split into ADP and $P_i$ cocking of the myosin head occurs.

4 Myosin crossbridge attaches to the actin filament.

6 As new ATP attaches to the myosin head, the crossbridge detaches.

5 Working stroke—the myosin head pivots and bends as it pulls on the actin filament.

**Muscle shortening results when thick and thin filaments slide past one another.**

# SELF-TEST QUESTIONS

## Recall/Understand

1. Which of these characteristics applies to vertebrate skeletal muscle?
   a. may bend but not extend body parts
   b. attached to bone by means of ligaments
   c. usually attached at each end to the same bone
   d. may rotate one body part with respect to another

2. Which of these terms refers to the connective tissue that joins bones together on either side of a joint?
   a. periosteum
   b. stratum corneum
   c. tendon
   d. ligament

3. Which of the following occur(s) in a resting muscle fibre?
   a. dark A bands containing overlapping thick and thin filaments with a central thin H zone composed only of thick filaments
   b. Z lines lying adjacent to H zones attached to thick filaments
   c. I bands composed of the same thick filaments seen in A bands
   d. disks of M line proteins, called the *A band*, separating the thick filaments

4. Which of these statements describes the sliding filament contractile mechanism?
   a. It causes lengthening of the sarcomere to separate the I regions.
   b. It causes thick and thin filaments to slide toward the centre of the H band, bringing the A lines closer together.
   c. It causes thick and thin filaments to slide toward the centre of the A band, bringing the Z lines closer together.
   d. It uses myosin crossbridges to stimulate delivery of $Ca^{2+}$ to the muscle fibre.

5. Where is the $Ca^{2+}$ that is directly involved in muscle contraction stored?
   a. in the T tubules
   b. in the cytosol
   c. in the sarcoplasmic reticulum
   d. in the extracellular fluid

## Apply/Analyze

6. Which of these statements describes how the force of contraction is adjusted in skeletal muscles?
   a. by controlling the recruitment of motor units
   b. by controlling the speed of contraction
   c. by contracting antagonistic muscle pairs
   d. by tetanic contractions

7. Suppose that you are having meat for dinner. As you cut through your schnitzel, you notice that it is white in colour. Which muscles are you most likely having for dinner?
   a. fast anaerobic fibres
   b. slow anaerobic fibres
   c. fast aerobic fibres
   d. slow aerobic fibres

8. You have found an animal that has highly specialized muscles containing a lot of gigantic mitochondria. Which of these animals have you most likely found?
   a. a frog
   b. an earthworm
   c. a fish
   d. a flying insect

9. You notice that one of your finger muscles is twitching. You understand that this is most likely a result of which of the following?
   a. multiple action potentials arriving at a neuromuscular junction without time for the muscle to relax
   b. multiple action potentials arriving at a neuromuscular junction allowing for relaxing
   c. a single action potential arriving at a neuromuscular junction
   d. a result of temporal summation at a neuromuscular junction

## Create/Evaluate

10. You have found a non-moving, non-breathing animal with stiff limbs. You conclude that it must have died. Which of the following did you base your conclusion on and why?
    a. Since the animal has stopped breathing, no new proteins are being synthesized, and the muscles cannot move.
    b. Since the animal has stopped breathing, no new ATP is being produced, and the bonds between myosin and actin cannot break.
    c. Since the animal has stopped breathing, no oxygen is available in the blood, and the tissues are not receiving any.
    d. Since the animal has stopped breathing, no new ATP is being produced, and new bonds between myosin and actin cannot form.

11. Which of these sequences depicts the hierarchy of muscle structure from smallest to largest?
    a. single muscle fibre; muscle; myofibril; bundle of muscle fibres
    b. myofibril; bundle of muscle fibres; single muscle fibre; muscle
    c. myofibril; single muscle fibre; bundle of muscle fibres; muscle
    d. single muscle fibre; bundle of muscle fibres; myofibril; muscle

12. Which of these characteristics of muscles allow them to conduct action potentials?
    a. flexibility
    b. strength
    c. excitability
    d. length

13. You are dissecting a muscle under a microscope and you focus in on an A band. Which muscle protein(s) occur in this band?
    a. tropomyosin, but not troponin
    b. actin and myosin
    c. myosin, but not actin
    d. troponin, but not tropomyosin

14. After cellulose, chitin is the most abundant polymer on Earth. Which of the following is most likely the reason for this?
    a. It has never been a target of some successful insecticides.
    b. It is not degraded by bacteria.
    c. It is the principal component of the exoskeletons of vertebrates.
    d. It is the principal component of the exoskeletons of arthropods.

15. Evaluate the steps of an earthworm's movement.

# Appendix A: Answers to Self-Test Questions

## Chapter 1
1. a 2. a 3. d 4. a 5. c 6. d 7. c
8. a 9. b 10. a 11. c 12. b 13. d
14. Eyes are usually not exposed to full sunlight for a very long period of time, such as the photosynthetic apparatus is. Damage due to exposure of photosystems can be repaired by removing damaged proteins and replacing them with newly synthesized ones, which is not possible in a damaged eye.
15. Melanin protects skin cells because it absorbs ultraviolet light, and it is increasingly synthesized upon exposure to the Sun, which results in the darker shade of her skin.

## Chapter 2
1. d 2. c 3. c 4. a 5. a 6. b 7. b
8. a 9. d 10. a 11. d 12. d 13. c
14. ribosomes, rough ER, transport vesicle, Golgi complex, secretory vesicle, plasma membrane
15. Anchoring junctions function to reinforce cell-to-cell connections made by adhesion molecules. Tight junctions seal the spaces between cells. Gap junctions create direct channels for communicating between adjacent cells.

## Chapter 3
1. c 2. d 3. b 4. a 5. b 6. c 7. c 8. d
9. c 10. d
11. As they dissolve, the sugar molecules raise their entropy. However, the crystals re-form because the water decreases in its order, changing from compact liquid to disordered vapour.
12. Any substance in ordered state (minimum entropy) will contain molecules with maximum free energy. On the contrary, any substance in disordered state (maximum entropy) will contain molecules with minimum free energy. The relationship is reversed.
13. In an exergonic reaction, reactants contain more free energy than the products; energy is released and the reaction is spontaneous. In an endergonic reaction, reactants contain less free energy than the products; energy is required and the reaction is not spontaneous.
14. At any time in a cell, there must be exergonic reactions happening to provide enough energy for endergonic reactions. In addition, the energy released by exergonic reactions must be higher than the energy needed for endergonic reactions because some energy is always transferred to heat (second law of thermodynamics).

## Chapter 4
1. a 2. c 3. b 4. c
5. Some proteins perform transport; others have enzymatic activities; some are a part of signal transduction process; and others are involved in attachment and/or recognition.
6. b 7. c 8. b 9. c 10. c 11. b
12. a 13. d
14. Passive transport occurs down the concentration gradient of the solute, and active transport occurs against the gradient of the transported solute. Active transport therefore requires a protein and energy to perform.
15. They are both a form of passive transport, but facilitated diffusion utilizes proteins to speed up the transport of solute across the membrane.

## Chapter 5
1. a 2. c 3. d 4. d 5. b 6. c 7. a
8. This patient might have defective mitochondria in his cells. This condition is common in a number of diseases. The reason why it was suspected is that, based on his symptoms, probably little ATP is synthesized, in spite of high oxygen consumption, since his cells dissipated a lot of heat (the patient was hot all the time).
9. b 10. c 11. d
12. Direct burning of glucose is an uncontrolled process; cellular respiration occurs in a series of steps and is therefore a form of controlled combustion.
13. Reduction is the acceptance of electrons during a redox reaction. Oxidation is the loss of electrons during a redox reaction.
14. Hydrogen and its electrons move from sugar to oxygen, forming water.
15. The process of oxidative phosphorylation produces the large number of ATP molecules needed for the endergonic reactions in the cell that we are so dependent on. One of the major sequences of proteins embedded in the mitochondrial membrane—called the electron transport chain—can accept electrons rich in energy. As the energized electrons fall from protein to protein in the ETC, they deposit energy that they carry. At the end of the ETC, there must be oxygen ions present to accept these energetically depleted electrons. If these energy-depleted electrons are not carried away by the oxygen ions, ATP production would stop. Cyanide exerts its deadly effects by reacting with the final protein in ETC, blocking oxygen from accepting electrons from this protein.

## Chapter 6
1. d 2. c 3. c 4. a 5. c
6. A group of pigment proteins form an antenna complex that surrounds a reaction centre. Light energy absorbed anywhere in the antenna complex is transferred to a special chlorophyll *a* molecule in the reaction centre. The absorbed light is converted to chemical energy when an excited electron from the chlorophyll *a* is transferred to a primary

acceptor, also in the reaction centre. High-energy electrons are passed out of the photosystem to the electron transport system.

7. Electrons move in a circular pathway from photosystem I through ferredoxin back to the plastoquinone pool, through the cytochrome complex and plastocyanin, and then back to photosystem I. Photosystem II does not operate in cyclic electron transport. The pathway generates proton pumping and thus leads to ATP production, but does not result in the synthesis of NADPH.

8. c 9. c 10. c 11. a 12. a 13. d

14. Photosystem I generates NADPH, and photosystem II generates ATP. Photosystem I has a shorter electron transport chain than has photosystem II. Photosystem I replenishes its electrons from photosystem II; photosystem II replenishes its electrons from splitting water.

15. Two alternative processes of carbon fixation to minimize photorespiration are found in $C_4$ and CAM plants. In both cases, carbon fixation produces the four-carbon oxaloacetate, which is processed to generate the $CO_2$ that feeds into the Calvin ($C_3$) cycle. In $C_4$ plants, carbon fixation and the Calvin cycle occur in different cell types: carbon fixation by the $C_4$ pathway takes place in mesophyll cells, and the Calvin cycle takes place in bundle sheath cells. In CAM plants, carbon fixation and the Calvin cycle occur at different times in mesophyll cells: carbon fixation by the $C_4$ pathway takes place at night, and the Calvin cycle takes place during the day.

## Chapter 7

1. c 2. d 3. a 4. b 5. b 6. b 7. d
8. b 9. c 10. d 11. d 12. d 13. b

14. These aneuploid cells likely arose due to failure of the microtubules to bind to the kinetochores of one replicated chromosome.

15. The experiment could compare cells growing in the presence and absence of chocolate flavonoids. One could observe the proportion of cells that are actively cycling in both treatments.

## Chapter 8

1. d 2. c 3. d 4. a 5. a 6. b

7. Mutations in somatic cells may give rise to cancer in an individual. Only mutations in meiotic cells would have the potential to be inherited by offspring and contribute to evolution of the species.

8. d 9. b 10. a

11. A recombination event between bio and met would create the necessary genotype in strain 1.

12. G2 cells would have 4 times the amount of DNA of a gamete. Telophase I cells would have 2 times the amount of DNA of a gamete. Telophase II cells would have the same amount of DNA as a gamete.

13. 13. d

14. During synapsis, the two reciprocally translocated chromosomes and the two normal chromosomes would form a cross shape as their homologous regions pair.

15. The two circles would fuse together to make one large circle.

## Chapter 9

1. c

2. (a) all *AB*; (b) 1/2 *AB* + 1/2 *aB*; (c) 1/2 *Ab* + 1/2 *ab*; (d) 1/4 *AB* + 1/4 *Ab* + 1/4 *aB* + 1/4 *ab*

3. (a) all *ABC*; (b) 1/2 *ABc* + 1/2 *aBc*; (c) 1/4 *ABC* + 1/4 *ABc* + 1/4 *aBC* + 1/4 *aBc*; (d) 1/8 *ABC* + 1/8 *ABc* + 1/8 *AbC* + 1/8 *Abc* + 1/8 *aBC* + 1/8 *aBc* + 1/8 *abC* + 1/8 *abc*

4. (a) The *CC* parent produces all *C* gametes, and the *Cc* parent produces 1/2 *C* and 1/2 *c* gametes. All offspring would have coloured seeds: half homozygous *CC* and half heterozygous *Cc*. (b) Both parents produce 1/2 *C* and 1/2 *c* gametes. Of the offspring, three-fourths would have coloured seeds (1/4 *CC* + 1/2 *Cc*) and one-fourth would have colourless seeds (1/4 *cc*). (c) The *Cc* parent produces 1/2 *C* gametes and 1/2 *c* gametes, and the *cc* parent produces all *c* gametes. Half the offspring are coloured (1/2 *Cc*) and half are colourless (1/2 *cc*).

5. The genotypes of the parents are *Tt* and *tt*.

6. (a) The taster parents could have a non-taster child, but non-taster parents are not expected to have a child who can taste PTC. The chance that they might have a taster child is 3/4. (b) The chance of a non-taster child being born to the taster couple is 1/4. (c) Because each combination of gametes is an independent event, the chance of the couple having a second child, or any child, who cannot taste PTC is expected to be 1/4.

7. (a) all *AaBB*; (b) *AABB* (1/16) + *AaBB* (1/8) + *aaBB* (1/16) + *AABb* (1/8) + *AaBb* (1/4) + *aaBb* (1/8) + *AAbb* (1/16) + *Aabb* (1/8) + *aabb* (1/16); (c) *AaBb* (1/4) + *Aabb* (1/4) + *aaBb* (1/4) + *aabb* (1/4); (d) *AABB* (1/4) + *AABb* (1/4) + *AaBB* (1/4) + *AaBb* (1/4)

8. Probably one gene controls pod colour. One allele, *G* for green pods, is dominant; the other allele, *g* for yellow pods, is recessive.

9. (a) The cross *RR* × *Rr* will produce 1/2 *RR* and 1/2 *Rr* offspring. (b) The cross *Rr* × *Rr* will produce 1/4 *RR*, 1/2 *Rr*, and 1/4 *rr* as combinations of alleles. However, the 1/4 *rr* combination is lethal, so it does not appear among the offspring. Therefore, the offspring will be born with only two types, *RR* and *Rr*, with twice as many *Rr* as *RR* in a 1:2 ratio (or 1/3 *RR* : 2/3 *Rr*).

10. (a) The parental cross is *GG TT RR* × *gg tt rr*. All offspring of this cross are expected to be tall plants with green pods and round seeds, or *Gg Tt Rr*. (b) When crossed, this heterozygous $F_1$ generation is expected to produce 8 different phenotypes among the offspring: green-tall-round, green-dwarf-round, yellow-tall-round, green-tall-wrinkled, yellow-dwarf-round, green-dwarf-wrinkled, yellow-tall-wrinkled, and yellow-dwarf-wrinkled, in a 27:9:9:9:3:3:3:1 ratio.

11. The genotypes are, for bird 1, *Ff Pp*; bird 2, *FF PP*; bird 3, *Ff PP*; and bird 4, *Ff Pp*.

12. Yes, it can be determined that the child is not hers because the father must be AB to have both an A and B child with a type O wife; none of the woman's children could have type O blood with an AB father.

13. The cross is expected to produce white, tabby, and black kittens in a 12:3:1 ratio.

14. The mother is homozygous recessive for both genes, and the father must be heterozygous for both genes. The child is homozygous recessive for both genes. The chance of having a child with normal hands is 1/2, and that of having a child with woolly hair is 1/2. Using the product rule of probability, the probability of having a child with normal hands and woolly hair is 1/2 × 1/2 = 1/4.

15. This diagram is incorrect because it does not show that meiosis results in gametes containing one allele from each of the two genes involved in this cross. The gametes should be *Mh*, *MH*, *mH*, and *mh*.

16. (a) Because the man can produce only 1 type of allele for each of the 10 genes, he can produce only 1 type of sperm cell with respect to these genes. (b) The woman can produce 2 types of alleles for each of her 2 heterozygous genes, so she can produce 2 × 2 = 4 different types of eggs with respect to the 10 genes. (c) In general, as the number of heterozygous genes increases, the number of possible types of gametes increases as $2^n$, where $n$ = the number of heterozygous genes.

17. (a) Use a standard testcross; that is, cross the guinea pig with rough black fur with a double-recessive individual, *rr bb* (smooth, white fur). (b) If your animal is homozygous *RR BB,* you would expect all the offspring to have rough black fur.

18. There are likely other genes that influence brown eye colour. Different brown-eyed people carry different alleles of these additional genes.

# Chapter 10

1. (a) All sons will be colour-blind. (b) None of the daughters will be colour-blind; however, all daughters will be heterozygous carriers of the trait.

2. Because this trait is probably carried on the Y chromosome, which a man transmits to all his sons, all will have hairy ears. None of the daughters will have hairy ears because they do not have a Y chromosome.

3. (a,b) The chance that her son will be colour-blind is 1:2, regardless of whether she marries a normal or colour-blind male.

4. All these questions can be answered from the pedigree. Polydactyly is caused by a dominant allele, and the trait is not sex linked. The genotypes of each person are as shown below.

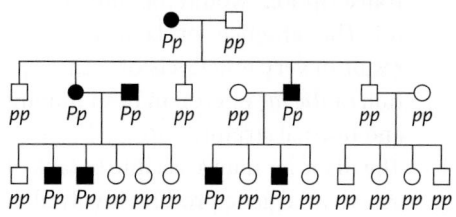

5. The sequence of the genes is *ADBC*.

6. c

7. Let the allele for wild-type grey body colour be b⁺, and the allele for black body be b. Let the allele for wild-type red eye colour be p⁺, and the allele for purple eyes be p. Then the parents are as follows:

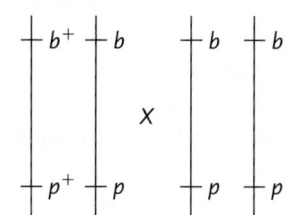

The F1 flies with black bodies and red eyes are as follows:

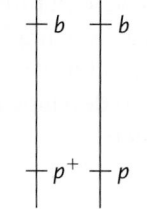

The flies with grey bodies and purple eyes are as shown:

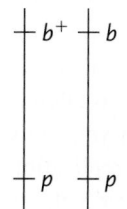

8. The genes are linked by their presence on the same chromosome (an autosome), but they are not sex linked. Because the F₁ females must have produced 600 gametes to give these 600 progeny, and because 42 + 30 of these were recombinant, the percentage of recombinant gametes is 72/600, or 12%, which implies that 12 map units separate the two genes.

9. One might suspect that a recessive allele is sex linked, and is carried on one of the two X chromosomes of the female parent in the cross. When present on the single X of the male (or if present on both Xs of a female), the gene is lethal.

10. One might suspect that some genes on the "inactivated" X chromosomes are in fact still expressed; that is, some genes may escape inactivation. Therefore, people with different numbers of X chromosomes would express different amounts of such gene products, regardless of X inactivation.

11. One could make a series of pair-wise test crosses; that is, cross *AaBb* with *aabb*. There should be four types of progeny and the two least frequent classes will represent the recombinants. The proportion of recombinants among the total will be the map distance between gene *a* and gene *b*. Repeat for other pairs of genes and then arrange in a linear series.

12. Kinshoo's trisomy 18 could have arisen from several different errors in chromosome partitioning: meiosis I or II in her mother, or meiosis I in her father.

# Chapter 11

1. b  2. a  3. a  4. d  5. c  6. a  7. d
8. d  9. a  10. a  11. c  12. b  13. c
14. This situation simply illustrates the definition of mutation. The original mismatch is DNA damage but is not a mutation yet. Only during the next round of replication will the incorrect T be paired with an A, giving rise to an AT pair in the chromosome where there was originally a GC pair. This is a mutation. The other daughter cell will receive a GC pair as usual.
15. The presence of the antibiotic does not create mutations. Rather, any of the mutational mechanisms in this chapter could occur in a gene that confers resistance to the antibiotic. This mutational event occurs *before* exposure to the antibiotic.

# Chapter 12

1. c  2. a  3. b  4. d  5. c  6. c  7. b
8. No. rRNA genes would be transcribed but not translated.
9. b  10. a  11. b
12. The normal tRNA would insert leucine at the codon UUA. The mutated tRNA would insert leucine at the codon UAA. The effect would likely be dramatic since translation would now read through UAA stop codons.
13. Enzymes 1 and 2 are alternative sources of compound C. Cells can still survive without either enzyme 1 or enzyme 2. However, enzymes 3 and 4 are essential.
14. We could move a gene from a eukaryote and have it expressed in a bacterium. Then we could compare the amino acid sequences.
15. Insertion of a transposable element is a dramatic change in the DNA sequence of a gene. That such an insertion would disrupt the normal function of a gene product is to be expected. Such insertions might increase enzyme activity by inactivating a repressor binding site.

# Chapter 13

1. c  2. c  3. d  4. b  5. d  6. c  7. d
8. c  9. a  10. d  11. b  12. a  13. c
14. (a) The presence of lactose would result in transcription of the *lac* operon in both mutant and normal strains. Since glucose is also present, CAP/cAMP would not be bound to the DNA of the normal strain. CAP/cAMP cannot bind at all in the mutant strain. Therefore, under these conditions, transcription in the two strains would be the same. (b) The presence of lactose would result in transcription of the lac operon in both mutant and normal strains. In the normal strain, the absence of glucose would result in binding of CAP/cAMP to the DNA with the resulting increase in transcription. CAP/cAMP binding is not possible in the mutant strain so transcription would be much less. (c) The absence of lactose would result in very low levels of transcription of the *lac* operon in both mutant and normal strains.
15. The disorder may arise due to lack of an essential gene product involved in muscle function. The mutation responsible may be carried on the X chromosome. X inactivation in heterozygous women may explain the distribution of normal versus affected tissue.

# Chapter 14

1. a  2. b  3. a  4. d  5. c  6. b  7. b
8. This is the experiment of cloning a sheep, which produced the clone Dolly. A diploid cell was isolated from a mammary gland of an adult white-faced ewe and propagated in tissue culture. The nucleus was removed from an unfertilized egg of a black-faced ewe, and the mammary gland cell was fused with the enucleated egg cell. Cells were cultured to produce a cluster that was implanted into the uterus of an adult black-faced ewe and the embryo developed in this surrogate mother.
9. c  10. a  11. c  12. d  13. a  14. d
15. Any scenario that describes a situation that requires identification of criminals or wrongly convicted people; identifying plants found on bodies for easier location of the crime scene; identifying paternity in criminal cases, *etc.* Bringing in samples that contain DNA from someone else (hair from a hairbrush, for example), or material from plants distant from the criminal's normal location would create "clues" that make solving the case much harder.

# Chapter 15

1. a  2. a  3. a  4. d  5. b  6. d
7.

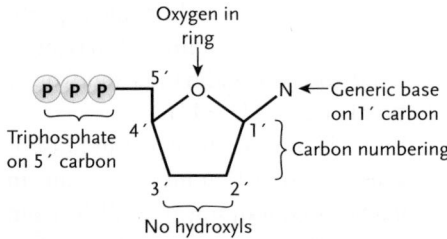

8. b  9. b  10. a  11. c  12. d
13. Gene knockout: researchers replace a normal gene with a defective one that cannot express a functional protein. Gene knockdown: RNA interference reduces the expression of a gene at the translation level.
14. Align the primer to the template in an antiparallel direction. Read each nucleotide complementary to the template starting *only* from the primer's 3′ end. You cannot sequence the primer, and there are only five nucleotides on the template that will attract the ddNTP.

| A | T | C | G |
|---|---|---|---|
|   |   |   |   |
|   |   |   | — |
|   |   | — |   |
| — |   |   |   |
|   | — |   |   |
|   |   | — |   |

15. Many studies are done on animals because of experimental concerns (e.g., homogeneity of genotypes, length of time to maturity, experimental design) and allow us to analyze the functions of genes using a variety of techniques. When we find a similar sequence in the human genome, we might already know much of that gene's function due to the animal studies. Because of the evolutionary connectedness of all life, we can use comparisons of genes from closely-related and more distantly-related organisms to see if a particular protein has a similar function or if it has diverged. The more we know about other organisms around us, the more we can take logical approaches to determine the functions of human genes based on their sequence alone.

# Chapter 16

1. c 2. c 3. d 4. b 5. c 6. c 7. d 8. d 9. b 10. a
11. Evolution is a change in the traits of a population over time. Natural selection is one of the mechanisms that can cause that change.
12. It is a non-random process because it selects individuals in a population with certain traits.
13. (1) Most organisms produce more than one or two offspring; (2) populations do not increase in size indefinitely; (3) food and other resources are limited for most populations.
14. (1) Individuals within populations exhibit variability in many characteristics; (2) many variations appear to be inherited by subsequent generations.
15. Monarch butterflies are able to ingest cardiac glycosides, and they benefit from this ability because they use these molecules to establish their own defence.

# Chapter 17

1. c 2. d 3. d 4. b 5. a 6. c 7. b 8. c 9. c 10. c 11. b 12. b
13. It considers the number of surviving offspring that an individual produces in comparison to the number of offspring that other individuals produce in the same population.
14. In the case of reciprocal gene flow, the populations would probably become more phenotypically similar to each other after some time. In the case of non-reciprocal gene flow, one of the populations may become more different than it was before the gene flow, while the other may remain the same as it was at the beginning of the process.

# Chapter 18

1. c 2. a 3. b 4. d 5. d 6. b 7. b 8. d 9. b 10. c 11. c 12. b
13. The concept cannot be applied to species known only from fossil records, to species that reproduce only asexually, or to species that do not overlap geographically or do not meet each other otherwise.
14. Individuals of the same species interbreed with no difficulty and their offspring look like their parents. Subspecies are local variants of a species. Individuals from different subspecies usually interbreed where their geographical distributions meet; their offspring often exhibit intermediate phenotypes.
15. Lions and tigers do not live in the same habitat, so they are naturally geographically isolated and do not come in contact unless captured. Since they are two species, their offspring would be a hybrid that is either sterile or has reduced fertility, hence exhibiting an example of the postzygotic reproductive barrier, which prevents it from being considered a separate species and present in the wilderness as such.

# Chapter 19

1. a 2. b 3. b 4. b 5. d 6. c 7. c 8. a 9. b 10. d 11. d 12. c
13. A monophyletic taxon includes an ancestor and all its descendants. A polyphyletic taxon includes species from different evolutionary lineages. A paraphyletic taxon includes an ancestor and some, but not all its descendants.
14. You are surprised, because you understand that the class Reptilia, even though it includes turtles, lizards, snakes, and crocodilians, which are descendants of a common ancestor, it does not include all descendants of archosaurs, namely birds. As such, class Reptilia can only be considered a paraphyletic taxon.
15. Convergent evolution is used when referring to phylogenetically or distantly related organisms, and parallel evolution when referring to more closely related organisms.

# Chapter 20

1. d 2. c 3. d 4. d 5. c 6. a 7. c 8. d 9. c 10. b 11. d 12. b
13. Improved predator detection; display of warning signs; more efficient walk over long distances; more efficient thermoregulation
14. This is an old notion, perhaps even a seductive idea, but it is dangerous to interpret the origin of a structure or function in terms of its current utility. It would be like saying that the human brain evolved in order to write symphonies, which is clearly nonsense.
15. The African emergence hypothesis suggests that all modern humans are descended from a fairly recent African ancestor, as early hominin descendants left Africa to establish populations elsewhere. The multiregional hypothesis suggests that populations of *H. erectus* and archaic humans spread through much of Europe and Asia, and that modern humans evolved from descendants of these earlier dispersals.

# Chapter 21

1. c 2. b 3. a 4. a 5. d 6. d 7. b 8. c 9. d 10. b 11. b 12. d
13. To determine relative dates, scientists order fossils found in different strata in sequence from the lowest (oldest)

to the highest (newest) strata. This sequencing reveals their relative ages. By using a technique called radiometric dating, scientists can estimate the age of a rock by noting how much of an unstable "parent" isotope has decayed to another form. By measuring the relative amounts of the parent radioisotope and its breakdown products, and comparing this ratio with the isotope's half-life—the time it takes for half of a given amount of radioisotope to decay—researchers can estimate the absolute age of the rock.

14. LUCA stands for Last Universal Common Ancestor, because the similarities across all domains of life present today indicate that only one of these primitive life forms has descendants that survive today.

15. Bacteria and archaea have circular chromosomes; eukaryotes have linear chromosomes. The location of DNA of prokaryotes is in the nucleoid region, and in eukaryotes it is in the nucleus. Chromosomes segregate by binary fission in prokaryotes, and by mitosis/meiosis in eukaryotes. Introns are rarely present in bacteria, but are common in archaea and eukaryotes.

# Chapter 22

1. c 2. a 3. b 4. c 5. c 6. d 7. a 8. d 9. d 10. c 11. d 12. c

13. Treatment is difficult because viruses are incorporated into cells, since they use the cell's machinery to replicate. Therefore, it is difficult to target them specifically with drugs. They do not react to antibiotics, and usually take their own course before being eliminated by the cells of their host's immune system.

14. The phage attaches to the host cell and injects its DNA into the cell. Expression of phage genes produces an enzyme that breaks down bacterial chromosomes. The phage DNA then replicates inside the cell. Viral heads and tail units synthesize and assemble into "new" phage particles. The cell then ruptures, releasing the phage particles.

15. The lytic cycle begins with a phage binding to the host cell and releasing its DNA into the host cell's cytoplasm. The viral DNA is initially linear, but once inside the host cell, it forms a circle. Viral genes produce enzymes that break down the cell's chromosomes and proteins, along with linear copies of viral DNA. New viral particles assemble, with DNA packed inside. Viral genes encode for the protein that breaks the cell open, releasing new viral particles out of the cell. In the lysogenic cycle, viral DNA integrates with the host cell's chromosome, allowing the viral DNA to be replicated along with the host cell's DNA. Following cell division, each daughter cell receives viral DNA incorporated in their own DNA.

# Chapter 23

1. b 2. c 3. c 4. c 5. b 6. a 7. b 8. a 9. d 10. a 11. a 12. b

13. Obligate anaerobes are poisoned by oxygen. They perform either fermentation or anaerobic respiration. Facultative anaerobes use oxygen when present, and utilize fermentation or anaerobic respiration when oxygen is not present. Obligate aerobes cannot survive without oxygen.

14. Gram-positive bacteria appear purple under the microscope, due to a stain they retain in their cells; Gram-negatives appear pink. This is because Gram-positive bacteria contain a thick peptidoglycan layer in their cell walls, and Gram-negative bacteria have a very thin layer. Gram-negative bacteria have an outer layer external to the peptidoglycan layer, which inhibits entry of penicillin, thus making the Gram-negative bacteria less sensitive to penicillin than are Gram-positive bacteria.

15. Methanogens are archaea that live in low-oxygen environments. They are obligate anaerobes living in swamps, lakes, marshes, and sewage works, but also in guts of ruminants, termites, dogs, and humans. Methanogens convert some gases into methane. Halophiles are salt-loving extremophiles, living in highly saline environments. Most are aerobic chemoheterotrophs. Extreme thermophiles live in extremely hot environments, such as hot springs and hydrothermal vents at ocean bottoms, which makes them unique among living organisms.

# Chapter 24

1. d 2. b 3. d 4. c 5. b 6. c 7. d 8. c 9. b 10. a

11. All animals are multicellular; protists are also unicellular. Animals have complex structures and internal organs. Protists do not have features that characterize animals, such as nerve cells, limbs, heart, tissues such as collagen.

12. Many protists can be photosynthetic and at the same time live as heterotrophs, which plants cannot do. Protists are not embryophytes like plants, and they do not have roots, stems, or leaves. Generally, photosynthetic protists live in aquatic environments, which is not true of land plants.

13. Most protists are aerobic, and are either heterotrophs or autotrophs. Many phototrophic protists may also live as heterotrophs. Some protists absorb small organic molecules from their environment.

14. Protists live in aqueous habitats, including aquatic or moist terrestrial environments such as oceans, lakes, ponds, streams, and moist soil, and within hosts. Their roles are different depending on the environment in which they live.

15. Reproduction in protists is asexual by mitosis and sexual by meiosis and gamete formation. Some protists reproduce utilizing both mitosis and meiosis, and their modes of cell division are often combined into a life cycle highly distinctive among the different protist groups.

# Chapter 25

1. c  2. b  3. b  4. b  5. a  6. d  7. c  8. d  9. d  10. c  11. c

12. The human embryo is diploid. It grows by mitosis into a full organism, and when it becomes adult and mature, it starts producing haploid gametes by meiosis. Male and female gametes fertilize, forming a diploid zygote/embryo. Humans do not reproduce asexually. Fungi reproduce sexually but also asexually. In the asexual cycle, haploid spores are produced by mitosis into mycelium, which produces spores again. In sexual reproduction, haploid spores grow into mycelium, which fuses with a compatible strain creating a binucleate mycelium (heterokaryotic stage). Karyogamy (fusion of nuclei) occurs later in the life cycle, creating diploid zygotes, which produce haploid spores by meiosis often within a fruiting body.

13. Similarities: Both penetrate root and increase surface area for absorption of nutrients. Differences: Arbuscular mycorrhizae have fungal hyphae that penetrate the cells of the root. In ectomycorrhizae, fungal hyphae form a sheath (called mantle) around a root and do not penetrate the cell walls of the root.

14. They break down organic matter, allowing nutrients to cycle in nature; some are edible; some damage our food; some are used in making alcoholic beverages; some help in baking processes; cause diseases of plants that humans are reliant on; cause diseases in humans, causing even death.

15. 15. You would need to find the evidence of absorptive nutrition, as this is the distinguishing characteristic of fungi.

# Chapter 26

1. c  2. d  3. c  4. c  5. b  6. b  7. a  8. d  9. d  10. d  11. b  12. a  13. b  14. c

15. Two multicellular stages alternate throughout the lifetime of land plants: a diploid sporophyte and a haploid gametophyte. Sporophyte produces haploid spores by meiosis that grow directly into gametophytes. Gametophytes produce haploid gametes by mitosis. Gametes must fuse together (fertilize) to form a diploid zygote, which will grow by mitosis into a sporophyte, and the cycle will resume.

# Chapter 27

1. b  2. c  3. d  4. c  5. a  6. b  7. d  8. c  9. c  10. a  11. d  12. d  13. a  14. a  15. b  16. b

17. This colonial, flagellated ancestor with unspecialized cells would have had a developmental reorganization that resulted in two cell layers. Certain cells became specialized for feeding and other functions. A developmental reorganization produced a two-layered animal with a sac-within-a-sac body plan. Such cell movements are similar to those that occur during the development of many animals. Associated with this, cells became specialized for different functions, such as the feeding cells giving rise to the digestive cavity.

18. Pizza cutting; crystal formations; graphical ornaments; spikes on a wheel, etc. Anything that shows body parts regularly arranged around a central axis.

19. *Hox* genes are homeotic genes that influence the three-dimensional shape of the animal and the locations of important structures such as eyes, wings, and legs, particularly along the head-to-tail axis of the body. *Hox* genes are arranged on chromosomes in a particular order, forming the *Hox* gene complex. Each gene in the complex governs the development of particular structures. Animal groups with the simplest structure, such as cnidarians, have two *Hox* genes. Those with more complex anatomy, such as insects, have 10. Chordates typically have up to 13 or 14. Lineages with many *Hox* genes generally have more complex anatomy than those with fewer *Hox* genes.

20. (1) Skin is waterproof: keratin and lipids in the cells make skin relatively impermeable to water. (2) Amniotic eggs can survive and develop on dry land because they have four specialized membranes and a hard or leathery shell perforated by microscopic pores. Amniotic eggs are resistant to desiccation. The membranes protect the developing embryo and facilitate gas exchange and excretion. The shell mediates the exchange of air and water between the egg and its environment. Developing amniote embryos can excrete uric acid, which is stored in the allantois of the embryo, which will later become the bladder. Generous supplies of yolk in the egg are the developing embryo's main energy source; albumin supplies water and other materials. There is no larval stage, and hatchling amniotes are miniature versions of the adult. Amniotic eggs are the ancestral condition, but in some reptiles and most mammals, development takes place within the body of the mother. (3) Some amniotes produce urea and/or uric acid as a waste product of nitrogen metabolism. Although ammonia is less expensive (metabolically) to produce, it is toxic and must be flushed away with water. Urea is much less toxic than ammonia and therefore easier to store and to void. Uric acid is even less toxic and, because it is insoluble, it can be stored or voided without risk while conserving water. (4) A skeleton provides support and points of attachment for muscles, allowing locomotion and survival on land.

# Chapter 28

1. c  2. c  3. d  4. c  5. b  6. b  7. b  8. b  9. c  10. c  11. a  12. a  13. c  14. b

15. An extirpated species no longer exists in one location in the wild, but occurs elsewhere in the wild. Endangered species face imminent extirpation or extinction.

# Chapter 29

1. a 2. b 3. a 4. b 5. a 6. c 7. a 8. b 9. a 10. d 11. d 12. d 13. d 14. a

15. Type I curves reflect high survivorship until late in life. Type II curves reflect a relatively constant rate of mortality in all age classes, a pattern that produces steadily declining survivorship. Type III curves reflect high juvenile mortality, followed by a period of low mortality once offspring reach a critical age and size.

# Chapter 30

1. c 2. b 3. a 4. b 5. d 6. a 7. b 8. c 9. b 10. b 11. c 12. d 13. d

14. Fundamental niche is the niche occupied in the absence of competition, and is wider. Realized niche is narrower, and is occupied in the presence of competition.

15. Gause grew cultures of two *Paramecium* species under constant laboratory conditions, regularly renewing food and removing wastes. Both species ate bacteria suspended in the culture medium. When grown alone, each species exhibited logistic growth. When grown together in the same dish, *Paramecium aurelia* persisted at high density, but *Paramecium caudatum* was almost eliminated. Gause explained such results by a competitive exclusion principle. Populations of two or more species cannot coexist indefinitely if they rely on the same limiting resources and exploit them in the same way. One species inevitably harvests resources more efficiently, produces more offspring than the other, and, by its actions, negatively affects the other species.

# Chapter 31

1. d 2. c 3. c 4. a 5. c 6. d 7. d 8. d 9. d 10. a 11. c 12. a

13. Each trophic level uses energy for its own maintenance, and each subsequent trophic level has less energy available from primary productivity. The biomass at each trophic level is proportional to the amount of chemical energy temporarily stored there. The reduction of energy and biomass affects sizes of populations of organisms at the top of a food web. Top predators can be relatively large animals, so the limited biomass present in the highest trophic levels is concentrated in relatively few animals.

14. Nitrogen fixation is a conversion of gaseous nitrogen ($N_2$) to ammonia ($NH_3$), which dissolves to form ammonium ($NH_4^+$). Nitrogen fixation is performed by nitrogen-fixing bacteria. Ammonification is a process of conversion of residues to ammonia, which dissolves to form ammonium. Ammonification is performed by bacteria and fungi. Nitrification is a conversion of ammonium to nitrite ($NO_2^-$), and subsequent conversion of nitrite to nitrate ($NO_3^-$). Nitrification is performed by bacteria. Denitrification is conversion of nitrate to gaseous nitrogen by bacteria.

15. Phosphorus becomes available to biological systems when wind and rainfall dissolve phosphates in rocks and carry them into adjacent soil and freshwater ecosystems. Runoff carries dissolved phosphorus into marine ecosystems, where it precipitates out of solution and is incorporated into marine sediments.

# Chapter 32

1. c 2. b 3. b 4. d 5. c 6. a 7. b 8. d 9. b 10. b 11. b 12. d 13. c 14. d

15. Imprinting occurs when animals learn the identity of a caregiver or the key features of a suitable mate during a critical period, a stage of development early in life. Classical conditioning happens when animals develop a mental association between two phenomena that are usually unrelated. Operant conditioning—trial-and-error learning—is another form of associative learning: animals learn to link a voluntary activity, an operant, with its favourable consequences, a reinforcement. Insight learning occurs when an animal abruptly learns to solve problems without apparent trial-and-error attempts at the solution. Habituation occurs when animals lose their responsiveness to frequent stimuli not immediately followed by the usual reinforcement.

# Chapter 33

1. c 2. d 3. b 4. a 5. a 6. c 7. b 8. c 9. b 10. d 11. a

12. Similarities: Both are complex tissues that conduct (transport) materials. Differences: Xylem transports water and minerals unidirectionally (from roots to shoots). It contains dead cells with thick, secondary walls. Phloem transports sugars and other solutes throughout the plant body parts. The cells of phloem are not dead.

13. They are both parts of the plant body and are involved in transport of materials. Roots grow underground; shoots grow above ground. Shoots are covered with waxy cuticle; roots are not. Both exhibit primary growth at their tips, and secondary growth. Roots have a layer of epidermis; shoots do not. Both can be modified.

14. The Casparian strip is impregnated with a waxy substance (suberin) that is impermeable to water, and blocks the apoplastic movement of water at the level of the endodermis. As such, it forces the water and the nutrients dissolved in it to pass through a selectively permeable plasma membrane. This way, the cells have control of what will reach the vascular tissues. At the same time, it also prevents the backflow of materials that are already inside the xylem.

15. The apoplastic pathway is movement of water through cell walls and tissue air spaces. At the level of the endodermis, it is blocked by the Casparian strip. The symplastic pathway is movement of water through the cytoplasm of the root cells via plasmodesmata, and is not blocked by the Casparian strip.

# Chapter 34

1. d 2. b 3. d 4. c 5. a 6. a 7. b 8. d 9. c 10. c 11. a 12. b

13. Transpirational pull, which relies on the properties of water. Transpiration is the evaporation of water molecules from above-ground plant parts. This process pulls the water from the lower tree parts. Due to the collective strength of the hydrogen bonds, along with cohesion and adhesion of water molecules to each other and to the xylem cells, the continuous thread of water is maintained, which travels from the bottom of a tall tree to the very tip of it.

14. These plants often have various adaptations to dry environments: thickened cuticle to prevent water loss; trichomes to reduce evaporation; sunken stomata; leaves reduced to thin spines; as well as physiological adaptations ($C_4$ and CAM metabolism).

15. Family Crassulaceae are plants that utilize crassulacean acid metabolism (CAM), such as jade plant, have fewer stomata than other types of plants, and they are mostly closed during the day when it is hottest and driest. At cooler temperatures during nights, CAM plants open their stomata to take in $CO_2$, converting it to malate. During the day, they free $CO_2$ from malate, and carbon fixation by Rubisco takes place, despite daily closure of their stomata. This adaptation prevents heavy loss of water by keeping stomata closed during high temperatures.

# Chapter 35

1. b 2. d 3. b 4. a 5. b 6. c 7. d 8. a 9. c 10. d 11. c 12. a

13. The three genes are expressed in the different whorls of the flower and provide the identity of sepals, petals, anthers, and carpel. Protein A gives identity to sepals and petals; these mutants can form only the anthers and carpel of the flower.

14. The genes responsible for this are *S* genes, and they usually have multiple alleles. A common type of incompatibility occurs when pollen and stigma carry an identical *S* gene. In some plants, when incompatible pollen contacts a stigma, a pollen tube grows normally, but a hormonal response soon causes the flower to drop off the plant, preventing fertilization. It is important because self-incompatibility prevents inbreeding and promotes genetic variation, which is the raw material for natural selection and adaptation.

15. "Stamen: filament and anther, containing pollen sac. Carpel: stigma, style, and ovary, containing ovules. A flower without a stamen would not be able to produce pollen, and hence potentially successfully reproduce with another individual plant of the same species. A flower without a carpel would not be able to get pollinated, and potentially fertilized by another plant of the same species. In conclusion, the plant without its reproductive parts will not be able to reproduce sexually."

# Chapter 36

1. d 2. b 3. b 4. c 5. b 6. d 7. a

8. Soil is a complex mix of mineral particles, chemical compounds, ions, decomposing organic matter, air, water, and assorted living organisms. Humus specifically refers to "decomposing parts of plants and animals, animal droppings, and other organic matter." Humus has a loose, crumbly texture that can absorb a great deal of water. Organic molecules in humus are reservoirs of nutrients, including nitrogen, phosphorus, and sulfur.

9. Ranked: oxygen, nitrogen, phosphorus, sulfur, iron. Oxygen is a component of all macromolecules, especially water, the most abundant molecule in a living cell. Nitrogen is required by every amino acid, nucleic acids, and to some extent other macromolecules and coenzymes. Proteins make up a significant component of a plant's dry mass. Phosphorus is needed for membrane lipids, nucleic acids, and a wide variety of coenzymes.

10. c 11. a

12. A chosen plant could be any, except an epiphyte or a parasite, and chosen deficiencies should cause some obvious change that can be seen in that type of plant (e.g., size of leaves, roots, or plant as a whole). Some prominent deficiencies could be purplish veins due to lack of phosphorus; or dwarfed size (reduced growth) due to lack of nitrogen or potassium; or changes in leaves, such as dead spots due to copper or nickel deficiency, etc. (refer to Table 36.1).

13. In response to a specific flavonoid released by soybean roots, bacterial genes called *nod* genes begin to be expressed. Products of the *nod* gene cause the tip of the root hair to curl toward the bacteria and trigger the release of bacterial enzymes that break down the root hair cell wall. As bacteria enter the cell and multiply, the plasma membrane forms a tube called an infection thread that extends into the root cortex, allowing the bacteria to invade cortex cells. The enclosed bacteria, now called bacteroids, enlarge and become immobile. Stimulated by still other *nod* gene products, cells of the root cortex begin to divide. This region of proliferating cortex cells forms the root nodule. Typically, each cell in a root nodule contains several thousand bacteroids; the plant takes up some of the nitrogen fixed by the bacteroids, and the bacteroids use some compounds produced by the plant.

14. Even though epiphytes grow on other plants, they are not parasites because they use the plant they live on for physical support and do not damage it.

15. Carnivorous plants usually live on nitrogen-poor soil, and they need to obtain nitrogen by attracting and capturing animals. They have evolved various ways of trapping animals.

# Chapter 37

1. d  2. b  3. d  4. c  5. a
6. Auxin promotes growth and elongation of stems; promotes formation of lateral roots and dormancy in lateral buds; promotes fruit development; inhibits leaf abscission; orients plants with respect to light and gravity.
7. a  8. b  9. a  10. c
11. Because of its ability to establish dormancy, ABA is deposited in seeds and can be applied to plants prior to shipping. A dormant plant is less susceptible to damage, and therefore is protected during harsh overwintering as well as the stresses that occur during transport of plants.
12. a
13. Wounding from herbivory releases systemin, which travels through the phloem to distant locations in the plant. Systemin binds membrane receptors on cells throughout the plant body, releasing chemicals such as jasmonate, which stimulate genes that produce defences such as protease inhibitors. By using the vascular system, a localized attack can invoke protection to other plant parts that might soon be susceptible.
14. a
15. Root and shoot tips produce gibberellins, ethylene, and cytokinins (mainly in root tips). Developing leaves produce auxins, gibberellins, ethylene (in leaf nodes), and brassinosteroids (also in shoots). Embryos produce auxins, gibberellins, brassinosteroids (young seeds), and jasmonates. Gibberellins promote elongation in shoots, roots, and leaves, and affect the embryo by elongation of the seed. Ethylene regulates elongation in stems and roots, and abscission of leaves. Cytokinins coordinate growth of shoots and roots, and inhibit senescence of leaves. Auxins promote growth in stems and the formation of lateral roots, and inhibit leaf abscission. Brassinosteroids stimulate growth and differentiation of vascular tissue. Jasmonates play roles in defence and plant responses to nutrient deficiencies. (Refer to Table 37.1.)

# Chapter 38

1. a  2. b  3. d  4. d  5. b  6. d  7. c  8. d  9. c  10. b  11. a  12. d
13. Skeletal: bundles of long, cylindrical, striated, contractile cells called muscle fibres. Functions in voluntary movements, and is found attached to bones of skeleton. Cardiac: cylindrical, striated cells with specialized intercalated disks. Found in the heart wall, and functions in involuntary contractions of the heart. Smooth: cells with tapered ends, with one nucleus in each cell. Found in walls of internal organs, they function in involuntary movement of internal organs.
14. Negative feedback: response shuts off the stimulus; results in homeostasis. Positive feedback: response enhances the stimulus; does not result in homeostasis.
15. Cartilage is very elastic, which allows it to resist compression and stay resilient. In the air passages, it serves the purpose of keeping the passages open but still flexible while breathing, aiding in unobstructed passing of the air.

# Chapter 39

1. a  2. b  3. a  4. c  5. c  6. b  7. c  8. a  9. a  10. d  11. b  12. b  13. c
14. Leafy green vegetables, whole grains, cheese, and nuts
15. Food containing electrolytes such as chlorine, magnesium, phosphorus, potassium, and sodium

# Chapter 40

1. c  2. c  3. d  4. d  5. b  6. a  7. a  8. b  9. b  10. a  11. d  12. c
13. In body tissues, some of the $CO_2$ released into the blood combines with water in the blood plasma to form $HCO_3^-$ and $H^+$. Most of the $CO_2$ diffuses into red blood cells, where some combines with hemoglobin and some with water to form $HCO_3^-$ and $H^+$. The $H^+$ formed by this reaction combines with hemoglobin, and the $HCO_3^-$ is transported out of red blood cells and into the plasma. In the lungs, most of the $HCO_3^-$ in the blood is transported back into red blood cells, where it combines with $H^+$ released from hemoglobin to form $CO_2$ and water. $CO_2$ diffuses from red blood cells and, along with the $CO_2$, into the blood plasma and then from the blood into the alveolar air.
14. All gases diffuse slower in water than in air, and the solubility of many gases is very different in water than in air. For the same volume, there is approximately 30 times the amount of $O_2$ in air as in water at the same partial pressure. These two factors require animals that live in water to breathe much more in order to obtain the same volume of $O_2$ as an animal that breathes air. Moreover, the density of water is about 1000 times that of air, and its viscosity is about 50 times that of air. Therefore, it takes significantly more energy to move water than air over a respiratory surface. On the other hand, $CO_2$ solubility is higher in water and so it is much easier to excrete $CO_2$.
15. In concurrent flow, the diffusion will eventually stop because the gradient driving diffusion would fall to zero half way along the length of the capillary. The net result is that less gas would be transferred.

# Chapter 41

1. a  2. b  3. a  4. d  5. b  6. c  7. d  8. d  9. d  10. c
11. inferior vena cava → right atrium → right ventricle → left and right pulmonary arteries → lungs
12. right and left pulmonary veins → left atrium → left ventricle → aorta → to systemic circuit
13. The key is in the enormous cross-sectional area of small capillaries. Every time blood vessels branch, the cross-sectional areas of the resulting two vessels is larger (not smaller) than the original vessel. This slows the speed of blood enough for efficient exchange

to occur across the large surface area of the small vessels.

14. The earliest animals had no circulatory system, from which later evolved open and closed circulatory systems. As such, Porifera, cnidarians, Platyhelminthes, and nematodes have no circulatory systems. The exceptions are echinoderms, which also have no circulatory system, even though they evolved later. Open circulatory systems are found in urochordates, cephalochordates, arthropods, and some annelids. Other annelids, cephalopod molluscs (squids and octopuses), most deuterostome vertebrates, and all vertebrates have closed circulatory systems.

15. The diving reflex consists of breath holding, a slowing of heart rate, and redistribution of the blood to the heart and brain. This is a defensive reflex because it protects diving animals that normally breathe using lungs from breathing under water. It produces changes in blood flow, which conserves oxygen for tissues that need it most (the heart and brain). It reduces the metabolic rate, which prolongs the period the animal can stay submerged.

## Chapter 42

1. a 2. d 3. a 4. c 5. d 6. b 7. b 8. c 9. a 10. d 11. d 12. b 13. b
14. Refer to Figure 42.13.
15. Refer to Figure 42.13.

## Chapter 43

1. a 2. d 3. c 4. a 5. c
6. Prothoracicotropic hormone (PTTH) stimulates the prothoracic glands to release ecdysone. The brain hormone ecdysone promotes growth of a new exoskeleton under the old one, and stimulates the release of other hormones that lead to the moult. If the concentration of juvenile hormone (JH) is high, the moult produces a larger larva. If the JH concentration is low, the moult leads to pupation. After the adult emerges from the pupa, JH levels rise again and help trigger fully mature sexual behaviour.

7. c 8. a 9. b 10. c 11. b 12. d 13. a
14. The posterior pituitary gland is an extension of the hypothalamus. It does not make its own hormones, but stores hormones made in the hypothalamus. The neurosecretory cells in the hypothalamus make ADH and oxytocin, which are transported to the posterior pituitary gland by axons, where they are released when the neurosecretory cells are stimulated. The anterior pituitary consists of endocrine cells that synthesize and secrete many different releasing or inhibiting hormones. These hormones stimulate endocrine cells in the anterior pituitary to release their hormones. Several of these hormones, such as ACTH, FSH, LH, and TSH, target other endocrine glands in the body. They also secrete hormones that do not affect other glands in the body, such as prolactin and growth hormone.

15. Endocrine system: In autocrine regulation, a local regulator acts on the same cells that release it. This is a common mechanism used by cells to either reduce or increase their sensitivity to other stimuli. In paracrine regulation, a cell releases signalling molecules that diffuse through the extracellular fluid and act on nearby cells. In both these instances, regulation is local rather than at a distance. In endocrine regulation, hormones are secreted into the blood or extracellular fluid by the cells of ductless secretory organs called endocrine glands. Nervous system: In neuroendocrine regulation, specialized neurosecretory neurons respond to and conduct electrical signals, but rather than synapsing with target cells, they release a neurohormone into the circulation when appropriately stimulated. The hormone is produced in the cell body and packaged in membrane-bound vesicles that are transported along the axon to the release sites. The neurohormone is usually distributed in blood or other body fluids, and elicits a response in target cells some distance away that have receptors for the neurohormone. In contrast, in neural regulation, neurons synapse directly with target cells, releasing neurotransmitters into a synapse or neuromuscular junction. Both neurohormones and neurotransmitters are secreted by neurons. Neurohormones are distinguished from neurotransmitters in that neurohormones affect distant target cells, whereas neurotransmitters affect adjacent cells.

## Chapter 44

1. c 2. a 3. d 4. d 5. d 6. b 7. a
8. The yolk sac is an extension of mesoderm and endoderm enclosing the yolk. It stores nutrients for the embryo. The chorion, produced from ectoderm and mesoderm, completely surrounds the embryo and yolk sac, and lines the inside of the shell. The chorion exchanges oxygen and carbon dioxide with the environment through the egg's shell. The amnion closes over the embryo to form the amniotic cavity. Cells of the amnion secrete amniotic fluid into the cavity, which bathes the embryo and provides an aquatic environment in which it can develop. The allantois stores nitrogenous wastes removed from the embryo. The part of the allantoic membrane lining the chorion forms a rich bed of capillaries connected to the embryo by arteries and veins. This circulatory system delivers carbon dioxide to the chorion and picks up the oxygen.

9. A diploid spermatogonium divides by meiosis. Meiosis I creates primary spermatocytes, which are diploid and with replicated chromosomes. It divides further into secondary spermatocytes, which are haploid, but still with duplicated chromosomes. Meiosis I is over. In meiosis II, haploid spermatocytes divide into spermatids, which are haploid and with a

single set of chromosomes. These mature into sperm, which are haploid as well.

10. d  11. b  12. c  13. a  14. c  15. b

# Chapter 45

1. c  2. b  3. a  4. d  5. c  6. b  7. c  8. a  9. d  10. a  11. d  12. b  13. c

14. Being radially symmetrical, these animals lack a head and therefore a cephalized brain. Instead, they have a series of ganglia connected by a nerve ring that surrounds the centrally located mouth. Neurons are organized into radial nerves. If the nerve serving an arm is cut, the arm can still move in response to stimuli, but not in coordination with the other arms.

15. In an electrical synapse, the plasma membranes of the presynaptic and postsynaptic cells make direct contact. In a chemical synapse, the plasma membranes of the presynaptic and postsynaptic cells are separated by a narrow synaptic cleft. In electrical synapses, ions flow through gap junctions that connect the two membranes, allowing impulses to pass directly to the postsynaptic cell. In chemical synapses, neurotransmitters diffuse across the cleft and bind to receptors in the plasma membrane of the postsynaptic cell. This binding opens the channels for ions to flow, potentially generating the impulse in the postsynaptic cell.

# Chapter 46

1. d  2. d  3. a  4. c  5. c  6. a  7. a  8. d  9. b  10. b  11. c  12. c  13. b  14. d

15. Constriction of circular muscles elongates the segments, pushing them forward. Setae anchor the segments to prevent backward sliding. Constriction of longitudinal muscles shortens the segments. It is obvious that earthworms have an antagonistic pair of muscles—circular and longitudinal muscles—that oppose each other, allowing the animal to move in one direction.

# Glossary

**3′ end** The end of a polynucleotide chain at which a hydroxyl group is bonded to the 3 carbon of a deoxyribose sugar. p. 256

**5′ cap** In eukaryotes, a guanine-containing nucleotide attached in a reverse orientation to the 5 end of pre-mRNA and retained in the mRNA produced from it. The 5′ cap on an mRNA is the site where ribosomes attach to initiate translation. p. 286

**5′ end** The end of a polynucleotide chain at which a phosphate group is bound to the 5 carbon of a deoxyribose sugar. p. 256

**10 nm chromatin fibre** The most fundamental level of chromatin packing of a eukaryotic chromosome, in which DNA winds for almost two turns around an eight-protein nucleosome core particle to form a nucleosome, and linker DNA extends between adjacent nucleosomes. The result is a beads-on-a-string type of structure with a 10 nm diameter. p. 155

**30 nm chromatin fibre** Level of chromatin packing of a eukaryotic chromosome in which histone H1 binds to the 10 nm chromatin fibre, causing it to package into a coiled structure about 30 nm in diameter and with about six nucleosomes per turn. Also referred to as a *solenoid*. p. 155

**A site** The site where the incoming aminoacyl-tRNA carrying the next amino acid to be added to the polypeptide chain binds to the mRNA. p. 291

**abductor muscle** Muscles that abduct or move a body part away from the body (the opposite action to an adductor muscle that moves a body part toward the midline). p. 666

**abiotic** Nonbiological, often in reference to physical factors in the environment. p. 494

**abscisic acid (ABA)** A plant hormone involved in the abscission of leaves, flowers, and fruits; dormancy of buds and seeds; and closing of stomata. p. 980

**abscission** In plants, the dropping of flowers, fruits, and leaves in response to environmental signals. p. 987

**absorb** The process by which cells take up substances such as nutrients. p. 1030

**absorption spectrum** Curve representing the amount of light absorbed at each wavelength. p. 130

**absorptive nutrition** Mode of nutrition in which an organism secretes digestive enzymes into its environment and then absorbs the small molecules thus produced. p. 588

**accommodation** A process by which the lens changes to enable the eye to focus on objects at different distances. p. 1225

**acetabulum** Socket of hip joint, receives head of femur. p. 700

**acid-growth hypothesis** A hypothesis to explain how the hormone auxin promotes the growth of plant cells; it suggests that auxin stimulates H pumps in the plasma membrane to move H from the cell interior into the cell wall, which increases wall acidity, making the wall expandable. p. 984

**acidity** The concentration of $H^+$ in a water solution, compared with the concentration of $OH^-$. p. 70

**acid precipitation** Rainfall with low pH, primarily created when gaseous sulfur dioxide ($SO_2$) dissolves in water vapour in the atmosphere, forming sulfuric acid. p. 963

**acid reflux** Heartburn in humans; caused by the imperfect closure of the gastroesophageal sphincter, allowing acidic stomach contents to enter the esophagus. p. 1041

**acoelomate** A body plan of bilaterally symmetrical animals that lack a body cavity (coelom) between the gut and the body wall. p. 646

**acorn worms** Sedentary marine animals living in U-shaped tubes or burrows in coastal sand or mud. p. 684

**acrosome** A specialized secretory vesicle on the head of an animal sperm, which helps the sperm penetrate the egg. p. 1164

**acrosome reaction** The process in which enzymes contained in the acrosome are released from an animal sperm and digest a path through the egg coats. p. 1178

**action potential** The abrupt and transient change in membrane potential that occurs when a neuron conducts an electrical impulse. p. 996

**action spectrum** Graph produced by plotting the effectiveness of light at each wavelength in driving photosynthesis. p. 131

**activation energy** The initial input of energy required to start a reaction. p. 64

**activator** A regulatory protein that controls the expression of one or more genes. p. 309

**active parental care** Parents' investment of time and energy in caring for offspring after they are born or hatched. p. 754

**active site** The region of an enzyme that recognizes and combines with a substrate molecule. p. 65

**active transport** The mechanism by which ions and molecules move against the concentration gradient across a membrane, from the side with the lower concentration to the side with the higher concentration. p. 88

**adaptive zone** A part of a habitat that may be occupied by a group of species exploiting the same resources in a similar manner. p. 704

**adenine** A purine that base-pairs with either thymine in DNA or uracil in RNA. p. 256

**adherens junction** Animal cell junction in which intermediate filaments are the anchoring cytoskeletal component. p. 46

**adhesion** The adherence of molecules to the walls of conducting tubes, as in plants. p. 45

**adipose tissue** Connective tissue containing large, densely clustered cells called adipocytes that are specialized for fat storage. p. 1014

**adrenal cortex** The outer region of the adrenal glands, which contains endocrine cells that secrete two major types of steroid hormones, the glucocorticoids and the mineralocorticoids. p. 1149

**adrenal medulla** The central region of the adrenal glands, which contains neurosecretory neurons that secrete the catecholamine hormones epinephrine and norepinephrine. p. 1149

**adrenocorticotropic hormone (ACTH)** A hormone that triggers hormone secretion by cells in the adrenal cortex. p. 1145

**adventitious** Formed in an unusual position. p. 901

**adventitious root** A root that develops from the stem or leaves of a plant. p. 901

**aerobe** An organism that requires oxygen for cellular respiration. p. 544

**afferent arteriole** The vessel that delivers blood to the glomerulus of the kidney. p. 1117

**afferent neuron** A neuron that transmits stimuli collected by a sensory receptor to an interneuron. p. 1201

**African emergence hypothesis** A hypothesis proposing that modern humans first evolved in Africa and then dispersed to other continents. p. 405

**agar** A gelatinous product extracted from certain red algae or seaweed used as a culture medium in the laboratory and as a gelling or stabilizing agent in foods. p. 175

**agarose gel electrophoresis** Technique by which DNA, RNA, or molecules are separated in a gel subjected to an electric field. p. 340

**age-specific fecundity** The average number of offspring produced by surviving females of a particular age. p. 752

**age-specific mortality** The proportion of individuals alive at the start of an age interval that died during that age interval. p. 752

**age-specific survivorship** The proportion of individuals alive at the start of an age interval that survived until the start of the next age interval. p. 752

**aggregate fruit** A fruit that develops from multiple separate carpels of a single flower, such as a raspberry or strawberry. p. 942

**albumin** The most abundant protein in blood plasma, important for osmotic balance and pH buffering; also, the portion of an egg that serves as the main source of nutrients and water for the embryo. p. 1084

**alcohol** A molecule of the form R—OH in which R is a chain of one or more carbon atoms, each of which is linked to hydrogen atoms. p. 80

**alcohol fermentation** Reaction in which pyruvate is converted into ethyl alcohol and $CO_2$ in a two-step series that also converts NADH into $NAD^+$. p. 117

**aldosterone** A mineralocorticoid hormone released from the adrenal cortex that increases the amount of Na reabsorbed from the urine in the kidneys and absorbed from foods in the intestine, reduces the amount of Na secreted by salivary and sweat glands, and increases the rate of K excretion by the kidneys, keeping Na and K balanced at the levels required for normal cellular function. p. 1150

**algin** Alginic acid, found in the cell walls of brown algae. p. 572

**allantoic membrane** Forms from mesoderm and endoderm that has bulged outward from the gut and encloses the allantois. p. 1186

**allantois** In an amniote egg, an extraembryonic membrane sac that fills much of the space between the chorion and the yolk sac and stores the embryo's nitrogenous wastes. p. 1186

**allele** One of two or more versions of a gene. p. 175

**allochthonous** Sediment or rock that originated far from its present position. p. 836

**allopatric speciation** The evolution of reproductive isolating mechanisms between two populations that are geographically separated. p. 440

**allopolyploidy** The genetic condition of having two or more complete sets of chromosomes from different parent species. p. 445

**all-or-nothing principle** No matter how strong the stimulus, action potentials are always the same size; they either occur or do not occur. p. 1205

**allosteric activator** Molecule that converts an enzyme with an allosteric site, a regulatory site outside the active site, from the inactive form to the active form. p. 69

**allosteric inhibitor** Molecule that converts an enzyme with an allosteric site, a regulatory site outside the active site, from the active form to the inactive form. p. 69

**allosteric site** A regulatory site outside the active site. p. 69

**alpine tundra** A biome that occurs on high mountaintops throughout the world, in which dominant plants form cushions and mats. p. 619

**alternation of generations** The regular alternation of mode of reproduction in the life cycle of an organism, such as the alternation between diploid (sporophyte) and haploid (gametophyte) phases in plants. p. 612

**alternative splicing** Mechanism that joins exons in different combinations to produce different mRNAs from a single gene. p. 288

**altricial** Newborns that are immobile and helpless for some considerable time after birth. p. 709

**altruism** A behavioural phenomenon in which individuals appear to sacrifice their own reproductive success to help other individuals. p. 873

**alveolus** (plural, **alveoli**) One of the millions of tiny air pockets in mammalian lungs, each surrounded by dense capillary networks. p. 1063

**amacrine cell** A type of neuron that forms lateral connections in the retina of the eye, connecting bipolar cells and ganglion cells. p. 1226

**amino acid** A molecule that contains both an amino and a carboxyl group. p. 30

**aminoacylation** The process of adding an amino acid to a tRNA. Also referred to as *charging*. p. 291

**aminoacyl–tRNA** A tRNA linked to its "correct" amino acid, which is the finished product of charging. p. 291

**aminoacyl–tRNA synthetase** An enzyme that catalyzes aminoacylation. p. 291

**ammocoetes** Larval lamprey eel. p. 689

**ammonification** A metabolic process in which bacteria and fungi convert organic nitrogen compounds into ammonia and ammonium ions; part of the nitrogen cycle. pp. 828, 967

**amniocentesis** Technique of prenatal diagnosis in which cells are obtained from the amniotic fluid. p. 243

**amnion** In an amniote egg, an extraembryonic membrane that encloses the embryo, forming the amniotic cavity and secreting amniotic fluid, which provides an aquatic environment in which the embryo develops. p. 1186

**Amniota** The monophyletic group of vertebrates that have an amnion during embryonic development. p. 1186

**amniote (amniotic) egg** A shelled egg that can survive and develop on land. p. 698

**amoeboid** Similar to an amoeba, particularly in type of movement. p. 651

**amphipathic** Containing a region that is hydrophobic and a region that is hydrophilic. p. 80

**amplification** An increase in the magnitude of each step as a signal transduction pathway proceeds. pp. 95, 1140

**amygdala** A grey-matter centre of the brain that works as a switchboard, routing information about experiences that have an emotional component through the limbic system. p. 1242

**anabolic pathway** Type of metabolic pathway in which energy is consumed to build complicated molecules from simpler ones; often called a biosynthetic pathway. p. 61

**anabolic reaction** Metabolic reaction that requires energy to assemble simple substances into more complex molecules. p. 102

**anabolic steroid** A steroid hormone that stimulates muscle development. p. 1151

**anaerobe** *See* facultative anaerobe and strict anaerobe. p. 118

**anaerobic respiration** The process by which molecules are oxidized to produce ATP via an electron transport chain and ATP synthase, but unlike aerobic respiration, oxygen is not the final electron acceptor. p. 544

**anaphase** The phase of mitosis during which the spindle separates sister chromatids and pulls them to opposite spindle poles. p. 155

**anapsid (lineage Anapsida)** A member of the group of amniote vertebrates with no temporal arches and no spaces on the sides of the skull (includes turtles). p. 699

**anatomy** The study of the structures of organisms. p. 882

**ancestral character state** A trait that was present in a distant common ancestor. p. 463

**anchoring junction** Cell junction that forms belts that run entirely around cells, "welding" adjacent cells together. p. 45

**androgen** One of a family of hormones that promote the development and maintenance of sex characteristics. pp. 1151, 1176

**aneuploid** An individual with extra or missing chromosomes. p. 237

**angiosperm** A flowering plant. Its egg-containing ovules mature into seeds within protected chambers called ovaries. p. 21

**animal behaviour** The responses of animals to specific internal and external stimuli. p. 846

**animal pole** The end of the egg where the egg nucleus is located, which typically gives rise to surface structures and the anterior end of the embryo. p. 1180

**anion** A negatively charged ion. pp. F-11, 1203

**annual** A herbaceous plant that completes its life cycle in one growing season and then dies. p. 889

**antagonistic pair** Two skeletal muscles, one of which flexes as the other extends to move joints. p. 1269

**antenna** (plural, **antennae**) A chemosensory appendage attached to the head of some adult arthropods. p. 131

**antenna complex** In photosystems, the sites at which light is absorbed and converted into chemical energy during photosynthesis, an aggregate of many chlorophyll pigments and a number of carotenoid pigments that serve as the primary site of absorbing light energy in the form of photons. p. 131

**anterior pituitary** The glandular part of the pituitary, composed of endocrine cells that synthesize and secrete several tropic and nontropic hormones. p. 1145

**anther** The pollen-bearing part of a stamen. p. 936

**antheridium** (plural, **antheridia**) In plants, a structure in which sperm are produced. p. 619

**Anthocerotophyta** The phylum comprising hornworts. p. 622

**Anthophyta** The phylum comprising flowering plants. p. 633

**antibiotic** A natural or synthetic substance that kills or inhibits the growth of bacteria and other microorganisms. p. 546

**antibody** A highly specific soluble protein molecule that circulates in the blood and lymph, recognizing and binding to antigens and clearing them from the body. p. 215

**anticodon** The three-nucleotide segment in tRNAs that pairs with a codon in mRNAs. p. 290

**antidiuretic hormone (ADH)** A hormone secreted by the posterior pituitary that increases water absorption in the kidneys, thereby increasing the volume of the blood. p. 1147

**anti-Müllerian hormone** The hormone that causes the Müllerian ducts to disappear; compare to testosterone stimulating the development of Wolffian ducts into a male reproductive tract. p. 1192

**antiparallel** Refers to strands of DNA that run in opposite directions. p. 258

**antiport** A secondary active transport mechanism in which a molecule moves through a membrane channel into a cell and powers the active transport of a second molecule out of the cell. Also referred to as *exchange diffusion.* p. 90

**aorta** A large artery from the heart that branches into arteries leading to all body regions except the lungs. p. 1087

**aortic body** One of several small clusters of chemoreceptors, baroreceptors, and supporting cells located along the aortic arch that measures changes in blood pressure and the composition of arterial blood flowing past it. p. 1086

**apical dominance** Inhibition of the growth of lateral buds in plants due to auxin diffusing down a shoot tip from the terminal bud. p. 895

**apical growth** Growth from the tip of a cell or tissue. p. 588

**apical meristem** A region of unspecialized dividing cells at the shoot tips and root tips of a plant. pp. 615, 888

**apical surface** The outer surface of epithelial cells. p. 1010

**apicomplexan** A group of parasitic organisms with specific structures in their apical complex to penetrate and enter the cells they parasitize. p. 568

**apomixis** In plants, the production of offspring without meiosis or formation of gametes. p. 947

**apomorphy** A derived character state. p. 463

**apoplast** The nonliving component of plant tissues, composed of cell walls and intercellular spaces. p. 917

**apoplastic pathway** The route followed by water moving through plant cell walls and intercellular spaces (the apoplast). *Compare* symplastic pathway. p. 917

**apoptosis** Programmed cell death. pp. 167, 1186

**aposematic** Refers to bright, contrasting patterns that advertise the unpalatability of poisonous or repellent species. p. 787

**appendicular skeleton** The bones constituting the pectoral (shoulder) and pelvic (hip) girdles and limbs of a vertebrate. p. 1266

**appendix** A fingerlike sac that extends from the cecum of the large intestine. p. 1045

**applied research** Research conducted with the goal of solving specific practical problems. p. 335

**aquaporin** A specialized protein channel that facilitates diffusion of water through cell membranes. p. 915

**aquatic succession** A process in which debris from rivers and runoff accumulates in a body of fresh water, causing it to fill in at the margins. p. 801

**aqueous humour** A clear fluid that fills the space between the cornea and the lens of the eye. p. 1225

**arbuscular mycorrhizas** Symbiotic association between a glomeromycete fungus and the roots of a wide range of plants, including nonvascular, nonseed, and seed plants. p. 965

**arbuscule** Highly branched hypha produced inside root cells by arbuscular mycorrhizal fungi; nutrient exchange site between plant and fungus. p. 594

**Archaea** One of two domains of prokaryotes; archaeans have some unique molecular and biochemical traits, but they also share some traits with Bacteria and other traits with Eukarya. p. 538

**archaeocytes** A major group of the domain Archaea, members of which are found in different extreme environments. They include methanogens, extreme halophiles, and some extreme thermophiles. *See also* Euryarchaeota. p. 651

**archegonium** (plural, **archegonia**) The flask-shaped structure in which bryophyte eggs form. p. 619

**archenteron** The central endoderm-lined cavity of an embryo at the gastrula stage, which forms the primitive gut. pp. 648, 1181

**Archosauromorpha** A diverse group of diapsids that comprises crocodilians, pterosaurs, and dinosaurs (including birds). p. 700

**arctic tundra** A treeless biome that stretches from the boreal forests to the polar ice cap in Europe, Asia, and North America. p. 619

**arteries** In vertebrates, vessels conducting blood away from the heart at relatively high pressure. p. 1081

**arteriole** A branch from a small artery at the point where it reaches the organ it supplies. p. 1090

**artificial selection** Selective breeding of animals or plants to ensure that certain desirable traits appear at higher frequency in successive generations. p. 399

**ascocarp** A reproductive body that bears or contains asci. p. 594

**ascospore** Spore formed by meiosis in the ascus, a saclike cell produced by ascomycete fungi. p. 596

**asexual reproduction** Any mode of reproduction in which a single individual gives rise to offspring without fusion of gametes, that is, without genetic input from another individual. *See also* vegetative reproduction. p. 1162

**assimilation efficiency** The ratio of the energy absorbed from consumed food to the total energy content of the food. p. 819

**association areas** Several areas surrounding the sensory and motor areas of the cerebral cortex that integrate information from the sensory areas, formulate responses, and pass them on to the primary motor area. p. 1244

**aster** Radiating array produced as microtubules extending from the centrosomes of cells grow in length and extent. p. 160

**astrocyte** A star-shaped glial cell that provides support to neurons in the vertebrate central nervous system. p. 1201

**atmospheric pressure** The density (thickness or thinness) of the air in the atmosphere; the pressure exerted on the surface of Earth due to the weight of the air above it stretching from the atmosphere to the surface of Earth. p. 1058

**atom** The smallest unit that retains the chemical and physical properties of an element. p. F-8

**atomic number** The number of protons in the nucleus of an atom. p. F-8

**ATP cycle** Continued breakdown and resynthesis of ATP. p. **63**

**ATP synthase** A membrane-spanning protein complex that couples the energetically favourable transport of protons across a membrane to the synthesis of ATP. p. 113

**atrial siphon** A tube through which invertebrate chordates expel digestive and metabolic wastes. p. 685

**atriopore** The hole in the body wall of a cephalochordate through which water is expelled from the body. p. 685

**atrioventricular node (AV node)** A region of the heart wall that receives signals from the sinoatrial node and conducts them to the ventricle. p. 1089

**atrioventricular valve (AV valve)** A valve composed of endocardium and connective tissue between each atrium and ventricle that prevents backflow of blood from the ventricle to the atrium during emptying of the heart. p. 1087

**atrium** (plural, **atria**) A body cavity or chamber surrounding the perforated pharynx of invertebrate chordates; also one of the chambers that receive blood returning to the heart. p. 685

**autocrine regulation** A local regulator acts on the same cells that release it. p. 1136

**autonomic nervous system** A subdivision of the peripheral nervous system that controls largely involuntary processes, including digestion, secretion by sweat glands, circulation of the blood, many functions of the reproductive and excretory systems, and contraction of smooth muscles in all parts of the body. p. 1247

**autopolyploidy** The genetic condition of having more than two sets of chromosomes from the same parent species. p. 444

**autosomal dominant inheritance** Pattern in which the allele that causes a trait is dominant, and only homozygous recessives are unaffected. p. 241

**autosomal recessive inheritance** Pattern in which individuals with a trait are homozygous for a recessive allele. p. 240

**autosome** Chromosome other than a sex chromosome. p. 231

**autotroph** An organism that produces its own food using $CO_2$ and other simple inorganic compounds from its environment and energy from the Sun or from oxidation of inorganic substances. pp. 126, **503**, 543

**auxin** Any of a family of plant hormones that stimulate growth by promoting cell elongation in stems and coleoptiles, inhibit abscission, govern responses to light and gravity, and have other developmental effects. p. 981

**auxotroph** Mutant strain that is unable to synthesize amino acids. p. 175

**Avogadro's number** The number $6.022 \times 10^{23}$, derived by dividing the atomic weight of any element by the weight of an atom of that element. p. F-19

***Avr* gene** A gene in certain plant pathogens that encodes a product triggering a defensive response in the plant. p. 991

**axial skeleton** The bones constituting the head and trunk of a vertebrate: the cranium, vertebral column, ribs, and sternum (breastbone). pp. 687, 1266

**axillary bud** Embryonic shoot that develops where a leaf meets the stem. p. 895

**axillary meristem** A cluster of totipotent cells found at the shoot nodes. These allow new shoots to form branches off the main shoot, and may convert to flowers in some species. p. 936

**axon** The single elongated extension of a neuron that conducts signals away from the cell body to another neuron or an effector. p. 1200

**axon hillock** A junction with the cell body of a neuron from which the axon arises. p. 1200

**axon terminal** A branch at the tip of an axon that ends as a small, buttonlike swelling. p. 1200

**axopods** Slender, raylike strands of cytoplasm supported internally by long bundles of microtubules. p. 572

**backbone (spine)** Vertebral column of vertebrates. p. 685

**Bacteria** One of the two domains of prokaryotes; collectively, bacteria are the most metabolically diverse organisms. p. 538

**bacterial flagellum** *See* flagellum. p. 31

**bacteriophage** A virus that infects bacteria. Also referred to as a *phage*. pp. 181, 254, 523

**bacteroid** A rod-shaped or branched bacterium in the root nodules of nitrogen-fixing plants. p. 968

**balancing selection** A type of natural selection in which more than one allele is actively maintained in a population. p. 425

**bark** The tough outer covering of woody stems and roots, comprising all the living and nonliving tissues between the vascular cambium and the stem surface. p. 904

**Barr body** The inactive, condensed X chromosome seen in the nucleus of female mammals. p. 235

**basal lamina** A membrane secreted at the inner surface of epithelial cells. p. 1011

**basal nucleus** (plural, **basal nuclei**) One of several grey-matter centres that surround the thalamus on both sides of the brain and moderate voluntary movements directed by motor centres in the cerebrum. p. 1242

**basal surface** The inner surface of epithelial cells. p. 1011

**base analogue** a chemical that can substitute for a normal base in RNA or DNA. p. 300

**base-excision repair** An excision repair mechanism that repairs nonbulky damage to DNA bases by removing the erroneous base and replacing it with the correct one complementary to the base on the other DNA strand. p. 271

**basement membrane** A membrane at the inner surface of epithelia in vertebrates. It consists of the basal lamina and a layer of connective tissue. p. 1011

**base-pair mismatch** An error in the assembly of a new nucleotide chain in which bases other than the correct ones pair together. p. 270

**basic research** Research conducted to search for explanations about natural phenomena to satisfy curiosity and advance collective knowledge of living systems. p. 334

**basidiocarp** A fruiting body of a basidiomycete; mushrooms are examples. p. 600

**basidiospore** A haploid sexual spore produced by basidiomycete fungi. p. 600

**basidium** (plural, **basidia**) A small, club-shaped structure in which sexual spores of basidiomycetes arise. p. 597

**basilar membrane** A stiff structural element within the cochlea. p. 1222

**behavioural isolation** A prezygotic reproductive isolating mechanism in which two species do not mate because of differences in courtship behaviour; also known as *ethological isolation*. p. 438

**biennial** A plant that completes its life cycle in two growing seasons and then dies; limited secondary growth occurs in some biennials. p. 889

**bile** A mixture of substances including bile salts, cholesterol, and bilirubin that is made in the liver, stored in the gallbladder, and used in the digestion of fats. p. 1039

**binary fission** Prokaryotic cell division—splitting or dividing into two parts. p. 151

**binomial** Relating to or consisting of two names or terms. p. 454

**binomial nomenclature** The naming of species with a two-part scientific name, the first indicating the genus and the second indicating the species. p. 454

**biofilm** A microbial community consisting of a complex aggregation of microorganisms attached to a surface. p. 546

**biogeochemical cycle** Any of several global processes in which a nutrient circulates between the abiotic environment and living organisms. pp. 544, 823

**biogeography** The study of the geographic distributions of plants and animals. p. 396

**bioinformatics** Field that fuses biology with mathematics and computer science and is used for the analysis of genome sequences. p. 371

**biological clock** An internal time-measuring mechanism that adapts an organism to recurring environmental changes. p. 997

**biological magnification** The increasing concentration of nondegradable poisons in the tissues of animals at higher trophic levels. p. 815

**biological research** The collective effort of individuals who have worked to understand how living systems function. p. F-2

**biological species concept** The definition of species based on the ability of populations to interbreed and produce fertile offspring. p. 434

**bioluminescent** Refers to an organism that glows or releases a flash of light, particularly when disturbed. p. 568

**biomass** The dry weight of biological material per unit area or volume of habitat. pp. 538, 817

**bioremediation** Applications of chemical and biological knowledge to decontaminate polluted environments. p. 538

**biotechnology** The manipulation of living organisms to produce useful products. p. 333

**biotic** Biological, often in reference to living components of the environment. p. 494

**bipedalism** The habit in animals of walking upright on two legs. p. 480

**bipolar cell** A type of neuron in the retina of the eye that connects the rods and cones with the ganglion cells. p. 1226

**blade** The expanded part of a leaf that provides a large surface area for absorbing sunlight and carbon dioxide. p. 897

**BLAST** The *Basic Local Alignment Search Tool* is a computer program which allows comparison of polypeptides or nucleic acids. p. 373

**blastocoel** A fluid-filled cavity in the blastula embryo. p. 1181

**blastocyst** An embryonic stage in mammals; a single cell–layered hollow ball of about 120 cells with a fluid-filled blastocoel in which a dense mass of cells is localized to one side. p. 1189

**blastodisc** A disclike layer of cells at the surface of the yolk produced by early cleavage divisions. p. 1185

**blastomere** A small cell formed during cleavage of the embryo. p. 1181

**blastopore** The opening at one end of the archenteron in the gastrula that gives rise to the mouth in protostomes and the anus in deuterostomes. p. 648

**blastula** The hollow ball of cells that is the result of cleavage divisions in an early embryo. p. 1181

**blending theory of inheritance** Theory suggesting that hereditary traits blend evenly in offspring through mixing of the blood of the two parents. p. 200

**blind spot** The point where the optic nerve exits the eye that lacks photoreceptors. p. 1226

**blood** A fluid connective tissue composed of blood cells suspended in a fluid extracellular matrix, plasma. p. 1015

**blood–brain barrier** A specialized arrangement of capillaries in the brain that prevents most substances dissolved in the blood from entering the cerebrospinal fluid and thus protects the brain and spinal cord from viruses, bacteria, and toxic substances that may circulate in the blood. p. 1240

**body plan** Description of the way that animals are built; the "blueprint" of cellular organization that encompasses such things as symmetry, segmentation, and formation and position of limbs. p. 645

**bolting** Rapid formation of a floral shoot in plant species that form rosettes, such as lettuce. p. 985

**bolus** The food mass after chewing. p. 1041

**bone** The densest form of connective tissue, in which living cells secrete the mineralized matrix of collagen and calcium salts that surrounds them; forms the skeleton. p. 1013

**boreal forest** A biome that is a circumpolar expanse of evergreen coniferous trees in Europe, Asia, and North America. p. 966

**Bowman's capsule** An infolded region at the proximal end of a nephron that cups around the glomerulus and collects the water and solutes filtered out of the blood. p. 1113

**brain** A single, organized collection of nervous tissue in an organism's head that forms the control centre of the nervous system and major sensory structures. p. 1200

**brain hormone** A peptide hormone secreted by neurosecretory neurons in the brain of insects. p. 1154

**brain stem** Consists of the pons and medulla; controls many vital body functions without conscious involvement or control by the cerebrum. p. 1239

**brassinosteroid** Any of a family of plant hormones that stimulate cell division and elongation and differentiation of vascular tissue. p. 988

**bronchi** The bronchi connect the trachea to the terminal airways, the bronchioles, leading to the alveoli in the lungs. p. 1065

**bronchiole** One of the small, branching airways in the lungs that lead into the alveoli. p. 1065

**brown adipose tissue** A specialized tissue in which the most intense heat generation by nonshivering thermogenesis takes place. p. 1128

**Bryophyta** The phylum of nonvascular plants, including mosses and their relatives. p. 621

**bryophyte** A general term for plants (such as mosses) that lack internal transport vessels. p. 619

**budding** A mode of asexual reproduction in which a new individual grows and develops while attached to the parent. pp. 588, 1162

**bulbourethral gland** One of two pea-sized glands on either side of the prostate gland that secrete a mucous fluid that is added to semen. p. 1176

**bulk feeder** An animal that consumes sizable food items whole or in large chunks. p. 1035

**bulk flow** The group movement of molecules in response to a difference in pressure between two locations. p. 919

**bulk-phase endocytosis (pinocytosis)** Mechanism by which extracellular water is taken into a cell together with any molecules that happen to be in solution in the water. p. 91

**calcitonin** A nontropic peptide hormone that lowers the level of $Ca^{2+}$ in the blood by inhibiting the ongoing dissolution of calcium from bone. p. 1148

**calcium pump ($Ca^{2+}$ pump)** Pump that pushes $Ca^{2+}$ from the cytoplasm to the cell exterior and from the cytosol into the vesicles of the endoplasmic reticulum. p. 89

**callus** An undifferentiated tissue that develops on or around a cut plant surface or in tissue culture. p. 948

**CAM plant** A $C_4$ plant that runs the Calvin and $C_4$ cycles at different times to circumvent photorespiration. CAM stands for "crassulacean acid metabolism." p. 141

**canines** Teeth located at the sides of the incisors specialized for biting and piercing. p. 1040

**capillary** The smallest-diameter blood vessel, with a wall that is one cell thick, which forms highly branched networks well adapted for diffusion of substances. p. 1082

**capsid** The protective layer of protein that surrounds the nucleic acid core of a virus. p. 522

**capsule** An external layer of sticky or slimy polysaccharides coating the cell wall in many prokaryotes. pp. 30, 542

**captaculum** (plural, **captacula**) In molluscs, a filamentous, tactile organ with an adhesive, suckerlike end used to gather small particles of food in the sand and pass them to the mouth. p. 668

**carapace** A protective outer covering that extends backward behind the head on the dorsal side of an animal, such as the shell of a turtle or lobster. p. 675

**carbon cycle** The global circulation of carbon atoms, especially via the processes of photosynthesis and respiration. p. 824

**cardiac cycle** The systole–diastole sequence of the heart. p. 1088

**cardiac muscle** The contractile tissue of the heart. p. 1016

**carnivore** An animal that primarily eats other animals. p. 710

**carotenoid** Molecule of yellow-orange pigment by which light is absorbed in photosynthesis. p. 20

**carotid bodies** Special sense organs that relay information to the brain about $O_2$ and $CO_2$ in the blood in the carotid arteries, which supply the brain. p. 1067

**carpel** The reproductive organ of a flower that houses an ovule and its associated structures. p. 936

**carrageenan** A chemical extracted from the red alga *Eucheuma* that is used to thicken and stabilize paints, dairy products such as pudding and ice cream, and many other creams and emulsions. p. 577

**carrier protein** Transport protein that binds a specific single solute and transports it across the lipid bilayer. p. 87

**carrying capacity** The maximum size of a population that an environment can support indefinitely. p. 758

**Cartagena Protocol on Biosafety** An international agreement that promotes biosafety as it relates to genetically modified organisms. p. 354

**cartilage** A tissue composed of sparsely distributed chondrocytes surrounded by networks of collagen fibres embedded in a tough but elastic matrix of the glycoprotein. p. 1013

**Casparian strip** A thin, waxy, impermeable band that seals abutting cell walls in roots; the strip helps control the type and amount of solutes that enter the stele by blocking the apoplastic pathway at the endodermis and forcing substances to pass through cells (the symplast). p. 918

**caspase** A protease involved in programmed cell death. p. 167

**catabolic pathway** Type of metabolic pathway in which energy is released by the breakdown of complex molecules to simpler compounds. p. 61

**catalyst** Substance with the ability to accelerate a spontaneous reaction without being changed by the reaction. p. 65

**catecholamine** Any of a class of compounds derived from the amino acid tyrosine that circulates in the bloodstream, including epinephrine and norepinephrine. p. 1150

**cation** A positively charged ion. pp. F-11, 1203

**cation exchange** Replacement of one cation with another, as on a soil particle. p. 963

**cDNA library** The entire collection of cloned cDNAs made from the mRNAs isolated from a cell. p. 336

**cecum** A blind pouch formed at the junction of the large and small intestines. p. 1045

**celestial navigation** Navigating by the positions of stars. p. 865

**cell adhesion molecule** A cell surface protein responsible for selectively binding cells together. p. 45

**cell body** The portion of the neuron containing genetic material and cellular organelles. p. 1200

**cell centre** *See* centrosome (cell centre). p. 41

**cell cycle** The sequence of events during which a cell experiences a period of growth followed by nuclear division and cytokinesis. p. 506

**cell differentiation** A process in which changes in gene expression establish cells with specialized structure and function. p. 934

**cell expansion** A mechanism that enlarges the cells in specific directions in a developing organ. p. 945

**cell junction** Junction that seals the spaces between cells and provides direct communication between cells. p. 45

**cell plate** In cytokinesis in plants, a new cell wall that forms between the daughter nuclei and grows laterally until it divides the cytoplasm. p. 157

**cell wall** A rigid external layer of material surrounding the plasma membrane of cells in plants, fungi, bacteria, and some protists, providing cell protection and support. p. 30

**cellular respiration** The process by which energy-rich molecules are broken down to produce energy in the form of ATP. p. 102

**cellular senescence** Loss of proliferative ability over time. p. 166

**cellular slime mould** Any of a variety of primitive organisms of the phylum Acrasiomycota, especially of the genus *Dictyostelium*; the life cycle is characterized by a slimelike amoeboid stage and a multicellular reproductive stage. p. 575

**cellulose** One of the primary constituents of plant cell walls, formed by chains of carbohydrate subunits. p. 886

**centimorgan** *See* map unit. p. 230

**central canal** The cavity of the neural tube becomes the fluid-filled ventricles of the brain and the central canal through the spinal cord. p. 1239

**central nervous system (CNS)** One of the two major divisions of the nervous system containing the brain and spinal cord. p. 1200

**central vacuole** A large, water-filled organelle in plant cells that maintains the turgor of the cell and controls movement of molecules between the cytosol and sap. pp. 44, 916

**centriole** A cylindrical structure consisting of nine triplets of microtubules in the centrosomes of most animal cells. pp. 41, 158

**centrosome (cell centre)** The main microtubule organizing centre of a cell, which organizes the microtubule cytoskeleton during interphase and positions many of the cytoplasmic organelles. pp. 41, 158

**cephalized An** animal's sense organs are concentrated at the anterior end (i.e., the head). p. 645

**cerebellum** The portion of the brain that receives sensory input from receptors in muscles and joints, from balance receptors in the inner ear, and from the receptors of touch, vision, and hearing. p. 1242

**cerebral cortex** A thin outer shell of grey matter covering a thick core of white matter within each hemisphere of the brain; the part of the forebrain responsible for information processing and learning. p. 1240

**cerebrospinal fluid** Fluid that circulates through the central canal of the spinal cord and the ventricles of the brain, cushioning the brain and spinal cord from jarring movements and impacts, as well as nourishing the CNS and protecting it from toxic substances. p. 1240

**cervix** The lower end of the uterus. p. 1023

**channel protein** Transport protein that forms a hydrophilic channel in a cell membrane through which water, ions, or other molecules can pass, depending on the protein. p. 85

**chaperone protein (chaperonin)** "Guide" protein that binds temporarily with newly synthesized proteins, directing their conformation toward the correct tertiary structure and inhibiting incorrect arrangements as the new proteins fold. p. F-35

**character** A heritable characteristic. pp. 200, 463

**character displacement** The phenomenon in which allopatric populations are morphologically similar and use similar resources, but sympatric populations are morphologically different and use different resources; may also apply to characters influencing mate choice. p. 791

**character state** One or more forms of a character used in a phylogenetic analysis. p. 463

**charging** *See* aminoacylation. p. 291

**charophyte** A member of the group of green algae most similar to the algal ancestors of land plants. p. 579

**checkpoint** Internal control of the cell cycle that prevents a critical phase from beginning until the previous phase is complete. p. 162

**chelicerae** The first pair of fanglike appendages near the mouth of an arachnid, used for biting prey and often modified for grasping and piercing. p. 673

**chelipeds** The legs of arthropods that terminate in a claw or pincer. p. 675

**chemical bond** Link formed when atoms of reactive elements combine into molecules. p. F-11

**chemical equation** A chemical reaction written in balanced form. p. F-15

**chemical reaction** A reaction that occurs when atoms or molecules interact to form new chemical bonds or break old ones. p. F-15

**chemical signal** Any secretion from one cell type that can alter the behaviour of a different cell that bears a receptor for it; a means of cell communication. p. 575

**chemical synapse** A type of communicating connection between two neurons or a neuron and an effector cell in which an electrical impulse arriving at an axon terminal of the presynaptic cell triggers release of a neurotransmitter that crosses the gap and binds to a receptor on the postsynaptic cell, triggering an electrical impulse in that cell. p. 1210

**chemiosmosis** Ability of cells to use the proton-motive force to do work. p. 113

**chemoautotroph** An organism that obtains energy by oxidizing inorganic substances such as hydrogen, iron, sulfur, ammonia, nitrites, and nitrates and uses carbon dioxide as a carbon source. p. 543

**chemoheterotroph** An organism that oxidizes organic molecules as an energy source and obtains carbon in organic form. p. 548

**chemoreceptor** A sensory receptor that detects specific molecules or chemical conditions such as acidity. p. 1215

**chemotroph** An organism that obtains energy by oxidizing inorganic or organic substances. p. 543

**chiasmata** *See* crossover. p. 192

**chief cell** Cell that secretes pepsinogen, the inactive precursor molecule of pepsin, in the gastric glands. p. 1041

**chitin** A polysaccharide that contains nitrogen and is present in the cell walls of fungi and the exoskeletons of arthropods. p. 45

**chloroplast** The site of photosynthesis in plant cells. p. 43

**chlorosis** An abnormal yellowing of plant tissues due to lack of chlorophyll; a sign of nutrient deficiency or infection by a pathogen. p. 959

**choanocyte** One of the inner layer of flagellated cells lining the body cavity of a sponge. p. 651

**Choanoflagellata** A group of minute, single-celled protists found in water; the flask-shaped body has a collar of closely packed microvilli that surrounds the single flagellum by which it moves and takes in food.  p. 576

**cholesterol**  The predominant sterol of animal cell membranes.  p. 82

**chorion**  In an amniote egg, an extraembryonic membrane that surrounds the embryo and yolk sac completely and exchanges oxygen and carbon dioxide with the environment; becomes part of the placenta in mammals.  p. 243

**chorionic villus**  (plural, **villi**) One of many treelike extensions from the chorion, which greatly increase the surface area of the chorion.  p. 1189

**chorionic villus sampling**  Technique of prenatal diagnosis in which cells are obtained from portions of the placenta that develop from tissues of the embryo.  p. 243

**chromatid**  One half of a replicated chromosome. Each chromatid contains one double helix of DNA.  p. 152

**chromatin**  The structural building block of a chromosome, which includes the complex of DNA and its associated proteins.  p. 32

**chromatin remodelling**  Process in which the state of the chromatin is changed so that the proteins that initiate transcription can bind to their promoters.  p. 320

**chromosome**  The nuclear unit of genetic information, consisting of a DNA molecule and associated proteins.  p. 152

**chromosome segregation**  The equal distribution of daughter chromosomes to each of the two cells that result from cell division.  p. 153

**chromosome theory of inheritance**  The principle that genes and their alleles are carried on the chromosomes.  p. 211

**chylomicron**  A small triglyceride droplet covered by a protein coat.  p. 1044

**chyme**  Digested content of the stomach released for further digestion in the small intestine.  p. 1044

**ciliary body**  A fine ligament in the eye that anchors the lens to a surrounding layer of connective tissue and muscle.  p. 1225

**cilium**  Motile structure, extending from a cell surface, that moves a cell through fluid or fluid over a cell.  p. 42

**circadian rhythm**  Any biological activity that is repeated in cycles, each about 24 hours long, independent of any shifts in environmental conditions.  pp. 17, 997

**circulatory system**  An organ system consisting of a fluid, a heart, and vessels for moving important molecules, and often cells, from one tissue to another.  p. 1080

**circumcision**  Removal of the prepuce for religious, cultural, or hygienic reasons.  p. 1177

**cisternae**  (singular, **cisterna**) Membranous channels and vesicles that make up the endoplasmic reticulum.  p. 35

**citric acid cycle**  Series of reactions in which acetyl groups are oxidized completely to carbon dioxide and some ATP molecules are synthesized. Also referred to as *Krebs cycle* and *tricarboxylic acid cycle*.  p. 108

**clade**  A monophyletic group of organisms that share homologous features derived from a common ancestor.  p. 456

**cladistics**  An approach to systematics that uses shared derived characters to infer the phylogenetic relationships and evolutionary history of groups of organisms.  p. 462

**claspers**  A pair of organs on the pelvic fins of male crustaceans and sharks, which help transfer sperm into the reproductive tract of the female.  p. 692

**classical conditioning**  A type of learning in which an animal develops a mental association between two phenomena that are usually unrelated.  p. 850

**classification**  An arrangement of organisms into hierarchical groups that reflect their relatedness.  p. 455

**clathrin**  The network of proteins that coat and reinforce the cytoplasmic surface of cell membranes.  p. 92

**cleavage**  Mitotic cell divisions of the zygote that produce a blastula from a fertilized ovum.  pp. 646, 1181

**climate**  The weather conditions prevailing over an extended period of time.  p. 139

**climax community**  A relatively stable, late successional stage in which the dominant vegetation replaces itself and persists until an environmental disturbance eliminates it, allowing other species to invade.  p. 801

**cline**  A pattern of smooth variation in a characteristic along a geographic gradient.  p. 436

**clitoris**  The structure at the junction of the labia minora in front of the vulva, homologous to the penis in the male.  p. 1171

**clone**  An individual genetically identical to an original cell from which it descended.  pp. 153, 175

**cloning vector**  DNA molecules into which a DNA fragment can be inserted to form a recombinant DNA molecule for cloning.  p. 336

**closed circulatory system**  A circulatory system in which the fluid, blood, is confined in blood vessels and is distinct from the interstitial fluid.  pp. 668, 1082

**cnidocyte**  A prey-capturing and defensive cell in the epidermis of cnidarians.  p. 653

**coactivator**  In eukaryotes, a large multiprotein complex that bridges between activators at an enhancer and proteins at the promoter and promoter proximal region to stimulate transcription.  p. 316

**coated pit**  A depression in the plasma membrane that contains receptors for macromolecules to be taken up by endocytosis.  p. 91

**coccoid**  Spherical prokaryotic cell.  p. 538

**cochlea**  A snail-shaped structure (in vertebrates) in the inner ear containing the organ of hearing.  pp. 538, 1221

**codominance**  Condition in which alleles have approximately equal effects in individuals, making the alleles equally detectable in heterozygotes.  p. 214

**codon**  Each three-letter word (triplet) of the genetic code.  p. 281

**coelom**  A fluid-filled body cavity in bilaterally symmetrical animals that is completely lined with derivatives of mesoderm.  p. 646

**coelomate**  A body plan of bilaterally symmetrical animals that have a coelom.  p. 646

**coenzymes**  Organic cofactors that include complex chemical groups of various kinds.  p. 67

**co-evolution**  The evolution of genetically based, reciprocal adaptations in two or more species that interact closely in the same ecological setting.  p. 778

**cofactor**  An inorganic or organic nonprotein group that is necessary for catalysis to take place.  p. 67

**cohesion–tension mechanism of water transport**  *See* cohesion–tension theory of water transport.  p. 919

**cohesion–tension theory of water transport**  Henry Dixon's explanation of the ascent of sap in terms of the relationship between transpiration and water's properties.  p. 919

**cohort**  A group of individuals of similar age.  p. 752

**coleoptile**  A protective sheath that covers the shoot apical meristem and plumule of the embryo in monocots, such as grasses, as it pushes up through soil.  p. 944

**coleorhiza** A sheath that encloses the radicle of an embryo until it breaks out of the seed coat and enters the soil as the primary root. p. 944

**collagen** Fibrous glycoprotein—very rich in carbohydrates—embedded in a network of proteoglycans. p. 1012

**collecting duct** A location where urine leaving individual nephrons is processed further. p. 1112

**collenchyma** One of three simple plant tissues. Flexibly supports rapidly growing plant parts. Its elongated cells are alive at maturity and often collectively form strands or a sheathlike cylinder under the dermal tissue of growing shoot regions and leaf stalks. p. 890

**colon** The main part of the large intestine. p. 1045

**colony** Multiple individual organisms of the same species living in a group. p. 562

**combinatorial gene regulation** The combining of a few regulatory proteins in particular ways so that the transcription of a wide array of genes can be controlled and a large number of cell types can be specified. p. 318

**commaless** The sequential nature of the words of the nucleic acid code, with no indicators such as commas or spaces to mark the end of one codon and the beginning of the next. p. 282

**commensalism** A symbiotic interaction in which one species benefits and the other is unaffected. p. 779

**companion cell** A specialized parenchyma cell that is connected to a mature sieve tube member by plasmodesmata and assists sieve tube members with both the uptake of sugars and the unloading of sugars in tissues. p. 893

**compass orientation** A wayfinding mechanism that allows animals to move in a particular direction, often over a specific distance or for a prescribed length of time. p. 865

**competitive exclusion principle** The ecological principle stating that populations of two or more species cannot coexist indefinitely if they rely on the same limiting resources and exploit them in the same way. p. 790

**competitive inhibition** Inhibition of an enzyme reaction by an inhibitor molecule that resembles the normal substrate closely enough that it fits into the active site of the enzyme. p. 68

**complementary base-pairing** Feature of DNA in which the specific purine–pyrimidine base pairs A–T (adenine–thymine) and G–C (guanine–cytosine) occur to bridge the two sugar–phosphate backbones. p. 257

**complementary DNA (cDNA)** A DNA molecule that is complementary to an mRNA molecule, synthesized by reverse transcriptase. p. 336

**complete metamorphosis** The form of metamorphosis in which an insect passes through four separate stages of growth: egg, larva, pupa, and adult. p. 678

**complex I** NADH dehydrogenase. p. 109

**complex II** Succinate dehydrogenase. p. 109

**complex III** Cytochrome complex. p. 109

**complex IV** Cytochrome oxidase. p. 109

**compound** A unit composed of more than one type of atom combined chemically in fixed numbers and ratios. p. F-11

**compound eye** The eye of most insects and some crustaceans, composed of many-faceted, light-sensitive units called ommatidia fitted closely together, each with its own refractive system and each forming a portion of an image. pp. 676, 1224

**concentration** The number of molecules or ions of a substance in a unit volume of space. p. F-18

**concentration gradient** The concentration difference that drives diffusion. p. 84

**concestor** Common ancestor. p. 373

**conduction** 1. The flow of heat between atoms or molecules in direct contact. 2. The flow of an action potential along an axon. *See also* propagation (conduction). pp. 1121, 1206

**cone** 1. In cone-bearing plants, a cluster of sporophylls. 2. In the vertebrate eye, a photoreceptor in the retina that is specialized for detection of different wavelengths (colours). pp. 625, 1225

**conformation** The overall three-dimensional shape of a protein. p. 66

**conformational change** Alteration in the three-dimensional shape of a protein. p. 1258

**conformers** Animals having internal environments that change as the external environment changes. p. 1019

**conidium** (plural, **conidia**) An asexually produced fungal spore. p. 596

**Coniferophyta** The major phylum of cone-bearing gymnosperms, most of which are substantial trees; includes pines, firs, and other conifers. p. 630

**connective tissue** Tissue with cells scattered through an extracellular matrix; forms layers in and around body structures that support other body tissues, transmit mechanical and other forces, and in some cases act as filters. p. 1012

**conodont** An abundant, bonelike fossil dating from the early Paleozoic era through the early Mesozoic era, now described as a feeding structure of some of the earliest vertebrates. p. 689

**consciousness** Awareness of oneself, one's identity, and one's surroundings, with understanding of the significance and likely consequences of events. p. 1245

**consumer** An organism that consumes other organisms in a community or ecosystem. p. 778

**contact inhibition** The inhibition of movement or proliferation of normal cells that results from cell–cell contact. p. 164

**contractile vacuole** A specialized cytoplasmic organelle that pumps fluid in a cyclical manner from within the cell to the outside by alternately filling and then contracting to release its contents at various points on the surface of the cell. p. 562

**control** Treatment that tells what would be seen in the absence of the experimental manipulation. p. F-3

**convection** The transfer of heat from a body to a fluid, such as air or water, that passes over its surface. p. 1121

**convergent evolution** The evolution of similar adaptations in distantly related organisms that occupy similar environments. p. 459

**corepressor** In the regulation of gene expression in bacteria, a regulatory molecule that combines with a repressor to activate it and shut off an operon. p. 313

**cork** A nonliving, impermeable secondary tissue that is one element of bark. p. 903

**cork cambium** A lateral meristem in plants that forms periderm, which in turn produces cork. p. 903

**cornea** The transparent layer that forms the front wall of the eye, covering the iris. p. 1224

**corpus callosum** A structure formed of thick axon bundles that connect the two cerebral hemispheres and coordinate their functions. p. 1243

**corpus luteum** Cells remaining at the surface of the ovary during the luteal phase; the structure acts as an endocrine gland, secreting several hormones: estrogens, large quantities of progesterone, and inhibin. p. 1174

**cortisol** The major glucocorticoid steroid hormone secreted by the adrenal cortex, which increases blood glucose by promoting breakdown of proteins and fats. p. 1150

**cotranslational import** A mechanism in which proteins end up on the inside (lumen) of the endoplasmic reticulum (ER) as they are translated by ribosome associated with the ER. p. 297

**cotransport** *See* symport. p. 90

**cotyledon** A leaf of a seed plant embryo; also known as a seed leaf. p. 944

**coupled reaction** Reaction that occurs when an exergonic reaction is joined to an endergonic reaction, producing an overall reaction that is exergonic. p. 63

**covalent bond** Bond formed by electron sharing between atoms. p. F-12

**cranial nerve** A nerve that connects the brain directly to the head, neck, and body trunk. p. 687

**cranium** The part of the skull that encloses the brain. p. 687

**crassulacean acid metabolism (CAM)** A biochemical variation of photosynthesis that was discovered in a member of the plant family Crassulaceae. Carbon dioxide is taken up and stored during the night to allow the stomata to remain closed during the daytime, decreasing water loss. pp. 141, 923

**Crenarchaeota** A major group of the domain Archaea, separated from the other archaeans based mainly on rRNA sequences. p. 551

**CRISPR (Clusters of Regularly Interspersed Short Palindromic Repeats)** A locus in sequenced bacterial and archaeal genomes that, with *cas* genes, encode an immune system against foreign bacteriophages and plasmids. Each CRISPR locus consists of repeated sequences about 40 bp long that have palindromic regions, and that are interspersed with unique sequences of about the same length. p. 348

**crista** (plural, **cristae**) Fold that expands the surface area of the inner mitochondrial membrane. p. 39

**critical period** A restricted stage of development early in life during which an animal has the capacity to respond to specific environmental stimuli. p. 850

**crop** Of birds, an enlargement of the digestive tube where the digestive contents are stored and mixed with lubricating mucus. p. 1038

**crosscurrent** Air passing through air capillaries and blood moving through blood capillaries travel at right angles to each other such that oxygen diffuses from the air capillaries into the blood at many points along the length of avian parabronchi. This results in higher partial pressures of $O_2$ in the blood leaving the lungs than is possible in the alveolar lungs of mammals. p. 1064

**crossing-over** The recombination process in meiosis, in which chromatids exchange segments. p. 190

**crossover** Site of recombination during meiosis. Also referred to as a *chiasmata*. p. 190

**cross-pollination** Fertilization of one plant by a different plant. p. 200

**cryptochrome** A light-absorbing protein that is sensitive to blue light and that may also be an important early step in various light-based growth responses. p. 994

**ctenidium** (plural, **ctenidia**) A comblike or featherlike structure. In mollusks they appear as gills, while in some insects they appear as rows of spines on their legs. p. 668

**C-terminal end** The end of an amino acid chain with a —COO group. p. 289

**cupula** In certain mechanoreceptors, a gelatinous structure with stereocilia extending into it that moves with pressure changes in the surrounding water; movement of the cupula bends the stereocilia, which triggers release of neurotransmitters. p. 1217

**cuticle** The outer layer of plants and some animals, which helps prevent desiccation by slowing water loss. pp. 614, 894

**C-value** Genome size of an organism. p. 378

**Cycadophyta** A phylum of palmlike gymnosperms known as cycads; the pollen-bearing and seed-bearing cones (strobili) occur on separate plants. p. 630

**cyclic AMP (cAMP)** In particular signal transduction pathways, a second messenger that activates protein kinases, which elicit the cellular response by adding phosphate groups to specific target proteins. cAMP functions in one of two major G protein–coupled receptor response pathways. p. 311

**cyclic electron transport** An electron transport pathway associated with photosystem I in photosynthesis that produces ATP without the synthesis of NADPH. p. 134

**cyclin** In eukaryotes, protein that regulates the activity of Cdk (cyclin-dependent kinase) and controls progression through the cell cycle. p. 162

**cyclin-dependent kinase (CDK)** A protein kinase that controls the cell cycle in eukaryotes. p. 163

**cytokinesis** Division of the cytoplasm into two daughter cells following the nuclear division stage of mitosis. p. 157

**cytokinin** A hormone that promotes and controls growth responses of plants. p. 986

**cytoplasm** All parts of the cell that surround the central nuclear or nucleoid region. p. 28

**cytoplasmic determinants** The mRNA and proteins stored in the egg cytoplasm that direct the first stages of animal development in the period before genes of the zygote become active. p. 1180

**cytoplasmic inheritance** Pattern in which inheritance follows that of genes in the cytoplasmic organelles, mitochondria, or chloroplasts. p. 244

**cytoplasmic streaming** Intracellular movement of cytoplasm. pp. 41, 589

**cytosine** A pyrimidine that base-pairs with guanine in nucleic acids. p. 256

**cytoskeleton** The interconnected system of protein fibres and tubes that extends throughout the cytoplasm of a eukaryotic cell. p. 28

**cytosol** Aqueous solution in the cytoplasm containing ions and various organic molecules. p. 28

**daily torpor** A period of inactivity and lowered metabolic rate that allows an endotherm to conserve energy when environmental temperatures are low. p. 1129

**day-neutral plant** A plant that flowers without regard to photoperiod. p. 998

**decomposer** A small organism, such as a bacterium or fungus, that feeds on the remains of dead organisms, breaking down complex biological molecules or structures into simpler raw materials. pp. 126, 778

**degeneracy (redundancy)** The feature of the genetic code in which, with two exceptions, more than one codon represents each amino acid. p. 282

**dehydration synthesis reaction** Reaction during which the components of a water molecule are removed, usually as part of the assembly of a larger molecule from smaller subunits. Also referred to as a *condensation reaction*. p. F-22

**deletion** Chromosomal alteration that occurs if a broken segment is lost from a chromosome. p. 236

**demographic transition model** A graphic depiction of the historical relationship between a country's economic development and its birth and death rates. p. 768

**demography** The statistical study of the processes that change a population's size and density through time. p. 752

**denaturation** A loss of both the structure and function of a protein due to extreme conditions that unfold it from its conformation. p. F-35

**dendrite** The branched extension of the nerve cell body that receives signals from other nerve cells. p. 1017

**denitrification** A metabolic process in which certain bacteria convert nitrites or nitrates into nitrous oxide and then into molecular nitrogen, which enters the atmosphere. p. 828

**density** Mass per unit volume. p. 1060

**density dependent** Description of environmental factors for which the strength of their effect on a population varies with the population's density. p. 1060

**density independent** Description of environmental factors for which the strength of their effect on a population does not vary with the population's density. p. 762

**deoxyribonucleic acid (DNA)** The large, double-stranded, helical molecule that contains the genetic material of all living organisms. p. 252

**deoxyribose** A five-carbon sugar to which the nitrogenous bases in nucleotides of DNA link covalently. p. F-36

**depolarized** State of the membrane (which was polarized at rest) as the membrane potential becomes less negative. p. 1204

**deposit feeder** An animal that consumes particles of organic matter from the solid substrate on which it lives. p. 1035

**derived character state** A new version of a trait found in the most recent common ancestor of a group. p. 463

**dermal tissue system** The plant tissue system that comprises the outer tissues of the plant body, including the epidermis and periderm; it serves as a protective covering for the plant body. p. 890

**dermis** The skin layer below the epidermis; it is packed with connective tissue fibres such as collagen, which resist compression, tearing, or puncture of the skin. p. 1126

**desmosome** Anchoring junction for which microfilaments anchor the junction in the underlying cytoplasm. p. 45

**determinate cleavage** A type of cleavage in protostomes in which each cell's developmental path is determined as the cell is produced. p. 647

**determinate growth** The pattern of growth in most animals in which individuals grow to a certain size and then their growth slows dramatically or stops. p. 888

**determination** Mechanism in which the developmental fate of a cell is set. p. 1183

**detritus** Dead organic matter. pp. 600, 778

**deuterostome** A division of the Bilateria in which blastopore forms the anus during development and the mouth appears later (includes Echinodermata and Chordata). p. 646

**diabetes mellitus** A disease that results from problems with insulin production or action. p. 1152

**diaphragm** A dome-shaped sheet of skeletal muscle separating the chest cavity from the abdominal cavity in mammals. p. 1067

**diapsid (lineage Diapsida)** A member of a group within the amniote vertebrates with a skull with two temporal arches. Their living descendants include lizards and snakes, crocodilians, and birds. p. 700

**diastole** The period of relaxation and filling of the heart between contractions. p. 1088

**diatom** Photosynthetic single-celled organisms with a glassy silica shell; also called bacillariophytes. p. 570

**dideoxynucleotide** A nucleotide that lacks hydroxyls at both the 2′ and 3′ positions on the pentose ring which terminates DNA elongation and is required for Sanger Sequencing. Abbreviated ddNTP. p. 363

**differentiation** Follows determination and involves the establishment of a cell-specific developmental program in the cells. Differentiation results in cell types with clearly defined structures and functions. p. 1183

**diffusion** The net movement of ions or molecules from a region of higher concentration to a region of lower concentration. p. 84

**digestion** The splitting of carbohydrates, proteins, lipids, and nucleic acids in foods into chemical subunits small enough to be absorbed into the body fluids and cells of an animal. p. 1030

**dihybrid** A zygote produced from a cross that involves two characters. p. 207

**dihybrid cross** A cross between two individuals that are heterozygous for two pairs of alleles. p. 207

**dikaryotic hyphae** Hyphae containing two separate nuclei in one cell. p. 596

**dioecious** Having male flowers and female flowers on different plants of the same species. p. 937

**diphyodont** Having two generations of teeth, milk (baby) teeth and adult teeth. p. 708

**diploblastic** An animal body plan in which adult structures arise from only two cell layers, the ectoderm and the endoderm. p. 645

**diploid** An organism or cell with two copies of each type of chromosome in its nucleus. p. 152

**directional selection** A type of selection in which individuals near one end of the phenotypic spectrum have the highest relative fitness. p. 421

**disclimax community** See disturbance climax (disclimax) community. p. 803

**discontinuous replication** Replication in which a DNA strand is formed in short lengths that are synthesized in the direction opposite to DNA unwinding. p. 264

**dispersion** The spatial distribution of individuals within a population's geographic range. p. 749

**disruptive selection** A type of natural selection in which extreme phenotypes have higher relative fitness than intermediate phenotypes. p. 422

**dissociation** The separation of water to produce hydrogen ions and hydroxide ions. p. 1071

**distal convoluted tubule** The tubule in the human nephron that drains urine into a collecting duct that leads to the renal pelvis. p. 1113

**disturbance climax (disclimax) community** An ecological community in which regular disturbance inhibits successional change. p. 803

**DNA** See deoxyribonucleic acid (DNA). p. 252

**DNA chip** See DNA microarray. p. 375

**DNA fingerprinting** Technique in which DNA samples are used to distinguish between individuals of the same species. p. 342

**DNA helicase** An enzyme that catalyzes the unwinding of DNA template strands. p. 263

**DNA ligase** In DNA replication, an enzyme that seals the nicks left after RNA primers are replaced with DNA. p. 264

**DNA methylation** Process in which a methyl group is added enzymatically to cytosine bases in the DNA. p. 320

**DNA microarray** A solid surface divided into a microscopic grid of thousands of spaces each containing thousands of copies of a DNA probe. DNA microarrays are used commonly for analysis of gene activity and for detecting differences between cell types. Also referred to as a *DNA chip*. p. 375

**DNA polymerase** An enzyme that assembles complementary nucleotide chains during DNA replication. p. 259

**DNA polymerase I** A specialized polymerase responsible for removing RNA primers and replacing them with DNA. p. 264

**DNA polymerase III** The main, "general-purpose" polymerase for replicating DNA. p. 264

**DNA technologies** Techniques to isolate, purify, analyze, and manipulate DNA sequences. p. 334

**DNA transposon** Transposable elements that transpose using a DNA intermediate. p. 383

**domain** In protein structure, a distinct, large structural subdivision produced in many proteins by the folding of the amino acid chain. In systematics, the highest taxonomic category; a group of cellular organisms with characteristics that set it apart as a major branch of the evolutionary tree. p. 83

**dominance hierarchy** A social system in which the behaviour of each individual is constrained by that individual's status in a highly structured social ranking. p. 871

**dominance** The masking effect of one allele over another. p. 203

**dominant** Refers to the allele expressed when more than one allele is present. p. 203

**dormancy** A period in the life cycle in which biological activity is suspended. pp. 945, 1001

**dorsal lip of the blastopore** A crescent-shaped depression rotated clockwise 90° on the embryo surface that marks the region derived from the grey crescent, to which cells from the animal pole move as gastrulation begins. p. 1183

**dosage compensation** In placental mammals, the effects of most genes carried on the X chromosome in females are equalized in females (who have two X chromosomes) and males (who have one X chromosome). p. 233

**double fertilization** The characteristic feature of sexual reproduction in flowering plants. In the embryo sac, one sperm nucleus unites with the egg to form a diploid zygote from which the embryo develops, and another unites with two polar nuclei to form the primary endosperm nucleus. p. 941

**double-helix model** Model of DNA consisting of two complementary sugar–phosphate backbones. p. 257

**driver gene** In the context of cancer, a gene that contains a *driver mutation*. p. 325

**driver mutation** In the context of cancer, a mutation that confers a selective growth advantage to the cell in which it occurs. p. 325

**duodenum** A short region of the small intestine where secretions from the pancreas and liver enter a common duct. p. 1042

**duplication** Chromosomal alteration that occurs if a segment is broken from one chromosome and inserted into its homologue. p. 236

**E site** The site where an exiting tRNA binds prior to its release from the ribosome. p. 291

**ecdysis** Shedding of the cuticle, exoskeleton, or skin; moulting. p. 291

**echolocating animal** An animal that makes squeaking or clicking noises, and then listens for the echoes that bounce back from objects in its environment. The animal stores the outgoing signal in its brain for comparison with returning echoes. p. 859

**ECM** *See* extracellular matrix (ECM). p. 45

**ecological efficiency** The ratio of net productivity at one trophic level to net productivity at the trophic level below it. p. 819

**ecological isolation** A prezygotic reproductive isolating mechanism in which species that live in the same geographic region occupy different habitats. p. 437

**ecological niche** The resources a population uses and the environmental conditions it requires over its lifetime. p. 790

**ecological pyramid** A diagram illustrating the effects of energy transfer from one trophic level to the next. p. 821

**ecosystem** A group of biological communities interacting with their shared physical environment. p. 814

**ecotone** A wide transition zone between adjacent communities. p. 793

**ectoderm** The outermost of the three primary germ layers of an embryo, which develops into epidermis and nervous tissue. pp. 645, 1181

**ectognathous** *Ecto* = outward; *gnathous* = having jaws. Insect mouthparts that project outward from the head and are not retracted within the head. p. 675

**ectomycorrhiza** A mycorrhiza that grows between and around the young roots of trees and shrubs but does not enter root cells. p. 965

**ectotherm** An animal that obtains its body heat primarily from the external environment. p. 1121

**effector** In signal transduction, a plasma membrane–associated enzyme, activated by a G protein, that generates one or more second messengers. In homeostatic feedback, the system that returns the condition to the set point if it has strayed away. pp. 1019, 1201

**efferent neuron** A neuron that carries the signals indicating a response away from the interneuron networks to the effectors. p. 1201

**egg** Nonmotile gamete. p. 1163

**egg cell** The female reproductive cell. p. 938

**Elasmobranchii** Cartilaginous fishes, including the skates and rays. p. 690

**elastin** A rubbery protein in some connective tissues that adds elasticity to the extracellular matrix. It is able to return to its original shape after being stretched, bent, or compressed. p. 1013

**electric signal** A means of animal communication in which a signaller emits an electric discharge that can be received by another individual. p. 859

**electrical synapse** A mechanical and electrically conductive link between two abutting neurons that is formed at the gap junction. p. 1210

**electrocardiogram (ECG)** Graphic representation of the electrical activity within the heart, detected by electrodes placed on the body. p. 1089

**electrochemical gradient** A difference in chemical concentration and electric potential across a membrane. pp. 89, 1203

**electromagnetic spectrum** The range of wavelengths or frequencies of electromagnetic radiation extending from gamma rays to the longest radio waves and including visible light. p. 6

**electron** Negatively charged particle outside the nucleus of an atom. p. 7

**electron microscope** A microscope that uses electrons to illuminate the specimen. p. 26

**electron shell** In chemistry and physics, may be thought of as an orbit followed by electrons around an atom's nucleus. Also known as *principal energy level*. p. F-10

**electron transfer system** Stage of cellular respiration in which high-energy electrons produced from glycolysis, pyruvate oxidation, and the citric acid cycle are delivered to oxygen by a sequence of electron carriers. p. 143

**electronegativity** The measure of an atom's attraction for the electrons it shares in a chemical bond with another atom. p. F-13

**electroreceptor** A specialized sensory receptor that detects electrical fields. pp. 691, 1233

**element** A pure substance that cannot be broken down into simpler substances by ordinary chemical or physical techniques. p. F-7

**elongation factor (EF)** Proteins that promote various steps in the elongation of peptides during translation. p. 292

**embryo** An organism in its early stage of reproductive development, beginning in the first moments after fertilization. p. 45

**embryo sac** The female gametophyte of angiosperms, within which the embryo develops; it usually consists of seven cells: an egg cell, an endosperm mother cell, and five other cells with fleeting reproductive roles. p. 938

**embryology** The study of embryos and their development. p. 1183

**embryonic stem cell** Stem cells in the mammalian embryo that can differentiate into any cell type. p. 346

**emergent property** New property that forms when simpler objects associate to increase the complexity of the resulting combination. p. F-1

**emigration** The movement of individuals out of a population. p. 752

**endemic species** A species that occurs in only one place on Earth. p. 734

**endergonic process** Reaction that can proceed only if free energy is supplied. p. 58

**endocrine gland** Any of several ductless secretory organs that secrete hormones into the blood or extracellular fluid. pp. 1012, 1137

**endocrine regulation** Hormones are secreted into the blood or extracellular fluid by the cells of ductless secretory organs called endocrine glands. p. 1136

**endocrine system** The system of glands that release their secretions (hormones) directly into the circulatory system. p. 1136

**endocytic vesicle** A vesicle that carries proteins and other molecules from the plasma membrane to destinations within the cell. p. 37

**endocytosis** In eukaryotes, the process by which molecules are brought into the cell from the exterior involving a bulging in of the plasma membrane that pinches off to form an endocytic vesicle. p. 37

**endoderm** The innermost of the three primary germ layers of an embryo, which develops into the gastrointestinal tract and, in some animals, the respiratory organs. pp. 645, 1181

**endodermis** The innermost layer of the root cortex; a selectively permeable barrier that helps control the movement of water and dissolved minerals into the stele. pp. 902, 918

**endomembrane system** In eukaryotes, a collection of interrelated internal membranous sacs that divide a cell into functional and structural compartments. p. 34

**endomycorrhiza** A mycorrhiza in which the fungal hyphae penetrate into cells of the root. p. 965

**endoparasite** A parasite that lives in the internal organs of its host organism. p. 781

**endoplasmic reticulum (ER)** In eukaryotes, an extensive interconnected network of cisternae that is responsible for the synthesis, transport, and initial modification of proteins and lipids. p. 35

**endorphin** One of a group of small proteins occurring naturally in the brain and around nerve endings that bind to opiate receptors and thus can raise the pain threshold. pp. 1147, 1232

**endoskeleton** A supportive internal body structure, such as bones, that provides support. p. 1266

**endosperm** Nutritive tissue inside the seeds of flowering plants. p. 941

**endosporous** Pattern of development in some plants (e.g., seed plants) in which the gametophyte develops inside the spore wall. p. 627

**endosymbiosis** A symbiotic association in which one symbiont or partner lives inside the other. p. 504

**endotherm** An animal that obtains most of its body heat from internal physiological sources. p. 1121

**endothermic** Refers to reactions that absorb energy. pp. 57, 708

**endotoxin** A lipopolysaccharide released from the outer membrane of the cell wall when a bacterium dies and lyses. p. 545

**energy** The capacity to do work. p. 54

**energy budget** The total amount of energy that an organism can accumulate and use to fuel its activities. p. 54

**energy coupling** The process by which ATP is brought in close contact with a reactant molecule involved in an endergonic reaction, and when the ATP is hydrolyzed, the terminal phosphate group is transferred to the reactant molecule. p. 63

**enhancer** In eukaryotes, a region at a significant distance from the beginning of a gene, containing regulatory sequences that determine whether the gene is transcribed at its maximum possible rate. p. 315

**enterocoelom** In deuterostomes, the body cavity pinched off by outpocketings of the archenteron. p. 648

**enthalpy** Potential energy in a system. p. 57

**entognathous** The mouth parts can be withdrawn into a capsule in the head. p. 675

**entropy** Disorder, in thermodynamics. p. 55

**envelope** Outer glycoprotein layer surrounding the capsid of some viruses, derived in part from host cell plasma membrane. p. 522

**enveloped virus** A virus that has a surface membrane derived from its host cell. p. 522

**enzymatic hydrolysis** A process in which chemical bonds are broken by the addition of $H^+$ and $OH^-$, the components of a molecule of water. p. 1036

**enzyme** Protein that accelerates the rate of a cellular reaction. p. 65

**epiblast** The top layer of the blastodisc. p. 1185

**epicotyls** The upper part of the axis of an early plant embryo, located between the cotyledons and the first true leaves. p. 944

**epidermis** A complex tissue that covers an organism's body in a single continuous layer or sometimes in multiple layers of tightly packed cells. pp. 894, 1126

**epididymis** A coiled storage tubule attached to the surface of each testis. p. 1176

**epigenetics** The study of changes to gene expression that do not arise from changes in the DNA sequence (i.e., mutations). Epigenetic changes may arise from chemical modification of bases (e.g., methylation), chromatin remodelling, protein or RNA binding, etc. p. 324

**epiglottis** A flaplike valve at the top of the trachea. p. 1041

**epinephrine** A nontropic amine hormone secreted by the adrenal medulla. p. 1150

**epiphyte** A plant that grows independently on other plants and obtains nutrients and water from the air. p. 970

**epistasis** Interaction of genes, with one or more alleles of a gene at one locus inhibiting or masking the effects of one or more alleles of a gene at a different locus. p. 216

**epithelial tissue** Tissue formed of sheetlike layers of cells that are usually joined tightly together, with little extracellular matrix material between them. They protect body surfaces from invasion by bacteria and viruses and secrete or absorb substances. p. 1010

**EPSP** *See* excitatory postsynaptic potential (EPSP). p. 1236

**equilibrium theory of island biogeography** A hypothesis suggesting that the number of species on an island is governed by a give and take between the immigration of new species to the island and the extinction of species already there. p. 805

**ER (endoplasmic reticulum) lumen** The enclosed space surrounded by a cisterna. p. 35

**erythrocyte** A red blood cell that contains hemoglobin, a protein that transports $O_2$ in blood. pp. 1069, 1084

**erythropoietin (EPO)** A hormone that stimulates stem cells in bone marrow to increase erythrocyte production. pp. 1085, 1070

**esophagus** A connecting passage of the digestive tube. p. 680

**essential amino acid** An amino acid that an animal cannot synthesize and must obtain from organic molecules in their food. p. 1031

**essential element** Any of a number of elements required by living organisms to ensure normal reproduction, growth, development, and maintenance. p. 957

**essential fatty acid** Any fatty acid that the body cannot synthesize but needs for normal metabolism. p. 1031

**essential nutrient** Any of the essential amino acids, fatty acids, vitamins, and minerals required in the diet of an animal. p. 1031

**estivation** Seasonal torpor in an animal that occurs in summer. p. 1129

**estradiol** A form of estrogen. p. 1151

**estrogen** Any of the group of female sex hormones. p. 1151

**ethology** A discipline that focuses on how animals behave. p. 850

**ethylene** A plant hormone that helps regulate seedling growth; stem elongation; the ripening of fruit; and the abscission of fruits, leaves, and flowers. p. 987

**eudicot** A plant belonging to the Eudicotyledones, one of the two major classes of angiosperms; their embryos generally have two seed leaves (cotyledons), and their pollen grains have three grooves. pp. 633, 889

**Eukarya** The domain that includes all eukaryotes, organisms that contain a membrane-bound nucleus within each of their cells; all protists, plants, fungi, and animals. p. 538

**eukaryote** Organism in which the DNA is enclosed in a nucleus. p. 29

**eukaryotic chromosome** A DNA molecule, with its associated proteins, in the nucleus of a eukaryotic cell. p. 32

**Euryarchaeota** A major group of the domain Archaea, members of which are found in different extreme environments. They include methanogens, extreme halophiles, and some extreme thermophiles. p. 551

**eusocial** A form of social organization, observed in some insect species, in which numerous related individuals—a large percentage of them sterile female workers—live and work together in a colony for the reproductive benefit of a single queen and her mate(s). p. 874

**eustachian tube** A duct leading from the air-filled middle ear to the throat that protects the eardrum from damage caused by changes in environmental atmospheric pressure. p. 1222

**evaporation** Heat transfer through the energy required to change a liquid to a gas. p. 1121

**evolution** The main unifying concept in biology, explaining how the diversity of life on Earth arose and how species change over time in response to changes in their abiotic and biotic environment. p. 414

**evolutionary adaptation** Characteristic or suite of characteristics that helps an organism survive longer or reproduce more under a particular set of environmental conditions; the accumulation of adaptive traits over time. p. 988

**exchange diffusion** *See* antiport. p. 90

**excitatory postsynaptic potential (EPSP)** The change in membrane potential caused when a neurotransmitter opens a ligand-gated $Na^+$ channel and $Na^+$ enters the cell, making it more likely that the postsynaptic neuron will generate an action potential. p. 1236

**excretion** The process that helps maintain the body's water and ion balance while ridding the body of metabolic wastes. p. 1106

**exergonic process** Reaction that has a negative $\Delta G$ because it releases free energy. p. 58

**exocrine gland** A gland that is connected to the epithelium by a duct and that empties its secretion at the epithelial surface. p. 1012

**exocytosis** In eukaryotes, the process by which a secretory vesicle fuses with the plasma membrane and releases the vesicle contents to the exterior. p. 36

**exodermis** In the roots of some plants, an outer layer of root cortex that may limit water losses from roots and help regulate the absorption of ions. p. 902

**exon** An amino acid–coding sequence present in pre-mRNA that is retained in a spliced mRNA that is translated to produce a polypeptide. p. 286

**exoskeleton** A hard external covering of an animal's body that blocks the passage of water and provides support and protection. pp. 673, 1266

**exothermic** Refers to processes that release energy. p. 57

**exotoxin** A toxic protein that leaks from or is secreted from a bacterium and interferes with the biochemical processes of body cells in various ways. p. 545

**experimental variable** The variable to which any difference in observations of experimental treatment subjects and control treatment subjects is attributed. p. F-3

**exploitative competition** Form of competition in which two or more individuals or populations use the same limiting resources. p. 788

**exponential model of population growth** Model that describes unlimited population growth. p. 756

**expression vector** A plasmid that can not only carry cloned genes but also drive their expression. p. 345

**external fertilization** The process in which sperm and eggs are shed into the surrounding water, occurring in most aquatic invertebrates, bony fishes, and amphibians. p. 1166

**external gill** A gill that extends out from the body and lacks a protective covering. p. 1062

**extracellular digestion** Digestion that takes place outside body cells, in a pouch or tube enclosed within the body. p. 653

**extracellular fluid** The fluid occupying the spaces between cells in multicellular animals. p. 1018

**extracellular matrix (ECM)** A molecular system that supports and protects cells and provides mechanical linkages. pp. 45, 164, 1012

**extra-embryonic membrane** A primary tissue layer extended outside the embryo that conducts nutrients from the yolk to the embryo, exchanges gases with the environment outside the egg, or stores metabolic wastes removed from the embryo. p. 1186

**F pilus** Structure on the cell surface that allows an $F^+$ donor bacterial cell to attach to an $F^-$ recipient bacterial cell. Also referred to as a *sex pilus*. p. 177

**$F^-$ cell** Recipient cell in conjugation between bacteria. p. 177

**$F^+$ cell** Donor cell in conjugation between bacteria. p. 177

**$F_1$ generation** The first generation of offspring from a genetic cross. p. 202

**$F_2$ generation** The second generation of offspring from a genetic cross. p. 202

**facilitated diffusion** Mechanism by which polar and charged molecules diffuse across membranes with the help of transport proteins. p. 85

**facilitation hypothesis** A hypothesis that explains ecological succession, suggesting that species modify the local environment in ways that make it less suitable for themselves but more suitable for colonization by species typical of the next successional stage. p. 802

**facultative anaerobe** An organism that can live in the presence or absence of oxygen, using oxygen when it is present and living by fermentation under anaerobic conditions. p. 544

**familial (hereditary) cancer** Cancer that runs in a family. p. 325

**family planning program** A program that educates people about ways to produce an optimal family size on an economically feasible schedule. p. 769

**fast block (to polyspermy)** The barrier set up by the wave of depolarization triggered when sperm and egg fuse, making it impossible for other sperm to enter the egg. p. 1168

**fast muscle fibre** A muscle fibre that contracts relatively quickly and powerfully. p. 1263

**fat** Neutral lipid that is semisolid at biological temperatures. p. 1031

**fat-soluble vitamin** A vitamin that dissolves in liquid fat or fatty oils, in addition to water. p. 1031

**fatty acid** One of two components of a neutral lipid, containing a single hydrocarbon chain with a carboxyl group linked at one end. p.38

**feather** A sturdy, lightweight structure of birds, derived from scales in the skin of their ancestors. p. 706

**feces** Condensed and compacted digestive contents in the large intestine. p. 1045

**feedback inhibition** In enzyme reactions, regulation in which the product of a reaction acts as a regulator of the reaction. Also referred to as *end-product inhibition*. p. 70

**fermentation** Process in which electrons carried by NADH are transferred to an organic acceptor molecule rather than to the electron transfer system. p. 117

**fertilization** The fusion of the nuclei of an egg and sperm cell, which initiates development of a new individual. pp. 183, 1164

**fetus** A developing human from the eighth week of gestation onward, at which point, the major organs and organ systems have formed. p. 1188

**fibre** In sclerenchyma, an elongated, tapered, thick-walled cell that gives plant tissue its flexible strength. p. 892

**fibrin** A protein necessary for blood clotting; fibrin forms a weblike mesh that traps

platelets and red blood cells and holds a clot together. p. 1086

**fibrinogen** A plasma protein that plays a central role in the blood-clotting mechanism. p. 1084

**fibronectin** A class of glycoproteins that aids in the attachment of cells to the extracellular matrix and helps hold the cells in position. p. 1012

**fibrous connective tissue** Tissue in which fibroblasts are sparsely distributed among dense masses of collagen and elastin fibres that are lined up in highly ordered, parallel bundles, producing maximum tensile strength and elasticity. p. 1013

**fibrous root system** A root system that consists of branching roots rather than a main taproot; roots tend to spread laterally from the base of the stem. p. 901

**filament** In flowers, the stalk of a stamen, which supports the anther. p. 936

**filtration** The nonselective movement of some water and a number of solutes—ions and small molecules, but not large molecules such as proteins—into the proximal end of the renal tubules through spaces between cells. p. 1106

**first law of thermodynamics** The principle that energy can be transferred and transformed but cannot be created or destroyed. p. 55

**fission** The mode of asexual reproduction in which the parent separates into two or more offspring of approximately equal size. p. 1162

**fitness** An individual's reproductive success. p. 400

**fixed action pattern** A highly stereotyped instinctive behaviour; when triggered by a specific cue, it is performed over and over in almost exactly the same way. p. 848

**flagellum** (plural, **flagella**) A long, threadlike, cellular appendage responsible for movement; found in both prokaryotes and eukaryotes, but with different structures and modes of locomotion. pp. 31, 542

**flame cell** The cell that forms the primary filtrate in the excretory system of many bilateria. The urine is propelled through ducts by the synchronous beating of cilia, resembling a flickering flame. p. 659

**floral meristem** The fate of either a shoot apical meristem or axillary meristems is stimulated to produce floral organs (sepals, petals, stamens, and carpels) instead of its normal products of shoots and leaves. p. 936

**flower** The reproductive structure of angiosperms, consisting of floral parts

grouped on a stem; the structure in which seeds develop. p. 632

**fluid feeder** An animal that obtains nourishment by ingesting liquids that contain organic molecules in solution. p. 1034

**fluid mosaic model** Model proposing that the membrane consists of a fluid phospholipid bilayer in which proteins are embedded and float freely. p. 78

**follicle cell** A cell that grows from ovarian tissue and nourishes the developing egg. p. 1165

**follicle** The ovum and follicle cells. p. 1173

**follicle-stimulating hormone (FSH)** The pituitary hormone that stimulates oocytes in the ovaries to continue meiosis and become follicles. During follicle enlargement, FSH interacts with luteinizing hormone to stimulate follicular cells to secrete estrogens. p. 1145

**food web** A set of interconnected food chains with multiple links. p. 619

**foreskin** A loose fold of skin that covers the glans of the penis. *See* prepuce. p. 1177

**fossil** The remains or traces of an organism of a past geologic age embedded and preserved in Earth's crust. p. 12

**founder effect** An evolutionary phenomenon in which a population that was established by just a few colonizing individuals has only a fraction of the genetic diversity seen in the population from which it was derived. p. 419

**fovea** The small region of the retina around which cones are concentrated in mammals and birds with eyes specialized for daytime vision. p. 1225

**fragmentation** A type of vegetative reproduction in plants in which cells or a piece of the parent break off and then develop into new individuals. pp. 947, 1162

**frameshift mutation** Mutation in a protein-coding gene that causes the reading frame of an mRNA transcribed from the gene to be altered, resulting in the production of a different, and non-functional, amino acid sequence in the polypeptide. p. 300

**free energy** The energy in a system that is available to do work. p. 54

**freeze-fracture technique** Technique in which experimenters freeze a block of cells rapidly and then fracture the block to split the lipid bilayer and expose the hydrophobic membrane interior. p. 79

**frequency-dependent selection** A form of natural selection in which rare phenotypes have a selective advantage simply because they are rare. p. 427

**fruit** A mature ovary, often with accessory parts, from a flower. pp. 632, 942

**fruiting body** In some fungi, a stalked, spore-producing structure such as a mushroom. p. 575

**functional groups** The atoms in reactive groups. p. F-23

**fundamental niche** The range of conditions and resources that a population can possibly tolerate and use. p. 790

**furculum** Wishbone in birds. p. 704

**furrow** In cytokinesis, a groove that girdles the cell and gradually deepens until it cuts the cytoplasm into two parts. p. 157

**G$_0$ phase** The phase of the cell cycle in eukaryotes in which many cell types stop dividing. p. 154

**G1 phase** The initial growth stage of the cell cycle in eukaryotes, during which the cell makes proteins and other types of cellular molecules but not nuclear DNA. p. 153

**G2 phase** The phase of the cell cycle in eukaryotes during which the cell continues to synthesize proteins and grow, completing interphase. p. 153

**gallbladder** The organ that stores bile between meals, when no digestion is occurring. p. 1044

**gametangium** (plural, **gametangia**) A cell or organ in which gametes are produced. pp. 592, 619

**gamete** A haploid cell; an egg or sperm. Haploid cells fuse during sexual reproduction to form a diploid zygote. pp. 183, 644

**gametic isolation** A prezygotic reproductive isolating mechanism caused by incompatibility between the sperm of one species and the eggs of another; may prevent fertilization. p. 439

**gametogenesis** The formation of male and female gametes. p. 1164

**gametophyte** An individual of the haploid generation produced when a spore germinates and grows directly by mitotic divisions in organisms that undergo alternation of generations. pp. 572, 612, 934

**ganglion** (plural, **ganglia**) A functional concentration of nervous system tissue composed principally of nerve cell bodies, usually lying outside the central nervous system. pp. 659, 1200

**ganglion cell** A type of neuron in the retina of the eye that receives visual information from photoreceptors via various intermediate cells such as bipolar cells, amacrine cells, and horizontal cells. p. 1226

**gap junction** A junction that opens direct channels allowing ions and small molecules to pass directly from one cell to another. pp. 46, 1010

**gas transport cascade** A cascade of steps that transport oxygen and carbon dioxide between the environment and mitochondria. p. 1058

**gastric glands** Glands in the mucosa of the stomach that contain cells that secrete some of the products needed to digest food. p. 1041

**gastric juice** A substance secreted by the stomach that contains the digestive enzyme pepsin. p. 1041

**gastric pits** Entrances to the gastric glands in the stomach lining. p. 1041

**gastrula** The developmental stage resulting when the cells of the blastula migrate and divide once cleavage is complete. p. 1181

**gastrulation** The second major process of early development in most animals, which produces an embryo with three distinct primary tissue layers. p. 1181

**gated channel** Ion transporter in a membrane that switches between open, closed, and intermediate states. p. 85

**gemma** (plural, **gemmae**) Small cell mass that forms in cuplike growths on a thallus. p. 621

**gemmules** Clusters of cells with a resistant covering that allows them to survive unfavourable conditions. p. 652

**gene** A unit containing the code for a protein molecule or one of its parts, or for functioning RNA molecules such as tRNA and rRNA. p. 28

**gene flow** The transfer of genes from one population to another through the movement of individuals or their gametes. p. 416

**gene-for-gene recognition** A mechanism in which plants can detect an attack by a specific pathogen; the product of a specific plant gene interacts with the product of a specific pathogen gene, triggering the plant's defensive response. p. 991

**gene isoform** One of the different forms of mRNAs produced by transcription of particular protein-coding genes. p. 289

**gene pool** The sum of all alleles at all gene loci in all individuals in a population. p. 414

**gene targeting** The knocking out, replacement, or addition of a gene in a genome. p. 346

**gene therapy** Correction of genetic disorders using genetic engineering techniques. p. 349

**general transcription factor** In eukaryotes, a protein that binds to the promoter of a gene in the area of the TATA box and recruits and orients RNA polymerase II to initiate transcription at the correct place. Also known as basal transcription factor. p. 279

**generalized compartment model** A model used to describe nutrient cycling in which two criteria—organic versus inorganic nutrients and available versus unavailable nutrients—define four compartments where nutrients accumulate. p. 823

**generalized transduction** Transfer of bacterial genes between bacteria using virulent phages that have incorporated random DNA fragments of the bacterial genome. p. 182

**generation time** The average time between the birth of an organism and the birth of its offspring. pp. 402, 751

**generative cell** A cell in the pollen grain (male gametophyte) of seed plants that will give rise to sperm. p. 937

**genetic code** The nucleotide information that specifies the amino acid sequence of a polypeptide. p. 281

**genetic counselling** Counselling that allows prospective parents to assess the possibility that they might have a child affected by a genetic disorder. p. 243

**genetic distance method** An approach to phylogenetic analysis that calculates the overall proportion of nucleotide bases that differ among species. p. 466

**genetic drift** Random fluctuations in allele frequencies as a result of chance events; usually reduces genetic variation in a population. p. 419

**genetic engineering** The use of DNA technologies to alter genes for practical purposes. p. 333

**genetic equilibrium** The point at which neither the allele frequencies nor the genotype frequencies in a population change in succeeding generations. p. 416

**genetic recombination** The process by which the combinations of alleles for different genes in two parental individuals become shuffled into new combinations in offspring individuals. p. 174

**genetically modified organism (GMO)** A transgenic organism. p. 354

**genomic imprinting** Pattern of inheritance in which the expression of a nuclear gene is based on whether an individual organism inherits the gene from the male or the female parent. p. 244

**genomic library** A collection of clones that contains a copy of every DNA sequence in a genome. p. 336

**genotype** The genetic constitution of an organism. p. 205

**genus** A Linnaean taxonomic category ranking below a family and above a species. p. 454

**geographic range** The overall spatial boundaries within which a population lives. p. 749

**germ cell** An animal cell that is set aside early in embryonic development and gives rise to the gametes. p. 1164

**germ layer** The layers (up to three) of cells produced during the early development of the embryo of most animals. p. 645

**germ-line gene therapy** Therapy in which a gene is introduced into germ-line cells of an animal to correct a genetic disorder. p. 349

**gestation** The period of mammalian development in which the embryo develops in the uterus of the mother. p. 708

**GH** *See* growth hormone (GH). p. 1145

**gibberellin** Any of a large family of plant hormones that regulate aspects of growth, including cell elongation. p. 984

**gill arch** One of the series of curved supporting structures between the slits in the pharynx of a chordate. p. 690

**gill slit** One of the openings in the pharynx of a chordate through which water passes out of the pharynx. p. 685

**Ginkgophyta** A plant phylum with a single living species, the ginkgo (or maidenhair) tree. p. 630

**gizzard** The part of the digestive tube that grinds ingested material into fine particles by muscular contractions of the wall. p. 1036

**gland** A cell or group of cells that produces and releases substances nearby, in another part of the body, or to the outside. p. 1012

**glans** A soft, caplike structure at the end of the penis, containing most of the nerve endings producing erotic sensations. p. 1177

**glial cell** A nonneuronal cell contained in the nervous tissue that physically supports and provides nutrients to neurons, provides electrical insulation between them, and scavenges cellular debris and foreign matter. pp. 1017, 1201

**globulin** A plasma protein that transports lipids (including cholesterol) and fat-soluble vitamins; a specialized subgroup of globulins, the immunoglobulins, constitute antibodies and other molecules contributing to the immune response. p. 1084

**glomerulus** A ball of blood capillaries surrounded by Bowman's capsule in the human nephron. p. 1113

**glucagon** A pancreatic hormone with effects opposite to those of insulin: it stimulates glycogen, fat, and protein degradation. p. 1152

**glucocorticoid** A steroid hormone secreted by the adrenal cortex that helps maintain the blood concentration of glucose and other fuel molecules. p. 1150

**glycocalyx** A carbohydrate coat covering the cell surface. p. 30

**glycogen** Energy-providing carbohydrates stored in animal cells. p. 115

**glycolysis** Stage of cellular respiration in which sugars such as glucose are partially oxidized and broken down into smaller molecules. p. 105

**Gnathostomata** The group of vertebrates with movable jaws. p. 688

**Golgi complex** In eukaryotes, the organelle responsible for the final modification, sorting, and distribution of proteins and lipids. p. 36

**Golgi tendon organ** A proprioceptor of tendons. p. 1219

**gonad** A specialized gamete-producing organ in which the germ cells collect. Gonads are the primary source of sex hormones in vertebrates: ovaries in the female and testes in the male. p. 1151

**gonadotropin** A hormone that regulates the activity of the gonads (ovaries and testes). p. 1145

**gonadotropin-releasing hormone (GnRH)** A tropic hormone secreted by the hypothalamus that causes the pituitary to make luteinizing hormone (LH) and follicle-stimulating hormone (FSH). p. 1151

**graded potential** A change in membrane potential that does not necessarily trigger an action potential. p. 1204

**Gram-negative** Describing bacteria that do not retain the stain used in the Gram stain procedure. p. 541

**Gram-positive** Describing bacteria that appear purple when stained using the Gram stain technique. p. 541

**Gram stain procedure** A procedure of staining bacteria to distinguish between types of bacteria with different cell wall compositions. p. 541

**granum** (plural, **grana**) Structure in the chloroplasts of higher plants formed by thylakoids stacked one on top of another. p. 44

**greater vestibular gland** One of two glands located slightly below and to the left and right of the opening of the vagina in women. They secrete mucus to provide lubrication, especially when the woman is sexually aroused. p. 1171

**greenhouse effect** A phenomenon in which certain gases foster the accumulation of heat in the lower atmosphere, maintaining warm temperatures on Earth. p. 830

**grey crescent** A crescent-shaped region of the underlying cytoplasm at the side opposite the point of sperm entry exposed after fertilization when the pigmented layer of cytoplasm rotates toward the site of sperm entry. p. 1183

**grey matter** Areas of densely packed nerve cell bodies and dendrites in the brain and spinal cord. p. 1246

**gross primary productivity** The rate at which producers convert solar energy into chemical energy. p. 817

**ground meristem** The primary meristematic tissue in plants that gives rise to ground tissues, mostly parenchyma. p. 896

**ground tissue system** One of the three basic tissue systems in plants; includes all tissues other than dermal and vascular tissues. p. 890

**growth hormone (GH)** A hormone that stimulates cell division, protein synthesis, and bone growth in children and adolescents, thereby causing body growth. p. 1145

**guanine** A purine that base-pairs with cytosine in nucleic acids. p. 256

**guard cell** Either of a pair of specialized crescent-shaped cells that control the opening and closing of stomata in plant tissue. p. 894

**guttation** The exudation of water from leaves as a result of strong root pressure. p. 922

**gymnosperm** A seed plant that produces "naked" seeds not enclosed in an ovary. p. 628

**H$^+$ pump** *See* proton pump. p. 89

**habitat** The specific environment in which a population lives, as characterized by its biotic and abiotic features. p. 749

**habituation** The learned loss of responsiveness to stimuli. p. 851

**half-life** The time it takes for half of a given amount of a radioisotope to decay. p. F-9

**haplodiploidy** A pattern of sex determination in insects in which females are diploid and males are haploid. p. 874

**haploid** An organism or cell with only one copy of each type of chromosome in its nuclei. p. 153

**Hardy–Weinberg principle** An evolutionary rule of thumb that specifies the conditions under which a population of diploid organisms achieves genetic equilibrium. p. 416

**harvesting efficiency** The ratio of the energy content of food consumed to with the energy content of food available. p. 819

**hCG** *See* human chorionic gonadotropin (hCG). p. 1179

**head–foot** In molluscs, the region of the body that provides the major means of locomotion and contains concentrations of nervous system tissues and sense organs. p. 665

**heartwood** The inner core of a woody stem; composed of dry tissue and nonliving cells that no longer transport water and solutes and may store resins, tannins, and other defensive compounds. p. 904

**heat of vaporization** The heat required to give water molecules enough energy of motion to break loose from liquid water and form a gas. p. F-16

**heat-shock protein (HSP)** Any of a group of chaperone proteins that are present in all cells in all life forms. They are induced when a cell undergoes various types of environmental stresses such as heat, cold, and oxygen deprivation. p. 992

**helical virus** A virus in which the protein subunits of the coat assemble in a rodlike spiral around the genome. p. 522

**heliotropism** Rotation of a plant's leaves and flowers (the inflorescence) to stay perpendicular to the Sun. p. 977

**hemoglobin** The $O_2$-carrying protein of the blood. p. 1084

**hemolymph** The circulatory fluid of invertebrates with open circulatory systems, including molluscs and arthropods. pp. 665, 1081

**hepatic portal vein** The blood vessel that leads to capillary networks in the liver. p. 1044

**Hepatophyta** The phylum that includes liverworts and their bryophyte relatives. p. 620

**herbicide** A compound that, at proper concentration, kills plants. p. 982

**herbivore** An animal that obtains energy and nutrients primarily by eating plants. p. 778

**hermaphroditism** The mechanism in which both mature egg-producing and mature sperm-producing tissue are present in the same individual. p. 1170

**heterodont** Having different teeth specialized for different jobs. p. 708

**heterosporous** Producing two types of spores, "male" microspores and "female" megaspores. p. 617

**heterotroph** An organism that acquires energy and nutrients by eating other organisms or their remains. pp. 502, 543, 644

**heterozygote** An individual with two different alleles of a gene. p. 203

**heterozygote advantage** An evolutionary circumstance in which individuals that are heterozygous at a particular locus have higher relative fitness than either homozygote. p. 425

**heterozygous** The state of possessing two different alleles of a gene. p. 203

**Hfr cell** A special donor cell that can transfer genes on a bacterial chromosome to a recipient bacterium. p. 178

**hibernation** Extended torpor during winter. p. 1129

**hierarchical genome sequencing** A method of determining the nucleotide order in a genome in which clones are assessed and carefully sequenced several times; contrast with whole-genome shotgun sequencing. p. 367

**hippocampus** An area of the brain that assists with the storage of long-term memories and is also responsible for the memory of the location of objects or individuals. p. 1242

**histone code** A regulatory mechanism for altering chromatin structure and, therefore, gene activity, based on signals in histone tails represented by chemical modification patterns. p. 320

**Holocephali** The chimeras, another group of cartilaginous fishes. p. 690

**homeostasis** A steady internal condition maintained by responses that compensate for changes in the external environment. pp. 1007, 1104

**homeostatic mechanism** Any process or activity responsible for homeostasis. p. 1007

**hominin** A member of a monophyletic group of primates, characterized by an erect bipedal stance, that includes modern humans and their recent ancestors. p. 480

**hominoid (Hominoidea)** A member of the monophyletic group of primates that includes apes and humans. p. 480

**homologous** Similar. p. 174

**homology** A characteristic shared by a set of species because they inherited it from their common ancestor. pp. 396, 459

**homoplasies** Characteristics shared by a set of species, often because they live in similar environments, but not present in their common ancestor; often the product of convergent evolution. p. 459

**homosporous** Producing only one type of spore. p. 617

**homozygote** An individual with two copies of the same allele. p. 203

**homozygous** State of possessing two copies of the same allele. p. 203

**horizon** A noticeable layer of soil, such as topsoil, with a distinct texture and composition that varies with soil type. p. 961

**horizontal cell** A type of neuron that forms lateral connections among photoreceptor cells in the retina of the eye. p. 1226

**horizontal gene transfer** Movement of genetic material between organisms other than by descent. p. 513

**hormone** Chemical released by the endocrine system that provides the communication that coordinates the activities of multicellular life. pp. 319, 979

**host** A species that is fed upon by a parasite. p. 504

**host race** A population of insects that may be reproductively isolated from other populations of the same species as a consequence of their adaptation to feed on a specific host plant species. p. 442

**human chorionic gonadotropin (hCG)** A hormone that keeps the corpus luteum in the ovary from breaking down. p. 1179

**humus** The organic component of soil remaining after decomposition of plants and animals, animal droppings, and other organic matter. p. 960

**hybrid** An organism produced by a mating between parents of different species or subspecies. p. 437

**hybrid breakdown** A postzygotic reproductive isolating mechanism in which hybrids are capable of reproducing, but their offspring have either reduced fertility or reduced viability. p. 439

**hybrid inviability** A postzygotic reproductive isolating mechanism in which a

**hybrid individual** has a low probability of survival to reproductive age. p. 439

**hybrid sterility** A postzygotic reproductive isolating mechanism in which hybrid offspring cannot form functional gametes. p. 439

**hybrid zone** A geographic area where the hybrid offspring of two divergent populations or species are common. p. 441

**hydration shell** A shell of any chemical species that acts as a solvent and surrounds a solute species. When the solvent is water it is often referred to as a *hydration shell* or *hydration sphere*. A classic example is when water molecules form a sphere around a metal ion. p. F-17

**hydrocarbon** Molecule consisting of carbon linked only to hydrogen atoms. p. 80

**hydrogen bond** Noncovalent bond formed by unequal electron sharing between hydrogen atoms and oxygen, nitrogen, or sulfur atoms. p. F-13

**hydrogeological cycle** The global cycling of water between the ocean, the atmosphere, land, freshwater ecosystems, and living organisms. p. 824

**hydrolysis** Reaction in which the components of a water molecule are added to functional groups as molecules are broken into smaller subunits. p. F-22

**hydrophilic** Refers to polar molecules that associate readily with water. p. F-13

**hydrophobic** Refers to nonpolar substances that are excluded by water and other polar molecules. p. F-13

**hydroponic culture** A method of growing plants not in soil but with the roots bathed in a solution that contains water and mineral nutrients. p. 956

**hydrostatic skeleton** A structure consisting of muscles and fluid that, by themselves, provide support for the animal or part of the animal; no rigid support, such as a bone, is involved. pp. 646, 1265

**hydroxyl group** Group consisting of an oxygen atom linked to a hydrogen atom on one side and to a carbon chain on the other side. p. 256

**hymen** A thin flap of tissue that partially covers the opening of the vagina. p. 1171

**hyomandibular bones** Bones that support the hyoid and throat. p. 690

**hyperpolarized** The condition of a neuron when its membrane potential is more negative than the resting value. p. 1204

**hypersensitive response** A plant defence that physically cordons off an infection site by surrounding it with dead cells. p. 991

**hyperthermia** Body temperature above the regulated set point. p. 1128

**hypertonic** Solution containing dissolved substances at higher concentrations than the cells it surrounds. p. 87

**hypha** (plural, **hyphae**) Any of the threadlike filaments that form the mycelium of a fungus. pp. 570, 588

**hypoblast** The bottom layer of a blastodisc. p. 1185

**hypodermis** The innermost layer of the skin that contains larger blood vessels and additional reinforcing connective tissue. p. 1126

**hypothalamus** The portion of the brain that contains centres regulating basic homeostatic functions of the body and contributing to the release of hormones. p. 1242

**hypothermia** A condition in which the core temperature falls below normal for a prolonged period. p. 1128

**hypothesis** A "working explanation" of observed facts. p. F-2

**hypotonic** Solution containing dissolved substances at lower concentrations than the cells it surrounds. p. 87

**hypoxic** Low environmental oxygen. p. 1057

**ileum** The third part of the small intestine in most higher vertebrates where vitamin $B_{12}$ and bile salts are absorbed. p. 1044

**imbibition** The movement of water into a seed as the water molecules are attracted to hydrophilic groups of stored proteins; the first step in germination. p. 945

**immigration** Movement of organisms into a population. p. 752

**immunoglobulin** A specific protein substance produced by plasma cells to aid in fighting infection. p. 1084

**imperfect flower** A type of incomplete flower that has stamens or carpels, but not both. p. 937

**imprinting** The process of learning the identity of a caretaker and potential future mate during a critical period. p. 850

**inbreeding** A special form of nonrandom mating in which genetically related individuals mate with each other. p. 423

**inbreeding depression** A decline in the average fitness of inbred individuals in a population. p. 424

**incisors** Flattened, chisel-shaped teeth of mammals, located at the front of the mouth, that are used to nip or cut food. p. 1040

**incomplete dominance** Condition in which the effects of recessive alleles can be detected to some extent in heterozygotes. p. 212

**incomplete metamorphosis** In certain insects, a life cycle characterized by the absence of a pupal stage between the immature and adult stages. p. 678

**incus** The second of the three sound-conducting middle ear bones in vertebrates, located between the malleus and the stapes. p. 1221

**independent assortment** Mendel's principle that the alleles of the genes that govern two characters segregate independently during formation of gametes. p. 207

**indeterminate cleavage** A type of cleavage, observed in many deuterostomes, in which the developmental fates of the first few cells produced by mitosis are not determined as soon as cells are produced. p. 647

**indeterminate growth** Growth that is not limited by an organism's genetic program, so that the organism grows for as long as it lives; typical of many plants. *Compare* determinate growth. p. 888

**induced mutation** A mutation that occurs when an organism is exposed either deliberately or accidentally to a physical or chemical mutagen. p. 300

**inducer** Concerning regulation of gene expression in bacteria, a molecule that turns on the transcription of the genes in an operon. p. 311

**inducible operon** Operon whose expression is increased by an inducer molecule. p. 311

**induction** A mechanism in which one group of cells (the inducer cells) causes or influences another nearby group of cells (the responder cells) to follow a particular developmental pathway. p. 1182

**infection thread** In the formation of root nodules on nitrogen-fixing plants, the tube formed by the plasma membrane of root hair cells as bacteria enter the cell. p. 968

**inflorescence** The arrangement of flowers on a stem. p. 934

**ingestion** The feeding methods used to take food into the digestive cavity. p. 1030

**inhibin** A peptide that, in females, is an inhibitor of follicle-stimulating hormone (FSH) secretion from the pituitary, thereby diminishing the signal for follicular growth. In males, inhibin inhibits FSH secretion from the pituitary, thereby decreasing spermatogenesis. p. 1174

**inhibiting hormone (IH)** A hormone released by the hypothalamus that inhibits the secretion of a particular anterior pituitary hormone. p. 1145

**inhibition hypothesis** A hypothesis suggesting that new species are prevented from occupying a community by whatever species are already present. p. 802

**inhibitory postsynaptic potential (IPSP)** A change in membrane potential caused when hyperpolarization occurs, pushing the neuron farther from threshold. p. 1236

**initiator codon** *See* start codon. p. 282

**inner boundary membrane** Membrane lying just inside the outer boundary membrane of a chloroplast, enclosing the stroma. p. 44

**inner cell mass** The dense mass of cells within the blastocyst that will become the embryo. p. 1189

**inner ear** That part of the ear, particularly the cochlea, that converts mechanical vibrations (sound) into neural messages that are sent to the brain. p. 1221

**inner mitochondrial membrane** Membrane surrounding the mitochondrial matrix. p. 39

**inorganic molecule** Molecule without carbon atoms in its structure. p. F-21

**inositol triphosphate (IP₃)** In particular, signal transduction pathways, a second messenger that activates transport proteins in the endoplasmic reticulum to release $Ca^{2+}$ into the cytoplasm. $IP_3$ is involved in one of two major G protein–coupled receptor response pathways. p. 981

**insertion sequence (IS)** A transposable element that contains only genes for its transposition. p. 382

**insertional mutagenesis** A transposon insertion event that disrupts a gene and thereby prevents synthesis of its protein. p. 300

**insight learning** A phenomenon in which animals can solve problems without apparent trial-and-error attempts at the solution. p. 851

**instar** The stage between successive moults in insects and other arthropods. p. 677

**instinctive behaviour** A genetically "programmed" response that appears in complete and functional form the first time it is used. p. 847

**insulin** A hormone secreted by beta cells in the islets of Langerhans, acting mainly on cells of nonworking skeletal muscles, liver cells, and adipose tissue (fat) to lower blood glucose, fatty acid, and amino acid levels and promote the storage of those molecules. p. 1152

**insulin-like growth factor (IGF)** A peptide that directly stimulates growth processes. p. 1145

**integral membrane protein** Protein embedded in a phospholipid bilayer. p. 83

**integration** The sorting and interpretation of neural messages and the determination of the appropriate response(s). p. 1200

**integrator** In homeostatic feedback, the control centre that compares a detected environmental change with a set point. p. 1019

**integument** Skin. In plants, the outer layer of an ovule. p. 937

**interference competition** Form of competition in which individuals fight over resources or otherwise harm each other directly. p. 788

**interkinesis** A brief interphase separating the two meiotic divisions. p. 187

**intermediate disturbance hypothesis** Hypothesis proposing that species richness is greatest in communities that experience fairly frequent disturbances of moderate intensity. p. 798

**intermediate-day plant** A plant that flowers only when day length falls between the values for long-day and short-day plants. p. 998

**intermediate filament** A cytoskeletal filament about 10 nm in diameter that provides mechanical strength to cells in tissues. p. 41

**internal fertilization** The process in which sperm are released by the male close to or inside the entrance of the reproductive tract of the female. p. 1166

**internal gill** A gill located within the body that has a cover providing physical protection for the gills. Water must be brought to internal gills. p. 1062

**interneuron** A neuron that integrates information to formulate an appropriate response. p. 1201

**internode** The region between two nodes on a plant stem. p. 895

**interphase** The first stage of the mitotic cell cycle, during which the cell grows and replicates its DNA before undergoing mitosis and cytokinesis. p. 153

**interspecific** Between species. p. 788

**interstitial fluid** The fluid occupying the spaces between cells in multicellular animals. p. 1018

**intestine** The portion of the digestive system where organic matter is hydrolyzed by enzymes secreted into the digestive tube. As muscular contractions of the intestinal wall move the mixture along, cells lining the intestine absorb the molecular subunits produced by digestion. p. 70

**intracellular digestion** The process in which cells take in food particles by endocytosis. p. 653

**intraspecific** Among same species. p. 759

**intraspecific competition** The dependence of two or more individuals in a population on the same limiting resource. pp. 759, 788

**intrinsic rate of increase** The maximum possible per capita population growth rate in a population living under ideal conditions. p. 757

**intron** A non–protein-coding sequence that interrupts the protein-coding sequence in a eukaryotic gene. Introns are removed by splicing in the processing of pre-mRNA to mRNA. p. 286

**inversion** Chromosomal alteration that occurs if a broken segment reattaches to the same chromosome from which it was lost, but in reversed orientation, so that the order of genes in the segment is reversed with respect to the other genes of the chromosome. p. 420

**inverted repeat** Enables the transposase enzyme to identify the ends of the transposable element when it catalyzes transposition. p. 382

**involution** The process by which cells migrate into the blastopore. p. 1184

**ion** A positively or negatively charged atom. pp. 10, F-11

**ionic bond** Bond that results from electrical attractions between atoms that have lost or gained electrons. p. 84

**IP₃** *See* inositol triphosphate (IP₃). p. 981

**iris** Of the eye, the coloured muscular membrane that lies behind the cornea and in front of the lens, which by opening or closing determines the size of the pupil and hence the amount of light entering the eye. p. 1224

**islets of Langerhans** Endocrine cells that secrete the peptide hormones insulin and glucagon into the bloodstream. p. 1152

**isotonic** Refers to the state of equal concentration of water inside and outside cells. p. 87

**isotope** A distinct form of the atoms of an element, with the same number of protons but a different number of neutrons. p. F-9

**jasmonate** Any of a group of plant hormones that help regulate aspects of growth and responses to stress, including attacks by predators and pathogens. p. 989

**jejunum** The second part of the small intestine in most higher vertebrates where most of the nutrients present in food are absorbed. p. 1044

**junk DNA** DNA sequences which have no apparent structural or protein information role but are otherwise useful for determining evolutionary and ancestry information. This DNA may reveal function with further investigation or be reactivated through mutation. p. 380

**juvenile hormones** A family of fatty acid hormones that govern metamorphosis and reproduction in insects and crustaceans. p. 1154

**karyogamy** In plants, the fusion of two sexually compatible haploid nuclei after cell fusion (plasmogamy). p. 589

**karyotype** A characteristic of a species consisting of the shapes and sizes of all of the chromosomes at metaphase. p. 155

**keeled sternum** The ventrally extended breastbone of a bird to which the flight muscles attach. p. 704

**ketone** A product of fat metabolism that accumulates when the body has insufficient insulin; the body cannot get glucose from the blood into the body's cells to use as energy and will instead begin to burn fat. p. 1152

**keystone species** A species that has a greater effect on community structure than its numbers might suggest. p. 791

**kin selection** Altruistic behaviour to close relatives, allowing them to produce proportionately more surviving copies of the altruist's genes than the altruist might otherwise have produced on its own. p. 872

**kinesis** A change in the rate of movement or the frequency of turning movements in response to environmental stimuli. p. 862

**kinetic energy** The energy of motion. p. 54

**kinetochore** A specialized structure consisting of proteins attached to a centromere that mediates the attachment and movement of chromosomes along the mitotic spindle. p. 155

**kingdom Animalia** The taxonomic kingdom that includes all living and extinct animals. p. 644

**kingdom Fungi** The taxonomic kingdom that includes all living or extinct fungi. p. 590

**kingdom Plantae** The taxonomic kingdom encompassing all living or extinct plants. p. 613

**knockout mouse** A mouse in which a gene in the genome has been knocked out so that its

function is lost. A knockout mouse is made by a gene targeting method. p. 346

**Korarchaeota** A group of Archaea recognized solely on the basis of rRNA coding sequences in DNA taken from environmental samples. p. 551

**K-selected species** Long-lived, slow-reproducing species that thrive in more stable environments. p. 763

**labia majora** A pair of fleshy, fat-padded folds that partially cover the labia minora. p. 1171

**labia minora** Two folds of tissue that run from front to rear on either side of the opening to the vagina. p. 1171

**lactate fermentation** Reaction in which pyruvate is converted into lactate. p. 117

**lagging strand** A DNA strand assembled discontinuously in the direction opposite to DNA unwinding. p. 264

**lagging strand template** The DNA template strand for the lagging strand. p. 264

**larynx** The voice box. p. 1065

**latent phase** The time during which a virus remains in the cell in an inactive form. p. 528

**lateral bud** A bud on the side of a plant stem from which a branch may grow. p. 528

**lateral geniculate nuclei** Clusters of neurons located in the thalamus that receive visual information from the optic nerves and send it on to the visual cortex. p. 1228

**lateral inhibition** Visual processing in which lateral movement of signals from a rod or cone proceeds to a horizontal cell and continues to bipolar cells with which the horizontal cell makes inhibitory connections, serving both to sharpen the edges of objects and enhance contrast in an image. p. 1226

**lateral line system** The complex of mechanoreceptors along the sides of some fishes and aquatic amphibians that detect vibrations in the water. pp. 691, 1217

**lateral meristem** A plant meristem that gives rise to secondary tissue growth. *Compare* primary meristem. p. 888

**lateral root** A root that extends away from the main root (or taproot). p. 900

**lateralization** A phenomenon in which some brain functions are more localized in one of the two hemispheres. p. 1245

**leaching** The process by which soluble materials in soil are washed into a lower layer of soil or are dissolved and carried away by water. p. 955

**leading strand** A DNA strand assembled in the direction of DNA unwinding. p. 264

**leading strand template** The "old" DNA used as a template for synthesis of "new" DNA in the direction of DNA unwinding. p. 264

**leaf primordium** (plural, **primordia**) A lateral outgrowth from the apical meristem that develops into a young leaf. p. 898

**learned behaviour** A response of an animal that depends on having a particular kind of experience during development. p. 847

**learning** A process in which experiences stored in memory change the behavioural responses of an animal. p. 1245

**left aortic arch** In mammals, leads blood way from the heart to the aorta. p. 708

**leghemoglobin** An iron-containing, red-pigmented protein produced in root nodules during the symbiotic association between *Bradyrhizobium* or *Rhizobium* and legumes. p. 968

**lek** A display ground where males each possess a small territory from which they court attentive females. p. 869

**lens** The transparent, biconvex intraocular tissue that helps bring rays of light to a focus on the retina. p. 1224

**Lepidosauromorpha** A monophyletic lineage of diapsids that includes both marine and terrestrial animals, represented today by sphenodontids, lizards, and snakes. p. 700

**leukocyte** A white blood cell, which eliminates dead and dying cells from the body, removes cellular debris, and participates in defending the body against invading organisms. p. 1084

**Leydig cell** A cell that produces the male sex hormones. p. 1176

**life cycle** The sequential stages through which individuals develop, grow, maintain themselves, and reproduce. p. 563

**life table** A chart that summarizes the demographic characteristics of a population. p. 752

**ligament** A fibrous connective tissue that connects bones to each other at a joint. p. 1013

**ligand-gated ion channel** A channel that opens or closes when a specific chemical, such as a neurotransmitter, binds to the channel. p. 1210

**light** The portion of the electromagnetic spectrum that humans can detect with their eyes. p. 6

**light-independent reaction** The second stage of photosynthesis, in which electrons are used as a source of energy to convert inorganic $CO_2$ to an organic form. Also referred to as the *Calvin cycle*. p. 134

**light microscope** Microscope that uses light to illuminate the specimen. p. 26

**lignin** A tough, rather inert polymer that strengthens the secondary walls of various plant cells and thus helps vascular plants grow taller and stay erect on land. p. 887

**limbic system** A functional network formed by parts of the thalamus, hypothalamus, and basal nuclei, along with other nearby grey-matter centres—the amygdala, hippocampus, and olfactory bulbs—sometimes called the "emotional brain." p. 1242

**limiting nutrient** An element in short supply within an ecosystem, the shortage of which limits productivity. p. 817

**lingual lipase** An enzyme that starts the breakdown of saturated fatty acids in the mouth of a mammal. p. 1040

**linkage map** Map of a chromosome showing the relative locations of genes based on recombination frequencies. p. 230

**linkage** The phenomenon of genes being located on the same chromosome. p. 227

**linked genes** Genes on the same chromosome. p. 227

**linker** A short segment of DNA extending between one nucleosome and the next in a eukaryotic chromosome. p. 155

**lipopolysaccharide (LPS)** A large molecule that consists of a lipid and a carbohydrate joined by a covalent bond. p. 541

**liver** A large organ whose may functions include aiding in digestion, removing toxins from the body, and regulating the chemicals in the blood. p. 1044

**loam** Any well-aerated soil composed of a mixture of sand, clay, silt, and organic matter. p. 961

**locus** The particular site on a chromosome at which a gene is located. pp. 211, 414

**logistic model of population growth** Model of population growth that assumes that a population's per capita growth rate decreases as the population gets larger. p. 758

**Lokiarchaeota** A candidate group of the domain Archaea, members of which contain more eukaryotic-like genes than any of the other known archaeal species. p. 551

**long-day plant** A plant that flowers in spring when dark periods become shorter and day length becomes longer. p. 998

**long-term memory** Memory that stores information from days to years or even for life. p. 1245

**long-term potentiation** A long-lasting increase in the strength of synaptic connections in activated neural pathways following brief periods of repeated stimulation. p. 1245

**loop of Henle** In mammals, a U-shaped bend of the proximal convoluted tubule. p. 1113

**loose connective tissue** A tissue formed of sparsely distributed cells surrounded by a more or less open network of collagen and other glycoprotein fibres. p. 1013

**lophophore** The circular or U-shaped fold with one or two rows of hollow, ciliated tentacles that surrounds the mouth of brachiopods, bryozoans, and phoronids and is used to gather food. p. 659

**lungs** A pair of invaginated respiratory surfaces buried in the body interior where they are less susceptible to drying out; the organs of respiration in mammals, birds, reptiles, and most amphibians. p. 1063

**luteinizing hormone (LH)** A hormone secreted by the pituitary that stimulates the growth and maturation of eggs in females and the secretion of testosterone in males. p. 1145

**Lycophyta** The plant phylum that includes club mosses and their close relatives. p. 624

**lymph** The interstitial fluid picked up by the lymphatic system. p. 1095

**lymph node** One of many small, bean-shaped organs spaced along the lymph vessels that contain macrophages and other leukocytes that attack invading disease organisms. p. 1097

**lymphatic system** An accessory system of vessels and organs that helps balance the fluid content of the blood and surrounding tissues and participates in the body's defences against invading disease organisms. p. 1095

**lymphocyte** A leukocyte that carries out most of its activities in the tissues and organs of the lymphatic system. Lymphocytes play major roles in immune responses. p. 1095

**lysed** Refers to a cell that has ruptured or undergone lysis. p. 526

**lysogenic cycle** Cycle in which the DNA of the bacteriophage is integrated into the DNA of the host bacterial cell and may remain for many generations. pp. 183, 526

**lysosome** Membrane-bound vesicle containing hydrolytic enzymes for the digestion of many complex molecules. p. 37

**lytic cycle** The series of events from infection of one bacterial cell by a phage through the release of progeny phages from lysed cells. pp. 182, 526

**macronucleus** In ciliophorans, a single large nucleus that develops from a micronucleus but loses all genes except those required for basic "housekeeping" functions of the cell and for ribosomal RNAs. p. 567

**macronutrient** A nutrient required for growth and maintenance in relatively large amounts. p. 957

**magnetoreceptor** A receptor found in some animals that navigate long distances that allows them to detect and use Earth's magnetic field as a source of directional information. p. 1233

**magnification** The ratio of an object as viewed to its real size. p. 27

**malleus** The outermost of the sound-conducting bones of the middle ear in vertebrates. p. 1221

**malnutrition** A condition resulting from a diet that lacks one or more essential nutrients. p. 1301

**Malpighian tubule** The main organ of excretion and osmoregulation in insects, helping them maintain water and electrolyte balance. pp. 676, 1109

**mammary glands** Specialized organs of female mammals that produce energy-rich milk, a watery mixture of fats, sugars, proteins, vitamins, and minerals. p. 321

**mantle** One or two folds of the body wall that lines the shell and secretes the substance that forms the shell in molluscs. p. 665

**mantle cavity** The protective chamber produced by the mantle in many molluscs. p. 665

**map unit** The unit of a linkage map, equivalent to a recombination frequency of 1%. Also referred to as a *centimorgan*. p. 230

**marsupium** An external pouch on the abdomen of many female marsupials, containing the mammary glands, and within which the young continue to develop after birth. p. 1170

**mass number** The total number of protons and neutrons in the atomic nucleus. p. F-9

**maternal chromosome** The chromosome derived from the female parent of an organism. p. 185

**maternal inheritance** A type of uniparental inheritance in which all progeny (both males and females) have the phenotype of the female parent. p. 244

**mating** The pairing of a male and a female for the purpose of sexual reproduction. p. 17

**mating systems** The social systems describing how males and females pair up. p. 868

**mating type** A genetically defined strain of an organism (such as a fungus) that can only mate with an organism of the opposite mating type; mating types are often designated + and –. p. 592

**matter** Anything that occupies space and has mass. p. F-7

**maxilla** (plural, **maxillae**) One of the paired head appendages posterior to the mouth used for feeding in arthropods. p. 691

**maximum likelihood method** A statistical technique that compares alternative phylogenetic trees with specific models of evolutionary change. p. 466

**mechanical isolation** A prezygotic reproductive isolating mechanism caused by differences in the structure of reproductive organs or other body parts. p. 438

**mechanoreceptor** A sensory receptor that detects mechanical energy, such as changes in pressure, body position, or acceleration. The auditory receptors in the ears are examples of mechanoreceptors. p. 1215

**medusa** (plural, **medusae**) The tentacled, usually bell-shaped, free-swimming sexual stage in the life cycle of a coelenterate. p. 653

**megapascal** A unit of pressure used to measure water potential. p. 915

**megaspore** A plant spore that develops into a female gametophyte; usually larger than a microspore. pp. 617, 938

**meiocyte** A cell that is destined to divide by meiosis. p. 186

**meiosis** The division of diploid cells to haploid progeny, consisting of two sequential rounds of nuclear and cellular division. p. 183

**meiosis I** The first division of the meiotic cell cycle in which homologous chromosomes pair and undergo an exchange of chromosome segments, and then the homologous chromosomes separate, resulting in two cells, each with the haploid number of chromosomes and with each chromosome still consisting of two chromatids. p. 186

**meiosis II** The second division of the meiotic cell cycle in which the sister chromatids in each of the two cells produced by meiosis I separate and segregate into different cells, resulting in four cells each with the haploid number of chromosomes. p. 186

**melanocyte-stimulating hormone (MSH)** A hormone secreted by the anterior pituitary that controls the degree of pigmentation in melanocytes. p. 1147

**melatonin** A peptide hormone secreted by the pineal gland that helps maintain daily biorhythms. p. 1153

**membrane potential** The electrical potential across a cell membrane due to the unequal distribution of positively and negatively charged molecules; it is negative under resting conditions. pp. 89, 1202

**memory** The storage and retrieval of a sensory or motor experience or a thought. p. 1245

**meninges** Three layers of connective tissue that surround and protect the spinal cord and brain. p. 1240

**menstrual cycle** A cycle of approximately 1 month in the human female during which an egg is released from an ovary and the uterus is prepared to receive the fertilized egg; if fertilization does not occur, the endometrium breaks down, which releases blood and tissue breakdown products from the uterus to the outside through the vagina. p. 1173

**meristem** An undifferentiated, permanently embryonic plant tissue that gives rise to new cells forming tissues and organs. p. 888

**mesenteries** Sheets of loose connective tissue, covered on both surfaces with epithelial cells, which suspend the abdominal organs in the coelom and provide lubricated, smooth surfaces that prevent chafing or abrasion between adjacent structures as the body moves. pp. 646, 1013

**mesoderm** The middle layer of the three primary germ layers of an animal embryo, from which the muscular, skeletal, vascular, and connective tissues develop. pp. 645, 1181

**mesohyl** The gelatinous middle layer of cells lining the body cavity of a sponge. p. 651

**mesophyll** The ground tissue located between the two outer leaf tissues, composed of loosely packed parenchyma cells that contain chloroplasts. p. 898

**messenger RNA (mRNA)** An RNA molecule that serves as a template for protein synthesis. p. 279

**metabolism** The biochemical reactions that allow a cell or organism to extract energy from its surroundings and use that energy to maintain itself, grow, and reproduce. p. 61

**metagenomics** The study of all DNA sequences, regardless of origin, isolated "in bulk" from ecosystems such as decaying animals, ocean water, termite gut, etc. p. 538

**metamorphosis** A reorganization of the form of certain animals during postembryonic development. p. 678

**metanephridium** (plural, **metanephridia**) The excretory tubule of most annelids and molluscs. p. 1108

**metaphase** The phase of mitosis during which the spindle reaches its final form and the spindle microtubules move the chromosomes into alignment at the spindle midpoint. p. 155

**metaphase plate** During cell division, chromosomes are located to a position at the spindle midpoint prior to them separating during anaphase. p. 187

**metastasis** The spreading of a malignant tumour through the blood system or the lymphatic system, forming new tumours at other locations in the body. p. 166

**micelle** A sphere composed of a single layer of lipid molecules. p. 81

**microbiome** The complete collection of microorganisms (bacteria, archaea, protists, yeasts, other fungi, and viruses) in the gut. p. 1046

**microclimate** The abiotic conditions immediately surrounding an organism. p. 801

**microfilament** A cytoskeletal filament composed of actin. p. 41

**micronucleus** In ciliophorans, one or more diploid nuclei that contain a complete complement of genes, functioning primarily in cellular reproduction. p. 567

**micronutrient** Any mineral required by an organism only in trace amounts. pp. 958, 1030

**microRNAs (miRNAs)** Small RNAs that regulate gene expression by binding to specific mRNAs and decreasing their translation. p. 322

**microscope** Instrument of microscopy with different magnifications and resolutions of specimens. p. 27

**microscopy** Technique for producing visible images of objects that are too small to be seen by the human eye. p. 26

**microspore** A plant spore from which a male gametophyte develops; usually smaller than a megaspore. pp. 617, 630

**microtubule** A cytoskeletal component formed by the polymerization of tubulin into rigid, hollow rods about 25 nm in diameter. p. 40

**microtubule organizing centre (MTOC)** An anchoring point near the centre of a eukaryotic cell from which most microtubules extend outward. p. 158

**middle ear** The air-filled cavity containing three small, interconnected bones: the malleus, incus, and stapes. p. 1220

**mineralocorticoid** A steroid hormone secreted by the adrenal cortex that regulates the levels of Na and K in the blood and extracellular fluid. p. 1150

**minimal medium** A growth medium containing the minimal ingredients that enable a nonmutant organism, such as *E. coli*, to grow. p. 175

**miRNA-induced silencing complex (miRISC)** Protein complex containing an miRNA that binds to sequences in the 3′ UTRs of target mRNAs, resulting in either inhibition of translation of the mRNAs or their degradation. p. 322

**mismatch repair** Repair system that removes mismatched bases from newly synthesized DNA strands. p. 270

**missense mutation** A base-pair substitution mutation in a protein-coding gene that results in a different amino acid in the encoded polypeptide than the normal one. p. 299

**mitochondrial matrix** The innermost compartment of the mitochondrion. p. 39

**mitochondrion** Membrane-bound organelle responsible for synthesis of most of the ATP in eukaryotic cells. p. 39

**mitosis** Nuclear division that produces daughter nuclei that are exact genetic copies of the parental nucleus. p. 152

**mitotic spindle** The complex of microtubules that orchestrate the separation of chromosomes during mitosis. p. 155

**mixotroph** An organisms that can act as an autotroph and a heterotroph. p. 564

**molarity (M)** The number of moles of a substance dissolved in 1 L of solution. p. F-19

**molars** Posterior-most teeth of mammals, with a broad chewing surface for grinding food. p. 1040

**mole (mol)** The atomic weight of an element or the molecular weight of a compound. p. F-19

**molecular clock** A technique for dating the time of divergence of two species or lineages, based on the number of molecular sequence differences between them. p. 469

**molecular weight** The weight of a molecule in grams, equal to the total mass number of its atoms. p. F-19

**molecule** A group of atoms held together with covalent bonds. p. F-11

**monocot** A plant belonging to the Monocotyledones, one of the two major classes of angiosperms; monocot embryos have a single seed leaf (cotyledon) and pollen grains with a single groove. pp. 633, 889

**monoecious** Having both "male" flowers (which possess only stamens) and "female" flowers (which possess only carpels). pp. 651, 936

**monogamy** A mating system in which one male and one female form a long-term association. p. 868

**monohybrid** An F₁ heterozygote produced from a genetic cross that involves a single character. p. 203

**monohybrid cross** A genetic cross between two individuals that are each heterozygous for the same pair of alleles. p. 205

**monomers** Identical or nearly identical subunits that link together to form polymers during polymerization. p. 498

**monophyletic taxon** A group of organisms that includes a single ancestral species and all of its descendants. p. 458

**monosaccharides** The smallest carbohydrates, containing three to seven carbon atoms. p. 64

**monotreme** A lineage of mammals that lay eggs instead of bearing live young. p. 708

**morphological species concept** The concept that all individuals of a species share measurable traits that distinguish them from individuals of other species. p. 434

**morula** The first stage of animal development, a solid ball or layer of blastomeres. p. 1181

**motif** A highly specialized region in a protein produced by the three-dimensional arrangement of amino acid chains within and between domains. p. 315

**motile** Capable of self-propelled movement. p. 644

**motor neuron** An efferent neuron that carries signals to skeletal muscle. p. 1201

**motor unit** A block of muscle fibres that is controlled by branches of the axon of a single efferent neuron. p. 1261

**moult-inhibiting hormone (MIH)** A peptide neurohormone secreted by cells in the eyestalks (extensions of the brain leading to the eyes). p. 1154

**mRNA** *See* messenger RNA (mRNA). p. 279

**mRNA splicing** Process that removes introns from pre-mRNAs and joins exons together. p. 287

**MTOC** *See* microtubule organizing centre (MTOC). p. 158

**mucosa** The lining of the gut that contains epithelial and glandular cells. p. 1039

**Müllerian duct** The bipotential primitive duct associated with the gonads that leads to a cloaca. p. 1192

**multiple alleles** More than two different alleles of a gene. p. 214

**multiple fruit** A fruit that develops from several ovaries in multiple flowers; examples are pineapples and mulberries. p. 942

**multipotent cell** A cell that gives rise to a cell with a particular function. p. 1182

**multiregional hypothesis** A hypothesis proposing that after archaic humans migrated from Africa to many regions on Earth, their different populations evolved into modern humans simultaneously. p. 485

**muscle fibre** A bundle of elongated, cylindrical cells that make up skeletal muscle. pp. 1015, 1256

**muscle spindle** A stretch receptor in muscle; a bundle of small, specialized muscle cells wrapped with the dendrites of afferent neurons and enclosed in connective tissue. p. 1219

**muscle tissue** Cells that have the ability to contract (shorten) forcibly. p. 1015

**muscle twitch** A single, weak contraction of a muscle fibre. p. 1260

**muscularis** The muscular coat of a hollow organ or tubular structure. p. 1039

**mutagen** A physical, chemical, or biological agent that produces a mutation. p. 300

**mutagenesis** The production of mutations in a laboratory by exposure to a mutagen. p. 300

**mutation** A spontaneous and heritable change in DNA. pp. 299, 401, 419

**mutualism** A symbiotic interaction between species in which both partners benefit. pp. 588, 780

**mycelium** A network of branching hyphae that constitutes the body of a multicellular fungus. pp. 570, 588

**mycobiont** The fungal component of a lichen. p. 601

**mycorrhiza** A mutualistic symbiosis in which fungal hyphae associate intimately with plant roots.  pp. 594, 965

**myofibril** A cylindrical contractile element about 1 m in diameter that runs lengthwise inside the muscle fibre cell.  p. 1256

**myogenic heart** A heart that maintains its contraction rhythm with no requirement for signals from the nervous system.  p. 1088

**myoglobin** An oxygen-storing protein closely related to hemoglobin.  p. 1262

**N-terminal end** The end of a polypeptide chain with an —$NH_3$ group.  p. 289

**Na$^+$/K$^+$ pump** Pump that pushes 3 Na$^+$ out of the cell and 2 K$^+$ into the cell in the same pumping cycle. Also referred to as the *sodium–potassium pump*.  p. 89

**nastic movement** In plants, a reversible response to non-directional stimuli, such as mechanical pressure or humidity.  p. 996

**natural selection** The evolutionary process by which alleles that increase the likelihood of survival and the reproductive output of the individuals that carry them become more common in subsequent generations.  p. 399

**navigation** A wayfinding mechanism in which an animal moves toward a specific destination, using both a compass and a "mental map" of where it is in relation to the destination.  p. 865

**negative feedback** The primary mechanism of homeostasis, in which a stimulus—a change in the external or internal environment—triggers a response that compensates for the environmental change.  p. 1019

**negative pressure breathing** Muscular contractions that expand the lungs, lowering the pressure of the air in the lungs and causing air to be pulled inward.  p. 1063

**nematocyst** A coiled thread, encapsulated in a cnidocyte, that cnidarians fire at prey or predators, sometimes releasing a toxin through its tip.  p. 653

**nephron** A specialized excretory tubule that contributes to osmoregulation and carries out excretion, found in all vertebrates.  p. 1110

**nerve** A bundle of axons enclosed in connective tissue and all following the same pathway.  p. 1200

**nerve cord** A bundle of nerves that extends from the central ganglia to the rest of the body, connected to smaller nerves.  p. 1238

**nerve net** A simple nervous system that coordinates responses to stimuli but has no central control organ or brain.  pp. 654, 1238

**nervous system** A communication system in which information flows along neurons in nerves.  p. 1200

**nervous tissue** Tissue that contains neurons, which serve as lines of communication and control between body parts.  p. 1017

**net primary productivity** The chemical energy remaining in an ecosystem after a producer's cellular respiration is deducted.  p. 817

**neural crest cells** A band of cells that arises early in the embryonic development of vertebrates near the region where the neural tube pinches off from the ectoderm; later, the cells migrate and develop into unique structures.  p. 1186

**neural plate** Ectoderm thickened and flattened into a longitudinal band, induced by notochord cells.  p. 1186

**neural regulation** Neurons synapse directly with target cells, releasing neurotransmitters into a synapse or neuromuscular junction.  p. 1137

**neural signalling** Communication between cells in an animal by neural signalling; involves the flow of information within neurons and between neurons within networks or circuits.  p. 1200

**neural tube** A hollow tube in vertebrate embryos that develops into the brain, spinal cord, spinal nerves, and spinal column.  p. 1239

**neuroendocrine regulation** Specialized neurosecretory neurons respond to and conduct electrical signals, but rather than synapsing with target cells, they release a neurohormone into the circulation.  p. 1137

**neurogenic heart** A heart that beats under the control of signals from the nervous system.  p. 1088

**neuromodulator** Any chemical substance that modulates (enhances or inhibits) the actions of a nerve. p. 1211

**neuromuscular junction** The junction between a nerve fibre and the muscle it supplies.  p. 1257

**neuron** An electrically active cell of the nervous system responsible for controlling behaviour and body functions.  pp. 1017, 1137, 1200

**neuronal circuit** Neurons connected together into functional circuits.  p. 1201

**neurosecretory neuron** A neuron that releases a neurohormone into the circulatory system when appropriately stimulated.  p. 1137

**neurotransmitter** A chemical released by an axon terminal at a chemical synapse.  p. 1210

**neurulation** The process in vertebrates by which organogenesis begins with development of the nervous system from ectoderm.  p. 1186

**neutron** Uncharged particle in the nucleus of an atom.  p. F-8

**nitrification** A metabolic process in which certain soil bacteria convert ammonia or ammonium ions into nitrites that are then converted by other bacteria to nitrates, a form usable by plants.  pp. 544, 828, 967

**nitrogen cycle** A biogeochemical cycle that moves nitrogen between the huge atmospheric pool of gaseous molecular nitrogen and several much smaller pools of nitrogen-containing compounds in soils, marine and freshwater ecosystems, and living organisms.  p. 827

**nitrogen fixation** A metabolic process in which certain bacteria and cyanobacteria convert molecular nitrogen into ammonia and ammonium ions, forms usable by plants.  pp. 544, 827, 967

**nitrogenous base** A nitrogen-containing molecule with the properties of a base.  p. 62

**nociceptor** A sensory receptor that detects tissue damage or noxious chemicals; their activity registers as pain.  p. 1215

**node** The point on a stem where one or more leaves are attached.  pp. 456, 895

**node of Ranvier** The gap between two Schwann cells, which exposes the axon membrane directly to extracellular fluids.  p. 1201

**nondisjunction** The failure of homologous pairs to separate during the first meiotic division or of chromatids to separate during the second meiotic division.  p. 237

**nonsense codon** *See* stop codon.  p. 237

**nonsense mutation** A base-pair substitution mutation in a gene in which the base-pair change results in a change from a sense codon to a nonsense codon in the mRNA. The polypeptide translated from the mRNA is shorter than the normal polypeptide because of the mutation.  p. 300

**nonshivering thermogenesis** The generation of heat by oxidative mechanisms in nonmuscle tissue throughout the body.  p. 1127

**nonvascular plant** *See* bryophyte.  p. 615

**norepinephrine** A nontropic amine hormone secreted by the adrenal medulla.  p. 1150

**not at risk** The category that identifies a species that is not at risk of extinction under current circumstances. p. 727

**notochord** A flexible rodlike structure constructed of fluid-filled cells surrounded by tough connective tissue, which supports a chordate embryo from head to tail. p. 685

**nucellus** The inner part of an ovule, containing the embryo sac; equivalent to a megasporangium. p. 937

**nuclear envelope** In eukaryotes, membranes separating the nucleus from the cytoplasm. p. 31

**nuclear localization signal** A short amino acid sequence in a protein that directs the protein to the nucleus. p. 298

**nuclear pore** Opening in the membrane of the nuclear envelope through which large molecules, such as RNA and proteins, move between the nucleus and the cytoplasm. p. 31

**nuclear pore complex** A large, octagonally symmetrical, cylindrical structure that functions to exchange molecules between the nucleus and cytoplasm and prevents the transport of material not meant to cross the nuclear membrane. A nuclear pore—a channel through the complex—is the path for the exchange of molecules. p. 31

**nucleoid** The central region of a prokaryotic cell with no boundary membrane separating it from the cytoplasm, where DNA replication and RNA transcription occur. pp. 29, 151, 538

**nucleolus** The nuclear site of rRNA transcription, processing, and ribosome assembly in eukaryotes. p. 32

**nucleosome** The basic structural unit of chromatin in eukaryotes, consisting of DNA wrapped around a histone core. p. 155

**nucleotide** The monomer of nucleic acids consisting of a five-carbon sugar, a nitrogenous base, and a phosphate. p. F-36

**nucleotide-excision repair** A type of excision repair mechanism for repairing DNA damage involving bulky distortion to the DNA. Nucleotide-excision repair involves recognition of the damage, removing the DNA segment with the damage, and replacing the removed DNA with new DNA. p. 271

**nucleus** The central region of eukaryotic cells, separated by membranes from the surrounding cytoplasm, where DNA replication and messenger RNA transcription occur. p. 29

**null hypothesis** A prediction of what researchers would see if a particular factor had no effect. p. 415

**nutrient** An organic or inorganic molecule required for growth, maintenance, or reproduction. p. 1030

**nutrition** The sum of the processes by which an animal or plant takes in and utilizes the substances necessary for maintenance, growth, and reproduction. p. 1030

**obligate aerobe** A microorganism that must use oxygen for cellular respiration and requires oxygen in its surroundings to support growth. p. 544

**obligate anaerobe** A microorganism that cannot use oxygen and can grow only in the absence of oxygen. p. 544

**ocellus** (plural, **ocelli**) The simplest eye, which detects light but does not form an image. pp. 659, 1224

**Okazaki fragment** Relatively short segment of DNA synthesized on the lagging strand at a replication fork. p. 264

**olfactory bulb** A grey-matter centre that relays inputs from odour receptors to both the cerebral cortex and the limbic system. p. 1242

**oligodendrocyte** A type of glial cell that populates the central nervous system and is responsible for producing myelin. p. 1201

**oligosaccharin** A complex carbohydrate that in plants serves as a signalling molecule and as a defence against pathogens. p. 989

**ommatidium** (plural, **ommatidia**) A faceted visual unit of a compound eye. p. 1224

**omnivore** An animal that feeds at several trophic levels, consuming plants, animals, and other sources of organic matter. p. 1030

**oncogene** A gene that, when deregulated, is capable of inducing one or more characteristics of cancer cells. pp. 167, 325

**one gene–one enzyme hypothesis** Hypothesis showing the direct relationship between genes and enzymes. p. 279

**one gene–one polypeptide hypothesis** Restatement of the one gene–one enzyme hypothesis, taking into account that some proteins consist of more than one polypeptide and not all proteins are enzymes. p. 279

**oocyte** A developing gamete that becomes an ootid at the end of meiosis. p. 651

**oogenesis** The process of producing eggs. p. 1164

**oogonium** (plural, **oogonia**) A cell that enters meiosis and gives rise to gametes, produced by mitotic divisions of the germ cells in females. p. 1164

**open circulatory system** An arrangement of internal transport in some invertebrates in which the vascular fluid, hemolymph, is released into sinuses, bathing organs directly, and is not always retained within vessels. pp. 666, 1081

**open reading frames (ORFs)** Segments of DNA sequence that contain start and stop codons. Such sequences are candidate genes. p. 371

**operant** Involves the modification of a behaviour by the effects (positive or negative) of its own consequences. p. 851

**operant conditioning** A form of associative learning in which animals learn to link a voluntary activity, an operant, with its favourable consequences, the reinforcement. p. 851

**operator** A DNA regulatory sequence that controls transcription of an operon. p. 309

**operculum** A lid or flap of the bone serving as the gill cover in some fishes. p. 693

**operon** A cluster of prokaryotic genes and the DNA sequences involved in their regulation. p. 309

**opisthosoma** The rear end of a chelicerate's body, derived from the abdomen in ancestral arthropods. p. 673

**opsin** One of several different proteins that bond covalently with the light-absorbing pigment of rods and cones (retinal). p. 1226

**optic chiasm** Location just behind the eyes where the optic nerves converge before entering the base of the brain, with a portion of each optic nerve crossing over to the opposite side. p. 1228

**oral hood** Soft fleshy structure at the anterior end of a cephalochordate that frames the opening of the mouth. p. 685

**orbital** The region of space where the electron "lives" most of the time. p. F-10

**organ** Two or more different tissues integrated into a structure that carries out a specific function. pp. 886, 1008

**organ of Corti** An organ within the cochlear duct that contains the sensory hair cells detecting sound vibrations transmitted to the inner ear. p. 1222

**organ system** The coordinated activities of two or more organs to carry out a major body function such as movement, digestion, or reproduction. pp. 1009, 1080

**organelles** The nucleus and other specialized internal structures and compartments of eukaryotic cells. p. 28

**organic molecule** Molecule based on carbon. p. 28

**organogenesis** The development of the major organ systems, giving rise to a free-living individual with the body organization characteristic of its species. p. 1181

**origin of replication (*ori*)** A specific region at which replication of a bacterial chromosome commences. p. 151

**orthologs** Genes in two or more different organisms that are closely related to one another evolutionarily, and perform the same function in every organism. p. 372

**osmoconformer** An animal in which the osmolarity of the cellular and extracellular solutions matches the osmolarity of the environment. p. 1105

**osmolality** A measure of the osmotic concentration of a solution. It is measured in osmoles (the number of solute molecules and ions) per kilogram of solvent. p. 1105

**osmolarity** The total solute concentration of a solution, measured in osmoles—the number of solute molecules and ions (in moles)—per litre of solution. p. 1105

**osmoregulator** An animal that uses control mechanisms to keep the osmolarity of cellular and extracellular fluids the same but at levels that may differ from the osmolarity of the surroundings. p. 1105

**osmosis** The passive transport of water across a selectively permeable membrane in response to solute concentration gradients, a pressure gradient, or both. pp. 87, 915

**osteoblast** A cell that produces the collagen and mineral of bone. p. 1013

**osteoclast** A cell that removes bone minerals and recycles them through the bloodstream. p. 1013

**osteocyte** A mature bone cell. p. 1013

**osteon** The structural unit of bone, consisting of a minute central canal surrounded by osteocytes embedded in concentric layers of mineral matter. p. 1013

**ostracoderm** One of an assortment of extinct, jawless fishes that were covered with bony armour. p. 689

**otolith** One of many small crystals of calcium carbonate embedded in the otolithic membrane of the hair cells. p. 1218

**outer boundary membrane** A smooth membrane that surrounds a chloroplast, enclosing the stroma. p. 44

**outer ear** The external structure of the ear, consisting of the pinna and meatus. p. 1220

**outer membrane** In Gram-negative bacteria, an additional boundary membrane that covers the peptidoglycan layer of the cell wall. p. 541

**outer mitochondrial membrane** The smooth membrane covering the outside of a mitochondrion. p. 39

**outgroup comparison** A technique used to identify ancestral and derived characters by comparing the group under study with more distantly related species that are not otherwise included in the analysis. p. 463

**oval window** An opening in the bony wall that separates the middle ear from the inner ear. p. 1221

**ovarian cycle** The cyclic events in the ovary leading to ovulation. p. 1173

**ovary** In animals, the female gonad, which produces female gametes and reproductive hormones. In flowering plants, the enlarged base of a carpel in which one or more ovules develop into seeds. pp. 936, 1151, 1164

**oviduct** The tube through which the egg moves from the ovary to the outside of the body. p. 1164

**oviparous** Referring to animals that lay eggs containing the nutrients needed for development of the embryo outside the mother's body. p. 1169

**ovoviviparous** Referring to animals in which fertilized eggs are retained within the body and the embryo develops using nutrients provided by the egg; eggs hatch inside the mother. p. 1170

**ovulation** The process in which oocytes are released into the oviducts as immature eggs. p. 1172

**ovule** In plants, the structure in a carpel in which a female gametophyte develops and fertilization takes place. pp. 628, 936

**ovum** (plural, **ova**) A female sex cell, or egg. p. 1164

**oxidation** The removal of electrons from a substance. p. 103

**oxidative phosphorylation** Synthesis of ATP in which ATP synthase uses an $H^+$ gradient built by the electron transfer system as the energy source to make the ATP. p. 113

**oxidized** Refers to a substance from which the electrons are removed during oxidation. p. 103

**oxytocin** A hormone that stimulates the ejection of milk from the mammary glands of a nursing mother. p. 1147

**P generation** The parental individuals used in an initial cross. p. 202

**P site** The site in the ribosome where the tRNA carrying the growing polypeptide chain is bound. p. 291

**pacemaker cell** A specialized cardiac muscle cell in the upper wall of the right atrium that sets the rate of contraction in the heart. p. 1089

**pancreas** A mixed gland composed of an exocrine portion that secretes digestive enzymes into the small intestine and an endocrine portion, the islets of Langerhans, that secretes insulin and glucagon. p. 1152

**parabronchi** In bird lungs, an array of fine, parallel tubes through which air flows, and across which a capillary network crosses in a perpendicular direction to produce a crosscurrent pattern of blood flow relative to the air flow. p. 1064

**paracrine regulation** A cell releases signalling molecules that diffuse through the extracellular fluid and act on nearby cells. p. 1136

**paralog** Genes that arise through duplication within a genome. p. 372

**paralogous chromosome** Duplicate copies of chromosomes that arise through nondisjunction. Contrast this with *homologous chromosomes*, which are similar chromosomes but do not arise through mistakes in the cell cycle. p. 384

**paraphyletic taxon** A group of organisms that includes an ancestral species and some, but not all, of its descendants. p. 458

**parasite** An organism that feeds on the tissues of or otherwise exploits its host. p. 562

**parasitism** A symbiotic interaction in which one species, the parasite, uses another, the host, in a way that is harmful to the host. pp. 588, 780

**parasympathetic division** The division of the autonomic nervous system that predominates during quiet, low-stress situations, such as while relaxing. p. 1248

**parathyroid gland** One of a pair of glands that produce parathyroid hormone (PTH) (found only in tetrapod vertebrates). p. 1149

**parathyroid hormone (PTH)** The hormone secreted by the parathyroid glands in response to a fall in blood $Ca^{2+}$ levels. p. 1149

**parental investment** The time and energy devoted to the production and rearing of offspring. p. 1193

**parthenogenesis** A mode of asexual reproduction in which animals produce offspring by the growth and development of an egg without fertilization. p. 1162

**partial diploid** A condition in which part of the genome of a haploid organism is diploid. Recipients in bacterial conjugation between an Hfr and an F cell become partial diploids for part of the Hfr bacterial chromosome. p. 180

**partial pressure** The individual pressure exerted by each gas within a mixture of gases. p. 1058

**parturition** The process of giving birth. p. 1191

**passenger mutation** In a typical tumour, the many mutations that do not have any effect on cancer progression. p. 325

**passive parental care** The amount of energy invested in offspring—in the form of the energy stored in eggs or seeds or energy transferred to developing young through a placenta—before they are born. p. 754

**passive transport** The transport of substances across cell membranes without expenditure of energy, as in diffusion. pp. 84, 915

**paternal chromosome** The chromosome derived from the male parent of an organism. p. 185

**pathogenesis-related (PR) protein** A hydrolytic enzyme that breaks down components of a pathogen's cell wall. p. 991

**PCR** See polymerase chain reaction (PCR). p. 338

**pectoral girdle** A bony or cartilaginous structure in vertebrates that supports and is attached to the forelimbs. p. 687

**pedicellaria** (plural, **pedicellariae**) Small pincer at the base of short spines in starfishes and sea urchins. p. 682

**pedigree** Chart that shows all parents and offspring for as many generations as possible, the sex of individuals in the different generations, and the presence or absence of a trait of interest. p. 240

**pedigree analysis** The study of a pedigree. p. 240

**pellicle** A layer of supportive protein fibres located inside the cell, just under the plasma membrane, providing strength and flexibility instead of a cell wall. p. 562

**pelvic girdle** A bony or cartilaginous structure in vertebrates that supports and is attached to the hindlimbs. p. 687

**pepsin** An enzyme made in the stomach that breaks down proteins. p. 70

**pepsinogen** The inactive precursor molecule for pepsin. p. 295

**peptide bond** A link formed by a dehydration synthesis reaction between the —NH$_2$ group of one amino acid and the —COOH group of a second. p. 291

**peptidoglycan** A polymeric substance formed from a polysaccharide backbone tied together by short polypeptides, which is the primary structural molecule of bacterial cell walls. p. 540

**peptidyl transferase** An enzyme that catalyzes the reaction in which an amino acid is cleaved from the tRNA in the P site of the ribosome and forms a peptide bond with the amino acid on the tRNA in the A site of the ribosome. p. 292

**peptidyl–tRNA** A tRNA linked to a growing polypeptide chain containing two or more amino acids. p. 292

**per capita growth rate** The difference between the per capita birth rate and the per capita death rate of a population. p. 757

**perception** The conscious awareness of our external and internal environments derived from the processing of sensory input. p. 1235

**perennial** A plant in which vegetative growth and reproduction continue year after year. p. 889

**perfusion** The flow of blood or other body fluids to the various organs of the body. p. 1061

**pericarp** The fruit wall. p. 942

**pericycle** A tissue of plant roots, located between the endodermis and the phloem, which gives rise to lateral roots. p. 902

**periderm** The outermost portion of bark; consists of cork, cork cambium, and secondary cortex. p. 904

**peripheral membrane protein** Protein held to membrane surfaces by noncovalent bonds formed with the polar parts of integral membrane proteins or membrane lipids. p. 84

**peripheral nervous system (PNS)** All nerve roots and nerves (motor and sensory) that supply the muscles of the body and transmit information about sensation (including pain) to the central nervous system. p. 1200

**peristalsis** The rippling motion of muscles in the intestine or other tubular organs characterized by the alternate contraction and relaxation of the muscles that propel the contents onward. p. 1037

**peritoneum** The thin tissue derived from mesoderm that lines the abdominal wall and covers most of the organs in the abdomen. p. 646

**peritubular capillary** A capillary of the network surrounding the glomerulus. p. 1114

**permafrost** Perpetually frozen ground below the topsoil. p. 252

**peroxisome** Microbody that produces hydrogen peroxide as a by-product. p. 296

**petal** Part of the corolla of a flower, often brightly coloured. p. 936

**petiole** The stalk by which a leaf is attached to a stem. p. 897

**phage** See bacteriophage. pp. 254, 523

**phagocytosis** Process in which some types of cells engulf bacteria or other cellular debris to break them down. pp. 37, 92

**pharynx** The throat. In some invertebrates, a protrusible tube used to bring food into the mouth for passage to the gastrovascular cavity; in mammals, the common pathway for air entering the larynx and food entering the esophagus. p. 1065

**phenomics** The study of gene function by identifying changes in phenotypes. p. 374

**phenotype** The outward appearance of an organism. p. 205

**phenotypic variation** Differences in appearance or function between individual organisms. p. 412

**phloem** The food-conducting tissue of a vascular plant. pp. 615, 893

**phloem sap** The solution of water and organic compounds that flows rapidly through the sieve tubes of flowering plants. p. 925

**phosphate group** Group consisting of a central phosphorus atom held in four linkages: two that bind —OH groups to the central phosphorus atom, a third that binds an oxygen atom to the central phosphorus atom, and a fourth that links the phosphate group to an oxygen atom. p. 53

**phosphodiester bond** The linkage of nucleotides in polynucleotide chains by a bridging phosphate group between the 5 carbon of one sugar and the 3 carbon of the next sugar in line. p. 256

**phospholipid** A phosphate-containing lipid. p. 80

**phosphorus cycle** A biogeochemical cycle in which weathering and erosion carry phosphate ions from rocks to soil and into streams and rivers, which eventually transport them to the ocean, where they are slowly incorporated into rocks. p. 829

**photoautotroph** A photosynthetic organism that uses light as its energy source and carbon dioxide as its carbon source. p. 126

**photobiont** The photosynthetic component of a lichen. p. 601

**photoheterotroph** An organism that uses light as the ultimate energy source but obtains carbon in organic form rather than as carbon dioxide. p. 543

**photon** Discrete particle or packet of energy. p. 7

**photoperiodism** The response of plants to changes in the relative lengths of light and dark periods in their environment during each 24 hour period. p. 997

**photophosphorylation** The synthesis of ATP coupled to the transfer of electrons energized by photons of light. p. 134

**photopigment** Light-absorbing pigment. p. 1224

**photopsin** One of three photopigments in which retinal is combined with different opsins. p. 1226

**photoreceptor** A sensory receptor that detects the energy of light. p. 1215

**photorespiration** A process that metabolizes a by-product of photosynthesis. p. 137

**photoreversible** The property of certain light-sensitive pigment proteins (such as phytochromes) in which light absorption triggers a shift from one conformation to another. p. 997

**photosynthesis** The conversion of light energy to chemical energy in the form of sugar and other organic molecules. p. 126

**photosystem** A large complex into which the light-absorbing pigments for photosynthesis are organized with proteins and other molecules. p. 128

**photosystem I** In photosynthesis, a protein complex in the thylakoid membrane that uses energy absorbed from sunlight to synthesize NADPH. p. 132

**photosystem II** In photosynthesis, a protein complex in the thylakoid membrane that uses energy absorbed from sunlight to synthesize ATP. p. 132

**phototroph** An organism that obtains energy from light. p. 543

**phototropism** The tendency of a plant shoot to bend toward a source of light. p. 981

**PhyloCode** A formal set of rules governing phylogenetic nomenclature. p. 464

**phylogenetic species concept** A concept that seeks to delineate species as the smallest aggregate population that can be united by shared derived characters. p. 435

**phylogenetic tree** A branching diagram depicting the evolutionary relationships of groups of organisms. p. 456

**phylogeny** The evolutionary history of a group of organisms. p. 456

**physiology** The study of the functions of organisms—the physicochemical processes of organisms. pp. 882, 1008

**phytoalexin** A biochemical that functions as an antibiotic in plants. p. 991

**phytochrome** A blue-green pigmented plant chromoprotein involved in the regulation of light-dependent growth processes. p. 997

**phytoplankton** Microscopic, free-flowing aquatic plants and protists. p. 562

**pigment** A molecule that can absorb photons of light. p. 7

**piloting** A wayfinding mechanism in which animals use familiar landmarks to guide their journey. p. 865

**pilus** (plural, **pili**) A hair or hairlike appendage on the surface of a prokaryote. pp. 31, 542

**pinacoderm** In sponges, an unstratified outer layer of cells. p. 651

**pineal gland** A light-sensitive, melatonin-secreting gland that regulates some biological rhythms. p. 1153

**pinna (outer ear)** The external structure of the outer ear, which concentrates and focuses sound waves. p. 1220

**pinocytosis** *See* bulk-phase endocytosis. p. 91

**pith** The soft, spongelike, central cylinder of the stems of most flowering plants, composed mainly of parenchyma. p. 896

**pituitary** A gland consisting mostly of two fused lobes suspended just below the hypothalamus by a slender stalk of tissue that contains both neurons and blood vessels; it interacts with the hypothalamus to control many physiological functions, including the activity of some other glands. p. 1145

**placenta** A specialized temporary organ that connects the embryo and fetus with the uterus in mammals, mediating the delivery of oxygen and nutrients. Analagous structures occur in other animals. pp. 709, 1170

**planula** a ciliated larval stage that settles and undergoes metamorphosis into the polyp form. p. 654

**plasma** The liquid component of blood in which a variety of cells are suspended. pp. 1018, 1084

**plasma membrane** The outer limit of the cytoplasm responsible for the regulation of substances moving into and out of cells. pp. 27, 78

**plasmid** A DNA molecule in the cytoplasm of certain prokaryotes, which often contains genes with functions that supplement those in the nucleoid and can replicate independently of the nucleoid DNA and be passed along during cell division. pp. 350, 540

**plasmodesma** (plural, **plasmodesmata**) A minute channel that perforates a cell wall and contains extensions of the cytoplasm that directly connect adjacent plant cells. p. 887

**plasmodial slime mould** A slime mould of the class Myxomycetes. p. 575

**plasmodium** The composite mass of plasmodial slime moulds consisting of individual nuclei suspended in a common cytoplasm surrounded by a single plasma membrane. p. 575

**plasmogamy** The sexual stage of fungi during which the cytoplasm of two genetically different partners fuse. p. 589

**plastids** A family of plant organelles. p. 43

**plastron** The ventral part of the shell of a turtle. p. 702

**platelet** An oval or rounded cell fragment enclosed in its own plasma membrane, which is found in the blood; they are produced in red bone marrow by the division of stem cells and contain enzymes and other factors that take part in blood clotting. p. 1086

**pleiotropy** Condition in which single genes affect more than one character of an organism. p. 218

**pleura** The double layer of epithelial tissue covering the outside of the lungs and the surrounding body wall. p. 1067

**ploidy** The number of chromosome sets of a cell or species. p. 153

**plumule** The rudimentary terminal bud of a plant embryo located at the end of the hypocotyl, consisting of the epicotyl and a cluster of tiny foliage leaves. p. 944

**pluripotent cell** A cell that can give rise to most, but not all, adult cell types. p. 1182

**poikilohydric** Having little control over internal water content. p. 614

**polar** A molecule having partially positive and negative ends. p. F-13

**polar body** A non-functional cell produced in oogenesis. p. 1165

**polar covalent bond** Bond in which electrons are shared unequally. p. F-13

**polar nucleus** In the embryo sac of a flowering plant, one of two nuclei that migrate into the centre of the sac, become housed in a

**central cell**, and eventually give rise to endosperm. p. 938

**polar transport**  Unidirectional movement of a substance from one end of a cell (or other structure) to the other.  p. 984

**polarity**  The unequal distribution of yolk and other components in a mature egg.  p. 1180

**pollen grain**  The male gametophyte of a seed plant.  pp. 628, 937

**pollen sac**  The microsporangium of a seed plant, in which pollen develops.  p. 936

**pollen tube**  A tube that grows from a germinating pollen grain through the tissues of a carpel and carries the sperm cells to the ovary.  p. 628

**pollination**  The transfer of pollen to a flower's reproductive parts by air currents or on the bodies of animal pollinators.  p. 200

**poly(A) tail**  The string of A nucleotides added posttranscriptionally to the 3 end of a pre-mRNA molecule and retained in the mRNA produced from it that enables the mRNA to be translated efficiently and protects it from attack by RNA-digesting enzymes in the cytoplasm.  p. 286

**polyandry**  A polygamous mating system in which one female mates with multiple males.  p. 868

**polygamy**  A mating system in which either males or females may have many mating partners.  p. 868

**polygenic inheritance**  Inheritance in which several to many different genes contribute to the same character.  p. 216

**polygyny**  A polygamous mating system in which one male mates with many females.  p. 868

**polyhedral virus**  A virus in which the coat proteins form triangular units that fit together like the parts of a geodesic sphere.  p. 522

**polymerase chain reaction (PCR)**  Process that amplifies a specific DNA sequence from a DNA mixture to an extremely large number of copies.  p. 338

**polymorphism**  The existence of discrete variants of a character among individuals in a population.  p. 341

**polyp**  The tentacled, usually sessile stage in the life cycle of a coelenterate.  p. 653

**polypeptide**  The chain of amino acids formed by sequential peptide bonds.  p. F-30

**polyphyletic taxon**  A group of organisms that belong to different evolutionary lineages and do not share a recent common ancestor.  p. 458

**polyploid**  An individual with one or more extra copies of the entire haploid complement of chromosomes.  p. 237

**polyploidy**  The condition of having one or more extra copies of the entire haploid complement of chromosomes.  p. 443

**polysaccharide**  Chain with more than 10 linked monosaccharide subunits.  p. 30

**polysome**  The entire structure of an mRNA molecule and the multiple associated ribosomes that are translating it simultaneously.  p. 293

**population**  All individuals of a single species that live together in the same place and time.  p. 399

**population density**  The number of individuals per unit area or per unit volume of habitat.  p. 749

**population genetics**  The branch of science that studies the prevalence and variation in genes among populations of individuals.  p. 414

**population size**  The number of individuals in a population at a specified time.  p. 749

**porocyte**  A cylindrical cell that allows water to pass.  p. 651

**portal vein**  A special vein that connects the capillaries of two structures.  p. 1044

**positive feedback**  A mechanism that intensifies or adds to a change in internal or external environmental condition.  p. 1023

**positive pressure breathing**  A gulping or swallowing motion that forces air into the lungs.  p. 1063

**posterior pituitary**  The neural portion of the pituitary, which stores and releases two hormones made by the hypothalamus, antidiuretic hormone and oxytocin.  p. 1145

**postsynaptic cell**  The neuron or the surface of an effector after a synapse that receives the signal from the presynaptic cell.  p. 1210

**postsynaptic membrane**  The plasma membrane of the postsynaptic cell.  p. 1210

**posttranslational import**  A process for sorting proteins that are translated on cytosolic ribosomes and then moved into organelles.  p. 298

**postzygotic isolating mechanism**  A reproductive isolating mechanism that acts after zygote formation.  p. 437

**potential energy**  Stored energy.  p. 54

**precocial**  Newborns that can stand immediately after birth and are soon able to run.  pp. 709, 1191

**precursor mRNA (pre-mRNA)**  The primary transcript of a eukaryotic protein-coding gene, which is processed to form messenger RNA.  p. 285

**predator**  Any organism that preys upon another. p. 778

**prediction**  A statement about what the researcher expects to happen to one variable if another variable changes.  p. F-3

**pregnancy**  The period of mammalian development in which the embryo develops in the uterus of the mother.  p. 1188

**premaxillae**  bone in vertebrates that bears the upper incisor teeth.  p. 691

**premolars**  Teeth located in pairs on each side of the upper and lower jaws of mammals, positioned behind the canines and in front of the molars.  p. 1040

**prenatal diagnosis**  Techniques in which cells derived from a developing embryo or its surrounding tissues or fluids are tested for the presence of mutant alleles or chromosomal alterations.  p. 243

**prepuce**  Foreskin; a loose fold of skin that covers the glans of the penis.  p. 1177

**pressure-flow mechanism**  In vascular plants, pressure that builds up at the source end of a sieve tube system and pushes solutes by bulk flow toward a sink, where they are removed.  p. 926

**presynaptic cell**  The neuron with an axon terminal on one side of the synapse that transmits the signal across the synapse to the dendrite or cell body of the postsynaptic cell.  p. 1210

**presynaptic membrane**  The plasma membrane of the axon terminal of a presynaptic cell, which releases neurotransmitter molecules into the synapse in response to the arrival of an action potential.  p. 1210

**prezygotic isolating mechanism**  A reproductive isolating mechanism that acts prior to the production of a zygote, or fertilized egg.  p. 437

**primary active transport**  Transport in which the same protein that transports a substance also hydrolyzes ATP to power the transport directly.  p. 89

**primary cell layers**  The ectoderm, mesoderm, and endoderm layers that form the embryonic tissues.  p. 1181

**primary cell wall**  The initial cell wall laid down by a plant cell.  p. 886

**primary consumer**  A herbivore, a member of the second trophic level.  pp. 778, 1030

**primary endosymbiosis** In the model for the origin of plastids in eukaryotes, the first event in which a eukaryotic cell engulfed a photosynthetic cyanobacterium. p. 580

**primary growth** The growth of plant tissues derived from apical meristems. *Compare* secondary growth. p. 888

**primary meristem** Root and shoot apical meristems, from which a plant's primary tissues develop. *Compare* lateral meristem. p. 896

**primary motor area** The area of the cerebral cortex that runs in a band just in front of the primary somatosensory area and is responsible for voluntary movement. p. 1244

**primary plant body** The portion of a plant that is made up of primary tissues. p. 888

**primary producer** An autotroph, usually a photosynthetic organism, a member of the first trophic level. pp. 126, 778

**primary somatosensory area** The area of the cerebral cortex that runs in a band across the parietal lobes of the brain and registers information on touch, pain, temperature, and pressure. p. 1243

**primary structure** The sequence of amino acids in a protein. pp. 83, F-30

**primary tissue** A plant tissue that develops from an apical meristem. p. 888

**primase** An enzyme that assembles the primer for a new DNA strand during DNA replication. p. 264

**primer** A short nucleotide chain made of RNA that is laid down as the first series of nucleotides in a new DNA strand or made of DNA for use in the polymerase chain reaction (PCR). p. 263

**primitive groove** In the development of birds, the sunken midline of the primitive streak that acts as a conduit for migrating cells to move into the blastocoel. p. 1185

**primitive streak** In the development of birds, the thickened region of the embryo produced by cells of the epiblast streaming toward the midline of the blastodisc. p. 1185

**principle of independent assortment** Mendel's principle that the alleles of the genes that govern two characters segregate independently during formation of gametes. p. 207

**principle of parsimony** A principle of systematic biology that states that a particular trait is unlikely to evolve independently in separate evolutionary lineages. p. 464

**principle of segregation** Mendel's principle that the pairs of alleles that control a character segregate as gametes are formed, with half the gametes carrying one allele and the other half carrying the other allele. p. 203

**prion** An infectious agent that contains only protein and does not include a nucleic acid molecule. p. 530

**probability** The possibility that an outcome will occur if it is a matter of chance. p. 205

**procambium** The primary meristem of a plant that develops into primary vascular tissue. p. 896

**product** An atom or molecule leaving a chemical reaction. p. F-15

**product rule** Mathematical rule in which the final probability is found by multiplying individual probabilities. p. 205

**production efficiency** The ratio of the energy content of new tissue produced to the energy assimilated from food. p. 819

**progesterone** A female sex hormone that stimulates growth of the uterine lining and inhibits contractions of the uterus. p. 1151

**progestin** A class of sex hormones synthesized by the gonads of vertebrates and active predominantly in females. p. 1151

**proglottid** One of the segmentlike repeating units that constitute the body of a tapeworm. p. 662

**programmable RNA-guided genome editing system** A molecular technique based on the CRISPR-Cas system that can cut and edit any sequence of DNA in a genome. p. 348

**prokaryote** Organism in which the DNA is suspended in the cell interior without separation from other cellular components by a discrete membrane. p. 29

**prokaryotic chromosome** A single, typically circular DNA molecule. p. 30

**prolactin (PRL)** A peptide hormone secreted by the anterior pituitary that stimulates breast development and milk secretion in mammals. pp. 1145, 1192

**prometaphase** A transition period between prophase and metaphase during which the microtubules of the mitotic spindle attach to the kinetochores and the chromosomes shuffle until they align in the centre of the cell. p. 155

**promiscuity** A mating system in which individuals do not form close pair bonds, and both males and females mate with multiple partners. p. 868

**promoter** The site to which RNA polymerase binds for initiating transcription of a gene. p. 283

**promoter proximal elements** Regulatory sequence within the promoter proximal region, a region upstream of a eukaryotic protein-coding gene. Regulatory proteins bind to promoter proximal elements. p. 315

**promoter proximal region** Upstream of a eukaryotic gene, a region containing regulatory sequences for transcription called promoter proximal elements. p. 315

**proofreading** A mechanism for DNA polymerase to back up and remove mispaired nucleotides from a newly synthesized DNA strand. p. 270

**propagation (conduction)** In animal nervous systems, the concept that the action potential does not need further trigger events to keep going. p. 1206

**property** The essence of a thing; the abilities that a particular object can demonstrate. p. F-1

**prophage** A viral genome inserted in the host cell DNA. pp. 183, 526

**prophase** The beginning phase of mitosis during which the duplicated chromosomes within the nucleus condense from a greatly extended state into compact, rodlike structures. p. 155

**proportion of reproducing individuals** percent of reproducing individuals in a poplation. p. 751

**prosoma** The fused head and thorax of chelicerates. p. 673

**prostaglandin** One of a group of local regulators derived from fatty acids that are involved in paracrine and autocrine regulation. p. 1174

**prostate gland** An accessory sex gland in males that adds a thin, milky fluid to the semen and adjusts the pH of the semen to the level of acidity best tolerated by sperm. p. 1176

**protein kinase** Enzyme that transfers a phosphate group from ATP to one or more sites on particular proteins. p. 95

**protein phosphatase** Enzyme that removes phosphate groups from target proteins. p. 95

**proteome** The complete set of proteins that can be expressed by the genome of an organism. p. 375

**proteomics** The study of the proteome. p. 375

**protist** Organism currently classified in the kingdom Protista. p. 560

**protobiont** The term given to a group of abiotically produced organic molecules that are surrounded by a membrane or membranelike structure. p. 499

**protoderm** The primary meristem that will produce stem epidermis. p. 896

**proton** Positively charged particle in the nucleus of an atom. p. F-8

**proton pump** Pump that moves hydrogen ions across membranes and pushes hydrogen ions across the plasma membrane from the cytoplasm to the cell exterior. Also referred to as *H⁺ pump*. p. 89

**protonema** The structure that arises when a liverwort or moss spore germinates and eventually gives rise to a mature gametophyte. p. 621

**protonephridium** The simplest form of invertebrate excretory tubule. p. 1108

**proton-motive force** Stored energy that contributes to ATP synthesis and to the cotransport of substances to and from mitochondria. p. 113

**proto-oncogene** A gene that encodes various kinds of proteins that stimulate cell division. Mutated proto-oncogenes contribute to the development of cancer. p. 326

**protostome** A division of the Bilateria in which the blastopore forms the mouth during development of the embryo and the anus appears later. p. 646

**prototroph** A strain that is able to synthesize the necessary amino acids. p. 175

**proximal convoluted tubule** The tubule between the Bowman's capsule and the loop of Henle in the nephron of the kidney, which carries and processes the filtrate. p. 1113

**pseudocoelom** A fluid- or organ-filled body cavity between the gut (a derivative of endoderm) and the muscles of the body wall (a derivative of mesoderm). p. 646

**pseudogene** A gene that is very similar to a functional gene at the DNA sequence level but that has one or more inactivating mutations that prevent it from producing a functional gene product. p. 373

**pseudopod** (plural, **pseudopodia**) A temporary cytoplasmic extension of a cell. p. 562

**psychrophile** An archaean or bacterium that grows optimally at temperatures in the range of −10 to −20°C. p. 553

**Pterophyta** The plant phylum of ferns and their close relatives. p. 624

**PTH** *See* parathyroid hormone (PTH). p. 1149

**pulmonary circuit** The circuit of the cardiovascular system that supplies the lungs. p. 1082

**pulvinus** (plural, **pulvini**) A jointlike, thickened pad of tissue at the base of a leaf or petiole; flexes when the leaf makes nastic movements. p. 996

**Punnett square** Method for determining the genotypes and phenotypes of offspring and their expected proportions. p. 207

**pupa** The nonfeeding stage between the larva and adult in the complete metamorphosis of some insects, during which the larval tissues are completely reorganized within a protective cocoon or hardened case. p. 678

**pupil** The dark centre in the middle of the iris through which light passes to the back of the eye. p. 1224

**purine** A type of nitrogenous base with two carbon–nitrogen rings. p. 497

**pyramid of biomass** A diagram that illustrates differences in standing crop biomass in a series of trophic levels. p. 821

**pyramid of energy** A diagram that illustrates the amount of energy that flows through a series of trophic levels. p. 820

**pyramid of numbers** A diagram that illustrates the number of individual organisms present in a series of trophic levels. p. 821

**pyrimidine** A type of nitrogenous base with one carbon–nitrogen ring. p. 497

**pyrosequencing** A measure of the pyrophosphate released by nucleotide addition as A, G, C, and T dNTPs are cycled across template DNAs. p. 367

**qualitative variation** Variation that exists in two or more discrete states, with intermediate forms often being absent. p. 412

**quantitative trait** A character that displays a continuous distribution of the phenotype involved, typically resulting from several to many contributing genes. p. 216

**quantitative variation** Variation that is measured on a continuum (such as height in human beings) rather than in discrete units or categories. p. 412

**quorum sensing** The use of signalling molecules by prokaryotes to communicate and to coordinate their behaviour. p. 547

**R gene** A resistance gene in a plant; dominant R alleles confer enhanced resistance to plant pathogens. p. 991

**radial cleavage** A cleavage pattern in deuterostomes in which newly formed cells lie directly above and below other cells of the embryo. p. 646

**radial symmetry** A body plan of organisms in which structures are arranged regularly around a central axis, like spokes radiating out from the centre of a wheel. p. 646

**radiation** The transfer of heat energy as electromagnetic radiation. p. 1121

**radicle** The rudimentary root of a plant embryo. p. 944

**radioactivity** The giving off of particles of matter and energy by decaying nuclei. p. 254

**radiometric dating** A dating method that uses measurements of certain radioactive isotopes to calculate the absolute ages in years of rocks and minerals. p. 509

**radula** The tooth-lined "tongue" of molluscs that scrapes food into small particles or drills through the shells of prey. p. 665

**random dispersion** A pattern of distribution in which the individuals in a population are distributed unpredictably in their habitat. p. 751

**rapid eye movement (REM) sleep** The period during deep sleep when the delta wave pattern is replaced by rapid, irregular beta waves characteristic of the waking state. The person's heartbeat and breathing rate increase, the limbs twitch, and the eyes move rapidly behind the closed eyelids. p. 1246

**reabsorption** The process in which some molecules (e.g., glucose and amino acids) and ions are transported by the transport epithelium back into the body fluid (animals with open circulatory systems) or into the blood in capillaries surrounding the tubules (animals with closed circulatory systems) as the filtered solution moves through the excretory tubule. p. 1106

**reactants** The atoms or molecules entering a chemical reaction. p. F-15

**reaction centre** Part of photosystems I and II in chloroplasts of plants. In the light-dependent reactions of photosynthesis, the reaction centre receives light energy absorbed by the antenna complex in the same photosystem. p. 132

**reading frame** A particular grouping of triplet bases read by transfer RNA during translation. pp. 283, 292

**realized niche** The range of conditions and resources that a population actually uses in nature. p. 790

**receptacle** The expanded tip of a flower stalk that bears floral organs. p. 936

**reception** In signal transduction, the binding of a signal molecule with a specific receptor in a target cell. p. 92

**receptive field** Each ganglion cell in the eye receives signals from a clearly defined set of photoreceptors constituting the receptive field for that cell. p. 1226

**receptor-mediated endocytosis** The selective uptake of macromolecules that bind to cell surface receptors concentrated in clathrin-coated pits. p. 91

**receptor protein** Protein that recognizes and binds molecules from other cells that act as chemical signals. p. 47

**recessive** An allele that is masked by a dominant allele. p. 203

**reciprocal altruism** Form of altruistic behaviour in which individuals help nonrelatives if they are likely to return the favour in the future. p. 873

**recognition protein** Protein in the plasma membrane that identifies a cell as part of the same individual or as foreign. p. 525

**recombinant** Phenotype with a different combination of traits from those of the original parents. p. 180

**recombinant DNA** DNA from two or more different sources joined together. p. 334

**rectum** The final segment of the large intestine. p. 1045

**red tide** A growth in dinoflagellate populations that causes red, orange, or brown discoloration of coastal ocean waters. p. 567

**reduced** Refers to a substance that receives electrons during reduction. p. 103

**reduction** The addition of electrons to a substance. p. 103

**reflex** A programmed movement that takes place without conscious effort, such as the sudden withdrawal of a hand from a hot surface. p. 1246

**refractory period** A period that begins at the peak of an action potential and lasts a few milliseconds, during which the threshold required for generation of an action potential is much higher than normal. p. 1205

**regulator** Animal that maintains factors of the internal environment in a relatively constant state. p. 1019

**regulatory protein** DNA-binding protein that binds to a regulatory sequence and affects the expression of an associated gene or genes. p. 309

**reinforcement** 1. The enhancement of reproductive isolation that had begun to develop while populations were geographically separated. 2. Encouraging or establishing a pattern of behaviour using a positive or negative stimulus. pp. 441, 851

**release factor v(RF)** A protein that recognizes stop codons in the A site of a ribosome translating an mRNA and terminates translation. Also referred to as the *termination factor*. p. 293

**releasing hormone (RH)** A peptide neurohormone that controls the secretion of hormones from the anterior pituitary. p. 1145

**renal artery** An artery that carries bodily fluids into the kidney. p. 1112

**renal cortex** The outer region of the mammalian kidney that surrounds the renal medulla. p. 1112

**renal medulla** The inner region of the mammalian kidney. p. 1112

**renal pelvis** The central cavity in the kidney where urine drains from collecting ducts. p. 1112

**renal vein** The vein that routes filtered blood away from the kidney. p. 1112

**renaturation** The reformation of a denatured protein into its folded, functional state. p. F-35

**replica plating** Technique for identifying and counting genetic recombinants in conjugation, transformation, or transduction experiments in which the colony pattern on a plate containing solid growth medium is pressed onto sterile velveteen and transferred to other plates containing different combinations of nutrients. p. 175

**replicates** Multiple subjects that receive either the same experimental treatment or the same control treatment. p. F-4

**replication bubble** A structure resulting from bidirectional DNA replication from a given origin. Two forks, travelling in opposite directions, create a bubble. p. 267

**replication fork** The region of DNA synthesis where the parental strands separate and two new daughter strands elongate. p. 263

**replisome** The key proteins and enzymes for replication assembled into a DNA replication complex. p. 266

**repolarized** The return of a membrane potential to its resting state from a state of depolarization or hyperpolarization. p. 1204

**repressible operon** Operon whose expression is prevented by a repressor molecule. p. 313

**repressor** A regulatory protein that prevents the operon genes from being expressed. p. 309

**reproduction** The process in which a parent or parents produce offspring. p. 183

**reproductive isolating mechanism** A biological characteristic that prevents the gene pools of two species from mixing. p. 437

**reproductive strategy** A set of behaviours that lead to reproductive success. p. 1162

**residual volume** The air that remains in lungs after a complete, forced exhalation. p. 1067

**resolution** The minimum distance two points in a specimen can be separated and still be seen as two points. p. 26

**resource partitioning** The use of different resources or the use of resources in different ways by species living in the same place. p. 791

**respiratory surface** A layer of epithelial cells that provides the interface between the body and the respiratory medium. p. 1060

**response** In signal transduction, the last stage in which the transduced signal causes the cell to change according to the signal and to the receptors on the cell. In the nervous system, the output resulting from the integration of neural messages. p. 92

**resting potential** A steady negative membrane potential exhibited by the membrane of a neuron that is not stimulated—that is, not conducting an impulse. p. 1202

**restriction endonuclease (restriction enzyme)** An enzyme that cuts DNA at a specific sequence. p. 335

**restriction fragment** A DNA fragment produced by cutting a long DNA molecule with a restriction enzyme. p. 335

**restriction fragment length polymorphisms (RFLPs)** When comparing different individuals, restriction enzyme–generated DNA fragments of different lengths from the same region of the genome. p. 341

**retina** A light-sensitive membrane lining the posterior part of the inside of the eye. p. 1224

**retrotransposon** A transposable element that transposes via an intermediate RNA copy of the transposable element. p. 383

**reversible** Refers to a reaction may go from left to right or from right to left, depending on conditions. p. 59

**rhizoid** A modified hypha that anchors a fungus to its substrate and absorbs moisture. p. 619

**rhizome** A horizontal, modified stem that can penetrate a substrate and anchor the plant. p. 623

**rhodopsin** The retinal–opsin photopigment. p. 1226

**rhynchocoel** A coelomic cavity that contains the proboscis of nemerteans. p. 662

**ribose** A five-carbon sugar to which the nitrogenous bases in nucleotides link covalently. p. F-36

**ribosomal RNA (rRNA)** The RNA component of ribosomes. p. 30

**ribosome** A ribonucleoprotein particle that carries out protein synthesis by translating mRNA into chains of amino acids. pp. 30, 279

**ribosome binding site** In translation initiation in prokaryotes, a sequence just upstream of the start codon that directs the small ribosomal subunit to bind and orient correctly for the complete ribosome to assemble and start translating in the correct spot. p. 291

**ribozyme** An RNA-based catalyst that is part of the biochemical machinery of all cells. p. 500

**ribulose 1,5-bisphosphate (RuBP) carboxylase oxygenase (Rubisco)** An enzyme that catalyzes the key reaction of the Calvin cycle, carbon fixation, in which $CO_2$ combines with RuBP (ribulose 1,5-bisphosphate) to form 3-phosphoglycerate. p. 136

**ring species** A species with a geographic distribution that forms a ring around uninhabitable terrain. p. 436

**RNA interference (RNAi)** The phenomenon of silencing a gene posttranscriptionally by a small, single-stranded RNA that is complementary to part of an mRNA. p. 321

**RNA polymerase** An enzyme that catalyzes the assembly of nucleotides into an RNA strand. p. 279

**rod** In the vertebrate eye, a type of photoreceptor in the retina that is specialized for detection of light at low intensities. pp. 538, 1225

**root** An anchoring structure in land plants that also absorbs water and nutrients and (in some plant species) stores food. p. 456

**root cap** A dome-shaped cell mass that forms a protective covering over the apical meristem in the tip of a plant root. p. 901

**root hair** A tubular outgrowth of the outer wall of a root epidermal cell; root hairs absorb much of a plant's water and minerals from the soil. p. 894

**root nodule** A localized swelling on a root in which symbiotic nitrogen-fixing bacteria reside. p. 967

**root pressure** The pressure that develops in plant roots as the result of osmosis, forcing xylem sap upward and out through leaves. *See also* guttation. p. 922

**root system** An underground (or submerged) network of roots with a large surface area that favours the rapid uptake of soil water and dissolved mineral ions. pp. 615, 888

**rough ER** Endoplasmic reticulum with many ribosomes studding its outer surface. p. 35

**round window** A thin membrane that faces the middle ear. p. 1222

***r*-selected species** A short-lived species adapted to function well in a rapidly changing environment. p. 763

**Rubisco** *See* ribulose 1,5-bisphosphate (RuBP) carboxylase oxygenase. p. 136

**S phase** The phase of the cell cycle during which DNA replication occurs. p. 153

**SA node** *See* sinoatrial node (SA node). p. 1089

**saccule** A fluid-filled chamber in the vestibular apparatus that provides information about the position of the head with respect to gravity (up versus down), as well as changes in the rate of linear movement of the body. p. 1218

**salicylic acid (SA)** In plants, a chemical synthesized following a wound that has multiple roles in plant defences, including interaction with jasmonates in signalling cascades. p. 991

**salivary amylase** A substance that hydrolyzes starches to the disaccharide maltose. p. 1040

**salivary gland** A gland that secretes saliva through a duct on the inside of the cheek or under the tongue; the saliva lubricates food and begins digestion. p. 1040

**saltatory conduction** A mechanism that allows small-diameter axons to conduct impulses rapidly. p. 1209

**saprotroph** An organism nourished by dead or decaying organic matter. p. 588

**sapwood** The newly formed outer wood located between heartwood and the vascular cambium. Compared with heartwood, it is wet, lighter in colour, and not as strong. p. 904

**sarcomere** The basic unit of contraction in a myofibril. p. 1256

**saturated fatty acid** Fatty acid with only single bonds linking the carbon atoms. p. 81

**savannah** A biome comprising grasslands with few trees, which grows in areas adjacent to tropical deciduous forests. p. 782

**schizocoelom** In protostomes, the body cavity that develops as inner and outer layers of mesoderm separate. p. 648

**schizocoelous** Having a coelom formed by a split in the mesoderm in segmented coelomates. p. 649

**Schwann cell** A type of glial cell in the peripheral nervous system that wraps nerve fibres with myelin and also secretes regulatory factors. p. 1201

**scientific method** An investigative approach in which scientists make observations about the natural world, develop working explanations about what they observe, and then test those explanations by collecting more information. p. F-2

**sclereid** A type of sclerenchyma cell; sclereids are typically short and have thick, lignified walls. p. 892

**sclerenchyma** A ground tissue in which cells develop thick secondary walls, which are commonly lignified and perforated by pits through which water can pass. p. 892

**sclerocyte** Specialized cells that secrete the mineralized structures in the body wall of some invertebrates. p. 651

**scolex** The anterior (head) of a tapeworm, adapted for fastening the worm to the intestinal epithelium of its host. p. 662

**scrotum** The baglike sac in which the testes are suspended in many mammals. p. 1175

**second law of thermodynamics** Principle that for any process in which a system changes from an initial to a final state, the total disorder of the system and its surroundings always increases. p. 56

**secondary active transport** Transport indirectly driven by ATP hydrolysis. p. 89

**secondary cell wall** A layer added to the cell wall of plants that is more rigid and may become many times thicker than the primary cell wall. p. 887

**secondary consumer** A carnivore that feeds on herbivores, a member of the third trophic level. pp. 778, 1030

**secondary contact** Contact after a period of geographical isolation. p. 441

**secondary endosymbiosis** In the model for the origin of plastids in eukaryotes, the second event, in which a non-photosynthetic eukaryote engulfed a photosynthetic eukaryote. p. 580

**secondary growth** Plant growth that originates at lateral meristems and increases the diameter of older roots and stems. *Compare* primary growth. p. 888

**secondary metabolite** Organic compound not required for the growth or survival of an organism; tends to be biologically active. p. 589

**secondary productivity** Energy stored in new consumer biomass as energy is transferred from producers to consumers. p. 818

**secondary structure** Regions of alpha helix, beta strand, or random coil in a polypeptide chain. pp. 83, F-30

**secondary succession** Predictable changes in species composition in an ecological community that develops after existing vegetation is destroyed or disrupted by an environmental disturbance. p. 801

**secondary tissue** In plants, the tissue that develops from lateral meristems. p. 888

**secretion** A selective process in which specific small molecules and ions are transported from the body fluids (in animals with open circulatory systems) or blood (in animals with closed circulatory systems) into the excretory tubules. In animal nutrition, secretion is one of the steps of the digestive process; it involves the release in the digestive tract of enzymes and other substances that aid the process of digestion, such as acids, emulsifiers, and lubricating mucus. p. 1106

**secretory vesicle** Vesicle that transports proteins to the plasma membrane. p. 36

**seed** The structure that forms when an ovule matures after a pollen grain reaches it and a sperm fertilizes the egg. p. 628

**seed coat** The outer protective covering of a seed. p. 944

**segment** A body structure that repeats along an anterior–posterior axis and itself has an anterior–posterior polarity. p. 648

**segregate** *See* principle of segregation. p. 203

**selective cell adhesion** A mechanism in which cells make and break specific connections to other cells or to the extracellular matrix. p. 1182

**selectively permeable** Membranes that selectively allow, impede, or block the passage of atoms and molecules. p. 499

**self-fertilization (self-pollination)** Fertilization in which sperm nuclei in pollen produced by anthers fertilize egg cells housed in the carpel of the same flower. Self-fertilization can also occur in hermaphroditic animals. pp. 200, 940

**self-incompatibility** In plants, the inability of a plant's pollen to fertilize ovules of the same plant. p. 940

**self-pollination** *See* self-fertilization. p. 200

**semen** The secretions of several accessory glands in which sperm are mixed prior to ejaculation. p. 1176

**semicircular canal** A part of the vestibular apparatus that detects rotational (spinning) motions. p. 1218

**semiconservative replication** The process of DNA replication in which the two parental strands separate and each serves as a template for the synthesis of new progeny double-stranded DNA molecules. p. 258

**semilunar (SL) valve** A flap of endocardium and connective tissue reinforced by fibres that prevent the valve from turning inside out. p. 1087

**seminal vesicle** A vesicle that secretes seminal fluid. p. 1176

**seminiferous tubule** One of the tiny tubes in the testes where sperm cells are produced, grow, and mature. p. 1176

**senescence** The biologically complex process of aging in mature organisms that leads to the death of cells and eventually the whole organism. p. 165

**sense codon** A codon that specifies an amino acid. p. 291

**sensitization** Increased responsiveness to mild stimuli after experiencing a strong stimulus; one of the simplest forms of memory. p. 1245

**sensor** A tissue or organ that detects a change in an external or internal factor such as pH, temperature, or the concentration of a molecule such as glucose. p. 1019

**sensory adaptation** A condition in which the effect of a stimulus is reduced if it continues at a constant level. p. 1235

**sensory hair cell** A hair cell that sends impulses along the auditory nerve to the brain when alternating changes of pressure agitate the basilar membrane on which the organ of Corti rests, moving the hair cells. p. 1216

**sensory neuron** A neuron that transmits stimuli collected by their sensory receptors to interneurons. p. 1201

**sensory receptor (transducer)** A receptor formed by the dendrites of afferent neurons or by specialized receptor cells making synapses with afferent neurons that pick up information about the external and internal environments of the animal. p. 1214

**sensory transduction** The conversion of a stimulus into a change in membrane potential. p. 1215

**sepal** One of the separate, usually green parts forming the calyx of a flower. p. 936

**septum** (plural, **septa**) A thin partition or cross wall that separates body segments. pp. 589, 662

**sequence alignment** A tool in genomics in which nucleotide or amino acid order between molecules from different sources are compared based on similarity; BLAST output is in the form of sequence alignments. p. 374

**sequential hermaphroditism** The form of hermaphroditism in which individuals change from one sex to the other. p. 1171

**serosa** The serous membrane: a thin membrane lining the closed cavities of the body; has two layers with a space between that is filled with serous fluid. p. 1040

**Sertoli cell** One of the supportive cells that completely surrounds developing spermatocytes in the seminiferous tubules. Follicle-stimulating hormone stimulates Sertoli cells to secrete a protein and other molecules that are required for spermatogenesis. p. 1176

**set point** The level at which the condition controlled by a homeostatic pathway is to be maintained. p. 1019

**sex chromosomes** Chromosomes that are different in male and female individuals of the same species. p. 190

**sex linkage** The genes carried on sex chromosomes can be inherited in a distinctly non-Mendelian pattern. p. 232

**sex-linked gene** Gene located on a sex chromosome. p. 231

**sex pilus** *See* F pilus. p. 177

**sexual dimorphism** Differences in the size or appearance of males and females. p. 869

**sexual reproduction** The mode of reproduction in which male and female parents produce offspring through the union of egg and sperm generated by meiosis. pp. 183, 1162

**sexual selection** A form of natural selection established by male competition for access to females and by the females' choice of mates. p. 424

**shoot system** The stems and leaves of a plant. pp. 616, 888

**short interfering RNAs (siRNAs)** Small RNA molecules that regulate expression of certain genes by binding to their mRNA and reducing translation. p. 322

**short-day plant** A plant that flowers in late summer or early autumn when dark periods become longer and light periods become shorter. p. 999

**short interfering RNAs (siRNAs)** Small RNA molecules that regulate expression of certain genes by binding to their mRNA and reducing translation. p. 322

**short-term memory** Information stored for seconds, minutes, or, at most, an hour or so. p. 1245

**sieve tube** A series of phloem cells joined end to end, forming a long tube through which nutrients are transported; seen mainly in flowering plants. p. 893

**sieve tube member** Any of the main conducting cells of phloem that connect end to end, forming a sieve tube. p. 893

**sign stimulus** A simple cue that triggers a fixed action pattern. p. 848

**signal peptide** A short segment of amino acids to which the signal recognition particle binds, temporarily blocking further translation. A signal peptide is found on polypeptides that are sorted to the endoplasmic reticulum. Also referred to as *signal sequence.* p. 297

**signal sequence** *See* signal peptide. p. 297

**signal transduction** The series of events by which a signal molecule released from a controlling cell causes a response (affects the function) of target cells with receptors for the signal. Target cells process the signal in the three sequential steps of reception, transduction, and response. p. 10

**silencing** Phenomenon in which methylation of cytosines in eukaryotic promoters inhibits transcription and turns the genes off. p. 320

**silent mutation** A base-pair substitution mutation in a protein-coding gene that does not alter the amino acid specified by the gene. p. 300

**simple diffusion** Mechanism by which certain small substances diffuse through the lipid part of a biological membrane. p. 85

**simple fruit** A fruit that develops from a single ovary; in many of them, at least one layer of the pericarp is fleshy and juicy. p. 942

**simulation modelling** An analytical method in which researchers gather detailed information about a system and then create a series of mathematical equations that predict how the components of the system interact and respond to change. p. 832

**simultaneous hermaphroditism** A form of hermaphroditism in which individuals develop functional ovaries and testes at the same time. p. 1170

**single-lens eye** An eye type that works by changing the amount of light allowed to enter into the eye and by focusing this incoming light with a lens. p. 1224

**single-stranded binding protein (SSB)** Protein that coats single-stranded segments of DNA, stabilizing the DNA for the replication process. p. 263

**sink** Any region of a plant where organic substances are being unloaded from the sieve tube system and used or stored. p. 925

**sinoatrial node (SA node)** The region of the heart that controls the rate and timing of cardiac muscle cell contraction. p. 1089

**siRNA-induced silencing complex (siRISC)** A group of proteins, recruited when siRNA binds to mRNA, that degrade the target mRNA. p. 322

**sister chromatid** One of two exact copies of a chromosome duplicated during replication. p. 153

**sister clades** Two evolutionary lineages (i.e., clades) that emerge from the same node in a phylogenetic tree. p. 456

**sister species** Two species that are descended from the same recent ancestral species. p. 456

**skeletal muscle** A muscle that connects to bones of the skeleton, typically made up of long and cylindrical cells that contain many nuclei. p. 1015

**SL valve** *See* semilunar (SL) valve. p. 1087

**sliding DNA clamp** A protein that encircles the DNA and binds to the DNA polymerase to tether the enzyme to the template, thereby making replication more efficient. p. 260

**slime layer** A coat typically composed of polysaccharides that is loosely associated with bacterial cells. p. 30

**slow block (to polyspermy)** The process in which enzymes released from cortical granules alter the egg coats within minutes after fertilization so that no other sperm can attach and penetrate to the egg. p. 1168

**slow muscle fibre** A muscle fibre that contracts relatively slowly and with low intensity. p. 1262

**small ribonucleoprotein particle** A complex of RNA and proteins. p. 287

**smooth ER** Endoplasmic reticulum with no ribosomes attached to its membrane surfaces. Smooth ER has various functions, including synthesis of lipids that become part of cell membranes. p. 36

**smooth muscle** A relatively small and spindle-shaped muscle cell in which actin and myosin molecules are arranged in a loose network rather than in bundles. p. 1016

**social behaviour** The interactions that animals have with other members of their species. p. 480

**sodium–potassium pump** *See* Na$^+$/K$^+$ pump. p. 89

**soil solution** A combination of water and dissolved substances that coats soil particles and partially fills pore spaces. p. 962

**solenoid** *See* 30 nm chromatin fibre. p. 155

**solute** The molecules of a substance dissolved in water. p. 84

**solution** Substance formed when molecules and ions separate and are suspended individually, surrounded by water molecules. p. F-17

**solvent** The water in a solution in which the hydration layer prevents polar molecules or ions from reassociating. p. F-17

**somatic cell** Any of the cells of an organism's body other than reproductive cells. pp. 183, 1164

**somatic embryo** A plant embryo that is genetically identical to the parent because it arose through asexual means. p. 947

**somatic gene therapy** Gene therapy in which genes are introduced into somatic cells. p. 349

**somatic nervous system** A subdivision of the peripheral nervous system controlling body movements that are primarily conscious and voluntary. p. 1248

**somites** Paired blocks of mesoderm cells along the vertebrate body axis that form during early vertebrate development and differentiate into dermal skin, bone, and muscle. p. 1187

**soredium** (plural, **soredia**) A specialized cell cluster produced by lichens, consisting of a mass of algal cells surrounded by fungal hyphae; soredia function like reproductive spores and can give rise to a new lichen. p. 601

**sorus** (plural, **sori**) A cluster of sporangia on the underside of a fern frond; reproductive spores arise by meiosis inside each sporangium. p. 625

**source** In plants, any region (such as a leaf) where organic substances are being loaded into the sieve tube system of phloem. p. 925

**Southern blot analysis** Technique in which labelled probes are used to detect specific DNA fragments that have been separated by gel electrophoresis. p. 342

**spatial summation** The summation of excitatory postsynaptic potentials produced by firing of different presynaptic neurons. pp. 1236, 1261

**specialized transduction** Transfer of bacterial genes between bacteria using temperate phages that have incorporated fragments of the bacterial genome as they make the transition from the lysogenic cycle to the lytic cycle. pp. 182, 527

**speciation** The process of species formation. p. 434

**species cluster** A group of closely related species recently descended from a common ancestor. p. 441

**species composition** The particular combination of species that occupy a site. p. 797

**species diversity** A community characteristic defined by species richness and the relative abundance of species. p. 795

**species fusion** Merger of two populations into one after the establishment of secondary contact. p. 441

**species richness** The number of species that live within an ecological community. p. 794

**specific epithet** The species name in a binomial. p. 454

**specific heat** The amount of heat required to increase the temperature of a given quantity of water. p. F-16

**sperm** Motile gamete. p. 1163

**spermatogenesis** The process of producing sperm. p. 1164

**spermatogonium** (plural, **spermatogonia**) A cell that enters meiosis and gives rise to gametes, produced by mitotic divisions of the germ cells in males. p. 1164

**spermatozoon** (plural, **spermatozoa**) Also called sperm; a haploid cell that develops into a mature sperm cell when meiosis is complete. p. 1164

**sphincter** A powerful ring of smooth muscle that forms a valve between major regions of the digestive tract. p. 1040

**spinal cord** A column of nervous tissue located within the vertebral column and directly connected to the brain. p. 1239

**spinal nerve** A nerve that carries signals between the spinal cord and the body trunk and limbs. p. 1246

**spindle pole** One of the pair of centrosomes in a cell undergoing mitosis from which bundles of microtubules radiate to form the part of the spindle from that pole. p. 155

**spine** See backbone. p. 685

**spiracle** An opening in the chitinous exoskeleton of an insect through which air enters and leaves the tracheal system. p. 1063

**spiral cleavage** The cleavage pattern in many protostomes in which newly produced cells lie in the space between the two cells immediately below them. p. 646

**spiral valve** A corkscrew-shaped fold of mucous membrane in the digestive system of elasmobranchs, which slows the passage of material and increases the surface area available for digestion and absorption. p. 691

**spliceosome** A complex formed between the pre-mRNA and small ribonucleoprotein particles, in which mRNA splicing takes place. p. 287

**spongocoel** The central cavity in a sponge. p. 651

**spontaneous mutation** A mutation that occurs naturally within a cell. p. 300

**spontaneous reaction** Chemical or physical reaction that occurs without outside help. p. 58

**sporadic (nonhereditary) cancer** Cancer that is not inherited. p. 325

**sporangium** (plural, **sporangia**) A single-celled or multicellular structure in fungi and plants in which spores are produced. p. 592

**spore** A haploid reproductive structure, usually a single cell, that can develop into a new individual without fusing with another cell; found in plants, fungi, and certain protists. p. 934

**sporophyll** A specialized leaf that bears sporangia (spore-producing structures). p. 625

**sporophyte** An individual of the diploid generation produced through fertilization in organisms that undergo alternation of generations; it produces haploid spores. pp. 572, 612, 934

**squalene** A liver oil found in sharks that is lighter than water, which increases their buoyancy. p. 691

**stability** The ability of a community to maintain its species composition and relative abundances when environmental disturbances eliminate some species from the community. p. 793

**stabilizing selection** A type of natural selection in which individuals expressing intermediate phenotypes have the highest relative fitness. p. 422

**stamen** A "male" reproductive organ in flowers, consisting of an anther (pollen producer) and a slender filament. p. 936

**standing crop biomass** The total dry weight of plants present in an ecosystem at a given time. p. 817

**stapes** The smallest of three sound-conducting bones in the middle ear of tetrapod vertebrates. pp. 696, 1221

**start codon** The first codon read in an mRNA in translation—AUG. Also referred to as the *initiator codon*. p. 282

**statocyst** A mechanoreceptor in invertebrates that senses gravity and motion using statoliths. p. 1216

**statolith** A movable starch- or carbonate-containing stonelike body involved in sensing gravitational pull. pp. 994, 1216

**stele** The central core of vascular tissue in roots and shoots of vascular plants; it consists of the xylem and phloem together with supporting tissues. p. 902

**stem cell** Undifferentiated cells in most multicellular organisms that can divide without differentiating and also can divide and differentiate into specialized cell types. pp. 346, 1011

**stereocilia** Microvilli covering the surface of hair cells clustered in the base of neuromasts. p. 1217

**steroid** A type of lipid derived from cholesterol. p. 319

**steroid hormone receptor** Internal receptor that turns on specific genes when it is activated by binding a signal molecule. p. 320

**steroid hormone response element** The DNA sequence to which the hormone receptor complex binds. p. 320

**sterol** Steroid with a single polar —OH group linked to one end of the ring framework and a complex, nonpolar hydrocarbon chain at the other end. p. 82

**sticky end** End of a DNA fragment, with a single-stranded structure that can form hydrogen bonds with a complementary sticky end on any other DNA molecule cut with the same enzyme. p. 335

**stigma** The receptive end of a carpel where deposited pollen germinates. p. 936

**stimulus** A component of a negative feedback control system maintaining homeostasis, specifically an environmental change that triggers a response. p. 1019

**stoma** (plural, **stomata**) The opening between a pair of guard cells in the epidermis of a plant leaf or stem, through which gases and water vapour pass. pp. 614, 894

**stomach** The portion of the digestive system in which food is stored and digestion begins. p. 46

**stop codon** A codon that does not specify amino acids. The three nonsense codons are UAG, UAA, and UGA. Also referred to as the *nonsense codon* and *termination codon*. p. 282

**stretch receptor** A proprioceptor in the muscles and tendons of vertebrates that detects the position and movement of the limbs. p. 1094

**strict aerobe** Cell with an absolute requirement for oxygen to survive, unable to live solely by fermentations. p. 118

**strict anaerobe** Organism in which fermentation is the only source of ATP. p. 118

**strobilus** *See* cone (of a plant). p. 625

**stroma** An inner compartment of a chloroplast, enclosed by two boundary membranes and containing a third membrane system. p. 44

**stromatolite** Fossilized remains of ancient cyanobacterial mats that carried out photosynthesis by the water-splitting reaction. p. 509

**style** The slender stalk of a carpel situated between the ovary and the stigma in plants. p. 936

**suberin** A waxy, waterproof substance present in cork cells. pp. 904, 918

**submucosa** A thick layer of elastic connective tissue that contains neuron networks and blood and lymph vessels. p. 1039

**subsoil** The region of soil beneath the topsoil that contains relatively little organic matter. p. 961

**subspecies** A taxonomic subdivision of a species. p. 435

**substrate** The particular reacting molecule or molecular group that an enzyme catalyzes. p. 21

**substrate-level phosphorylation** An enzyme-catalyzed reaction that transfers a phosphate group from a substrate to ADP. p. 106

**succession** The change from one community type to another. p. 799

**sugar–phosphate backbone** Structure in a polynucleotide chain that is formed when deoxyribose sugars are linked by phosphate groups in an alternating sugar–phosphate–sugar–phosphate pattern. p. 256

**sum rule** Mathematical rule in which the final probability is found by summing individual probabilities. p. 205

**surface tension** The force that places surface water molecules under tension, making them more resistant to separation than the underlying water molecules. p. F-17

**survivorship curve** Graphic display of the rate of survival of individuals over a species' life span. p. 753

**suspension feeder** An animal that ingests small food items suspended in water. pp. 651, 1035

**suspensor** In seed plants, a stalklike row of cells that develops from a zygote and helps position the embryo close to the nourishing endosperm. p. 943

**swallowing reflex** An involuntary action produced by contractions of muscles in the walls of the pharynx that direct food into the esophagus. p. 1041

**swim bladder** A gas-filled internal organ that helps fish maintain buoyancy. p. 694

**swimmeret** small paddle-like fin used in swimming. p. 675

**symbiont** An organism living in symbiosis with another organism; the symbionts are not usually closely related. p. 588

**symbiosis** An interspecific interaction in which the ecological relations of two or more species are intimately tied together. p. 504

**sympathetic division** Division of the autonomic nervous system that predominates in situations involving stress, danger, excitement, or strenuous physical activity. p. 1248

**sympatric speciation** Speciation that occurs without the geographic isolation of populations. p. 442

**symplast** The living component of plant tissue, composed of protoplasts interconnected by plasmodesmata. p. 917

**symplastic pathway** The route taken by water that moves through the cytoplasm of plant cells (the symplast). *Compare* apoplastic pathway. p. 917

**symport** The transport of two molecules in the same direction across a membrane. Also referred to as *cotransport*. p. 90

**synapomorphy** A derived character state found in two or more species. p. 463

**synapse** A site where a neuron makes a communicating connection with another neuron or an effector such as a muscle fibre or gland. p. 1210

**Synapsida** A group of amniotes with one temporal arch on each side of the head, which includes living mammals. p. 700

**synapsis** Process in meiosis in which homologous chromosomes come together and pair. Also known as *pairing*. p. 186

**synaptic cleft** A narrow gap that separates the plasma membranes of the presynaptic and postsynaptic cells. p. 1210

**synaptonemal complex** A protein framework that tightly holds together homologous chromosomes as they pair. p. 190

**synteny** Blocks of genes that are in the same order as those found in another species, indicating a common ancestor prior to genetic alterations. p. 384

**synthetic biology** A new interdisciplinary field in which synthetic biologists combine standardized parts (DNA sequences) to design and build modified regulatory networks to study the organization of natural systems in living cells, and to create novel networks with potential benefits in a wide range of biotechnologies. p. 355

**systematics** The branch of biology that studies the diversity of life and its evolutionary relationships. p. 454

**systemic acquired resistance** A plant defence response to microbial invasion; defensive chemicals including salicylic acid may spread throughout a plant, rendering healthy tissues less vulnerable to infection. p. 992

**systemic circuit** In amphibians, the branch of a double blood circuit that receives oxygenated blood and provides the blood supply for most of the tissues and cells of a body. p. 1082

**systemin** A plant peptide hormone that functions in defence responses to wounds. p. 990

**systole** The period of contraction and emptying of the heart. p. 1088

**T (transverse) tubule** The tubule that passes in a transverse manner from the sarcolemma across a myofibril of striated muscle. p. 1257

**T₃** *See* triiodothyronine (T₃). p. 1148

**T₄** *See* thyroxine (T₄). p. 1148

**tactile signal** A means of animal communication in which the signaller uses touch to convey a message to the signal receiver. p. 859

**taiga** *See* boreal forest. p. 818

**taproot system** A root system consisting of a single main root from which lateral roots can extend; often stores starch. p. 900

**target cell** A cell with receptor protein for a hormone. p. 1136

**TATA box** A regulatory DNA sequence found in the promoters of many eukaryotic genes transcribed by RNA polymerase II. p. 315

**taxis** A behavioural response that is directed either toward or away from a specific stimulus. p. 862

**taxon** (plural, **taxa**) A name designating a group of organisms included within a category in the Linnaean taxonomic hierarchy. p. 455

**taxonomic hierarchy** A system of classification based on arranging organisms into ever more inclusive categories. p. 455

**taxonomy** The science of the classification of organisms into an ordered system that indicates natural relationships. p. 454

**telomerase** An enzyme that adds telomere repeats to chromosome ends. p. 268

**telomeres** Repeats of simple-sequence DNA that maintain the ends of linear chromosomes. p. 268

**telophase** The final phase of mitosis, during which the spindle disassembles, the chromosomes decondense, and the nuclei re-form. p. 155

**temperate bacteriophage** Bacteriophage that may enter an inactive phase (lysogenic cycle) in which the host cell replicates and passes on the bacteriophage DNA for generations before the phage becomes active and kills the host (lytic cycle). pp. 182, 525

**temperate deciduous forest** A forested biome found at low to middle altitudes at temperate latitudes, with warm summers, cold winters, and annual precipitation between 75 and 250 cm. p. 795

**temperate grassland** A nonforested biome that stretches across the interiors of most continents, where winters are cold and snowy and summers are warm and fairly dry. p. 818

**temperate rainforest** A coniferous forest biome supported by heavy rain and fog, which grows where winters are mild and wet and the summers are cool. p. 572

**template strand** The DNA strand that is copied into an RNA molecule during gene transcription. p. 279

**temporal isolation** A prezygotic reproductive isolating mechanism in which species live in the same habitat but breed at different times of day or different times of year. p. 438

**temporal summation** The summation of several excitatory postsynaptic potentials produced by successive firing of a single presynaptic neuron over a short period of time. pp. 1236, 1260

**tendon** A type of fibrous connective tissue that attaches muscles to bones. p. 1013

**terminal bud** A bud that develops at the apex of a shoot. p. 895

**termination codon** *See* stop codon. p. 282

**termination factor** *See* release factor (RF). p. 293

**terminator** Specific DNA sequence for a gene that signals the end of transcription of a gene.

Terminators are common for prokaryotic genes. p. 285

**tertiary consumer** A carnivore that feeds on other carnivores, a member of the fourth trophic level. p. 797

**testcross** A genetic cross between an individual with the dominant phenotype and a homozygous recessive individual. p. 207

**testis** (plural, **testes**) The male gonad. In male vertebrates, secretes androgens and steroid hormones that stimulate and control the development and maintenance of male reproductive systems. pp. 1151, 1164

**testosterone** A hormone produced by the testes, responsible for the development of male secondary sex characteristics and the functioning of the male reproductive organs. pp. 1151, 1176

**tetanus** A situation in which a muscle fibre cannot relax between stimuli, and twitch summation produces a peak level of continuous contraction. p. 1260

**tetrad** Homologous pair consisting of four chromatids. p. 187

**Tetrapoda** A monophyletic lineage of vertebrates that includes animals with four feet, legs, or leglike appendages. p. 688

**T-even bacteriophage** Virulent bacteriophages, T2, T4, and T6, that have been valuable for genetic studies of bacteriophage structure and function. p. 525

**thalamus** A major switchboard of the brain that receives sensory information and relays it to the regions of the cerebral cortex concerned with motor responses to sensory information of that type. p. 1242

**thallus** (plural, **thalli**) A plant body not differentiated into stems, roots, or leaves. pp. 601, 620

**theory** A broadly applicable idea or hypothesis that has been confirmed by every conceivable test. p. F-5

**thermal acclimatization** A set of physiological changes in ectotherms in response to seasonal shifts in environmental temperature, allowing the animals to attain good physiological performance at both winter and summer temperatures. p. 1124

**thermodynamics** The study of the energy flow during chemical and physical reactions. p. 54

**thermoreceptor** A sensory receptor that detects the flow of heat energy. p. 1215

**thermoregulation** The control of body temperature. p. 1120

**thick filament** A type of filament in striated muscle composed of myosin molecules; they

interact with thin filaments to shorten muscle fibres during contraction. p. 1256

**thigmomorphogenesis** A plant response to a mechanical disturbance, such as frequent strong winds; includes inhibition of cellular elongation and production of thick-walled supportive tissue. p. 978

**thigmotropism** Growth in response to contact with a solid object. p. 995

**thin filament** A type of filament in striated muscle composed of actin, tropomyosin, and troponin molecules; interacts with thick filaments to shorten muscle fibres during contraction. p. 1256

**threshold potential** In signal conduction by neurons, the membrane potential at which the action potential fires. p. 1204

**thylakoids** Flattened, closed sacs that make up a membrane system within the stroma of a chloroplast. p. 44

**thymine** A pyrimidine that base-pairs with adenine. p. 256

**thymine dimer** A particular type of DNA damage caused by lower-energy, non-ionizing radiation such as UV light. p. 300

**thymus** An organ of the lymphatic system that plays a role in filtering viruses, bacteria, damaged cells, and cellular debris from the lymph and bloodstream and in defending the body against infection and cancer. p. 1097

**thyroid gland** A gland located beneath the voice box (larynx) that secretes hormones regulating growth and metabolism. p. 1148

**thyroid-stimulating hormone (TSH)** A hormone that stimulates the thyroid gland to grow in size and secrete thyroid hormones. p. 1145

**thyroxine ($T_4$)** The main hormone of the thyroid gland, responsible for controlling the rate of metabolism in the body. p. 1148

**Ti (tumour-inducing) plasmid** A plasmid used to make transgenic plants. p. 350

**tidal volume** The volume of air entering and leaving the lungs during inhalation and exhalation. p. 1067

**tight junction** Region of tight connection between membranes of adjacent cells. p. 46, 1010

**time lag** The delayed response of organisms to changes in environmental conditions. p. 759

**tissue** A group of cells and intercellular substances with the same structure that function as a unit to carry out one or more specialized tasks. pp. 886, 888, 1008

**tolerance hypothesis** Hypothesis asserting that ecological succession proceeds because competitively superior species replace competitively inferior ones. p. 803

**tonoplast** The membrane that surrounds the central vacuole in a plant cell. pp. 44, 916

**topoisomerase** An enzyme that relieves the overtwisting and strain of DNA ahead of the replication fork. p. 263

**topsoil** The rich upper layer of soil where most plant roots are located; it generally consists of sand, clay particles, and humus. p. 961

**torpor** A sleeplike state produced when a lowered set point greatly reduces the energy required to maintain body temperature, accompanied by reductions in metabolic, nervous, and physical activity. p. 1129

**totipotency** The ability to develop into any type of cells. p. 887

**totipotent** Having the capacity to produce cells that can develop into or generate a new organism or body part. pp. 947, 1182

**trachea** In insects, an extensively branched, air-conducting tube formed by invagination of the outer epidermis of the animal and reinforced by rings of chitin. In vertebrates, the windpipe, which branches into the bronchi. p. 1065

**tracheal system** A branching network of tubes that carries air from small openings in the exoskeleton of an insect to tissues throughout its body. p. 676

**tracheid** A conducting cell of xylem, usually elongated and tapered. p. 892

**traditional systematics** An approach to systematics that uses phenotypic similarities and differences to infer evolutionary relationships, grouping together species that share both ancestral and derived characters. p. 461

**trait** A particular variation in a genetic or phenotypic character. p. 200

**transcription** The mechanism by which the information encoded in DNA is made into a complementary RNA copy. p. 279

**transcription factor** Protein that recognizes and binds to the TATA box and then recruits the polymerase. pp. 285, 315

**transcription initiation complex** Combination of general transcription factors with RNA polymerase II. p. 315

**transcription unit** A region of DNA that transcribes a single primary transcript. pp. 283, 309

**transcriptome** The complete set of RNA transcripts from a given cell under given conditions. pp. 289, 375

**transcriptomics** The study of the transcriptome. p. 375

**transduction** In cell signalling, the process of changing a signal into the form necessary to cause the cellular response. In prokaryotes, the process in which DNA is transferred from donor to recipient bacterial cells by an infecting bacteriophage. p. 92

**transfer cell** Any of the specialized cells that form when large amounts of solutes must be loaded or unloaded into the phloem; they facilitate the short-distance transport of organic solutes from the apoplast into the symplast. p. 926

**transfer RNA (tRNA)** The RNA that brings amino acids to the ribosome for addition to the polypeptide chain. p. 512

**transformation** The conversion of the hereditary type of a cell by the uptake of DNA released by the breakdown of another cell. pp. 180, 254

**transgenic** Refers to an organism that has been modified to contain genetic information from an external source. p. 345

**transit sequence** A part of a gene sequence that targets the protein product to an organelle, endoplasmic lumen, etc. p. 298

**transition state** An intermediate arrangement of atoms and bonds that both the reactants and the products of a reaction can assume. p. 64

**translation** The use of the information encoded in the RNA to assemble amino acids into a polypeptide. p. 279

**translocation** In genetics, a chromosomal alteration that occurs if a broken segment is attached to a different, nonhomologous chromosome. In vascular plants, the long-distance transport of substances by xylem and phloem. pp. 236, 925

**transmission** In neural signalling, the sending of a message along a neuron and then to another neuron or to a muscle or gland. p. 1200

**transpiration** The evaporation of water from a plant, principally from the leaves. p. 919

**transport epithelium** A layer of cells with specialized transport proteins in their plasma membranes. p. 1106

**transport protein** A protein embedded in the cell membrane that forms a channel allowing selected polar molecules and ions to pass across the membrane. p. 27

**transposable element (TE)** A sequence of DNA that can move from one place to another within the genome of a cell. p. 382

**transposase** An enzyme that catalyzes some of the reactions inserting or removing the transposable element from the DNA. p. 382

**transposition** Mechanism of movement of transposable elements involving nonhomologous recombination. p. 382

**transposon** A bacterial transposable element with an inverted repeat sequence at each end enclosing a central region with one or more genes. p. 382

**transverse tubule** *See* T (transverse) tubule. p. 1257

**trichocyst** A dartlike protein thread that can be discharged from a surface organelle for defence or to capture prey. p. 567

**trichome** A single-celled or multicellular outgrowth from the epidermis of a plant that provides protection and shade and often gives the stems or leaves a hairy appearance. p. 894

**triglyceride** A nonpolar compound produced when a fatty acid binds by a dehydration synthesis reaction at each of glycerol's three —OH-bearing sites. p. 115

**triiodothyronine ($T_3$)** A hormone secreted by the thyroid gland that regulates metabolism. p. 1148

**trimester** A division of human gestation, three months in length. p. 1188

**triploblastic** An animal body plan in which adult structures arise from three primary germ layers: endoderm, mesoderm, and ectoderm. p. 645

**trochophore** The small, free-swimming, ciliated aquatic larva of various invertebrates, including certain molluscs and annelids. p. 659

**trophic cascade** The effects of predator–prey interactions that reverberate through other population interactions at two or more trophic levels in an ecosystem. p. 822

**trophic level** A position in a food chain or web that defines the feeding habits of organisms. p. 797

**trophoblast** The outer single layer of cells of the blastocyst. p. 1189

**trophozoite** Motile, feeding stage of *Giardia* and other single-celled protists. p. 559

**tropical forest** Any forest that grows between the Tropics of Capricorn and Cancer, a region characterized by high temperature and rainfall and thin, nutrient-poor topsoil. p. 630

**tropism** The turning or bending of an organism or one of its parts toward or away from an external stimulus, such as light, heat, or gravity. p. 981

**true-breeding** Refers to an individual that passes traits without change from one generation to the next. p. 201

**tube cell** The cell in a pollen grain (male gametophyte) of a seed plant that will give rise to the pollen tube. p. 937

**tumour-inducing plasmid** *See* Ti (tumour-inducing) plasmid. p. 351

**tumour suppressor gene** A gene that encodes proteins that inhibit cell division. p. 326

**turgid** A cell with high internal hydrostatic pressure. p. 916

**turgor pressure** The internal hydrostatic pressure within plant cells; the normal fullness or tension produced by the fluid content of plant and animal cells. p. 916

**turnover rate** The rate at which one generation of producers in an ecosystem is replaced by the next. p. 821

**tympanum** A thin membrane in the auditory canal that vibrates back and forth when struck by sound waves. pp. 696, 1220

**umbilical cord** A long tissue with blood vessels linking the embryo and the placenta. p. 349

**umbilicus** Navel; the scar left when the short length of umbilical cord still attached to the infant after birth dries and shrivels within a few days. p. 1189

**uncinate process** Forward-protrusion from rib in birds. p. 704

**undernutrition** A condition in animals in which intake of organic fuels is inadequate or whose assimilation of such fuels is abnormal. p. 1031

**undulating membrane** In parabasalid protists, a finlike structure formed by a flagellum buried in a fold of the cytoplasm that facilitates movement through thick and viscous fluids. An expansion of the plasma membrane in some flagellates that is usually associated with a flagellum. p. 565

**uniform dispersion** A pattern of distribution in which the individuals in a population are evenly spaced in their habitat. p. 750

**uniparental inheritance** A pattern of inheritance in which all progeny (both males and females) have the phenotype of only one of the parents p. 244

**universal** A feature of the nucleic acid code, with the same codons specifying the same amino acids in all living organisms. p. 282

**unreduced gamete** A gamete that contains the same number of chromosomes as a somatic cell. p. 444

**unsaturated** Fatty acid with one or more double bonds linking the carbons. p. 81

**ureter** The tube through which urine flows from the renal pelvis to the urinary bladder. p. 1113

**urethra** The tube through which urine leaves the bladder. In most animals, the urethra opens to the outside. p. 1113

**urinary bladder** A storage sac located outside the kidneys. p. 1113

**uterine cycle** The menstrual cycle. p. 1173

**uterus** A specialized saclike organ in which the embryo develops in viviparous animals. p. 1173

**utricle** A fluid-filled chamber of the vestibular apparatus that provides information about the position of the head with respect to gravity (up versus down), as well as changes in the rate of linear movement of the body. p. 1218

**vagina** The muscular canal that leads from the cervix to the exterior. p. 1171

**valence electron** An electron in the outermost energy level of an atom. p. F-10

**van der Waals forces** Weak molecular attractions over short distances. p. F-14

**vas deferens** (plural, **vasa deferentia**) The tube through which sperm travel from the epididymis to the urethra in the male reproductive system. p. 1176

**vascular bundle** A cord of plant vascular tissue; often multistranded with both xylem and phloem. p. 896

**vascular cambium** A lateral meristem that produces secondary vascular tissues in plants. p. 903

**vascular plant** A plant with xylem, phloem, and usually well-developed roots, stems, and leaves. p. 615

**vascular tissue** In plants, tissue that transports water and nutrients or the products of photosynthesis through the plant body. p. 615

**vascular tissue system** One of the three tissue systems in plants that provide the foundation for plant organs; it consists of transport tubes for water and nutrients. p. 890

**vegetal pole** The end of the egg opposite the animal pole, which typically gives rise to internal structures such as the gut and the posterior end of the embryo. p. 1180

**vegetative** (growth) Accumulation of mass and more cells through mitotic divisions alone. Vegetative growth is involved with accumulating nutrients, often preceding reproductive growth strategies, such as converting a stem that makes leaves into a flower-producing structure. p. 936

**vegetative reproduction** Asexual reproduction in plants by which new individuals arise (or are created) without seeds or spores; examples include fragmentation from the parent plant or the use of cuttings by gardeners. p. 947

**vein** In a plant, a vascular bundle that forms part of the branching network of conducting and supporting tissues in a leaf or other expanded plant organ. In an animal, a vessel that carries the blood back to the heart. pp. 899, 1081

**ventilation** The flow of the respiratory medium (air or water, depending on the animal) over the respiratory surface. p. 1061

**ventricle** In the brain, an irregularly shaped cavity containing cerebrospinal fluid. In the heart, a chamber that pumps blood out of the heart. p. 1239

**venule** A capillary that merges into the small veins leaving an organ. p. 1090

**vernalization** The stimulation of flowering by a period of low temperature. p. 1000

**vertical gene transfer** Inheritance from one generation to the next. p. 513

**vesicle** A small, membrane-bound compartment that transfers substances between parts of the endomembrane system. p. 34

**vessel** In plants, one of the tubular conducting structures of xylem, typically several centimetres long; most angiosperms and some other vascular plants have xylem vessels. p. 892

**vessel member** Any of the short cells joined end to end in tubelike columns in xylem. p. 892

**vestibular apparatus** The specialized sensory structure of the inner ear of most terrestrial vertebrates that is responsible for perceiving the position and motion of the head and, therefore, for maintaining equilibrium and for coordinating head and body movements. p. 1218

**vestigial structure** An anatomical feature of living organisms that no longer retains its function. p. 396

**virion** A complete virus particle. p. 524

**viroid** A plant pathogen that consists of strands or circles of RNA, smaller than any viral DNA or RNA molecule, that have no protein coat. p. 530

**virulent bacteriophage** Bacteriophage that kills its host bacterial cells during each cycle of infection. p. 525

**virus** An infectious agent that contains either DNA or RNA surrounded by a protein coat. p. 254

**visceral mass** In molluscs, the region of the body containing the internal organs. p. 665

**viscosity** The measure of a fluid's resistance to flow; the state of being thick, sticky, and semifluid in consistency, due to internal friction. p. 1060

**visual signal** A means of communication in which animals use facial expressions or body language to send messages to other individuals. p. 856

**vital capacity** The maximum tidal volume of air that an individual can inhale and exhale. p. 1067

**vitamin** An organic molecule required in small quantities that the animal cannot synthesize for itself. p. 1031

**vitamin D** A steroidlike molecule that increases the absorption of $Ca^{2+}$ and phosphates from ingested food by promoting the synthesis of a calcium-binding protein in the intestine; it also increases the release of $Ca^{2+}$ from bone in response to parathyroid hormone. p. 1149

**vitelline coat** A gel-like matrix of proteins, glycoproteins, or polysaccharides immediately outside the plasma membrane of an egg cell. p. 1164

**vitreous humour** The jellylike substance that fills the main chamber of the eye, between the lens and the retina. p. 1225

**viviparous** Referring to animals that retain the embryo within the mother's body and nourish it during at least early embryo development. pp. 709, 1170

**voltage-gated ion channel** A membrane-embedded protein that opens and closes as the membrane potential changes. p. 1205

**vulva** The external female sex organs. p. 1171

**water lattice** An arrangement formed when a water molecule in liquid water establishes an average of 3.4 hydrogen bonds with its neighbours. p. F-15

**water potential** The potential energy of water, representing the difference in free energy between pure water and water in cells and solutions; it is the driving force for osmosis. p. 915

**water-soluble vitamin** A vitamin with a high proportion of oxygen and nitrogen able to form hydrogen bonds with water. p. 1031

**water vascular system** A locomotor system, including internal canals and tube feet, unique to Echinodermata. p. 680

**wetland** A highly productive ecotone often at the border between a freshwater biome and a terrestrial biome. p. 632

**white matter** The myelinated axons that surround the grey matter of the central nervous system. p. 1246

**whole-genome shotgun sequencing** A method of determining the nucleotide order in a genome in which the genome is fragmented and pieces are sequenced directly then assembled; contrast with hierarchical genome sequencing. p. 367

**whorl** A concentric arrangement of modified leaves that make up a flower. The outermost whorl is the sepals, with petals and stamens found respectively nearer the centre. The carpels make up the innermost whorl. p. 936

**wild-type** Normal genotype. p. 227

**wilting** The drooping of leaves and stems caused by a loss of turgor. p. 916

**wobble hypothesis** Hypothesis stating that the complete set of 61 sense codons can be read by fewer than 61 distinct tRNAs because of particular pairing properties of the bases in the anticodons. p. 291

**Wolffian duct** A bipotential primitive duct associated with the gonads that leads to a cloaca. p. 1192

**wood** The secondary xylem of trees and shrubs, lying under the bark and consisting largely of cellulose and lignin. p. 904

**X chromosome** Sex chromosome that occurs paired in female cells and single in male cells. p. 232

**X-linked recessive inheritance** Pattern in which displayed traits are due to inheritance of recessive alleles carried on the X chromosome. p. 242

**X-ray diffraction** Method for deducing the position of atoms in a molecule. p. 257

**xylem** The plant vascular tissue that distributes water and nutrients. p. 892

**xylem sap** The dilute solution of water and solutes that flows in the xylem. p. 919

**Y chromosome** Sex chromosome that is paired with an X chromosome in male cells. p. 190

**yolk** The portion of an egg that serves as the main energy source for the embryo. p. 1180

**yolk sac** In an amniote egg, an extraembryonic membrane that encloses the yolk. p. 1186

**zero population growth** A circumstance in which the birth rate of a population equals the death rate. p. 757

**zona pellucida** A gel-like matrix of proteins, glycoproteins, or polysaccharides immediately outside the plasma membrane of the egg cell. p. 1164

**zone of cell division** The region in a growing root that consists of the root apical meristem and the actively dividing cells behind it. p. 902

**zone of elongation** The region in a root where newly formed cells grow and elongate. p. 902

**zone of maturation** The region in a root above the zone of elongation where cells do not increase in length but may differentiate further and take on specialized roles. p. 902

**zooplankton** Small, usually microscopic, animals that float in aquatic habitats. p. 562

**zygosporangium** A thick-walled sporangium in which spores are produced, characteristic of Zygomycetes. p. 592

**zygospore** A multinucleate, thick-walled sexual spore in some fungi that is formed from the union of two gametes. p. 592

**zygote** A fertilized egg. pp. 183, 644, 1164

# Index

*The letter* i *denotes an illustration;* t *denotes a table;* b *denotes a box;* **bold** *denotes a defined or introduced term.*

A bands, 1257
A site, **291**, 292
Aardvarks (*Orycteropus afer*), 782
Aardwolf, 712i
ABC model, 936
Abdomen, 679
Abductor muscles, **666**
Abiotic, **494**
Abomasum, 1047
ABP1 (auxin binding protein 1), 984
Abscisic acid (ABA), 979t, 981, **988**–989
Abscission, **987**, 988i
Absolute ages, 509
Absorbed, **1030**
Absorption, of digestive products, 1037, 1044–1045, 1046i
Absorption spectrum, 16, 16i
    of light energy, 129i, 129–**130**, 130i
Absorptive nutrition, **588**
Acacia tree (*Acacia cornigera*), 780, 780i
Acanthodii, class, 690
Accessory fruits, 942, 942i
Accommodation, **1225**, 1226i
*Acetabularia*, 578i
Acetabulum, 700i
Acetyl coenzyme A (acetyl-CoA), 104, 108
Acetyl groups, oxidizing to carbon dioxide, 108–109, 110i
Acetylcholine, 1094b, 1094i, 1213t
Achenes, 942
Acheulian culture, 485
Achondroplasia, 212, 212i, 241, 241i
Acid precipitation, **963**
Acid reflux, **1041**
Acid-growth hypothesis, **984**, 986i
Acidity, **70**
Acids, **F-19b**
Acoela, 648, 658
Acoelomate, **646**, 647i
Acorn worms, 682i, **684**
Acoustical signals, 856
Aquatic snails (*Lymnaea elodes*), 761
Acquired characteristics, 394, 395i
Acquired immunodeficiency syndrome (AIDS), 470, 524t, 527
*Acropora palmata*, 568i
Acrosome, **1208**
Acrosome reaction, **1222**
Actinopterygian, 694
Actinopterygii, class, 693–695
Actins, 39
Action potentials, **996**, **1203**, 1205i, 1206–1207i
    conduction of, 1206–1210, 1258
    frequency of, 1262i
    graded potentials, 1204
    ion movements through plasma membrane, 1205–1206
    propagation of, 1208i
    as rapid and reversible, 1204–1205
    resting membrane potential, 1202–1204
    saltatory conduction, 1209i
    skeletal muscles and, 1260–1261
Action spectrum, **131**
Activation energy, 58, 64i, 64–65, 65i, 67, 67i
Activation gate, 1205, 1206i
Activator, **309**, **315**–316, 316i, 317i
Active membrane transport, **88**–90, 91i
Active parental care, 754

Active site, **66**, 67i
Active transport, **915**, 918, 1116
Adaptation, 399–**400**. *See also* Sensory adaptation
Adaptive behaviours, 848
Adaptive zones, **704**
Adductor muscle, 666i
Adenine (A), 256i, **256**, F-36, F-37b, 986
Adenosine deaminase deficiency (ADA), 349
Adenosine-triphosphate (ATP)
    formation, 8–10, 9i
        generating, 132i, 134–137
        lactate production, 1264
        muscle fibres and, 1258–1259
        in oxidation-reduction reactions, 502
        regenerating, 63i, 63–64
Adenovirus, 524t
Adherens junction, **46**
Adhesion, **45**, 919, 920
ADH-stimulated water reabsorption, 1118b, 1119i
Adipocytes, 1014
Adipose tissue, 1014i, **1014**–1015
ADP, 62–63, 63i, 1258
Adrenal cortex, 1139, 1143i, 1143t, 1144t, 1146i, **1149**, 1150i, 1150–1151, 1151i
Adrenal glands, 1139
Adrenal medulla, 1139, 1143i, 1144t, 1149i, **1149**–1150, 1150i
Adrenocorticotropic hormone (ACTH), 1143t, **1145**, 1146i, 1150, 1151i
Adsorption, 963
Adult stem cells, 346
Adventitious roots, **901**, 902i
*Aegina citrea*, 656i
Aerobes, **544**
Afferent arteriole, 1113i, **1117**
Afferent neuron, **1201**, 1202i, 1215i
Afferent system, 1248i
African cichlid fish, 854, 854i
African emergence hypothesis, **485**, 486i
African lions (*Panthera leo*), 870–871
African ostrich, 396i
African pancake tortoises (*Malacochersus tornieri*), 785
Agar, **577**
Agar block method, 983b, 995
*Agaricus bisporus*, 599i
Agarose gel electrophoresis, **340**, 340b, 340i, 341, 342, 343b, 343i
Age, 754–755
Age pyramids, 768i
Age structure, **751**, 767–768, 768i
Age-specific fecundity, **752**
Age-specific mortality, **752**
Age-specific survivorship, **752**
Aggregate fruits, 942i, **942**
Agnathan, 689–690, 690i
Agre, Peter, 85
Agricultural land, 818t
Agriculture, 729i, 729–730
*Agrobacterium*, 986
AIDS (Acquired immunodeficiency syndrome), 470, 524t, 527
Air pollution, 601
Air sacs, 1064i, 1065i
Airways, in mammals, 1065–1066, 1066i
Albinism, 212, 212i
Albumin, 698i, **1084**
Alcohol (ethanol), 1214t
Alcohol fermentation, **117**–118, 118i
Alcohols, **80**
Alders, 828
Aldosterone, 1117, 1139–1140, 1144t, **1150**–1151
Alexandra, Czarina, 242

Alexis, Crown Prince, 242
Algae, 1i, 27i, 138, 184i, 561, 792b, 792i
    carbon dioxide and, 138i, 138–139
Algae bloom, 149–150, 150i
Algal ancestors (of plants), 613, 618i
Algin, **572**
ALH84001, 493
Alien species, 731–733
Alkaline hydrothermal vents, 502, 503i
Alkaline solutions, F-19b
Alkaptonuria, 278
Allantoic membrane, 1186i, **1186**
Allantois, **1186**
Allard, Henry, 997
Allee effect, 761
Allele frequencies, 414, 415, 416t, 417i,
    417b–418b, 422
Alleles, **175**, **203**, 414i, **414**
Allelopathy, 750
Alligators, 703i, 703–704
Allochthonous, **836**
Allolactose, 310–311
Allopatric speciation, 440i, **440**–441, 791
Allopolyploidy, 444i, **445**–446
All-or-nothing principle, **1205**
Allosteric activator, **69**
Allosteric inhibitor, **69**
Allosteric regulation, 69i
Allosteric site, **69**
Alpha cells, 1152
α-glucose, F-25b
α-helix, 83, F-32b, F-32i
Alpine tundra, 619i, **619**, 818t
Alternation of generations life cycle, 184, 612i, **612**,
    **934**, 935i
Alternative hypothesis, 498
Alternative splicing, 288i, **288**–289, 321
Altman, Sydney, 500
Altricial species, **1192**
Altriciality, **709**
Altruism, **873**
Alvarez, Gonzao, 424
Alveoli, **1063**, 1064i, 1066i, **1066**
Alzheimer's disease, 102
Amacrine cell, **1226**
*Amanita phalloides*, 278i, 599
Amanitin, 278i
American chestnut tree, 733
American ginseng, 723–724, 724i
American Sign Language (ASL), 861
Ames, Jack, 846–847
Amine hormones, 1150
Amino acid residues, F-28b
Amino acids, 30, 84i, F-28b, F-29i
    adding to tRNAs, 292, 293i
    as essential elements for animals, 1031
    neurotransmitters and, 1214t
    transfer RNA (tRNA) and, 289–291
Amino group, F-23b
Amino peptidase, 1045i
Aminoacyl-tRNA, **291**–292
Aminoacyl-tRNA synthetase, **291**
Aminocylation, **291**, 292i
Ammocoetes, **689**
Ammonia (NH3), 544, 1107, 1107i
Ammonification, 828t, **828**, **967**
Ammonium, 967, 967i
Amniocentesis, 243i
Amnion, 698, 698i, 1186i, **1186**, 1189–1190
Amniota, 464, **1186**
Amniote (amniotic) eggs, 698i, 698–701,
    **698**
Amniote ancestry, 699i
Amniotes, 698–701
*Amoeba proteus*, 563i

Amoebas, 572, 574, 575i
Amoeboid cell, **651**
Amoebozoa, 563i
Amphetamines, 1213t
Amphibia, class, 464, 696–698
Amphibians, 1083
    circulatory system, 1083i
    cleavage and gastrulation, 1183–1184, 1184i
    as ectotherms, 1123–1124
    ectothermy in, 1123–1124
    examples of, 697i
    excretions from, 1111
    fossils, 696i
    gas exchange in, 1063, 1064i
    modern, 696–698
    osmoregulation and excretion in, 1111
    positive pressure breathing, 1063–1064, 1064i
    reproductive systems of, 1167i
    thyroid hormones and, 1148
Amphipathic, **80**
Amphipathic molecules, F-39b
Amplexus, 1166, 1167i
Amplification, 95i, **95**, 338, 342, **1140**, 1143
*Amp*^R gene, 336, 337i
Ampulla, 680, 1219i
Amygdala, **1242**
Amylases, 1036
Amylose, F-27i
Amyoplasts, 994, 995i
Amyotrophic lateral sclerosis, 102
Anabolic pathways, 61i, **61**–62
Anabolic reactions, **102**, 115
Anabolic steroids, **1151**
Anaerobic metabolism, 506
Anaerobic respiration, 118, **544**
Anagenesis, 456
Anal sphincter, 1045–1046, 1046i
Analogous characters, 459, 459i
Anaphase, **155**, 157i, 164b, 164i, 191i
Anaphase I, 187, 189i, 190, 191i
Anaphase II, 187, 189i
Anaphase spindle, 162i
Anapsid (lineage Anapsida), 698, 699i
Anapsida, 699i, **700**
Anaspid, 700i
Anatomy, **882**, **1008**
Ancestral character state, **463**
Ancestral characters, 462
Ancestral green alga, 613, 618i
Ancestry, DNA fingerprinting in establishment of, 344
Anchoring junctions, **45**–46, 46i, **1009**, 1010i
Ancient DNA (aDNA), 251–252
Anderson, W. French, 349
Andersson, Malte, 425
Androgens, 1144t, **1151**, **1176**
Anemones, 653–658
Aneuploids, 237–239
Anfinsen, Christian, F-35b
Angiosperms, 21i, 615t, 617i, 618i, 623t, **632**–637, 635b, 635i, 934–935, 936.
    *See also* Flowering plants
Angiotensin II, 1117
Angiotensinconverting enzyme (ACE), 1117
Anglerfish, 1035i, 1036
*Angraecum sesquipedale*, 637
*Anguillicola crassus*, 671i
Animal behaviour, 845–**846**
    changing, 851i, 851–852
    communication, 856–861, 857i, 858i, 859i, 860i
    environment and, 846–848
    eusocial animals, 874i, 874–876, 875i
    genes and, 846–848
    home range and territory, 862–863
    hormones and, 853i, 853–854
    human social behaviour, 876–877, 877i
    instinct, 848–850

Biological evolution, 400–403
Biological hot spots, 797
Biological magnification, 815i, **815**
Biological molecules, damaging light on, 14–17
Biological reactions, role of enzymes in, 64–67
Biological research, **F-2**
Biological rhythms, pineal gland and, 1153
Biological species concept, **434**
Biology, scientific basis of, F-2b–F-5b
Bioluminescence, 21–23, 22i
Bioluminescent, **568**
Bioluminescent dinoflagellates, 568i
Biomass, **538**, **817**, 819i, 821–823
Bioremediation, **538**, 598
Biosphere, 60–61, 61i
Biotechnology, **333**–334
Biotic, **494**
Biotin, 1032t
Bipedal locomotion, 478b
Bipedalism, **480**, 481–484
Bipolar cell, **1226**
Bird flu, 739–740
Birds, 704i, 704–708. *See also* Aves, class
  bills, 705i, 705–706, 706i, 1021b, 1021i
  circulatory system, 1083i
  cleavage and gastrulation, 1184–1185, 1185i, 1189
  crosscurrent exchange in, 1065i, 1069
  daily and seasonal rhythms of, 1128–1129
  digestion in, 1038i, 1039
  eggs, 706i
  evolution of, 462, 707i
  finches, Darwin's, 400
  flightless, 396i
  homologous characters, 460, 460i
  lungs and air sacs in, 1064i, 1065i
  osmoregulation and excretion in, 1111
  retina of, 1225–1226
  salt glands, 1111i
  signs of stress, 739–740
  skeletons, 704i, 705i
  uric acid from, 1107
  using phylogenetic trees to test hypotheses, 469
Birds of paradise, 433, 433i
Birth, 483–484, 1191–1192, 1192i, 1193i
Birth control methods, 1179t
Birth control pills, 770i, 770–771
Birth weight, 422, 422b, 422i
*Biston* moths, 401
Bivalve molluscs, 734
Bivalves, 666i, 666–667
Bivalvia, class, 666–667
Black rhino, 721–723, 723i
Blackburn, Elizabeth, 268
Bladders, 1109, 1109i, 1112i, 1112–1113, 1113i
Blades, **897**
Blake, P. R., 877
BLAST (Basic Local Alignment Search Tool) program, **373**–374, 374i
Blastocoel, **1181**, 1185i
Blastocyst, **1189**, 1190i
Blastodisc, 1185i, **1185**
Blastomere, **1181**
Blastopore, **648**
Blastula, **1181**
Blending theory of inheritance, **200**
Blind spot, **1226**
Blobel, Günter, 297–298
Blood, 1014i, **1015**
  components of, 1084i, 1084–1086, 1139
  composition of, 1085t
  erythrocytes, 1084i, 1084–1086
  gas exchange with, 1068–1069
  maintaining flow, 1093–1095
  platelets, 1086
  reservoirs of, 1093

Blood Ca$^{2+}$, 1149, 1149i
Blood clots, 1086
Blood doping, 1070
Blood flow, 1091i, 1092i, 1093–1095
Blood glucose, 1152, 1152i
Blood pressure, 1090, 1093–1095, 1139–1140
Blood root plant, 996i
Blood types, 214–215, 215t, 216i
Blood vessels, 1090–1093
  in annelids, 664i
  of circulatory system, 1090i, 1090–1093
  veins, 1093
  venules, 1093
Blood volume, 1093
Blood-brain barrier, 1093, 1240–1241, **1240**
Blood-feeding insects, 780–781, 781i
Blue jay, 418, 418i
Blue tits (*Cyanistes caeruleus*), 862, 862i
Bluegill sunfishes, 783, 783i
Blue-headed wrasse, 440i
Blue-stain fungi, 596, 596i
Blue-white screening, 336, 337b, 337i
Bobolink (*Dolichonyx oryzivorus*), 720, 720i
Bodmer, Walter, 422b
Body axes, 1224i
Body cavity, 646, 647i
Body language, 484, 484i, 861
Body lever, 1270i
Body movements, 1242, 1255–1256, 1266i
Body plans, 645i, **645**, 647i, 648i, 652i, 653i, 665i, 667i, 677i
Body position, receptors for, 1216–1218
Body size, 751i
Body symmetry, 645i, 645–646
Body temperature, 1120i, 1120–1121
Bolas spiders, 858
Bolting, **985**, 986i
Bolus, **1041**
Bombykol, 858
Bone tissue, **1013**–1014, 1014i, 1267
Bones
  bat, 1271i
  bird, 1271i
  interactions with muscles, 1267–1271
  joints, 1269, 1269i
  pterosaur, 1271i
Bonner, James, 998
Bonobos (*Pan paniscus*), 876
Bony fishes, 693–695
Boreal forest, 818t, 819i, **966**
Boron, as essential plant nutrient, 958t
*Borrelia burgdorferi*, 540
Bosch, Carl, 828
Botulin, 545, 545i
Bouchard, Lucien, 545
Bovine spongiform encephalopathy (BSE), 530–531, 531i
Bowman's capsule, 1113i, **1113**, 1114–1115, 1115t
Box jellyfish, 656
Boyer, Herbert, 336
Brachiopoda, phylum, 650, 669i, 669–670
*Bradyrhizobium*, 967–968
Brain, **1200**
  activity in, 1242i
  basal nuclei, thalamus, and hypothalamus, 1242–1243
  brain stem, 1241–1242
  cerebellum, 1242
  cerebral cortex, 1243
  cerebrum, 1243i
  development of, 1239–1240, 1240i
  hormonally induced changes in structure of, 853, 853i
  of mammals, 1241i
  neural integration, evolutionary trends in, 1237–1239
  role in central nervous system, 1239–1245
  spinal cord and, 1246–1247
  structures of, 1241i
  ventilation controlled by, 1067–1068

Development
    animals. *See* Animal development
    in flowering plants, 933–934
    thyroid hormones and, 1148
Devonian period, 618, 624
D-form, F-25b
Diabetes mellitus, **1152**
Diagnostic characteristics, 434i
Dial, Kenneth P., 706
Diaphragm, in mammalian respiratory system, 1066i, 1067i, **1067**, 1068i
Diapsida, 699i, **700**
Diapsids, 700i, 702–704
Diarrhea, 1045
Diastole, **1088**
Diastolic blood pressure, 1090
Diatomaceous earth, 570–571
Diatoms, **570**–571, 571i
Diaz, Sandra, 793
Diazepam (Valium), 1214t
2,4-Dichlorophenoxyacetic acid (2,4-D), 730i, 730–731, 982
2,5-Dichlorophenol, 731i
*Dictyostelium discoideum*, 575, 576i
Dideoxynucleotide, **363**
Dideoxynucleotide sequencing, 363–366, 364b–366b, 364–366i, 367
*Didinium*, 560i
Diencephalon, 1239, 1240i
Difference, in meiosis, 185–186
Differentiation, 887–888, 949, **1183**
Diffusion, **84**–85, 1059i, 1060i
    across body surface, 1061–1062, 1062i
    across membranes, 59, 59i
    exchanging gas by simple, 1061–1062
    passive transport based on, 84–85, 85i
Diffusion coefficient, 1059
Digestion, **1030**, 1036–1048
Digestive processes
    in animals, 1036–1039, 1038i, 1048–1049
    regulation of, 1048–1049, 1049i
Digestive system, 1017i, 1036–1048, 1040i
Digger wasps (*Philanthus triangulum*), 865, 866i
Dihybrid, **207**
Dihybrid cross, **207**
Dikaryon, 599–600
Dikaryotic hyphae, **596**
Dikaryotic mycelium, 605
*Dinobryon*, 562i
Dinoflagellates, 22, 567i, 567–568, 568i
Dinosaurs, 700i, 720, 721
Dioecious, **936**, 938i
Dipeptidase, 1045i
Diphyodont, **708**
Diploblastic body plan, **645**
Diploid, **152**
Diploid generations, 934–935, 935i
Diploid organisms, 427t
Diploid stage (of life cycle), 183–184, 612, 612i, 616–617, 617i, 621i, 626i, 631i, 636i
Diploidy, 425
Diplomonad, **565**
Diplonemids, 564, 565b
Direct flight muscles, 679i
Directional selection, 421i, **421**–422
Disaccharidases, F-25b–F-26b, 1045i
Disassociation of water and pH, F-19b–F-20b
Disclimax community, **803**
Discontinuous replication, **264**
Dishevlled gene, 850
Disk, 682
Disorder, 55
Dispersal, 485, 802, 802i, 833i, 876
Dispersal agents, 418
Dispersion, 55–57, 56i, **749**
Dispersive replication model, 259, 260i, 261b, 261i
Display order, as characteristic of life, 495i
Disruptive selection, 421i, **422**–423, 423i
Dissociation, **1071**

Distal convoluted tubule, 1113i, **1113**, 1115t, 1116
Distal end, 1106, 1109
Distinctiveness of species, 434
Distole, 1088i
Distribution, 749–751
Disturbance, effect on community characteristics, 798–799, 799i, 803
Disturbance climax, **803**
Disulfide bridges, F-33b, F-33i
Divergence, 712i
Diversification, 385
Diversity, in mammals, 710–712
Diversity of Animals
    agnathans: hagfishes and lampreys, conodonts, and ostracoderms, 689–690
    amniote origin and Mesozoic radiations, 698–701
    animal phylogeny and classification, 649–650
    Aves: birds, 704–708
    deuterostomes, 680–687
    early tetrapods and modern amphibians, 696–698
    ecdysozoan protostomes, 670–680
    evolutionary convergence and mammalian diversity: tails to teeth, 710–712
    jawed fishes, 690–693
    key innovations in animal evolution, 645–648
    lophotrochozoan protostomes, 659–670
    Mammalia: monotremes, marsupials, and placentals, 708–713
    phylum Chordata, 684–687
    phylum Echinodermata, 680–684
    phylum Hemichordata, 682i, 684
    phylum Porifera, 651–652
    subclass Testudinata: turtles and tortoises, 702
    vertebrate origin and diversification, 687–689
    what is an animal? 644–645
Division, in cell cycles, 150i, 150–151
Division of labour, 506–507
Dixon, Henry, 919
DNA. *See* Deoxyribonucleic acid (DNA)
DNA chips, **375**. *See also* DNA microarrays
DNA cloning, 334i, 334–341, 335i
DNA double helix, **2**, 257–258, 258i, F-38b, F-38i
DNA fingerprinting, 342–344, 344i
DNA helicase, **263**
DNA hybridization, 343b
DNA libraries, 336–338
DNA ligase, **264**, 266t, 336, 341
DNA methylation, **320**
DNA microarrays, 361i, **375**, 376i
DNA molecule, 257
DNA polymerase I, **264**, 266t
DNA polymerase III, **264**, 266t
DNA polymerases, **259**–264, 262i, 263i, 264i, 270i, 271
DNA repair mechanisms, 270–271, 271i
DNA replication, 260i
    enzymes in, 264–266
    major proteins of, 266t
    mechanisms to correct errors in, 270–271
    molecular model of, 265i
    multiple enzymes in, 264–266, 266i
    proteins of, 266, 266t
DNA sequencing, 363–367, 411–412, 414
DNA synthesis, 263
DNA technologies, **334**
    application of, 341–355
    DNA cloning. *See* DNA cloning
    as subject of public concern, 354–355
    why it matters, 333–334
DNA transposons, **383**
DNA-directed RNA synthesis, 283–285, 284i
Dobbenstein, B., 297–298
Dobzhansky, Theodosius, 394
Dodders, 970, 971i
Dodo, 724, 724i
Dogwood, 896i
Do-it-yourself (DIY) biology, 333
Dolly (cloned sheep), 350, 351
Dolphins, 397i, 873, 1057i, 1161i
Domains, **83**

Dominance, **203**, 871–872
Dominant, **203**
Dominant alleles, 203
Donoghue, Michael J., 635b
Dopamine, 1213t
Dormancy, **945**, 1001i, **1001**
Dorsal, 646
Dorsal lip of the blastopore, **1184**
D'Ortous de Mairan, Jean-Jacques, 17
Dosage compensation, **233**
Double blood circuits, 1082–1083
Double-crested cormorants (*Phalacrocorax auritus*), 766
Double fertilization, 636i, 939i, 941, 941i, **941**
Double helix, **2**, 257–258, 258i, F-38b, F-38i
Double-helix model, **257**–258, 258i
Double-stranded DNA, six reading frames of, 371i
Doudna, Jennifer, 348
Douglas fir (*Pseudotsuga menziesii*), 913, 1001, 1001i
Down syndrome, 238, 239i
Downy mildew, 570i
Dragonflies, 677i, 866
Driver gene, **325**
Driver mutation, **325**
*Drosophila* spp. (fruit fly), 155–156, 227, 228b, 228i, 229i, 230, 230i, 233i, 234b, 234i, 438, 439, 440, 443, 678i, 845, 850, 1164, 1167i, 1229i
Drugs, affecting neurotransmission, 1213–1214t
Dry rot, 601, 601i
Drylands, 740
Duchenne muscular dystrophy (DMD), 241i, 242, 342
Duck-billed platypus, 710i
Ducks (*Anas platyrhynchos*), 750i
Ducks, sexual selection, 443i, 443–444
Duffy-negative prevalence, 748i
*Dugesia*, 1108, 1109i
Dung, fossilized, 484
*Dunkleosteus*, 690, 691i
Duodenum, 1044i, **1044**
Duplication, 236i, **236**, **420**
Dust mites, 674i
*Dvl* gene, 850
Dwarf mongooses, 711i
Dwarfism, 985
Dyneins, 41

*E. coli*, 30, 30i, 1046
    bacteriophages and, 525i, 525–526
    binary fission, 545i
    cell cycle in, 151
    as chemoheterotroph, 548
    comparison of K12 and human genomes, 381t
    experimental evolution, 403, 404b, 404i
    genetic engineering of to make insulin, 345i, 345–346
    genetic recombination in, 175–176, 178i, 179i
    genome of, 379, 380i, 381t
    Gram-positive bacteria, 546
    Hershey-Chase experiments, 254–255, 255b, 255i
    population growth, 756
    transforming of DNA into, 336, 345i
    transforming of plasmids into, 337b, 337i
E site, **291**
"Eagle" alarm, 485
Ears, 1219i, 1221i, 1222i
Earth, 495–496, 496i
    history of, F-42–F-44
Earthworms, 662, 664i, 732i, 1035, 1038, 1038i, 1109i, 1266i
Eastern pondmussel, 732i
Eastern song sparrow, 1021b, 1021i
Ecdysis, **650**, 677
Ecdysone, 1154, 1154i
Ecdysozoa protosteomes, 670i, 670–680
Echinodermata, phylum, 680–684
Echinoderms, 683i, 1238i, 1239, 1266
Echinoidea, class, 682i, 682–684

Echolocating animal, 859–860
Echolocation, 736, 855, 859–860
Eclectus parrot, 20, 20i
Ecological communities, 794i
Ecological efficiency, **819**–820
Ecological isolation, 437t, **437**
Ecological niche, **790**, 791i
Ecological pyramids, **821**
Ecology, role of light in, 20–21
Economic development, 768–769
Economic growth, 767
*Eco*RI, 335, 335i
Ecosystem pyramids, 821–823
Ecosystems, 813–**814**
    carbon, 830–832
    caves, 836–838
    cities, 838–839
    connections within and among, 815–816
    energy and, 816–823
    modelling, 832i, 832–833
    nutrient cycling, 823–830
    pitcher plant ecosystems, 834–836
    samples, 834–839
    scale and species, 833–834
Ecotones, 793
Ectoderm, **645**, **1181**, 1182t, 1185, 1185i, 1186–1187
Ectognathous, **676**
Ectomycorrhizae, **965**–966, 966i
Ectoparasites, 781–782
Ectotherms, **1121**–1124, 1122i, 1124i
Ectothermy, 1122–1125
Edidin, Michael A., 79b
Effector, **1019**–1020, 1020i, 1022i, **1201**, 1202i
Efferent arteriole, 1113i
Efferent neuron, **1201**, 1202i, 1248i
Egg cell, **938**
Egg coats, 1164
Eggs, 706i, **1163**–1165, 1166i
Egyptian rousette bats (*Rousettus aegyptiacus*), 866, 867i
Eimer's organs, 856, 857i
Eisenberg, Robert, 761
Eisner, Thomas, 731
Ejaculation, 1178
Elasmobranchii, **690**
Elasmobranchs, 691, 692i, 1110
Elastin, **1013**
Electric fishes, 1233i
Electric signals, **859**
Electrical synapses, 1210i, **1210**
Electricity-generating bacteria, 543
Electrocardiogram (ECG), 1089i, **1089**
Electrochemical gradient, **89**, **1203**
Electrolocation, 1233i
Electrolyte balance, 1116
Electromagnetic radiation, 6, 14, 14i, 1121i
Electromagnetic spectrum, **6**–7, 7i, 129i, 129–130
Electron acceptor, 103
Electron donor, 103
Electron microscope, **26**
Electron microscopy, 28i
Electron shells, **F-10b**, F-10i
Electron transfer system, **143**
Electron transport chain (ETC), 104
Electron transport/electron transport chain, 109–112, 109–114, 111i, 112i, 502, 505
    electrons moving along, 111i, 112
    uncoupling chemiosmosis and, 113–114, 114i
Electronegativity, **F-13b**
Electrons, 7i, **7**, 129i, 129–130, 130i, F-10b
Electroreceptors, **691**, **1233**
Electrosensors, 1216i
Element, **F-7b**–F-8b
Elephants, 749, 750i, 763, 764, 1127i, 1128
Elimination, as a process from ingestion of food, 1037
Elkhorn coral, 568i

Fish, 1081i
  balancing water and salt content in, 1110i
  bony, 693–695
  circulatory system, 1070i, 1083i
  as ectotherms, 1123
  fins, 691i
  jawed, 690–693, 691i
  osmoregulation and excretion in, 1110–1111
Fisher, Donald, 925b
Fission, **1162**, 1163i
Fitness, **400**, 420
5' cap, **286**
5' end, **256**, 258, 258i, 259, 262i
Five-lined skink (*Eumeces fasciatus*), 753, 753i
Fixation, 136
Fixed action pattern, **848**
Flaccid cell, 917i
Flagella, 31, **31**, 42, 43i, **542**–543, 651
Flame cells, **659**, 1109i
Flatulence, 1046–1047
Flatworms, 11i, 11–12, 658, 659–662, 660i, 732, 732i, 1039, 1061i, 1062i, 1080, 1108, 1109i, 1224i, 1238i, 1239
*Flavivirus*, 524t
Flavonoids, 969i
Fleas, 677i
Fleming, Alexander, 393
Flexion, 1270i
Flight, 679, 679i, 1271
  muscles, 679, 679i, 1264, 1265i
Floral meristems, **936**
"Florigen," 1000
Flower colour locus, 415, 417i, 417b–418b
Flowering plants, 632–637
  adaptive success, 634–635, 635b
  asexual reproduction in, 947i, 947–949
  chemical signal, 1000, 1000i
  co-evolution with animal pollinators, 636–637, 637i
  development, 933–934
  early development of form and function, 949
  fertilization, 941
  formation of gametes, 936–940
  fossil record, 633
  germination, 945
  groups by type of growth and lifespan, 889
  life cycle of, 636i, 935i
  monocots and eudicots, 633–634
  origin of, 633
  photoperiodism and, 998–1000
  pollination in, 940–941
  reproduction, 933–935
  sexual reproduction in, 939i
  structure of, 936i, 936–940
  tissues, 891t
Flowers, 439, **632**, 633i
Fluid, in circulatory systems, 1081
Fluid feeders, 1034i, **1034**
Fluid mosaic model, 78i, **78**–80
Flunitrazepam (Rohypnol, the "date rape" drug), 1214t
Fluorescence, 130
Fluoxetine (Prozac), 1213t
Fly agaric mushroom, 598i
Flying fringe-lipped bat (*Trachops cirrhosus*), 779i
Flying sphinx moth, 1123i
Folic acid, 1032t
Follicle, **1165**, 1173i, **1173**
Follicle cell, **1165**
Follicle-stimulating hormone (FSH), 1144t, **1145**, 1173–1174, 1174i, 1177
Fontaine, Colin, 793
Food, competition for, 871
Food as fuel, 102–103
Food chain, 350, 797–798
Food web, **619**, 796i, 816, 816i, 822
Food-associated learning, 846
Foot, 481–482
Foot-and-mouth disease, 524t

Foothill yellow-legged frogs, 1123
Footprints, 481i
Foraminifera, 573
Forams, 573, 574i
Forcipules, 675i
Forebrain, 1239–1240, 1240i
Forelimbs, 1270i
Forensics, DNA fingerprinting in, 342, 344
Foreskin, **1177**
Forster, Peter, 861
Fossil record, 395–396, 480, 481i, 485
Fossilized dung, 484
Fossils, **12**, 509i, 633i
  earliest, 508i, 508–509, 509i
  evidence of evolution, 395–396
  feet, legs, and pelvis, 481–482
  formation of, 507
  hands, 483
  hominin fossil record, 480
  hominins, 478b–480b, 480
  pelvis and birth, 483–484
  radiometric dating, 509, 511b
  record, 507–509
  shoulders and arms, 482–483
  value of, 507
Founder effect, **419**
Four-o'clock plant (*Mirabilis jalapa*), 997
Fovea, **1225**
*FOXP2* gene, 485
Fragmentation, **947**, **1162**, 1163i
Frameshift mutation, 299i, **300**
Franklin, Benjamin, 999
Franklin, Rosalind, 257, 257i, 258
Free energy, **54**, 57–59, 62, 62i, 102
Free-running, 17
Freeze tolerance, 1008i
Freeze-fracture technique, **79**, 80b, 80i
Frequency, of action potentials, 1208, 1262i
Frequency, of traits, 413
Frequency-dependent selection, 427
Freshwater ecosystems, 818t, 821
Freshwater fish, excretions from, 1111
Freshwater osmoregulators, 1108
Frisch, Karl von, 859
Frogs, 696–698, 697i, 760i, 1148i, 1167i, 1181i, 1184i, 1237i
Frontal lobe, 1243i
Fructose, F-25i
Fruit, **632**
Fruit fly (*Drosophila* spp.), 227, 228b, 228i, 229i, 230, 230i, 233i, 234b, 234i, 438, 439, 440, 443, 678i, 845, 850, 1164, 1167i, 1229i
Fruit ripening, 987–988
Fruit wall, 942
Fruiting bodies, 548–549, 549i, **575**, 589i
Fruits, **942**–943
Frye, David, 79b
Frye-Edidin experiment, 79b, 79i
*Fucus gardneri*, 560i
Fuel molecules, 103i, 1030–1031
Fuel selection, 863
Fuelling animals, 1030–1031
Fulcrum, 1269, 1270i
Full siblings, 873i
Function, of cells, 26–29
Functional analysis of genome, 363
Functional groups, **F-23b**
Functional magnetic resonance imaging (fMRI), 1241, 1242i
Functional proteins, posttranslational regulation and, 323, 324i
Fundamental niche, **790**–791, 791i
Fungal cells, 27i
Fungal phyla, 590t
Fungi, 512, 587–588, 588i
  characteristics of, 588–589
  evolution and diversity of, 590–600
  life cycles, 184i, 184–185
  lifestyles of, 600–605

lineages of, 590–600
little brown myotis and, 724–725
phylogeny of, 590t, 591i
structure of, 588i
symbiotic associations with, 614
Fungi Imperfecti, 596
Furchgott, R. H., 1094b
Furculum, **704**
Furrowing, **157**, 160i

$G_0$ phase, **154**
$G_1$ phase, 153i, **153**–154, 154i, 156i
$G_1$/S checkpoint, 163
$G_2$ phase, 153i, **153**, 156i
$G_2$/M checkpoint, 163
G3P molecule, 136
GA1, 985
Gächter, Simon, 877
Galápagos Islands, 399–400
Galápagos marine iguana, 1124
Galápagos mockingbirds, 400i
Gallbladder, **1044**
Gallery forest, 751
Gametangium (plural, gametangia), **592, 619**, 620i
Gametes, **183, 612, 644**, 936–940, 1166
Gametic isolation, 437t, **439**
Gametogenesis, **1164**–1166
Gametophytes, 184, **572, 612**, 617–619, 620i, 621i, 625, 626i, 627i, 630, 636i, **934**–935, 935i, 937–940, 939i
Gammaaminobutyric acid (GABA), 1214t
Ganglia (singular, ganglion), **659, 1200**, 1237–1239
Ganglion cell, **1226**
Gangliosides, 214
Gap junctions, 46i, **46**–47, 1010i, **1010**
Gar, 693, 693i
Garden pea (*Pisum sativum*), 942
Garner, Wightman, 997
Garrod, Archibald, 278
Gas bladders, 571i
Gas composition of atmosphere, 1059t
Gas exchange, 897–899, 1057–1058, 1059i, 1103–1104
adaptations for, 1061i
animals that breathe water vs. air, 1060
with blood, 1068–1069
general principles of, 1058–1061, 1059i
mammalian respiratory system, 1065–1068
mechanisms of gas transport, 1069–1072
organs, 1061–1064
surfaces, 1059–1061
transport in blood, 1069–1072
Gas transport cascade, **1058**, 1059i
Gases, in plasma, 1084
Gassner, Gustav, 1000
Gastric emptying, 1042
Gastric glands, **1041**, 1043i
Gastric juice, **1041**–1042
Gastric lipase, 1045i
Gastric lumen, 1043i
Gastric pits, **1041**, 1043i
Gastrin, 1048, 1049i, 1139
Gastrodermis, 653–654
Gastroenteritis, 524t
Gastrointestinal cavities and tracts, 1036–1039, 1040–1041
Gastropoda, class, 667i, 667–668
Gastrotricha, phylum, 662
Gastrovascular cavity, 653
Gastrula, **1181**
Gastrulation, **1181**, 1182i, 1183–1185, 1184i, 1185i
Gated channel, **85**–86, 86i
Gause, G. F., 790b, 790i
Geese, snow, 413i
Gel electrophoresis, 340, 340b, 340i, 414
Gemmae, **621**
Gemmules, **652**
GenBank, 362–363

Gene cloning, 341
Gene duplication, 373i, 384, 384i, 420i
Gene effects, 233–235
Gene expression, 374–375, 376i, 382
loss of regulatory controls in cancer, 325–327
posttranscriptional, translational, and posttranslational regulation, 321–324
regulation of, 307–308
regulation of in prokaryotic cells, 308–314
Gene flow, **416**, 418, 418i, 423t, 427i, 435–436
Gene function, 371, 374
Gene imprinting, 245
Gene isoforms, **289**
Gene knockdown, 374
Gene knockout, 374
Gene machines, 334
Gene of interest, 334, 336, 337b, 337i
Gene pool, 414i, **414**
Gene sequences, 512
Gene structure and expression, 277–278
connection between DNA, RNA, and protein, 278–283
transcription, 283–285
translation, 289–298
Gene targeting, **346**
Gene therapy, **349**–350
Gene-for-gene recognition, 990t, **991**–992, 992i
Genera, 626
General Conference of Weights and Measures, F-5b
General transcription factor (basal transcription factor), **315**, 317i
Generalized compartment model, **823**–824
Generalized transduction, 181i, **182**, 526
Generation time, **402**, 403i, 751i, **751**, 758i
Generative cell, **937**
Genes, **28**. *See also* Genetics
in ABC model, 937i
animal behaviour and, 846–848
classes of implicated in cancer, 325–327
determining function of in genome, 374
FOXP2 gene, 485
gene-enzyme relationship, 281i
mapping by conjugation, 180
testing independence in crosses, 207, 210i
testing predicted outcomes in crosses, 208b, 208i
Genes, chromosomes, and human genetics, 2
chromosomal alterations affecting inheritance, 236–240
genetic counselling, 240–244
genetic linkage and recombination, 226–231
nontraditional patterns of inheritance, 244–245
sex-linked genes, 231–235, 232i
Genetic code, **281**–283, 283i
Genetic cohesiveness, 434
Genetic counselling, 240–244, **243**
Genetic diseases, 325, 341–342
Genetic disorders, prediction of, 243–244
Genetic distance method, **466**, 468b
Genetic distinctness, 434
Genetic divergence, 443–444
Genetic diversity, 174, 190–193, 1163
Genetic drift, **419**, 423t
Genetic engineering, **333**, 341
of animals, 346
of bacteria to produce proteins, 345–346
as latest addition to biotechnoloy, 333–334
methods of for animals, 346–349
of plants, 350–351
as subject of public concern, 354–355
use of DNA technologies to alter genes of cell or organism, 344–353
Genetic equilibrium, **416**
Genetic information, supporting theory of endosymbiosis, 505
Genetic linkage, recombination and, 226–231, 228b, 228i
Genetic recombination, 173–**174**, 190–192
in bacteria, 175–183, 177b, 177i, 541b
conceptual model, 174i
in eukaryotes, 183–193, 184i

Great Salt Lake, 550i
Great sharks, 735, 735i
Great Tit (*Parus major*), 761i
Great white sharks, 691
Great Zimbabwe R, 731
Greater vestibular gland, **1171**
Green algae, 560i, 578i, 578–579, 579i, 580i
Greenhouse effect, 830i, **830**–831, 831i
Greenhouse gases, 830–832
Grey crescent, **1183**
Grey matter, 1241i, **1246**
Grey reef shark, 692i
Grey vireo, 856, 857i
Grey whales, 865, 868
Grey wolf (*Canis lupus*), 737i, 737–738, 873, 1029i
Greylag geese (*Anser anser*), 850
Grieder, Carol, 268
Griffin, Donald R., 736
Griffith, Frederick, 180, 252, 253b
Grip, 483, 483i
Gross primary productivity, **817**
Ground finches, 422, 423i
Ground meristem, **896**, 902
Ground tissue system, **890**
Ground tissues, 890–892, 891i, 891t
Group living, 871i, 871–872, 872i
Growth
    abscisic acid (ABA) and, 988–989
    auxins and, 981–984
    brassinosteroids and, 988
    in cell cycles, 150i, 150–151
    as characteristic of life, 495i
    jasmonates and, 989
    oligosaccharins and, 989
    population. *See* Population growth
Growth factors, 1136–1137, 1144t
Growth hormone (GH), 1139, 1144t, **1145**, 1146i, 1147i
Growth rings, 905, 906i
Guanine (G), 256i, **256**, F-36b, F-37b
Guard cells, **894**, 923i
GUG, 371
Guglielmo, Chris, 863
Guppies (*Poecilia reticulata*), 754–755, 755i
Gut layers, in mammals, 1039–1040, 1040i
Gut microbiomes, 1046–1048, 1050b–1051b
Guttation, 922i, **922**
Gymnophiona, 698
Gymnosperms, 615t, 617i, 618i, 623t, **628**–632
Gypsum, 963i
Gypsy moths, 679

$H^+$ pump, **89**
Haber, Edgar, F-35b
Haber, Fritz, 828
Habitat, **749**, 833i
Habitat selection, 862, 862i
Habituation, **851**
Hadza of Tanzania, 484
Haeckel, Ernst, 645
Hafted tool, 483
Hagfish, 689, 689i, 689–690
Hahn, Beatrice H., 471
*Haikouichthys*, 688i
Hair follicles, 1126
Haldane, John, 497
Half-life, **509**, **F-9b**, F-09b–F-10b, F-10i
Half-siblings, 873i
*Halobacterium*, 9i, 9–10
Halophiles, 551–552
*Haloquadratum walsbyi*, 539i
Halteres, 1217, 1217i
Hamilton, William D., 872, 874
Hammer-headed bats (*Hypsignathus monstrosus*), 869
Hamner, Karl, 998
Hand, 483, 483i

Hand axe, 479i
Handicap hypothesis, 870
Hands, 483, 483i
Hanson, Jean, 1259b
Haplodiploidy, **874**, 875i
Haploid, **153**
Haploid generations, 934–935, 935i
Haploid stage (of life cycle), 184, 185, 612i, 617i, 621i, 626i, 631i, 636i
Hardy, G. H., 416
Hardy-Weinberg Principle, 415–**416**, 417b–418b, 424
Harlequin frogs, 592
Hartl, Daniel, 420
Hartwell, Leland, 162
Harvesters, humans as, 734–736
Harvesting efficiency, **819**
Haselton, Martie, 1172b
Haustorial roots, 970
Hawaii, 733
Hawkins, April, 693i
Hawkmoth, 637i
Haworth projection, F-24i
Hawthorn (*Crataegus* spp.), 442, 442i
Hayflick, Leonard, 165–166
Hayflick factors, 166
HbA allele (hemoglobin), 426
HbS allele (sickle cell), 426, 427i
HCl, 1048
Head–foot, **666**
Health Canada, 354, 393
Hearing
    mechanoreceptors and, 1220–1222
    in vertebrates, 1220–1222
Heart, 1086i, 1086–1087
    arterial blood pressure cycles, 1090
    cardiac cycle, 1088–1089
    in circulatory systems, 1081
    cycle of contraction and relaxation, 1088, 1088i
    heartbeat, 1088
    organization of, 1087i
Heart rate, 1093
Heart valves, 1093i
Heartbeat, 1094
Heartburn, 1041
Heartwood, **904**, 906i
Heat detection, 1231–1232
Heat exchanges, with environment, 1121, 1125–1126
Heat of vaporization, **F-16b**
Heat-shock proteins (HSP), **992**–993
Heat-shock responses, as plant chemical defence, 990t
Hedge sparrow (*Prunella modularis*), 849i
Heinrich, Bernd, 861
Helical virus, 522i, **522**
Helicases, 263, 263i, 264i, 266t
*Helicobacter pylori*, 548, 1042
Heliotropism, **977**
Hematocrit, 1085t
Hemicellulose, 887i
Hemichordata, phylum, 682i, 684
Hemocoel, 646
Hemocyanin, 669
Hemocytes, 1084
Hemoglobin, 426, 1015, 1069–1071, 1070i, 1071i, 1073b, **1085**
Hemoglobin-$O_2$ equilibrium curve, 1069, 1071i
Hemolymph, **666**, **1081**, 1082i, 1108, 1109i
Hemophilia, 235, 242
Hemorrhagic eye disease, 524t
Hendry, Andrew P., 422
Hennig, Willi, 462
Hepadnavirus, 524t
Hepatic portal vein, **1044**
Hepatitis A virus, 524t
Hepatitis B, 524t
Hepatitis C, 524t
    therapy, 529b

Hepatophyta, 618i, **620**–621, 623t
Herbicide, **982**
Herbivores, **778**, 783, 784, 792, 792b, 793i, 817, 1041i, 1047
Herbivory, 778t
Hereditary enamel hypoplasia, 241i, 243
Heritable changes, 401
Heritable variation, 412
Hermaphroditism, 1170i, **1170**–1171
Hermichordata, phylum, 684
Heron Island Reef, 798
Herpes, 524t
Herpesvirus 4 (Epstein–Barr virus), 524t
Herpesviruses, 528
Herring gull, 848, 849b, 849i
Herrmann, Esther, 876
Hershey, Alfred D., 254–255, 255b
Hershko, Avram, 323
Hervieux, Dave, 737, 738
Heske, E. J., 803
Hesperornis, 707
Heterodont, **708**
Heterosporous, 617i, **617**–618, 627, 628
Heterotrophic plants, 611i
Heterotrophs, **502**–503, **543**, 588, **644**, 797
Heterozygosity, 423–424
Heterozygote advantage, **425**–427, 427i
Heterozygotes, **203**, 214, 240–241
Heterozygous, **203**
Hexapoda, subphylum, 675–680
Hexokinase, 65, 66i
Hfr cells, **178**–180
Hibernation, 754, **1129**
*Hibiscus*, 637i
Hierarchical genome sequencing, **367**, 370i
Hierarchy of complexity, F-1–F-2
High altitude, 1057, 1058i, 1073b
High blood pressure, 1090
High-affinity state, 69
Higher brain functions, 1243–1245
Hindbrain, 1239, 1240i
Hippocampus, **1242**
Hippocrates, 453
Hirudinea, class, 662
Histone acetyltransferase, 320
Histone code, **321**
Histone deacetylase, 320
Histones, 159i, 320i
History of life, phylogeny, 453–454, 462i
*HLA* haplotypes, 485
*HLA-B*73* allele, 485
Hoary bats (*Lasiurus cinereus*), 865, 865i
Hoatzin, 1047, 1048i
Holder, R. L., 482
Holdfasts, 572
Holocephali, **690**
Holothuroidea, class, 682i, 684
Home range, 862–863
Homeostasis, **1007**, 1018–1023, **1104**, 1149i
  as characteristic of life, 495i
  factors regulated by, 1019
  negative feedback mechanisms, 1019–1022, 1020i
  positive feedback mechanism, 1023
Homeostatic mechanism, **1007**
Homeostatic regulation, 1138–1139
Homing pigeons (*Columba livia*), 866, 1233
Hominin, 478i, 478b–480b, **480**, 481i, 485, 487
Hominoids, **480**
*Homo*, 478b, 478i, 482–483
*Homo antecessor*, 478i
*Homo erectus*, 478b, 478i, 479i, **479b**–480b, 483
*Homo ergaster*, 478i
*Homo floresiensis*, **480b**
*Homo georgicus*, 487
*Homo habilis*, 478b, 478i, **479b**
*Homo heidelbergensis*, 478i

*Homo neanderthalensis*, 477, 478b, 478i, **480**, 485
*Homo sapiens*, 478b, 478i, **480b**
  Anthropocene and, 720
  brain size, 478b
  dispersal, 485
  hand, 482i
  language, 485
  scapula, 482i
  skeleton, 481i
Homologous, **174**
Homologous characters, 459i, 459–460
Homologous chromosomes, 211i
Homologous genes, 372
Homologous pair, 185
Homologous traits, 396i
Homologous transfusion, 1070
Homology, **397**, **459**, 460i
Homoplasy, **459**, 464
Homosporous, 617, 627
Homozygote, **203**
Homozygous, **203**
Homozygous recessives, 240–241
Höner, O. P., 876
Honesty, 876–877
Honey badgers, (*Mellivora cape*), 780
Honeybees, 307–308, 308i, 679i, 736, 853i, 853–854, 859, 859i, 874, 874i, 875i, 1022, 1123
Honeyguide birds (*Indicator indicator*), 780, 848–849
Hooded warblers, 730, 730i
Hooke, Robert, 25, 26i
Hookworms (*Ancylostoma duodenale* and *Necator americanus*), 770
Horizon, **961**–962
Horizons, soil, 961i, 961–962
Horizontal cells, **1226**
Horizontal gene transfer (HGT), 513–514, **513**–514, 514i, 515i, 540, 546, 604
Hormonal controls, 1049i
Hormones, **319**, F-28t, **1136**
  animal behaviour and, 853i, 853–854
  binding to receptors, 1139, 1140i
  body processes, 1139
  in endocrine control, 1136–1139
  environmental stimuli and, 1138
  evolutionary conserved, 1137
  growth and development, 1138
  homeostatic regulation, 1138–1139
  hydrophilic, 1139
  mechanisms of, 1139–1144
  reguating cardiac output and arteriole diameter with, 1095
  regulating body processes with coordinated hormone secretion, 1139
  regulating by feedback pathways, 1138i, 1138–1139
  regulating cardiac output and arteriole diameter with, 1095
  reproductive, 1173, 1177–1178
  target cells and, 1140–1143
Hormones (plant), 979t, **979**–989
  abscisic acid, 988–989
  auxins, 981–984
  brassinosteroids, 988
  cytokinins, 986–987
  ethylene, 987–988
  gibberellins, 984–986
  jasmonates, 989
  oligosaccharins, 989
  second messengers, 981
  signal transduction pathways and, 980, 980i
Horned lizards, 1123
Hornworts, 622, 622i
Horsehair worms, 672
Horses, 439, 439i
Horseshoe crabs, 674, 720, 786
Horseshoe worms, 669
Horsetails, 626–627, 627i, 959
Horvitz, Robert, 167
Host, **504**, 527i
Host race, **442**
House cats, 731–732

House dust mites, 674i
House sparrow, 437i
Houseflies, 678i
*Hox* genes, 645, 646i, 687, 688i
Hudson's Bay Company, 764, 765i
Human. *See Homo sapiens*
Human ABO blood group, 215, 215t, 216i
Human chorionic gonadotropin (hCG), **1179**
Human evolution, application of comparative genomics to understanding of, 383–384
Human genetics. *See* Genes, chromosomes, and human genetics
Human genome
    compared to bacterial genome, 378–381
    comparison of *E. coli* K12 and, 381t
    dispersal, 485
    profile of, 379–381, 381i
Human Genome Project (HGP), 362
Human herpesvirus, 524t
Human immunodeficiency virus (HIV), 470–471, 471i, 524t, 527i, 527–528
Humans
    adrenal cortex, 1150i
    adrenal medulla, 1150i
    birth, 1191–1192, 1192i
    brain development, 1240i
    dentition, 1041i
    digestion in, 1038i
    digestive system, 1039, 1040i
    ears, 1219i, 1221i
    embryo, 1191i
    embryonic development of, 1188–1193, 1189i, 1190i
    endocrine glands in, 1143i, 1143–1144t
    essential elements for, 1031–1034
    eye structure, 1225i
    as harvesters, 734–736
    hypothalamus, 1145i
    as invasive species, 734, 734i
    large intestine in, 1045–1048
    location variation in population growth rates, 767i
    lungs, 1061i
    mouth, pharynx, and esophagus, 1040–1041
    nutritional requirements, 1031–1034
    organ systems, 1017i
    ovaries and testes, 1151i
    parathyroid glands, 1149i
    pineal gland, 1153i
    pituitary gland, 1145i
    population growth, 739, 766i, 766–770
    respiratory system in, 1066i
    as root problem for conservation, 739
    small intestines in, 1042–1045, 1043i, 1045i, 1046i
    social behaviour, 876–877, 877i
    stomach in, 1041–1042, 1043i, 1044i, 1045i
    taste receptors, 1230i
    thyroid gland, 1148i
    urinary system in, 1112i, 1112–1113
    vocal cues to ovulation, 1172b, 1172i
Humans and evolution, 477–487
    dispersal, 486i
    evolutionary impacts, 393–394
    features that do not fossilize, 484–485
    fossil hominins, 478b–480b
    hominin fossil record, 480, 481i
    hominins and the species concept, 485–487
    impacts, 393–394
    morphology and bipedalism, 481–484
    skeletons, 481i
    social networks, 484
    species concepts, 485, 487
Hummingbirds, 637i, 706i, 856, 1034i, 1080i, 1129
Humpback whale, 411, 411i, 1035i, 1036
Humulin, 345–346, 1152
Humus, **960–961**
Hunt, R. Timothy, 163
Huntington disease, 102
Husky, 1022i, 1127i

Hutton, James, 395
Huxley, Andrew, 1259b
Huxley, Hugh, 1259b
Huxley, Thomas, 403
Hyacinth macaws, 859i
Hybrid, **437**
Hybrid breakdown, 437t, 439, **440**
Hybrid inviability, 437t, 439, **439**
Hybrid sterility, 437t, 439, **439**, 443
Hybrid vigour, 425
Hybrid zones, **441**, 442i
*Hydra*, 1153
Hydrangea, 413, 413i
Hydras, 654i, 656, 657i, 1080, 1081i
Hydration shell, **F-17b**
Hydrocarbons, **80**, F-21b
Hydrogen, as essential plant nutrient, 957, 958t
Hydrogen bonds, F-11, **F-13b**–F-14b, F-15b–F-16b, F-14b, F-14i, F-33b, F-33i
Hydrogeological cycle, **824**, 825i
Hydroids, 653–658
Hydrolysis, 62, **F-22b**, F-22i
Hydrolysis reactions, F-22b
Hydrophilic, **80**, **F-13b**
Hydrophilic hormones, 1139, 1140i
Hydrophobic, **80**, **F-13b**
Hydrophobic effects, 81
Hydrophobic hormones, 1139–1140, 1140i
Hydrophobic interactions, F-17b, F-33b
Hydroponic culture, **956**–957, 957b, 957i, 959
Hydroponics, 956–957, 957b, 957i
Hydrostatic movement, 1266, 1266i
Hydrostatic pressure, 1090
Hydrostatic skeletons, **646**, 673, 1265i, **1265**–1266, 1266i
Hydrothermal vent, 544i
Hydroxyapatite, 1013
Hydroxyl group, **256**, F-23b
Hydrozoa, class, 656
Hygrophorus (scarlet hood), 598i
Hymen, **1171**
Hyomandibular bones, **690**
Hyperosmotic, 1105, 1108, 1110–1111, 1112
Hyperosmotic urine, 1114
Hyperpolarization, 1204i, **1204**
Hypersensitive response, 990t, 991i, **991**
Hypertension, 1090
Hyperthermia, **1128**
Hyperthyroidism, 1148
Hypertonic, **87**, 88i
Hyphae, **570**, 588i, **588**–589, 594, 602
Hypoblast, **1185**
Hypocotyl, 944
Hypodermis, 1126i, **1126**
Hypoosmotic, 1105, 1110, 1114, 1115
Hypothalamus, 1048–1049, 1117, 1117i, 1125, 1127–1128, 1138i, 1143i, 1143t, 1145i, 1145–1147, 1146i, 1151i, 1155, **1242**–1243
Hypothermia, **1128**
Hypothesis, **F-2b**, F-3i, F-3b–F-4b, 469
Hypothyroidism, 1148
Hypotonic, **87**, 88i
Hypoxic, **1057**, 1058i

I bands, 1257
Iceberg lettuce (*Lactuca* sp.), 985
Icefish, 1124i
*Ichthyostega*, 696
*Ideonella sakiaiensis 201-F6*, 731
*Igf2* gene, 245, 245i
Ileum, **1044**
Illumina/Solexa method for DNA sequencing, 367
Imbibition, **945**
Immigration, **752**, 805i, 805–806, 807
Immune response, 1097
Immune system, 485, 1016i
Immunoglobulins, **1084**
Imperfect flower, **936**

Invertebrates, 12
  chemoreceptors, 1229–1230
  circulatory system, 1081–1082
  ectothermy in, 1122–1123
  endocrine systems in, 1153–1154
  eyes of, 1223–1225
  hearing in, 1220
  muscles, 1264
  nervous systems, 1238i, 1238–1239
  as osmoconformers, 1108
  osmoregulation and excretion in, 1108–1110
  as osmoregulators, 1108
Inverted repeat, **382**, 383
Involution, **1184**
Iodine, 1033t
Ionic bonds, **84**, F-11b, F-12i, F-33b, F-33i
Ionizing radiation, 14
Ionophores, 113
Ions, **10**, **F-11b**, 918, 1084, 1110, 1139, 1205–1206
Iris, **1224**
Irish potato famine, 569–570
Iron
  deficiencies in, 960i, 1033i
  as essential plant nutrient, 958t, 959
  sources, functions, and effects of deficiencies in humans, 1033t
*Isistius plutodus*, 691
Island biogeography, equilibrium theory of, 805–807
Island foxes (*Urocyon littoralis*), 766
Islets of Langerhans, 1143i, 1144t, **1152**–1153
Isoforms, 289
Isolated system, 55, 55i
Isoleucine, 70, 70i
Isomers, F-24b–F-25b
Isoosmotic, 1105, 1110, 1114
Isoprenes, F-39b
Isotonic, **87**, 88i
Isotopes, **F-9b**
Isthmus of Panama, 440, 440i

Jack pine, 614i
Jackrabbits, 783, 1127i, 1128
Jacky dragons, 725i, 725–726
Jacob, François, 180, 309–310
Jade plant, 947
Jambiyas, 723
Jasmonates, 979t, **989**, 990–991, 990t
Jawed fish, 690–693, 691i
Jawless fish, 689–690
Jaws, 691i
Jeffreys, Alec, 342
Jejunum, **1044**
Jellies, 653–658
Jellyfish, 656, 1080
Jensen, Keith, 876
Jet lag, 18–19, 19i
Jet propulsion, 669
Johnson, Robert T., 162
Joint-legged animals, 673–680
Joints, 1269, 1269i
Jordano, P., 802
Jumping genes, 174. *See also* Mobile elements
Junctions, 1009–1010, 1010i
Junk DNA, 289, **380**
Juvenile hormone (JH), 678i, 678–679, 853, 1154i, **1154**
Juvenile mortality, 753
Juxtamedullary nephrons, 1114

K+ channels, 1205
K+ ions, 1203
Kalashnikov assault rifles, 723, 723i
Kandel, Eric, 1246
Kangaroo rat, 803, 803i, 1117–1118, 1118b
Kangaroos, 710i
*Karenia brevis*, 567i
Karyogamy, **589**

Karyotype, **155**, 159i
Keast, Allen, 791
Keeled sternum, **704**
Keeling, Patrick, 564, 580
Kelp, 572
  beds and reefs, 818t
Kentucky bluegrass (*Poa pratensis*), 947
Keratin, 1012, 1126
Kernel, 944, 944i
Ketone, **1153**
Keystone species, **791**
Khorana, H. Gobind, 282
Kidd, Karen A., 771
Kidney bean (*Phaseolus vulgaris*), 944, 944i, 946i
Kidneys, 1114i
  ADH-stimulated water reabsorption in, 1118–1119i
  in mammals, 1112i, 1112–1113, 1113i
  in marine fish, 1110–1111
  regulation of in mammals, 1116–1117
Kidneyshell mussels, 732i
Killer whales (*Orcinus orca*), 727, 727i, 860
Killifish (*Rivulus hartii*), 755, 755i
Kin selection, 872–874, 873i, 876
Kinesins, 41, 42i
Kinesis, **862**
Kinetic barrier, 64
Kinetic energy, **54**, 56, 56i
Kinetochore, **155**, 162i, 164b, 164i
Kinetoplast, 565
Kinetoplastids, 564–565
King penguin, 20, 20i
Kingdom Animalia, 644
Kingdom Fungi, **590**
Kingdom Plantae, **613**, 614i
Kingdome of Animalia, **644**
Kinorhyncha, phylum, 648, 670, 670i
Kirtland's warblers (*Dendroica kirtlandii*), 782, 862
Kissing bugs (*Rhodnius prolixus*), 781i
Klinefelter syndrome, 239t
Klironomos, J. N., 795
Knee joint, 1269i
Knepper, Mark, 1118b
Knockout mouse, **346**, 347b, 347i, 349, 850
Koalas, 710i, 783
Korarchaeota, **551**, 553
Kornberg, Roger, 285
Krakatoa explosion, 739, 805
Krebs, Charles, 765
Krebs cycle. *See* Citric acid cycle
*k*-selected species, 763i, **763**–764, 764i, 798, 801–802
Kuru, 530

Labia majora, **1171**
Labia minora, **1171**
Labium, 678i
*lac* operon, 309i, 309–311, 310i
Lac repressor, 310, 310i
  protein, 375
Lactate fermentation, **117**–118
Lactate production, 1264
Lactic acid, 1264
*Lactobacillus*, 550
Lactose, F-26i
*lacZ+* gene, 336, 337b, 337i
Lady-of-the-night orchid (*Brassavola flagellaris*), 971i
Lagging strand, **264**
  template, **264**, 267, 267i
Lahr, M. Mirazón, 876
Lake and stream, 818t, 819i, 822
Lake Erie, 829
Lamarck, Jean Baptiste de, 394
Lambda, 526i, 526–527
*Lambeosaurus*, 701i
Lamp shells, 669–670

Linker, **155**, 159i
Linnaeus, Carolus, 394, 454–456, 458
Linné, Carl von. *See* Linnaeus, Carolus
Linoleic acid, 1031
Lipases, 1036, 1045i
Lipid bilayer, 27–28, 29i, 80b, 80i
Lipid fabric, of cell membranes, 80–82
Lipid molecules, 78–79
Lipid soluble hormones, 1139
Lipid spheres, 499–500
Lipids, F-38–F-39, F-22b
Lipopolysaccharides (LPSs), **542**
Liposomes, 81i, 499, 499i
Lithotrophs, 544
Little brown myotis (*Myotis lucifugus*), 724–725, 725i, 736, 764, 860, 860i
Liver, 1044i, **1044**–1045
Liver fluke, 661i
Liverworts, 620i, 620–621
Lizards, 702–703, 703i, 725i, 725–726, 753, 761, 762b, 762i, 1123–1124, 1124i
Loam, **961**
Lobster, 648, 669, 676i, 1216–1217
Local controls, regulating arteriole diameter with, 1095
Lock-and-key hypothesis, 66
Locus, 211i, 414i, **414**
Lodgepole pine (*Pinus contorta*), 961
Loewi, Otto, 1212b
Logistic model of population growth, 758i, 758t, **758**–760, 759i
Lohmann, Kenneth, 1234b
Lokiarchaeota, **551**, 553
Long-day plant, 999i, **999**
Long-distance transport, 914i, 919–924
Longlining, 736i
Long-term memory, **1245**
Long-term potentiation, **1245**
Loons, 1255, 1256i
Loop of Henle, **1113**, 1114i, 1115, 1115t, 1116
Loose connective tissue, **1013**, 1014i
Lophophorate, 670
Lophophore, **659**, 669i
Lophotrochozoa, 650
Lophotrochozoa protostomes, 659–670, 660i
Lorenz, Konrad, 850
Loricifera, phylum, 671
Lotka, Alfred J., 790
Lou Gehrig's disease, 102
Low-affinity state, 69
Lower Fraser Valley, 722i
Lubchenco, Jane, 792, 792b
LUCA (Last Universal Common Ancestor), 378, 512–513, 513i
*Lucernaria quadricornis*, 657i
"Lucy," 478b, 478i
Luft, Rolf, 101
Luft syndrome, 102
Lumen, 1036, 1045i
Luna moths, 677i
Lunge feeding, 1036
Lungfish, 695, 695i
Lungs, **1063**–1064, 1068i
   in birds, 1065i
   in humans, 1066i
   in mammalian respiratory system, 1064i, 1065–1068, 1066i
   in terrestrial mammals, 1117
   in vertebrates, 1063–1064
Luteinizing hormone (LH), 1144t, **1145**, 1173–1174, 1174i, 1177
Lycophyta, 618i, 623t, **624**
Lycophyte tree, 624i
Lycophytes (club mosses), 616i, 617i, 625, 625i
*Lycopodium*, 617i, 625, 625i
Lyell, Charles, 395
Lyme disease, 540
Lymph, **1095**
Lymph node, 1096i, **1097**
Lymph vessels, 1096i
Lymphatic system, **1080**, **1095**–1097, 1096i
Lymphocytes, 1085t, **1095**

Lynx, 764–765, 765i
Lysed, **526**
Lysogenic cycle, 182i, **183**, 526i, **526**–527
Lysosomal storage diseases, 38
Lysosomes, 37i, **37**–39
Lysozymes, 525–526, F-33i
Lytic cycle, 182i, **182**, 526i, 526–527, **526**

M line, 1257
MacArthur, Robert, 797, 805
MacArthur–Wilson model, 805–806
MacLeod, Colin, 254
*Macrocystis pyrifera*, 571i
Macroevolution, 433–434
   genetic mechanisms of speciation, 443–446
   geography of spciation, 440–443
   reproductive isolation, 437–440
   species, 434–437
Macrominerals, 1033t
Macromolecules, 494, 496, 499–502
Macronucleus, **567**
Macronutrients, 956–959, **957**, 958t, **1030**
Macrophages, 1085, 1085t
"Mad cow disease," 530
Magnesium
   as a cation, 963
   deficiencies in, 960i
   as essential plant nutrient, 957, 958t, 959
   in soil, 963–964
   sources, functions, and effects of deficiencies in humans, 1033t
Magnetic sense, in sea turtles, 1234b, 1234i
Magnetoreceptors, **1233**
Magnification, **26**
MagR proteins, 845
Mahaleb cherry (*Prunus mahaleb*), 802, 802i
Maherali, H., 795
Maintenance of high species richness, 804
Malaria (*Plasmodium falciparum*), 453–454, 454i, 568, 569i, 747–749, 748i
Malaria Initiative, 748i
Malarial parasite, 426, 427i
Males, in reproduction, 1175–1178, 1176i, 1177i, 1178i
Malignant, 325
Mallard duck (Anas platyrhynchos), 443i
Malleus, 1221i, **1221**
Malnourishment, 762
Malnutrition, **1031**
Malpighian tubules, **676**, 1108, 1109i, **1109**–1110
Malthus, Thomas, 398
Maltose, F-26i
Mammalia, class
   diversity, 710–712
   evolutionary convergence and mammalian diversity, 710–712
   phylogeny, 709i
   radiation of, 708–710
   teeth, 709i, 711–712, 712i, 713i, 1040, 1041i
   variations, 708–710
Mammals
   brains of, 1241i
   circulatory system, 1070i, 1083i
   daily and seasonal rhythms of, 1128–1129, 1129i
   digestion in, 1038i, 1039–1048, 1040i
   embryonic development of, 1188–1193
   endocrine glands in, 1143i
   fertilization, 1179i
   forelimbs and locomotion, 397i
   osmoregulation and excretion in, 1112i, 1112–1119
   phylogenies, 709i
   reproductive systems of, 1167i
   respiratory system in, 1065–1068, 1066i
   retina of, 1225–1226
   sexual reproduction in, 1171–1180
   skeletons, 1268i
   teeth, 709i, 711–712, 712i, 713i, 1040, 1041i
   urinary system in, 1112–1113
   water-conserving adaptations, 1117–1119

Metazoa, 644, 644i, 645, 649i, 650, 652
Metencephalon, 1239, 1240i
Meteorites, 493
Methane, 831i, 1047, F-13i
Methanogens, 551
*Methanosarcina*, 552i
Methyl bromide, 806
Methyl salicylate, 993i
Methylation, of DNA, 320
Methylphenidate (Ritalin), 1213t
Mexican cavefish (*Astyanax mexicanus*), 814, 814i, 836, 836i
Micelle, 81i, **81**
Michael Smith Labor, 528
Michel, Andrew P., 443
*Micrasterias*, 560i
Microbiome, **1046**–1048, 1050b–1051b
Microbodies, 297
Microclimate, **801**
Microevolution, 411–**412**
    agents of, 416–423
    evolutionary agents, 416–423
    maintenance of variation, 425–427
    population genetics, 414–416
    variation in natural populations, 412–413
Microfilaments, 39–41, 40i, **41**
Micronucleus, **567**
Micronutrients, 956–959, 958t, **958**, **1030**
Microphylls, 616, 616i
*Microplana termitophaga*, 660, 660i
Micropyle, **938**, 941
MicroRNAs (miRNAs), 322i, **322**, 327, 371
Microscopes, 2, 25, 26i, **26**–27
Microscopic tubules, excretion and, 1106, 1106i
Microscopy, **26**
Microsporangia, 937
Microspore mother cells, 937
Microspores, 617i, **618**, 627, **630**, 631i, 937, **937**
Microsporocytes, 631i
Microtubule motor proteins, 163i
Microtubule organizing centre (MTOC), **158**
Microtubules, 39, 40i, **40**–41, 42, 158, 162i
Microvilli, 1042, 1043i, 1044
Midbrain, 1240i
Middle ear, **1220**–1221, 1221i
Midges (*Metriocnemus knabi*), 835, 835i
Miescher, Joahnn Friedrich, 252
Migration
    animal behaviour and, 845–846, 846i, 863–868, 864i, 865i, 867b
    reasons for, 866–868
Migratory birds, 708, 727, 754, 867b, 867–868, 1008i
Migratory locusts (*Locusta migratoria*), 760–761, 761i
Mildew, 597i
Milk, 1192
Milkweed (*Asclepias* spp.), 784, 784i, 863, 864i
Miller, Stanley, 497, 497i
Miller-Urey experiment, 497i, 497–498
Milliosmoles, 1105
Millipede, 675, 675i
Mimicry, 787, 788i, 856
*Mimosa*, 977, 978i
*Mimosa pudica*, 996, 996i
Mineral licks, 851–852
Mineralocorticoids, **1150**–1151
Minerals
    availability of in soil, 957–958, 963i
    deficiencies in, 1033i
    as essential animal nutrient, 1031
    long-distance transport of in xylem, 919–924
    plant nutrition, 957–958
    sources, functions, and effects of deficiencies in humans, 1033t
Minimal medium (MM), **175**, 278–279, 280b, 280i
Miramichi River, 1103, 1104i

miRNA-induced silencing complex (miRISC), **322**
Mismatch repair, **270**–271, 271i
Missense mutation, 299i, **299**–300, 300i
Mitchell, Peter, 113
Mites, 674i, 835
Mitochondria, **39**, 101–102
    cellular respiration and, 39, 39i
    in endosymbiosis, 504, 505i
    in horizontal gene transfer, 514i
    membranes and compartments of, 105, 105i
    protein sorting to the, 297
Mitochondrial DNA (mtDNA), 469, 477, 480
Mitochondrial matrix, **39**
Mitochondrion, 105
Mitosis, 149i, **152**–153, 164b, 1165i
    compared with meiosis, 191i
    in eukaryotes, 184i
    eukaryotic cell cycle and, 152i, 152–158, 153i, 156i, 157i, 158i, 160i
    flowering plants and, 938, 939i
    in reproduction, 1164, 1165i, 1169
    stages after interphase, 154–156, 156i, 157i, 158i, 164
Mitotic cell division, **1182**
Mitotic spindle, **155**, 160–161, 161i, 162i
Mitotic spindle checkpoint, 163
Mixotrophs, **564**
Modelling, 873
Modern synthesis of evolution, 400
Molarity (M), **F-19b**
Molars, **479**, **1040**
Mole, **F-19b**
Molecular analysis, 662
Molecular clocks, **469**, **480**
Molecular hydrogen, F-12b, F-13i
Molecular phylogenetic analyses, 469–471
Molecular phylogeny, 649i, 649–650
Molecular sequences, 461, 464
Molecular techniques, 401–402
Molecular weight, **F-19b**
Molecules, **F-11**
    as neurotransmitters, 1213
    units of measure in, 27i
Mollusca, phylum, 646, 665i, 665–669, 666i
Molluscs, 511i, 660i, 734, 1122, 1238i, 1266
Molybdenum, as essential plant nutrient, 958t
Monarch butterflies (*Danaus plexippus*), 463i, 863, 864i
Monera, 512
Monet, Claude, 5i, 5–6, 10
Mongooses (*Herpestes auropunctatus*), 765–766
Monkeys, 485
Monoamines, 1213t
Monocots, 623t, 634i, **634**, **889**, 890t, 898i, 899i
    development of, 946i
    root systems, 904i
    seeds, 944, 944i
Monocytes, 1085t
Monod, Jacques, 309–310
Monoecious, **651**, **936**, 938i
Monogamy, **868**–869
Monogenea, 661, 662
Monohybrid, **203**
Monohybrid cross, **205**
Monomers, **498**
Monophyletic, 620
Monophyletic taxa (singular, monophyletic taxon), 458i, **458**
Monoplacophora, class, 666
Monosaccharides, F-24b–F-25b, **64**
Monotremata, 708–713
Monotremes, **708**
*Monotropa uniflora*, 611, 611i, 612
Monterey pine (*Pinus radiata*), 733
Moorhead, Paul, 165–166
Moose (*Alces alces*), 727–728, 803, 846, 851, 851i, 1060i, 1121i
*Morchella esculenta*, 595, 595i
Morel, 595, 595i

Navarro, Arcadi, 446
Navigation, 845, **865**, 866
Neandertal. *See Homo neanderthalensis*
Nectar, 636
Nectar guides, 637
Negative feedback, **1019**–1022
Negative feedback control, 1149i
Negative feedback mechanisms, 1085
  blood and, 1085
  coordination of body processes, 1139
  glucocorticoids and epinephrine, 1151i
  homeostasis and, 1019–1022, 1020i
  homeostatic regulation, 1138, 1138i
  male reproductive hormones, 1177–1178,
    1178i
  of parathyroid hormone, 1149i
  in reproduction, 1178i
  thermoregulation, 1120
Negative gene regulation, 313
Negative pressure breathing, **1063**
Nematocyst, **653**, 654i
Nematoda, phylum, 671i, 671–672
Nematodes, 1080
Nematode-trapping fungus, 596i
*Nematodinium*, 581i
Nematomorpha, phylum, 672
Nematozoa, 670
Nemertea, phylum, 648, 662–665, 665i
Nemertodermatidae, 658
Neodermata, 661
Neonicotinoid pesticides, 736
Nephrons, 1103i, **1110**, 1112i, 1113i, 1114i, 1146i
  filtration, reabsorption, and secretion in, 1115–1116, 1115t
  hyperosmotic urine from, 1114
  specialized functions of, 1113–1114
Nerve cells, 1017. *See also* Neurons
Nerve cord, **1239**
Nerve impulses, 1203, 1207, 1212b, 1212i
Nerve nets, **654**, 1238
Nerves, 664i, **1200**
Nervous system, 1016i, 1136i, 1200–1206, **1200**, 1238i
Nervous tissue, 1009i, **1017**–1018
Nest parasites, 856
Net primary productivity, **817**, 818, 818i, 818t, 819i
Networking, 893b
Networks, **1201**, 1237–1239
Neural anatomy, animal behaviour and, 855i, 855–856, 856i
Neural circuits, specialization in, 1201
Neural control, 1199–1200
  action potentials and, 1202–1206
  basis of information flow in nervous system, 1200–1206
  brains, 1239–1245
  central nervous system (CNS), 1236–1247
  chemoreceptors, 1229–1231
  electroreceptors, 1233
  ganglia, 1239–1245
  integrating incoming signals with neurons, 1236–1237
  integration, 1236–1247
  magnetoreceptors, 1233
  nerves, 1239–1245
  networks, 1239–1245
  organization of neurons, 1200–1202
  peripheral nervous system (PNS), 1247–1249
  reception, 1214–1220
  sensory coding, 1235
  sensory inputs, 1214–1220
  signal initiation by neurons, 1206–1207
  thermoreceptors and nociceptors, 1231–1233
Neural crest cells, **1186**–1187, 1187i
Neural integration, 1237–1239
  evolutionary trends in, 1237–1239
  hearing and mechanoreceptors, 1220–1222
  of incoming signals, 1236–1237
  mechanoreceptors, **1215**, 1216–1222
  photoreceptors and vision, 1223–1229

  sensory integration, 1236–1237
  tactile and spatial senses, 1216–1220
Neural plate, **1186**
Neural regulation, 1136i, **1137**
Neural signalling, **1200**, 1201i, 1202i, 1258i
Neural tube, 1186–1187, 1187i, **1239**, 1240i
Neuroendocrine regulation, 1136i, **1137**
Neurogenic hearts, **1089**
Neurohormones, 1137
Neuromasts, 1218i
Neuromodulators, **1211**
Neuromuscular junction, 1137, **1257**
Neuronal circuit, **1201**
Neurons, 1017i, **1017**, **1137**, **1200**, 1201i
  functioning as circuits, 1200
  integrating incoming signals by, 1236–1237, 1237i
  organization of, 1200–1202
  signal initiation by, 1206–1207
  specialization in, 1201
  synapses and, 1210–1213
Neuropeptides, 1214t
Neurophysiology, animal behaviour and, 852, 852i
Neurosecretory neurons, **1137**, 1138
*Neurospora crassa*, 278, 587, 594, 597i
Neurotransmitters, **1210**, 1213–1214t, 1215i
  exocytosis and, 1212–1213
  ions and, 1213
  molecules as, 1213
Neurulation, **1186**
Neutrons, **F-8b**
Neutrophil, 1085t
New France, 226i
New Guinea, 433
New World knifefish, 859
New York Declaration on Forests, 730
Niacin, 1032t
Niagara Falls, 55, 56i
Niches, 790–792, 791i
Nicholas II, Czar, 242
Nickel, as essential plant nutrient, 958t, 959
Nicotinamide adenine dinucleotide (NAD$^+$), 103–104, 104i
Nicotine, 1213t
Niedergerke, Rolf, 1259b
Nirenberg, Marshall, 281–282
*Nitella*, 579
Nitrate
  as an anion, 963
  production and assimilation of, 967, 967i
Nitric oxide (NO), 994, 1095
Nitrification, **544**, 828t, **828**, **967**
Nitrifying bacteria, 967
Nitrogen, 544, 827–828
  assimilation of, 967
  in atmosphere, 1059t
  in commercial fertilizers, 960
  deficiencies in, 960i
  as essential plant nutrient, 957, 958t, 959–960, 966–967
  plants obtaining from soil, 967i
Nitrogen compounds, from animals, 1107i, 1107–1108, 1109i
Nitrogen cycle, **826**–828, 827i, 828t, 829i, 966–967
Nitrogen fixation, **544**, **826**–828, 828t, 967–968, **967**, 969i
Nitrogen-fixing bacteria, 967
Nitrogenous base, **62**
Nitroglycerin, 1094b
Nitrous oxide (NO), 831i, 1214t
Nociceptors, **1215**, 1232–1233
*Nod* gene, 968, 969i
Node, **456**, 457i, **895**, 896i
Nodes of Ranvier, **1202**, 1203i
Nomarski (differential interference contrast), 28i
Nomenclature, 454–456
Noncoding RNA genes, 371
Noncompetitive activation, 69i
Noncompetitive inhibition, 68–70, 69i
Nondisjunction, **237**–240, 238i, 239i

Photopsin, **1228**
Photoreceptors, **1215**
Photoreceptors and vision, 1223–1229
  invertebrate eyes, 1223–1225
  neural pathways for, 1228i
  opsin pigments, 1226–1228
  radiant energy, detection and perception, 1223,
    1223b
  retina of mammals and birds, 1225–1226
  rhodopsin as a photoreceptor, 10, 10i
  sensory transduction, 1226
  structure of rods and cones, 1227i
  vertebrate eyes, 1225
  visual cortex, 1228–1229
  visual processing, 1226
Photorespiration, **137**–142, 138i, 141i
Photoreversible, **997**
Photosensors, 1216i
Photosynthesis, 6, 8, 14, 102, 125–**126**, 523–524
  appartus for, 128–132
  Calvin cycle and, 9, 9i, 127, 127i, 134–137
  cellular respiration compared with, 142–143
  chloroplasts and, 127
  $CO_2$-concentrating mechanisms, 137–142
  in dim environments, 635b, 635i
  global perspective of, 128
  greenhouse gases and, 831–832
  leaves and, 897–899
  light reactions and, 127, 127i, 132–134
  linked with cellular respiration, 102i
  overview of, 126–128
  as an oxidation-reduction process, 126–127
  photorespiration, 137–142
  primary productivity, 817
  process of, 142i
  in protists, 561, 563
  shoot systems and, 888
Photosynthetic electron transport, 132i,
    132–133
Photosystem I, 132i, **132**, 133i
Photosystem II, 15, 15i, 132i, **132**, 133i
Photosystems, **128**
  photosynthetic pigments in, 131i, 131–132
Phototaxis, 10
Phototrophs, **543**
Phototropisms, **981**, 982b, 982i, 993–994, 994i
*Phronima*, 675, 676i
Phycobilins, 577
PhyloCode, **464**
Phylogenetic analyses, sources of data, 458–461
Phylogenetic species concept, **435**
Phylogenetic trees, **456**–458, 457i, 462i
  of Bacteria and Archaea, 548i
  comparative method, 469, 470i
  public health and, 470–471, 471i
  as research tools, 469
  techniques to identify optimal, 464–466
  traditional vs. cladistic classifications, 462i
  using genetic distances to construct, 468b, 468i
Phylogenetics, 649–650
Phylogeny, 453–454, **456**
  animal, 649i, 649–650
  cladistics, 462i
  classification, 458, 462i
  deuterostome, 681i
  evolution of birds, 462
  inference, 469
  land plants, 618i
  mammal, 709i
  molecular phylogenetic analyses, 469–471
*Physarum*, 560i
*Physarum polycephalum*, 575
Physical disturbances, 798
Physiological performance, thermoregulation and optimal, 1120i,
    1120–1121

Physiology, 863, **882**, 1008. *See also* Organization and physiology of animals
Phytoalexins, 990t, **991**
Phytochrome, 11, 11i, **997**, 998i
Phytohormones, 979
*Phytophthora infestans*, 570, 570i
Phytoplankton, **562**, 567, 797, 822, 822i
Picornavirus, 524t
Pigeons, 1038i, 1039
Pigment molecules, 129i, 129–130, 130i
Pigments, 7–8, **7**, 8i, 1226–1228
Pigs, 396, 397i, 783
Pike–cichlid (*Crenicichla alta*), 755, 755i
Pili, **31**, **542**–543, 543i
*Pilobolus*, 594, 594i
Piloting, 845, **865**–866, 866i
Pinacoderm, **651**
Pine life cycle, 631i
Pine trees, 630, 631i, 906i
Pineal gland, 1143i, 1144t, 1153i, **1153**, 1155
Pineapple (*Ananus comosus*), 942i, 943
Pinnae, 1222i
Pinocytosis, **91**, 93i
Pintail duck, 443i
Piranhas, 694, 695i
Pit organs, 1232i
Pitcher plant ecosystems, 834–836, 835i, 836i
Pitcher plants, 599, 750i, 782, 783i, 835i, 959, 970
Pith, **896**
Pituitary dwarfs, 1147, 1147i
Pituitary giants, 1147i
Pituitary gland, 1138i, 1138–1139, 1145i, 1145–1147, **1145**,
    1146i
*Pitx1*, 402
Placenta, **709**, **1170**, 1189, 1190i
Placental, 708–713
Placental mammals, 1170
Placodermi, class, 690
Placozoa, phylum, 652–653, 653i
Planaria, 11i, 12, 12i
Planarian, 1238i
Plant body, organization of, 885–886
  dermal tissues, 894
  ground tissues, 890–892
  plant tissue systems, 890–894
  primary shoot systems, 895–899
  root systems, 900–903
  secondary growth, 903–907
  structure and growth, 886–889
  vascular tissues, 892–893
Plant cells, 27i, 33i
  cell walls in, 44–45, 45i
  central vacuoles, 44
  life cycles, 184i
  structure of, 43–45
  viruses affecting, 528
Plant nutrition, 955–956
  absorbing nutrients, 964–971
  adaptations of for obtaining and absorbing nutrients, 970, 971i
  deficiencies in, 959–960, 960i
  requirements for, 956–960
  root adaptations, 964–971
  soil, 960–964
Plant pharming, 353
Plant tissue culture, 948b, 948i, 948–949
Plantae, 512, 561i, 577–579
Plants, 611–612
  algal ancestors of, 613, 618i
  angiosperms, 632–637
  breeding techniques, 446
  colour in, 20–21
  compared to animals, 882
  convergent evolution, 459i
  desiccation-tolerant, 614
  diploid phase, 616–617
  flowering plants, 632–637, 636i

Plants (*continued*)
  formation of mitotic spindles by, 158–161
  genetic engineering of, 350–351
  gymnosperms, 628–632
  land plants, defining characteristics of, 612
  land plants, phylogenetic relationships between major groups of, 618i
  life cycles, 184
  lignified water-conducting cells, 615
  long-distance transport, 914i
  long-distance transport of water and mineralsin xylem, 919–924
  nonvascular plants, 615, 619–622
  phyla and characteristics, 623t
  plant phyla and major characteristics, 623t
  pollination in, 20–21, 21i
  polyploidy, 444i
  root and shoot systems, 615–616
  seedless vascular plants, 622–627, 623t
  short-distance transport, 914i
  signals and responses. *See* Signals and responses (plants)
  symbiotic associations with fungi, 614
  transition of to life on land, 613–619
  transport in, 913–914, 914i
  transport of organic substances in phloem, 924–927
  trends in evolution of, 615t
  uptake and transport of water and solutes by roots, 917–918
  vascular plants, 615, 617–619
  viruses, 523
  water and solute movement in, 914–917
Planula, **654**
Plasma, 1018i, **1018**–1019, 1071–1072, **1084**
Plasma membrane, **27**, 29i, 30–31, **78**, 505–506, 1085t, 1139, 1140i, 1142b, 1142i, 1205–1206
  receptors, 1142b, 1142i
Plasmids, 540i, **540**
Plasmodesmata (singular, plasmodesma), 44–45, **887**, 917
Plasmodial slime moulds, **575**
Plasmodium, 568, 569i, **575**
*Plasmodium vivax*, 747–749, 748i
Plasmogamy, **589**
*Plasmopara viticola*, 570i
Plastic microbeads, 731, 731i
Plasticity, **888**
Plastids, **43**–44, 1029
Plastron, **702**
Platelets, 1084, 1084i, **1086**, 1092
Platyhelminthes, phylum, 659–662, 660i
Platys, 443
Pleiotropy, **218**–219, 219i
Pleura, 1066i, **1067**
*Pleurobrachia pileus*, 651i
Ploidy, **153**, 187
Plumule, **944**
Pluripotent cells, 346, **1182**
*Pneumocystis jirovecii*, 596
Pneumonia, 524t
Pneumonia bacteria, 252, 253b, 253i
Poaching, 723
Poikilohydric, **614**, 625
Poinsettia (*Euphorbia pulcherrima*), 999i
Point mutation, 420i, **420**
Poison claws, 675i
Polar, **F-13b**
Polar amino acids, F-29i
Polar bear, 726, 729i, 1059i
Polar body, **1165i**, 1166i
Polar capsules, 657
Polar covalent bond, **F-13b**
Polar nuclei, **938**
Polar transport, 984i, **984**
Polarity, F-13b–F-14b, **1180**
Polio, 524t
Pollen, 628, 631i, 637
Pollen grains, **628**, 630, 631i, **937**, 939i, 940i
Pollen sac, 636i, **936**, 939i

Pollen tube, **628**, 629i, 631i, 636i
Pollination, 20–21, 21i, **628**, 631i, 736, 802i, 941i
Pollination networks, 793, 793i
Pollinators, 438–439, 439i, 637, 637i
Poly (A) tail, **286**
Polyadenylation signal, 286
Polyandry, **868**
Polychaeta, class, 662
Polyethylene terephthalate (PET), 731
Polygamy, **868**
Polygenic inheritance, **216**–217, 218i
Polygyny, **868**, 869
Polyhedral virus, 522i, **522**
Polymerase, 528–529
Polymerase chain reaction (PCR), **338**–341, 339b, 339i, 341, 344i, 461, 779
Polymers, synthesis of, 498–499, 499i
Polymorphic development, 644
Polymorphism, **413**, **414**, 427
Polynesians, 734, 734i
Polynucleotide chain, 256i, 256–257
Polypeptide chains, 292–293, 295i
Polypeptides, 279, 294–295, 375, 933, **F-30b**, F-30i, F-31i
Polyphyletic taxon, 458i, **458**
Polyplacophora, class, 666, 666i
Polyploids, **237**, 239–240
Polyploidy, **443**, 444i, 444–446
Polyps, 653i, **653**, 654i, 655i, 657i
Polyribosome, 293
Polysaccharides, F-26b, F-27i, **30**, 887
Polysome, **293**, 297i
Polyspermy, 1168–1169
*Polytrichum*, 621i
Ponderosa pine, 631i
*Pongo labelii*, 482i
Population, 399i, **399**, 412
Population bottlenecks, 419, 419i
Population characteristics, 749i, 749–751
Population control, human administered, 765–766
Population cycles, 764–765
Population density, 749i, **749**
Population dispersion, 749–751
Population ecology
  birth control pills, 770–771
  demography, 752–753
  evolution of life histories, 753–755
  future of, 770
  human administered population control, 765–766
  human population growth, 766–770
  introduction to, 749
  malaria and, 747–749, 748i
  models of population growth, 756–760
  population characteristics, 749i, 749–751
  population regulation, 760–765
Population genetics, **414**–416
  genetic structure, 415, 416t
  Hardy-Weinberg Principle, 416
Population growth, 398i. *See also* Exponential model of population growth; Logistic model of population growth
  age structure and, 767–768
  economic development, 768–769
  human, 766–770
  models of, 756i, 756–760
  strategies for, 763–764
Population size, 749i, **749**, 758t
Populations
  genetic structure, 415
  genetic variations within, 414–415, 415i
Porcupines, 785–786, 786i
Porifera, phylum, 651i, 651–652
  body plan, 652i
Porocytes, 651
Portal vein, **1145**
Positive feedback, **1023**
Positive feedback cycles, 1138–1139
Positive feedback mechanism, homeostasis and, 1023

Positive gene regulation, 311
Positive pressure breathing, **1063**, 1064i
Positron emission tomography (PET), 1241, 1242i
Postembryonic development in insects, 678i
Posterior pituitary, 1117i, 1143i, 1144t, **1145**, 1146i, 1147
Postsynaptic cell, **1210**
Postsynaptic membrane, **1211**
Postsynaptic neuron, 1236–1237, 1237i
Posttranscriptional regulation, 321–324
Posttranslational import, **298**
Posttranslational regulation, 321–324
Postzygotic isolating mechanisms, 437t, **437**, 439–440
Potassium, 923i
    as a cation, 963
    in commercial fertilizers, 960
    deficiencies in, 960i, 1033i
    as essential animal nutrient, 1032
    as essential plant nutrient, 958t
    in soil, 963–964
    sources, functions, and effects of deficiencies in humans, 1033t
Potato blight, 569–570, 570i
Potato cod (*Epinephelus tukula*), 778i
Potato leaf (*Solanum tuberosum*), 991i
Potatoes, 899i, 947, 947i
Potential energy, **54**, 111i, 112i, 112–113
Potential support ratio (PSR), 769
Power grip, 483, 483i
Poxvirus, 524t
*Praeconvoluta castinea*, 658i
Prakash, Om, 447b
Praying mantids, 677i
Praying mantis, 785i
Pre-capillary sphincter muscles, 1091
Precision grip, 483, 483i
Precocial species, **1192**
Precociality, **709**
Precursor cell, 346
Precursor mRNA (pre-mRNA), **285**–287, 286i
Predation, 654i, 761, 778t, 784, 803i
Predator-prey model, 764–765, 765i
Predators, **778**, 791
Prediction, 243i, 243–244, **F-3b**
Predisposition, 326
Pregnancy, 483–484, **1188**
Pregnancy rates, 1179t
Premaxillae, **691i**
Premolars, 709i, **1040**
Pre-mRNA processing, variations in, 321
Prenatal diagnosis, 243i, **243**
Prepuce, **1177**
Pressure, 915–916
Pressure, receptors for, 1216
Pressure-flow mechanism, **926**, 927i
Presynaptic cell, **1210**
Presynaptic membrane, **1210**–1211
Prevalence of rule violation (PRV), 877
Prezygotic isolating mechanisms, 437t, **437**–439
Prezygotic isolation, 443i
Priapulida, phylum, 671
Primary active transport, **89**, 90i
Primary cell layers, **1181**, 1182t
Primary cell wall, **886**–887, 887i
Primary consumer, 778, 796i, 797, 816, **1030**
Primary electron acceptor, 131, 131i
Primary endocymbiosis, 580, **580**, 581i
Primary growth, **888**, 896, 897i, 903i, 905i
Primary meristem, **896**
Primary motor area, **1244**
Primary phloem, 905, 907i
    cells, 904
Primary plant body, **888**
Primary producers, **126**, **778**, 796i, 797, 817i
Primary productivity, 817–818, 821–822, 822i

Primary shoot systems, 895–899
Primary somatosensory area, **1243**, 1244i
Primary structure, **84**, **F-30b**, F-31b, F-31i
Primary succession, **799**–801, 800i
Primary tissues, **888**
Primary xylem, 905, 907i
Primase, 264i, **264**, 266t
Primer, **263**–264, 264i, 338, 364b–365b
Primitive groove, **1185**
Primitive streak, **1185**
Principle of independent assortment, **207**, 209b, 209i
Principle of parsimony, **464**, 467i
Principle of segregation, **203**–205, 204b, 204i
*Principles of Geology: An Attempt to Explain the Former Changes of the Earth's Surface by Reference to Causes Now in Operation* (Lyell), 395
Prions, **530**–531
Probability, 205i, **205**–207, 206i
Procambium, **896**, 907i
Processes. *See* Systems and processes
Product rule, 205i, **205**
Production efficiency, **819**
Products, **F-15b**
Progesterone, 770, 770i, **1151**, 1174, 1174i
Progestins, **1151**
Proglottids, **662**
Prognghorn antelope, 863
Programmable RNA-guided genome editing system, **348b**, 348i
Programmed cell death, 167, 1187–1188
Prohibited Plant List of Canada, 605
Prokaryotes, **29**
Prokaryotic cells, 29
    asexual reproduction in, 544–545
    cell walls in, 540–542, 541i, 542i
    vs. eukaryotic cells, 538–543
    flagella and pili, 542–543
    internal structures, 540
    living in communities attached to surface, 546–548
    metabolic diversity, 543–544
    nucleus of, 31–32
    regulation of gene expression in, 308–314
    structure and function, 538–548, 539i
    structure and organization of, 30i, 30–31
Prokaryotic chromosome, **30**
Prokaryotic organisms, cell cycles in, 151i, 151–152
Prokarytic genomes, 371
Prolactin (PRL), 1144t, **1145**, 1146i, **1192**
Prometaphase, **155**, 156i
Prometaphase I, 187, 188i
Prometaphase II, 187
Promiscuity, **868**, 869
Promoter, **283**
Promoter proximal elements, **315**
Promoter proximal region, **315**
Pronghorn antelope, 863i, 1047i
Proofreading, 270i, **270**
Prop roots, 901, 902i
Propagation, 1162, 1164i
Propagation rate, 1208–1210
Propane, combustion of, 64, 65i
Property, **F-1**
Prophage, **183**, 527
Prophase, **155**, 156i, 191i
Prophase I, 186i, 187, 188i, 190–191, 191i
Prophase II, 187, 188i
Proportion of reproducing individuals, **751**
Proprioceptors, 1216–1218
Prosoma, **673**
Prostaglandins, 1144t , **1174**–1175
Prostate gland, **1176**
Prosthetic groups, F-34b
Protease inhibitors, 990i
Proteases, 1036
Proteasome, 323
Protective viruses, 523
Protein coat, 522, 522i

Protein deficiency, 1031
Protein domains, F-34b, F-34i
Protein factories, turning domestic animals into, 350
Protein kinases, **95**, 163, 375, 1139
Protein phosphatase, 95
Protein sorting, 297–298, 298i
Protein synthesis
    in animals, 1031
    translational regulation and rate of, 323
Protein variability, 288–289
Protein-coding genes, 334, 363, 371, 373, 375, 379, 379t, 380i
Protein-coding sequence, sequences interrupting the, 286–287
Protein-interaction networks, 377
Proteins, **2**, F-22b, F-28, F-28b–F-36b, F-28t
    cell membrane, 82–84, 83i
    connection between RNA, DNA and, 278–283
    determining location of in cells, 375, 377i
    enzymatic digestion of, 1045i
    folding and denaturation, F-35b
    identifying interactions among, 375–377, 377i
    levels of structure, F-30b–F-31b
    oxidizing, 115, 116i
    in plasma, 1084
    Rubisco, 136–137, 137i
    sorting to cytoplasm, 297
Proteobacteria, 548–549
Proteoglycans, 47, 47i
Proteomes, 361–362, **375**
Proteomics, **375**–377
Prothoracic glands, 1154
Prothoracicotropic hormone (PTTH), 1154, 1154i
Protist cells, 27i
Protista, 512
Protists, 559–**560**, 560i
    vs. animals, 561–562
    characteristics of, 561–562
    Chromalveolates, 566–572
    eukaryotes, 560–561
    Excavata, 564–566
    habitats, 562
    lineage of eukaryotic supergroups, 561i, 563–579
    metabolism, 563
    Plantae, 577–579
    primary and secondary endosymbiosis, 580
    reproduction, 563
    Rhizaria, 572–574
    structure of, 562–563, 563i
    Unikont, 574–577
Protobiont, **499**
Proto-chloroplast, 514
Protoderm, **896**
Proto-mitochondrion, 514
Proton gradient, 111i, 113, 132–133
Proton pumps (H⁺ pumps), 9, **89**
Proton translocation, 113
Proton-motive force, **113**
Protonema, 621i, **622**
Protonephridium, **1108**, 1109i
Protons, F-8b
Proto-oncogenes, **326**
Protosome
    ecdysozoan, 670–680
    lophotrochozoan, 659–670
Protostomes, **646**–648, 647i, 648i, 650, 658–659, 1080
Prototrophs, **175**
Protozoa, 564
Proximal convoluted tubule, 1113i, **1113**, 1115–1116, 1115t
Pruetz, Jill, 847
Prusiner, Stanley, 531
*Pseudoceros dimidiatus*, 660i
Pseudocoelom, **646**
Pseudocoelomate, 647i

Pseudogenes, 371, **373**, 380
*Pseudonitzschia*, 571
Pseudopodia, **562**
Pseudopods, 574, 575i
*Psilotum*, 626, 627i
Psychrophiles, **552**
Pterophyta, 618i, 623t, **624**, 625–627
*Pteropsis*, 690i
Public health, 767
Pufferfish, 384, 384i
Pulmonary arteries, 1087, 1087i
Pulmonary circuit, **1082**, 1087, 1087i, 1090, 1096i
Pulmonary veins, 1087, 1087i
Pulvini, **996**–997
Punnett square, 206i, **207**, 209b, 209i, 242i
Pupa, **678**
Pupil, **1224**
Pure-breeding, 201b
Purines, 256, 257, **497**, F-37i, F-38b
Purkinje fibres, 1089
Purple monkey-flower, 439, 439i
Pycnogonids, 673, 673i
Pyloric sphincter, 1042
Pyramid of biomass, 821i, **821**
Pyramid of energy, 821i, **821**–823
Pyramid of numbers, **821**, 822i
Pyrimidines, 256, 257, **497**, F-37i, F-38b
*Pyrobolus*, 552
Pyrosequencing, **367**, 368–369, 368–369i
Pyruvate oxidation, 106–109
    citric acid cycle and, 105, 105i, 106–109, 109i, 110i
    metabolic pathway of, 117i
    reactions of, 108i
    reactions to, 109i
Pythons, 1034i

Quackgrass (*Elymus repens*), 896, 935
Qualitative variation, **412**–413, 413i
Quanta, 129
Quantitative PCR (qPCR), 340–341
Quantitative trait, **216**
Quantitative variation, 412i, **412**
Quantum physics, F-1
Quaternary consumers, 796i
Quaternary structure, F-30b, F-31i, F-33b
Quorum sensing, 22, **547**

*R* allele, 991
*R* gene, **991**, 992i
Rabies, 524t
Raccoons (*Procyon lotor*), 741
Radial canal, 680
Radial cleavage, **646**–647, 680
Radial cuts, 891i
Radial symmetry, 645i, **646**
Radiant energy, detection and perception of, 1223, 1223b
Radiation, 325, **1121**
Radicle, **944**
Radioactivity, **254**
Radioisotope, F-8b–F-9b, 255i, 511b
Radiolaria, 572, 574i
Radiometric dating, **509**, 511b
Radula, **666**
Rainbow mussel, 732i
Ramaria (coral fungus), 598i
Random dispersion, **751**
Random fertilization, 193
Random mutation, 400–401
Random segregation, 192
*Ranunculus ficaria*, 21i
Rao, Potu N., 162
*Raphanobrassica*, 446
Rapid eye movement (REM) sleep, **1246**
Raspberries, 942, 942i
Rasputin, 242

Resolution, **26**
Resource partitioning, 791i, **791**
Resource use efficiency (RUE), 733, 733i
Respiratory, **1057**
Respiratory intermediates, utilizing for anabolic reactions, 115
Respiratory medium, 1060
Respiratory surface, **1060**–1061, 1061i
Respiratory system, 1017i. *See also* Gas exchange
    in humans, 1066i
    in mammals, 1065–1068
Response, 94i, **1200**, 1202i
    in peripheral nervous system, 1247–1249
    in signal pathway, 92
Resting membrane potential, 1202–1204
Resting position, 1265i
Resting potential, **1203**, 1204i
Restriction endonucleases (restriction enzyme), 335–336,
    **335**–336, 341
Restriction enzymes, 336
Restriction fragment length polymorphisms (RFLPs), **342**
Restriction fragments, **335**, 341
Restriction sites, 335, 335i, 336, 345
Results, interpretation of, F-3i
Retina, **1224**, 1227i
    of mammals and birds, 1225–1226
    visual processing in, 1226
Retrotransposons, 383i, **383**
Retrovirus, 524t
Reverse transcriptase, 334, 336, 338, 338i, 383i
Reversible, **59**
Reznick, David, 755
Rhabdovirus, 524t
Rhamphorynchus meunsteri, 700i
Rhino horn, 721, 723, 723i
Rhinovirus, 524t
Rhizaria, 561i, 572–574
*Rhizobium*, 542i, 544, 967–968
*Rhizobium radiobacter*, 351, 352b, 351i
Rhizoids, **619**, 620, 621i, 622, 625, 626
Rhizomes, 624i, **624**, 626, 626i, 896–897, 899i
*Rhizomnium*, 620i
Rhizomorphs, 588i
*Rhizopus nigricans*, 594i
*Rhizopus stolonifer*, 594, 594i
*Rhodnius prolixus*, 1155b, 1155i
Rhodophyta, 577–578
Rhodopsin, 10, 10i, **1226**
Rhynchocoel, **665**
*Rhynia*, 623–624, 624i
*Rhynia gwynne-vaughnii*, 624i
Ribbon worm, 662–665, 665i
Ribonuclease, F-35i
Ribonucleic acid (RNA), 2, 254, F-36, F-37b
Ribose, 259, **F-36b**
Ribosomal RNA (rRNA), **30**, 548
Ribosomal subunits, 291–292, 293i
Ribosome binding site, **291**
Ribosomes, **30**, 34, 34i, **279**, 289–291, **291**, 293i, 293–294, 296i,
    512, 540
Ribozyme, 500i, **500**
Ribulose-1,5-bisphosphate (RuBP) carboxylase/oxygenase (Rubisco),
    **136**–138, 137i, 375
Rice, 353, 353i
Rice (*Oryza sativa*), 934, 934i
*Riftia pachyptila*, 643–644, 644i
Ring canal, 680
Ring species, 436i, **436**
Ringworm, 596
Ritualized, 856
RNA
    connection between DNA, protein and, 278–283
    flow of information from DNA to, 500, 500i
    replaced by DNA, 501, 501i
RNA interference (RNAi), **321**, 374

RNA polymerase, 278, **279**, 316i
RNA primers, 263–264, 264i
RNA replication, 528
RNA synthesis, 283–285, 284i
Rods, **538**, **1225**, 1227i
Rods and cones, 1225–1226
Rolling circle, 180
Rolling circle replication, 177
Roosting bats (*Kerivoula hardwickii*), 782
Root cap, **901**
Root cortex, 902
Root hair, **894**, 895i
Root nodules, 968i, **968**, 969i, 978i
Root pressure, 922i, **922**
Root systems, **616**, 882, 886, 888, **888**
    absorbing essential nutrients through, 964
    eudicot vs. monocot, 890t
    in plants, 900–903
    structure of, 901–903
    tissues of, 902–903
Root tip, 903i
Root xylem, 917–918
Roots, **456**, 615–**616**
    adaptations of for obtaining and absorbing nutrients, 964–971
    of banyan trees, 885
    secondary growth, 903–905
    secretions from, 964
    types of, 902i
    uptake and transport of water and solutes by, 917–918
Root–soil interactions, 962i, 962–964
Rose, Irwin, 323
Rotifera, phylum, 659, 659i
Rotifers (*Habrotrocha rosa*), 835, 835i
Rough ER, 35i, **35**–36
Round dance, 859, 859i, 861
Round pigtoe mussel, 732i
Round window, **1222**
Roundworms (*Ascaris lumbricoides*), 770, 671i, 671–672
Royal kingbird (*Onychorhynchus coronatus*), 856, 858i
Royal penguins, 871, 872i
rRNA genes, 371
*r*-selected species, 763i, **763**–764, 764i, 798, 801–802
*Rsl4* gene, 964
Rubisco, **136**–137, 137i, 137–138, 138i
Rubisco. *See* Ribulose 1,5-bisphosphate (RuBP) carboxylase oxygenase (Rubisco)
Ruffed grouse (*Bonasa umbellus*), 764
Ruminant mammals, 1047, 1047i
Russian Revolution, 242
Rust, 605
Rust fungus, 605i
Rye, 605
Rye plants (*Secale cereale*), 944

*S* allele, 940, 941i
S bacteria, 252
S phase, 153i, **153**, 154i
Sac fungi, 595i
*Saccharomyces cerevisiae*, 587
Saccule, **1218**, 1219, 1219i
Sachs, Julius von, 956–957
Safari hunts, 728–729
Sage grouse, 869, 869i, 870
Salamander, 436, 436i, 696–698, 697i, 1238i
Salem witch trials, possible connection of to lysergic acid, 596
Salicylic acid (SA), 979t, 990t, **991**, 992, 993i
Saliva, 1040
Salivary amylase, **1040**, 1045i
Salivary glands, **1040**
Salmon, 833–834, 834i, 865, 1060i, 1120i
*Salmonella*, 539i, 546
Salt glands, 1111, 1111i
Salt licks, 851–852
Saltatory conduction, 1208–1210, 1209i, **1209**–1210
Sand dollar, 682

Sandy soils, 961
Sanger, Frederick, 363
Sanger sequencing. *See* Dideoxynucleotide sequencing
Sap, 784, 784i
*Saprolegnia parasitica*, 570i
Saprotrophic fungi, 600–601
Saprotrophs, **588**, 592
Sapwood, **904**–905, 906i
Sarcomeres, 1257–1260, **1257**, 1258i, 1262i
Sarcoplasmic reticulum, **1257**
Sarcopterygians, 695i
Sarcopterygii, class, 695, 695i
*Sarracenia purpurea*, 836i
SARS (Severe Acute Respiratory Syndrome), 524t, 528
Saturated fatty acid, **81**
Saturation kinetics, 87i
Saurischian dinosaurs, 700i, 701i
Savannah, **782**, 818t, 819i
Savigny's agama, 1123–1124
Sawfish, 692i
*Scala Naturae* (Scale of Nature), 394
Scale, F-7
Scale of interactions, 833–834
Scale of nature, 394, 394i
Scalidophora, 670
Scallops, 666–667, 735
Scanning electron microscopy (SEM), 28i
Scaphopoda, class, 668
Scapula, 482, 482i
Scarlet cup fungus, 595i
Scarlet monkey-flower, 439i
Scherer, Stephen, 477
Schizocoelom, **648**
Schizocoelous, **649**
Schleiden, Matthias, 25
Schoener, Amy, 806
Schoener, Tom (Thomas W.), 761, 762b, 762i, 788
Schulz, Jonathan, 877
Schwann, Theodor, 25
Schwann cells, 1166, **1201**–1202, 1203i
Schwarzenegger, Arnold, 394, 395i
Scientific method, **F-2b**, F-3i
Scientific theory, F-5b
Sclereids, 892i, **892**
Sclerenchyma, 891t, 892i, **892**, 896
Sclerocytes, **651**
Scolex, **662**, 663i
Scorpion, 674i
Scott, Becky, 1070–1071, 1071i
Scrapie, 530
Scrotum, **1175**–1176
Scyphozoa, class, 656, 657i
Sea anemones, 656i, 1037i, 1080, 1238i, 1265i
Sea cucumber, 680, 682i, 684
Sea hares (*Aplysia* species), 851
Sea horses, 1193i
Sea level atmosphere, 1059t
Sea lily, 680
Sea lions, 1271i
Sea otters (*Enhydra lutris*), 572, 572i, 846–847
Sea slug, 1029, 1030i
Sea squirt, 685
Sea star, 680, 683i, 1238i
Sea star (*Pisaster ochraceus*), 680, 683i, 1238i, 792b, 792i
Sea turtles, 736i, 1234b, 1234i, 1271i
Sea urchins (*Pisaster brevispinus*), 680, 682, 682i, 846, 1223b, 1223i, 1226i, 1227
Seals, 1126, 1175i
Second law of thermodynamics, 55–57, 56i, **56**, 59–60
Second messengers, **981**
Secondary active transport, **89**–90, 92i
Secondary cell wall, **887**, 892i, 893b

Secondary consumer, **778**, 796i, 816, **1030**
Secondary contact, 440i, **441**–442
Secondary endosymbiosis, 573, 580, **580**, 581i
Secondary growth, **888**, 903–907, 905i, 906i, 907i
Secondary metabolites, **589**, 991
Secondary phloem, 905i, 906, 907i
    cells, 904
Secondary productivity, 818–819
Secondary structure, **84**, **F-30b**, F-31i, F-32b
Secondary succession, **801**
Secondary tissues, **888**
Secondary xylem, 905, 905i, 906, 907i
Secretin, 1049i
Secretion of enzymes, 1106i, **1106**
    as a process from ingestion of food, 1037
    as a tubule function in excretion, 1106
Secretory vesicles, **36**, 90–91
Sedimentation, 507, 508i, 824
Seed coat, 630, 631i, 939i, **944**
Seed ferns, 624, 633
Seedless vascular plants, 618i, 622–627, 623t
Seeds, **628**–630, 629i
    protecting and nourishing plant embryos, 628–630, 942–945
    structure of, 944i
    suppressing growth in, 988–989
Segmentation, 648, 664i
Segmented worms, 662
Segments, **648**
Segregate, **203**
Segregation, principle of, **203**–205, 204b, 204i
*Selaginella*, 617i
*Selaginella densa*, 625, 625i
    sporophytes, 625i
*Selaginella strobilus*, 617i
Selection pressures, 399i, 402
Selective breeding, 398i, 398–399
Selective cell adhesion, **1182**
Selective permeability, 1104–1105
Selective pressures, 420
Selectively permeable, **499**
Selenium, 959
Self-fertilization (self-pollination), **200**, **940**
Self-incompatibility, **940**, 941i
Selfing, 940
Self-pollination, **200**
Semen, **1176**
Semicircular canals, **1218**, 1219i
Semiconservative replication, **258**–259, 260i, 261b, 261i
Semilunar (SL) valves, 1087i, **1087**
Seminal vesicle, **1176**
Seminiferous tubules, **1176**, 1177i
Senegal galagos (*Galago senegalensis*), 847, 847i
Senescence, **987**–988
Sense codons, **282**, **291**
Sensilla, 1229
Sensitization, **1246**
Sensors, **1019**
Sensory adaptation, **1235**
Sensory cell membrane proteins, 1216i
Sensory coding, 1235
Sensory cortex, 1244i
Sensory hair cell, **1216**
Sensory inputs, 1214–1220
Sensory neuron, 855, 1201i, **1201**
Sensory receptor (transducer), **1214**–1216, 1215i
Sensory regions, of cerebral cortex, 1243–1244
Sensory systems, 855–856, 857i
Sensory transduction, **1215**, 1226
Sepals, **936**
Septum (plural, septa), 589i, **589**, 654, **662**, 1087i
Seq4You, 361–362
Sequence alignment, 374i, **374**

repression of, 316–318
  simultaneous translation and, 297i
  supporting theory of endosymbiosis, 505
  of *trp* operon, 311–314, 313i
Transcription factors, **285**, **315**, 949, 964
Transcription initiation, 314–320
Transcription initiation complex, **315**, 316i
Transcription unit, **283**, **309**
Transcriptome, **289**, **375**
Transcriptomics, 374–**375**
Transducing phage, 182
Transduction, 94i, 181i, **181**–183, 526, 1217i
  as DNA source for recombination, 181i, 181–183, 182i
  in signal pathway, 92
Transfer cell, **926**, 927i
Transfer RNA (tRNA), 282, 289–291, 290i, **512**
Transformation, **180**–181, 252, 254–**255**
Transforming DNA (T DNA), 351
Transforming principle, 252
Transgene, 345
Transgenic, **345**
Transgenic crops, 350–353, 353i
Transient killer whales, 727, 860
Transit sequence, **298**
Transition state, 67
Translation, **279**, 280b, 280i
  gene to polypeptide, 279
  in horizontal gene transfer, 514i
  initiation in eukaryotes, 294i
  mRNA-directed polypeptide synthesis, 289–298, 290i
  in prokaryotic and eukaryotic cells, 281i
  simultaneous transcription and, 297i
  supporting theory of endosymbiosis, 505
  termination of, 296i
Translational regulation, 321–324
Translocation, **236**, 237i, **925**
  as chromosomal alterations, 236i, 236–237
Translocation pressure, 925b
Transmembrane pathway, 917, 918i
Transmembrane protein, 83–84, 84i
Transmission, **1200**, 1201i, 1202i, 1247–1249
Transmission electron microscopy (TEM), 28i
Transpiration, 919, 920i, 921, 922–923
Transpiration–photosynthesis compromise, 922
Transport, 9
  in animals. *See* Circulatory system
  in plants. *See* Plants
Transport epithelium, **1106**
Transport mechanisms, characteristics of, 89t
Transport proteins, **27**–28, 85–87, 86i
Transportation, as key function of membrane proteins, 83, 83i
Transposable element sequences, 380
Transposable element (TE), 382i, **382**–384, 383i
Transposase, **382**
Transposition, 382i, **382**
Transposons, **382**
Transverse cuts, 891i
Transverse tubule. *See* T (transverse) tubule
Tree frogs, 460–461, 461i, 1107, 1108, 1111i
Tree of Life, 435, 456, 509–514
  Darwin's, 515i
  domains, 513i, 513t
  gene sequence analysis, 512
  horizontal gene transfer, 515i
Trematoda, class, 661
Trembling aspen (*Populus tremuloides*), 961
*Treponema pallidum*, 550i
Triacylglycerols, F-40b
*Triceratops*, 701i
Trichocysts, **567**
Trichomes, **894**, 895i
*Trichomonas vaginalis*, 565, 566i

*Trichonympha*, 566i
*Trichoplax adherens*, 652–653, 653i
Triglycerides, **115**, F-40b, F-41i
Triiodothyronine (T$_3$), 1144t, **1148**
Trillium, 634i
Trimesters, **1188**
Trimethylamine oxide (TMAO), 1110
Triple X females, 238
Triple-X syndrome, 239t
Triploblastic body plan, **645**
Triploids, 237
Trisomy 21, 238
Triticale (grass), 633i
Trivers, Robert, 873
TRNA structure, 289–291, 290i
Trochophore, 659i, **659**
Troglophiles, 813
Trogloxenes, 813
Trophic cascade, **822**
Trophic interactions, 793, 793i, 796–797
Trophic level, 796i, **797**, 816
Trophoblast, **1189**
Trophozoites, **559**
Trophy hunting, 729
Tropical deciduous forest, 818t, 819i
Tropical forests, **630**, 793
Tropical orchid, 970, 971i
Tropical rainforests, 818t, 819i, 955–956, 956i
Tropism, **981**, 993
Troponin, 1257
*trp* operon, 311–314, 312i, 313i
True-breeding, **201b**
Truffles (*Tuber melanosporum*), 595, 966
*Trypanosoma brucei*, 564, 566i
Trypsin, 1045i
Tryptophan biosynthesis, 311–314, 313i
Tsunami of December 2004, 739
Tuatara, 701
Tube cell, **937**
Tube foot, 680
Tubers, 896–897, 899i
Tubeworm, 643
Tubules, 1106i
Tubulins, 39
*Tullimonstrum gregarium*, 686i
Tully monster, 686, 686i
Tumour suppressor genes, **326**–327, 327i
Tumour-inducing plasmid. *See* Ti (tumour-inducing) plasmid
Tumours, 325
Tundra, 818t, 819i
Tunicate, 686i
Turbellaria, class, 659
Turgid, **916**, 917i
Turgor pressure, **916**–917, 925b, 926
Turner syndrome, 239t
Turnover rates, **821**
Turtles, 702, 702i, 1234b, 1234i
*Twenty Thousand Leagues under the Sea* (Verne), 22
Twinflower (*Linnaea borealis*), 634i
Twitch summation, 1260, 1262i
Tymbal, 679
Tympanic canal, 1221i
Tympanum, **696**, 1220i, **1220**
Type 1 diabetes, 1152–1153
Type 2 diabetes, 1152–1153
Type I survivorship curves, 753
Type II survivorship curves, 753
Type III survivorship curves, 753
Typhlosoles, 1038
Tyrosine kinase (TK), 644i

UAA, 371
UAG, 371
Ubiquitin, 323, 324i
Uddin, Mohammed, 477